Annotated Instructor's Edition

Introductory and Intermediate Algebra

Second Edition

Margaret L. Lial
American River College

John Hornsby
University of New Orleans

Terry McGinnis

Addison Wesley

Boston San Francisco New York
London Toronto Sydney Tokyo Singapore Madrid
Mexico City Munich Paris Cape Town Hong Kong Montreal

Publisher	Greg Tobin
Executive Editor	Maureen O'Connor
Editorial Project Management	Ruth Berry and Suzanne Alley
Editorial Assistants	Melissa Wright and Jolene Lehr
Managing Editor/Production Supervisor	Ron Hampton
Text and Cover Design	Dennis Schaefer
Supplements Production	Sheila C. Spinney
Production Services	Elm Street Publishing Services, Inc.
Media Producer	Lorie Reilly
Marketing Manager	Dona Kenly
Marketing Coordinator	Heather Rosefsky
Prepress Services Buyer	Caroline Fell
Technical Art Supervisor	Joseph K. Vetere
Art Creation and Composition	Pre-Press Company, Inc.
First Print Buyer	Hugh Crawford
Cover Photo Credits	© Ron Johnson/Index Stock Imagery; Walter Bibikow/Index Stock Imagery; Tina Buckman/Index Stock Imagery

Photo Credits All photos from PhotoDisk except the following:
Bill Aron/PhotoEdit, p. 366; Bill Bachman/Photo Researchers, Inc., p. 155 right; Bettmann/CORBIS, p. 521; Dick Blume/Syracruse Newpapers/The Image Works, p. 715; Cleve Bryant/PhotoEdit, p. 634 right; Nigel Cattlin, Holt Studios International/Photo Researchers, Inc., pp. 361, 373; John Coletti/Stock Boston, p. 787; Bob Collins III/The Image Works, p. 688; Paul Conklin/PhotoEdit, p. 585 left; Gary A. Conner/PhotoEdit, pp. 178, 605; Greg Crisp/SportsChrome USA, p. 586 left; Bob Daemmrich/The Image Works, p. 340 left; Bob Daemmrich/Stock Boston, p. 886 top; Michael Dwyer/Stock Boston, p. 572; Kathy Ferguson/PhotoEdit, p. 388; Eric Fowke/PhotoEdit, p. 265; Tony Freeman/PhotoEdit, pp. 184, 223, 828, 833; Spencer Grant/PhotoEdit, p. 846; Jeff Greenberg/PhotoEdit, p. 154; Charles Gupton/Stock Boston, pp. 321, 374; Courtesy, John Hornsby, pp. 105, 147, 150, 167; Iowa State University, p. 779; D. Jennings/The Image Works, p. 634 left; Doug Martin/Photo Researchers, Inc., pp. 737, 744; Mary Ellen Matthews/Photofest, p. 372; NASA, pp. 360, 451 top, 451 bottom, 596, 855, 876, 886 bottom; Eric Neurath/Stock Boston, p. 771; Michael Newman/PhotoEdit, pp. 259, 689, 728, 743, 845; Jonathan Nourok/PhotoEdit, p. 594; Richard Pasley/Stock Boston, pp. 169, 189; Charles Pefley/Stock Boston, p. 733; Photofest, pp. 213, 392, 785, 827; Phyllis Picardi/Stock Boston, p. 807; A. Ramey/PhotoEdit, p. 896 left; Randall/The Image Works, pp. 589, 597; Reuters News/Media Inc./CORBIS, pp. 128, 155 left, 537, 577 bottom; Mark Richards/PhotoEdit, p. 370; Brian Spurlock/SportsChrome USA, pp. 363, 586 right; Jamie Squire/Allsport, p. 290; Rob Tringali, Jr./SportsChrome USA, pp. 25, 52, 183; Dana White/PhotoEdit, p. 215; David Young-Wolff/PhotoEdit, pp. 781, 895; Michael Zito/SportsChrome USA, pp. 194, 585 right.

Library of Congress Cataloging-in-Publication Data

Lial, Margaret L.

Introductory and intermediate algebra.—2 ed./Margaret L. Lial, John Hornsby, Terry McGinnis.

p. cm.

Includes index.

ISBN 0-321-06461-5 (Student Edition)

ISBN 0-321-08871-9 (Annotated Instructor's Edition)

1. Algebra. I. Title: Introductory and intermediate algebra. II. Hornsby, John. III. McGinnis, Terry. IV. Title.

QA152.3 .L56 2002

512.9—dc21 2001046375

1 2 3 4 5 6 7 8 9 10 WC 04 03 02 01

Contents

List of Applications

List of Focus on Real-Data Applications

Preface

The second edition of *Introductory and Intermediate Algebra* continues our ongoing commitment to provide the best possible text and supplements package to help instructors teach and students succeed. To that end, we have tried to address the diverse needs of today's students through an attractive design, updated figures and graphs, helpful features, careful explanations of topics, and an expanded package of supplements and study aids. We have also taken special care to respond to the suggestions of users and reviewers and have added many new examples and exercises based on their feedback. Students who have completed a course in introductory algebra—as well as those who require further review of basic algebraic concepts before taking additional courses in mathematics, business, science, nursing, or other fields—will benefit from the text's student-oriented approach.

This text is part of a series that also includes the following books:

- *Essential Mathematics*, by Lial and Salzman
- *Basic College Mathematics*, Sixth Edition, by Lial, Salzman, and Hestwood
- *Prealgebra*, Second Edition, by Lial and Hestwood
- *Introductory Algebra*, Seventh Edition, by Lial, Hornsby, and McGinnis
- *Intermediate Algebra with Early Functions and Graphing*, Seventh Edition, by Lial, Hornsby, and McGinnis.

What's New in This Edition?

We believe students and instructors will welcome the following new features.

New, Real-Life Applications We are always on the lookout for interesting data to use in real-life applications. As a result, we have included many new or updated examples and exercises throughout the text that focus on real-life applications of mathematics. These applied problems provide a modern flavor that will appeal to and motivate students. (See pp. 224, 230, and 516.) A comprehensive List of Applications appears at the beginning of the text.

New Figures and Photos Today's students are more visually oriented than ever. Thus, we have made a concerted effort to add mathematical figures, diagrams, tables, and graphs whenever possible. (See pp. 136, 183, and 194.) Many of the graphs use a style similar to that seen by students in today's print and electronic media. Photos have also been incorporated to enhance applications in examples and exercises.

Increased Emphasis on Problem Solving Introduced in Chapter 2, our six-step problem-solving method has been refined and integrated throughout the text. The six steps, *Read*, *Assign a Variable*, *Write an Equation*, *Solve*, *State the Answer*, and *Check*, are emphasized in boldface type and repeated in examples and exercises to reinforce the problem-solving process for students. (See pp. 127, 132, and 139.)

Study Skills Component A desk-light icon at key points in the text directs students to a separate *Study Skills Workbook* containing activities correlated directly to the text. (See pp. 33, 217, and 315.) This unique workbook explains *how* the brain actually learns, so students understand *why* the study tips presented will help them succeed in the course. Students are introduced to the workbook in an updated To the Student section at the beginning of the text.

Focus on Real-Data Applications These one-page activities present a relevant and in-depth look at how mathematics is used in the real world. Designed to help instructors answer the often-asked question, "When will I ever use this stuff?," these activities ask students to read and interpret data from newspaper articles, the Internet, and other familiar, real sources. (See pp. 90, 212, and 450.) The activities are well-suited to collaborative work and can also be completed by individuals or used for open-ended class discussions. Instructor teaching notes and extensions for the activities are provided in the *Printed Test Bank and Instructor's Resource Guide.*

Diagnostic Pretest A diagnostic pretest is now included on p. xxix and covers all the material in the book, much like a sample final exam. This pretest can be used to facilitate student placement in the correct chapter according to skill level.

Chapter Openers New chapter openers feature real-world applications of mathematics that are relevant to students and tied to specific material within the chapters. Examples of topics include higher education costs, credit card debt, and political affiliation. (See pp. 169, 221, and 321—Chapters 3, 4, and 5.)

Calculator Tips These optional tips, marked with calculator icons, offer basic information and instruction for students using calculators in the course. (See pp. 375, 378, and 449.) In addition, a new Introduction to Calculators has been included at the beginning of the text.

Test Your Word Power To help students understand and master mathematical vocabulary, this new feature has been incorporated in each chapter summary. Key terms from the chapter are presented along with four possible definitions in a multiple-choice format. Answers and examples illustrating each term are provided. (See pp. 94, 304, and 453.)

WHAT FAMILIAR FEATURES HAVE BEEN RETAINED?

We have retained the popular features of previous editions of the text, some of which follow.

Learning Objectives Each section begins with clearly stated, numbered objectives, and the included material is directly keyed to these objectives so that students know exactly what is covered in each section. (See pp. 65, 239, and 396.)

Cautions and Notes One of the most popular features of previous editions, Caution and Note boxes warn students about common errors and emphasize important ideas throughout the exposition. (See pp. 33, 114, and 198.) There are more of these in the seventh edition than in the sixth, and the new text design makes them easier to spot; Cautions are highlighted in bright yellow and Notes are highlighted in green.

Margin Problems Margin problems, with answers immediately available at the bottom of the page, are found in every section of the text. (See pp. 149, 258, and 396.) This key feature allows students to immediately practice the material covered in the examples in preparation for the exercise sets. Based on reviewer feedback, we have added more margin exercises to the seventh edition.

Ample and Varied Exercise Sets The text contains a wealth of exercises to provide students with opportunities to practice, apply, connect, and extend the algebraic skills they are learning. Numerous illustrations, tables, graphs, and photos have been added to the exercise sets to help students visualize the problems they are solving. Problem types include writing, estimation, and calculator exercises as well as applications and multiple-choice, matching, true/false, and fill-in-the-blank problems. In the *Annotated Instructor's Edition* of the text, writing exercises are marked with icons so that instructors may assign these problems at their discretion. Exercises suitable for calculator work are marked in both the student and instructor editions with calculator icons. (See pp. 37, 143, and 411.)

Relating Concepts Exercises Formerly titled Mathematical Connections, these sets of exercises help students tie together topics and develop problem-solving skills as they compare and contrast ideas, identify and describe patterns, and extend concepts to new situations. (See pp. 206, 314, and 350.) These exercises make great collaborative activities for pairs or small groups of students.

Summary Exercises Three sets of in-chapter summary exercises on linear and absolute value equations and inequalities, factoring, and rational expressions provide students with the all-important *mixed* practice problems they need to master these typically difficult topics. (See pp. 207, 501, and 573.)

Ample Opportunity for Review Each chapter concludes with a Chapter Summary that features Key Terms with definitions and helpful graphics, New Symbols, Test Your Word Power, and a Quick Review of each section's content with additional examples. A comprehensive set of Chapter Review Exercises, keyed to individual sections, is included, as are Mixed Review Exercises and a Chapter Test. Beginning with Chapter 2, each chapter concludes with a set of Cumulative Review Exercises that cover material going back to Chapters R and 1. (See pp. 157–168, 383–394, and 453–464.)

What Content Changes Have Been Made?

We have worked hard to fine-tune and polish presentations of topics throughout the text based on user and reviewer feedback. Some of the content changes include the following:

- New Chapter R on fractions, decimals, and percents is included for student review and reference.
- Multiplication and division of real numbers are consolidated in Section 1.6.
- In Chapter 5, Systems of Linear Equations, the substitution method (Section 5.2) is covered before the elimination method (Section 5.3). Solving linear systems of equations by matrix methods is included in a new Section 5.6.
- Chapter 6 on exponents and polynomials has been reorganized for increased continuity.
- Factoring trinomials by grouping and factoring trinomials using FOIL are treated in separate sections in Chapter 7.
- Variation, formerly covered in Section 4.6, is now included in Section 8.6.
- Functions are introduced early as in the previous edition, but are more fully integrated throughout the text. We now introduce graphs of simple rational functions in Chapter 8 and radical functions in Chapter 9.
- Rational exponents are included in a new Section 9.2.
- Quadratic functions and graphs are presented earlier in the text when quadratic equations are solved (Chapter 10).
- The presentation on solving quadratic and rational inequalities in Section 10.8 has been rewritten to build on the graphing concepts presented in the preceding sections.
- The material on exponential and logarithmic functions (Chapter 11) is now placed before conic sections (Chapter 12) instead of after it.
- Four new appendices have been included. Appendix A provides a review of sets. Appendix B covers determinants and Cramer's Rule, formerly included in the chapter on systems of linear equations. Appendix C covers synthetic division. Appendix D reviews exponents, polynomials, and factoring.

What Supplements Are Available?

Our extensive supplements package includes an *Annotated Instructor's Edition*, testing materials, solutions manuals, tutorial software, videotapes, and a state-of-the-art Web site. For more information about any of the following supplements, please contact your Addison-Wesley sales consultant.

For the Student

***Student's Solutions Manual* (ISBN 0-321-09217-1)** The *Student's Solutions Manual* provides detailed solutions to the odd-numbered section exercises and to all margin, Relating Concepts, Summary, Chapter Review, Chapter Test, and Cumulative Review exercises.

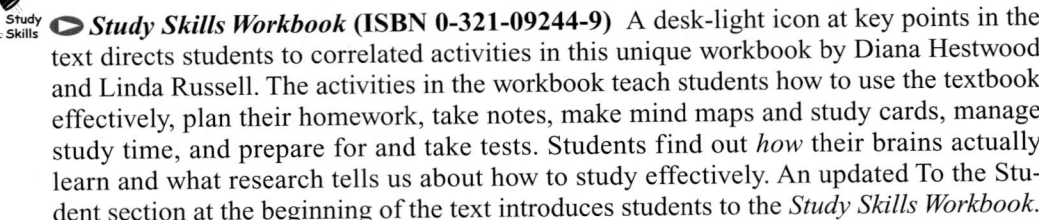

***Study Skills Workbook* (ISBN 0-321-09244-9)** A desk-light icon at key points in the text directs students to correlated activities in this unique workbook by Diana Hestwood and Linda Russell. The activities in the workbook teach students how to use the textbook effectively, plan their homework, take notes, make mind maps and study cards, manage study time, and prepare for and take tests. Students find out *how* their brains actually learn and what research tells us about how to study effectively. An updated To the Student section at the beginning of the text introduces students to the *Study Skills Workbook*.

Addison-Wesley Math Tutor Center The Addison-Wesley Math Tutor Center is staffed by qualified college mathematics instructors who tutor students on examples and exercises from the textbook. Tutoring is provided via toll-free telephone, toll-free fax, e-mail, and the Internet. White Board technology allows tutors and students to actually see problems being worked while they "talk" in real time over the Internet during tutoring sessions. The Math Tutor Center is accessed through a registration number that can be bundled free with a new textbook or purchased separately.

***InterAct Math® Tutorial Software* (ISBN 0-321-09222-8)** This interactive CD-ROM tutorial software provides algorithmically generated practice exercises that are correlated at the objective level to the content of the text. Every exercise in the program is accompanied by an example and a guided solution designed to involve students in the solution process. Selected problems also include a video clip to help students visualize concepts. The software tracks student activity and scores and can generate printed summaries of students' progress. Instructors can use the InterAct Math® Plus course-management software to create, administer, and track tests and monitor student performance during practice sessions. (See For the Instructor.)

***InterAct MathXL:* www.mathxl.com** InterAct MathXL is a Web-based tutorial system that enables students to take practice tests and receive personalized study plans based on their results. Practice tests are correlated directly to the section objectives in the text, and once a student has taken a practice test, the software scores the test and generates a study plan that identifies strengths, pinpoints topics where more review is needed, and links directly to InterAct Math® tutorial software for additional practice and review. A course-management feature allows instructors to create and administer tests and view students' test results, study plans, and practice work. Students gain access to the InterAct MathXL Web site through a password-protected subscription, which can either be bundled free with a new copy of the text or purchased separately.

***Real-to-Reel Videotape Series* (ISBN 0-321-09225-2)** This series of videotapes, created specifically for *Introductory and Intermediate Algebra*, Second Edition, features an engaging team of lecturers who provide comprehensive lessons on every objective in the text. The videos include a stop-the-tape feature that encourages students to pause the video, work through the example presented on their own, and then resume play to watch the video instructor go over the solution.

***Digital Video Tutor* (ISBN 0-321-09226-0)** This supplement provides the entire set of Real-to-Reel videotapes for the text in digital format on CD-ROM, making it easy and convenient for students to watch video segments from a computer, either at home or on campus. Available for purchase with the text at minimal cost, the Digital Video Tutor is ideal for distance learning and supplemental instruction.

MyMathLab.com

***Web Site:* www.MyMathLab.com** Ideal for lecture-based, lab-based, and on-line courses, MyMathLab.com provides students with a centralized point of access to the wide variety of on-line resources available with this text. The pages of the actual book are loaded into MyMathLab.com, and as students work through a section of the on-line text, they can link directly from the pages to supplementary resources (such as tutorial software, interactive animations, and audio and video clips) that provide instruction, exploration, and practice beyond what is offered in the printed book. MyMathLab.com generates personalized study plans for students and allows instructors to track all student work on tutorials, quizzes, and tests.

For the Instructor

***Annotated Instructor's Edition* (ISBN 0-321-08871-9)** The *Annotated Instructor's Edition* provides answers to all text exercises in color next to the corresponding problems. To assist instructors in assigning homework problems, icons identify writing and calculator exercises.

***Instructor's Solutions Manual* (ISBN 0-321-09218-X)** The *Instructor's Solutions Manual* provides complete solutions to all even-numbered section exercises.

***Answer Book* (ISBN 0-321-09220-1)** The *Answer Book* provides answers to all the exercises in the text.

***Printed Test Bank and Instructor's Resource Guide* (ISBN 0-321-09219-8)** The *Printed Test Bank* portion of this manual contains two diagnostic pretests, six free-response and two multiple-choice test forms per chapter, and two final exams. The *Instructor's Resource Guide* portion of the manual contains teaching suggestions for each chapter, additional practice exercises for every objective of every section, a correlation guide from the first to the second edition, phonetic spellings for all key terms in the text, and teaching notes and extensions for the Focus on Real-Data Applications in the text.

***TestGen-EQ with QuizMaster EQ* (ISBN 0-321-09221-X)** This fully networkable software enables instructors to create, edit, and administer tests using a computerized test bank of questions organized according to the chapter content of the text. Six question formats are available, and a built-in question editor allows the user to create graphs, import graphics, and insert mathematical symbols and templates, variables, or text. An "Export to HTML" feature allows practice tests to be posted to the Internet, and instructors can use QuizMaster-EQ to post quizzes to a local computer network so that students can take them on-line and have their results tracked automatically.

***Web Site:* www.MyMathLab.com** In addition to providing a wealth of resources for lecture-based courses, MyMathLab.com gives instructors a quick and easy way to create a complete on-line course based on *Introductory and Intermediate Algebra*, Second Edition. MyMathLab.com is hosted nationally at no cost to instructors, students, or schools, and it provides access to an interactive learning environment where all content is keyed directly to the text. Using a customized version of Blackboard™ as the course-management platform, MyMathLab.com lets instructors administer preexisting tests and quizzes or create their own. It provides detailed tracking of all student work as well as a wide array of communication tools for course participants. Within MyMathLab.com, students link directly from on-line pages of their text to supplementary resources such as tutorial software, interactive animations, and audio and video clips.

Acknowledgments

The comments, criticisms, and suggestions of users, nonusers, instructors, and students have positively shaped this textbook over the years, and we are most grateful for the many responses we have received. The feedback gathered for this revision of the text was particularly helpful, and we especially wish to thank the following individuals who provided invaluable suggestions:

Mary Kay Abbey, *Montgomery College*
Jannette Avery, *Monroe Community College*
Randall Allbritton, *Daytona Beach Community College*
Sonya Armstrong, *West Virginia State College*
Linda Beattie, *Western New Mexico University*
Linda Beller, *Brevard Community College*
Jean Bolyard, *Fairmont State College*
Tim C. Caldwell, *Meridian Community College*
Dawn Cox, *Cochise College*
Julie Dewan, *Mohawk Valley Community College*
Bill Dunn, *Las Positas College*
Lucy Edwards, *Las Positas College*
Rob Farinelli, *Community College of Allegheny—Boyce Campus*
J. Lloyd Harris, *Gulf Coast Community College*
Edith Hays, *Texas Woman's University*
Anthony Hearn, *Community College of Philadelphia*
Karen Heavin, *Morehead State University*
Christine Heinecke Lehmann, *Purdue University—North Central*
Elizabeth Heston, *Monroe Community College*
Matthew Hudock, *St. Philips College*
Mel Jacobson, *Snow College*
Salley Keely, *Clark College*
Harriet Kiser, *Floyd College*
Jeffrey Kroll, *Brazosport College*
Barbara Krueger, *Cochise College*
Valerie Lazzara, *Palm Beach Community College*
Sandy Lofstock, *California Lutheran University*
Valerie H. Maley, *Cape Fear Community College*
Susan McClory, *San Jose State University*
Jeffrey Mills, *Ohio State University*
Linda Murphy, *Northern Essex Community College*
Larry Potanski, *Pueblo Community College*
Janice Rech, *University of Nebraska at Omaha*
Diann Robinson, *Ivy Tech State College—Lafayette*
Rachael Schettenhelm, *Southern Connecticut State University*
Dwight Smith, *Prestonburg Community College*
Lee Ann Spahr, *Durham Technical Community College*
Theresa Stalder, *University of Illinois—Chicago*
Barbara Strauch, *DeVry Institute of Technology*
Cora S. West, *Florida Community College at Jacksonville*
Mark Tom, *College of the Sequoias*
Jackie Wing, *Angelina College*
Gabriel Yimesghen, *Community College of Philadelphia*
Karl Zilm, *Lewis and Clark Community College*

Our sincere thanks go to these dedicated individuals at Addison-Wesley who worked long and hard to make this revision a success: Maureen O'Connor, Ruth Berry, Ron Hampton, Dennis Schaefer, Dona Kenly, Suzanne Alley, and Jolene Lehr.

While Kitty Pellissier did her usual outstanding job checking the answers to all the exercises, she also reviewed the entire manuscript and provided invaluable content suggestions during both the writing and production processes. Steven Pusztai of Elm Street Publishing Services provided his customary excellent production work. We are most grateful to Peg Crider for researching and writing the Focus on Real-Data Applications feature; Paul Van Erden for his accurate and useful index; Becky Troutman for preparing the comprehensive List of Applications; Abby Tanenbaum for writing the new Diagnostic Pretest; and Randall Allbritton, Linda Buchanan, Scott Higinbotham, Valerie Maley, Laurie Semarne, and Sharon Testone for accuracy checking the manuscript.

As an author team, we are committed to the goal stated earlier in this Preface—to provide the best possible text and supplements package to help instructors teach and students succeed. We are most grateful to all those over the years who have aspired to this goal with us. As we continue to work toward it, we would welcome any comments or suggestions you might have. Please feel free to send your comments via e-mail to math@awl.com.

Margaret L. Lial
John Hornsby
Terry McGinnis

Feature Walk-Through

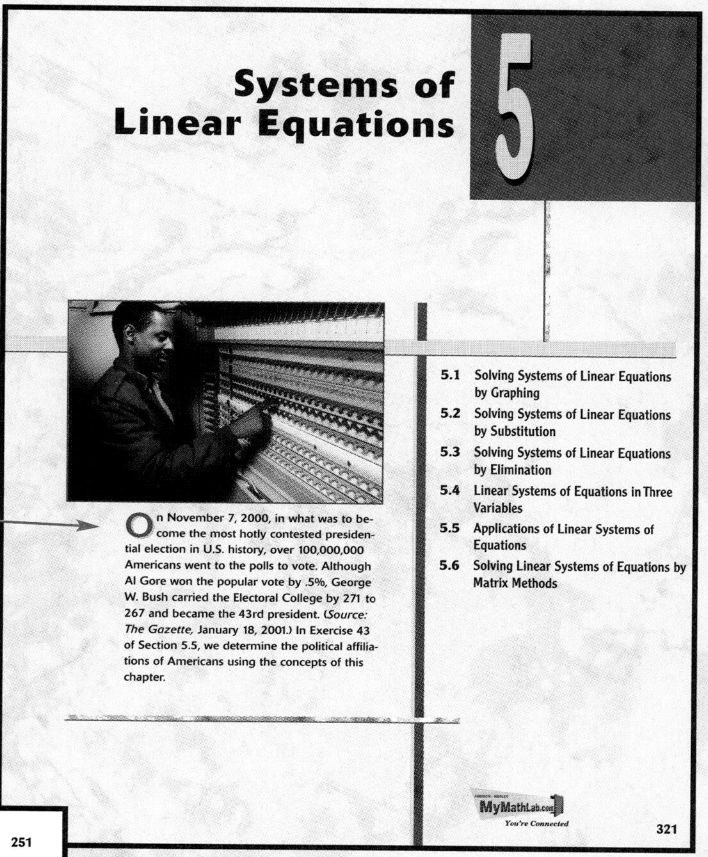

Systems of Linear Equations

5

On November 7, 2000, in what was to become the most hotly contested presidential election in U.S. history, over 100,000,000 Americans went to the polls to vote. Although Al Gore won the popular vote by .5%, George W. Bush carried the Electoral College by 271 to 267 and became the 43rd president. (*Source: The Gazette,* January 18, 2001.) In Exercise 43 of Section 5.5, we determine the political affiliations of Americans using the concepts of this chapter.

321

New! Chapter Openers New chapter openers feature real-world applications of mathematics that are relevant to students and tied to specific material within the chapters. (page 321)

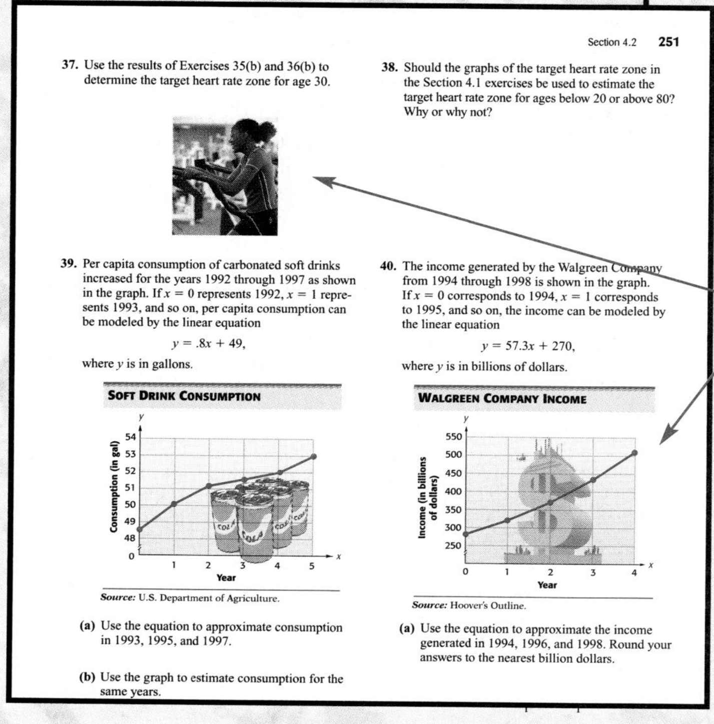

Section 4.2 251

37. Use the results of Exercises 35(b) and 36(b) to determine the target heart rate zone for age 30.

38. Should the graphs of the target heart rate zone in the Section 4.1 exercises be used to estimate the target heart rate zone for ages below 20 or above 80? Why or why not?

39. Per capita consumption of carbonated soft drinks increased for the years 1992 through 1997 as shown in the graph. If $x = 0$ represents 1992, $x = 1$ represents 1993, and so on, per capita consumption can be modeled by the linear equation

$$y = .8x + 49,$$

where y is in gallons.

Source: U.S. Department of Agriculture.

(a) Use the equation to approximate consumption in 1993, 1995, and 1997.

(b) Use the graph to estimate consumption for the same years.

40. The income generated by the Walgreen Company from 1994 through 1998 is shown in the graph. If $x = 0$ corresponds to 1994, $x = 1$ corresponds to 1995, and so on, the income can be modeled by the linear equation

$$y = 57.3x + 270,$$

where y is in billions of dollars.

Source: Hoover's Outline.

(a) Use the equation to approximate the income generated in 1994, 1996, and 1998. Round your answers to the nearest billion dollars.

Figures and Photos Today's students are more visually oriented than ever. Thus, a concerted effort has been made to add mathematical figures, diagrams, tables, and graphs whenever possible. Many of the graphs use a style similar to that seen by students in today's print and electronic media. Photos have been incorporated to enhance applications in examples and exercises. (page 251)

Relating Concepts Formerly titled *Mathematical Connections,* these sets of exercises help students tie together topics and develop problem-solving skills as they compare and contrast ideas, identify and describe patterns, and extend concepts to new situations. These exercises make great collaborative activities for pairs or small groups of students. (page 350)

350 Chapter 5 Systems of Linear Equations

RELATING CONCEPTS (Exercises 39–44) FOR INDIVIDUAL OR GROUP WORK

Attending the movies is one of America's favorite forms of entertainment. The graph shows how attendance gradually increased from 1991 to 1996. In 1991, attendance was 1141 *million, as represented by the point* $P(1991, 1141)$*. In 1996, attendance was* 1339 *million, as represented by the point* $Q(1996, 1339)$*. We can find an equation of line segment PQ using a system of equations, and then we can use the equation to approximate the attendance in any of the years between 1991 and 1996.* **Work Exercises 39–44 in order.**

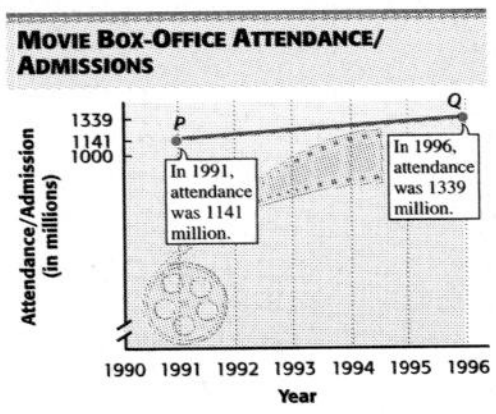

Source: Motion Picture Association of America.

39. The line segment has an equation that can be written in the form $y = ax + b$. Using the coordinates of point P with $x = 1991$ and $y = 1141$, write an equation in the variables a and b.

40. Using the coordinates of point Q with $x = 1996$ and $y = 1339$, write a second equation in the variables a and b.

41. Write the system of equations formed from the two equations in Exercises 39 and 40, and solve the system using the elimination method.

42. What is the equation of the segment PQ?

43. Let $x = 1993$ in the equation of Exercise 42, and solve for y. How does the result compare with the actual figure of 1244 million?

44. The data points for the years 1991 through 1996 do not lie in a perfectly straight line. Explain the pitfalls of relying too heavily on using the equation in Exercise 42 to predict attendance.

Focus on **Real-Data Applications**

What Do I Have to Average on My Tests to Get the Grade I Want?

On the first day of class, you are typically given a syllabus that describes the course requirements. If the syllabus includes a grading scale for homework, tests, projects, and final exam, then you should be able to predict the points you need on the final exam to earn a specific grade.

One intermediate algebra teacher bases final grades on points earned for three major exams, a comprehensive final exam, a daily activities grade (scaled), and lab participation and completion. The number of points available for each activity is given in the Graded Classwork table on the left. The teacher strictly adheres to the point ranges given in the Grade Distribution table on the right. A grade of IP (In Progress) is given to a student who participates fully but fails to achieve the course objectives.

GRADED CLASSWORK

Activity	Points Available
Homework and vocabulary	45
Daily activities (scaled)	55
Lab participation and completion	100
Major exams (3 at 100 pt)	300
Final exam	150
Total points	650

GRADE DISTRIBUTION

Grade	Points Required
A	585–650
B	520–584
C	455–519
IP	< 455 and active
F	< 455 and inactive

Notice that exams account for 450 of the possible 650 points. The remaining 200 points should be fairly easy to earn by keeping up with the day-to-day course requirements.

Assumption: You earn a "baseline" number of points based on the following criteria.

1. You earn *all* of the homework and vocabulary points.
2. You earn a minimum of 50 points based on daily activities.
3. You earn a minimum of 90 lab participation and completion points.

For Group Discussion

1. Assume that you earn the baseline number of points. Let x represent the test points to be earned. Write and solve linear inequalities to find the minimum number of points that you need in test scores to earn grades no lower than A, B, and C. What "test average" is each minimum score? Round *up* to the nearest whole percent.

2. To keep your scholarship, you must earn a B in the course. Write a compound inequality to find the range of points that you need in test scores to earn a B average. Solve the inequality. What range of "test averages" are those minimum scores? Round *up* to the nearest whole percent.

3. Mark does not like to do the homework or participate in labs. Assume that Mark earns only 15 points in homework and vocabulary, 40 points in daily activities, and 50 points in lab participation. Write and solve linear inequalities to find the minimum number of points that Mark needs in test scores to earn grades no lower than A, B, and C. What "test average" is each minimum score? Round *up* to the nearest whole percent.

212

New! Focus on Real-Data Applications These one-page activities found throughout the text present even more relevant and in-depth looks at how mathematics is used in the real world. Designed to help instructors answer the often-asked question, "When will I ever use this stuff?," these activities ask students to read and interpret data from newspaper articles, the Internet, and other familiar, real sources. The activities are well suited to collaborative work and can also be completed by individuals or used for open-ended class discussions. (page 212)

Calculator Tip Figure 10 shows how a graphing calculator displays the preceding two matrices. Work with matrices is made much easier by using technology when available. Consult your owner's manual for details.

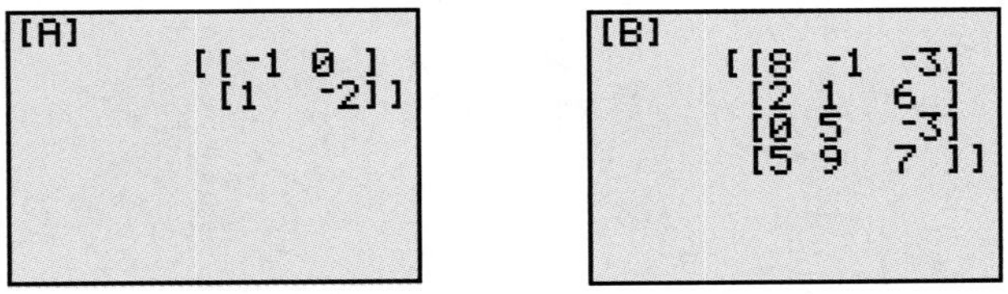

Figure 10

New! Calculator Tips These optional tips, marked with calculator icons, offer basic information and instruction for students using calculators in the course. (page 375)

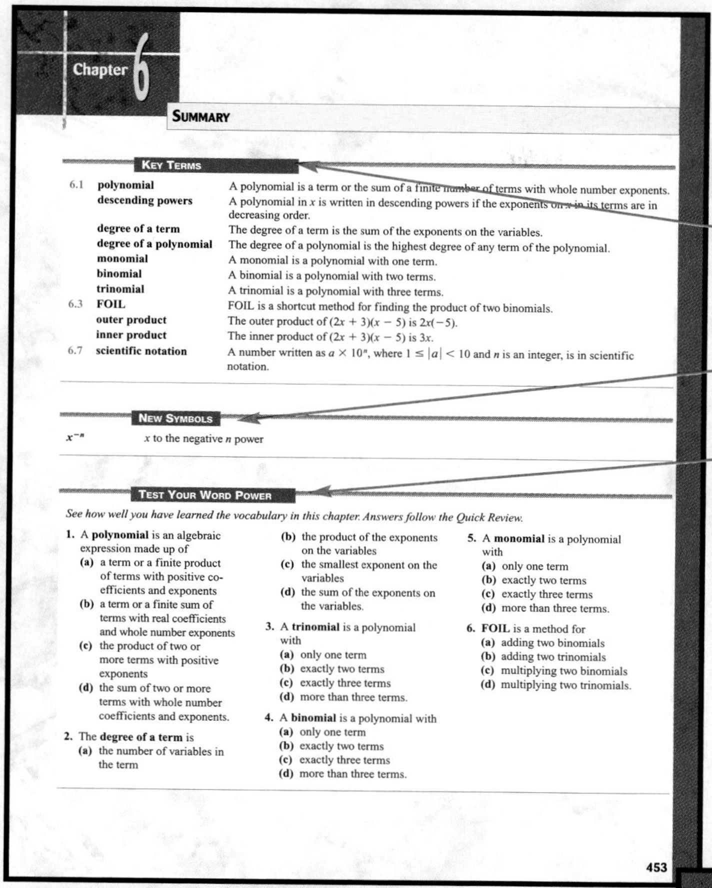

Chapter 6

SUMMARY

KEY TERMS

6.1	**polynomial**	A polynomial is a term or the sum of a finite number of terms with whole number exponents.
	descending powers	A polynomial in x is written in descending powers if the exponents on x in its terms are in decreasing order.
	degree of a term	The degree of a term is the sum of the exponents on the variables.
	degree of a polynomial	The degree of a polynomial is the highest degree of any term of the polynomial.
	monomial	A monomial is a polynomial with one term.
	binomial	A binomial is a polynomial with two terms.
	trinomial	A trinomial is a polynomial with three terms.
6.3	**FOIL**	FOIL is a shortcut method for finding the product of two binomials.
	outer product	The outer product of $(2x + 3)(x - 5)$ is $2x(-5)$.
	inner product	The inner product of $(2x + 3)(x - 5)$ is $3x$.
6.7	**scientific notation**	A number written as $a \times 10^n$, where $1 \le \lvert a \rvert < 10$ and n is an integer, is in scientific notation.

NEW SYMBOLS

x^{-n} x to the negative n power

TEST YOUR WORD POWER

See how well you have learned the vocabulary in this chapter. Answers follow the Quick Review.

1. A **polynomial** is an algebraic expression made up of
   (a) a term or a finite product of terms with positive coefficients and exponents
   (b) a term or a finite sum of terms with real coefficients and whole number exponents
   (c) the product of two or more terms with positive exponents
   (d) the sum of two or more terms with whole number coefficients and exponents.
2. The **degree of a term** is
   (a) the number of variables in the term
   (b) the product of the exponents on the variables
   (c) the smallest exponent on the variables
   (d) the sum of the exponents on the variables.
3. A **trinomial** is a polynomial with
   (a) only one term
   (b) exactly two terms
   (c) exactly three terms
   (d) more than three terms.
4. A **binomial** is a polynomial with
   (a) only one term
   (b) exactly two terms
   (c) exactly three terms
   (d) more than three terms.
5. A **monomial** is a polynomial with
   (a) only one term
   (b) exactly two terms
   (c) exactly three terms
   (d) more than three terms.
6. **FOIL** is a method for
   (a) adding two binomials
   (b) adding two trinomials
   (c) multiplying two binomials
   (d) multiplying two trinomials.

453

End-of-Chapter Material One of the most admired features of the Lial textbooks is the extensive and well-thought-out end-of-chapter material. At the end of each chapter, students will find:

Key Terms are listed, defined, and referenced back to the appropriate section number. (page 453)

New Symbols are listed for easy reference and study.

New! Test Your Word Power To help students understand and master mathematical vocabulary, Test Your Word Power has been incorporated in each Chapter Summary. Students are quizzed on Key Terms from the chapter in a multiple-choice format. Answers and examples illustrating each term are provided.

A Chapter Test helps students practice for the real thing. (page 461)

New! Study Skills Component A desk-light icon at key points in the text directs students to a separate *Study Skills Workbook* containing activities correlated directly to the text. This unique workbook explains how the brain actually learns, so students understand *why* the study tips presented will help them succeed in the course.

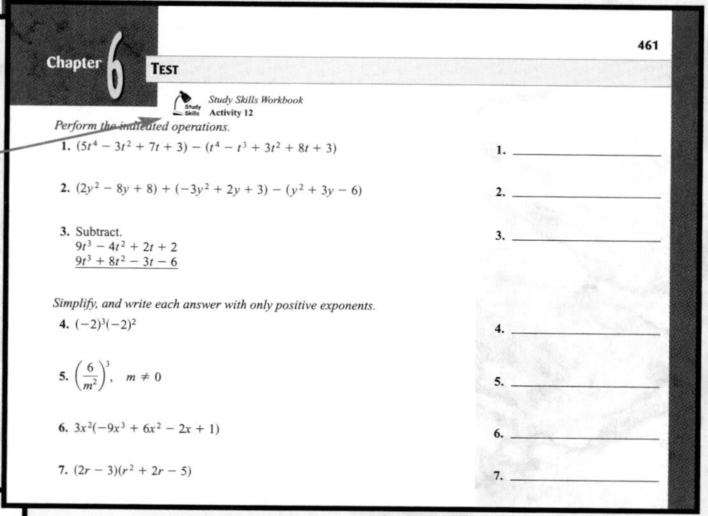

Chapter 6 TEST 461

Study Skills Workbook Activity 12

Perform the indicated operations.

1. $(5t^4 - 3t^2 + 7t + 3) - (t^4 - t^3 + 3t^2 + 8t + 3)$ 1. ______
2. $(2y^2 - 8y + 8) + (-3y^2 + 2y + 3) - (y^2 + 3y - 6)$ 2. ______
3. Subtract.   3. ______
   $9t^3 - 4t^2 + 2t + 2$
   $9t^3 + 8t^2 - 3t - 6$

Simplify, and write each answer with only positive exponents.

4. $(-2)^3(-2)^2$ 4. ______
5. $\left(\frac{6}{m^2}\right)^3, \quad m \neq 0$ 5. ______
6. $3x^2(-9x^3 + 6x^2 - 2x + 1)$ 6. ______
7. $(2r - 3)(r^2 + 2r - 5)$ 7. ______

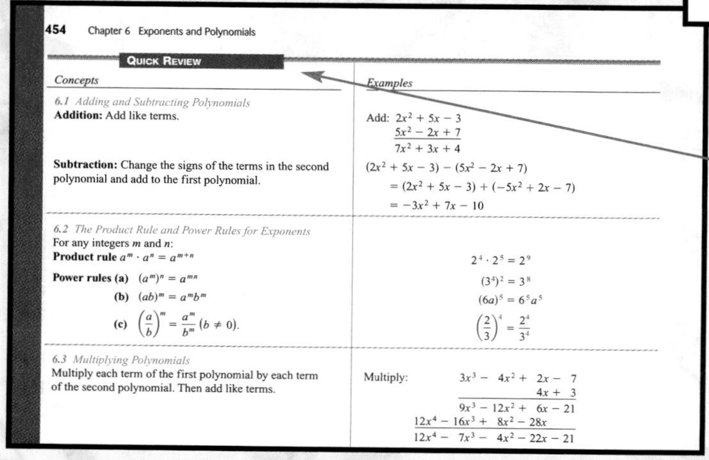

454 Chapter 6 Exponents and Polynomials

QUICK REVIEW

Concepts	Examples
6.1 Adding and Subtracting Polynomials **Addition:** Add like terms.	Add: $2x^2 + 5x - 3$; $5x^2 - 2x + 7$; $7x^2 + 3x + 4$
Subtraction: Change the signs of the terms in the second polynomial and add to the first polynomial.	$(2x^2 + 5x - 3) - (5x^2 - 2x + 7)$ $= (2x^2 + 5x - 3) + (-5x^2 + 2x - 7)$ $= -3x^2 + 7x - 10$
6.2 The Product Rule and Power Rules for Exponents For any integers m and n: **Product rule** $a^m \cdot a^n = a^{m+n}$	$2^4 \cdot 2^5 = 2^9$
Power rules (a) $(a^m)^n = a^{mn}$	$(3^4)^2 = 3^8$
(b) $(ab)^m = a^m b^m$	$(6a)^5 = 6^5 a^5$
(c) $\left(\frac{a}{b}\right)^m = \frac{a^m}{b^m} \quad (b \neq 0)$.	$\left(\frac{2}{3}\right)^4 = \frac{2^4}{3^4}$
6.3 Multiplying Polynomials Multiply each term of the first polynomial by each term of the second polynomial. Then add like terms.	Multiply: $3x^3 - 4x^2 + 2x - 7$; $4x + 3$; $9x^3 - 12x^2 + 6x - 21$; $12x^4 - 16x^3 + 8x^2 - 28x$; $12x^4 - 7x^3 - 4x^2 - 22x - 21$

Quick Review sections give students not only the main concepts from the chapter (referenced back to the appropriate section), but also an adjacent example of each concept. (page 454)

Review Exercises are keyed to the appropriate sections so that students can refer to examples of that type of problem if they need help. (page 457)

Chapter 6 REVIEW EXERCISES

[6.1] *Combine terms where possible in each polynomial. Write the answer in descending powers of the variable. Give the degree of the answer. Identify the polynomial as a* monomial, binomial, trinomial, *or* none of these.

1. $9m^2 + 11m^2 + 2m^2$

2. $-4p + p^3 - p^2 + 8p + 2$

3. $12a^5 - 9a^4 + 8a^3 + 2a^2 - a + 3$

4. $-7y^5 - 8y^4 - y^5 + y^4 + 9y$

Add or subtract as indicated.

5. Add.
$$\begin{array}{r} -2a^3 + 5a^2 \\ \underline{-3a^3 - a^2} \end{array}$$

6. Add.
$$\begin{array}{r} 4r^3 - 8r^2 + 6r \\ \underline{-2r^3 + 5r^2 + 3r} \end{array}$$

7. Subtract.
$$\begin{array}{r} 6y^2 - 8y + 2 \\ \underline{-5y^2 + 2y - 7} \end{array}$$

8. Subtract.
$$\begin{array}{r} -12k^4 - 8k^2 + 7k - 5 \\ \underline{k^4 + 7k^2 + 11k + 1} \end{array}$$

9. $(2m^3 - 8m^2 + 4) + (8m^3 + 2m^2 - 7)$

10. $(-5y^2 + 3y + 11) + (4y^2 - 7y + 15)$

11. $(6p^2 - p - 8) - (-4p^2 + 2p + 3)$

12. $(12r^4 - 7r^3 + 2r^2) - (5r^4 - 3r^3 + 2r^2 + 1)$

[6.2] *Use the product rule or power rules to simplify each expression. Write the answer in exponential form.*

13. $4^3 \cdot 4^8$ **14.** $(-5)^6(-5)^5$ **15.** $(-8x^4)(9x^3)$ **16.** $(2x^2)(5x^3)(x^9)$

MIXED REVIEW EXERCISES

Perform the indicated operations. Write with positive exponents. Assume that no denominators are equal to 0.

87. $19^0 - 3^0$ **88.** $(3p)^4(3p^{-7})$ **89.** 7^{-2}

90. $(-7 + 2k)^2$ **91.** $\dfrac{2y^3 + 17y^2 + 37y + 7}{2y + 7}$ **92.** $\left(\dfrac{6r^2s}{5}\right)^4$

93. $-m^5(8m^2 + 10m + 6)$ **94.** $\left(\dfrac{1}{2}\right)^{-5}$ **95.** $(25x^2y^3 - 8xy^2 + 15x^3y) \div (5x)$

96. $(6r^{-2})^{-1}$ **97.** $(2x + y)^3$ **98.** $2^{-1} + 4^{-1}$

99. $(a + 2)(a^2 - 4a + 1)$ **100.** $(5y^3 - 8y^2 + 7) - (-3y^3 + y^2 + 2)$

101. $(2r + 5)(5r - 2)$ **102.** $(12a + 1)(12a - 1)$

103. Find a polynomial that represents the area of the rectangle shown.

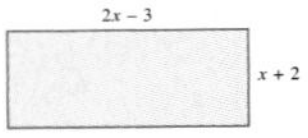

104. If the side of a square has a measure represented by $5x^4 + 2x^2$, what polynomial represents its area?

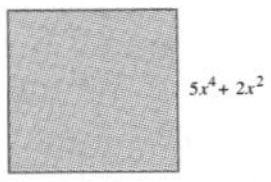

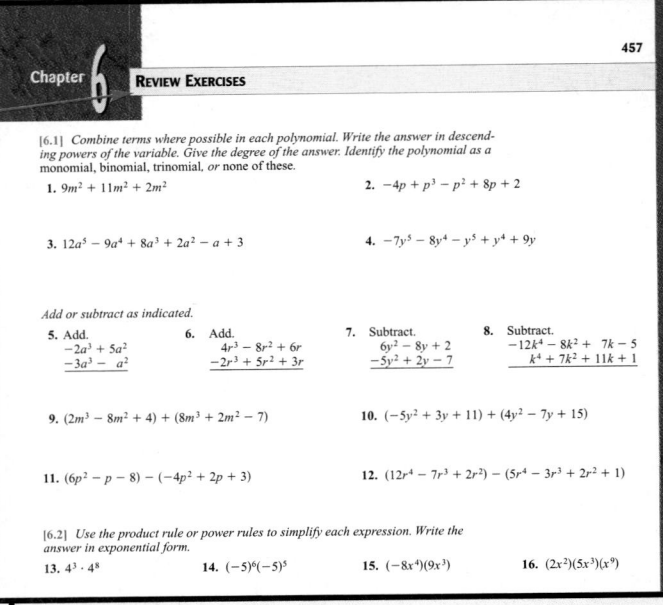

Mixed Review Exercises require students to solve problems without the help of section references. (page 460)

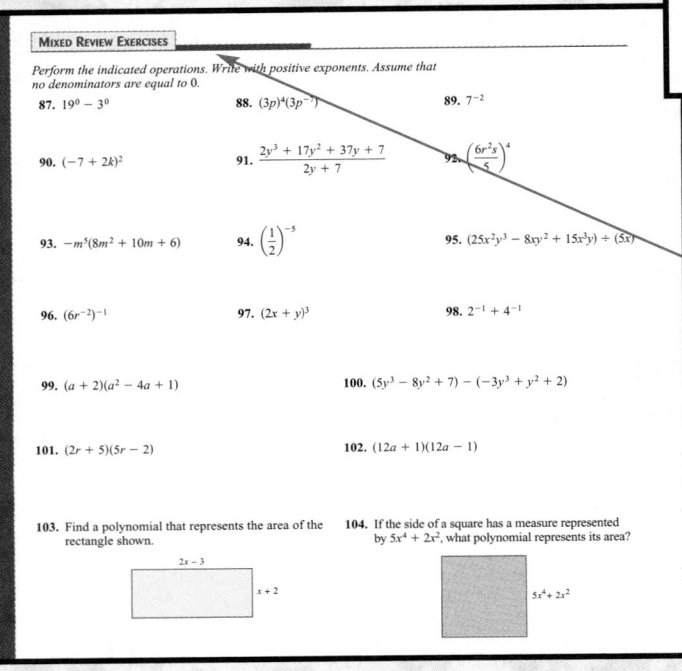

Cumulative Review Exercises gather various types of exercises from preceding chapters to help students remember and retain what they are learning throughout the course. (page 463)

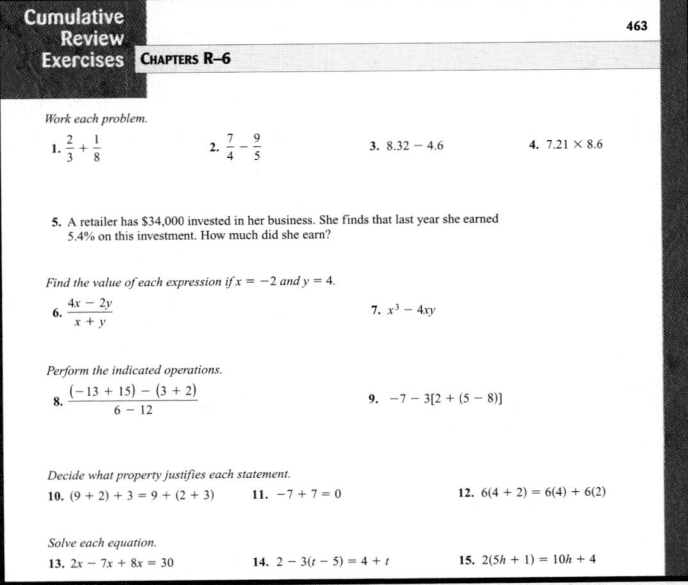

Cumulative Review Exercises CHAPTERS R–6

Work each problem.

1. $\dfrac{2}{3} + \dfrac{1}{8}$ **2.** $\dfrac{7}{4} - \dfrac{9}{5}$ **3.** $8.32 - 4.6$ **4.** 7.21×8.6

5. A retailer has \$34,000 invested in her business. She finds that last year she earned 5.4% on this investment. How much did she earn?

Find the value of each expression if $x = -2$ *and* $y = 4$.

6. $\dfrac{4x - 2y}{x + y}$ **7.** $x^3 - 4xy$

Perform the indicated operations.

8. $\dfrac{(-13 + 15) - (3 + 2)}{6 - 12}$ **9.** $-7 - 3[2 + (5 - 8)]$

Decide what property justifies each statement.

10. $(9 + 2) + 3 = 9 + (2 + 3)$ **11.** $-7 + 7 = 0$ **12.** $6(4 + 2) = 6(4) + 6(2)$

Solve each equation.

13. $2x - 7x + 8x = 30$ **14.** $2 - 3(t - 5) = 4 + t$ **15.** $2(5h + 1) = 10h + 4$

An Introduction to Calculators

There is little doubt that the appearance of handheld calculators three decades ago and the later development of scientific and graphing calculators have changed the methods of learning and studying mathematics forever. For example, computations with tables of logarithms and slide rules made up an important part of mathematics courses prior to 1970. Today, with the widespread availability of calculators, these topics are studied only for their historical significance.

Most consumer models of calculators are inexpensive. At first, however, they were costly. One of the first consumer models available was the Texas Instruments SR-10, which sold for about $150 in 1973. It could perform the four operations of arithmetic and take square roots, but could do very little more.

Today, calculators come in a large array of different types, sizes, and prices. *For the course for which this textbook is intended, the most appropriate type is the scientific calculator*, which costs $10–$20.

In this introduction, we explain some of the features of scientific and graphing calculators. However, remember that calculators vary among manufacturers and models, and that while the methods explained here apply to many of them, they may not apply to your specific calculator. For this reason, it is important to remember that *this introduction is only a guide and is not intended to take the place of your owner's manual.* Always refer to the manual in the event you need an explanation of how to perform a particular operation.

Scientific Calculators

Scientific calculators are capable of much more than the typical four-function calculator that you might use for balancing your checkbook. Most scientific calculators use *algebraic logic*. (Models sold by Texas Instruments, Sharp, Casio, and Radio Shack, for example, use algebraic logic.) A notable exception is Hewlett-Packard, a company whose calculators use *Reverse Polish Notation* (RPN). In this introduction, we explain the use of calculators with algebraic logic.

Arithmetic Operations To perform an operation of arithmetic, simply enter the first number, press the operation key ((+), (−), (×), or (÷)), enter the second number, and then press the (=) key. For example, to add 4 and 3, use the following keystrokes.

(4) (+) (3) (=) [7]

Change Sign Key The key marked (+/−) allows you to change the sign of a display. This is particularly useful when you wish to enter a negative number. For example, to enter −3, use the following keystrokes.

(3) (+/−) [− 3]

Memory Key Scientific calculators can hold a number in memory for later use. The label of the memory key varies among models; two of these are M and STO. The M+ and M− keys allow you to add to or subtract from the value currently in memory. The memory recall key, labeled MR, RM, or RCL, allows you to retrieve the value stored in memory.

Suppose that you wish to store the number 5 in memory. Enter 5, then press the key for memory. You can then perform other calculations. When you need to retrieve the 5, press the key for memory recall.

If a calculator has a constant memory feature, the value in memory will be retained even after the power is turned off. Some advanced calculators have more than one memory. It is best to read the owner's manual for your model to see exactly how memory is activated.

Clearing/Clear Entry Keys These keys allow you to clear the display or clear the last entry entered into the display. They are usually marked C and CE. In some models, pressing the C key once will clear the last entry, while pressing it twice will clear the entire operation in progress.

Second Function Key This key is used in conjunction with another key to activate a function that is printed *above* an operation key (and not on the key itself). It is usually marked 2nd. For example, suppose you wish to find the square of a number, and the squaring function (explained in more detail later) is printed above another key. You would need to press 2nd before the desired squaring function can be activated.

Square Root Key Pressing the square root key, $\sqrt{x}$, will give the square root (or an approximation of the square root) of the number in the display. For example, to find the square root of 36, use the following keystrokes.

3 6 $\sqrt{x}$ 6

The square root of 2 is an example of an irrational number (Chapter 9). The calculator will give an approximation of its value, since the decimal for $\sqrt{2}$ never terminates and never repeats. The number of digits shown will vary among models. To find an approximation of $\sqrt{2}$, use the following keystrokes.

2 $\sqrt{x}$ 1.4142136 An approximation for $\sqrt{2}$

Squaring Key The x^2 key allows you to square the entry in the display. For example, to square 35.7, use the following keystrokes.

3 5 . 7 x^2 1274.49

The squaring key and the square root key are often found on the same key, with one of them being a second function (that is, activated by the second function key previously described).

Reciprocal Key The key marked 1/x is the reciprocal key. (When two numbers have a product of 1, they are called *reciprocals*. See Chapter 1.) Suppose that you wish to find the reciprocal of 5. Use the following keystrokes.

5 1/x 0.2

Inverse Key Some calculators have an inverse key, marked INV. Inverse operations are operations that "undo" each other. For example, the operations of squaring and taking the square root are inverse operations. The use of the INV key varies among different models of calculators, so read your owner's manual carefully.

Exponential Key The key marked x^y or y^x allows you to raise a number to a power. For example, if you wish to raise 4 to the fifth power (that is, find 4^5, as explained in Chapter 1), use the following keystrokes.

4 x^y 5 =   1024

Root Key Some calculators have this key specifically marked $\sqrt[x]{x}$ or $\sqrt[x]{y}$; with others, the operation of taking roots is accomplished by using the inverse key in conjunction with the exponential key. Suppose, for example, your calculator is of the latter type and you wish to find the fifth root of 1024. Use the following keystrokes.

1 0 2 4 INV x^y 5 =   4

Notice how this "undoes" the operation explained in the exponential key discussion.

Pi Key The number π is an important number in mathematics. It occurs, for example, in the area and circumference formulas for a circle. By pressing the π key, you can display the first few digits of π. (Because π is irrational, the display shows only an approximation.) One popular model gives the following display when the π key is pressed.

3.1415927   An approximation for π

Methods of Display When decimal approximations are shown on scientific calculators, they are either *truncated* or *rounded*. To see how a particular model is programmed, evaluate 1/18 as an example. If the display shows .0555555 (last digit 5), it truncates the display. If it shows .0555556 (last digit 6), it rounds the display.

When very large or very small numbers are obtained as answers, scientific calculators often express these numbers in scientific notation (Chapter 6). For example, if you multiply 6,265,804 by 8,980,591, the display might look like this:

5.6270623 13

The 13 at the far right means that the number on the left is multiplied by 10^{13}. This means that the decimal point must be moved 13 places to the right if the answer is to be expressed in its usual form. Even then, the value obtained will only be an approximation: 56,270,623,000,000.

Graphing Calculators

Graphing calculators are becoming increasingly popular in mathematics classrooms. While you are not expected to have a graphing calculator to study from this book, we include the following as background information and reference should your course or future courses require the use of graphing calculators.

Basic Features

Graphing calculators provide many features beyond those found on scientific calculators. In addition to the typical keys found on scientific calculators, they have keys that can be used to create graphs, make tables, analyze data, and change settings. One of the major differences between graphing and scientific calculators is that a graphing calculator has a larger viewing screen with graphing capabilities. The screens below illustrate the graphs of $y = x$ and $y = x^2$.

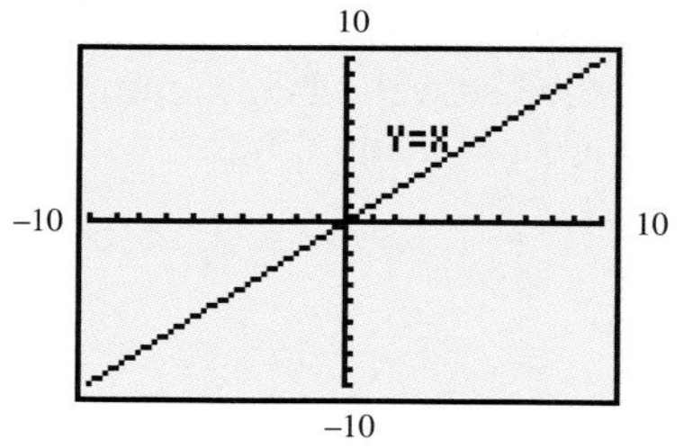

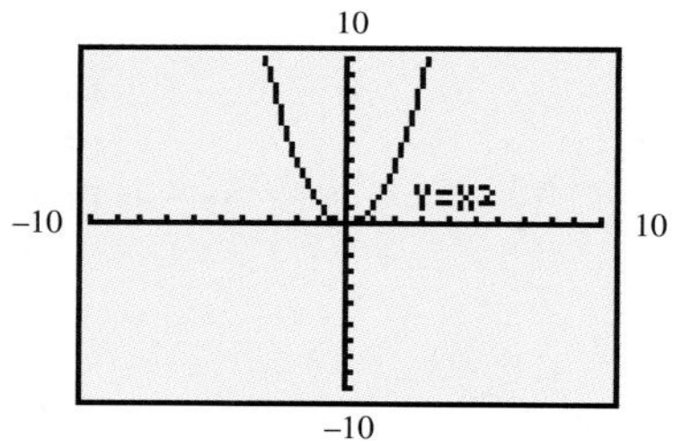

If you look closely at the screens, you will see that the graphs appear to be jagged rather than smooth, as they should be. The reason for this is that graphing calculators have much lower resolution than computer screens. Because of this, graphs generated by graphing calculators must be interpreted carefully.

Editing Input

The screen of a graphing calculator can display several lines of text at a time. This feature allows you to view both previous and current expressions. If an incorrect expression is entered, an error message is displayed. The erroneous expression can be viewed and corrected by using various editing keys, much like a word-processing program. You do not need to enter the entire expression again. Many graphing calculators can also recall past expressions for editing or updating. The screen on the left below shows how two expressions are evaluated. The final line is entered incorrectly, and the resulting error message is shown in the screen on the right.

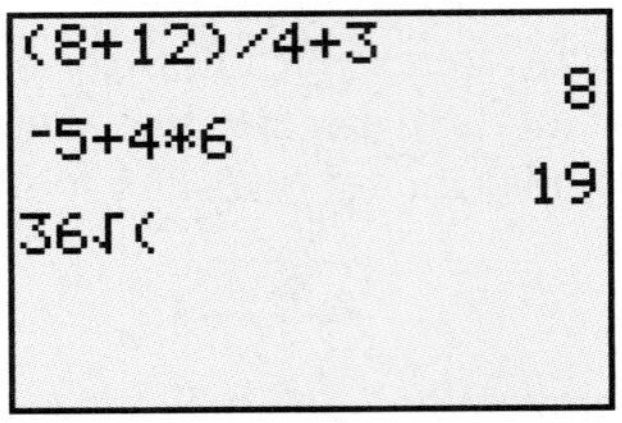

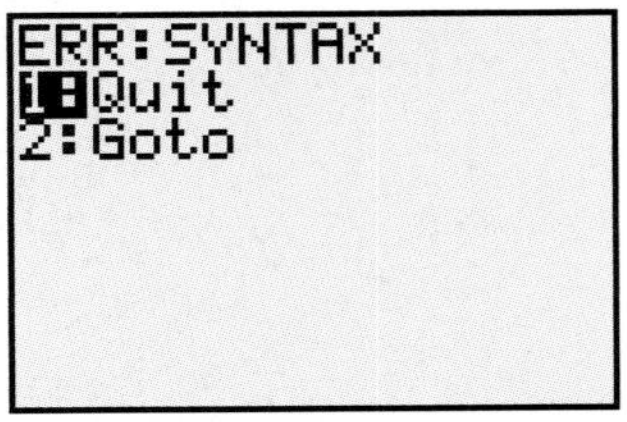

Order of Operations

Arithmetic operations on graphing calculators are usually entered as they are written in mathematical expressions. For example, to evaluate $\sqrt{36}$ on a typical scientific calculator, you would first enter 36 and then press the square root key. As seen above, this is not the correct syntax for a graphing calculator. To find this root, you would first press the square root key, and then enter 36. See the screen on the left below. The order of operations on a graphing calculator is also important, and current models assist the user by inserting parentheses when typical errors might occur. The open parenthesis that follows the square root symbol is automatically entered by the calculator so that an expression such as $\sqrt{2 \times 8}$ will not be calculated incorrectly as $\sqrt{2} \times 8$. Compare the two entries and their results in the screen on the right.

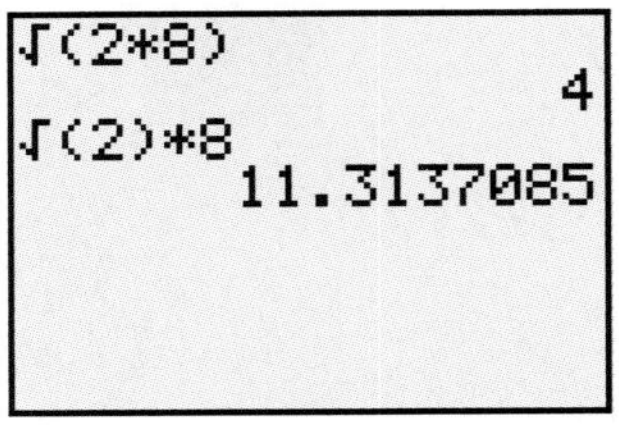

Viewing Windows

The viewing window for a graphing calculator is similar to the viewfinder in a camera. A camera usually cannot take a photograph of an entire view of a scene. The camera must be centered on some object and can capture only a portion of the available scenery. A camera with a zoom lens can photograph different views of the same scene by zooming in and out. Graphing calculators have similar capabilities. The *xy*-coordinate plane is infinite. The calculator screen can only show a finite, rectangular region in the plane, and it must be specified before the graph can be drawn. This is done by setting both minimum and maximum values for the *x*- and *y*-axes. The scale (distance between tick marks) is usually specified as well. Determining an appropriate viewing window for a graph is often a challenge, and many times it will take a few attempts before a satisfactory window is found.

The screen on the left shows a standard viewing window, and the graph of $y = 2x + 1$ is shown on the right. Using a different window would give a different view of the line.

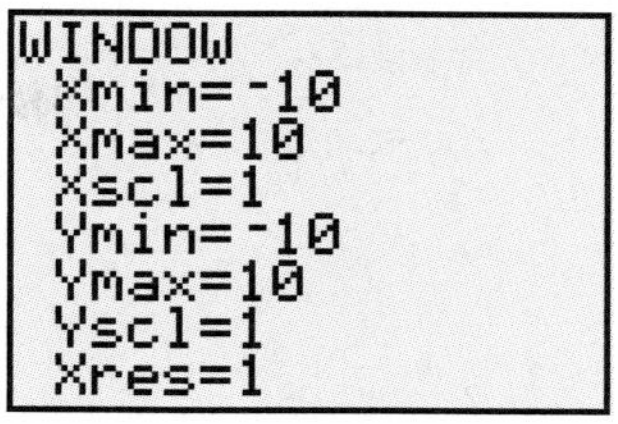

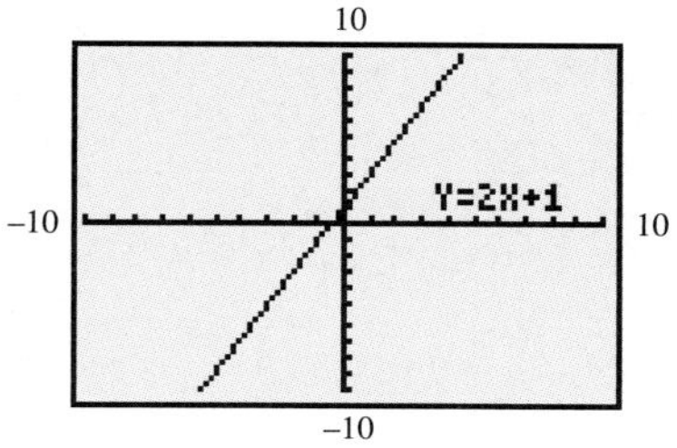

Locating Points on a Graph: Tracing and Tables

Graphing calculators allow you to trace along the graph of an equation and display the coordinates of points on the graph. See the screen on the left below, which indicates that the point (2, 5) lies on the graph of $y = 2x + 1$. Tables for equations can also be displayed. The screen on the right shows a partial table for this same equation. Note the middle of the screen, which indicates that when $x = 2$, $y = 5$.

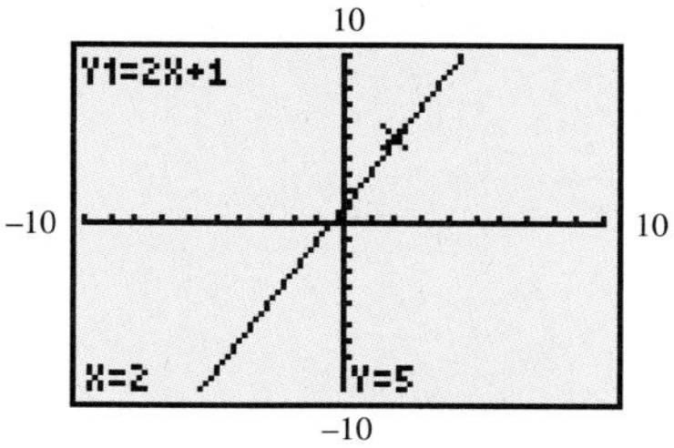

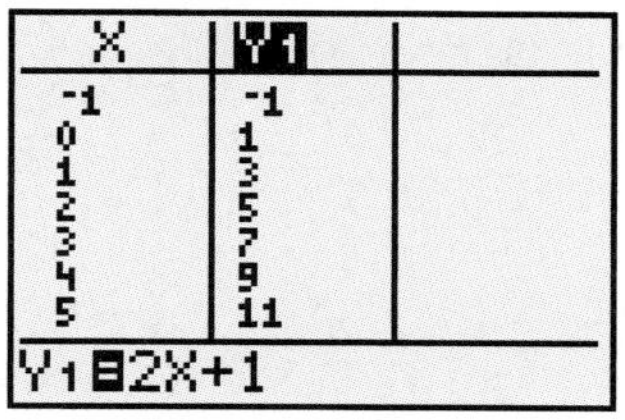

Additional Features

There are many features of graphing calculators that go far beyond the scope of this book. These calculators can be programmed, much like computers. Many of them can solve equations at the stroke of a key, analyze statistical data, and perform symbolic algebraic manipulations. Mathematicians from the past would have been amazed by today's calculators. Many important equations in mathematics cannot be solved by hand. However, their solutions can often be approximated using a calculator. Calculators also provide the opportunity to ask "What if . . . ?" more easily. Values in algebraic expressions can be altered and conjectures tested quickly.

Final Comments

Despite the power of today's calculators, they cannot replace human thought. ***In the entire problem-solving process, your brain is the most important component.*** Calculators are only tools and, like any tool, they must be used appropriately in order to enhance our ability to understand mathematics. Mathematical insight may often be the quickest and easiest way to solve a problem; a calculator may neither be needed nor appropriate. By applying mathematical concepts, you can make the decision whether or not to use a calculator.

To the Student: Success in Algebra

There are two main reasons students have difficulty with mathematics:

- Students start in a course for which they do not have the necessary background knowledge.
- Students don't know how to study mathematics effectively.

Your instructor can help you decide whether this is the right course for you. We can give you some study tips.

Studying mathematics *is* different from studying subjects like English and history. The key to success is regular practice. This should not be surprising. After all, can you learn to play the piano or ski well without a lot of regular practice? The same is true for learning mathematics. Working problems nearly every day is the key to becoming successful. Here is a list of things that will help you succeed in studying algebra.

1. *Attend class regularly.* Pay attention to what your instructor says and does in class, and take careful notes. In particular, note the problems the instructor works on the board and copy the complete solutions. Keep these notes separate from your homework to avoid confusion when you review them later.
2. Don't hesitate to *ask questions in class.* It is not a sign of weakness but of strength. There are always other students with the same question who are too shy to ask.
3. *Read your text carefully.* Many students read only enough to get by, usually only the examples. Reading the complete section will help you solve the homework problems. Most exercises are keyed to specific examples or objectives that will explain the procedures for working them.
4. Before you start on your homework assignment, *rework the problems the teacher worked in class.* This will reinforce what you have learned. Many students say, "I understand it perfectly when you do it, but I get stuck when I try to work the problem myself."
5. Do your homework assignment only *after reading the text* and reviewing your notes from class. Check your work against the answers in the back of the book. If you get a problem wrong and are unable to understand why, mark that problem and ask your instructor about it. Then practice working additional problems of the same type to reinforce what you have learned.
6. *Work as neatly as you can.* Write your symbols clearly, and make sure the problems are clearly separated from each other. Working neatly will help you to think clearly and also make it easier to review the homework before a test.
7. After you complete a homework assignment, *look over the text again.* Try to identify the main ideas that are in the lesson. Often they are clearly highlighted or boxed in the text.
8. *Use the chapter test at the end of each chapter as a practice test.* Work through the problems under test conditions, without referring to the text or the answers until you are finished. You may want to time yourself to see how long it takes you. When you finish, check your answers against those in the back of the book, and study the problems you missed.

9. *Keep all quizzes and tests that are returned to you,* and use them when you study for future tests and the final exam. These quizzes and tests indicate what concepts your instructor considers to be most important. Be sure to correct any problems on these tests that you missed, so you will have the corrected work to study.

10. *Don't worry if you do not understand a new topic right away.* As you read more about it and work through the problems, you will gain understanding. Each time you review a topic you will understand it a little better. Few people understand each topic completely right from the start.

Reading a list of study tips is a good start, but you may need some help actually *applying* the tips to your work in this math course.

Study Skills Watch for this icon as you work in this textbook, particularly in the first few chapters. It will direct you to one of 12 activities in the *Study Skills Workbook* that comes with this text. Each activity helps you to actually *use* a study skills technique. These techniques will greatly improve your chances for success in this course.

- Find out *how your brain learns new material.* Then use that information to set up effective ways to learn math.
- Find out *why short-term memory is so short* and what you can do to help your brain remember new material weeks and months later.
- Find out *what happens when you "blank out" on a test* and simple ways to prevent it from happening.

All the activities in the *Study Skills Workbook* are practical ways to enjoy and succeed at math. Whether you need help with note taking, managing homework, taking tests, or preparing for a final exam, you'll find specific, clearly explained ideas that really work because they're based on research about how the brain learns and remembers.

Diagnostic Pretest

Study Skills Workbook
Activity 1

[Chapter R]

1. Perform the indicated operations. Write answers in lowest terms.

(a) $\frac{42}{5} \div \frac{7}{15}$ **(b)** $6\frac{7}{8} + 3\frac{2}{3}$

1. (a) 18
(b) $\frac{253}{24}$ or $10\frac{13}{24}$

2. Subtract $38 - 9.678$.

2. 28.322

3. **(a)** Convert .99% to a decimal.

(b) Convert 4.72 to a percent.

3. (a) $.0099$
(b) 472%

[Chapter 1]

Perform the indicated operations.

4. $(-3)(-8) - 4(-2)^3$

5. $\dfrac{-6 + |-11 + 5|}{4^2 - (-9)}$

6. Evaluate $\dfrac{6r - 2s^2}{-3t}$ if $r = -5$, $s = -3$, and $t = 4$.

4. 56
5. 0
6. 4

[Chapter 2]

7. Solve and check $-8(x - 3) + 12x = 15 - (2x + 3)$.

7. $\{-2\}$

8. The two largest cities in the United States are New York and Los Angeles. On July 1, 1998, the population of New York was about 3,822,610 greater than the population of Los Angeles, and there were a total of about 11,017,722 people living in these two cities. Find the population of each city, using these population estimates. Do not round your answer. (*Source: The World Almanac and Book of Facts,* 2000.)

8. New York: 7,420,166; Los Angeles: 3,597,556

9. Find the measure of each marked angle.

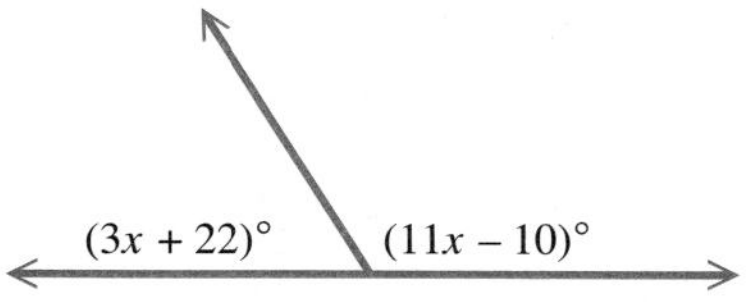

9. 58°, 122°

[Chapter 3]

Solve each inequality. Give the solution set in both interval and graph forms.

10. $3x - 2(x - 7) \geq 4(3x + 2) + x$

10. $\left(-\infty, \frac{1}{2}\right]$

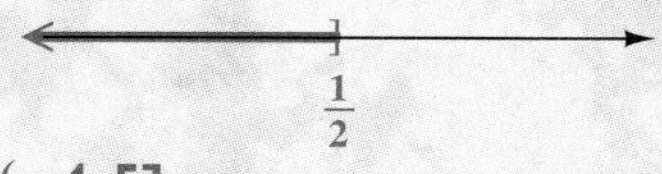

11. $-8t < 32$ and $3t - 5 \leq 10$

11. $(-4, 5]$

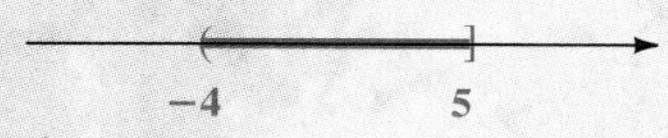

12. Solve $|4 - 5y| = |3y + 9|$.

12. $\left\{-\frac{5}{8}, \frac{13}{2}\right\}$

[Chapter 4]

13. Find the x- and y-intercepts and graph the equation $3x - 5y = -15$.

13. x-intercept: $(-5, 0)$

y-intercept: $(0, 3)$

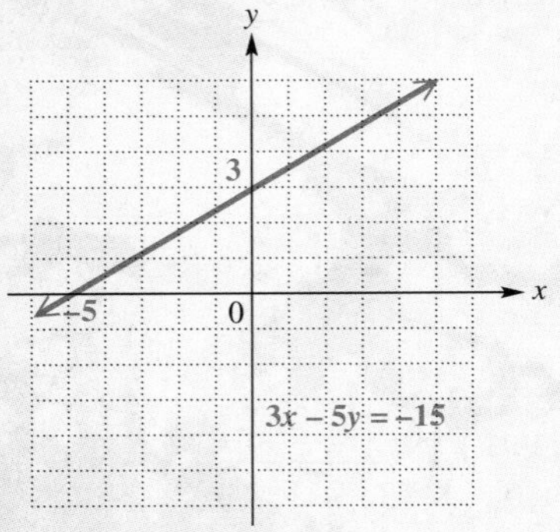

14. Find the slope of the line through $(5, -12)$ and $(-9, 10)$.

14. $-\frac{11}{7}$

15. Graph $4x + 3y < -12$.

15.

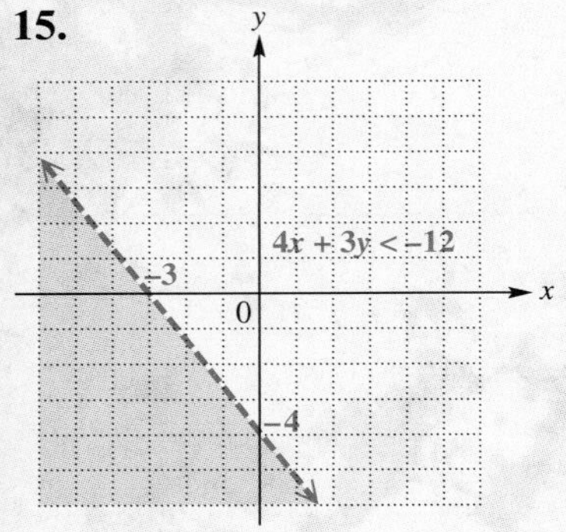

16. The median ages for first marriage for women in the United States from 1994–1998 are shown in the table.

Marriage Age	24.5	24.5	24.8	25.0	25.0
Year	1994	1995	1996	1997	1998

Source: World Almanac and Book of Facts, 2000.

Which set of ordered pairs from the table is a function? Explain.

A. (Marriage Age, Year) **B.** (Year, Marriage Age)

16. **B; Set A includes two ordered pairs with the same first component and different second components, so it is not a function.**

[Chapter 5]

Solve each system.

17. $-2x + 5y = 11$
$y = x + 7$

18. $2x + 3y = 1$
$3x - 4y = 27$

19. $3x + y - z = -2$
$x - 2y + z = 8$
$-2x + 3y + 3z = 1$

17. $\{(-8, -1)\}$

18. $\{(5, -3)\}$

19. $\{(1, -2, 3)\}$

20. A party mix is made by combining nuts that sell for \$3.50 per lb with raisins that sell for \$1.50 per lb. How much of each should be used to get 32 lb of a mix that will sell for \$2.75 per lb?

20. 20 lb of nuts, 12 lb of raisins

[Chapter 6]

21. Subtract $(4m^3 - 5m^2 + m - 8) - (6m^3 - 5m^2 + 10m - 3)$.

21. $-2m^3 - 9m - 5$

22. Multiply $(7z + 3w)^2$.

22. $49z^2 + 42zw + 9w^2$

23. Evaluate the expression $5^{-1} + 2^{-1} - 3^0$.

23. $-\frac{3}{10}$

24. (a) Write 445,000,000 in scientific notation.

(b) Write 2.34×10^{-4} without exponents.

24. (a) 4.45×10^8

(b) .000234

[Chapter 7]

25. Factor $3x^2 + 2x - 8$.

25. $(3x - 4)(x + 2)$

26. Solve $t^2 - 2t = 15$.

26. $\{-3, 5\}$

27. The length of the cover of a road atlas is 4 in. more than the width. The area is 165 in.^{2}. Find the dimensions of the cover.

27. 15 in. by 11 in.

[Chapter 8]

28. Multiply $\frac{z^2 - 16}{z^2 - 4z - 5} \cdot \frac{z^2 - 10z + 25}{z^2 - 9z + 20}$.

28. $\frac{z + 4}{z + 1}$

29. Subtract $\frac{5x}{x - 3} - \frac{4}{x + 3}$.

29. $\frac{5x^2 + 11x + 12}{(x + 3)(x - 3)}$

30. Simplify the complex fraction.

$$\frac{16 - \frac{1}{x^2}}{\frac{4}{x} - \frac{1}{x^2}}$$

30. $4x + 1$

[Chapter 9]

Simplify each expression. Assume that all variables represent positive real numbers.

31. $(-64m^{15}n^{-9})^{2/3}$

32. $\sqrt[3]{250y^7z^{11}}$

31. $\frac{16m^{10}}{n^6}$

32. $5y^2z^3\sqrt[3]{2yz^2}$

33. Solve $\sqrt{2x - 5} + 4 = x$.

33. $\{7\}$

34. Multiply $(8 - 5i)(8 + 5i)$.

34. 89

35. $\left\{-5, -\frac{1}{3}\right\}$

36. $\left\{\frac{-5 + \sqrt{37}}{6}, \frac{-5 - \sqrt{37}}{6}\right\}$

37. east: 60 mi; south: 45 mi

38. vertex: $(3, 5)$

domain: $(-\infty, \infty)$

range: $(-\infty, 5]$

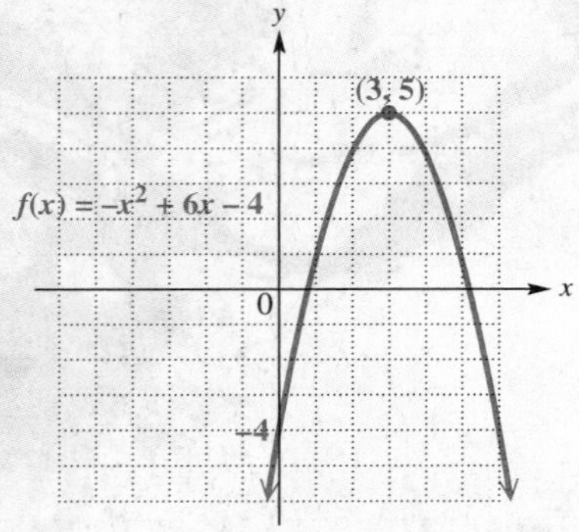

39. $f^{-1}(x) = \sqrt[3]{x + 8}$

40. $\{2\}$

41. $\{27\}$

42. $\{8\}$

43. (a) 12

(b) 13

(c) $4x^2 - 4x + 4$

(d) $2x^2 + 5$

44.

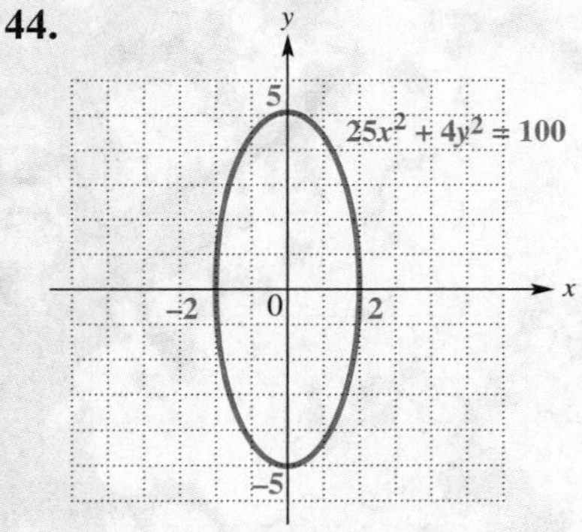

45. $\{(-1, -3), (3, 5)\}$

[Chapter 10]

Solve each equation.

35. $(3x + 8)^2 = 49$

36. $3y^2 + 5y - 1 = 0$

37. Two cars left the same intersection at the same time, one heading due east and the other heading due south. Some time later, they were exactly 75 mi apart. The car headed east had gone 15 mi farther than the car headed south. How far had each car traveled?

38. Graph $f(x) = -x^2 + 6x - 4$. Give the vertex, domain, and range.

[Chapter 11]

39. Find $f^{-1}(x)$ for the one-to-one function with $f(x) = x^3 - 8$.

Solve.

40. $5^{3x+2} = 25^{2x}$

41. $\log_9 x = \frac{3}{2}$

42. $\log_2 x + \log_2(x - 6) = 4$

[Chapter 12]

43. Let $f(x) = x^2 + 3$ and $g(x) = 2x - 1$. Find each of the following.

(a) $(f \circ g)(2)$

(b) $(g \circ f)(2)$

(c) $(f \circ g)(x)$

(d) $(g \circ f)(x)$

44. Graph $25x^2 + 4y^2 = 100$.

45. Solve the system

$$\begin{aligned} y &= x^2 - 4 \\ 2x - y &= 1. \end{aligned}$$

Prealgebra Review

R

R.1 FRACTIONS

OBJECTIVES

1. Identify prime numbers.
2. Write numbers in prime factored form.
3. Write fractions in lowest terms.
4. Multiply and divide fractions.
5. Add and subtract fractions.

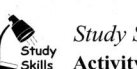

Study Skills — *Study Skills Workbook* **Activity 2**

Studying algebra requires good arithmetic skills. Most people do not get much practice using fractions, so we review the rules for fractions in this section.

The numbers used most often in everyday life are the **whole numbers,**

$$0, 1, 2, 3, 4, 5, \ldots$$

and **fractions,** such as

$$\frac{1}{3}, \frac{5}{4}, \quad \text{and} \quad \frac{11}{12}.$$

The parts of a fraction are named as follows.

$$\text{Fraction bar} \longrightarrow \frac{4}{7} \begin{array}{l} \leftarrow \text{Numerator} \\ \leftarrow \text{Denominator} \end{array}$$

If the numerator of a fraction is smaller than the denominator, we call it a **proper fraction.** A proper fraction has a value less than 1. If the numerator is greater than the denominator, the fraction is an **improper fraction.** An improper fraction, which has a value greater than 1, is often written as a **mixed number.** For example, $\frac{12}{5}$ may be written as $2\frac{2}{5}$. In algebra, we prefer to use the improper form because it is easier to work with. In applications, we usually convert answers to mixed number form, which is more meaningful.

1 Identify prime numbers. In work with fractions, we will need to write the numerators and denominators as products. A **product** is the answer to a multiplication problem. When 12 is written as the product $2 \cdot 6$, for example, 2 and 6 are called **factors** of 12. Other factors of 12 are 1, 3, 4, and 12. A whole number is **prime** if it has exactly two different factors (itself and 1). The first dozen primes are listed here.

$$2, 3, 5, 7, 11, 13, 17, 19, 23, 29, 31, 37$$

A whole number greater than 1 that is not prime is called a **composite number.** For example, 4, 6, 8, 9, and 12 are composite numbers. The number 1 is neither prime nor composite.

1 Tell whether each number is prime or composite.

(a) 12

(b) 13

(c) 27

(d) 59

(e) 1806

2 Write each number in prime factored form.

(a) 70

(b) 72

(c) 693

(d) 97

ANSWERS

1. **(a)** composite **(b)** prime **(c)** composite **(d)** prime **(e)** composite

2. **(a)** $2 \cdot 5 \cdot 7$ **(b)** $2 \cdot 2 \cdot 2 \cdot 3 \cdot 3$ **(c)** $3 \cdot 3 \cdot 7 \cdot 11$ **(d)** 97 is prime.

Example 1 Distinguishing between Prime and Composite Numbers

Decide whether each number is prime or composite.

(a) 33

33 has factors of 3 and 11 as well as 1 and 33, so it is composite.

(b) 43

Since there are no numbers other than 1 and 43 itself that divide *evenly* into 43, the number 43 is prime.

(c) 9832

9832 can be divided by 2, giving $2 \cdot 4916$, so it is composite.

Work Problem 1 at the Side.

2 Write numbers in prime factored form.

As mentioned earlier, to factor a number means to write it as the product of two or more numbers. Factoring is just the reverse of multiplying two numbers to get the product.

Multiplication	Factoring
$6 \cdot 3 = 18$	$18 = 6 \cdot 3$
↑ ↑ ↑	↑ ↑ ↑
Factors Product	Product Factors

In algebra, a dot is used instead of the × symbol to indicate multiplication because × may be confused with the letter x. Each composite number can be written as the product of prime numbers in only one way (disregarding the order of the factors). A number written using factors that are all prime numbers is in **prime factored form.** We will write the factored form with the prime factors in order by size, although any ordering is correct.

Example 2 Writing Numbers in Prime Factored Form

Write each number in prime factored form.

(a) 35

Factor 35 as the product of the prime factors 5 and 7, or as

$$35 = 5 \cdot 7.$$

(b) 24

A handy way to keep track of the factors is to use a tree, as shown below. The prime factors are circled.

		24
Divide by the smallest prime, 2, to get	$24 = 2 \cdot 12.$	(2) · 12
Now divide 12 by 2 to find factors of 12.	$24 = 2 \cdot 2 \cdot 6$	(2) · 6
Since 6 can be factored as $2 \cdot 3$, $24 = 2 \cdot 2 \cdot 2 \cdot 3$, where all factors are prime.	$24 = 2 \cdot 2 \cdot 2 \cdot 3$	(2) · (3)

Work Problem 2 at the Side.

3 Write fractions in lowest terms.

We use prime factors to write fractions in *lowest terms*. A fraction is in **lowest terms** when the numerator and denominator have no factors in common (other than 1). We write a fraction in this form by using the following facts.

Properties of 1

Any nonzero number divided by itself is equal to 1.

Any number multiplied by 1 remains the same.

For example,

$$\frac{3}{3} = 1, \quad \frac{8}{8} = 1, \quad \text{and} \quad 17 \cdot 1 = 17.$$

Writing a Fraction in Lowest Terms

Step 1 Write the numerator and denominator in prime factored form.

Step 2 Replace each pair of factors common to the numerator and denominator with 1.

Step 3 Multiply the remaining factors in the numerator and in the denominator.

(This procedure is sometimes called "simplifying the fraction.")

Example 3 **Writing Fractions in Lowest Terms**

Write each fraction in lowest terms.

(a) $\frac{10}{15} = \frac{2 \cdot 5}{3 \cdot 5} = \frac{2}{3} \cdot \frac{5}{5} = \frac{2}{3} \cdot 1 = \frac{2}{3}$

Since 5 is a common factor of 10 and 15, we use the first property of 1 to replace $\frac{5}{5}$ with 1.

(b) $\frac{15}{45} = \frac{3 \cdot 5}{3 \cdot 3 \cdot 5} = \frac{1 \cdot 3 \cdot 5}{3 \cdot 3 \cdot 5} = \frac{1}{3} \cdot \frac{3}{3} \cdot \frac{5}{5} = \frac{1}{3} \cdot 1 \cdot 1 = \frac{1}{3}$

Multiplying by 1 in the numerator does not change the value of the numerator and makes it possible to rewrite the expression as the product of three fractions in the next step.

(c) $\frac{150}{200}$

It is not always necessary to factor into *prime* factors in Step 1. Here, if you see that 50 is a common factor of the numerator and the denominator, factor as follows:

$$\frac{150}{200} = \frac{3 \cdot 50}{4 \cdot 50} = \frac{3}{4} \cdot 1 = \frac{3}{4}.$$

NOTE

When you are writing a fraction in lowest terms, look for the largest common factor in the numerator and the denominator. If none is obvious, factor the numerator and the denominator into prime factors. *Any* common factor can be used, and the fraction can be simplified in stages. For example,

$$\frac{150}{200} = \frac{15 \cdot 10}{20 \cdot 10} = \frac{3 \cdot 5 \cdot 10}{4 \cdot 5 \cdot 10} = \frac{3}{4}.$$

Work Problem 3 at the Side.

3 Write each fraction in lowest terms.

(a) $\frac{8}{14}$

(b) $\frac{35}{42}$

(c) $\frac{120}{72}$

ANSWERS

3. (a) $\frac{4}{7}$ **(b)** $\frac{5}{6}$ **(c)** $\frac{5}{3}$

4 Find each product, and write it in lowest terms.

(a) $\frac{5}{8} \cdot \frac{2}{10}$

(b) $\frac{1}{10} \cdot \frac{12}{5}$

(c) $\frac{7}{9} \cdot \frac{12}{14}$

(d) $3\frac{1}{3} \cdot 1\frac{3}{4}$

ANSWERS

4. (a) $\frac{1}{8}$ **(b)** $\frac{6}{25}$ **(c)** $\frac{2}{3}$ **(d)** $\frac{35}{6}$ or $5\frac{5}{6}$

4 Multiply and divide fractions.

Multiplying Fractions

To multiply two fractions, multiply the numerators to get the numerator of the product, and multiply the denominators to get the denominator of the product. The product must be written in lowest terms.

In practice, we will show the products of the numerator and the denominator in factored form to make it easier to write the product in lowest terms. We often simplify before performing the multiplication, as shown in the next example.

Example 4 Multiplying Fractions

Find each product, and write it in lowest terms.

(a) $\frac{3}{8} \cdot \frac{4}{9} = \frac{3 \cdot 4}{8 \cdot 9}$ Multiply numerators. Multiply denominators.

$= \frac{3 \cdot 4}{2 \cdot 4 \cdot 3 \cdot 3}$ Factor.

$= \frac{1}{2 \cdot 3} = \frac{1}{6}$ Write in lowest terms.

(b) $2\frac{1}{3} \cdot 5\frac{1}{2} = \frac{7}{3} \cdot \frac{11}{2}$ Write as improper fractions.

$= \frac{77}{6}$ or $12\frac{5}{6}$ Multiply numerators and denominators.

Work Problem 4 at the Side.

Two fractions are **reciprocals** of each other if their product is 1. For example, $\frac{3}{4}$ and $\frac{4}{3}$ are reciprocals because

$$\frac{3}{4} \cdot \frac{4}{3} = 1.$$

The numbers $\frac{7}{11}$ and $\frac{11}{7}$ are reciprocals also. Other examples are $\frac{1}{5}$ and 5, $\frac{4}{9}$ and $\frac{9}{4}$, and 16 and $\frac{1}{16}$.

Because division is the opposite or inverse of multiplication, we use reciprocals to divide fractions.

Dividing Fractions

To divide two fractions, multiply the first fraction by the reciprocal of the second. The result is called the **quotient.**

The reason this method works will be explained in Section 1.6. However, as an example, we know that $20 \div 10 = 2$, and $20 \cdot \frac{1}{10} = 2$.

Example 5 **Dividing Fractions**

Find each quotient, and write it in lowest terms.

(a) $\frac{3}{4} \div \frac{8}{5} = \frac{3}{4} \cdot \frac{5}{8} = \frac{3 \cdot 5}{4 \cdot 8} = \frac{15}{32}$

Multiply by the reciprocal of the second fraction.

(b) $\frac{3}{4} \div \frac{5}{8} = \frac{3}{4} \cdot \frac{8}{5} = \frac{3 \cdot 8}{4 \cdot 5} = \frac{3 \cdot 4 \cdot 2}{4 \cdot 5} = \frac{6}{5}$

(c) $\frac{5}{8} \div 10 = \frac{5}{8} \div \frac{10}{1} = \frac{5}{8} \cdot \frac{1}{10} = \frac{1}{16}$

Write 10 as $\frac{10}{1}$.

(d) $1\frac{2}{3} \div 4\frac{1}{2} = \frac{5}{3} \div \frac{9}{2}$ Write as improper fractions.

$= \frac{5}{3} \cdot \frac{2}{9}$ Multiply by the reciprocal of the second fraction.

$= \frac{10}{27}$

CAUTION

Notice that *only* the second fraction (the divisor) is replaced by its reciprocal in the multiplication.

Work Problem 5 at the Side.

5 Add and subtract fractions. The result of adding two numbers is called the **sum** of the numbers. For example, since $2 + 3 = 5$, the sum of 2 and 3 is 5.

Adding Fractions

To find the sum of two fractions with the *same* denominator, add their numerators and keep the *same* denominator.

Example 6 **Adding Fractions with the Same Denominator**

Add. Write sums in lowest terms.

(a) $\frac{3}{7} + \frac{2}{7} = \frac{3+2}{7} = \frac{5}{7}$ Denominator does not change.

(b) $\frac{2}{10} + \frac{3}{10} = \frac{2+3}{10} = \frac{5}{10} = \frac{1}{2}$ Write in lowest terms.

Work Problem 6 at the Side.

5 Find each quotient, and write it in lowest terms.

(a) $\frac{3}{10} \div \frac{2}{7}$

(b) $\frac{3}{4} \div \frac{7}{16}$

(c) $\frac{4}{3} \div 6$

(d) $3\frac{1}{4} \div 1\frac{2}{5}$

6 Add. Write sums in lowest terms.

(a) $\frac{3}{5} + \frac{4}{5}$

(b) $\frac{5}{14} + \frac{3}{14}$

ANSWERS

5. (a) $\frac{21}{20}$ **(b)** $\frac{12}{7}$ **(c)** $\frac{2}{9}$ **(d)** $\frac{65}{28}$ or $2\frac{9}{28}$

6. (a) $\frac{7}{5}$ **(b)** $\frac{4}{7}$

If the fractions to be added do not have the same denominator, the procedure above can still be used, but only *after* the fractions are rewritten with a common denominator. For example, to rewrite $\frac{3}{4}$ as a fraction with a denominator of 32,

$$\frac{3}{4} = \frac{?}{32},$$

we must find the number that can be multiplied by 4 to give 32. Since $4 \cdot 8 = 32$, we use the number 8. By the second property of 1, we can multiply the numerator and the denominator by 8.

$$\frac{3}{4} = \frac{3}{4} \cdot \mathbf{1} = \frac{3}{4} \cdot \frac{\mathbf{8}}{\mathbf{8}} = \frac{3 \cdot \mathbf{8}}{4 \cdot \mathbf{8}} = \frac{24}{32}$$

Finding the Least Common Denominator (LCD)

Step 1 Factor all denominators to prime factored form.

Step 2 The LCD is the product of every (different) factor that appears in any of the factored denominators. If a factor is repeated, use the largest number of repeats as factors of the LCD.

Step 3 Write each fraction with the LCD as the denominator, using the second property of 1.

Example 7 Adding Fractions with Different Denominators

Add. Write sums in lowest terms.

(a) $\frac{4}{15} + \frac{5}{9}$

Step 1 To find the LCD, we first factor both denominators to prime factored form.

$$15 = 5 \cdot \mathbf{3} \quad \text{and} \quad 9 = \mathbf{3} \cdot 3$$

3 is a factor of both denominators.

Step 2

$$\text{LCD} = \underbrace{5 \cdot 3}_{15} \cdot 3 = 45 \quad (\text{with } 3 \cdot 3 \text{ from } 9)$$

In this example, the LCD needs one factor of 5 and two factors of 3 because the second denominator has two factors of 3.

Step 3 Now we can use the second property of 1 to write each fraction with 45 as the denominator.

$$\frac{4}{15} = \frac{4}{15} \cdot \frac{\mathbf{3}}{\mathbf{3}} = \frac{12}{45} \quad \text{and} \quad \frac{5}{9} = \frac{5}{9} \cdot \frac{\mathbf{5}}{\mathbf{5}} = \frac{25}{45}$$

Now add the two equivalent fractions to get the required sum.

$$\frac{4}{15} + \frac{5}{9} = \frac{12}{45} + \frac{25}{45} = \frac{37}{45}$$

Continued on Next Page

(b) $3\frac{1}{2} + 2\frac{3}{4} = \frac{7}{2} + \frac{11}{4}$ Change to improper fractions.

$= \frac{14}{4} + \frac{11}{4}$ Get a common denominator.

$= \frac{25}{4}$ or $6\frac{1}{4}$ Add.

(c) $45\frac{2}{3} + 73\frac{1}{2}$

We could use an alternative vertical method here, adding the whole numbers and the fractions separately.

$$\begin{array}{rcl} 45\frac{2}{3} & = & 45\frac{4}{6} \\ +\ 73\frac{1}{2} & = & 73\frac{3}{6} \\ \hline \end{array}$$

$$118\frac{7}{6} = 118 + \left(1 + \frac{1}{6}\right) = 119\frac{1}{6}$$

Work Problem 7 at the Side.

The **difference** between two numbers is found by subtracting the numbers. For example, $9 - 5 = 4$, so the difference between 9 and 5 is 4. We find the difference between two fractions as follows.

Subtracting Fractions

To find the difference between two fractions with the *same* denominator, subtract their numerators and keep the *same* denominator.

If the fractions have *different* denominators, write them with a common denominator first.

Example 8 Subtracting Fractions

Subtract. Write differences in lowest terms.

(a) $\frac{15}{8} - \frac{3}{8} = \frac{15 - 3}{8} = \frac{12}{8} = \frac{3}{2}$ Lowest terms

(b) $\frac{15}{16} - \frac{4}{9}$

Since $16 = 2 \cdot 2 \cdot 2 \cdot 2$ and $9 = 3 \cdot 3$ have no common factors, the LCD is $16 \cdot 9 = 144$.

$\frac{15}{16} - \frac{4}{9} = \frac{15 \cdot 9}{16 \cdot 9} - \frac{4 \cdot 16}{9 \cdot 16}$ Get a common denominator.

$= \frac{135}{144} - \frac{64}{144}$

$= \frac{71}{144}$ Subtract numerators; keep the same denominator.

Continued on Next Page

7 Add. Write sums in lowest terms.

(a) $\frac{7}{30} + \frac{2}{45}$

(b) $\frac{17}{10} + \frac{8}{27}$

(c) $2\frac{1}{8} + 1\frac{2}{3}$

(d) $132\frac{4}{5} + 28\frac{3}{4}$

Answers

7. (a) $\frac{5}{18}$ **(b)** $\frac{539}{270}$ **(c)** $\frac{91}{24}$ or $3\frac{19}{24}$ **(d)** $161\frac{11}{20}$

(c) $2\frac{1}{2} - 1\frac{3}{4}$

First, change the mixed numbers $2\frac{1}{2}$ and $1\frac{3}{4}$ to improper fractions.

$$2\frac{1}{2} - 1\frac{3}{4} = \frac{5}{2} - \frac{7}{4} \quad \text{Write as improper fractions.}$$

$$= \frac{10}{4} - \frac{7}{4} \quad \text{Get a common denominator.}$$

$$= \frac{3}{4} \quad \text{Subtract.}$$

Work Problem 8 at the Side.

We often see mixed numbers used in applications of mathematics.

Example 9 Solving an Applied Problem Requiring Addition of Fractions

The diagram below appears in the book *Woodworker's 39 Sure-Fire Projects.* It is a view of a corner bookcase/desk. Add the fractions shown in the diagram to find the height of the bookcase/desk to the top of the writing surface.

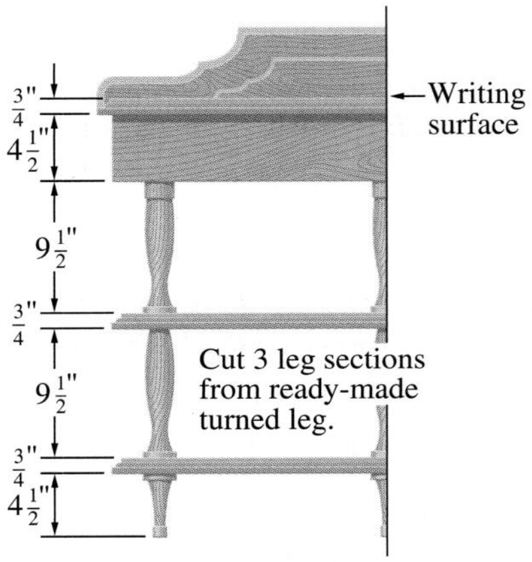

We must find the following sum (" means inches).

$$\frac{3}{4} + 4\frac{1}{2} + 9\frac{1}{2} + \frac{3}{4} + 9\frac{1}{2} + \frac{3}{4} + 4\frac{1}{2}$$

Change the mixed numbers to improper fractions.

$$\frac{3}{4} + \frac{9}{2} + \frac{19}{2} + \frac{3}{4} + \frac{19}{2} + \frac{3}{4} + \frac{9}{2}$$

The LCD is 4. Change all fractions to fourths.

$$\frac{3}{4} + \frac{18}{4} + \frac{38}{4} + \frac{3}{4} + \frac{38}{4} + \frac{3}{4} + \frac{18}{4}$$

Now we can add and simplify the answer.

$$\frac{3}{4} + \frac{18}{4} + \frac{38}{4} + \frac{3}{4} + \frac{38}{4} + \frac{3}{4} + \frac{18}{4} = \frac{121}{4} \text{ or } 30\frac{1}{4}$$

The height is $30\frac{1}{4}$ in.

Work Problem 9 at the Side.

---

8 Subtract.

(a) $\frac{9}{11} - \frac{3}{11}$

(b) $\frac{13}{15} - \frac{5}{6}$

(c) $2\frac{3}{8} - 1\frac{1}{2}$

(d) $50\frac{1}{4} - 32\frac{2}{3}$

9 Solve the problem.

To make a three-piece outfit from the same fabric, Wei Jen needs $1\frac{1}{4}$ yd for the blouse, $1\frac{2}{3}$ yd for the skirt, and $2\frac{1}{2}$ yd for the jacket. How much fabric does she need?

ANSWERS

8. **(a)** $\frac{6}{11}$ **(b)** $\frac{1}{30}$ **(c)** $\frac{7}{8}$ **(d)** $17\frac{7}{12}$

9. $5\frac{5}{12}$ yd

Example 10 Solving an Applied Problem Requiring Division of Fractions

An upholsterer needs $2\frac{1}{4}$ yd of fabric to recover a chair. How many chairs can be covered with $23\frac{2}{3}$ yd of fabric?

It helps to understand the problem if we replace the fractions with whole numbers. Suppose each chair requires 2 yd, and we have 24 yd of fabric. Dividing 24 by 2 gives the number of chairs (12) that can be recovered. To solve the original problem, we must divide $23\frac{2}{3}$ by $2\frac{1}{4}$.

$$23\frac{2}{3} \div 2\frac{1}{4} = \frac{71}{3} \div \frac{9}{4}$$

$$= \frac{71}{3} \cdot \frac{4}{9}$$

$$= \frac{284}{27} \text{ or } 10\frac{14}{27}$$

Thus, 10 chairs can be recovered with some fabric left over.

Work Problem 10 at the Side.

10 Solve the problem.

A gallon of paint covers 500 ft^2. (ft^2 means square feet.) To paint his house, Tram needs enough paint to cover 4200 ft^2. How many gallons of paint should he buy?

Answers

10. $8\frac{2}{5}$ gal are needed, so he must buy 9 gal.

Focus on **Real-Data Applications**

Quantity of Fabric Needed to Sew a Quilt

Quilting is a popular craft. Quilts are often based on an underlying square grid, called a **block.** Blocks are typically sewn from square pieces forming patterns of 4, 9, 16, 25, and so on. The square pieces (or triangular pieces that form squares) are cut from various colored fabrics and are arranged to create a pleasing design.

The quilt design *Infinity*, shown on the left, is based solely on squares (no triangles). The enlarged underlying block design is shown on the right. Each block is constructed of 4-in. finished squares. Pieces of fabric are cut into $4\frac{1}{2}$ in. squares, allowing $\frac{1}{4}$ in. for seams. The quilt top is made of 9 blocks. The inner border is made of four strips finished to size 4 in. by 84 in., and the backing is folded to form the 4-in. outer border. You should be able to verify that the finished quilt measures 100 in. by 100 in.

Infinity Quilt

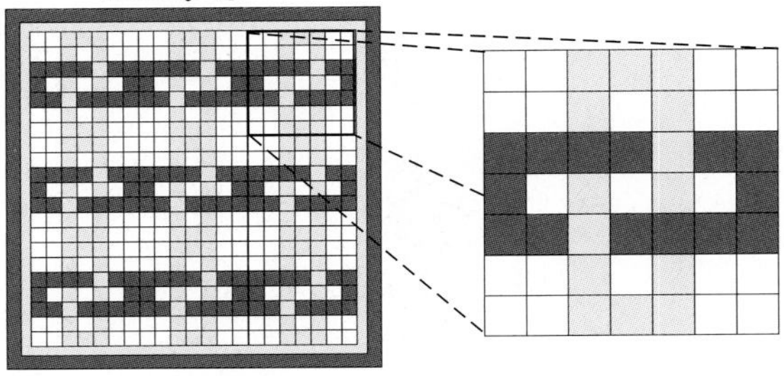

Block Design

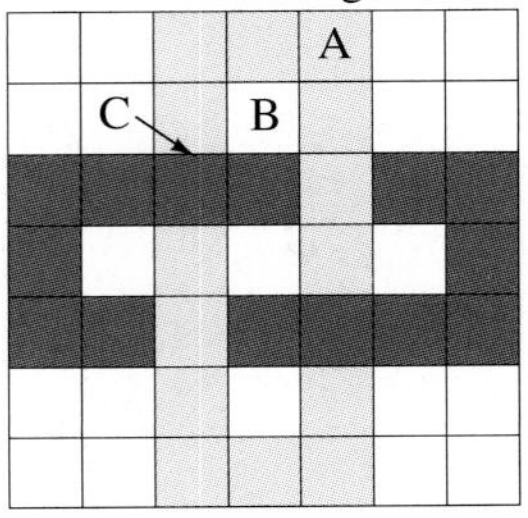

For Group Discussion

Cotton fabrics used in quilting are typically sold by the yard in widths of 45 in. The selvage edges are discarded, so allow 44 in. maximum width as you work these problems.

1. For each block, how many squares make up

   Color A? 14   Color B? 21   Color C? 14

Answers to Problems 2–5 will vary. Answers given here are based on the solution provided in the *Printed Test Bank and Instructor's Resource Guide.*

2. Determine the amount of fabric needed to sew the inner border (color A). Sketch and label a diagram to illustrate how the fabric would be cut from the yardage purchased. Also show the unused portion of fabric. **18 in. by 93 in. piece cut from 3 yd of fabric; balance used for squares**
3. Determine the amount of fabric needed to sew the backing and outer border (Color C). Assume that the backing is cut large enough to fold over to make the outer border. Sketch and label a diagram to illustrate how the fabric would be cut from the yardage purchased, including the unused portion of fabric. **approximately $9\frac{3}{4}$ yd**
4. Sketch a diagram to show the number of $4\frac{1}{2}$ in. squares that can be cut from a 9 in. by 18 in. piece of fabric. **See cutting diagram in *Extension* in *Notes to Teacher,* provided in the *Printed Test Bank and Instructor's Resource Guide.***
5. Determine the amount of fabric of each color needed to construct the *Infinity Quilt* top (minus the border). (*Hint:* Use the sketches from Problems 2, 3, and 4.) **Color A: unused piece of 3 yd from Problem 2; color B: $2\frac{5}{8}$ yd; color C: unused piece of fabric from Problem 3 plus $\frac{1}{8}$ yd**
6. What is your recommendation for the total amount of fabric of each color needed for this quilt? **Answers will vary.**

Teaching notes and an extension for this activity are provided in the *Printed Test Bank and Instructor's Resource Guide.*

R.1 EXERCISES

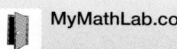

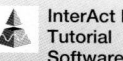

FOR EXTRA HELP: Student's Solutions Manual · MyMathLab.com · InterAct Math Tutorial Software · AW Math Tutor Center · www.mathxl.com · Digital Video Tutor CD 1 Videotape 1

Decide whether each statement is true *or* false. *If it is* false, *say why.*

Study Skills Workbook **Activity 3**

1. In the fraction $\frac{3}{7}$, 3 is the numerator and 7 is the denominator.

true

2. The mixed number equivalent of $\frac{41}{5}$ is $8\frac{1}{5}$.

true

3. The fraction $\frac{17}{51}$ is in lowest terms.

False; the fraction $\frac{17}{51}$ can be simplified to $\frac{1}{3}$.

4. The reciprocal of $\frac{8}{2}$ is $\frac{4}{1}$.

False; the reciprocal of $\frac{8}{2} = 4$ is $\frac{2}{8} = \frac{1}{4}$.

5. The product of 8 and 2 is 10.

False; *product* indicates multiplication, so the product of 8 and 2 is 16.

6. The difference between 12 and 2 is 6.

False; *difference* indicates subtraction, so the difference between 12 and 2 is 10.

Identify each number as prime, composite, or neither. See Example 1.

7. 19 — **prime**

8. 29 — **prime**

9. 52 — **composite**

10. 99 — **composite**

11. 2468 — **composite**

12. 3125 — **composite**

13. 1 — **neither**

14. 14 — **composite**

Write each number in prime factored form. See Example 2.

15. 30 — $2 \cdot 3 \cdot 5$

16. 40 — $2 \cdot 2 \cdot 2 \cdot 5$

17. 252 — $2 \cdot 2 \cdot 3 \cdot 3 \cdot 7$

18. 168 — $2 \cdot 2 \cdot 2 \cdot 3 \cdot 7$

19. 124 — $2 \cdot 2 \cdot 31$

20. 165 — $3 \cdot 5 \cdot 11$

21. 29 — 29

22. 31 — 31

Write each fraction in lowest terms. See Example 3.

23. $\frac{8}{16}$ — $\frac{1}{2}$

24. $\frac{4}{12}$ — $\frac{1}{3}$

25. $\frac{15}{18}$ — $\frac{5}{6}$

26. $\frac{16}{20}$ — $\frac{4}{5}$

27. $\frac{15}{75}$ — $\frac{1}{5}$

28. $\frac{24}{64}$ — $\frac{3}{8}$

29. $\frac{144}{120}$ — $\frac{6}{5}$

30. $\frac{132}{77}$ — $\frac{12}{7}$

31. For the fractions $\frac{p}{q}$ and $\frac{r}{s}$, which can serve as a common denominator?

A. $q \cdot s$

B. $q + s$

C. $p \cdot r$

D. $p + r$

A

32. Which is the correct way to write $\frac{16}{24}$ in lowest terms?

A. $\frac{16}{24} = \frac{8+8}{8+16} = \frac{8}{16} = \frac{1}{2}$

B. $\frac{16}{24} = \frac{4 \cdot 4}{4 \cdot 6} = \frac{4}{6}$

C. $\frac{16}{24} = \frac{8 \cdot 2}{8 \cdot 3} = \frac{2}{3}$

D. $\frac{16}{24} = \frac{14+2}{21+3} = \frac{2}{3} + \frac{2}{3} = \frac{4}{3}$

C

Find each product or quotient, and write it in lowest terms. See Examples 4 and 5.

33. $\frac{4}{5} \cdot \frac{6}{7}$

$\frac{24}{35}$

34. $\frac{5}{9} \cdot \frac{10}{7}$

$\frac{50}{63}$

35. $\frac{1}{10} \cdot \frac{12}{5}$

$\frac{6}{25}$

36. $\frac{6}{11} \cdot \frac{2}{3}$

$\frac{4}{11}$

37. $\frac{15}{4} \cdot \frac{8}{25}$

$\frac{6}{5}$

38. $\frac{4}{7} \cdot \frac{21}{8}$

$\frac{3}{2}$

39. $2\frac{2}{3} \cdot 5\frac{4}{5}$

$\frac{232}{15}$ or $15\frac{7}{15}$

40. $3\frac{3}{5} \cdot 7\frac{1}{6}$

$\frac{129}{5}$ or $25\frac{4}{5}$

41. $\frac{5}{4} \div \frac{3}{8}$

$\frac{10}{3}$

42. $\frac{7}{6} \div \frac{9}{10}$

$\frac{35}{27}$

43. $\frac{32}{5} \div \frac{8}{15}$

12

44. $\frac{24}{7} \div \frac{6}{21}$

12

45. $\frac{3}{4} \div 12$

$\frac{1}{16}$

46. $\frac{2}{5} \div 30$

$\frac{1}{75}$

47. $2\frac{5}{8} \div 1\frac{15}{32}$

$\frac{84}{47}$ or $1\frac{37}{47}$

48. $2\frac{3}{10} \div 7\frac{4}{5}$

$\frac{23}{78}$

49. In your own words, explain how to divide two fractions.

Multiply the first fraction (the dividend) by the reciprocal of the second fraction (the divisor) to divide two fractions.

50. In your own words, explain how to add two fractions that have different denominators.

To add two fractions with different denominators, find a common denominator, change each fraction to an equivalent fraction with that denominator, add numerators, and place the sum over the common denominator.

Find each sum or difference, and write it in lowest terms. See Examples 6–8.

51. $\frac{7}{12} + \frac{1}{12}$

$\frac{2}{3}$

52. $\frac{3}{16} + \frac{5}{16}$

$\frac{1}{2}$

53. $\frac{5}{9} + \frac{1}{3}$

$\frac{8}{9}$

54. $\frac{4}{15} + \frac{1}{5}$

$\frac{7}{15}$

55. $3\frac{1}{8} + \frac{1}{4}$

$\frac{27}{8}$ or $3\frac{3}{8}$

56. $5\frac{3}{4} + \frac{2}{3}$

$\frac{77}{12}$ or $6\frac{5}{12}$

57. $\frac{7}{12} - \frac{1}{9}$

$\frac{17}{36}$

58. $\frac{11}{16} - \frac{1}{12}$

$\frac{29}{48}$

59. $6\frac{1}{4} - 5\frac{1}{3}$

$\frac{11}{12}$

60. $8\frac{4}{5} - 7\frac{4}{9}$

$\frac{61}{45}$ or $1\frac{16}{45}$

61. $\frac{5}{3} + \frac{1}{6} - \frac{1}{2}$

$\frac{4}{3}$

62. $\frac{7}{15} + \frac{1}{6} - \frac{1}{10}$

$\frac{8}{15}$

Use the chart, which appears on a package of Quaker Quick Grits, to answer the questions in Exercises 63 and 64.

63. How many cups of water would be needed for eight microwave servings?

6 cups

64. How many tsp of salt would be needed for five stove top servings? (*Hint:* 5 is halfway between 4 and 6.)

$\frac{3}{8}$ tsp

	Microwave	Stove Top		
Servings	1	1	4	6
Water	$\frac{3}{4}$ cup	1 cup	3 cups	4 cups
Grits	3 Tbsp	3 Tbsp	$\frac{3}{4}$ cup	1 cup
Salt (optional)	Dash	Dash	$\frac{1}{4}$ tsp	$\frac{1}{2}$ tsp

Solve each applied problem. See Examples 9 and 10.

65. A motel owner has decided to expand his business by buying a piece of property next to the motel. The property has an irregular shape, with five sides as shown in the figure. Find the total distance around the piece of property. This is called the *perimeter* of the figure.

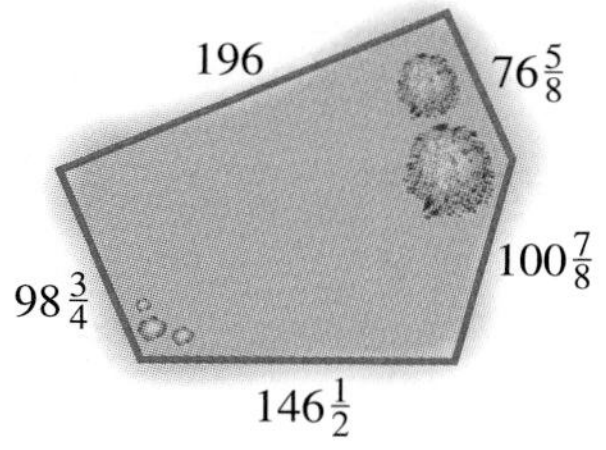

Measurements in feet

$618\frac{3}{4}$ ft

66. A triangle has sides of lengths $5\frac{1}{4}$ ft, $7\frac{1}{2}$ ft, and $10\frac{1}{8}$ ft. Find the perimeter of the triangle. See Exercise 65.

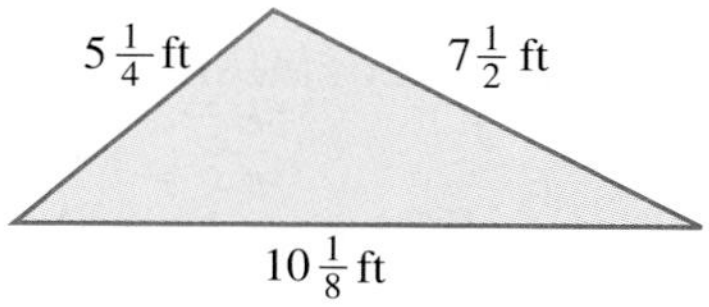

$22\frac{7}{8}$ ft

67. A hardware store sells a 40-piece socket wrench set. The measure of the largest socket is $\frac{3}{4}$ in., while the measure of the smallest socket is $\frac{3}{16}$ in. What is the difference between these measures?

$\frac{9}{16}$ in.

68. Two sockets in a socket wrench set have measures of $\frac{9}{16}$ in. and $\frac{3}{8}$ in. What is the difference between these two measures?

$\frac{3}{16}$ in.

69. Under existing standards, most of the holes in Swiss cheese must have diameters between $\frac{11}{16}$ and $\frac{13}{16}$ in. To accommodate new high-speed slicing machines, the USDA wants to reduce the minimum size to $\frac{3}{8}$ in. How much smaller is $\frac{3}{8}$ in. than $\frac{11}{16}$ in.? (*Source:* U.S. Department of Agriculture.)

$\frac{5}{16}$ in.

70. Tex's favorite recipe for barbecue sauce calls for $2\frac{1}{3}$ cups of tomato sauce. The recipe makes enough barbecue sauce to serve 7 people. How much tomato sauce is needed for 1 serving?

$\frac{1}{3}$ cup

More than 8 million immigrants were admitted to the United States between 1990 and 1997. The pie chart gives the fractional number from each region of birth for these immigrants. Use the chart to answer the following questions.

U.S. IMMIGRANTS BY REGION OF BIRTH

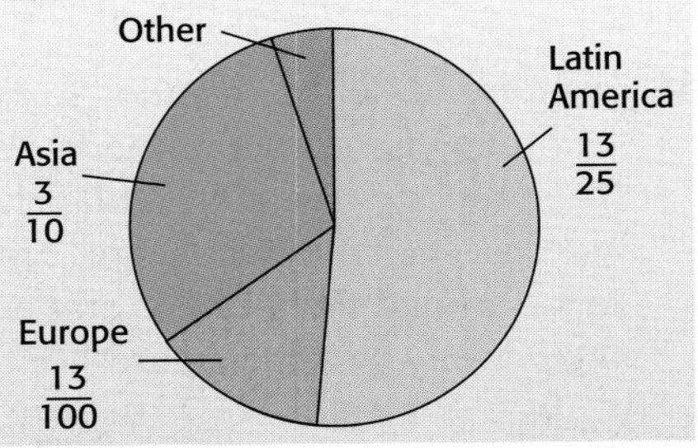

Source: U.S. Bureau of the Census.

71. What fractional part of the immigrants were from other regions?

$\frac{1}{20}$

72. What fractional part of the immigrants were from Latin America or Asia?

$\frac{41}{50}$

73. How many (in millions) were from Europe?

more than $1\frac{1}{25}$ million

R.2 Decimals and Percents

Objectives

1. Write decimals as fractions.
2. Add and subtract decimals.
3. Multiply and divide decimals.
4. Write fractions as decimals.
5. Convert percents to decimals and decimals to percents.

Fractions are one way to represent parts of a whole. Another way is with a **decimal fraction** or **decimal,** a number written with a decimal point, such as 9.4. Each digit in a decimal number has a place value, as shown below.

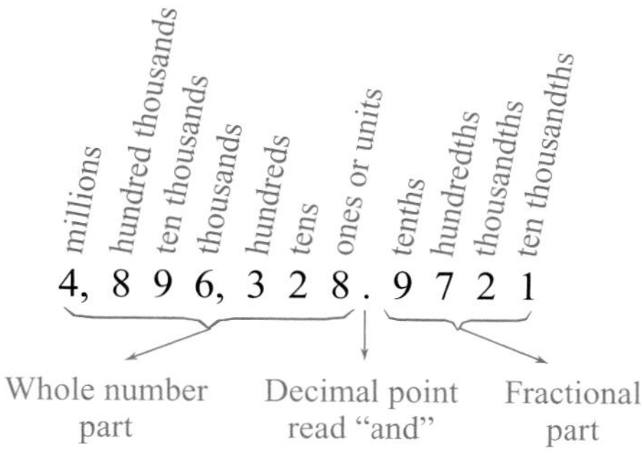

Each successive place value is ten times larger than the place value to its right and is one-tenth as large as the place value to its left.

Prices are often written as decimals. The price \$14.75 means 14 dollars and 75 cents, or 14 dollars and $\frac{75}{100}$ of a dollar.

1 Write decimals as fractions. Place value is used to write a decimal number as a fraction. For example, since the last digit (that is, the digit farthest to the right) of .67 is in the *hundredths* place,

$$.67 = \frac{67}{\mathbf{100}}.$$

Similarly, $.9 = \frac{9}{10}$ and $.25 = \frac{25}{100}$. Digits to the left of the decimal point indicate whole numbers, so 12.342 is the sum of 12 and .342, and

$$12.342 = 12 + .342 = 12 + \frac{342}{1000} = \frac{12{,}000}{1000} + \frac{342}{1000} = \frac{12{,}342}{1000}.$$

These examples suggest the following rule.

Converting a Decimal to a Fraction

Read the name using the correct place value. Write it in fraction form just as you read it. The denominator will be a **power of 10,** a number like 10, 100, 1000, and so on.

For example, we read .16 as "sixteen hundredths" and write it in fraction form as $\frac{16}{100}$. The same thing is accomplished by counting the number of digits to the right of the decimal point, then writing the given number without a decimal point over a denominator of 1 followed by that number of zeros.

Example 1 **Writing Decimals as Fractions**

Write each decimal as a fraction. Do not write in lowest terms.

(a) .95

We read .95 as 95 hundredths, so the fraction form is $\frac{95}{100}$. Using the shortcut method, since there are two places to the right of the decimal point, there will be two zeros in the denominator.

Continued on Next Page

1 Write each decimal as a fraction. Do not write in lowest terms.

(a) .8

(b) .431

(c) 20.58

2 Add or subtract as indicated.

(a)
$$\begin{array}{r} 68.9 \\ 42.72 \\ +\ 8.973 \\ \hline \end{array}$$

(b)
$$\begin{array}{r} 32.5 \\ -\ 21.72 \\ \hline \end{array}$$

(c) $42.83 + 71 + 3.074$

(d) $351.8 - 2.706$

$$\underset{\text{2 places}}{.95} = \underset{\text{2 zeros}}{\frac{95}{100}}$$

(b) $\underset{\text{3 places}}{.056} = \underset{\text{3 zeros}}{\frac{56}{1000}}$

(c) $\underset{\text{4 places}}{4.2095} = 4 + .2095 = 4 + \underset{\text{4 zeros}}{\frac{2095}{10,000}} = \frac{42,095}{10,000}$

Work Problem 1 at the Side.

2 Add and subtract decimals. In the next example, we explain addition and subtraction of decimals.

Example 2 Adding and Subtracting Decimals

Add or subtract as indicated.

(a) $6.92 + 14.8 + 3.217$

Place the digits of the numbers in columns, with decimal points lined up so that tenths are in one column, hundredths in another column, and so on.

$$\begin{array}{r} 6.92 \\ 14.8 \\ +\ \ 3.217 \\ \hline 24.937 \end{array} \quad \text{Decimal points lined up}$$

A good way to avoid errors is to attach zeros to make all the numbers the same length. For example,

$$\begin{array}{r} 6.92 \\ 14.8 \\ +\ \ 3.217 \\ \hline \end{array} \quad \text{becomes} \quad \begin{array}{r} 6.920 \\ 14.800 \\ 1\ \ 3.217 \\ \hline 24.937. \end{array} \quad \text{Attach zeros.}$$

(b) $47.6 - 32.509$

Write the numbers in columns, attaching zeros to 47.6.

$$\begin{array}{r} 47.6 \\ -\ 32.509 \\ \hline \end{array} \quad \text{becomes} \quad \begin{array}{r} 47.600 \\ -\ \ 32.509 \\ \hline 15.091 \end{array}$$

(c) $3 - .253$

A whole number is assumed to have the decimal point at the right of the number. Write 3 as 3.000; then subtract.

$$\begin{array}{r} 3.000 \\ -\ \ \ .253 \\ \hline 2.747 \end{array}$$

Work Problem 2 at the Side.

3 Multiply and divide decimals. We multiply decimals by slightly modifying multiplication of whole numbers. We will sometimes use the times symbol, ×, instead of a dot to avoid confusion with the decimal point.

ANSWERS

1. (a) $\frac{8}{10}$ (b) $\frac{431}{1000}$ (c) $\frac{2058}{100}$
2. (a) 120.593 (b) 10.78 (c) 116.904 (d) 349.094

Multiplying Decimals

Ignore the decimal points and multiply as if the numbers were whole numbers. Then add together the number of **decimal places** (digits to the *right* of the decimal point) in each number being multiplied. Place the decimal point in the answer that many digits from the right.

Example 3 **Multiplying Decimals**

Multiply.

(a) 29.3 × 4.52

Multiply as if the numbers were whole numbers.

```
   29.3     1 decimal place in first number
×  4.52     2 decimal places in second number
    586     | 1 + 2 = 3
  1465      |
 1172       ↓
132.436     3 decimal places in answer
```

(b) 7.003 × 55.8

```
   7.003    3 decimal places
×   55.8    1 decimal place
   56024    | 3 + 1 = 4
  35015     |
 35015      ↓
390.7674    4 decimal places
```

(c) 31.42 × 65

```
  31.42     2 decimal places
×    65     0 decimal places
  15710     | 2 + 0 = 2
 18852      ↓
2042.30     2 decimal places
```

The final 0 here can be dropped and the result can be expressed as 2042.3.

Work Problem 3 at the Side.

To divide decimals, convert the divisor to a whole number.

Dividing Decimals

Change the **divisor** (the number you are dividing *by*) into a whole number by moving the decimal point as many places as necessary to the right. Move the decimal point in the **dividend** (the number you are dividing *into*) to the right by the same number of places. Move the decimal point straight up and then divide as with whole numbers.

```
               5  ← Quotient
Divisor → 25)125
              ↑
           Dividend
```

3 Multiply.

(a) 2.13 × .05

(b) 9.32 × 1.4

(c) 300.2 × .052

(d) 42,001 × .012

ANSWERS

3. **(a)** .1065 **(b)** 13.048 **(c)** 15.6104 **(d)** 504.012

4 Divide.

(a) $14.9\overline{)451.47}$

(b) $.37\overline{)5.476}$

(c) $375.1 \div 3.001$

Example 4 **Dividing Decimals**

Divide.

(a) $233.45 \div 11.5$

Write the problem as follows.

$$11.5\overline{)233.45}$$

To change 11.5 into a whole number, move the decimal point one place to the right. Move the decimal point in 233.45 the same number of places to the right, to get 2334.5.

$$11.5.\overline{)233.4.5} \qquad \text{Move one decimal place to the right.}$$

To see why this works, write the division in fraction form and multiply by $\frac{10}{10}$ or 1.

$$\frac{233.45}{11.5} \cdot \frac{10}{10} = \frac{2334.5}{115}$$

The result is the same as when we moved the decimal point one place to the right in the divisor and the dividend.

Move the decimal point straight up and divide as with whole numbers.

$$\begin{array}{r} 20.3 \\ 115\overline{)2334.5} \\ \underline{230} \\ 345 \\ \underline{345} \\ 0 \end{array} \qquad \text{Move decimal point straight up.}$$

In the second step of the division, 115 does not divide into 34, so we used zero as a placeholder in the quotient.

(b) $73.85\overline{)1852.882}$ (Round the answer to two decimal places.)

Move the decimal point two places to the right in 73.85, to get 7385. Do the same thing with 1852.882, to get 185288.2.

$$73.85.\overline{)1852.88.2}$$

Move the decimal point straight up and divide as with whole numbers.

$$\begin{array}{r} 25.089 \\ 7385\overline{)185288.200} \\ \underline{14770} \\ 37588 \\ \underline{36925} \\ 66320 \\ \underline{59080} \\ 72400 \\ \underline{66465} \\ 5935 \end{array}$$

We carried out the division to three decimal places so that we could round to two decimal places, getting the quotient 25.09.

Work Problem 4 at the Side.

ANSWERS

4. (a) 30.3 **(b)** 14.8
(c) 124.99 (rounded)

A shortcut can be used when multiplying or dividing by powers of 10.

Multiplying or Dividing by Powers of 10

To *multiply* by a power of 10, move the decimal point to the *right* as many places as the number of zeros.

To *divide* by a power of 10, move the decimal point to the *left* as many places as the number of zeros.

In both cases, insert 0s as placeholders if necessary.

Example 5 **Multiplying and Dividing by Powers of 10**

Multiply or divide as indicated.

(a) $48.731 \times 100 = 48.73.1 = 4873.1$

We moved the decimal point two places to the right because 100 has two zeros.

(b) $48.7 \div 1000 = .048.7 = .0487$

We moved the decimal point three places to the left because 1000 has three zeros. We needed to insert a zero in front of the 4 to do this.

Work Problem 5 at the Side.

To avoid misplacing the decimal point, check your work by estimating the answer. To get a quick estimate, round the numbers so that only the first digit is not zero, using the rule for rounding. For more accurate estimates, the numbers could be rounded to the first two or even three nonzero digits.

Rule for Rounding

If the digit to become 0 or be dropped is 5 or more, round up by adding 1 to the final digit to be kept.

If the digit to become 0 or be dropped is 4 or less, do not round up.

For example, to estimate the answer to Example 2(a), round

6.92 to 7, 14.8 to 10, and 3.217 to 3.

(6.92: 5 or more; 14.8: 4 or less; 3.217: 4 or less)

Since $7 + 10 + 3 = 20$, the answer of 24.937 is reasonable. In Example 4(a), round 233.45 to 200 and 11.5 to 10. Since $200 \div 10 = 20$, the answer of 20.3 is reasonable.

4 **Write fractions as decimals.**

Writing a Fraction as a Decimal

Because a fraction bar indicates division, write a fraction as a decimal by dividing the denominator into the numerator.

5 Multiply or divide as indicated.

(a) 294.72×10

(b) 19.5×1000

(c) $4.793 \div 100$

(d) $960.1 \div 10$

ANSWERS

5. **(a)** 2947.2 **(b)** 19,500 **(c)** .04793 **(d)** 96.01

6 Convert to decimals. For repeating decimals, write the answer two ways: using the bar notation and rounding to the nearest thousandth.

(a) $\frac{2}{9}$

(b) $\frac{17}{20}$

(c) $\frac{1}{11}$

Example 6 Writing Fractions as Decimals

Write each fraction as a decimal.

(a) $\frac{19}{8}$

$$\begin{array}{r} 2.375 \\ 8\overline{)19.000} \\ \underline{16} \\ 3\,0 \\ \underline{2\,4} \\ 60 \\ \underline{56} \\ 40 \\ \underline{40} \\ 0 \end{array}$$

$\frac{19}{8} = 2.375$

(b) $\frac{2}{3}$

$$\begin{array}{r} .6666\ldots \\ 3\overline{)2.0000\ldots} \\ \underline{1\,8} \\ 20 \\ \underline{18} \\ 20 \\ \underline{18} \\ 20 \end{array}$$

The remainder in the division in part (b) is never 0. Because 2 is always left after the subtraction, this quotient is a **repeating decimal.** A convenient notation for a repeating decimal is a bar over the digit (or digits) that repeats. For instance, we can write .6666 . . . as $.\overline{6}$. In applications, we often round repeating decimals to as many places as needed. For example, rounding to the *nearest thousandth,*

$$\frac{2}{3} = .667. \quad \text{An approximation}$$

CAUTION

When rounding, be careful to distinguish between *thousandths* and *thousands* or between *hundredths* and *hundreds,* and so on.

Work Problem 6 at the Side.

5 Convert percents to decimals and decimals to percents. An important application of decimals is in work with percents. The word **percent** means "per one hundred." Percent is written with the sign %. One percent means "one per one hundred" or "one one-hundredth."

$$\mathbf{1\% = .01 \quad \text{or} \quad 1\% = \frac{1}{100}}$$

Example 7 Converting Percents and Decimals

(a) Write 73% as a decimal.
Since 1% = .01,

$$73\% = 73 \cdot 1\% = 73 \times .01 = .73.$$

Also, 73% can be written as a decimal using the fraction form $1\% = \frac{1}{100}$.

$$73\% = 73 \cdot 1\% = 73 \cdot \left(\frac{1}{100}\right) = \frac{73}{100} = .73$$

(b) Write 125% as a decimal.

$$125\% = 125 \cdot 1\% = 125 \times .01 = 1.25$$

Continued on Next Page

ANSWERS
6. **(a)** $.\overline{2}$, .222 **(b)** .85 **(c)** $.\overline{09}$, .091

(c) Write $3\frac{1}{2}\%$ as a decimal.

First write the fractional part as a decimal.

$$3\frac{1}{2}\% = (3 + .5)\% = 3.5\%$$

Now change the percent to decimal form.

$$3.5\% = 3.5 \times .01 = .035$$

(d) Write .32 as a percent.

Since .32 means 32 hundredths, write .32 as $32 \times .01$. Finally, replace .01 with 1%.

$$.32 = 32 \times \mathbf{.01} = 32 \times \mathbf{1\%} = 32\%$$

(e) Write 2.63 as a percent.

$$2.63 = 263 \times .01 = 263 \times 1\% = 263\%$$

NOTE

A quick way to change from a percent to a decimal is to move the decimal point two places to the left. To change from a decimal to a percent, move the decimal point two places to the right.

Decimal ← (Divide by 100; Move 2 places left.) — Percent

Decimal — (Multiply by 100; Move 2 places right.) → Percent

Example 8 Converting Percents and Decimals by Moving the Decimal Point

Convert each percent to a decimal and each decimal to a percent.

(a) 45% = .45

(b) 250% = 2.50

(c) .57 = 57%

(d) 1.5 = 1.50 = 150%

(e) .327 = 32.7%

Work Problem 7 at the Side.

Calculator Tip In this book, we do not use 0 in the ones place for decimal fractions between 0 and 1. Many calculators (and other books) will show 0.45 instead of just .45 to emphasize that there is a 0 in the ones place. Graphing calculators do *not* show 0 in the ones place. Either way is correct.

7 Convert as indicated.

(a) 23% to a decimal

(b) 310% to a decimal

(c) .71 to a percent

(d) 1.32 to a percent

(e) .685 to a percent

ANSWERS

7. (a) .23 **(b)** 3.10 **(c)** 71% **(d)** 132% **(e)** 68.5%

Focus on

Real-Data Applications

Decimalization of Stock Prices

When the New York Stock Exchange (NYSE) was founded in 1792, Thomas Jefferson suggested that stock prices be based on a decimal system. Instead, stock prices were based on the Spanish milled dollar. Even before the United States began minting its own coinage, the Spanish *eight-reales* coin, or the Spanish milled dollar, had been a commonly used currency and continued to be legal currency until 1857. The bits of the Spanish coin—the four reales, two reales, and one real—were the legendary *pieces of eight* famous in pirate and treasure lore.

The NYSE decision to base stock prices on an archaic coin resulted in the continuing practice of representing a **price per share** as a mixed number with fractional parts of $\frac{1}{2}$, $\frac{1}{4}$, $\frac{1}{8}$, or $\frac{1}{16}$. After two centuries, the Securities Exchange Commission (SEC) and the NYSE proposed a change in stock pricing to a decimal system consistent with that used by foreign stock exchanges. If they had only listened to Thomas Jefferson!

On August 28, 2000, the U.S. stock markets began the 8-month process of decimalization, to be completed by April 9, 2001. The pilot program included seven stocks on the New York Stock Exchange and six stocks on the American Stock Exchange. *Bond markets will continue to use a fraction-based pricing scheme.*

One of the primary issues had been whether to price stocks in one-cent increments or five-cent increments. Under the fraction-based pricing scheme, there are only 16 price changes per \$1.00. At five-cent increments, there would be 20 price changes per \$1.00 compared to 100 price changes per dollar for one-cent increments. Trading in smaller increments will increase competition because it will lower the spread between "bid" and "ask" prices—the difference between what a buyer is willing to pay for a security and what the seller is offering for a security. The volumes of trades could increase dramatically with one-cent price increments.

For the purpose of discussion only, assume that stocks are priced in five-cent increments. Assume that on April 9, 2001, you own 50 shares of Allied Technology, priced at $\$65\frac{7}{16}$ or \$65.4375 per share, resulting in an equity value of

$$\$65.4375 \times 50 = \$3271.875.$$

With decimalization, the price per share must be adjusted to the nearest nickel less than the original price, or \$65.40. Since the equity is unchanged, the new number of shares is

$$\$3271.875 \div \$65.40 = 50.02866972,$$

which is reported to the nearest thousandth as 50.029 shares. For a one-cent incremental scheme, the adjusted price would have been \$65.43 and the adjusted number of shares 50.006.

For Group Discussion

For each stock given, calculate the equity, the adjusted price per share, and the number of shares (to the nearest thousandth).

	Before Decimalization			After Decimalization	
Stock	Number of Shares	Price per Share	Equity	Price per Share	Number of Shares
1. **Aeroflex (five-cent pricing)**	50	$\$61\frac{7}{8}$	\$3093.75	\$61.85	50.020
2. **Philadelphia Suburban (one-cent pricing)**	100	$\$23\frac{1}{16}$	\$2306.25	\$23.06	100.011

Teaching notes and an extension for this activity are provided in the *Printed Test Bank and Instructor's Resource Guide.*

R.2 EXERCISES

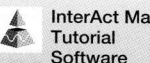

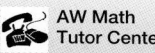

FOR EXTRA HELP: Student's Solutions Manual | MyMathLab.com | InterAct Math Tutorial Software | AW Math Tutor Center | www.mathxl.com | Digital Video Tutor CD 1 Videotape 1

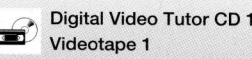

1. In the decimal 367.9412, name the digit that is in each place value.

(a) tens 6 **(b)** tenths 9 **(c)** thousandths 1

(d) ones or units 7 **(e)** hundredths 4

2. Write a numeral that has 5 in the thousands place, 0 in the tenths place, and 4 in the ten thousandths place.

Answers will vary. One example is 5243.0164.

3. For the decimal number 46.249, round to the place value indicated.

(a) hundredths 46.25 **(b)** tenths 46.2

(c) ones or units 46 **(d)** tens 50

4. Round each decimal to the nearest thousandth.

(a) $.\overline{8}$ .889 **(b)** $.\overline{5}$ .556

(c) .9762 .976 **(d)** .8642 .864

5. For the sum 35.89 + 24.1, which is the best estimate?
A. 40 **B.** 50 **C.** 60 **D.** 70

C

6. For the difference 119.83 − 52.4, which is the best estimate?
A. 40 **B.** 50 **C.** 60 **D.** 70

D

7. For the product 84.9 × 98.3, which is the best estimate?
A. 7000 **B.** 8000 **C.** 80,000 **D.** 70,000

B

8. For the quotient 9845.3 ÷ 97.2, which is the best estimate?
A. 10 **B.** 1000 **C.** 100 **D.** 10,000

C

Write each decimal as a fraction. Do not write in lowest terms. See Example 1.

9. .4 $\frac{4}{10}$ **10.** .6 $\frac{6}{10}$ **11.** .64 $\frac{64}{100}$ **12.** .82 $\frac{82}{100}$

13. .138 $\frac{138}{1000}$ **14.** .104 $\frac{104}{1000}$ **15.** 3.805 $\frac{3805}{1000}$ **16.** 5.166 $\frac{5166}{1000}$

Add or subtract as indicated. Make sure that your answer is reasonable by estimating first. Show your estimate, then the exact answer. See Example 2.

17. 25.32 + 109.2 + 8.574
139; 143.094

18. 90.527 + 32.43 + 589.83 + 399.327
1120; 1112.114

19. 28.73 − 3.12
27; 25.61

20. 46.88 − 13.45
40; 33.43

21. 43.5 − 28.17
10; 15.33

22. 345.1 − 56.31
240; 288.79

23. 32.56 + 47.356 + 1.8
82; 81.716

24. 75.22 + 123.96 + 3.897
184; 203.077

25. 18 − 2.789
17; 15.211

26. 29 − 8.582
21; 20.418

Multiply or divide as indicated. Make sure that your answer is reasonable by estimating first. Show your estimate, then the exact answer. See Examples 3–5.

27. .2 × .03
.006; .006

28. .07 × .004
.00028; .00028

29. 12.8 × 9.1
90; 116.48

30. 34.04 × .56
18; 19.0624

31. 57.2 ÷ 8
6; 7.15

32. 73.36 ÷ 14
7; 5.24

33. 19.967 ÷ 9.74
2; 2.05

34. 44.4788 ÷ 5.27
8; 8.44

35. 57.116 × 100 6000; 5711.6

36. .094 × 1000 100; 94

37. 1.62 ÷ 10 .2; .162

38. 24.03 ÷ 100 .2; .2403

39. Explain in your own words how to add or subtract decimals.

To add or subtract decimals, line up the decimal points in a column, add or subtract as usual, and move the decimal point straight down in the sum or difference.

40. Explain in your own words how to **(a)** multiply decimals and **(b)** divide decimals.

(a) To multiply decimals, multiply as usual, then count the total number of digits to the right of the decimal points in the numbers being multiplied. This total is the number of places to the right of the decimal point in the product.

(b) To divide decimals, move the decimal points in both the divisor and the dividend as many places to the right as necessary to make the divisor a whole number. Divide as usual. Move the decimal point straight up into the quotient.

Write each fraction as a decimal. For repeating decimals, write the answer two ways: using the bar notation and rounding to the nearest thousandth. See Example 6.

41. $\frac{1}{8}$ .125

42. $\frac{7}{8}$ .875

43. $\frac{1}{4}$ .25

44. $\frac{3}{4}$ .75

45. $\frac{5}{9}$ $.\overline{5}$; .556

46. $\frac{8}{9}$ $.\overline{8}$; .889

47. $\frac{1}{6}$ $.1\overline{6}$; .167

48. $\frac{5}{6}$ $.8\overline{3}$; .833

49. In your own words, explain how to convert a decimal to a percent.

To convert a decimal to a percent, move the decimal point two places to the right and attach a percent symbol (%).

50. In your own words, explain how to convert a percent to a decimal.

To convert a percent to a decimal, move the decimal point two places to the left and drop the percent symbol.

Convert each percent to a decimal. See Examples 7(a)–(c), 8(a), and 8(b).

51. 54% .54

52. 39% .39

53. 117% 1.17

54. 189% 1.89

55. 2.4% .024

56. 3.1% .031

57. $6\frac{1}{4}\%$ .0625

58. $5\frac{1}{2}\%$ .055

59. .8% .008

60. .9% .009

Convert each decimal to a percent. See Examples 7(d), 7(e), and 8(c)–(e).

61. .75 75%

62. .83 83%

63. .004 .4%

64. .005 .5%

65. 1.28 128%

66. 2.35 235%

67. .3 30%

68. .6 60%

One method of converting a fraction to a percent is to first convert the fraction to a decimal, as shown in Example 6, and then convert the decimal to a percent, as shown in Examples 7 and 8. Convert each fraction to a percent in this way.

69. $\frac{3}{4}$ 75%

70. $\frac{1}{4}$ 25%

71. $\frac{5}{6}$ $83.\overline{3}\%$

72. $\frac{11}{16}$ 68.75%

73. Brand new tires have a tread of about $\frac{10}{32}$ in. By law, if 80% of the tread is worn off, the tire needs to be replaced.

(a) What fraction of an inch of tread (in $\frac{1}{32}$ of an inch) indicates that a new tire is needed? $\frac{2}{32}$

(b) How much tread wear (in $\frac{1}{32}$ of an inch) remains (according to the legal limit) if the tread depth is $\frac{4}{32}$? $\frac{2}{32}$

1 The Real Number System

Positive and negative numbers indicate position with respect to a starting point. A common example is the thermometer—temperatures are either "above zero" (positive) or "below zero" (negative). Another example is the number of yards gained (positive) or lost (negative) from the line of scrimmage in football. Exercises 63 and 64 of Section 1.4 are familiar examples of our need for positive and negative numbers to keep track of finances.

1.1 Exponents, Order of Operations, and Inequality

Objectives

1. Use exponents.
2. Use the order of operations guidelines.
3. Use more than one grouping symbol.
4. Know the meanings of $\neq$, $<$, $>$, $\leq$, and $\geq$.
5. Translate word statements to symbols.
6. Reverse the direction of inequality statements.

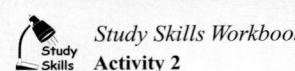

Study Skills Workbook **Activity 2**

1 Find the value of each exponential expression.

(a) 6^2

(b) 3^5

(c) $\left(\frac{3}{4}\right)^2$

(d) $\left(\frac{1}{2}\right)^4$

(e) $(.4)^3$

Answers

1. (a) 36 **(b)** 243 **(c)** $\frac{9}{16}$ **(d)** $\frac{1}{16}$ **(e)** .064

In preparation for the study of algebra, we begin by introducing some basic ideas and vocabulary that we will be using throughout the course.

1 Use exponents. In algebra, we use a raised dot for multiplication as shown in Chapter R, where we factored a number as the product of its prime factors. For example, 81 is written in prime factored form as

$$81 = 3 \cdot 3 \cdot 3 \cdot 3,$$

where the factor 3 appears four times. Repeated factors are written in an abbreviated form by using an *exponent*. The prime factored form of 81 is written with an exponent as

$$\underbrace{3 \cdot 3 \cdot 3 \cdot 3}_{\text{4 factors of 3}} = 3^4.$$

(Exponent: 4; Base: 3)

The number 4 is the **exponent** and 3 is the **base** in the **exponential expression** 3^4. Exponents are also called **powers.** We read 3^4 as "3 to the fourth power" or simply "3 to the fourth."

Example 1 Finding Values of Exponential Expressions

Find the value of each exponential expression.

(a) 5^2

$$\underbrace{5 \cdot 5}_{} = 25 \qquad \text{5 is used as a factor 2 times.}$$

Read 5^2 as "5 to the second power" or, more commonly, "5 squared."

(b) 6^3

$$\underbrace{6 \cdot 6 \cdot 6}_{} = 216 \qquad \text{6 is used as a factor 3 times.}$$

Read 6^3 as "6 to the third power" or, more commonly, "6 cubed."

(c) 2^5

$$2 \cdot 2 \cdot 2 \cdot 2 \cdot 2 = 32 \qquad \text{2 is used as a factor 5 times.}$$

Read 2^5 as "2 to the fifth power."

(d) 7^4

$$7 \cdot 7 \cdot 7 \cdot 7 = 2401 \qquad \text{7 is used as a factor 4 times.}$$

Read 7^4 as "7 to the fourth power."

(e) $\left(\frac{2}{3}\right)^3$

$$\frac{2}{3} \cdot \frac{2}{3} \cdot \frac{2}{3} = \frac{8}{27} \qquad \text{$\frac{2}{3}$ is used as a factor 3 times.}$$

Work Problem 1 at the Side.

2 Use the order of operations guidelines. Many problems involve more than one operation. To indicate the order in which the operations should be performed, we often use *grouping symbols.* If no grouping symbols are used, we apply the order of operations discussed below.

Consider the expression $5 + 2 \cdot 3$. To show that the multiplication should be performed before the addition, parentheses can be used to write

$$5 + (2 \cdot 3) = 5 + 6 = 11.$$

If addition is to be performed first, the parentheses should group $5 + 2$ as follows.

$$(5 + 2) \cdot 3 = 7 \cdot 3 = 21$$

Other grouping symbols used in more complicated expressions are brackets [ ], braces { }, and fraction bars. (For example, in $\frac{8-2}{3}$, the expression $8 - 2$ is considered to be grouped in the numerator.)

To work problems with more than one operation, use the following **order of operations.** This order is used by most calculators and computers.

Order of Operations

If grouping symbols are present, simplify within them, innermost first (and above and below fraction bars separately), in the following order.

Step 1 Apply all exponents.

Step 2 Do any multiplications or divisions in the order in which they occur, working from left to right.

Step 3 Do any additions or subtractions in the order in which they occur, working from left to right.

If no grouping symbols are present, start with Step 1.

A dot has been used to show multiplication; another way to show multiplication is with parentheses. For example, 3(7) means $3 \cdot 7$ or 21. Also, $3(4 + 5)$ means 3 times the sum of 4 and 5. By the order of operations, the sum in parentheses must be found first, then the product.

Example 2 Using the Order of Operations

Find the value of each expression.

(a) $4 \cdot 5 - 6$

Using the order of operations given in the box, first multiply 4 and 5, then subtract 6 from the product.

$$4 \cdot 5 - 6 = 20 - 6 \quad \text{Multiply.}$$
$$= 14 \quad \text{Subtract.}$$

(b) $9(6 + 11)$

Work first inside the parentheses.

$$9(6 + 11) = 9(17) \quad \text{Add inside parentheses.}$$
$$= 153 \quad \text{Multiply.}$$

Continued on Next Page

(c) $6 \cdot 8 + 5 \cdot 2$

Perform any multiplications from left to right, then add.

$$
\begin{aligned}
6 \cdot 8 + 5 \cdot 2 &= 48 + 10 && \text{Multiply.} \\
&= 58 && \text{Add.}
\end{aligned}
$$

(d)
$$
\begin{aligned}
2(5 + 6) + 7 \cdot 3 &= 2(11) + 7 \cdot 3 && \text{Add inside parentheses.} \\
&= 22 + 21 && \text{Multiply.} \\
&= 43 && \text{Add.}
\end{aligned}
$$

(e) $9 + 2^3 - 5$

Following the order of operations, calculate 2^3 first.

$$
\begin{aligned}
9 + 2^3 - 5 &= 9 + 8 - 5 && \text{Use the exponent.} \\
&= 12 && \text{Add, then subtract.}
\end{aligned}
$$

Work Problem 2 at the Side.

3 Use more than one grouping symbol. An expression with double parentheses, such as the expression $2(8 + 3(6 + 5))$, can be confusing. We avoid confusion by using square brackets, [ ], in place of one pair of parentheses.

Example 3 Using Brackets and Fraction Bars

Find the value of each expression.

(a) $2[8 + 3(6 + 5)]$

Begin inside the parentheses. Then follow the order of operations.

$$
\begin{aligned}
2[8 + 3(6 + 5)] &= 2[8 + 3(11)] && \text{Add.} \\
&= 2[8 + 33] && \text{Multiply.} \\
&= 2[41] && \text{Add.} \\
&= 82 && \text{Multiply.}
\end{aligned}
$$

(b) $\dfrac{4(5 + 3) + 3}{2(3) - 1}$

Simplify the numerator and denominator separately.

$$
\begin{aligned}
\frac{4(5 + 3) + 3}{2(3) - 1} &= \frac{4(8) + 3}{2(3) - 1} && \text{Add inside parentheses.} \\
&= \frac{32 + 3}{6 - 1} && \text{Multiply.} \\
&= \frac{35}{5} && \text{Add and subtract.} \\
&= 7 && \text{Divide.}
\end{aligned}
$$

Work Problem 3 at the Side.

Calculator Tip Calculators follow the order of operations given in this section. You may want to try some of the examples to see that your calculator gives the same answers. Be sure to use the parentheses keys to insert parentheses where they are needed. To work Example 3(b) with a calculator, you must put parentheses around the numerator and the denominator.

2 Find the value of each expression.

(a) $7 + 3 \cdot 8$

(b) $2 \cdot 9 + 7 \cdot 3$

(c) $7 \cdot 6 - 3(8 + 1)$

(d) $2 + 3^2 - 5$

3 Find the value of each expression.

(a) $9[(4 + 8) - 3]$

(b) $\dfrac{2(7 + 8) + 2}{3 \cdot 5 + 1}$

ANSWERS

2. (a) 31 **(b)** 39 **(c)** 15 **(d)** 6

3. (a) 81 **(b)** 2

4 Know the meanings of ≠, <, >, ≤, and ≥. So far we have used only the symbols of arithmetic, such as +, −, ·, and ÷ and the equality symbol =. The equality symbol with a slash through it means "is *not* equal to." For example,

$$7 \neq 8$$

indicates that 7 is not equal to 8.

If two numbers are not equal, then one of the numbers must be less than the other. The symbol < represents "is less than," so "7 is less than 8" is written as

$$7 < 8.$$

Also, we write "6 is less than 9" as $6 < 9$.

The symbol > means "is greater than." We write "8 is greater than 2" as

$$8 > 2.$$

The statement "17 is greater than 11" becomes $17 > 11$.

Keep the meanings of the symbols < and > clear by remembering that the symbol always points to the *smaller* number.

Smaller number → **8** < 15

15 > **8** ← Smaller number

Work Problem 4 at the Side.

Two other symbols, ≤ and ≥, also represent the idea of inequality. The symbol ≤ means "is less than or equal to," so

$$5 \leq 9$$

means "5 is less than or equal to 9." If either the < part or the = part is true, then the inequality ≤ is true. The statement $5 \leq 9$ is true because $5 < 9$ is true. Also, $8 \leq 8$ is true because $8 = 8$ is true. But $13 \leq 9$ is not true because neither $13 < 9$ nor $13 = 9$ is true.

The symbol ≥ means "is greater than or equal to";

$$9 \geq 5$$

is true because $9 > 5$ is true.

Example 4 Using the Symbols ≤ and ≥

Tell whether each statement is *true* or *false*.

(a) $15 \leq 20$ The statement $15 \leq 20$ is true because $15 < 20$.

(b) $12 \geq 12$ Since $12 = 12$, this statement is true.

(c) $\dfrac{6}{15} \geq \dfrac{2}{3}$

To compare fractions, write them with a common denominator. Here, 15 is a common denominator and $\frac{2}{3} = \frac{10}{15}$. Now decide whether $\frac{6}{15} \geq \frac{10}{15}$ is true or false. Both statements $\frac{6}{15} > \frac{10}{15}$ and $\frac{6}{15} = \frac{10}{15}$ are false; therefore, $\frac{6}{15} \geq \frac{2}{3}$ is false.

Work Problem 5 at the Side.

5 Translate word statements to symbols. Word phrases or statements often must be converted to symbols in algebra. The next example illustrates this.

4 Write each statement in words, then decide whether it is *true* or *false*.

(a) $7 < 5$

(b) $12 > 6$

(c) $4 \neq 10$

(d) $28 \neq 4 \cdot 7$

5 Tell whether each statement is *true* or *false*.

(a) $30 \leq 40$

(b) $25 \geq 10$

(c) $40 \leq 10$

(d) $21 \leq 21$

(e) $3 \geq 3$

ANSWERS

4. (a) Seven is less than five. False
(b) Twelve is greater than six. True
(c) Four is not equal to ten. True
(d) Twenty-eight is not equal to four times seven. False

5. (a) true **(b)** true **(c)** false **(d)** true **(e)** true

6 Write in symbols.

(a) Nine equals eleven minus two.

(b) Seventeen is less than thirty.

(c) Eight is not equal to ten.

(d) Fourteen is greater than twelve.

(e) Thirty is less than or equal to fifty.

(f) Two is greater than or equal to two.

7 Write each statement with the inequality symbol reversed.

(a) $8 < 10$

(b) $3 > 1$

(c) $9 \leq 15$

(d) $6 \geq 2$

ANSWERS

6. (a) $9 = 11 - 2$ (b) $17 < 30$ (c) $8 \neq 10$ (d) $14 > 12$ (e) $30 \leq 50$ (f) $2 \geq 2$

7. (a) $10 > 8$ (b) $1 < 3$ (c) $15 \geq 9$ (d) $2 \leq 6$

Example 5 Converting Words to Symbols

Write each word statement in symbols.

(a) Twelve **equals** ten **plus** two. $12 = 10 + 2$

(b) Nine **is less than** ten. $9 < 10$
Compare this with 9 less than 10, which is written $10 - 9$.

(c) Fifteen **is not equal to** eighteen. $15 \neq 18$

(d) Seven **is greater than** four. $7 > 4$

(e) Thirteen **is less than or equal to** forty. $13 \leq 40$

(f) Six **is greater than or equal to** six. $6 \geq 6$

Work Problem 6 at the Side.

6 **Reverse the direction of inequality statements.** Any statement with $<$ can be converted to one with $>$, and any statement with $>$ can be converted to one with $<$. We do this by reversing both the order of the numbers and the direction of the symbol. For example, the statement $6 < 10$ can be written as $10 > 6$.

Exchange numbers.

$6 < 10$ becomes $10 > 6$

Reverse symbol.

Example 6 Converting between < and >

Parts (a)–(d) show the same statements written in two equally correct ways.

(a) $9 < 16$, $16 > 9$ **(b)** $5 > 2$, $2 < 5$

(c) $3 \leq 8$, $8 \geq 3$ **(d)** $12 \geq 5$, $5 \leq 12$

Note that in each inequality, the point of the symbol is directed toward the smaller number.

Work Problem 7 at the Side.

Here is a summary of the symbols of equality and inequality.

SYMBOLS OF EQUALITY AND INEQUALITY

Symbol	Meaning	Example
$=$	Is equal to	$.5 = \frac{1}{2}$ means .5 is equal to $\frac{1}{2}$.
$\neq$	Is not equal to	$3 \neq 7$ means 3 is not equal to 7.
$<$	Is less than	$6 < 10$ means 6 is less than 10.
$>$	Is greater than	$15 > 14$ means 15 is greater than 14.
$\leq$	Is less than or equal to	$4 \leq 8$ means 4 is less than or equal to 8.
$\geq$	Is greater than or equal to	$1 \geq 0$ means 1 is greater than or equal to 0.

CAUTION

The symbols of equality and inequality are used to write mathematical *sentences*. They differ from the symbols for operations ($+$, $-$, $\cdot$, and $\div$), discussed earlier, which are used to write mathematical *expressions* that represent a number. For example, compare the sentence $4 < 10$, which gives the relationship between 4 and 10, with the expression $4 + 10$, which tells how to operate on 4 and 10 to get the number 14. This distinction between sentences and expressions will be important throughout your study of algebra.

1.1 EXERCISES

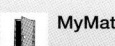

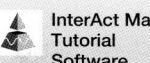

FOR EXTRA HELP: Student's Solutions Manual; MyMathLab.com; InterAct Math Tutorial Software; AW Math Tutor Center; www.mathxl.com; Digital Video Tutor CD 1 Videotape 2

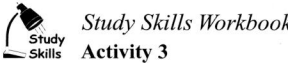

Study Skills Workbook **Activity 3**

Decide whether each statement is true *or* false. *If it is* false, *explain why.*

1. Exponents are also called powers.

true

2. Some grouping symbols are $+, -, \cdot$, and $\div$.

False; $+, -, \cdot$, and $\div$ are operation symbols.

3. When evaluated, $4 + 3(8 - 2)$ is equal to 42.

False; using the guidelines for order of operations gives $4 + 3(8 - 2) = 4 + 3(6) = 4 + 18 = 22$.

4. $3^3 = 9$

False; $3^3 = 3 \cdot 3 \cdot 3 = 27$.

5. The statement "4 is 12 less than 16" is interpreted $4 = 12 - 16$.

False; the correct translation is $4 = 16 - 12$.

6. The statement "6 is 4 less than 10" is interpreted $6 < 10 - 4$.

False; the correct translation is $6 = 10 - 4$.

Find the value of each exponential expression. See Example 1.

7. 7^2 **49** **8.** 4^2 **16** **9.** 12^2 **144** **10.** 14^2 **196**

11. 4^3 **64** **12.** 5^3 **125** **13.** 10^3 **1000** **14.** 11^3 **1331**

15. 3^4 **81** **16.** 6^4 **1296** **17.** 4^5 **1024** **18.** 3^5 **243**

19. $\left(\frac{2}{3}\right)^4$ **$\frac{16}{81}$** **20.** $\left(\frac{3}{4}\right)^3$ **$\frac{27}{64}$** **21.** $(.04)^3$ **.000064** **22.** $(.05)^4$ **.00000625**

23. When evaluating $(4^2 + 3^3)^4$, what is the *last* exponent that would be applied? Explain your answer.

The 4 would be applied last because we work first inside the parentheses.

24. Which are not grouping symbols—parentheses, brackets, fraction bars, exponents?

exponents

Find the value of each expression. See Examples 2 and 3.

25. $13 + 9 \cdot 5$ **58** **26.** $11 + 7 \cdot 6$ **53** **27.** $20 - 4 \cdot 3 + 5$ **13** **28.** $18 - 7 \cdot 2 + 6$ **10**

29. $9 \cdot 5 - 13$ **32** **30.** $7 \cdot 6 - 11$ **31** **31.** $18 - 2 + 3$ **19** **32.** $22 - 8 + 9$ **23**

33. $\frac{1}{4} \cdot \frac{2}{3} + \frac{2}{5} \cdot \frac{11}{3}$ **$\frac{49}{30}$** **34.** $\frac{9}{4} \cdot \frac{2}{3} + \frac{4}{5} \cdot \frac{5}{3}$ **$\frac{17}{6}$** **35.** $9 \cdot 4 - 8 \cdot 3$ **12** **36.** $11 \cdot 4 + 10 \cdot 3$ **74**

37. $2.5(1.9) + 4.3(7.3)$ **36.14** **38.** $4.3(1.2) + 2.1(8.5)$ **23.01** **39.** $10 + 40 \div 5 \cdot 2$ **26**

40. $12 + 8^2 \div 8 - 4$ **16** **41.** $18 - 2(3 + 4)$ **4** **42.** $30 - 3(4 + 2)$ **12**

43. $5[3 + 4(2^2)]$ **95** **44.** $6\left[\frac{3}{4} + 8\left(\frac{1}{2}\right)^3\right]$ **$\frac{21}{2}$** **45.** $\left(\frac{3}{2}\right)^2\left[\left(11 + \frac{1}{3}\right) - 6\right]$ **12**

46. $4^2[(13 + 4) - 8]$ **144** **47.** $\frac{8 + 6(3^2 - 1)}{3 \cdot 2 - 2}$ **14** **48.** $\frac{8 + 2(8^2 - 4)}{4 \cdot 3 - 10}$ **64**

49. $\dfrac{4(7+2)+8(8-3)}{6(4-2)-2^2}$ **$\dfrac{19}{2}$**

50. $\dfrac{6(5+1)-9(1+1)}{5(8-4)-2^3}$ **$\dfrac{3}{2}$**

Tell whether each statement is true *or* false. *In Exercises 53–62, first simplify each expression involving an operation. See Example 4.*

51. $8 \geq 17$ **false**

52. $10 \geq 41$ **false**

53. $17 \leq 18 - 1$ **true**

54. $12 \geq 10 + 2$ **true**

55. $6 \cdot 8 + 6 \cdot 6 \geq 0$ **true**

56. $4 \cdot 20 - 16 \cdot 5 \geq 0$ **true**

57. $6[5 + 3(4 + 2)] \leq 70$ **false**

58. $6[2 + 3(2 + 5)] \leq 135$ **false**

59. $\dfrac{9(7-1) - 8 \cdot 2}{4(6-1)} > 3$ **false**

60. $\dfrac{2(5+3) + 2 \cdot 2}{2(4-1)} > 1$ **true**

61. $8 \leq 4^2 - 2^2$ **true**

62. $10^2 - 8^2 > 6^2$ **false**

Write each word statement in symbols. See Example 5.

63. Fifteen is equal to five plus ten.
$15 = 5 + 10$

64. Twelve is equal to twenty minus eight.
$12 = 20 - 8$

65. Nine is greater than five minus four.
$9 > 5 - 4$

66. Ten is greater than six plus one.
$10 > 6 + 1$

67. Sixteen is not equal to nineteen.
$16 \neq 19$

68. Three is not equal to four.
$3 \neq 4$

69. Two is less than or equal to three.
$2 \leq 3$

70. Five is less than or equal to nine.
$5 \leq 9$

Write each statement in words and decide whether it is true *or* false. *(Hint: To compare fractions, write them with the same denominator.)*

71. $7 < 19$
Seven is less than nineteen. True

72. $9 < 10$
Nine is less than ten. True

73. $\dfrac{1}{3} \neq \dfrac{3}{10}$
One-third is not equal to three-tenths. True

74. $\dfrac{10}{7} \neq \dfrac{3}{2}$
Ten-sevenths is not equal to three-halves. True

75. $8 \geq 11$
Eight is greater than or equal to eleven. False

76. $4 \leq 2$
Four is less than or equal to two. False

Write each statement with the inequality symbol reversed. See Example 6.

77. $5 < 30$ **$30 > 5$**

78. $8 > 4$ **$4 < 8$**

79. $12 \geq 3$ **$3 \leq 12$**

80. $25 \leq 41$ **$41 \geq 25$**

The table shows results of a science literacy survey by Jon Miller of the International Center for the Advancement of Science Literacy in Chicago. Use this table to answer Exercises 81–83.

Country	Science Literacy Index
United States	56
Netherlands	52
France	50
Canada	45
Greece	38
Japan	36

81. Which countries scored more than 50?
United States and Netherlands

82. Which countries scored at most 40?
Greece and Japan

83. For which countries were scores not less than 50?
United States, Netherlands, and France

1.2 VARIABLES, EXPRESSIONS, AND EQUATIONS

OBJECTIVES

1. Evaluate algebraic expressions, given values for the variables.
2. Convert phrases from words to algebraic expressions.
3. Identify solutions of equations.
4. Translate word statements to equations.
5. Distinguish between expressions and equations.

Study Skills *Study Skills Workbook* **Activity 4**

To make general statements about numbers in algebra, letters called **variables** are used to represent numbers. Different numbers can replace the variables to form specific statements. For example, in Section 1.7 we will see the statement

$$a + b = b + a.$$

This statement is true for any replacements of the variables a and b, such as 2 for a and 5 for b, which gives the true statement

$$2 + 5 = 5 + 2.$$

An **algebraic expression** is a collection of numbers, variables, operation symbols, and grouping symbols, such as parentheses, square brackets, or fraction bars. For example,

$$x + 5, \quad 2m - 9, \quad \text{and} \quad 8p^2 + 6(p - 2)$$

are all algebraic expressions. In $2m - 9$, the expression $2m$ means $2 \cdot m$, the product of 2 and m, and $8p^2$ represents the product of 8 and p^2. Also, $6(p - 2)$ means the product of 6 and $p - 2$.

1 Evaluate algebraic expressions, given values for the variables. An algebraic expression has different numerical values for different values of the variables.

Example 1 Evaluating Expressions Given Values of the Variable

Find the value of each algebraic expression if $m = 5$ and then if $m = 9$.

(a) $8m$

$8m = 8 \cdot 5$	Let $m = 5$.	$8m = 8 \cdot 9$	Let $m = 9$.
$= 40$	Multiply.	$= 72$	Multiply.

(b) $3m^2$

$3m^2 = 3 \cdot 5^2$	Let $m = 5$.	$3m^2 = 3 \cdot 9^2$	Let $m = 9$.
$= 3 \cdot 25$	Square.	$= 3 \cdot 81$	Square.
$= 75$	Multiply.	$= 243$	Multiply.

CAUTION

In Example 1(b), notice that $3m^2$ means $3 \cdot m^2$; it *does not* mean $3m \cdot 3m$. Unless parentheses are used, the exponent refers only to the variable or number just before it. To write $3m \cdot 3m$ with exponents, use parentheses: $3m \cdot 3m = (3m)^2$.

Work Problem 1 at the Side.

Example 2 Evaluating Expressions with More Than One Variable

Find the value of each expression if $x = 5$ and $y = 3$.

(a) $2x + 5y$

$2x + 5y = 2 \cdot 5 + 5 \cdot 3$	Replace x with 5 and y with 3.
$= 10 + 15$	Multiply.
$= 25$	Add.

Continued on Next Page

1 Find the value of each expression if $p = 3$.

(a) $6p$

(b) $p + 12$

(c) $5p^2$

ANSWERS

1. (a) 18 **(b)** 15 **(c)** 45

2 Find the value of each expression if $x = 6$ and $y = 9$.

(a) $4x + 7y$

(b) $\dfrac{4x - 2y}{x + 1}$

(c) $2x^2 + y^2$

ANSWERS

2. (a) 87 **(b)** $\frac{6}{7}$ **(c)** 153

(b) $\dfrac{9x - 8y}{2x - y}$

$$\frac{9x - 8y}{2x - y} = \frac{9 \cdot 5 - 8 \cdot 3}{2 \cdot 5 - 3} \quad \text{Replace } x \text{ with 5 and } y \text{ with } 3.$$

$$= \frac{45 - 24}{10 - 3} \quad \text{Multiply.}$$

$$= \frac{21}{7} \quad \text{Subtract.}$$

$$= 3 \quad \text{Divide.}$$

(c) $x^2 - 2y^2$

$$x^2 - 2y^2 = 5^2 - 2 \cdot 3^2 \quad \text{Replace } x \text{ with 5 and } y \text{ with } 3.$$

$$= 25 - 2 \cdot 9 \quad \text{Use the exponents.}$$

$$= 25 - 18 \quad \text{Multiply.}$$

$$= 7 \quad \text{Subtract.}$$

Work Problem 2 at the Side.

Calculator Tip An Introduction to Calculators in the front of this book explains how to perform arithmetic operations and evaluate exponentials with a calculator.

2 Convert phrases from words to algebraic expressions.

Problem Solving

Sometimes variables must be used to change word phrases into algebraic expressions. This process will be important later for solving applied problems.

Example 3 Using Variables to Change Word Phrases into Algebraic Expressions

Change each word phrase to an algebraic expression. Use x as the variable to represent the number.

(a) The sum of a number and 9
"Sum" is the answer to an addition problem. This phrase translates as

$$x + 9 \quad \text{or} \quad 9 + x.$$

(b) 7 minus a number
"Minus" indicates subtraction, so the translation is

$$7 - x.$$

Note that $x - 7$ would *not* be correct because we cannot subtract in either order and get the same results.

(c) A number subtracted from 12
Since a number is subtracted *from* 12, write this as

$$12 - x.$$

Compare this result with "12 is subtracted from a number," which is $x - 12$.

Continued on Next Page

(d) The **product** of 11 and a number

$$11 \cdot x \quad \text{or} \quad 11x$$

(e) 5 **divided by** a number

$$\frac{5}{x}$$

(f) The **product of** 2 and the **difference** between a number and 8

$$2(x - 8)$$

CAUTION

Notice that in translating the words "the difference between a number and 8" the order is kept the same: $x - 8$. "The difference between 8 and a number" would be written $8 - x$.

Work Problem 3 at the Side.

3 Identify solutions of equations. An **equation** is a statement that two expressions are equal. Examples of equations are

$$x + 4 = 11, \quad 2y = 16, \quad \text{and} \quad 4p + 1 = 25 - p.$$

To **solve** an equation, we must find all values of the variable that make the equation true. Such values of the variable are called the **solutions** of the equation.

Example 4 Deciding Whether a Number Is a Solution of an Equation

Decide whether the given number is a solution of the equation.

(a) Is 7 a solution of $5p + 1 = 36$?

$$5p + 1 = 36$$
$$5 \cdot 7 + 1 = 36 \quad \text{Replace } p \text{ with 7.}$$
$$35 + 1 = 36 \quad \text{Multiply.}$$
$$36 = 36 \quad \text{True}$$

The number 7 is a solution of the equation.

(b) Is $\frac{14}{3}$ a solution of $9m - 6 = 32$?

$$9m - 6 = 32$$
$$9 \cdot \frac{14}{3} - 6 = 32 \quad \text{Replace } m \text{ with } \tfrac{14}{3}.$$
$$42 - 6 = 32 \quad \text{Multiply.}$$
$$36 = 32 \quad \text{False}$$

The number $\frac{14}{3}$ is not a solution of the equation.

Work Problem 4 at the Side.

4 Translate word statements to equations. We have seen how to translate phrases from words to expressions. Sentences given in words are translated as equations.

3 Write as an algebraic expression. Use x as the variable.

(a) The sum of 5 and a number

(b) A number minus 4

(c) A number subtracted from 48

(d) The product of 6 and a number

(e) 9 multiplied by the sum of a number and 5

4 Decide whether the given number is a solution of the equation.

(a) $p - 1 = 3$; 2

(b) $2k + 3 = 15$; 7

(c) $8p - 11 = 5$; 2

ANSWERS

3. **(a)** $5 + x$ **(b)** $x - 4$ **(c)** $48 - x$ **(d)** $6x$ **(e)** $9(x + 5)$

4. **(a)** no **(b)** no **(c)** yes

5 Change each sentence to an equation. Let x represent the number.

(a) Three times the sum of a number and 13 is 19.

(b) Five times a number is subtracted from 21, giving 15.

6 Decide whether each is an equation or an expression.

(a) $2x + 5y - 7$

(b) $\dfrac{3x - 1}{5}$

(c) $2x + 5 = 7$

(d) $\dfrac{x}{y - 3} = 4x$

ANSWERS

5. **(a)** $3(x + 13) = 19$ **(b)** $21 - 5x = 15$

6. **(a)** expression **(b)** expression **(c)** equation **(d)** equation

Example 5 **Translating Word Sentences to Equations**

Change each word sentence to an equation. Let x represent the number.

(a) Twice the sum of a number and four is six.

"Twice" means two times. The word *is* suggests equals. With x representing the number, translate as follows.

Twice	the sum of a number and four	is	six.
↓	↓	↓	↓
$2 \cdot$	$(x + 4)$	$=$	6

$$2(x + 4) = 6$$

(b) Nine more than five times a number is 49.

"Nine more than" means "nine is added to." Use x to represent the unknown number.

Nine	more than	five times a number	is	49.
↓	↓	↓	↓	↓
9	$+$	$5x$	$=$	49

$$9 + 5x = 49$$

(c) Seven less than three times a number is eleven.

Here, 7 is *subtracted* from three times a number to get 11.

Three times a number	less	seven	is	eleven.
↓	↓	↓	↓	↓
$3x$	$-$	7	$=$	11

$$3x - 7 = 11$$

Work Problem 5 at the Side.

5 **Distinguish between expressions and equations.** Students often have trouble distinguishing between equations and expressions. Remember that an equation is a sentence (with an = symbol); an expression is a phrase that represents a number.

$4x + 5 = 9$	$4x + 5$
↑	↑
Equation	Expression

Example 6 **Distinguishing between Equations and Expressions**

Decide whether each is an equation or an expression.

(a) $2x - 5y$

There is no equals sign, so this is an expression.

(b) $2x = 5y$

Because of the equals sign, this is an equation.

Work Problem 6 at the Side.

1.2 EXERCISES

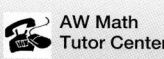

FOR EXTRA HELP: Student's Solutions Manual | MyMathLab.com | InterAct Math Tutorial Software | AW Math Tutor Center | www.mathxl.com | Digital Video Tutor CD 1 Videotape 2

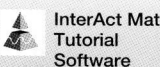

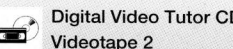

Fill in each blank with the correct response.

1. If $x = 3$, then the value of $x + 7$ is 10.

2. If $x = 1$ and $y = 2$, then the value of $4xy$ is 8.

3. "The sum of 12 and x" is represented by the expression $12 + x$. If $x = 9$, the value of that expression is 21.

4. Will the equation $x = x + 4$ ever have a solution? no

5. $2x + 3$ is an expression (equation/expression), while $2x + 3 = 8$ is an equation (equation/expression).

Exercises 6–10 cover some of the concepts introduced in this section. Give a short explanation for each.

6. Why is $2x^3$ not the same as $2x \cdot 2x \cdot 2x$? Explain, using an exponent to write $2x \cdot 2x \cdot 2x$.

$2x^3 = 2 \cdot x \cdot x \cdot x$, while $2x \cdot 2x \cdot 2x = (2x)^3$.

7. If the words *more than* in Example 5(b) were changed to *less than,* how would the equation be changed?

The equation would be $5x - 9 = 49$.

8. Explain in your own words why, when evaluating the expression $4x^2$ for $x = 3$, 3 must be squared *before* multiplying by 4.

The exponent 2 applies only to the base x, and exponentials must be evaluated before products.

9. There are many pairs of values of x and y for which $2x + y$ will equal 6. Name two such pairs and describe how you determined them.

Answers will vary. Two such pairs are $x = 0, y = 6$ and $x = 1, y = 4$. To find a pair, choose one number, substitute it for a variable, then calculate the value for the other variable.

10. Suppose that for the equation $3x - y = 9$, the value of x is given as 4 . What would be the corresponding value of y? How do you know this?

The value for y is 3. If $x = 4$, then $3x = 12$, and 3 subtracted from 12 equals 9.

*Find the numerical value of each expression if **(a)** x = 4 and **(b)** x = 6. See Example 1.*

11. $4x^2$
(a) 64 **(b)** 144

12. $5x^2$
(a) 80 **(b)** 180

13. $\dfrac{3x - 5}{2x}$
(a) $\dfrac{7}{8}$ **(b)** $\dfrac{13}{12}$

14. $\dfrac{4x - 1}{3x}$
(a) $\dfrac{5}{4}$ **(b)** $\dfrac{23}{18}$

15. $\dfrac{6.459x}{2.7}$ (to the nearest thousandth)
(a) 9.569 **(b)** 14.353

16. $\dfrac{.74x^2}{.85}$ (to the nearest thousandth)
(a) 13.929 **(b)** 31.341

17. $3x^2 + x$
(a) 52 **(b)** 114

18. $2x + x^2$
(a) 24 **(b)** 48

*Find the numerical value of each expression if **(a)** x = 2 and y = 1 and **(b)** x = 1 and y = 5. See Example 2.*

19. $3(x + 2y)$
(a) 12 **(b)** 33

20. $2(2x + y)$
(a) 10 **(b)** 14

21. $x + \dfrac{4}{y}$
(a) 6 **(b)** $\dfrac{9}{5}$

22. $y + \dfrac{8}{x}$
(a) 5 **(b)** 13

23. $\dfrac{x}{2} + \dfrac{y}{3}$
(a) $\dfrac{4}{3}$ **(b)** $\dfrac{13}{6}$

24. $\dfrac{x}{5} + \dfrac{y}{4}$
(a) $\dfrac{13}{20}$ **(b)** $\dfrac{29}{20}$

25. $\dfrac{2x + 4y - 6}{5y + 2}$
(a) $\dfrac{2}{7}$ **(b)** $\dfrac{16}{27}$

26. $\dfrac{4x + 3y - 1}{2x + y}$
(a) 2 **(b)** $\dfrac{18}{7}$

27. $2y^2 + 5x$
(a) 12 **(b)** 55

28. $6x^2 + 4y$
(a) 28 **(b)** 26

29. $\dfrac{3x + y^2}{2x + 3y}$
(a) 1 **(b)** $\dfrac{28}{17}$

30. $\dfrac{x^2 + 1}{4x + 5y}$
(a) $\dfrac{5}{13}$ **(b)** $\dfrac{2}{29}$

31. $.841x^2 + .32y^2$

(a) 3.684 (b) 8.841

32. $.941x^2 + .2y^2$

(a) 3.964 (b) 5.941

Change each word phrase to an algebraic expression. Use x to represent the number. See Example 3.

33. Twelve times a number

$12x$

34. Thirteen added to a number

$x + 13$

35. Two subtracted from a number

$x - 2$

36. Eight subtracted from a number

$x - 8$

37. Four times a number, subtracted from seven

$7 - 4x$

38. Three times a number, subtracted from fourteen

$14 - 3x$

39. The difference between twice a number and 6

$2x - 6$

40. The difference between 6 and half a number

$6 - \frac{x}{2}$

41. 12 divided by the sum of a number and 3

$\frac{12}{x + 3}$

42. The difference between a number and 5, divided by 12

$\frac{x - 5}{12}$

43. The product of 6 and four less than a number

$6(x - 4)$

44. The product of 9 and five more than a number

$9(x + 5)$

45. In the phrase "four more than the product of a number and 6," does the word *and* signify the operation of addition? Explain.

The word *and* does not signify addition here. In the phrase "the product of a number and 6," *and* connects two quantities to be multiplied.

46. Suppose that the directions on a test read "Solve the following expressions." How would you politely correct the person who wrote these directions?

An expression cannot be solved; it merely indicates a series of operations to be performed. An equation can be solved.

Decide whether the given number is a solution of the equation. See Example 4.

47. Is 7 a solution of $p - 5 = 12$?

no

48. Is 10 a solution of $x + 6 = 15$?

no

49. Is 1 a solution of $5m + 2 = 7$?

yes

50. Is 1 a solution of $3x + 5 = 8$?

yes

51. Is $\frac{1}{5}$ a solution of $6p + 4p + 9 = 11$?

yes

52. Is $\frac{12}{5}$ a solution of $2x + 3x + 8 = 20$?

yes

53. Is 3 a solution of
$2y + 3(y - 2) = 14$?

no

54. Is 2 a solution of
$6a + 2(a + 3) = 14$?

no

55. Is $\frac{1}{3}$ a solution of
$\frac{z + 4}{2 - z} = \frac{13}{5}$?

yes

56. Is $\frac{13}{4}$ a solution of
$\frac{x + 6}{x - 2} = \frac{37}{5}$?

yes

57. Is 4.3 a solution of
$3r^2 - 2 = 53.47$?

yes

58. Is 3.7 a solution of
$2x^2 + 1 = 28.38$?

yes

Change each sentence to an equation. Use x to represent the number. See Example 5.

59. The sum of a number and 8 is 18.

$x + 8 = 18$

60. A number minus three equals 1.

$x - 3 = 1$

61. Five more than twice a number is 5.

$2x + 5 = 5$

62. The product of 2 and the sum of a number and 5 is 14.

$2(x + 5) = 14$

63. Sixteen minus three-fourths of a number is 13.

$16 - \frac{3}{4}x = 13$

64. The sum of six-fifths of a number and 2 is 14.

$\frac{6}{5}x + 2 = 14$

65. Three times a number is equal to 8 more than twice the number.

$3x = 2x + 8$

66. Twelve divided by a number equals $\frac{1}{3}$ times that number.

$\frac{12}{x} = \frac{1}{3}x$

Identify each as an expression *or an* equation. *See Example 6.*

67. $3x + 2(x - 4)$

expression

68. $5y - (3y + 6)$

expression

69. $7t + 2(t + 1) = 4$

equation

70. $9r + 3(r - 4) = 2$

equation

RELATING CONCEPTS (Exercises 71–74) FOR INDIVIDUAL OR GROUP WORK

A mathematical model *is an equation that describes the relationship between two quantities. For example, based on data from the U.S. Bureau of Labor Statistics, average hourly earnings of production workers in manufacturing industries in the United States from 1990 through 1997 are approximated by the equation* $y = .319x - 624.31$, *where x represents the year and y represents the hourly earnings in dollars. Use this model to approximate the hourly earnings during each year. Compare with the actual earnings given in parentheses.*

71. 1990 ($10.83)

$10.50; less by $.33

72. 1994 ($12.07)

$11.78; less by $.29

73. 1996 ($12.37)

$12.41; more by $.04

74. 1997 ($13.17)

$12.73; less by $.44

1.3 Real Numbers and the Number Line

Objectives

1. Use integers to express numbers in applications.
2. Graph rational numbers on the number line.
3. Tell which of two real numbers is smaller.
4. Find the opposite of a real number.
5. Find the absolute value of a real number.

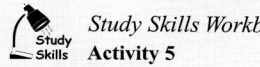

Study Skills: *Study Skills Workbook* **Activity 5**

In Chapter R, we introduced the set of whole numbers. We use set braces, { }, to enclose the elements of a set.

Whole Numbers

$$\{0, 1, 2, 3, 4, 5, \ldots\}$$

The numbers used for counting are called the **natural numbers.**

Natural Numbers

$$\{1, 2, 3, 4, 5, \ldots\}$$

These numbers, along with many others, can be represented on **number lines** like the one in Figure 1. We draw a number line by choosing any point on the line and labeling it 0. Choose any point to the right of 0 and label it 1. The distance between 0 and 1 gives a unit of measure used to locate other points, as shown in Figure 1. The points labeled in Figure 1 correspond to the first few whole numbers.

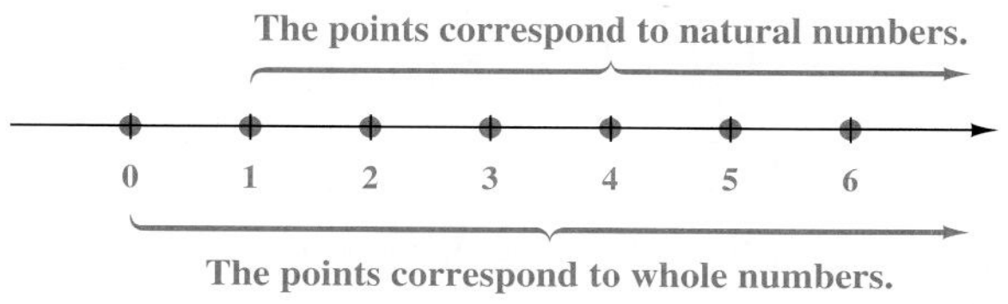

Figure 1

1 Use integers to express numbers in applications.

The natural numbers are located to the right of 0 on the number line. But numbers may also be placed to the left of 0. For each natural number we can place a corresponding number to the left of 0. These numbers, written -1, -2, -3, -4, and so on, are shown in Figure 2. Each is the **opposite** or **negative** of a natural number. The natural numbers, their opposites, and 0 form a new set of numbers called the **integers.**

Integers

$$\{\ldots, -3, -2, -1, 0, 1, 2, 3, \ldots\}$$

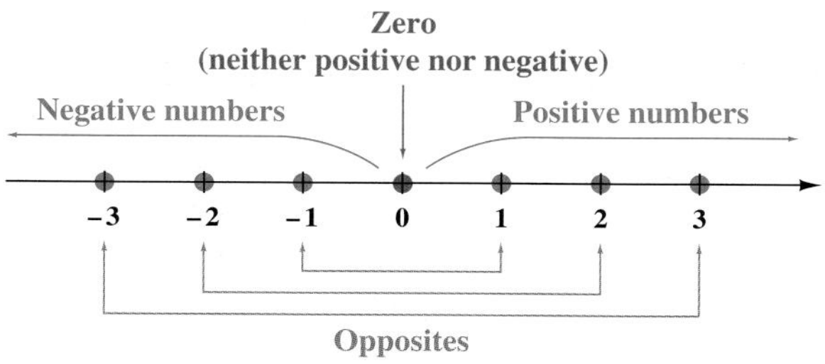

The points correspond to integers.

Figure 2

1 Use an integer to express the number(s) in each application.

(a) Erin discovers that she has spent $53 more than she has in her checking account.

(b) The record high Fahrenheit temperature in the United States was 134° in Death Valley, California on July 10, 1913. (*Source: The World Almanac and Book of Facts,* 2000.)

(c) A football team gained 5 yd, then lost 10 yd on the next play.

2 Graph each number on the number line.

$$-3, \frac{17}{8}, -2.75, 1\frac{1}{2}, -\frac{3}{4}$$

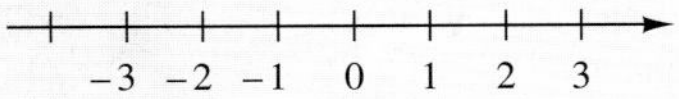

ANSWERS

1. (a) −53 **(b)** 134 **(c)** 5, −10

2.

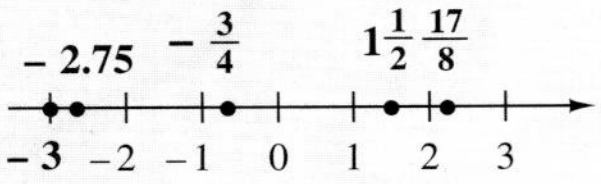

There are many practical applications of negative numbers. For example, a Fahrenheit temperature on a cold January day might be −10°, and a business that spends more than it takes in has a negative "profit."

Example 1 **Using Negative Numbers in Applications**

Use an integer to express the number in each application.

(a) The lowest Fahrenheit temperature ever recorded in meteorological records was 129° below zero at Vostok, Antarctica, on July 21, 1983. (*Source: The World Almanac and Book of Facts,* 2000.)
Use −129° because "below zero" indicates a negative number.

(b) The shore surrounding the Dead Sea is 1340 ft below sea level. (*Source: Microsoft Encarta Encyclopedia 2000.*)
Again, "below sea level" indicates a negative number, −1340.

Work Problem 1 at the Side.

2 **Graph rational numbers on the number line.** Not all numbers are integers. For example, $\frac{1}{2}$ is not; it is a number halfway between the integers 0 and 1. Also, $3\frac{1}{4}$ is not an integer. These numbers and others that are quotients of integers are **rational numbers.** (The name comes from the word *ratio,* which indicates a quotient.)

Rational Numbers

{numbers that can be written as quotients of integers, with denominators not 0}

Since any integer can be written as the quotient of itself and 1, all integers are also rational numbers. For example, $-5 = \frac{-5}{1}$. A decimal number that comes to an end (terminates), such as .23, is a rational number: $.23 = \frac{23}{100}$. Decimal numbers that repeat in a fixed block of digits, such as $.3333\ldots = .\overline{3}$ and $.454545\ldots = .\overline{45}$, are also rational numbers. For example, $.\overline{3} = \frac{1}{3}$.

As shown in Figures 1 and 2, to **graph** a number, we place a dot on the number line at the point that corresponds to the number. The number is called the **coordinate** of the point. Think of the graph of a set of numbers as a picture of the set.

Example 2 **Graphing Rational Numbers**

Graph each number on the number line.

$$-\frac{3}{2}, -\frac{2}{3}, \frac{1}{2}, 1\frac{1}{3}, \frac{23}{8}, 3\frac{1}{4}$$

To locate the improper fractions on the number line, write them as mixed numbers or decimals. The graph is shown in Figure 3.

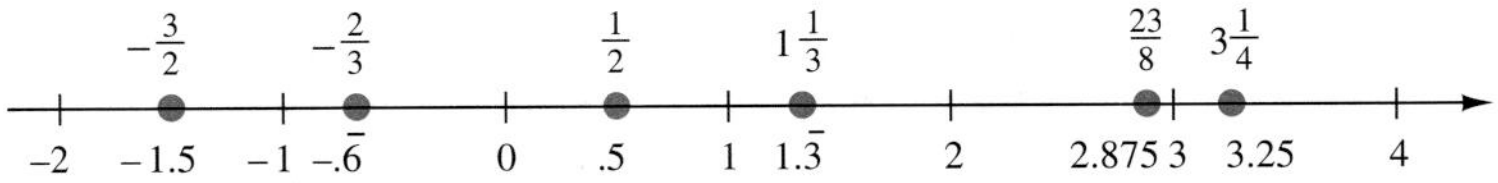

Figure 3

Work Problem 2 at the Side.

Although many numbers are rational, not all are. For example, a square that measures one unit on a side has a diagonal whose length is the square root of 2, written $\sqrt{2}$. See Figure 4. It can be shown that $\sqrt{2}$ cannot be written as a quotient of integers. Because of this, $\sqrt{2}$ is not rational; it is **irrational**. Other examples of irrational numbers are $\sqrt{3}$, $\sqrt{7}$, $-\sqrt{10}$, and π (the ratio of the circumference of a circle to its diameter).

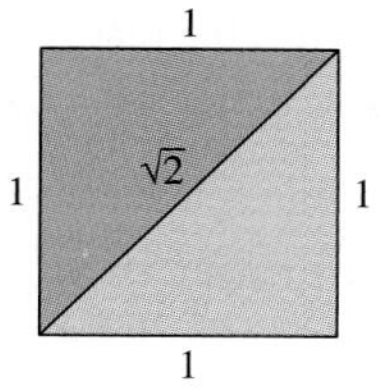

Figure 4

Irrational Numbers

{nonrational numbers represented by points on the number line}

The decimal form of an irrational number neither terminates nor repeats. Irrational numbers are discussed in Chapter 9.

Both rational and irrational numbers can be represented by points on the number line and are called **real numbers.**

Real Numbers

{all numbers that are either rational or irrational}

All the numbers mentioned so far are real numbers. The relationships between the various types of numbers are shown in Figure 5. Notice that any real number is either a rational number or an irrational number.

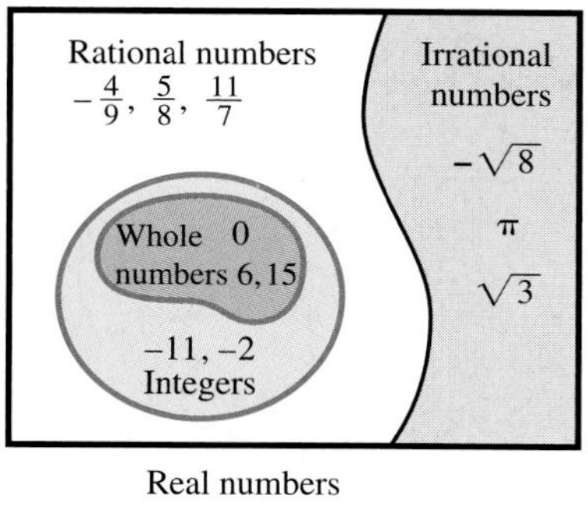

Figure 5

3 **Tell which of two real numbers is smaller.** Given any two whole numbers, we can tell which number is smaller. But what about two negative numbers, as in the set of integers? Moving from 0 to the right along a number line, the positive numbers corresponding to the points on the number line *increase.* For example, $8 < 12$, and 8 is to the left of 12 on a number line. We extend this ordering to all real numbers.

3 Tell whether each statement is *true* or *false*.

(a) $-2 < 4$

(b) $6 > -3$

(c) $-9 < -12$

(d) $-4 \geq -1$

(e) $-6 \leq 0$

Ordering of the Real Numbers

For any two real numbers a and b, **a is less than b** if a is to the left of b on a number line.

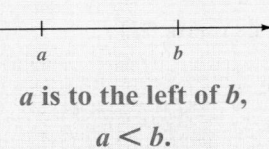

***a* is to the left of *b*,**

$$a < b.$$

This means that any negative number is smaller than 0, and any negative number is smaller than any positive number. Also, 0 is smaller than any positive number.

Example 3 **Determining the Order of Real Numbers**

Is it true that $-3 < -1$?

To find out, locate -3 and -1 on a number line, as shown in Figure 6. Because -3 is to the left of -1 on the number line, -3 is smaller than -1. The statement $-3 < -1$ is true.

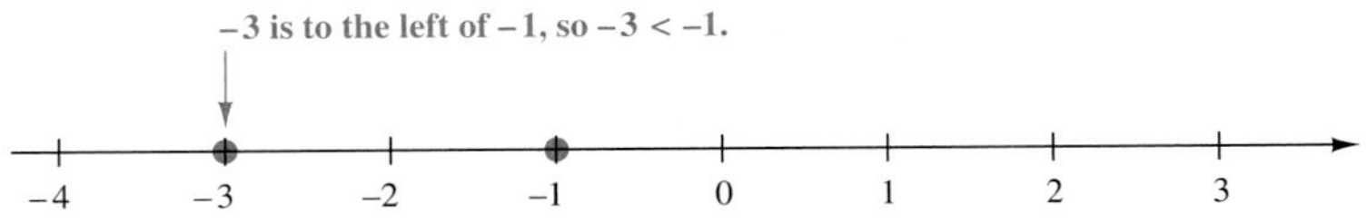

Figure 6

Work Problem 3 at the Side.

4 **Find the opposite of a real number.** Earlier, we saw that every positive integer has a negative integer that is its opposite or negative. This is true for every real number except 0, which is its own opposite.* A characteristic of pairs of opposites is that they are the same distance from 0 on the number line but in opposite directions. See Figure 7.

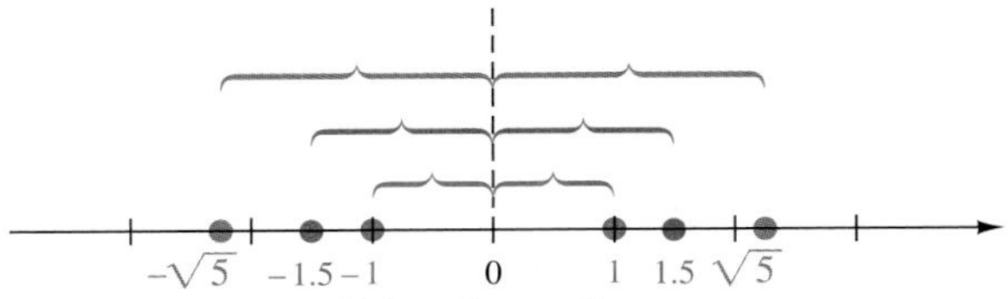

Pairs of opposites

Figure 7

We indicate the opposite of a number by writing the symbol − in front of the number. For example, the opposite of 7 is -7 (read "negative 7"). We could write the opposite of -4 as $-(-4)$, but we know that 4 is the opposite of -4. Since a number can have only one opposite, $-(-4)$ and 4 must represent the same number, so

$$-(-4) = 4.$$

This idea can be generalized.

---

* The opposite (or negative) of a number is also called the *additive inverse* of the number, as we shall see in Section 1.7.

ANSWERS

3. **(a)** true **(b)** true **(c)** false **(d)** false **(e)** true

Double Negative Rule

For any real number a,

$$-(-a) = a.$$

The following chart shows several numbers and their opposites.

Number	Opposite
-4	$-(-4)$, or 4
-3	3
0	0
5	-5
19	-19

The chart suggests the following rule.

Except for 0, the opposite of a number is found by changing the sign of the number.

Work Problem 4 at the Side.

5 Find the absolute value of a real number. As previously mentioned, opposites are numbers the same distance from 0 on the number line but on opposite sides of 0. Another way to say this is to say that opposites have the same *absolute value*. The **absolute value** of a number is the undirected distance between 0 and the number on the number line. The symbol for the absolute value of the number a is $|a|$, read "the absolute value of a." For example, the distance between 2 and 0 on the number line is 2 units, so

$$|2| = 2.$$

Also, the distance between -2 and 0 on the number line is 2, so

$$|-2| = 2.$$

Since distance is a physical measurement, which is never negative, we can make the following statement.

The absolute value of a number can never be negative.

For example,

$$|12| = 12 \quad \text{and} \quad |-12| = 12$$

because both 12 and -12 lie at a distance of 12 units from 0 on the number line. Since the distance of 0 from 0 is 0 units, we have

$$|0| = 0.$$

Example 4 Evaluating Absolute Value

Simplify.

(a) $|5| = 5$

(b) $|-5| = 5$

(c) $-|-5| = -(5) = -5$ Replace $|-5|$ with 5.

Continued on Next Page

4 Find the opposite of each number.

(a) 6

(b) 15

(c) -9

(d) -12

(e) 0

ANSWERS

4. **(a)** -6 **(b)** -15 **(c)** 9 **(d)** 12 **(e)** 0

(d) $-|-13| = -(13) = -13$

(e) $|8 - 5|$
Simplify within the absolute value bars first.

$$|8 - 5| = |3| = 3$$

(f) $-|8 - 5| = -|3| = -3$

(g) $-|12 - 3| = -|9| = -9$

Parts (e)–(g) in Example 5 show that absolute value bars also act as grouping symbols. You must perform any operations within absolute value bars before finding the absolute value.

Work Problem 5 at the Side.

5 Simplify.

(a) $|-6|$

(b) $|9|$

(c) $-|15|$

(d) $-|-9|$

(e) $|9 - 4|$

(f) $-|32 - 2|$

ANSWERS

5. (a) 6 **(b)** 9 **(c)** -15 **(d)** -9 **(e)** 5 **(f)** -30

1.3 EXERCISES

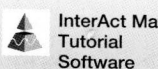

FOR EXTRA HELP — Student's Solutions Manual | MyMathLab.com | InterAct Math Tutorial Software | AW Math Tutor Center | www.mathxl.com | Digital Video Tutor CD 1 Videotape 2

In Exercises 1–6, give an example of a number that satisfies each given condition.

1. An integer between 3.5 and 4.5

4

2. A rational number between 3.8 and 3.9

One example is 3.85. There are others.

3. A whole number that is not positive and is less than 1

0

4. A whole number greater than 4.5

One example is 5. There are others.

5. An irrational number that is between $\sqrt{11}$ and $\sqrt{13}$

One example is $\sqrt{12}$. There are others.

6. A real number that is neither negative nor positive

0

*List all numbers from each set that are **(a)** natural numbers, **(b)** whole numbers, **(c)** integers, **(d)** rational numbers, **(e)** irrational numbers, **(f)** real numbers.*

7. $\left\{-9, -\sqrt{7}, -1\frac{1}{4}, -\frac{3}{5}, 0, \sqrt{5}, 3, 5.9, 7\right\}$

(a) 3, 7 (b) 0, 3, 7 (c) −9, 0, 3, 7

(d) $-9, -1\frac{1}{4}, -\frac{3}{5}, 0, 3, 5.9, 7$

(e) $-\sqrt{7}, \sqrt{5}$ (f) All are real numbers.

8. $\left\{-5.3, -5, -\sqrt{3}, -1, -\frac{1}{9}, 0, 1.2, 4, \sqrt{12}\right\}$

(a) 4 (b) 0, 4 (c) −5, −1, 0, 4

(d) $-5.3, -5, -1, -\frac{1}{9}, 0, 1.2, 4$

(e) $-\sqrt{3}, \sqrt{12}$ (f) All are real numbers.

Use an integer to express each number representing a change *in the following applications. See Example 1.*

9. In February 1998, the number of housing starts in the United States increased from the previous month by 93,000 units. (*Source: Wall Street Journal.*)

93,000

10. The Wolfsburg, Germany, Volkswagen plant turns out 1550 fewer cars per day than it did in 1991. (*Source:* Klebnikov, P., "Bringing Back the Beetle," *Forbes,* April 7, 1997.)

−1550

11. Between 1980 and 1990, the population of the District of Columbia decreased by 31,532. (*Source:* U.S. Bureau of the Census.)

−31,532

12. In 1994, Taiwan produced 159,376 more passenger cars than commercial vehicles. (*Source:* American Automobile Manufacturers Association.)

159,376

Graph each group of numbers on a number line. See Example 2.

13. 0, 3, −5, −6

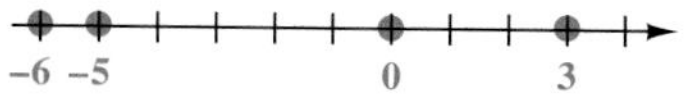

14. 2, 6, −2, −1

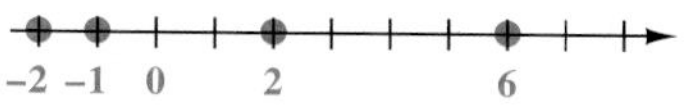

15. −2, −6, −4, 3, 4

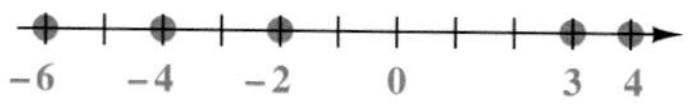

16. −5, −3, −2, 0, 4

17. $\frac{1}{4}, 2\frac{1}{2}, -3\frac{4}{5}, -4, -\frac{13}{8}$

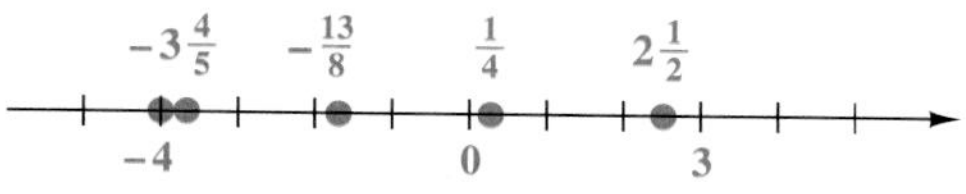

18. $5\frac{1}{4}, \frac{41}{9}, -2\frac{1}{3}, 0, -3\frac{2}{5}$

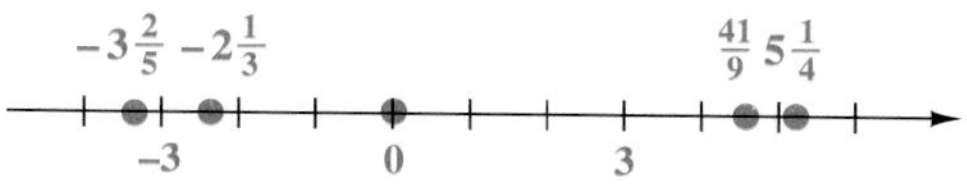

Select the smaller number in each pair. See Example 3.

19. $-11, -4$ **-11**

20. $-9, -16$ **-16**

21. $-21, 1$ **-21**

22. $-57, 3$ **-57**

23. $0, -100$ **-100**

24. $-215, 0$ **-215**

25. $-\frac{2}{3}, -\frac{1}{4}$ **$-\frac{2}{3}$**

26. $-\frac{3}{8}, -\frac{9}{16}$ **$-\frac{9}{16}$**

Decide whether each statement is true *or* false. *See Example 3.*

27. $8 < -16$
false

28. $12 < -24$
false

29. $-3 < -2$
true

30. $-10 < -9$
true

For each number, ***(a)*** *find its opposite and* ***(b)*** *find its absolute value.*

31. -2
(a) 2 (b) 2

32. -8
(a) 8 (b) 8

33. 6
(a) -6 (b) 6

34. 11
(a) -11 (b) 11

35. $-\frac{3}{4}$
(a) $\frac{3}{4}$ (b) $\frac{3}{4}$

36. $-\frac{1}{3}$
(a) $\frac{1}{3}$ (b) $\frac{1}{3}$

Simplify. See Example 4.

37. $|-7|$ **7**

38. $|-3|$ **3**

39. $-|12|$ **-12**

40. $-|23|$ **-23**

41. $-|-14|$ **-14**

42. $-|-19|$ **-19**

43. $|13 - 4|$ **9**

44. $|8 - 7|$ **1**

Decide whether each statement is true *or* false.

45. $|-8| < 7$
false

46. $|-6| \geq -|6|$
true

47. $4 \leq |4|$
true

48. $-|-3| > 2$
false

49. Students often say "The absolute value of a number is always positive." Is this true? If not, explain.
No; the statement is false for one number, 0.

50. If the absolute value of a number is equal to the number itself, what must be true about the number?
It must be greater than or equal to 0.

To answer the questions in Exercises 51–54, refer to the table, which gives the changes in producer price indexes for two recent years.

Commodity	Change from 1995 to 1996	Change from 1996 to 1997
Food	4.9	4.0
Transportation	3.9	1.3
Apparel	−.5	.9
Video/Audio equipment	−2.6	−2.2
Shelter	5.3	5.3

Source: U.S. Bureau of Labor Statistics.

51. What commodity for which years represents the greatest decrease?
video/audio equipment from 1995–1996

52. What commodity for which years represents the least change?
apparel from 1995–1996

53. Which has smaller absolute value, the change for video/audio equipment from 1995 to 1996 or from 1996 to 1997?
1996–1997

54. Which has greater absolute value, the change for apparel from 1995 to 1996 or from 1996 to 1997?
1996–1997

1.4 Addition of Real Numbers

OBJECTIVES

1. Add two numbers with the same sign.
2. Add numbers with different signs.
3. Add mentally.
4. Use the order of operations with real numbers.
5. Translate words and phrases that indicate addition.

1 Add two numbers with the same sign. We can use the number line to explain addition of real numbers. Later, we will give the rules for addition. Recall that the answer to an addition problem is called the **sum.**

Example 1 Adding with the Number Line

Use the number line to find the sum $2 + 3$.

Add the positive numbers 2 and 3 by starting at 0 and drawing an arrow two units to the *right,* as shown in Figure 8. This arrow represents the number 2 in the sum $2 + 3$. Next, from the right end of this arrow draw another arrow three units to the right. The number below the end of this second arrow is 5, so $2 + 3 = 5$.

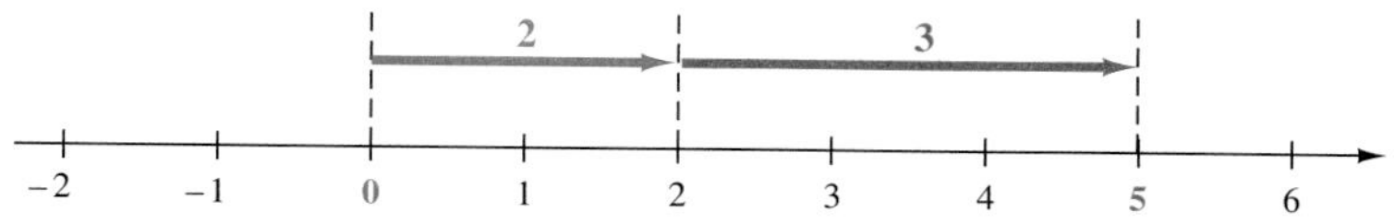

Figure 8

Example 2 Adding with the Number Line

Use the number line to find the sum $-2 + (-4)$. (Parentheses are placed around the -4 to avoid the confusing use of + and − next to each other.)

To add the negative numbers -2 and -4 on the number line, we start at 0 and draw an arrow two units to the *left,* as shown in Figure 9. From the left end of this first arrow, we draw a second arrow four units to the left. We draw the arrow to the left to represent the addition of the *negative* number, -4. The number below the end of this second arrow is -6, so $-2 + (-4) = -6$.

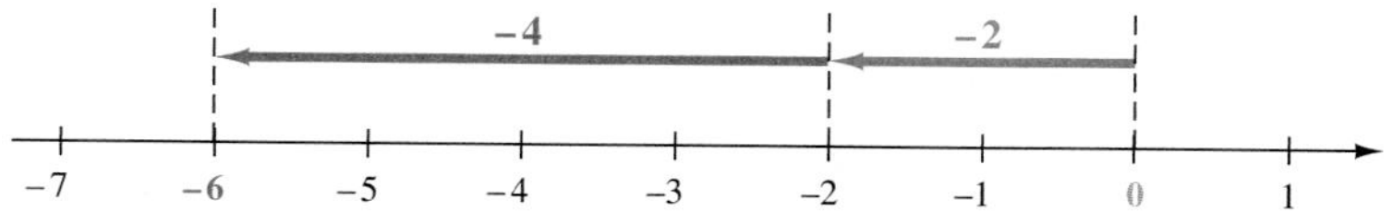

Figure 9

Work Problem 1 at the Side.

1 Use a number line to find each sum.

(a) $1 + 4$

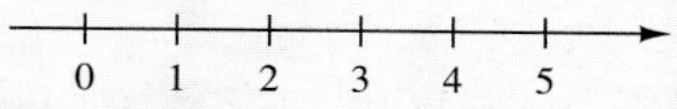

(b) $-2 + (-5)$

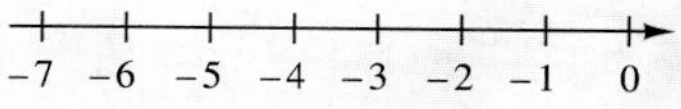

In Example 2, we found that the sum of the two negative numbers -2 and -4 is a negative number whose distance from 0 is the sum of the distance of -2 from 0 and the distance of -4 from 0. That is, *the sum of two negative numbers is the negative of the sum of their absolute values.*

$$-2 + (-4) = -(|-2| + |-4|) = -(2 + 4) = -6$$

> To add two numbers having the same sign, add the absolute values of the numbers. Give the result the same sign as the numbers being added.
>
> *Example:* $-4 + (-3) = -7$.

ANSWERS

1. (a) $1 + 4 = 5$

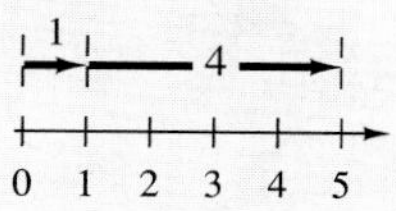

(b) $-2 + (-5) = -7$

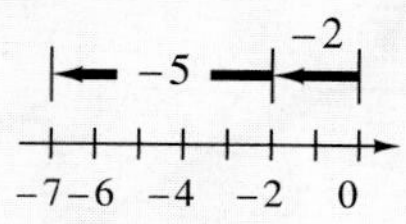

Example 3 Adding Two Negative Numbers

Find each sum.

(a) $-2 + (-9) = -11$ The sum of two negative numbers is negative.

(b) $-8 + (-12) = -20$ **(c)** $-15 + (-3) = -18$

Work Problem 2 at the Side.

2 Add numbers with different signs.

We use the number line again to illustrate the sum of a positive number and a negative number.

Example 4 Adding Numbers with Different Signs

Use the number line to find the sum $-2 + 5$.

We find the sum $-2 + 5$ on the number line by starting at 0 and drawing an arrow two units to the left. From the left end of this arrow, we draw a second arrow five units to the right, as shown in Figure 10. The number below the end of this second arrow is 3, so $-2 + 5 = 3$.

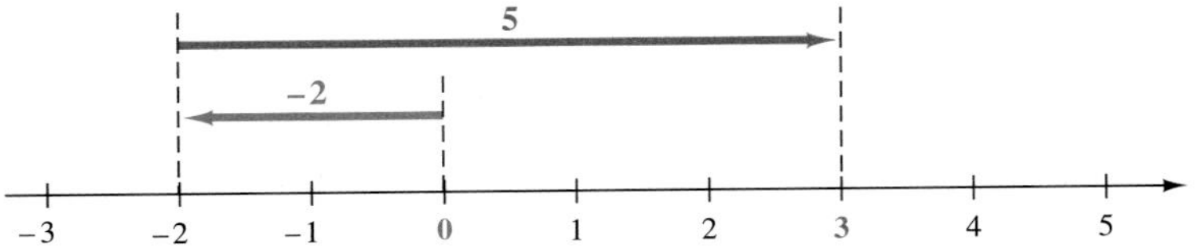

Figure 10

Work Problem 3 at the Side.

Addition of numbers with different signs also can be defined using absolute value.

> To add numbers with different signs, first find the difference between the absolute values of the numbers. Give the answer the same sign as the number with the larger absolute value.
>
> *Example:* $-12 + 6 = -6$.

For example, to add -12 and 5, we find their absolute values: $|-12| = 12$ and $|5| = 5$; then we find the difference between these absolute values: $12 - 5 = 7$. Since $|-12| > |5|$, the sum will be negative, so $-12 + 5 = -7$.

Calculator Tip The (−) or (+/−) key is used to input a negative number in some scientific calculators. Try using your calculator to add negative numbers.

3 Add mentally.

While a number line is useful in showing the rules for addition, it is important to be able to find sums mentally.

Example 5 Adding a Positive Number and a Negative Number

Check each answer, trying to work the addition mentally. If you have trouble, use a number line.

(a) $7 + (-4) = 3$

(b) $-8 + 12 = 4$

Continued on Next Page

---

2 Find each sum.

(a) $-7 + (-3)$

(b) $-12 + (-18)$

(c) $-15 + (-4)$

3 Use a number line to find each sum.

(a) $6 + (-3)$

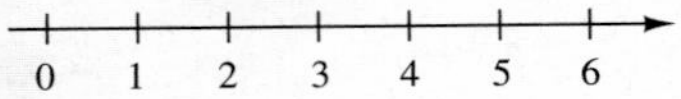

(b) $-5 + 1$

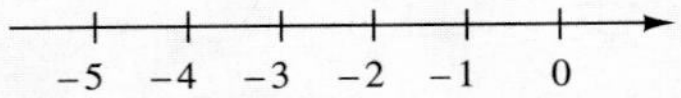

ANSWERS

2. (a) -10 **(b)** -30 **(c)** -19

3. (a) $6 + (-3) = 3$

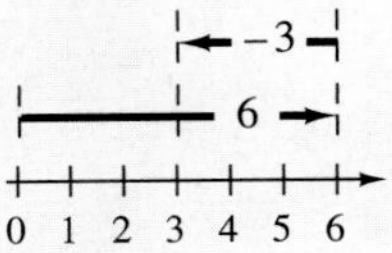

(b) $-5 + 1 = -4$

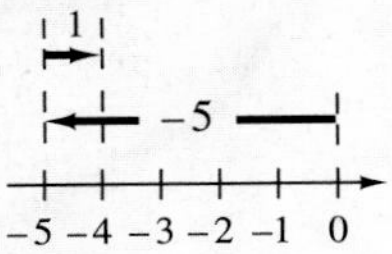

(c) $-\frac{1}{2} + \frac{1}{8} = -\frac{4}{8} + \frac{1}{8} = -\frac{3}{8}$ Remember to find a common denominator first.

(d) $\frac{5}{6} + \left(-1\frac{1}{3}\right) = \frac{5}{6} + \left(-\frac{4}{3}\right) = \frac{5}{6} + \left(-\frac{8}{6}\right) = -\frac{3}{6} = -\frac{1}{2}$

(e) $-4.6 + 8.1 = 3.5$

Work Problem 4 at the Side.

The rules for adding signed numbers are summarized below.

Adding Signed Numbers

Same sign Add the absolute values of the numbers. Give the sum the same sign as the numbers being added.

Different signs Find the difference between the larger absolute value and the smaller. Give the answer the sign of the number having the larger absolute value.

4 Use the order of operations with real numbers. Sometimes a problem involves square brackets, [ ]. As we mentioned earlier, brackets are treated just like parentheses. We do the calculations inside the brackets until a single number is obtained. Remember to use the order of operations given in Section 1.1 for adding more than two numbers.

Example 6 **Adding with Brackets**

Find each sum.

(a) $-3 + [4 + (-8)]$

First work inside the brackets. Follow the order of operations given in Section 1.1.

$$-3 + [4 + (-8)] = -3 + (-4) = -7$$

(b) $8 + [(-2 + 6) + (-3)] = 8 + [4 + (-3)] = 8 + 1 = 9$

Work Problem 5 at the Side.

5 Translate words and phrases that indicate addition. Let's now look at the interpretation of words and phrases that involve addition. Problem solving often requires translating words and phrases into symbols. We began this process with translating simple phrases in Section 1.1.

The word *sum* indicates addition. There are other key words and phrases that also indicate addition. Some of these are given in the chart below.

Word or Phrase	Example	Numerical Expression and Simplification
Sum of	The *sum of* −3 and 4	$-3 + 4 = 1$
Added to	5 *added to* −8	$-8 + 5 = -3$
More than	12 *more than* −5	$(-5) + 12 = 7$
Increased by	−6 *increased by* 13	$-6 + 13 = 7$
Plus	3 *plus* 14	$3 + 14 = 17$

4 Check each answer, trying to work the addition mentally. If you have trouble, use a number line.

(a) $-8 + 2 = -6$

(b) $-15 + 4 = -11$

(c) $17 + (-10) = 7$

(d) $\frac{3}{4} + \left(-1\frac{3}{8}\right) = -\frac{5}{8}$

(e) $-9.5 + 3.8 = -5.7$

5 Find each sum.

(a) $2 + [7 + (-3)]$

(b) $6 + [(-2 + 5) + 7]$

(c) $-9 + [-4 + (-8 + 6)]$

ANSWERS
4. All are correct.
5. (a) 6 **(b)** 16 **(c)** −15

Example 7 Translating Words and Phrases

Write a numerical expression for each phrase, and simplify the expression.

(a) The **sum of** -8 and 4 and 6

$$-8 + 4 + 6 = (-8 + 4) + 6 = -4 + 6 = 2$$

Notice that parentheses were placed around $-8 + 4$, and this addition was done first, using the order of operations given earlier.

(b) 3 **more than** -5, **increased by** 12

$$-5 + 3 + 12 = (-5 + 3) + 12 = -2 + 12 = 10$$

Work Problem 6 at the Side.

Gains (or increases) and losses (or decreases) sometimes appear in applied problems. When they do, the gains may be interpreted as positive numbers and the losses as negative numbers.

Example 8 Interpreting Gains and Losses

The Tennessee Titans football team gained 3 yd on first down, lost 12 yd on second down, and then gained 13 yd on third down. How many yards did the team gain or lose altogether?

The gains are represented by positive numbers and the loss by a negative number.

$$3 + (-12) + 13$$

Add from left to right.

$$3 + (-12) + 13 = [3 + (-12)] + 13 = (-9) + 13 = 4$$

The team gained 4 yd altogether.

Work Problem 7 at the Side.

---

6 Write a numerical expression for each phrase, and simplify the expression.

(a) 4 more than -12

(b) The sum of 6 and -7

(c) -12 added to -31

(d) 7 increased by the sum of 8 and -3

7 Solve the problem.

A football team lost 8 yd on first down, lost 5 yd on second down, and then gained 7 yd on third down. How many yards did the team gain or lose altogether?

ANSWERS

6. **(a)** $-12 + 4$; -8 **(b)** $6 + (-7)$; -1
(c) $-31 + (-12)$; -43
(d) $7 + [8 + (-3)]$; 12

7. The team lost 6 yd.

1.4 EXERCISES

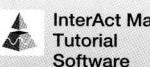

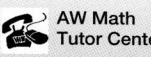

FOR EXTRA HELP: Student's Solutions Manual; MyMathLab.com; InterAct Math Tutorial Software; AW Math Tutor Center; www.mathxl.com; Digital Video Tutor CD 1 Videotape 2

By the order of operations, what is the first step you would use to simplify each expression?

1. $4[3(-2 + 5) - 1]$ Add −2 and 5.

2. $[-4 + 7(-6 + 2)]$ Add −6 and 2.

3. $9 + ([-1 + (-3)] + 5)$ Add −1 and −3.

4. $[(-8 + 4) + (-6)] + 5$ Add −8 and 4.

Find each sum. See Examples 1–6.

5. $6 + (-4)$ 2

6. $8 + (-5)$ 3

7. $12 + (-15)$ −3

8. $4 + (-8)$ −4

9. $-7 + (-3)$ −10

10. $-11 + (-4)$ −15

11. $-10 + (-3)$ −13

12. $-16 + (-7)$ −23

13. $-12.4 + (-3.5)$ −15.9

14. $-21.3 + (-2.5)$ −23.8

15. $10 + [-3 + (-2)]$ 5

16. $13 + [-4 + (-5)]$ 4

17. $5 + [14 + (-6)]$ 13

18. $7 + [3 + (-14)]$ −4

19. $-3 + [5 + (-2)]$ 0

20. $-7 + [10 + (-3)]$ 0

21. $-8 + [3 + (-1) + (-2)]$ −8

22. $-7 + [5 + (-8) + 3]$ −7

23. $\frac{9}{10} + \left(-\frac{3}{5}\right)$ $\frac{3}{10}$

24. $\frac{5}{8} + \left(-\frac{17}{12}\right)$ $-\frac{19}{24}$

25. $-\frac{1}{6} + \frac{2}{3}$ $\frac{1}{2}$

26. $-\frac{6}{25} + \frac{19}{20}$ $\frac{71}{100}$

27. $2\frac{1}{2} + \left(-3\frac{1}{4}\right)$ $-\frac{3}{4}$

28. $-4\frac{3}{8} + 6\frac{1}{2}$ $\frac{17}{8}$ or $2\frac{1}{8}$

29. $7.8 + (-9.4)$ −1.6

30. $14.7 + (-10.1)$ 4.6

31. $-7.1 + [3.3 + (-4.9)]$ −8.7

32. $-9.5 + [-6.8 + (-1.3)]$ −17.6

33. $[-8 + (-3)] + [-7 + (-7)]$ −25

34. $[-5 + (-4)] + [9 + (-2)]$ −2

Work each problem. (*Source:* Population Reference Bureau.) *See Example 8.*

35. Based on census population projections for 2020, New York will lose 5 seats in the U.S. House of Representatives, Pennsylvania will lose 4 seats, and Ohio will lose 3. Write a signed number that represents the total number of seats these three states are projected to lose.

−12

36. Michigan is projected to lose 3 seats in the U.S. House of Representatives and Illinois 2 in 2020. The states projected to gain the most seats are California with 9, Texas with 5, Florida with 3, Georgia with 2, and Arizona with 2. Write a signed number that represents the algebraic sum of these changes.

+16

Perform each operation, and then determine whether the statement is true *or* false. *Try to do all work mentally. See Examples 5 and 6.*

37. $-11 + 13 = 13 + (-11)$ **true**

38. $16 + (-9) = -9 + 16$ **true**

39. $-10 + 6 + 7 = -3$ **false**

40. $-12 + 8 + 5 = -1$ **false**

41. $18 + (-6) + (-12) = 0$ **true**

42. $-5 + 21 + (-16) = 0$ **true**

43. $|-8 + 10| = -8 + (-10)$ **false**

44. $|-4 + 6| = -4 + (-6)$ **false**

45. $2\frac{1}{5} + \left(-\frac{6}{11}\right) = -\frac{6}{11} + 2\frac{1}{5}$ **true**

46. $-1\frac{1}{2} + \frac{5}{8} = \frac{5}{8} + \left(-1\frac{1}{2}\right)$ **true**

47. $-7 + [-5 + (-3)] = [(-7) + (-5)] + 3$ **false**

48. $6 + [-2 + (-5)] = [(-4) + (-2)] + 5$ **true**

RELATING CONCEPTS (Exercises 49–52) FOR INDIVIDUAL OR GROUP WORK

Recall the rules for adding signed numbers introduced in this section, and ***work Exercises 49–52 in order.***

49. Suppose that the sum of two numbers is negative, and you know that one of the numbers is positive. What can you conclude about the other number?

It must be negative and have the larger absolute value.

50. If you are asked to solve the equation $x + 5 = -7$ from a set of numbers, why could you immediately eliminate any positive numbers as possible solutions? (Remember how you answered Exercise 49.)

The sum of a positive number and 5 cannot be -7.

51. Suppose that the sum of two numbers is positive, and you know that one of the numbers is negative. What can you conclude about the other number?

It must be positive and have the larger absolute value.

52. If you are asked to solve the equation $x + (-8) = 2$ from a set of numbers, why could you immediately eliminate any negative numbers as possible solutions? (Remember how you answered Exercise 51.)

The sum of a negative number and -8 cannot be 2.

53. In your own words, explain how to add two negative numbers.

Add the absolute values of the numbers. The sum will be negative.

54. In your own words, explain how to add a positive number and a negative number. Give two cases.

Subtract the smaller absolute value from the larger absolute value. The number with larger absolute value determines the sign of the sum. If that number is positive, the sum will be positive. If that number is negative, the sum will be negative.

Write a numerical expression for each phrase, and simplify the expression. See Example 7.

55. The sum of -5 and 12 and 6

$-5 + 12 + 6$; 13

56. The sum of -3 and 5 and -12

$-3 + 5 + (-12)$; -10

57. 14 added to the sum of -19 and -4

[−19 + (−4)] + 14; −9

58. -2 added to the sum of -18 and 11

(−18 + 11) + (−2); −9

59. The sum of -4 and -10, increased by 12

[−4 + (−10)] + 12; −2

60. The sum of -7 and -13, increased by 14

[−7 + (−13)] + 14; −6

61. 4 more than the sum of 8 and -18

[8 + (−18)] + 4; −6

62. 10 more than the sum of -4 and -6

[−4 + (−6)] + 10; 0

Solve each problem. See Example 8.

63. Kramer owed Jerry \$10 for snacks raided from the refrigerator. Kramer later borrowed \$70 from George to finance his latest get-rich scheme. What positive or negative number represents Kramer's financial status?

−\$80

64. Shalita's checking account balance is \$54.00. She then takes a gamble by writing a check for \$89.00. What is her new balance? (Write the balance as a signed number.)

−\$35.00

65. The surface, or rim, of a canyon is at altitude 0. On a hike down into the canyon, a party of hikers stops for a rest at 130 m below the surface. They then descend another 54 m. What is their new altitude? (Write the altitude as a signed number.)

−184 m

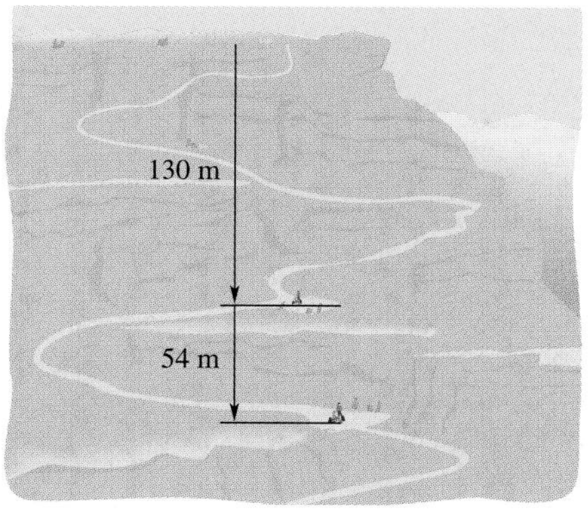

66. A pilot announces to the passengers that the current altitude of their plane is 34,000 ft. Because of some unexpected turbulence, the pilot is forced to descend 2100 ft. What is the new altitude of the plane? (Write the altitude as a signed number.)

31,900 ft

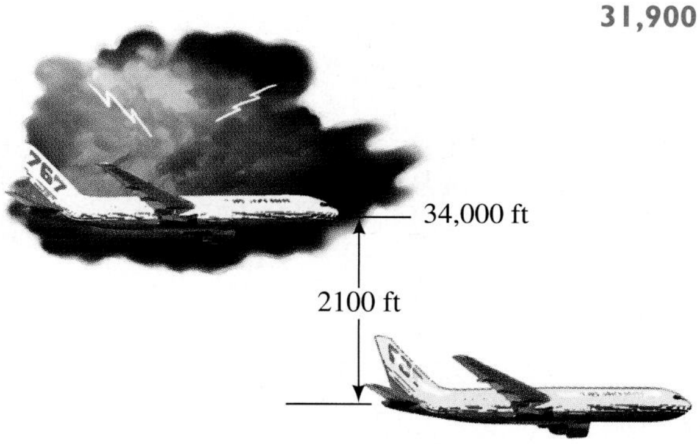

67. On three consecutive passes, Troy Aikman of the Dallas Cowboys passed for a gain of 6 yd, was sacked for a loss of 12 yd, and passed for a gain of 43 yd. What positive or negative number represents the total net yardage for the plays? **37 yd**

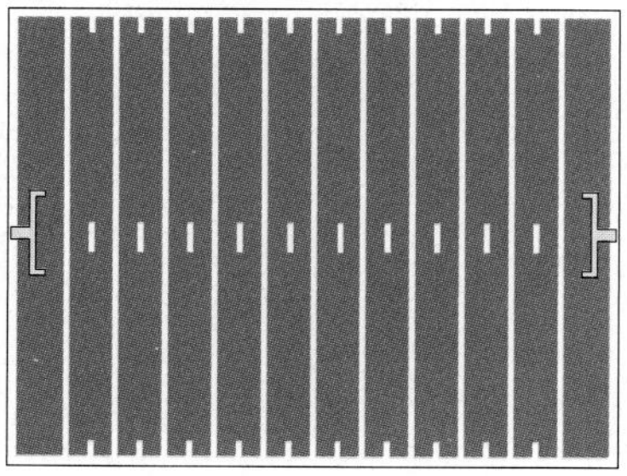

68. On a series of three consecutive running plays, Peyton Manning of the Indianapolis Colts gained 4 yd, lost 3 yd, and lost 2 yd. What positive or negative number represents his total net yardage for the series of plays? **−1 yd**

69. The lowest temperature ever recorded in Arkansas was -29°F. The highest temperature ever recorded there was 149°F more than the lowest. What was this highest temperature? (*Source: World Almanac and Book of Facts,* 2000.)

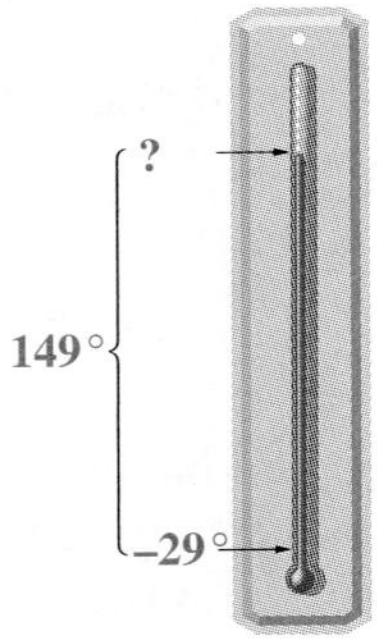

120°F

70. On January 23, 1943, the temperature rose 49°F in two minutes in Spearfish, South Dakota. If the starting temperature was -4°F, what was the temperature two minutes later?

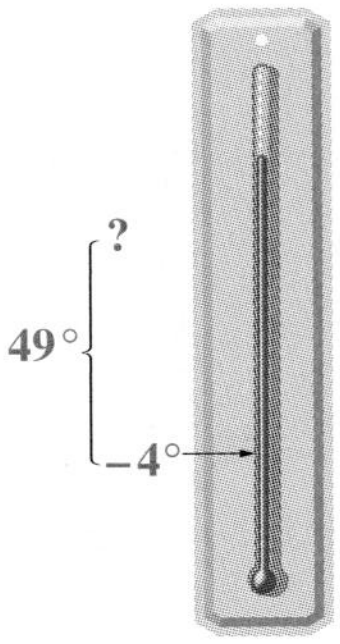

45°F

71. Jennifer owes \$153 to a credit card company. She makes a \$14 purchase with the card, and then pays \$60 on the account. What is her current balance as a signed number?

−\$107

72. A female polar bear weighed 660 lb when she entered her winter den. She lost 45 lb during each of the first two months of hibernation, and another 205 lb before leaving the den with her two cubs in March. How much did she weigh when she left the den?

365 lb

73. Jim Yee owes \$870.00 on his MasterCard account. He returns two items costing \$35.90 and \$150.00 and receives credits for these on the account. Next, he makes a purchase of \$82.50, and then two more purchases of \$10.00 each. He finally makes a payment of \$500.00. What is his new account balance?

\$286.60

74. A welder working with stainless steel must use precise measurements. Suppose a welder attaches two pieces of steel that are each 3.60 in. long, and then attaches an additional three pieces that are each 9.10 in. long. She finally cuts off a piece that is 7.60 in. long. Find the length of the welded piece of steel.

26.90 in.

1.5 Subtraction of Real Numbers

Objectives

1. Find a difference.
2. Use the definition of subtraction.
3. Work subtraction problems that involve brackets.
4. Translate words and phrases that indicate subtraction.

1 Find a difference. As we mentioned earlier, the answer to a subtraction problem is called a **difference.** Differences between signed numbers can be found by using a number line. Addition and subtraction are opposite operations. Thus, because *addition* of a positive number on the number line is shown by drawing an arrow to the *right, subtraction* of a positive number is shown by drawing an arrow to the *left.*

Example 1 Subtracting with the Number Line

Use the number line to find the difference $7 - 4$.

To find the difference $7 - 4$ on the number line, begin at 0 and draw an arrow 7 units to the *right.* From the right end of this arrow, draw an arrow 4 units to the *left,* as shown in Figure 11. The number at the end of the second arrow shows that $7 - 4 = 3$.

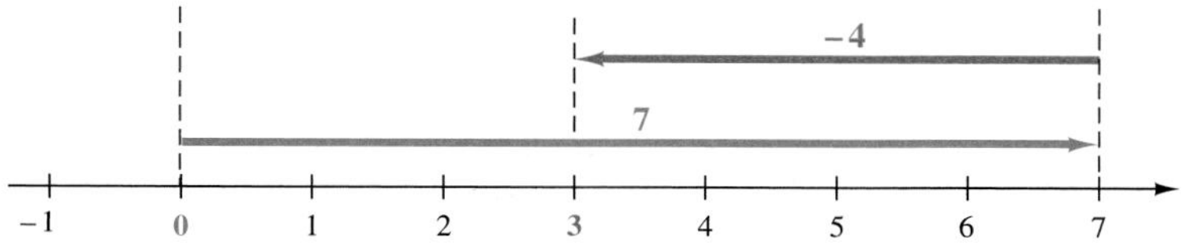

Figure 11

Work Problem 1 at the Side.

1 Use the number line to find each difference.

(a) $5 - 1$

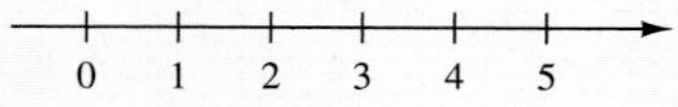

(b) $6 - 2$

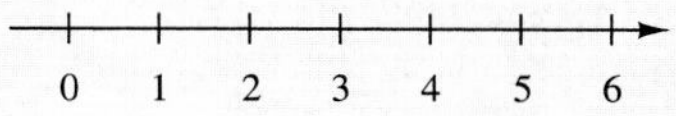

2 Use the definition of subtraction. The procedure used in Example 1 to find $7 - 4$ is exactly the same procedure that would be used to find $7 + (-4)$, so

$$7 - 4 = 7 + (-4).$$

This shows that *subtracting* a positive number from a larger positive number is the same as *adding* the opposite of the smaller number to the larger. We use this idea to define subtraction for all real numbers.

Subtraction

For any real numbers a and b,

$$a - b = a + (-b).$$

Example: $4 - 9 = 4 + (-9) = -5$.

That is, to *subtract b* from *a*, *add the opposite* (or *negative*) of *b* to *a*. This definition leads to the following procedure for subtracting signed numbers.

Subtracting Signed Numbers

Step 1 Change the subtraction symbol to addition, and change the sign of the number being subtracted.

Step 2 Add, as in the previous section.

Answers

1. (a) $5 - 1 = 4$

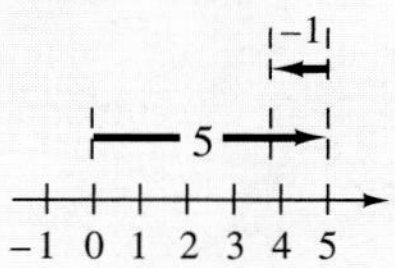

(b) $6 - 2 = 4$

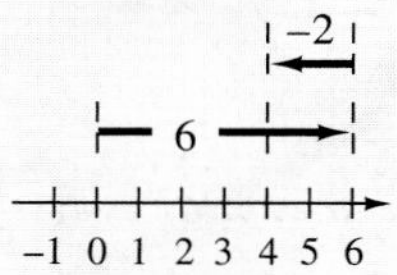

2 Subtract.

(a) $6 - 10$

(b) $-2 - 4$

(c) $3 - (-5)$

(d) $-8 - (-12)$

(e) $\frac{5}{4} - \left(-\frac{3}{7}\right)$

Example 2 **Using the Definition of Subtraction**

Subtract.

No change; Change − to +.; Opposite of 3

(a) $12 - 3 = 12 + (-3) = 9$

(b) $5 - 7 = 5 + (-7) = -2$

(c) $8 - 15 = 8 + (-15) = -7$

No change; Change − to +.; Opposite of −5

(d) $-3 - (-5) = -3 + (5) = 2$

(e) $-6 - (-9) = -6 + (9) = 3$

(f) $\frac{3}{8} - \left(-\frac{4}{5}\right) = \frac{15}{40} - \left(-\frac{32}{40}\right) = \frac{15}{40} + \frac{32}{40} = \frac{47}{40}$

Work Problem 2 at the Side.

Subtraction can be used to reverse the result of an addition problem. For example, if 4 is added to a number and then subtracted from the sum, the original number is the result.

$$12 + 4 = 16 \quad \text{and} \quad 16 - 4 = 12$$

The symbol − has now been used for three purposes:

1. to represent subtraction, as in $9 - 5 = 4$;
2. to represent negative numbers, such as -10, -2, and -3;
3. to represent the opposite (or negative) of a number, as in "the opposite (or negative) of 8 is -8."

We may see more than one use in the same problem, such as $-6 - (-9)$, where -9 is subtracted from -6. The meaning of the symbol depends on its position in the algebraic expression.

3 **Work subtraction problems that involve brackets.** As before, with problems that have both parentheses and brackets, first do any operations inside the parentheses and brackets. Work from the inside out. Because subtraction is defined in terms of addition, the order of operations from Section 1.1 can still be used.

Example 3 **Subtracting with Grouping Symbols**

Perform each operation.

(a)
$$\begin{aligned} -6 - [2 - (8 + 3)] &= -6 - [2 - 11] \\ &= -6 - [2 + (-11)] \quad \text{Change } - \text{ to } +. \\ &= -6 - (-9) \\ &= -6 + (9) = 3 \end{aligned}$$

Continued on Next Page

ANSWERS

2. (a) -4 (b) -6 (c) 8 (d) 4 (e) $\frac{47}{28}$

(b) $5 - \left[\left(-\frac{1}{3} - \frac{1}{2}\right) - (4 - 1)\right] = 5 - \left[\left(-\frac{1}{3} + \left(-\frac{1}{2}\right)\right) - 3\right]$

$= 5 - \left[\left(-\frac{5}{6}\right) - 3\right]$

$= 5 - \left[\left(-\frac{5}{6}\right) + (-3)\right]$

$= 5 - \left(-\frac{23}{6}\right)$

$= 5 + \frac{23}{6} = \frac{53}{6}$

Work Problem 3 at the Side.

3 Perform each operation.

(a) $2 - [(-3) - (4 + 6)]$

(b) $[(5 - 7) + 3] - 8$

(c) $6 - [(-1 - 4) - 2]$

4 Translate words and phrases that indicate subtraction. Now we translate words and phrases that involve subtraction of real numbers. *Difference* is one of them. Some others are given in the chart below.

Word or Phrase	Example	Numerical Expression and Simplification
Difference between	The *difference between* −3 and −8	$-3 - (-8) = -3 + 8 = 5$
Subtracted from	12 *subtracted from* 18	$18 - 12 = 6$
Less than	6 *less than* 5	$5 - 6 = 5 + (-6) = -1$
Decreased by	9 *decreased by* −4	$9 - (-4) = 9 + 4 = 13$
Minus	−8 *minus* 5	$-8 - 5 = -8 + (-5) = -13$

CAUTION

When you are subtracting two numbers, it is important that you write them in the correct order, because, in general, $a - b \neq b - a$. For example, $5 - 3 \neq 3 - 5$. For this reason, it is important to *think carefully before interpreting an expression involving subtraction!* (This problem does not arise for addition.)

Example 4 **Translating Words and Phrases**

Write a numerical expression for each phrase, and simplify the expression.

(a) The **difference between** −8 and 5

When "difference between" is used, write the numbers in the order they are given.

$$-8 - 5 = -8 + (-5) = -13$$

(b) 4 **subtracted from** the sum of 8 and −3

Here the operation of addition is also used, as indicated by the word *sum*. First, add 8 and −3. Next, subtract 4 from this sum.

$$[8 + (-3)] - 4 = 5 - 4 = 1$$

Continued on Next Page

ANSWERS
3. (a) 15 **(b)** −7 **(c)** 13

4 Write a numerical expression for each phrase, and simplify the expression.

(a) The difference between -5 and -12

(b) -2 subtracted from the sum of 4 and -4

(c) 7 less than -2

(d) 9, decreased by 10 less than 7

5 Solve the problem.

The highest elevation in Argentina is Mt. Aconcagua, which is 6960 m above sea level. The lowest point in Argentina is the Valdes Peninsula, 40 m below sea level. Find the difference between the highest and lowest elevations.

ANSWERS

4. **(a)** $-5-(-12)$; 7
(b) $[4+(-4)]-(-2)$; 2
(c) $-2-7$; -9
(d) $9-(7-10)$; 12

5. 7000 m

(c) 4 **less than** -6

Be careful with order here. 4 must be taken *from* -6, so write -6 first.

$$-6-4=-6+(-4)=-10$$

Notice that "4 less than -6" differs from "4 *is less than* $-$ 6." The statement "4 is less than -6" is symbolized as $4<-6$ (which is a false statement).

(d) 8, **decreased by** 5 **less than** 12

First, write "5 less than 12" as $12-5$. Next, subtract $12-5$ from 8.

$$8-(12-5)=8-7=1$$

Work Problem 4 at the Side.

We have seen a few applications of signed numbers in earlier sections. The next example involves subtraction of signed numbers.

Example 5 Solving a Problem Involving Subtraction

The record high temperature of 134°F in the United States was recorded at Death Valley, California, in 1913. The record low was -80°F, at Prospect Creek, Alaska, in 1971. See Figure 12. What is the difference between these highest and lowest temperatures? (*Source: World Almanac and Book of Facts,* 2000.)

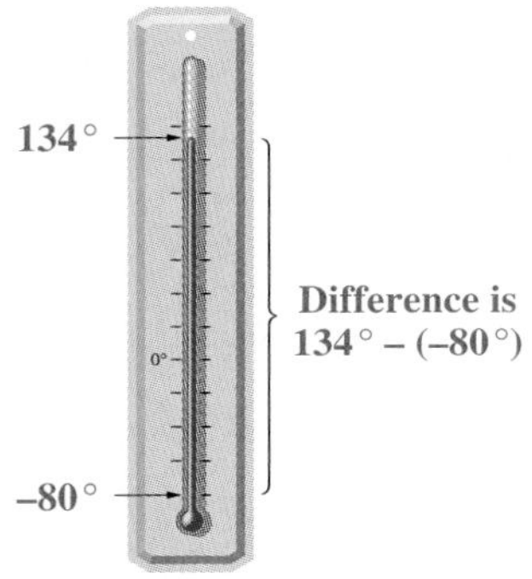

Figure 12

We must subtract the lowest temperature from the highest temperature.

$$134-(-80)=134+80 \quad \text{Use the definition of subtraction.}$$
$$=214 \quad \text{Add.}$$

The difference between the two temperatures is 214°F.

Work Problem 5 at the Side.

1.5 EXERCISES

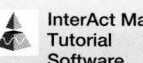

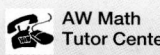

FOR EXTRA HELP: Student's Solutions Manual | MyMathLab.com | InterAct Math Tutorial Software | AW Math Tutor Center | www.mathxl.com | Digital Video Tutor CD 1 Videotape 3

Fill in each blank with the correct response.

1. By the definition of subtraction, in order to perform the subtraction $-6 - (-8)$, we must add the opposite of $\underline{-8}$ to $\underline{-6}$.

2. By the order of operations, to simplify $8 - [3 - (-4 - 5)]$, the first step is to subtract $\underline{5}$ from $\underline{-4}$.

3. "The difference between 7 and 12" translates as $\underline{7 - 12}$, while "the difference between 12 and 7" translates as $\underline{12 - 7}$.

4. $-9 - (-3) = -9 + \underline{3}$

5. $-8 - 4 = -8 + \underline{-4}$

6. $-19 - 22 = -19 + \underline{-22}$

Find each difference. See Examples 1–3.

7. $-7 - 3$ -10

8. $-12 - 5$ -17

9. $-10 - 6$ -16

10. $-13 - 16$ -29

11. $7 - (-4)$ 11

12. $9 - (-6)$ 15

13. $6 - (-13)$ 19

14. $13 - (-3)$ 16

15. $-7 - (-3)$ -4

16. $-8 - (-6)$ -2

17. $3 - (4 - 6)$ 5

18. $6 - (7 - 14)$ 13

19. $-3 - (6 - 9)$ 0

20. $-4 - (5 - 12)$ 3

21. $\frac{1}{2} - \left(-\frac{1}{4}\right)$ $\frac{3}{4}$

22. $\frac{1}{3} - \left(-\frac{4}{3}\right)$ $\frac{5}{3}$

23. $-\frac{3}{4} - \frac{5}{8}$ $-\frac{11}{8}$

24. $-\frac{5}{6} - \frac{1}{2}$ $-\frac{4}{3}$

25. $\frac{5}{8} - \left(-\frac{1}{2} - \frac{3}{4}\right)$ $\frac{15}{8}$

26. $\frac{9}{10} - \left(\frac{1}{8} - \frac{3}{10}\right)$ $\frac{43}{40}$

27. $4.4 - (-9.2)$ 13.6

28. $6.7 - (-12.6)$ **19.3**

29. $-7.4 - 4.5$ **-11.9**

30. $-5.4 - 9.6$ **-15.0**

31. $-5.2 - (8.4 - 10.8)$ **-2.8**

32. $-9.6 - (3.5 - 12.6)$ **$-.5$**

33. $[(-3.1) - 4.5] - (.8 - 2.1)$ **-6.3**

34. $[(-7.8) - 9.3] - (.6 - 3.5)$ **-14.2**

35. $-12 - [(9 - 2) - (-6 - 3)]$ **-28**

36. $-4 + [(-6 - 9) - (-7 + 4)]$ **-16**

37. $-8 + [(-3 - 10) - (-4 + 1)]$ **-18**

38. $\left(-\frac{3}{4} - \frac{5}{2}\right) - \left(-\frac{1}{8} - 1\right)$ **$-\frac{17}{8}$**

39. $\left(-\frac{3}{8} - \frac{2}{3}\right) - \left(-\frac{9}{8} - 3\right)$ **$\frac{37}{12}$**

40. $[-34.99 + (6.59 - 12.25)] - 8.33$ **-48.98**

41. $[-12.25 - (8.34 + 3.57)] - 17.88$ **-42.04**

42. Explain in your own words how to subtract signed numbers.

To subtract signed numbers, add the opposite of the second number to the first number.

43. We know that, in general, $a - b \neq b - a$. Find two pairs of values for a and b so that $a - b = b - a$.

For example, let $a = 1, b = 1$ or let $a = 2, b = 2$. In general, choose $a = b$.

Simplify each expression. Use the order of operations.

44. $-3 - (-4) - 5$ **-4**

45. $8 - (-3) - 9 + 6$ **8**

46. $-5 - 2 + 4 - 8 - (-6)$ **-5**

47. Make up a subtraction problem so that the difference between two negative numbers is a negative number.

For example, $-8 - (-2) = -6$.

48. Make up a subtraction problem so that the difference between two negative numbers is a positive number.

For example, $-2 - (-8) = 6$.

Write a numerical expression for each phrase and simplify. See Example 4.

49. The difference between 4 and -8

$4 - (-8); 12$

50. The difference between 7 and -14

$7 - (-14); 21$

51. 8 less than -2

$-2 - 8; -10$

52. 9 less than -13

$-13 - 9; -22$

53. The sum of 9 and -4, decreased by 7

$[9 + (-4)] - 7; -2$

54. The sum of 12 and -7, decreased by 14

$[12 + (-7)] - 14; -9$

55. 12 less than the difference between 8 and -5

$[8 - (-5)] - 12; 1$

56. 19 less than the difference between 9 and -2

$[9 - (-2)] - 19; -8$

Solve each problem. See Example 5.

57. The coldest temperature recorded in Chicago, Illinois, was -35°F in 1996. The record low in South Dakota was set in 1936 and was 23°F lower than -35°F. What was the record low in South Dakota? (*Source: World Almanac and Book of Facts,* 2000.)

-58°F

58. No one knows just why humpback whales love to heave their 45-ton bodies out of the water, but leap they do. Mark and Debbie, two researchers based on the island of Maui, noticed that one of their favorite whales, "Pineapple," leaped 15 ft above the surface of the ocean while her mate cruised 12 ft below the surface. What is the difference between these two heights? **27 ft**

59. The top of Mount Whitney, visible from Death Valley, has an altitude of 14,494 ft above sea level. The bottom of Death Valley is 282 ft below sea level. Using 0 as sea level, find the difference between these two elevations. (*Source: World Almanac and Book of Facts,* 2000.)

14,776 ft

60. A chemist is running an experiment under precise conditions. At first, she runs it at $-174.6°$F. She then lowers the temperature by 2.3°F. What is the new temperature for the experiment?

$-176.9°$F

61. Chris owed his brother \$10. He later borrowed \$70. What positive or negative number represents his present financial status?

$-\$80$

62. Francesca has \$15 in her purse, and Emilio has a debt of \$12. Find the difference between these amounts.

\$27

63. For the year 1999, one health club showed a profit of \$76,000, while another showed a loss of \$29,000. Find the difference between these amounts.

\$105,000

64. At 1:00 A.M., a plant worker found that a dial reading was 7.904. At 2:00 A.M., she found the reading to be -3.291. Find the difference between these two readings.

11.195

The average sales prices of new single-family homes in the United States for the years 1990 through 1995 are shown in the table. Complete the table, determining the change from one year to the next by subtraction.

	Year	Average Sales Price	Change from Previous Year
	1990	\$149,800	
	1991	\$147,200	$-\$2600$
65.	1992	\$144,100	$-\$3100$
66.	1993	\$147,700	\$3600
67.	1994	\$154,500	\$6800
68.	1995	\$158,700	\$4200

Source: U.S. Bureau of the Census.

In Exercises 69–72, suppose that x represents a positive number and y represents a negative number. Determine whether the given expression must represent a positive number or a negative number.

69. $x - y$

positive

70. $y - x$

negative

71. $x + |y|$

positive

72. $y - |x|$

negative

1.6 Multiplication and Division of Real Numbers

In this section we learn how to multiply positive and negative numbers. The result of multiplication is called the **product.** We already know how to multiply positive numbers and that the product of two positive numbers is positive. We also know that the product of 0 and any positive number is 0, and we extend that property to all real numbers.

Multiplication Property of 0

For any real number a,

$$a \cdot 0 = 0 \cdot a = 0.$$

1 Find the product of numbers with different signs. To define the product of numbers with different signs so that the result is consistent with multiplication of positive numbers, look at the following pattern.

$$\begin{aligned} 3 \cdot 5 &= 15 \\ 3 \cdot 4 &= 12 \\ 3 \cdot 3 &= 9 \\ 3 \cdot 2 &= 6 \\ 3 \cdot 1 &= 3 \\ 3 \cdot 0 &= 0 \\ 3 \cdot (-1) &= ? \end{aligned}$$

The products decrease by 3.

What should $3(-1)$ equal? Since multiplication can also be considered repeated addition, the product $3(-1)$ represents the sum

$$-1 + (-1) + (-1) = -3,$$

so the product should be -3, which fits the pattern. Also,

$$3(-2) = -2 + (-2) + (-2) = -6.$$

Work Problem 1 at the Side.

The results from Problem 1 maintain the pattern in the list above, which suggests the following rule.

The product of a positive number and a negative number is negative.
Example: $6(-3) = -18$.

Example 1 Multiplying a Positive Number and a Negative Number

Find each product using the multiplication rule.

(a) $8(-5) = -(8 \cdot 5) = -40$ **(b)** $-7(2) = -(7 \cdot 2) = -14$

(c) $-9\left(\frac{1}{3}\right) = -3$ **(d)** $-6.2(4.1) = -25.42$

Work Problem 2 at the Side.

Objectives

1. Find the product of numbers with different signs.
2. Find the product of two negative numbers.
3. Use the reciprocal of a number to apply the definition of division.
4. Use the order of operations when multiplying and dividing signed numbers.
5. Evaluate expressions involving variables.
6. Translate words and phrases involving multiplication and division.
7. Translate simple sentences into equations.

1 Find each product by finding the sum of three numbers.

(a) $3(-3)$

(b) $3(-4)$

(c) $3(-5)$

2 Find each product.

(a) $2(-6)$

(b) $7(-8)$

(c) $-9(2)$

(d) $-16\left(\frac{5}{32}\right)$

(e) $4.56(-10)$

Answers

1. (a) -9 **(b)** -12 **(c)** -15
2. (a) -12 **(b)** -56 **(c)** -18 **(d)** $-\frac{5}{2}$ **(e)** -45.6

3 Find each product.

(a) $-5(-6)$

(b) $-7(-3)$

(c) $-8(-5)$

(d) $-11(-2)$

(e) $-17(3)(-7)$

(f) $-41(2)(-13)$

ANSWERS
3. **(a)** 30 **(b)** 21 **(c)** 40 **(d)** 22 **(e)** 357 **(f)** 1066

2 **Find the product of two negative numbers.** The product of two positive numbers is positive, and the product of a positive number and a negative number is negative. What about the product of two negative numbers? Look at another pattern.

$$\begin{aligned} -5(4) &= -20 \\ -5(3) &= -15 \\ -5(2) &= -10 \\ -5(1) &= -5 \\ -5(0) &= 0 \\ -5(-1) &= ? \end{aligned}$$

The products increase by 5.

The numbers on the left of the equals signs (in color) decrease by 1 for each step down the list. The products on the right increase by 5 for each step down the list. To maintain this pattern, $-5(-1)$ should be 5 more than $-5(0)$, or 5 more than 0, so

$$-5(-1) = 5.$$

The pattern continues with

$$\begin{aligned} -5(-2) &= 10 \\ -5(-3) &= 15 \\ -5(-4) &= 20 \\ -5(-5) &= 25, \end{aligned}$$

and so on. This pattern suggests the next rule.

> The product of two negative numbers is positive.
>
> *Example:* $-5(-4) = 20$.

Example 2 **Multiplying Two Negative Numbers**

Find each product using the multiplication rule.

(a) $-9(-2) = 18$

(b) $-6(-12) = 72$

(c) $-2(4)(-1) = -8(-1) = 8$

(d) $3(-5)(-2) = -15(-2) = 30$

Work Problem 3 at the Side.

Here is a summary of the results for multiplying signed numbers.

> **Multiplying Signed Numbers**
>
> The product of two numbers having the *same* sign is *positive,* and the product of two numbers having *different* signs is *negative.*

3 **Use the reciprocal of a number to apply the definition of division.** Recall that the result of division is called the **quotient.** In the previous section we saw that the difference between two numbers is found by adding the opposite of the second number to the first. Similarly, the *quotient* of two numbers involves multiplying by the *reciprocal* of the second number.

Reciprocals

Pairs of numbers whose product is 1 are called **reciprocals** of each other.

Since $8 \cdot \frac{1}{8} = \frac{8}{8} = 1$ and $\frac{5}{4} \cdot \frac{4}{5} = \frac{20}{20} = 1,$

the reciprocal of 8 is $\frac{1}{8}$, and that of $\frac{5}{4}$ is $\frac{4}{5}$. The following table shows several numbers and their reciprocals.

Number	Reciprocal
4	$\frac{1}{4}$
-5	$\frac{1}{-5}$ or $-\frac{1}{5}$
$\frac{3}{4}$	$\frac{4}{3}$
$-\frac{5}{8}$	$-\frac{8}{5}$
0	None

By definition, the product of a number and its reciprocal is 1. But the multiplication property of 0 says that the product of 0 and any number is 0. Thus,

0 has no reciprocal.

Work Problem 4 at the Side.

By definition, the quotient of a and b is the product of a and the reciprocal of b.

Division

The quotient $\frac{a}{b}$ of real numbers a and b, with $b \neq 0$, is

$$\frac{a}{b} = a \cdot \frac{1}{b}.$$

Example: $\frac{8}{-4} = 8\left(-\frac{1}{4}\right) = -2.$

This definition indicates that b, the number to divide by, cannot be 0. Since 0 has no reciprocal,

$\frac{1}{0}$ is not a number and *division by* 0 *is undefined.* If a division problem requires division by 0, write "undefined."

NOTE

While division *by* 0 is undefined, we may divide 0 by any nonzero number.

$$\text{If } a \neq 0, \text{ then } \frac{0}{a} = 0.$$

Because division is defined in terms of multiplication, all the rules for multiplying signed numbers also apply to dividing them.

4 Complete the table.

Number	*Reciprocal*
(a) 6	
(b) -2	
(c) $\frac{2}{3}$	
(d) $-\frac{1}{4}$	
(e) 0	

ANSWERS

4. (a) $\frac{1}{6}$ (b) $\frac{1}{-2} = -\frac{1}{2}$ (c) $\frac{3}{2}$ (d) -4 (e) none

5 Find each quotient.

(a) $\frac{42}{7}$

(b) $\frac{-36}{(-2)(-3)}$

(c) $\frac{-12.56}{-.4}$

(d) $\frac{10}{7} \div \left(-\frac{24}{5}\right)$

(e) $\frac{-3}{0}$

(f) $\frac{0}{-53}$

6 Find each quotient.

(a) $\frac{-8}{-2}$

(b) $\frac{-16.4}{2.05}$

(c) $\frac{1}{4} \div \left(-\frac{2}{3}\right)$

ANSWERS

5. **(a)** 6 **(b)** -6 **(c)** 31.4 **(d)** $-\frac{25}{84}$ **(e)** undefined **(f)** 0

6. **(a)** 4 **(b)** -8 **(c)** $-\frac{3}{8}$

Example 3 Using the Definition of Division

Find each quotient.

(a) $\frac{12}{3} = 12 \cdot \frac{1}{3} = 4$

(b) $\frac{5(-2)}{2} = -10 \cdot \frac{1}{2} = -5$

(c) $\frac{-1.47}{-7} = -1.47 \cdot \left(-\frac{1}{7}\right) = .21$

(d) $-\frac{2}{3} \div \left(-\frac{5}{4}\right) = -\frac{2}{3} \cdot \left(-\frac{4}{5}\right) = \frac{8}{15}$

(e) $\frac{-10}{0}$ Undefined

(f) $\frac{0}{13} = 0 \quad \frac{0}{a} = 0 \quad (a \neq 0)$

Work Problem 5 at the Side.

When dividing fractions, multiplying by the reciprocal works well. However, using the definition of division directly with integers is awkward. It is easier to divide in the usual way, then determine the sign of the answer. The following rule for division can be used instead of multiplying by the reciprocal.

Dividing Signed Numbers

The quotient of two numbers having the *same* sign is *positive;* the quotient of two numbers having *different* signs is *negative.*

Examples: $\frac{-15}{-5} = 3$ and $\frac{-15}{5} = -3$.

Example 4 Dividing Signed Numbers

Find each quotient.

(a) $\frac{8}{-2} = -4$

(b) $\frac{-4.5}{-.09} = 50$

(c) $-\frac{1}{8} \div \left(-\frac{3}{4}\right) = -\frac{1}{8} \cdot \left(-\frac{4}{3}\right) = \frac{1}{6}$

Work Problem 6 at the Side.

From the definitions of multiplication and division of real numbers,

$$\frac{-40}{8} = -40 \cdot \frac{1}{8} = -5 \quad \text{and} \quad \frac{40}{-8} = 40\left(\frac{1}{-8}\right) = -5, \text{ so}$$

$$\frac{-40}{8} = \frac{40}{-8}.$$

Based on this example, the quotient of a positive number and a negative number can be written in any of the following three forms.

For any positive real numbers a and b,

$$\frac{-a}{b} = \frac{a}{-b} = -\frac{a}{b}.$$

The form $\frac{a}{-b}$ is seldom used.

Similarly, the quotient of two negative numbers can be expressed as the quotient of two positive numbers.

For any positive real numbers a and b,

$$\frac{-a}{-b} = \frac{a}{b}.$$

4 **Use the order of operations when multiplying and dividing signed numbers.**

Example 5 **Using the Order of Operations**

Simplify.

(a) $-9(2) - (-3)(2)$

First find all products, working from left to right.

$$\begin{aligned} -9(2) - (-3)(2) &= -18 - (-6) \\ &= -18 + 6 \\ &= -12 \end{aligned}$$

(b) $\begin{aligned}[t] -6(-2) - 3(-4) &= 12 - (-12) \\ &= 12 + 12 \\ &= 24 \end{aligned}$

(c) $\dfrac{5(-2) - 3(4)}{2(1 - 6)}$

Follow the order of operations. Simplify the numerator and denominator separately. Then divide or write in lowest terms.

$$\begin{aligned} \frac{5(-2) - 3(4)}{2(1 - 6)} &= \frac{-10 - 12}{2(-5)} && \text{Multiply in numerator. Subtract in denominator.} \\ &= \frac{-22}{-10} && \text{Subtract in numerator. Multiply in denominator.} \\ &= \frac{11}{5} && \text{Write in lowest terms.} \end{aligned}$$

Work Problem 7 at the Side.

The rules for operations with signed numbers are summarized here.

Operations with Signed Numbers

Addition

Same sign Add the absolute values of the numbers. The sum has the same sign as the numbers.

$$-4 + (-6) = -10$$

Different signs Subtract the number with the smaller absolute value from the one with the larger. Give the sum the sign of the number having the larger absolute value.

$$4 + (-6) = -(6 - 4) = -2$$

(continued)

7 Perform the indicated operations.

(a) $-3(4) - 2(6)$

(b) $-8[-1 - (-4)(-5)]$

(c) $\dfrac{6(-4) - 2(5)}{3(2 - 7)}$

(d) $\dfrac{-6(-8) + 3(9)}{-2[4 - (-3)]}$

ANSWERS

7. (a) -24 **(b)** 168 **(c)** $\frac{34}{15}$ **(d)** $-\frac{75}{14}$

Subtraction
Add the opposite of the second number to the first number.

$$8 - (-3) = 8 + 3 = 11$$

Multiplication and Division
Same sign The product or quotient of two numbers with the same sign is positive.

$$-5(-6) = 30 \quad \text{and} \quad \frac{-36}{-12} = 3$$

Different signs The product or quotient of two numbers with different signs is negative.

$$-5(6) = -30 \quad \text{and} \quad \frac{18}{-6} = -3$$

Division by 0 is undefined.

5 Evaluate expressions involving variables. The next examples show numbers substituted for variables where the rules for operating with signed numbers must be used.

Example 6 Evaluating Expressions for Numerical Values

Evaluate each expression, given that $x = -1$, $y = -2$, and $m = -3$.

(a) $(3x + 4y)(-2m)$

First substitute the given values for the variables. Then use the order of operations to find the value of the expression.

$(3x + 4y)(-2m) = [3(-1) + 4(-2)][-2(-3)]$	Put parentheses around the number for each variable.
$= [-3 + (-8)][6]$	Find the products.
$= (-11)(6)$	Add inside the brackets.
$= -66$	Multiply.

(b) $2x^2 - 3y^2$

Use parentheses as shown.

$2(-1)^2 - 3(-2)^2 = 2(1) - 3(4)$	Substitute, then apply the exponents.
$= 2 - 12$	Multiply.
$= -10$	Subtract.

(c) $\dfrac{4y^2 + x}{m}$

$\dfrac{4(-2)^2 + (-1)}{-3} = \dfrac{4(4) + (-1)}{-3}$	Substitute, then apply the exponent.
$= \dfrac{16 + (-1)}{-3}$	Multiply.
$= \dfrac{15}{-3}$	Add.
$= -5$	Divide.

Notice how the fraction bar was used as a grouping symbol.

Work Problem 8 at the Side.

8 Evaluate each expression.

(a) $2x - 7(y + 1)$
if $x = -4$ and $y = 3$

(b) $2x^2 - 4y^2$
if $x = -2$ and $y = -3$

(c) $\dfrac{4x - 2y}{-3x}$
if $x = 2$ and $y = -1$

ANSWERS

8. **(a)** -36 **(b)** -28 **(c)** $-\frac{5}{3}$

6 Translate words and phrases involving multiplication and division. Just as there are words and phrases that indicate addition or subtraction, certain words and phrases indicate multiplication or division. The chart gives some phrases indicating multiplication.

Word or Phrase	Example	Numerical Expression and Simplification
Product of	The *product of* -5 and -2	$-5(-2) = 10$
Times	13 *times* -4	$13(-4) = -52$
Twice (meaning "2 times")	*Twice* 6	$2(6) = 12$
Of (used with fractions)	$\frac{1}{2}$ *of* 10	$\frac{1}{2}(10) = 5$
Percent of	12% *of* -16	$.12(-16) = -1.92$

Example 7 Translating Words and Phrases

Write a numerical expression for each phrase and simplify. Use the order of operations.

(a) The **product of** 12 and the sum of 3 and -6
Here 12 is multiplied by "the sum of 3 and -6."

$$12[3 + (-6)] = 12(-3) = -36$$

(b) **Three times** the difference between 4 and -11

$$3[4 - (-11)] = 3(4 + 11) = 3(15) = 45$$

(c) Two-thirds **of** the sum of -5 and -3

$$\frac{2}{3}[-5 + (-3)] = \frac{2}{3}(-8) = -\frac{16}{3}$$

(d) 15% **of** the difference between 14 and -2
Remember that 15% = .15.

$$.15[14 - (-2)] = .15(14 + 2) = .15(16) = 2.4$$

Work Problem 9 at the Side.

The word *quotient* refers to the answer in a division problem. In algebra, a quotient is usually represented with a fraction bar; the symbol ÷ is seldom used. When translating an applied problem involving division, use a fraction bar. The chart gives some key phrases associated with division.

Word or Phrase	Example	Numerical Expression and Simplification
Quotient of	The *quotient of* -24 and 3	$\frac{-24}{3} = -8$
Divided by	-16 *divided by* -4	$\frac{-16}{-4} = 4$
Ratio of	The *ratio of* 2 to 3	$\frac{2}{3}$

When translating a phrase involving division, we write the first number named as the numerator and the second as the denominator.

9 Write a numerical expression for each phrase and simplify.

(a) The product of 6 and the sum of -5 and -4

(b) Twice the difference between 8 and -4

(c) Three-fifths of the sum of 2 and -7

(d) 20% of the sum of 9 and -4

ANSWERS
9. **(a)** $6[(-5) + (-4)]$; -54
(b) $2[8 - (-4)]$; 24
(c) $\frac{3}{5}[2 + (-7)]$; -3
(d) $.20[9 + (-4)]$; 1

10 Write a numerical expression for each phrase, and simplify the expression.

(a) The quotient of 20 and the sum of 8 and -3

(b) The product of -9 and 2, divided by the difference between 5 and -1

11 Write each sentence in symbols, using x to represent the number.

(a) Twice a number is -6.

(b) The difference between -8 and a number is -11.

(c) The sum of 5 and a number is 8.

(d) The quotient of a number and -2 is 6.

ANSWERS

10. (a) $\frac{20}{8+(-3)}$; 4

(b) $\frac{-9(2)}{5-(-1)}$; -3

11. (a) $2x = -6$

(b) $-8 - x = -11$

(c) $5 + x = 8$

(d) $\frac{x}{-2} = 6$

Example 8 Translating Words and Phrases

Write a numerical expression for each phrase, and simplify the expression.

(a) The **quotient** of 14 and the sum of -9 and 2

"Quotient" indicates division. The number 14 is the numerator and "the sum of -9 and 2" is the denominator.

$$\frac{14}{-9+2} = \frac{14}{-7} = -2$$

(b) The product of 5 and -6, **divided by** the difference between -7 and 8

The numerator of the fraction representing the division is obtained by multiplying 5 and -6. The denominator is found by subtracting -7 and 8.

$$\frac{5(-6)}{-7-8} = \frac{-30}{-15} = 2$$

Work Problem 10 at the Side.

7 Translate simple sentences into equations. In this section and the previous two sections, important words and phrases involving the four operations of arithmetic have been introduced. We can use these words and phrases to translate sentences into equations. This skill will be useful later when solving applied problems in Section 2.4.

Example 9 Translating Sentences into Equations

Write each sentence with symbols, using x to represent the number.

(a) Three **times** a number **is** -18.

The word *times* indicates multiplication, and the word *is* translates as the equals sign (=).

$$3x = -18$$

(b) The **sum** of a number and 9 **is** 12.

$$x + 9 = 12$$

(c) The **difference between** a number and 5 **is** 0.

$$x - 5 = 0$$

(d) The **quotient of** 24 and a number **is** -2.

$$\frac{24}{x} = -2$$

Work Problem 11 at the Side.

CAUTION

It is important to recognize the distinction between the types of problems found in Example 8 and Example 9. In Example 8, the phrases translate as *expressions,* while in Example 9, the sentences translate as *equations.* Remember that an equation is a sentence, while an expression is a phrase.

$$\underbrace{\frac{5(-6)}{-7-8}}_{\text{Expression}} \qquad \qquad \underbrace{3x = -18}_{\text{Equation}}$$

1.6 EXERCISES

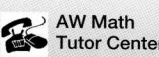

FOR EXTRA HELP: Student's Solutions Manual; MyMathLab.com; InterAct Math Tutorial Software; AW Math Tutor Center; www.mathxl.com; Digital Video Tutor CD 1 Videotape 3

Fill in each blank with one of the following: greater than 0, less than 0, equal to 0.

1. The product or the quotient of two numbers with the same sign is **greater than 0**.

2. The product or the quotient of two numbers with different signs is **less than 0**.

3. If three negative numbers are multiplied together, the product is **less than 0**.

4. If two negative numbers are multiplied and then their product is divided by a negative number, the result is **less than 0**.

5. If a negative number is squared and the result is added to a positive number, the final answer is **greater than 0**.

6. The reciprocal of a negative number is **less than 0**.

Find each product. See Examples 1 and 2.

7. $-7(4)$ **-28**
8. $-8(5)$ **-40**
9. $5(-6)$ **-30**
10. $-4(-20)$ **80**
11. $-8(0)$ **0**
12. $0(-12)$ **0**
13. $-\frac{3}{8}\left(-\frac{20}{9}\right)$ **$\frac{5}{6}$**
14. $-\frac{5}{4}\left(-\frac{6}{25}\right)$ **$\frac{3}{10}$**
15. $-6.8(.35)$ **-2.38**
16. $-4.6(.24)$ **-1.104**
17. $-6\left(-\frac{1}{4}\right)$ **$\frac{3}{2}$**
18. $-8\left(-\frac{1}{2}\right)$ **4**

Find each quotient. See Examples 3 and 4.

19. $\frac{-15}{5}$ **-3**
20. $\frac{-18}{6}$ **-3**
21. $\frac{20}{-10}$ **-2**
22. $\frac{28}{-4}$ **-7**
23. $\frac{-160}{-10}$ **16**
24. $\frac{-260}{-20}$ **13**
25. $\frac{0}{-3}$ **0**
26. $\frac{-6}{0}$ **undefined**
27. $\frac{-10.252}{-.4}$ **25.63**
28. $\frac{-29.584}{-.8}$ **36.98**
29. $\left(-\frac{3}{4}\right) \div \left(-\frac{1}{2}\right)$ **$\frac{3}{2}$**
30. $\left(-\frac{3}{16}\right) \div \left(-\frac{5}{8}\right)$ **$\frac{3}{10}$**

31. Which expression is undefined?

A. $\dfrac{5-5}{5+5}$ **B.** $\dfrac{5+5}{5+5}$ **C.** $\dfrac{5-5}{5-5}$ **D.** $\dfrac{5-5}{5}$ **C**

32. What is the reciprocal of .4? **2.5**

Perform each indicated operation. See Example 5.

33. $\dfrac{-5(-6)}{9-(-1)}$ **3**

34. $\dfrac{-12(-5)}{7-(-5)}$ **5**

35. $\dfrac{-21(3)}{-3-6}$ **7**

36. $\dfrac{-40(3)}{-2-3}$ **24**

37. $\dfrac{-10(2)+6(2)}{-3-(-1)}$ **4**

38. $\dfrac{8(-1)+6(-2)}{-6-(-1)}$ **4**

39. $\dfrac{-27(-2)-(-12)(-2)}{-2(3)-2(2)}$ **−3**

40. $\dfrac{-13(-4)-(-8)(-2)}{(-10)(2)-4(-2)}$ **−3**

41. $\dfrac{3^2-4^2}{7(-8+9)}$ **−1**

42. Explain the method you would use to evaluate $3x + 2y$ if $x = -3$ and $y = 4$.

Substitute −3 for x and 4 for y to get $3(-3) + 2(4)$. Next, find the two products: $3(-3) = -9$ and $2(4) = 8$. Finally, add the products to get −1.

43. If x and y are both replaced by negative numbers, is the value of $4x + 8y$ positive or negative? What about $4x - 8y$?

negative; impossible to tell

Evaluate each expression if $x = 6$, $y = -4$, and $a = 3$. See Example 6.

44. $5x - 2y + 3a$ **47**

45. $6x - 5y + 4a$ **68**

46. $(2x + y)(3a)$ **72**

47. $(5x - 2y)(-2a)$ **−228**

48. $\left(\dfrac{1}{3}x - \dfrac{4}{5}y\right)\left(-\dfrac{1}{5}a\right)$ $-\dfrac{78}{25}$

49. $\left(\dfrac{5}{6}x + \dfrac{3}{2}y\right)\left(-\dfrac{1}{3}a\right)$ **1**

50. $(-5 + x)(-3 + y)(3 - a)$ **0**

51. $(6 - x)(5 + y)(3 + a)$ **0**

52. $-2y^2 + 3a$ **−23**

53. $5x - 4a^2$ -6

54. $\dfrac{2y^2 - x}{a - 3}$ undefined

55. $\dfrac{xy + 8a}{x - y}$ 0

Write a numerical expression for each phrase and simplify. See Examples 7 and 8.

56. The product of -9 and 2, added to 9

$9 + (-9)(2); -9$

57. The product of 4 and -7, added to -12

$-12 + 4(-7); -40$

58. Twice the product of -1 and 6, subtracted from -4

$-4 - 2(-1)(6); 8$

59. Twice the product of -8 and 2, subtracted from -1

$-1 - 2(-8)(2); 31$

60. The product of 12 and the difference between 9 and -8

$12[9 - (-8)]; 204$

61. The product of -3 and the difference between 3 and -7

$-3[3 - (-7)]; -30$

62. Four-fifths of the sum of -8 and -2

$\frac{4}{5}[-8 + (-2)]; -8$

63. Three-tenths of the sum of -2 and -28

$\frac{3}{10}[-2 + (-28)]; -9$

64. The quotient of -12 and the sum of -5 and -1

$\dfrac{-12}{-5 + (-1)}; 2$

65. The quotient of -20 and the sum of -8 and -2

$\dfrac{-20}{-8 + (-2)}; 2$

66. The sum of 15 and -3, divided by the product of 4 and -3

$\dfrac{15 + (-3)}{4(-3)}; -1$

67. The sum of -18 and -6, divided by the product of 2 and -4

$\dfrac{-18 + (-6)}{2(-4)}; 3$

68. The product of $-\frac{1}{2}$ and $\frac{3}{4}$, divided by $-\frac{2}{3}$

$\frac{-\frac{1}{2}\left(\frac{3}{4}\right)}{-\frac{2}{3}}; \frac{9}{16}$

69. The product of $-\frac{2}{3}$ and $-\frac{1}{5}$, divided by $\frac{1}{7}$

$\frac{-\frac{2}{3}\left(-\frac{1}{5}\right)}{\frac{1}{7}}; \frac{14}{15}$

Write each sentence with symbols, using x to represent the number. See Example 9.

70. Six times a number is -42.

$6x = -42$

71. Four times a number is -36.

$4x = -36$

72. The quotient of a number and 3 is -3.

$\frac{x}{3} = -3$

73. The quotient of a number and 4 is -1.

$\frac{x}{4} = -1$

74. 6 less than a number is 2.

$x - 6 = 2$

75. 7 less than a number is 5.

$x - 7 = 5$

76. When 15 is divided by a number, the result is -5.

$\frac{15}{x} = -5$

77. When 6 is divided by a number, the result is -3.

$\frac{6}{x} = -3$

RELATING CONCEPTS (Exercises 78–83) FOR INDIVIDUAL OR GROUP WORK

To find the average of a group of numbers, we add the numbers and then divide the sum by the number of terms added. ***Work Exercises 78–81 in order,*** *to find the average of* 23, 18, 13, −4, *and* −8. *Then find the averages in Exercises 82 and 83.*

78. Find the sum of the given group of numbers.

42

79. How many numbers are in the group?

5

80. Divide your answer for Exercise 78 by your answer for Exercise 79. Give the quotient as a mixed number.

$8\frac{2}{5}$

81. What is the average of the given group of numbers?

$8\frac{2}{5}$

82. What is the average of all integers between -10 and 14, including both -10 and 14?

2

83. What is the average of the integers between -15 and -10, including -15 and -10?

$-12\frac{1}{2}$

1.7 Properties of Real Numbers

If you are asked to find the sum

$$3 + 89 + 97,$$

you might mentally add $3 + 97$ to get 100, and then add $100 + 89$ to get 189. While the order of operations guidelines say to add (or multiply) from left to right, the fact is we may change the order of the terms (or factors) and group them in any way we choose without affecting the sum (or product). This is an example of a shortcut we use in everyday mathematics that is justified by the properties of real numbers introduced in this section. In the following statements, *a, b,* and *c* represent real numbers.

Objectives

1. Use the commutative properties.
2. Use the associative properties.
3. Use the identity properties.
4. Use the inverse properties.
5. Use the distributive property.

1 Use the commutative properties. The word *commute* means to go back and forth. Many people commute to work or to school. If you travel from home to work and follow the same route from work to home, you travel the same distance each time. The **commutative properties** say that if two numbers are added or multiplied in any order, they give the same result.

$$a + b = b + a \quad \text{Addition}$$
$$ab = ba \quad \text{Multiplication}$$

Example 1 Using the Commutative Properties

Use a commutative property to complete each statement.

(a) $-8 + 5 = 5 +$ _____

By the commutative property for addition, the missing number is -8 because $-8 + 5 = 5 + (-8)$.

(b) $-2(7) =$ _____ (-2)

By the commutative property for multiplication, the missing number is 7, since $-2(7) = 7(-2)$.

Work Problem 1 at the Side.

2 Use the associative properties. When we *associate* one object with another, we tend to think of those objects as being grouped together. The **associative properties** say that when we add or multiply three numbers, we can group them in any manner and get the same answer.

$$(a + b) + c = a + (b + c) \quad \text{Addition}$$
$$(ab)c = a(bc) \quad \text{Multiplication}$$

Example 2 Using the Associative Properties

Use an associative property to complete each statement.

(a) $8 + (-1 + 4) = (8 +$ _____ $) + 4$

The missing number is -1.

(b) $[2(-7)]6 = 2$ _____

The missing expression on the right should be $[(-7)6]$.

Work Problem 2 at the Side.

1 Complete each statement. Use a commutative property.

(a) $x + 9 = 9 +$ _____

(b) $-12(4) =$ _____ (-12)

(c) $5x = x \cdot$ _____

2 Complete each statement. Use an associative property.

(a) $(9 + 10) + (-3)$
$= 9 + [$_____ $+ (-3)]$

(b) $-5 + (2 + 8)$
$= ($_____$) + 8$

(c) $10[-8(-3)] =$ _____

Answers

1. **(a)** x **(b)** 4 **(c)** 5
2. **(a)** 10 **(b)** $-5 + 2$ **(c)** $[10(-8)](-3)$

By the associative property of addition, the sum of three numbers will be the same no matter how the numbers are "associated" in groups. For this reason, parentheses can be left out in many addition problems. For example, both

$$(-1 + 2) + 3 \quad \text{and} \quad -1 + (2 + 3)$$

can be written as

$$-1 + 2 + 3.$$

In the same way, parentheses also can be left out of many multiplication problems.

Example 3 **Distinguishing between the Associative and Commutative Properties**

(a) Is $(2 + 4) + 5 = 2 + (4 + 5)$ an example of the associative or the commutative property?

The order of the three numbers is the same on both sides of the equals sign. The only change is in the grouping, or association, of the numbers. Therefore, this is an example of the associative property.

(b) Is $6(3 \cdot 10) = 6(10 \cdot 3)$ an example of the associative or the commutative property?

The same numbers, 3 and 10, are grouped on each side. On the left, however, 3 appears first in $(3 \cdot 10)$. On the right, 10 appears first. Since the only change involves the order of the numbers, this statement is an example of the commutative property.

(c) Is $(8 + 1) + 7 = 8 + (7 + 1)$ an example of the associative or the commutative property?

In the statement, both the order and the grouping are changed. On the left, the order of the three numbers is 8, 1, and 7. On the right it is 8, 7, and 1. On the left, 8 and 1 are grouped, and on the right, 7 and 1 are grouped. Therefore, both the associative and the commutative properties are used.

Work Problem 3 at the Side.

We can use the commutative and associative properties to simplify expressions.

Example 4 **Using the Commutative and Associative Properties**

The commutative and associative properties make it possible to choose pairs of numbers that are easy to add or multiply.

(a)
$$\begin{aligned} 23 + 41 + 2 + 9 + 25 &= (41 + 9) + (23 + 2) + 25 \\ &= 50 + 25 + 25 \\ &= 100 \end{aligned}$$

(b)
$$\begin{aligned} 25(69)(4) &= 25(4)(69) \\ &= 100(69) \\ &= 6900 \end{aligned}$$

Work Problem 4 at the Side.

3 Decide whether each statement is an example of a commutative property, an associative property, or both.

(a) $2(4 \cdot 6) = (2 \cdot 4)6$

(b) $(2 \cdot 4)6 = (4 \cdot 2)6$

(c) $(2 + 4) + 6 = 4 + (2 + 6)$

4 Find the sum:

$5 + 18 + 29 + 31 + 12.$

ANSWERS

3. (a) associative **(b)** commutative **(c)** both

4. 95

3 Use the identity properties. The identity or value of a real number is left unchanged when identity properties are applied. The **identity properties** say that the sum of 0 and any number equals that number, and the product of 1 and any number equals that number.

$$a + 0 = a \quad \text{and} \quad 0 + a = a$$
$$a \cdot 1 = a \quad \text{and} \quad 1 \cdot a = a$$

The number 0 leaves the identity, or value, of any real number unchanged by addition. For this reason, 0 is called the **identity element for addition** or the **additive identity.** Since multiplication by 1 leaves any real number unchanged, 1 is the **identity element for multiplication** or the **multiplicative identity.**

Example 5 Using the Identity Properties

These statements are examples of the identity properties.

(a) $-3 + 0 = -3$ **(b)** $1 \cdot 25 = 25$

Work Problem 5 at the Side.

We use the identity property for multiplication to write fractions in lowest terms and to get common denominators.

Example 6 Using the Identity Element for Multiplication to Simplify Expressions

Simplify each expression.

(a) $\frac{49}{35}$

$$\begin{aligned} \frac{49}{35} &= \frac{7 \cdot 7}{5 \cdot 7} && \text{Factor.} \\ &= \frac{7}{5} \cdot \frac{7}{7} && \text{Write as a product.} \\ &= \frac{7}{5} \cdot 1 && \text{Property of 1} \\ &= \frac{7}{5} && \text{Identity property} \end{aligned}$$

(b) $\frac{3}{4} + \frac{5}{24}$

$$\begin{aligned} \frac{3}{4} + \frac{5}{24} &= \frac{3}{4} \cdot 1 + \frac{5}{24} && \text{Identity property} \\ &= \frac{3}{4} \cdot \frac{6}{6} + \frac{5}{24} && \text{Use } 1 = \tfrac{6}{6} \text{ to get a common denominator.} \\ &= \frac{18}{24} + \frac{5}{24} && \text{Multiply.} \\ &= \frac{23}{24} && \text{Add.} \end{aligned}$$

Work Problem 6 at the Side.

5 Use an identity property to complete each statement.

(a) $9 + 0 =$ ______

(b) ______ $+ (-7) = -7$

(c) ______ $\cdot 1 = 5$

6 Use an identity property to simplify each expression.

(a) $\frac{85}{105}$

(b) $\frac{9}{10} - \frac{53}{50}$

ANSWERS

5. (a) 9 **(b)** 0 **(c)** 5

6. (a) $\frac{17}{21}$ **(b)** $-\frac{4}{25}$

7 Complete each statement so that it is an example of either an identity property or an inverse property. Tell which property is used.

(a) $-6 + \_\_\_\_ = 0$

(b) $\frac{4}{3} \cdot \_\_\_\_ = 1$

(c) $-\frac{1}{9} \cdot \_\_\_\_ = 1$

(d) $275 + \_\_\_\_ = 275$

4 **Use the inverse properties.** Each day before you go to work or school, you probably put on your shoes before you leave. Before you go to sleep at night, you probably take them off, and this leads to the same situation that existed before you put them on. These operations from everyday life are examples of inverse operations. The **inverse properties** of addition and multiplication lead to the additive and multiplicative identities, respectively. The opposite of a, $-a$, is the **additive inverse** of a and the reciprocal of a, $\frac{1}{a}$, is the **multiplicative inverse** of the nonzero number a. The sum of the numbers a and $-a$ is 0, and the product of the nonzero numbers a and $\frac{1}{a}$ is 1.

$$a + (-a) = 0 \quad \text{and} \quad -a + a = 0$$

$$a \cdot \frac{1}{a} = 1 \quad \text{and} \quad \frac{1}{a} \cdot a = 1 \quad (a \neq 0)$$

Example 7 **Using the Inverse Properties**

The following statements are examples of the inverse properties.

(a) $\frac{2}{3} \cdot \frac{3}{2} = 1$ **(b)** $(-5)\left(-\frac{1}{5}\right) = 1$

(c) $-\frac{1}{2} + \frac{1}{2} = 0$ **(d)** $4 + (-4) = 0$

Work Problem 7 at the Side.

5 **Use the distributive property.** The everyday meaning of the word *distribute* is "to give out from one to several." An important property of real number operations involves this idea.

Look at the value of the following expressions.

$$2(5 + 8) = 2(13) = 26$$
$$2(5) + 2(8) = 10 + 16 = 26$$

Since both expressions equal 26,

$$2(5 + 8) = 2(5) + 2(8).$$

This result is an example of the *distributive property*, the only property involving *both* addition and multiplication. With this property, a product can be changed to a sum or difference. This idea is illustrated by the divided rectangle in Figure 13.

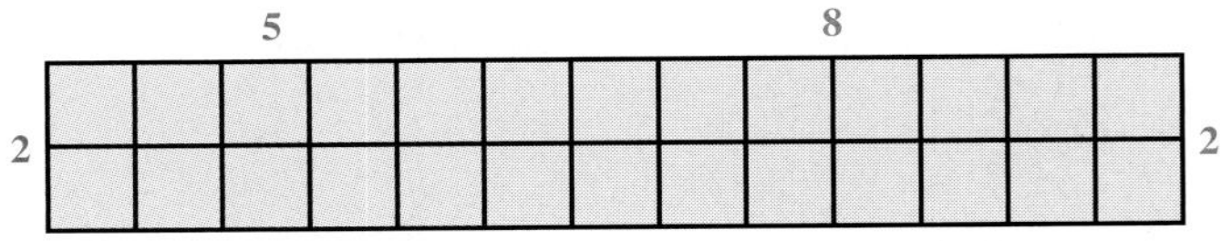

The area of the left part is 2(5) = 10.
The area of the right part is 2(8) = 16.
The total area is 2(5 + 8) = 26 or the total area is
2(5) + 2(8) = 10 + 16 = 26.
Thus, 2(5 + 8) = 2(5) + 2(8).

Figure 13

The **distributive property** says that multiplying a number a by a sum of numbers $b + c$ gives the same result as multiplying a by b and a by c and then adding the two products.

$$a(b + c) = ab + ac \quad \text{and} \quad (b + c)a = ba + ca$$

ANSWERS

7. **(a)** 6; inverse **(b)** $\frac{3}{4}$; inverse **(c)** -9; inverse **(d)** 0; identity

As the arrows show, the a outside the parentheses is "distributed" over the b and c inside. The distributive property is also valid for subtraction.

$$a(b - c) = ab - ac \quad \text{and} \quad (b - c)a = ba - ca$$

The distributive property also can be extended to the sum (or difference) of more than two numbers.

$$a(b + c + d) = ab + ac + ad$$

Example 8 **Using the Distributive Property**

Use the distributive property to rewrite each expression.

(a) $5(9 + 6) = 5 \cdot 9 + 5 \cdot 6$ Distributive property
$= 45 + 30$ Multiply.
$= 75$ Add.

(b) $4(x + 5 + y) = 4x + 4 \cdot 5 + 4y$ Distributive property
$= 4x + 20 + 4y$ Multiply.

(c) $-2(x + 3) = -2x + (-2)(3)$ Distributive property
$= -2x + (-6)$ Multiply.
$= -2x - 6$

(d) $3(k - 9) = 3k - 3 \cdot 9$ Distributive property
$= 3k - 27$ Multiply.

(e) $6 \cdot 8 + 6 \cdot 2$

The distributive property says that $a(b + c) = ab + ac$. This can be reversed to read $ab + ac = a(b + c)$. We use this form of the distributive property to write a sum like $6 \cdot 8 + 6 \cdot 2$ with a common factor (of 6) as a product.

$ab + ac = a(b + c)$ Distributive property
$6 \cdot 8 + 6 \cdot 2 = 6(8 + 2)$ Let $a = 6$, $b = 8$, and $c = 2$.
$= 6(10)$
$= 60$

(f) $8(3r + 11t + 5z) = 8(3r) + 8(11t) + 8(5z)$ Distributive property
$= (8 \cdot 3)r + (8 \cdot 11)t + (8 \cdot 5)z$ Associative property
$= 24r + 88t + 40z$

Work Problem 8 at the Side.

The symbol $-a$ may be interpreted as $-1 \cdot a$. Similarly, when a negative sign precedes an expression within parentheses, it may also be interpreted as a factor of -1. Thus, we can use the distributive property to remove the parentheses from expressions such as $-(2y + 3)$. We do this by first writing $-(2y + 3)$ as $-1 \cdot (2y + 3)$.

$-(2y + 3) = -1 \cdot (2y + 3)$ $-a = -1 \cdot a$
$= -1 \cdot (2y) + (-1) \cdot (3)$ Distributive property
$= -2y - 3$ Multiply.

8 Use the distributive property to rewrite each expression.

(a) $2(p + 5)$

(b) $-4(y + 7)$

(c) $5(m - 4)$

(d) $9 \cdot k + 9 \cdot 5$

(e) $3a - 3b$

(f) $7(2y + 7k - 9m)$

ANSWERS

8. **(a)** $2p + 10$ **(b)** $-4y - 28$
(c) $5m - 20$ **(d)** $9(k + 5)$
(e) $3(a - b)$ **(f)** $14y + 49k - 63m$

9 Write without parentheses.

(a) $-(3k - 5)$

(b) $-(2 - r)$

(c) $-(-5y + 8)$

(d) $-(-z + 4)$

ANSWERS

9. **(a)** $-3k + 5$ **(b)** $-2 + r$ **(c)** $5y - 8$ **(d)** $z - 4$

Example 9 **Using the Distributive Property to Remove Parentheses**

Write without parentheses.

(a) $-(7r - 8) = -1(7r) + (-1)(-8)$ Distributive property

$= -7r + 8$ Multiply.

(b) $-(-9w + 2) = -1(-9w + 2)$

$= 9w - 2$

Work Problem 9 at the Side.

The properties discussed here are the basic properties of real numbers that justify how we add and multiply in algebra. You should know them by name because we will be referring to them frequently. Here is a summary of these properties.

Properties of Addition and Multiplication

For any real numbers a, b, and c, the following properties hold.

Commutative properties $a + b = b + a$ $ab = ba$

Associative properties $(a + b) + c = a + (b + c)$

$(ab)c = a(bc)$

Identity properties There is a real number 0 such that

$a + 0 = a$ and $0 + a = a$.

There is a real number 1 such that

$a \cdot 1 = a$ and $1 \cdot a = a$.

Inverse properties For each real number a, there is a single real number $-a$ such that

$a + (-a) = 0$ and $(-a) + a = 0$.

For each nonzero real number a, there is a single real number $\frac{1}{a}$ such that

$a \cdot \frac{1}{a} = 1$ and $\frac{1}{a} \cdot a = 1$.

Distributive property $a(b + c) = ab + ac$

$(b + c)a = ba + ca$

1.7 EXERCISES

FOR EXTRA HELP: Student's Solutions Manual · MyMathLab.com · InterAct Math Tutorial Software · AW Math Tutor Center · MathXL www.mathxl.com · Digital Video Tutor CD 2 Videotape 3

Match each item in Column I with the correct choice from Column II. Choices may be used once, more than once, or not at all.

I

1. Identity element for addition B
2. Identity element for multiplication F
3. Additive inverse of a C
4. Multiplicative inverse, or reciprocal, of the nonzero number a I
5. The only number that has no multiplicative inverse B
6. An example of the associative property A
7. An example of the commutative property G
8. An example of the distributive property H

II

A. $(5 \cdot 4) \cdot 3 = 5 \cdot (4 \cdot 3)$
B. 0
C. $-a$
D. -1
E. $5 \cdot 4 \cdot 3 = 60$
F. 1
G. $(5 \cdot 4) \cdot 3 = 3 \cdot (5 \cdot 4)$
H. $5(4 + 3) = 5 \cdot 4 + 5 \cdot 3$
I. $\frac{1}{a}$

Decide whether each statement is an example of the commutative, associative, identity, inverse, or distributive property. See Examples 1, 2, 3, and 5–8.

9. $\frac{2}{3}(-4) = -4\left(\frac{2}{3}\right)$
commutative property

10. $6\left(-\frac{5}{6}\right) = \left(-\frac{5}{6}\right)6$
commutative property

11. $-6 + (12 + 7) = (-6 + 12) + 7$
associative property

12. $(-8 + 13) + 2 = -8 + (13 + 2)$
associative property

13. $-6 + 6 = 0$
inverse property

14. $12 + (-12) = 0$
inverse property

15. $\left(\frac{2}{3}\right)\left(\frac{3}{2}\right) = 1$
inverse property

16. $\left(\frac{5}{8}\right)\left(\frac{8}{5}\right) = 1$
inverse property

17. $2.34 \cdot 1 = 2.34$
identity property

18. $-8.456 \cdot 1 = -8.456$
identity property

19. $(4 + 17) + 3 = 3 + (4 + 17)$
commutative property

20. $(-8 + 4) + (-12) = -12 + (-8 + 4)$
commutative property

21. $6(x + y) = 6x + 6y$
distributive property

22. $14(t + s) = 14t + 14s$
distributive property

23. $-\frac{5}{9} = -\frac{5}{9} \cdot \frac{3}{3} = -\frac{15}{27}$

identity property

24. $\frac{13}{12} = \frac{13}{12} \cdot \frac{7}{7} = \frac{91}{84}$

identity property

25. $5(2x) + 5(3y) = 5(2x + 3y)$

distributive property

26. $3(5t) - 3(7r) = 3(5t - 7r)$

distributive property

27. What number(s) satisfy each condition? **(a)** a number that is its own additive inverse **(b)** two numbers that are their own multiplicative inverses **(a) 0 (b) 1, −1**

28. The distributive property holds for multiplication with respect to addition. Is there a distributive property for addition with respect to multiplication? That is, does $a + b \cdot c = (a + b)(a + c)$? If not, give an example to show why.

No. For example, $2 + (3 \cdot 4) \neq (2 + 3) \cdot (2 + 4)$.

29. Evaluate $25 - (6 - 2)$ and $(25 - 6) - 2$. Use the results to explain why subtraction is or is not associative.

$25 - (6 - 2) = 25 - 4 = 21$ and $(25 - 6) - 2 = 19 - 2 = 17$. Since these results are different, subtraction is not associative.

30. Suppose that a student shows you the following work.

$$-2(5 - 6) = -2(5) - 2(6) = -10 - 12 = -22$$

The student has made a very common error. Explain the error and then work the problem correctly.

In the first step, using the distributive property, the second product should be −2 times −6 (not 6). The correct steps are

$$-2(5 - 6) = (-2)(5) + (-2)(-6) = -10 + 12 = 2.$$

Write a new expression that is equal to the given expression, using the given property. Then simplify the new expression if possible. See Examples 1, 2, 5, 7, and 8.

31. $r + 7$; commutative

$7 + r$

32. $t + 9$; commutative

$9 + t$

33. $s + 0$; identity

s

34. $w + 0$; identity

w

35. $-6(x + 7)$; distributive

$-6x + (-6)7; -6x - 42$

36. $-5(y + 2)$; distributive

$-5y + (-5)2; -5y - 10$

37. $(w + 5) + (-3)$; associative

$w + [5 + (-3)]; w + 2$

38. $(b + 8) + (-10)$; associative

$b + [8 + (-10)]; b - 2$

39. Explain how the procedure of changing $\frac{3}{4}$ to $\frac{9}{12}$ requires the use of the multiplicative identity element, 1.

We must multiply $\frac{3}{4}$ by 1 in the form $\frac{3}{3}$: $\frac{3}{4} \cdot \frac{3}{3} = \frac{9}{12}$.

Use the properties of this section to simplify each expression. See Example 4.

40. $26 + 8 - 26 + 12$

20

41. $-\frac{3}{8} + \frac{2}{5} + \frac{8}{5} + \frac{3}{8}$

2

42. $\frac{9}{7}(-.38)\left(\frac{7}{9}\right)$

$-.38$

Use the distributive property to rewrite each expression. Simplify if possible. See Example 8.

43. $5 \cdot 3 + 5 \cdot 17$

$5(3 + 17)$; 100

44. $15 \cdot 6 + 5 \cdot 6$

$(15 + 5)6$; 120

45. $4(t + 3)$

$4t + 12$

46. $5(w + 4)$

$5w + 20$

47. $-8(r + 3)$

$-8r - 24$

48. $-11(x + 4)$

$-11x - 44$

49. $-5(y - 4)$

$-5y + 20$

50. $-9(g - 4)$

$-9g + 36$

51. $-\frac{4}{3}(12y + 15z)$

$-16y - 20z$

52. $-\frac{2}{5}(10b + 20a)$

$-4b - 8a$

53. $8 \cdot z + 8 \cdot w$

$8(z + w)$

54. $4 \cdot s + 4 \cdot r$

$4(s + r)$

55. $7(2v) + 7(5r)$

$7(2v + 5r)$

56. $13(5w) + 13(4p)$

$13(5w + 4p)$

57. $8(3r + 4s - 5y)$

$24r + 32s - 40y$

58. $2(5u - 3v + 7w)$

$10u - 6v + 14w$

59. $-3(8x + 3y + 4z)$

$-24x - 9y - 12z$

60. $-5(2x - 5y + 6z)$

$-10x + 25y - 30z$

Use the distributive property to write each expression without parentheses. See Example 9.

61. $-(4t + 5m)$

$-4t - 5m$

62. $-(9x + 12y)$

$-9x - 12y$

63. $-(-5c - 4d)$

$5c + 4d$

64. $-(-13x - 15y)$

$13x + 15y$

65. $-(-3q + 5r - 8s)$

$3q - 5r + 8s$

66. $-(-4z + 5w - 9y)$

$4z - 5w + 9y$

67. "Getting out of bed" and "taking a shower" are not commutative. Give an example of another pair of everyday activities that are not commutative.

Answers will vary. For example, "putting on your socks" and "putting on your shoes"

68. Are "going upstairs" and "going downstairs" commutative?

no

69. True or false: "preparing a meal" and "eating a meal" are commutative.

false

70. The phrase "dog biting man" has two different meanings, depending on how the words are associated.

(dog biting) man or dog (biting man)

Give another example of a three-word phrase that has different meanings depending on how the words are associated.

Answers will vary. For example, "defective merchandise counter"

71. Use parentheses to show how the associative property can be used to give two different meanings to "foreign sales clerk."

(foreign sales) clerk; foreign (sales clerk)

72. Use parentheses to show two different meanings for "new cook book."

(new cook) book; new (cook book)

Relating Concepts (Exercises 73–76) For Individual or Group Work

In Section 1.6 we used a pattern to see that the product of two negative numbers is a positive number. In the exercises that follow, we show another justification for determining the sign of the product of two negative numbers. ***Work Exercises 73–76 in order.***

73. Evaluate the expression $-3[5 + (-5)]$ by using the order of operations.

0

74. Write the expression in Exercise 73 using the distributive property. Do not simplify the products.

$-3(5) + (-3)(-5)$

75. The product $-3(5)$ should be one of the terms you wrote when answering Exercise 74. Based on the results in Section 1.6, what is this product?

-15

76. In Exercise 73, you should have obtained 0 as the answer. Now, consider the following, using the results of Exercises 73 and 75.

$$-3[5 + (-5)] = -3(5) + (-3)(-5)$$
$$0 = -15 + ?$$

The question mark represents the product $-3(-5)$. When added to -15, it must give a sum of 0. Therefore, $-3(-5)$ must equal what?

The product $-3(-5)$ must equal 15, since it is the additive inverse of -15.

1.8 SIMPLIFYING EXPRESSIONS

OBJECTIVES

1. Simplify expressions.
2. Identify terms and numerical coefficients.
3. Identify like terms.
4. Combine like terms.
5. Simplify expressions from word phrases.

1 Simplify expressions. In this section, we show how to simplify expressions using the properties of addition and multiplication introduced in the previous section.

Example 1 Simplifying Expressions

Simplify each expression.

(a) $4x + 8 + 9$

Since $8 + 9 = 17$, $4x + 8 + 9 = 4x + 17$.

(b) $4(3m - 2n)$

Use the distributive property.

$$\begin{aligned} 4(3m - 2n) &= 4(3m) - 4(2n) \\ &= 12m - 8n \end{aligned}$$

(c)

$$\begin{aligned} 6 + 3(4k + 5) &= 6 + 3(4k) + 3(5) && \text{Distributive property} \\ &= 6 + 12k + 15 && \text{Multiply.} \\ &= 21 + 12k && \text{Add.} \end{aligned}$$

(d)

$$\begin{aligned} 5 - (2y - 8) &= 5 - 1(2y - 8) && -a = -1 \cdot a \\ &= 5 - 2y + 8 && \text{Distributive property} \\ &= 13 - 2y && \text{Add.} \end{aligned}$$

NOTE

Although the steps were not shown, in Examples 1(c) and 1(d) we mentally used the commutative and associative properties to add in the last step. In practice, these steps are usually left out, but we should realize that they are used whenever the ordering in a sum is rearranged.

Work Problem 1 at the Side.

1 Simplify each expression.

(a) $9k + 12 - 5$

(b) $7(3p + 2q)$

(c) $2 + 5(3z - 1)$

(d) $-3 - (2 + 5y)$

2 Identify terms and numerical coefficients. A **term** is a number, a variable, or a product or quotient of a number and one or more variables raised to powers. Examples of terms include

$$-9x^2, \quad 15y, \quad -3, \quad 8m^2n, \quad \frac{2}{p}, \quad \text{and} \quad k.$$

The **numerical coefficient,** or simply coefficient, of the term $9m$ is 9; the numerical coefficient of $-15x^3y^2$ is -15; the numerical coefficient of x is 1; and the numerical coefficient of 8 is 8. In the expression $\frac{x}{3}$, the numerical coefficient of x is $\frac{1}{3}$ since $\frac{x}{3} = \frac{1x}{3} = \frac{1}{3}x$.

CAUTION

It is important to be able to distinguish between *terms* and *factors.* For example, in the expression $8x^3 + 12x^2$, there are two terms, $8x^3$ and $12x^2$. Terms are separated by a + or − sign. On the other hand, in the one-term expression $(8x^3)(12x^2)$, $8x^3$ and $12x^2$ are *factors.* Factors are multiplied.

ANSWERS

1. (a) $9k + 7$ (b) $21p + 14q$ (c) $15z - 3$ (d) $-5 - 5y$

2 Give the numerical coefficient of each term.

(a) $15q$

(b) $-2m^3$

(c) $-18m^7q^4$

(d) $-r$

(e) $\frac{5x}{4}$

3 Identify each pair of terms as *like* or *unlike*.

(a) $9x, 4x$

(b) $-8y^3, 12y^2$

(c) $5x^2y^4, 5x^4y^2$

(d) $7x^2y^4, -7x^2y^4$

(e) $13kt, 4tk$

Here are some examples of terms and their numerical coefficients.

Term	Numerical Coefficient
$-7y$	-7
$34r^3$	34
$-26x^5yz^4$	-26
$-k$	-1
r	1
$\frac{3x}{8} = \frac{3}{8}x$	$\frac{3}{8}$

Work Problem 2 at the Side.

3 Identify like terms. Terms with exactly the same variables (including the same exponents) are called **like terms.** For example, $9m$ and $4m$ have the same variables and are like terms. Also, $6x^3$ and $-5x^3$ are like terms. The terms $-4y^3$ and $4y^2$ have different exponents and are **unlike terms.** Here are some additional examples.

Like terms	$5x$ and $-12x$	$3x^2y$ and $5x^2y$
Unlike terms	$4xy^2$ and $5xy$	$8x^2y^3$ and $7x^3y^2$

Work Problem 3 at the Side.

4 Combine like terms. Recall the distributive property:

$$x(y + z) = xy + xz.$$

As seen in the previous section, this statement can also be written "backward" as

$$xy + xz = x(y + z).$$

This form of the distributive property may be used to find the sum or difference of like terms. For example,

$$3x + 5x = (3 + 5)x = 8x.$$

This process is called **combining like terms.**

CAUTION

Remember that *only like terms* may be combined.

Example 2 Combining Like Terms

Combine like terms in each expression.

(a) $9m + 5m$
Use the distributive property as given above.

$$9m + 5m = (9 + 5)m = 14m$$

(b) $6r + 3r + 2r = (6 + 3 + 2)r = 11r$ Distributive property

(c) $\frac{3}{4}x + x = \frac{3}{4}x + 1x = \left(\frac{3}{4} + 1\right)x = \frac{7}{4}x$ (Note: $x = 1x$.)

Continued on Next Page

ANSWERS
2. (a) 15 (b) -2 (c) -18 (d) -1 (e) $\frac{5}{4}$
3. (a) like (b) unlike (c) unlike (d) like (e) like

(d) $16y^2 - 9y^2 = (16 - 9)y^2 = 7y^2$

(e) $32y + 10y^2$ cannot be combined because $32y$ and $10y^2$ are unlike terms. The distributive property cannot be used here to combine coefficients.

Work Problem 4 at the Side.

When an expression involves parentheses, the distributive property is used both "forward" and "backward" to combine like terms, as shown in the following example.

Example 3 Simplifying Expressions Involving Like Terms

Simplify each expression.

(a)
$$\begin{aligned} 14y + 2(6 + 3y) &= 14y + 2(6) + 2(3y) && \text{Distributive property} \\ &= 14y + 12 + 6y && \text{Multiply.} \\ &= 20y + 12 && \text{Combine like terms.} \end{aligned}$$

(b)
$$\begin{aligned} 9k - 6 - 3(2 - 5k) &= 9k - 6 - 3(2) - 3(-5k) && \text{Distributive property} \\ &= 9k - 6 - 6 + 15k && \text{Multiply.} \\ &= 24k - 12 && \text{Combine like terms.} \end{aligned}$$

(c)
$$\begin{aligned} -(2 - r) + 10r &= -1(2 - r) + 10r && -(2 - r) = -1(2 - r) \\ &= -1(2) - 1(-r) + 10r && \text{Distributive property} \\ &= -2 + r + 10r && \text{Multiply.} \\ &= -2 + 11r && \text{Combine like terms.} \end{aligned}$$

(d)
$$\begin{aligned} 5(2a^2 - 6a) - 3(4a^2 - 9) &= 10a^2 - 30a - 12a^2 + 27 && \text{Distributive property} \\ &= -2a^2 - 30a + 27 && \text{Combine like terms.} \end{aligned}$$

Work Problem 5 at the Side.

5 Simplify expressions from word phrases. Earlier we saw how to translate words, phrases, and statements into expressions and equations. Now we can simplify translated expressions by combining like terms.

Example 4 Translating Words into a Mathematical Expression

Write the following phrase as a mathematical expression and simplify: four times a number, subtracted from the sum of twice the number and 4.

Let x represent the number.

The sum of twice the number and 4 → $(2x + 4)$; Four times the number → $4x$

$$(2x + 4) - 4x \qquad \text{Write with symbols.}$$

which simplifies to

$$-2x + 4 \qquad \text{Combine like terms.}$$

Work Problem 6 at the Side.

CAUTION

In Example 4, we are dealing with an expression to be simplified, *not* an equation to be solved.

---

4 Combine like terms.

(a) $4k + 7k$

(b) $4r - r$

(c) $5z + 9z - 4z$

(d) $8p + 8p^2$

(e) $5x - 3y + 2x - 5y - 3$

5 Simplify.

(a) $10p + 3(5 + 2p)$

(b) $7z - 2 - (1 + z)$

(c) $-(3k^2 + 5k) + 7(k^2 - 4k)$

6 Write each phrase as a mathematical expression, and simplify by combining like terms.

(a) Three times a number, subtracted from the sum of the number and 8

(b) Twice a number added to the sum of 6 and the number

ANSWERS

4. (a) $11k$ **(b)** $3r$ **(c)** $10z$ **(d)** cannot be combined **(e)** $7x - 8y - 3$

5. (a) $16p + 15$ **(b)** $6z - 3$ **(c)** $4k^2 - 33k$

6. (a) $(x + 8) - 3x; -2x + 8$ **(b)** $2x + (6 + x); 3x + 6$

Focus on

Real-Data Applications

Algebraic Expressions and Tuition Costs

Algebraic expressions are useful in real-life scenarios in which the same set of instructions are repeated for different choices of numbers. Below is the description of how tuition and fees are calculated for "Resident of District" students at North Harris Montgomery Community College District (NHMCCD) in Texas for 2000–2001. The information is given in the college's schedule and can be found at the Web site www.nhmccd.edu.*

Fees Required at NHMCCD

[*Residents of the district pay*] tuition at the rate of \$26 per credit hour, a \$4 per credit hour technology fee, and a registration fee of \$12.

For Group Discussion

1. Calculate the tuition and fees for a student who is a resident of the district and who enrolls at NHMCCD for the specified number of credit hours. Let x represent the number of credit hours. Pay attention to the *process* used in your calculations so that you can write the algebraic expression for x credit hours.

   (a) 3 credit hours: \$102 **(b)** 9 credit hours: \$282

   (c) 12 credit hours: \$372 **(d)** x credit hours: $30x + 12$ dollars

Write the algebraic expression that represents the tuition and fees for each institution for one semester. Let x represent the number of credit hours. If you have difficulty, first calculate the costs for 3 or 9 credit hours and focus on the process that you used to get the answer.

2. American River College, California (nonresident student) www.arc.losrios.cc.ca.us*
   Enrollment: \$11 per unit; parking: \$30 per semester; an additional nonresident enrollment: \$134 per unit; other fees: \$8 $11x + 30 + 134x + 8 = 145x + 38$ **dollars**

3. Austin Community College, Texas (out-of-district student) www.austin.cc.tx.us*
   Tuition: \$31 per credit hour; parking: \$10 per year; an additional out-of-district tuition: \$75 per credit hour; student service fee: \$3 $31x + 10 + 75x + 3 = 106x + 13$ **dollars**

4. Valdosta State University, Georgia (in-state student) www.valdosta.edu*
   Matriculation: \$78 per credit hour; health fee: \$66; student services fee: \$78; athletics fees: \$97; technology fee: \$38; parking fee: \$25; special fees also apply. $78x + 66 + 78 + 97 + 38 + 25 = 78x + 304$ **dollars, minimum**

5. Your college tuition and fees **Answers will vary.**

***Note** that URLs sometimes change, although that is unlikely for academic institutions. If the Web address given does not work, use a search engine, such as www.yahoo.com, to find the new URL.

Teaching notes for this activity are provided in the *Printed Test Bank and Instructor's Resource Guide.*

1.8 EXERCISES

FOR EXTRA HELP: Student's Solutions Manual; MyMathLab.com; InterAct Math Tutorial Software; AW Math Tutor Center; www.mathxl.com; Digital Video Tutor CD 2 Videotape 3

Decide whether each statement is true *or* false.

1. $6t + 5t^2 = 11t^3$

false

2. $9xy^2 - 3x^2y = 6xy$

false

3. $8r^2 + 3r - 12r^2 + 4r = -4r^2 + 7r$

true

4. $4 + 3t^3 = 7t^3$

false

In Exercises 5–8, choose the letter of the correct response.

5. Which is true for all real numbers x? C

A. $6 + 2x = 8x$ **B.** $6 - 2x = 4x$
C. $6x - 2x = 4x$ **D.** $3 + 8(4x - 6) = 11(4x - 6)$

6. Which is an example of a pair of like terms? C

A. $6t, 6w$ **B.** $-8x^2y, 9xy^2$
C. $5ry, 6yr$ **D.** $-5x^2, 2x^3$

7. Which is an example of a term with numerical coefficient 5? A

A. $5x^3y^7$ **B.** x^5 **C.** $\frac{x}{5}$ **D.** 5^2xy^3

8. Which is a correct translation for "six times a number, subtracted from the product of eleven and the number" (if x represents the number)? B

A. $6x - 11x$ **B.** $11x - 6x$
C. $(11 + x) - 6x$ **D.** $6x - (11 + x)$

Simplify each expression. See Example 1.

9. $4r + 19 - 8$ $4r + 11$

10. $7t + 18 - 4$ $7t + 14$

11. $5 + 2(x - 3y)$ $5 + 2x - 6y$

12. $8 + 3(s - 6t)$ $8 + 3s - 18t$

13. $-2 - (5 - 3p)$ $-7 + 3p$

14. $-10 - (7 - 14r)$ $-17 + 14r$

Give the numerical coefficient of each term.

15. $-12k$ -12

16. $-23y$ -23

17. $5m^2$ 5

18. $-3n^6$ -3

19. xw 1

20. pq 1

21. $-x$ -1

22. $-t$ -1

23. 74 74

24. 98 98

25. Give an example of a pair of like terms with the variable x, such that one of them has a negative numerical coefficient, one has a positive numerical coefficient, and their sum has a positive numerical coefficient.

Answers will vary. For example, $-3x$ and $4x$

26. Give an example of a pair of unlike terms such that each term has x as the only variable.

Answers will vary. For example, x^2 and x^3

Identify each group of terms as like *or* unlike.

27. $8r, -13r$

like

28. $-7a, 12a$

like

29. $5z^4, 9z^3$

unlike

30. $8x^5, -10x^3$

unlike

31. $4, 9, -24$

like

32. $7, 17, -83$

like

33. x, y

unlike

34. t, s

unlike

35. There is an old saying "You can't add apples and oranges." Explain how this saying can be applied to Objective 3 in this section.

We cannot "add" unlike terms, so we must be able to identify like terms in order to combine them.

36. Explain how the distributive property is used in combining $6t + 5t$ to get $11t$.

The variable t has been "distributed." By the distributive property, $6t + 5t = (6 + 5)t = 11t$.

Simplify each expression. See Examples 2 and 3.

37. $5 - 2(x - 3)$ **$11 - 2x$**

38. $-8 - 3(2x + 4)$ **$-20 - 6x$**

39. $-\frac{4}{3} + 2t + \frac{1}{3}t - 8 - \frac{8}{3}t$ **$-\frac{1}{3}t - \frac{28}{3}$**

40. $-\frac{5}{6} + 8x + \frac{1}{6}x - 7 - \frac{7}{6}$ **$\frac{49}{6}x - 9$**

41. $-5.3r + 4.9 - (2r + .7) + 3.2r$ **$-4.1r + 4.2$**

42. $2.7b + 5.8 - (3b + .5) - 4.4b$ **$-4.7b + 5.3$**

43. $2y^2 - 7y^3 - 4y^2 + 10y^3$ **$-2y^2 + 3y^3$**

44. $9x^4 - 7x^6 + 12x^4 + 14x^6$ **$21x^4 + 7x^6$**

45. $13p + 4(4 - 8p)$ **$-19p + 16$**

46. $5x + 3(7 - 2x)$ **$-x + 21$**

47. $-\frac{4}{3}(y - 12) - \frac{1}{6}y$ **$-\frac{3}{2}y + 16$**

48. $-\frac{7}{5}(t - 15) - \frac{3}{2}$ **$-\frac{7}{5}t + \frac{39}{2}$**

49. $-5(5y - 9) + 3(3y + 6)$ **$-16y + 63$**

50. $-3(2t + 4) + 8(2t - 4)$ **$10t - 44$**

Write each phrase as a mathematical expression. Use x to represent the number. Combine like terms when possible. See Example 4.

51. Five times a number, added to the sum of the number and three

$(x + 3) + 5x; 6x + 3$

52. Six times a number, added to the sum of the number and six

$(x + 6) + 6x; 7x + 6$

53. A number multiplied by -7, subtracted from the sum of 13 and six times the number

$(13 + 6x) - (-7x); 13 + 13x$

54. A number multiplied by 5, subtracted from the sum of 14 and eight times the number

$(14 + 8x) - 5x; 14 + 3x$

55. Six times a number added to -4, subtracted from twice the sum of three times the number and 4

$2(3x + 4) - (-4 + 6x); 12$

56. Nine times a number added to 6, subtracted from triple the sum of 12 and 8 times the number

$3(12 + 8x) - (6 + 9x); 30 + 15x$

57. Write the expression $9x - (x + 2)$ using words, as in Exercises 51–56.

Wording may vary. One example is "the difference between 9 times a number and the sum of the number and 2."

58. Write the expression $2(3x + 5) - 2(x + 4)$ using words, as in Exercises 51–56.

Wording may vary. One example is "the difference between twice the sum of three times a number and 5, and twice the sum of the number and 4."

RELATING CONCEPTS (Exercises 59–62) FOR INDIVIDUAL OR GROUP WORK

A manufacturer has fixed costs of \$1000 *to produce widgets. Each widget costs* \$5 *to make. The fixed cost to produce gadgets is* \$750, *and each gadget costs* \$3 *to make.*
Work Exercises 59–62 in order.

59. Write an expression for the cost to make x widgets. (*Hint:* The cost will be the sum of the fixed cost and the cost per item times the number of items.)

$1000 + 5x$ (dollars)

60. Write an expression for the cost to make y gadgets.

$750 + 3y$ (dollars)

61. Write an expression for the total cost to make x widgets and y gadgets.

$1000 + 5x + 750 + 3y$ (dollars)

62. Simplify the expression you wrote in Exercise 61.

$1750 + 5x + 3y$ (dollars)

Chapter 1

SUMMARY

Study Skills Workbook
Activity 6

KEY TERMS

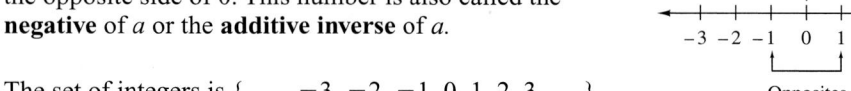

1.1	**exponent**	An exponent, or **power**, is a number that indicates how many times a factor is repeated. 3^4 ← Exponent; 3 ← Base
	base	The base is the number that is a repeated factor when written with an exponent.
	exponential expression	A number written with an exponent is an exponential expression.
1.2	**variable**	A variable is a symbol, usually a letter, used to represent an unknown number.
	algebraic expression	An algebraic expression is a collection of numbers, variables, operation symbols, and grouping symbols.
	equation	An equation is a statement that says two expressions are equal.
	solution	A solution of an equation is any value of the variable that makes the equation true.
1.3	**whole numbers**	The set of whole numbers is $\{0, 1, 2, 3, 4, 5, \ldots\}$.
	natural numbers	The set of natural numbers is $\{1, 2, 3, 4, \ldots\}$.
	number line	The number line shows the ordering of the real numbers on an infinite line.
	opposite	The opposite of a number a is the number that is the same distance from 0 on the number line as a, but on the opposite side of 0. This number is also called the **negative** of a or the **additive inverse** of a.
	integers	The set of integers is $\{\ldots, -3, -2, -1, 0, 1, 2, 3, \ldots\}$.
	negative number	A negative number is located to the *left* of 0 on the number line.
	positive number	A positive number is located to the *right* of 0 on the number line.
	rational numbers	A rational number is a number that can be written as the quotient of two integers, with denominator not 0.
	coordinate	The number that corresponds to a point on the number line is the coordinate of that point.
	irrational numbers	An irrational number is a real number that is not a rational number.
	real numbers	Real numbers are numbers that can be represented by points on the number line, or all rational and irrational numbers.
	absolute value	The absolute value of a number is the distance between 0 and the number on the number line.
1.4	**sum**	The answer to an addition problem is called the sum.
1.5	**difference**	The answer to a subtraction problem is called the difference.
1.6	**product**	The answer to a multiplication problem is called the product.
	reciprocal	Pairs of numbers whose product is 1 are called reciprocals or **multiplicative inverses** of each other.
	quotient	The answer to a division problem is called the quotient.
1.7	**identity element for addition**	When the identity element for addition, which is 0, is added to a number, the number is unchanged.
	identity element for multiplication	When a number is multiplied by the identity element for multiplication, which is 1, the number is unchanged.
1.8	**term**	A term is a number, a variable, or a product or quotient of a number and one or more variables raised to powers.
	numerical coefficient	The numerical factor in a term is its numerical coefficient.
	like terms	Terms with exactly the same variables (including the same exponents) are called like terms.

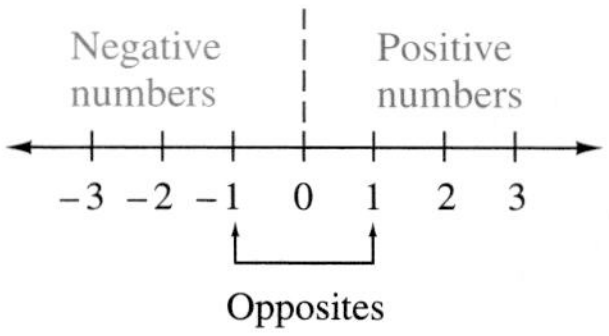

New Symbols

a^n	n factors of a	$a(b)$, $(a)b$, $(a)(b)$, $a \cdot b$, or ab	a times b
$=$	is equal to	$\frac{a}{b}$, a/b, or $a \div b$	a divided by b
$\neq$	is not equal to	$\{\ \}$	set braces
$<$	is less than	$\lvert x \rvert$	absolute value of x
$\leq$	is less than or equal to	$\frac{1}{x}$	the multiplicative inverse or reciprocal of x ($x \neq 0$)
$>$	is greater than		
$\geq$	is greater than or equal to		

Test Your Word Power

See how well you have learned the vocabulary in this chapter. Answers follow the Quick Review.

1. The **product** is
- **(a)** the answer in an addition problem
- **(b)** the answer in a multiplication problem
- **(c)** one of two or more numbers that are added to get another number
- **(d)** one of two or more numbers that are multiplied to get another number.

2. A number is **prime** if
- **(a)** it cannot be factored
- **(b)** it has just one factor
- **(c)** it has only itself and 1 as factors
- **(d)** it has at least two different factors.

3. An **exponent** is
- **(a)** a symbol that tells how many numbers are being multiplied
- **(b)** a number raised to a power
- **(c)** a number that tells how many times a factor is repeated
- **(d)** one of two or more numbers that are multiplied.

4. A **variable** is
- **(a)** a symbol used to represent an unknown number
- **(b)** a value that makes an equation true
- **(c)** a solution of an equation
- **(d)** the answer in a division problem.

5. An **integer** is
- **(a)** a positive or negative number
- **(b)** a natural number, its opposite, or zero
- **(c)** any number that can be graphed on a number line
- **(d)** the quotient of two numbers.

6. A **coordinate** is
- **(a)** the number that corresponds to a point on a number line
- **(b)** the graph of a number
- **(c)** any point on a number line
- **(d)** the distance from 0 on a number line.

7. The **absolute value** of a number is
- **(a)** the graph of the number
- **(b)** the reciprocal of the number
- **(c)** the opposite of the number
- **(d)** the distance between 0 and the number on a number line.

8. A **term** is
- **(a)** a numerical factor
- **(b)** a number, a variable, or a product or quotient of numbers and variables raised to powers
- **(c)** one of several variables with the same exponents
- **(d)** a sum of numbers and variables raised to powers.

9. A **numerical coefficient** is
- **(a)** the numerical factor in a term
- **(b)** the number of terms in an expression
- **(c)** a variable raised to a power
- **(d)** the variable factor in a term.

Quick Review

Concepts | *Examples*

1.1 Exponents, Order of Operations, and Inequality

Order of Operations

If necessary, simplify within parentheses or brackets and above and below fraction bars, using the following steps.

Step 1 Apply all exponents.

Step 2 Do any multiplications or divisions from left to right.

Step 3 Do any additions or subtractions from left to right.

$$\frac{9(2+6)}{2} - 2(2^3 + 3) = 36 - 2(8 + 3)$$
$$= 36 - 2(11)$$
$$= 36 - 22$$
$$= 14$$

1.2 Variables, Expressions, and Equations

Evaluate an expression with a variable by substituting a given number for the variable.

Evaluate $2x + y^2$ if $x = 3$ and $y = -4$.

$$2x + y^2 = 2(3) + (-4)^2$$
$$= 6 + 16$$
$$= 22$$

Values of a variable that make an equation true are solutions of the equation.

Is 2 a solution of $5x + 3 = 18$?

$$5(2) + 3 = 18$$
$$13 = 18 \quad \text{False}$$

2 is not a solution.

1.3 Real Numbers and the Number Line

Ordering Real Numbers

a is less than b if a is to the left of b on the number line.

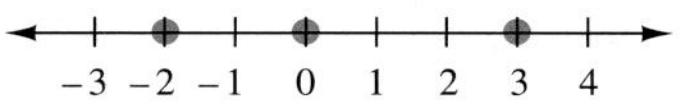

$-2 < 3 \qquad 3 > 0 \qquad 0 < 3$

The opposite or additive inverse of a is $-a$.

$-(5) = -5 \qquad -(-7) = 7 \qquad -0 = 0$

The absolute value of a, $|a|$, is the distance between a and 0 on the number line.

$|13| = 13 \qquad |0| = 0 \qquad |-5| = 5$

1.4 Addition of Real Numbers

To add two numbers with the same sign, add their absolute values. The sum has that same sign.

$$9 + 4 = 13$$
$$-8 + (-5) = -13$$

To add two numbers with different signs, subtract their absolute values. The sum has the sign of the number with larger absolute value.

$$7 + (-12) = -5$$
$$-5 + 13 = 8$$

1.5 Subtraction of Real Numbers

To subtract signed numbers:

Change the subtraction symbol to addition, and change the sign of the number being subtracted. Add as in the previous section.

$$5 - (-2) = 5 + 2 = 7$$
$$-3 - 4 = -3 + (-4) = -7$$
$$-2 - (-6) = -2 + 6 = 4$$

Concepts	*Examples*
1.6 Multiplication and Division of Real Numbers	
The product (or quotient) of two numbers having the *same sign* is *positive*; the product (or quotient) of two numbers having *different signs* is *negative.*	$6 \cdot 5 = 30$ $\quad (-7)(-8) = 56$ $\frac{10}{2} = 5$ $\quad \frac{-24}{-6} = 4$ $-6(5) = -30$ $\quad 6(-5) = -30$ $-18 \div 9 = \frac{-18}{9} = -2$ $\quad 49 \div (-7) = \frac{49}{-7} = -7$
To divide a by b, multiply a by the reciprocal of b.	$\frac{10}{\frac{2}{3}} = 10 \div \frac{2}{3} = 10 \cdot \frac{3}{2} = 15$
Division *by* 0 is undefined.	$\frac{0}{5} = 0$ $\quad \frac{5}{0}$ is undefined.
1.7 Properties of Real Numbers	
Commutative Properties	
$a + b = b + a$	$7 + (-1) = -1 + 7$
$ab = ba$	$5(-3) = (-3)5$
Associative Properties	
$(a + b) + c = a + (b + c)$	$(3 + 4) + 8 = 3 + (4 + 8)$
$(ab)c = a(bc)$	$[-2(6)](4) = -2[6(4)]$
Identity Properties	
$a + 0 = a$ $\quad 0 + a = a$	$-7 + 0 = -7$ $\quad 0 + (-7) = -7$
$a \cdot 1 = a$ $\quad 1 \cdot a = a$	$9 \cdot 1 = 9$ $\quad 1 \cdot 9 = 9$
Inverse Properties	
$a + (-a) = 0$ $\quad -a + a = 0$	$7 + (-7) = 0$ $\quad -7 + 7 = 0$
$a \cdot \frac{1}{a} = 1$ $\quad \frac{1}{a} \cdot a = 1 \; (a \neq 0)$	$-2\left(-\frac{1}{2}\right) = 1$ $\quad -\frac{1}{2}(-2) = 1$
Distributive Properties	
$a(b + c) = ab + ac$	$5(4 + 2) = 5(4) + 5(2)$
$(b + c)a = ba + ca$	$(4 + 2)5 = 4(5) + 2(5)$
1.8 Simplifying Expressions	
Only like terms may be combined.	$-3y^2 + 6y^2 + 14y^2 = 17y^2$ $-8a^5b^3 + 2a^3b^5 - 6a^5b^3 + 5a^3b^5 = -14a^5b^3 + 7a^3b^5$ $4(3 + 2x) - 6(5 - x) = 12 + 8x - 30 + 6x$ $= 14x - 18$

ANSWERS TO TEST YOUR WORD POWER

1. (b) *Example:* The product of 2 and 5, or 2 times 5, is 10. **2. (c)** *Examples:* 2, 3, 11, 41, 53 **3. (c)** *Example:* In 2^3, the number 3 is the exponent (or power), so 2 is a factor three times; $2^3 = 2 \cdot 2 \cdot 2 = 8$. **4. (a)** *Examples:* *a, b, c* **5. (b)** *Examples:* $-9, 0, 6$ **6. (a)** *Example:* The point graphed three units to the right of 0 on a number line has coordinate 3. **7. (d)** *Examples:* $|2| = 2$ and $|-2| = 2$ **8. (b)** *Examples:* $6, \frac{x}{2}, -4ab^2$ **9. (a)** *Examples:* The term 3 has numerical coefficient 3, $8z$ has numerical coefficient 8, and $-10x^4y$ has numerical coefficient -10.

Chapter 1

REVIEW EXERCISES

If you need help with any of these Review Exercises, look in the section indicated in brackets.

[1.1] *Find the value of each exponential expression.*

1. 5^4 625

2. $(.03)^4$ .00000081

3. $.21^3$ .009261

4. $\left(\frac{5}{2}\right)^3$ $\frac{125}{8}$

Find the value of each expression.

5. $-13 + 8 \cdot 5$ 27

6. $5[4^2 + 3(2^3)]$ 200

7. $\frac{7(3^2 - 5)}{2 \cdot 6 - 16}$ -7

8. $\frac{3(9 - 4) + 5(8 - 3)}{2^3 - (5 - 3)}$ $\frac{20}{3}$

Write each word statement in symbols.

9. Thirteen is less than seventeen. $13 < 17$

10. Five plus two is not equal to ten. $5 + 2 \neq 10$

11. Write $6 < 15$ in words. Six is less than fifteen.

12. Construct a false statement that involves addition on the left side, the symbol $\geq$, and division on the right side.

Answers will vary. One example is $-4 + (-7) \geq \frac{12}{-3}$.

[1.2] *Evaluate each expression if $x = 6$ and $y = 3$.*

13. $2x + 6y$ 30

14. $4(3x - y)$ 60

15. $\frac{x}{3} + 4y$ 14

16. $\frac{x^2 + 3}{3y - x}$ 13

Change each word phrase to an algebraic expression. Use x to represent the number.

17. Six added to a number $x + 6$

18. A number subtracted from eight $8 - x$

19. Nine subtracted from six times a number $6x - 9$

20. Three-fifths of a number added to 12 $12 + \frac{3}{5}x$

Decide whether the given number is a solution of the equation.

21. $5x + 3(x + 2) = 22$; 2 yes

22. $\frac{t + 5}{3t} = 1$; 6 no

Change each word sentence to an equation. Use x to represent the number.

23. Six less than twice a number is 10. $2x - 6 = 10$

24. The product of a number and 4 is 8. $4x = 8$

Identify each of the following as either an equation *or an* expression.

25. $5r - 8(r + 7) = 2$ equation

26. $2y + (5y - 9) + 2$ expression

[1.3] *Graph each group of numbers on a number line.*

27. $-4, -\frac{1}{2}, 0, 2.5, 5$

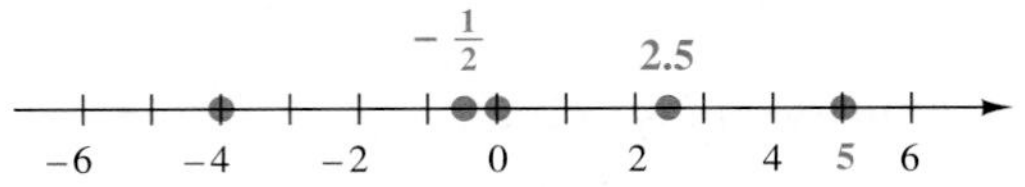

28. $-2, -3, |-3|, |-1|$

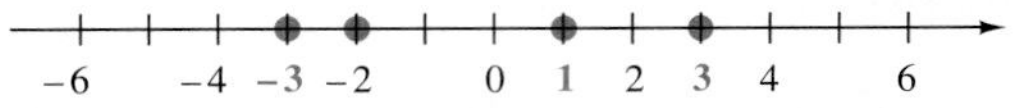

29. $-3\frac{1}{4}, \frac{14}{5}, -1\frac{1}{8}, \frac{5}{6}$

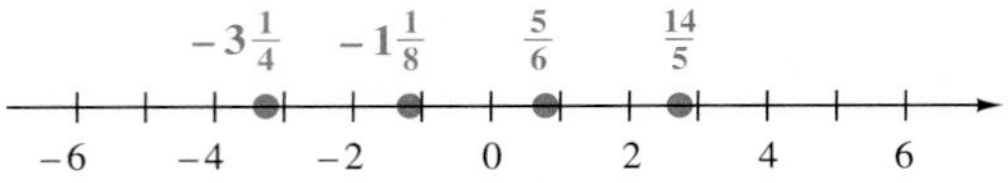

30. $|-4|, -|-3|, -|-5|, -6$

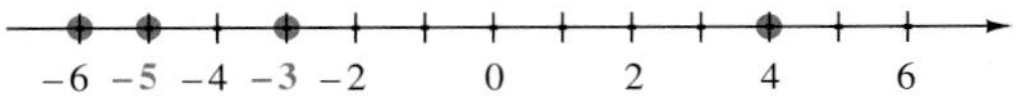

Select the smaller number in each pair.

31. $-10, 5$ **-10**

32. $-8, -9$ **-9**

33. $-\frac{2}{3}, -\frac{3}{4}$ **$-\frac{3}{4}$**

34. $0, -|23|$ **$-|23|$**

Decide whether each statement is true *or* false.

35. $12 > -13$ **true**

36. $0 > -5$ **true**

37. $-9 < -7$ **true**

38. $-13 > -13$ **false**

Simplify by finding the absolute value.

39. $-|3|$ **-3**

40. $-|-19|$ **-19**

41. $-|9 - 2|$ **-7**

42. $|15 - 6|$ **9**

[1.4] *Find each sum.*

43. $-10 + 4$ **-6**

44. $14 + (-18)$ **-4**

45. $-8 + (-9)$ **-17**

46. $\frac{4}{9} + \left(-\frac{5}{4}\right)$ **$-\frac{29}{36}$**

47. $[-6 + (-8) + 8] + [9 + (-13)]$ **-10**

48. $(-4 + 7) + (-11 + 3) + (-15 + 1)$ **-19**

Write a numerical expression for each phrase, and simplify the expression.

49. 19 added to the sum of -31 and 12
$(-31 + 12) + 19; 0$

50. 13 more than the sum of -4 and -8
$[-4 + (-8)] + 13; 1$

Solve each problem.

51. Tri Nguyen has \$18 in his checking account. He then writes a check for \$26. What negative number represents his balance?
−\$8

52. The temperature at noon on an August day in Houston was 93°F. After a thunderstorm, it dropped 6°. What was the new temperature?
87°F

[1.5] *Find each difference.*

53. $-7 - 4$ **−11**

54. $-12 - (-11)$ **−1**

55. $5 - (-2)$ **7**

56. $-\frac{3}{7} - \frac{4}{5}$ $-\frac{43}{35}$

57. $2.56 - (-7.75)$ **10.31**

58. $(-10 - 4) - (-2)$ **−12**

59. $(-3 + 4) - (-1)$ **2**

60. $|5 - 9| - |-3 + 6|$ **1**

Write a numerical expression for each phrase, and simplify the expression.

61. The difference between −4 and −6
$-4 - (-6); 2$

62. Five less than the sum of 4 and −8
$[4 + (-8)] - 5; -9$

63. In the 1969–1970 school year, the percent of high school graduates among 17-year-olds reached a maximum of 76.9%. This percent decreased by 5.5% in 1979–1980 and then increased by 2.8% in 1989–1990. What percent of 17-year-olds graduated in 1990? (*Source:* National Center for Education Statistics, U.S. Department of Education.) **74.2%**

64. The 1988 Women's Olympic Downhill Skiing champion, Marina Kiehl, from West Germany, finished the course in 1 min, 25.86 sec. The winning time of the 1994 champion, Katja Seizinger of Germany, increased by 10.07 sec. Seizinger won again in 1998. Her time decreased by 7.04 sec. What was Seizinger's winning time in 1998? (*Source: World Almanac and Book of Facts,* 1999.)
1 min, 28.89 sec

65. Explain in your own words how the subtraction problem $-8 - (-6)$ is performed.
The first step is to change subtracting −6 to adding its opposite, 6. So the problem becomes −8 + 6. This sum is −2.

66. Can the difference of two negative numbers be positive? Explain with an example.
Yes; for example, $-2 - (-6) = -2 + 6 = 4$, a positive number.

The bar graph shows the federal budget outlays for national defense for the years 1990–1998. Use a signed number to represent the change in outlay for each time period. For example, the change from 1995 to 1996 was \$253.3 − \$259.6 = −\$6.3 billion.

67. 1991–1992 **\$25.1 billion**

68. 1993–1994 **−\$11.3 billion**

69. 1996–1997 **\$5.0 billion**

70. 1997–1998 **−\$2.2 billion**

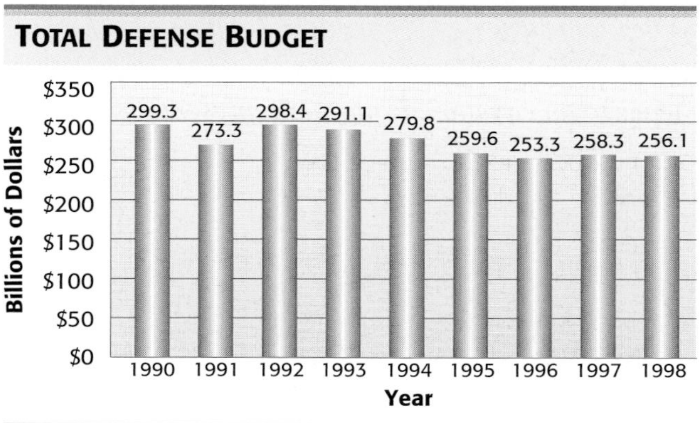

Source: U.S. Office of Management and Budget.

[1.6] *Perform the indicated operations.*

71. $(-12)(-3)$ 36

72. $15(-7)$ -105

73. $\left(-\frac{4}{3}\right)\left(-\frac{3}{8}\right)$ $\frac{1}{2}$

74. $(-4.8)(-2.1)$ 10.08

75. $5(8-12)$

-20

76. $(5-7)(8-3)$

-10

77. $2(-6)-(-4)(-3)$

-24

78. $3(-10)-5$

-35

79. $\frac{-36}{-9}$ 4

80. $\frac{220}{-11}$ -20

81. $\frac{1}{2} \div \frac{2}{3}$ $\frac{3}{4}$

82. $-33.9 \div (-3)$ 11.3

83. $\frac{-5(3)-1}{8-4(-2)}$

-1

84. $\frac{5(-2)-3(4)}{-2[3-(-2)]+10}$

undefined

85. $\frac{10^2-5^2}{8^2+3^2-(-2)}$

1

86. $\frac{(.6)^2+(.8)^2}{(-1.2)^2-(-.56)}$

.5

Evaluate each expression if $x=-5$, $y=4$, *and* $z=-3$.

87. $6x-4z$

-18

88. $5x+y-z$

-18

89. $5x^2$

125

90. $z^2(3x-8y)$

-423

Write a numerical expression for each phrase, and simplify the expression.

91. Nine less than the product of -4 and 5

$-4(5)-9; -29$

92. Five-sixths of the sum of 12 and -6

$\frac{5}{6}[12+(-6)]; 5$

93. The quotient of 12 and the sum of 8 and -4

$\frac{12}{8+(-4)}; 3$

94. The product of -20 and 12, divided by the difference between 15 and -15

$\frac{-20(12)}{15-(-15)}; -8$

Translate each sentence to an equation, using x to represent the number.

95. The quotient of a number and the sum of the number and 5 is -2.

$\frac{x}{x+5}=-2$

96. 3 less than 8 times a number is -7.

$8x-3=-7$

[1.7] *Decide whether each statement is an example of the commutative, associative, identity, inverse, or distributive property.*

97. $6 + 0 = 6$

identity property

98. $5 \cdot 1 = 5$

identity property

99. $-\frac{2}{3}\left(-\frac{3}{2}\right) = 1$

inverse property

100. $17 + (-17) = 0$

inverse property

101. $5 + (-9 + 2) = [5 + (-9)] + 2$

associative property

102. $w(xy) = (wx)y$

associative property

103. $3x + 3y = 3(x + y)$

distributive property

104. $(1 + 2) + 3 = 3 + (1 + 2)$

commutative property

Use the distributive property to rewrite each expression. Simplify if possible.

105. $7y + y$

$(7 + 1)y$; $8y$

106. $-12(4 - t)$

$-12 \cdot 4 - 12(-t)$; $-48 + 12t$

107. $3(2s) + 3(4y)$

$3(2s + 4y)$; $6s + 12y$

108. $-(-4r + 5s)$

$-1(-4r) + (-1)(5s)$; $4r - 5s$

[1.8] *Use the distributive property as necessary and combine like terms.*

109. $16p^2 - 8p^2 + 9p^2$

$17p^2$

110. $4r^2 - 3r + 10r + 12r^2$

$16r^2 + 7r$

111. $-8(5k - 6) + 3(7k + 2)$

$-19k + 54$

112. $2s - (-3s + 6)$

$5s - 6$

113. $-7(2t - 4) - 4(3t + 8) - 19(t + 1)$

$-45t - 23$

114. $3.6t^2 + 9t - 8.1(6t^2 + 4t)$

$-45t^2 - 23.4t$

Translate each phrase into a mathematical expression. Use x to represent the number, and combine like terms when possible.

115. Seven times a number, subtracted from the product of -2 and three times the number

$-2(3x) - 7x$; $-13x$

116. The quotient of 9 more than a number and 6 less than the number

$\frac{x + 9}{x - 6}$

117. In Exercise 115, does the word *and* signify addition? Explain.

No. The use of *and* there indicates the two quantities that are to be multiplied.

118. Write the expression $3(4x - 6)$ using words, as in Exercises 115 and 116.

Answers may vary. For example, "3 times the difference between 4 times a number and 6"

Mixed Review Exercises*

Perform the indicated operations.

119. $[(-2) + 7 - (-5)] + [-4 - (-10)]$ **16**

120. $\left(-\frac{5}{6}\right)^2$ $\mathbf{\frac{25}{36}}$

121. $-|(-7)(-4)| - (-2)$ **−26**

122. $\frac{6(-4) + 2(-12)}{5(-3) + (-3)}$ $\mathbf{\frac{8}{3}}$

123. $\frac{3}{8} - \frac{5}{12}$ $\mathbf{-\frac{1}{24}}$

124. $\frac{12^2 + 2^2 - 8}{10^2 - (-4)(-15)}$ $\mathbf{\frac{7}{2}}$

125. $\frac{8^2 + 6^2}{7^2 + 1^2}$ **2**

126. $-16(-3.5) - 7.2(-3)$ **77.6**

127. $2\frac{5}{6} - 4\frac{1}{3}$ $\mathbf{-1\frac{1}{2}}$

128. $-8 + [(-4 + 17) - (-3 - 3)]$ **11**

129. $-\frac{12}{5} \div \frac{9}{7}$ $\mathbf{-\frac{28}{15}}$

130. $(-8 - 3) - 5(2 - 9)$ **24**

131. $[-7 + (-2) - (-3)] + [8 + (-13)]$ **−11**

132. $\frac{15}{2} \cdot \left(-\frac{4}{5}\right)$ **−6**

Write a numerical expression or an equation for each problem, and simplify it if possible. Use x as the variable, and specify what it represents.

133. In 2000, a company spent \$1400 less on advertising than in the previous year. The total spent for this purpose over these two years was \$25,800. How much was spent in 2000?

$2x - 1400 = 25{,}800$; *x* represents the amount spent in 1999.

134. The quotient of a number and 14 less than three times the number

$\frac{x}{3x - 14}$; *x* represents the number.

---

* The order of exercises in this final group does not correspond to the order in which topics occur in the chapter. This random ordering should help you prepare for the chapter test in yet another way.

Chapter 1 Test

Study Skills Workbook
Activity 7

Decide whether the statement is true *or* false.

1. $4[-20 + 7(-2)] \leq -135$

1. true

2. $(-3)^2 + 2^2 = 5^2$

2. false

3. Graph the numbers -1, -3, $|-4|$, and $|-1|$ on the number line.

3. 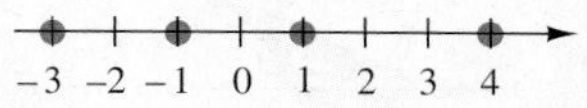

Select the smaller number from each pair.

4. $6, -|-8|$

4. $-|-8|$ (or -8)

5. $-.742, -1.277$

5. -1.277

6. Write in symbols: The quotient of -6 and the sum of 2 and -8. Simplify the expression.

6. $\dfrac{-6}{2 + (-8)}$; 1

7. If a and b are both negative, is $\dfrac{a + b}{a \cdot b}$ positive or negative?

7. negative

Perform the indicated operations whenever possible.

8. $-2 - (5 - 17) + (-6)$

8. 4

9. $-5\frac{1}{2} + 2\frac{2}{3}$

9. $-2\frac{5}{6}$

10. $-6 - [-7 + (2 - 3)]$

10. 2

11. $4^2 + (-8) - (2^3 - 6)$

11. 6

12. $(-5)(-12) + 4(-4) + (-8)^2$

12. 108

13. $\dfrac{-7 - |-6 + 2|}{-5 - (-4)}$

13. 11

14. $\frac{30}{27}$

14. $\dfrac{30(-1-2)}{-9[3-(-2)]-12(-2)}$

In Exercises 15 and 16, evaluate each expression if $x = -2$ and $y = 4$.

15. -70

15. $3x - 4y^2$

16. 3

16. $\dfrac{5x + 7y}{3(x + y)}$

17. 178°F

17. The highest Fahrenheit temperature ever recorded in Idaho was 118°, while the lowest was −60°. What is the difference between these highest and lowest temperatures? (*Source: World Almanac and Book of Facts,* 2000.)

Match each example in Column I with a property in Column II.

18. D
19. A
20. E
21. B
22. C

	I	II
18.	$3x + 0 = 3x$	**A.** Commutative
19.	$(5 + 2) + 8 = 8 + (5 + 2)$	**B.** Associative
20.	$-3(x + y) = -3x + (-3y)$	**C.** Inverse
21.	$-5 + (3 + 2) = (-5 + 3) + 2$	**D.** Identity
22.	$-\frac{5}{3}\left(-\frac{3}{5}\right) = 1$	**E.** Distributive

23. $-9x^2 - 6x - 8$

23. Simplify $-2(3x^2 + 4) - 3(x^2 + 2x)$ by using the distributive property and combining like terms.

24. identity and distributive properties

24. What properties are used to show that $-(3x + 1) = -3x - 1$?

25. **(a)** 18 **(b)** −18 **(c)** The distributive property tells us that the two methods produce equal results.

25. Consider the expression $-6[5 + (-2)]$.
(a) Evaluate it by first working within the brackets.
(b) Evaluate it by using the distributive property.
(c) Why must the answers in items (a) and (b) be the same?

Linear Equations and Applications

2

After Lee Ann Spahr pumped 5.0 gal of gasoline, the display showing the price read $7.90. When she finished pumping the gasoline, the price display read $21.33. How many gallons did she pump?

During the course of a day, it is likely that you use the concepts of ratio, proportion, and percent to solve simple problems. In Example 5 of Section 2.6, we use a proportion to answer the question posed here.

2.1 The Addition Property of Equality

Objectives

1. Identify linear equations.
2. Use the addition property of equality.
3. Simplify equations, and then use the addition property of equality.
4. Solve equations that have no solution or infinitely many solutions.

To solve applied problems, we must be able to solve equations. The simplest type of equation is a *linear equation*. Methods for solving linear equations will be introduced in this section. We will be using the definitions and properties of real numbers that we learned in Chapter 1.

1 Identify linear equations. We begin with a definition.

Linear Equation in One Variable

A **linear equation in one variable** can be written in the form

$$Ax + B = C$$

for real numbers A, B, and C, with $A \neq 0$.

For example,

$$4x + 9 = 0, \quad 2x - 3 = 5, \quad \text{and} \quad x = 7$$

are linear equations in one variable (x). The final two can be written in the specified form using properties developed in this chapter. However,

$$x^2 + 2x = 5, \quad \frac{1}{x} = 6, \quad \text{and} \quad |2x + 6| = 0$$

are *not* linear equations.

As we saw in Chapter 1, a solution of an equation is a number that makes the equation true when it replaces the variable. Equations that have exactly the same solutions are **equivalent equations**. Linear equations are solved by using a series of steps to produce a simpler equivalent equation of the form

$$x = \text{a number}.$$

2 Use the addition property of equality. In the equation $x - 5 = 2$, both $x - 5$ and 2 represent the same number because this is the meaning of the equals sign. To solve the equation, we change the left side from $x - 5$ to just x. This is done by adding 5 to $x - 5$. To keep the two sides equal, we must also add 5 to the right side.

$x - 5 = 2$	Given equation
$x - 5 + 5 = 2 + 5$	Add 5 to each side.
$x + 0 = 7$	Additive inverse property
$x = 7$	Additive identity property

The solution of the given equation is 7. Check by replacing x with 7 in the original equation.

Check:	$x - 5 = 2$		Original equation
	$7 - 5 = 2$	?	Let $x = 7$.
	$2 = 2$		True

Since the final equation is true, 7 checks as the solution.

To solve the equation, we added the same number to each side. The **addition property of equality** justifies this step.

Addition Property of Equality

If A, B, and C are real numbers, then the equations

$$A = B \quad \text{and} \quad A + C = B + C$$

are equivalent equations.

In words, we can add the same number to each side of an equation without changing the solution.

In the addition property, C represents a real number. This means that any quantity that represents a real number can be added to each side of an equation to change it to an equivalent equation.

The set of all solutions of an equation is called its **solution set.** We write a solution set using set braces. For example, the solution set of $x - 5 = 2$ is $\{7\}$.

Example 1 Using the Addition Property of Equality

Solve $x - 16.2 = 7.5$.

If the left side of this equation were just x, the solution would be known. Get x alone by using the addition property of equality, adding 16.2 to each side.

$$x - 16.2 = 7.5$$
$$x - 16.2 + \mathbf{16.2} = 7.5 + \mathbf{16.2} \qquad \text{Add 16.2 to each side.}$$
$$x = 23.7 \qquad \text{Combine terms.}$$

Here we combined the steps that change $x - 16.2 + 16.2$ to $x + 0$ and $x + 0$ to x. We will combine these steps from now on. Check by substituting 23.7 for x in the original equation.

Check:

$$x - 16.2 = 7.5 \qquad \text{Original equation}$$
$$\mathbf{23.7} - 16.2 = 7.5 \quad ? \qquad \text{Let } x = 23.7.$$
$$7.5 = 7.5 \qquad \text{True}$$

Since the check results in a true statement, $\{23.7\}$ is the solution set.

Work Problem 1 at the Side.

The addition property of equality says that the same number may be *added* to each side of an equation. In Chapter 1, subtraction was defined as addition of the opposite. Thus, we can also use the following rule when solving an equation.

The same number may be subtracted from each side of an equation without changing the solution.

For example, to solve $x + 5 = 10$, subtract 5 from each side to get $x = 5$.

Work Problem 2 at the Side.

Example 2 Subtracting a Variable Expression

Solve $\frac{3}{5}k + 17 = \frac{8}{5}k$.

Get all terms with variables on the same side of the equation. One way to do this is to subtract $\frac{3}{5}k$ from each side.

Continued on Next Page

1 Solve.

(a) $m - 2.9 = -6.4$

(b) $y - 4.1 = 6.3$

2 Solve.

(a) $a + 2 = -3$

(b) $r + 16 = 22$

ANSWERS

1. (a) $\{-3.5\}$ **(b)** $\{10.4\}$

2. (a) $\{-5\}$ **(b)** $\{6\}$

$$\frac{3}{5}k + 17 = \frac{8}{5}k$$

$$\frac{3}{5}k + 17 - \frac{3}{5}k = \frac{8}{5}k - \frac{3}{5}k \quad \text{Subtract } \tfrac{3}{5}k \text{ from each side.}$$

$$17 = 1k \quad \text{Combine terms; } \tfrac{5}{5}k = 1k.$$

$$17 = k \quad \text{Identity property}$$

From now on we will skip the step that changes $1k$ to k. Check the solution by replacing k with 17 in the original equation. The solution set is $\{17\}$.

Another way to solve the equation in Example 2 is to first subtract $\frac{8}{5}k$ from each side.

$$\frac{3}{5}k + 17 = \frac{8}{5}k$$

$$\frac{3}{5}k + 17 - \frac{8}{5}k = \frac{8}{5}k - \frac{8}{5}k \quad \text{Subtract } \tfrac{8}{5}k \text{ from each side.}$$

$$17 - k = 0 \quad \text{Combine terms.}$$

$$17 - k - 17 = 0 - 17 \quad \text{Subtract 17 from each side.}$$

$$-k = -17 \quad \text{Combine terms; additive inverse}$$

This result gives the value of $-k$, but not of k itself. However, it does say that the additive inverse of k is -17, which means that k must be 17, the same result we obtained in Example 2.

$$-k = -17$$
$$k = 17$$

(This result can also be justified using the multiplication property of equality, covered in Section 2.2.) We can make the following generalization.

If a is a number and $-x = a$, then $x = -a$.

Work Problem 3 at the Side.

3 Simplify equations, and then use the addition property of equality. Sometimes an equation must be simplified as a first step in its solution.

Example 3 Using the Distributive Property to Simplify an Equation

Solve $3(2 + 5x) - (1 + 14x) = 6$.

$$3(2 + 5x) - (1 + 14x) = 6$$

$$3(2 + 5x) - 1(1 + 14x) = 6 \quad -(1 + 14x) = -1(1 + 14x)$$

$$6 + 15x - 1 - 14x = 6 \quad \text{Distributive property}$$

$$x + 5 = 6 \quad \text{Combine terms.}$$

$$x + 5 - 5 = 6 - 5 \quad \text{Subtract 5 from each side.}$$

$$x = 1 \quad \text{Combine terms.}$$

Check by substituting 1 for x in the original equation. The solution set is $\{1\}$.

Work Problem 4 at the Side.

---

3 (a) Solve $\frac{7}{2}m + 1 = \frac{9}{2}m$.

(b) What is the solution set of $-x = 6$?

(c) What is the solution set of $-x = -12$?

4 Solve.

(a) $-(5 - 3r) + 4(-r + 1) = 1$

(b) $-3(m - 4) + 2(5 + 2m) = 29$

ANSWERS
3. (a) $\{1\}$ (b) $\{-6\}$ (c) $\{12\}$
4. (a) $\{-2\}$ (b) $\{7\}$

4 Solve equations that have no solution or infinitely many solutions. Every equation solved so far has had exactly one solution. Sometimes this is not the case, as shown in the next examples.

Example 4 **Solving an Equation That Has Infinitely Many Solutions**

Solve $5x - 15 = 5(x - 3)$.

$$5x - 15 = 5(x - 3)$$
$$5x - 15 = 5x - 15 \quad \text{Distributive property}$$
$$5x - 15 + 15 = 5x - 15 + 15 \quad \text{Add 15 to each side.}$$
$$5x = 5x \quad \text{Combine terms.}$$
$$5x - 5x = 5x - 5x \quad \text{Subtract } 5x \text{ from each side.}$$
$$0 = 0$$

The final step leads to an equation that contains no variables ($0 = 0$ in this case). Whenever such a statement is true, as it is in this example, *any* real number is a solution. (Try several replacements for x in the given equation to see that they all satisfy the equation.) An equation with both sides exactly the same, like $0 = 0$, is called an **identity.** An identity is true for all replacements of the variables. We indicate this by writing {all real numbers} as the solution set.

CAUTION

When you are solving an equation like the one in Example 4, do not write {0} as the solution set. While 0 is a solution, there are infinitely many other solutions.

Example 5 **Solving an Equation That Has No Solution**

Solve $2x + 3(x + 1) = 5x + 4$.

$$2x + 3(x + 1) = 5x + 4$$
$$2x + 3x + 3 = 5x + 4 \quad \text{Distributive property}$$
$$5x + 3 = 5x + 4 \quad \text{Combine terms.}$$
$$5x + 3 - 5x = 5x + 4 - 5x \quad \text{Subtract } 5x \text{ from each side.}$$
$$3 = 4 \quad \text{Combine terms.}$$

Again, the variable has disappeared, but this time a false statement ($3 = 4$) results. Whenever this happens in solving an equation, it is a signal that the equation has no solution. Its solution set is the **empty set** (or **null set**), symbolized $\emptyset$.

Work Problem 5 at the Side.

5 Solve each equation.

(a) $2(x - 6) = 2x - 12$

(b) $3x + 6(x + 1) = 9x - 4$

ANSWERS

5. (a) {all real numbers} **(b)** $\emptyset$

Focus on

Real-Data Applications

The Magic Number in Sports

National League

East Division

	W	L	Pct.	GB
Atlanta	86	60	.589	—
New York	84	62	.575	2
Florida	69	76	.476	16.5
Montreal	61	84	.421	24.5
Philadelphia	60	85	.414	25.5

Central Division

	W	L	Pct.	GB
St. Louis	86	61	.585	—
Cincinnati	75	72	.510	11
Milwaukee	64	82	.438	21.5
Houston	63	83	.432	22.5
Pittsburgh	61	84	.421	24
Chicago	60	86	.411	25.5

West Division

	W	L	Pct.	GB
San Francisco	87	58	.600	—
Arizona	78	66	.542	8.5
Colorado	75	70	.517	12
Los Angeles	75	71	.514	12.5
San Diego	71	76	.483	17

American League

East Division

	W	L	Pct.	GB
New York	84	59	.587	—
Boston	76	68	.528	8.5
Toronto	75	70	.517	10
Baltimore	66	80	.452	19.5
Tampa Bay	61	85	.418	24.5

Central Division

	W	L	Pct.	GB
Chicago	87	58	.600	—
Cleveland	77	65	.542	8.5
Detroit	71	74	.490	16
Kansas City	68	78	.466	19.5
Minnesota	63	82	.434	24

West Division

	W	L	Pct.	GB
Seattle	80	66	.548	—
Oakland	77	67	.535	2
Anaheim	74	72	.507	6
Texas	66	80	.452	14

The climax of any sports season is the playoffs. Baseball fans eagerly debate predictions of which team will win the pennant for their division. The *magic number* for each first place team is often used to predict the division winner. The **magic number** is the required number of additional wins by the first-place team that would exceed by one the maximum number of wins of the second-place team.

The baseball league standings on September 15, 2000 are shown at the left. There were 162 regulation games in the 2000 baseball season.

For Group Discussion

To calculate the magic number, consider the following conditions.

The number of wins for the first-place team (W_1) plus the magic number (M) is one more than the sum of the number of wins to date (W_2) and the number of games remaining in the season (N_2) for the second-place team.

1. First, use the variable definitions to write an equation involving the magic number. Second, solve the equation for the magic number. Write the formula for the magic number.

$M = W_2 + N_2 + 1 - W_1$

2. Find the magic number for each team. The number of games remaining in the season for the second-place team is calculated as

$$N_2 = 162 - (W_2 + L_2).$$

(a) NL East: Atlanta vs New York
Magic No. 15

(b) NL Central: St. Louis vs Cincinnati
Magic No. 5

(c) NL West: San Francisco vs Arizona
Magic No. 10

(d) AL East: New York vs Boston
Magic No. 11

(e) AL Central: Chicago vs Cleveland
Magic No. 11

(f) AL West: Seattle vs Oakland
Magic No. 16

Teaching notes and an extension for this activity are provided in the *Printed Test Bank and Instructor's Resource Guide.*

2.1 EXERCISES

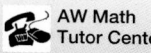

FOR EXTRA HELP — Student's Solutions Manual; MyMathLab.com; InterAct Math Tutorial Software; AW Math Tutor Center; www.mathxl.com; Digital Video Tutor CD 2 Videotape 4

1. Which of the pairs of equations are equivalent equations?

A. $x + 2 = 6$ and $x = 4$ **B.** $10 - x = 5$ and $x = -5$

C. $x + 3 = 9$ and $x = 6$ **D.** $4 + x = 8$ and $x = -4$

A and C

2. Decide whether each is an expression or an equation. If it is an expression, simplify it. If it is an equation, solve it.

(a) $5x + 8 - 4x + 7$ — expression; $x + 15$

(b) $-6y + 12 + 7y - 5$ — expression; $y + 7$

(c) $5x + 8 - 4x = 7$ — equation; $\{-1\}$

(d) $-6y + 12 + 7y = -5$ — equation; $\{-17\}$

3. Which of the following are not linear equations in one variable?

A. $x^2 - 5x + 6 = 0$ **B.** $x^3 = x$

C. $3x - 4 = 0$ **D.** $7x - 6x = 3 + 9x$

A and B

4. Refer to the definition of linear equation in one variable given in this section. Why is the restriction $A \neq 0$ necessary?

If $A = 0$, the equation $Ax + B = C$ becomes $B = C$; with no variable, it is not a linear equation.

Solve each linear equation by inspection (that is, do not write out any steps).

5. $x + 1 = 5$ — $\{4\}$

6. $x - 2 = 4$ — $\{6\}$

7. $x - 10 = 0$ — $\{10\}$

8. $x + 7 = 0$ — $\{-7\}$

Solve each equation by using the addition property of equality. Check each solution. See Examples 1, 2, 4, and 5.

9. $x - 4 = 8$ — $\{12\}$

10. $x - 8 = 9$ — $\{17\}$

11. $7 + r = -3$ — $\{-10\}$

12. $8 + k = -4$ — $\{-12\}$

13. $\frac{9}{7}r - 3 = \frac{2}{7}r$ — $\{3\}$

14. $\frac{8}{5}w - 6 = \frac{3}{5}w$ — $\{6\}$

15. $5.6x + 2 = 4.6x$ — $\{-2\}$

16. $9.1x - 5 = 8.1x$ — $\{5\}$

17. $3p + 6 = 10 + 2p$ — $\{4\}$

18. $8x - 4 = -6 + 7x$ — $\{-2\}$

19. $1.2x - 4 = .2x - 4$ — $\{0\}$

20. $7.7r + 6 = 6.7r + 6$ — $\{0\}$

21. $3x + 9 = 3x + 8$ — $\emptyset$

22. $-2x + 5 = -2x$ — $\emptyset$

23. $8x + 1 = 1 + 8x$ — {all real numbers}

24. $4w - 5 = -5 + 4w$ — {all real numbers}

Solve each equation. First simplify each side of the equation as much as possible. Check each solution. See Examples 3, 4, and 5.

25. $10x + 5x + 7 - 8 = 12x + 3 + 2x$
{4}

26. $7p + 4p + 13 - 7 = 7p + 9 + 3p$
{3}

27. $6x + 5 - 7x + 3 = 5x - 6x - 4$
$\emptyset$

28. $4x - 3 - 8x + 1 = 5x - 9x + 7$
$\emptyset$

29. $5.2q - 4.6 - 7.1q = -2.1 - 1.9q - 2.5$
{all real numbers}

30. $-4.0x + 2.7 - 1.6x = 1.3 - 5.6x + 1.4$
{all real numbers}

31. $\frac{5}{7}x + \frac{1}{3} = \frac{2}{5} - \frac{2}{7}x + \frac{2}{5}$ $\left\{\frac{7}{15}\right\}$

32. $\frac{6}{7}s - \frac{3}{4} = \frac{4}{5} - \frac{1}{7}s + \frac{1}{6}$ $\left\{\frac{103}{60}\right\}$

33. $(5x + 6) - (3 + 4x) = 10$ {7}

34. $(8r - 3) - (7r + 1) = -6$ {−2}

35. $2(p + 5) - (9 + p) = -3$ {−4}

36. $4(k - 6) - (3k + 2) = -5$ {21}

37. $-6(2x + 1) + (13x - 7) = 0$ {13}

38. $-5(3w - 3) + (1 + 16w) = 0$ {−16}

39. $10(-2x + 1) = -14(x + 2) + 38 - 6x$
{all real numbers}

40. $2(2 - 3r) = 5(1 - r) - r - 1$
{all real numbers}

41. $-2(8p + 2) - 3(2 - 7p) = 2(4 + 2p)$ {18}

42. $-5(1 - 2z) + 4(3 - z) = 7(3 + z)$ {−14}

43. $4(7x - 1) + 3(2 - 5x) = 4(3x + 5) - 6$ {12}

44. $9(2m - 3) - 4(5 + 3m) = 5(4 + m) - 3$ {64}

45. In your own words, state how you would find the solution of a linear equation if your next-to-last step reads "$-x = 5$."
Since the opposite of x is 5, x must be -5.

46. If the final step in solving a linear equation leads to the statement $0 = 0$, why is it incorrect to say that {0} is the solution set of the equation? What is the solution set of the equation?
While 0 is one solution, there are infinitely many other solutions. The solution set is {all real numbers}.

47. Write an equation where 6 must be added to each side to solve the equation, and the solution is a negative number.
Answers will vary. One example is $x - 6 = -8$.

48. Write an equation where $\frac{1}{2}$ must be subtracted from each side, and the solution is a positive number.
Answers will vary. One example is $x + \frac{1}{2} = 1$.

2.2 THE MULTIPLICATION PROPERTY OF EQUALITY

The addition property of equality alone is not enough to solve some equations, such as $3x + 2 = 17$.

$$3x + 2 = 17$$

$$3x + 2 - 2 = 17 - 2 \quad \text{Subtract 2 from each side.}$$

$$3x = 15 \quad \text{Combine terms.}$$

Notice that the coefficient of x on the left side is 3, not 1 as desired. We must develop a method that leads to an equation of the form

$$x = \text{a number.}$$

1 Use the multiplication property of equality. If $3x = 15$, then $3x$ and 15 both represent the same number. Multiplying both $3x$ and 15 by the same number will also result in an equality. The **multiplication property of equality** states that we can multiply each side of an equation by the same nonzero number without changing the solution.

Multiplication Property of Equality

If A, B, and C $(C \neq 0)$ represent real numbers, then the equations

$$A = B \quad \text{and} \quad AC = BC$$

have exactly the same solution.

In words, we can multiply each side of an equation by the same nonzero number without changing the solution.

This property can be used to solve $3x = 15$. The $3x$ on the left must be changed to $1x$, or x, instead of $3x$. To isolate x, multiply each side of the equation by $\frac{1}{3}$. We use $\frac{1}{3}$ because $\frac{1}{3}$ is the reciprocal of 3, and $\frac{1}{3} \cdot 3 = \frac{3}{3} = 1$.

$$3x = 15$$

$$\frac{1}{3}(3x) = \frac{1}{3} \cdot 15 \quad \text{Multiply each side by } \tfrac{1}{3}.$$

$$\left(\frac{1}{3} \cdot 3\right)x = \frac{1}{3} \cdot 15 \quad \text{Associative property}$$

$$1x = 5 \quad \text{Multiplicative inverse property}$$

$$x = 5 \quad \text{Multiplicative identity property}$$

The solution set of the equation is $\{5\}$. We can check this result in the original equation. We will sometimes combine the last two steps shown in the preceding example.

Work Problem 1 at the Side.

Just as the addition property of equality permits *subtracting* the same number from each side of an equation, the multiplication property of equality permits *dividing* each side of an equation by the same nonzero number. For example, the equation $3x = 15$, which we just solved by multiplication, could also be solved by dividing each side by 3, as follows.

$$3x = 15$$

$$\frac{3x}{3} = \frac{15}{3} \quad \text{Divide each side by 3.}$$

$$x = 5$$

OBJECTIVES

1. Use the multiplication property of equality.
2. Use the multiplication property of equality to solve equations with decimals.
3. Simplify equations, and then use the multiplication property of equality.
4. Use the multiplication property of equality to solve equations such as $-r = 4$.

1 Check that $\{5\}$ is the solution set of $3x = 15$.

ANSWERS

1. Since $3(5) = 15$, the solution set of $3x = 15$ is $\{5\}$.

2 Solve.

(a) $-6p = -14$

(b) $3r = -12$

(c) $-2m = 16$

We can divide each side of an equation by the same nonzero number without changing the solution. Do not, however, divide each side by a variable, as that may result in losing a valid solution.

NOTE

In practice, it is usually easier to multiply on each side if the coefficient of the variable is a fraction, and divide on each side if the coefficient is an integer. For example, to solve

$$-\frac{3}{4}x = 12,$$

it is easier to multiply by $-\frac{4}{3}$, the reciprocal of $-\frac{3}{4}$, than to divide by $-\frac{3}{4}$. On the other hand, to solve

$$-5x = -20,$$

it is easier to divide by -5 than to multiply by $-\frac{1}{5}$.

Example 1 **Dividing Each Side of an Equation by a Nonzero Number**

Solve $25p = 30$.

Transform the equation so that p (instead of $25p$) is on the left by using the multiplication property of equality. Divide each side of the equation by 25, the coefficient of p.

$$25p = 30$$

$$\frac{25p}{25} = \frac{30}{25} \qquad \text{Divide by 25.}$$

$$p = \frac{30}{25} = \frac{6}{5} \qquad \text{Write in lowest terms.}$$

To check, substitute $\frac{6}{5}$ for p in the original equation.

Check:

$$25p = 30$$

$$\frac{25}{1}\left(\frac{6}{5}\right) = 30 \quad ? \qquad \text{Let } p = \tfrac{6}{5}.$$

$$30 = 30 \qquad \text{True}$$

The solution set is $\{\frac{6}{5}\}$.

Work Problem 2 at the Side.

In the next two examples, multiplication produces the solution more quickly than division would.

Example 2 **Using the Multiplication Property of Equality**

Solve $\frac{a}{4} = 3$.

Replace $\frac{a}{4}$ by $\frac{1}{4}a$, since division by 4 is the same as multiplication by $\frac{1}{4}$. To get a alone on the left, multiply each side by 4, the reciprocal of the coefficient of a.

Continued on Next Page

ANSWERS

2. (a) $\left\{\frac{7}{3}\right\}$ **(b)** $\{-4\}$ **(c)** $\{-8\}$

$$\frac{a}{4} = 3$$

$$\frac{1}{4}a = 3 \qquad \text{Change } \tfrac{a}{4} \text{ to } \tfrac{1}{4}a.$$

$$4 \cdot \frac{1}{4}a = 4 \cdot 3 \qquad \text{Multiply by 4.}$$

$$a = 12 \qquad \text{Multiplicative inverse property; multiplicative identity property}$$

Check that 12 is the solution.

Check:

$$\frac{a}{4} = 3 \qquad \text{Original equation}$$

$$\frac{12}{4} = 3 \quad ? \qquad \text{Let } a = 12.$$

$$3 = 3 \qquad \text{True}$$

The solution set is $\{12\}$.

Work Problem 3 at the Side.

Example 3 Using the Multiplication Property of Equality

Solve $\frac{3}{4}h = 6$.

Transform the equation so that h is alone on the left by multiplying each side of the equation by $\frac{4}{3}$. Use $\frac{4}{3}$ because $\frac{4}{3} \cdot \frac{3}{4}h = 1 \cdot h = h$.

$$\frac{3}{4}h = 6$$

$$\frac{4}{3}\left(\frac{3}{4}h\right) = \frac{4}{3} \cdot 6 \qquad \text{Multiply by } \tfrac{4}{3}.$$

$$1 \cdot h = \frac{4}{3} \cdot \frac{6}{1} \qquad \text{Multiplicative inverse property}$$

$$h = 8 \qquad \text{Multiplicative identity property; multiply fractions.}$$

Check by substitution in the original equation. The solution set is $\{8\}$.

Work Problem 4 at the Side.

2 Use the multiplication property of equality to solve equations with decimals.

Example 4 Solving an Equation with Decimals

Solve $2.1x = 6.09$.

Divide each side by 2.1.

$$2.1x = 6.09$$

$$\frac{2.1x}{\mathbf{2.1}} = \frac{6.09}{\mathbf{2.1}}$$

You may use a calculator to simplify the work at this point.

$$x = 2.9 \qquad \text{Divide.}$$

Check that the solution set is $\{2.9\}$.

Work Problem 5 at the Side.

3 Solve.

(a) $\frac{y}{5} = 5$

(b) $\frac{p}{4} = -6$

4 Solve.

(a) $-\frac{5}{6}t = -15$

(b) $\frac{3}{4}k = -21$

5 Solve.

(a) $-.7m = -5.04$

(b) $12.5k = -63.75$

ANSWERS

3. (a) $\{25\}$ **(b)** $\{-24\}$
4. (a) $\{18\}$ **(b)** $\{-28\}$
5. (a) $\{7.2\}$ **(b)** $\{-5.1\}$

6 Solve.

(a) $4r - 9r = 20$

(b) $7m - 5m = -12$

7 Solve.

(a) $-m = 2$

(b) $-p = -7$

ANSWERS
6. **(a)** $\{-4\}$ **(b)** $\{-6\}$
7. **(a)** $\{-2\}$ **(b)** $\{7\}$

3 **Simplify equations, and then use the multiplication property of equality.** In the next example, it is necessary to simplify the equation before using the multiplication property of equality.

Example 5 **Simplifying an Equation**

Solve $5m + 6m = 33$.

$$5m + 6m = 33$$
$$11m = 33 \qquad \text{Combine terms.}$$
$$\frac{11m}{11} = \frac{33}{11} \qquad \text{Divide by 11.}$$
$$1m = 3 \qquad \text{Divide.}$$
$$m = 3 \qquad \text{Multiplicative identity property}$$

Check that the solution set is $\{3\}$.

Work Problem 6 at the Side.

4 **Use the multiplication property of equality to solve equations such as $-r = 4$.** The following example shows how to solve equations where the coefficient of the variable is understood to be -1.

Example 6 **Using the Multiplication Property of Equality When the Coefficient of the Variable Is −1**

Solve $-r = 4$.

On the left side, change $-r$ to r by first writing $-r$ as $-1 \cdot r$.

$$-r = 4$$
$$-1 \cdot r = 4 \qquad -r = -1 \cdot r$$
$$-1(-1 \cdot r) = -1 \cdot 4 \qquad \text{Multiply by } -1\text{, since } -1(-1) = 1.$$
$$[-1(-1)] \cdot r = -4 \qquad \text{Associative property}$$
$$1 \cdot r = -4 \qquad \text{Multiplicative inverse property}$$
$$r = -4 \qquad \text{Multiplicative identity property}$$

Check this solution.

Check:
$$-r = 4 \qquad \text{Original equation}$$
$$-(-4) = 4 \quad ? \qquad \text{Let } r = -4.$$
$$4 = 4 \qquad \text{True}$$

The solution, -4, checks, so the solution set is $\{-4\}$.

Work Problem 7 at the Side.

2.2 Exercises

FOR EXTRA HELP: Student's Solutions Manual; MyMathLab.com; InterAct Math Tutorial Software; AW Math Tutor Center; www.mathxl.com; Digital Video Tutor CD 2 Videotape 4

Solve each equation by inspection.

1. $3x = 12$
$\{4\}$

2. $4x = 36$
$\{9\}$

3. $\frac{1}{2}x = -4$
$\{-8\}$

4. $\frac{1}{3}x = -2$
$\{-6\}$

By what number is it necessary to multiply each side of each equation in order to obtain just x on the left side? Do not actually solve these equations.

5. $\frac{2}{3}x = 8$
$\frac{3}{2}$

6. $\frac{4}{5}x = 6$
$\frac{5}{4}$

7. $.1x = 3$
10

8. $.01x = 8$
100

9. $-\frac{9}{2}x = -4$
$-\frac{2}{9}$

10. $-\frac{8}{3}x = -11$
$-\frac{3}{8}$

11. $-x = .36$
-1

12. $-x = .29$
-1

By what number is it necessary to divide each side of each equation in order to obtain just x on the left side? Do not actually solve these equations.

13. $6x = 5$
6

14. $7x = 10$
7

15. $-4x = 13$
-4

16. $-13x = 6$
-13

17. $.12x = 48$
$.12$

18. $.21x = 63$
$.21$

19. $-x = 23$
-1

20. $-x = 49$
-1

21. In the statement of the multiplication property of equality in this section, there is a restriction that $C \neq 0$. What would happen if you multiplied each side of an equation by 0?

If each side of an equation were multiplied by 0, the resulting equation would be $0 = 0$. This is true, but does not help to solve the equation.

22. Which equation does not require the use of the multiplication property of equality?

A. $3x - 5x = 6$ **B.** $-\frac{1}{4}x = 12$ **C.** $5x - 4x = 7$ **D.** $\frac{x}{3} = -2$ C

Solve each equation, and check your solution. See Examples 1–6.

23. $2m = 15$
$\left\{\frac{15}{2}\right\}$

24. $3m = 10$
$\left\{\frac{10}{3}\right\}$

25. $3a = -15$
$\{-5\}$

26. $5k = -70$
$\{-14\}$

27. $10t = -36$
$\left\{-\frac{18}{5}\right\}$

28. $4s = -34$
$\left\{-\frac{17}{2}\right\}$

29. $-6x = -72$
$\{12\}$

30. $-8x = -64$
$\{8\}$

31. $2r = 0$

$\{0\}$

32. $5x = 0$

$\{0\}$

33. $-y = 12$

$\{-12\}$

34. $-t = 14$

$\{-14\}$

35. $.2t = 8$

$\{40\}$

36. $.9x = 18$

$\{20\}$

37. $\frac{1}{4}y = -12$

$\{-48\}$

38. $\frac{1}{5}p = -3$

$\{-15\}$

39. $\frac{x}{7} = -5$

$\{-35\}$

40. $\frac{k}{8} = -3$

$\{-24\}$

41. $-\frac{7}{9}c = \frac{3}{5}$

$\left\{-\frac{27}{35}\right\}$

42. $-\frac{5}{6}d = \frac{4}{9}$

$\left\{-\frac{8}{15}\right\}$

43. $4x + 3x = 21$

$\{3\}$

44. $9x + 2x = 121$

$\{11\}$

45. $3r - 5r = 10$

$\{-5\}$

46. $9p - 13p = 24$

$\{-6\}$

47. $5m + 6m - 2m = 63$

$\{7\}$

48. $11r - 5r + 6r = 168$

$\{14\}$

49. $5x + 2 = 8x + 8$

$\{-2\}$

50. $2y - 4 = 7y + 1$

$\{-1\}$

51. $9w - 5w + 3 = -w$

$\left\{-\frac{3}{5}\right\}$

52. $7 + 6k - 2k = 8$

$\left\{\frac{1}{4}\right\}$

53. Write an equation that requires the use of the multiplication property of equality, where each side must be multiplied by $\frac{2}{3}$, and the solution is a negative number.

Answers will vary. One example is $\frac{3}{2}x = -6$.

54. Write an equation that requires the use of the multiplication property of equality, where each side must be divided by 100, and the solution is not an integer.

Answers will vary. One example is $100x = 17$.

Write an equation using the information given in the problem. Use x to represent the number. Then solve the equation, and give the required number.

55. Three times a number is 18 more than five times the number. Find the number.

$3x = 18 + 5x$; -9; The number is -9.

56. If four times a number is added to three times the number, the result is the sum of five times the number and 10. Find the number.

$4x + 3x = 5x + 10$; 5; The number is 5.

2.3 More on Solving Linear Equations

1 Learn the four steps for solving a linear equation, and apply them. In this section, we use the addition and multiplication properties together to solve more complicated equations. We will use the following four-step method.

Solving Linear Equations

Step 1 **Simplify each side separately.** Clear parentheses using the distributive property, if needed, and combine terms.

Step 2 **Isolate the variable term on one side.** Use the addition property if necessary so that the variable term is on one side of the equation and a number is on the other.

Step 3 **Isolate the variable.** Use the multiplication property if necessary to get the equation in the form $x =$ a number.

Step 4 **Check.** Check the proposed solution by substituting into the *original* equation.

The check is used only to catch errors in carrying out the steps.

Example 1 Using the Four Steps to Solve an Equation

Solve the equation $3r + 4 - 2r - 7 = 4r + 3$.

We use the four steps described above.

Step 1

$$3r + 4 - 2r - 7 = 4r + 3$$

$$r - 3 = 4r + 3 \qquad \text{Combine terms.}$$

Step 2

$$r - 3 + 3 = 4r + 3 + 3 \qquad \text{Add 3.}$$

$$r = 4r + 6$$

$$r - 4r = 4r + 6 - 4r \qquad \text{Subtract } 4r.$$

$$-3r = 6 \qquad \text{Combine terms.}$$

Step 3

$$\frac{-3r}{-3} = \frac{6}{-3} \qquad \text{Divide by } -3.$$

$$r = -2 \qquad \tfrac{-3}{-3} = 1;\ 1r = r$$

Step 4 Substitute -2 for r in the original equation to check.

$$3r + 4 - 2r - 7 = 4r + 3$$

$$3(-2) + 4 - 2(-2) - 7 = 4(-2) + 3 \quad ? \quad \text{Let } r = -2.$$

$$-6 + 4 + 4 - 7 = -8 + 3 \quad ? \quad \text{Multiply.}$$

$$-5 = -5 \qquad \text{True}$$

The solution, -2, checks, so the solution set is $\{-2\}$.

NOTE

In Step 2 of Example 1, we added and subtracted the terms in such a way that the variable term ended up on the left side of the equation. Choosing differently would have put the variable term on the right side of the equation.

Work Problem 1 at the Side.

Objectives

1 Learn the four steps for solving a linear equation, and apply them.

2 Solve equations by clearing fractions and decimals.

1 Solve.

(a) $5y - 7y + 6y - 9 = 3 + 2y$

(b) $-3k - 5k - 6 + 11 = 2k - 5$

Answers

1. **(a)** $\{6\}$ **(b)** $\{1\}$

2 Solve.

(a) $7(p - 2) + p = 2p + 4$

(b) $3(m + 5) - 1 + 2m = 5(m + 2)$

Example 2 Using the Four Steps to Solve an Equation

Solve the equation $4(k - 3) - k = k - 6$.

Step 1

$$4(k - 3) - k = k - 6$$

$$4k - 12 - k = k - 6 \quad \text{Distributive property}$$

$$3k - 12 = k - 6 \quad \text{Combine terms.}$$

Step 2

$$3k - 12 + 12 = k - 6 + 12 \quad \text{Add 12.}$$

$$3k = k + 6 \quad \text{Combine terms.}$$

$$3k - k = k + 6 - k \quad \text{Subtract } k.$$

$$2k = 6 \quad \text{Combine terms.}$$

Step 3

$$\frac{2k}{2} = \frac{6}{2} \quad \text{Divide by 2.}$$

$$k = 3$$

Step 4 Check this answer by substituting 3 for k in the original equation. Remember to do all the work inside the parentheses first.

$$4(k - 3) - k = k - 6$$

$$4(3 - 3) - 3 = 3 - 6 \quad ? \quad \text{Let } k = 3.$$

$$4(0) - 3 = 3 - 6 \quad ? \quad 3 - 3 = 0$$

$$0 - 3 = 3 - 6 \quad ? \quad 4(0) = 0$$

$$-3 = -3 \quad \text{True}$$

The solution set is $\{3\}$.

Work Problem 2 at the Side.

Example 3 Using the Four Steps to Solve an Equation

Solve the equation $8a - (3 + 2a) = 3a + 1$.

Step 1 Simplify.

$$8a - (3 + 2a) = 3a + 1$$

$$8a - 1(3 + 2a) = 3a + 1 \quad \text{Multiplicative identity property}$$

$$8a - 3 - 2a = 3a + 1 \quad \text{Distributive property}$$

$$6a - 3 = 3a + 1 \quad \text{Combine terms.}$$

Step 2 First, add 3 to each side; then subtract $3a$.

$$6a - 3 + 3 = 3a + 1 + 3 \quad \text{Add 3.}$$

$$6a = 3a + 4 \quad \text{Combine terms.}$$

$$6a - 3a = 3a + 4 - 3a \quad \text{Subtract } 3a.$$

$$3a = 4 \quad \text{Combine terms.}$$

Step 3

$$\frac{3a}{3} = \frac{4}{3} \quad \text{Divide by 3.}$$

$$a = \frac{4}{3}$$

Step 4 Check that the solution set is $\{\frac{4}{3}\}$.

ANSWERS

2. **(a)** $\{3\}$ **(b)** $\emptyset$

CAUTION

Be very careful with signs when solving an equation like the one in Example 3. When clearing parentheses in the expression

$$8a - (3 + 2a),$$

remember that the $-$ sign acts like a factor of -1, changing the sign of *every* term in the parentheses. Thus,

$$8 - (3 + 2a) = 8 - 3 - 2a.$$

Change to $-$ in both terms.

Work Problem 3 at the Side.

3 Solve.

(a) $7m - (2m - 9) = 39$

(b) $4x + 2(3 - 2x) = 6$

Example 4 Using the Four Steps to Solve an Equation

Solve the equation $4(8 - 3t) = 32 - 8(t + 2)$.

Step 1

$$4(8 - 3t) = 32 - 8(t + 2)$$

$$32 - 12t = 32 - 8t - 16 \quad \text{Distributive property}$$

$$32 - 12t = 16 - 8t \quad \text{Combine terms.}$$

Step 2

$$32 - 12t - 32 = 16 - 8t - 32 \quad \text{Subtract 32.}$$

$$-12t = -16 - 8t \quad \text{Combine terms.}$$

$$-12t + 8t = -16 - 8t + 8t \quad \text{Add } 8t.$$

$$-4t = -16 \quad \text{Combine terms.}$$

Step 3

$$\frac{-4t}{-4} = \frac{-16}{-4} \quad \text{Divide by } -4.$$

$$t = 4$$

Step 4 Check this solution in the original equation.

$$4(8 - 3t) = 32 - 8(t + 2)$$

$$4(8 - 3 \cdot 4) = 32 - 8(4 + 2) \quad ? \quad \text{Let } t = 4.$$

$$4(8 - 12) = 32 - 8(6) \quad ?$$

$$4(-4) = 32 - 48 \quad ?$$

$$-16 = -16 \quad \text{True}$$

The solution, 4, checks, so the solution set is $\{4\}$.

Work Problem 4 at the Side.

4 Solve.

(a) $2(4 + 3r) = 3(r + 1) + 11$

(b) $2 - 3(2 + 6z) = 4(z + 1) + 18$

2 **Solve equations by clearing fractions and decimals.** We clear an equation of fractions by multiplying each side by the LCD of all the fractions in the equation. It is a good idea to do this before starting the four-step method to avoid working with fractions.

Example 5 Solving an Equation with Fractions as Coefficients

Solve $\frac{2}{3}x - \frac{1}{2}x = -\frac{1}{6}x - 2$.

The least common denominator of all the fractions in the equation is 6. Start by multiplying each side of the equation by 6.

Continued on Next Page

ANSWERS

3. (a) $\{6\}$ **(b)** {all real numbers}

4. (a) $\{2\}$ **(b)** $\left\{-\frac{13}{11}\right\}$

5 Solve $\frac{1}{4}x - 4 = \frac{3}{2}x + \frac{3}{4}x$.

$$\frac{2}{3}x - \frac{1}{2}x = -\frac{1}{6}x - 2$$

$$6\left(\frac{2}{3}x - \frac{1}{2}x\right) = 6\left(-\frac{1}{6}x - 2\right) \quad \text{Multiply by 6.}$$

$$6\left(\frac{2}{3}x\right) + 6\left(-\frac{1}{2}x\right) = 6\left(-\frac{1}{6}x\right) + 6(-2) \quad \text{Distributive property}$$

$$4x - 3x = -x - 12$$

Now use the four steps to solve this equivalent equation.

Step 1 $\quad x = -x - 12 \quad$ Combine terms.

Step 2 $\quad x + \mathbf{x} = -x - 12 + \mathbf{x} \quad$ Add x.

$\quad 2x = -12 \quad$ Combine terms.

Step 3 $\quad \frac{2x}{\mathbf{2}} = \frac{-12}{\mathbf{2}} \quad$ Divide by 2.

$\quad x = -6$

Step 4 Check by substituting -6 for x in the original equation.

$$\frac{2}{3}(-6) - \frac{1}{2}(-6) = -\frac{1}{6}(-6) - 2 \quad ? \quad \text{Let } x = -6.$$

$$-4 + 3 = 1 - 2 \quad ?$$

$$-1 = -1 \quad \text{True}$$

The solution set is $\{-6\}$.

CAUTION

When clearing an equation of fractions, be sure to multiply *every* term on each side of the equation by the LCD.

6 Solve $.06(100 - x) + .04x = .05(92)$.

Work Problem 5 at the Side.

The multiplication property is also used to clear an equation of decimals.

Example 6 Solving an Equation with Decimals as Coefficients

Solve $.1t + .05(20 - t) = .09(20)$.

The decimals are expressed as tenths and hundredths. Choose the smallest exponent on 10 needed to eliminate the decimals; in this case, use $10^2 = 100$. A number can be multiplied by 100 by moving the decimal point two places to the right.

$$\mathbf{.10}t + \mathbf{.05}(20 - t) = \mathbf{.09}(20) \quad .1 = .10$$

$$10t + 5(20 - t) = 9(20) \quad \text{Multiply by 100.}$$

Now use the four steps.

Step 1 $\quad 10t + 5(20) + 5(-t) = 180 \quad$ Distributive property

$\quad 10t + 100 - 5t = 180$

$\quad 5t + 100 = 180 \quad$ Combine terms.

Step 2 $\quad 5t + 100 - \mathbf{100} = 180 - \mathbf{100} \quad$ Subtract 100.

$\quad 5t = 80 \quad$ Combine terms.

Step 3 $\quad \frac{5t}{\mathbf{5}} = \frac{80}{\mathbf{5}} \quad$ Divide by 5.

$\quad t = 16$

Step 4 Check to see that $\{16\}$ is the solution set.

Work Problem 6 at the Side.

ANSWERS
5. $\{-2\}$
6. $\{70\}$

2.3 Exercises

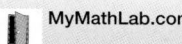

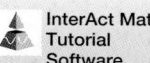

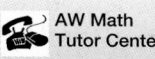

FOR EXTRA HELP: Student's Solutions Manual; MyMathLab.com; InterAct Math Tutorial Software; AW Math Tutor Center; www.mathxl.com; Digital Video Tutor CD 2 Videotape 4

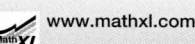

Solve each equation, and check your solution. See Examples 1–4.

1. $5m + 8 = 7 + 4m$
$\{-1\}$

2. $4r + 2 = 3r - 6$
$\{-8\}$

3. $10p + 6 = 12p - 4$
$\{5\}$

4. $-5x + 8 = -3x + 10$
$\{-1\}$

5. $7r - 5r + 2 = 5r - r$
$\{1\}$

6. $9p - 4p + 6 = 7p - 3p$
$\{-6\}$

7. $x + 3 = -(2x + 2)$
$\left\{-\frac{5}{3}\right\}$

8. $2x + 1 = -(x + 3)$
$\left\{-\frac{4}{3}\right\}$

9. $4(2x - 1) = -6(x + 3)$
$\{-1\}$

10. $6(3w + 5) = 2(10w + 10)$
$\{5\}$

11. $6(4x - 1) = 12(2x + 3)$
$\emptyset$

12. $6(2x + 8) = 4(3x - 6)$
$\emptyset$

13. $3(2x - 4) = 6(x - 2)$
{all real numbers}

14. $3(6 - 4x) = 2(-6x + 9)$
{all real numbers}

15. After correctly working through several steps of the solution of a linear equation, a student obtains the equation $7x = 3x$. Then the student divides each side by x to get $7 = 3$ and gives $\emptyset$ as the solution set. Is this correct? If not, explain why.

No, it is incorrect to divide each side by a variable. If $-3x$ is added to each side, the equation becomes $4x = 0$, so $x = 0$ is the correct solution, and $\{0\}$ is the correct solution set.

16. Which linear equation does *not* have {all real numbers} as its solution set?

A. $5x = 4x + x$ **B.** $2(x + 6) = 2x + 12$ **C.** $\frac{1}{2}x = .5x$ **D.** $3x = 2x$

D

17. Explain in your own words the major steps used in solving a linear equation that does not contain fractions or decimals as coefficients.

Simplify each side separately. Use the addition property to get all variable terms on one side of the equation and all numbers on the other, then combine terms. Use the multiplication property to get the equation in the form x = a number. Check the solution.

18. Explain in your own words the major steps used in solving a linear equation that contains fractions or decimals as coefficients.

Multiply both sides by the LCD of all fractions in the equation or by the power of 10 that makes all decimal coefficients whole numbers. Then follow the steps outlined in the answer for Exercise 17.

Solve each equation by first clearing it of fractions or decimals. See Examples 5 and 6.

19. $-\frac{2}{7}r + 2r = \frac{1}{2}r + \frac{17}{2}$

{7}

20. $\frac{3}{5}t - \frac{1}{10}t = t - \frac{5}{2}$

{5}

21. $\frac{1}{9}(y + 18) + \frac{1}{3}(2y + 3) = y + 3$

{0}

22. $-\frac{1}{4}(x - 12) + \frac{1}{2}(x + 2) = x + 4$

{0}

23. $-\frac{5}{6}q - \left(q - \frac{1}{2}\right) = \frac{1}{4}(q + 1)$

$\left\{\frac{3}{25}\right\}$

24. $\frac{2}{3}k - \left(k + \frac{1}{4}\right) = \frac{1}{12}(k + 4)$

$\left\{-\frac{7}{5}\right\}$

25. $.30(30) + .15x = .20(30 + x)$

{60}

26. $.20(60) + .05x = .10(60 + x)$

{120}

27. $.92x + .98(12 - x) = .96(12)$

{4}

28. $1.00x + .05(12 - x) = .10(63)$

{6}

29. $.02(5000) + .03x = .025(5000 + x)$

{5000}

30. $.06(10{,}000) + .08x = .072(10{,}000 + x)$

{15,000}

Relating Concepts (Exercises 31–36) For Individual or Group Work

Work Exercises 31–36 in order.

31. Evaluate the term $100ab$ for $a = 2$ and $b = 4$.

800

32. Will you get the same answer as in Exercise 31 if you evaluate $(100a)b$ for $a = 2$ and $b = 4$? Why or why not?

Yes, you will get $(100 \cdot 2) \cdot 4 = 800$. This is a result of the associative property of multiplication.

33. Is the term $(100a)(100b)$ equivalent to $100ab$? Why or why not?

No, because $(100a)(100b) = 10{,}000ab \neq 100ab$.

34. If your answer to Exercise 33 is *no,* explain why the distributive property is not involved.

The distributive property involves the operation of addition as well.

35. The simplest way to solve the equation $.05(x + 2) + .10x = 2.00$ is to begin by multiplying each side by 100. If we do this, the first term on the left becomes $100(.05)(x + 2)$. Is this expression equivalent to $[100(.05)](x + 2)$? Explain. (*Hint:* Compare to Exercises 31 and 32 with $a = .05$ and $b = x + 2$.)

Yes; the associative property of multiplication is used.

36. Students often want to "distribute" the 100 to both .05 and $(x + 2)$ in the expression $100(.05)(x + 2)$. Is this correct? (*Hint:* See Exercises 34 and 35.)

no

Solve each equation, and check your solution. See Examples 1–6.

37. $-3(5z + 24) + 2 = 2(3 - 2z) - 4$

$\left\{-\frac{72}{11}\right\}$

38. $-2(2s - 4) - 8 = -3(4s + 4) - 1$

$\left\{-\frac{13}{8}\right\}$

39. $-(6k - 5) - (-5k + 8) = -3$

$\{0\}$

40. $-(4y + 2) - (-3y - 5) = 3$

$\{0\}$

41. $\frac{1}{3}(x + 3) + \frac{1}{6}(x - 6) = x + 3$

$\{-6\}$

42. $\frac{1}{2}(x + 2) + \frac{3}{4}(x + 4) = x + 5$

$\{4\}$

43. $.30(x + 15) + .40(x + 25) = 25$

$\{15\}$

44. $.10(x + 80) + .20x = 14$

$\{20\}$

45. $4(x + 3) = 2(2x + 8) - 4$

{all real numbers}

46. $4(x + 8) = 2(2x + 6) + 20$

{all real numbers}

47. $8(t - 3) + 4t = 6(2t + 1) - 10$

$\emptyset$

48. $9(v + 1) - 3v = 2(3v + 1) - 8$

$\emptyset$

Write the answer to each problem as an algebraic expression.

49. Two numbers have a sum of 12. One number is q. Find the other number.

$12 - q$

50. The product of two numbers is 13. One number is k. What is the other number?

$\frac{13}{k}$

51. A bank teller has t dollars in ten-dollar bills. How many ten-dollar bills does the teller have?

$\frac{t}{10}$

52. A plane ticket costs b dollars for an adult and d dollars for a child. Find the total cost of 5 adult and 3 child tickets.

$5b + 3d$

2.4 An Introduction to Applications of Linear Equations

Objectives

1. Learn the six steps for solving applied problems.
2. Solve problems involving unknown numbers.
3. Solve problems involving sums of quantities.
4. Solve problems involving supplementary and complementary angles.
5. Solve problems involving consecutive integers.

1 Learn the six steps for solving applied problems. We now look at how algebra is used to solve applied problems. It must be emphasized that many *meaningful* applications of mathematics require concepts that are beyond the level of this book. Some of the problems you will encounter will seem "contrived," and to some extent they are. But the skills you will develop in solving simple problems will help you in solving more realistic problems in chemistry, physics, biology, business, and other fields.

In earlier sections we learned how to translate words, phrases, and sentences into mathematical expressions and equations. Now we will use these translations to solve applied problems using algebra. While there is no specific method that enables you to solve all kinds of applied problems, the following six-step method is suggested.

Solving an Applied Problem

Step 1 **Read** the problem carefully until you understand what is given and what is to be found.

Step 2 **Assign a variable** to represent the unknown value, using diagrams or tables as needed. Write down what the variable represents. If necessary, express any other unknown values in terms of the variable.

Step 3 **Write an equation** using the variable expression(s).

Step 4 **Solve** the equation.

Step 5 **State the answer.** Does it seem reasonable?

Step 6 **Check** the answer in the words of the *original* problem.

The third step in solving an applied problem is often the hardest. Begin to translate the problem into an equation by writing the given phrases as mathematical expressions. In transforming an applied problem into an algebraic equation, replace any words that mean *equal* or *same* with an = sign. Other forms of the verb "to be," such as *is, are, was,* and *were,* also translate this way. The = sign leads to an equation to be solved.

2 Solve problems involving unknown numbers. Some of the simplest applied problems involve unknown numbers.

Example 1 Finding the Value of an Unknown Number

The product of 4, and a number decreased by 7, is 100. What is the number?

Step 1 **Read** the problem carefully. Decide what you are being asked to find.

Step 2 **Assign a variable** to represent the unknown quantity. In this problem, we are asked to find a number, so we write

$$\text{Let } x = \text{the number.}$$

There are no other unknown quantities to find.

Continued on Next Page

1 Use the six steps to solve the problem. Give the equation, using x as the variable, and give the answer.

If 5 is added to the product of 9 and a number, the result is 19 less than the number. Find the number.

Step 3 **Write an equation.**

The product of 4,	and	a number	decreased by	7,	is	100.
$4 \cdot$		$(x$	$-$	$7)$	$=$	100

Because of the commas in the given problem, writing the equation as $4x - 7 = 100$ is incorrect. The equation $4x - 7 = 100$ corresponds to the statement "The product of 4 and a number, decreased by 7, is 100."

Step 4 **Solve** the equation.

$$4(x - 7) = 100$$
$$4x - 28 = 100 \quad \text{Distributive property}$$
$$4x - 28 + 28 = 100 + 28 \quad \text{Add 28.}$$
$$4x = 128 \quad \text{Combine terms.}$$
$$x = 32 \quad \text{Divide by 4.}$$

Step 5 **State the answer.** The number is 32.

Step 6 **Check.** When 32 is decreased by 7, we get $32 - 7 = 25$. If 4 is multiplied by 25, we get 100, as required. The answer, 32, is correct.

Work Problem 1 at the Side.

3 Solve problems involving sums of quantities. A common type of problem in elementary algebra involves finding two quantities when the sum of the quantities is known.

In general, to solve such problems, choose a variable to represent one of the unknowns and then represent the other quantity in terms of the same variable, using information contained in the problem. Then write an equation based on the words of the problem. The next example illustrates these ideas.

Example 2 Finding the Numbers of Olympic Medals Won by the United States

In the 2000 Olympics, U.S. contestants won 14 more gold than silver medals. They won a total of 64 gold and silver medals. How many of each type medal were won? (*Source:* United States Olympic Committee.)

Step 1 **Read** the problem. We are given information about the total number of gold and silver medals, and we are asked to find the number of each kind.

Step 2 **Assign a variable.**

Let $x =$ the number of silver medals.

Then $x + 14 =$ the number of gold medals.

Step 3 **Write an equation.**

The total	is	the number of silver	plus	the number of gold.
64	$=$	x	$+$	$(x + 14)$

Continued on Next Page

ANSWERS
1. $9x + 5 = x - 19$; -3

Step 4 **Solve** the equation.

$$64 = 2x + 14 \qquad \text{Combine terms.}$$
$$64 - 14 = 2x + 14 - 14 \qquad \text{Subtract 14.}$$
$$50 = 2x \qquad \text{Combine terms.}$$
$$25 = x \qquad \text{Divide by 2.}$$

Step 5 **State the answer.** Because x represents the number of silver medals, the U.S. athletes won 25 silver medals. Because $x + 14$ represents the number of gold medals, they won $25 + 14 = 39$ gold medals.

Step 6 **Check.** Since there were 39 gold and 25 silver medals, the total number of medals was $39 + 25 = 64$. Because $39 - 25 = 14$, there were 14 more gold medals than silver medals. This information agrees with what is given in the problem, so the answers check.

Work Problem 2 at the Side.

2 Solve the problem.

On one day of their vacation, Annie drove three times as far as Jim. Altogether they drove 84 mi that day. Find the number of miles driven by each.

NOTE

The problem in Example 2 could also have been solved by letting x represent the number of gold medals. Then $x - 14$ would represent the number of silver medals. The equation would then be

$$64 = x + (x - 14).$$

The solution of this equation is 39, which is the number of gold medals. The number of silver medals would then be $39 - 14 = 25$. The answers are the same, whichever approach is used.

Sometimes it is necessary to find three unknown quantities in an applied problem. Frequently the three unknowns are compared in *pairs.* When this happens, it is usually easiest to let the variable represent the unknown found in both pairs. The next example illustrates this.

Example 3 **Dividing a Board into Pieces**

The instructions for a woodworking project call for three pieces of wood. The longest piece must be twice the length of the middle-sized piece, and the shortest piece must be 10 in. shorter than the middle-sized piece. Maria Gonzales has a board 70 in. long that she wishes to use. How long can each piece be?

Step 1 **Read** the problem. There will be three answers.

Step 2 **Assign a variable.** Since the middle-sized piece appears in both pairs of comparisons, let x represent the length, in inches, of the middle-sized piece. We have

$$x = \text{the length of the middle-sized piece,}$$
$$2x = \text{the length of the longest piece, and}$$
$$x - 10 = \text{the length of the shortest piece.}$$

A sketch is helpful here. See Figure 1.

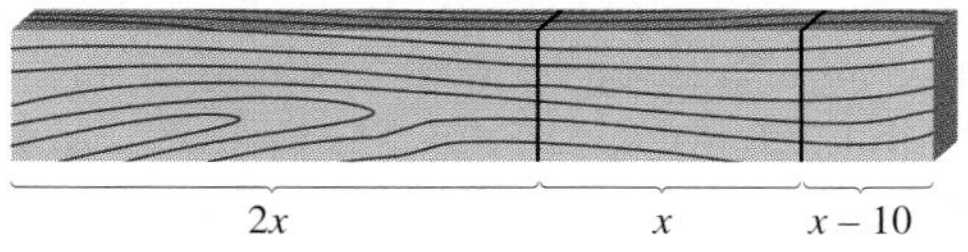

Figure 1

Continued on Next Page

ANSWERS

2. Jim: 21 mi; Annie: 63 mi

3 Solve the problem.
A piece of pipe is 50 in. long. It is cut into three pieces. The longest piece is 10 in. more than the middle-sized piece, and the shortest piece measures 5 in. less than the middle-sized piece. Find the lengths of the three pieces.

4 Solve the problem.
At a meeting of the local stamp club, each member brought two nonmembers. If a total of 27 people attended, how many were members and how many were nonmembers?

ANSWERS
3. longest: 25 in.
middle: 15 in.
shortest: 10 in.
4. members: 9; nonmembers: 18

Step 3 **Write an equation.**

Longest		Middle-sized		Shortest	is	Total length
$2x$	$+$	x	$+$	$(x - 10)$	$=$	70

Step 4 **Solve.**

$$4x - 10 = 70 \quad \text{Combine terms.}$$
$$4x - 10 + \mathbf{10} = 70 + \mathbf{10} \quad \text{Add 10.}$$
$$4x = 80 \quad \text{Combine terms.}$$
$$x = 20 \quad \text{Divide by 4.}$$

Step 5 **State the answer.** The middle-sized piece is 20 in. long, the longest piece is $2(20) = 40$ in. long, and the shortest piece is $20 - 10 = 10$ in. long.

Step 6 **Check.** The sum of the lengths is 70 in. All conditions of the problem are satisfied.

Work Problem 3 at the Side.

Example 4 Analyzing a Gasoline/Oil Mixture

A lawn trimmer uses a mixture of gasoline and oil. The mixture contains 16 oz of gasoline for each ounce of oil. If the tank holds 68 oz of the mixture, how many ounces of oil and how many ounces of gasoline does it require when it is full?

Step 1 **Read** the problem. We must find how many ounces of oil and gasoline are needed to fill the tank.

Step 2 **Assign a variable.** Let x = the number of ounces of oil required. Then $16x$ = the number of ounces of gasoline required.

Step 3 **Write an equation.**

Amount of gasoline		Amount of oil	is	Total amount in tank
$16x$	$+$	x	$=$	68

Step 4 **Solve.**

$$17x = 68 \quad \text{Combine terms.}$$
$$x = 4 \quad \text{Divide by 17.}$$

Step 5 **State the answer.** The lawn trimmer requires 4 oz of oil and $16(4) = 64$ oz of gasoline when full.

Step 6 **Check.** Since $4 + 64 = 68$, and 64 is 16 times 4, the answers check.

Work Problem 4 at the Side.

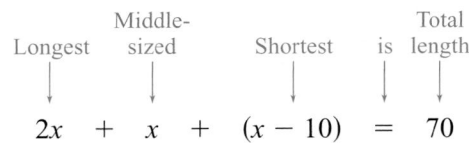

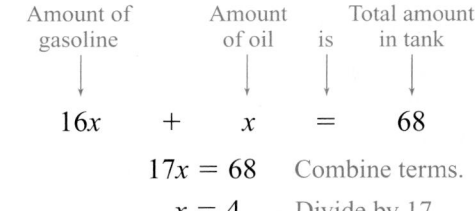

4 **Solve problems involving supplementary and complementary angles.** The next example deals with concepts from geometry. An angle can be measured by a unit called the degree (°). Two angles whose sum is 90° are said to be **complementary,** or complements of each other. An angle that measures 90° is a **right angle.** Two angles whose sum is 180° are said to be **supplementary,** or supplements of each other. One angle *supplements* the other to form a **straight angle** of 180°. See Figure 2. If x represents the degree measure of an angle, then

$90 - x$ represents the degree measure of its complement, and

$180 - x$ represents the degree measure of its supplement.

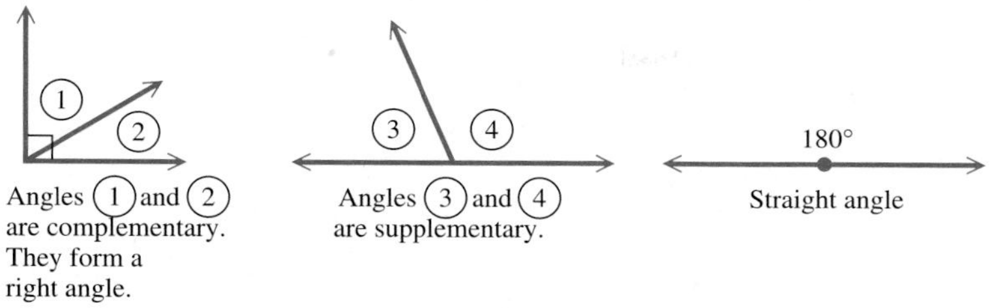

Figure 2

Example 5 Finding the Measure of an Angle

Find the measure of an angle whose supplement is 10° more than twice its complement.

Step 1 **Read** the problem. We are to find the measure of an angle, given information about its complement and its supplement.

Step 2 **Assign a variable.**

Let x = the degree measure of the angle.

Then $90 - x$ = the degree measure of its complement;

$180 - x$ = the degree measure of its supplement.

Step 3 **Write an equation.**

Supplement	is	10	more than	twice		its complement.
↓	↓	↓	↓	↓		↓
$180 - x$	$=$	10	$+$	2	$\cdot$	$(90 - x)$

Step 4 **Solve.**

$$180 - x = 10 + 180 - 2x \quad \text{Distributive property}$$
$$180 - x = 190 - 2x \quad \text{Combine terms.}$$
$$180 - x + \mathbf{2x} = 190 - 2x + \mathbf{2x} \quad \text{Add } 2x.$$
$$180 + x = 190 \quad \text{Combine terms.}$$
$$180 + x - \mathbf{180} = 190 - \mathbf{180} \quad \text{Subtract 180.}$$
$$x = 10$$

Step 5 **State the answer.** The measure of the angle is 10°.

Step 6 **Check.** The complement of 10° is 80° and the supplement of 10° is 170°. 170° is equal to 10° more than twice 80° ($170 = 10 + 2(80)$ is true); therefore, the answer is correct.

Work Problem 5 at the Side.

5 Solve problems involving consecutive integers. Two integers that differ by 1 are called **consecutive integers.** For example, 3 and 4, 6 and 7, and -2 and -1 are pairs of consecutive integers. In general, if x represents an integer, $x + 1$ represents the next larger consecutive integer.

Consecutive *even* integers, such as 8 and 10, differ by 2. Similarly, consecutive *odd* integers, such as 9 and 11, also differ by two. In general, if x represents an even integer, $x + 2$ represents the next larger consecutive even integer. The same holds true for odd integers; that is, if x is an odd integer, $x + 2$ is the next larger odd integer.

5 Find each angle measure.

(a) The supplement of an angle that measures 92°

(b) An angle whose complement has twice its measure

(c) An angle such that twice its complement is 30° less than its supplement

ANSWERS
5. (a) 88° **(b)** 30° **(c)** 30°

6 Solve the problem.
Find two consecutive integers whose sum is -45.

7 Solve the problem.
Find two consecutive even integers such that six times the smaller added to the larger gives a sum of 86.

Example 6 Finding Consecutive Integers

Two pages that face each other in this book have 569 as the sum of their page numbers. What are the page numbers?

Step 1 **Read** the problem. Because the two pages face each other, they must have page numbers that are consecutive integers.

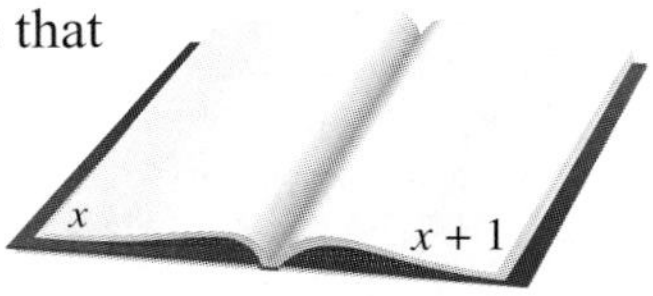

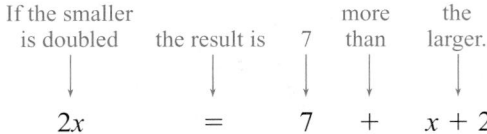

Step 2 **Assign a variable.**

Let $x =$ the smaller page number.

Then $x + 1 =$ the larger page number.

Step 3 **Write an equation.** Because the sum of the page numbers is 569, the equation is

$$x + (x + 1) = 569.$$

Step 4 **Solve.**

$$x + (x + 1) = 569$$
$$2x + 1 = 569 \quad \text{Combine terms.}$$
$$2x = 568 \quad \text{Subtract 1.}$$
$$x = 284 \quad \text{Divide by 2.}$$

Step 5 **State the answer.** The smaller page number is 284, and the larger page number is $284 + 1 = 285$.

Step 6 **Check.** The sum of 284 and 285 is 569. The answers are correct.

Work Problem 6 at the Side.

In the final example, we do not number the steps. See if you can identify them.

Example 7 Finding Consecutive Odd Integers

If the smaller of two consecutive odd integers is doubled, the result is 7 more than the larger of the two integers. Find the two integers.

Let x be the smaller integer. Since the two numbers are consecutive *odd* integers, then $x + 2$ is the larger. Now write an equation.

If the smaller is doubled	the result is	7	more than	the larger.
↓	↓	↓	↓	↓
$2x$	$=$	7	$+$	$x + 2$

Solve the equation.

$$2x = 7 + x + 2$$
$$2x = 9 + x \quad \text{Combine terms.}$$
$$2x - x = 9 + x - x \quad \text{Subtract } x.$$
$$x = 9 \quad \text{Combine terms.}$$

The first integer is 9 and the second is $9 + 2 = 11$. To check the answers, we see that when 9 is doubled, we get 18, which is 7 more than the larger odd integer, 11. The answers are correct.

Work Problem 7 at the Side.

ANSWERS
6. $-23, -22$
7. 12, 14

2.4 EXERCISES

FOR EXTRA HELP Student's Solutions Manual | MyMathLab.com | InterAct Math Tutorial Software | AW Math Tutor Center | www.mathxl.com | Digital Video Tutor CD 2 Videotape 5

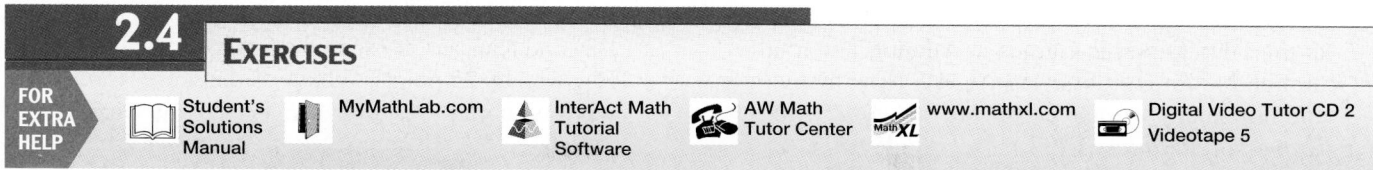

1. In your own words, write the general procedure for solving applications as outlined in this section.

The procedure should include the following steps: read the problem carefully; assign a variable to represent the unknown to be found; write down variable expressions for any other unknown quantities; translate into an equation; solve the equation; state the answer; check your solution.

2. List some of the words that translate as "=" when writing an equation to solve an applied problem.

Some examples are *is, are, were,* and *was.*

3. Suppose that a problem requires you to find the number of cars on a dealer's lot. Which one of the following would not be a reasonable answer? Justify your answer.

A. 0 **B.** 45 **C.** 1 **D.** $6\frac{1}{2}$

D; there cannot be a fractional number of cars.

4. Suppose that a problem requires you to find the number of hours a light bulb is on during a day. Which one of the following would not be a reasonable answer? Justify your answer.

A. 0 **B.** 4.5 **C.** 13 **D.** 25

D; a day cannot have more than 24 hr.

Solve each problem. See Example 1.

5. If 2 is subtracted from a number and this difference is tripled, the result is 6 more than the number. Find the number. **6**

6. If 3 is added to a number and this sum is doubled, the result is 2 more than the number. Find the number. **−4**

7. The sum of three times a number and 7 more than the number is the same as the difference between −11 and twice the number. What is the number? **−3**

8. If 4 is added to twice a number and this sum is multiplied by 2, the result is the same as if the number is multiplied by 3 and 4 is added to the product. What is the number? **−4**

Solve each problem. See Examples 2–4.

9. The U.S. Senate has 100 members. During the 106th session (1999–2001), there were 10 more Republicans than Democrats. How many Democrats and Republicans were there in the Senate? (*Source: The World Almanac and Book of Facts,* 2000.) **45 Democrats; 55 Republicans**

10. The total number of Democrats and Republicans in the U.S. House of Representatives during the 106th session was 434. There were 12 fewer Democrats than Republicans. How many members of each party were there? (*Source: The World Almanac and Book of Facts,* 2000.)

211 Democrats; 223 Republicans

11. There were 2783 more men than women competing in the 1996 Olympic Games in Atlanta. The total number of competitors was 10,341. How many men and how many women competed? (*Source: The Universal Almanac,* 1997.)

6562 men; 3779 women

12. In the first NFL Championship, played in 1967, Green Bay and Kansas City scored a total of 45 points. Green Bay won by 25 points. What was the score? (*Source:* www.nfl.com.) **Green Bay: 35; Kansas City: 10**

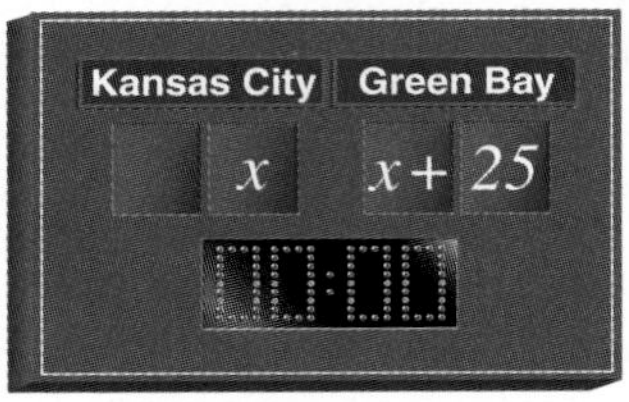

13. The largest recorded dog is an English mastiff named Zorba, who weighs 63 lb more than an average lioness. The sum of the two animals' weights is 623 lb. How much do the dog and the lioness each weigh? (*Source: The Guinness Book of Records,* 1996.) **dog: 343 lb; lioness: 280 lb**

14. In the 1998 U.S. Senior Open, Hale Irwin finished with a score of 1 more than the winner, Vicente Fernandez. The sum of their scores was 571. Find their scores. (*Source:* Television coverage.)
Fernandez: 285; Irwin: 286

15. In one day, Akilah Cadet received 13 packages. Federal Express delivered three times as many as Airborne Express, while United Parcel Service delivered 2 fewer than Airborne Express. How many packages did each service deliver to Akilah?

Airborne Express: 3; Federal Express: 9; United Parcel Service: 1

16. In his job at the post office, Eddie Thibodeaux works a 6.5-hr day. He sorts mail, sells stamps, and does supervisory work. One day he sold stamps twice as long as he sorted mail, and he supervised .5 hr longer than he sorted mail. How many hours did he spend at each task?

sorting mail: 1.5 hr; selling stamps: 3 hr; supervising: 2 hr

17. Venus is 31.2 million mi farther from the sun than Mercury, while Earth is 57 million mi farther from the sun than Mercury. If the total of the distances from these three planets to the sun is 196.2 million mi, how far away from the sun is Mercury? (All distances given here are *mean* (*average*) distances.) (*Source: The Universal Almanac,* 1997.)

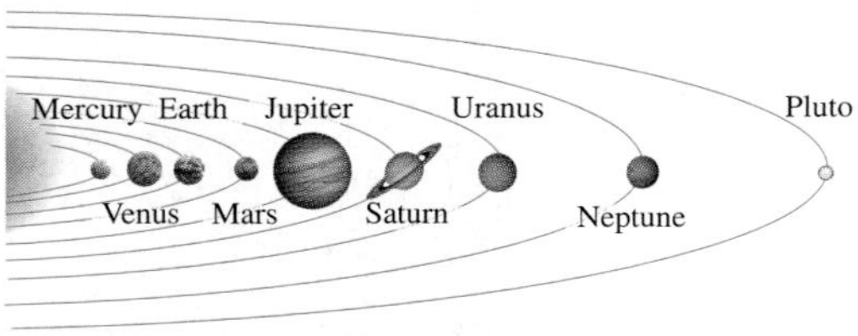

36 million mi

18. Together, Saturn, Jupiter, and Mars have a total of 36 known satellites (moons). Jupiter has 2 fewer satellites than Saturn, and Mars has 16 fewer satellites than Saturn. How many known satellites does Mars have? (*Source: The World Almanac and Book of Facts,* 2000.) **2**

19. The sum of the measures of the angles of any triangle is 180°. In triangle ABC, angles A and B have the same measure, while the measure of angle C is 60° larger than each of A and B. What are the measures of the three angles? **A and B: 40°; C: 100°**

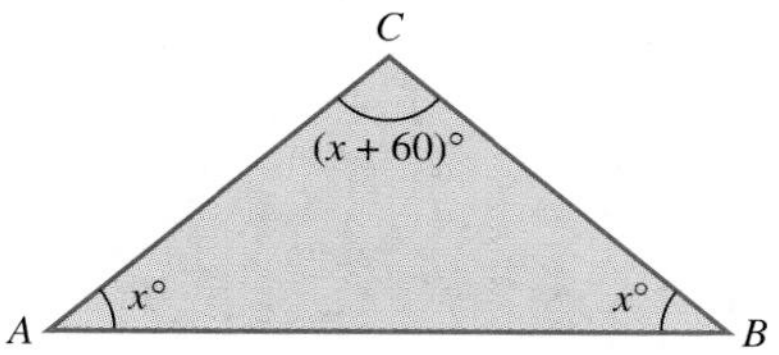

20. Nagaraj Nanjappa has a party-length submarine sandwich 59 in. long. He wants to cut it into three pieces so that the middle piece is 5 in. longer than the shortest piece and the shortest piece is 9 in. shorter than the longest piece. How long should the three pieces be?

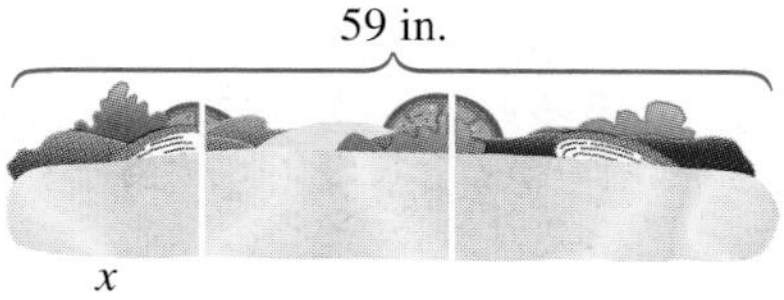

shortest piece: 15 in.; middle piece: 20 in.; longest piece: 24 in.

Solve each problem. See Example 4.

21. The September 11, 2000, issue of *Coin World* listed the value of a "Mint State-65" (uncirculated) 1950 Jefferson nickel minted at Denver as $\frac{7}{6}$ the value of a similar condition 1945 nickel minted at Philadelphia. Together the total value of the two coins is \$26.00. What is the value of each coin?

1950 Denver nickel: \$14.00; 1945 Philadelphia nickel: \$12.00

22. The largest sheep ranch in the world is located in Australia. The number of sheep on the ranch is $\frac{8}{3}$ the number of uninvited kangaroos grazing on the pastureland. Together, herds of these two animals number 88,000. How many sheep and how many kangaroos roam the ranch? (*Source: The Guinness Book of Records,* 1996.)

sheep: 64,000; kangaroos: 24,000

23. In 1988, a dairy in Alberta, Canada, created a sundae with approximately 1 lb of topping for every 83.2 lb of ice cream. The total of the two ingredients weighed approximately 45,225 lb. To the nearest tenth of a pound, how many pounds of ice cream and how many pounds of topping were there? (*Source: The Guinness Book of Records,* 1996.)

ice cream: 44,687.9 lb; topping: 537.1 lb

24. A husky running the Iditarod (a thousand-mile race between Anchorage and Nome, Alaska) burns $5\frac{3}{8}$ calories in exertion for every 1 calorie burned in thermoregulation in extreme cold. According to one scientific study, a husky in top condition burns an amazing total of 11,200 calories per day. How many calories are burned for exertion, and how many are burned for regulation of body temperature? Round answers to the nearest whole number.

exertion: 9443; regulating body temperature: 1757

Solve each problem. See Example 5.

25. Find the measure of an angle whose complement is four times its measure. **18°**

26. Find the measure of an angle whose supplement is three times its measure. **45°**

27. Find the measure of an angle whose supplement measures 39° more than twice its complement.

39°

28. Find the measure of an angle whose supplement measures 38° less than three times its complement.

26°

29. Find the measure of an angle such that the difference between the measures of its supplement and three times its complement is 10°. **50°**

30. Find the measure of an angle such that the sum of the measures of its complement and its supplement is 160°. **55°**

Solve each problem. See Examples 6 and 7.

31. The numbers on two consecutively numbered gym lockers have a sum of 137. What are the locker numbers? **68, 69**

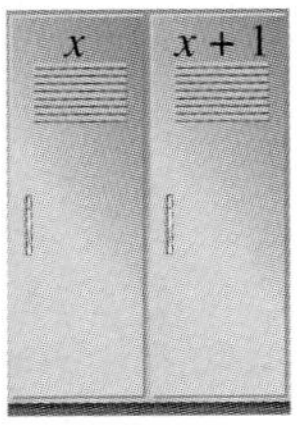

32. The sum of two consecutive checkbook check numbers is 357. Find the numbers. **178, 179**

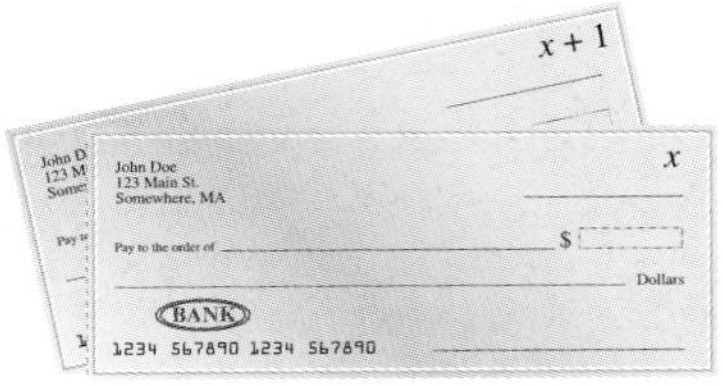

33. Find two consecutive even integers such that the smaller added to three times the larger gives a sum of 46. **10, 12**

34. Find two consecutive odd integers such that twice the larger is 17 more than the smaller. **13, 15**

35. Two pages that are back-to-back in this book have 203 as the sum of their page numbers. What are the page numbers? **101, 102**

36. Two houses on the same side of the street have house numbers that are consecutive even integers. The sum of the integers is 58. What are the two house numbers? **28, 30**

37. When the smaller of two consecutive integers is added to three times the larger, the result is 43. Find the integers. **10, 11**

38. If five times the smaller of two consecutive integers is added to three times the larger, the result is 59. Find the integers. **7, 8**

Apply the ideas of this section to solve Exercises 39 and 40, based on the graphs.

39. In a recent year, the funding for Head Start programs increased by .55 billion dollars from the funding in the previous year. The following year, the increase was .20 billion dollars more. For those three years, the total funding was 9.64 billion dollars. How much was funded in each of these years? (*Source:* U.S. Department of Health and Human Services.) **\$2.78 billion, \$3.33 billion, \$3.53 billion**

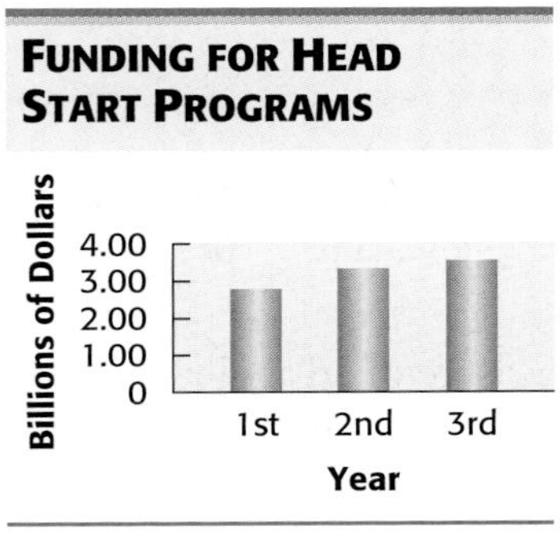

40. According to data provided by the National Safety Council for a recent year, the number of serious injuries per 100,000 participants in football, bicycling, and golf is illustrated in the graph. There were 800 more in bicycling than in golf, and there were 1267 more in football than in bicycling. Altogether there were 3179 serious injuries per 100,000 participants. How many such serious injuries were there in each sport? **football: 2171; bicycling: 904; golf: 104**

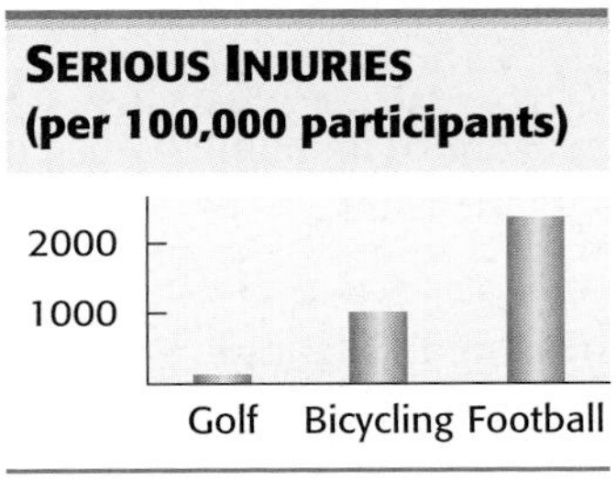

2.5 FORMULAS AND APPLICATIONS FROM GEOMETRY

OBJECTIVES

1. Solve a formula for one variable, given the values of the other variables.
2. Use a formula to solve an applied problem.
3. Solve problems involving vertical angles and straight angles.
4. Solve a formula for a specified variable.

Many applied problems can be solved with formulas. For example, formulas exist for geometric figures such as squares and circles, for distance, for money earned on bank savings, and for converting English measurements to metric measurements. The formulas used in this book are given on the inside covers.

1 Solve a formula for one variable, given the values of the other variables. Given the values of all but one of the variables in a formula, we can find the value of the remaining variable by using the methods introduced in this chapter.

In Example 1, we use the idea of *area*. The **area** of a plane (two-dimensional) geometric figure is a measure of the surface covered by the figure.

Example 1 Using a Formula to Evaluate a Variable

Find the value of the remaining variable in each formula.

(a) $A = LW$; $A = 64$, $L = 10$

As shown in Figure 3, this formula gives the area of a rectangle with length L and width W.

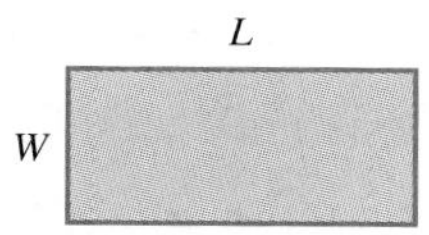

Rectangle
$A = LW$

Figure 3

Substitute the given values into the formula and then solve for W.

$$A = LW$$

$$64 = 10W \quad \text{Let } A = 64 \text{ and } L = 10.$$

$$6.4 = W \quad \text{Divide by 10.}$$

Check that the width of the rectangle is 6.4.

(b) $A = \frac{1}{2}h(b + B)$; $A = 210$, $B = 27$, $h = 10$

This formula gives the area of a trapezoid with parallel sides of lengths b and B and distance h between the parallel sides. See Figure 4.

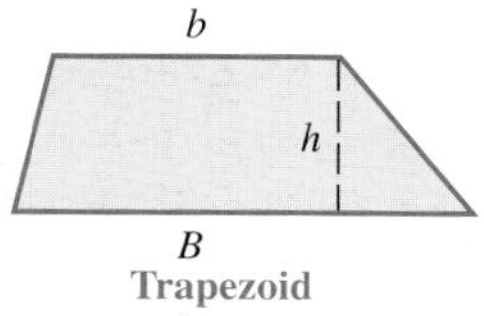

Trapezoid
$A = \frac{1}{2}h(b + B)$

Figure 4

Again, begin by substituting the given values into the formula.

$$A = \frac{1}{2}h(b + B)$$

$$210 = \frac{1}{2}(10)(b + 27) \quad A = 210, h = 10, B = 27$$

Continued on Next Page

Now solve for b.

$$210 = 5(b + 27) \quad \text{Multiply.}$$
$$210 = 5b + 135 \quad \text{Distributive property}$$
$$210 - \mathbf{135} = 5b + 135 - \mathbf{135} \quad \text{Subtract 135.}$$
$$75 = 5b \quad \text{Combine terms.}$$
$$\frac{75}{\mathbf{5}} = \frac{5b}{\mathbf{5}} \quad \text{Divide by 5.}$$
$$15 = b$$

Check that the length of the shorter parallel side, b, is 15.

Work Problem 1 at the Side.

2 Use a formula to solve an applied problem. As the next examples show, formulas are often used to solve applied problems. *It is a good idea to draw a sketch when a geometric figure is involved.* Example 2 uses the idea of *perimeter.* The **perimeter** of a plane (two-dimensional) geometric figure is the distance around the figure, that is, the sum of the lengths of its sides. We use the six steps introduced in the previous section.

Example 2 Finding the Width of a Rectangular Lot

A rectangular lot has perimeter 80 m and length 25 m. Find the width of the lot.

Step 1 **Read.** We are told to find the width of the lot.

Step 2 **Assign a variable.** Let W = the width of the lot in meters. See Figure 5.

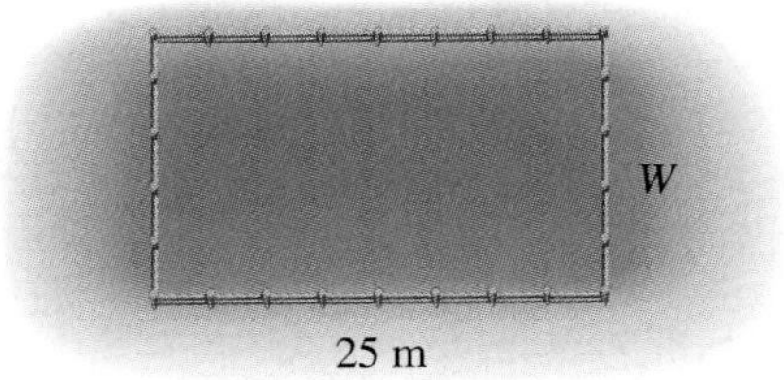

Figure 5

Step 3 **Write an equation.** The formula for the perimeter of a rectangle is

$$P = 2L + 2W.$$

Find the width by substituting 80 for P and 25 for L in the formula.

$$\mathbf{80} = 2(\mathbf{25}) + 2W \quad P = 80, L = 25$$

Step 4 **Solve** the equation.

$$80 = 50 + 2W \quad \text{Multiply.}$$
$$80 - \mathbf{50} = 50 + 2W - \mathbf{50} \quad \text{Subtract 50.}$$
$$30 = 2W \quad \text{Combine terms.}$$
$$15 = W \quad \text{Divide by 2.}$$

Step 5 **State the answer.** The width is 15 m.

Step 6 **Check.** If the width is 15 m and the length is 25 m, the distance around the rectangular lot (perimeter) is $2(25) + 2(15) = 50 + 30 = 80$ m, as required.

Work Problem 2 at the Side.

1 Find the value of the remaining variable in each formula.

(a) $I = prt$; $I = \$246$, $r = .06$, $t = 2$

(b) $P = 2L + 2W$; $P = 126$, $W = 25$

2 Solve the problem.

A farmer has 800 m of fencing material to enclose a rectangular field. The width of the field is 175 m. Find the length of the field.

ANSWERS

1. **(a)** $p = \$2050$ **(b)** $L = 38$
2. 225 m

Example 3 Finding the Height of a Triangular Sail

The area of a triangular sail of a sailboat is 126 ft^2. (Recall that ft^2 means "square feet.") The base of the sail is 12 ft. Find the height of the sail.

Step 1 **Read.** We must find the height of the triangular sail.

Step 2 **Assign a variable.** Let h = the height of the sail in feet. See Figure 6.

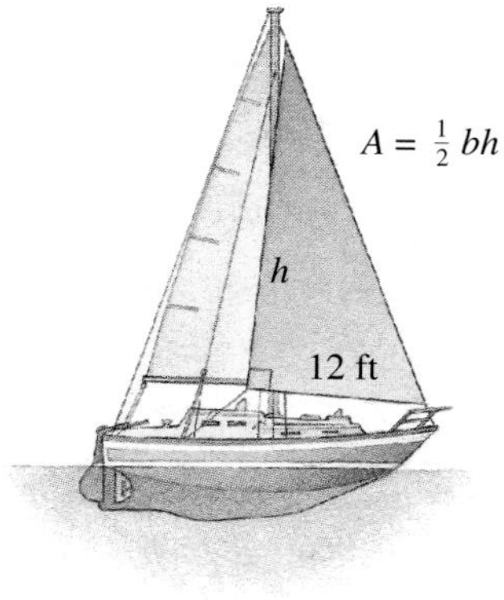

Figure 6

Step 3 **Write an equation.** The formula for the area of a triangle is $A = \frac{1}{2}bh$, where A is the area, b is the base, and h is the height. Using the information given in the problem, substitute 126 for A and 12 for b in the formula.

$$A = \frac{1}{2}bh$$

$$\mathbf{126} = \frac{1}{2}(\mathbf{12})h \qquad A = 126,\ b = 12$$

Step 4 **Solve** the equation.

$$126 = 6h \qquad \text{Multiply.}$$

$$21 = h \qquad \text{Divide by 6.}$$

Step 5 **State the answer.** The height of the sail is 21 ft.

Step 6 **Check** to see that the values $A = 126$, $b = 12$, and $h = 21$ satisfy the formula for the area of a triangle.

Work Problem ❸ at the Side.

3 Solve problems involving vertical angles and straight angles.

Figure 7 shows two intersecting lines forming angles that are numbered ①, ②, ③, and ④. Angles ① and ③ lie "opposite" each other. They are called **vertical angles.** Another pair of vertical angles is ② and ④. In geometry, it is shown that vertical angles have equal measures.

Now look at angles ① and ②. When their measures are added, we get the measure of a **straight angle,** which is 180°. There are three other such pairs of angles: ② and ③, ③ and ④, and ① and ④.

The next example uses these ideas.

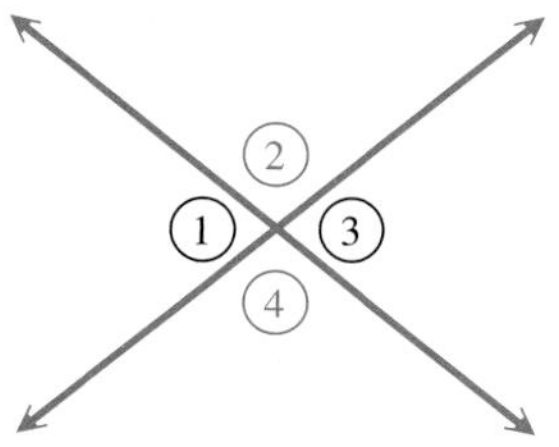

Figure 7

❸ Solve the problem.
The area of a triangle is 120 m^2. The height is 24 m. Find the length of the base of the triangle.

ANSWERS
3. 10 m

4 Find the measure of each marked angle.

(a)

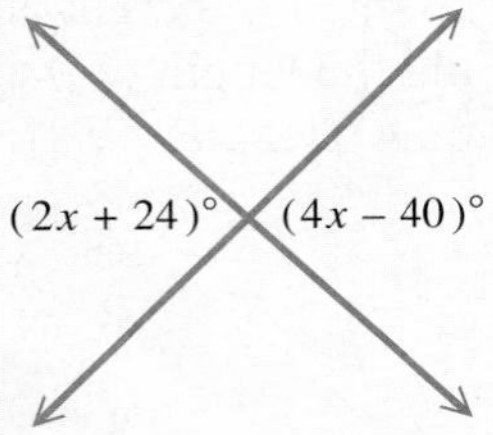

(b)

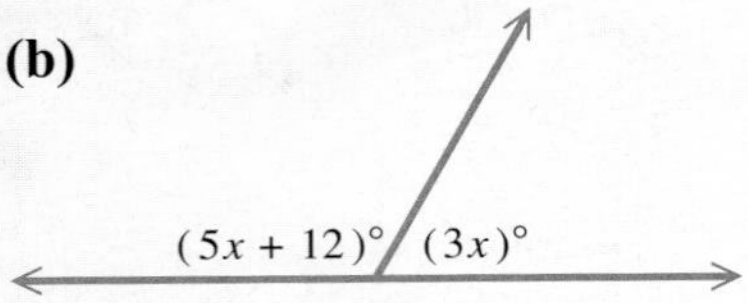

Example 4 Finding Angle Measures

Refer to the appropriate figure in each part.

(a) Find the measure of each marked angle in Figure 8.

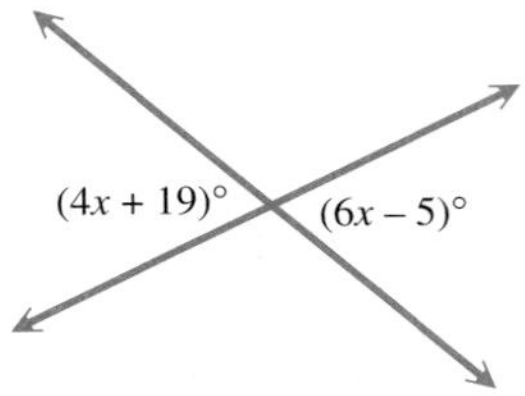

Figure 8

Since the marked angles are vertical angles, they have equal measures. Set $4x + 19$ equal to $6x - 5$ and solve.

$$4x + 19 = 6x - 5$$
$$-4x + 4x + 19 = -4x + 6x - 5 \quad \text{Add } -4x.$$
$$19 = 2x - 5$$
$$19 + 5 = 2x - 5 + 5 \quad \text{Add 5.}$$
$$24 = 2x$$
$$12 = x \quad \text{Divide by 2.}$$

Since $x = 12$, one angle has measure $4(12) + 19 = 67$ degrees. The other has the same measure, since $6(12) - 5 = 67$ as well. Each angle measures 67°.

(b) Find the measure of each marked angle in Figure 9.

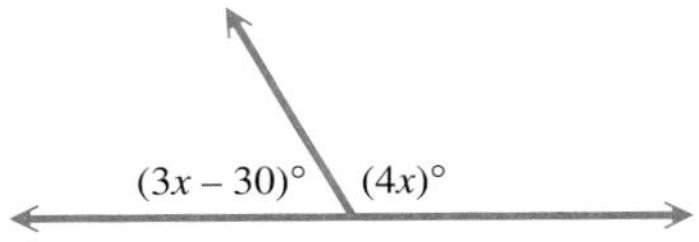

Figure 9

The measures of the marked angles must add to 180° because together they form a straight angle. The equation to solve is

$$(3x - 30) + 4x = 180.$$
$$7x - 30 = 180 \quad \text{Combine terms.}$$
$$7x - 30 + 30 = 180 + 30 \quad \text{Add 30.}$$
$$7x = 210$$
$$x = 30 \quad \text{Divide by 7.}$$

To find the measures of the angles, replace x with 30 in the two expressions.

$$3x - 30 = 3(30) - 30 = 90 - 30 = 60$$
$$4x = 4(30) = 120$$

The two angle measures are 60° and 120°.

Work Problem 4 at the Side.

ANSWERS

4. (a) Both measure 88°. **(b)** 117° and 63°

4 Solve a formula for a specified variable. Sometimes it is necessary to solve a large number of problems that use the same formula. For example, a surveying class might need to solve several problems that involve the formula for the area of a rectangle, $A = LW$. Suppose that in each problem the area (A) and the length (L) of a rectangle are given, and the width (W) must be found. Rather than solving for W each time the formula is used, it would be simpler to rewrite the *formula* so that it is solved for W. This process is called **solving for a specified variable.**

In solving a formula for a specified variable, we treat the specified variable as if it were the *only* variable in the equation, and treat the other variables as if they were numbers. We use the same steps to solve the equation for the specified variable that we have used to solve equations with just one variable.

5 **(a)** Solve $I = prt$ for t.

(b) Solve $P = a + b + c$ for a.

Example 5 Solving for a Specified Variable

Solve $A = LW$ for W.

Think of undoing what has been done to W. Since W is multiplied by L, undo the multiplication by dividing each side of $A = LW$ by L.

$$A = LW$$

$$\frac{A}{L} = \frac{LW}{L} \qquad \text{Divide by } L.$$

$$\frac{A}{L} = W \qquad \tfrac{L}{L} = 1;\ 1W = W$$

The formula is now solved for W.

Work Problem 5 at the Side.

Example 6 Solving for a Specified Variable

Solve $P = 2L + 2W$ for L.

We want to get L alone on one side of the equation. We begin by subtracting $2W$ from each side.

$$P = 2L + 2W$$

$$P - 2W = 2L + 2W - 2W \qquad \text{Subtract } 2W.$$

$$P - 2W = 2L \qquad \text{Combine terms.}$$

$$\frac{P - 2W}{2} = \frac{2L}{2} \qquad \text{Divide by 2.}$$

$$\frac{P - 2W}{2} = L \qquad \tfrac{2}{2} = 1;\ 1L = L$$

The last step gives the formula solved for L, as required.

ANSWERS

5. **(a)** $t = \frac{I}{pr}$ **(b)** $a = P - b - c$

6 **(a)** Solve $A = p + prt$ for t.

(b) Solve $Ax + By = C$ for y.

Example 7 Solving for a Specified Variable

Solve $F = \frac{9}{5}C + 32$ for C. (This is the formula for converting from Celsius to Fahrenheit.)

We need to isolate C on one side of the equation. First undo the addition of 32 to $\frac{9}{5}C$ by subtracting 32 from each side.

$$F = \frac{9}{5}C + 32$$

$$F - 32 = \frac{9}{5}C + 32 - 32 \qquad \text{Subtract 32.}$$

$$F - 32 = \frac{9}{5}C$$

Now multiply each side by $\frac{5}{9}$. Use parentheses on the left.

$$\frac{5}{9}(F - 32) = \frac{5}{9} \cdot \frac{9}{5}C \qquad \text{Multiply by } \tfrac{5}{9}.$$

$$\frac{5}{9}(F - 32) = C$$

This last result is the formula for converting temperatures from Fahrenheit to Celsius.

Work Problem 6 at the Side.

ANSWERS

6. **(a)** $t = \frac{A - p}{pr}$ **(b)** $y = \frac{C - Ax}{B}$

2.5 EXERCISES

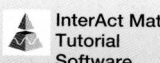

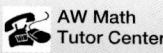

1. In your own words, explain what is meant by each term.

(a) Perimeter of a plane geometric figure

The perimeter of a plane geometric figure is the distance around the figure.

(b) Area of a plane geometric figure

The area of a plane geometric figure is the measure of the surface covered or enclosed by the figure.

2. Perimeter is to a polygon as **circumference** is to a circle.

3. If a formula has exactly five variables, how many values would you need to be given in order to find the value of any one variable? **four**

4. Look at the drawings of a rectangle and a trapezoid at the beginning of this section. Discuss their similarities and their differences.

One of their similarities is that both have a pair of parallel sides. They differ because the other pair of opposite sides are parallel in a rectangle, but are not in the trapezoid. Also, the rectangle has four equal angles (all right angles), but the trapezoid does not have four equal angles.

Decide whether perimeter or area would be used to solve a problem concerning the measure of the quantity.

5. Sod for a lawn **area**

6. Carpeting for a bedroom **area**

7. Baseboards for a living room **perimeter**

8. Fencing for a yard **perimeter**

9. Fertilizer for a garden **area**

10. Tile for a bathroom **area**

11. Determining the cost of planting rye grass in a lawn for the winter **area**

12. Determining the cost of replacing a linoleum floor with a wood floor **area**

In the following exercises a formula is given, along with the values of all but one of the variables in the formula. Find the value of the variable that is not given. (When necessary, use 3.14 as an approximation for π.) See Example 1.

13. $P = 2L + 2W$ (perimeter of a rectangle); $L = 8$, $W = 5$

$P = 26$

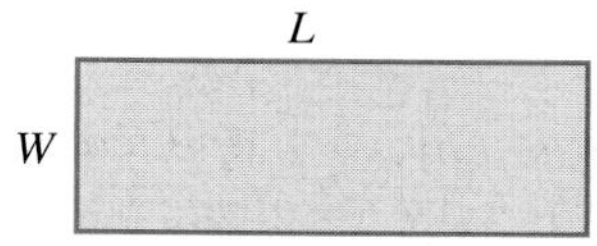

14. $P = 2L + 2W$; $L = 6$, $W = 4$

$P = 20$

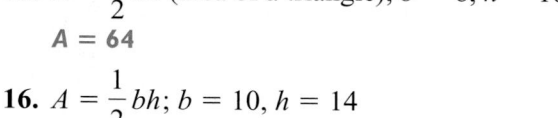

15. $A = \frac{1}{2}bh$ (area of a triangle); $b = 8$, $h = 16$

$A = 64$

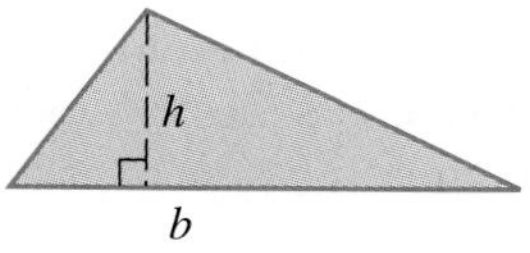

16. $A = \frac{1}{2}bh$; $b = 10$, $h = 14$

$A = 70$

17. $P = a + b + c$ (perimeter of a triangle); $P = 12$, $a = 3$, $c = 5$ **$b = 4$**

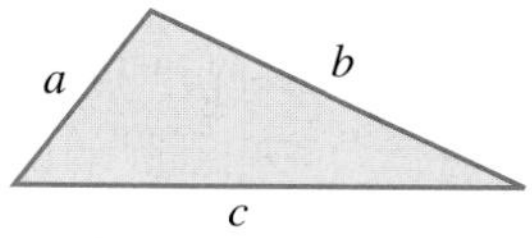

18. $P = a + b + c$; $P = 15$, $a = 3$, $b = 7$ **$c = 5$**

19. $d = rt$ (distance formula); $d = 252$, $r = 45$ **$t = 5.6$**

20. $d = rt$; $d = 100$, $t = 2.5$ **$r = 40$**

21. $I = prt$ (simple interest); $p = 7500$, $r = .035$, $t = 6$ **$I = 1575$**

22. $I = prt$; $p = 5000$, $r = .025$, $t = 7$ **$I = 875$**

23. $C = 2\pi r$ (circumference of a circle); $C = 16.328$ **$r = 2.6$**

24. $C = 2\pi r$; $C = 8.164$ **$r = 1.3$**

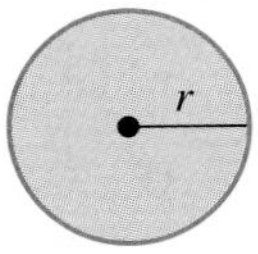

25. $A = \pi r^2$ (area of a circle); $r = 4$ **$A = 50.24$**

26. $A = \pi r^2$; $r = 12$ **$A = 452.16$**

*The **volume** of a three-dimensional object is a measure of the space occupied by the object. For example, we would need to know the volume of a gasoline tank in order to know how many gallons of gasoline it would take to completely fill the tank. In the following exercises, a formula for the volume (V) of a three-dimensional object is given, along with values for the other variables. Evaluate V. (Use 3.14 as an approximation for π.) See Example 1.*

27. $V = LWH$ (volume of a rectangular box); $L = 10$, $W = 5$, $H = 3$ **$V = 150$**

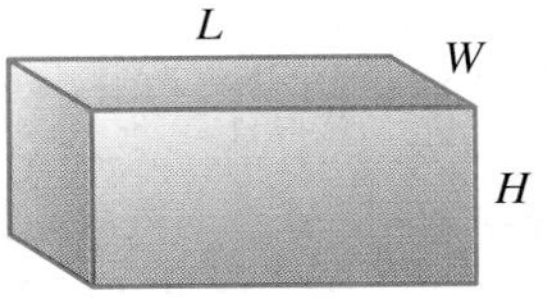

28. $V = LWH$; $L = 12$, $W = 8$, $H = 4$ **$V = 384$**

29. $V = \frac{1}{3}Bh$ (volume of a pyramid); $B = 12$, $h = 13$ **$V = 52$**

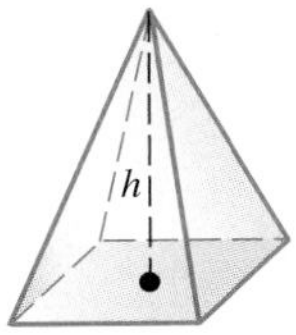

30. $V = \frac{1}{3}Bh$; $B = 36$, $h = 4$ **$V = 48$**

31. $V = \frac{4}{3}\pi r^3$ (volume of a sphere); $r = 12$ **$V = 7234.56$**

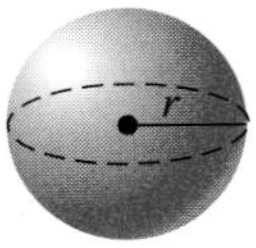

32. $V = \frac{4}{3}\pi r^3$; $r = 6$ **$V = 904.32$**

Use a formula to write an equation for each application, and then use the problem-solving method of Section 2.4 to solve. (Use 3.14 as an approximation for π.) Formulas are found on the inside covers of this book. See Examples 2 and 3.

33. Recently, a prehistoric ceremonial site dating to about 3000 B.C. was discovered at Stanton Drew in southwestern England. The site, which is larger than Stonehenge, is a nearly perfect circle, consisting of nine concentric rings that probably held upright wooden posts. Around this timber temple is a wide, encircling ditch enclosing an area with a diameter of 443 ft. Find this enclosed area to the nearest thousand square feet. (*Source: Archaeology,* vol. 51, no. 1, Jan./Feb. 1998.) **about 154,000 ft^2**

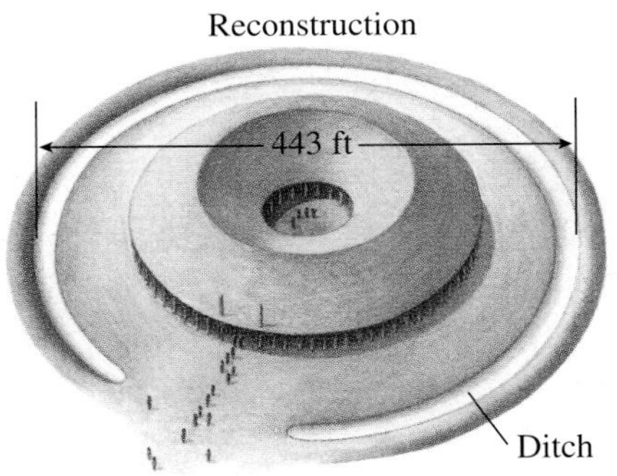

34. The Skydome in Toronto, Canada, is the first stadium with a hard-shell, retractable roof. The steel dome is 630 ft in diameter. To the nearest foot, what is the circumference of this dome? (*Source:* www.4ballparks.com.) **about 1978 ft**

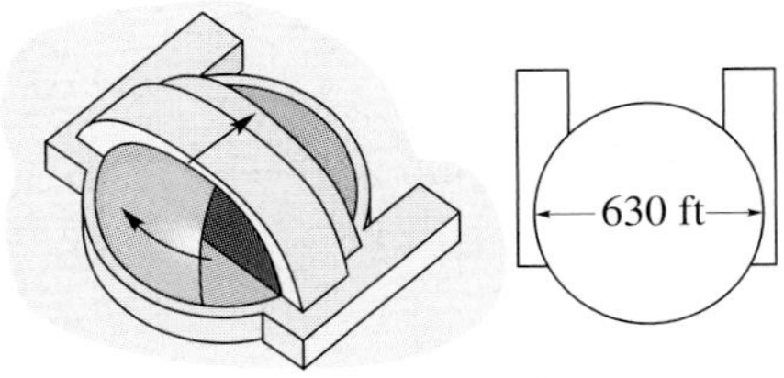

35. The *Daily Banner,* published in Roseberg, Oregon, in the 19th century, had page size 3 in. by 3.5 in. What was the perimeter? What was the area? (*Source: The Guinness Book of Records*, 1994.)
perimeter: 13 in.; area: 10.5 in.^{2}

36. The newspaper *The Constellation,* printed in 1859 in New York City as part of the Fourth of July celebration, had length 51 in. and width 35 in. What was the perimeter? What was the area? (*Source: The Guinness Book of Records*, 1994.)
perimeter: 172 in.; area: 1785 in.^{2}

37. The largest drum ever constructed was played at the Royal Festival Hall in London in 1987. It had a diameter of 13 ft. What was the area of the circular face of the drum? (*Hint:* Use $A = \pi r^2$.) (*Source: The Guinness Book of Records*, 1994.)
132.665 ft^2

38. What was the circumference of the drum described in Exercise 37? (*Hint:* Use $C = 2\pi r$.)
40.82 ft

39. The survey plat depicted here shows two lots that form a trapezoid. The measures of the parallel sides are 115.80 ft and 171.00 ft. The height of the trapezoid is 165.97 ft. Find the combined area of the two lots. Round your answer to the nearest hundredth of a square foot.
23,800.10 ft^2

40. Lot A in the figure is in the shape of a trapezoid. The parallel sides measure 26.84 ft and 82.05 ft. The height of the trapezoid is 165.97 ft. Find the area of Lot A. Round your answer to the nearest hundredth of a square foot.
9036.24 ft^2

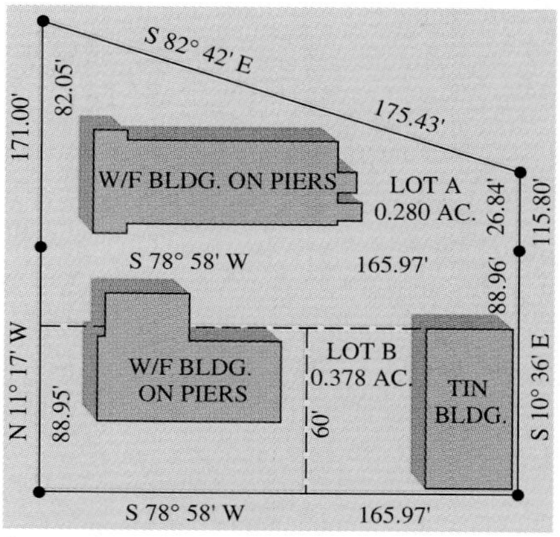

Source: Property survey in New Roads, Louisiana.

41. The U.S. Postal Service requires that any box sent through the mail have length plus girth (distance around) totaling no more than 108 in. The maximum volume that meets this condition is contained by a box with a square end 18 in. on each side. What is the length of the box? What is the maximum volume?

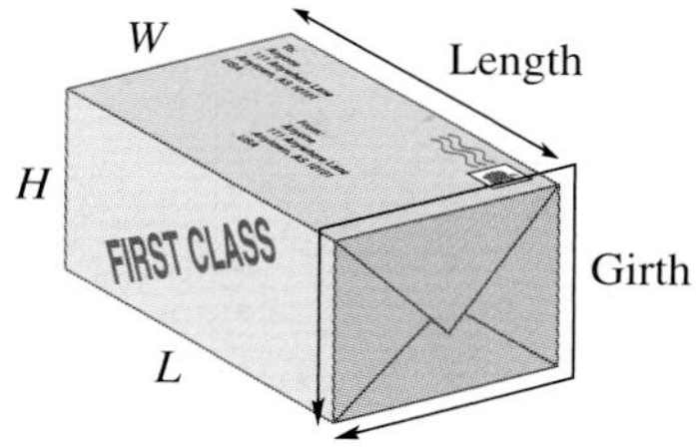

length: 36 in.; volume: 11,664 in.^{3}

42. The largest box of popcorn was filled by students in Jacksonville, Florida. The box was approximately 40 ft long, $20\frac{2}{3}$ ft wide, and 8 ft high. To the nearest cubic foot, what was the volume of the box? (*Source: The Guinness Book of Records,* 1998.)

6613 ft^3

Find the measure of each marked angle. See Example 4.

43.

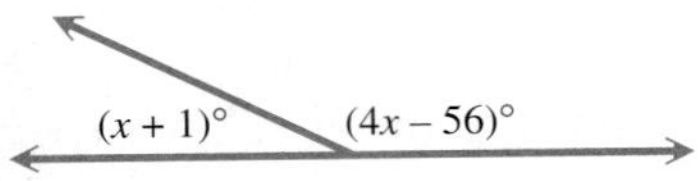

48°, 132°

44.

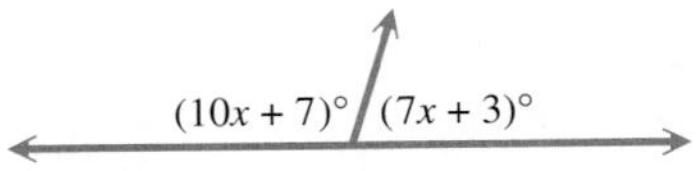

107°, 73°

45.

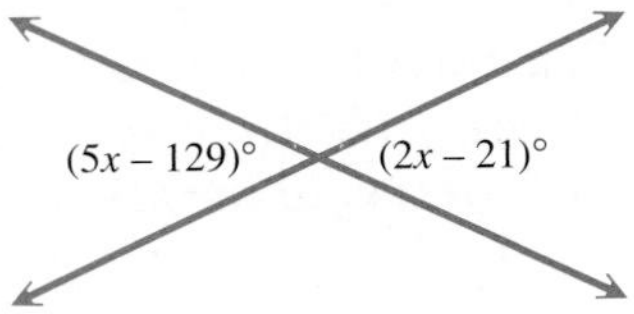

51°, 51°

46.

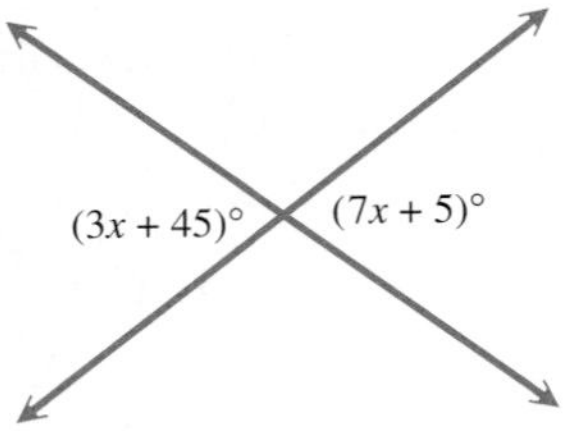

75°, 75°

47.

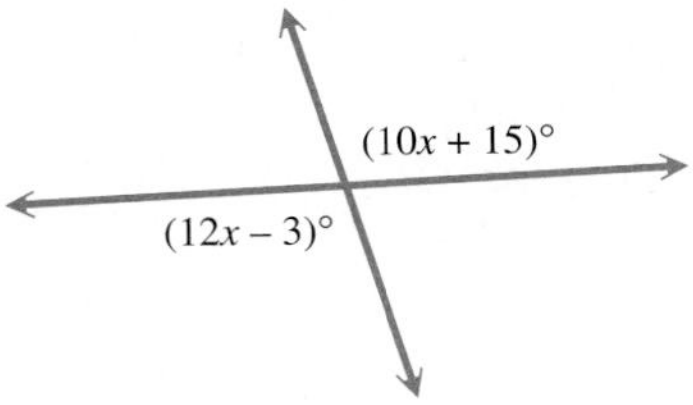

105°, 105°

48.

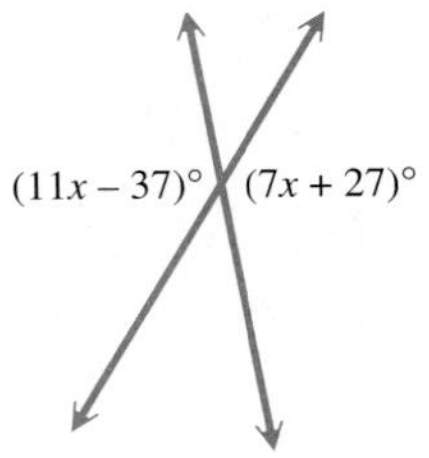

139°, 139°

Solve each formula for the specified variable. See Examples 5–7.

49. $d = rt$ for t

$t = \frac{d}{r}$

50. $d = rt$ for r

$r = \frac{d}{t}$

51. $V = LWH$ for H

$H = \frac{V}{LW}$

52. $A = LW$ for L

$L = \frac{A}{W}$

53. $P = a + b + c$ for b

$b = P - a - c$

54. $P = a + b + c$ for a

$a = P - b - c$

55. $I = prt$ for r

$r = \frac{I}{pt}$

56. $I = prt$ for p

$p = \frac{I}{rt}$

57. $A = \frac{1}{2}bh$ for h

$h = \frac{2A}{b}$

58. $A = \frac{1}{2}bh$ for b

$b = \frac{2A}{h}$

59. $P = 2L + 2W$ for W

$W = \frac{P - 2L}{2}$ or $W = \frac{P}{2} - L$

60. $A = p + prt$ for r

$r = \frac{A - p}{pt}$

61. $V = \frac{1}{3}\pi r^2 h$ for h

$h = \frac{3V}{\pi r^2}$

62. $V = \pi r^2 h$ for h

$h = \frac{V}{\pi r^2}$

63. $C = \frac{5}{9}(F - 32)$ for F

$F = \frac{9}{5}C + 32$

2.6 Ratio, Proportion, and Percent

OBJECTIVES

1. Write ratios.
2. Solve proportions.
3. Solve applied problems using proportions.
4. Find percentages and percents.

1 Write ratios. A **ratio** is a comparison of two quantities using a quotient.

Ratio

The ratio of the number a to the number b is written

$$a \text{ to } b, \quad a:b, \quad \text{or} \quad \frac{a}{b}.$$

This last way of writing a ratio is most common in algebra.

Percents are ratios where the second number is always 100. For example, 50% represents the ratio of 50 to 100, 27% represents the ratio of 27 to 100, and so on.

Example 1 Writing a Word Phrase as a Ratio

Write a ratio for each word phrase.

(a) The ratio of 5 hr to 3 hr is

$$\frac{5 \text{ hr}}{3 \text{ hr}} = \frac{5}{3}.$$

(b) To find the ratio of 6 hr to 3 days, first convert 3 days to hours.

$$\begin{aligned} 3 \text{ days} &= 3 \cdot 24 \\ &= 72 \text{ hr} \end{aligned}$$

The ratio of 6 hr to 3 days is thus

$$\frac{6 \text{ hr}}{3 \text{ days}} = \frac{6 \text{ hr}}{72 \text{ hr}} = \frac{6}{72} = \frac{1}{12}.$$

Work Problem 1 at the Side.

1 Write each ratio.

(a) 9 women to 5 women

(b) 4 in. to 1 ft

An example of the use of a ratio is in unit pricing, to see which size of an item offered in different sizes produces the best price per unit. To do this, set up the ratio of the price of the item to the number of units on the label. Then divide to obtain the price per unit.

Example 2 Finding the Price per Unit

The Winn-Dixie supermarket in Mandeville, Louisiana, charges the following prices for a box of trash bags.

Size	Price
10-count	\$1.28
20-count	\$2.68
30-count	\$3.88

Which size is the best buy? That is, which size has the lowest unit price?

Continued on Next Page

ANSWERS

1. (a) $\frac{9}{5}$ (b) $\frac{4}{12} = \frac{1}{3}$

To find the best buy, write ratios comparing the price for each box size to the number of units (bags) per box. The results in the following table are rounded to the nearest thousandth.

Size	Unit Cost (dollars per bag)
10-count	$\frac{\$1.28}{10} = \$.128$ ← The best buy
20-count	$\frac{\$2.68}{20} = \$.134$
30-count	$\frac{\$3.88}{30} = \$.129$

Because the 10-count size produces the lowest unit cost, it is the best buy. This example shows that buying the largest size does not always provide the best buy, although this is often true.

Work Problem ❷ at the Side.

❷ Solve the problem.

The local supermarket charges the following prices for a popular brand of pancake syrup.

Size	Price
36-oz	\$3.89
24-oz	\$2.79
12-oz	\$1.89

Which size is the best buy? What is the unit cost for that size?

2 Solve proportions. A ratio is used to compare two numbers or amounts. A **proportion** says that two ratios are equal. For example,

$$\frac{3}{4} = \frac{15}{20}$$

is a proportion that says that the ratios $\frac{3}{4}$ and $\frac{15}{20}$ are equal. In the proportion

$$\frac{a}{b} = \frac{c}{d},$$

a, b, c, and *d* are the **terms** of the proportion. Beginning with the proportion

$$\frac{a}{b} = \frac{c}{d}$$

and multiplying each side by the common denominator, *bd,* gives

$$bd \cdot \frac{a}{b} = bd \cdot \frac{c}{d}$$

$$\frac{b}{b}(d \cdot a) = \frac{d}{d}(b \cdot c) \qquad \text{Associative and commutative properties}$$

$$ad = bc. \qquad \text{Commutative and identity properties}$$

The products *ad* and *bc* are found by multiplying diagonally, as shown below.

$$\frac{a}{b} = \frac{c}{d}$$

bc

ad

For this reason, *ad* and *bc* are called **cross products.**

In the discussion that follows, we assume that no denominators are 0.

If $\frac{a}{b} = \frac{c}{d}$, then the cross products *ad* and *bc* are equal.

Also, if $ad = bc$, then $\frac{a}{b} = \frac{c}{d}$.

ANSWERS

2. 36-oz; \$.108 per oz

From this rule, if $\frac{a}{b} = \frac{c}{d}$ then $ad = bc$. However, if $\frac{a}{c} = \frac{b}{d}$, then $ad = cb$, or $ad = bc$. This means that the two proportions are equivalent, and

$$\text{the proportion } \frac{a}{b} = \frac{c}{d} \text{ can always be written as } \frac{a}{c} = \frac{b}{d}.$$

Sometimes one form is more convenient to work with than the other.

Four numbers are used in a proportion. If any three of these numbers are known, the fourth can be found.

Example 3 **Finding an Unknown in a Proportion**

Solve the proportion $\frac{5}{9} = \frac{x}{63}$.

The cross products must be equal.

$$\begin{aligned} 5 \cdot 63 &= 9 \cdot x && \text{Cross products} \\ 315 &= 9x && \text{Multiply.} \\ 35 &= x && \text{Divide by 9.} \end{aligned}$$

The proportion is true when $x = 35$, so the solution set is $\{35\}$.

Work Problem 3 at the Side.

CAUTION

The cross product method cannot be used directly if there is more than one term on either side.

Example 4 **Solving an Equation Using Cross Products**

Solve the equation $\frac{m-2}{5} = \frac{m+1}{3}$.

Find the cross products.

$$\begin{aligned} 3(m-2) &= 5(m+1) && \text{Be sure to use parentheses.} \\ 3m - 6 &= 5m + 5 && \text{Distributive property} \\ 3m &= 5m + 11 && \text{Add 6.} \\ -2m &= 11 && \text{Subtract } 5m. \\ m &= -\frac{11}{2} && \text{Divide by } -2. \end{aligned}$$

The solution set is $\{-\frac{11}{2}\}$.

Work Problem 4 at the Side.

NOTE

When you set cross products equal to each other, you are really multiplying each ratio in the proportion by a common denominator.

3 **Solve applied problems using proportions.** Proportions are useful in many practical applications. We continue to use the six-step method, although the steps are not numbered here.

3 Solve each proportion.

(a) $\frac{y}{6} = \frac{35}{42}$

(b) $\frac{a}{24} = \frac{15}{16}$

4 Solve each equation.

(a) $\frac{z}{2} = \frac{z+1}{3}$

(b) $\frac{p+3}{3} = \frac{p-5}{4}$

ANSWERS

3. **(a)** $\{5\}$ **(b)** $\left\{\frac{45}{2}\right\}$

4. **(a)** $\{2\}$ **(b)** $\{-27\}$

5 Solve the problem.

Twelve gal of diesel fuel costs \$20.88. How much would 16.5 gal of the same fuel cost?

Example 5 Applying Proportions

After Lee Ann Spahr pumped 5.0 gal of gasoline, the display showing the price read \$7.90. When she finished pumping the gasoline, the price display read \$21.33. How many gallons did she pump?

We will solve this problem by setting up a proportion, with prices in the numerators and gallons in the denominators. Make sure that the corresponding numbers appear together.

Let x = the number of gallons she pumped. Then

$$\begin{array}{rcl} \text{Price} \rightarrow \dfrac{\$7.90}{5.0} \leftarrow \text{Gallons} & = & \dfrac{\$21.33}{x} \begin{array}{l}\leftarrow \text{Price}\\ \leftarrow \text{Gallons}\end{array} \\ 7.90x & = & 5.0(21.33) \quad \text{Cross products} \\ 7.90x & = & 106.65 \quad \text{Multiply.} \\ x & = & 13.5. \quad \text{Divide by 7.90.} \end{array}$$

She pumped a total of 13.5 gal. Check this answer. Notice that the way the proportion was set up uses the fact that the unit price is the same, no matter how many gallons are purchased.

Calculator Tip Using a calculator to perform the arithmetic in Example 5 reduces the possibility of errors.

Work Problem 5 at the Side.

4 Find percentages and percents. We can use the techniques for solving proportions to solve percent problems. Recall, the decimal point is moved two places to the left to change a percent to a decimal number.

Calculator Tip Many calculators have a percent key that does this automatically.

We can solve a percent problem by writing it as the proportion

$$\frac{\textit{amount}}{\textit{base}} = \frac{\textit{percent}}{100} \quad \text{or} \quad \frac{a}{b} = \frac{p}{100}.$$

The amount, or **percentage,** is compared to the **base** (the whole amount). Since *percent* means *per 100,* we compare the numerical value of the percent to 100. Thus, we write 50% as

$$\frac{p}{100} = \frac{50}{100}.$$

ANSWERS

5. \$28.71

Example 6 **Finding Percentages**

Solve each problem.

(a) Find 15% of 600.

Here, the base is 600, the percent is 15, and we must find the percentage.

$$\frac{a}{b} = \frac{p}{100}$$

$$\frac{a}{\mathbf{600}} = \frac{\mathbf{15}}{100}$$

$$100a = 600(15) \quad \text{Cross products}$$

$$a = \frac{600(15)}{100} \quad \text{Divide by 100.}$$

$$a = 90$$

Thus, 15% of 600 is 90.

(b) A DVD with a regular price of \$18 is on sale this week at 22% off. Find the amount of the discount and the sale price of the disc.

The discount is 22% of \$18. We want to find a, given b is 18 and p is 22.

$$\frac{a}{b} = \frac{p}{100}$$

$$\frac{a}{\mathbf{18}} = \frac{\mathbf{22}}{100}$$

$$100a = 18(22) \quad \text{Cross products}$$

$$100a = 396$$

$$a = 3.96 \quad \text{Divide by 100.}$$

The amount of the discount on the DVD is \$3.96, and the sale price is \$18.00 − \$3.96 = \$14.04.

Work Problem 6 at the Side.

Example 7 **Solving an Applied Percent Problem**

A newspaper ad offered a set of tires at a sale price of \$258. The regular price was \$300. What percent of the regular price were the savings?

The savings amounted to \$300 − \$258 = \$42. We can now restate the problem: What percent of 300 is 42? Substitute into the percent proportion. We have $a = 42$, $b = 300$, and p is to be found.

$$\frac{a}{b} = \frac{p}{100}$$

$$\frac{\mathbf{42}}{\mathbf{300}} = \frac{p}{100}$$

$$300p = 4200 \quad \text{Cross products}$$

$$p = 14 \quad \text{Divide by 300.}$$

The sale price represented a 14% savings.

Work Problem 7 at the Side.

6 Solve each problem.

(a) Find 20% of 70.

(b) Find the discount on a television set with a regular price of \$270 if the set is on sale at 25% off. Find the sale price of the set.

7 Solve each problem.

(a) 90 is what percent of 360?

(b) The interest in 1 yr on deposits of \$11,000 was \$682. What percent interest was paid?

Answers

6. **(a)** 14 **(b)** \$67.50; \$202.50

7. **(a)** 25% **(b)** 6.2%

Focus on Real-Data Applications

Currency Exchange

When you travel between countries, you need to exchange your U.S. dollars for the local currency. The exchange rate between currencies changes daily, and you can easily find the updated rates using the Internet. The table shown here was taken from the Bloomberg Currency Calculator Web page.

WESTERN EUROPE CURRENCY RATES

Currency	Currency per 1 unit of USD			
	Symbol	Value	Net Chg	Pct Chg
British Pound	GBP	.6614	+.003	+.4557
Euro	EUR	1.0453	−.0052	−.4950
Danish Krone	DKK	7.7996	−.0367	−.4683
German Mark (based on Euro vs. dollar)	DEM	2.0445	−.0101	−.4915

Source: Bloomberg L.P.

On June 30, 2000, the currency exchange rate from U.S. dollars to British pounds was given as:

\$1.00 U.S. was equivalent to £.6614 (British pounds).

You can set up a proportion to convert dollars to British pounds. For example, suppose you want to determine how many British pounds is equivalent to \$50.00.

$$\frac{\$1}{£.6614} = \frac{\$50}{£x} \quad \text{or} \quad \frac{1}{.6614} = \frac{50}{x}$$

$$1(x) = .6614(50)$$

$$x = 33.07$$

So 33.07 British pounds is equivalent to 50 U.S. dollars.

For Group Discussion

1. Based on the currency exchange rates in the table above, find the amount of the local currency equivalent to \$50 U.S. and find the number of U.S. dollars equivalent to 200 units of the local currency.

   (a) \$50 = **389.98** Danish Krone and 200 Krone = **25.64** dollars

   (b) \$50 = **102.23** German Marks and 200 Marks = **97.82** dollars

   (c) \$50 = **52.27** Euros and 200 Euros = **191.33** dollars

2. Set up a proportion to find the number of U.S. dollars equivalent to £1 (British pound).

   £1 (British) was equivalent to \$ **1.51** (U.S.).

3. From problem 2, you should recognize the conversion rate based on £1 as the expression $\frac{1}{.6614}$. What is the mathematical term that describes the relationship between the conversion rates .6614 and $\frac{1}{.6614}$? **reciprocals**

Teaching notes and an extension for this activity are provided in the *Printed Test Bank and Instructor's Resource Guide.*

2.6 EXERCISES

FOR EXTRA HELP: Student's Solutions Manual | MyMathLab.com | InterAct Math Tutorial Software | AW Math Tutor Center | www.mathxl.com | Digital Video Tutor CD 2 Videotape 5

1. Match each ratio in Column I with the ratio equivalent to it in Column II.

I	II
(a) 75 to 100	**A.** 80 to 100
(b) 5 to 4	**B.** 50 to 100
(c) $\frac{1}{2}$	**C.** 3 to 4
(d) 4 to 5	**D.** 15 to 12

(a) C **(b)** D **(c)** B **(d)** A

2. Give three different, equivalent forms of the ratio $\frac{4}{3}$.

Answers will vary. Three examples are $\frac{8}{6}$, $\frac{12}{9}$, and $\frac{40}{30}$.

Write a ratio for each word phrase. In Exercises 7–10, first write the amounts with the same units. Write fractions in lowest terms. See Example 1.

3. 60 ft to 70 ft

$\frac{6}{7}$

4. 40 mi to 30 mi

$\frac{4}{3}$

5. 72 dollars to 220 dollars

$\frac{18}{55}$

6. 120 people to 90 people

$\frac{4}{3}$

7. 30 in. to 8 ft

$\frac{5}{16}$

8. 20 yd to 8 ft

$\frac{15}{2}$

9. 16 min to 1 hr

$\frac{4}{15}$

10. 24 min to 2 hr

$\frac{1}{5}$

A supermarket was surveyed to find the prices charged for items in various sizes. Find the best buy (based on price per unit) for each item. See Example 2.

11. Seasoning mix

8-oz size: $1.75

17-oz size: $2.88

17-oz size

12. Red beans

1-lb package: $.89

2-lb package: $1.79

1-lb package

13. Prune juice

32-oz can: $1.95

48-oz can: $2.89

64-oz can: $3.29

64-oz can

14. Corn oil

24-oz bottle: $2.08

64-oz bottle: $3.94

128-oz bottle: $7.65

128-oz bottle

15. Artificial sweetener packets

50-count: $1.19

100-count: $1.85

250-count: $3.79

500-count: $6.38

500-count

16. Chili (no beans)

7.5-oz can: $1.19

10.5-oz can: $1.29

15-oz can: $1.78

25-oz can: $2.59

25-oz can

17. Extra crunchy peanut butter

12-oz size: $1.49

28-oz size: $1.99

40-oz size: $3.99

28-oz size

18. Tomato ketchup

14-oz size: $.93

32-oz size: $1.19

44-oz size: $2.19

32-oz size

19. Explain how percent and ratio are related.

A percent is a ratio where the basis of comparison is 100. For example, 27% represents the ratio of 27 to 100.

20. Explain the distinction between *ratio* and *proportion.*

A ratio is a comparison, while a proportion is a statement that two ratios are equal.

Solve each equation. See Examples 3 and 4.

21. $\frac{k}{4} = \frac{175}{20}$ **{35}**

22. $\frac{x}{6} = \frac{18}{4}$ **{27}**

23. $\frac{49}{56} = \frac{z}{8}$ **{7}**

24. $\frac{z}{80} = \frac{20}{100}$ **{16}**

25. $\frac{3y - 2}{5} = \frac{6y - 5}{11}$ **{−1}**

26. $\frac{2r + 8}{4} = \frac{3r - 9}{3}$ **{10}**

27. $\frac{5k + 1}{6} = \frac{3k - 2}{3}$ **{5}**

28. $\frac{2p + 7}{3} = \frac{p - 1}{4}$ $\left\{-\frac{31}{5}\right\}$

29. $\frac{3m - 2}{5} = \frac{4 - m}{3}$ $\left\{\frac{13}{7}\right\}$

Solve each problem involving proportion. See Example 5.

30. A chain saw requires a mixture of 2-cycle engine oil and gasoline. According to the directions on a bottle of Oregon 2-cycle Engine Oil, for a 50 to 1 ratio requirement, approximately 2.5 fluid oz of oil are required for 1 gal of gasoline. For 2.75 gal, how many fluid ounces of oil are required?

6.875 fluid oz

31. The directions on the bottle mentioned in Exercise 30 indicate that if the ratio requirement is 24 to 1, approximately 5.5 oz of oil are required for 1 gal of gasoline. If gasoline is to be mixed with 22 oz of oil, how much gasoline is to be used?

4 gal

32. In a recent year, the average exchange rate between British pounds and U.S. dollars was 1 pound to \$1.6762. Margaret went to London and exchanged her U.S. currency for British pounds, and received 400 pounds. How much in U.S. dollars did Margaret exchange?

\$670.48

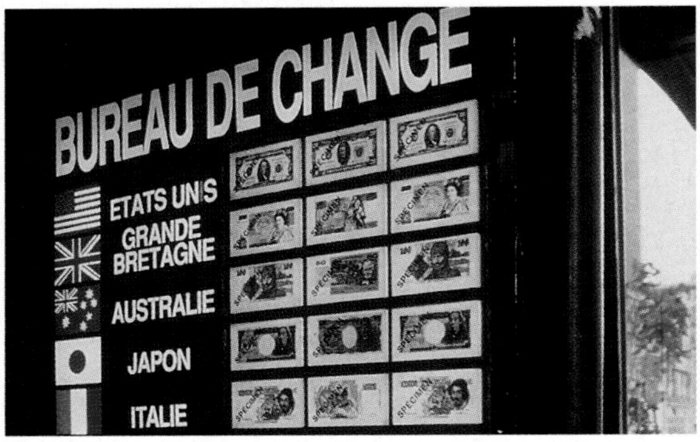

33. If 3 U.S. dollars can be exchanged for 4.5204 Swiss francs, how many Swiss francs can be obtained for \$49.20? (Round to the nearest hundredth.)

74.13 francs

34. If 6 gal of premium unleaded gasoline cost \$11.34, how much would it cost to completely fill a 15-gal tank?

\$28.35

35. If sales tax on a \$16.00 compact disc is \$1.32, how much would the sales tax be on a \$120.00 compact disc player?

\$9.90

36. The distance between Kansas City, Missouri, and Denver is 600 mi. On a certain wall map, this is represented by a length of 2.4 ft. On the map, how many feet would there be between Memphis and Philadelphia, two cities that are actually 1000 mi apart?

4 ft

37. The distance between Singapore and Tokyo is 3300 mi. On a certain wall map, this distance is represented by 11 in. The actual distance between Mexico City and Cairo is 7700 mi. How far apart are they on the same map?

$25\frac{2}{3}$ in.

38. Biologists tagged 500 fish in Willow Lake on October 5. At a later date they found 7 tagged fish in a sample of 700. Estimate the total number of fish in Willow Lake to the nearest hundred.

50,000 fish

39. On May 13 researchers at Argyle Lake tagged 840 fish. When they returned a few weeks later, their sample of 1000 fish contained 18 that were tagged. Give an approximation of the fish population in Argyle Lake to the nearest hundred.

46,700 fish

Answer each question about percent. See Example 6.

40. What is 48.6% of 19? **9.234**

41. What is 26% of 480? **124.8**

42. What percent of 48 is 96? **200%**

43. What percent of 30 is 36? **120%**

44. 12% of what number is 3600? **30,000**

45. 25% of what number is 150? **600**

46. 78.84 is what percent of 292? **27%**

47. .392 is what percent of 28? **1.4%**

Use mental techniques to answer the questions in Exercises 48–50. Try to avoid using paper and pencil or a calculator.

48. Jane Gunton bought a boat five years ago for $5000 and sold it this year for $2000. What percent of her original purchase did she lose on the sale?

A. 40% **B.** 50% **C.** 20% **D.** 60%

D

49. The 1990 U.S. Census showed that the population of Alabama was 4,040,587, with 25.3% represented by African-Americans. What is the best estimate of the African-American population in Alabama? (*Source:* U.S. Bureau of the Census.)

A. 500,000 **B.** 750,000
C. 1,000,000 **D.** 1,500,000

C

50. The 1990 U.S. Census showed that the population of New Mexico was 1,515,069, with 38.2% being Hispanic. What is the best estimate of the Hispanic population of New Mexico? (*Source:* U.S. Bureau of the Census.)

A. 600,000 **B.** 60,000
C. 750,000 **D.** 38,000 **A**

Work each problem. Round all money amounts to the nearest dollar and percents to the nearest tenth. See Examples 6 and 7.

51. In 1998, the U.S. civilian labor force consisted of 137,673,000 persons. Of this total, 6,210,000 were unemployed. What was the percent of unemployment? (*Source:* U.S. Bureau of Labor Statistics.)
4.5%

52. In 1998, the U.S. labor force (excluding agricultural employees, self-employed persons, and the unemployed) consisted of 116,730,000 persons. Of this total, 16,211,000 were union members. What percent of this labor force belonged to unions? (*Source:* U.S. Bureau of Labor Statistics.) **13.9%**

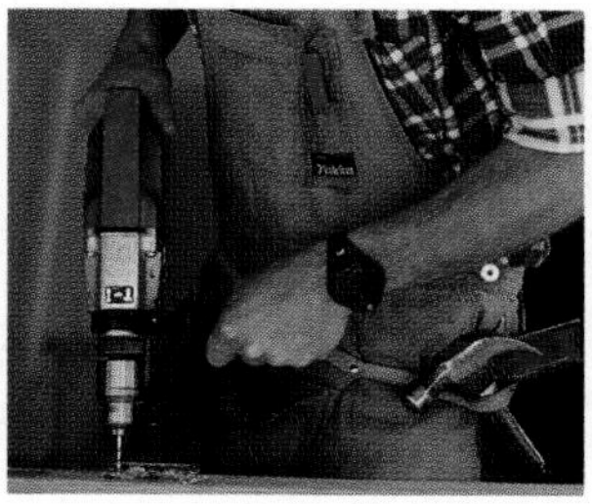

53. During former President George Bush's tenure, he vetoed a total of 44 bills. Fifteen of these were pocket vetoes. What percent of his vetoes were *not* pocket vetoes? (*Source:* Senate Library.) **65.9%**

54. During 1996 and 1997, the total public and private school enrollment in the United States was 51,375,000. Of this total, 12.7% of the students were enrolled in private schools. How many students were enrolled in public schools? (*Source:* National Center for Education Statistics, U.S. Department of Education.)

44,850,375

55. A family of four with a monthly income of \$3800 plans to spend 8% of this amount on entertainment. How much will be spent on entertainment?

\$304

56. Quinhon Dac Ho earns \$3200 per month. He wants to save 12% of this amount. How much will he save?

\$384

57. The 1916 dime minted in Denver is quite rare. The 1979 edition of *A Guide Book of United States Coins* listed its value in Extremely Fine condition as \$625. The 1997 value had increased to \$2400. What was the percent increase in the value of this coin?

284%

58. Here is a common business problem. If the sales tax rate is 6.5% and I have collected \$3400 in sales tax, how much were my sales?

\$52,308

The Consumer Price Index, issued by the U.S. Bureau of Labor Statistics, provides a means of determining the purchasing power of the U.S. dollar from one year to the next. Using the period from 1982 to 1984 as a measure of 100.0, the Consumer Price Index in each year from 1990 to 1998 is shown here. To use the Consumer Price Index to predict a price in a particular year, we can set up a proportion and compare it with a known price in another year, as follows:

$$\frac{\text{price in year } A}{\text{index in year } A} = \frac{\text{price in year } B}{\text{index in year } B}.$$

Year	Consumer Price Index
1990	130.7
1991	136.2
1992	140.3
1993	144.5
1994	148.2
1995	152.4
1996	156.9
1997	160.5
1998	163.0

Source: U.S. Bureau of Labor Statistics.

Use the Consumer Price Index figures in the table to find the amount that would be charged for the use of the same amount of electricity that cost \$225 *in 1990. Give your answer to the nearest dollar.*

59. in 1995 **\$262**

60. in 1996 **\$270**

61. in 1997 **\$276**

62. in 1998 **\$281**

RELATING CONCEPTS (Exercises 63–66) FOR INDIVIDUAL OR GROUP WORK

In Section 2.3 we solved equations with fractions by first multiplying each side of the equation by the common denominator. A proportion with a variable is this kind of equation. ***Work Exercises 63–66 in order.*** *The steps justify the method of solving a proportion by cross products.*

63. What is the LCD of the fractions in the equation $\frac{x}{6} = \frac{2}{5}$? **30**

64. Solve the equation in Exercise 63 as follows.

(a) Multiply each side by the LCD. What equation do you get? **$5x = 12$**

(b) Solve the equation from part (a) by dividing each side by the coefficient of x. $\left\{\frac{12}{5}\right\}$

65. Solve the equation in Exercise 63 using cross products. $\left\{\frac{12}{5}\right\}$

66. Compare your solutions from Exercises 64 and 65. What do you notice?

Both methods give the same solution set.

Chapter 2

Summary

Key Terms

2.1

linear equation A linear equation in one variable is an equation that can be written in the form $Ax + B = C$, for real numbers A, B, and C, with $A \neq 0$.

equivalent equations Equations that have the same solutions are equivalent equations.

solution set The solution set of an equation is the set of all its solutions.

identity An identity is an equation that is true for all replacements of the variable.

2.4

complementary angles Two angles whose measures have a sum of 90° are complementary angles.

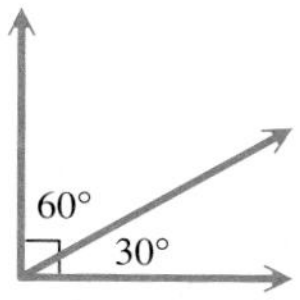

right angle A right angle measures 90°.

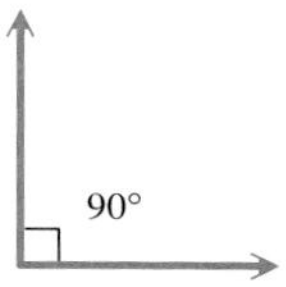

supplementary angles Two angles whose measures have a sum of 180° are supplementary angles.

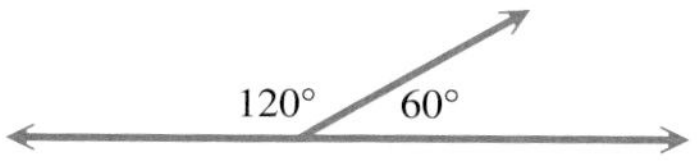

straight angle A straight angle measures 180°.

consecutive integers Two integers that differ by 1 are consecutive integers.

2.5

area The area of a plane geometric figure is a measure of the surface covered by the figure.

perimeter The perimeter of a plane geometric figure is the distance around the figure, that is, the sum of the length of its sides.

vertical angles Vertical angles are angles formed by intersecting lines. They have the same measure.

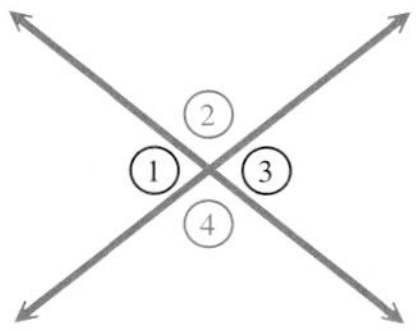

2.6

ratio A ratio is a comparison of two quantities using a quotient.

proportion A proportion is a statement that two ratios are equal.

cross products The method of cross products provides a way of determining whether a proportion is true.

$$\frac{a}{b} = \frac{c}{d}$$

terms In the proportion $\frac{a}{b} = \frac{c}{d}$, a, b, c, and d are the terms.

NEW SYMBOLS

$\emptyset$ empty (null) set

***a* to *b*, *a* : *b*, or** $\frac{a}{b}$ the ratio of a to b

TEST YOUR WORD POWER

See how well you have learned the vocabulary in this chapter. Answers follow the Quick Review.

1. A **solution set** is the set of numbers that
- **(a)** make an expression undefined
- **(b)** make an equation false
- **(c)** make an equation true
- **(d)** make an expression equal to 0.

2. Complementary angles are angles
- **(a)** formed by two parallel lines
- **(b)** whose sum is 90°
- **(c)** whose sum is 180°
- **(d)** formed by perpendicular lines.

3. Supplementary angles are angles
- **(a)** formed by two parallel lines
- **(b)** whose sum is 90°
- **(c)** whose sum is 180°
- **(d)** formed by perpendicular lines.

4. A **ratio**
- **(a)** compares two quantities using a quotient
- **(b)** says that two quotients are equal
- **(c)** is a product of two quantities
- **(d)** is a difference between two quantities.

5. A **proportion**
- **(a)** compares two quantities using a quotient
- **(b)** says that two ratios are equal
- **(c)** is a product of two quantities
- **(d)** is a difference between two quantities.

QUICK REVIEW

Concepts	*Examples*
2.1 The Addition Property of Equality The same number may be added to (or subtracted from) each side of an equation without changing the solution.	Solve. $x - 6 = 12$ $x - 6 + \mathbf{6} = 12 + \mathbf{6}$ Add 6. $x = 18$ Combine terms. The solution set is $\{18\}$.
2.2 The Multiplication Property of Equality Each side of an equation may be multiplied (or divided) by the same nonzero number without changing the solution.	Solve. $\frac{3}{4}x = -9$ $\mathbf{\frac{4}{3}} \cdot \frac{3}{4}x = \mathbf{\frac{4}{3}}(-9)$ Multiply by $\frac{4}{3}$. $x = -12$ The solution set is $\{-12\}$.

Concepts	*Examples*
2.3 *More on Solving Linear Equations* *Step 1* Simplify each side separately. *Step 2* Isolate the variable term on one side. *Step 3* Isolate the variable. *Step 4* Check.	Solve. $2x + 2(x + 1) = 14 + x$ $2x + 2x + 2 = 14 + x$ Distributive property $4x + 2 = 14 + x$ Combine terms. $4x + 2 - x - 2 = 14 + x - x - 2$ Subtract x; subtract 2. $3x = 12$ Combine terms. $\frac{3x}{3} = \frac{12}{3}$ Divide by 3. $x = 4$ *Check:* $2(4) + 2(4 + 1) \stackrel{?}{=} 14 + 4$ Let $x = 4$. $18 = 18$ True The solution set is $\{4\}$.
2.4 *An Introduction to Applications of Linear Equations* *Step 1* Read. *Step 2* Assign a variable. *Step 3* Write an equation. *Step 4* Solve the equation. *Step 5* State the answer. *Step 6* Check.	One number is 5 more than another. Their sum is 21. What are the numbers? We are looking for two numbers. Let x represent the smaller number. Then $x + 5$ represents the larger number. $x + (x + 5) = 21$ $2x + 5 = 21$ Combine terms. $2x + 5 - 5 = 21 - 5$ Subtract 5. $2x = 16$ Combine terms. $\frac{2x}{2} = \frac{16}{2}$ Divide by 2. $x = 8$ The numbers are 8 and 13. 13 is 5 more than 8, and $8 + 13 = 21$. It checks.
2.5 *Formulas and Applications from Geometry* To find the value of one of the variables in a formula, given values for the others, substitute the known values into the formula.	Find L if $A = LW$, given that $A = 24$ and $W = 3$. $24 = L \cdot 3$ $A = 24, W = 3$ $\frac{24}{3} = \frac{L \cdot 3}{3}$ Divide by 3. $8 = L$
To solve a formula for one of the variables, isolate that variable by treating the other variables as numbers and using the steps for solving equations.	Solve $P = 2L + 2W$ for W. $P - 2L = 2L + 2W - 2L$ Subtract $2L$. $P - 2L = 2W$ Combine terms. $\frac{P - 2L}{2} = \frac{2W}{2}$ Divide by 2. $\frac{P - 2L}{2} = W$ or $W = \frac{P - 2L}{2}$

Concepts	*Examples*
2.6 Ratio, Proportion, and Percent To write a ratio, express quantities in the same units.	4 ft to 8 in. = 48 in. to 8 in. $= \frac{48}{8} = \frac{6}{1}$
To solve a proportion, use the method of cross products.	Solve $\frac{x}{12} = \frac{35}{60}$. $60x = 12 \cdot 35$ Cross products $60x = 420$ Multiply. $\frac{60x}{60} = \frac{420}{60}$ Divide by 60. $x = 7$ The solution set is $\{7\}$.
To solve a percent problem, use the proportion $\frac{\text{amount}}{\text{base}} = \frac{\text{percent}}{100}$.	

ANSWERS TO TEST YOUR WORD POWER

1. (c) *Example:* $\{8\}$ is the solution set of $2x + 5 = 21$. **2. (b)** *Example:* Angles with measures 35° and 55° are complementary angles. **3. (c)** *Example:* Angles with measures 112° and 68° are supplementary angles. **4. (a)** *Example:* $\frac{7 \text{ in.}}{12 \text{ in.}} = \frac{7}{12}$ **5. (b)** *Example:* $\frac{2}{3} = \frac{8}{12}$

Chapter 2 REVIEW EXERCISES

[2.1–2.3] *Solve each equation. Check the solution.*

1. $x - 7 = 2$

{9}

2. $4r - 6 = 10$

{4}

3. $5x + 8 = 4x + 2$

{−6}

4. $8t = 7t + \frac{3}{2}$

$\left\{\frac{3}{2}\right\}$

5. $(4r - 8) - (3r + 12) = 0$

{20}

6. $7(2x + 1) = 6(2x - 9)$

$\left\{-\frac{61}{2}\right\}$

7. $-\frac{6}{5}y = -18$

{15}

8. $\frac{1}{2}r - \frac{1}{6}r + 3 = 2 + \frac{1}{6}r + 1$

{0}

9. $3x - (-2x + 6) = 4(x - 4) + x$

∅

10. $.10(x + 80) + .20x = 8 + .30x$

{all real numbers}

[2.4] *Solve each problem.*

11. If 7 is added to five times a number, the result is equal to three times the number. Find the number.

$-\frac{7}{2}$

12. If 4 is subtracted from twice a number, the result is 36. Find the number.

20

13. The land area of Hawaii is 5213 mi^2 greater than that of Rhode Island. Together, the areas total 7637 mi^2. What is the area of each state?

Hawaii: 6425 mi^2; Rhode Island: 1212 mi^2

14. The height of Seven Falls in Colorado is $\frac{5}{2}$ the height (in feet) of Twin Falls in Idaho. The sum of the heights is 420 ft. Find the height of each.

Seven Falls: 300 ft; Twin Falls: 120 ft

15. The supplement of an angle measures 10 times the measure of its complement. What is the measure of the angle (in degrees)?

80°

16. Find two consecutive odd integers such that when the smaller is added to twice the larger, the result is 24 more than the larger integer.

11, 13

[2.5] *A formula is given in each exercise, along with the values for all but one of the variables. Find the value of the variable that is not given. (For Exercises 19 and 20, use* 3.14 *as an approximation for* π.*)*

17. $A = \frac{1}{2}bh$; $A = 44$, $b = 8$ $h = 11$

18. $A = \frac{1}{2}h(b + B)$; $b = 3$, $B = 4$, $h = 8$ $A = 28$

19. $C = 2\pi r$; $C = 29.83$ $r = 4.75$

20. $V = \frac{4}{3}\pi r^3$; $r = 6$ $V = 904.32$

Solve each formula for the specified variable.

21. $A = LW$ for L $\quad L = \frac{A}{W}$

22. $A = \frac{1}{2}h(b + B)$ for h $\quad h = \frac{2A}{b + B}$

Find the measure of each marked angle.

23.

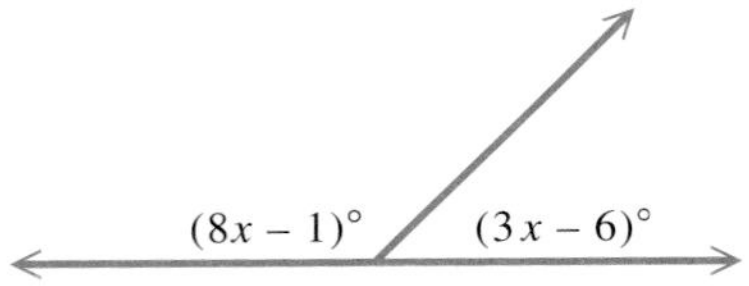

135°, 45°

24.

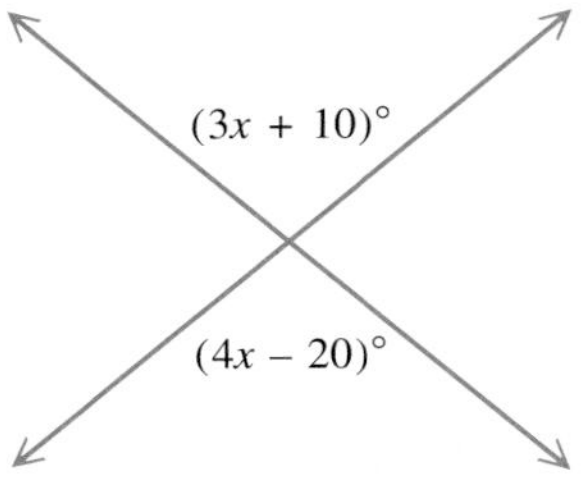

100°, 100°

Solve each application of geometry.

25. A cinema screen in Indonesia has length 92.75 ft and width 70.5 ft. What is the perimeter? What is the area? (*Source: The Guinness Book of Records*, 1994.)

perimeter: 326.5 ft; area: 6538.875 ft^2

26. The Ziegfield Room in Reno, Nevada, has a circular turntable on which its showgirls dance. The circumference of the turntable is 62.5 ft. What is the diameter of the turntable? What is the radius? What is its area? (Use 3.14 as an approximation for π.) (*Source: The Guinness Book of Records*, 1994.)

diameter: approximately 19.9 ft;
radius: approximately 9.95 ft;
area: approximately 311 ft^2

[2.6] *Write a ratio for each word phrase. Write fractions in lowest terms.*

27. 60 cm to 40 cm $\quad \frac{3}{2}$

28. 5 days to 2 weeks $\quad \frac{5}{14}$

29. 90 in. to 10 ft $\quad \frac{3}{4}$

30. 3 mo to 3 yr $\quad \frac{1}{12}$

Solve each proportion.

31. $\frac{p}{21} = \frac{5}{30}$ $\quad \left\{\frac{7}{2}\right\}$

32. $\frac{5 + x}{3} = \frac{2 - x}{6}$ $\quad \left\{-\frac{8}{3}\right\}$

33. $\frac{y}{5} = \frac{6y - 5}{11}$ $\quad \left\{\frac{25}{19}\right\}$

34. Explain how 40% can be expressed as a ratio of two whole numbers.

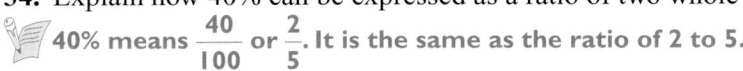

40% means $\frac{40}{100}$ or $\frac{2}{5}$. It is the same as the ratio of 2 to 5.

Solve each problem involving proportion.

35. If 2 lb of fertilizer will cover 150 ft^2 of lawn, how many pounds would be needed to cover 500 ft^2?

$6\frac{2}{3}$ lb

36. If 8 oz of medicine must be mixed with 20 oz of water, how many ounces of medicine must be mixed with 90 oz of water?

36 oz

37. An enlarged version of the chair used by George Washington at the Constitutional Convention casts a shadow 18 ft long at the same time a vertical pole 12 ft high casts a shadow 4 ft long. How tall is the chair? (*Source: The Guinness Book of Records*, 1994.) **54 ft**

38. The distance between two cities on a road map is 32 cm. The two cities are actually 150 km apart. The distance on the map between two other cities is 80 cm. How far apart are these cities? **375 km**

39. What is 23% of 76? **17.48**

40. What percent of 12 is 21? **175%**

41. 6 is what percent of 18? **$33\frac{1}{3}\%$**

42. 36% of what number is 900? **2500**

43. Gwen and John paid \$25,407.00 for their 1999 Chevrolet conversion van. The sales tax rate was 8.75%, and the tax was added to that amount. What was the final price for the van? (*Source:* Author Hornsby's sales receipt.) **\$27,630.11**

44. Ruth, from the mathematics editorial division of Addison-Wesley, took a community college faculty out to dinner. The bill was \$304.75. Ruth added a 15% tip, and paid for the meal with her corporate credit card. What was the total price she paid? **\$350.46**

Mixed Review Exercises

Solve each problem.

45. $\frac{y}{7} = \frac{y-5}{2}$ **{7}**

46. $I = prt$ for r **$r = \frac{I}{pt}$**

47. $-2x = -4 - 2(2 - x)$ **{2}**

48. $2k - 5 = 4k + 13$ **{−9}**

49. $.05x + .02x = 4.9$ **{70}**

50. $2 - 3(y - 5) = 4 + y$ **$\left\{\frac{13}{4}\right\}$**

51. $9x - (7x + 2) = 3x + (2 - x)$ **$\emptyset$**

52. $\frac{1}{3}s + \frac{1}{2}s + 7 = \frac{5}{6}s + 5 + 2$ **{all real numbers}**

53. One of the tallest candles ever constructed was exhibited at the 1897 Stockholm Exhibition. If it cast a shadow 5 ft long at the same time a vertical pole 32 ft high cast a shadow 2 ft long, how tall was the candle? (*Source: The Guinness Book of Records*, 1994.)

80 ft

54. Two-thirds of a number added to the number is 10. What is the number?

6

55. Rita and Bobby commute to work. Rita travels three times as far as Bobby each day, and together they travel 112 mi. How far does each travel? **Rita: 84 mi; Bobby: 28 mi**

56. Mike defeated William in an election. Mike had twice as many votes as William, and together they had 1800 votes. How many votes did each of the candidates receive?

Mike: 1200 votes; William: 600 votes

57. In the 2000 Olympic Games in Sydney, Australia, the United States and Russia earned a total of 185 medals. The United States earned 9 more medals than Russia. How many medals did each country earn? (*Source: Times Picayune,* October 2, 2000.)

United States: 97;
Russia: 88

58. Of the 58 medals earned by the host country, Australia, in the 2000 Olympics, there were 9 more silver than gold medals, and 8 fewer bronze than silver medals. How many of each medal did Australia earn? (*Source: Times Picayune*, October 2, 2000.)

gold: 16; silver: 25; bronze: 17

59. The perimeter of a triangle is 96 m. One side is twice as long as another, and the third side is 30 m long. What is the length of the longest side?

44 m

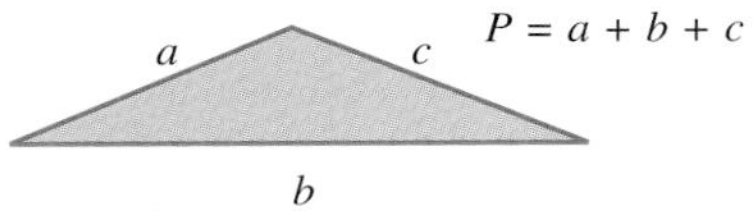

60. The perimeter of a rectangle is 288 ft. The length is 4 ft longer than the width. Find the width.

70 ft

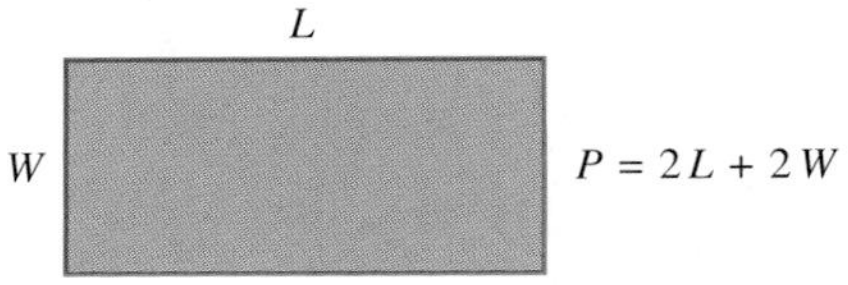

61. The perimeter of a rectangle is 75 in. The width is 17 in. What is the length?

$20\frac{1}{2}$ in.

62. The area of a triangle is 182 in.^{2}. The height is 14 in. Find the length of the base.

26 in.

63. Find the best buy based on unit pricing for spaghetti sauce.

Size	Price
$15\frac{1}{2}$-oz	\$1.19
32-oz	\$1.69
48-oz	\$2.69

32-oz size

64. Find the measure of each marked angle.

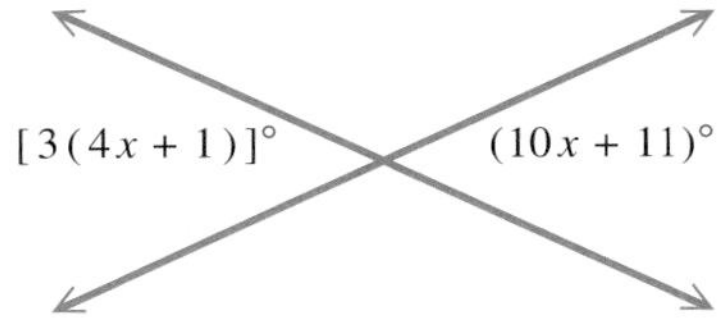

51°, 51°

Chapter 2 Test

Study Skills Workbook
Activity 8

Solve each equation, and check the solution.

1. $3x - 7 = 11$

1. {6}

2. $5x + 9 = 7x + 21$

2. {−6}

3. $2 - 3(x - 5) = 3 + (x + 1)$

3. $\left\{\frac{13}{4}\right\}$

4. $2.3x + 13.7 = 1.3x + 2.9$

4. {−10.8}

5. $7 - (m - 4) = -3m + 2(m + 1)$

5. ∅

6. $-\frac{4}{7}x = -12$

6. {21}

7. $.06(x + 20) + .08(x - 10) = 4.6$

7. {30}

8. $-8(2x + 4) = -4(4x + 8)$

8. {all real numbers}

This problem refers to the 1997 All-Star basketball game held February 9 in Cleveland. (Source: The ESPN 1998 Information Please Sports Almanac.)

9. The East won the game by 12 points. The total of the East and West team scores was 252. What was the final score of the game?

9. East: 132; West: 120

10. The high scorer of the game was Glenn Rice, playing for the Eastern Conference. He scored 7 more points than Latrell Sprewell, the high scorer on the Western Conference team. The total number of points scored by both players was 45. How many points did Rice score?

10. 26 points

11. The three largest islands in the Hawaiian island chain are Hawaii (the Big Island), Maui, and Kauai. Together, their areas total 5300 mi^2. The island of Hawaii is 3293 mi^2 larger than the island of Maui, and Maui is 177 mi^2 larger than Kauai. What is the area of each island?

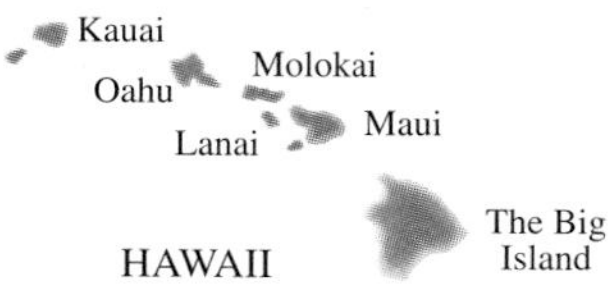

11. Hawaii: 4021 mi^2; Maui: 728 mi^2; Kauai: 551 mi^2

12. 50°

12. Find the measure of an angle if its supplement measures 10° more than three times its complement.

13. (a) $W = \frac{P - 2L}{2}$ or $W = \frac{P}{2} - L$

(b) 18

13. The formula for the perimeter of a rectangle is $P = 2L + 2W$.

(a) Solve for W.

(b) If $P = 116$ and $L = 40$, find the value of W.

Find the measure of each marked angle.

14. 100°, 80°

15. 75°, 75°

14.

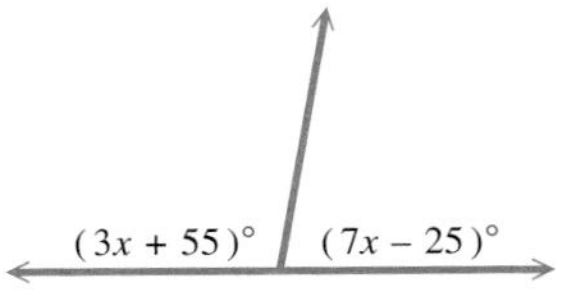

15.

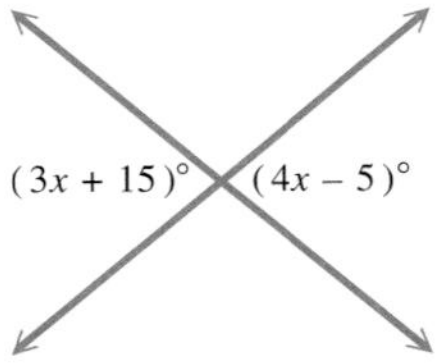

Solve each proportion.

16. {6}

16. $\frac{z}{8} = \frac{12}{16}$

17. {−29}

17. $\frac{y + 5}{3} = \frac{y - 3}{4}$

18. 8 slices for $2.19

18. Which is the better buy for processed cheese slices: 8 slices for $2.19 or 12 slices for $3.30?

19. 2300 mi

19. The distance between Milwaukee and Boston is 1050 mi. On a certain map, this distance is represented by 42 in. On the same map, Seattle and Cincinnati are 92 in. apart. What is the actual distance between Seattle and Cincinnati?

20. 236%

20. In 1997, the Tampa Bay Lightning hockey team had debt of about $177 million, with a franchise value of only $75 million. What percent of the franchise value was the debt? (*Source:* Ozanian, M. K., "Fields of Debt," *Forbes,* December 15, 1997, vol. 160, no. 13.)

Cumulative Review Exercises CHAPTERS R–2

Beginning with this chapter, each chapter in the text will conclude with a set of cumulative review exercises designed to cover the major topics from the beginning of the course. This feature will allow you to constantly review topics that have been introduced up to that point.

Write each fraction in lowest terms.

1. $\frac{15}{40}$ $\frac{3}{8}$

2. $\frac{108}{144}$ $\frac{3}{4}$

Perform the indicated operations.

3. $\frac{5}{6} + \frac{1}{4} + \frac{7}{15}$ $\frac{31}{20}$

4. $16\frac{7}{8} - 3\frac{1}{10}$ $\frac{551}{40}$ or $13\frac{31}{40}$

5. $\frac{9}{8} \cdot \frac{16}{3}$ 6

6. $\frac{3}{4} \div \frac{5}{8}$ $\frac{6}{5}$

7. $4.8 + 12.5 + 16.73$ 34.03

8. $56.3 - 28.99$ 27.31

9. $67.8(.45)$ 30.51

10. $236.46 \div 4.2$ 56.3

11. In making dresses, Earth Works uses $\frac{5}{8}$ yd of trim per dress. How many yards of trim would be used to make 56 dresses?
35 yd

12. A cook wants to increase a recipe for Quaker Quick Grits that serves 4 to make enough for 10 people. The recipe calls for 3 cups of water. How much water will be needed to serve 10?
$7\frac{1}{2}$ cups

13. Pythagoras weighs $71\frac{1}{4}$ lb and Fred weighs $28\frac{3}{8}$ lb. How much do the two dogs weigh together?
$99\frac{5}{8}$ lb

14. A purchasing agent bought 3 Executive Single-Pedestal Desks at \$1099.99 each and 3 chairs for \$159.99, \$189.99, and \$199.99. What was the final bill (without tax)? (*Source:* Office Depot catalog "The Big Book," 2000.)
\$3849.94

Tell whether each inequality is true *or* false.

15. $\frac{8(7) - 5(6 + 2)}{3 \cdot 5 + 1} \geq 1$ true

16. $\frac{4(9 + 3) - 8(4)}{2 + 3 - 3} \geq 2$ true

Perform the indicated operations.

17. $-11 + 20 + (-2)$ 7

18. $13 + (-19) + 7$ 1

19. $9 - (-4)$ 13

20. $-2(-5)(-4)$ −40

21. $\frac{4 \cdot 9}{-3}$ −12

22. $\frac{8}{7 - 7}$ undefined

23. $(-5 + 8) + (-2 - 7)$ −6

24. $(-7 - 1)(-4) + (-4)$ 28

25. $\frac{-3 - (-5)}{1 - (-1)}$ 1

26. $\dfrac{6(-4) - (-2)(12)}{3^2 + 7^2}$ **0**

27. $\dfrac{(-3)^2 - (-4)(2^4)}{5 \cdot 2 - (-2)^3}$ $\dfrac{73}{18}$

28. $\dfrac{-2(5^3) - 6}{4^2 + 2(-5) + (-2)}$ **−64**

Find the value of each expression when $x = -2$, $y = -4$, and $z = 3$.

29. $xz^3 - 5y^2$ **−134**

30. $\dfrac{xz - y^3}{-4z}$ $-\dfrac{29}{6}$

Name the property illustrated by each equation.

31. $7(k + m) = 7k + 7m$

distributive property

32. $3 + (5 + 2) = 3 + (2 + 5)$

commutative property

33. $7 + (-7) = 0$

inverse property

34. $3.5(1) = 3.5$

identity property

Simplify each expression by combining terms.

35. $4p - 6 + 3p - 8$

$7p - 14$

36. $-4(k + 2) + 3(2k - 1)$

$2k - 11$

Solve each equation, and check the solution.

37. $2r - 6 = 8$

$\{7\}$

38. $2(p - 1) = 3p + 2$

$\{-4\}$

39. $4 - 5(a + 2) = 3(a + 1) - 1$

$\{-1\}$

40. $2 - 6(z + 1) = 4(z - 2) + 10$

$\left\{-\dfrac{3}{5}\right\}$

41. $-(m - 1) = 3 - 2m$

$\{2\}$

42. $\dfrac{y - 2}{3} = \dfrac{2y + 1}{5}$

$\{-13\}$

43. $\dfrac{2x + 3}{5} = \dfrac{x - 4}{2}$

$\{26\}$

44. $\dfrac{2}{3}y + \dfrac{3}{4}y = -17$

$\{-12\}$

Solve each formula for the indicated variable.

45. $P = a + b + c$ for c $c = P - a - b$

46. $P = 4s$ for s $s = \dfrac{P}{4}$

Solve each problem.

47. The purchasing agent in Exercise 14 paid a sales tax of $6\frac{1}{4}\%$ on his purchase. What was the final bill, including tax? **$4090.56**

48. A car has a price of $5000. For trading in her old car, Shannon D'hemecourt will get 25% off. Find the price of the car with the trade-in. **$3750**

49. Jennifer Johnston bought textbooks at the college bookstore for $244.33, including 6% sales tax. What did the books cost?

$230.50

50. Carter Fenton received a bill from his credit card company for $104.93. The bill included interest at $1\frac{1}{2}\%$ per month for one month and a $5.00 late charge. How much did his purchases amount to?

$98.45

51. The perimeter of a rectangle is 98 cm. The width is 19 cm. Find the length. **30 cm**

52. The area of a triangle is 104 in.^{2}. The base is 13 in. Find the height.

16 in.

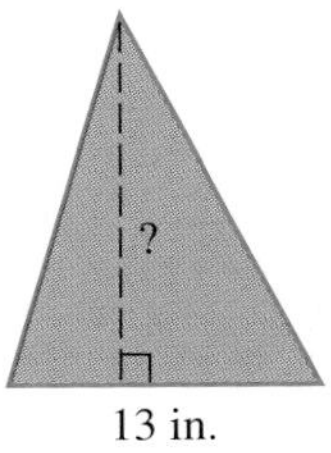

3 Linear Inequalities and Absolute Value

The cost of a college education has risen rapidly in the last decade. Average higher education tuition and fees increased by 50.2% from the 1990–1991 school year to the 1998–1999 school year. (*Source: World Almanac and Book of Facts,* 2000.) In Example 8 of Section 3.2, we apply the concepts of this chapter to college student expenses.

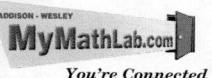

3.1 Linear Inequalities in One Variable

Objectives

1. Graph intervals on a number line.
2. Solve linear inequalities using the addition property.
3. Solve linear inequalities using the multiplication property.
4. Solve linear inequalities with three parts.
5. Solve applied problems using linear inequalities.

Solving inequalities is closely related to solving equations. In this section we introduce properties for solving inequalities.

Inequalities are algebraic expressions related by

$<$	"is less than,"	$\leq$	"is less than or equal to,"
$>$	"is greater than,"	$\geq$	"is greater than or equal to."

We solve an inequality by finding all real number solutions for it. For example, the solution set of $x \leq 2$ includes *all* real numbers that are less than or equal to 2, not just the integers less than or equal to 2. For example, $-2.5, -1.7, -1, \frac{1}{2}, \sqrt{2}, \frac{7}{4}$, and 2, are real numbers less than or equal to 2 and are therefore solutions of $x \leq 2$.

1 Graph intervals on a number line. A good way to show the solution set of an inequality is by graphing. We graph all the real numbers satisfying $x \leq 2$ by placing a square bracket at 2 on a number line and drawing an arrow extending from the bracket to the left (to represent the fact that all numbers less than 2 are also part of the graph). The graph is shown in Figure 1.

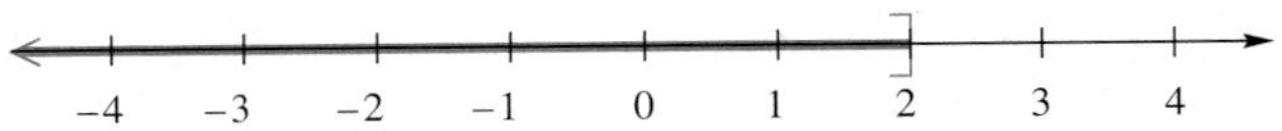

Figure 1

The set of numbers less than or equal to 2 is an example of an **interval** on the number line. To write intervals, we use **interval notation.** For example, using this notation, the interval of all numbers less than or equal to 2 is written $(-\infty, 2]$. The negative infinity symbol $-\infty$ does not indicate a number. It is used to show that the interval includes all real numbers less than 2. As on the number line, the square bracket indicates that 2 is included in the solution set. A parenthesis is always used next to the infinity symbol. The set of real numbers is written in interval notation as $(-\infty, \infty)$.

Example 1 Graphing Intervals Written in Interval Notation on Number Lines

Write each inequality in interval notation and graph it.

(a) $x > -5$

The statement $x > -5$ says that x can represent any number greater than -5, but x cannot equal -5. This interval is written $(-5, \infty)$. We show this solution set on a number line by placing a parenthesis at -5 and drawing an arrow to the right, as in Figure 2. The parenthesis at -5 shows that -5 is *not* part of the graph.

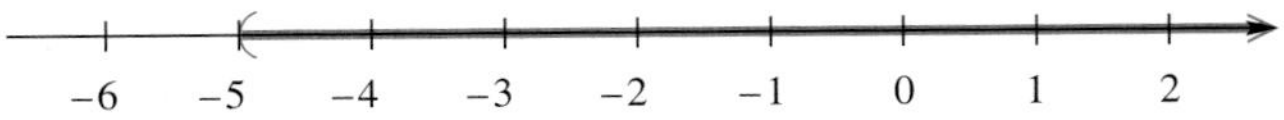

Figure 2

(b) $-1 \leq x < 3$

This statement is read "-1 is less than or equal to x *and* x is less than 3." Thus, we want the set of numbers that are *between* -1 and 3, with -1 included and 3 excluded. In interval notation, we write the solution set as

Continued on Next Page

$[-1, 3)$, using a square bracket at -1 because it is part of the graph and a parenthesis at 3 because it is not part of the graph. The graph is shown in Figure 3.

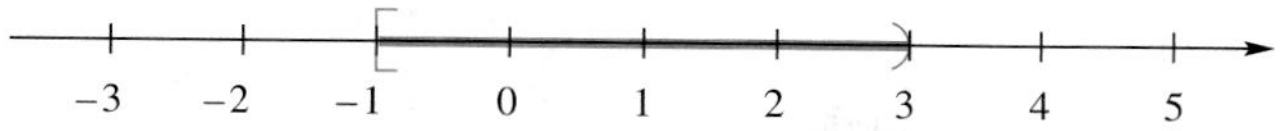

Figure 3

Work Problem 1 at the Side.

We now summarize the various types of intervals. The notation used in the second column of the table, such as $\{x|x < b\}$, is called **set-builder notation.** This notation is convenient to use when it is not possible to list all the elements of a set.

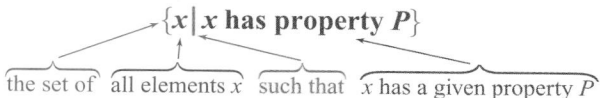

$\{x|x$ **has property** $P\}$

the set of | all elements x | such that | x has a given property P

Type of Interval	Set	Interval Notation	Graph
Open interval	$\{x\|a < x\}$	(a, ∞)	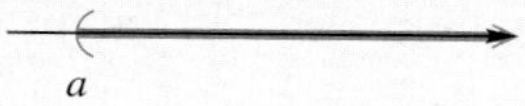
	$\{x\|a < x < b\}$	(a, b)	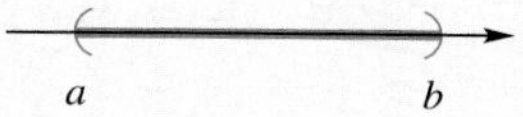
	$\{x\|x < b\}$	$(-\infty, b)$	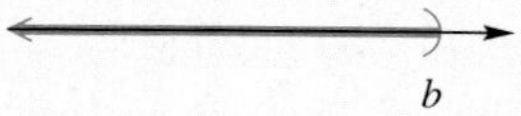
	$\{x\|x$ is a real number$\}$	$(-\infty, \infty)$	
Half-open interval	$\{x\|a \leq x\}$	$[a, \infty)$	
	$\{x\|a < x \leq b\}$	$(a, b]$	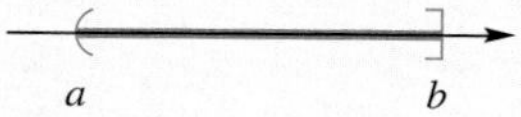
	$\{x\|a \leq x < b\}$	$[a, b)$	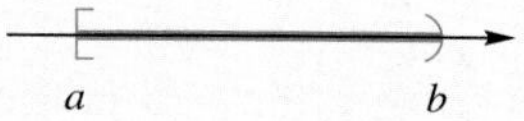
	$\{x\|x \leq b\}$	$(-\infty, b]$	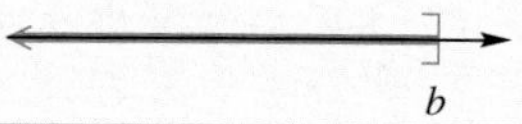
Closed interval	$\{x\|a \leq x \leq b\}$	$[a, b]$	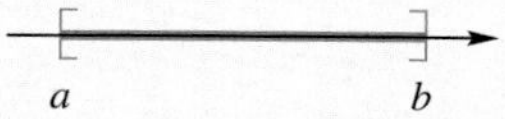

An **inequality** says that two expressions are *not* equal. Solving inequalities is similar to solving equations.

Linear Inequality in One Variable

A **linear inequality in one variable** can be written in the form

$$Ax + B < C,$$

where A, B, and C are real numbers, with $A \neq 0$.

Examples of linear inequalities in one variable include

$$x + 5 < 2, \quad y - 3 \geq 5, \quad \text{or} \quad 2k + 5 \leq 10.$$

(Throughout this section we give definitions and rules only for $<$, but they are also valid for $>$, $\leq$, and $\geq$.)

1 Write each inequality in interval notation and graph it.

(a) $x < -1$

(b) $x \geq -3$

(c) $-4 \leq x < 2$

ANSWERS

1. (a) $(-\infty, -1)$

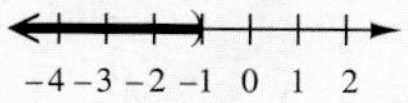

(b) $[-3, \infty)$

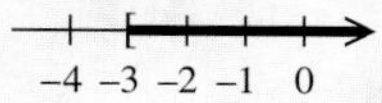

(c) $[-4, 2)$

2 Solve each inequality, check your solutions, and graph the solution set.

(a) $p + 6 < 8$

(b) $8y < 7y - 6$

2 Solve linear inequalities using the addition property. We solve an inequality by finding all numbers that make the inequality true. Usually, an inequality has an infinite number of solutions. These solutions, like solutions of equations, are found by producing a series of simpler equivalent inequalities. **Equivalent inequalities** are inequalities with the same solution set. We use the addition and multiplication properties of inequality to produce equivalent inequalities.

Addition Property of Inequality

For all real numbers A, B, and C, the inequalities

$$A < B \quad \text{and} \quad A + C < B + C$$

are equivalent.

In words, adding the same number to each side of an inequality does not change the solution set.

As with equations, the addition property can be used to *subtract* the same number from each side of an inequality.

Example 2 Using the Addition Property of Inequality

Solve $x - 7 < -12$.

Add 7 to each side.

$$x - 7 + 7 < -12 + 7 \qquad \text{Add 7.}$$
$$x < -5$$

Check: Substitute -5 for x in the equation $x - 7 = -12$. The result should be a true statement.

$$x - 7 = -12$$
$$-5 - 7 = -12 \quad ? \qquad \text{Let } x = -5.$$
$$-12 = -12 \qquad \text{True}$$

This shows that -5 is the boundary point. Now we test a number on each side of -5 to verify that numbers *less than* -5 make the inequality true. We choose -4 and -6.

$$x - 7 < -12$$

$-4 - 7 < -12$? Let $x = -4$.	$-6 - 7 < -12$? Let $x = -6$.
$-11 < -12$ False	$-13 < -12$ True
-4 is not in the solution set.	-6 is in the solution set.

The check confirms that $(-\infty, -5)$, graphed in Figure 4, is the correct solution set.

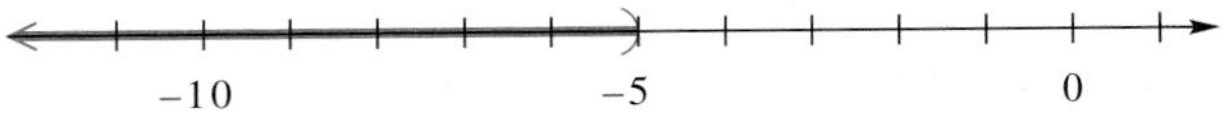

Figure 4

Work Problem **2** at the Side.

Example 3 Using the Addition Property of Inequality

Solve the inequality $14 + 2m \leq 3m$, and graph the solution set.

Continued on Next Page

ANSWERS

2. (a) $(-\infty, 2)$

(b) $(-\infty, -6)$

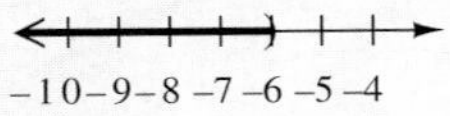

First, subtract $2m$ from each side.

$$14 + 2m \le 3m$$
$$14 + 2m - 2m \le 3m - 2m \quad \text{Subtract } 2m.$$
$$14 \le m \quad \text{Combine like terms.}$$

The inequality $14 \le m$ (14 is less than or equal to m) can also be written $m \ge 14$ (m is greater than or equal to 14). Notice that in each case, the inequality symbol points to the smaller number, 14.

Check:

$$14 + 2m = 3m$$
$$14 + 2(14) = 3(14) \quad ? \quad \text{Let } m = 14.$$
$$42 = 42 \quad \text{True}$$

So 14 satisfies the equality part of $\le$. Choose 10 and 15 as test points.

$$14 + 2m < 3m$$

$14 + 2(10) < 3(10)$? Let $m = 10$.	$14 + 2(15) < 3(15)$? Let $m = 15$.
$34 < 30$ False	$44 < 45$ True
10 is not in the solution set.	15 is in the solution set.

The check confirms that $[14, \infty)$ is the correct solution set. See Figure 5.

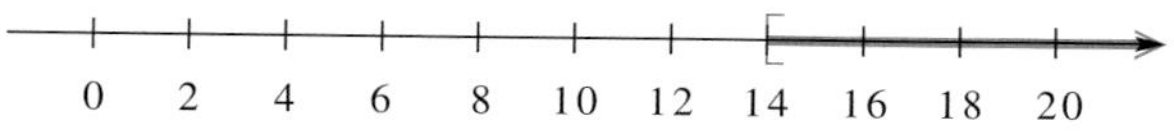

Figure 5

CAUTION

Errors often occur in graphing inequalities when the variable term is on the right side. (This is probably due to the fact that we read from left to right.) To guard against such errors, it is a good idea to rewrite these inequalities so that the variable is on the left, as discussed in Example 3.

Work Problem 3 at the Side.

3 Solve linear inequalities using the multiplication property. Solving an inequality such as $3x \le 15$ requires dividing each side by 3, using the *multiplication property of inequality*, which is a little more involved than the multiplication property of *equality*. To see how the multiplication property of inequality works, start with the true statement

$$-2 < 5.$$

Multiply each side by, say, 8.

$$-2(8) < 5(8) \quad \text{Multiply by 8.}$$
$$-16 < 40 \quad \text{True}$$

This gives a true statement. Start again with $-2 < 5$, and multiply each side by -8.

$$-2(-8) < 5(-8) \quad \text{Multiply by } -8.$$
$$16 < -40 \quad \text{False}$$

The result, $16 < -40$, is false. To make it true, we must change the direction of the inequality symbol to get

$$16 > -40. \quad \text{True}$$

Work Problem 4 at the Side.

3 Solve $2k - 5 \ge 1 + k$, check, and graph the solution set.

4 Multiply both sides of each inequality by -5. Then insert the correct symbol, either $<$ or $>$, in the first blank, and fill in the other blank in part (b).

(a) $7 < 8$

-35 ______ -40

(b) $-1 > -4$

5 ______ ______

ANSWERS

3. $[6, \infty)$

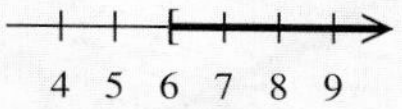

4. (a) $>$ **(b)** $<$; 20

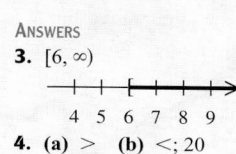

5 Solve each inequality, check, and graph the solution set.

(a) $2y < -10$

(b) $-7k \geq 8$

(c) $-9m < -81$

As these examples suggest, multiplying each side of an inequality by a *negative* number reverses the direction of the inequality symbol. The same is true for dividing by a negative number since division is defined in terms of multiplication.

Multiplication Property of Inequality

For all real numbers A, B, and C, with $C \neq 0$,
(a) the inequalities

$$A < B \quad \text{and} \quad AC < BC$$

are equivalent **if $C > 0$**;
(b) the inequalities

$$A < B \quad \text{and} \quad AC > BC$$

are equivalent **if $C < 0$**.

In words, each side of an inequality may be multiplied by a *positive* number without changing the direction of the inequality symbol. ***Multiplying or dividing by a* negative *number requires that we reverse the inequality symbol.***

CAUTION

Remember to reverse the direction of the inequality symbol when multiplying or dividing by a *negative* number.

Example 4 Using the Multiplication Property of Inequality

Solve each inequality, and graph the solution set.

(a) $5m \leq -30$

Use the multiplication property to divide each side by 5. Since $5 > 0$, do *not* reverse the inequality symbol.

$$5m \leq -30$$

$$\frac{5m}{5} \leq \frac{-30}{5} \quad \text{Divide by 5.}$$

$$m \leq -6$$

Check that the solution set is the interval $(-\infty, -6]$, graphed in Figure 6.

Figure 6

(b) $-4k \leq 32$

Divide each side by -4. Since $-4 < 0$, reverse the inequality symbol.

$$-4k \leq 32$$

$$\frac{-4k}{-4} \geq \frac{32}{-4} \quad \text{Divide by } -4 \text{ and reverse the symbol.}$$

$$k \geq -8$$

Check the solution set. Figure 7 shows the graph of the solution set, $[-8, \infty)$.

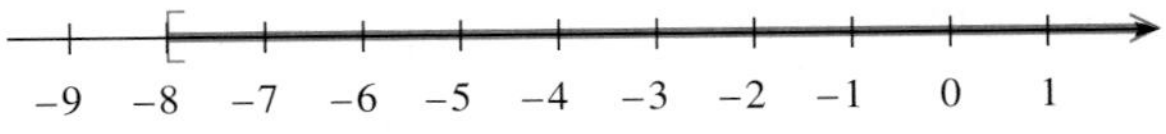

Figure 7

Work Problem 5 at the Side.

ANSWERS

5. (a) $(-\infty, -5)$

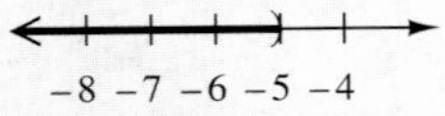

(b) $\left(-\infty, -\frac{8}{7}\right]$

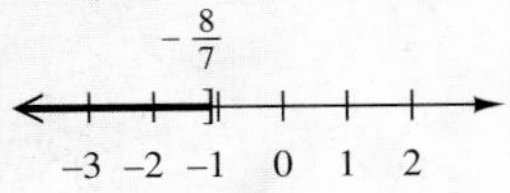

(c) $(9, \infty)$

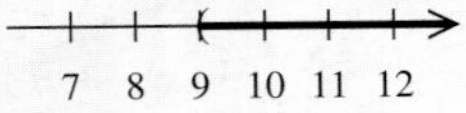

The steps used in solving a linear inequality are given below.

Solving a Linear Inequality

Step 1 **Simplify each side separately.** Simplify each side of the inequality as much as possible by using the distributive property to clear parentheses and by combining like terms as needed.

Step 2 **Isolate the variable terms on one side.** Use the addition property of inequality to get all terms with variables on one side of the inequality and all numbers on the other side.

Step 3 **Isolate the variable.** Use the multiplication property of inequality to change the inequality to the form $x < k$ or $x > k$.

Remember: Reverse the direction of the inequality symbol ***only*** when ***multiplying or dividing each side of an inequality by a*** **negative** ***number.***

Example 5 Solving a Linear Inequality Using the Distributive Property

Solve $-3(x + 4) + 2 \geq 7 - x$, and graph the solution set.

$$-3x - 12 + 2 \geq 7 - x \quad \text{Distributive property}$$
$$-3x - 10 \geq 7 - x$$
$$-3x - 10 + \mathbf{x} \geq 7 - x + \mathbf{x} \quad \text{Add } x.$$
$$-2x - 10 \geq 7$$
$$-2x - 10 + \mathbf{10} \geq 7 + \mathbf{10} \quad \text{Add 10.}$$
$$-2x \geq 17$$
$$\frac{-2x}{\mathbf{-2}} \leq \frac{17}{\mathbf{-2}} \quad \text{Divide by } -2\text{; change } \geq \text{ to } \leq.$$
$$x \leq -\frac{17}{2}$$

Figure 8 shows the graph of the solution set, $(-\infty, -\frac{17}{2}]$.

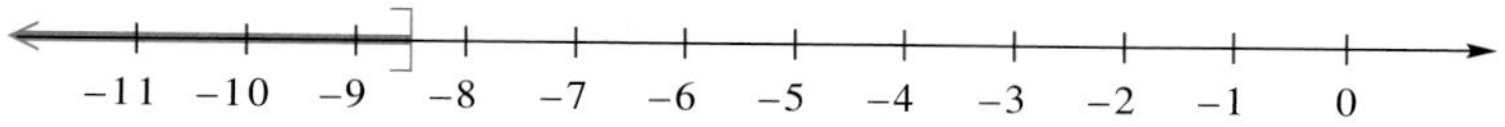

Figure 8

Example 6 Solving a Linear Inequality with Fractions

Solve $-\frac{2}{3}(r - 3) - \frac{1}{2} < \frac{1}{2}(5 - r)$, and graph the solution set.

To clear fractions, multiply each side by the least common denominator, 6.

$$-\frac{2}{3}(r - 3) - \frac{1}{2} < \frac{1}{2}(5 - r)$$
$$-4(r - 3) - 3 < 3(5 - r) \quad \text{Multiply by 6.}$$

Step 1
$$-4r + 12 - 3 < 15 - 3r \quad \text{Distributive property}$$
$$-4r + 9 < 15 - 3r$$

Continued on Next Page

6 Solve, check, and graph the solution set of each inequality.

(a) $5 - 3(m - 1) \leq 2(m + 3) + 1$

(b) $\frac{1}{4}(m + 3) + 2 \leq \frac{3}{4}(m + 8)$

Step 2

$$3r - 4r + 9 < 3r + 15 - 3r \quad \text{Add } 3r.$$
$$-r + 9 < 15$$
$$-r + 9 - 9 < 15 - 9 \quad \text{Subtract 9.}$$
$$-r < 6$$

Step 3 To solve for r, multiply each side of the inequality by -1. Since -1 is negative, change the direction of the inequality symbol.

$$-1(-r) > -1(6) \quad \text{Multiply by } -1, \text{ change } < \text{ to } >.$$
$$r > -6$$

Check that the solution set is $(-6, \infty)$. See Figure 9.

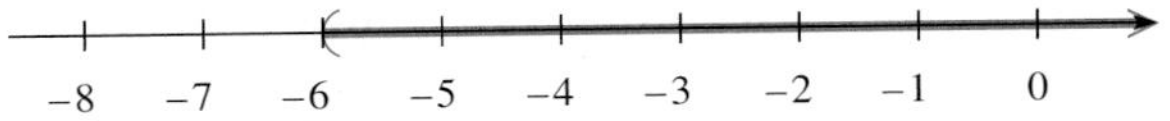

Figure 9

Work Problem 6 at the Side.

4 **Solve linear inequalities with three parts.** For some applications, it is necessary to work with an inequality such as

$$3 < x + 2 < 8,$$

where $x + 2$ is *between* 3 and 8. To solve this inequality, we subtract 2 from each of the three parts of the inequality, giving

$$3 - 2 < x + 2 - 2 < 8 - 2$$
$$1 < x < 6.$$

Thus, x must be between 1 and 6, so $x + 2$ will be between 3 and 8. The solution set, $(1, 6)$, is graphed in Figure 10.

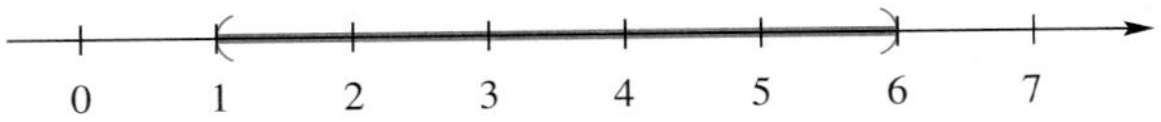

Figure 10

CAUTION

When inequalities have three parts, the order of the parts is important. It would be *wrong* to write an inequality as $8 < x + 2 < 3$, since this would imply that $8 < 3$, a false statement. In general, three-part inequalities are written so that the symbols point in the same direction, and both point toward the smaller number.

Example 7 **Solving a Three-Part Inequality**

Solve the inequality $-2 \leq -3k - 1 \leq 5$, and graph the solution set.

Begin by adding 1 to each of the three parts to isolate the variable term in the middle.

$$-2 + 1 \leq -3k - 1 + 1 \leq 5 + 1 \quad \text{Add 1 to each part.}$$
$$-1 \leq -3k \leq 6$$
$$\frac{-1}{-3} \geq \frac{-3k}{-3} \geq \frac{6}{-3} \quad \text{Divide each part by } -3; \text{ reverse the inequality symbols.}$$
$$\frac{1}{3} \geq k \geq -2$$
$$-2 \leq k \leq \frac{1}{3} \quad \text{Rewrite in the order on the number line.}$$

Continued on Next Page

ANSWERS

6. (a) $\left[\frac{1}{5}, \infty\right)$

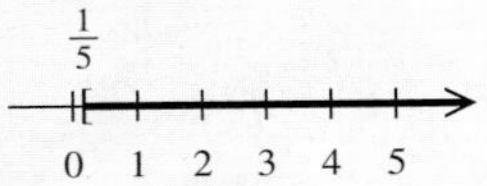

(b) $\left[-\frac{13}{2}, \infty\right)$

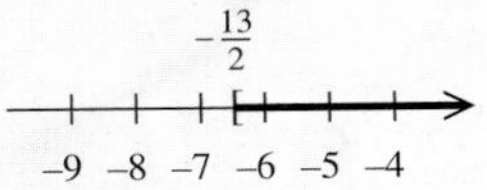

Check that the solution set is $\left[-2, \frac{1}{3}\right]$, as shown in Figure 11.

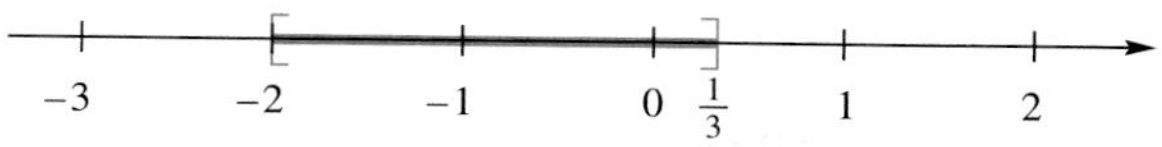

Figure 11

Work Problem 7 at the Side.

Examples of the types of solution sets to be expected from solving linear equations or linear inequalities are shown below.

SOLUTIONS OF LINEAR EQUATIONS AND INEQUALITIES

Equation or Inequality	Typical Solution Set	Graph of Solution Set
Linear equation $5x + 4 = 14$	$\{2\}$	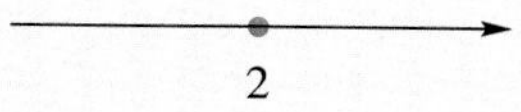
Linear inequality $5x + 4 < 14$	$(-\infty, 2)$	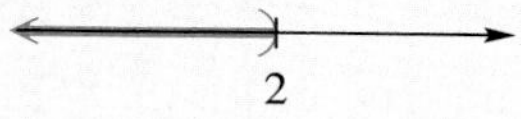
$5x + 4 > 14$	$(2, \infty)$	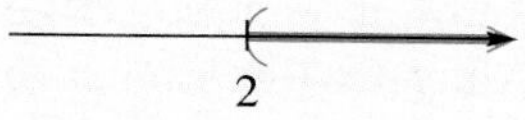
Three-part inequality $-1 \leq 5x + 4 \leq 14$	$[-1, 2]$	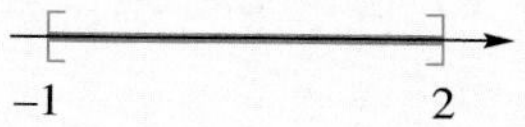

5 **Solve applied problems using linear inequalities.** In addition to the familiar "is less than" and "is greater than," the expressions "is no more than" and "is at least" also indicate inequalities. Expressions for inequalities sometimes appear in applied problems. The table below shows how to interpret these expressions.

Word Expression	Interpretation
a is at least *b*	$a \geq b$
a is no less than *b*	$a \geq b$
a is at most *b*	$a \leq b$
a is no more than *b*	$a \leq b$

In Examples 8 and 9, we show how to solve applied problems with inequalities. We use the six problem-solving steps from Chapter 2, changing Step 3 to "Write an inequality" instead of "Write an equation."

Example 8 **Using a Linear Inequality to Solve a Rental Problem**

A rental company charges \$15 to rent a chain saw, plus \$2 per hr. Al Ghandi can spend no more than \$35 to clear some logs from his yard. What is the *maximum* amount of time he can use the rented saw?

Step 1 **Read** the problem again.

Step 2 **Assign a variable.** Let $h =$ the number of hours he can rent the saw.

Continued on Next Page

7 Solve, check, and graph the solution set of each inequality.

(a) $-3 \leq x - 1 \leq 7$

(b) $5 < 3x - 4 < 9$

ANSWERS

7. (a) $[-2, 8]$

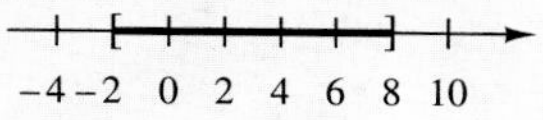

(b) $\left(3, \frac{13}{3}\right)$

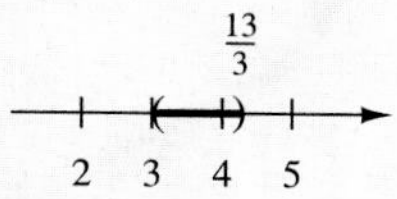

Step 3 **Write an inequality.** He must pay \$15, plus \$2h, to rent the saw for h hours, and this amount must be *no more than* \$35.

Cost of renting	is no more than	35 dollars.	
$15 + 2h$	$\leq$	35	

Step 4 **Solve.**

$$2h \leq 20 \quad \text{Subtract 15.}$$
$$h \leq 10 \quad \text{Divide by 2.}$$

Step 5 **State the answer.** He can use the saw for a maximum of 10 hr. (Of course, he may use it for less time, as indicated by the inequality $h \leq 10$.)

Step 6 **Check.** If Al uses the saw for 10 hr, he will spend $15 + 2(10) = 35$ dollars, the maximum amount.

Work Problem 8 at the Side.

8 Solve the problem.
Maureen O'Connor can rent a car from Ames for \$48 per day plus 10¢ per mile, or from Hughes at \$40 per day plus 15¢ per mile. She plans to use the car for 3 days. What number of miles would make Hughes cost at most as much as Ames?

Example 9 Finding an Average Test Score

Martha has scores of 88, 86, and 90 on her first three algebra tests. An average score of at least 90 will earn an A in the class. What possible scores on her fourth test will earn her an A average?

Let x represent the score on the fourth test. Her average score must be at least 90. To find the average of four numbers, add them and then divide by 4.

$$\underbrace{\frac{88 + 86 + 90 + x}{4}}_{\text{Average}} \underbrace{\geq}_{\text{is at least}} \underbrace{90}_{90.}$$

$$\frac{264 + x}{4} \geq 90 \quad \text{Add the scores.}$$

$$264 + x \geq 360 \quad \text{Multiply by 4.}$$

$$x \geq 96 \quad \text{Subtract 264.}$$

She must score 96 or more on her fourth test.

Check: $$\frac{88 + 86 + 90 + 96}{4} = \frac{360}{4} = 90$$

A score of 96 or more will give an average of at least 90, as required.

Work Problem 9 at the Side.

9 Solve the problem.
Michael has grades of 92, 90, and 84 on his first three tests. What grade must he make on his fourth test in order to keep an average of at least 90?

ANSWERS
8. 480 mi or less
9. at least 94

3.1 EXERCISES

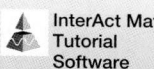

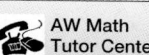

FOR EXTRA HELP: Student's Solutions Manual; MyMathLab.com; InterAct Math Tutorial Software; AW Math Tutor Center; www.mathxl.com; Digital Video Tutor CD 3 Videotape 6

Match each inequality with the correct graph or interval notation.

1. $x \leq 3$ **D**

2. $x > 3$ **C**

3. $x < 3$ **B**

4. $x \geq 3$ **A**

5. $-3 \leq x \leq 3$ **F**

6. $-3 < x < 3$ **E**

A. 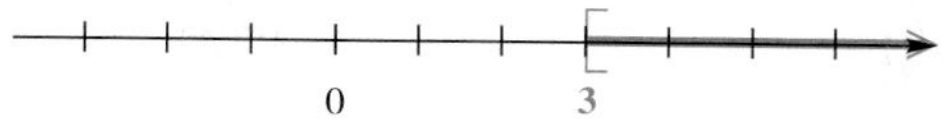

B. 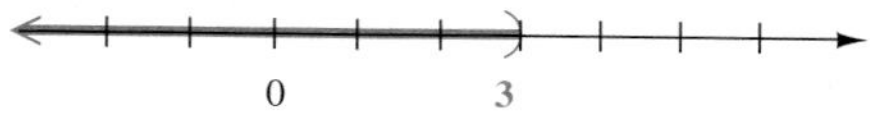

C. $(3, \infty)$

D. $(-\infty, 3]$

E. $(-3, 3)$

F. $[-3, 3]$

7. Explain how you will determine whether to use parentheses or brackets when graphing the solution set of an inequality.

Use a parenthesis when an endpoint is not included; use a bracket when it is included.

8. Describe the steps used to solve a linear inequality. Explain when it is necessary to reverse the inequality symbol.

Simplify each side separately using the distributive property and combining terms. Get all variable terms on one side of the inequality and numbers on the other side. Get the variable with a coefficient of 1 on one side of the inequality sign and a number on the other side. The inequality sign must be reversed when multiplying or dividing each side by a negative number.

Solve each inequality, giving its solution set in both interval and graph forms. Check your answers. See Examples 1–6.

9. $4x + 1 \geq 21$

$[5, \infty)$

10. $5t + 2 \geq 52$

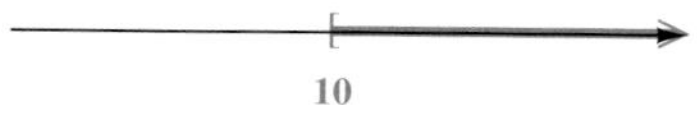

$[10, \infty)$

11. $\dfrac{3k - 1}{4} > 5$

$(7, \infty)$

12. $\dfrac{5z - 6}{8} < 8$

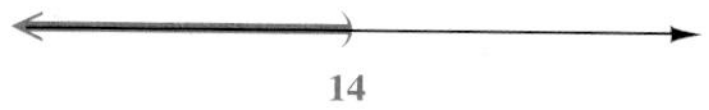

$(-\infty, 14)$

13. $-4x < 16$

$(-4, \infty)$

14. $-2m > 10$

$(-\infty, -5)$

15. $-\frac{3}{4}r \geq 30$

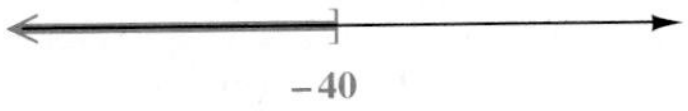

$(-\infty, -40]$

16. $-\frac{2}{3}y \leq 12$

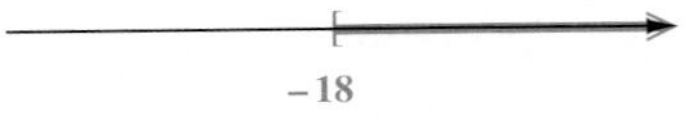

$[-18, \infty)$

17. $-1.3m \geq -5.2$

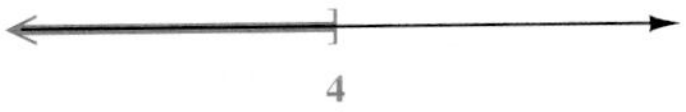

$(-\infty, 4]$

18. $-2.5y \leq -1.25$

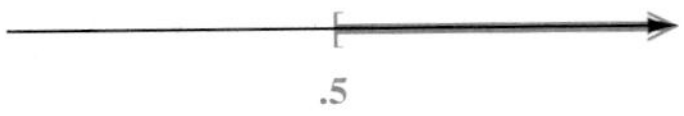

$[.5, \infty)$

19. $\frac{2k-5}{-4} > 5$

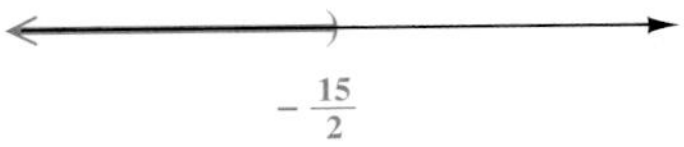

$\left(-\infty, -\frac{15}{2}\right)$

20. $\frac{3z-2}{-5} < 6$

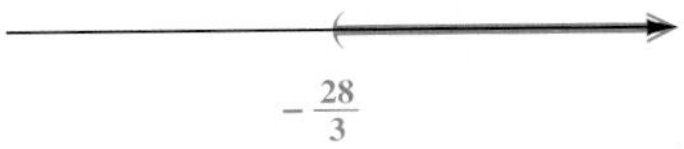

$\left(-\frac{28}{3}, \infty\right)$

21. $y + 4(2y - 1) \geq y$

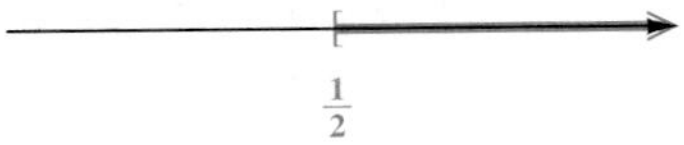

$\left[\frac{1}{2}, \infty\right)$

22. $m - 2(m - 4) \leq 3m$

$[2, \infty)$

23. $-(4 + r) + 2 - 3r < -14$

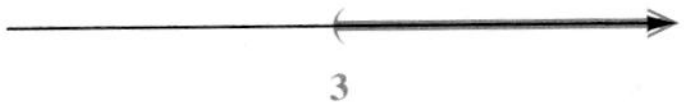

$(3, \infty)$

24. $-(9 + k) - 5 + 4k \geq 4$

$[6, \infty)$

25. $-3(z - 6) > 2z - 2$

$(-\infty, 4)$

26. $-2(y + 4) \leq 6y + 16$

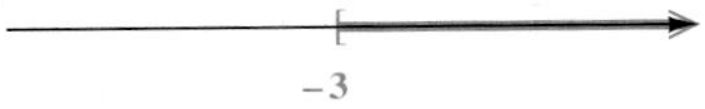

$[-3, \infty)$

27. $\frac{2}{3}(3k - 1) \geq \frac{3}{2}(2k - 3)$

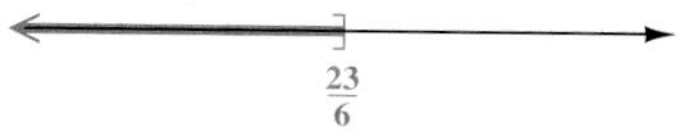

$\left(-\infty, \frac{23}{6}\right]$

28. $\frac{7}{5}(10m - 1) < \frac{2}{3}(6m + 5)$

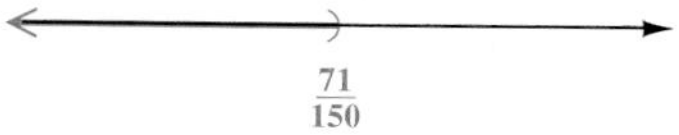

$\left(-\infty, \frac{71}{150}\right)$

29. $-\frac{1}{4}(p + 6) + \frac{3}{2}(2p - 5) < 10$

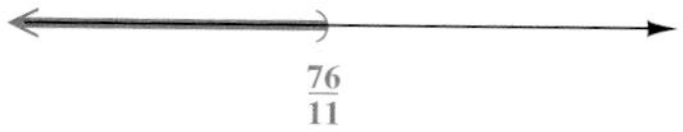

$\left(-\infty, \frac{76}{11}\right)$

30. $\frac{3}{5}(k - 2) - \frac{1}{4}(2k - 7) \leq 3$

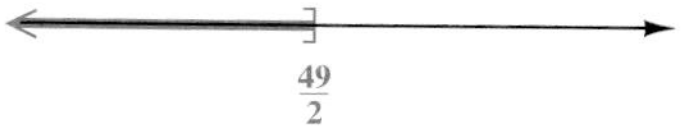

$\left(-\infty, \frac{49}{2}\right]$

RELATING CONCEPTS (Exercises 31–35) FOR INDIVIDUAL OR GROUP WORK

Work Exercises 31–35 in order.

31. Solve the linear equation

$$5(x + 3) - 2(x - 4) = 2(x + 7),$$

and graph the solution set on a number line. $\{-9\}$

32. Solve the linear inequality

$$5(x + 3) - 2(x - 4) > 2(x + 7),$$

and graph the solution set on a number line. $(-9, \infty)$

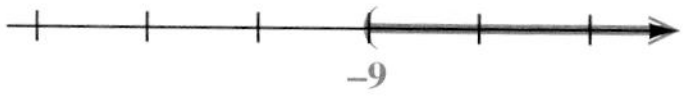

33. Solve the linear inequality

$$5(x + 3) - 2(x - 4) < 2(x + 7),$$

and graph the solution set on a number line. $(-\infty, -9)$

34. Graph all the solution sets of the equation and inequalities in Exercises 31–33 on the same number line. What set do you obtain? **We obtain the set of all real numbers.**

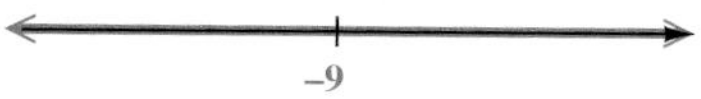

35. Based on the results of Exercises 31–33, complete the following using a conjecture (educated guess): The solution set of

$$-3(x + 2) = 3x + 12$$

is $\{-3\}$, and the solution set of

$$-3(x + 2) < 3x + 12$$

is $(-3, \infty)$. Therefore the solution set of

$$-3(x + 2) > 3x + 12$$

is $\underline{(-\infty, -3)}$.

36. Which is the graph of $-2 < x$?

A. 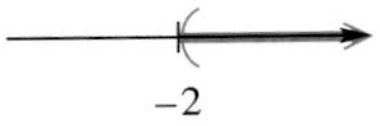

B. 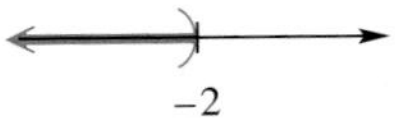

C. 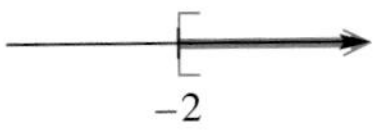

D. 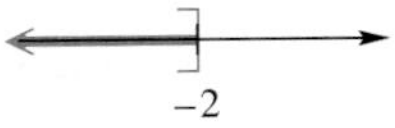

A

Solve each inequality, giving its solution set in both interval and graph forms. Check your answers. See Example 7.

37. $-4 < x - 5 < 6$

$(1, 11)$

38. $-1 < x + 1 < 8$

$(-2, 7)$

39. $-9 \leq k + 5 \leq 15$

$[-14, 10]$

40. $-4 \leq m + 3 \leq 10$

$[-7, 7]$

41. $-6 \leq 2(z + 2) \leq 16$

$[-5, 6]$

42. $-15 < 3(p + 2) < -12$

$(-7, -6)$

43. $-16 < 3t + 2 < -10$

$(-6, -4)$

44. $-1 \leq \dfrac{2x - 5}{6} \leq 5$

$\left[-\dfrac{1}{2}, \dfrac{35}{2}\right]$

45. $-3 \leq \dfrac{3m + 1}{4} \leq 3$

$\left[-\dfrac{13}{3}, \dfrac{11}{3}\right]$

The July 14th weather forecast by time of day for the 2000 U.S. Olympic Track and Field Trials, held July 14–23, 2000, in Sacramento, California, is shown in the figure. Use this graph to work Exercises 46–49.

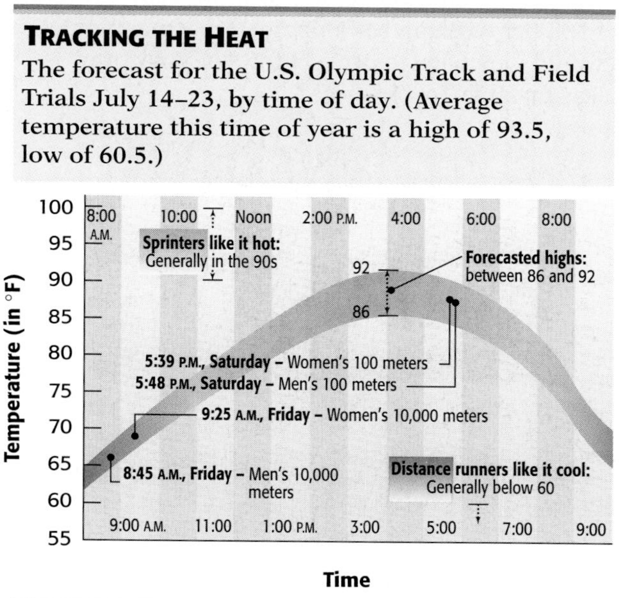

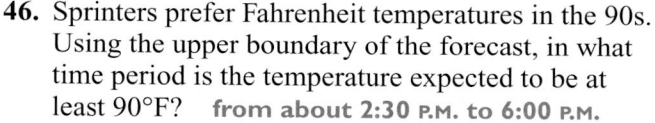

Source: Accuweather, Bee research.

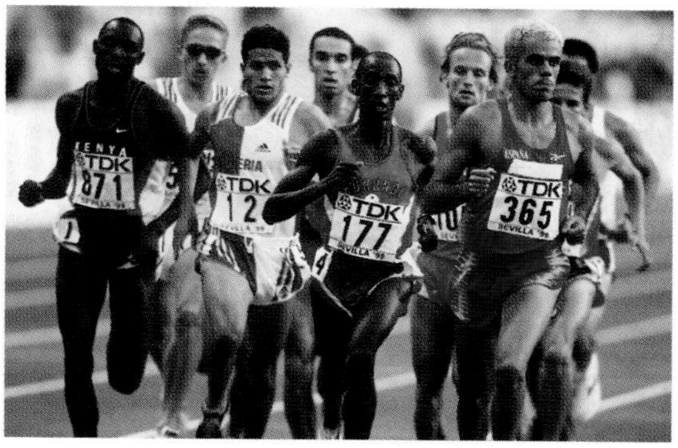

46. Sprinters prefer Fahrenheit temperatures in the 90s. Using the upper boundary of the forecast, in what time period is the temperature expected to be at least 90°F? **from about 2:30 P.M. to 6:00 P.M.**

47. Distance runners prefer cool temperatures. During what time period are temperatures predicted to be no more than 70°F? Use the lower forecast boundary. **from about 8:00 A.M. to 10:15 A.M. and after about 9:00 P.M.**

48. What range of temperatures is predicted for the Women's 100-m event? **about 84°F–91°F**

49. What range of temperatures is forecast for the Men's 10,000-m event? **about 65°F–67°F**

Solve each problem. See Examples 8 and 9.

50. Margaret Westmoreland earned scores of 90 and 82 on her first two tests in English Literature. What score must she make on her third test to keep an average of 84 or greater?

at least 80

51. Jacques d'Hemecourt scored 92 and 96 on his first two tests in Methods in Teaching Mathematics. What score must he make on his third test to keep an average of 90 or greater?

at least 82

52. A couple wishes to rent a car for one day while on vacation. Ford Automobile Rental wants \$15.00 per day and 14¢ per mi, while Chevrolet-For-A-Day wants \$14.00 per day and 16¢ per mi. After how many miles would the price to rent the Chevrolet exceed the price to rent a Ford?

50 mi

53. Jane and Terry Brandsma went to Mobile, Alabama, for a week. They needed to rent a car, so they checked out two rental firms. Avis wanted \$28 per day, with no mileage fee. Downtown Toyota wanted \$108 per week and 14¢ per mi. How many miles would they have to drive before the Avis price is less than the Toyota price?

628.6 mi

A product will produce a profit only when the revenue (R) from selling the product exceeds the cost (C) of producing it. Find the smallest whole number of units x that must be sold for each business to show a profit for the item described.

54. Peripheral Visions, Inc. finds that the cost to produce x studio-quality videotapes is

$$C = 20x + 100,$$

while the revenue produced from them is $R = 24x$ (C and R in dollars).

26 tapes

55. Speedy Delivery finds that the cost to make x deliveries is

$$C = 3x + 2300,$$

while the revenue produced from them is $R = 5.50x$ (C and R in dollars).

921 deliveries

56. A BMI (body mass index) between 19 and 25 is considered healthy. Use the formula

$$\text{BMI} = \frac{704 \times (\text{weight in pounds})}{(\text{height in inches})^2}$$

to find the weight range w, to the nearest pound, that gives a healthy BMI for each height. (*Source: Washington Post.*)

(a) 72 in. 140 to 184 lb

(b) Your height in inches Answers will vary.

57. To achieve the maximum benefit from exercising, the heart rate in beats per minute should be in the target heart rate zone (*THR*). For a person aged A, the formula is

$$.7(220 - A) \le THR \le .85(220 - A).$$

Find the *THR* to the nearest whole number for each age. (*Source:* Hockey, Robert V., *Physical Fitness: The Pathway to Healthful Living,* Times Mirror/Mosby College Publishing, 1989.)

(a) 35 130 to 157 beats per min

(b) Your age Answers will vary.

3.2 Set Operations and Compound Inequalities

The table shows symptoms of an overactive thyroid and an underactive thyroid.

Underactive Thyroid	Overactive Thyroid
Sleepiness, s	Insomnia, i
Dry hands, d	Moist hands, m
Intolerance of cold, c	Intolerance of heat, h
Goiter, g	Goiter, g

Source: The Merck Manual of Diagnosis and Therapy, 16th Edition, Merck Research Laboratories, 1992.

Let N be the set of symptoms for an underactive thyroid, and let O be the set of symptoms for an overactive thyroid. Suppose we are interested in the set of symptoms that are found in *both* sets N *and* O. In this section we discuss the use of the words *and* and *or* as they relate to sets and inequalities.

Objectives

1. Find the intersection of two sets.
2. Solve compound inequalities with the word *and.*
3. Find the union of two sets.
4. Solve compound inequalities with the word *or.*

1 **Find the intersection of two sets.** The intersection of two sets is defined using the word *and.*

Intersection of Sets

For any two sets A and B, the **intersection** of A and B, symbolized $A \cap B$, is defined as follows:

$$A \cap B = \{x \mid x \text{ is an element of } A \textbf{ and } x \text{ is an element of } B\}.$$

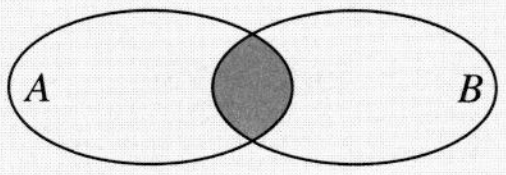

Example 1 Finding the Intersection of Two Sets

Let $A = \{1, 2, 3, 4\}$ and $B = \{2, 4, 6\}$. Find $A \cap B$.

The set $A \cap B$ contains those elements that belong to both A *and* B: the numbers 2 and 4. Therefore,

$$A \cap B = \{1, 2, 3, 4\} \cap \{2, 4, 6\}$$
$$= \{2, 4\}.$$

Work Problem 1 at the Side.

1 List the elements in each set.

(a) $A \cap B$, if $A = \{3, 4, 5, 6\}$ and $B = \{5, 6, 7\}$

(b) $N \cap O$ (Refer to the thyroid table.)

A **compound inequality** consists of two inequalities linked by a connective word such as *and* or *or.* Examples of compound inequalities are

$$x + 1 \le 9 \quad \textbf{and} \quad x - 2 \ge 3$$

and

$$2x > 4 \quad \textbf{or} \quad 3x - 6 < 5.$$

2 **Solve compound inequalities with the word *and.*** Use the following steps.

Solving a Compound Inequality with *and*

Step 1 Solve each inequality in the compound inequality individually.

Step 2 Since the inequalities are joined with *and*, the solution set of the compound inequality will include all numbers that satisfy both inequalities in Step 1 (the intersection of the solution sets).

Answers

1. (a) $\{5, 6\}$ **(b)** $\{g\}$

2 Solve each compound inequality, and graph the solution set.

(a) $x < 10$ and $x > 2$

(b) $x + 3 \leq 1$ and $x - 4 \geq -12$

3 Solve

$2x \geq x - 1$ and $3x \geq 3 + 2x$,

and graph the solution set.

Example 2 Solving a Compound Inequality with *and*

Solve the compound inequality

$$x + 1 \leq 9 \quad \text{and} \quad x - 2 \geq 3.$$

Step 1 Solve each inequality in the compound inequality individually.

$$\begin{aligned} x + 1 &\leq 9 & &\text{and} & x - 2 &\geq 3 \\ x + 1 - 1 &\leq 9 - 1 & &\text{and} & x - 2 + 2 &\geq 3 + 2 \\ x &\leq 8 & &\text{and} & x &\geq 5 \end{aligned}$$

Step 2 Because the inequalities are joined with the word *and*, the solution set will include all numbers that satisfy both inequalities in Step 1 at the same time. Thus, the compound inequality is true whenever $x \leq 8$ and $x \geq 5$ are both true. The top graph in Figure 12 shows $x \leq 8$, and the bottom graph shows $x \geq 5$.

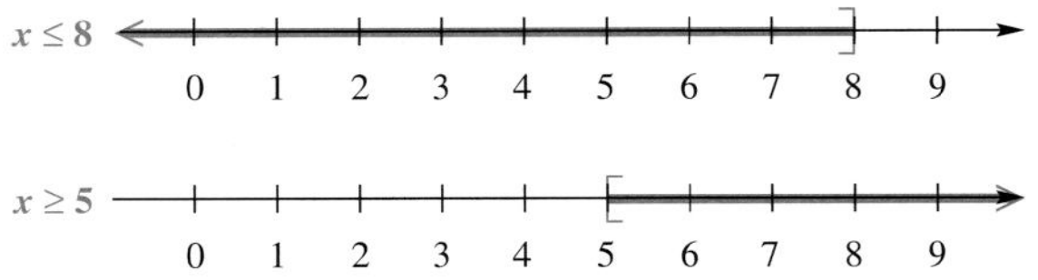

Figure 12

Find the intersection of the two graphs in Figure 12 to get the solution set of the compound inequality. The intersection of the two graphs in Figure 13 shows that the solution set in interval notation is [5, 8].

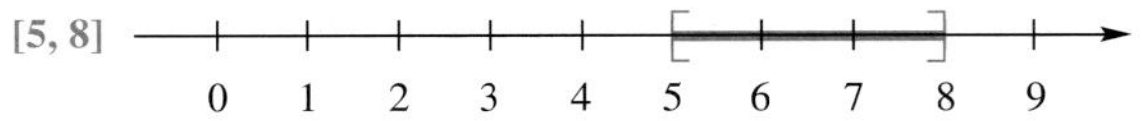

Figure 13

Work Problem 2 at the Side.

Example 3 Solving a Compound Inequality with *and*

Solve the compound inequality

$$-3x - 2 > 5 \quad \text{and} \quad 5x - 1 \leq -21.$$

Step 1 Solve each inequality separately.

$$\begin{aligned} -3x - 2 &> 5 & &\text{and} & 5x - 1 &\leq -21 \\ -3x &> 7 & &\text{and} & 5x &\leq -20 \\ x &< -\frac{7}{3} & &\text{and} & x &\leq -4 \end{aligned}$$

The graphs of $x < -\frac{7}{3}$ and $x \leq -4$ are shown in Figure 14.

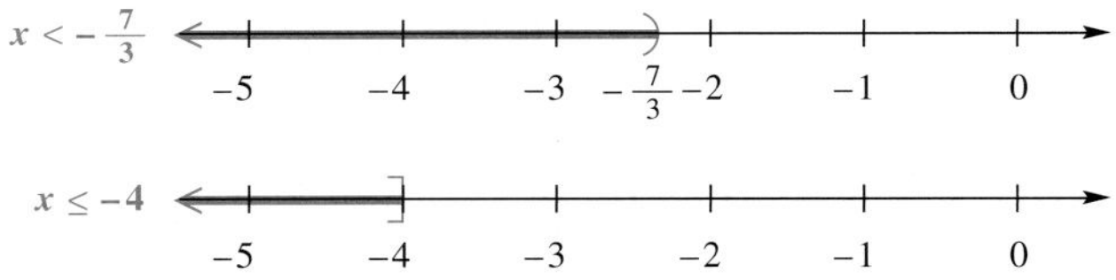

Figure 14

Step 2 Now find all values of x that satisfy both conditions; that is, the real numbers that are less than $-\frac{7}{3}$ and also less than or equal to -4. As shown by the graph in Figure 15, the solution set is $(-\infty, -4]$.

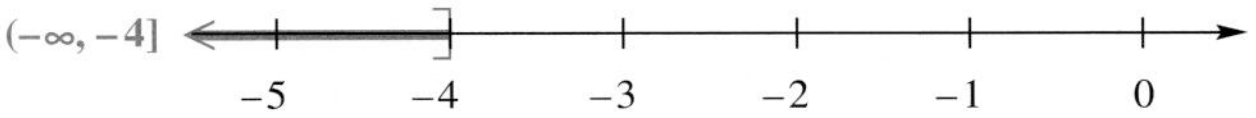

Figure 15

Work Problem 3 at the Side.

ANSWERS

2. (a) (2, 10)

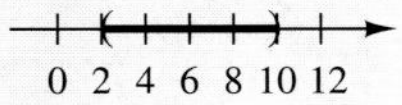

(b) $[-8, -2]$

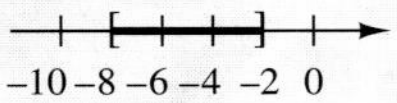

3. $[3, \infty)$

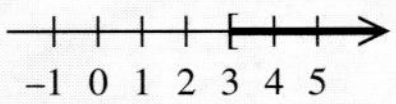

Example 4 Solving a Compound Inequality with *and*

Solve $x + 2 < 5$ and $x - 10 > 2$.

First solve each inequality separately.

$$x + 2 < 5 \quad \text{and} \quad x - 10 > 2$$
$$x < 3 \quad \text{and} \quad x > 12$$

The graphs of $x < 3$ and $x > 12$ are shown in Figure 16.

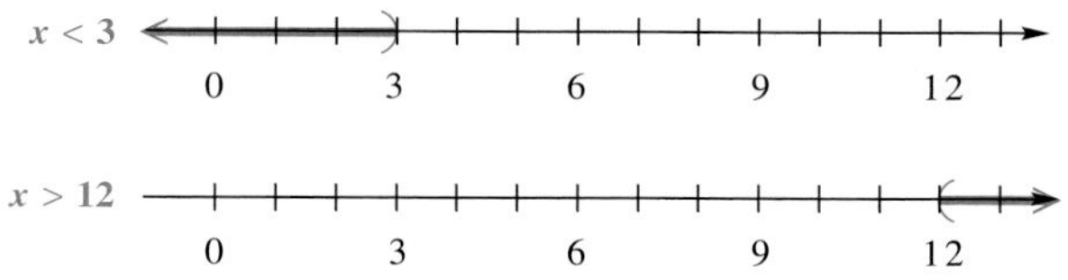

Figure 16

There is no number that is both less than 3 *and* greater than 12, so the given compound inequality has no solution. The solution set is $\emptyset$. See Figure 17.

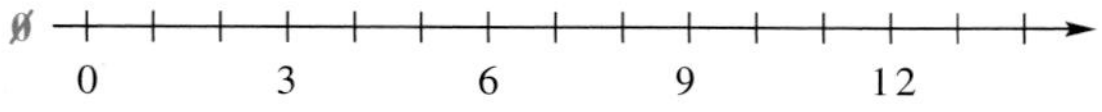

Figure 17

Work Problem 4 at the Side.

3 Find the union of two sets. The union of two sets is defined using the word *or*.

Union of Sets

For any two sets A and B, the **union** of A and B, symbolized $A \cup B$, is defined as follows:

$$A \cup B = \{x \mid x \text{ is an element of } A \textbf{ or } x \text{ is an element of } B\}.$$

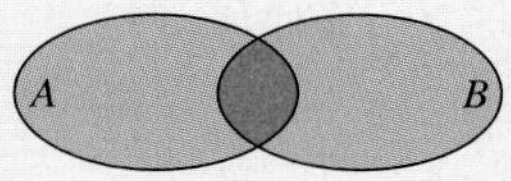

Example 5 Finding the Union of Two Sets

Let $A = \{1, 2, 3, 4\}$ and $B = \{2, 4, 6\}$. Find $A \cup B$.

Begin by listing all the elements of set A: 1, 2, 3, 4. Then list any additional elements from set B. In this case the elements 2 and 4 are already listed, so the only additional element is 6. Therefore,

$$A \cup B = \{1, 2, 3, 4\} \cup \{2, 4, 6\}$$
$$= \{1, 2, 3, 4, 6\}.$$

The union consists of all elements in either A *or* B (or both).

In Example 5, notice that although the elements 2 and 4 appeared in both sets A and B, they are written only once in $A \cup B$.

Work Problem 5 at the Side.

4 Solve.

(a) $x < 5$ and $x > 5$

(b) $x + 2 > 3$ and $2x + 1 < -3$

5 List the elements in each set.

(a) $A \cup B$, if $A = \{3, 4, 5, 6\}$ and $B = \{5, 6, 7\}$

(b) $N \cup O$ from the thyroid table at the beginning of this section

ANSWERS

4. (a) $\emptyset$ **(b)** $\emptyset$

5. (a) $\{3, 4, 5, 6, 7\}$ **(b)** $\{s, d, c, g, i, m, h\}$

6 Give each solution set in both interval and graph forms.

(a) $x + 2 > 3$ or
$2x + 1 < -3$

(b) $y - 1 > 2$ or
$3y + 5 < 2y + 6$

4 **Solve compound inequalities with the word *or*.** Use the following steps.

Solving a Compound Inequality with *or*

Step 1 Solve each inequality in the compound inequality individually.

Step 2 Since the inequalities are joined with *or,* the solution set includes all numbers that satisfy either one of the two inequalities in Step 1 (the union of the solution sets).

Example 6 Solving a Compound Inequality with *or*

Solve $6x - 4 < 2x$ or $-3x \leq -9$.

Step 1 Solve each inequality separately.

$$6x - 4 < 2x \quad \text{or} \quad -3x \leq -9$$
$$4x < 4$$
$$x < 1 \quad \text{or} \quad x \geq 3$$

The graphs of these two inequalities are shown in Figure 18.

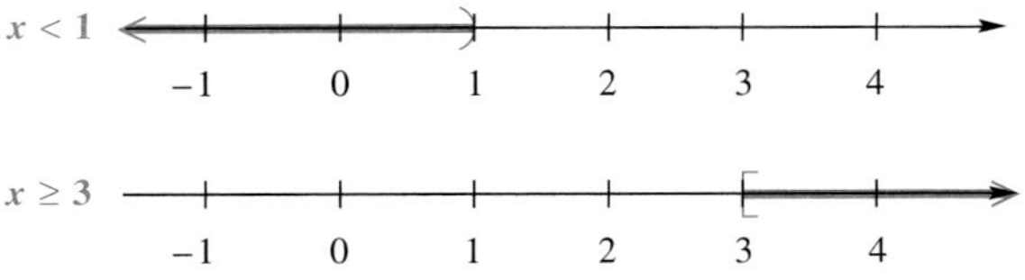

Figure 18

Step 2 Since the inequalities are joined with *or*, find the union of the two solution sets. The union is shown in Figure 19 and is written $(-\infty, 1) \cup [3, \infty)$.

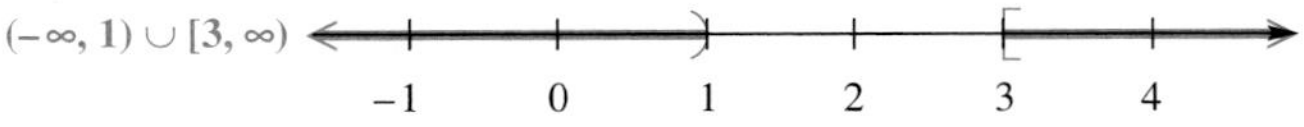

Figure 19

CAUTION

When inequalities are used to write the solution set in Example 6, it *should* be written as

$$x < 1 \quad \text{or} \quad x \geq 3,$$

which keeps the numbers 1 and 3 in their order on the number line. Writing $3 \leq x < 1$ would imply that $3 \leq 1$, which is ***FALSE.*** There is no other way to write the solution set of such a union.

Work Problem 6 at the Side.

Example 7 Solving a Compound Inequality with *or*

Solve $-4x + 1 \geq 9$ or $5x + 3 \geq -12$.

First, solve each inequality separately.

$$-4x + 1 \geq 9 \quad \text{or} \quad 5x + 3 \geq -12$$
$$-4x \geq 8 \quad \text{or} \quad 5x \geq -15$$
$$x \leq -2 \quad \text{or} \quad x \geq -3$$

Continued on Next Page

ANSWERS

6. (a) $(-\infty, -2) \cup (1, \infty)$

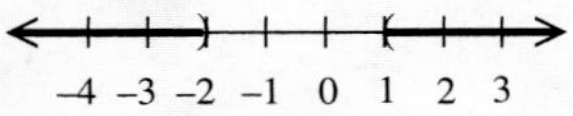

(b) $(-\infty, 1) \cup (3, \infty)$

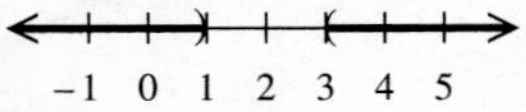

The graphs of these two inequalities are shown in Figure 20.

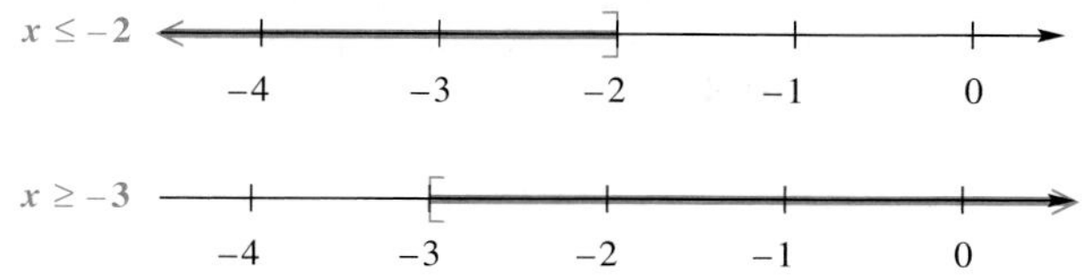

Figure 20

By taking the union, we obtain every real number as a solution, since every real number satisfies at least one of the two inequalities. The set of all real numbers is written in interval notation as $(-\infty, \infty)$ and graphed as in Figure 21.

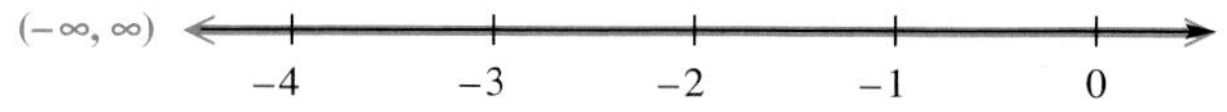

Figure 21

Work Problem 7 at the Side.

Example 8 Applying Intersection and Union

Average expenses for full-time college students during the 1997–1998 academic year are shown in the table.

COLLEGE EXPENSES IN 1997–1998 (IN DOLLARS)

Type of Expense	Public Schools	Private Schools
Tuition and fees	2365	13,013
Board rates	2180	2742
Dormitory charges	2243	2990

Source: U.S. National Center for Education Statistics, *Digest of Education Statistics,* annual.

Use the table to list the elements of each set.

(a) The set of expenses that are less than \$2500 for public schools *and* greater than \$3000 for private schools

The only expense that satisfies both conditions is for tuition and fees, so the set is

{Tuition and fees}.

(b) The set of expenses that are less than \$2200 for public schools *or* are greater than \$3000 for private schools

Here, an expense that satisfies at least one of the conditions is in the set. Only the public school expense for board rates is less than \$2200, and only the private school expense for tuition and fees is greater than \$3000, so the set is

{Tuition and fees, Board rates}.

Work Problem 8 at the Side.

7 Solve.

(a) $2x + 1 \le 9$ or $2x + 3 \le 5$

(b) $3x - 2 \le 13$ or $x + 5 \ge 7$

8 Refer to the table in Example 8. List the elements in each set.

(a) The set of expenses less than \$2500 for public schools and less than \$3000 for private schools

(b) The set of expenses greater than \$10,000 or less than \$2000

ANSWERS

7. **(a)** $(-\infty, 4]$ **(b)** $(-\infty, \infty)$

8. **(a)** {Board rates, Dormitory charges} **(b)** {Tuition and fees}

Focus on *Real-Data Applications*

Comparing Long-Distance Costs

Cellular phones are becoming popular tools for both local and long-distance phone calls. Frequently, rate plans include long-distance telephoning as an option if the calls are made from within the home area. The plans vary among different companies and often offer a limited number of "anytime" minutes. Information about the rate plans offered by different cellular phone companies is readily available on the Internet.

Using the Internet, you have found the following pricing schemes for both regular and the cellular phones.

- The long-distance plan for the *in-home* phone costs \$6.95 per month plus \$.05 per min for long-distance calls both within your state or between states, with no limit to the number of minutes of call time.

- One option for the *cellular* phone is a flat monthly fee of \$59.99 that includes 450 min of "anytime" local or long-distance calls.

Note: Basic phone rates are *not* included in the in-home plan, but since you intend to have an in-home phone anyway, you can disregard those costs. Also, calls in excess of the limits for the cellular plan are expensive: \$.35 per minute over the maximum. You do *not* expect to exceed the number of minutes included in the basic cellular rate plan, so do not worry about those extra charges.

For Group Discussion

The question is "Which plan is more economical?" Of course, economy is only one of the criteria that you will use when deciding whether to use your in-home phone or a cellular phone for long-distance calls, but it is one of the most important issues.

Let x represent the number of minutes of long-distance calls in a month.

1. Write an expression that represents the monthly costs for the in-home rate plan. **$.05x + 6.95$**
2. Write the expression that represents the monthly cost for the cellular rate plan. **59.99**
3. The question is: "How many minutes of long-distance calls would you have to make in one month with the in-home phone to exceed the cost of the cellular phone plan?" Write a linear inequality that states that the in-home rate plan costs more than the cellular rate plan. **$.05x + 6.95 > 59.99$**
4. Solve the linear inequality and answer the question posed in Problem 3. What does your answer mean in terms of comparing phone costs? **$x > 1061$ min; The in-home phone charges are never more expensive than the cellular phone if the number of minutes per month is limited to 450.**
5. Suppose you use the cellular phone plan for 450 min (the maximum number of minutes without incurring excess charges). How much more money would you pay compared to the in-home plan? **\$30.54**

Teaching notes and an extension for this activity are provided in the *Printed Test Bank and Instructor's Resource Guide.*

3.2 EXERCISES

FOR EXTRA HELP: Student's Solutions Manual | MyMathLab.com | InterAct Math Tutorial Software | AW Math Tutor Center | www.mathxl.com | Digital Video Tutor CD 3 Videotape 6

Decide whether each statement is true *or* false. *If it is* false, *explain why.*

1. The union of the solution sets of $2x + 1 = 3$, $2x + 1 > 3$, and $2x + 1 < 3$ is $(-\infty, \infty)$.

true

2. The intersection of the sets $\{x \mid x \geq 5\}$ and $\{x \mid x \leq 5\}$ is $\emptyset$.

False; The intersection is $\{5\}$.

3. The union of the sets $(-\infty, 6)$ and $(6, \infty)$ is $\{6\}$.

False; The union is $(-\infty, 6) \cup (6, \infty)$.

4. The intersection of the sets $[6, \infty)$ and $(-\infty, 6]$ is $\{6\}$.

true

Let $A = \{1, 2, 3, 4, 5, 6\}$, $B = \{1, 3, 5\}$, $C = \{1, 6\}$, *and* $D = \{4\}$. *Specify each set. See Examples 1 and 5.*

5. $A \cap D$

$\{4\}$ or D

6. $B \cap C$

$\{1\}$

7. $B \cap \emptyset$

$\emptyset$

8. $A \cap \emptyset$

$\emptyset$

9. $A \cup B$

$\{1, 2, 3, 4, 5, 6\}$ or A

10. $B \cup D$

$\{1, 3, 4, 5\}$

11. $B \cup C$

$\{1, 3, 5, 6\}$

12. $C \cup B$

$\{1, 3, 5, 6\}$

Two sets are specified by graphs. Graph the intersection of the two sets.

13.

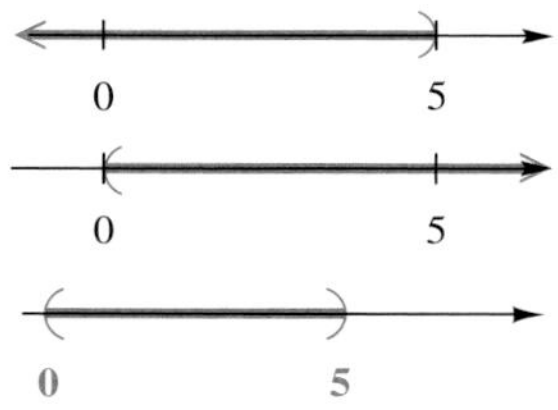

14.

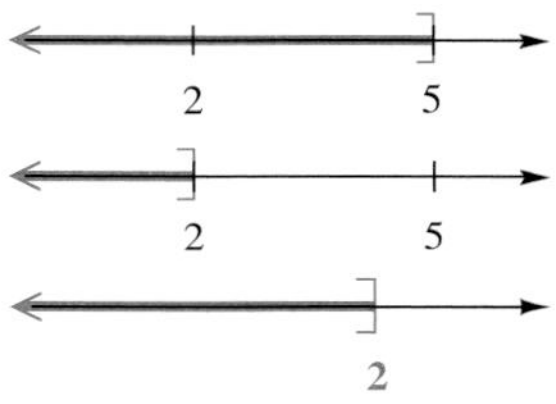

15.

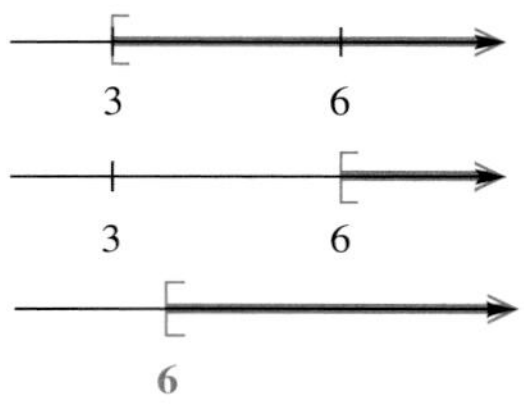

Two sets are specified by graphs. Graph the union of the two sets.

16.

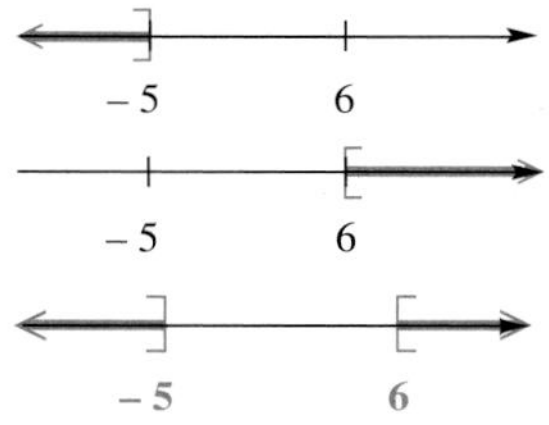

17.

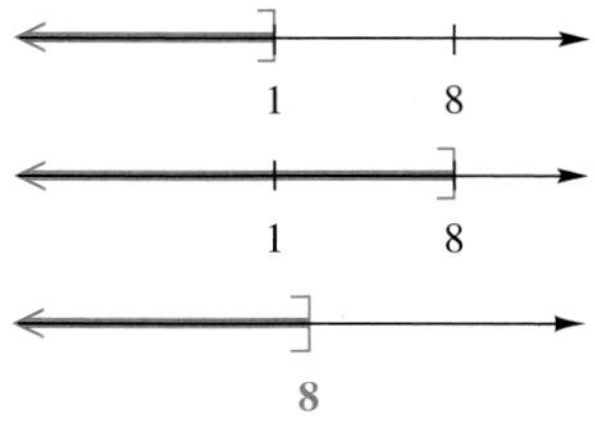

18.

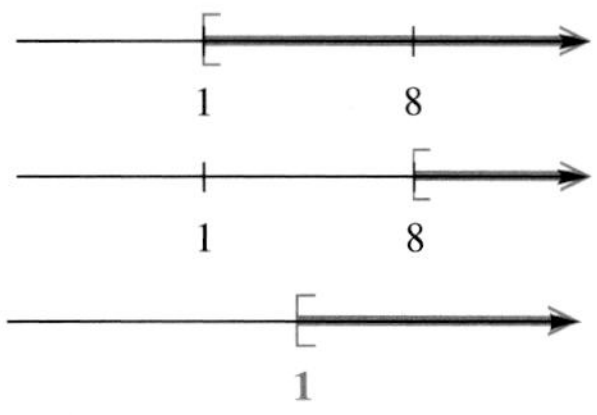

19. Give an example of intersection applied to a real-life situation.

Answers will vary. One example is: The intersection of two streets is the region common to *both* streets.

20. A compound inequality uses one of the words *and* or *or*. Explain how you will determine whether to use *intersection* or *union* when graphing the solution set.

If the word is *and*, use intersection. If the word is *or*, use union.

For each compound inequality, give the solution set in both interval and graph forms. See Examples 2–4.

21. $x < 2$ and $x > -3$

$(-3, 2)$

22. $x < 5$ and $x > 0$

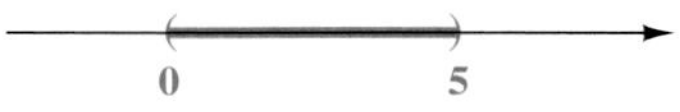

$(0, 5)$

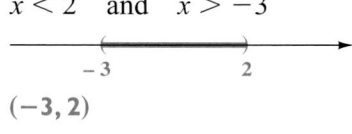

23. $x \leq 2$ and $x \leq 5$

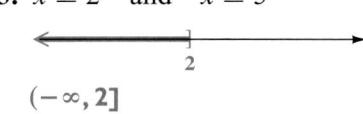

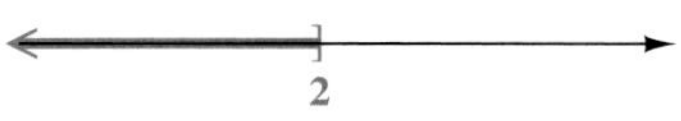

$(-\infty, 2]$

24. $x \geq 3$ and $x \geq 6$

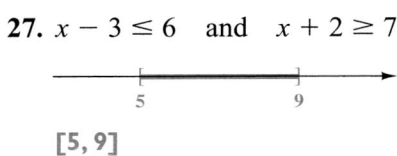

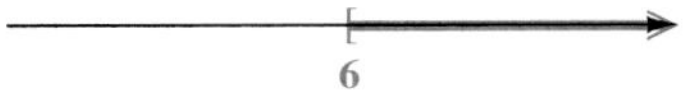

$[6, \infty)$

25. $x \leq 3$ and $x \geq 6$

$\emptyset$

26. $x \leq -1$ and $x \geq 3$

$\emptyset$

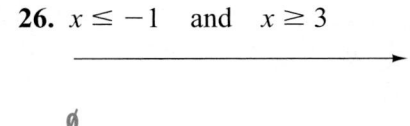

27. $x - 3 \leq 6$ and $x + 2 \geq 7$

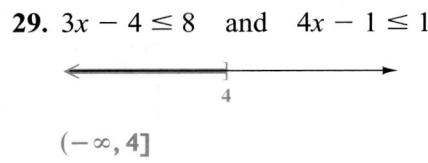

$[5, 9]$

28. $x + 5 \leq 11$ and $x - 3 \geq -1$

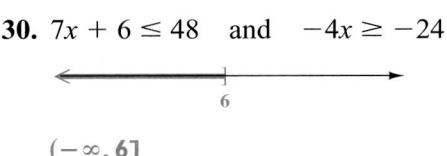

$[2, 6]$

29. $3x - 4 \leq 8$ and $4x - 1 \leq 15$

$(-\infty, 4]$

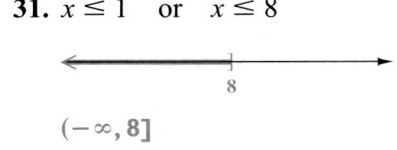

30. $7x + 6 \leq 48$ and $-4x \geq -24$

$(-\infty, 6]$

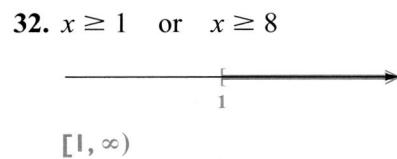

For each compound inequality, give the solution set in both interval and graph forms. See Examples 6 and 7.

31. $x \leq 1$ or $x \leq 8$

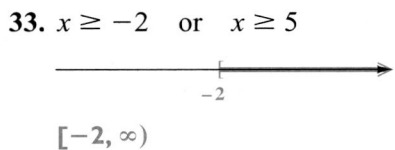

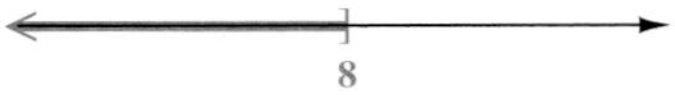

$(-\infty, 8]$

32. $x \geq 1$ or $x \geq 8$

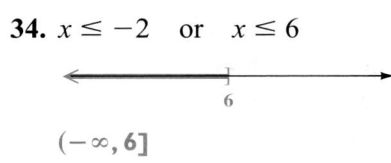

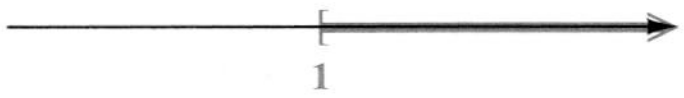

$[1, \infty)$

33. $x \geq -2$ or $x \geq 5$

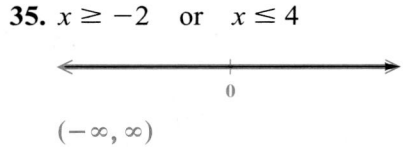

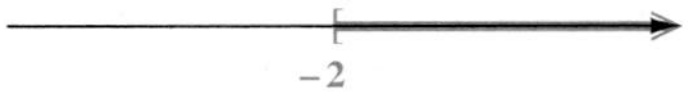

$[-2, \infty)$

34. $x \leq -2$ or $x \leq 6$

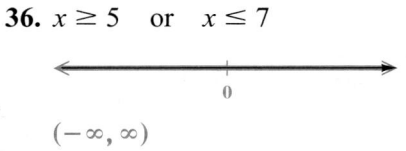

$(-\infty, 6]$

35. $x \geq -2$ or $x \leq 4$

$(-\infty, \infty)$

36. $x \geq 5$ or $x \leq 7$

$(-\infty, \infty)$

37. $x + 2 > 7$ or $x - 1 < -6$

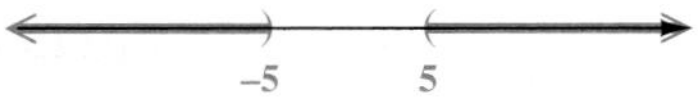

$(-\infty, -5) \cup (5, \infty)$

38. $x + 1 > 3$ or $x + 4 < 2$

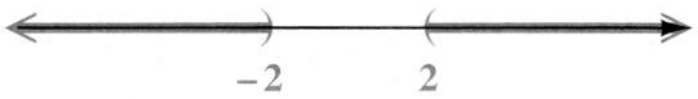

$(-\infty, -2) \cup (2, \infty)$

39. $4x - 8 > 0$ or $4x - 1 < 7$

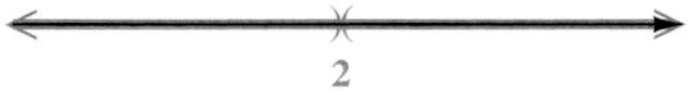

$(-\infty, 2) \cup (2, \infty)$

40. $3x < x + 12$ or $3x - 8 > 10$

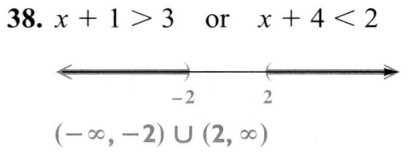

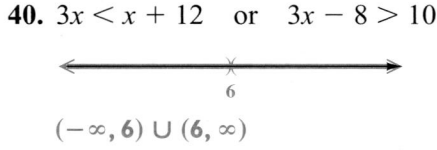

$(-\infty, 6) \cup (6, \infty)$

Express each set in the simplest interval form.

41. $(-\infty, -1] \cap [-4, \infty)$

$[-4, -1]$

42. $[-1, \infty) \cap (-\infty, 9]$

$[-1, 9]$

43. $(-\infty, -6] \cap [-9, \infty)$

$[-9, -6]$

44. $(5, 11] \cap [6, \infty)$

$[6, 11]$

45. $(-\infty, 3) \cup (-\infty, -2)$

$(-\infty, 3)$

46. $[-9, 1] \cup (-\infty, -3)$

$(-\infty, 1]$

47. $[3, 6] \cup (4, 9)$

$[3, 9)$

48. $[-1, 2] \cup (0, 5)$

$[-1, 5)$

For each compound inequality, state whether intersection or union should be used. Then give the solution set in both interval and graph forms. See Examples 2, 3, 4, 6, and 7.

49. $x < -1$ and $x > -5$

intersection; $(-5, -1)$

50. $x > -1$ and $x < 7$

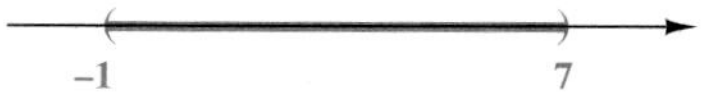

intersection; $(-1, 7)$

51. $x < 4$ or $x < -2$

union; $(-\infty, 4)$

52. $x < 5$ or $x < -3$

union; $(-\infty, 5)$

53. $x + 1 \geq 5$ and $x - 2 \leq 10$

intersection; $[4, 12]$

54. $2x - 6 \leq -18$ and $2x \geq -18$

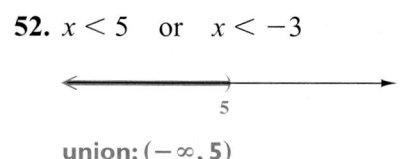

intersection; $[-9, -6]$

55. $-3x \leq -6$ or $-3x \geq 0$

union; $(-\infty, 0] \cup [2, \infty)$

56. $-8x \leq -24$ or $-5x \geq 15$

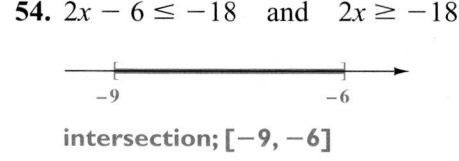

union; $(-\infty, -3] \cup [3, \infty)$

RELATING CONCEPTS (Exercises 57–60) FOR INDIVIDUAL OR GROUP WORK

The figures represent the backyards of neighbors Luigi, Mario, Than, and Joe. Find the area and the perimeter of each yard. Suppose that each resident has 150 *ft of fencing and enough sod to cover* 1400 ft^2 *of lawn.*

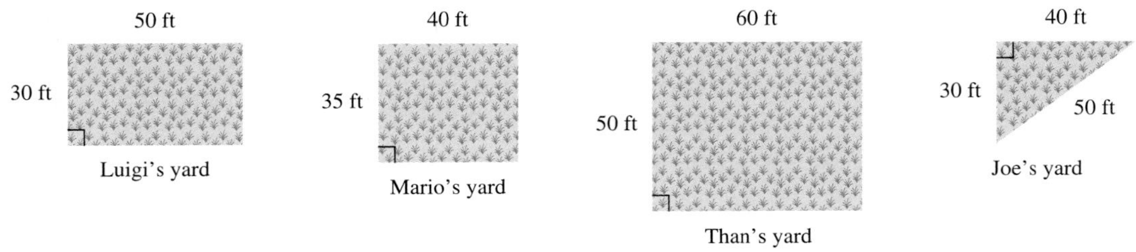

Give the name or names of the residents whose yards satisfy each description.

57. The yard can be fenced *and* the yard can be sodded.

Mario, Joe

58. The yard can be fenced *and* the yard cannot be sodded.

none of them

59. The yard cannot be fenced *and* the yard can be sodded.

none of them

60. The yard cannot be fenced *and* the yard cannot be sodded.

Luigi, Than

Use the graphs to answer Exercises 61 and 62. See Example 8.

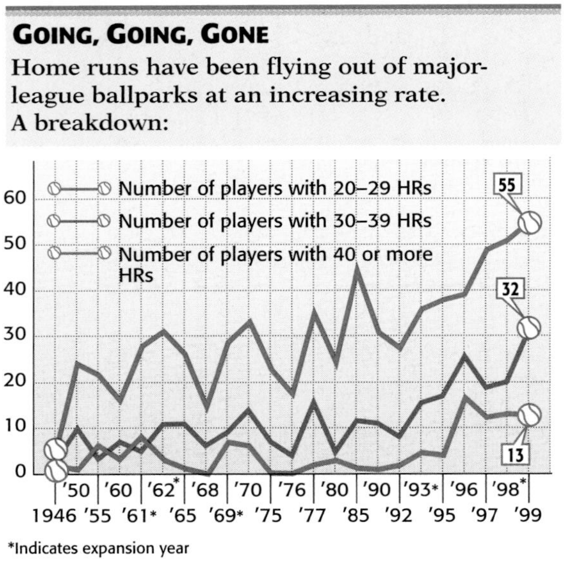

Source: Bee research.

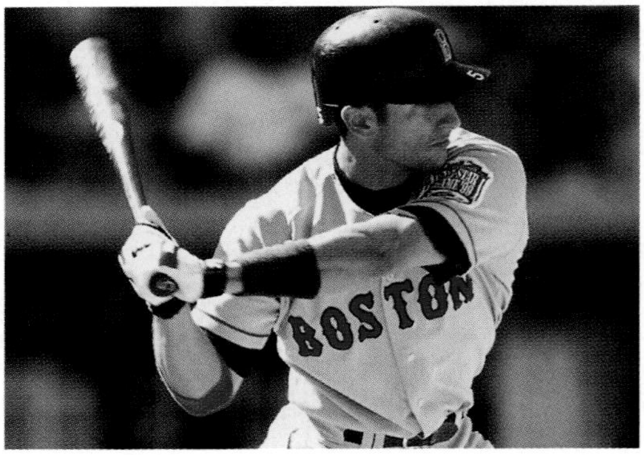

61. In which years did the number of players with 30–39 with home runs exceed 20 *and* the number of players with 40 or more home runs exceed 45?

none

62. In which years was the number of players 20–29 home runs less than 20 *or* the number of players with 30–39 home runs

1946, 1960, 1968, 1976, 1996, 1998, 1999

3.3 ABSOLUTE VALUE EQUATIONS AND INEQUALITIES

In a production line, quality is controlled by randomly choosing items from the line and checking to see how selected measurements vary from the optimum measure. These differences are sometimes positive and sometimes negative, so they are expressed with absolute value. For example, a machine that fills quart milk cartons might be set to release 1 qt plus or minus 2 oz per carton. Then the number of ounces in each carton should satisfy the *absolute value inequality* $|x - 32| \le 2$, where x is the number of ounces.

OBJECTIVES

1. Use the distance definition of absolute value.
2. Solve equations of the form $|ax + b| = k$, for $k > 0$.
3. Solve inequalities of the form $|ax + b| < k$ and of the form $|ax + b| > k$, for $k > 0$.
4. Solve absolute value equations that involve rewriting.
5. Solve equations of the form $|ax + b| = |cx + d|$.
6. Solve special cases of absolute value equations and inequalities.

1 Use the distance definition of absolute value. In Chapter 1 we saw that the absolute value of a number x, written $|x|$, represents the distance from x to 0 on the number line. For example, the solutions of $|x| = 4$ are 4 and -4, as shown in Figure 22.

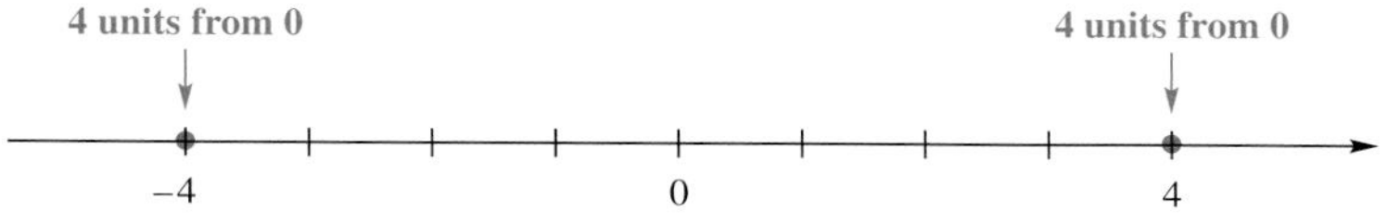

$x = -4$ or $x = 4$

Figure 22

Because absolute value represents distance from 0, it is reasonable to interpret the solutions of $|x| > 4$ to be all numbers that are *more* than 4 units from 0. The set $(-\infty, -4) \cup (4, \infty)$ fits this description. Figure 23 shows the graph of the solution set of $|x| > 4$. Because the graph consists of two separate intervals, the solution set is described using *or* as

$$x < -4 \quad \text{or} \quad x > 4.$$

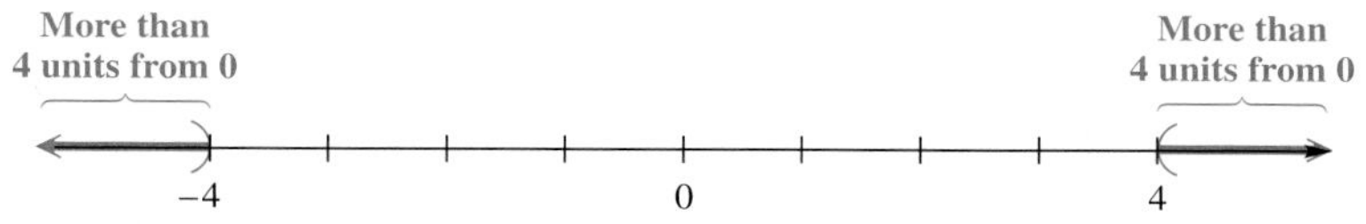

$x < -4$ or $x > 4$

Figure 23

The solution set of $|x| < 4$ consists of all numbers that are *less* than 4 units from 0 on the number line. Another way of thinking of this is to think of all numbers *between* -4 and 4. This set of numbers is given by $(-4, 4)$, as shown in Figure 24. Here, the graph shows that $-4 < x < 4$, which means $x > -4$ *and* $x < 4$.

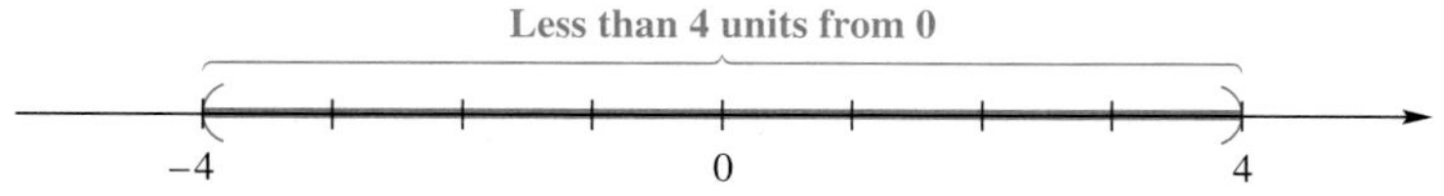

$-4 < x < 4$

Figure 24

Work Problem 1 at the Side.

The equation and inequalities just described are examples of **absolute value equations and inequalities.** They involve the absolute value of a variable expression and generally take the form

$$|ax + b| = k, \qquad |ax + b| > k, \qquad \text{or} \qquad |ax + b| < k,$$

where k is a positive number. From Figures 22–24, we see that

$|x| = 4$ has the same solution set as $x = -4$ **or** $x = 4$,
$|x| > 4$ has the same solution set as $x < -4$ **or** $x > 4$,
$|x| < 4$ has the same solution set as $x > -4$ **and** $x < 4$.

1 Graph the solution set of each equation or inequality.

(a) $|x| = 3$

(b) $|x| > 3$

(c) $|x| < 3$

ANSWERS

1. (a)

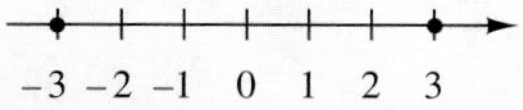

(b)

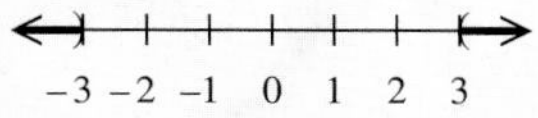

(c)

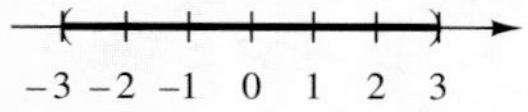

Thus, we can solve an absolute value equation or inequality by solving the appropriate compound equation or inequality.

Solving Absolute Value Equations and Inequalities

Let k be a positive real number, and p and q be real numbers.

1. To solve $|ax + b| = k$, solve the compound equation

$$ax + b = k \quad \text{or} \quad ax + b = -k.$$

The solution set is usually of the form $\{p, q\}$, which includes two numbers.

2. To solve $|ax + b| > k$, solve the compound inequality

$$ax + b > k \quad \text{or} \quad ax + b < -k.$$

The solution set is of the form $(-\infty, p) \cup (q, \infty)$, which consists of two separate intervals.

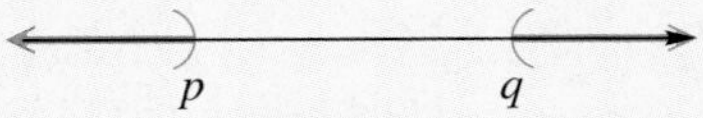

3. To solve $|ax + b| < k$, solve the compound inequality

$$-k < ax + b < k.$$

The solution set is of the form (p, q), a single interval.

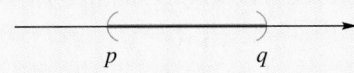

NOTE

Some people prefer to write the compound statements in parts 1 and 2 of the summary as

$$ax + b = k \quad \text{or} \quad -(ax + b) = k$$

and

$$ax + b > k \quad \text{or} \quad -(ax + b) > k.$$

These forms are equivalent to those we give in the summary and produce the same results.

2 **Solve equations of the form $|ax + b| = k$, for $k > 0$.** The next example shows how we use a compound equation to solve a typical absolute value equation. Remember that because absolute value refers to distance from the origin, each absolute value equation will have two parts.

Example 1 **Solving an Absolute Value Equation**

Solve $|2x + 1| = 7$.

For $|2x + 1|$ to equal 7, $2x + 1$ must be 7 units from 0 on the number line. This can happen only when $2x + 1 = 7$ or $2x + 1 = -7$. This is the first case in the preceding summary. Solve this compound equation as follows.

$$2x + 1 = 7 \quad \text{or} \quad 2x + 1 = -7$$
$$2x = 6 \quad \text{or} \quad 2x = -8$$
$$x = 3 \quad \text{or} \quad x = -4$$

Continued on Next Page

Check by substitution in the original absolute value equation to verify that the solution set is $\{-4, 3\}$. The graph is shown in Figure 25.

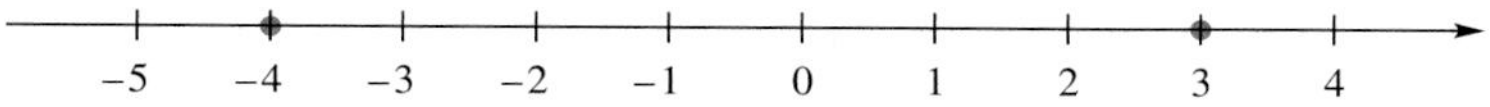

Figure 25

Work Problem 2 at the Side.

3 **Solve inequalities of the form $|ax + b| < k$ and of the form $|ax + b| > k$, for $k > 0$.**

Example 2 Solving an Absolute Value Inequality with >

Solve $|2x + 1| > 7$.

By part 2 of the summary, this absolute value inequality is rewritten as

$$2x + 1 > 7 \quad \text{or} \quad 2x + 1 < -7,$$

because $2x + 1$ must represent a number that is *more* than 7 units from 0 on either side of the number line. Now, solve the compound inequality.

$$\begin{aligned} 2x + 1 &> 7 \quad \text{or} \quad & 2x + 1 &< -7 \\ 2x &> 6 \quad \text{or} \quad & 2x &< -8 \\ x &> 3 \quad \text{or} \quad & x &< -4 \end{aligned}$$

Check these solutions. The solution set is $(-\infty, -4) \cup (3, \infty)$. See Figure 26. Notice that the graph consists of two intervals.

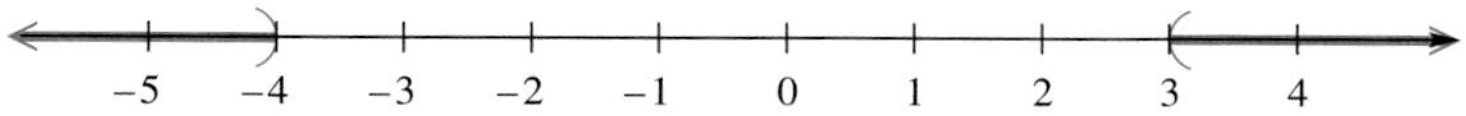

Figure 26

Work Problem 3 at the Side.

Example 3 Solving an Absolute Value Inequality with <

Solve $|2x + 1| < 7$.

The expression $2x + 1$ must represent a number that is less than 7 units from 0 on either side of the number line. Another way of thinking of this is to realize that $2x + 1$ must be between -7 and 7. As part 3 of the summary shows, this is written as the three-part inequality

$$-7 < 2x + 1 < 7.$$

We solved such inequalities in Section 3.1 by working with all three parts at the same time.

$$\begin{aligned} -7 &< 2x + 1 < 7 & \\ -8 &< 2x < 6 & \text{Subtract 1 from each part.} \\ -4 &< x < 3 & \text{Divide each part by 2.} \end{aligned}$$

Check that the solution set is $(-4, 3)$, so the graph consists of the single interval shown in Figure 27.

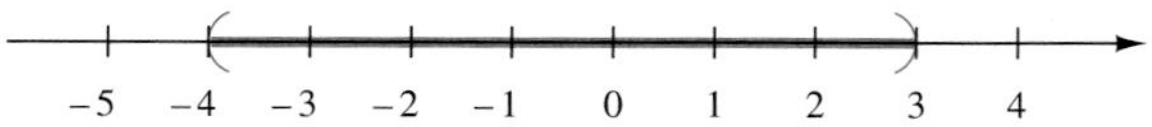

Figure 27

Work Problem 4 at the Side.

2 Solve each equation, check, and graph the solution set.

(a) $|x + 2| = 3$

(b) $|3x - 4| = 11$

3 Solve each inequality, check, and graph the solution set.

(a) $|x + 2| > 3$

(b) $|3x - 4| \geq 11$

4 Solve each inequality, check, and graph the solution set.

(a) $|x + 2| < 3$

(b) $|3x - 4| \leq 11$

ANSWERS

2. **(a)** $\{-5, 1\}$

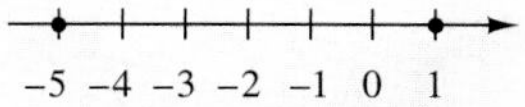

(b) $\left\{-\frac{7}{3}, 5\right\}$

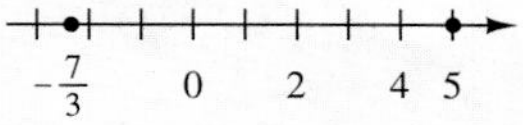

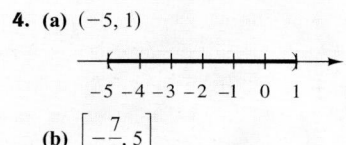

3. **(a)** $(-\infty, -5) \cup (1, \infty)$

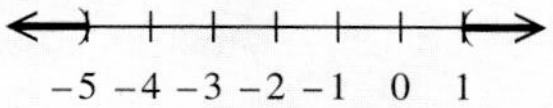

(b) $\left(-\infty, -\frac{7}{3}\right] \cup [5, \infty)$

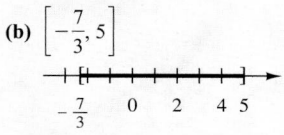

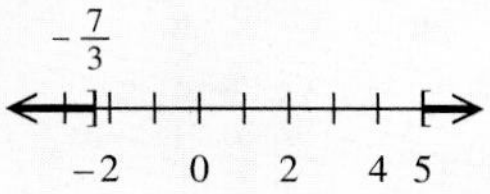

4. **(a)** $(-5, 1)$

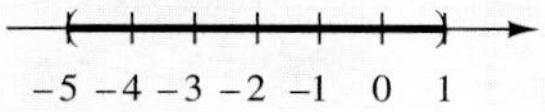

(b) $\left[-\frac{7}{3}, 5\right]$

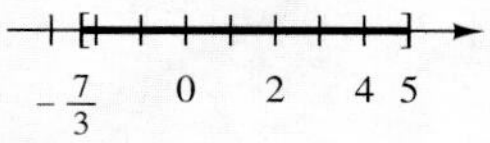

5 **(a)** Solve $|5a + 2| - 9 = -7$.

(b) Solve $|m + 2| - 3 > 2$, and graph the solution set.

(c) Solve, and graph the solution set.

$|3a + 2| + 4 \leq 15$

Look back at Figures 25, 26, and 27, with the graphs of $|2x + 1| = 7$, $|2x + 1| > 7$, and $|2x + 1| < 7$. If we find the union of the three sets, we get the set of all real numbers. This is because for any value of x, $|2x + 1|$ will satisfy one and only one of the following: it is equal to 7, greater than 7, or less than 7.

CAUTION

When solving absolute value equations and inequalities of the types in Examples 1, 2, and 3, remember the following.

1. The methods described apply when the constant is alone on one side of the equation or inequality and is *positive.*
2. Absolute value equations and absolute value inequalities in the form $|ax + b| > k$ translate into "or" compound statements.
3. Absolute value inequalities in the form $|ax + b| < k$ translate into "and" compound statements, which may be written as three-part inequalities.
4. An "or" statement *cannot* be written in three parts. It would be incorrect to use

$$-7 > 2x + 1 > 7$$

in Example 2, because this would imply that $-7 > 7$, which is *false.*

4 **Solve absolute value equations that involve rewriting.** Sometimes an absolute value equation or inequality requires some rewriting before it can be set up as a compound statement, as shown in the next example.

Example 4 **Solving an Absolute Value Equation That Requires Rewriting**

Solve the equation $|x + 3| + 5 = 12$.

First get the absolute value alone on one side of the equals sign by subtracting 5 from each side.

$$|x + 3| + 5 - 5 = 12 - 5 \quad \text{Subtract 5.}$$
$$|x + 3| = 7$$

Now use the method shown in Example 1.

$$x + 3 = 7 \quad \text{or} \quad x + 3 = -7$$
$$x = 4 \quad \text{or} \quad x = -10$$

Check that the solution set is $\{4, -10\}$ by substituting into the original equation.

We use a similar method to solve an absolute value *inequality* that requires rewriting.

Work Problem 5 at the Side.

5 **Solve equations of the form $|ax + b| = |cx + d|$.** By definition, for two expressions to have the same absolute value, they must either be equal or be negatives of each other.

ANSWERS

5. (a) $\left\{-\frac{4}{5}, 0\right\}$

(b) $(-\infty, -7) \cup (3, \infty)$

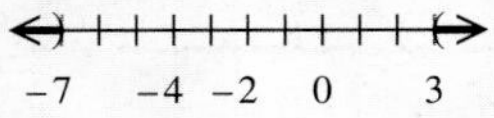

(c) $\left[-\frac{13}{3}, 3\right]$

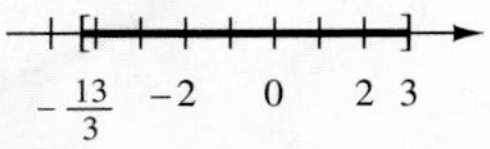

Solving $|ax + b| = |cx + d|$

To solve an absolute value equation of the form

$$|ax + b| = |cx + d|,$$

solve the compound equation

$$ax + b = cx + d \quad \textbf{or} \quad ax + b = -(cx + d).$$

6 Solve each equation.

(a) $|k - 1| = |5k + 7|$

(b) $|4r - 1| = |3r + 5|$

Example 5 Solving an Equation with Two Absolute Values

Solve the equation $|z + 6| = |2z - 3|$.

This equation is satisfied either if $z + 6$ and $2z - 3$ are equal to each other, or if $z + 6$ and $2z - 3$ are negatives of each other. Thus,

$$z + 6 = 2z - 3 \quad \text{or} \quad z + 6 = -(2z - 3).$$

Solve each equation.

$$\begin{aligned} z + 6 &= 2z - 3 &\quad \text{or} \quad z + 6 &= -2z + 3 \\ 9 &= z & 3z &= -3 \\ & & z &= -1 \end{aligned}$$

Check that the solution set is $\{9, -1\}$.

Work Problem **6** at the Side.

6 **Solve special cases of absolute value equations and inequalities.** When a typical absolute value equation or inequality involves a *negative* constant or *0* alone on one side, use the properties of absolute value to solve. Keep the following in mind.

1. The absolute value of an expression can never be negative: $|a| \geq 0$ for all real numbers a.

2. The absolute value of an expression equals 0 only when the expression is equal to 0.

The next two examples illustrate these special cases.

7 Solve each equation.

(a) $|6x + 7| = -5$

(b) $\left|\dfrac{1}{4}x - 3\right| = 0$

Example 6 Solving Special Cases of Absolute Value Equations

Solve each equation.

(a) $|5r - 3| = -4$

Since the absolute value of an expression can never be negative, there are no solutions for this equation. The solution set is $\emptyset$.

(b) $|7x - 3| = 0$

The expression $7x - 3$ will equal 0 *only* if

$$7x - 3 = 0$$

$$x = \frac{3}{7}.$$

Checking shows that the solution set is $\{\frac{3}{7}\}$, with just one element.

Work Problem **7** at the Side.

Answers

6. (a) $\{-1, -2\}$ (b) $\left\{-\frac{4}{7}, 6\right\}$

7. (a) $\emptyset$ (b) $\{12\}$

8 Solve.

(a) $|x| > -1$

(b) $|y| < -5$

(c) $|k + 2| \leq 0$

ANSWERS

8. **(a)** $(-\infty, \infty)$ **(b)** $\emptyset$ **(c)** $\{-2\}$

Example 7 **Solving Special Cases of Absolute Value Inequalities**

Solve each inequality.

(a) $|x| \geq -4$

The absolute value of a number is always greater than or equal to 0. For this reason, $|x| \geq -4$ is true for *all* real numbers. The solution set is $(-\infty, \infty)$.

(b) $|k + 6| - 3 < -5$

Add 3 to each side to get the absolute value expression alone on one side.

$$|k + 6| < -2$$

There is no number whose absolute value is less than -2, so this inequality has no solution. The solution set is $\emptyset$.

(c) $|m - 7| + 4 \leq 4$

Subtracting 4 from each side gives

$$|m - 7| \leq 0.$$

The value of $|m - 7|$ will never be less than 0. However, $|m - 7|$ will equal 0 when $m = 7$. Therefore, the solution set is $\{7\}$.

Work Problem 8 at the Side.

3.3 Exercises

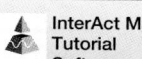

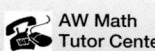

FOR EXTRA HELP: Student's Solutions Manual; MyMathLab.com; InterAct Math Tutorial Software; AW Math Tutor Center; www.mathxl.com; Digital Video Tutor CD 3 Videotape 6

Match each absolute value equation or inequality in Column I with the graph of its solution set in Column II.

1.

I	
$\lvert x\rvert = 5$	E
$\lvert x\rvert < 5$	C
$\lvert x\rvert > 5$	D
$\lvert x\rvert \leq 5$	B
$\lvert x\rvert \geq 5$	A

II

A. 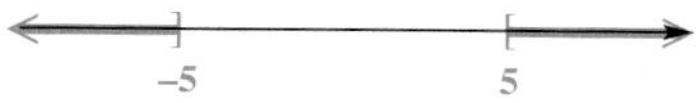

B. 

C. 

D. 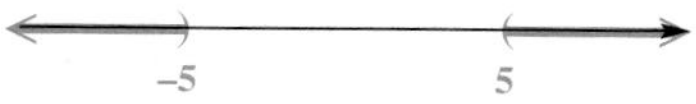

E. 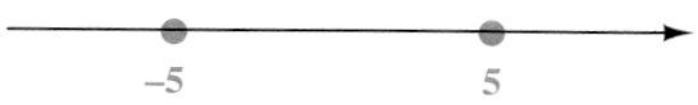

2.

I	
$\lvert x\rvert = 9$	E
$\lvert x\rvert > 9$	D
$\lvert x\rvert \geq 9$	A
$\lvert x\rvert < 9$	C
$\lvert x\rvert \leq 9$	B

II

A. 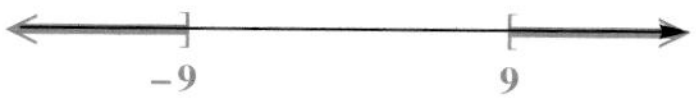

B. 

C. 

D. 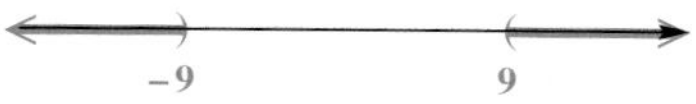

E. 

3. Explain when to use *and* and when to use *or* if you are solving an absolute value equation or inequality of the form $|ax + b| = k$, $|ax + b| < k$, or $|ax + b| > k$, where k is a positive number.

Use *or* for the equality statement and the $>$ statement. Use *and* for the $<$ statement.

4. How many solutions will $|ax + b| = k$ have if **(a)** $k = 0$; **(b)** $k > 0$; **(c)** $k < 0$?

(a) one (b) two (c) none

Solve each equation. See Example 1.

5. $|x| = 12$
$\{-12, 12\}$

6. $|k| = 14$
$\{-14, 14\}$

7. $|4x| = 20$
$\{-5, 5\}$

8. $|5x| = 30$
$\{-6, 6\}$

9. $|y - 3| = 9$
$\{-6, 12\}$

10. $|p - 5| = 13$
$\{-8, 18\}$

11. $|2x + 1| = 7$
$\{-4, 3\}$

12. $|2y + 3| = 19$
$\{-11, 8\}$

13. $|4r - 5| = 17$
$\left\{-3, \frac{11}{2}\right\}$

14. $|5t - 1| = 21$
$\left\{-4, \frac{22}{5}\right\}$

15. $|2y + 5| = 14$
$\left\{-\frac{19}{2}, \frac{9}{2}\right\}$

16. $|2x - 9| = 18$
$\left\{-\frac{9}{2}, \frac{27}{2}\right\}$

17. $\left|\frac{1}{2}x + 3\right| = 2$
$\{-10, -2\}$

18. $\left|\frac{2}{3}q - 1\right| = 5$
$\{-6, 9\}$

19. $\left|1 - \frac{3}{4}k\right| = 7$
$\left\{-8, \frac{32}{3}\right\}$

20. $\left|2 - \frac{5}{2}m\right| = 14$
$\left\{-\frac{24}{5}, \frac{32}{5}\right\}$

Solve each inequality, and graph the solution set. See Example 2.

21. $|x| > 3$

$(-\infty, -3) \cup (3, \infty)$

22. $|y| > 5$

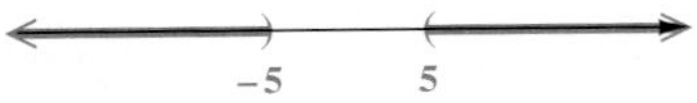

$(-\infty, -5) \cup (5, \infty)$

23. $|k| \geq 4$

$(-\infty, -4] \cup [4, \infty)$

24. $|r| \geq 6$

$(-\infty, -6] \cup [6, \infty)$

25. $|t + 2| > 10$

$(-\infty, -12) \cup (8, \infty)$

26. $|r + 5| > 20$

$(-\infty, -25) \cup (15, \infty)$

27. $|3x - 1| \geq 8$

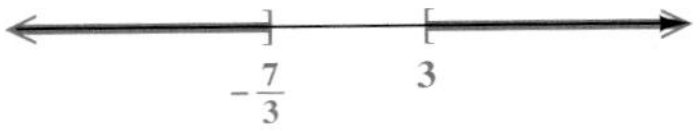

$\left(-\infty, -\frac{7}{3}\right] \cup [3, \infty)$

28. $|4x + 1| \geq 21$

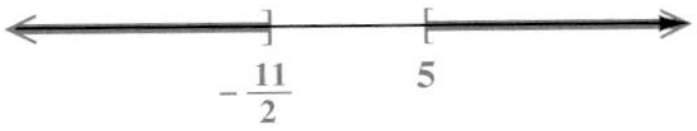

$\left(-\infty, -\frac{11}{2}\right] \cup [5, \infty)$

29. $|3 - x| > 5$

$(-\infty, -2) \cup (8, \infty)$

30. $|5 - x| > 3$

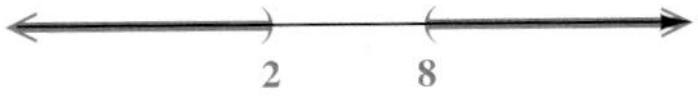

$(-\infty, 2) \cup (8, \infty)$

31. The graph of the solution set of $|2x + 1| = 9$ is given here.

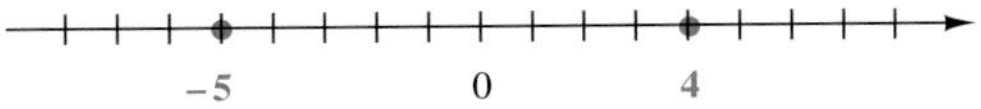

Without actually doing the algebraic work, graph the solution set of each inequality, referring to the graph above.

(a) $|2x + 1| < 9$

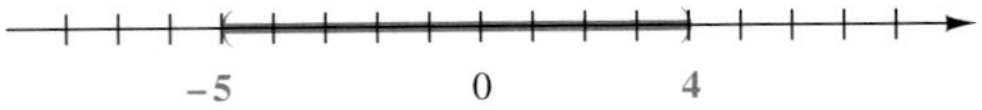

(b) $|2x + 1| > 9$

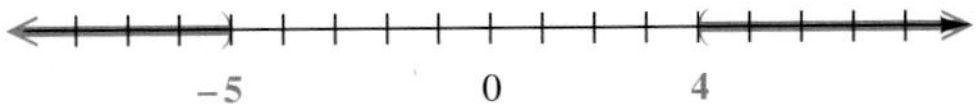

32. The graph of the solution set of $|3y - 4| < 5$ is given here.

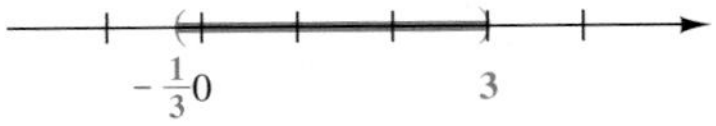

Without actually doing the algebraic work, graph the solution set of the equation and the inequality, referring to the graph above.

(a) $|3y - 4| = 5$

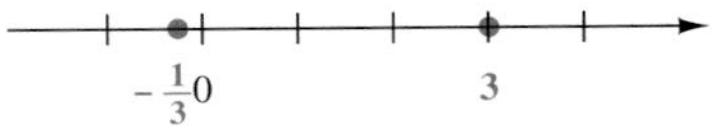

(b) $|3y - 4| > 5$

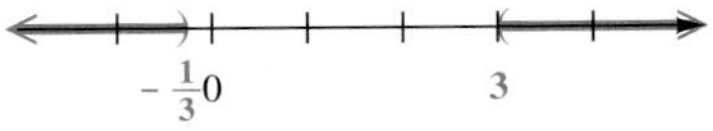

Solve each inequality, and graph the solution set. See Example 3. (Hint: Compare your answers to those in Exercises 21–30.)

33. $|x| \leq 3$

$[-3, 3]$

34. $|y| \leq 5$

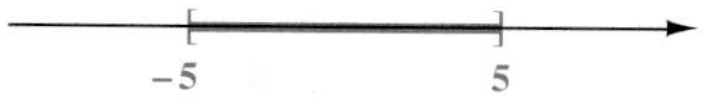

$[-5, 5]$

35. $|k| < 4$

$(-4, 4)$

36. $|r| < 6$

$(-6, 6)$

37. $|t + 2| \leq 10$

$[-12, 8]$

38. $|r + 5| \leq 20$

$[-25, 15]$

39. $|3x - 1| < 8$

$\left(-\frac{7}{3}, 3\right)$

40. $|4x + 1| < 21$

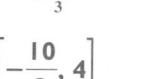

$\left(-\frac{11}{2}, 5\right)$

41. $|3 - x| \leq 5$

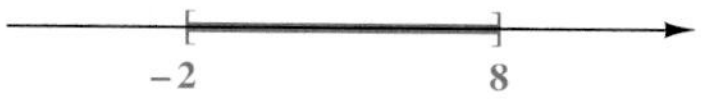

$[-2, 8]$

42. $|5 - x| \leq 3$

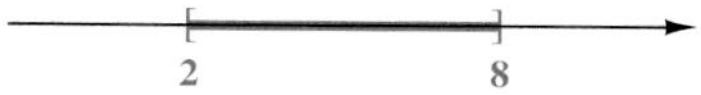

$[2, 8]$

Exercises 43–50 represent a sampling of the various types of absolute value equations and inequalities covered in Exercises 1–42. Decide which method of solution applies, find the solution set, and graph. See Examples 1–3.

43. $|-4 + k| > 9$

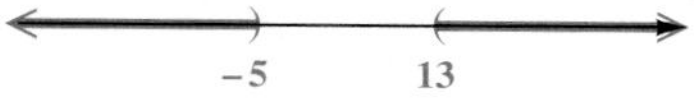

$(-\infty, -5) \cup (13, \infty)$

44. $|-3 + t| > 8$

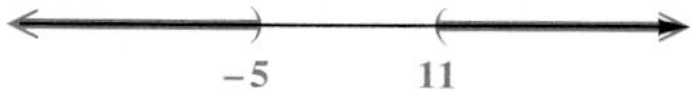

$(-\infty, -5) \cup (11, \infty)$

45. $|7 + 2z| = 5$

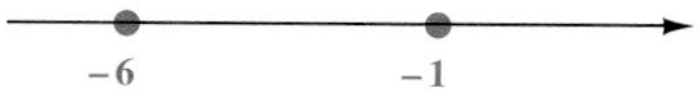

$\{-6, -1\}$

46. $|9 - 3p| = 3$

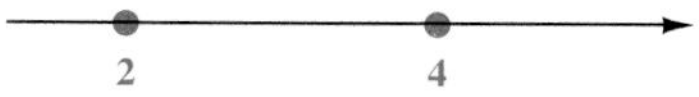

$\{2, 4\}$

47. $|3r - 1| \leq 11$

$\left[-\frac{10}{3}, 4\right]$

48. $|2s - 6| \leq 6$

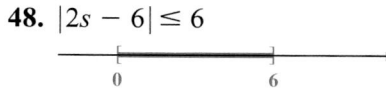

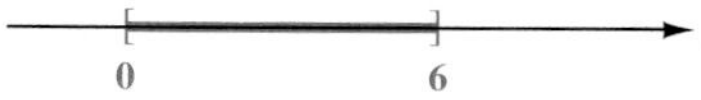

$[0, 6]$

49. $|-6x - 6| \leq 1$

$\left[-\frac{7}{6}, -\frac{5}{6}\right]$

50. $|-2x - 6| \leq 5$

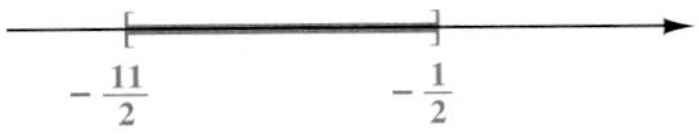

$\left[-\frac{11}{2}, -\frac{1}{2}\right]$

Solve each equation or inequality. Give the solution set in set notation for equations and in interval notation for inequalities. See Example 4.

51. $|x| - 1 = 4$

$\{-5, 5\}$

52. $|y| + 3 = 10$

$\{-7, 7\}$

53. $|x + 4| + 1 = 2$

$\{-5, -3\}$

54. $|y + 5| - 2 = 12$

$\{-19, 9\}$

55. $|2x + 1| + 3 > 8$

$(-\infty, -3) \cup (2, \infty)$

56. $|6x - 1| - 2 > 6$

$\left(-\infty, -\frac{7}{6}\right) \cup \left(\frac{3}{2}, \infty\right)$

57. $|x + 5| - 6 \leq -1$

$[-10, 0]$

58. $|r - 2| - 3 \leq 4$

$[-5, 9]$

Solve each equation. See Example 5.

59. $|3x + 1| = |2x + 4|$

$\{-1, 3\}$

60. $|7x + 12| = |x - 8|$

$\left\{-\frac{10}{3}, -\frac{1}{2}\right\}$

61. $\left|m - \frac{1}{2}\right| = \left|\frac{1}{2}m - 2\right|$

$\left\{-3, \frac{5}{3}\right\}$

62. $\left|\frac{2}{3}r - 2\right| = \left|\frac{1}{3}r + 3\right|$

$\{-1, 15\}$

63. $|6x| = |9x + 1|$

$\left\{-\frac{1}{3}, -\frac{1}{15}\right\}$

64. $|13y| = |2y + 1|$

$\left\{-\frac{1}{15}, \frac{1}{11}\right\}$

65. $|2p - 6| = |2p + 11|$

$\left\{-\frac{5}{4}\right\}$

66. $|3x - 1| = |3x + 9|$

$\left\{-\frac{4}{3}\right\}$

Solve each equation or inequality. See Examples 6 and 7.

67. $|12t - 3| = -8$

$\emptyset$

68. $|13w + 1| = -3$

$\emptyset$

69. $|4x + 1| = 0$

$\left\{-\frac{1}{4}\right\}$

70. $|6r - 2| = 0$

$\left\{\frac{1}{3}\right\}$

71. $|2q - 1| < -6$

$\emptyset$

72. $|8n + 4| < -4$

$\emptyset$

73. $|x + 5| > -9$

$(-\infty, \infty)$

74. $|x + 9| > -3$

$(-\infty, \infty)$

75. $|7x + 3| \leq 0$

$\left\{-\frac{3}{7}\right\}$

76. $|4x - 1| \leq 0$

$\left\{\frac{1}{4}\right\}$

77. $|5x - 2| \geq 0$

$(-\infty, \infty)$

78. $|4 + 7x| \geq 0$

$(-\infty, \infty)$

79. $|10z + 7| > 0$

$\left(-\infty, -\frac{7}{10}\right) \cup \left(-\frac{7}{10}, \infty\right)$

80. $|4x + 1| > 0$

$\left(-\infty, -\frac{1}{4}\right) \cup \left(-\frac{1}{4}, \infty\right)$

81. The 1998 recommended daily intake (RDI) of calcium for females aged 19–50 is 1000 mg/day. (*Source: World Almanac and Book of Facts,* 2000.) Actual vitamin needs vary from person to person. Write an absolute value inequality to express the RDI plus or minus 100 mg and solve it.

$|x - 1000| \leq 100; 900 \leq x \leq 1100$

82. The average clotting time of blood is 7.45 sec with a variation of plus or minus 3.6 sec. Write this statement as an absolute value inequality and solve it.

$|x - 7.45| \leq 3.6; 3.85 \leq x \leq 11.05$

RELATING CONCEPTS (Exercises 83–86) FOR INDIVIDUAL OR GROUP WORK

The ten tallest buildings in Kansas City, Missouri, are listed along with their heights.

Building	Height (in feet)
One Kansas City Place	632
AT&T Town Pavilion	590
Hyatt Regency	504
Kansas City Power and Light	476
City Hall	443
Fidelity Bank and Trust Building	433
1201 Walnut	427
Federal Office Building	413
Commerce Tower	407
City Center Square	404

Source: World Almanac and Book of Facts, 2001.

Use this information to ***work Exercises 83–86 in order.***

83. To find the average of a group of numbers, we add the numbers and then divide by the number of items added. Use a calculator to find the average of the heights.

472.9 ft

84. Let k represent the average height of these buildings. If a height x satisfies the inequality

$$|x - k| < t,$$

then the height is said to be within t ft of the average. Using your result from Exercise 83, list the buildings that are within 50 ft of the average.

1201 Walnut, Fidelity Bank and Trust Building, City Hall, Kansas City Power and Light, Hyatt Regency

85. Repeat Exercise 84, but find the buildings that are within 75 ft of the average.

City Center Square, Commerce Tower, Federal Office Building, 1201 Walnut, Fidelity Bank and Trust Building, City Hall, Kansas City Power and Light, Hyatt Regency

86. (a) Write an absolute value inequality that describes the height of a building that is *not* within 75 ft of the average.

$|x - 472.9| \geq 75$

(b) Solve the inequality you wrote in part (a).

$x \geq 547.9$ **or** $x \leq 397.9$

(c) Use the result of part (b) to find the buildings that are not within 75 ft of the average.

AT&T Town Pavilion, One Kansas City Place

(d) Confirm that your answer to part (c) makes sense by comparing it with your answer to Exercise 85.

It makes sense because it includes all buildings *not* listed earlier.

Summary Exercises on SOLVING LINEAR AND ABSOLUTE VALUE EQUATIONS AND INEQUALITIES

Students often have difficulty distinguishing between the various types of equations and inequalities introduced in Chapters 2 and 3. This section of miscellaneous equations and inequalities provides practice in solving all such types. You might wish to refer to the boxes in these chapters that summarize the various methods of solution.

Solve each equation or inequality.

1. $4z + 1 = 49$
$\{12\}$

2. $|m - 1| = 6$
$\{-5, 7\}$

3. $6q - 9 = 12 + 3q$
$\{7\}$

4. $3p + 7 = 9 + 8p$
$\left\{-\frac{2}{5}\right\}$

5. $|a + 3| = -4$
$\emptyset$

6. $2m + 1 \le m$
$(-\infty, -1]$

7. $8r + 2 \ge 5r$
$\left[-\frac{2}{3}, \infty\right)$

8. $4(a - 11) + 3a = 20a - 31$
$\{-1\}$

9. $2q - 1 = -7$
$\{-3\}$

10. $|3q - 7| - 4 = 0$
$\left\{1, \frac{11}{3}\right\}$

11. $6z - 5 \le 3z + 10$
$(-\infty, 5]$

12. $|5z - 8| + 9 \ge 7$
$(-\infty, \infty)$

13. $9y - 3(y + 1) = 8y - 7$
$\{2\}$

14. $|y| \ge 8$
$(-\infty, -8] \cup [8, \infty)$

15. $9y - 5 \ge 9y + 3$
$\emptyset$

16. $13p - 5 > 13p - 8$
$(-\infty, \infty)$

17. $|q| < 5.5$
$(-5.5, 5.5)$

18. $4z - 1 = 12 + z$
$\left\{\frac{13}{3}\right\}$

19. $\frac{2}{3}y + 8 = \frac{1}{4}y$
$\left\{-\frac{96}{5}\right\}$

20. $-\frac{5}{8}y \ge -20$
$(-\infty, 32]$

21. $\frac{1}{4}p < -6$
$(-\infty, -24)$

22. $7z - 3 + 2z = 9z - 8z$
$\left\{\frac{3}{8}\right\}$

23. $\frac{3}{5}q - \frac{1}{10} = 2$
$\left\{\frac{7}{2}\right\}$

24. $|r - 1| < 7$
$(-6, 8)$

25. $r + 9 + 7r = 4(3 + 2r) - 3$
$(-\infty, \infty)$

26. $6 - 3(2 - p) < 2(1 + p) + 3$
$(-\infty, 5)$

27. $|2p - 3| > 11$
$(-\infty, -4) \cup (7, \infty)$

28. $\frac{x}{4} - \frac{2x}{3} = -10$
$\{24\}$

29. $|5a + 1| \leq 0$
$\left\{-\frac{1}{5}\right\}$

30. $5z - (3 + z) \geq 2(3z + 1)$
$\left(-\infty, -\frac{5}{2}\right]$

31. $-2 \leq 3x - 1 \leq 8$
$\left[-\frac{1}{3}, 3\right]$

32. $-1 \leq 6 - x \leq 5$
$[1, 7]$

33. $|7z - 1| = |5z + 3|$
$\left\{-\frac{1}{6}, 2\right\}$

34. $|p + 2| = |p + 4|$
$\{-3\}$

35. $|1 - 3x| \geq 4$
$(-\infty, -1] \cup \left[\frac{5}{3}, \infty\right)$

36. $\frac{1}{2} \leq \frac{2}{3}r \leq \frac{5}{4}$
$\left[\frac{3}{4}, \frac{15}{8}\right]$

37. $-(m + 4) + 2 = 3m + 8$
$\left\{-\frac{5}{2}\right\}$

38. $\frac{p}{6} - \frac{3p}{5} = p - 86$
$\{60\}$

39. $-6 \leq \frac{3}{2} - x \leq 6$
$\left[-\frac{9}{2}, \frac{15}{2}\right]$

40. $|5 - y| < 4$
$(1, 9)$

41. $|y - 1| \geq -6$
$(-\infty, \infty)$

42. $|2r - 5| = |r + 4|$
$\left\{\frac{1}{3}, 9\right\}$

43. $8q - (1 - q) = 3(1 + 3q) - 4$
$(-\infty, \infty)$

44. $8y - (y + 3) = -(2y + 1) - 12$
$\left\{-\frac{10}{9}\right\}$

45. $|r - 5| = |r + 9|$
$\{-2\}$

46. $|r + 2| < -3$
$\emptyset$

47. $2x + 1 > 5$ or $3x + 4 < 1$
$(-\infty, -1) \cup (2, \infty)$

48. $1 - 2x \geq 5$ and $7 + 3x \geq -2$
$[-3, -2]$

Chapter 3

SUMMARY

KEY TERMS

3.1

interval An interval is a portion of a number line.

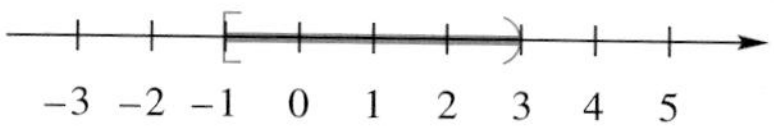

The interval [−1, 3)

interval notation The notation used to indicate an interval on the number line is called interval notation.

inequality An inequality is a mathematical statement that two expressions are not equal.

linear inequality in one variable A linear inequality in the variable x can be written in the form $Ax + B < C$, $Ax + B \leq C$, $Ax + B > C$, or $Ax + B \geq C$, where A, B, and C are real numbers, with $A \neq 0$.

equivalent inequalities Equivalent inequalities are inequalities with the same solution set.

3.2

intersection The intersection of two sets A and B is the set of elements that belong to both A and B.

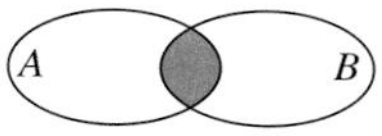

compound inequality A compound inequality is formed by joining two inequalities with a connective word, such as *and* or *or*.

union The union of two sets A and B is the set of elements that belong to either A or B (or both).

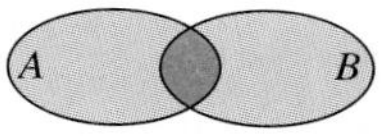

3.3

absolute value equation; absolute value inequality Absolute value equations and inequalities are equations and inequalities that involve the absolute value of a variable expression.

NEW SYMBOLS

∞	infinity	$\{x \mid x \text{ has property } P\}$	set-builder notation
$-\infty$	negative infinity	$\cap$	set intersection
$(-\infty, \infty)$	the set of real numbers	$\cup$	set union

TEST YOUR WORD POWER

See how well you have learned the vocabulary in this chapter. Answers follow the Quick Review.

1. An **inequality** is
   (a) a statement that two algebraic expressions are equal
   (b) a point on a number line
   (c) an equation with no solutions
   (d) a statement with algebraic expressions related by $<$, $\leq$, $>$, or $\geq$.

2. **Interval notation** is
   (a) a portion of a number line
   (b) a special notation for describing a point on a number line
   (c) a way to use symbols to describe an interval on a number line
   (d) a notation to describe unequal quantities.

3. The **intersection** of two sets A and B is the set of elements that belong
   (a) to both A and B
   (b) to either A or B, or both
   (c) to either A or B, but not both
   (d) to just A.

4. The **union** of two sets A and B is the set of elements that belong
   (a) to both A and B
   (b) to either A or B, or both
   (c) to either A or B, but not both
   (d) to just B.

Quick Review

Concepts	Examples

3.1 Linear Inequalities in One Variable

Solving Linear Inequalities in One Variable

Step 1 Simplify each side of the inequality by clearing parentheses and combining like terms.

Step 2 Use the addition property of inequality to get all terms with variables on one side and all terms without variables on the other side.

Step 3 Use the multiplication property of inequality to write the inequality in the form $x < k$ or $x > k$.

If an inequality is multiplied or divided by a *negative* number, the inequality symbol *must be reversed.*

Solve $3(x + 2) - 5x \leq 12$.

$$3x + 6 - 5x \leq 12$$
$$-2x + 6 \leq 12$$
$$-2x \leq 6$$
$$\frac{-2x}{-2} \geq \frac{6}{-2}$$
$$x \geq -3$$

The solution set $[-3, \infty)$ is graphed below.

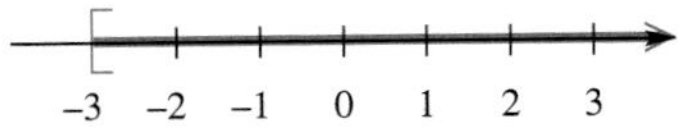

3.2 Set Operations and Compound Inequalities

Solving a Compound Inequality

Step 1 Solve each inequality in the compound inequality individually.

Step 2 If the inequalities are joined with *and*, the solution set is the intersection of the two individual solution sets.

If the inequalities are joined with *or*, the solution set is the union of the two individual solution sets.

Solve $x + 1 > 2$ and $2x < 6$.

$$x + 1 > 2 \quad \text{and} \quad 2x < 6$$
$$x > 1 \quad \text{and} \quad x < 3$$

The solution set is $(1, 3)$.

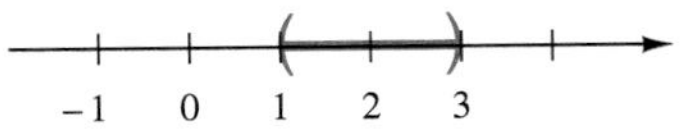

Solve $x \geq 4$ or $x \leq 0$.
The solution set is $(-\infty, 0] \cup [4, \infty)$.

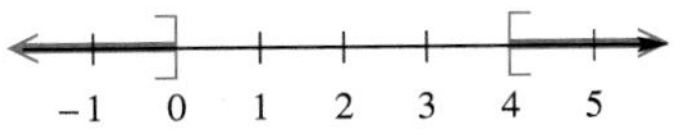

3.3 Absolute Value Equations and Inequalities

Let k be a positive number.
To solve $|ax + b| = k$, solve the compound equation

$$ax + b = k \quad \text{or} \quad ax + b = -k.$$

Solve $|x - 7| = 3$.

$$x - 7 = 3 \quad \text{or} \quad x - 7 = -3$$
$$x = 10 \quad \text{or} \quad x = 4$$

The solution set is $\{4, 10\}$.

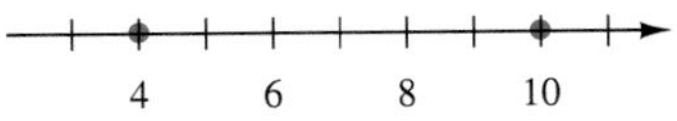

To solve $|ax + b| > k$, solve the compound inequality

$$ax + b > k \quad \text{or} \quad ax + b < -k.$$

Solve $|x - 7| > 3$.

$$x - 7 > 3 \quad \text{or} \quad x - 7 < -3$$
$$x > 10 \quad \text{or} \quad x < 4$$

The solution set is $(-\infty, 4) \cup (10, \infty)$.

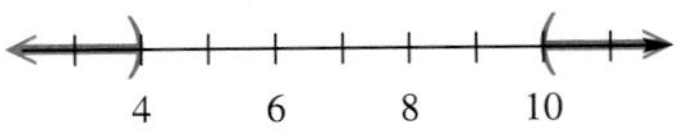

Concepts	*Examples*
3.3 Absolute Value Equations and Inequalities (continued) To solve $\|ax + b\| < k$, solve the compound inequality $-k < ax + b < k.$	Solve $\|x - 7\| < 3$. $-3 < x - 7 < 3$ $4 < x < 10$ The solution set is (4, 10). 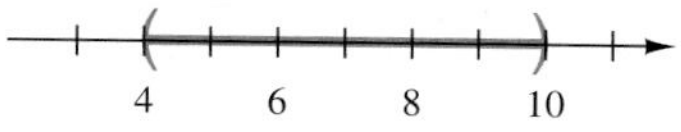
To solve an absolute value equation of the form $\|ax + b\| = \|cx + d\|,$ solve the compound equation $ax + b = cx + d \quad \text{or} \quad ax + b = -(cx + d).$	Solve $\|x + 2\| = \|2x - 6\|$. $x + 2 = 2x - 6$ or $x + 2 = -(2x - 6)$ $x = 8$ $\qquad$ $x + 2 = -2x + 6$ $3x = 4$ $x = \frac{4}{3}$ The solution set is $\{\frac{4}{3}, 8\}$.

ANSWERS TO TEST YOUR WORD POWER

1. (d) *Examples:* $x < 5$, $7 + 2y \geq 11$, $-5 < 2z - 1 \leq 3$ **2. (c)** *Examples:* $(-\infty, 5]$, $(1, \infty)$, $[-3, 3)$ **3. (a)** *Example:* If $A = \{2, 4, 6, 8\}$ and $B = \{1, 2, 3\}$, $A \cap B = \{2\}$. **4. (b)** *Example:* Using the preceding sets A and B, $A \cup B = \{1, 2, 3, 4, 6, 8\}$.

Focus on

Real-Data Applications

What Do I Have to Average on My Tests to Get the Grade I Want?

On the first day of class, you are typically given a syllabus that describes the course requirements. If the syllabus includes a grading scale for homework, tests, projects, and final exam, then you should be able to predict the points you need on the final exam to earn a specific grade.

One intermediate algebra teacher bases final grades on points earned for three major exams, a comprehensive final exam, a daily activities grade (scaled), and lab participation and completion. The number of points available for each activity is given in the Graded Classwork table on the left. The teacher strictly adheres to the point ranges given in the Grade Distribution table on the right. A grade of IP (In Progress) is given to a student who participates fully but fails to achieve the course objectives.

GRADED CLASSWORK

Activity	Points Available
Homework and vocabulary	45
Daily activities (scaled)	55
Lab participation and completion	100
Major exams (3 at 100 pt)	300
Final exam	150
Total points	650

GRADE DISTRIBUTION

Grade	Points Required
A	585–650
B	520–584
C	455–519
IP	<455 and active
F	<455 and inactive

Notice that exams account for 450 of the possible 650 points. The remaining 200 points should be fairly easy to earn by keeping up with the day-to-day course requirements.

Assumption: You earn a "baseline" number of points based on the following criteria.

1. You earn *all* of the homework and vocabulary points.
2. You earn a minimum of 50 points based on daily activities.
3. You earn a minimum of 90 lab participation and completion points.

For Group Discussion

1. Assume that you earn the baseline number of points. Let x represent the test points to be earned. Write and solve linear inequalities to find the minimum number of points that you need in test scores to earn grades no lower than A, B, and C. What "test average" is each minimum score? Round *up* to the nearest whole percent. **A: $185 + x \geq 585$; $x \geq 400$; 89%; B: $185 + x \geq 520$; $x \geq 335$; 75%; C: $185 + x \geq 455$; $x \geq 270$; 60%**

2. To keep your scholarship, you must earn a B in the course. Write a compound inequality to find the range of points that you need in test scores to earn a B average. Solve the inequality. What range of "test averages" are those minimum scores? Round *up* to the nearest whole percent. **$520 \leq 185 + x \leq 584$; $335 \leq x \leq 399$; 75% $\leq$ average $\leq$ 89%**

3. Mark does not like to do the homework or participate in labs. Assume that Mark earns only 15 points in homework and vocabulary, 40 points in daily activities, and 50 points in lab participation. Write and solve linear inequalities to find the minimum number of points that Mark needs in test scores to earn grades no lower than A, B, and C. What "test average" is each minimum score? Round *up* to the nearest whole percent. **A: $105 + x \geq 585$; $x \geq 480$; impossible; B: $105 + x \geq 520$; $x \geq 415$; 93%; C: $105 + x \geq 455$; $x \geq 350$; 78%**

Teaching notes and an extension for this activity are provided in the *Printed Test Bank and Instructor's Resource Guide.*

Chapter 3 REVIEW EXERCISES

[3.1] *Solve each inequality. Give the solution set in both interval and graph forms.*

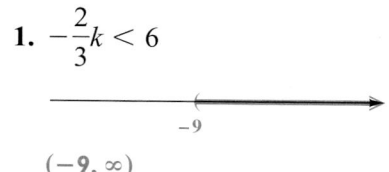

1. $-\frac{2}{3}k < 6$

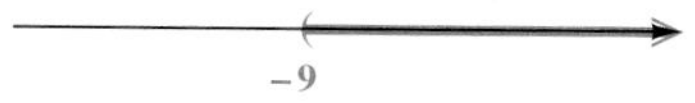

$(-9, \infty)$

2. $-5x - 4 \geq 11$

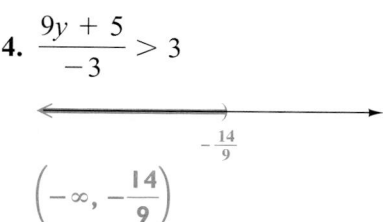

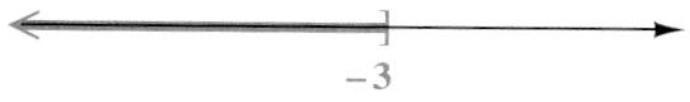

$(-\infty, -3]$

3. $\frac{6a + 3}{-4} < -3$

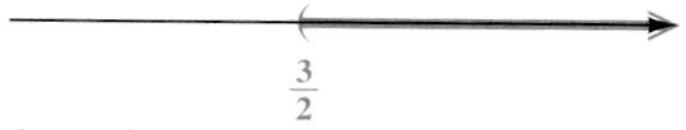

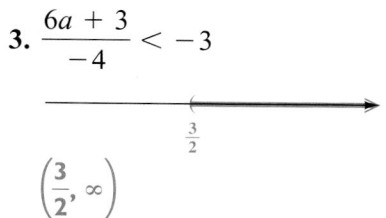

$\left(\frac{3}{2}, \infty\right)$

4. $\frac{9y + 5}{-3} > 3$

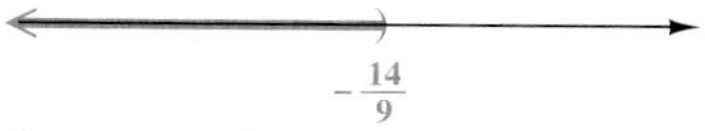

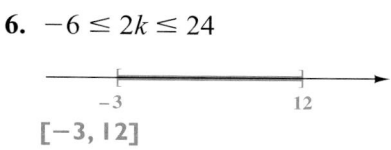

$\left(-\infty, -\frac{14}{9}\right)$

5. $5 - (6 - 4k) \geq 2k - 7$

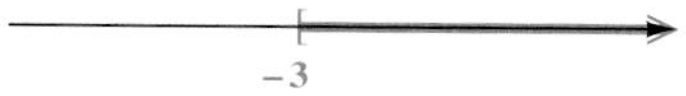

$[-3, \infty)$

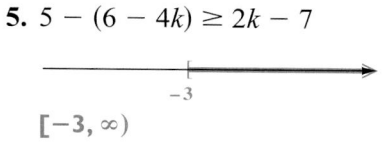

6. $-6 \leq 2k \leq 24$

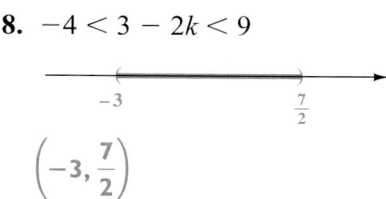

$[-3, 12]$

7. $8 \leq 3y - 1 < 14$

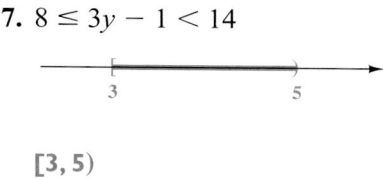

$[3, 5)$

8. $-4 < 3 - 2k < 9$

$\left(-3, \frac{7}{2}\right)$

9. The perimeter of a rectangular playground must be no greater than 120 m. The width of the playground must be 22 m. Find the possible lengths of the playground.

38 m or less

10. The hit movie *Titanic* earned more in Europe than in the United States. The average movie ticket in London, for example, costs the equivalent of \$10.59. (*Source: Parade* magazine, September 13, 1998.) A student group from the United States is touring London and wishes to see the movie there. If \$1000 is available to purchase tickets and the group receives a \$50 discount from the tour company, how many tickets can be purchased?

99 tickets or less

11. To pass algebra, a student must have an average of at least 70% on five tests. On the first four tests, a student has grades of 75%, 79%, 64%, and 71%. What possible grades on the fifth test would guarantee a passing grade in the class?

any grade greater than or equal to 61%

12. While solving the inequality

$$10x + 2(x - 4) < 12x - 13,$$

a student did all the work correctly and obtained the statement $-8 < -13$. The student did not know what to do at this point, because the variable "disappeared." How would you explain to the student the interpretation of this result?

Because the statement $-8 < -13$ is *false*, the inequality has no solution.

[3.2] *Let* $A = \{a, b, c, d\}$, $B = \{a, c, e, f\}$, *and* $C = \{a, e, f, g\}$. *Find each set.*

13. $A \cap B$

{a, c}

14. $A \cap C$

{a}

15. $B \cup C$

{a, c, e, f, g}

16. $A \cup C$

{a, b, c, d, e, f, g}

Solve each compound inequality. Give the solution set in both interval and graph forms.

17. $x > 6$ and $x < 9$

(6, 9)

18. $x + 4 > 12$ and $x - 2 < 12$

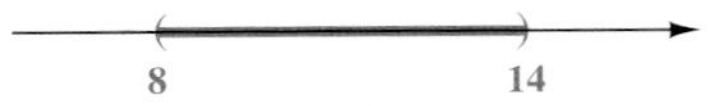

(8, 14)

19. $x > 5$ or $x \leq -3$

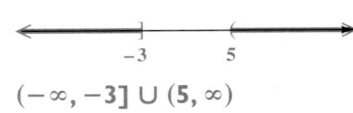

$(-\infty, -3] \cup (5, \infty)$

20. $x \geq -2$ or $x < 2$

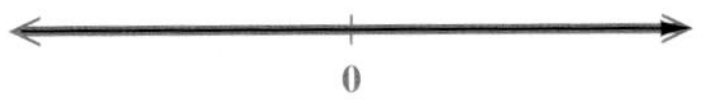

$(-\infty, \infty)$

21. $x - 4 > 6$ and $x + 3 \leq 10$

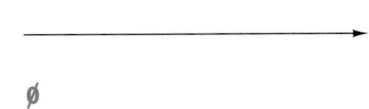

∅

22. $-5x + 1 \geq 11$ or $3x + 5 \geq 26$

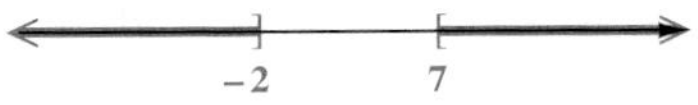

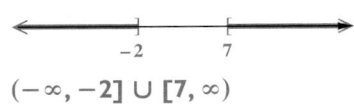

$(-\infty, -2] \cup [7, \infty)$

Express each union or intersection in simplest interval form.

23. $(-3, \infty) \cap (-\infty, 4)$

$(-3, 4)$

24. $(-\infty, 6) \cap (-\infty, 2)$

$(-\infty, 2)$

25. $(4, \infty) \cup (9, \infty)$

$(4, \infty)$

26. $(1, 2) \cup (1, \infty)$

$(1, \infty)$

27. The table shows the median weekly earnings of full-time workers by occupation for men and women.

Occupation	Men	Women
Managerial and professional specialty	\$ 852	\$616
Mathematical and computer scientists	\$1005	\$754
Waiters and waitresses	\$ 300	\$264
Bus drivers	\$ 482	\$354

Source: U.S. Bureau of Labor Statistics.

Give the occupation that satisfies each description.

(a) The median earnings for men are less than \$900 *and* for women are greater than \$500.

managerial and professional specialty

(b) The median earnings for men are greater than \$900 *or* for women are greater than \$600.

managerial and professional specialty, mathematical and computer scientists

[3.3] *Solve each absolute value equation.*

28. $|x| = 7$

$\{-7, 7\}$

29. $|y + 2| = 9$

$\{-11, 7\}$

30. $|3k - 7| = 8$

$\left\{-\frac{1}{3}, 5\right\}$

31. $|z - 4| = -12$

$\emptyset$

32. $|2k - 7| + 4 = 11$

$\{0, 7\}$

33. $|4a + 2| - 7 = -3$

$\left\{-\frac{3}{2}, \frac{1}{2}\right\}$

34. $|3p + 1| = |p + 2|$

$\left\{-\frac{3}{4}, \frac{1}{2}\right\}$

35. $|2m - 1| = |2m + 3|$

$\left\{-\frac{1}{2}\right\}$

Solve each absolute value inequality. Give the solution set in both interval and graph forms.

36. $|p| < 14$

$(-14, 14)$

37. $|-y + 6| \leq 7$

$[-1, 13]$

38. $|2p + 5| \leq 1$

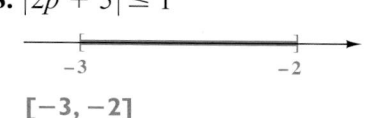

$[-3, -2]$

39. $|x + 1| \geq -3$

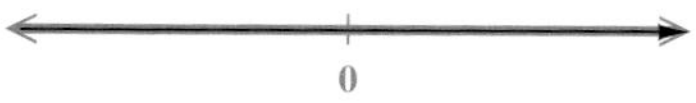

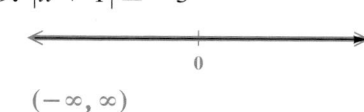

$(-\infty, \infty)$

40. $|5r - 1| > 9$

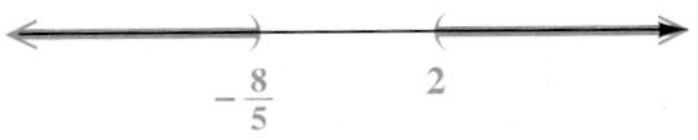

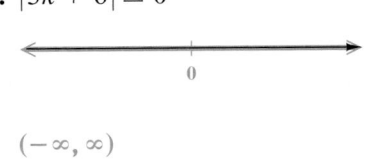

$\left(-\infty, -\frac{8}{5}\right) \cup (2, \infty)$

41. $|3k + 6| \geq 0$

$(-\infty, \infty)$

Mixed Review Exercises

Solve.

42. $(7 - 2k) + 3(5 - 3k) \geq k + 8$

$\left(-\infty, \frac{7}{6}\right]$

43. $x < 5$ and $x \geq -4$

$[-4, 5)$

44. $\frac{3}{4}(a - 2) - \frac{1}{3}(5 - 2a) < -2$

$\left(-\infty, \frac{14}{17}\right)$

45. To qualify for a company pension plan, an employee must average at least \$1000 per month in earnings. During the first four months of the year, an employee made \$900, \$1200, \$1040, and \$760. What possible amounts earned during the fifth month will qualify the employee?

any amount greater than or equal to \$1100

46. $-5r \geq -10$

$(-\infty, 2]$

47. $|7x - 2| > 9$

$(-\infty, -1) \cup \left(\frac{11}{7}, \infty\right)$

48. $|2x - 10| = 20$

$\{-5, 15\}$

49. $|m + 3| \leq 13$

$[-16, 10]$

50. $x \geq -2$ or $x < 4$

$(-\infty, \infty)$

51. $|m - 1| = |2m + 3|$

$\left\{-4, -\frac{2}{3}\right\}$

In Exercises 52 and 53, sketch the graph of each solution set.

52. $x > 6$ and $x < 8$

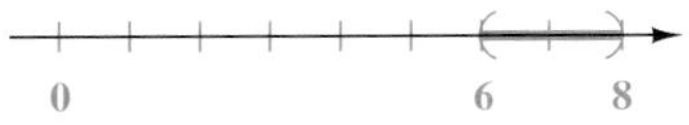

53. $-5x + 1 \geq 11$ or $3x + 5 \geq 26$

54. If $k < 0$, what is the solution set of

(a) $|5x + 3| < k$, **(b)** $|5x + 3| > k$, **(c)** $|5x + 3| = k$?

(a) $\emptyset$

(b) $(-\infty, \infty)$

(c) $\emptyset$

Chapter 3 Test

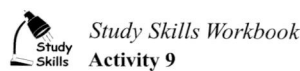

Study Skills Workbook
Activity 9

1. What is the special rule that must be remembered when multiplying or dividing each side of an inequality by a negative number?

1. Reverse the direction of the inequality symbol.

Solve each inequality. Give the solution set in both interval and graph forms.

2. $4 - 6(x + 3) \leq -2 - 3(x + 6) + 3x$

2. $[1, \infty)$

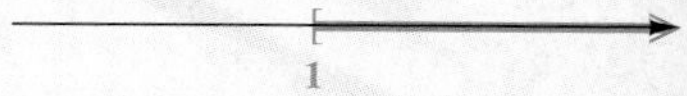

3. $-\frac{4}{7}x > -16$

3. $(-\infty, 28)$

4. $-6 \leq \frac{4}{3}x - 2 \leq 2$

4. $[-3, 3]$

5. Which one of the following inequalities is equivalent to $x < -3$?

A. $-3x < 9$ **B.** $-3x > -9$ **C.** $-3x > 9$ **D.** $-3x < -9$

5. C

6. The graph shows the number (in millions) of U.S. citizen departures to Europe. During which years were departures to Europe

(a) at least 8 million, **(b)** less than 7 million,

(c) between 7 million and 9 million?

6. (a) 1993–1998

(b) 1985–1989

(c) 1990, 1993–1995

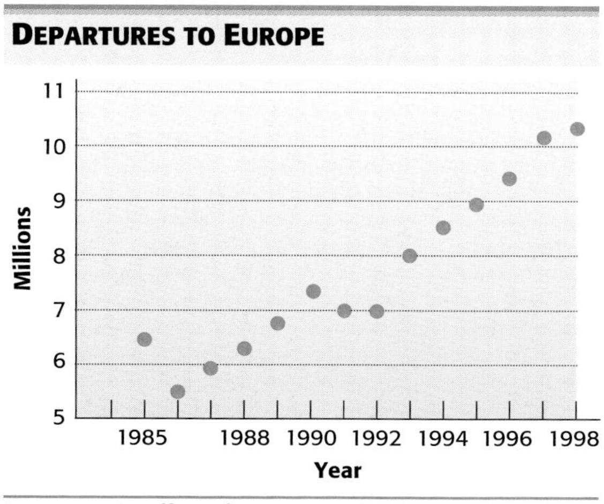

Source: U.S. Office of Tourism Industries.

Solve each problem.

7. A student must have an average of at least 80% on the four tests in a course to get a B. The student had 83%, 76%, and 79% on the first three tests. What minimum percent on the fourth test would guarantee a B in the course?

7. 82%

8. $[500, \infty)$

8. A product will break even or produce a profit only if the revenue R (in dollars) from selling the product is at least the cost C (in dollars) of producing it. Suppose that the cost to produce x units of carpet is $C = 50x + 5000$, while the revenue is $R = 60x$. For what values of x is R at least equal to C?

9. (a) $\{1, 5\}$

(b) $\{1, 2, 5, 7, 9, 12\}$

9. Let $A = \{1, 2, 5, 7\}$ and $B = \{1, 5, 9, 12\}$. Find

(a) $A \cap B$, **(b)** $A \cup B$.

10. $\{2\}$

10. Solve $x \leq 2$ and $x \geq 2$.

Solve each compound or absolute value inequality. For Exercises 11–14, give the solution set in both interval and graph forms.

11. $[2, 9)$

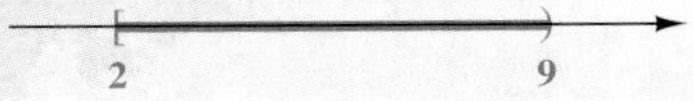

11. $3k \geq 6$ and $k - 4 < 5$

12. $(-\infty, 3) \cup [6, \infty)$

12. $-4x \leq -24$ or $4x - 2 < 10$

13. $\left[-\frac{5}{2}, 1\right]$

13. $|4x + 3| \leq 7$

14. $\left(-\infty, -\frac{7}{6}\right) \cup \left(\frac{17}{6}, \infty\right)$

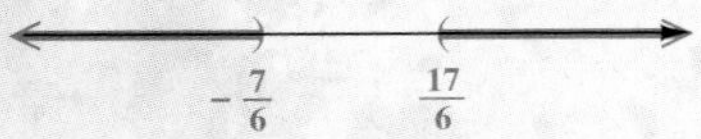

14. $|5 - 6x| > 12$

15. $\emptyset$

15. $|7 - x| \leq -1$

Solve each absolute value equation.

16. $\left\{-\frac{5}{3}, 3\right\}$

16. $|3k - 2| + 1 = 8$

17. $\left\{-\frac{5}{7}, \frac{11}{3}\right\}$

17. $|3 - 5x| = |2x + 8|$

Cumulative Review Exercises

Chapters R–3

1. Write $\frac{108}{144}$ in lowest terms.
$\frac{3}{4}$

2. True or false? $\frac{8(7) - 5(6 + 2)}{3 \cdot 5 + 1} \geq 1$
true

Perform the indicated operations.

3. $\frac{5}{6} + \frac{1}{4} - \frac{7}{15}$ **$\frac{37}{60}$**

4. $\frac{9}{8} \cdot \frac{16}{3} \div \frac{5}{8}$ **$\frac{48}{5}$**

5. $9 - (-4) + (-2)$ **11**

6. $\frac{-4(9)(-2)}{-3^2}$ **-8**

7. $|-7 - 1|(-4) + (-4)$ **-36**

Evaluate each exponential expression.

8. $(-5)^3$ **-125**

9. $\left(\frac{3}{2}\right)^4$ **$\frac{81}{16}$**

Evaluate each expression if $x = 2$, $y = -3$, and $z = 4$.

10. $-2y + 4(x - 3z)$ **-36**

11. $\frac{3x^2 - y^2}{4z}$ **$\frac{3}{16}$**

Name each property illustrated.

12. $7(k + m) = 7k + 7m$
distributive property

13. $3 + (5 + 2) = 3 + (2 + 5)$
commutative property

14. Simplify $-4(k + 2) + 3(2k - 1)$ by combining terms.
$2k - 11$

Solve each equation, and check the solution.

15. $4 - 5(a + 2) = 3(a + 1) - 1$
$\{-1\}$

16. $\frac{2}{3}y + \frac{3}{4}y = -17$
$\{-12\}$

17. $\frac{2x + 3}{5} = \frac{x - 4}{2}$
$\{26\}$

18. $|3m - 5| = |m + 2|$
$\left\{\frac{3}{4}, \frac{7}{2}\right\}$

19. $3x + 4y = 24$ for y
$y = \frac{24 - 3x}{4}$

20. $A = P(1 + ni)$ for n
$n = \frac{A - P}{iP}$

Solve each inequality. Give the solution set in both interval and graph forms.

21. $3 - 2(x + 7) \leq -x + 3$

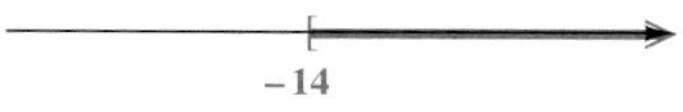

$[-14, \infty)$

22. $-4 < 5 - 3x \leq 0$

$\left[\frac{5}{3}, 3\right)$

23. $2x + 1 > 5$ or $2 - x > 2$

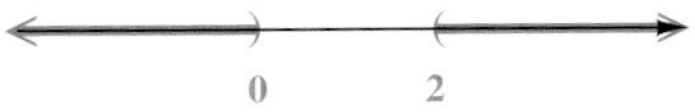

$(-\infty, 0) \cup (2, \infty)$

24. $|-7k + 3| \geq 4$

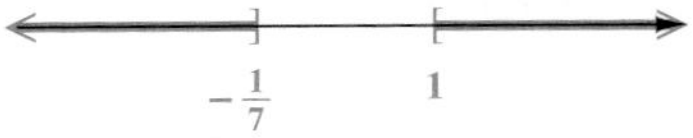

$\left(-\infty, -\frac{1}{7}\right] \cup [1, \infty)$

Solve each problem.

25. Find the measures of the marked angles.

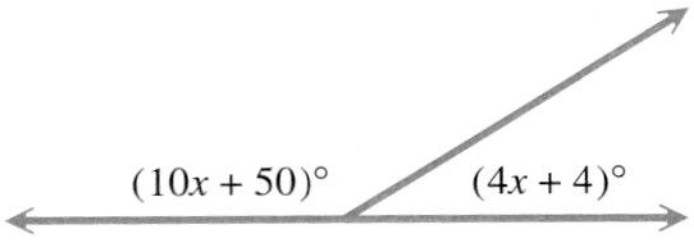

140°, 40°

26. A dietician must use three foods, A, B, and C, in a diet. He must include twice as many grams of food A as food C, and 5 g of food B. The three foods must total at most 24 g. What is the largest amount of food C that the dietician can use?

$6\frac{1}{3}$ g

27. Lorie Reilly got scores of 88 and 78 on her first two tests. What score must she make on her third test to keep an average of 80 or greater?

74 or greater

28. The distance between two cities on a road map is 11 in. The cities are actually 308 mi apart. The distance between two other cities on the map is 15 in. What is the actual distance between those cities?

420 mi

29. Since 1975, the number of daily newspapers has steadily declined.

Year	Number of Daily Newspapers
1975	1756
1980	1745
1985	1676
1990	1611
1995	1533
1996	1520
1997	1509
1998	1489

Source: Statistical Abstract of the United States, 1999.

According to the table,

(a) by how much did the number of daily newspapers decrease between 1990 and 1998?

122

(b) by what *percent* did the number of daily newspapers decrease from 1990 to 1998?

7.6%

30. For a woven hanging, Miguel Hidalgo needs three pieces of yarn, which he will cut from a 40 cm piece. The longest piece is to be 3 times as long as the middle-sized piece, and the shortest piece is to be 5 cm shorter than the middle-sized piece. What lengths should he cut?

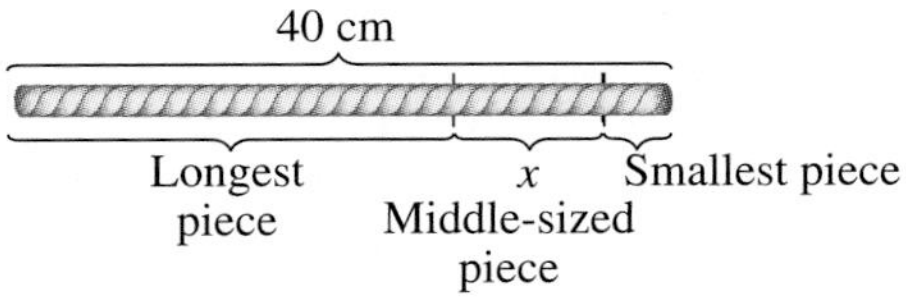

4 cm; 9 cm; 27 cm

Graphs of Linear Equations and Inequalities; Functions

4

U.S. debt from credit cards continues to increase. In recent years, college campuses have become fertile territory as credit card companies pitch their plastic to students at bookstores, student unions, and sporting events. As a result, three out of four undergrads now have at least one credit card and carry an average balance of $2748. (*Source:* Nellie Mae.) In Example 6 of Section 4.2, we use the concepts of this chapter to investigate credit card debt.

4.1 Reading Graphs; Linear Equations in Two Variables

Objectives

1. Interpret graphs.
2. Write a solution as an ordered pair.
3. Decide whether a given ordered pair is a solution of a given equation.
4. Complete ordered pairs for a given equation.
5. Complete a table of values.
6. Plot ordered pairs.

We live in an age of information. Graphs provide a quick way to organize and communicate much of this information. They can also be used to analyze data, make predictions, or simply entertain us. To prepare for the material in this chapter, we begin by looking at some graphs typically seen in newspapers, magazines, and other print and electronic media.

1 Interpret graphs. There are many ways to represent the relationship between two quantities. *Circle graphs, bar graphs,* and *line graphs* are often used for this purpose.

In a **circle graph** or **pie chart,** a circle is used to indicate the total of all the categories represented. The circle is divided into *sectors*, or wedges (like pieces of a pie), whose sizes show the relative magnitudes of the categories. The sum of all the fractional parts of the graph must be 1 (for 1 whole circle).

Example 1 **Interpreting a Circle Graph**

The 1999 market share for satellite-TV home subscribers is shown in the circle graph in Figure 1.

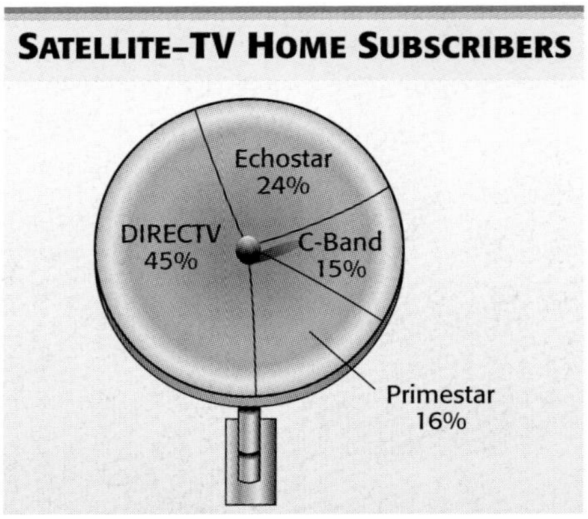

Source: Skyreport.com; *USA Today*.

Figure 1

The number of subscribers reached 12 million in August 1999.

(a) Which provider had the largest share of the home subscriber market in August 1999? What was that share?

In the circle graph, the sector for DIRECTV is the largest, so DIRECTV had the largest market share, 45%.

(b) Estimate the number of home subscribers to DIRECTV in August 1999.

A market share of 45% can be rounded to 50%, or .5. We multiply .5 (or $\frac{1}{2}$) by the total number of subscribers, 12 million. A good estimate for the number of DIRECTV subscribers would be

$$.5(12) = 6 \text{ million.}$$

Continued on Next Page

(c) How many actual home subscribers to DIRECTV were there?

To find the answer, we multiply the actual percent from the graph for DIRECTV, 45% or .45, by the number of subscribers, 12 million:

$$.45(12) = 5.4.$$

Thus, 5.4 million homes subscribed to DIRECTV. This is reasonable given our estimate in part (b).

Work Problem 1 at the Side.

A **bar graph** is used to show comparisons. It consists of a series of bars arranged either vertically or horizontally. In a bar graph, values from two categories are paired with each other.

Example 2 Interpreting a Bar Graph

The bar graph in Figure 2 compares average monthly savings, including retirement plans, for five countries.

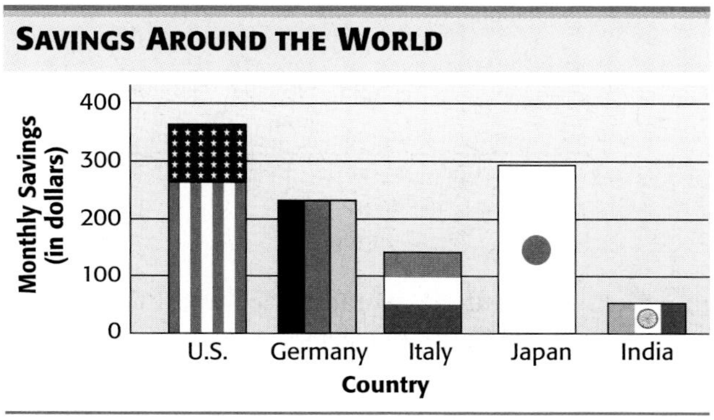

Source: Taylor Nelson–Sofres for American Express.

Figure 2

(a) Which country has the largest average monthly savings? the smallest?

The tallest bar corresponds to the United States, so the United States has the largest average monthly savings. India (with the shortest bar) has the smallest savings.

(b) Which countries have average monthly savings greater than $200?

Locate 200 on the vertical scale and follow the line across to the right. Three countries, the United States, Germany, and Japan, have bars that extend above the line for 200, so they have average monthly savings greater than $200.

(c) Estimate the average monthly savings for Japan and Italy.

Locate the top of the bar for Japan and move horizontally across to the vertical scale to see that average monthly savings in Japan is about $300.

Follow the top of the bar for Italy across to the vertical scale to see that this bar is almost halfway between $100 and $200. Average monthly savings in Italy is about $150.

(d) Find the difference between average monthly savings in Japan and Italy. Interpret this result.

Use the results from part (c) to see that the difference is about $\$300 - 150 = \$150$. Average monthly savings in Japan is about twice as much as that in Italy.

Work Problem 2 at the Side.

1 Refer to the circle graph in Figure 1.

(a) Which provider had the smallest market share in August 1999?

(b) Estimate the number of home subscribers to Echostar.

(c) How many actual home subscribers to Echostar were there?

2 Refer to the bar graph in Figure 2.

(a) Which countries have average monthly savings less than $150?

(b) Estimate the average monthly savings for Germany and India.

ANSWERS

1. (a) C-Band

(b) .25 or $\frac{1}{4}$ of 12 million = 3 million

(c) .24(12) = 2.88 million

2. (a) Italy and India

(b) Germany: about $230; India: about $50

3 Refer to the line graph in Figure 3.

(a) Which year had the highest average PC price?

(b) Estimate the average price of a PC in 1994.

(c) About how much did average PC prices decline from 1994 to 1999?

A **line graph** is used to show changes or trends in data over time. To form a line graph, we connect a series of points representing data with line segments.

Example 3 Interpreting a Line Graph

The line graph in Figure 3 shows average prices for personal computers (PCs) for the years 1993 through 1999.

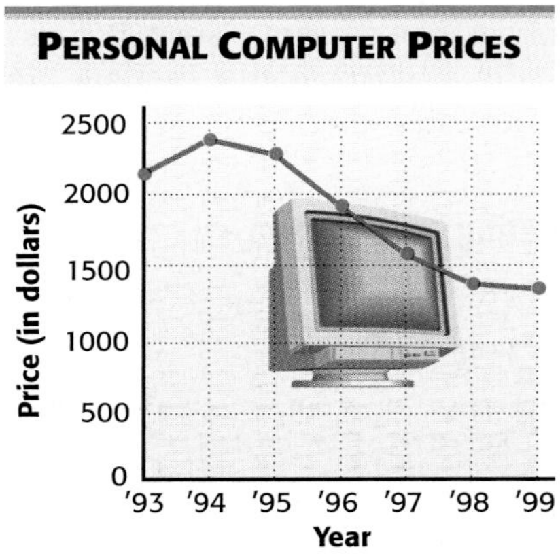

Source: CNW Marketing/Research; *USA Today*.

Figure 3

(a) Between which years did the average price of a PC increase?

The line between 1993 and 1994 rises, so PC prices increased from 1993 to 1994.

(b) What has been the general trend in average PC prices since 1994?

The line graph falls from 1994 to 1999, so PC prices have been decreasing over these years.

(c) Estimate average PC prices in 1996 and 1999. About how much did PC prices decline between 1996 and 1999?

Move up from 1996 on the horizontal scale to the point plotted for 1996. Then move across to the vertical scale. The average price of a PC in 1996 was about \$2000.

The point for 1999 is a little more than halfway between the lines for \$1000 and \$1500, so estimate the average price in 1999 at about \$1300.

Between 1996 and 1999, PC prices declined about

$$\$2000 - 1300 = \$700.$$

Work Problem 3 at the Side.

Many everyday situations, such as those illustrated in Examples 2 and 3, involve two quantities that are related. The equations and applications we discussed in Chapter 2 had only one variable. In this chapter, we extend those ideas to *linear equations in two variables.*

ANSWERS

3. **(a)** 1994 **(b)** about \$2400 **(c)** about \$1100

Linear Equation in Two Variables

A **linear equation in two variables** is an equation that can be written in the form

$$Ax + By = C,$$

where A, B, and C are real numbers and A and B are not both 0.

Some examples of linear equations in two variables in this form, called *standard form,* are

$$3x + 4y = 9, \quad x - y = 0, \quad \text{and} \quad x + 2y = -8.$$

NOTE

Other linear equations in two variables, such as

$$y = 4x + 5 \quad \text{and} \quad 3x = 7 - 2y,$$

are not written in standard form but could be. We will discuss the forms of linear equations in more detail in Section 4.4.

2 **Write a solution as an ordered pair.** Recall that a *solution* of an equation is a number that makes the equation true when it replaces the variable. For example, the linear equation in one variable $x - 2 = 5$ has solution 7, since replacing x with 7 gives a true statement.

A solution of a linear equation in *two* variables requires *two* numbers, one for each variable. For example, a true statement results when we replace x with 2 and y with 13 in the equation $y = 4x + 5$ since

$$13 = 4(2) + 5. \quad \text{Let } x = 2, y = 13.$$

The pair of numbers $x = 2$ and $y = 13$ gives one solution of the equation $y = 4x + 5$. The phrase "$x = 2$ and $y = 13$" is abbreviated

x-value → (2, 13) ← y-value

Ordered pair

with the x-value, 2, and the y-value, 13, given as a pair of numbers written inside parentheses. *The x-value is always given first.* A pair of numbers such as (2, 13) is called an **ordered pair.** As the name indicates, the order in which the numbers are written is important. The ordered pairs (2, 13) and (13, 2) are not the same. The second pair indicates that $x = 13$ and $y = 2$.

Work Problem 4 at the Side.

3 **Decide whether a given ordered pair is a solution of a given equation.** We substitute the x- and y-values of an ordered pair into a linear equation in two variables to see whether the ordered pair is a solution of the equation.

4 Write each solution as an ordered pair.

(a) $x = 5$ and $y = 7$

(b) $y = 6$ and $x = -1$

(c) $y = 4$ and $x = -3$

(d) $x = 3$ and $y = -12$

ANSWERS

4. **(a)** $(5, 7)$ **(b)** $(-1, 6)$ **(c)** $(-3, 4)$ **(d)** $(3, -12)$

5 Decide whether each ordered pair is a solution of the equation $5x + 2y = 20$.

(a) (0, 10)

$$5x + 2y = 20$$
$$5(\quad) + 2(\quad) = 20$$
$$\_\_\_\_ + 20 = 20$$
$$\_\_\_\_ = 20$$

Is (0, 10) a solution?

(b) (2, −5)

(c) (3, 2)

(d) (−4, 20)

6 Complete each ordered pair for the equation $y = 2x - 9$.

(a) (5,)

$$y = 2x - 9$$
$$y = 2(\quad) - 9$$
$$y = \_\_\_\_ - 9$$
$$y = \_\_\_\_$$

The ordered pair is ____.

(b) (2,)

(c) (, 7)

(d) (, −13)

ANSWERS

5. **(a)** 0; 10; 0; 20; yes **(b)** no **(c)** no **(d)** yes

6. **(a)** 5; 10; 1; (5, 1) **(b)** (2, −5) **(c)** (8, 7) **(d)** (−2, −13)

Example 4 Deciding Whether Ordered Pairs Are Solutions of an Equation

Decide whether each ordered pair is a solution of the equation $2x + 3y = 12$.

(a) (3, 2)

To see whether (3, 2) is a solution of the equation $2x + 3y = 12$, substitute 3 for x and 2 for y in the equation.

$$2x + 3y = 12$$
$$2(3) + 3(2) \stackrel{?}{=} 12 \quad \text{Let } x = 3; \text{ let } y = 2.$$
$$6 + 6 \stackrel{?}{=} 12$$
$$12 = 12 \quad \text{True}$$

This result is true, so (3, 2) is a solution of $2x + 3y = 12$.

(b) (−2, −7)

$$2x + 3y = 12$$
$$2(-2) + 3(-7) \stackrel{?}{=} 12 \quad \text{Let } x = -2; \text{ let } y = -7.$$
$$-4 + (-21) \stackrel{?}{=} 12$$
$$-25 = 12 \quad \text{False}$$

This result is false, so (−2, −7) is *not* a solution of $2x + 3y = 12$.

Work Problem 5 at the Side.

4 Complete ordered pairs for a given equation. Choosing a number for one variable in a linear equation makes it possible to find the value of the other variable.

Example 5 Completing Ordered Pairs

Complete each ordered pair for the equation $y = 4x + 5$.

(a) (7,)

In this ordered pair, $x = 7$. (Remember that x always comes first.) To find the corresponding value of y, replace x with 7 in the equation.

$$y = 4x + 5$$
$$y = 4(7) + 5 \quad \text{Let } x = 7.$$
$$y = 28 + 5$$
$$y = 33$$

The ordered pair is (7, 33).

(b) (, −3)

In this ordered pair, $y = -3$. Find the value of x by replacing y with −3 in the equation; then solve for x.

$$y = 4x + 5$$
$$-3 = 4x + 5 \quad \text{Let } y = -3.$$
$$-8 = 4x \quad \text{Subtract 5 from each side.}$$
$$-2 = x \quad \text{Divide each side by 4.}$$

The ordered pair is (−2, −3).

Work Problem 6 at the Side.

5 **Complete a table of values.** Ordered pairs are often displayed in a **table of values.** The table may be written either vertically or horizontally.

Example 6 **Completing Tables of Values**

Complete the table of values for each equation.

(a) $x - 2y = 8$

x	y
2	
10	
	0
	-2

To complete the first two ordered pairs, let $x = 2$ and $x = 10$, respectively.

If	$x = 2,$	If	$x = 10,$
then	$x - 2y = 8$	then	$x - 2y = 8$
becomes	$2 - 2y = 8$	becomes	$10 - 2y = 8$
	$-2y = 6$		$-2y = -2$
	$y = -3.$		$y = 1.$

Now complete the last two ordered pairs by letting $y = 0$ and $y = -2$, respectively.

If	$y = 0,$	If	$y = -2,$
then	$x - 2y = 8$	then	$x - 2y = 8$
becomes	$x - 2(0) = 8$	becomes	$x - 2(-2) = 8$
	$x - 0 = 8$		$x + 4 = 8$
	$x = 8.$		$x = 4.$

The completed table of values follows.

x	y
2	-3
10	1
8	0
4	-2

The corresponding ordered pairs are

$$(2, -3), (10, 1), (8, 0), \text{ and } (4, -2).$$

Notice that each ordered pair is a solution of the given equation.

(b) $x = 5$

x	y
	-2
	6
	3

Continued on Next Page

7 Complete the table of values for each equation.

(a) $2x - 3y = 12$

x	y
0	
	0
3	
	-3

(b) $y = 4$

x	y
-3	
2	
5	

8 Name the quadrant in which each point in the figure is located.

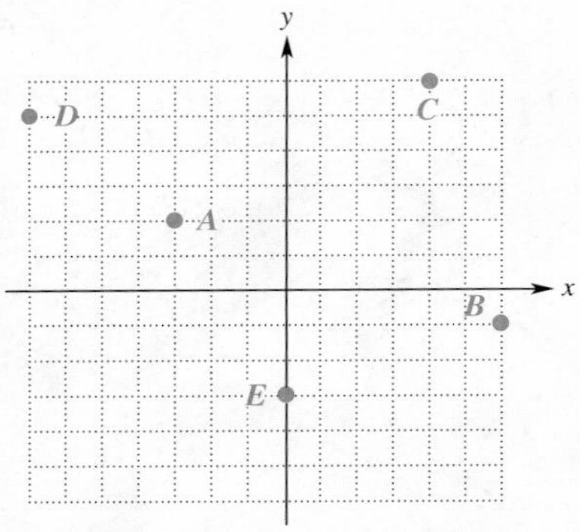

ANSWERS

7. (a)

x	y
0	-4
6	0
3	-2
$\frac{3}{2}$	-3

(b)

x	y
-3	4
2	4
5	4

8. *A*, II; *B*, IV; *C*, I; *D*, II; *E*, no quadrant

The given equation is $x = 5$. No matter which value of y is chosen, the value of x is always the same, 5.

x	y
5	-2
5	6
5	3

The corresponding ordered pairs are $(5, -2)$, $(5, 6)$, and $(5, 3)$.

NOTE

We can think of $x = 5$ in Example 6(b) as an equation in two variables by rewriting $x = 5$ as $x + 0y = 5$. This form of the equation shows that for any value of y, the value of x is 5. Similarly, $y = 4$ is the same as $0x + y = 4$.

Work Problem 7 at the Side.

6 **Plot ordered pairs.** In Chapter 2, we saw that linear equations in *one* variable had either one, zero, or an infinite number of real number solutions. These solutions could be graphed on *one* number line. Every linear equation in *two* variables has an infinite number of ordered pairs as solutions. Each choice of a number for one variable leads to a particular real number for the other variable.

To graph these solutions, represented as the ordered pairs (x, y), we need *two* number lines, one for each variable. These two number lines are drawn as shown in Figure 4. The horizontal number line is called the **x-axis,** and the vertical line is called the **y-axis.** Together, the x-axis and y-axis form a **rectangular coordinate system.** It is also called the **Cartesian coordinate system,** in honor of René Descartes (1596–1650), the French mathematician who is credited with its invention.

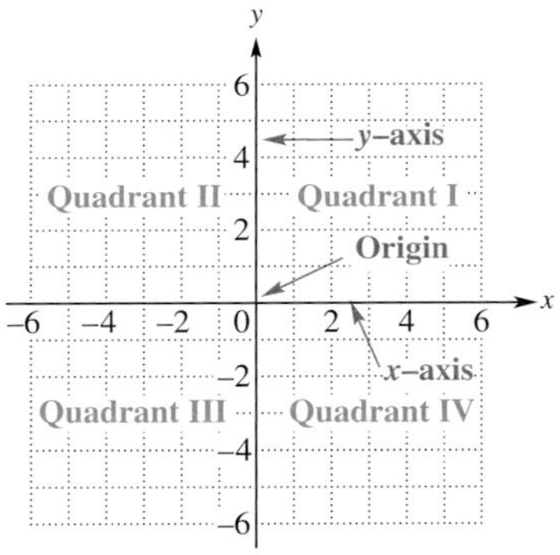

Figure 4

The coordinate system is divided into four regions, called **quadrants.** These quadrants are numbered counterclockwise, as shown in Figure 4. Points on the axes themselves are not in any quadrant. The point at which the x-axis and y-axis meet is called the **origin.** The origin, labeled 0 in Figure 4, is the point corresponding to $(0, 0)$.

Work Problem 8 at the Side.

The x-axis and y-axis determine a **plane,** a flat surface similar to a sheet of paper. By referring to the two axes, every point in the plane can be associated with an ordered pair. The numbers in the ordered pair are called the **coordinates** of the point. For example, locate the point associated with the ordered pair (2, 3) by starting at the origin. Since the x-coordinate is 2, go 2 units to the right along the x-axis. Then, since the y-coordinate is 3, turn and go up 3 units on a line parallel to the y-axis. The point (2, 3) is **plotted** in Figure 5. From now on, we will refer to the point with x-coordinate 2 and y-coordinate 3 as the point (2, 3).

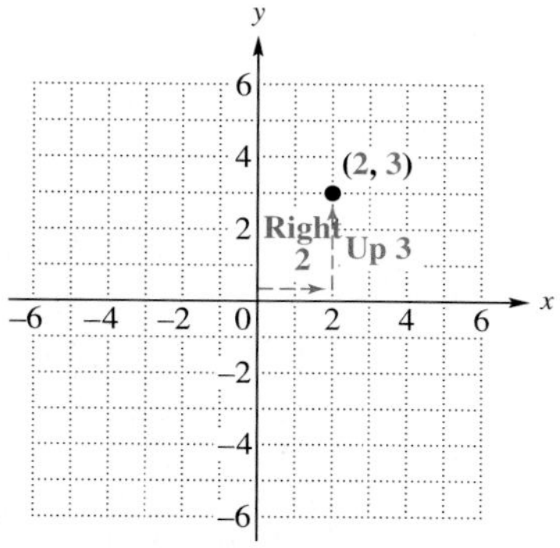

Figure 5

NOTE

When we graph on a number line, one number corresponds to each point. On a plane, however, both numbers in the ordered pair are needed to locate a point. The ordered pair is a name for the point.

Example 7 Plotting Ordered Pairs

Plot each ordered pair on a coordinate system.

(a) (1, 5) **(b)** (−2, 3) **(c)** (−1, −4) **(d)** (7, −2)

(e) $\left(\frac{3}{2}, 2\right)$ **(f)** (5, 0) **(g)** (0, −3)

See Figure 6. In part (c), locate the point (−1, −4) by first going 1 unit to the left along the x-axis. Then turn and go 4 units down, parallel to the y-axis. Plot the point $\left(\frac{3}{2}, 2\right)$ in part (e) by first going $\frac{3}{2}$ $\left(\text{or } 1\frac{1}{2}\right)$ units to the right along the x-axis. Then turn and go 2 units up, parallel to the y-axis.

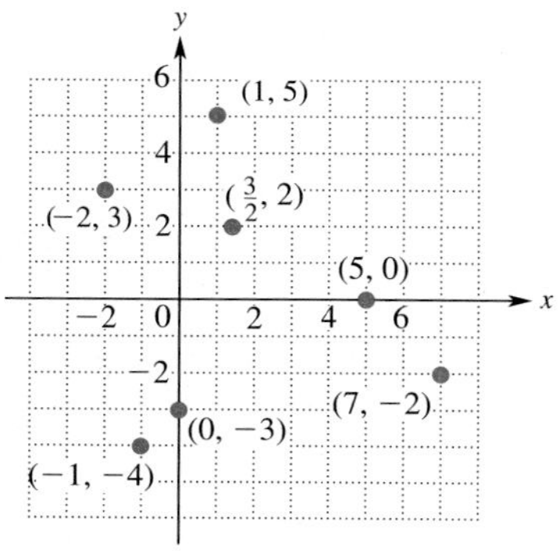

Figure 6

Work Problem 9 at the Side.

9 Plot each ordered pair on a coordinate system.

(a) (3, 5)

(b) (−2, 6)

(c) (−4, 0)

(d) (−5, −2)

(e) (5, −2)

(f) (0, −6)

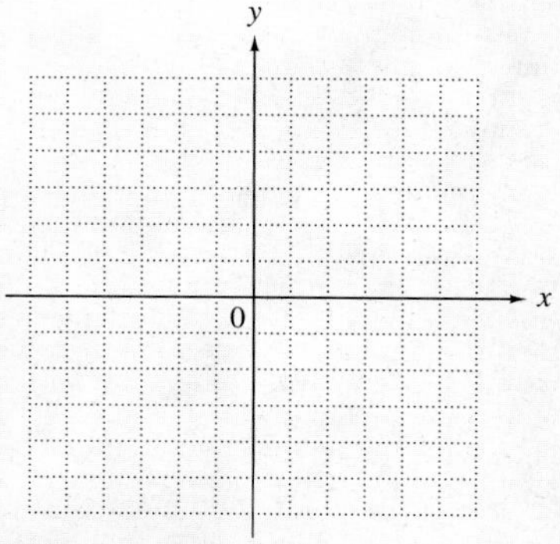

ANSWERS

9.

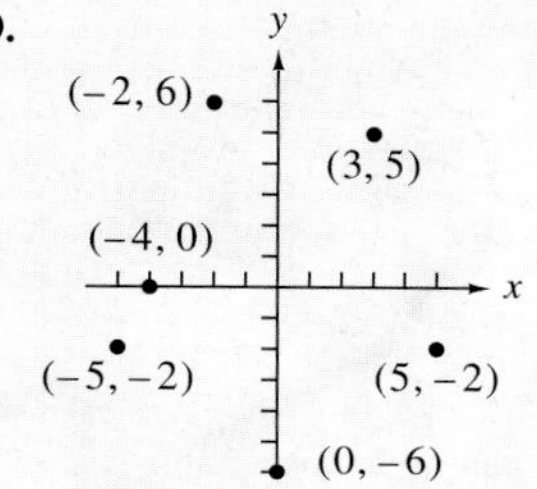

Sometimes we can use a linear equation to mathematically describe, or *model,* a real-life situation, as shown in the next example.

Example 8 **Completing Ordered Pairs to Estimate Annual Costs of Doctors' Visits**

The amount Americans pay annually for doctors' visits has increased steadily from 1990 through 2000. This amount can be closely approximated by the linear equation

Cost (y) — Year (x)

$$y = 34.3x - 67{,}693,$$

which relates x, the year, and y, the cost in dollars. (*Source:* U.S. Health Care Financing Administration.)

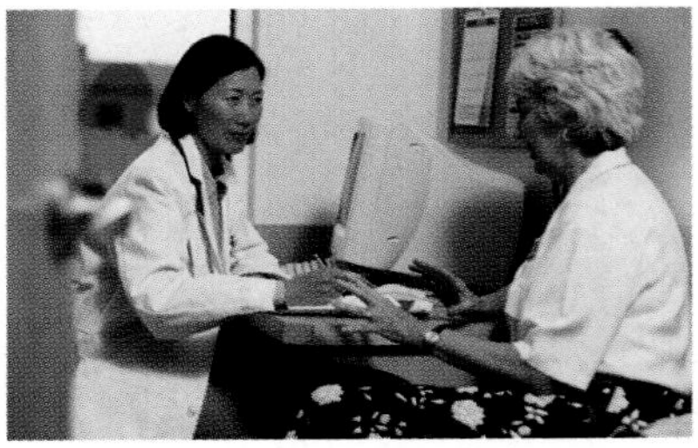

(a) Complete the table of values for this linear equation.

x (Year)	y (Cost)
1990	
1996	
2000	

To find y when $x = 1990$, substitute into the equation.

$$y = 34.3(1990) - 67{,}693 \quad \text{Let } x = 1990.$$
$$y = 564 \quad \text{Use a calculator.}$$

This means that in 1990, Americans each spent about \$564 on doctors' visits.

Work Problem 10 at the Side.

Including the results from Problem 10 at the side gives the completed table that follows.

x (Year)	y (Cost)
1990	564
1996	770
2000	907

We can write the results from the table of values as ordered pairs (x, y). Each year x is paired with its cost y:

$$(1990, 564), \quad (1996, 770), \quad \text{and} \quad (2000, 907).$$

Continued on Next Page

10 Refer to the linear equation in Example 8.

(a) Find the y-value for $x = 1996$. Round to the nearest whole number.

(b) Find the y-value for $x = 2000$. Interpret your result.

ANSWERS

10. **(a)** $y = 770$
(b) $y = 907$; In 2000, Americans each spent about \$907 on doctors' visits.

(b) Graph the ordered pairs found in part (a).

The ordered pairs are graphed in Figure 7. This graph of ordered pairs of data is called a **scatter diagram.** Notice how the axes are labeled: x represents the year, and y represents the cost in dollars. Different scales are used on the two axes. Here, each square represents two units in the horizontal direction and 100 units in the vertical direction. Because the numbers in the first ordered pair are so large, we show a break in the axes near the origin.

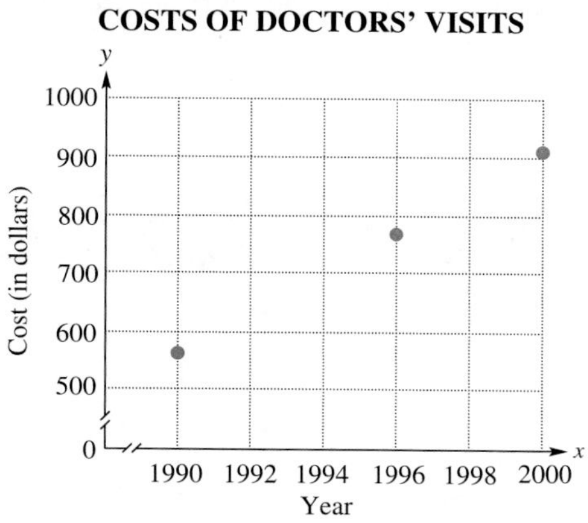

Figure 7

A scatter diagram enables us to tell whether two quantities are related to each other. In Figure 7, the plotted points could be connected to form a straight *line,* so the variables x (year) and y (cost) have a *line*ar relationship. The increase in costs is also reflected.

CAUTION

The equation in Example 8 is valid only for the years 1990 through 2000 because it was based on data for those years. Do not assume that this equation would provide reliable data for other years since the data for those years may not follow the same pattern.

Focus on *Real-Data Applications*

Linear or Nonlinear? That Is the Question about Windchill

The **windchill factor** measures the cooling effect that the wind has on one's skin. The table gives the windchill factor for various wind speeds and temperatures.

WINDCHILL FACTOR

Wind Speed (mph)	Air Temperature (°Fahrenheit) 35	30	25	20	15	10	5	0	−5	−10	−15	−20	−25	−30	−35
4	35	30	25	20	15	10	5	0	−5	−10	−15	−20	−25	−30	−35
5	32	27	22	16	11	6	0	−5	−10	−15	−21	−26	−31	−36	−42
10	22	16	10	3	−3	−9	−15	−22	−27	−34	−40	−46	−52	−58	−64
15	16	9	2	−5	−11	−18	−25	−31	−38	−45	−51	−58	−65	−72	−78
20	12	4	−3	−10	−17	−24	−31	−39	−46	−53	−60	−67	−74	−81	−88
25	8	1	−7	−15	−22	−29	−36	−44	−51	−59	−66	−74	−81	−88	−96
30	6	−2	−10	−18	−25	−33	−41	−49	−56	−64	−71	−79	−86	−93	−101
35	4	−4	−12	−20	−27	−35	−43	−52	−58	−67	−74	−82	−89	−97	−105
40	3	−5	−13	−21	−29	−37	−45	−53	−60	−69	−76	−84	−92	−100	−107
45	2	−6	−14	−22	−30	−38	−46	−54	−62	−70	−78	−85	−93	−102	−109

Source: USA Today.

The data in the table represents the relationships between two different sets of variable quantities: Windchill versus Air Temperature and Windchill versus Wind Speed. The question is whether either of these relationships is linear, that is, whether the data points, when graphed, could be connected to form a straight line.

Example 1 Windchill versus Air Temperature

Choose one measure of wind speed to keep constant, such as 15 mph. Complete the table with Air Temperature (AT) as the *input* and Windchill (WC) as the *output*. Both variables are measured in degrees Fahrenheit.

AT	35	30	25	20	15	10	5	0	−5	−10	−15	−20	−25	−30	−35
WC	16	9	2	−5	−11	−18	−25	−31	−38	−45	−51	−58	−65	−72	−78

Example 2 Windchill versus Wind Speed

Choose one measure of air temperature to keep constant, such as 10°F. Complete the table with Wind Speed (WS) as the *input* and Windchill (WC) as the *output*. Wind speed is measured in mph.

WS	4	5	10	15	20	25	30	35	40	45
WC	10	6	−9	−18	−24	−29	−33	−35	−37	−38

For Group Discussion

1. Refer to the Windchill versus Air Temperature data (Example 1).
   (a) Write the data as ordered pairs. (35, 16), (30, 9), (25, 2), (20, −5), (15, −11), (10, −18), (5, −25), and so on
   (b) On a sheet of graph paper, draw and label a rectangular coordinate system. Use a scale of 5 on the x-axis and the y-axis. Make a scatter diagram of the data. Does the graph represent a linear relationship? yes
2. Repeat Problem 1 using the Windchill versus Wind Speed data (Example 2).
   (a) (4, 10), (5, 6), (10, −9), (15, −18), (20, −24), (25, −29), and so on (b) no

Teaching notes and an extension for this activity are provided in the *Printed Test Bank and Instructor's Resource Guide.*

4.1 EXERCISES

FOR EXTRA HELP — Student's Solutions Manual · MyMathLab.com · InterAct Math Tutorial Software · AW Math Tutor Center · www.mathxl.com · Digital Video Tutor CD 3 Videotape 7

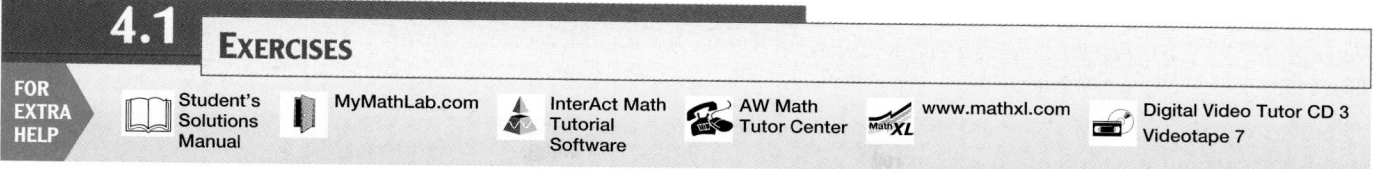

On February 13, 2000, Peanuts *fans bid farewell to this popular comic strip. The circle graph shows the results of a survey of adults to determine their favorite* Peanuts *characters. Use the circle graph to work Exercises 1–4. See Example 1.*

FAVORITE *PEANUTS* CHARACTERS

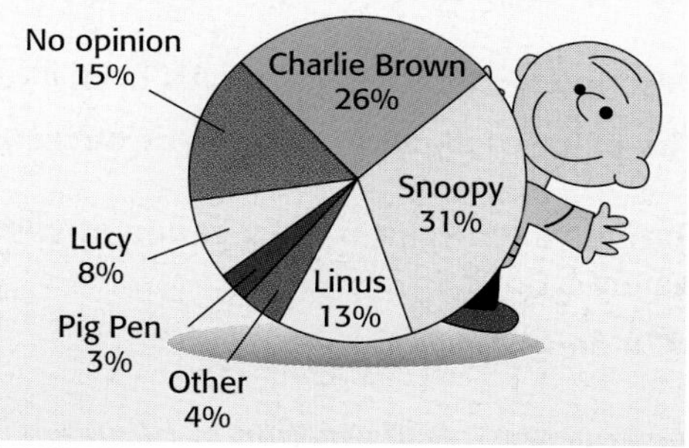

Source: *USA Today*/CNN/Gallop Poll conducted nationwide February 4–6, 2000.

1. Which *Peanuts* character was most popular? What percent of those surveyed named this character as their favorite?

Snoopy; 31%

2. A random sample of 2500 adults is surveyed.

(a) Estimate how many would be expected to name Lucy as their favorite *Peanuts* character. (*Hint*: To estimate, round 8% to 10%.)

about 250 adults

(b) Use the actual figure from the graph to determine how many adults would name Lucy as their favorite character. Is this answer reasonable based on your estimate in part (a)?

200 adults; yes

3. Regardless of the number of adults surveyed, how many would we expect to name Charlie Brown as their favorite *Peanuts* character compared to Linus?

Since 26% is twice as much as 13%, we can expect twice as many adults to favor Charlie Brown.

4. Using the group of 2500 adults, confirm your answer to Exercise 3.

Charlie Brown: 650; Linus: 325. As expected, the number for Charlie Brown is twice that for Linus.

The bar graph compares egg production in millions of eggs for six states in June 1999. Use the bar graph to work Exercises 5–8. See Example 2.

EGG PRODUCTION

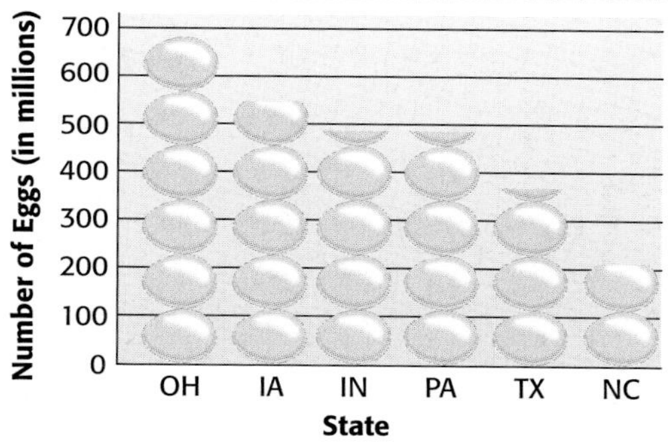

Source: Iowa Agricultural Statistics.

5. Name the top two egg-producing states in June 1999. Estimate their production.

Ohio (OH): about 680 million eggs; Iowa (IA): about 550 million eggs

6. Which states had egg production less than 400 million eggs?

Texas (TX) and North Carolina (NC)

7. Which states appear to have had equal production? Estimate this production.

Indiana (IN) and Pennsylvania (PA); about 490 million eggs each

8. How does egg production in Ohio compare to egg production in North Carolina?

Egg production in Ohio is more than three times egg production in North Carolina.

The line graph shows the average price, adjusted for inflation, that Americans have paid for a gallon of gasoline for selected years since 1970. Use the line graph to work Exercises 9–12. See Example 3.

AVERAGE GASOLINE PRICES

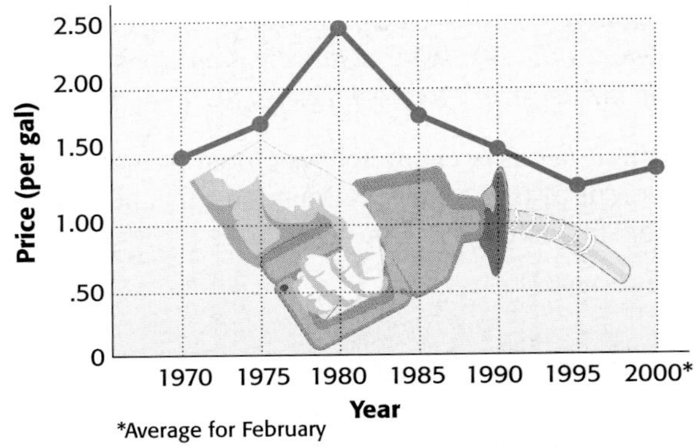

Source: American Petroleum Institute; AP research.

9. Over which period of years did the greatest increase in the price of a gallon of gas occur? About how much was this increase?

from 1975 to 1980; about \$.75

10. Estimate the price of a gallon of gas during 1985, 1990, 1995, and 2000.

1985: \$1.80; 1990: \$1.55; 1995: \$1.30; 2000: \$1.40

11. Describe the trend in gas prices from 1980 to 1995.

The price of a gallon of gas was decreasing.

12. During which year(s) did a gallon of gas cost approximately \$1.50?

1970 and 1990

Use the concepts of this section to fill in each blank with the correct response.

13. The symbol (x, y) **does** (does/does not) represent an ordered pair, while the symbols $[x, y]$ and $\{x, y\}$ **do not** (do/do not) represent ordered pairs.

14. The point whose graph has coordinates $(-4, 2)$ is in quadrant **II**.

15. The point whose graph has coordinates $(0, 5)$ lies on the **y**-axis.

16. The ordered pair (4, **3**) is a solution of the equation $y = 3$.

17. The ordered pair (**6**, -2) is a solution of the equation $x = 6$.

18. The ordered pair $(3, 2)$ is a solution of the equation $2x - 5y =$ **-4**.

Decide whether each ordered pair is a solution of the given equation. See Example 4.

19. $x + y = 9$; $(0, 9)$ **yes**

20. $x + y = 8$; $(0, 8)$ **yes**

21. $2x - y = 6$; $(4, 2)$ **yes**

22. $2x + y = 5$; $(3, -1)$ **yes**

23. $4x - 3y = 6$; $(2, 1)$ **no**

24. $5x - 3y = 15$; $(5, 2)$ **no**

25. $y = \frac{2}{3}x$; $(-6, -4)$ **yes**

26. $y = -\frac{1}{4}x$; $(-8, 2)$ **yes**

27. $x = -6$; $(5, -6)$ **no**

28. $y = 2$; $(2, 4)$ **no**

29. Do $(4, -1)$ and $(-1, 4)$ represent the same ordered pair? Explain.

No. For two ordered pairs (x, y) to be equal, the x-values must be equal and the y-values must be equal. Here we have $4 \neq -1$ and $-1 \neq 4$.

30. Explain why it would be easier to find the corresponding y-value for $x = \frac{1}{3}$ in the equation $y = 6x + 2$ than it would be for $x = \frac{1}{7}$.

Substituting $\frac{1}{3}$ for x in $y = 6x + 2$ gives $y = 6\left(\frac{1}{3}\right) + 2 = 2 + 2 = 4$. Because $6\left(\frac{1}{7}\right) = \frac{6}{7}$, calculating y requires working with fractions.

Complete each ordered pair for the equation $y = 2x + 7$. See Example 5.

31. (2,) **11**

32. (0,) **7**

33. (, 0) $-\frac{7}{2}$

34. (, −3) **−5**

Complete each ordered pair for the equation $y = -4x - 4$. See Example 5.

35. (0,) **−4**

36. (, 0) **−1**

37. (, 16) **−5**

38. (, 24) **−7**

Complete each table of values. In Exercises 39–42, write the results as ordered pairs. See Example 6.

39. $2x + 3y = 12$

x	y
0	**4**
6	0
−6	8

(0, 4); (6, 0); (−6, 8)

40. $4x + 3y = 24$

x	y
0	**8**
6	0
3	4

(0, 8); (6, 0); (3, 4)

41. $3x - 5y = -15$

x	y
0	**3**
−5	0
−15	−6

(0, 3); (−5, 0); (−15, −6)

42. $4x - 9y = -36$

x	y
−9	0
0	**4**
9	8

(−9, 0); (0, 4); (9, 8)

43. $x = -9$

x	y
−9	6
−9	2
−9	−3

44. $x = 12$

x	y
12	3
12	8
12	0

45. $y = -6$

x	y
8	**−6**
4	**−6**
−2	**−6**

46. $y = -10$

x	y
4	**−10**
0	**−10**
−4	**−10**

47. $x - 8 = 0$

x	y
8	8
8	3
8	0

48. $y + 2 = 0$

x	y
9	**−2**
2	**−2**
0	**−2**

Give the ordered pairs for the points labeled A–F in the figure.

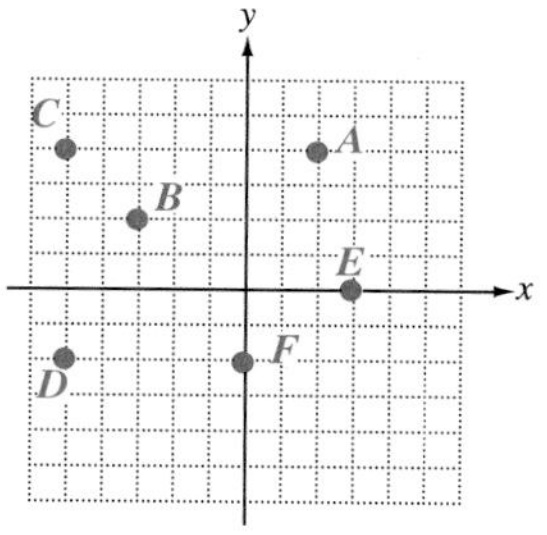

49. *A* **(2, 4)**

50. *B* **(−3, 2)**

51. *C* **(−5, 4)**

52. *D* **(−5, −2)**

53. *E* **(3, 0)**

54. *F* **(0, −2)**

Fill in each blank with the word positive *or the word* negative.

The point with coordinates (x, y) is in

55. quadrant III if x is **negative** and y is **negative**.

56. quadrant II if x is **negative** and y is **positive**.

57. quadrant IV if x is **positive** and y is **negative**.

58. quadrant I if x is **positive** and y is **positive**.

59. A point (x, y) has the property that $xy < 0$. In which quadrant(s) must the point lie? Explain.

If $xy < 0$, then either $x < 0$ and $y > 0$ or $x > 0$ and $y < 0$. If $x < 0$ and $y > 0$, then the point lies in quadrant II. If $x > 0$ and $y < 0$, then the point lies in quadrant IV.

60. A point (x, y) has the property that $xy > 0$. In which quadrant(s) must the point lie? Explain.

If $xy > 0$, then either $x > 0$ and $y > 0$ or $x < 0$ and $y < 0$. If $x > 0$ and $y > 0$, then the point lies in quadrant I. If $x < 0$ and $y < 0$, then the point lies in quadrant III.

Plot each ordered pair on the rectangular coordinate system provided. See Example 7.

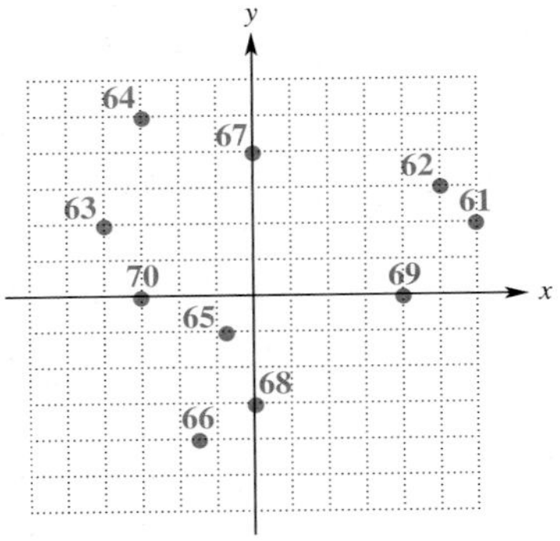

61. $(6, 2)$ **62.** $(5, 3)$ **63.** $(-4, 2)$

64. $(-3, 5)$ **65.** $\left(-\frac{4}{5}, -1\right)$ **66.** $\left(-\frac{3}{2}, -4\right)$

67. $(0, 4)$ **68.** $(0, -3)$ **69.** $(4, 0)$ **70.** $(-3, 0)$

Complete each table of values, and then plot the ordered pairs. See Examples 6 and 7.

71. $x - 2y = 6$

x	y
0	−3
6	0
2	−2
4	−1

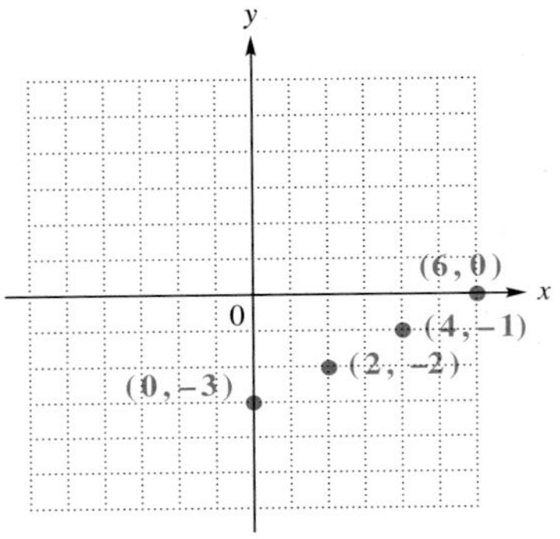

72. $2x - y = 4$

x	y
0	−4
2	0
1	−2
−1	−6

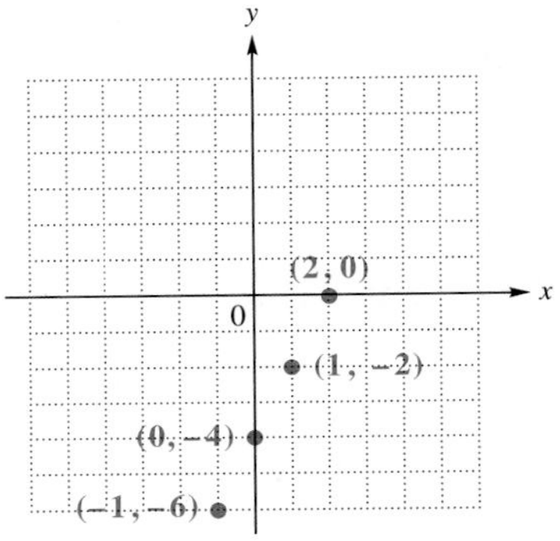

73. $3x - 4y = 12$

x	y
0	−3
4	0
−4	−6
$-\frac{4}{3}$	−4

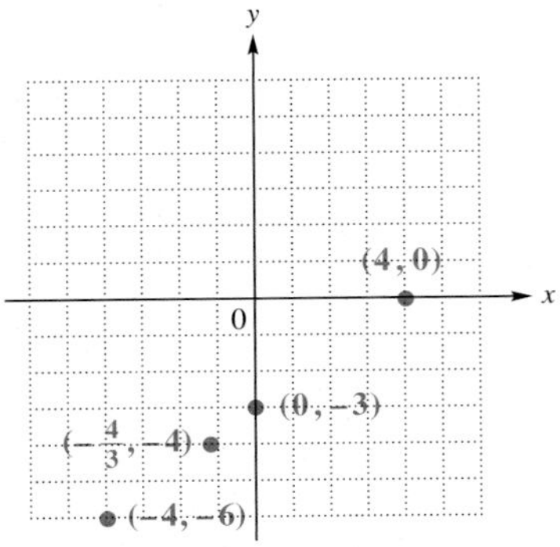

74. $2x - 5y = 10$

x	y
0	−2
5	0
−5	−4
$-\frac{5}{2}$	−3

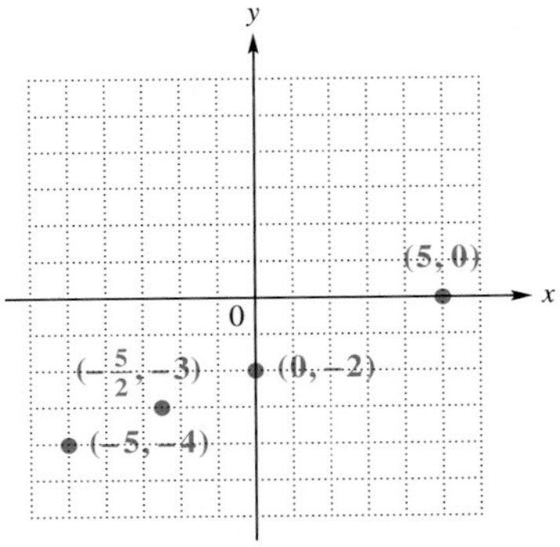

75. $y + 4 = 0$

x	y
0	−4
5	−4
−2	−4
−3	−4

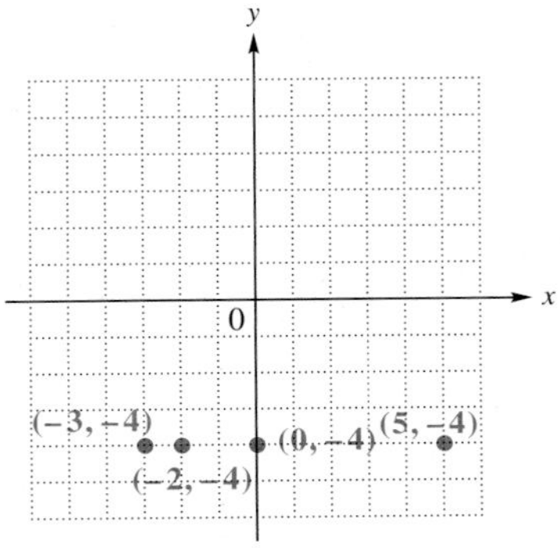

76. $x - 5 = 0$

x	y
5	1
5	0
5	6
5	−4

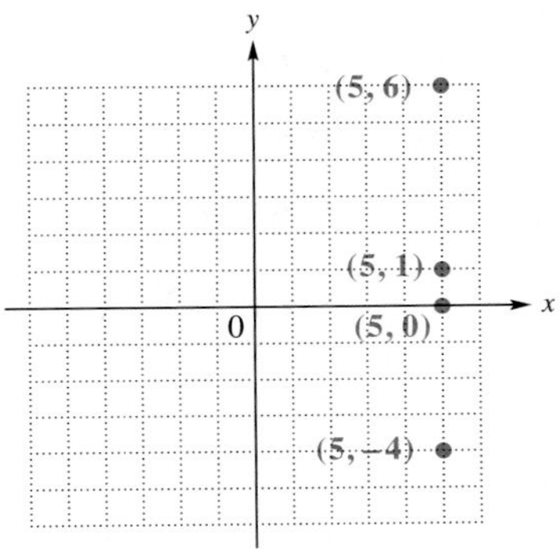

77. Look at the graphs of the ordered pairs in Exercises 71–76. Describe the pattern indicated by the plotted points.

The points in each graph appear to lie on a straight line.

Work each problem. See Example 8.

78. The table shows on-line retail spending in billions of dollars.

Year	Spending (in billions)
1998	7.8
1999	14.9
2000*	23.1
2001*	34.6
2002*	53.0

*Projected
Source: Jupiter Communications.

(a) Write the data from the table as ordered pairs (x, y), where x represents the year and y represents on-line spending in billions of dollars.

(1998, 7.8), (1999, 14.9), (2000, 23.1), (2001, 34.6), (2002, 53.0)

(b) What does the ordered pair (2003, 78.0) mean in the context of this problem?

(2003, 78.0) indicates that on-line spending in 2003 is projected to be 78.0 billion dollars.

(c) Make a scatter diagram of the data using the ordered pairs from part (a).

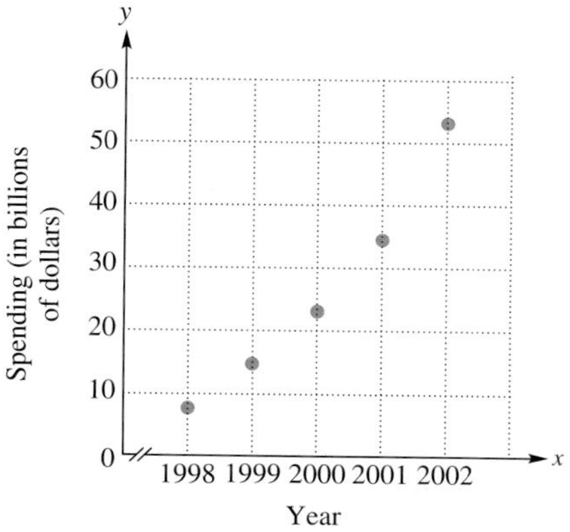

See the graph.

(d) Describe the pattern indicated by the points on the scatter diagram. What is the trend in on-line spending?

The points lie approximately on a straight line. On-line spending is increasing each year.

79. The table shows the rate (in percent) at which 4-year college students graduate within 5 years.

Year	Rate (%)
1996	53.3
1997	52.8
1998	52.1
1999	51.6

Source: ACT.

(a) Write the data from the table as ordered pairs (x, y), where x represents the year and y represents graduation rate.

(1996, 53.3), (1997, 52.8), (1998, 52.1), (1999, 51.6)

(b) What does the ordered pair (1995, 54.0) mean in the context of this problem?

(1995, 54.0) means that in 1995, the graduation rate for 4-year college students within 5 years was 54.0%.

(c) Make a scatter diagram of the data using the ordered pairs from part (a).

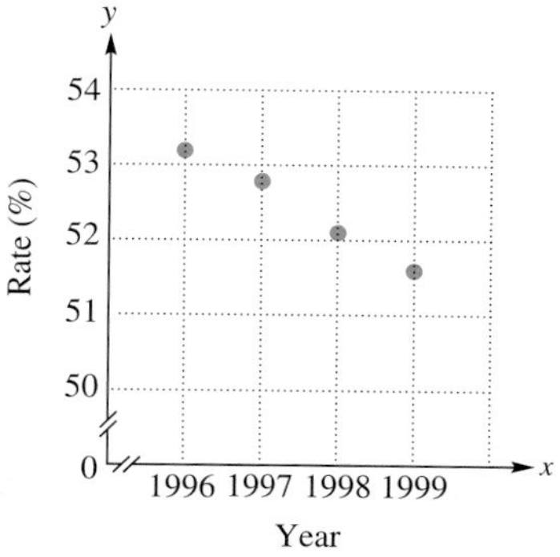

See the graph.

(d) Describe the pattern indicated by the points on the scatter diagram. What is happening to graduation rates for 4-year college students within 5 years?

The points appear to lie on a straight line. Graduation rates for 4-year college students within 5 years are decreasing.

80. The maximum benefit for the heart from exercising occurs if the heart rate is in the target heart rate zone. The lower limit of this target zone can be approximated by the linear equation

$$y = -.7x + 154,$$

where x represents age and y represents heartbeats per minute. (*Source:* Hockey, R. V., *Physical Fitness: The Pathway to Healthy Living*, Times Mirror/Mosby College Publishing, 1989.)

(a) Complete the table of values for this linear equation.

Age	Heartbeats (per minute)
20	140
40	126
60	112
80	98

See the table.

(b) Write the data from the table of values as ordered pairs.

(20, 140), (40, 126), (60, 112), (80, 98)

(c) Make a scatter diagram of the data. Do the points lie in an approximately linear pattern?

TARGET HEART RATE ZONE

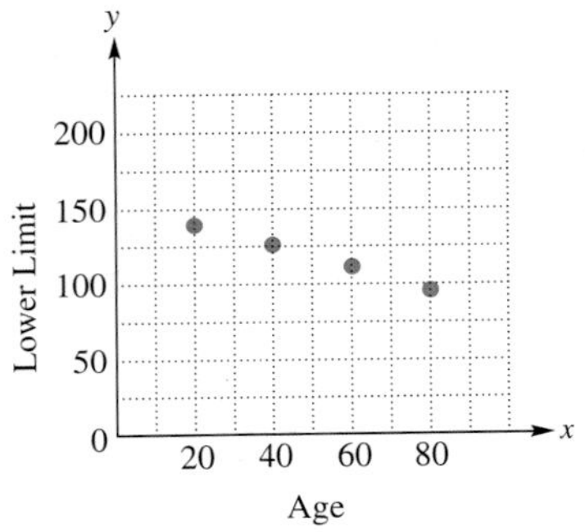

See the graph; Yes.

81. (See Exercise 80.) The upper limit of the target heart rate zone can be approximated by the linear equation

$$y = -.8x + 186,$$

where x represents age and y represents heartbeats per minute. (*Source:* Hockey, R. V., *Physical Fitness: The Pathway to Healthy Living*, Times Mirror/Mosby College Publishing, 1989.)

(a) Complete the table of values for this linear equation.

Age	Heartbeats (per minute)
20	170
40	154
60	138
80	122

See the table.

(b) Write the data from the table of values as ordered pairs.

(20, 170), (40, 154), (60, 138), (80, 122)

(c) Make a scatter diagram of the data. Describe the pattern indicated by the data.

TARGET HEART RATE ZONE

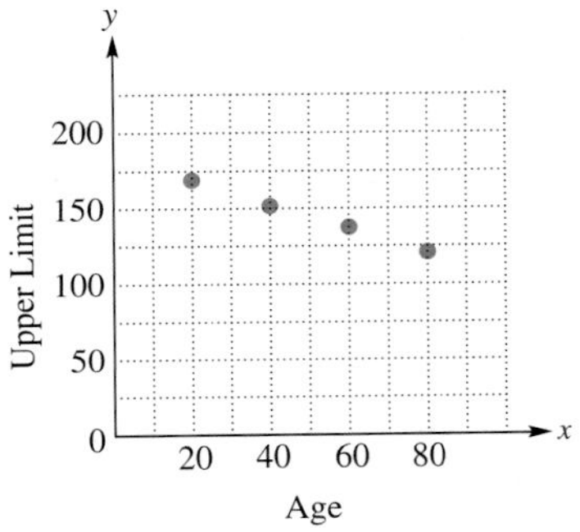

See the graph; The points lie in a linear pattern.

82. Refer to Exercises 80 and 81. What is the target heart rate zone for age 20? age 40?

between 140 and 170; between 126 and 154

4.2 GRAPHING LINEAR EQUATIONS IN TWO VARIABLES

OBJECTIVES

1. Graph linear equations by plotting ordered pairs.
2. Find intercepts.
3. Graph linear equations where the intercepts coincide.
4. Graph linear equations of the form $y = k$ or $x = k$.
5. Use a linear equation to model data.

1 Graph linear equations by plotting ordered pairs. There are infinitely many ordered pairs that satisfy an equation in two variables. We find ordered pairs that are solutions of the equation $x + 2y = 7$ by choosing as many values of x (or y) as we wish and then completing each ordered pair.

For example, if we choose $x = 1$, then $y = 3$, so the ordered pair (1, 3) is a solution of the equation $x + 2y = 7$.

$$1 + 2(3) = 1 + 6 = 7$$

Work Problem 1 at the Side.

Figure 8 shows a graph of all the ordered pairs found for $x + 2y = 7$ above and in Problem 1 at the side.

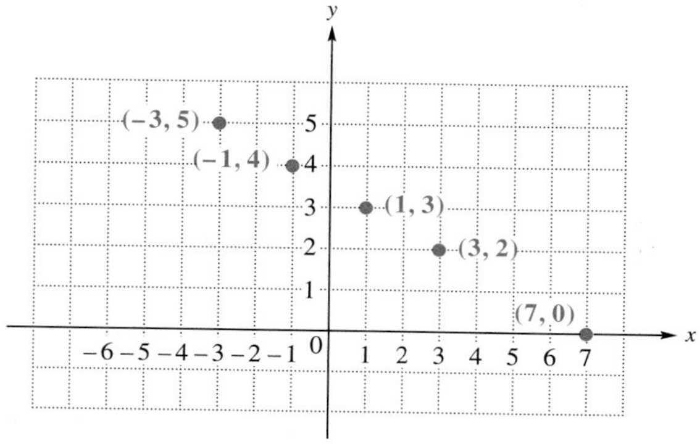

Figure 8

Notice that the points plotted in this figure all appear to lie on a straight line. The line that goes through these points is shown in Figure 9. In fact, all ordered pairs satisfying the equation $x + 2y = 7$ correspond to points that lie on this same straight line. This line gives a "picture" of all the solutions of the equation $x + 2y = 7$. Only a portion of the line is shown here, but it extends indefinitely in both directions, as suggested by the arrowhead on each end of the line.

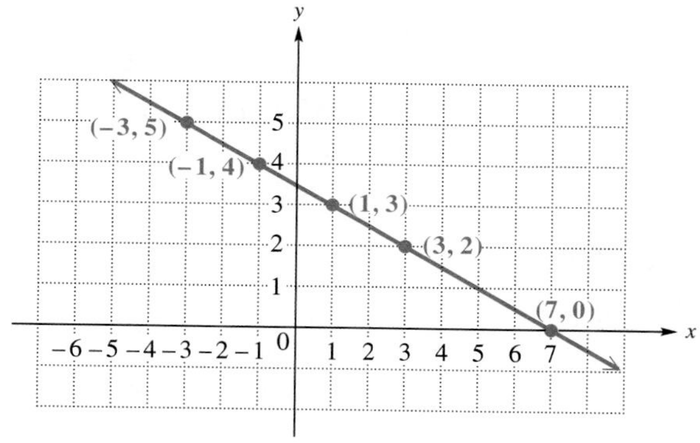

Figure 9

The line in Figure 9 is called the **graph** of the equation $x + 2y = 7$, and the process of plotting the ordered pairs and drawing the line through the corresponding points is called **graphing.** The preceding discussion can be generalized.

1 Complete each ordered pair for the equation $x + 2y = 7$.

(a) (−3,)

(b) (3,)

(c) (−1,)

(d) (7,)

ANSWERS

1. (a) (−3, 5) **(b)** (3, 2) **(c)** (−1, 4) **(d)** (7, 0)

The graph of any linear equation in two variables is a straight line.

(Notice that the word *line* appears in the term "*line*ar equation.")

Because two distinct points determine a line, a straight line can be graphed by finding any two different points on the line. However, it is a good idea to plot a third point as a check.

Example 1 **Graphing a Linear Equation**

Graph the linear equation $y = -\frac{3}{2}x + 3$.

Although this equation is not in the form $Ax + By = C$, it *could* be put in that form, so it is a linear equation. For most linear equations, two different points on the graph can be found by first letting $x = 0$ and then letting $y = 0$.

If $x = 0$, then

$$y = -\frac{3}{2}x + 3$$
$$y = -\frac{3}{2}(0) + 3 \quad \text{Let } x = 0.$$
$$y = 0 + 3$$
$$y = 3.$$

If $y = 0$, then

$$y = -\frac{3}{2}x + 3$$
$$0 = -\frac{3}{2}x + 3 \quad \text{Let } y = 0.$$
$$\frac{3}{2}x = 3$$
$$\frac{2}{3} \cdot \frac{3}{2}x = \frac{2}{3} \cdot 3$$
$$x = 2.$$

This gives the ordered pairs (0, 3) and (2, 0). Get a third point (as a check) by letting x or y equal some other number. For example, let $x = -2$. (Any number could be used, but a multiple of 2 makes multiplying by $-\frac{3}{2}$ easier.) Replace x with -2 in the given equation.

$$y = -\frac{3}{2}x + 3$$
$$y = -\frac{3}{2}(-2) + 3 \quad \text{Let } x = -2.$$
$$y = 3 + 3$$
$$y = 6$$

These three ordered pairs are shown in the table with Figure 10. Plot the corresponding points, then draw a line through them. This line, shown in Figure 10, is the graph of $y = -\frac{3}{2}x + 3$.

x	y
0	3
2	0
−2	6

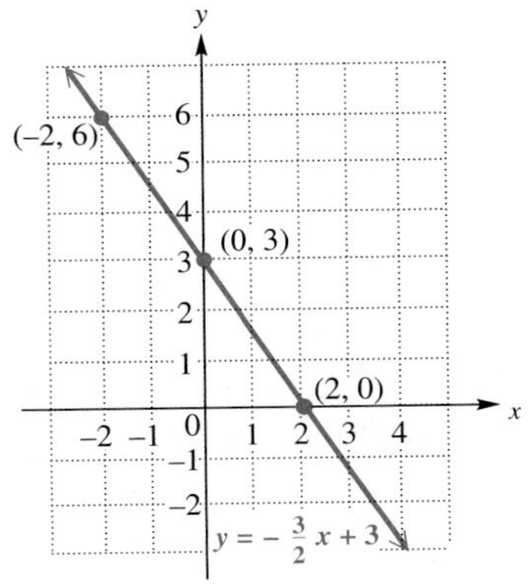

Figure 10

CAUTION

When graphing a linear equation as in Example 1, all three points should lie on the same straight line. If they don't, double-check the ordered pairs you found.

Work Problem 2 at the Side.

Example 2 Graphing a Linear Equation

Graph the linear equation $4x = 5y + 20$.

As before, at least two different points are needed to draw the graph. First let $x = 0$ and then let $y = 0$ to complete two ordered pairs.

$$\begin{aligned} 4x &= 5y + 20 \\ 4(0) &= 5y + 20 \quad \text{Let } x = 0. \\ 0 &= 5y + 20 \\ -5y &= 20 \\ y &= -4 \end{aligned} \qquad \begin{aligned} 4x &= 5y + 20 \\ 4x &= 5(0) + 20 \quad \text{Let } y = 0. \\ 4x &= 20 \\ x &= 5 \end{aligned}$$

The ordered pairs are $(0, -4)$ and $(5, 0)$. Get a third ordered pair (as a check) by choosing some number other than 0 for x or y. We choose $y = 2$. Replacing y with 2 in the equation $4x = 5y + 20$ leads to the ordered pair $\left(\frac{15}{2}, 2\right)$, or $\left(7\frac{1}{2}, 2\right)$.

Plot the three ordered pairs $(0, -4)$, $(5, 0)$, and $\left(\frac{15}{2}, 2\right)$, and draw a line through them. This line, shown in Figure 11, is the graph of $4x = 5y + 20$.

x	y
0	-4
5	0
$7\frac{1}{2}$	2

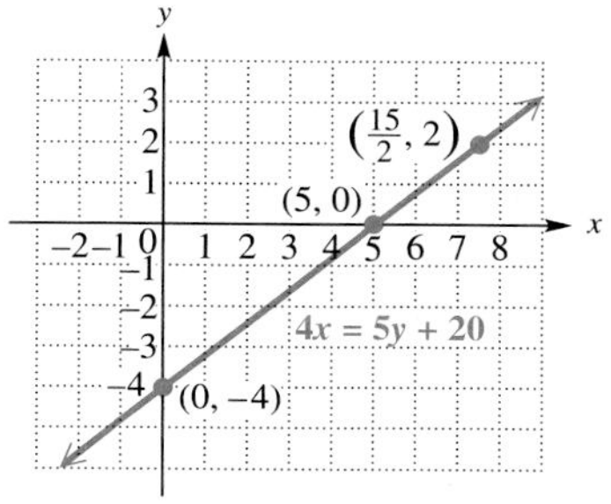

Figure 11

Work Problem 3 at the Side.

2 Find intercepts. In Figure 11, the graph crosses or intersects the y-axis at $(0, -4)$ and the x-axis at $(5, 0)$. For this reason, $(0, -4)$ is called the **y-intercept,** and $(5, 0)$ is called the **x-intercept** of the graph. The intercepts are particularly useful for graphing linear equations, as in Examples 1 and 2. (In general, any point on the y-axis has x-coordinate 0, and any point on the x-axis has y-coordinate 0.) The intercepts are found by replacing, in turn, each variable with 0 in the equation and solving for the value of the other variable.

Finding Intercepts

To find the x-intercept, let $y = 0$ in the given equation and solve for x. Then $(x, 0)$ is the x-intercept.

To find the y-intercept, let $x = 0$ in the given equation and solve for y. Then $(0, y)$ is the y-intercept.

2 Complete the table of values, and graph the linear equation.

$x + y = 6$

x	y
0	
	0
2	

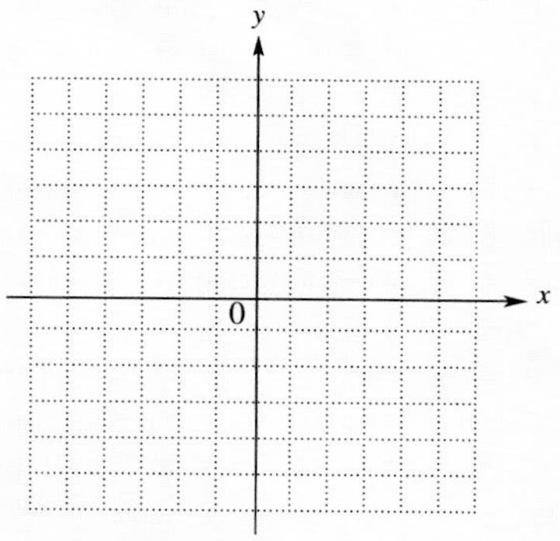

3 Make a table of values, and graph the linear equation.

$2x = 3y + 6$

x	y

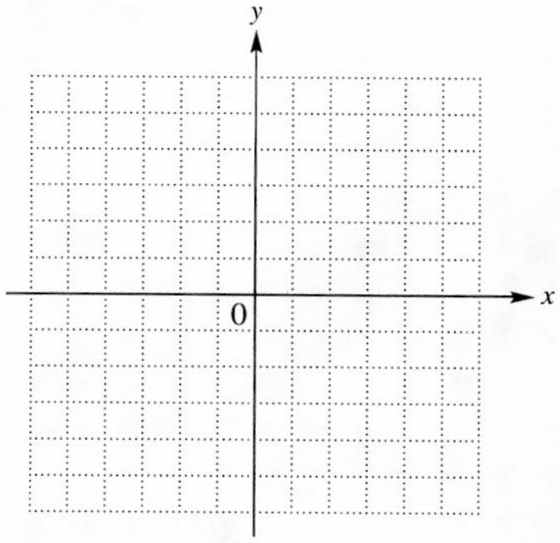

ANSWERS

2.

x	y
0	6
6	0
2	4

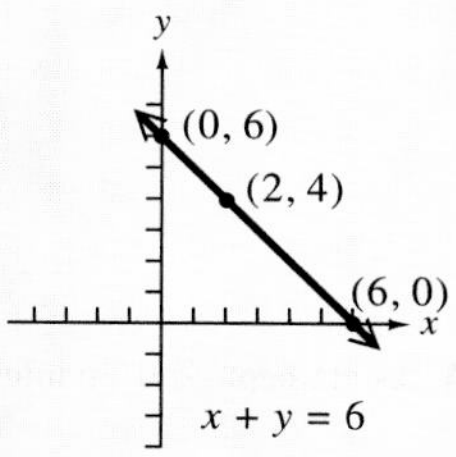

3.

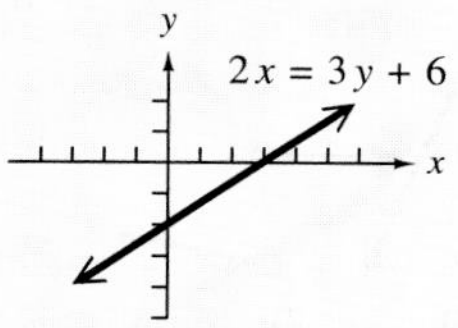

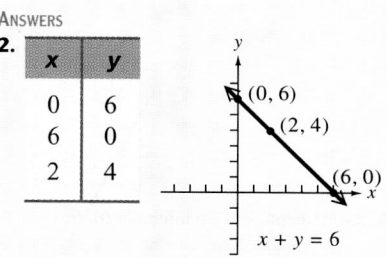

From the results in Example 5, we make the following observations.

Horizontal and Vertical Lines

The graph of the linear equation $y = k$, where k is a real number, is the horizontal line with y-intercept $(0, k)$ and no x-intercept.

The graph of the linear equation $x = k$, where k is a real number, is the vertical line with x-intercept $(k, 0)$ and no y-intercept.

Work Problem 6 at the Side.

The different forms of linear equations from this section and the methods of graphing them are summarized below.

Graphing Linear Equations

Equation — **Graphing Method** — **Example**

$y = k$ — Draw a horizontal line through $(0, k)$.

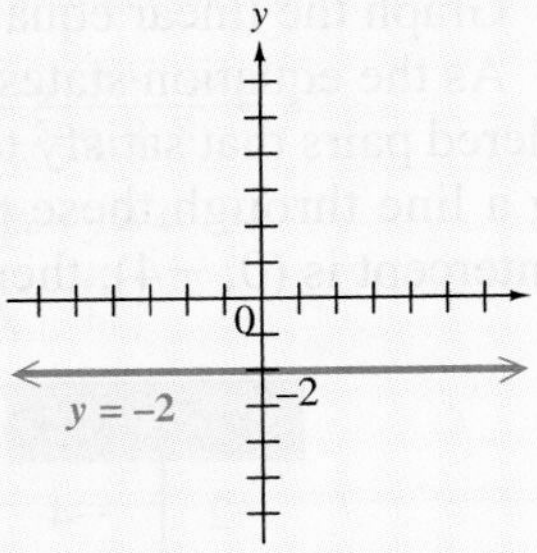

$x = k$ — Draw a vertical line through $(k, 0)$.

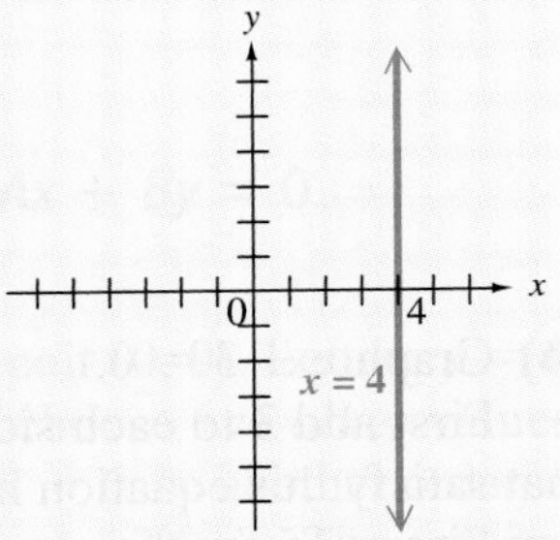

$Ax + By = 0$ — Graph goes through $(0, 0)$. To get additional points that lie on the graph, choose any values for x or y, except 0.

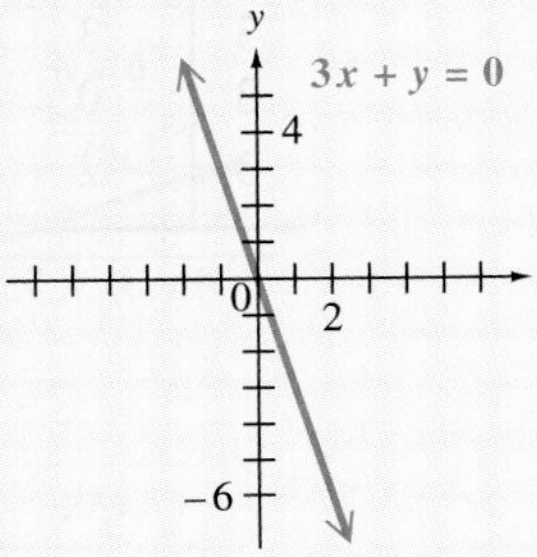

(continued)

6 Graph each equation.

(a) $y = -5$

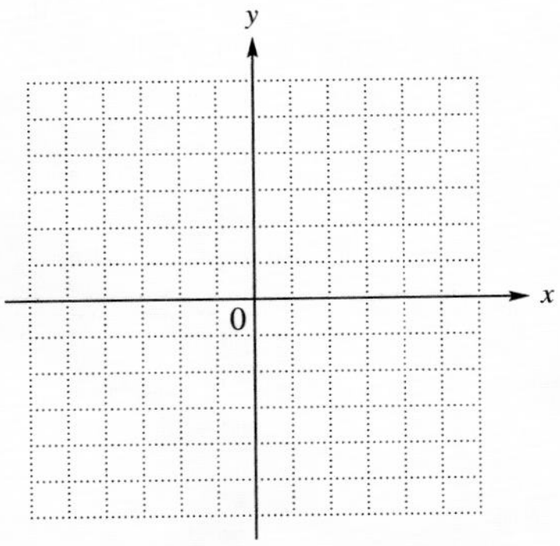

(b) $x + 4 = 6$

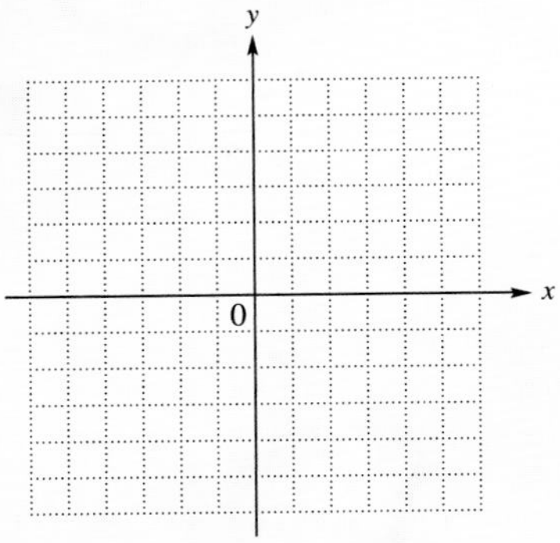

ANSWERS

6. (a)

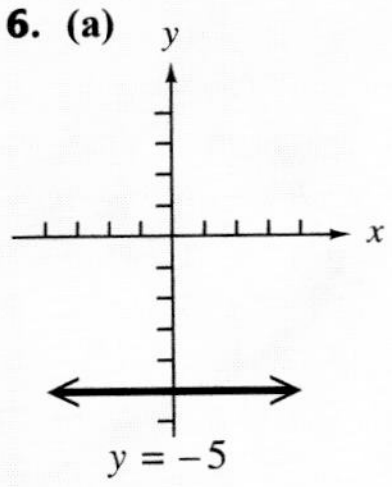

(b)

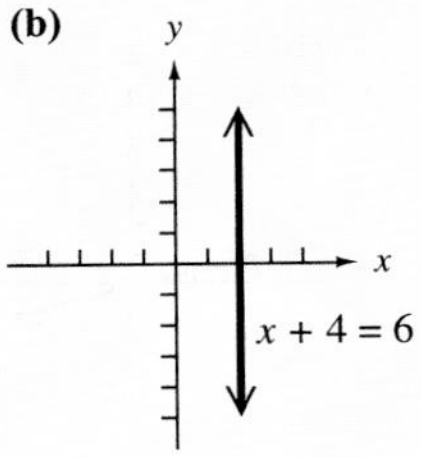

$Ax + By = C$ $A, B,$ and $C \neq 0$	Find any two points on the line. A good choice is to find the intercepts. Let $x = 0$, and find the corresponding value of y; then let $y = 0$, and find x. As a check, get a third point by choosing a value of x or y that has not yet been used.	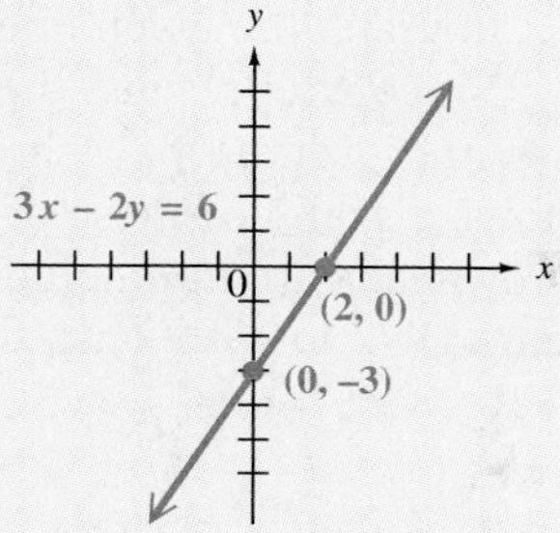

Work Problem 7 at the Side.

5 Use a linear equation to model data.

Example 6 Using a Linear Equation to Model Credit Card Debt

Credit card debt in the United States increased steadily from 1992 through 1999. The amount of debt y in billions of dollars can be modeled by the linear equation

$$y = 47.3x + 281,$$

where $x = 0$ represents 1992, $x = 1$ represents 1993, and so on. (*Source:* Board of Governors of the Federal Reserve System.)

(a) Use the equation to approximate credit card debt in the years 1992, 1993, and 1999.

For 1992: $y = 47.3(0) + 281$ Replace x with 0.
$y = 281$ billion dollars

For 1993: $y = 47.3(1) + 281$ Replace x with 1.
$y = 328.3$ billion dollars

For 1999: $y = 47.3(7) + 281$ $1999 - 1992 = 7$; replace x with 7.
$y = 612.1$ billion dollars

Continued on Next Page

7 Match the information about the graphs with the linear equations in A–D.

A. $x = 5$
B. $2x - 5y = 8$
C. $y - 2 = 3$
D. $x + 4y = 0$

(a) The graph of the equation is a horizontal line.

(b) The graph of the equation goes through the origin.

(c) The graph of the equation is a vertical line.

(d) The graph of the equation goes through $(9, 2)$.

ANSWERS
7. (a) C **(b)** D **(c)** A **(d)** B

8 Use the graph and the equation in Example 6 to approximate credit card debt in 1997.

(b) Write the information from part (a) as three ordered pairs, and use them to graph the given linear equation.

Since x represents the year and y represents the debt in billions of dollars, the ordered pairs are (0, 281), (1, 328.3), and (7, 612.1). Figure 16 shows a graph of these ordered pairs and the line through them. (Note that arrowheads are not included with the graphed line since the data are for the years 1992 to 1999 only, that is, from $x = 0$ to $x = 7$.)

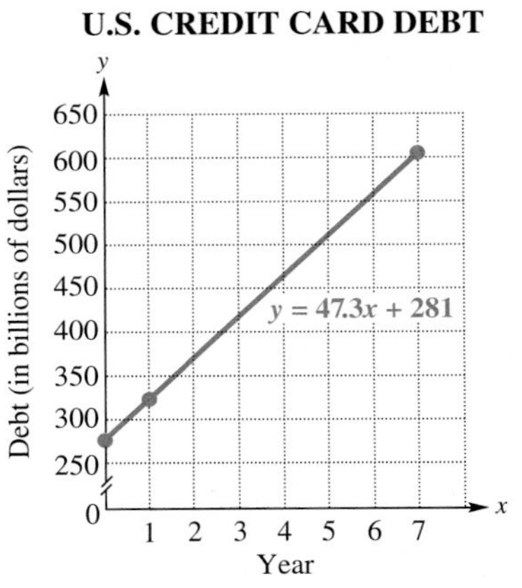

Figure 16

(c) Use the graph and then the equation to approximate credit card debt in 1996.

For 1996, $x = 4$. On the graph, find 4 on the horizontal axis and move up to the graphed line, then across to the vertical axis. It appears that credit card debt in 1996 was about 470 billion dollars.

To use the equation, substitute 4 for x.

$$y = 47.3(4) + 281 \qquad \text{Let } x = 4.$$

$$y = 470.2 \text{ billion dollars}$$

This result is quite similar to our estimate using the graph.

Work Problem 8 at the Side.

ANSWERS

8. about 510 billion dollars; 517.5 billion dollars

4.2 EXERCISES

FOR EXTRA HELP: Student's Solutions Manual | MyMathLab.com | InterAct Math Tutorial Software | AW Math Tutor Center | MathXL www.mathxl.com | Digital Video Tutor CD 3 Videotape 7

Complete the given ordered pairs for each equation. Then graph each equation by plotting the points and drawing a line through them. See Examples 1 and 2.

1. $y = -x + 5$ **5; 5; 3**

$(0, \quad), (\quad, 0), (2, \quad)$

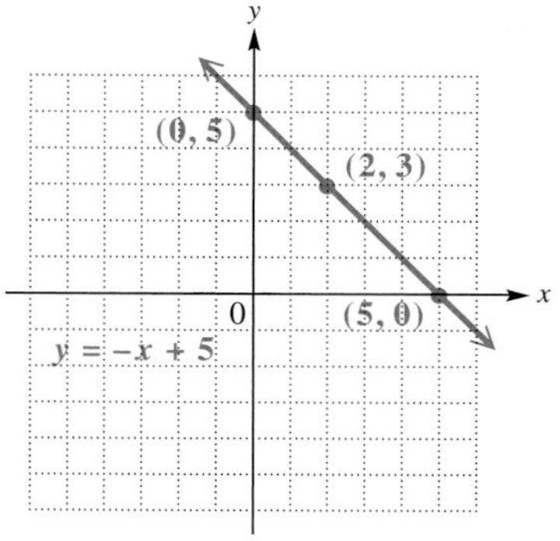

2. $y = x - 2$ **−2; 2; 3**

$(0, \quad), (\quad, 0), (5, \quad)$

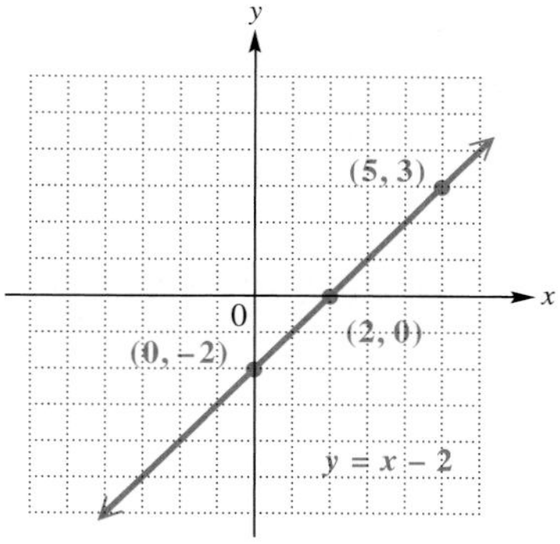

3. $y = \frac{2}{3}x + 1$ **1; 3; −1**

$(0, \quad), (3, \quad), (-3, \quad)$

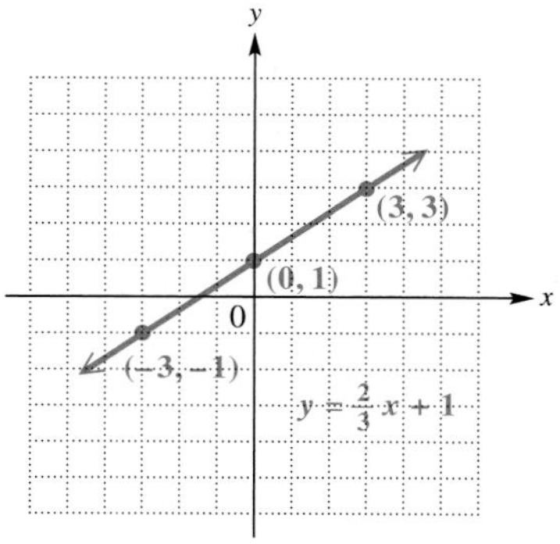

4. $y = -\frac{3}{4}x + 2$ **2; −1; 5**

$(0, \quad), (4, \quad), (-4, \quad)$

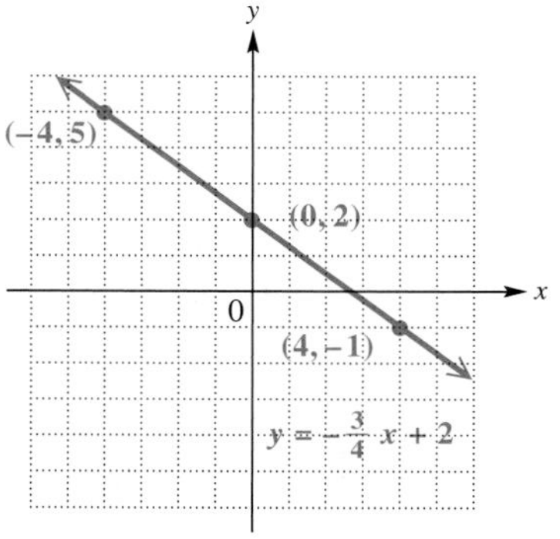

5. $3x = -y - 6$ **−6; −2; −5**

$(0, \quad), (\quad, 0), \left(-\frac{1}{3}, \quad\right)$

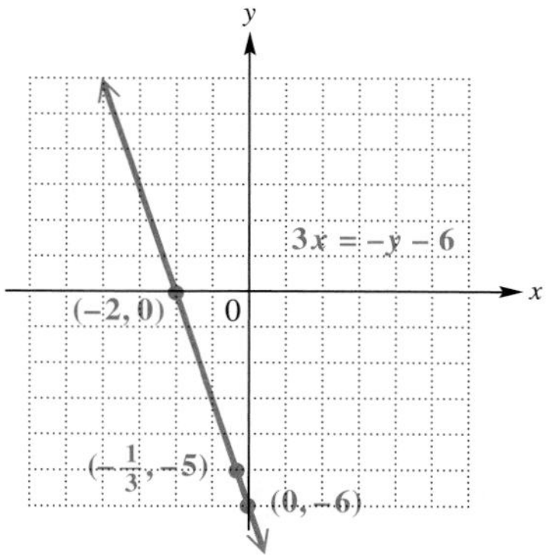

6. $x = 2y + 3$ **3; $-\frac{3}{2}$; 4**

$(\quad, 0), (0, \quad), \left(\quad, \frac{1}{2}\right)$

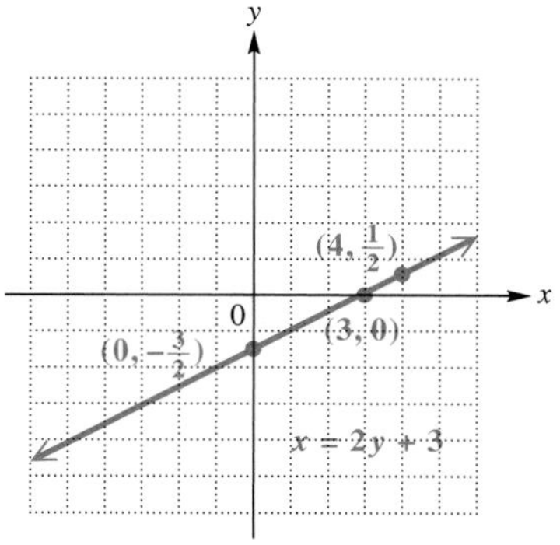

Match the information about each graph in Column I with the correct linear equation in Column II.

I	II
7. The graph of the equation has y-intercept $(0, -4)$. **A**	**A.** $3x + y = -4$
8. The graph of the equation has $(0, 0)$ as x-intercept and y-intercept. **C**	**B.** $x - 4 = 0$
9. The graph of the equation does not have an x-intercept. **D**	**C.** $y = 4x$
10. The graph of the equation has x-intercept $(4, 0)$. **B**	**D.** $y = 4$

Find the intercepts for the graph of each equation. See Example 3.

11. $2x - 3y = 24$

x-intercept:

y-intercept:

(12, 0); (0, −8)

12. $-3x + 8y = 48$

x-intercept:

y-intercept:

(−16, 0); (0, 6)

13. $x + 6y = 0$

x-intercept:

y-intercept:

(0, 0); (0, 0)

14. $3x - y = 0$

x-intercept:

y-intercept:

(0, 0); (0, 0)

15. A student attempted to graph $4x + 5y = 0$ by finding intercepts. She first let $x = 0$ and found y; then she let $y = 0$ and found x. In both cases, the resulting point was (0, 0). She knew that she needed at least two points to graph the line, but was unsure what to do next because finding intercepts gave her only one point. How would you explain to her what to do next?

Choose a value *other than* 0 for either x or y. For example, if $x = -5$, $y = 4$.

16. What is the equation of the x-axis? What is the equation of the y-axis?

$y = 0$; $x = 0$

Graph each linear equation. See Examples 1–5.

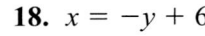

17. $x = y + 2$

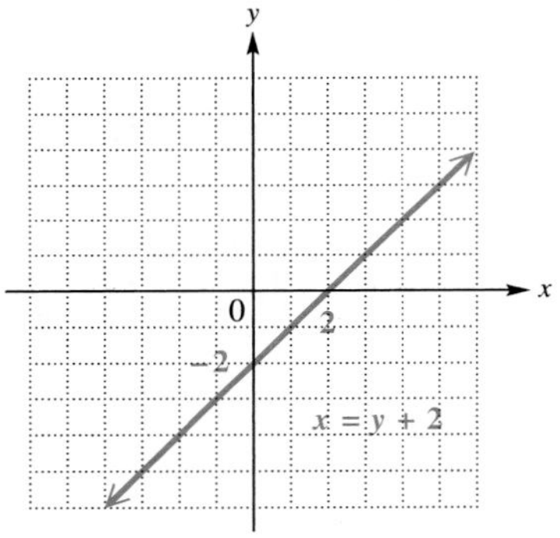

18. $x = -y + 6$

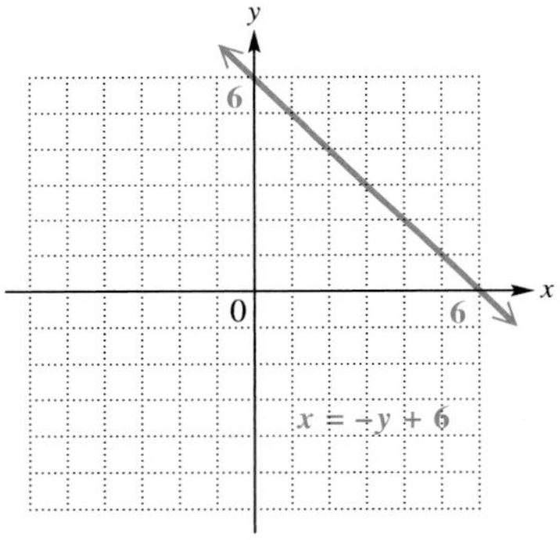

19. $x - y = 4$

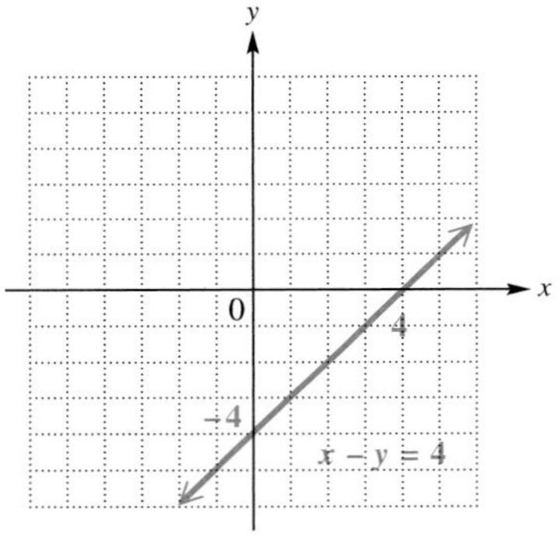

20. $x - y = 5$

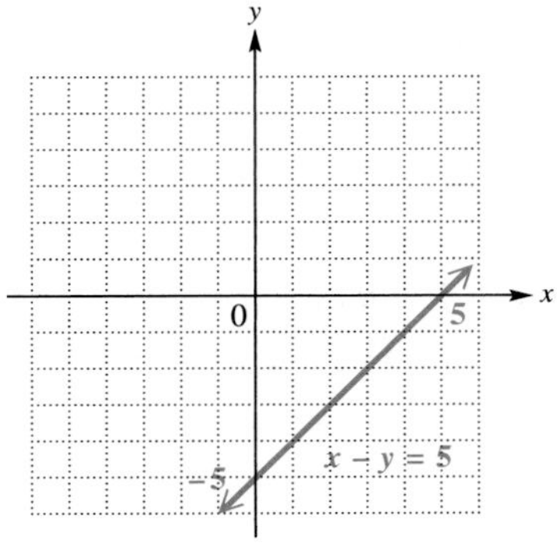

21. $2x + y = 6$

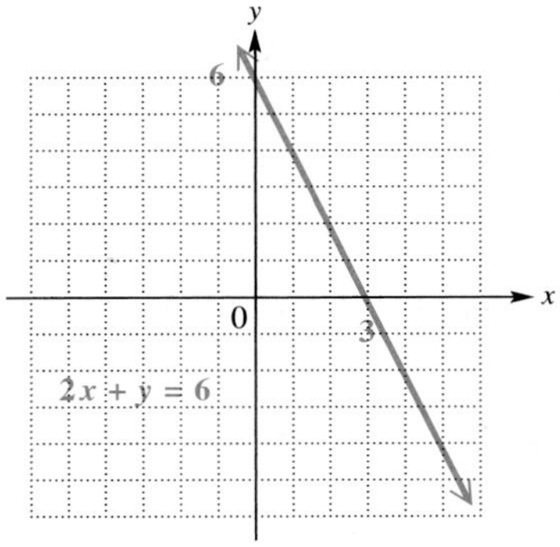

22. $-3x + y = -6$

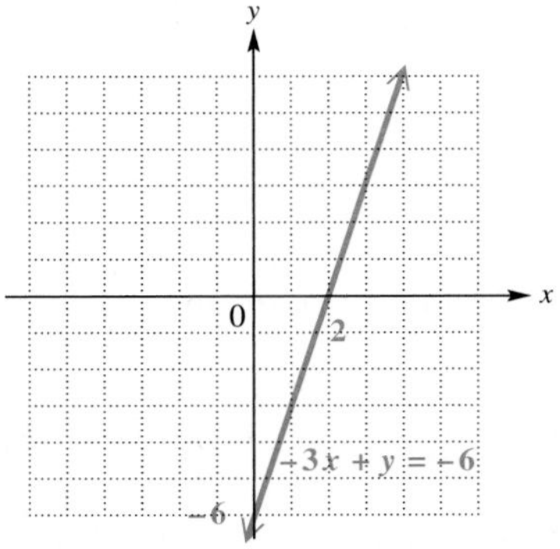

23. $3x + 7y = 14$

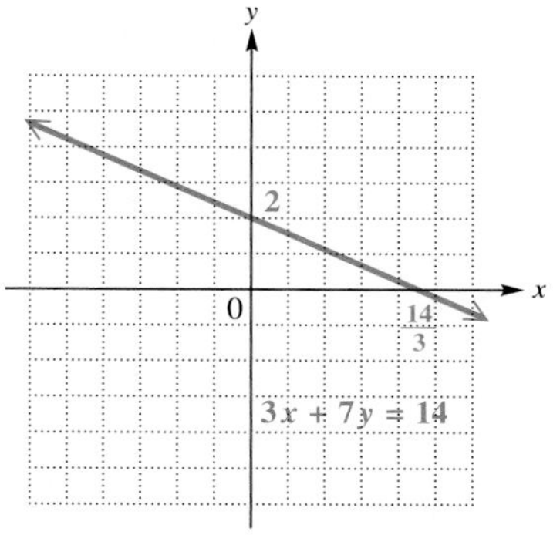

24. $6x - 5y = 18$

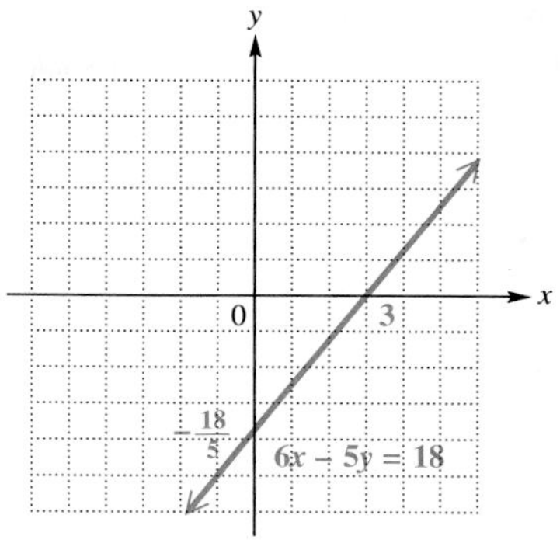

25. $y - 2x = 0$

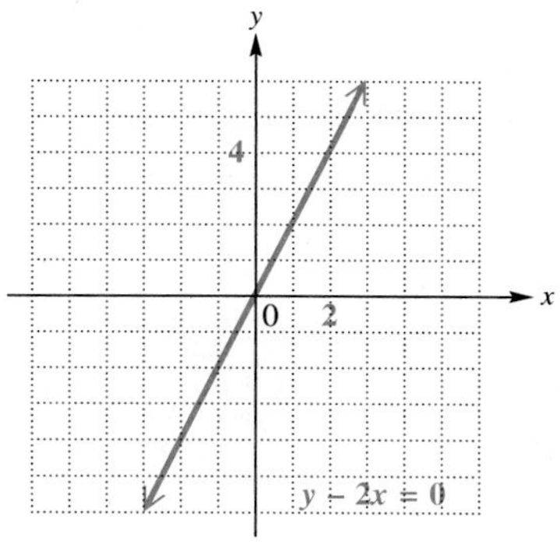

26. $y + 3x = 0$

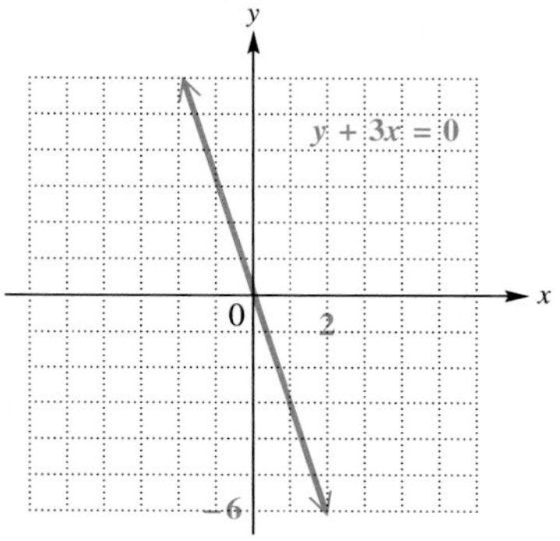

27. $y = -6x$

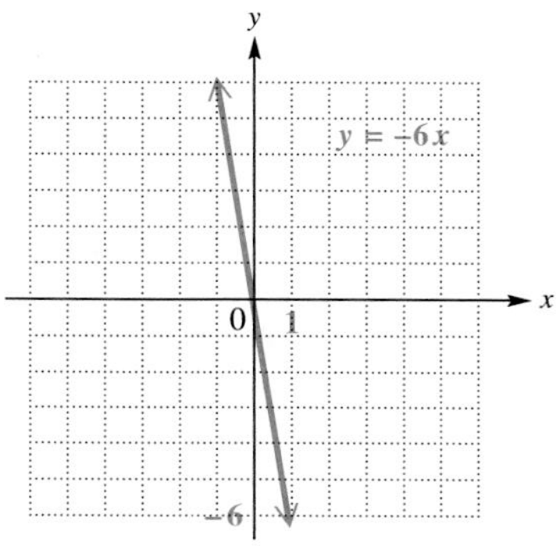

28. $x = 4$

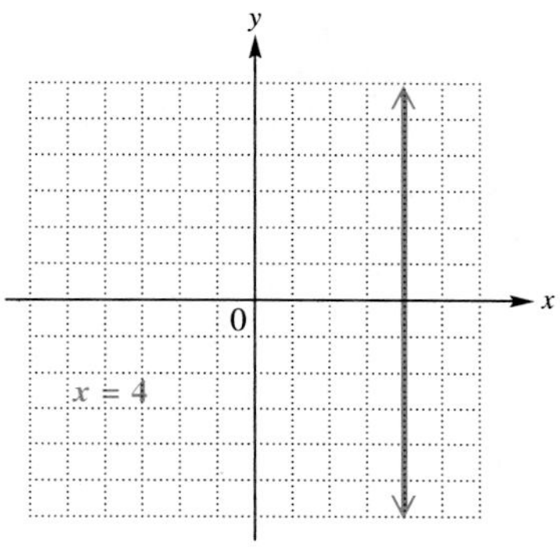

29. $x = -2$

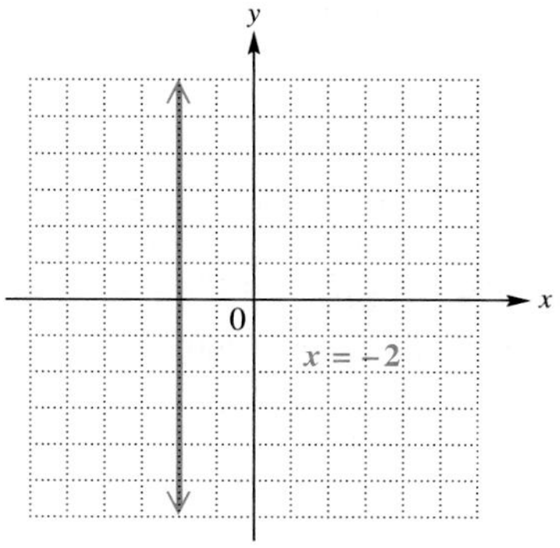

30. $y + 1 = 0$

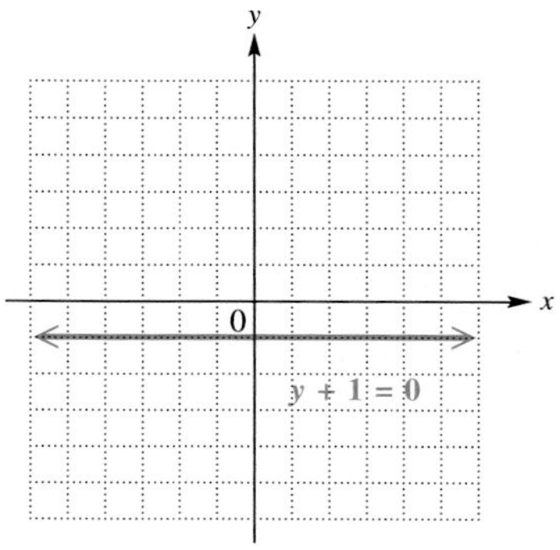

31. $y - 3 = 0$

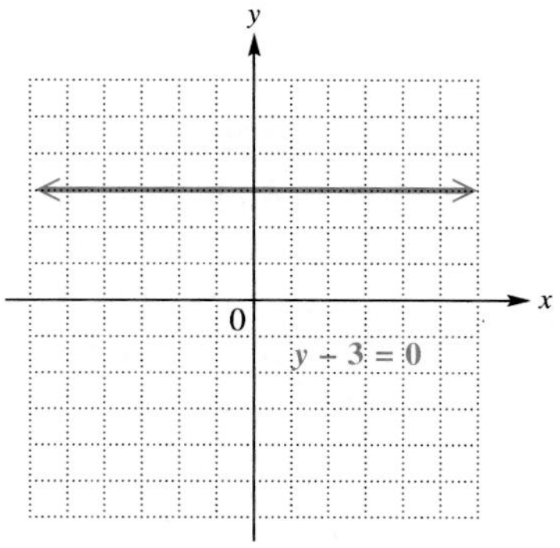

32. Write a few sentences summarizing how to graph a linear equation in two variables.

Find two ordered pairs that satisfy the equation. (The intercepts are good choices.) As a check, find a third ordered pair. Plot the corresponding points on a coordinate system. Draw a straight line through the points.

Solve each problem. See Example 6.

33. The height y (in centimeters) of a woman is related to the length of her radius bone x (from the wrist to the elbow) and is approximated by the linear equation

$$y = 3.9x + 73.5.$$

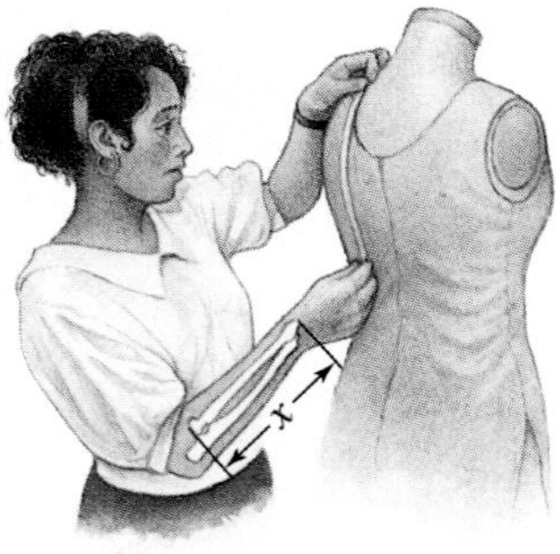

(a) Use the equation to find the approximate heights of women with radius bones of lengths 20 cm, 26 cm, and 22 cm.

151.5 cm, 174.9 cm, 159.3 cm

(b) Graph the equation using the data from part (a).

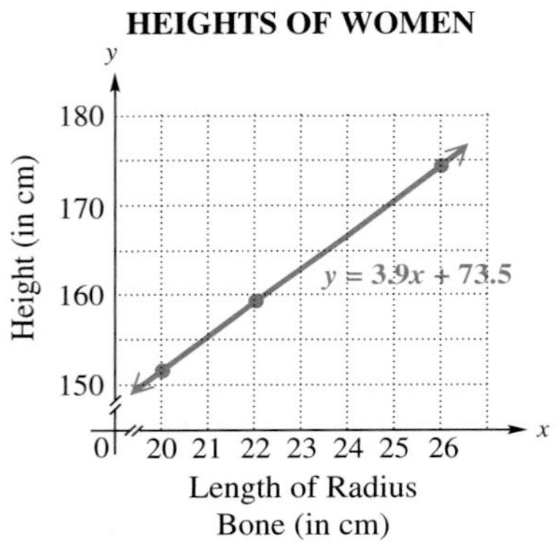

See the graph.

(c) Use the graph to estimate the length of the radius bone in a woman who is 167 cm tall. Then use the equation to find the length of this radius bone to the nearest centimeter. (*Hint:* Substitute for y in the equation.)

24 cm; 24 cm

34. The weight y (in pounds) of a man taller than 60 in. can be roughly approximated by the linear equation

$$y = 5.5x - 220,$$

where x is the height of the man in inches.

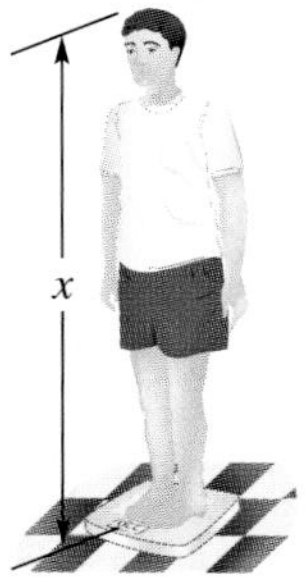

(a) Use the equation to approximate the weights of men whose heights are 62 in., 66 in., and 72 in.

121 lb, 143 lb, 176 lb

(b) Graph the equation using the data from part (a).

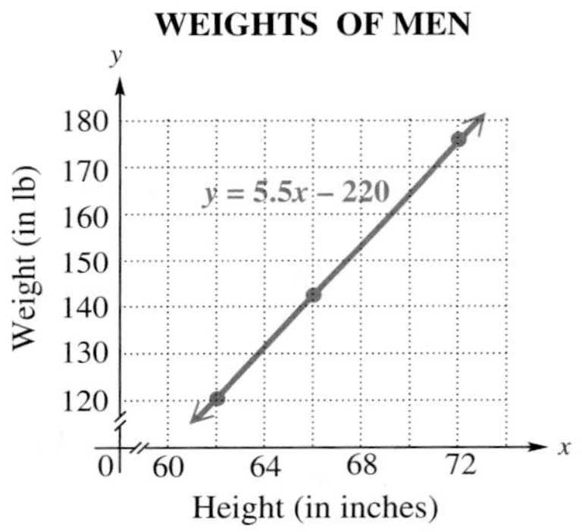

See the graph.

(c) Use the graph to estimate the height of a man who weighs 155 lb. Then use the equation to find the height of this man to the nearest inch. (*Hint:* Substitute for y in the equation.)

68 in.; 68 in.

35. Refer to Section 4.1 Exercise 80. Draw a line through the points you plotted in the scatter diagram there.

(a) Use the graph to estimate the lower limit of the target heart rate zone for age 30. **130**

(b) Use the linear equation given there to approximate the lower limit for age 30. **133**

(c) How does the approximation using the equation compare to the estimate from the graph?

They are quite close.

36. Refer to Section 4.1 Exercise 81. Draw a line through the points you plotted in the scatter diagram there.

(a) Use the graph to estimate the upper limit of the target heart rate zone for age 30. **160**

(b) Use the linear equation given there to approximate the upper limit for age 30. **162**

(c) How does the approximation using the equation compare to the estimate from the graph?

They are quite close.

37. Use the results of Exercises 35(b) and 36(b) to determine the target heart rate zone for age 30.

between 133 and 162

38. Should the graphs of the target heart rate zone in the Section 4.1 exercises be used to estimate the target heart rate zone for ages below 20 or above 80? Why or why not?

No. To go beyond the given data at either end assumes that the graph continues in the same way, which may not be true.

39. Per capita consumption of carbonated soft drinks increased for the years 1992 through 1997 as shown in the graph. If $x = 0$ represents 1992, $x = 1$ represents 1993, and so on, per capita consumption can be modeled by the linear equation

$$y = .8x + 49,$$

where y is in gallons.

SOFT DRINK CONSUMPTION

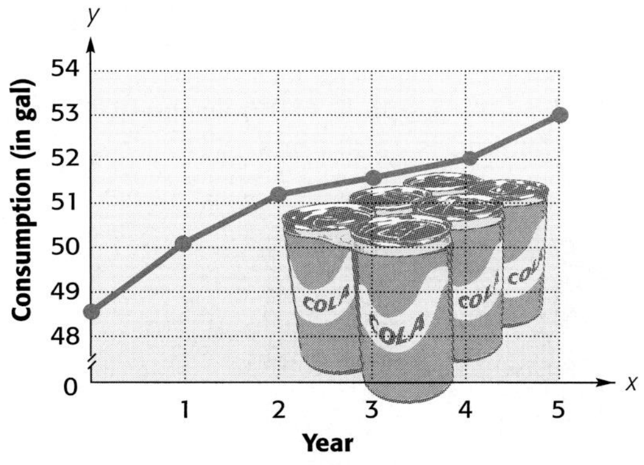

Source: U.S. Department of Agriculture.

(a) Use the equation to approximate consumption in 1993, 1995, and 1997.

1993: 49.8 gal; 1995: 51.4 gal; 1997: 53 gal

(b) Use the graph to estimate consumption for the same years.

1993: 50.1 gal; 1995: 51.6 gal; 1997: 53 gal

(c) How do the approximations using the equation compare to the estimates from the graph?

The corresponding values are quite close.

40. The income generated by the Walgreen Company from 1994 through 1998 is shown in the graph. If $x = 0$ corresponds to 1994, $x = 1$ corresponds to 1995, and so on, the income can be modeled by the linear equation

$$y = 57.3x + 270,$$

where y is in billions of dollars.

WALGREEN COMPANY INCOME

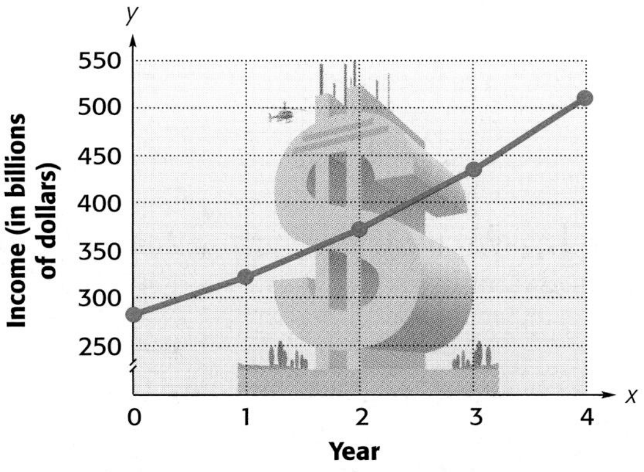

Source: Hoover's Outline.

(a) Use the equation to approximate the income generated in 1994, 1996, and 1998. Round your answers to the nearest billion dollars.

1994: \$270 billion; 1996: \$385 billion; 1998: \$499 billion

(b) Use the graph to estimate the income for the same years.

1994: \$280 billion; 1996: \$375 billion; 1998: \$510 billion

(c) How do the approximations using the equation compare to the estimates from the graph?

The figures are within about \$10 billion of each other, so they are fairly close.

41. The graph shows the value of a certain sport utility vehicle over the first 5 yr of ownership.

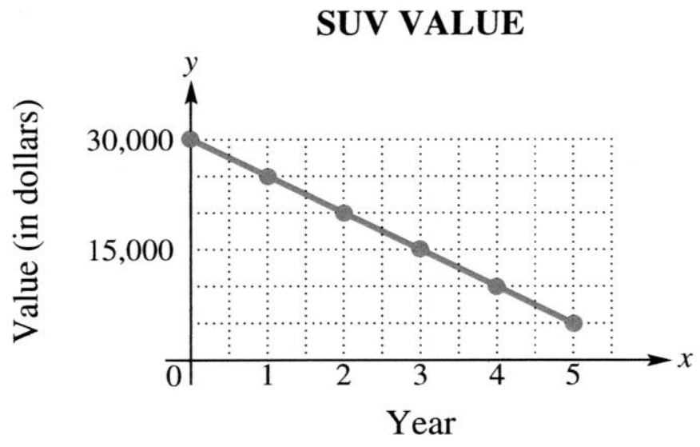

Use the graph to do the following.

(a) Determine the initial value of the SUV.

$30,000

(b) Find the *depreciation* (loss in value) from the original value after the first 3 yr.

$15,000

(c) What is the annual or yearly depreciation in each of the first 5 yr?

$5000

(d) What does the ordered pair (5, 5000) mean in the context of this problem?

After 5 yr, the SUV has a value of $5000.

42. Demand for an item is often closely related to its price. As price increases, demand decreases, and as price decreases, demand increases. Suppose demand for a video game is 2000 units when the price is $40, and demand is 2500 units when the price is $30.

(a) Let x be the price and y be the demand for the game. Graph the two given pairs of prices and demands.

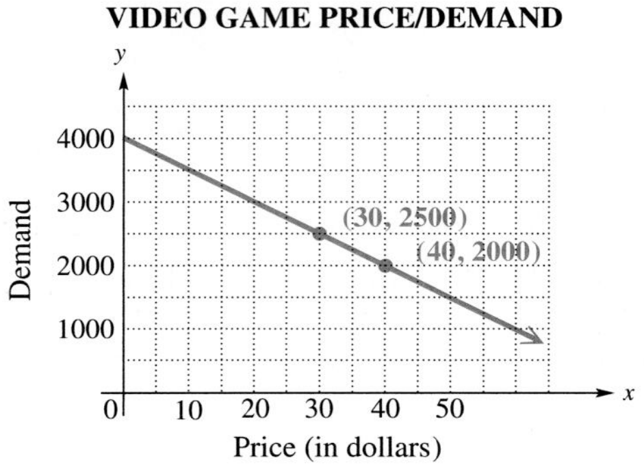

See the graph.

(b) Assume the relationship is linear. Draw a line through the two points from part (a). From your graph, estimate the demand if the price drops to $20. **3000 units**

(c) Use the graph to estimate the price if the demand is 3500 units. **$10**

43. The graph of the linear equation for credit card debt from Example 6,

$$y = 47.3x + 281,$$

where $x = 0$ represents 1992, and so on, and y is in billions of dollars, is shown in the figure. The actual data for 1992 through 1999 is also plotted.

(a) In general, how well does the linear equation model the actual data?

The equation is a fairly good model.

(b) Use the plotted points to estimate the actual credit card debt for 1996. How does it compare to the answer in Example 6(c)?

The actual debt for 1996 is about 500 billion dollars; this is about 30 billion dollars more than the amount given by the equation.

(c) Should this equation be used to predict credit card debt for the year 2002? Why or why not?

No. Data for future years might not follow the same pattern, so the linear equation would not be a reliable model.

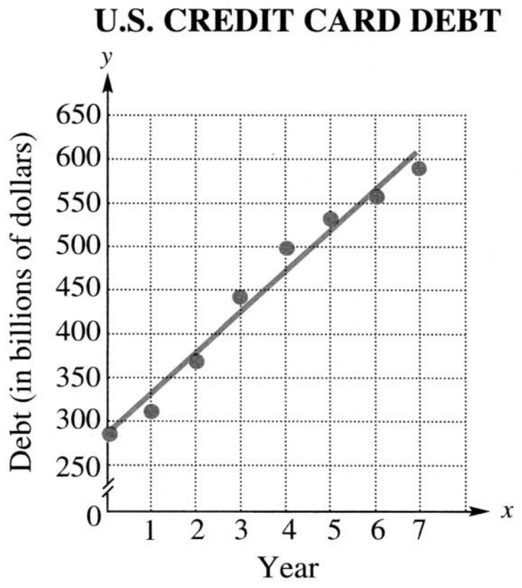

Source: Board of Governors of the Federal Reserve System.

4.3 SLOPE

OBJECTIVES

1. Find the slope of a line given two points.
2. Find the slope from the equation of a line.
3. Use slope to determine whether two lines are parallel, perpendicular, or neither.
4. Solve problems involving average rate of change.

An important characteristic of the lines we graphed in the previous section is their slant or "steepness." See Figure 17.

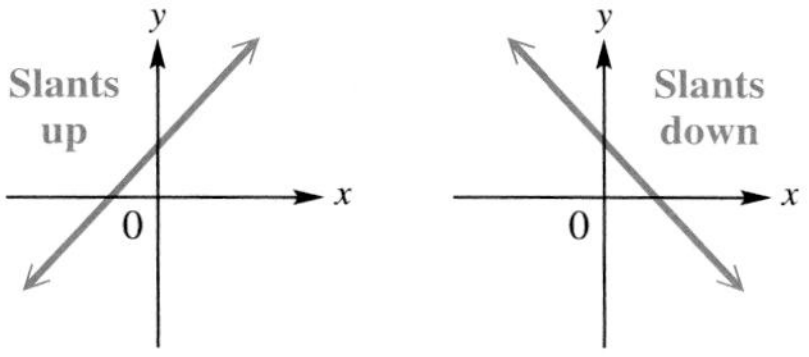

Figure 17

One way to measure the steepness of a line is to compare the vertical change in the line to the horizontal change while moving along the line from one fixed point to another. This measure of steepness is called the *slope* of the line.

1 Find the slope of a line given two points. Figure 18 shows a line through two nonspecific points (x_1, y_1) and (x_2, y_2). (This notation is called **subscript notation.** Read x_1 as "x-sub-one" and x_2 as "x-sub-two.")

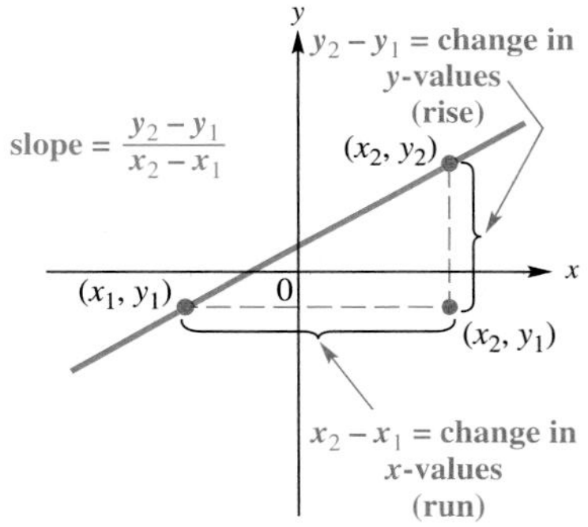

Figure 18

Moving along the line from the point (x_1, y_1) to the point (x_2, y_2) causes y to change by $y_2 - y_1$ units. This is the vertical change or **rise.** Similarly, x changes by $x_2 - x_1$ units, which is the horizontal change or **run.** (In both cases, the change is expressed as a *difference*.) Remember from Section 2.6 that one way to compare two numbers is by using a ratio. Slope is the ratio of the vertical change in y to the horizontal change in x. Traditionally, the letter m represents slope. The slope m of a line is defined as follows.

Slope Formula

The **slope** of the line through the points (x_1, y_1) and (x_2, y_2) is

$$m = \frac{\text{change in } y}{\text{change in } x} = \frac{y_2 - y_1}{x_2 - x_1}, \quad \text{if } x_1 \neq x_2.$$

Work Problem 1 at the Side.

The slope of a line tells how fast y changes for each unit of change in x; that is, the slope gives the rate of change in y for each unit of change in x.

1 Find $\frac{y_2 - y_1}{x_2 - x_1}$ for the following values.

(a) $y_2 = 4, y_1 = -1,$
$x_2 = 3, x_1 = 4$

(b) $x_1 = 3, x_2 = -5,$
$y_1 = 7, y_2 = -9$

(c) $x_1 = 2, x_2 = 7,$
$y_1 = 4, y_2 = 9$

ANSWERS
1. (a) -5 **(b)** 2 **(c)** 1

The idea of slope is used in many everyday situations. See Figure 19. For example, a highway with a 10% or $\frac{1}{10}$ grade (or slope) rises 1 m for every 10 m horizontally. Architects specify the pitch of a roof using slope; a $\frac{5}{12}$ roof means that the roof rises 5 ft for every 12 ft in the horizontal direction. The slope of a stairwell also indicates the ratio of the vertical rise to the horizontal run. In the figure, the slope of the stairwell is $\frac{8}{10}$ or $\frac{4}{5}$.

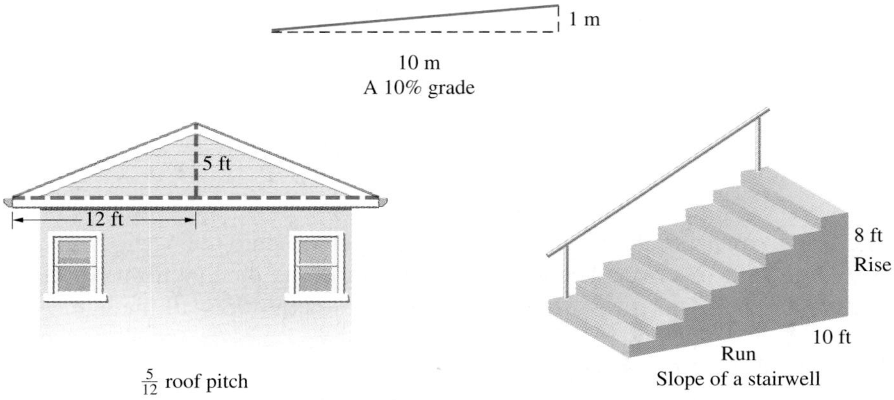

Figure 19

Example 1 Finding Slopes of Lines

Find the slope of each line.

(a) The line through $(1, -2)$ and $(-4, 7)$

Use the slope formula. Let $(-4, 7) = (x_2, y_2)$ and $(1, -2) = (x_1, y_1)$. Then

$$\text{slope } m = \frac{\text{change in } y}{\text{change in } x} = \frac{y_2 - y_1}{x_2 - x_1} = \frac{7 - (-2)}{-4 - 1} = \frac{9}{-5} = -\frac{9}{5}.$$

See Figure 20.

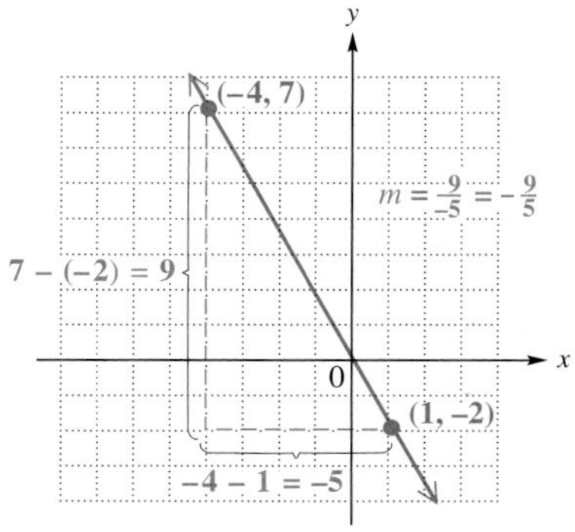

Figure 20

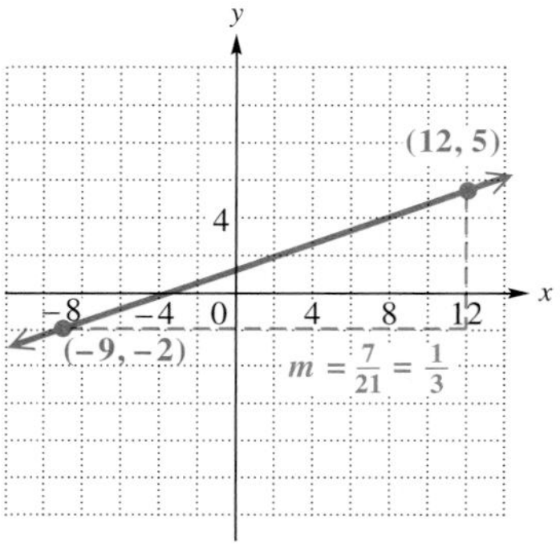

Figure 21

(b) The line through $(-9, -2)$ and $(12, 5)$

$$m = \frac{y_2 - y_1}{x_2 - x_1} = \frac{5 - (-2)}{12 - (-9)} = \frac{7}{21} = \frac{1}{3}$$

See Figure 21. The same slope is obtained by subtracting in reverse order.

$$m = \frac{-2 - 5}{-9 - 12} = \frac{-7}{-21} = \frac{1}{3}$$

CAUTION

It makes no difference which point is (x_1, y_1) or (x_2, y_2); however, it is important to be consistent. Start with the x- and y-values of one point (either one) and subtract the corresponding values of the other point. Also, the slope of a line is the same for *any* two points on the line.

Work Problem 2 at the Side.

In Example 1(a) the slope is negative and the corresponding line in Figure 20 falls from left to right. The slope in Example 1(b) is positive and the corresponding line in Figure 21 rises from left to right. These facts can be generalized.

Positive and Negative Slopes

A line with positive slope rises from left to right.

A line with negative slope falls from left to right.

Example 2 Finding the Slope of a Horizontal Line

Find the slope of the line through $(-8, 4)$ and $(2, 4)$.

$$m = \frac{y_2 - y_1}{x_2 - x_1} = \frac{4 - 4}{-8 - 2} = \frac{0}{-10} = 0 \quad \text{Zero slope}$$

As shown in Figure 22, the line through the given points is horizontal. *All horizontal lines have slope 0* since the difference in y-values is always 0.

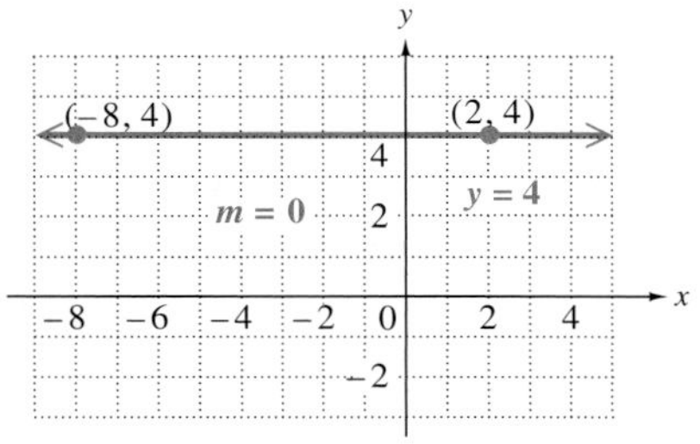

Figure 22

Example 3 Finding the Slope of a Vertical Line

Find the slope of the line through $(6, 2)$ and $(6, -4)$.

$$m = \frac{y_2 - y_1}{x_2 - x_1} = \frac{2 - (-4)}{6 - 6} = \frac{6}{0} \quad \text{Undefined slope}$$

Because division by 0 is undefined, this line has undefined slope. (This is why the slope formula at the beginning of this section had the restriction $x_1 \neq x_2$.) The graph in Figure 23 on the next page shows that this line is vertical. All points on a vertical line have the same x-value, so *all vertical lines have undefined slope.*

Continued on Next Page

2 Find the slope of each line.

(a) Through $(6, -2)$ and $(5, 4)$

(b) Through $(-3, 5)$ and $(-4, -7)$

(c) Through $(6, -8)$ and $(-2, 4)$ (Find this slope in two different ways as in Example 1(b).)

ANSWERS

2. (a) -6 **(b)** 12 **(c)** $-\frac{3}{2}; -\frac{3}{2}$

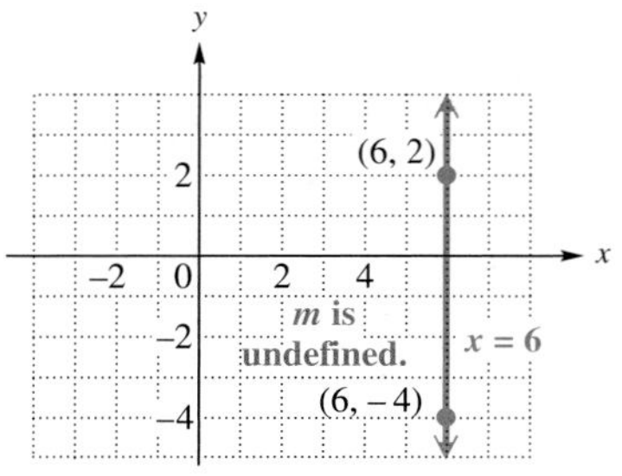

Figure 23

Slopes of Horizontal and Vertical Lines

Horizontal lines, which have equations of the form $y = k$, have **slope 0.**

Vertical lines, which have equations of the form $x = k$, have **undefined slope.**

Work Problem 3 at the Side.

2 Find the slope from the equation of a line. The slope of a line can be found directly from its equation. For example, the slope of the line

$$y = -3x + 5$$

can be found using any two points on the line. We get these two points by first choosing two different values of x and then finding the corresponding values of y. Choose $x = -2$ and $x = 4$.

$$\begin{aligned} y &= -3x + 5 \\ y &= -3(-2) + 5 \quad \text{Let } x = -2. \\ y &= 6 + 5 \\ y &= 11 \end{aligned} \qquad \begin{aligned} y &= -3x + 5 \\ y &= -3(4) + 5 \quad \text{Let } x = 4. \\ y &= -12 + 5 \\ y &= -7 \end{aligned}$$

The ordered pairs are $(-2, 11)$ and $(4, -7)$. Now use the slope formula.

$$m = \frac{11 - (-7)}{-2 - 4} = \frac{18}{-6} = -3$$

The slope, -3, is the same number as the coefficient of x in the equation $y = -3x + 5$. It can be shown that this always happens, *as long as the equation is solved for y.* This fact is used to find the slope of a line from its equation.

Finding the Slope of a Line from Its Equation

Step 1 Solve the equation for y.

Step 2 The slope is given by the coefficient of x.

NOTE

We will see in the next section that the equation $y = -3x + 5$ is written using a special form of the equation of a line,

$$y = mx + b,$$

called *slope-intercept form.*

---

3 Find the slope of each line.

(a) Through $(2, 5)$ and $(-1, 5)$

(b) Through $(3, 1)$ and $(3, -4)$

(c) With equation $y = -1$

(d) With equation $x - 4 = 0$

Answers

3. (a) 0 **(b)** undefined **(c)** 0 **(d)** undefined

Example 4 **Finding Slopes from Equations**

Find the slope of each line.

(a) $2x - 5y = 4$

Step 1 Solve the equation for y.

$$2x - 5y = 4$$
$$-5y = -2x + 4 \quad \text{Subtract } 2x.$$
$$y = \frac{2}{5}x - \frac{4}{5} \quad \text{Divide by } -5.$$

Step 2 The slope is given by the coefficient of x, so the slope is $\frac{2}{5}$.

(b) $8x + 4y = 1$
Solve for y.

$$4y = -8x + 1 \quad \text{Subtract } 8x.$$
$$y = -2x + \frac{1}{4} \quad \text{Divide by 4.}$$

The slope of this line is given by the coefficient of x, which is -2.

Work Problem 4 at the Side.

4 Find the slope of each line.

(a) $y = -\frac{7}{2}x + 1$

(b) $3x + 2y = 9$

(c) $y + 4 = 0$

(d) $x + 3 = 7$

3 **Use slope to determine whether two lines are parallel, perpendicular, or neither.** Two lines in a plane that never intersect are **parallel.** We use slopes to tell whether two lines are parallel. For example, Figure 24 shows the graphs of $x + 2y = 4$ and $x + 2y = -6$. These lines appear to be parallel. Solving for y, we find that both $x + 2y = 4$ and $x + 2y = -6$ have slope $-\frac{1}{2}$. Nonvertical parallel lines always have equal slopes.

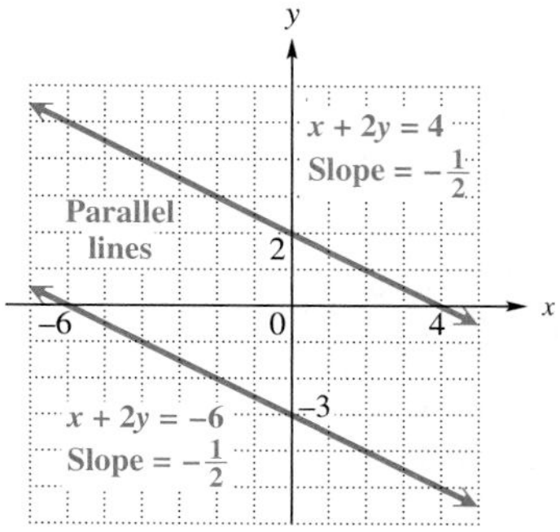

Figure 24

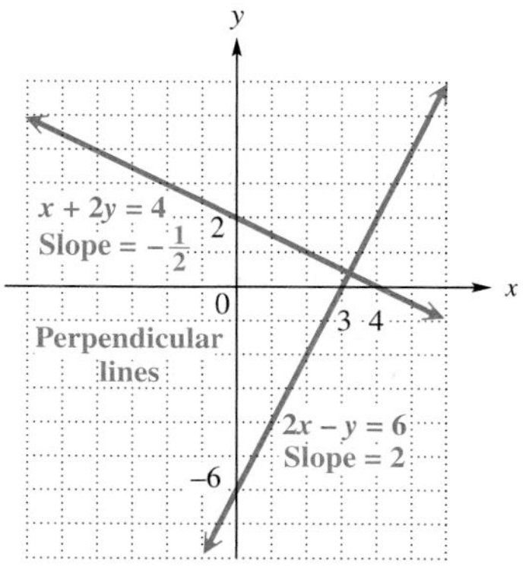

Figure 25

Figure 25 shows the graphs of $x + 2y = 4$ and $2x - y = 6$. These lines appear to be **perpendicular** (intersect at a 90° angle). Solving for y shows that the slope of $x + 2y = 4$ is $-\frac{1}{2}$, while the slope of $2x - y = 6$ is 2. The product of $-\frac{1}{2}$ and 2 is

$$-\frac{1}{2}(2) = -1.$$

This is true in general; the product of the slopes of two perpendicular lines (neither of which is vertical) is always -1.

Slopes of Parallel and Perpendicular Lines

Two lines with the same slope are parallel.

Two lines whose slopes have a product of -1 are perpendicular.

ANSWERS

4. **(a)** $-\frac{7}{2}$ **(b)** $-\frac{3}{2}$ **(c)** 0 **(d)** undefined

5 Decide whether each pair of lines is *parallel*, *perpendicular*, or *neither*.

(a) $x + y = 6$
$x + y = 1$

(b) $3x - y = 4$
$x + 3y = 9$

(c) $2x - y = 5$
$2x + y = 3$

(d) $3x - 7y = 35$
$7x - 3y = -6$

ANSWERS
5. **(a)** parallel **(b)** perpendicular **(c)** neither **(d)** neither

Example 5 Deciding Whether Lines Are Parallel, Perpendicular, or Neither

Decide whether each pair of lines is *parallel, perpendicular,* or *neither.*

(a) $x + 2y = 7$
$-2x + y = 3$

Find the slope of each line by first solving each equation for y.

$x + 2y = 7$	$-2x + y = 3$
$2y = -x + 7$	$y = 2x + 3$
$y = -\frac{1}{2}x + \frac{7}{2}$	
Slope is $-\frac{1}{2}$.	Slope is 2.

Because the slopes are not equal, the lines are not parallel. Check the product of the slopes: $-\frac{1}{2}(2) = -1$. The two lines are perpendicular because the product of their slopes is -1. See Figure 26.

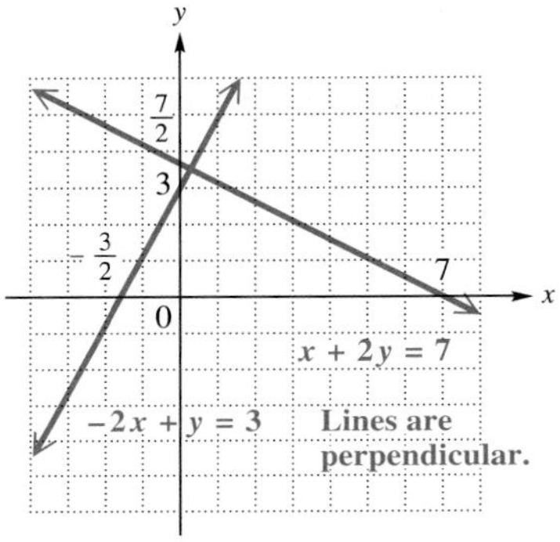

Figure 26

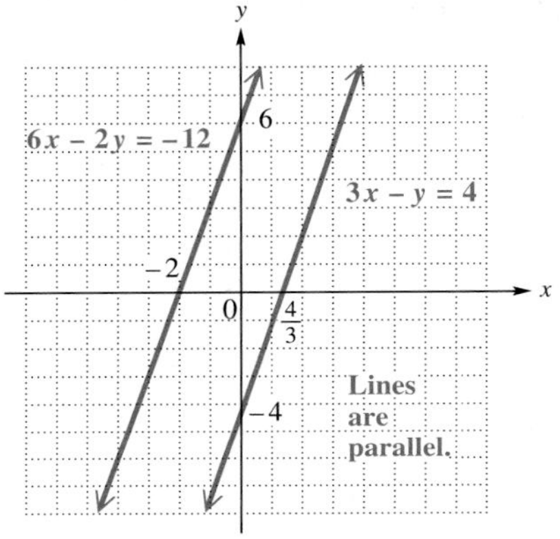

Figure 27

(b) $3x - y = 4$ Solve for y. $y = 3x - 4$
$6x - 2y = -12$ ⟶ $y = 3x + 6$

Both lines have slope 3, so the lines are parallel. See Figure 27.

(c) $4x + 3y = 6$ Solve for y. $y = -\frac{4}{3}x + 2$
$2x - y = 5$ ⟶ $y = 2x - 5$

Here the slopes are $-\frac{4}{3}$ and 2. These lines are neither parallel nor perpendicular.

(d) $5x - y = 1$
$x - 5y = -10$

Solving each equation for y gives

$$y = 5x - 1$$
$$y = \frac{1}{5}x + 2.$$

The slopes are 5 and $\frac{1}{5}$. The lines are not parallel, nor are they perpendicular. (Be careful! $5\left(\frac{1}{5}\right) = 1$, not -1.)

Work Problem 5 at the Side.

4 **Solve problems involving average rate of change.** We know that the slope of a line is the ratio of the change in y (vertical) to the change in x (horizontal). This idea can be applied to real-life situations. The slope gives the average rate of change in y per unit of change in x, where the value of y depends on the value of x. The next example further illustrates this idea of average rate of change. We assume a linear relationship between x and y.

6 Use the ordered pairs (1997, 10) and (2000, 20.8), which are plotted in Figure 28, to find the average rate of change. How does it compare to the average rate of change found in Example 6?

Example 6 Interpreting Slope as Average Rate of Change

The graph in Figure 28 approximates the percent of U.S. households owning multiple personal computers in the years 1997–2001. Find the average rate of change in percent per year.

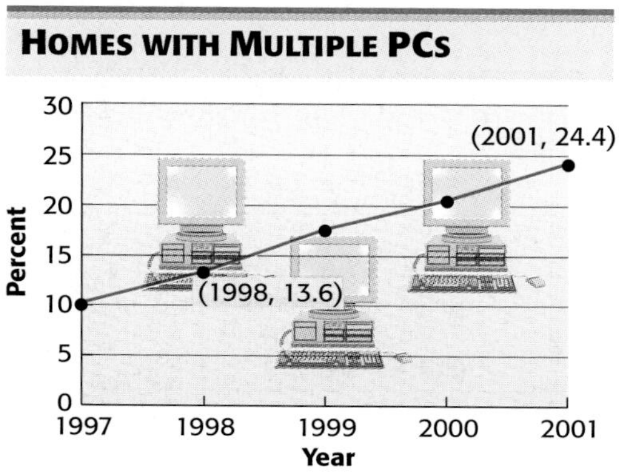

Source: The Yankee Group.

Figure 28

To use the slope formula, we need two pairs of data. From the graph, if $x = 1998$, then $y = 13.6$ and if $x = 2001$, then $y = 24.4$, so we have the ordered pairs (1998, 13.6) and (2001, 24.4). By the slope formula,

$$\text{average rate of change} = \frac{y_2 - y_1}{x_2 - x_1} = \frac{24.4 - 13.6}{2001 - 1998} = \frac{10.8}{3} = 3.6.$$

This means that the number of U.S. households owning multiple computers *increased* by 3.6% each year in the period from 1997 to 2001.

Work Problem 6 at the Side.

ANSWERS

6. 3.6; It is the same.

Focus on
Real-Data Applications

"Ins and Outs" of Algebraic Expressions

An algebraic expression such as $3x + 2$ represents both a *process* (what to do) and a *concept* (the result). To illustrate this idea, choose a number. Multiply by 3, then add 2. What is your answer? Now choose a different number and repeat this procedure. Did you get the same answer?

The examples in the table imitate the activity that you just finished. Compare the examples to the generalization.

	Example 1	Example 2	Example 3	Generalization
Choose a number.	5	-3.1	$\frac{2}{5}$	x
Multiply by 3.	$3 \times 5 = 15$	$-3.1 \times 3 = -9.3$	$\frac{2}{5} \times 3 = \frac{6}{5}$	$3x$
Add 2.	$3 \times 5 + 2 = 15 + 2$	$-3.1 \times 3 + 2 = -9.3 + 2$	$\frac{2}{5} \times 3 + 2 = \frac{6}{5} + 2$	$3x + 2$
What is the answer?	17	-7.3	$\frac{16}{5}$	$3x + 2$

As these examples illustrate, $3x + 2$ represents both the arithmetic procedure and the answer. Remember that $3x + 2$ is a number in the same way that x is a number. The variable x is the **input** and the expression $3x + 2$ represents the **output** or the "answer" as well as the step-by-step process for calculating the output.

Algebraic expressions are useful in real-life scenarios that describe the relationship between two variables, the input and the output.

For Group Discussion

For each scenario, define the input and the output, and write an expression that represents the relationship between those two variables.

1. R. Conniff claims that a hummingbird's heart beats about 1200 times per minute in flight. (*Source: Smithsonian.*)

What is the input? **the number of minutes of a hummingbird's flight**

What is the output? **the number of times that the hummingbird's heart beats**

Write an expression for the number of times that a hummingbird's heart beats during x minutes of flight. $1200x$

2. D. Webster claims that malaria kills one child every 30 seconds. (*Source: Smithsonian.*)

What is the input? **the number of seconds**

What is the output? **the number of children who die of malaria**

Write an expression for the number of children who die of malaria after x seconds. $\frac{x}{30}$

Teaching notes for this activity are provided in the *Printed Test Bank and Instructor's Resource Guide.*

4.3 EXERCISES

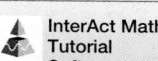

FOR EXTRA HELP: Student's Solutions Manual · MyMathLab.com · InterAct Math Tutorial Software · AW Math Tutor Center · www.mathxl.com · Digital Video Tutor CD 3 Videotape 7

1. In the context of the graph of a straight line, what is meant by "rise"? What is meant by "run"?

Rise is the vertical change between two different points on a line. Run is the horizontal change between two different points on a line.

Use the coordinates of the indicated points to find the slope of each line. See Example 1.

2.

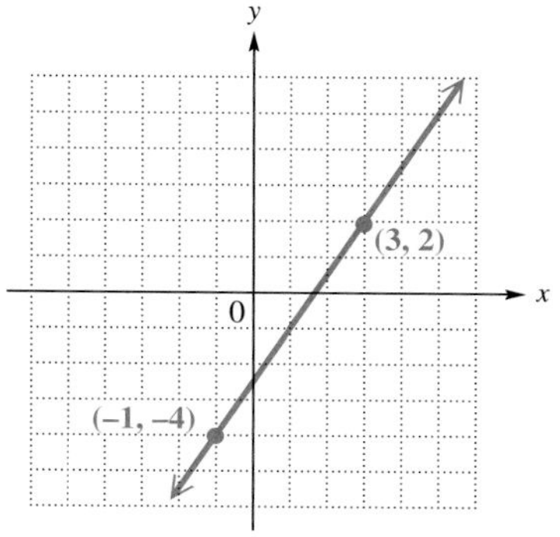

$\frac{3}{2}$

3.

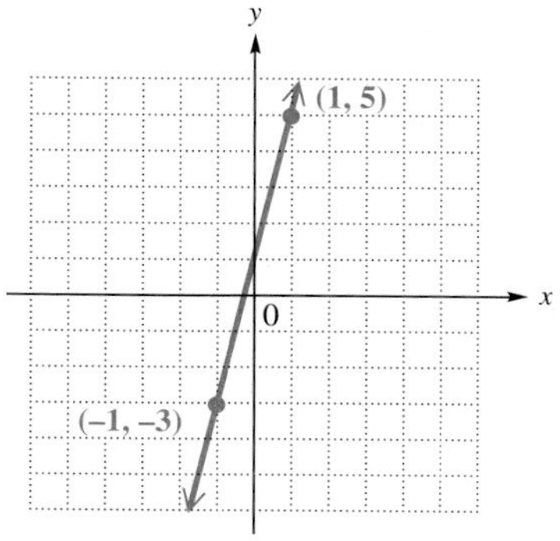

4

4.

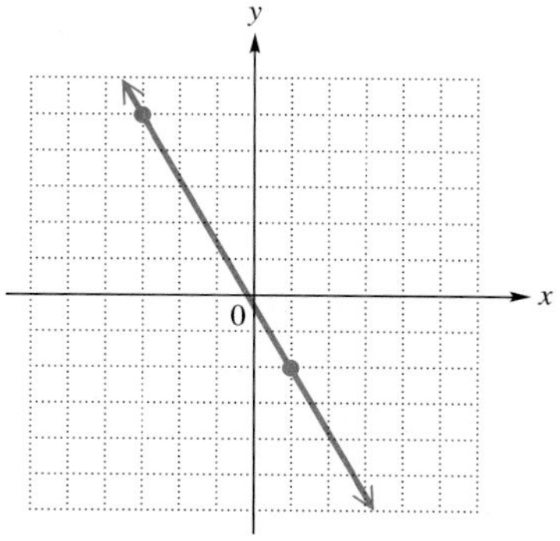

$-\frac{7}{4}$

5.

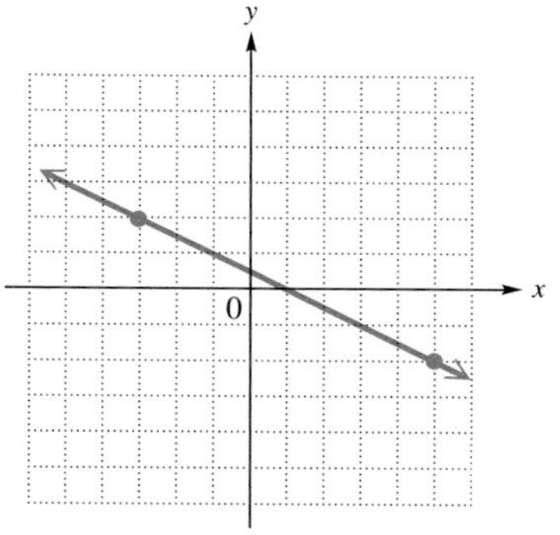

$-\frac{1}{2}$

6.

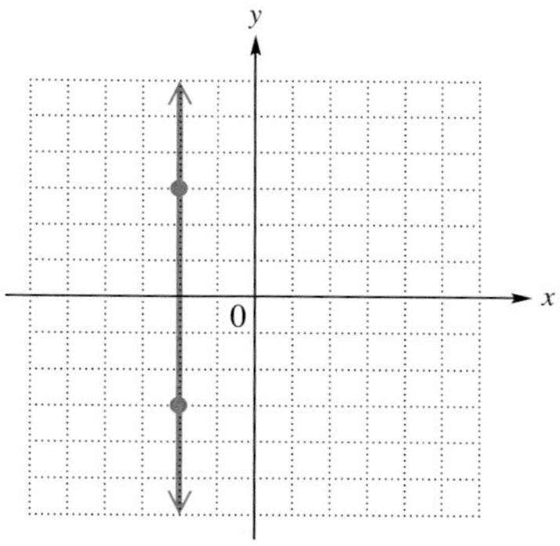

undefined

7.

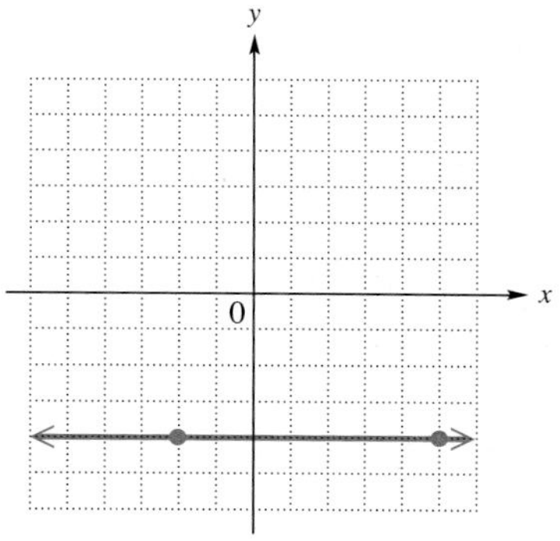

0

8. Look at the graph in Exercise 2, and answer the following.

(a) Start at the point $(-1, -4)$ and count vertically up to the horizontal line that goes through the other plotted point. What is this vertical change? (Remember: "up" means positive, "down" means negative.) **6**

(b) From this new position, count horizontally to the other plotted point. What is this horizontal change? (Remember: "right" means positive, "left" means negative.) **4**

(c) What is the quotient of the numbers found in parts (a) and (b)? $\frac{6}{4}$ *or* $\frac{3}{2}$

What do we call this number? **slope of the line**

9. Refer to Exercise 8. If we were to *start* at the point (3, 2) and *end* at the point $(-1, -4)$, would the answer to part (c) be the same? Explain why or why not.

Yes, the answer would be the same. It doesn't matter which point you start with. The slope would be expressed as the quotient of -6 and -4, which simplifies to $\frac{3}{2}$.

On the given coordinate system, sketch the graph of a straight line with the indicated slope.

10. Negative

11. Positive

12. Undefined

13. Zero

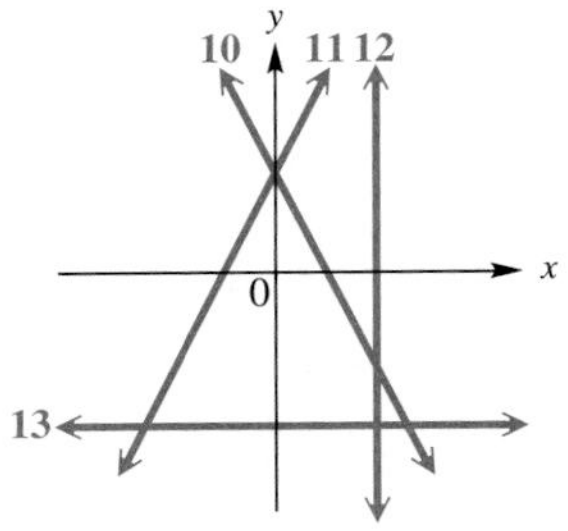

Answers will vary.

14. Explain in your own words what is meant by the *slope* of a line.

The slope of a line is the ratio (or quotient) of the rise, the change in *y*, and the run, the change in *x*.

15. A student found the slope of the line through the points (2, 5) and $(-1, 3)$ and got $-\frac{2}{3}$ as his answer. He showed his work as

$$\frac{3-5}{2-(-1)} = \frac{-2}{3} = -\frac{2}{3}.$$

Is he correct? If not, find his error and give the correct slope.

His answer is incorrect. Because he found the difference $3 - 5 = -2$ in the numerator, he should have subtracted in the same order in the denominator to get $-1 - 2 = -3$. The correct slope is $\frac{-2}{-3} = \frac{2}{3}$.

Find the slope of the line through each pair of points. See Examples 1–3.

16. $(4, -1)$ and $(-2, -8)$

$\frac{7}{6}$

17. $(1, -2)$ and $(-3, -7)$

$\frac{5}{4}$

18. $(-8, 0)$ and $(0, -5)$

$-\frac{5}{8}$

19. $(0, 3)$ and $(-2, 0)$

$\frac{3}{2}$

20. $(-4, -5)$ and $(-5, -8)$

3

21. $(-2, 4)$ and $(-3, 7)$

-3

22. $(6, -5)$ and $(-12, -5)$

0

23. $(4, 3)$ and $(-6, 3)$

0

24. $(-8, 6)$ and $(-8, -1)$

undefined

25. $(-12, 3)$ and $(-12, -7)$

undefined

26. $(3.1, 2.6)$ and $(1.6, 2.1)$

$\frac{1}{3}$

27. $\left(-\frac{7}{5}, \frac{3}{10}\right)$ and $\left(\frac{1}{5}, -\frac{1}{2}\right)$

$-\frac{1}{2}$

Find the slope of each line. See Example 4.

28. $y = 2x - 3$

2

29. $y = 5x + 12$

5

30. $2y = -x + 4$

$-\frac{1}{2}$

31. $4y = x + 1$

$\frac{1}{4}$

32. $-6x + 4y = 4$

$\frac{3}{2}$

33. $3x - 2y = 3$

$\frac{3}{2}$

34. $y = 4$

0

35. $x = 6$

undefined

The figure at the right shows a line that has a positive slope (because it rises from left to right) and a positive y-value for the y-intercept (because it intersects the y-axis above the origin).

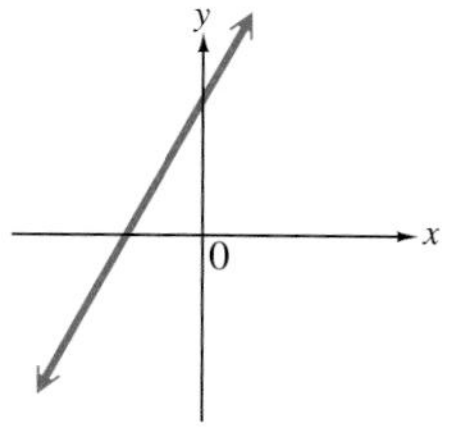

*For each figure in Exercises 36–41, decide whether **(a)** the slope is* positive, negative, *or* 0 *and whether **(b)** the y-value of the y-intercept is* positive, negative, *or* 0.

36. (a) **negative**
(b) **negative**

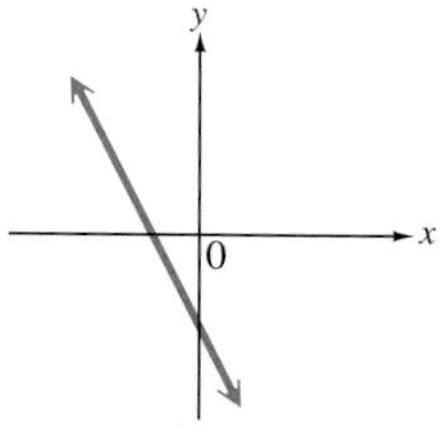

37. (a) **negative**
(b) **0**

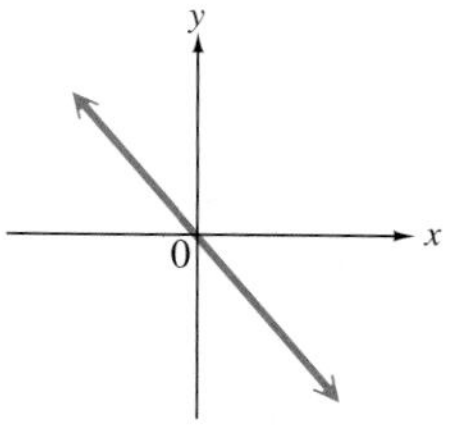

38. (a) **positive**
(b) **0**

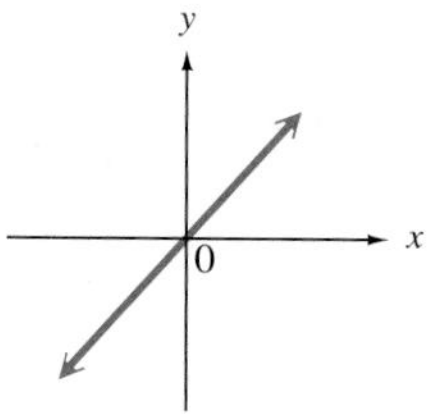

39. (a) **positive**
(b) **negative**

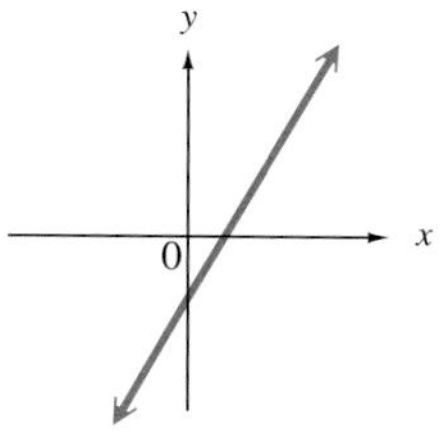

40. (a) **0**
(b) **positive**

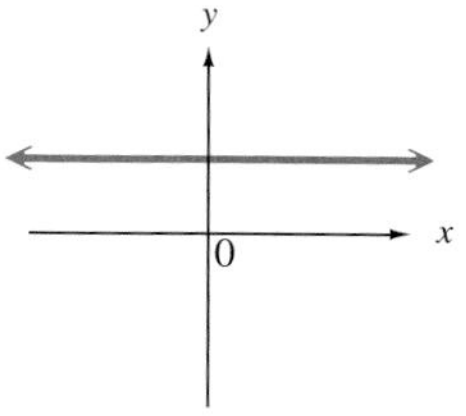

41. (a) **0**
(b) **negative**

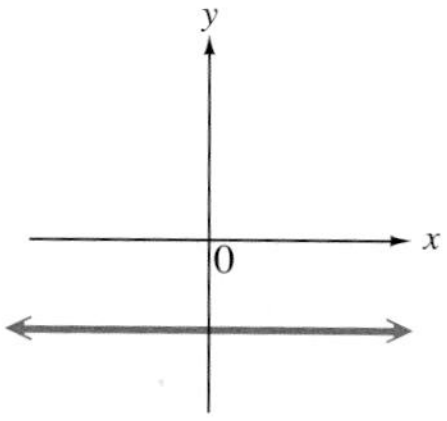

In each pair of equations, give the slope of each line, and then determine whether the two lines are parallel, perpendicular, *or* neither *parallel nor perpendicular. See Example 5.*

42. $2x + 5y = 4$
$4x + 10y = 1$

$-\frac{2}{5}$; $-\frac{2}{5}$; parallel

43. $-4x + 3y = 4$
$-8x + 6y = 0$

$\frac{4}{3}$; $\frac{4}{3}$; parallel

44. $8x - 9y = 6$
$8x + 6y = -5$

$\frac{8}{9}$; $-\frac{4}{3}$; neither

45. $5x - 3y = -2$
$3x - 5y = -8$

$\frac{5}{3}$; $\frac{3}{5}$; neither

46. $3x - 2y = 6$
$2x + 3y = 3$

$\frac{3}{2}$; $-\frac{2}{3}$; perpendicular

47. $3x - 5y = -1$
$5x + 3y = 2$

$\frac{3}{5}$; $-\frac{5}{3}$; perpendicular

48. What is the slope (or pitch) of this roof?

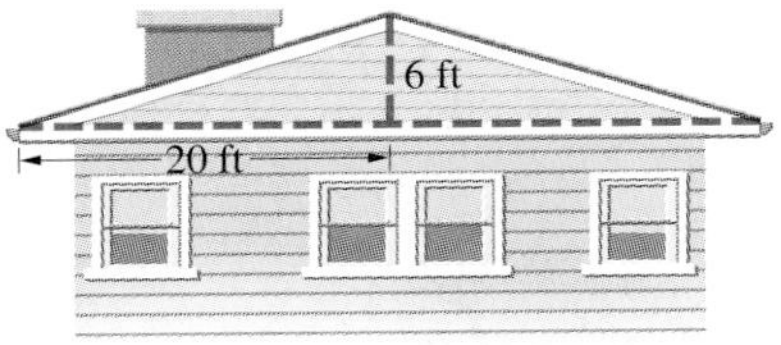

$\frac{3}{10}$

49. What is the slope (or grade) of this hill?

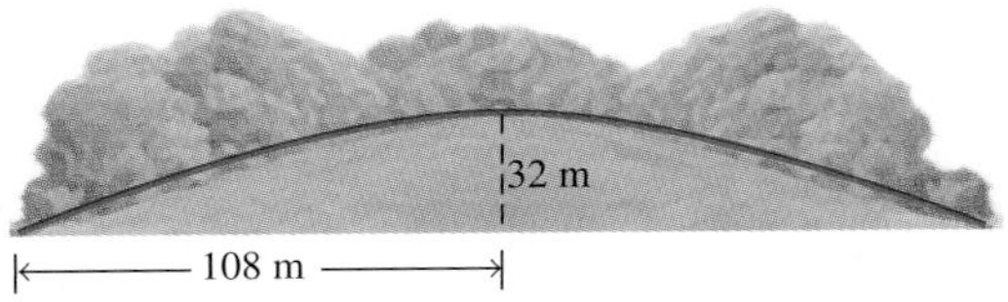

$\frac{8}{27}$

RELATING CONCEPTS (Exercises 50–55) FOR INDIVIDUAL OR GROUP WORK

Figure A gives the public school enrollment (in thousands) in grades 9–12 in the United States. Figure B gives the (average) number of public school students per computer.

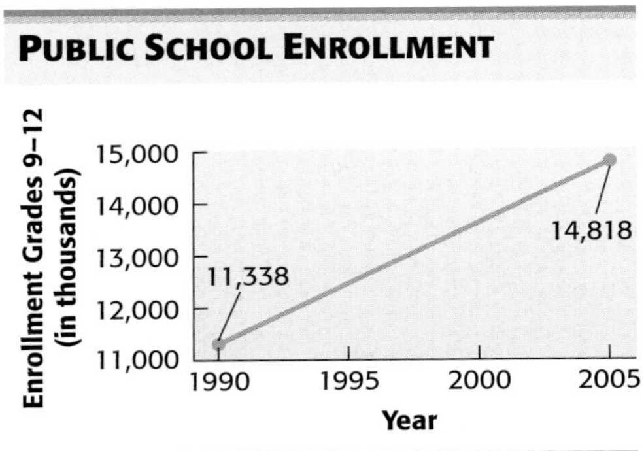

Source: *Digest of Educational Statistics*, annual, and *Projections of Educational Statistics*, annual.

Figure A

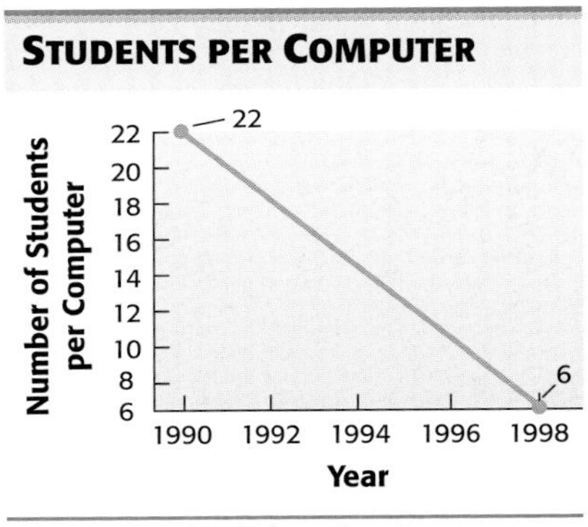

Source: *Quality Education Data.*

Figure B

Work Exercises 50–55 in order.

50. Use the ordered pairs (1990, 11,338) and (2005, 14,818) to find the slope of the line in Figure A. Note that enrollment is given in thousands.

232 thousand or 232,000

51. The slope of the line in Figure A is positive (positive/negative). This means that during the period represented, enrollment increased (increased/decreased).

52. The slope of a line represents its *rate of change.* Based on Figure A, what was the increase in students *per year* during the period shown?

232,000 students

53. Use the given ordered pairs to find the slope of the line in Figure B. -2

54. The slope of the line in Figure B is negative (positive/negative). This means that during the period represented, the number of students per computer decreased (increased/decreased).

55. Based on Figure B, what was the decrease in the number of students per computer *per year* during the period shown?

2 students per computer

Use the concept of slope to solve each problem.

56. The upper deck at Comiskey Park in Chicago has produced, among other complaints, displeasure with its steepness. It's been compared to a ski jump. It is 160 ft from home plate to the front of the upper deck and 250 ft from home plate to the back. The top of the upper deck is 63 ft above the bottom. What is its slope?

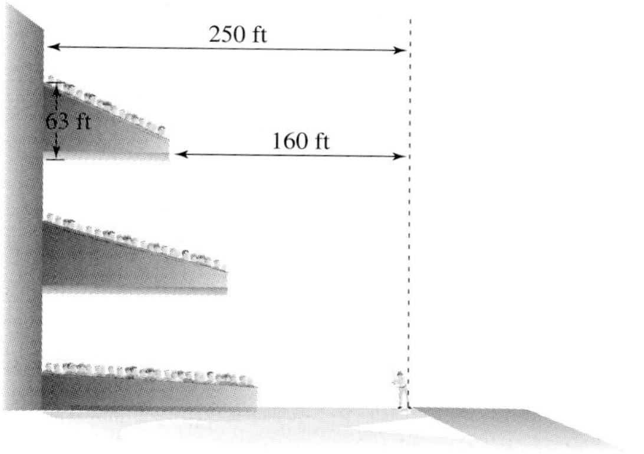

$\frac{7}{10}$

57. When designing the new FleetCenter arena in Boston to replace the old Boston Garden, architects were careful to design the ramps leading up to the entrances so that circus elephants would be able to march up the ramps. The maximum grade (or slope) that an elephant will walk on is 13%. Suppose that such a ramp was constructed with a horizontal run of 150 ft. What would be the maximum vertical rise the architects could use?

19.5 ft

Use the idea of average rate of change to solve each problem. See Example 6.

58. Merck pharmaceutical company research and development expenditures (in millions of dollars) in recent years are closely approximated by the graph.

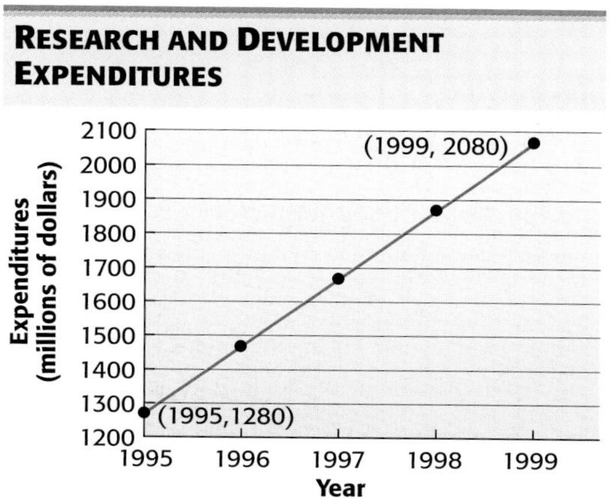

Source: Merck & Co., Inc. 1999 Annual Report.

(a) Use the given ordered pairs to determine the average rate of change in these expenditures per year.

\$200 million per yr

(b) Explain how a positive rate of change is interpreted in this situation.

The positive slope means expenditures *increased* an average of \$200 million each year.

59. The graph provides a good approximation of the number of food stamp recipients (in millions) during 1994–1998.

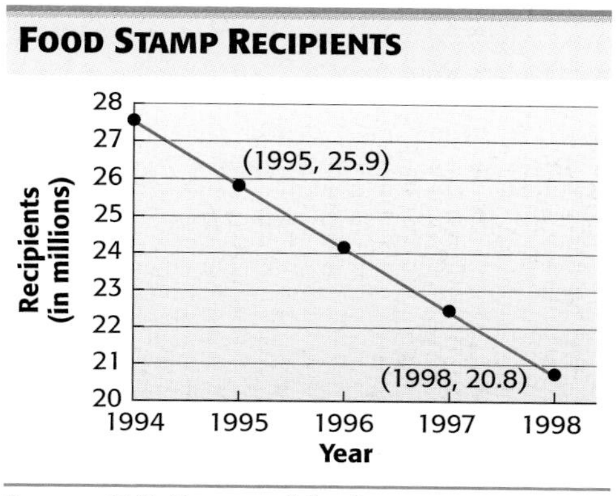

Source: U.S. Bureau of the Census.

(a) Use the given ordered pairs to find the average rate of change in food stamp recipients per year during this period.

-1.7 million recipients per yr

(b) Interpret what a negative slope means in this situation.

The negative slope means the numbers of recipients *decreased* by 1.7 million each year.

60. The table gives book publishers' approximate net dollar sales (in millions) from 1995 through 2000.

BOOK PUBLISHERS' SALES

Year	Sales (in millions)
1995	19,000
1996	20,000
1997	21,000
1998	22,000
1999	23,000
2000	24,000

Source: Book Industry Study Group.

(a) Find the average rate of change for 1995–1996, 1995–1999, and 1998–2000. What do you notice about your answers? What does this tell you?

1000 million/yr; 1000 million/yr; 1000 million/yr; The average rate of change is the same. This is true because the data points lie on a straight line.

(b) Calculate the rates of change in part (a) as percents. What do you notice?

5.3%, 5.3%, 4.5%; They are all approximately 5%.

61. The table gives the number of cellular telephone subscribers (in thousands) from 1994 through 1999.

CELLULAR TELEPHONE SUBSCRIBERS

Year	Subscribers (in thousands)
1994	24,134
1995	33,786
1996	44,043
1997	55,312
1998	69,209
1999	86,047

Source: Cellular Telecommunications Industry Association, Washington, D.C. *State of the Cellular Industry* (Annual).

(a) Find the average rate of change in subscribers for 1994–1995, 1995–1996, and so on.

9652 thousand; 10,257 thousand; 11,269 thousand; 13,897 thousand; 16,838 thousand

(b) Is the average rate of change in successive years approximately the same? If the ordered pairs in the table were plotted, could an approximately straight line be drawn through them?

no; no

RELATING CONCEPTS (Exercises 62–67) FOR INDIVIDUAL OR GROUP WORK

In these exercises we investigate a method of determining whether three points lie on the same straight line. (Such points are said to be **collinear.***) The points we consider are* $A(3, 1)$, $B(6, 2)$, *and* $C(9, 3)$. ***Work Exercises 62–67 in order.***

62. Find the slope of segment AB.

$\frac{1}{3}$

63. Find the slope of segment BC.

$\frac{1}{3}$

64. Find the slope of segment AC.

$\frac{1}{3}$

65. If slope of AB = slope of BC = slope of AC, then A, B, and C are collinear. Use the results of Exercises 62–64 to show that this statement is satisfied.

$\frac{1}{3} = \frac{1}{3} = \frac{1}{3}$ **is true.**

66. Use the slope formula to determine whether the points $(1, -2)$, $(3, -1)$, and $(5, 0)$ are collinear.

They are collinear.

67. Repeat Exercise 66 for the points $(0, 6)$, $(4, -5)$, and $(-2, 12)$.

They are not collinear.

4.4 EQUATIONS OF LINES

OBJECTIVES

1. Write an equation of a line given its slope and y-intercept.
2. Graph a line given its slope and a point on the line.
3. Write an equation of a line given its slope and any point on the line.
4. Write an equation of a line given two points on the line.
5. Write an equation of a line parallel or perpendicular to a given line.
6. Find an equation of a line that fits a data set.

In the previous section, we found the slope (steepness) of a line from the equation of the line by solving the equation for y. In that form, the slope is the coefficient of x. For example, the slope of the line with equation $y = 2x + 3$ is 2, the coefficient of x. What does the number 3 represent? If $x = 0$, the equation becomes

$$y = 2(0) + 3 = 0 + 3 = 3.$$

Since $y = 3$ corresponds to $x = 0$, $(0, 3)$ is the y-intercept of the graph of $y = 2x + 3$. An equation like $y = 2x + 3$ that is solved for y is said to be in **slope-intercept form** because both the slope and the y-intercept of the line can be read directly from the equation.

Slope-Intercept Form

The slope-intercept form of the equation of a line with slope m and y-intercept $(0, b)$ is

$$y = mx + b.$$

NOTE

The slope-intercept form is the most useful form for a linear equation because of the information we can determine from it. It is also the form used by graphing calculators and the one that describes a *linear function*, an important concept in mathematics. (See Section 4.6.)

1 Write an equation of a line given its slope and y-intercept. Given the slope and y-intercept of a line, we can use the slope-intercept form to find an equation of the line.

Example 1 Finding an Equation of a Line

Find an equation of the line with slope $\frac{2}{3}$ and y-intercept $(0, -1)$.

Here $m = \frac{2}{3}$ and $b = -1$, so the equation is

Slope → m; y-intercept → b

$$y = mx + b$$

$$y = \frac{2}{3}x - 1.$$

Work Problem 1 at the Side.

2 Graph a line given its slope and a point on the line. We can use the slope and y-intercept to graph a line. For example, to graph $y = \frac{2}{3}x - 1$, first locate the y-intercept $(0, -1)$ on the y-axis. From the definition of slope and the fact that the slope of this line is $\frac{2}{3}$,

$$m = \frac{\text{change in } y}{\text{change in } x} = \frac{2}{3}.$$

1 Find an equation of the line with the given slope and y-intercept.

(a) slope $\frac{1}{2}$; y-intercept $(0, -4)$

(b) slope -1; y-intercept $(0, 8)$

(c) slope 3; y-intercept $(0, 0)$

(d) slope 0; y-intercept $(0, 2)$

ANSWERS

1. (a) $y = \frac{1}{2}x - 4$ **(b)** $y = -x + 8$ **(c)** $y = 3x$ **(d)** $y = 2$

2 Graph each line,

(a) Through $(-1, 2)$, with slope $\frac{3}{2}$

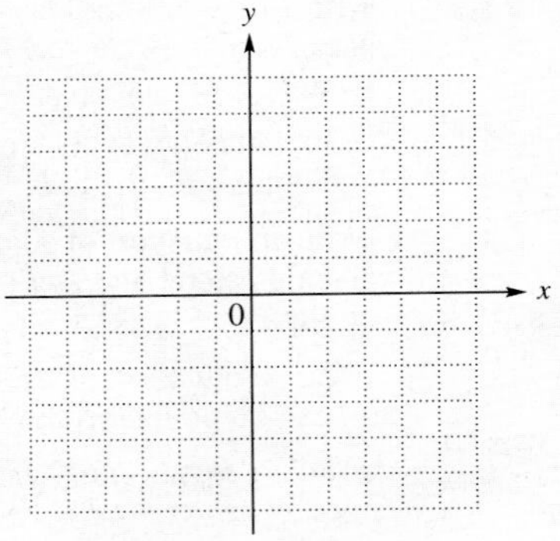

(b) Through $(2, -3)$, with slope $-\frac{1}{3}$

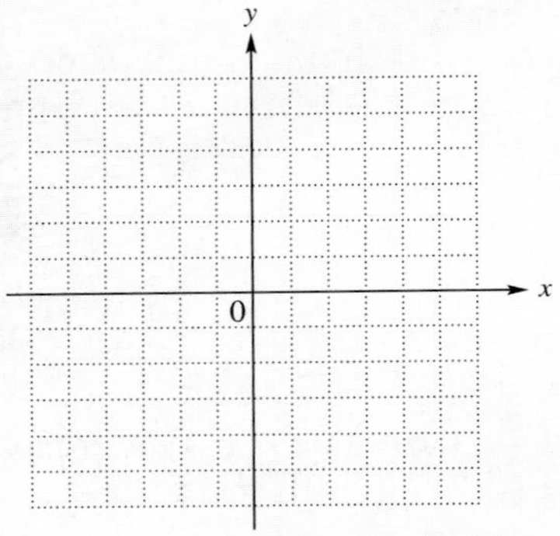

ANSWERS

2. (a)

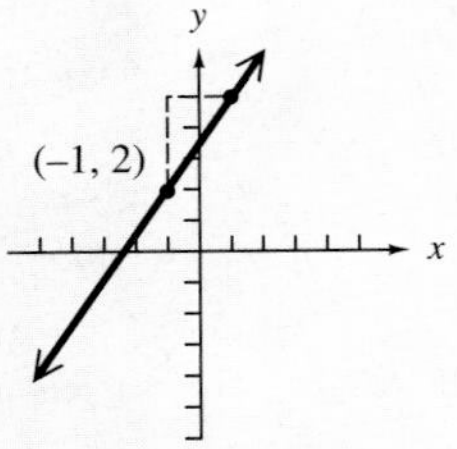

(b)

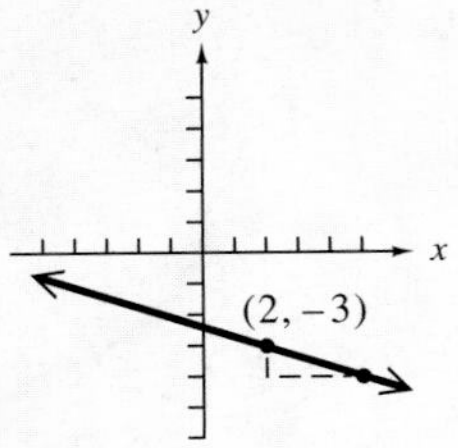

Recall that slope indicates the change in y (the rise) compared to the change in x (the run) between two points on the line. A slope of $\frac{2}{3}$ indicates the line rises 2 units for a run of 3 units. We can find another point P on the graph by counting from the y-intercept 2 units up and then counting 3 units to the right. We then draw the line through point P and the y-intercept, as shown in Figure 29.

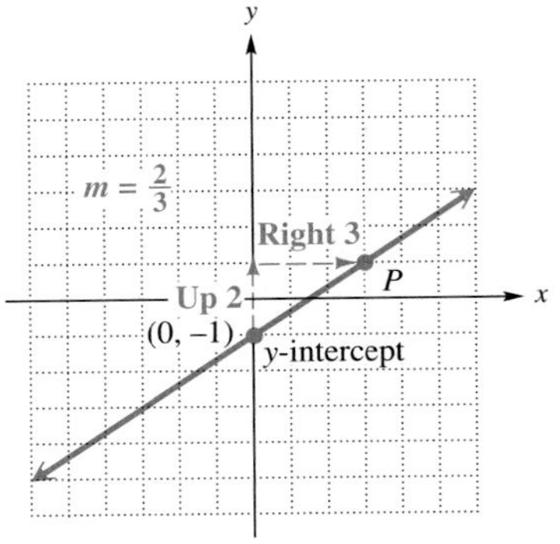

Figure 29

This method can be extended to graph a line given its slope and any point on the line.

Example 2 Graphing a Line Given a Point and the Slope

Graph the line through $(-2, 3)$ with slope -4.

First, locate the point $(-2, 3)$. Write the slope as

$$m = \frac{\text{change in } y}{\text{change in } x} = -4 = \frac{-4}{1}.$$

Locate another point on the line by counting 4 units down (because of the negative sign) and then 1 unit to the right. Finally, draw the line through this new point P and the given point $(-2, 3)$. See Figure 30.

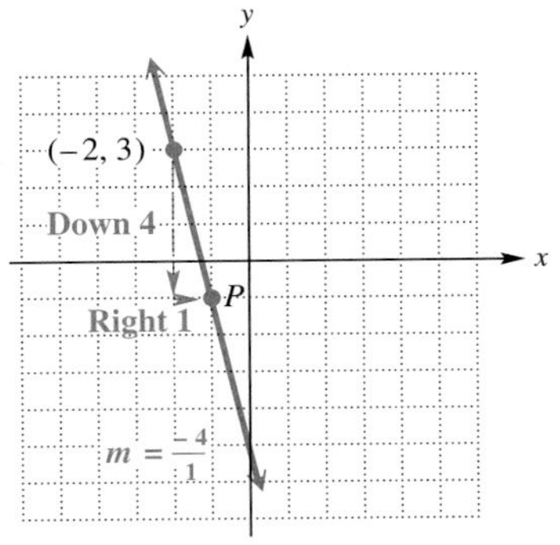

Figure 30

NOTE

In Example 2, we could have written the slope as $\frac{4}{-1}$ instead. In this case, we would move 4 units up from $(-2, 3)$ and then 1 unit to the left (because of the negative sign). Verify that this produces the same line.

Work Problem 2 at the Side.

3 Write an equation of a line given its slope and any point on the line. Let m represent the slope of a line and (x_1, y_1) represent a given point on the line. Let (x, y) represent any other point on the line. Then by the slope formula,

$$\frac{y - y_1}{x - x_1} = m \quad \text{or} \quad y - y_1 = m(x - x_1).$$

This result is the **point-slope form** of the equation of a line.

Point-Slope Form

The point-slope form of the equation of a line with slope m going through (x_1, y_1) is

$$y - y_1 = m(x - x_1).$$

This very important result should be memorized.

Example 3 Using the Point-Slope Form to Write Equations

Find an equation of each line. Write the equation in slope-intercept form.

(a) Through $(-2, 4)$, with slope -3

The given point is $(-2, 4)$ so $x_1 = -2$ and $y_1 = 4$. Also, $m = -3$. Substitute these values into the point-slope form.

$$y - y_1 = m(x - x_1) \quad \text{Point-slope form}$$
$$y - 4 = -3[x - (-2)] \quad \text{Let } x_1 = -2, y_1 = 4, m = -3.$$
$$y - 4 = -3(x + 2)$$
$$y - 4 = -3x - 6 \quad \text{Distributive property}$$
$$y = -3x - 2 \quad \text{Add 4.}$$

The last equation is in slope-intercept form.

(b) Through $(4, 2)$, with slope $\frac{3}{5}$

Use the point-slope form.

$$y - y_1 = m(x - x_1)$$
$$y - 2 = \frac{3}{5}(x - 4) \quad \text{Let } x_1 = 4, y_1 = 2, m = \tfrac{3}{5}.$$
$$y - 2 = \frac{3}{5}x - \frac{12}{5} \quad \text{Distributive property}$$
$$y = \frac{3}{5}x - \frac{12}{5} + \frac{10}{5} \quad \text{Add } 2 = \tfrac{10}{5}.$$
$$y = \frac{3}{5}x - \frac{2}{5} \quad \text{Combine terms.}$$

We did not clear fractions after the substitution step because we want the equation in slope-intercept form—that is, solved for y.

Work Problem 3 at the Side.

3 Find an equation for each line. Write answers in slope-intercept form.

(a) Through $(-1, 3)$, with slope -2

$$y - y_1 = m(x - x_1)$$
$$y - \_\_\_\_ = \_\_\_\_ [x - (\quad)]$$
$$y - 3 = -2(x + \_\_\_\_)$$
$$y - 3 = -2x - \_\_\_\_$$
$$y = \_\_\_\_$$

(b) Through $(5, 2)$, with slope $-\frac{1}{3}$

ANSWERS

3. (a) 3; −2; −1; 1; 2; $-2x + 1$

(b) $y = -\frac{1}{3}x + \frac{11}{3}$

4 Write an equation in slope-intercept form for the line through each pair of points.

(a) $(-3, 1)$ and $(2, 4)$

(b) $(2, 5)$ and $(-1, 6)$

4 **Write an equation of a line given two points on the line.** We can also use the point-slope form to find an equation of a line when two points on the line are known.

Example 4 **Finding the Equation of a Line Given Two Points**

Find an equation of the line through the points $(-2, 5)$ and $(3, 4)$. Write the equation in slope-intercept form.

First, find the slope of the line, using the slope formula.

$$\text{slope } m = \frac{y_2 - y_1}{x_2 - x_1} = \frac{5 - 4}{-2 - 3} = \frac{1}{-5} = -\frac{1}{5}$$

Now use either $(-2, 5)$ or $(3, 4)$ and the point-slope form. Using $(3, 4)$ gives

$$y - y_1 = m(x - x_1)$$

$$y - 4 = -\frac{1}{5}(x - 3) \qquad \text{Let } x_1 = 3, y_1 = 4, m = -\tfrac{1}{5}.$$

$$y - 4 = -\frac{1}{5}x + \frac{3}{5} \qquad \text{Distributive property}$$

$$y = -\frac{1}{5}x + \frac{3}{5} + \frac{20}{5} \qquad \text{Add } 4 = \tfrac{20}{5}.$$

$$y = -\frac{1}{5}x + \frac{23}{5}. \qquad \text{Combine terms.}$$

The same result would be found using $(-2, 5)$ for (x_1, y_1).

Work Problem 4 at the Side.

Many of the linear equations in Sections 4.1–4.3 were given in the form $Ax + By = C$, called **standard form.** We define the standard form of a linear equation as follows.

Standard Form

A linear equation is in standard form if it is written as

$$Ax + By = C,$$

where A, B, and C are integers and $A > 0$, $B \neq 0$.

NOTE

The above definition of standard form is not the same in all texts. A linear equation can be written in this form in many different, equally correct, ways. For example, $3x + 4y = 12$, $6x + 8y = 24$, and $9x + 12y = 36$ all represent the same set of ordered pairs. Let us agree that $3x + 4y = 12$ is preferable to the other forms because the greatest common factor of 3, 4, and 12 is 1.

5 **Write an equation of a line parallel or perpendicular to a given line.** As mentioned in the previous section, parallel lines have the same slope and perpendicular lines have slopes with product -1.

ANSWERS

4. **(a)** $y = \frac{3}{5}x + \frac{14}{5}$ **(b)** $y = -\frac{1}{3}x + \frac{17}{3}$

Example 5 Finding Equations of Parallel or Perpendicular Lines

Find the equation in slope-intercept form of the line passing through the point $(-4, 5)$ and **(a)** parallel to the line $2x + 3y = 6$; **(b)** perpendicular to the line $2x + 3y = 6$.

(a) The slope of the line $2x + 3y = 6$ can be found by solving for y.

$$2x + 3y = 6$$

$$3y = -2x + 6 \qquad \text{Subtract } 2x.$$

$$y = -\frac{2}{3}x + 2 \qquad \text{Divide by 3.}$$

└ Slope

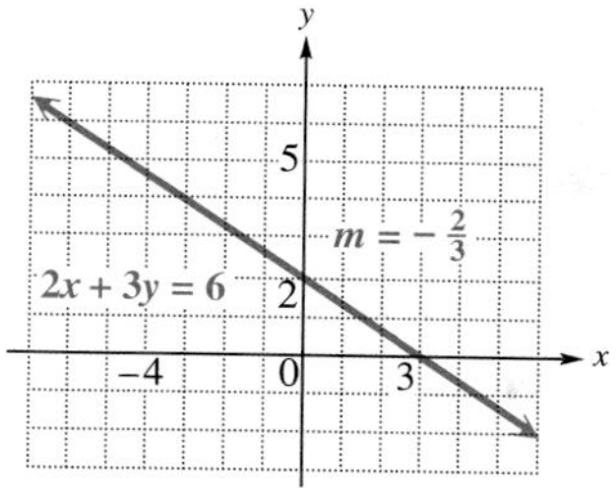

The slope is given by the coefficient of x, so $m = -\frac{2}{3}$. See the figure. The required equation of the line through $(-4, 5)$ and parallel to $2x + 3y = 6$ must also have slope $-\frac{2}{3}$. To find this equation, use the point-slope form, with $(x_1, y_1) = (-4, 5)$ and $m = -\frac{2}{3}$.

$$y - y_1 = m(x - x_1)$$

$$y - 5 = -\frac{2}{3}[x - (-4)] \qquad y_1 = 5,\ m = -\tfrac{2}{3},\ x_1 = -4$$

$$y - 5 = -\frac{2}{3}(x + 4)$$

$$y - 5 = -\frac{2}{3}x - \frac{8}{3} \qquad \text{Distributive property}$$

$$y = -\frac{2}{3}x - \frac{8}{3} + \frac{15}{3} \qquad \text{Add } 5 = \tfrac{15}{3}.$$

$$y = -\frac{2}{3}x + \frac{7}{3} \qquad \text{Combine terms.}$$

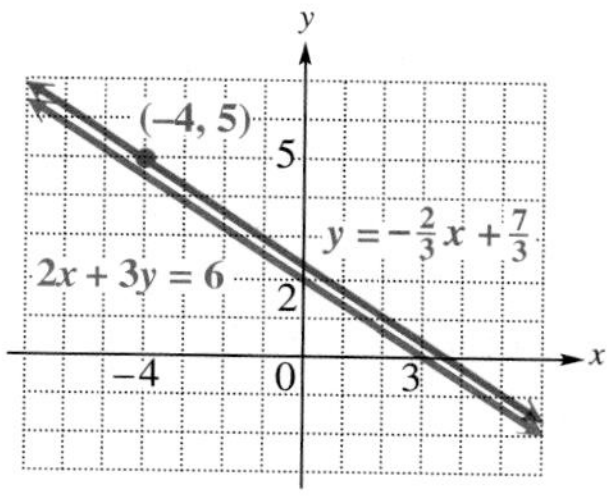

We did not clear fractions after the substitution step here because we want the equation in slope-intercept form—that is, solved for y. Both lines are shown in the figure.

(b) To be perpendicular to the line $2x + 3y = 6$, a line must have a slope that is the negative reciprocal of $-\frac{2}{3}$, which is $\frac{3}{2}$. Use the point $(-4, 5)$ and slope $\frac{3}{2}$ in the point-slope form to get the equation of the perpendicular line shown in the figure.

$$y - y_1 = m(x - x_1)$$

$$y - 5 = \frac{3}{2}[x - (-4)] \qquad y_1 = 5,\ m = \tfrac{3}{2},\ x_1 = -4$$

$$y - 5 = \frac{3}{2}(x + 4)$$

$$y - 5 = \frac{3}{2}x + 6 \qquad \text{Distributive property}$$

$$y = \frac{3}{2}x + 11 \qquad \text{Add 5.}$$

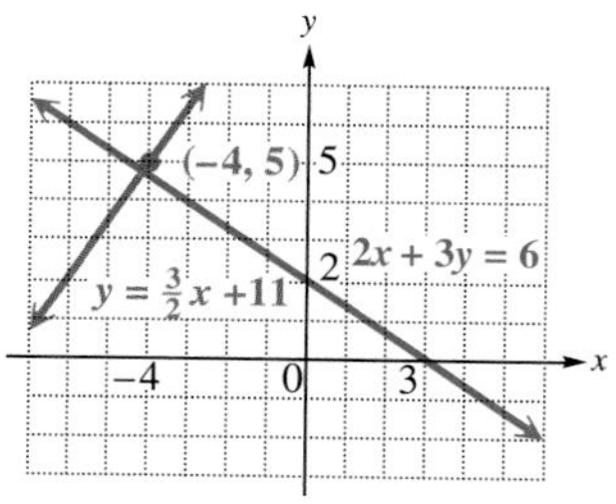

Work Problem 5 at the Side.

5 Write an equation in slope-intercept form of the line passing through the point $(-8, 3)$ and

(a) parallel to the line $2x - 3y = 10$.

(b) perpendicular to the line $2x - 3y = 10$.

ANSWERS

5. **(a)** $y = \frac{2}{3}x + \frac{25}{3}$ **(b)** $y = -\frac{3}{2}x - 9$

A summary of the various forms of linear equations follows.

Summary of Forms of Linear Equations

$x = k$	**Vertical Line** Slope is undefined. x-intercept is $(k, 0)$.
$y = k$	**Horizontal Line** Slope is 0. y-intercept is $(0, k)$.
$y = mx + b$	**Slope-Intercept Form** Slope is m. y-intercept is $(0, b)$.
$y - y_1 = m(x - x_1)$	**Point-Slope Form** Slope is m. Line passes through (x_1, y_1).
$Ax + By = C$	**Standard Form** $(A > 0)$ Slope is $-\frac{A}{B}$ $(B \neq 0)$. x-intercept is $(\frac{C}{A}, 0)$ $(A \neq 0)$. y-intercept is $(0, \frac{C}{B})$ $(B \neq 0)$.

6 Find an equation of a line that fits a data set. Earlier in this chapter, we gave linear equations that modeled real data, such as annual costs of doctors' visits and amounts of credit card debt, and then used these equations to estimate or predict values. Using the information in this section, we can now develop a procedure to find such an equation if the given set of data *fits* a linear pattern—that is, its graph consists of points lying close to a straight line.

Example 6 **Finding an Equation of a Line That Describes Data**

The table lists the average annual cost (in dollars) of tuition and fees at public 4-year colleges for selected years. Year 1 represents 1991, year 3 represents 1993, and so on. Plot the data and find an equation that approximates it.

Year	Cost (in dollars)
1	2137
3	2527
5	2860
7	3111
9	3356

Source: The College Board.

Continued on Next Page

Letting y represent the cost in year x, we plot the data as shown in Figure 31.

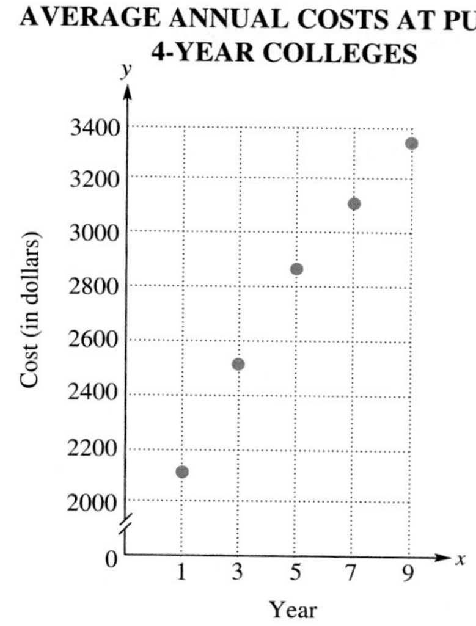

Figure 31

The points appear to lie approximately in a straight line. We can use two of the data pairs and the point-slope form of the equation of a line to get an equation that describes the relationship between the year and the cost. We choose the ordered pairs (3, 2527) and (7, 3111) from the table and find the slope of the line through these points.

$$m = \frac{y_2 - y_1}{x_2 - x_1} \quad \text{Slope formula}$$

$$m = \frac{3111 - 2527}{7 - 3} \quad \text{Let } (7, 3111) = (x_2, y_2) \text{ and } (3, 2527) = (x_1, y_1).$$

$$m = 146$$

As we might expect, the slope, 146, is positive, indicating that tuition and fees increased \$146 each year. Now use this slope and the point (3, 2527) in the point-slope form to find an equation of the line.

$$y - y_1 = m(x - x_1) \quad \text{Point-slope form}$$

$$y - 2527 = 146(x - 3) \quad \text{Substitute for } x_1, y_1, \text{ and } m.$$

$$y - 2527 = 146x - 438 \quad \text{Distributive property}$$

$$y = 146x + 2089 \quad \text{Add 2527.}$$

To see how well this equation approximates the ordered pairs in the data table, let $x = 9$ (for 1999) and find y.

$$y = 146x + 2089 \quad \text{Equation of the line}$$

$$y = 146(9) + 2089 \quad \text{Substitute 9 for } x.$$

$$y = 3403$$

The corresponding value in the table for $x = 9$ is 3356, so the equation approximates the data reasonably well. With caution, the equation could be used to predict values for years that are not included in the table.

6 Use the points (1, 2137) and (7, 3111) to find an equation in slope-intercept form that approximates the data of Example 6. (Round the slope to the nearest tenth.) How well does this equation approximate the cost in 1999?

NOTE

In Example 6, if we had chosen two different data points, we would have gotten a slightly different equation.

Work Problem 6 at the Side.

Here is a summary of what is needed to find the equation of a line.

Finding the Equation of a Line

To find the equation of a line, you need

1. a point on the line, and
2. the slope of the line.

If two points are known, first find the slope and then use the point-slope form.

ANSWERS

6. $y = 162.3x + 1974.7$ or $y = 162.3x + 1974.9$ (depending on the point used in the point-slope form); The equation gives $y \approx 3435$ when $x = 9$, which is a reasonably good approximation.

4.4 Exercises

FOR EXTRA HELP Student's Solutions Manual | MyMathLab.com | InterAct Math Tutorial Software | AW Math Tutor Center | www.mathxl.com | Digital Video Tutor CD 3 Videotape 8

Match the correct equation in Column II with the description given in Column I.

I		II
1. Slope $= -2$, through the point $(4, 1)$	D	**A.** $y = 4x$
2. Slope $= -2$, y-intercept $(0, 1)$	C	**B.** $y = \frac{1}{4}x$
3. Through the points $(0, 0)$ and $(4, 1)$	B	**C.** $y = -2x + 1$
4. Through the points $(0, 0)$ and $(1, 4)$	A	**D.** $y - 1 = -2(x - 4)$

Use the geometric interpretation of slope (rise divided by run, from Section 4.3) to find the slope of each line. Then, by identifying the y-intercept from the graph, write the slope-intercept form of the equation of the line.

5.

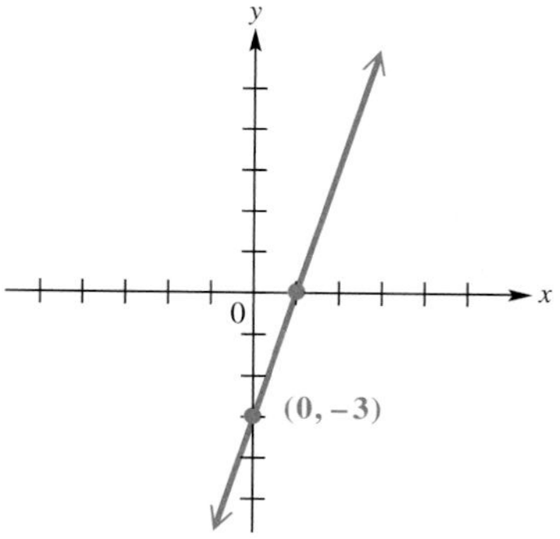

$y = 3x - 3$

6.

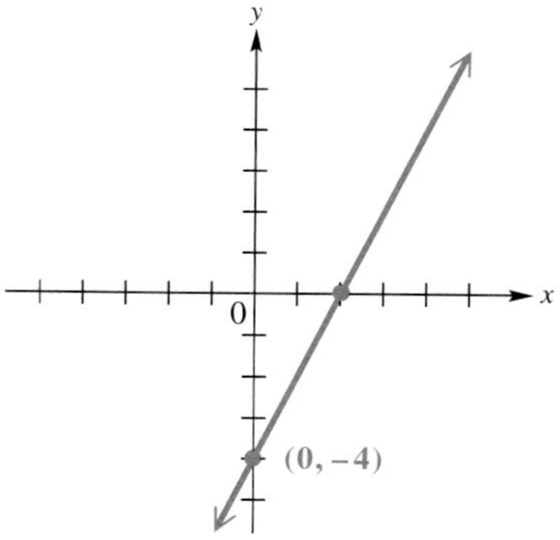

$y = 2x - 4$

7.

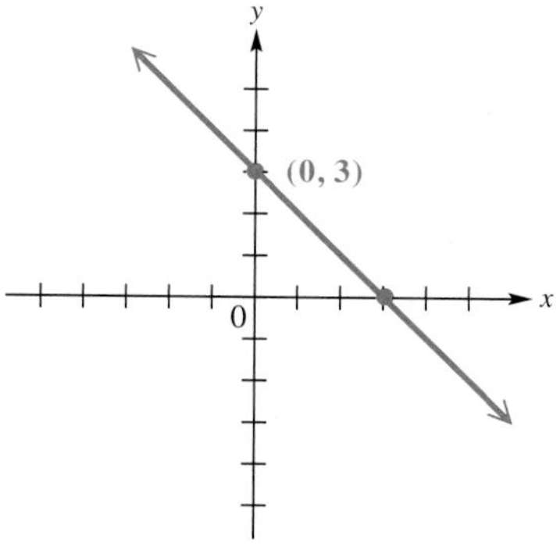

$y = -x + 3$

8.

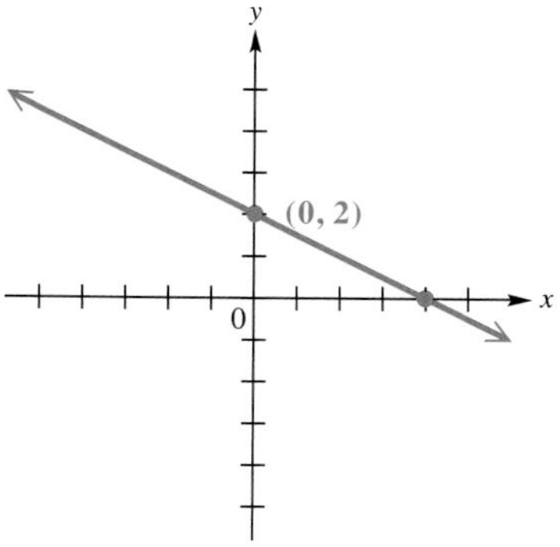

$y = -\frac{1}{2}x + 2$

Write the equation of the line with the given slope and y-intercept. See Example 1.

9. slope 4; y-intercept $(0, -3)$

$y = 4x - 3$

10. slope -5; y-intercept $(0, 6)$

$y = -5x + 6$

11. slope 0; y-intercept $(0, 3)$

$y = 3$

12. slope 3; y-intercept $(0, 0)$

$y = 3x$

13. Explain why the equation of a vertical line cannot be written in the form $y = mx + b$.

A vertical line has undefined slope, so there is no value for *m*. Also, there is no y-intercept, so there can be no value for *b*.

14. Match each equation with the graph that would most closely resemble its graph.

(a) $y = x + 3$ C

(b) $y = -x + 3$ B

(c) $y = x - 3$ A

(d) $y = -x - 3$ D

A.

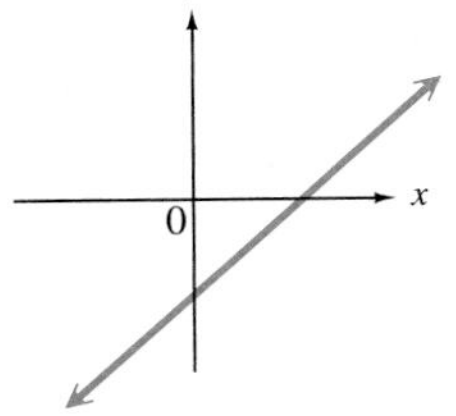

B.

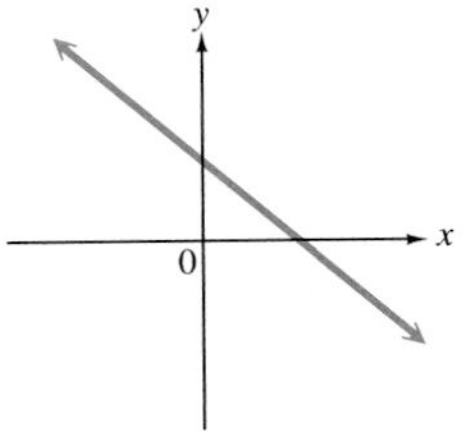

C.

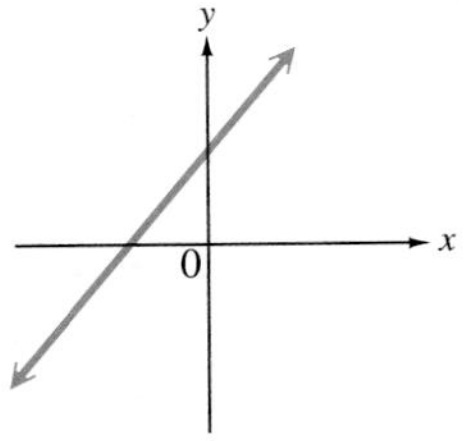

D.

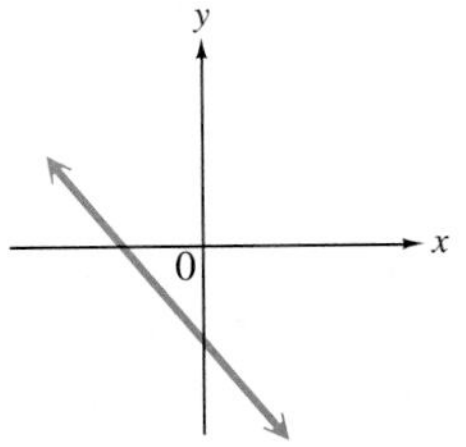

Graph the line through the given point with the given slope. (In Exercises 21–24, recall the types of lines having slope 0 and undefined slope.) Give the slope-intercept form of the equation of the line if possible. See Example 2.

15. $(-2, 3)$, $m = \frac{1}{2}$

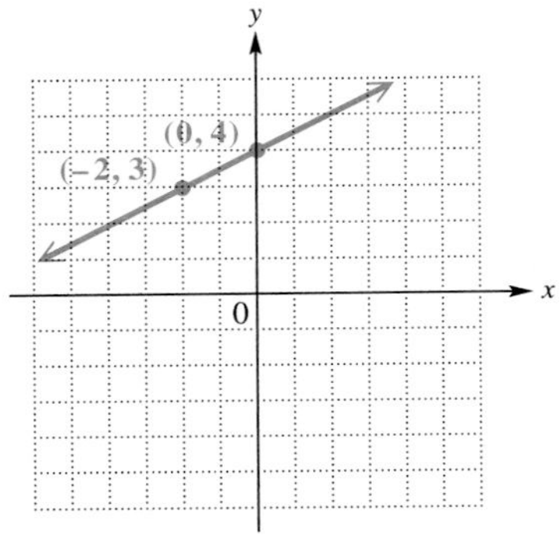

$y = \frac{1}{2}x + 4$

16. $(-4, -1)$, $m = \frac{3}{4}$

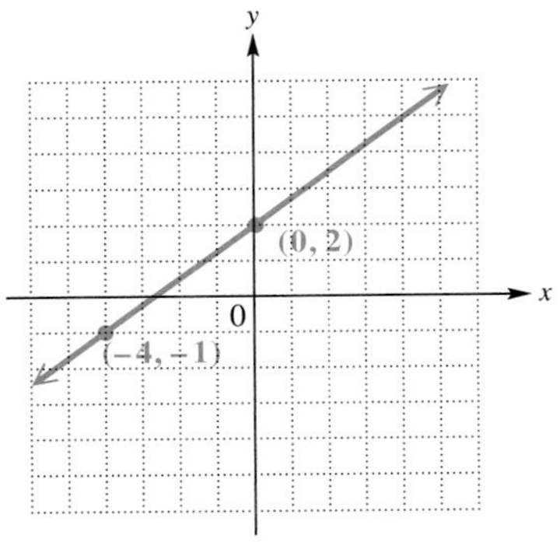

$y = \frac{3}{4}x + 2$

17. $(1, -5)$, $m = -\frac{2}{5}$

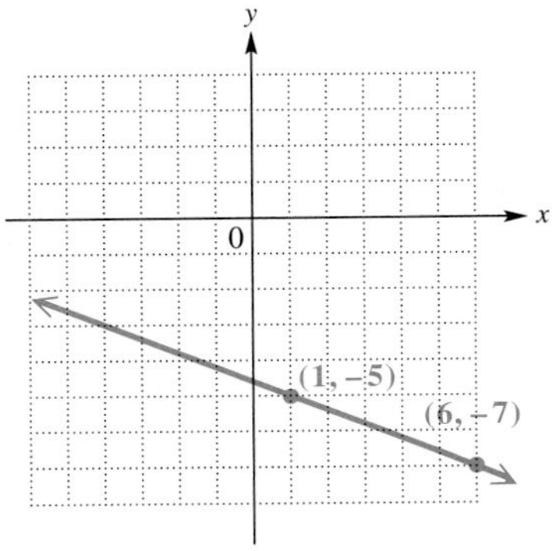

$y = -\frac{2}{5}x - \frac{23}{5}$

18. $(2, -1)$, $m = -\frac{1}{3}$

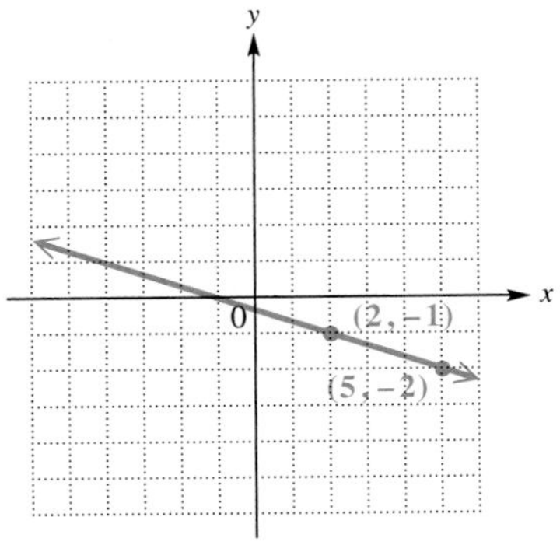

$y = -\frac{1}{3}x - \frac{1}{3}$

19. $(0, 2)$, $m = 3$

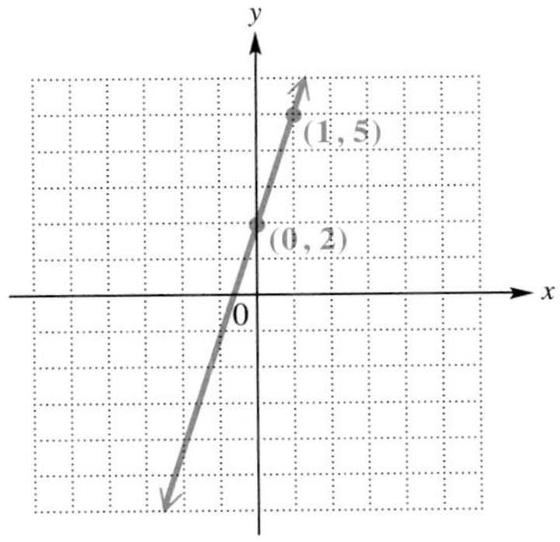

$y = 3x + 2$

20. $(0, -5)$, $m = -2$

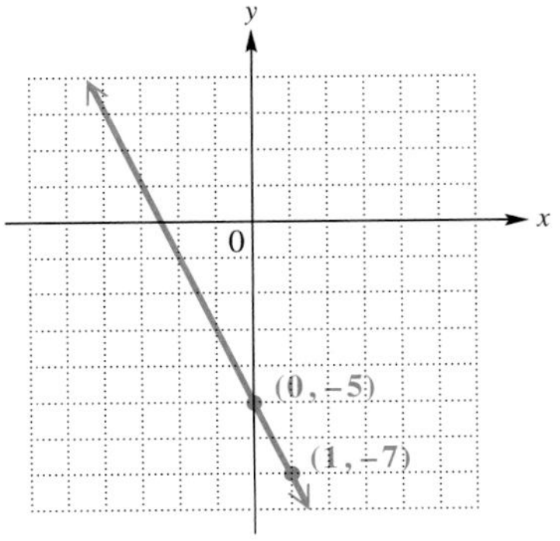

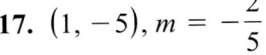

$y = -2x - 5$

21. $(3, 2)$, $m = 0$

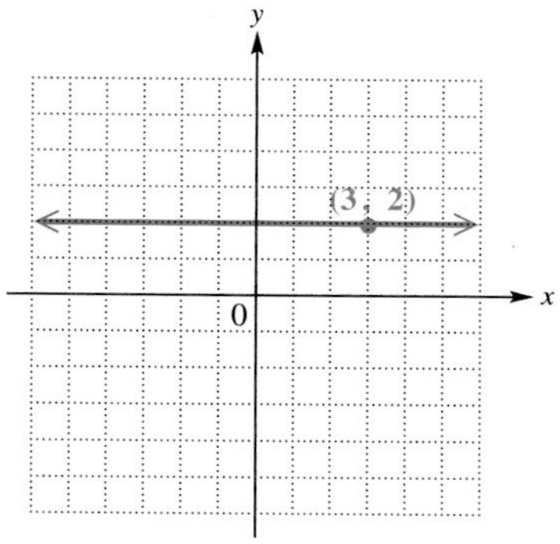

$y = 2$

22. $(-2, 3)$, $m = 0$

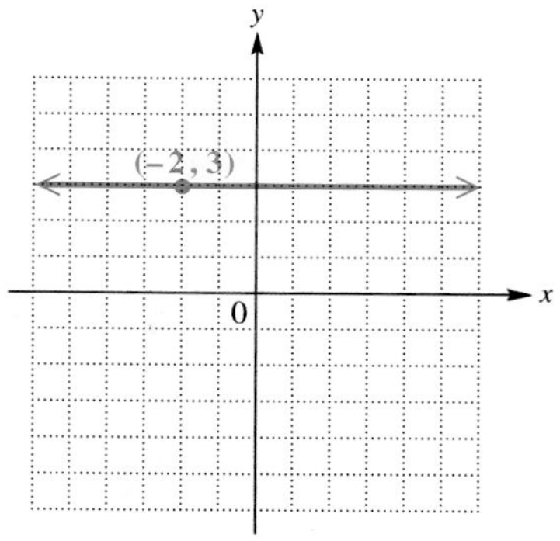

$y = 3$

23. $(3, -2)$, undefined slope

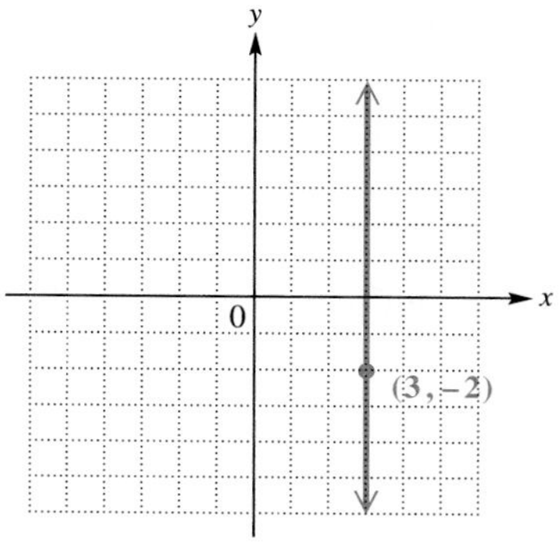

$x = 3$ (no slope-intercept form)

24. $(2, 4)$, undefined slope

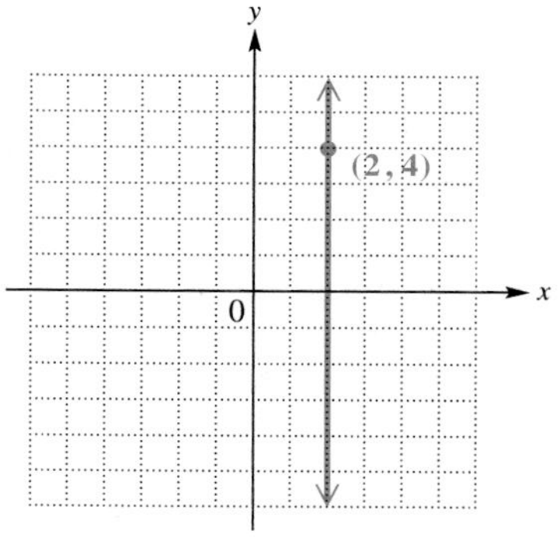

$x = 2$ (no slope-intercept form)

25. What is the common name given to the vertical line whose x-intercept is the origin?

the y-axis

26. What is the common name given to the line with slope 0 whose y-intercept is the origin?

the x-axis

Write an equation of the line through the given point with the given slope. Write the equation in slope-intercept form. See Example 3.

27. $(4, 1)$, $m = 2$

$y = 2x - 7$

28. $(2, 7)$, $m = 3$

$y = 3x + 1$

29. $(3, -10)$, $m = -2$

$y = -2x - 4$

30. $(2, -5)$, $m = -4$

$y = -4x + 3$

31. $(-2, 5)$, $m = \frac{2}{3}$

$y = \frac{2}{3}x + \frac{19}{3}$

32. $(-4, 1)$, $m = \frac{3}{4}$

$y = \frac{3}{4}x + 4$

33. If a line passes through the origin and a second point whose x- and y-coordinates are equal, what is an equation of the line?

$y = x$ (There are other forms as well.)

34. What is the only point common to both lines $y = x$ and $y = -x$?

the origin $(0, 0)$

Write an equation, in slope-intercept form if possible, of the line through each pair of points. See Example 4.

35. (8, 5) and (9, 6)

$y = x - 3$

36. (4, 10) and (6, 12)

$y = x + 6$

37. $(-1, -7)$ and $(-8, -2)$

$y = -\frac{5}{7}x - \frac{54}{7}$

38. $(-2, -1)$ and $(3, -4)$

$y = -\frac{3}{5}x - \frac{11}{5}$

39. $(0, -2)$ and $(-3, 0)$

$y = -\frac{2}{3}x - 2$

40. $(-4, 0)$ and $(0, 2)$

$y = \frac{1}{2}x + 2$

41. (3, 5) and $(3, -2)$

$x = 3$ (no slope-intercept form)

42. $(3, -5)$ and $(-1, -5)$

$y = -5$

43. $\left(\frac{1}{2}, \frac{3}{2}\right)$ and $\left(-\frac{1}{4}, \frac{5}{4}\right)$

$y = \frac{1}{3}x + \frac{4}{3}$

44. $\left(-\frac{2}{3}, \frac{8}{3}\right)$ and $\left(\frac{1}{3}, \frac{7}{3}\right)$

$y = -\frac{1}{3}x + \frac{22}{9}$

RELATING CONCEPTS (Exercises 45–52) FOR INDIVIDUAL OR GROUP WORK

If we think of ordered pairs of the form (C, F), then the two most common methods of measuring temperature, Celsius and Fahrenheit, can be related as follows: When $C = 0$, $F = 32$, and when $C = 100$, $F = 212$. ***Work Exercises 45–52 in order.***

45. Write two ordered pairs relating these two temperature scales. (0, 32); (100, 212)

46. Find the slope of the line through the two points.

$\frac{9}{5}$

47. Use the point-slope form to find an equation of the line. (Your variables should be C and F rather than x and y.)

$F - 32 = \frac{9}{5}(C - 0)$

48. Write an equation for F in terms of C.

$F = \frac{9}{5}C + 32$

49. Use the equation from Exercise 48 to write an equation for C in terms of F.

$C = \frac{5}{9}(F - 32)$

50. Use the equation from Exercise 48 to find the Fahrenheit temperature when $C = 30$.

86°

51. Use the equation from Exercise 49 to find the Celsius temperature when $F = 50$.

10°

52. For what temperature is $F = C$?

−40°

Write an equation in slope-intercept form of the line satisfying the given conditions. See Example 5.

53. Through $(2, -3)$, parallel to $3x = 4y + 5$

$y = \frac{3}{4}x - \frac{9}{2}$

54. Through $(-1, 4)$, perpendicular to $2x + 3y = 8$

$y = \frac{3}{2}x + \frac{11}{2}$

55. Through (8, 5), perpendicular to $2x - y = 7$

$y = -\frac{1}{2}x + 9$

56. Through $(-2, -2)$, parallel to $-x + 2y = 10$

$y = \frac{1}{2}x - 1$

57. Perpendicular to $x - 2y = 7$, y-intercept $(0, -3)$

$y = -2x - 3$

58. Parallel to $5x = 2y + 10$, y-intercept (0, 4)

$y = \frac{5}{2}x + 4$

The cost to produce x items is, in some cases, expressed as $y = mx + b$. The number b gives the fixed cost *(the cost that is the same no matter how many items are produced), and the number m is the* variable cost *(the cost to produce an additional item). Use this information to work Exercises 59 and 60.*

59. It costs \$400 to start up a business of selling snow cones. Each snow cone costs \$.25 to produce.

(a) What is the fixed cost? **\$400**

(b) What is the variable cost? **\$.25**

(c) Write the cost equation. $y = .25x + 400$

(d) What will be the cost to produce 100 snow cones, based on the cost equation? **\$425**

(e) How many snow cones will be produced if total cost is \$775? **1500**

60. It costs \$2000 to purchase a copier, and each copy costs \$.02 to make.

(a) What is the fixed cost? **\$2000**

(b) What is the variable cost? **\$.02**

(c) Write the cost equation. $y = .02x + 2000$

(d) What will be the cost to produce 10,000 copies, based on the cost equation? **\$2200**

(e) How many copies will be produced if total cost is \$2600? **30,000**

For each situation, **(a)** *write an equation in the form $y = mx + b$;* **(b)** *find and interpret the ordered pair associated with the equation for $x = 5$; and* **(c)** *answer the question.*

61. A membership to the Midwest Athletic Club costs \$99 plus \$39 per month. (*Source:* Midwest Athletic Club.) Let x represent the number of months selected. How much does the first year's membership cost?

(a) $y = 39x + 99$ (b) (5, 294); The cost of a 5-month membership is \$294. (c) \$567

62. A rental car costs \$50 plus \$.20 per mile. Let x represent the number of miles driven, so y represents the total charge to the renter. How many miles was the car driven if the renter paid \$84.60?

(a) $y = .20x + 50$ (b) (5, 51); The charge for driving 5 mi is \$51. (c) 173 mi

Solve each problem. See Example 6.

63. The table lists the average annual cost (in dollars) of tuition and fees at private 4-year colleges for selected years, where year 1 represents 1991, year 3 represents 1993, and so on.

Year	Cost (in dollars)
1	10,017
3	11,025
5	12,432
7	13,785
9	15,380

Source: The College Board.

(a) Write five ordered pairs for the data.

(1, 10,017), (3, 11,025), (5, 12,432), (7, 13,785), (9, 15,380)

(b) Plot the ordered pairs. Do the points lie approximately in a straight line?

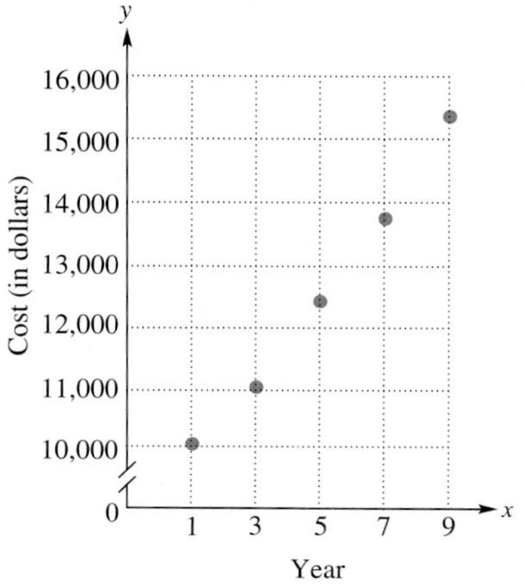

See the graph; Yes.

(c) Use the ordered pairs (3, 11,025) and (9, 15,380) to find the equation of a line that approximates the data. Write the equation in slope-intercept form. (Round the slope to the nearest tenth.)

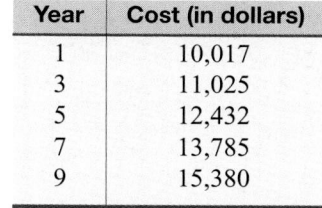

$y = 725.8x + 8847.6$ or $y = 725.8x + 8847.8$ (depending on the point used)

(d) Use the equation from part (c) to estimate the average annual cost at private 4-year colleges in 2003. (*Hint:* What is the value of x for 2003?) **\$18,283**

64. The table gives heavy-metal nuclear waste (in thousands of metric tons) from spent reactor fuel now stored temporarily at reactor sites, awaiting permanent storage. (*Source:* "Burial of Radioactive Nuclear Waste Under the Seabed," *Scientific American*, January 1998.)

Year x	Waste y
1995	32
2000*	42
2010*	61
2020*	76

*Estimates by the U.S. Department of Energy.

Let $x = 0$ represent 1995, $x = 5$ represent 2000 (since $2000 - 1995 = 5$), and so on.

(a) For 1995, the ordered pair is (0, 32). Write ordered pairs for the data for the other years given in the table.

(5, 42), (15, 61), (25, 76)

(b) Plot the ordered pairs (x, y). Do the points lie approximately in a straight line?

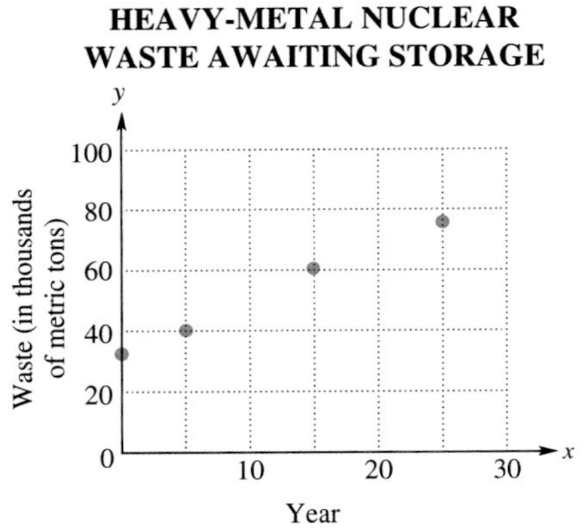

See the graph; Yes.

(c) Use the ordered pairs (0, 32) and (25, 76) to find the equation of a line that approximates the other ordered pairs. Write the equation in slope-intercept form.

$y = 1.76x + 32$

(d) Use the equation from part (c) to estimate the amount of nuclear waste in 2005. (*Hint:* What is the value of x for 2005?)

49.6 thousand or 49,600 metric tons

65. The graph shows the percent of women in the civilian labor force for selected years from 1955 through 1995.

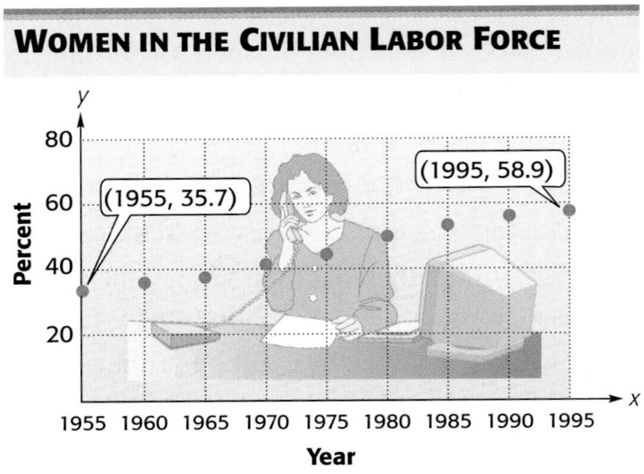

Source: U.S. Bureau of Labor Statistics.

(a) Use the points (1955, 35.7) and (1995, 58.9) to find a linear equation in slope-intercept form that approximates the data points.

$y = .58x - 1098.2$

(b) Use the equation from part (a) to predict the percent for 1996. How does the result compare to the actual value of 59.3%?

59.5%; This result is very close to the actual figure of 59.3%.

66. Median household income of African Americans increased in recent years, as shown in the bar graph.

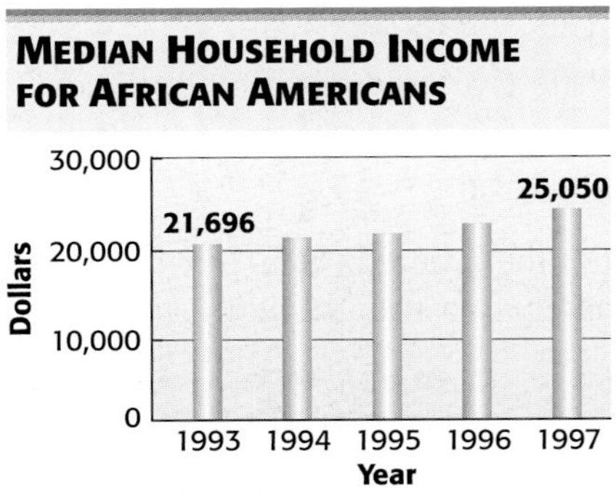

Source: U.S. Bureau of the Census.

(a) Use the information given for the years 1993 and 1997, letting $x = 3$ represent 1993, $x = 7$ represent 1997, and y represent the median income, to write an equation in slope-intercept form that models median household income.

$y = 838.5x + 19{,}180.5$

(b) Use the equation to approximate the median income for 1995. How does your result compare to the actual value, \$23,583?

\$23,373; It is close to the actual value.

4.5 GRAPHING LINEAR INEQUALITIES IN TWO VARIABLES

OBJECTIVES

1. Graph linear inequalities in two variables.
2. Graph the intersection of two linear inequalities.
3. Graph the union of two linear inequalities.

1 Graph linear inequalities in two variables. In Chapter 3 we graphed linear inequalities in one variable on the number line. In this section we will graph linear inequalities in two variables on a rectangular coordinate system.

Linear Inequality in Two Variables

An inequality that can be written as

$$Ax + By < C \quad \text{or} \quad Ax + By > C,$$

where A, B, and C are real numbers and A and B are not both 0, is a **linear inequality in two variables.**

Also, $\leq$ and $\geq$ may replace $<$ and $>$ in the definition.

A line divides the plane into three regions: the line itself and the two half-planes on either side of the line. Recall that graphs of linear inequalities in one variable are intervals on the number line that sometimes include endpoints. The graphs of linear inequalities in two variables are *regions* in the real number plane and may include *boundary lines*. The **boundary line** for the inequality $Ax + By < C$ or $Ax + By > C$ is the graph of the *equation* $Ax + By = C$. To graph a linear inequality in two variables, follow these steps.

Graphing a Linear Inequality

Step 1 **Draw the boundary.** Draw the graph of the straight line that is the boundary. Make the line solid if the inequality involves $\leq$ or $\geq$; make the line dashed if the inequality involves $<$ or $>$.

Step 2 **Choose a test point.** Choose any point not on the line as a test point.

Step 3 **Shade the appropriate region.** Shade the region that includes the test point if it satisfies the original inequality; otherwise, shade the region on the other side of the boundary line.

Example 1 Graphing a Linear Inequality

Graph $3x + 2y \geq 6$.

Step 1 First graph the line $3x + 2y = 6$. The graph of this line, the boundary of the graph of the inequality, is shown in Figure 32.

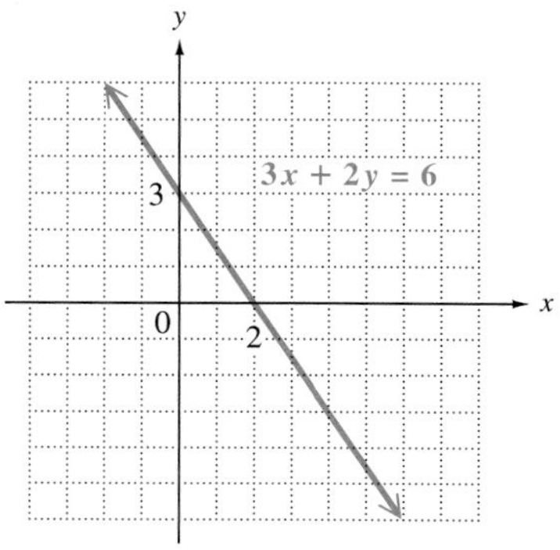

Figure 32

Continued on Next Page

Step 2 The graph of the inequality $3x + 2y \geq 6$ includes the points of the line $3x + 2y = 6$ and either the points *above* the line $3x + 2y = 6$ or the points *below* that line. To decide which, select any point not on the line $3x + 2y = 6$ as a test point. The origin, (0, 0), is often a good choice. Substitute the values from the test point (0, 0) for x and y in the inequality $3x + 2y > 6$.

$$3(0) + 2(0) > 6 \quad ?$$
$$0 > 6 \quad \text{False}$$

Step 3 Because the result is false, (0, 0) does *not* satisfy the inequality, and so the solution set includes all points on the other side of the line. This region is shaded in Figure 33.

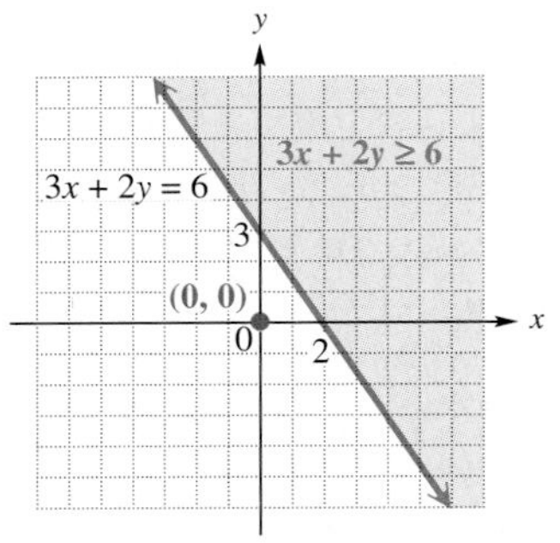

Figure 33

Work Problem 1 at the Side.

1 Graph each inequality.

(a) $x + y \leq 4$

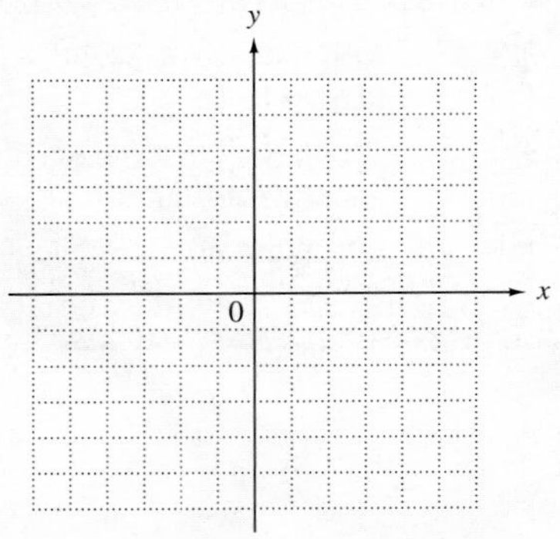

(b) $3x + y \geq 6$

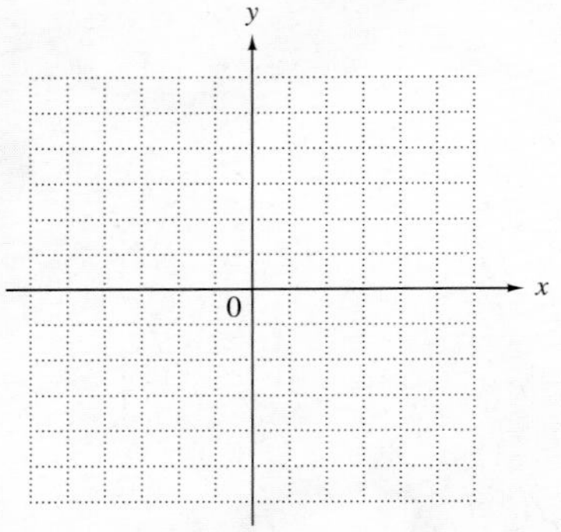

If the inequality is written in the form $y > mx + b$ or $y < mx + b$, the inequality symbol indicates which half-plane to shade.

If $y > mx + b$, shade **above** the boundary line;
if $y < mx + b$, shade **below** the boundary line.

This method works *only* if the inequality is solved for y.

Example 2 Graphing a Linear Inequality

Graph $x - 3y < 4$.

First graph the boundary line, shown in Figure 34. The points of the boundary line do not belong to the inequality $x - 3y < 4$ (because the inequality symbol is $<$, not $\leq$). For this reason, the line is dashed. Now solve the inequality for y.

$$x - 3y < 4$$
$$-3y < -x + 4$$
$$y > \frac{x}{3} - \frac{4}{3} \quad \text{Multiply by } -\tfrac{1}{3}\text{; change } < \text{ to } >.$$

Because of the *is greater than* symbol, shade *above* the line. As a check, choose a test point not on the line, say (1, 2), and substitute for x and y in the original inequality.

$$1 - 3(2) < 4 \quad ?$$
$$-5 < 4 \quad \text{True}$$

Continued on Next Page

ANSWERS

1. (a)

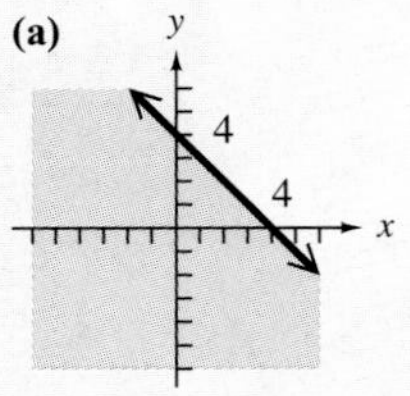

(b)

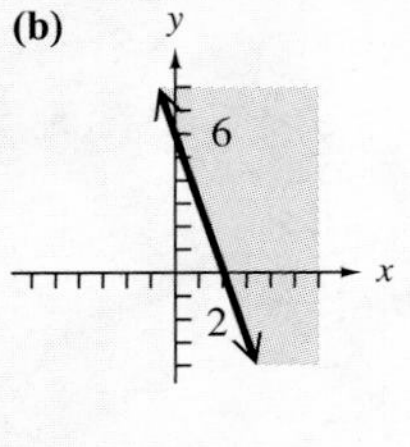

This result agrees with the decision to shade above the line. The solution set, graphed in Figure 34, includes only those points in the shaded half-plane (not those on the line).

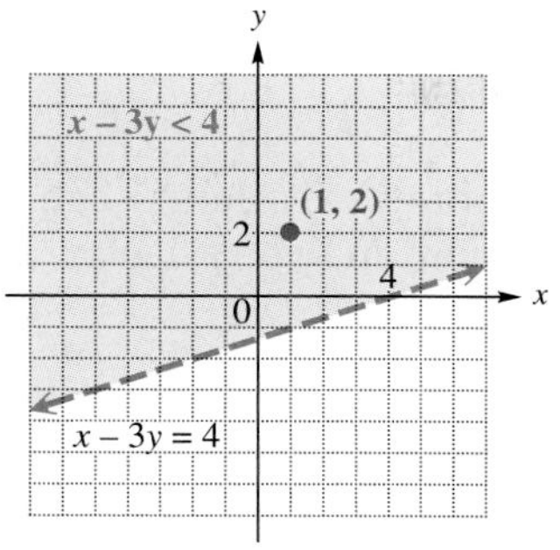

Figure 34

Work Problem ❷ at the Side.

❷ Graph each inequality.

(a) $x - y > 2$

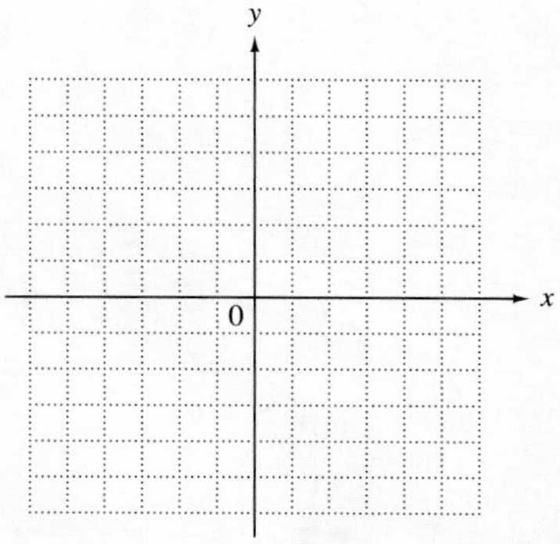

(b) $3x + 4y < 12$

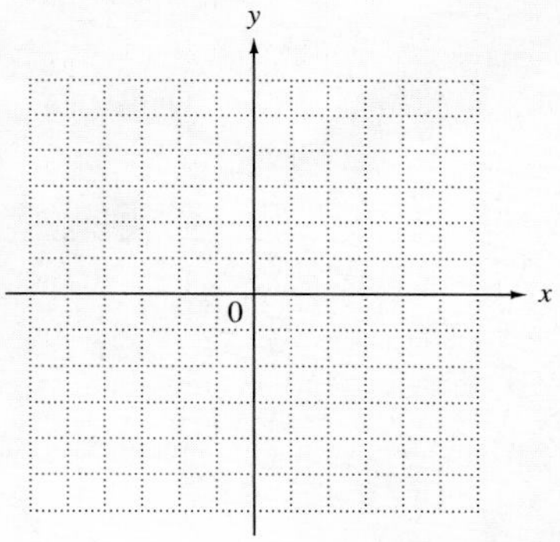

2 **Graph the intersection of two linear inequalities.** In Section 3.2 we discussed how the words *and* and *or* are used with compound inequalities. In that section, the inequalities had one variable. Those ideas can be extended to include inequalities in two variables. A pair of inequalities joined with the word *and* is interpreted as the intersection of the solution sets of the inequalities. The graph of the intersection of two or more inequalities is the region of the plane where all points satisfy all of the inequalities at the same time.

Example 3 Graphing the Intersection of Two Inequalities

Graph $2x + 4y \geq 5$ and $x \geq 1$.

To begin, we graph each of the two inequalities $2x + 4y \geq 5$ and $x \geq 1$ separately. The graph of $2x + 4y \geq 5$ is shown in Figure 35(a), and the graph of $x \geq 1$ is shown in Figure 35(b).

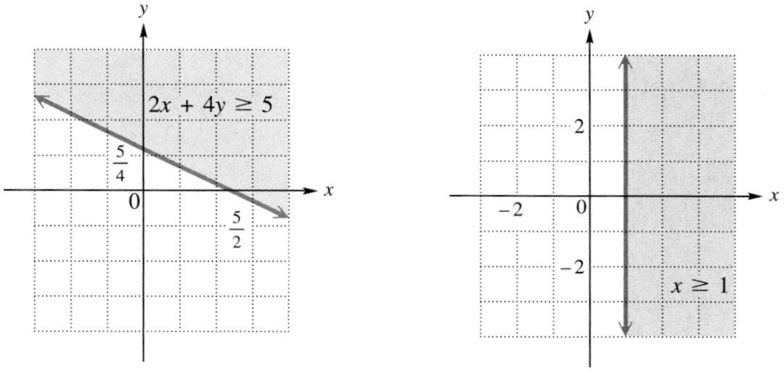

(a) (b)

Figure 35

In practice, the two graphs in Figure 35 are graphed on the same axes. Then we use heavy shading to identify the intersection of the graphs, as shown in Figure 36.

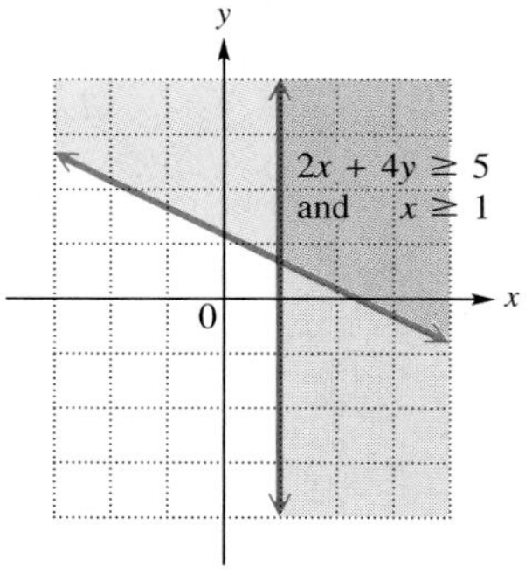

Figure 36

Continued on Next Page

ANSWERS

2. (a)

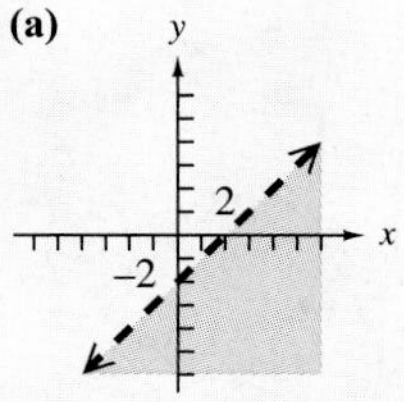

(b)

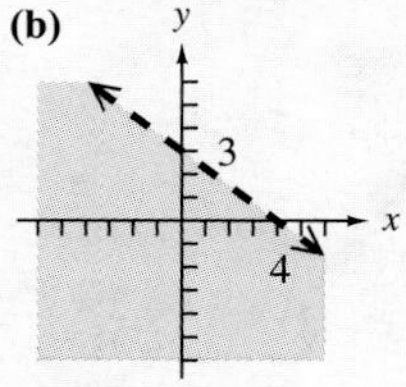

3 Graph $x - y \leq 4$ and $x \geq -2$.

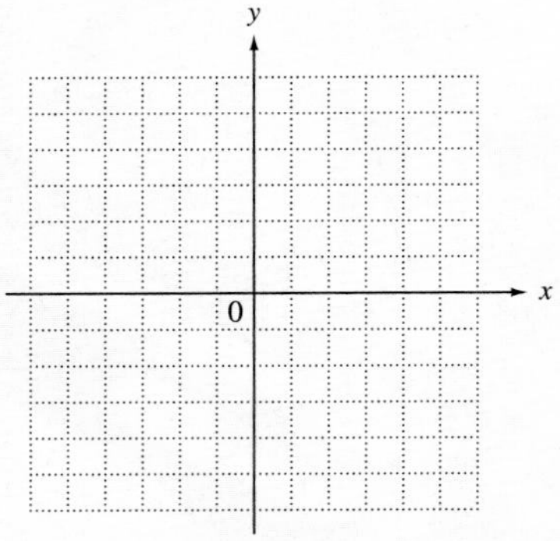

4 Graph $7x - 3y < 21$ or $x > 2$.

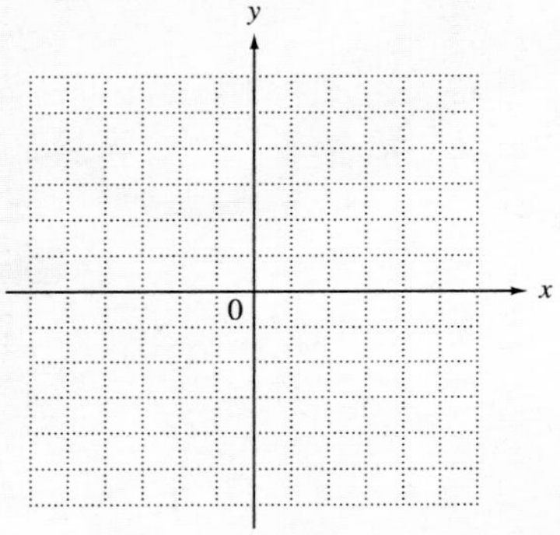

ANSWERS

3.

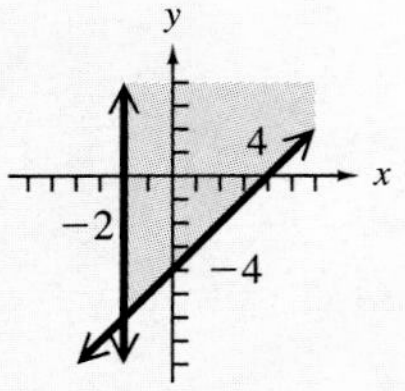

4.

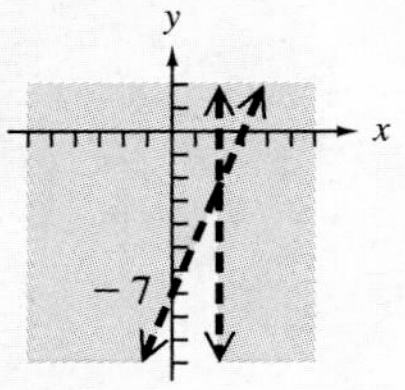

To check, we can use a test point from each of the four regions formed by the intersection of the boundary lines. Verify that only ordered pairs in the heavily shaded region satisfy both inequalities.

Work Problem 3 at the Side.

Calculator Tip Graphing calculators can graph inequalities in two variables, as well as equations in two variables. Refer to your owner's manual for specific directions.

3 Graph the union of two linear inequalities. When two inequalities are joined by the word *or*, we must find the union of the graphs of the inequalities. The graph of the union of two inequalities includes all of the points that satisfy either inequality.

Example 4 Graphing the Union of Two Inequalities

Graph $2x + 4y \geq 5$ or $x \geq 1$.

The graphs of the two inequalities are shown in Figure 35 on the previous page. The graph of the union is shown in Figure 37.

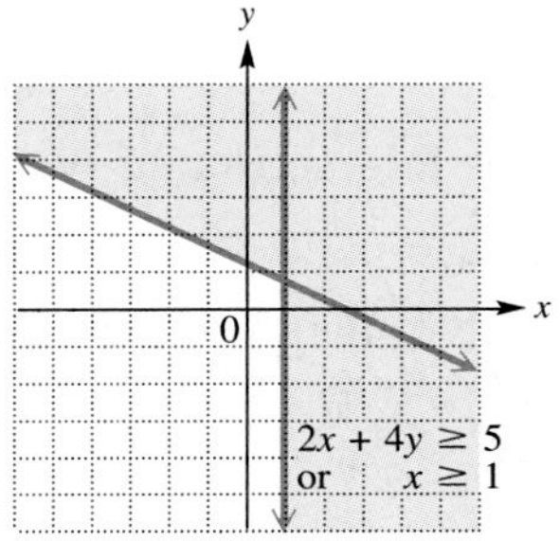

Figure 37

Work Problem 4 at the Side.

4.5 EXERCISES

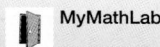

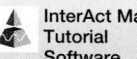

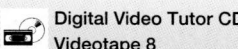

FOR EXTRA HELP: Student's Solutions Manual | MyMathLab.com | InterAct Math Tutorial Software | AW Math Tutor Center | www.mathxl.com | Digital Video Tutor CD 4 Videotape 8

In each statement, fill in the first blank with either solid *or* dashed. *Fill in the second blank with* above *or* below.

1. The boundary of the graph of $y \le -x + 2$ will be a <u>solid</u> line, and the shading will be <u>below</u> the line.

2. The boundary of the graph of $y < -x + 2$ will be a <u>dashed</u> line, and the shading will be <u>below</u> the line.

3. The boundary of the graph of $y > -x + 2$ will be a <u>dashed</u> line, and the shading will be <u>above</u> the line.

4. The boundary of the graph of $y \ge -x + 2$ will be a <u>solid</u> line, and the shading will be <u>above</u> the line.

5. How is the boundary line $Ax + By = C$ used in graphing either $Ax + By < C$ or $Ax + By > C$?

The graph of $Ax + By = C$ divides the plane into two regions. In one of these regions, the ordered pairs satisfy $Ax + By < C$; in the other, they satisfy $Ax + By > C$.

6. Describe the two methods discussed in the text for deciding which region is the solution set of a linear inequality in two variables.

One method is choosing any test point not on the boundary line and substituting the coordinates into the inequality. If the test point satisfies the inequality, the solution set is the region where it is located; if not, the solution set is the other region. The second method is writing the inequality in the form $y < mx + b$ or $y > mx + b$. The form $y < mx + b$ indicates the solution set is the region *below* the boundary line; $y > mx + b$ indicates the solution set is *above* the boundary line.

Graph each linear inequality. See Examples 1 and 2.

7. $x + y \le 2$

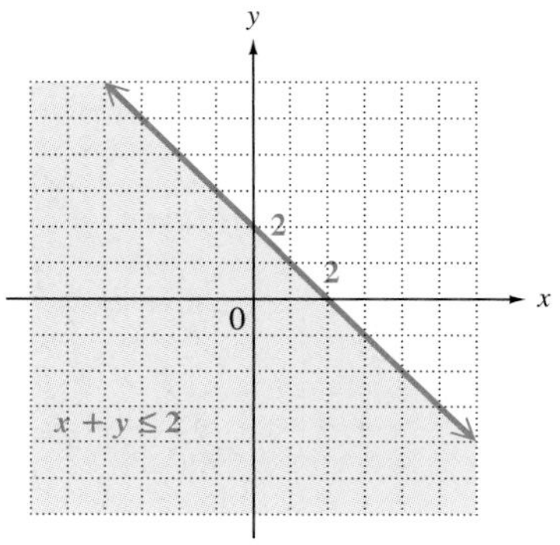

8. $x + y \le -3$

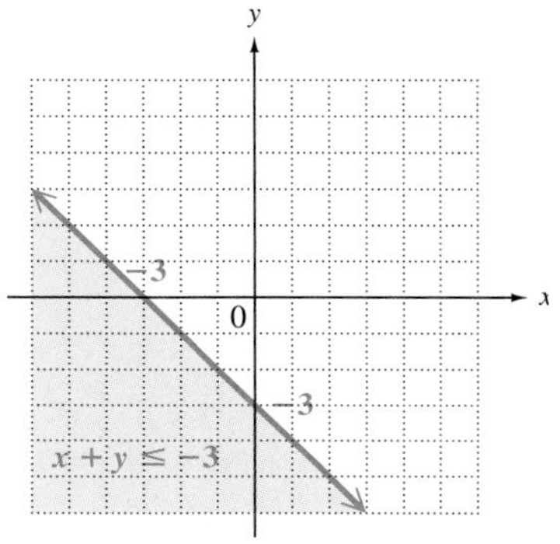

9. $4x - y < 4$

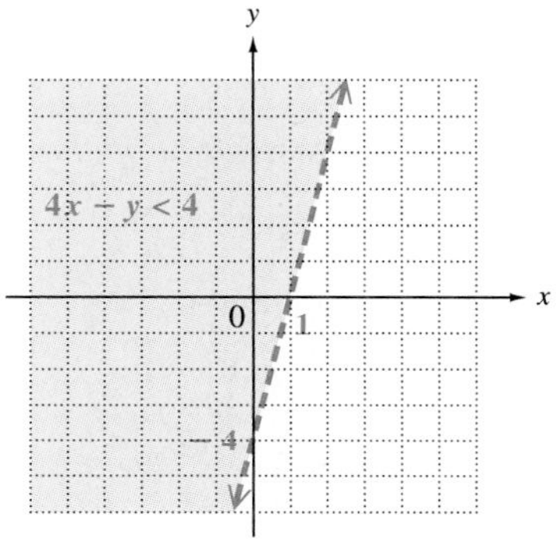

10. $3x - y < 3$

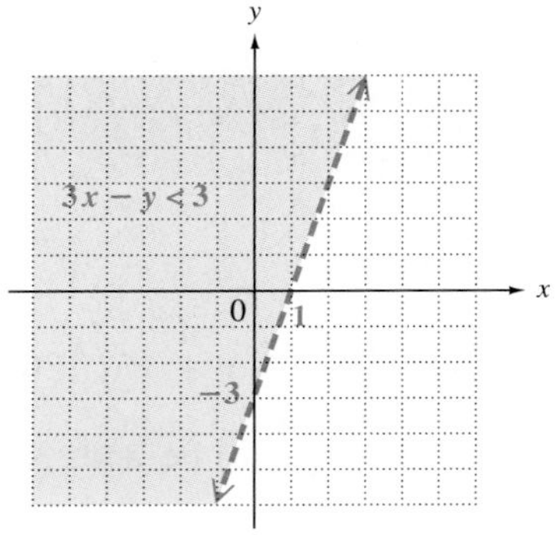

11. $x + 3y \geq -2$

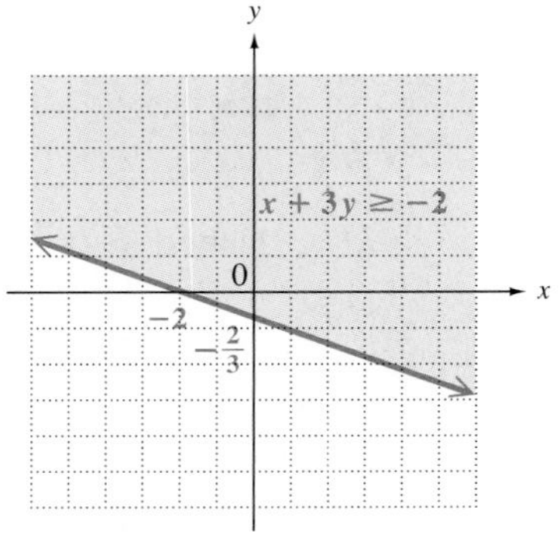

12. $x + 4y \geq -3$

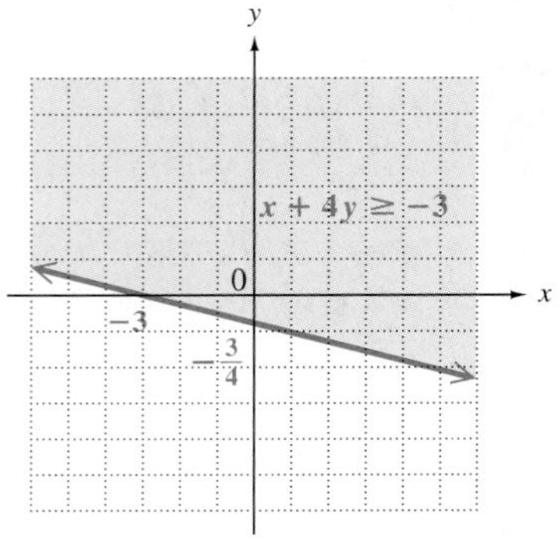

13. $x + y > 0$

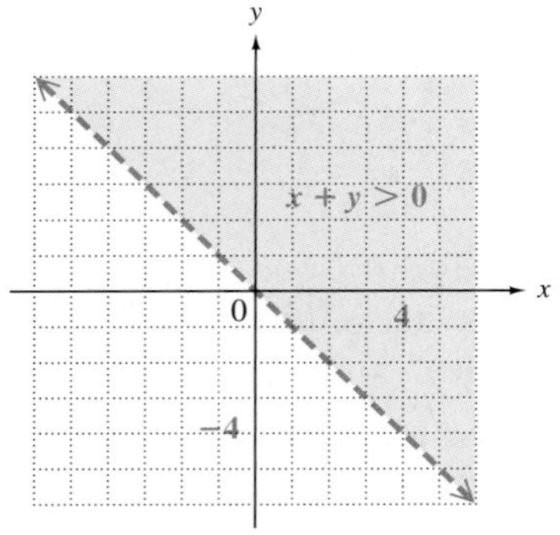

14. $x + 2y > 0$

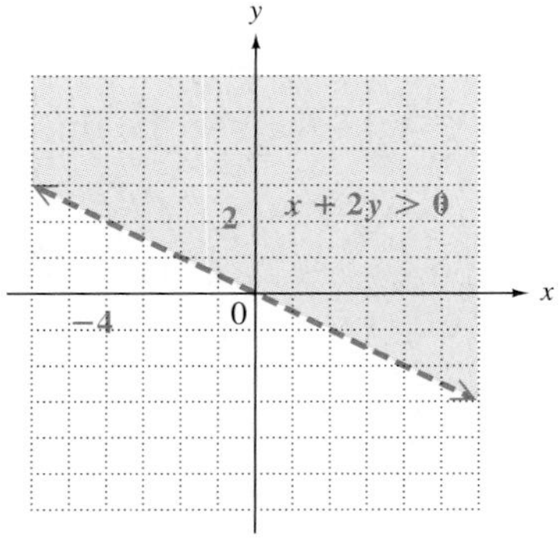

15. $x - 3y \leq 0$

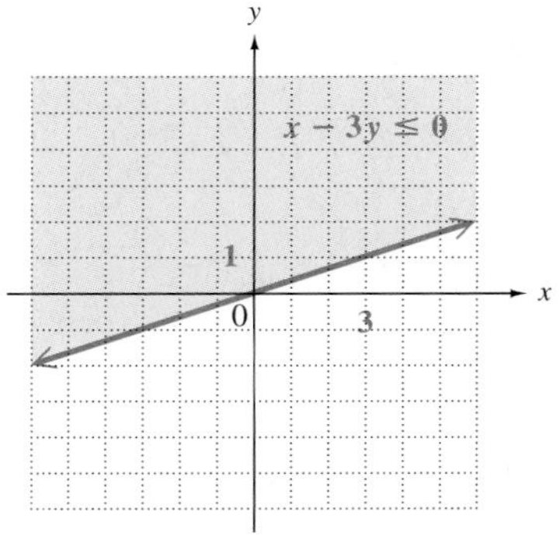

16. $x - 5y \leq 0$

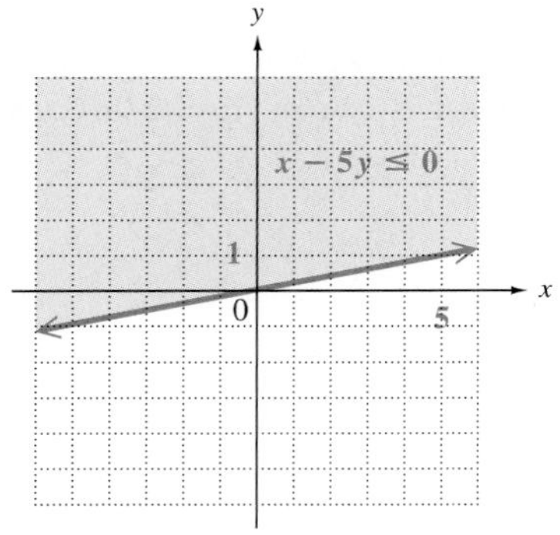

17. $y < x$

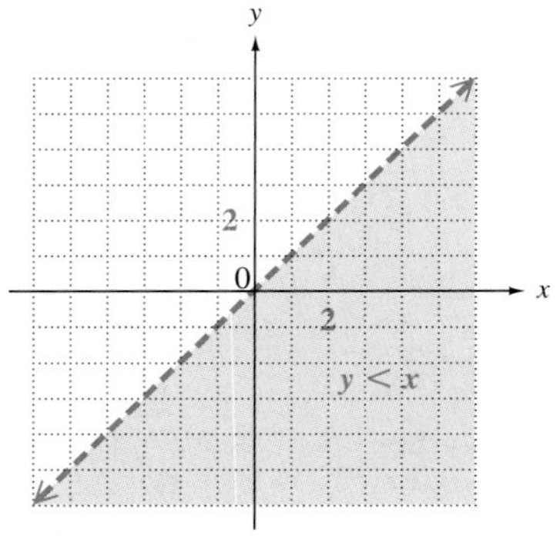

18. $y \leq 4x$

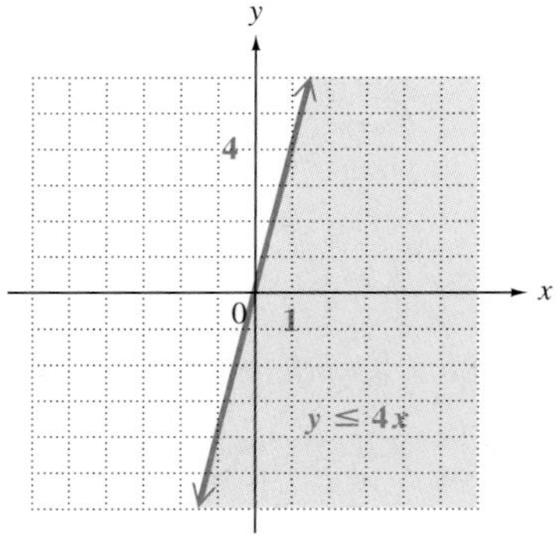

Graph the intersection of each pair of inequalities. See Example 3.

19. $x + y \leq 1$ and $x \geq 1$

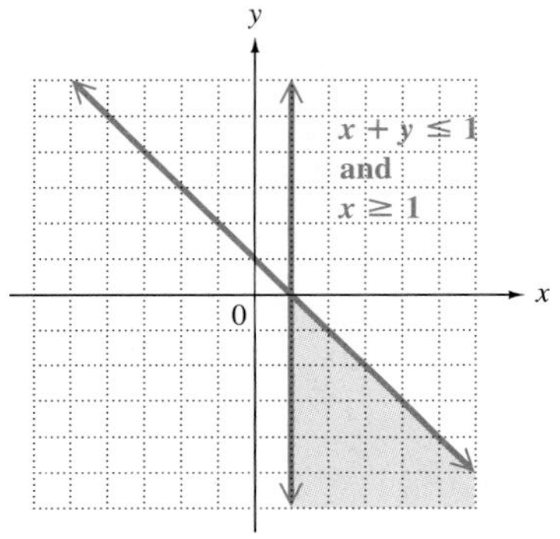

20. $x - y \geq 2$ and $x \geq 3$

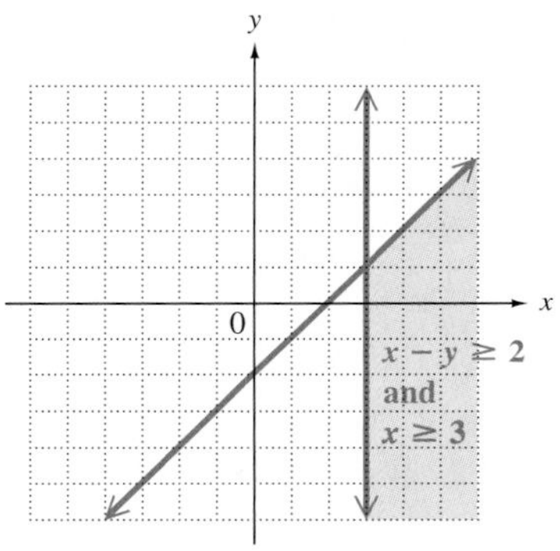

21. $2x - y \geq 2$ and $y < 4$

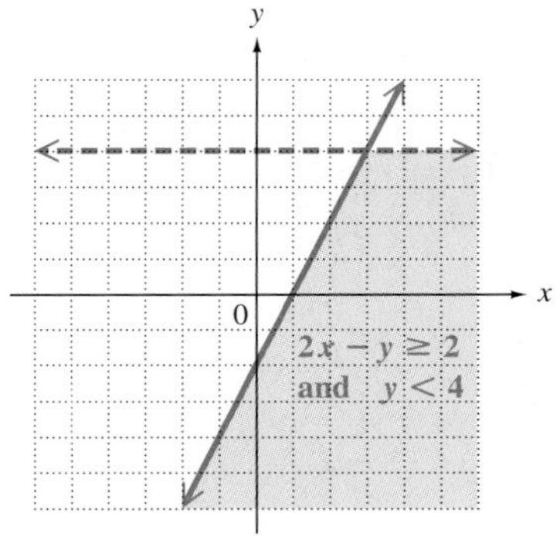

22. $3x - y \geq 3$ and $y < 3$

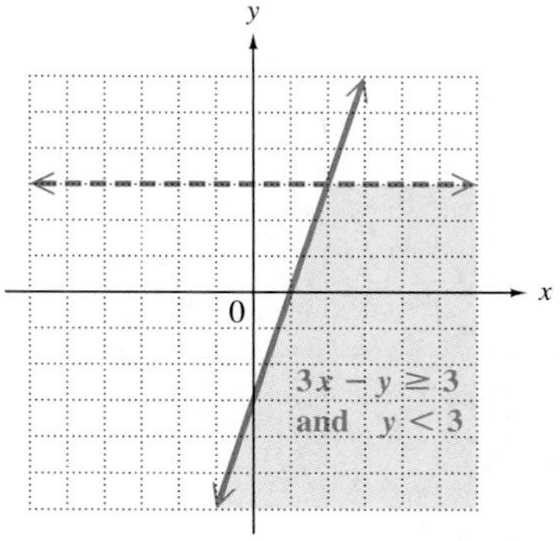

23. $x + y > -5$ and $y < -2$

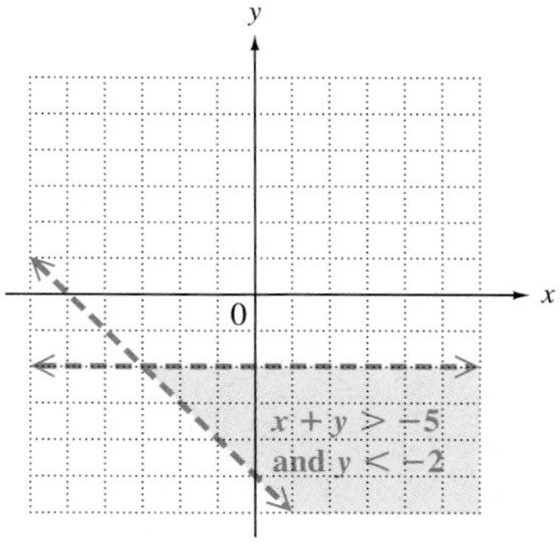

24. $6x - 4y < 10$ and $y > 2$

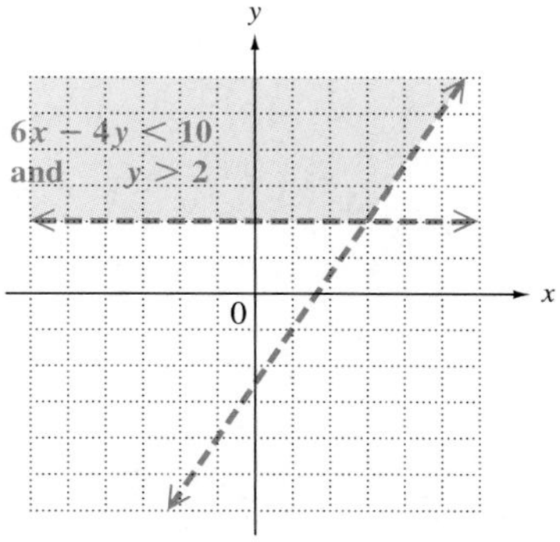

Use the method described in Section 3.3 to write each inequality as a compound inequality, and graph its solution set in the rectangular coordinate plane.

25. $|x| \geq 3$

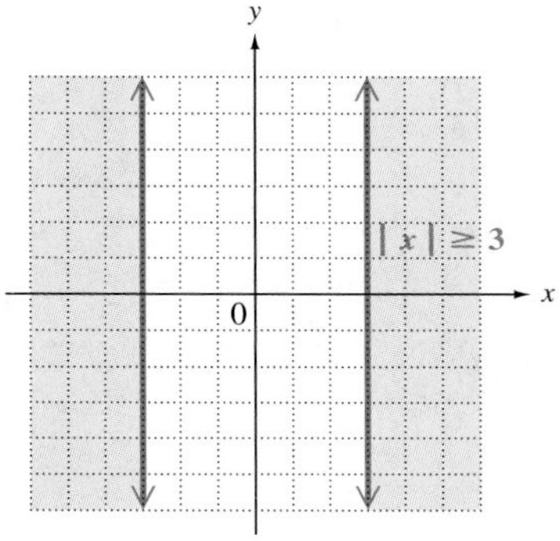

26. $|y| < 5$

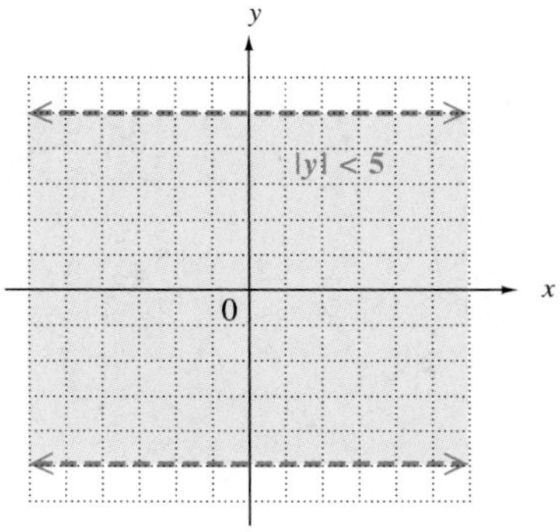

27. $|y + 1| < 2$

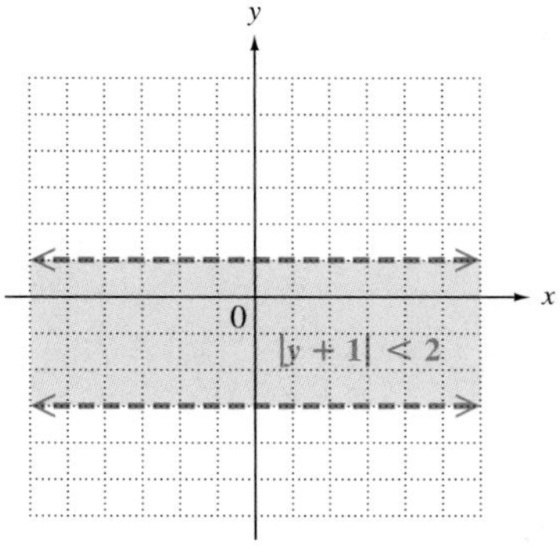

28. $|x - 2| \geq 1$

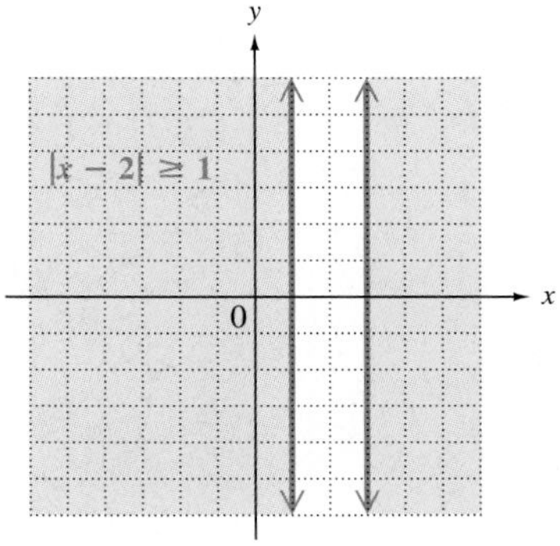

Graph the union of each pair of inequalities. See Example 4.

29. $x - y \geq 1$ or $y \geq 2$

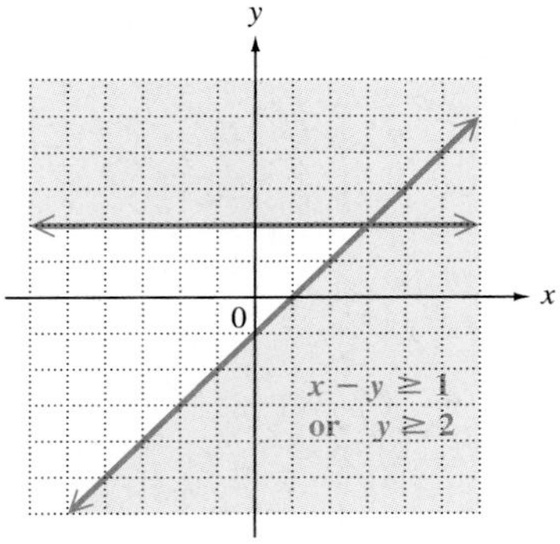

30. $x + y \leq 2$ or $y \geq 3$

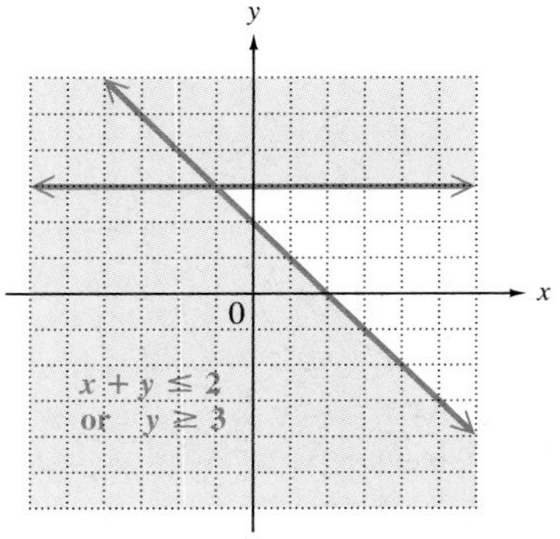

31. $x - 2 > y$ or $x < 1$

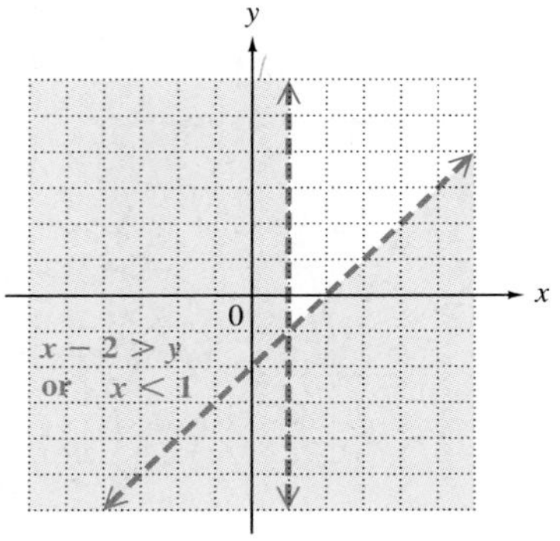

32. $x + 3 < y$ or $x > 3$

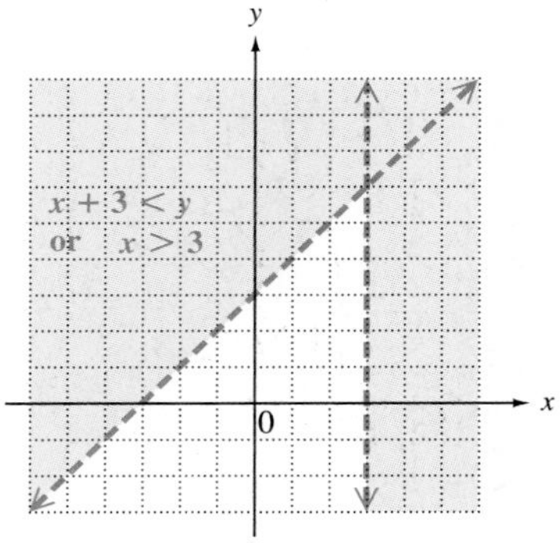

33. $3x + 2y < 6$ or $x - 2y > 2$

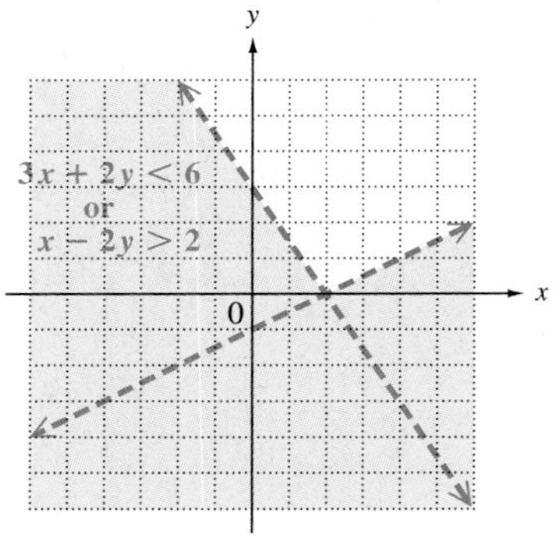

34. $x - y \geq 1$ or $x + y \leq 4$

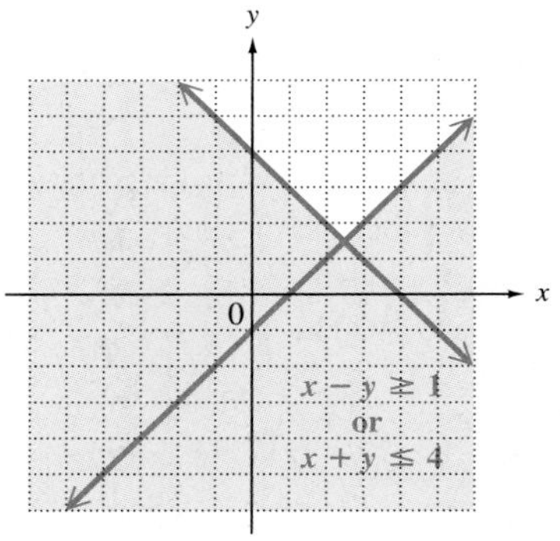

Solve each problem. In part (a), $x \geq 0$ and $y \geq 0$, so graph only the part of the inequality in quadrant I.

35. A company will ship x units of merchandise to outlet I and y units of merchandise to outlet II. The company must ship a total of at least 500 units to these two outlets. This can be expressed by writing

$$x + y \geq 500.$$

(a) Graph the inequality.

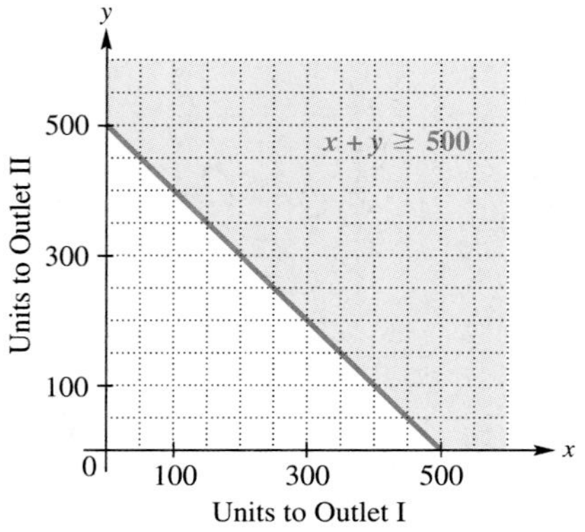

(b) Give two ordered pairs that satisfy the inequality.

(500, 0) and (200, 400); Other answers are possible.

36. A toy manufacturer makes stuffed bears and geese. It takes 20 min to sew a bear and 30 min to sew a goose. There is a total of 480 min of sewing time available to make x bears and y geese. These restrictions lead to the inequality

$$20x + 30y \geq 480.$$

(a) Graph the inequality.

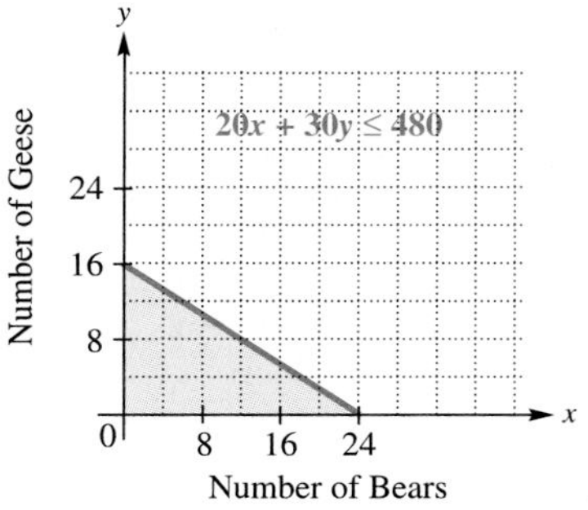

(b) Give two ordered pairs that satisfy the inequality.

(16, 1) and (20, 2); Other answers are possible.

4.6 Introduction to Functions

Objectives

1. Define relation and function.
2. Find domain and range.
3. Identify functions.
4. Use function notation.
5. Identify linear functions.

It is often useful to describe one quantity in terms of another; for example, the growth of a plant is related to the amount of light it receives, the demand for a product is related to the price of the product, the cost of a trip is related to the distance traveled, and so on. To represent these corresponding quantities, it is helpful to use ordered pairs.

For example, we can indicate the relationship between the demand for a product and its price by writing ordered pairs in which the first number represents the price and the second number represents the demand. Then the ordered pair (5, 1000) would indicate a demand for 1000 items when the price of the item is \$5. Since the demand depends on the price charged, we place the price first and the demand second. The ordered pair is an abbreviation for the sentence "If the price is 5 (dollars), then the demand is for 1000 (items)." Similarly, the ordered pairs (3, 5000) and (10, 250) show that a price of \$3 produces a demand for 5000 items, and a price of \$10 produces a demand for 250 items.

In this example, the demand depends on the price of the item. For this reason, demand is called the *dependent variable,* and price is called the *independent variable.* Generalizing, if the value of the variable y depends on the value of the variable x, then y is the **dependent variable** and x is the **independent variable.**

Independent variable → x, Dependent variable → y

$$(x, y)$$

1 Define relation and function. Since related quantities can be written using ordered pairs, the concept of *relation* can be defined as follows.

Relation

A **relation** is a set of ordered pairs.

For example, the sets

$$F = \{(1, 2), (-2, 5), (3, -1)\} \quad \text{and} \quad G = \{(-4, 1), (-2, 1), (-2, 0)\}$$

are both relations. A special kind of relation, called a *function,* is very important in mathematics and its applications.

Function

A **function** is a relation in which, for each value of the first component of the ordered pairs, there is *exactly one value* of the second component.

Of the two examples of a relation just given, only set F is a function, because for each x-value, there is exactly one y-value. In set G, the last two ordered pairs have the same x-value paired with two different y-values, so G is a relation, but not a function.

$$F = \{(\mathbf{1}, 2), (\mathbf{-2}, 5), (\mathbf{3}, -1)\} \qquad \text{Function}$$

Different x-values

$$G = \{(-4, 1), (\mathbf{-2}, 1), (\mathbf{-2}, 0)\} \qquad \text{Not a function}$$

Same x-value

In a function, there is *exactly one* value of the dependent variable, the second component, for each value of the independent variable, the first component. This is what makes functions so important in applications. It would not be as useful, for example, to know a price/demand relationship that gave more than one demand for a given price.

Another way to think of a functional relationship is to think of the independent variable as an input and the dependent variable as an output. A calculator is an input-output machine, for example. To find 8^2, we input 8, press the squaring key, and see that the output is 64. Inputs and outputs can also be determined from a graph or a table.

A third way to describe a function is to give a rule that tells how to determine the dependent variable for a specific value of the independent variable. The rule may be given in words: the dependent variable is twice the independent variable. Usually the rule is an equation:

$$y = 2x.$$

↑ Dependent variable (y) ↑ Independent variable (x)

This is the most efficient way to define a function.

Example 1 **Determining Independent and Dependent Variables of Functions**

Determine the independent and dependent variables for each function. Give an example of an ordered pair belonging to the function.

(a) The 2000 Summer Olympics medal winners in men's basketball were {(gold, United States), (silver, France), (bronze, Lithuania)}. (*Source:* espn.go.com/oly/summer00/)

The independent variable (the first component in each ordered pair) is the type of medal; the dependent variable (the second component) is the recipient. Any of the three ordered pairs could be given as an example.

(b) A calculator that finds squares using the squaring key

The independent variable (the input) is any real number, since any number can be squared. The dependent variable is the nonnegative square. For example, (9, 81) belongs to this function.

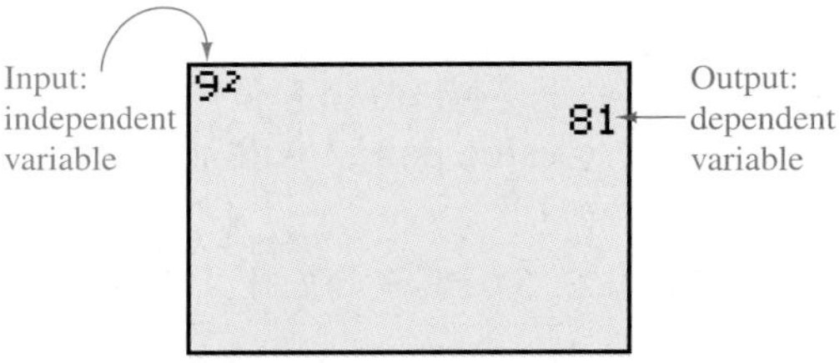

Continued on Next Page

(c) The graph of the relationship between the number of gallons of water in a small swimming pool and time in hours

The independent variable is the number of hours, and the dependent variable is the number of gallons of water in the pool. One ordered pair is (25, 3000).

GALLONS OF WATER IN A POOL AT TIME *t*

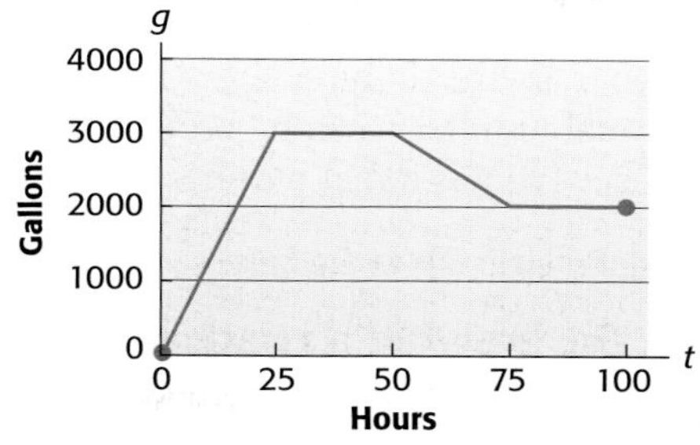

(d) Petroleum imports in millions of barrels per day for selected years given in the table

The independent variable is the year; the dependent variable is the number of barrels of petroleum. An example of an ordered pair is (1994, 9.00).

U.S. PETROLEUM IMPORTS

Year	Barrels Per Day (in millions)
1994	9.00
1995	8.84
1996	9.40
1997	10.16
1998	10.71

Source: World Almanac and Book of Facts, 2000.

(e) $y = 3x + 4$

The independent variable is x, and the dependent variable is y. One ordered pair is $(\frac{1}{3}, 5)$.

Work Problem 1 at the Side.

2 Find domain and range.

Domain and Range

In a relation, the set of all values of the independent variable (x) is the **domain;** the set of all values of the dependent variable (y) is the **range.**

Example 2 Determining Domains and Ranges of Relations

Give the domain and range of each function in Example 1.

(a) The domain is the type of medal, {gold, silver, bronze}, and the range is the set of winning countries, {United States, France, Lithuania}.

(b) Here, the domain is any real number, written $\{x | x \text{ is a real number}\}$ or $(-\infty, \infty)$. The range is restricted to nonnegative numbers, written $[0, \infty)$.

(c) The domain includes all possible values of t, the time in hours, which is the interval [0, 100]. The range is the set of the number of gallons at time t, the interval [0, 3000].

Continued on Next Page

1 Determine the independent variable, the dependent variable, and an ordered pair for each function.

(a) The reciprocal key on a calculator

(b) The graph given in Section 4.3, Exercise 58 (See page 265.)

(c) The table given in Section 4.3, Exercise 61 and repeated here

Year	Subscribers (in thousands)
1994	24,134
1995	33,786
1996	44,043
1997	55,312
1998	69,209
1999	86,047

Source: Cellular Telecommunications Industry Association, Washington, D.C., *State of the Cellular Industry* (Annual).

(d) $y = \frac{1}{2}x$

ANSWERS

1. (a) independent variable: any nonzero real number; dependent variable: any nonzero real number; $\left(-\frac{2}{3}, -\frac{3}{2}\right)$ **(b)** independent variable: the year; dependent variable: expenditures (in millions of dollars); any ordered pair corresponding to a point on the graph **(c)** independent variable: the year; dependent variable: the number of subscribers; any ordered pair from the table **(d)** independent variable: x; dependent variable: y; $(-10, -5)$ is one example.

2 Give the domain and range for each function.

(a) The reciprocal key on a calculator

(b) The graph given in Section 4.3, Exercise 59 (See page 265.)

(c) The table given in Section 4.3, Exercise 61 and repeated in margin Problem 1(c)

(d) $y = \frac{1}{2}x$

3 Give the domain and range of each relation.

(a)

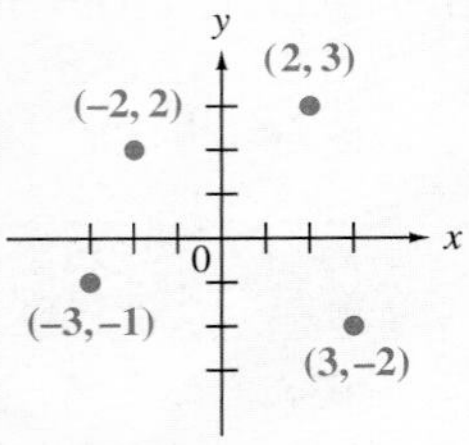

(b)

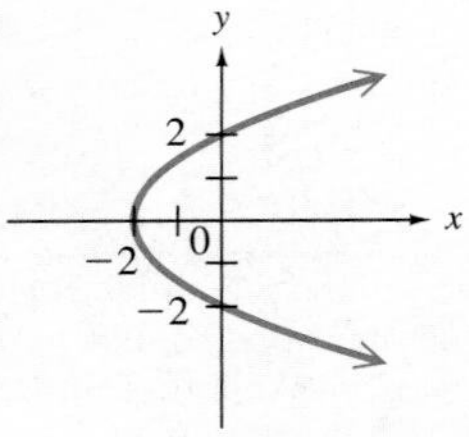

(c)

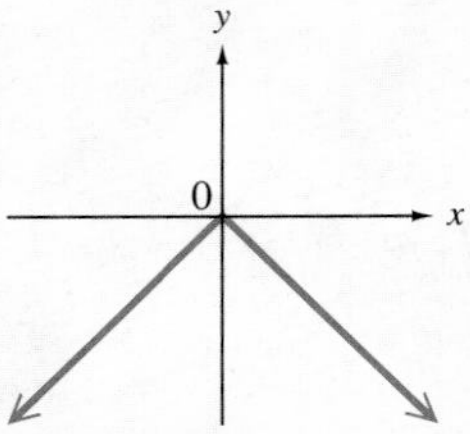

(d) The domain is the set of years, $\{1994, 1995, 1996, 1997, 1998\}$; the range is the set of petroleum imports (in millions of barrels per day) shown in the table, $\{9.00, 8.84, 9.40, 10.16, 10.71\}$.

(e) In the defining equation (or rule), $y = 3x + 4$, x can be any real number, so the domain is $\{x \mid x \text{ is a real number}\}$ or $(-\infty, \infty)$. Since every real number y can be produced by some value of x, the range is also the set $\{y \mid y \text{ is a real number}\}$ or $(-\infty, \infty)$.

Work Problem 2 at the Side.

The **graph of a relation** is the graph of its ordered pairs. The graph gives a picture of the relation, which can be used to determine its domain and range.

Example 3 Finding Domains and Ranges from Graphs

Give the domain and range of each relation.

(a)

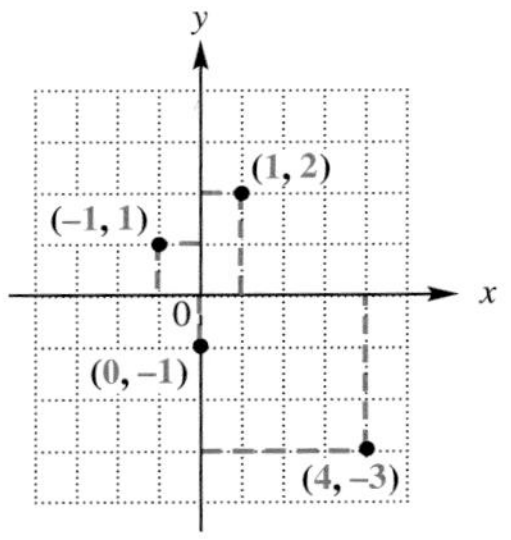

The domain is the set of x-values,

$$\{-1, 0, 1, 4\}.$$

The range is the set of y-values,

$$\{-3, -1, 1, 2\}.$$

(b)

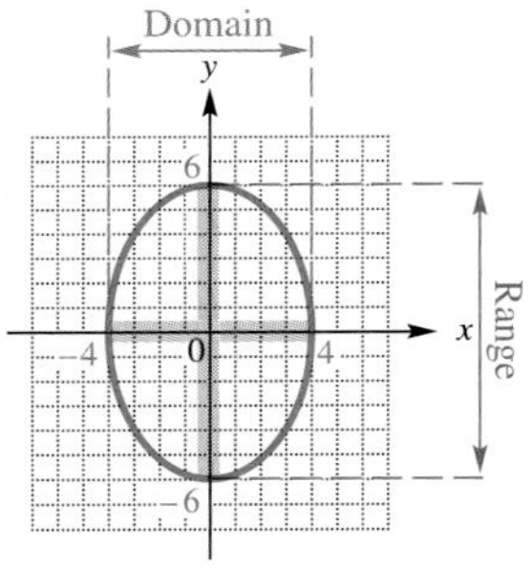

The x-values of the points on the graph include all numbers between -4 and 4, inclusive. The y-values include all numbers between -6 and 6, inclusive. Using interval notation,

the domain is $[-4, 4]$;

the range is $[-6, 6]$.

(c)

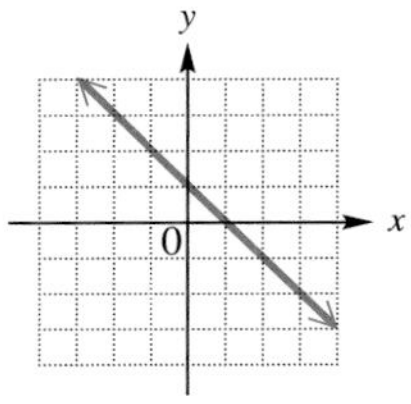

The arrowheads indicate that the line extends indefinitely left and right, as well as up and down. Therefore, both the domain and the range include all real numbers, written $(-\infty, \infty)$.

(d)

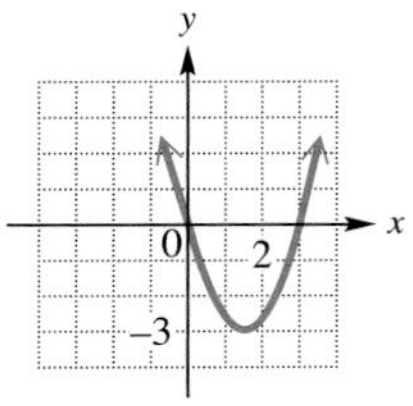

The arrowheads indicate that the graph extends indefinitely left and right, as well as upward. The domain is $(-\infty, \infty)$. Because there is a least y-value, -3, the range includes all numbers greater than or equal to -3, written $[-3, \infty)$.

Work Problem 3 at the Side.

ANSWERS

2. (a) domain: $(-\infty, 0) \cup (0, \infty)$; range: $(-\infty, 0) \cup (0, \infty)$
(b) domain: $[1994, 1998]$; range: approximately $[20.8, 27.6]$
(c) domain: $\{1994, 1995, 1996, 1997, 1998, 1999\}$; range: $\{24{,}134, 33{,}786, 44{,}043, 55{,}312, 69{,}209, 86{,}047\}$
(d) domain: $(-\infty, \infty)$; range: $(-\infty, \infty)$

3. (a) domain: $\{-3, -2, 2, 3\}$; range: $\{-2, -1, 2, 3\}$
(b) domain: $[-2, \infty)$; range: $(-\infty, \infty)$
(c) domain: $(-\infty, \infty)$; range: $(-\infty, 0]$

Relations are often defined by equations, such as $y = 2x + 3$ and $y^2 = x$. It is sometimes necessary to determine the domain of a relation from its equation. In this book, the following agreement on the domain of a relation is assumed.

Agreement on Domain

The domain of a relation is assumed to be all real numbers that produce real numbers when substituted for the independent variable.

To illustrate this agreement, since any real number can be used as a replacement for x in $y = 2x + 3$, the domain of this function is the set of real numbers. As another example, the function defined by $y = \frac{1}{x}$ has all real numbers except 0 as domain, since y is undefined if $x = 0$. In general, the domain of a function defined by an algebraic expression is all real numbers, except those numbers that lead to division by 0 or, as we will see in Chapter 9, an even root of a negative number.

3 Identify functions. Most of the relations we have seen in the examples are functions—that is, each x-value corresponds to exactly one y-value. Now we look at ways to determine whether a given relation, defined graphically, is a function.

In a function each value of x leads to only one value of y, so any vertical line drawn through the graph of a function must intersect the graph in at most one point. This is the *vertical line test for a function*.

Vertical Line Test

If every vertical line intersects the graph of a relation in no more than one point, then the relation represents a function.

For example, the graph shown in Figure 38(a) is not the graph of a function since a vertical line intersects the graph in more than one point. The graph in Figure 38(b) does represent a function.

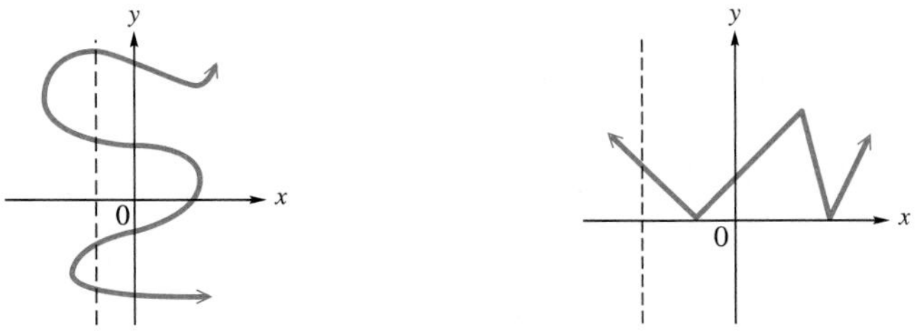

(a) (b)

Figure 38

Work Problem 4 at the Side.

The vertical line test is a simple method for identifying a function defined by a graph. It is more difficult to decide whether a relation defined by an equation is a function. The next example gives some hints that may help.

4 Use the vertical line test to decide which graphs represent functions.

A.

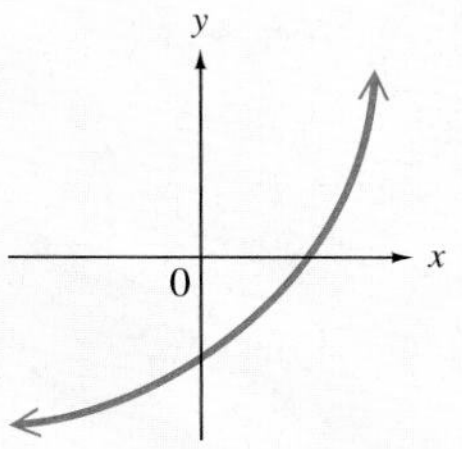

B.

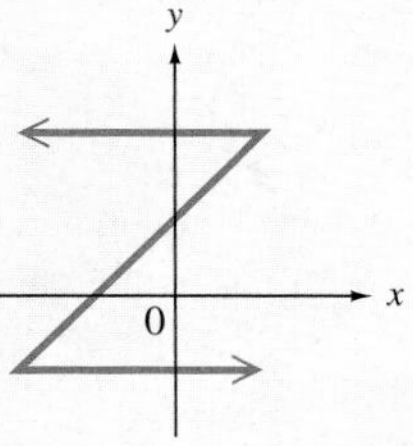

C.

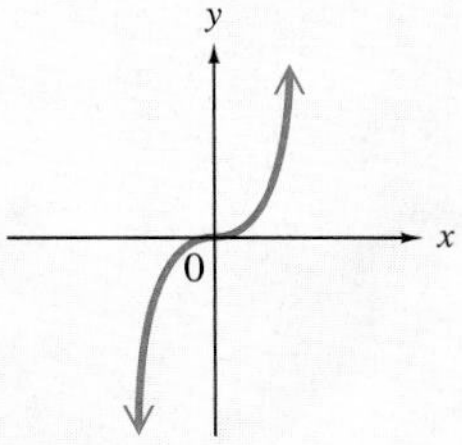

ANSWERS

4. A and C are graphs of functions.

5 Decide whether each relation defines a function, and give the domain.

(a) $y = 6x + 12$

(b) $y \leq 4x$

(c) $y = \dfrac{1}{3x - 2}$

(d) $y^2 = 25x$

ANSWERS

5. (a) yes; $(-\infty, \infty)$ **(b)** no; $(-\infty, \infty)$

(c) yes; $\left(-\infty, \frac{2}{3}\right) \cup \left(\frac{2}{3}, \infty\right)$

(d) no; $[0, \infty)$

Example 4 **Identifying Functions**

Decide whether each relation defines a function, and give the domain.

(a) $y = 2x - 1$

For any choice of x in the domain, there is exactly one corresponding value for y, so this equation defines a function. Since any real number can be used for x, the domain is the set of real numbers, $(-\infty, \infty)$.

(b) $y^2 = x$

The ordered pairs (16, 4) and (16, −4) both satisfy this equation. Since one value of x, 16, corresponds to two values of y, 4 and −4, this equation does not define a function. Because x is equal to the square of y, the values of x must always be nonnegative. The domain of the relation is $[0, \infty)$.

(c) $y \leq x - 1$

By definition, y is a function of x if every value of x leads to exactly one value of y. In this example, a particular value of x, say 1, corresponds to many values of y. The ordered pairs (1, 0), (1, −1), (1, −2), (1, −3), and so on, all satisfy the inequality. For this reason, an inequality does not define a function. Any number can be used for x, so the domain is the set of real numbers, $(-\infty, \infty)$.

(d) $y = \dfrac{5}{x - 1}$

Given any value of x in the domain, we find y by subtracting 1, then dividing the result into 5. This process produces exactly one value of y for each value in the domain, so this equation defines a function. The domain includes all real numbers except those that make the denominator 0. We find these numbers by setting the denominator equal to 0 and solving for x.

$$x - 1 = 0$$
$$x = 1$$

Thus, the domain includes all real numbers except 1. In interval notation this is written as

$$(-\infty, 1) \cup (1, \infty).$$

Work Problem 5 at the Side.

In summary, three variations of the definition of function are given here.

Variations of the Definition of Function

1. A **function** is a relation in which, for each value of the first component of the ordered pairs, there is exactly one value of the second component.
2. A **function** is a set of ordered pairs in which no first component is repeated.
3. A **function** is a rule or correspondence that assigns exactly one range value to each domain value.

4 **Use function notation.** When a function f is defined with a rule or an equation using x and y for the independent and dependent variables, we say "y is a function of x" to emphasize that *y depends on x*. We use the notation

$$y = f(x)$$

to express this. (In this special notation the parentheses do not indicate multiplication.) The letter f stands for *function*. For example, if $y = 2x - 7$, we write

$$f(x) = 2x - 7.$$

When you see the notation $f(x)$, remember that it is just another name for the dependent variable y. This **function notation** is useful for simplifying certain statements. For example, if $y = f(x) = 9x - 5$, then replacing x with 2 gives

$$\begin{aligned} y &= f(2) \\ &= 9 \cdot 2 - 5 \\ &= 18 - 5 \\ &= 13. \end{aligned}$$

The statement "if $x = 2$, then $y = 13$" is abbreviated with function notation as

$$f(2) = 13.$$

Read $f(2)$ as "f of 2" or "f at 2." Also,

$$f(0) = 9 \cdot 0 - 5 = -5, \quad \text{and} \quad f(-3) = 9(-3) - 5 = -32.$$

These ideas and the symbols used to represent them can be illustrated as follows.

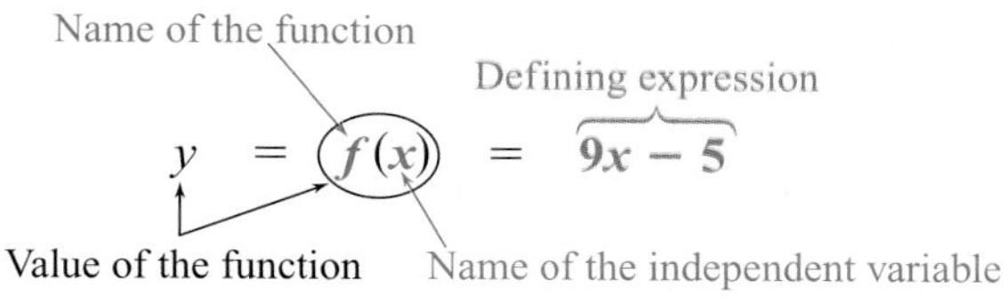

CAUTION

The symbol $f(x)$ *does not* indicate "f times x," but represents the y-value for the indicated x-value. As just shown, $f(2)$ is the y-value that corresponds to the x-value 2.

Example 5 **Using Function Notation**

Let $f(x) = -x^2 + 5x - 3$. Find the following.

(a) $f(2)$

Replace x with 2.

$$\begin{aligned} f(2) &= -2^2 + 5 \cdot 2 - 3 \\ &= -4 + 10 - 3 \\ &= 3 \end{aligned}$$

Continued on Next Page

6 Find $f(-3)$, $f(p)$, and $f(m + 1)$.

(a) $f(x) = 6x - 2$

(b) $f(x) = \dfrac{-3x + 5}{2}$

(c) $f(x) = \dfrac{1}{6}x - 1$

(b) $$f(-1) = -(-1)^2 + 5(-1) - 3 = -1 - 5 - 3 = -9$$

(c) $f(q)$
Replace x with q.

$$f(q) = -q^2 + 5q - 3$$

The replacement of one variable with another is important in later courses.

Sometimes letters other than f, such as g, h, or capital letters F, G, and H are used to name functions.

Example 6 Using Function Notation

Let $g(x) = 2x + 3$. Find and simplify the following.

(a) $g(a + 1)$
Replace x with $a + 1$.

$$g(a + 1) = 2(a + 1) + 3 = 2a + 2 + 3 = 2a + 5$$

(b) $$g\left(\frac{1}{b + 4}\right) = 2\left(\frac{1}{b + 4}\right) + 3 = \frac{2}{b + 4} + 3$$

Work Problem 6 at the Side.

If a function is defined by an equation with x and y, not with function notation, use the following steps to find $f(x)$.

Finding an Expression for $f(x)$

Step 1 Solve the equation for y.

Step 2 Replace y with $f(x)$.

Example 7 Writing Equations Using Function Notation

Rewrite each equation using function notation. Then find $f(-2)$ and $f(a)$.

(a) $y = x^2 + 1$
This equation is already solved for y. Since $y = f(x)$,

$$f(x) = x^2 + 1.$$

To find $f(-2)$, let $x = -2$.

$$f(-2) = (-2)^2 + 1 = 4 + 1 = 5$$

Find $f(a)$ by letting $x = a$: $f(a) = a^2 + 1$.

Continued on Next Page

ANSWERS

6. (a) -20; $6p - 2$; $6m + 4$

(b) 7; $\dfrac{-3p + 5}{2}$; $\dfrac{-3m + 2}{2}$

(c) $-\dfrac{3}{2}$; $\dfrac{1}{6}p - 1$; $\dfrac{1}{6}(m + 1) - 1$ or $\dfrac{1}{6}m - \dfrac{5}{6}$

(b) $x - 4y = 5$

First solve $x - 4y = 5$ for y. Then replace y with $f(x)$.

$$x - 4y = 5$$
$$x - 5 = 4y$$
$$y = \frac{x-5}{4} \quad \text{so} \quad f(x) = \frac{1}{4}x - \frac{5}{4}$$

Now find $f(-2)$ and $f(a)$.

$$f(-2) = \frac{1}{4}(-2) - \frac{5}{4} = -\frac{7}{4}$$
$$f(a) = \frac{1}{4}a - \frac{5}{4}$$

Work Problem 7 at the Side.

7 Rewrite each equation using function notation. Then find $f(-1)$.

(a) $y = x^3 + 2$

(b) $x^2 - 4y = 3$

5 **Identify linear functions.** Our first two-dimensional graphing was of straight lines. Linear equations (except for $x = c$) define *linear functions.*

Linear Function

A function that can be defined by

$$f(x) = mx + b$$

for real numbers m and b is a **linear function.**

Recall from Section 4.4 that m is the slope of the line and $(0, b)$ is the y-intercept. A linear function defined by $f(x) = d$ (whose graph is a horizontal line) is sometimes called a **constant function.** The domain of any linear function is $(-\infty, \infty)$. The range of a nonconstant linear function is $(-\infty, \infty)$, while the range of the constant function with $f(x) = d$ is $\{d\}$.

In later chapters of this book, we will learn about several other types of functions.

ANSWERS

7. (a) $f(x) = x^3 + 2$; 1

(b) $f(x) = \frac{x^2 - 3}{4}$ or $f(x) = \frac{1}{4}x^2 - \frac{3}{4}$; $-\frac{1}{2}$

Focus on Real-Data Applications

Linear or Nonlinear? That Is the Question about College Tuition

The data used in this table was taken from the fee schedule for North Harris Montgomery Community College for fall semester, 2000.

Credit Hours, x	Change in x	Resident Tuition Costs, y	Change in y
0		12	
3	$3 - 0 = 3$	102	$102 - 12 = 90$
6	$6 - 3 = 3$	192	$192 - 102 = 90$
9	$9 - 6 = 3$	282	$282 - 192 = 90$
12	**$12 - 9 = 3$**	372	**$372 - 282 = 90$**
15	**$15 - 12 = 3$**	462	**$462 - 372 = 90$**

Source: Credit schedule for North Harris Montgomery Community College District.

The data represents the relationship between the number of credit hours enrolled (*input*, or *domain*) and the tuition costs (*output*, or *range*). Is this relationship linear?

For Group Discussion

RESIDENT TUITION COSTS

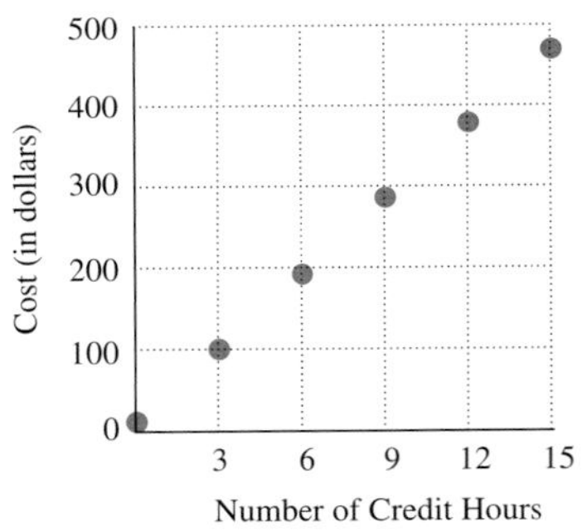

1. Complete the change in x and change in y columns of the table.

2. Graph the ordered-pair data (x, y) and observe the shape of the graph. If the graph approximates a line, then the data represents a linear relationship. Is the relationship linear? **yes**

3. **(a)** Linear relationships change at a constant rate. For example,

$$\frac{\text{change in fees, } y}{\text{change in credit hours, } x} = \frac{192 - 102}{6 - 3} = \frac{90}{3} = \underline{\mathbf{30}}.$$

If this ratio is approximately the same for all successive ordered pairs, then the data is linear. Calculate this ratio for a different set of ordered pairs. Did you get the same result? **yes**

(b) What is the rate of change, or slope, of the line? **30**

4. The y-intercept is the range value (*output*) associated with a domain value (*input*) of 0. From the table, predict the cost to enroll in 0 credit hours. What might the y-intercept represent in this situation? **\$12; registration fee**

5. Write an equation for a linear function that represents the relationship between number of credit hours and tuition costs. Use function notation. **$f(x) = 30x + 12$**

Teaching notes for this activity are provided in the *Printed Test Bank and Instructor's Resource Guide.*

4.6 EXERCISES

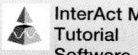

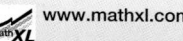

FOR EXTRA HELP: Student's Solutions Manual | MyMathLab.com | InterAct Math Tutorial Software | AW Math Tutor Center | www.mathxl.com MathXL | Digital Video Tutor CD 4 Videotape 8

1. In an ordered pair of a relation, is the first element the independent or the dependent variable?

independent variable

2. Give an example of a relation that is not a function, having domain $\{-3, 2, 6\}$ and range $\{4, 6\}$. (There are many possible correct answers.)

One example is $\{(-3, 4), (2, 4), (2, 6), (6, 4)\}$.

3. Explain what is meant by each term.

(a) Relation **(b)** Domain of a relation
(c) Range of a relation **(d)** Function

(a) A relation is a set of ordered pairs. (b) The domain is the set of all first components (x-values). (c) The range is the set of all second components (y-values). (d) A function is a relation in which each domain element is paired with one and only one range element.

Decide whether each relation is a function, and give the domain and the range. Use the vertical line test in Exercises 11–13. See Examples 1–3.

4. $\{(5, 1), (3, 2), (4, 9), (7, 3)\}$

function; domain: $\{5, 3, 4, 7\}$; range: $\{1, 2, 9, 3\}$

5. $\{(8, 0), (5, 4), (9, 3), (3, 9)\}$

function; domain: $\{8, 5, 9, 3\}$; range: $\{0, 4, 3, 9\}$

6. $\{(2, 4), (0, 2), (2, 6)\}$

not a function; domain: $\{2, 0\}$; range: $\{4, 2, 6\}$

7. $\{(9, -2), (-3, 5), (9, 1)\}$

not a function; domain: $\{9, -3\}$; range: $\{-2, 5, 1\}$

8. The set containing certain countries and their predicted life expectancy estimates for persons born in 2050 is {(U.S., 83.9), (Japan, 90.91), (Canada, 85.26), (Britain, 83.79), (France, 87.01), (Germany, 83.12), (Italy, 82.26)}. (*Source:* Shripad Tuljapurkar, Mountain View Research, Los Altos, California.)

function; domain: {U.S., Japan, Canada, Britain, France, Germany, Italy}; range: {83.9, 90.91, 85.26, 83.79, 87.01, 83.12, 82.26}

9. An input-output machine accepts negative real numbers as input, and outputs their squares.

function; domain: $(-\infty, 0)$; range: $(0, \infty)$

10.

U.S. Voting-Age Population in 2000 (in millions)	
Hispanic	21.3
Native American	1.6
Asian American	8.2
African American	24.6
White	152.0

Source: U.S. Bureau of the Census.

function; domain: {Hispanic, Native American, Asian American, African American, White}; range in millions: {21.3, 1.6, 8.2, 24.6, 152.0}

11.

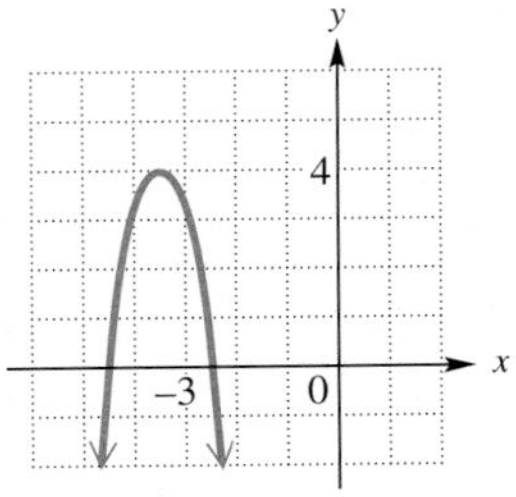

function; domain: $(-\infty, \infty)$; range: $(-\infty, 4]$

12.

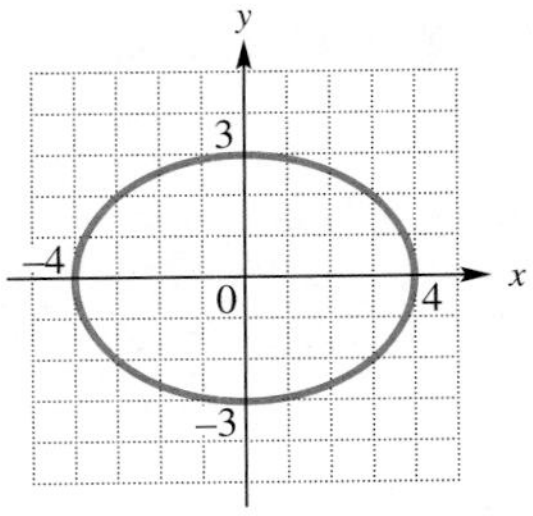

not a function; domain: $[-4, 4]$; range: $[-3, 3]$

13.

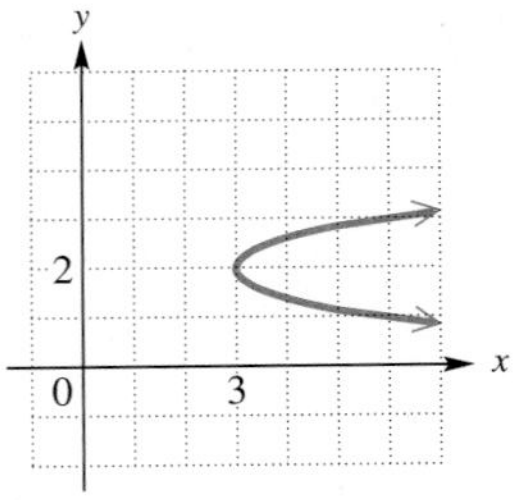

not a function; domain: $[3, \infty)$; range: $(-\infty, \infty)$

14. Describe the use of the vertical line test.

The vertical line test is used to determine whether a graph is that of a function. Any vertical line will intersect the graph of a function in at most one point.

Decide whether each relation defines y as a function of x. Give the domain. See Example 4.

15. $y = x^2$

function; domain: $(-\infty, \infty)$

16. $y = x^3$

function; domain: $(-\infty, \infty)$

17. $x = y^6$

not a function; domain: $[0, \infty)$

18. $x = y^4$

not a function; domain: $[0, \infty)$

19. $x + y < 4$

not a function; domain: $(-\infty, \infty)$

20. $x - y < 3$

not a function; domain: $(-\infty, \infty)$

21. $y = |x|$

function; domain: $(-\infty, \infty)$

22. $y = -|x|$

function; domain: $(-\infty, \infty)$

23. $xy = 1$

function; domain: $(-\infty, 0) \cup (0, \infty)$

24. $xy = -3$

function; domain: $(-\infty, 0) \cup (0, \infty)$

25. $y = 2x - 6$

function; domain: $(-\infty, \infty)$

26. $y = -6x + 8$

function; domain: $(-\infty, \infty)$

27. $y = \dfrac{2}{x - 9}$

function; domain: $(-\infty, 9) \cup (9, \infty)$

28. $y = \dfrac{-7}{x - 16}$

function; domain: $(-\infty, 16) \cup (16, \infty)$

29. $y = \dfrac{1}{4x + 2}$

function; domain: $\left(-\infty, -\frac{1}{2}\right) \cup \left(-\frac{1}{2}, \infty\right)$

30. $y = \dfrac{1}{9 - 2x}$

function; domain: $\left(-\infty, \frac{9}{2}\right) \cup \left(\frac{9}{2}, \infty\right)$

31. Refer to the graph to answer the questions.

GALLONS OF WATER IN A POOL AT TIME *t*

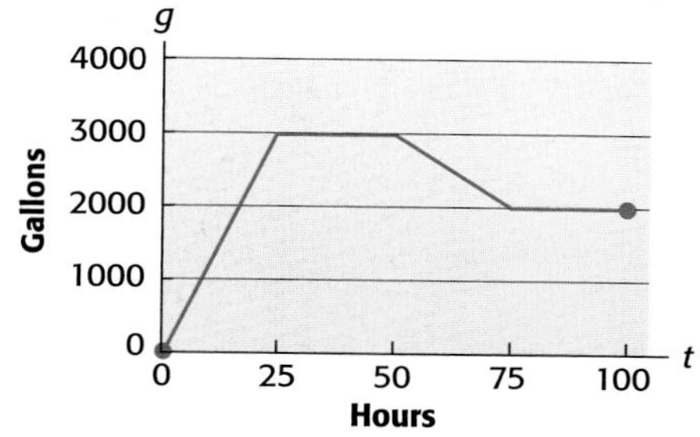

(a) What numbers are possible values of the dependent variable? **[0, 3000]**

(b) For how long is the water level increasing? decreasing? **25 hr; 25 hr**

(c) How many gallons are in the pool after 90 hr? **2000 gal**

(d) Call this function f. What is $f(0)$? What does it mean in this example? **$f(0) = 0$; The pool is empty at time 0.**

32. The graph shows the daily megawatts of electricity used on a record-breaking summer day in Sacramento, California.

ELECTRICITY USE

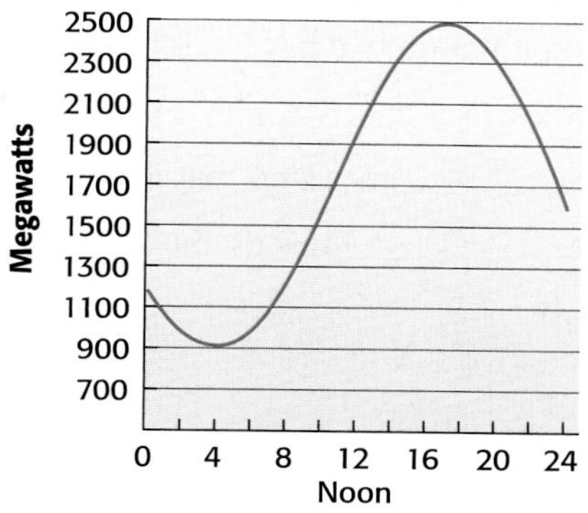

Source: Sacramento Municipal Utility District.

(a) Is this the graph of a function? **yes**

(b) What is the domain? **[0, 24]**

(c) Estimate the number of megawatts used at 8 A.M. **1200 megawatts**

(d) At what time was the most electricity used? the least electricity? **at 17 hr or 5 P.M.; at 4 A.M.**

33. Give an example of a function from everyday life. (*Hint:* Fill in the blanks: _______ depends on _______, so _______ is a function of _______.)

Here is one example. The cost of gasoline; number of gallons purchased; cost; number of gallons

34. Choose the correct response: The notation $f(3)$ means

A. the variable f times 3 or $3f$

B. the value of the dependent variable when the independent variable is 3

C. the value of the independent variable when the dependent variable is 3

D. f equals 3.

B

Let $f(x) = -3x + 4$ *and* $g(x) = -x^2 + 4x + 1$. *Find the following. See Examples 5 and 6.*

35. $f(0)$

4

36. $f(-3)$

13

37. $g(-2)$

−11

38. $g(10)$

−59

39. $f(p)$

$-3p + 4$

40. $g(k)$

$-k^2 + 4k + 1$

41. $f(-x)$

$3x + 4$

42. $g(-x)$

$-x^2 - 4x + 1$

43. $f(x + 2)$

$-3x - 2$

44. $g\left(-\frac{1}{x}\right)$

$-\frac{1}{x^2} - \frac{4}{x} + 1$

45. $g\left(\frac{p}{3}\right)$

$-\frac{p^2}{9} + \frac{4p}{3} + 1$

46. $f(3t - 2)$

$-9t + 10$

47. Fill in each blank with the correct response.

The equation $2x + y = 4$ has a straight **line** as its graph. One point that lies on the graph is (3, **−2**). If we solve the equation for y and use function notation, we have a **linear** function defined by $f(x) =$ **−2x + 4**. For this function, $f(3) =$ **−2**, meaning that the point (**3**, **−2**) lies on the graph of the function.

48. Which of the following defines a linear function?

A. $y = \dfrac{x-5}{4}$ **B.** $y = \dfrac{1}{x}$

C. $y = x^2$ **D.** $y = \sqrt{x}$

A

An equation that defines y as a function of x is given. ***(a)*** *Solve for y in terms of x, and replace y with the function notation f(x).* ***(b)*** *Find f(3). See Example 7.*

49. $x + 3y = 12$

(a) $f(x) = \dfrac{12 - x}{3}$ **(b)** 3

50. $x - 4y = 8$

(a) $f(x) = \dfrac{8 - x}{-4}$ **(b)** $-\dfrac{5}{4}$

51. $y + 2x^2 = 3$

(a) $f(x) = 3 - 2x^2$ **(b)** −15

52. $y - 3x^2 = 2$

(a) $f(x) = 2 + 3x^2$ **(b)** 29

53. $4x - 3y = 8$

(a) $f(x) = \dfrac{8 - 4x}{-3}$ **(b)** $\dfrac{4}{3}$

54. $-2x + 5y = 9$

(a) $f(x) = \dfrac{9 + 2x}{5}$ **(b)** 3

Solve each problem.

55. Suppose that a taxicab driver charges \$1.50 per mi.

(a) Fill in the table with the correct response for the price $f(x)$ she charges for a trip of x miles.

x	f(x)
0	\$0
1	\$1.50
2	\$3.00
3	\$4.50

(b) The linear function that gives a rule for the amount charged is $f(x) =$ **1.50x**.

(c) Graph this function for the domain {0, 1, 2, 3}.

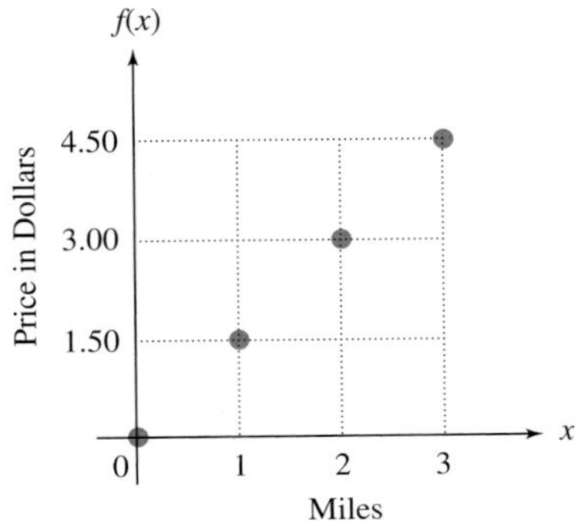

56. Suppose that a package weighing x pounds costs $f(x)$ dollars to mail to a given location, where

$$f(x) = 2.75x.$$

(a) What is the value of $f(3)$?

8.25 (dollars)

(b) In your own words, describe what 3 and the value $f(3)$ mean in part (a), using the terms *independent variable* and *dependent variable.*

3 is the value of the independent variable, which represents a package weight of 3 lb; f(3) = \$8.25 is the value of the dependent variable representing the cost to mail a 3-lb package.

(c) How much would it cost to mail a 5-lb package? Write the answer using function notation.

\$13.75; f(5) = 13.75

Chapter 4

SUMMARY

KEY TERMS

4.1

circle graph — A circle graph is a circle divided into sectors (or wedges) whose sizes show the relative magnitudes of the categories of data represented.

bar graph — A bar graph is a series of bars used to show comparisons between two categories of data.

line graph — A line graph consists of a series of points that are connected with line segments and is used to show changes or trends in data.

linear equation in two variables — An equation that can be written in the form $Ax + By = C$ is a linear equation in two variables. (A and B are real numbers that cannot both be 0.)

ordered pair — A pair of numbers written between parentheses in which order is important is called an ordered pair.

table of values — A table showing selected ordered pairs of numbers that satisfy an equation is called a table of values.

x-axis — The horizontal axis in a coordinate system is called the x-axis.

y-axis — The vertical axis in a coordinate system is called the y-axis.

rectangular (Cartesian) coordinate system — An x-axis and y-axis at right angles form a coordinate system.

quadrants — A coordinate system divides the plane into four regions called quadrants.

origin — The point at which the x-axis and y-axis intersect is called the origin.

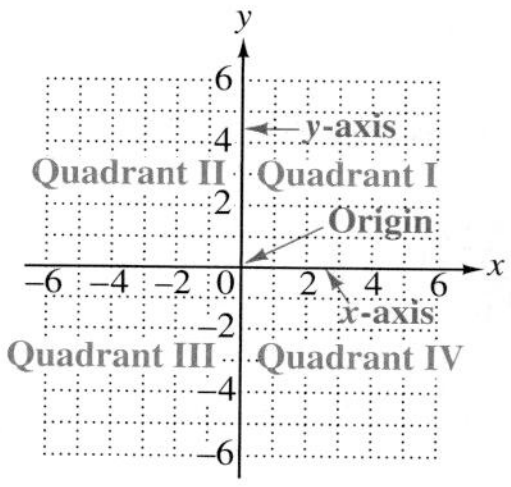

plane — A flat surface determined by two intersecting lines is a plane.

coordinates — The numbers in an ordered pair are called the coordinates of the corresponding point.

plot — To plot an ordered pair is to find the corresponding point on a coordinate system.

scatter diagram — A graph of ordered pairs of data is a scatter diagram.

4.2

graph — The graph of an equation is the set of all points that correspond to the ordered pairs that satisfy the equation.

graphing — The process of plotting the ordered pairs that satisfy a linear equation and drawing a line through them is called graphing.

y-intercept — If a graph intersects the y-axis at k, then the y-intercept is $(0, k)$.

x-intercept — If a graph intersects the x-axis at k, then the x-intercept is $(k, 0)$.

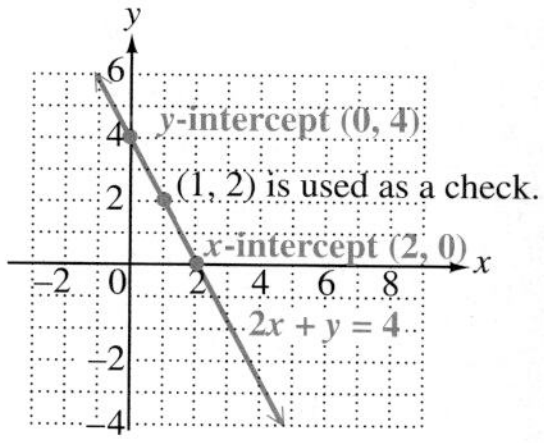

4.3

rise — Rise is the vertical change between two different points on a line.

run — Run is the horizontal change between two different points on a line.

slope — The slope of a line is the ratio of the change in y compared to the change in x when moving along the line from one point to another.

parallel lines — Two lines in a plane that never intersect are parallel.

perpendicular lines — Perpendicular lines intersect at a 90° angle.

4.5

linear inequality in two variables — An inequality that can be written in the form $Ax + By < C$, $Ax + By > C$, $Ax + By \leq C$, or $Ax + By \geq C$ is a linear inequality in two variables.

boundary line — In the graph of a linear inequality, the boundary line separates the region that satisfies the inequality from the region that does not satisfy the inequality.

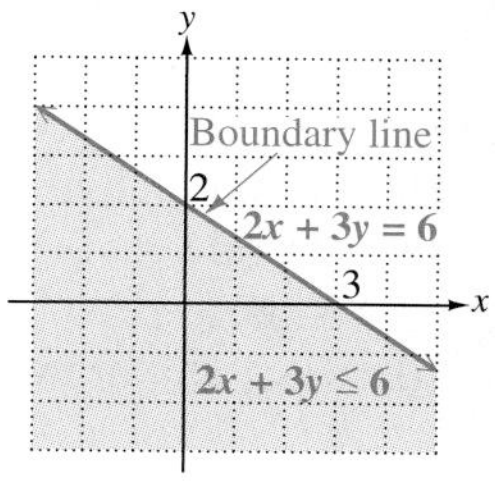

(*continued*)

4.6 **dependent variable** If the quantity y depends on x, then y is called the dependent variable in a relation between x and y.

independent variable If y depends on x, then x is the independent variable in a relation between x and y.

relation A relation is a set of ordered pairs of real numbers.

function A function is a set of ordered pairs in which each value of the first component, x, corresponds to exactly one value of the second component, y.

domain The domain of a relation is the set of first components (x-values) of the ordered pairs of the relation.

range The range of a relation is the set of second components (y-values) of the ordered pairs of the relation.

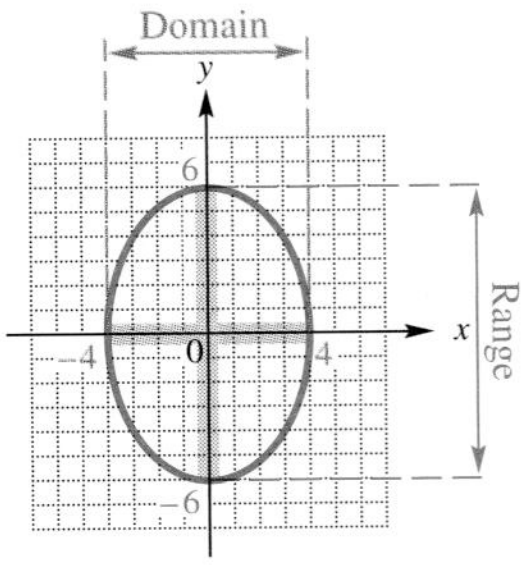

graph of a relation The graph of a relation is the graph of the ordered pairs of the relation.

function notation The function notation $f(x)$ is another way to represent the dependent variable y for the function f.

linear function A function that is defined by $f(x) = mx + b$ is a linear function.

constant function A constant function is a linear function of the form $f(x) = d$, for a real number d.

New Symbols

(a, b)	ordered pair
x_1	a specific value of the variable x (read "x sub one")
m	slope
$f(x)$	function of x (read "f of x")

Test Your Word Power

See how well you have learned the vocabulary in this chapter. Answers follow the Quick Review.

1. An **ordered pair** is a pair of numbers written
   (a) in numerical order between brackets
   (b) between parentheses or brackets
   (c) between parentheses in which order is important
   (d) between parentheses in which order does not matter.

2. The **coordinates** of a point are
   (a) the numbers in the corresponding ordered pair
   (b) the solution of an equation
   (c) the values of the x- and y-intercepts
   (d) the graph of the point.

3. A **linear equation in two variables** is an equation that can be written in the form
   (a) $Ax + By < C$
   (b) $ax = b$
   (c) $y = x^2$
   (d) $Ax + By = C$.

4. An **intercept** is
   (a) the point where the x-axis and y-axis intersect
   (b) a pair of numbers written between parentheses in which order matters
   (c) one of the four regions determined by a rectangular coordinate system
   (d) the point where a graph intersects the x-axis or the y-axis.

5. The **slope** of a line is
   (a) the measure of the run over the rise of the line
   (b) the distance between two points on the line
   (c) the ratio of the change in y to the change in x along the line
   (d) the horizontal change compared to the vertical change of two points on the line.

6. In a relationship between two variables x and y, the **independent variable** is
   (a) x, if x depends on y
   (b) x, if y depends on x
   (c) either x or y
   (d) the larger of x and y.

7. In a relationship between two variables x and y, the **dependent variable** is
(a) y, if y depends on x
(b) y, if x depends on y
(c) either x or y
(d) the smaller of x and y.

8. A **relation** is
(a) a set of ordered pairs
(b) the ratio of the change in y to the change in x along a line
(c) the set of all possible values of the independent variable
(d) all the second elements of a set of ordered pairs.

9. A **function** is
(a) the numbers in an ordered pair
(b) a set of ordered pairs in which each x-value corresponds to exactly one y-value
(c) a pair of numbers written between parentheses in which order matters
(d) the set of all ordered pairs that satisfy an equation.

10. The **domain** of a function is
(a) the set of all possible values of the dependent variable y
(b) a set of ordered pairs
(c) the difference between the x-values
(d) the set of all possible values of the independent variable x.

11. The **range** of a function is
(a) the set of all possible values of the dependent variable y
(b) a set of ordered pairs
(c) the difference between the y-values
(d) the set of all possible values of the independent variable x.

QUICK REVIEW

Concepts	*Examples*
4.1 Reading Graphs; Linear Equations in Two Variables Circle graphs, bar graphs, and line graphs are several ways to represent the relationship between two variables.	The bar graph indicates that in 2002, worldwide revenue from Internet security software is estimated to be about \$7.4 billion. 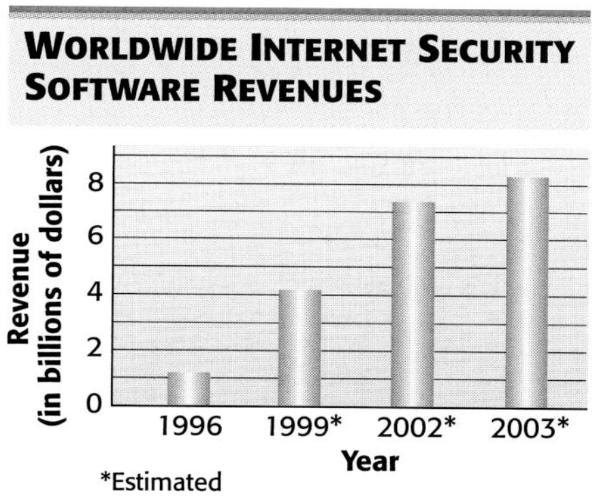 **Source:** International Data Corp.

(*continued*)

Concepts	*Examples*

4.1 Reading Graphs; Linear Equations in Two Variables (continued)

An ordered pair is a solution of an equation if it makes the equation a true statement.

Is $(2, -5)$ or $(0, -6)$ a solution of $4x - 3y = 18$?

$4(2) - 3(-5) = 23 \neq 18$	$4(0) - 3(-6) = 18$
$(2, -5)$ is not a solution.	$(0, -6)$ is a solution.

If a value of either variable in an equation is given, the value of the other variable can be found by substitution.

Complete the ordered pair $(0, \quad)$ for $3x = y + 4$.

$$3(0) = y + 4 \qquad \text{Let } x = 0.$$
$$0 = y + 4$$
$$-4 = y$$

The ordered pair is $(0, -4)$.

To plot the ordered pair $(-3, 4)$, start at the origin, go 3 units to the left, and from there go 4 units up.

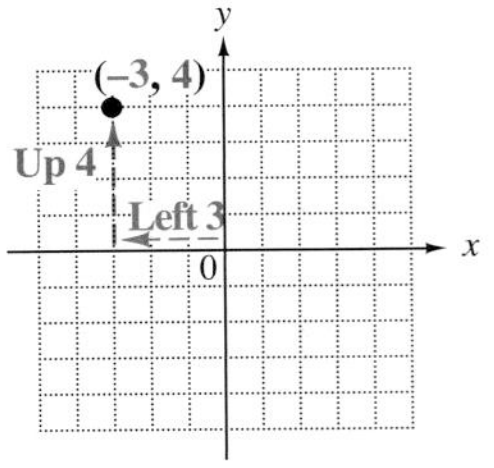

4.2 Graphing Linear Equations in Two Variables

Graphing a Linear Equation

Step 1 Find at least two ordered pairs that are solutions of the equation.

Step 2 Plot the corresponding points.

Step 3 Draw a straight line through the points.

Graph $x - 2y = 4$.

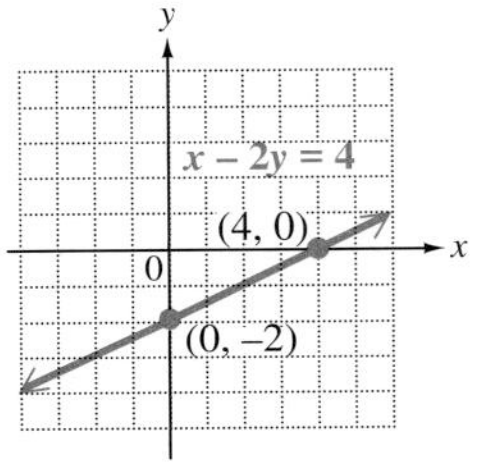

4.3 Slope

The slope of the line through (x_1, y_1) and (x_2, y_2) is

$$m = \frac{\text{change in } y}{\text{change in } x} = \frac{y_2 - y_1}{x_2 - x_1} \quad (x_1 \neq x_2).$$

The line through $(-2, 3)$ and $(4, -5)$ has slope

$$m = \frac{-5 - 3}{4 - (-2)} = \frac{-8}{6} = -\frac{4}{3}.$$

Horizontal lines have slope 0.

The line $y = -2$ has slope 0.

Vertical lines have undefined slope.

The line $x = 4$ has undefined slope.

Parallel lines have equal slopes.

$y = 2x + 5$	$4x - 2y = 6$
	$-2y = -4x + 6$
	$y = 2x - 3$
$m = 2$	$m = 2$

These lines are **parallel**.

Concepts	*Examples*
4.3 Slope (continued)	
The slopes of perpendicular lines are negative reciprocals (with a product of -1).	$y = 3x - 1$ $m = 3$ $x + 3y = 4$ $3y = -x + 4$ $y = -\frac{1}{3}x + \frac{4}{3}$ $m = -\frac{1}{3}$ These lines are **perpendicular**.
To find the slope of a line from its equation, solve for y. The slope is the coefficient of x.	Find the slope: $3x - 4y = 12$. $-4y = -3x + 12$ $y = \frac{3}{4}x - 3$ The slope is $\frac{3}{4}$.
4.4 Equations of Lines **Slope-Intercept Form** $\boldsymbol{y = mx + b}$ m is the slope. $(0, b)$ is the y-intercept.	Find an equation of the line with slope 2 and y-intercept $(0, -5)$. $y = 2x - 5$
Point-Slope Form $\boldsymbol{y - y_1 = m(x - x_1)}$ m is the slope. (x_1, y_1) is a point on the line.	Find an equation of the line with slope $-\frac{1}{2}$ through $(-4, 5)$. $y - 5 = -\frac{1}{2}[x - (-4)]$ $y - 5 = -\frac{1}{2}(x + 4)$ $y - 5 = -\frac{1}{2}x - 2$ $y = -\frac{1}{2}x + 3$
Standard Form $\boldsymbol{Ax + By = C}$ A, B, and C are integers and $A > 0$, $B \neq 0$.	This equation is written in standard form as $x + 2y = 6,$ with $A = 1$, $B = 2$, and $C = 6$.

Concepts	*Examples*
4.5 Graphing Linear Inequalities in Two Variables	
Graphing a Linear Inequality	
Step 1 Draw the graph of the line that is the boundary. Make the line solid if the inequality involves $\leq$ or $\geq$; make the line dashed if the inequality involves $<$ or $>$.	Graph $2x - 3y \leq 6$. Draw the graph of $2x - 3y = 6$. Use a solid line because the symbol $\leq$ is used.
Step 2 Choose any point not on the line as a test point.	Choose $(1, 2)$. $2(1) - 3(2) = 2 - 6 \leq 6$ True
Step 3 Shade the region that includes the test point if the test point satisfies the original inequality; otherwise, shade the region on the other side of the boundary line.	Shade the side of the line that includes $(1, 2)$. 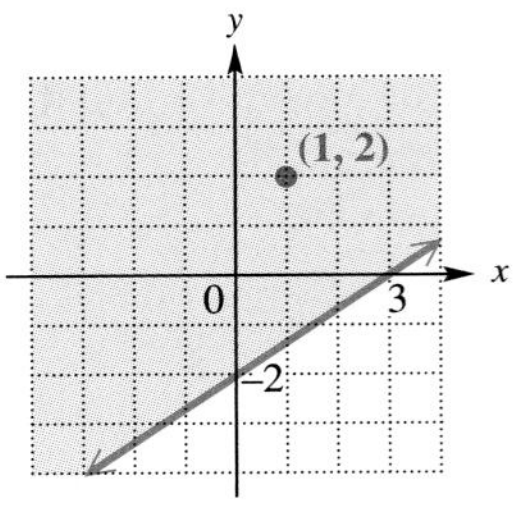
4.6 Introduction to Functions	
To evaluate a function using function notation (that is, $f(x)$ notation) for a given value of x, substitute the value wherever x appears.	If $f(x) = x^2 - 7x + 12$, then $f(1) = 1^2 - 7(1) + 12 = 6$.
To write the equation that defines a function in function notation, solve the equation for y.	Write $2x + 3y = 12$ in function notation. $3y = -2x + 12$; $y = -\frac{2}{3}x + 4$
Then replace y with $f(x)$.	$f(x) = -\frac{2}{3}x + 4$

Answers to Test Your Word Power

1. (c) *Examples:* (0, 3), (3, 8), (4, 0) **2. (a)** *Example:* The point associated with the ordered pair (1, 2) has x-coordinate 1 and y-coordinate 2. **3. (d)** *Examples:* $3x + 2y = 6$, $x = y - 7$, $4x = y$ **4. (d)** *Example:* In Figure 10 of Section 4.2, the x-intercept is (2, 0) and the y-intercept is (0, 3). **5. (c)** *Example:* The line through (3, 6) and (5, 4) has slope $\frac{4 - 6}{5 - 3} = \frac{-2}{2} = -1$. **6. (b)** *Example:* See Answer 7, which follows. **7. (a)** *Example:* When borrowing money, the amount you borrow (independent variable) determines the size of your payments (dependent variable). **8. (a)** *Example:* The set $\{(2, 0), (4, 3), (6, 6), (8, 9)\}$ defines a relation. **9. (b)** *Example:* The relation given in Answer 8 is a function since each x-value corresponds to exactly one y-value. **10. (d)** *Example:* In the function in Answer 8, the domain is the set of x-values, $\{2, 4, 6, 8\}$. **11. (a)** *Example:* In the function in Answer 8, the range is the set of y-values, $\{0, 3, 6, 9\}$.

Chapter 4 REVIEW EXERCISES

[4.1] *The line graph shows average prices for a gallon of gasoline in Cedar Rapids, Iowa, from June 1999 through June 2000. Use the graph to work Exercises 1–4.*

GAS PRICES: JUNE 1999–JUNE 2000

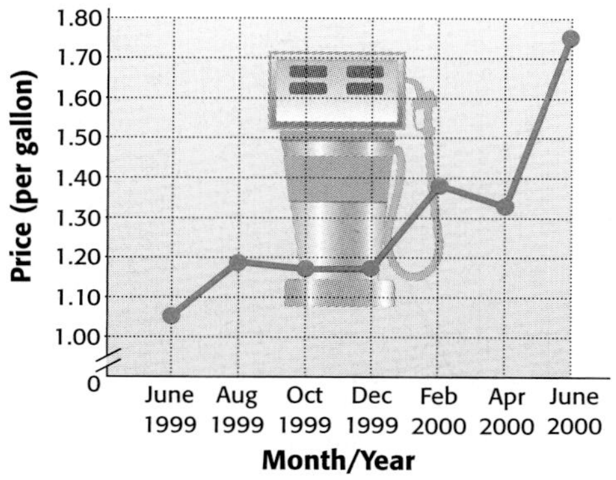

Source: Iowa DNR.

1. About how much did a gallon of gas cost in June 1999? In June 2000?

$1.05 per gal; $1.75 per gal

2. How much did the price of a gallon of gas increase over this 1-year period? What percent increase is this?

$.70 per gal; about 67%

3. During which months did the biggest increase in the price of a gallon of gas occur? About how much did the price increase during this time?

between April and June 2000; about $.40 per gal

4. Between which months did the price of a gallon of gas decrease?

August–October 1999 and February–April 2000

Complete the given ordered pairs for each equation.

5. $y = 3x + 2$ $\quad(-1,\ \ ), (0,\ \ ), (\ \ , 5)$

-1; 2; 1

6. $4x + 3y = 6$ $\quad(0,\ \ ), (\ \ , 0), (-2,\ \ )$

2; $\frac{3}{2}$; $\frac{14}{3}$

Decide whether each ordered pair is a solution of the given equation.

7. $x + y = 7$; $(2, 5)$

yes

8. $2x + y = 5$; $(-1, 3)$

no

9. $3x - y = 4$; $\left(\frac{1}{3}, -3\right)$

yes

Plot each ordered pair on the given coordinate system.

10. $(2, 3)$

11. $(-4, 2)$

12. $(3, 0)$

13. $(0, -6)$

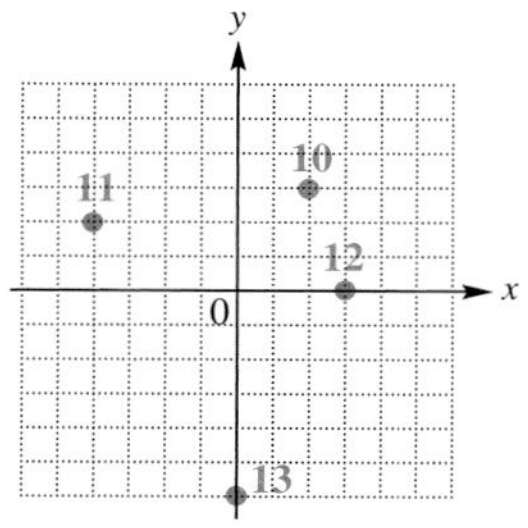

14. If $x > 0$ and $y < 0$, in what quadrant(s) must (x, y) lie? Explain.

x is positive in quadrants I and IV; y is negative in quadrants III and IV. Thus, if x is positive and y is negative, (x, y) must lie in quadrant IV.

15. On what axis does the point $(k, 0)$ lie for any real value of k? the point $(0, k)$? Explain.

In the ordered pair $(k, 0)$, the y-value is 0, so the point lies on the x-axis. In the ordered pair $(0, k)$, the x-value is 0, so the point lies on the y-axis.

[4.2] *Find the intercepts for each equation.*

16. $y = 2x + 5$
x-intercept:
y-intercept:

$\left(-\frac{5}{2}, 0\right)$; $(0, 5)$

17. $2x + y = -7$
x-intercept:
y-intercept:

$\left(-\frac{7}{2}, 0\right)$; $(0, -7)$

18. $3x + 2y = 8$
x-intercept:
y-intercept:

$\left(\frac{8}{3}, 0\right)$; $(0, 4)$

Graph each linear equation.

19. $2x - y = 3$

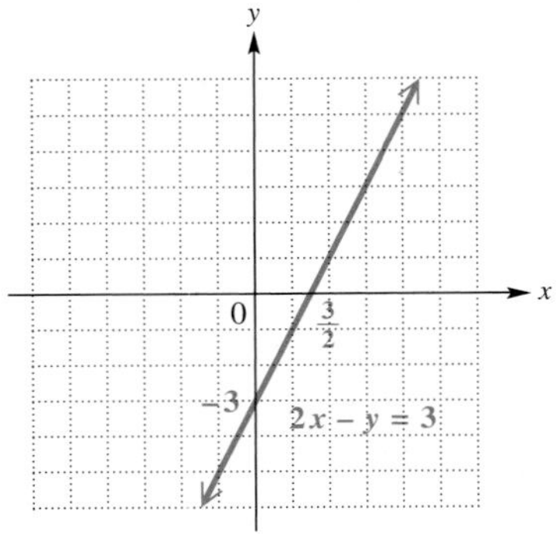

20. $x + 2y = -4$

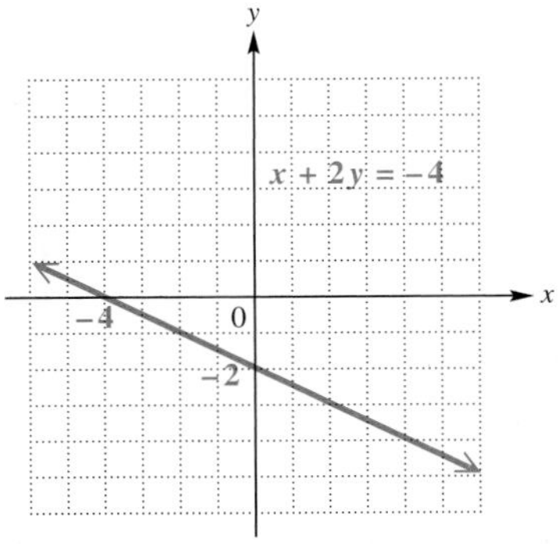

21. $x + y = 0$

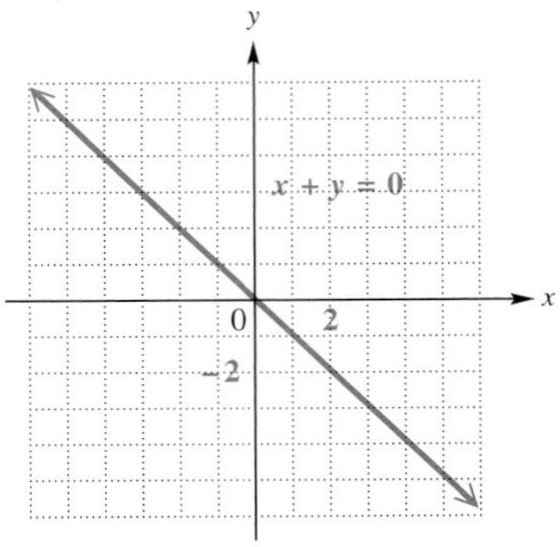

[4.3] *Find the slope of each line.*

22. Through $(2, 3)$ and $(-4, 6)$

$-\frac{1}{2}$

23. Through $(2, 5)$ and $(2, 8)$

undefined

24. $y = 3x - 4$

3

25. $\frac{3}{2}$

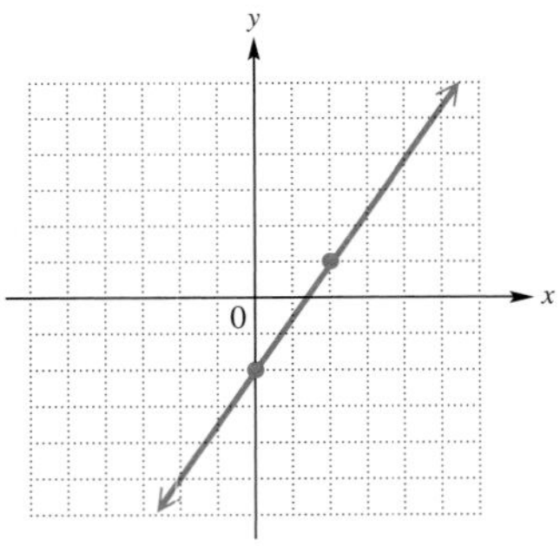

26. $-\frac{1}{3}$

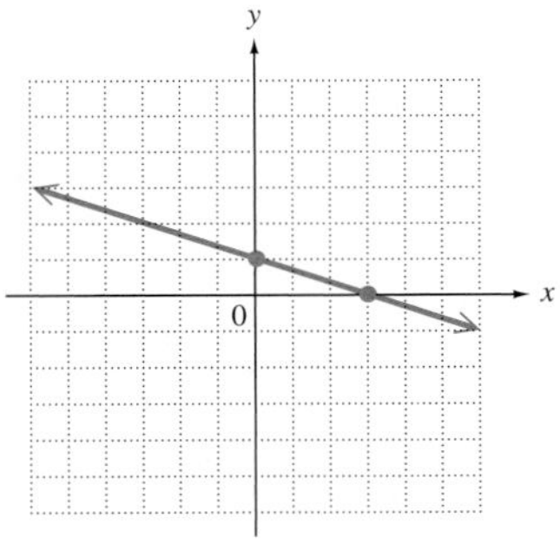

27. $y = 4$

0

28. The line having these points $\frac{3}{2}$

x	y
0	1
2	4
6	10

29. (a) A line parallel to the graph of $y = 2x + 3$ 2

(b) A line perpendicular to the graph of $y = -3x + 3$

$\frac{1}{3}$

Decide whether each pair of lines is parallel, perpendicular, *or* neither.

30. $3x + 2y = 6$
$6x + 4y = 8$

parallel

31. $x - 3y = 1$
$3x + y = 4$

perpendicular

32. $x - 2y = 8$
$x + 2y = 8$

neither

33. If the pitch of a roof is $\frac{1}{4}$, how many feet in the horizontal direction correspond to a rise of 3 ft?

12 ft

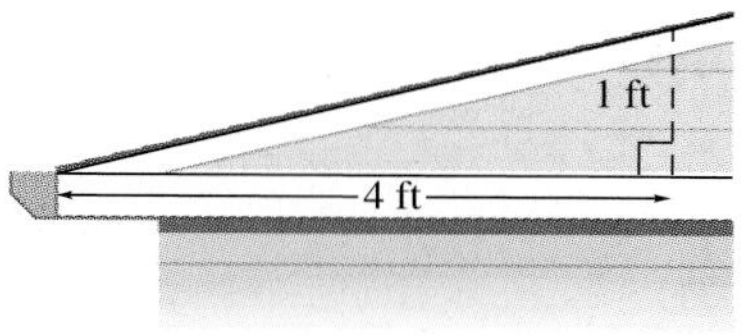

34. Family income in the United States has steadily increased for many years (primarily due to inflation). In 1970 the median family income was about $10,000 per yr. In 1998 it was about $47,000 per yr. Find the average rate of change of median family income over that period. (*Source:* U.S. Bureau of the Census.)

$1321 per yr

[4.4] *Write an equation in slope-intercept form (if possible) for each line.*

35. Slope $\frac{3}{5}$; y-intercept $(0, -8)$

$y = \frac{3}{5}x - 8$

36. Slope $-\frac{1}{3}$; y-intercept $(0, 5)$

$y = -\frac{1}{3}x + 5$

37. Slope 0; y-intercept $(0, 12)$

$y = 12$

38. Undefined slope; through $(2, 7)$

$x = 2$

39. Through $(2, -5)$ and $(1, 4)$

$y = -9x + 13$

40. Through $(-3, -1)$ and $(2, 6)$

$y = \frac{7}{5}x + \frac{16}{5}$

41. Parallel to $4x - y = 3$ and through $(6, -2)$

$y = 4x - 26$

42. Perpendicular to $2x - 5y = 7$ and through $(0, 1)$

$y = -\frac{5}{2}x + 1$

43. The Waste Management and Recycling Division of Sacramento County is responsible for managing the disposal of solid waste, including the operation of a landfill. The graph shows the remaining capacity (in millions of tons) at the county landfill during the past few years. These points appear to lie close to a straight line. The equation of this line can be used to project future landfill capacity.

(a) Write an equation in slope-intercept form of the line shown through the points $(0, 5.6)$ and $(2.5, 3.2)$.

$y = -.96x + 5.6$

(b) Use the equation from part (a) to estimate the remaining capacity of the landfill in 2001.

.8 million or 800,000 tons

(c) Based on the graph, when will the capacity of the landfill be used up? Explain. **near the end of 2001; The graphed line intersects the x-axis right before 2002.**

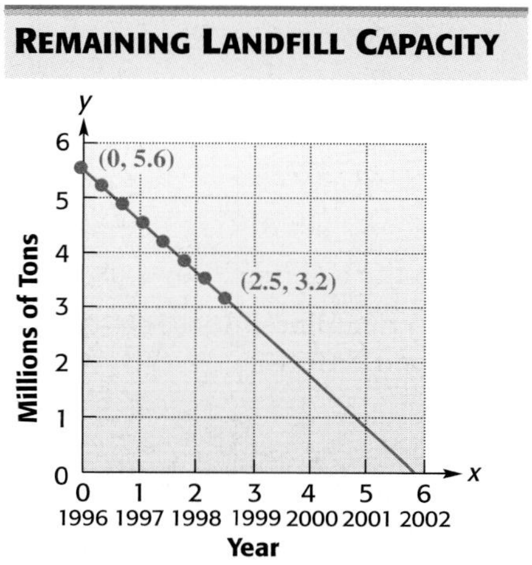

Source: Waste Management and Recycling Division, Sacramento County Public Works Agency, 1998 Report.

[4.5] *Graph each linear inequality.*

44. $3x + 5y > 9$

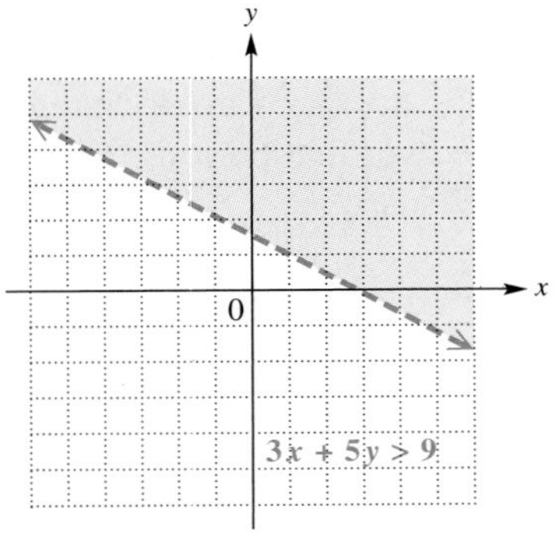

45. $2x - 3y > -6$

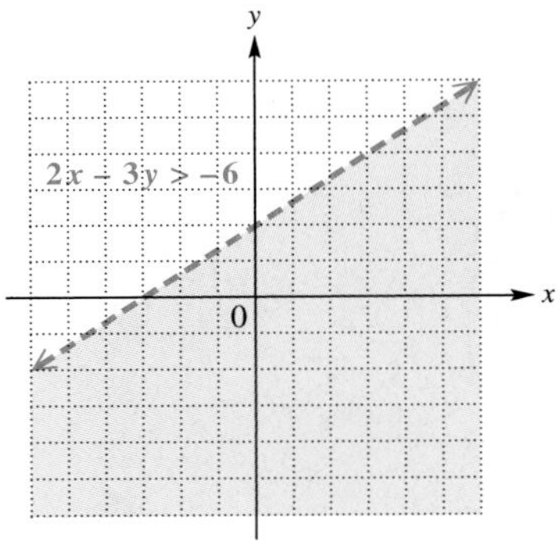

46. $x \geq 2$ or $y \geq 2$

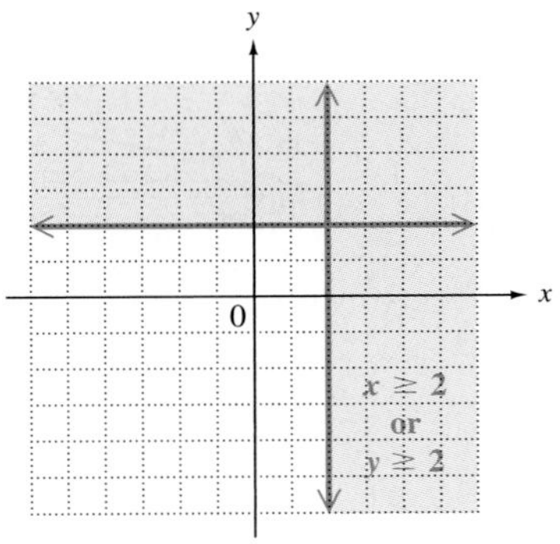

[4.6] *Give the domain and range of each relation. Identify any functions.*

47. $\{(-4, 2), (-4, -2), (1, 5), (1, -5)\}$

domain: $\{-4, 1\}$;
range: $\{2, -2, 5, -5\}$;
not a function

48.

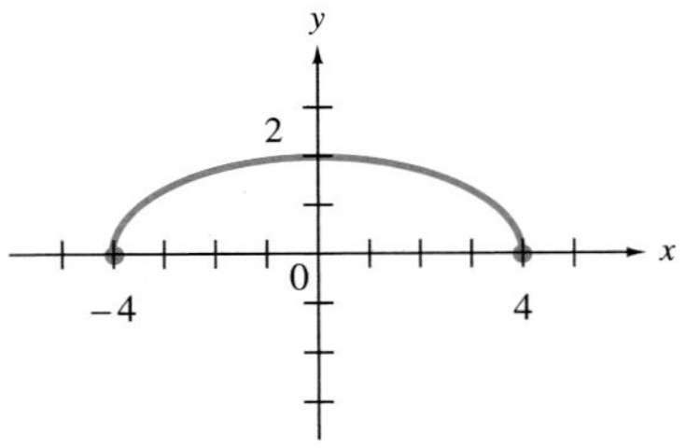

domain: $[-4, 4]$;
range: $[0, 2]$;
function

Determine whether each relation defines y as a function of x. Identify any linear functions. Give the domain in each case.

49. $y = 3x - 3$

function; linear function;
domain: $(-\infty, \infty)$

50. $y < x + 2$

not a function;
domain: $(-\infty, \infty)$

51. $y = |x - 4|$

function;
domain: $(-\infty, \infty)$

52. $y = \dfrac{1}{x + 7}$

function; domain:
$(-\infty, -7) \cup (-7, \infty)$

53. $x = y^2$

not a function;
domain: $[0, \infty)$

54. $y = \dfrac{7}{x - 36}$

function; domain:
$(-\infty, 36) \cup (36, \infty)$

55. Explain the test that allows us to determine whether a graph is that of a function.

If no vertical line intersects the graph in more than one point, then it is the graph of a function.

Given $f(x) = -2x^2 + 3x - 6$, *find each of the following.*

56. $f(0)$

-6

57. $f(3)$

-15

58. $f(p)$

$-2p^2 + 3p - 6$

59. $f(-k)$

$-2k^2 - 3k - 6$

60. The equation $2x^2 - y = 0$ defines y as a function of x. Rewrite it using $f(x)$ notation, and find $f(3)$.

$f(x) = 2x^2$; 18

Mixed Review Exercises

In Exercises 61–66, match each statement to the appropriate graph or graphs in A–D. Graphs may be used more than once.

A.

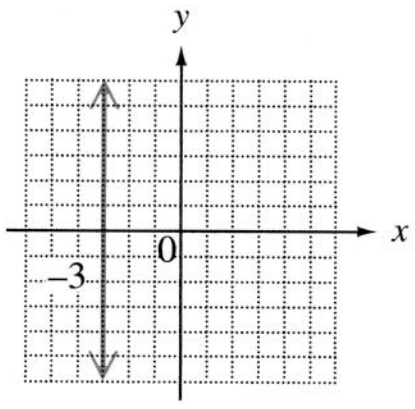

B.

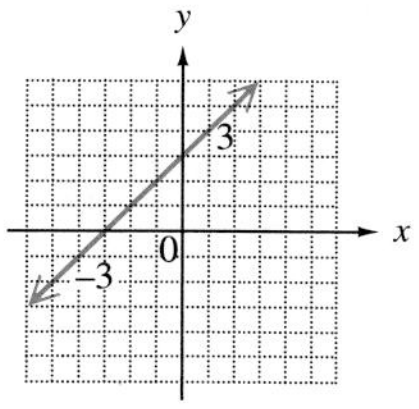

C.

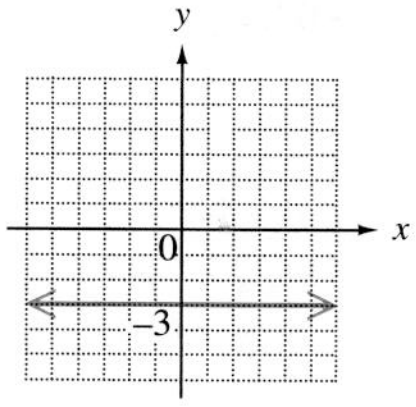

D.

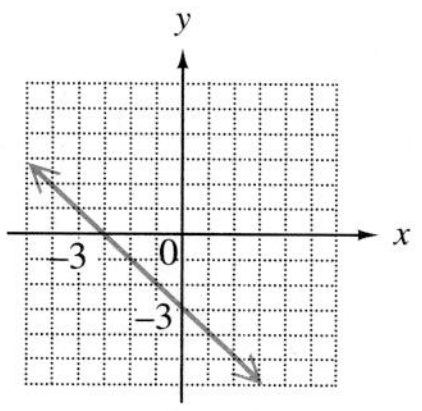

61. The line shown in the graph has undefined slope.
A

62. The graph of the equation has y-intercept $(0, -3)$.
C, D

63. The graph of the equation has x-intercept $(-3, 0)$.
A, B, D

64. The line shown in the graph has negative slope.
D

65. The graph is that of the equation $y = -3$. C

66. The line shown in the graph has slope 1. B

Find the intercepts and the slope of each line. Then graph the line.

67. $y = -2x - 5$
x-intercept:
y-intercept:
slope:

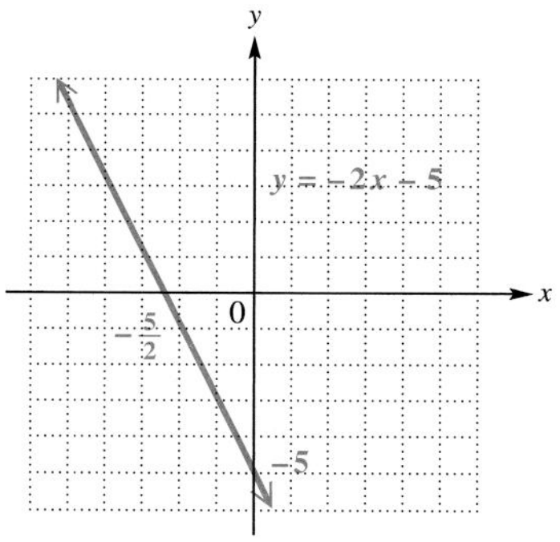

$\left(-\frac{5}{2}, 0\right)$; $(0, -5)$; -2

68. $x + 3y = 0$
x-intercept:
y-intercept:
slope:

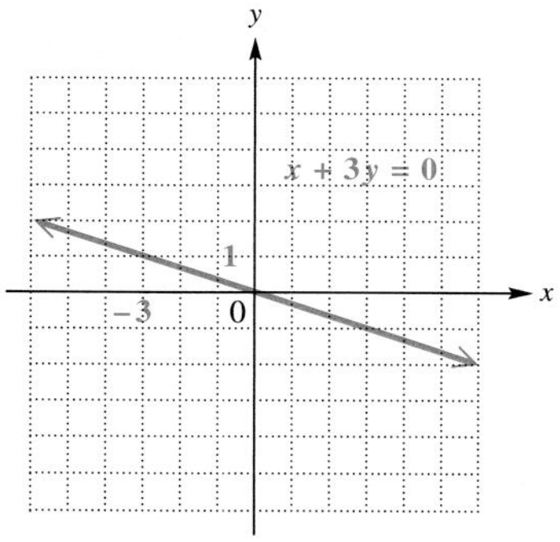

$(0, 0)$; $(0, 0)$; $-\frac{1}{3}$

69. $y - 5 = 0$
x-intercept:
y-intercept:
slope:

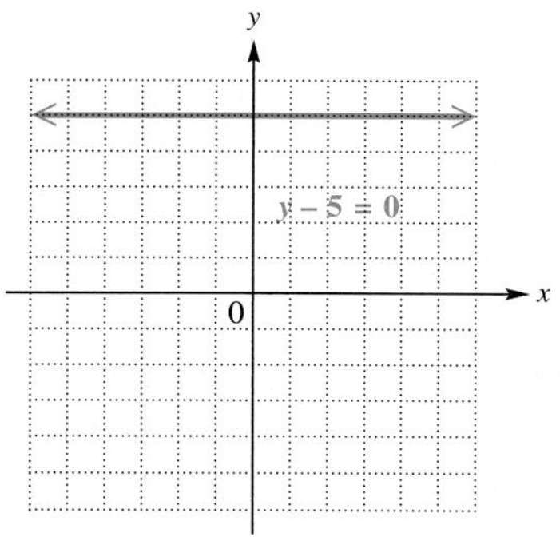

no x-intercept; $(0, 5)$; 0

Write an equation in slope-intercept form for each line.

70. $m = -\frac{1}{4}$; $b = -\frac{5}{4}$

$y = -\frac{1}{4}x - \frac{5}{4}$

71. Through $(8, 6)$; $m = -3$

$y = -3x + 30$

72. Through $(3, -5)$ and $(-4, -1)$

$y = -\frac{4}{7}x - \frac{23}{7}$

Graph each inequality.

73. $y < -4x$

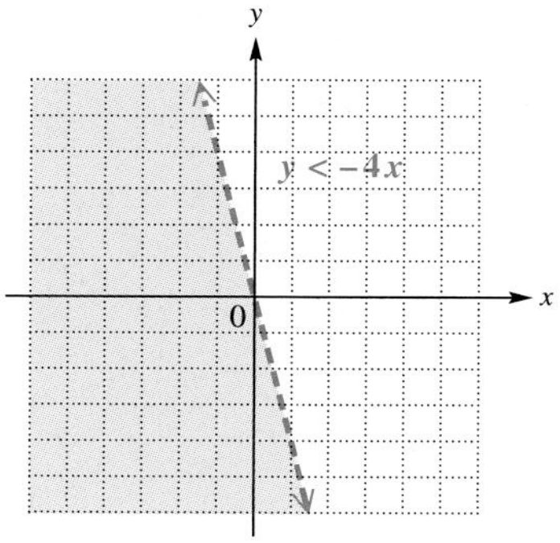

74. $x - 2y \leq 6$

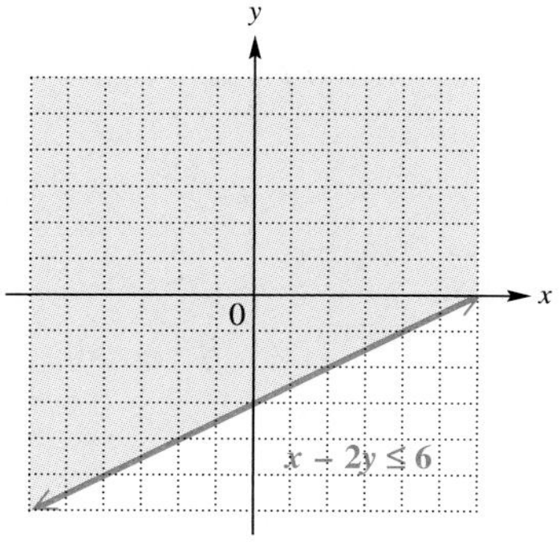

RELATING CONCEPTS (Exercises 75–83) FOR INDIVIDUAL OR GROUP WORK

The total amount spent in billions of dollars on video rentals in the United States from 1996 through 2000 is shown in the graph. Use the graph to ***work Exercises 75–83 in order.***

VIDEO RENTALS

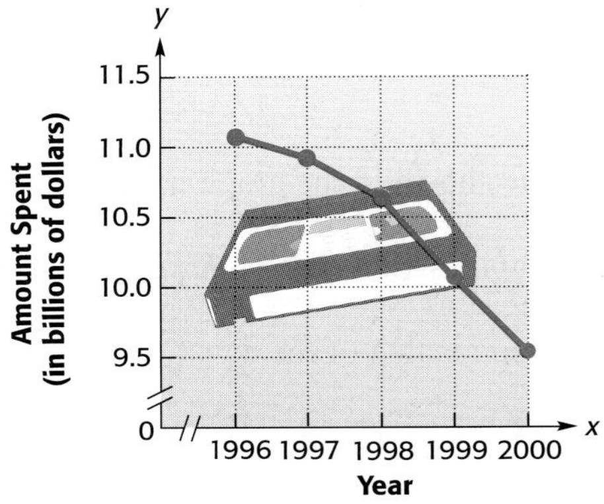

Source: Blockbuster.

75. About how much did the amount spent on video rentals decrease during the years shown in the graph?
about $1.5 billion

76. Since the points of the graph lie approximately in a linear pattern, a straight line can be used to model the data. Will this line have positive or negative slope? Explain.

It will have negative slope since the total spent on video rentals is decreasing over these years.

77. The table gives the actual amounts spent on video rentals in 1996 and 2000. Write two ordered pairs for the data. **(1996, 11.1), (2000, 9.6)**

Year x	Amount y (in billions of dollars)
1996	11.1
2000	9.6

78. Use the ordered pairs from Exercise 77 to find the equation of a line that models the data. Write the equation in slope-intercept form.

$y = -.375x + 759.6$

79. Based on the equation you found in Exercise 78, what is the slope of the line? Does it agree with your answer in Exercise 76?

$-.375$; Yes, the slope is negative.

80. Use the equation from Exercise 78 to approximate the amount spent on video rentals from 1997 through 1999, and complete the table. Round your answers to the nearest tenth.

x	y
1996	11.1
1997	**10.7**
1998	**10.4**
1999	**10.0**
2000	9.6

81. The actual amounts spent on video rentals are given in the following ordered pairs.

(1996, 11.1), (1997, 10.9), (1998, 10.6), (1999, 10.1), (2000, 9.6)

How do the actual amounts compare to those you found in Exercise 80 using the linear equation?

The actual amounts are fairly close to those given by the equation.

82. Since the equation in Exercise 78 models the data fairly well, use it to predict the amount that will be spent on video rentals in 2002. **$8.9 billion**

83. Discuss reasons why the amount spent on video rentals has been decreasing in recent years.

Answers will vary.

Chapter 4 TEST

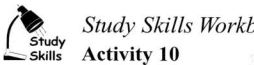

Study Skills Workbook
Activity 10

1. Complete these ordered pairs for the equation $3x + 5y = -30$: (0,), (, 0), (, −3).

2. Is (4, −1) a solution of $4x - 7y = 9$?

3. How do you find the x-intercept of the graph of a linear equation in two variables? How do you find the y-intercept?

Graph each linear equation. Give the x- and y-intercepts.

4. $3x + y = 6$

5. $y - 2x = 0$

6. $x + 3 = 0$

1. **−6, −10, −5**

2. **no**

3. **To find the x-intercept, let $y = 0$, and to find the y-intercept, let $x = 0$.**

4. x-intercept: **(2, 0)**
y-intercept: **(0, 6)**

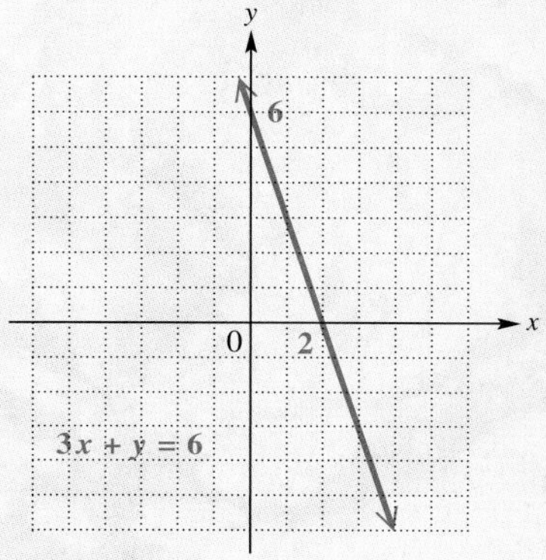

5. x-intercept: **(0, 0)**
y-intercept: **(0, 0)**

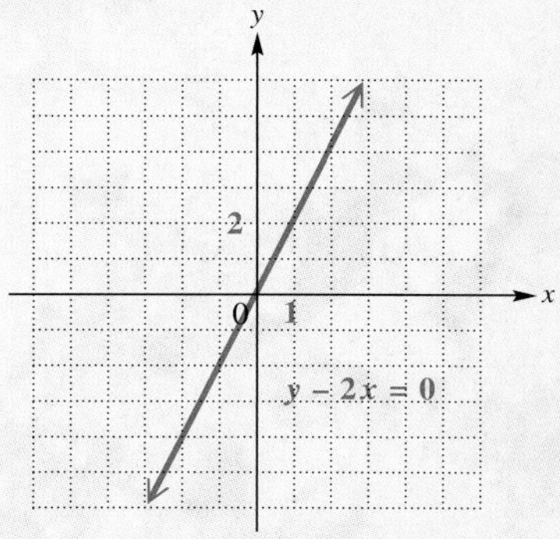

6. x-intercept: **(−3, 0)**
y-intercept: **none**

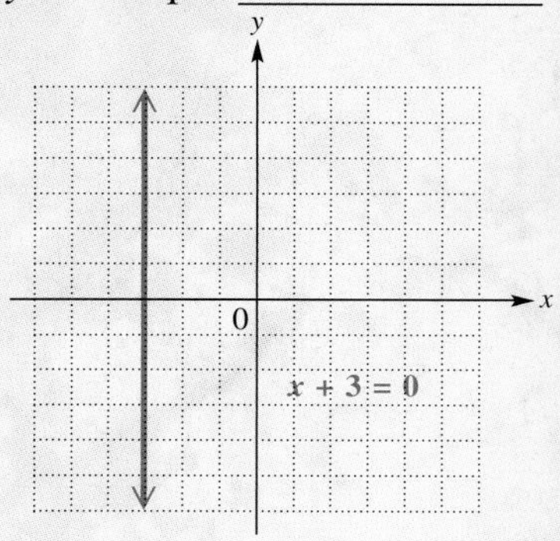

7. x-intercept: $(4, 0)$
y-intercept: $(0, -4)$

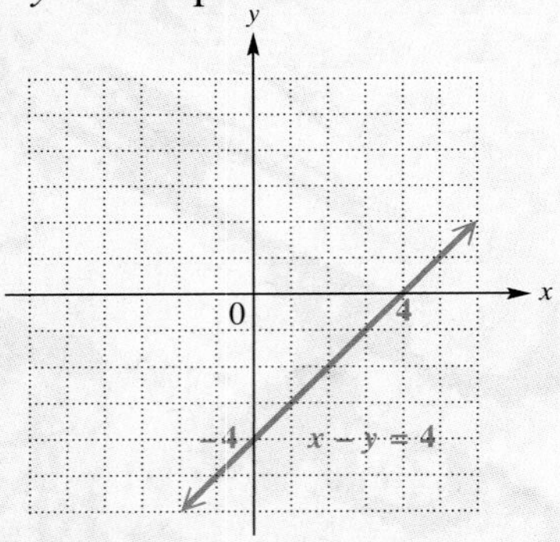

7. $x - y = 4$

Find the slope of each line.

8. $-\frac{8}{3}$

8. Through $(-4, 6)$ and $(-1, -2)$

9. -2

9. $2x + y = 10$

10. undefined

10. $x + 12 = 0$

11. $\frac{5}{2}$

11. 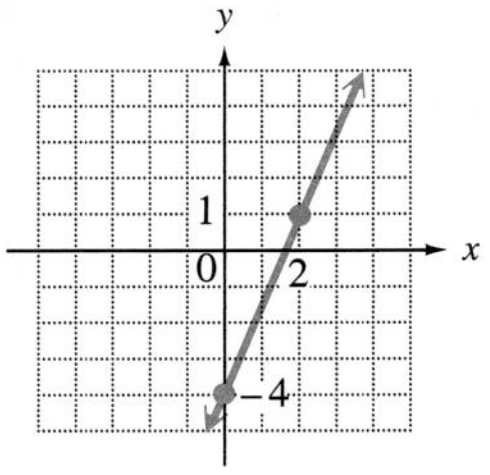

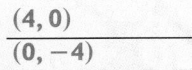

Write an equation in slope-intercept form for each line.

12. $y = 2x + 6$

12. Through $(-1, 4)$; $m = 2$

13. $y = \frac{5}{2}x - 4$

13. The line in Exercise 11

14. Through $(-7, 2)$;

(a) parallel to $3x + 5y = 6$

(b) perpendicular to $y = 2x$

14. (a) $y = -\frac{3}{5}x - \frac{11}{5}$

(b) $y = -\frac{1}{2}x - \frac{3}{2}$

15. Graph $x + y \leq 3$.

15.

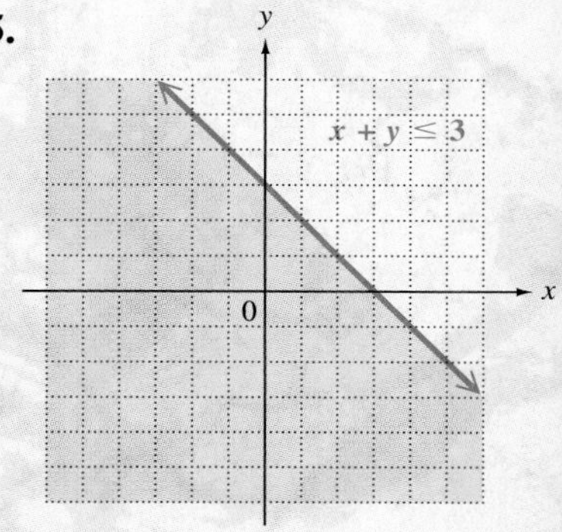

16. Which of the following is the graph of a function?

A.

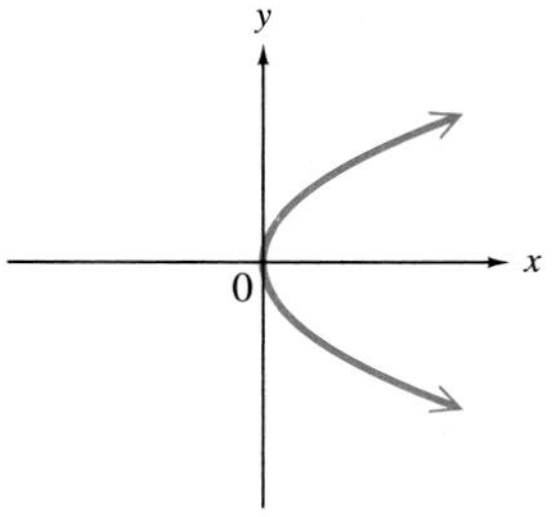

B.

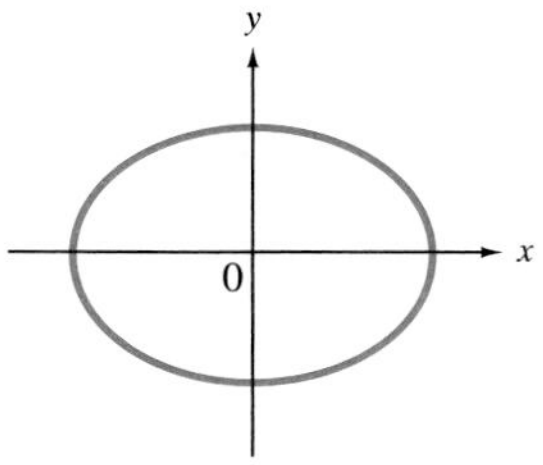

C.

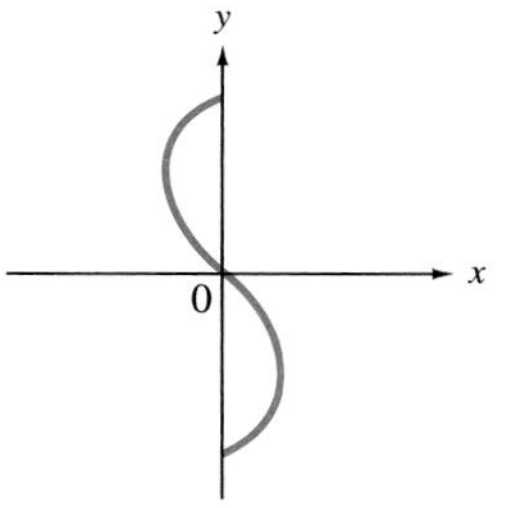

D.

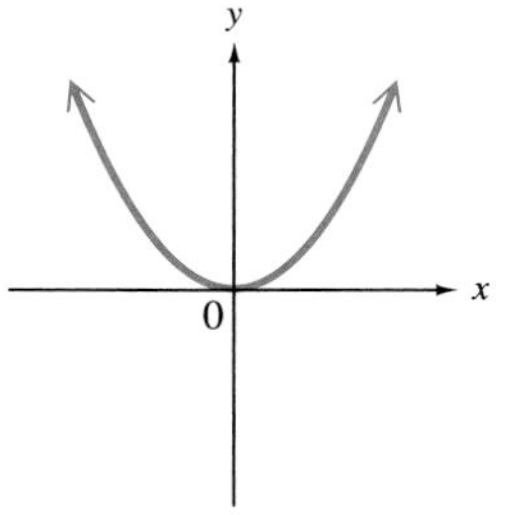

16. D

17. For the function defined by $f(x) = x^4 - 3$,

(a) give the domain, **(b)** find $f(-1)$.

17. (a) $(-\infty, \infty)$

(b) -2

18. B; The set in A includes, for example, the two ordered pairs (8.8, 1993) and (8.8, 1994). In a function, no value of the independent variable can correspond to more than one value of the dependent variable.

18. Deaths per 1000 population from 1993 through 1997 are shown in the table.

Death Rate	8.8	8.8	8.8	8.7	8.6
Year	1993	1994	1995	1996	1997

Source: U.S. National Center for Health Statistics.

Which set of ordered pairs from the table is a function? Explain.

A. {Death Rate, Year} **B.** {Year, Death Rate}

The graph shows total food and drink sales at U.S. restaurants from 1970 through 2000, where 1970 corresponds to $x = 0$. Use the graph to work Exercises 19–22.

WHAT'S FOR DINNER?

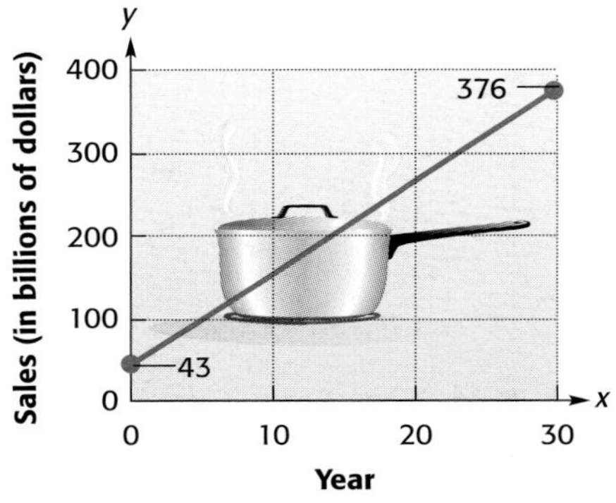

Source: National Restaurant Association.

19. The slope is positive since food and drink sales are increasing.

19. Is the slope of the line in the graph positive or negative? Explain.

20. (0, 43), (30, 376); 11.1

20. Write two ordered pairs for the data points shown in the graph. Use them to find the slope of the line.

21. 1990: $265 billion; 1995: $320.5 billion

21. The linear equation

$$y = 11.1x + 43$$

approximates food and drink sales y in billions of dollars, where $x = 0$ again represents 1970. Use the equation to approximate food and drink sales for 1990 and 1995.

22. In 2000, food and drink sales were $376 billion.

22. What does the ordered pair (30, 376) mean in the context of this problem?

Cumulative Review Exercises CHAPTERS R–4

Perform the indicated operations.

1. $10\frac{5}{8} - 3\frac{1}{10}$ **$\frac{301}{40}$ or $7\frac{21}{40}$**

2. $\frac{3}{4} \div \frac{1}{8}$ **6**

3. $5 - (-4) + (-2)$ **7**

4. $\frac{(-3)^2 - (-4)(2^4)}{5(2) - (-2)^3}$ **$\frac{73}{18}$ or $4\frac{1}{18}$**

5. True or false? $\frac{4(3 - 9)}{2 - 6} \geq 6$ **true**

6. Find the value of $xz^3 - 5y^2$ when $x = -2, y = -3$, and $z = -1$. **-43**

7. What property does $3(-2 + x) = -6 + 3x$ illustrate? **distributive property**

8. Simplify $-4p - 6 + 3p + 8$ by combining terms. **$-p + 2$**

Solve.

9. $2z - 5 + 3z = 4 - (z + 2)$ **$\left\{\frac{7}{6}\right\}$**

10. $\frac{3a - 1}{5} + \frac{a + 2}{2} = -\frac{3}{10}$ **$\{-1\}$**

11. $V = \frac{1}{3}\pi r^2 h$ for h **$h = \frac{3V}{\pi r^2}$**

12. $3 - 2(m + 3) < 4m$ **$\left(-\frac{1}{2}, \infty\right)$**

13. $2k + 4 < 10$ and $3k - 1 > 5$ **$(2, 3)$**

14. $2k + 4 > 10$ or $3k - 1 < 5$ **$(-\infty, 2) \cup (3, \infty)$**

15. $|5x + 3| = 13$ **$\left\{-\frac{16}{5}, 2\right\}$**

16. $|x + 2| < 9$ **$(-11, 7)$**

17. $|2y - 5| \geq 9$ **$(-\infty, -2] \cup [7, \infty)$**

Solve each problem.

18. The gap in average annual earnings by level of education continues to increase. Based on the most recent statistics available, a person with a bachelor's degree can expect to earn $17,583 more each year than someone with a high school diploma. Together the individuals would earn $63,373. How much can a person at each level of education expect to earn? (*Source:* U.S. Bureau of the Census.) **high school diploma: $22,895; bachelor's degree: $40,478**

19. Mount Mayon in the Philippines is the most perfectly shaped conical volcano in the world. Its base is a perfect circle with circumference 80 mi, and it has a height of about 8200 ft. (One mile is 5280 ft.) Find the radius of the circular base to the nearest mile. (*Hint:* This problem has some unneeded information.) (*Source: Microsoft Encarta Encyclopedia 2000.*) **13 mi**

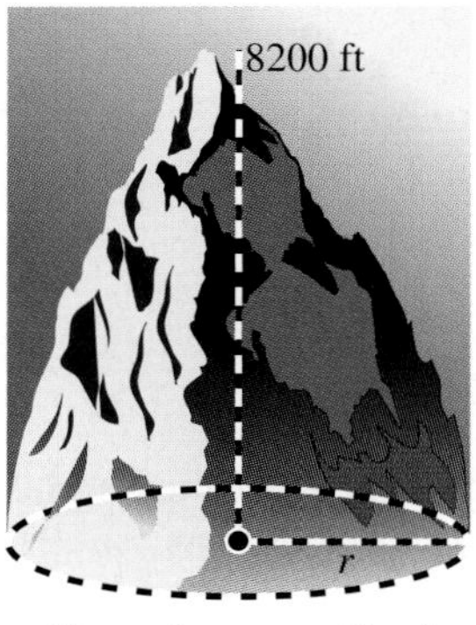

Circumference = 80 mi

20. The winning times in seconds for the women's 1000 m speed skating event in the Winter Olympics for the years 1960 through 1998 can be closely approximated by the linear equation

$$y = -.4685x + 95.07,$$

where x is the number of years since 1960. That is, $x = 4$ represents 1964, $x = 8$ represents 1968, and so on. (*Source: The Universal Almanac,* 1998.)

(a) Use this equation to complete the table of values. Round times to the nearest hundredth of a second.

x	y
12	**89.45**
28	**81.95**
36	**78.20**

(b) What does the ordered pair (20, 85.7) mean in the context of the problem?

In 1980, the winning time was 85.7 sec.

21. Baby boomers are expected to inherit \$10.4 trillion from their parents over the next 45 yr, an average of \$50,000 each. The circle graph shows how they plan to spend their inheritances.

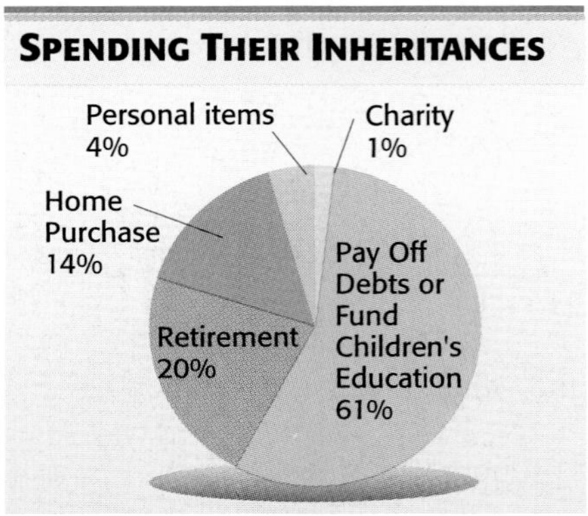

Source: First Interstate Bank Trust and Private Banking Group.

(a) How much is expected to go toward retirement? **\$10,000**

(b) Use the answer from part (a) to estimate the amount expected to go toward paying off debts or funding children's education.

about \$30,000

Consider the linear equation $-3x + 4y = 12$. *Find the following.*

22. The x- and y-intercepts

(−4, 0); (0, 3)

23. The slope

$\frac{3}{4}$

24. The graph

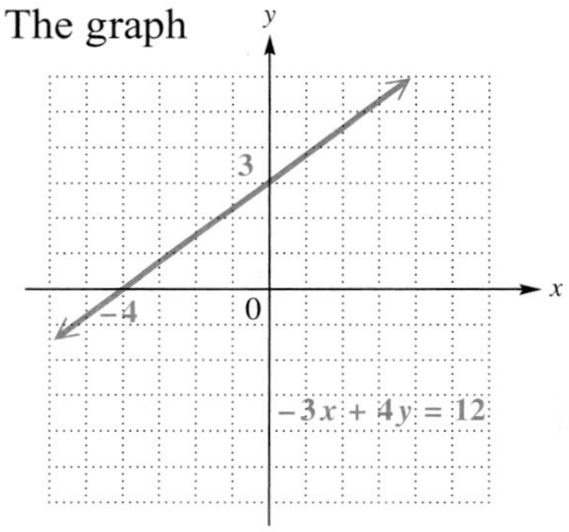

Write an equation in slope-intercept form for each line.

25. Through (2, −5) with slope 3 $y = 3x - 11$

26. Through (0, 4) and (2, 4) $y = 4$

Use the graph to answer Exercises 27 and 28.

27. What is the slope of the line segment joining the points for 1992 and 2000? **10.5**

28. Which one of the two line segments shown has a greater slope?
the segment for 1992 through 2000

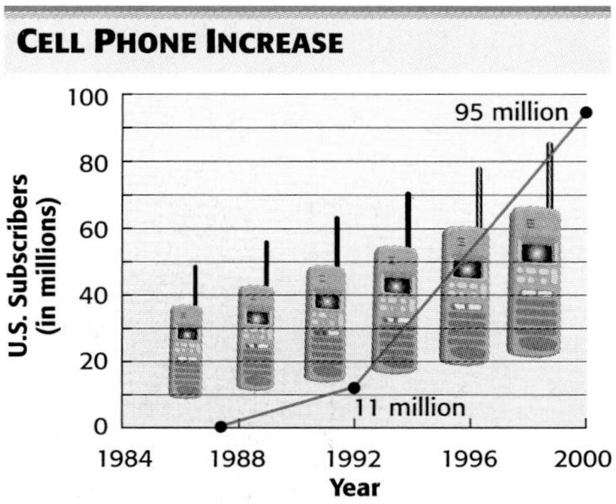

Source: Cellular Telecommunications Industry Association, Intel Corp.

Systems of Linear Equations

5

On November 7, 2000, in what was to become the most hotly contested presidential election in U.S. history, over 100,000,000 Americans went to the polls to vote. Although Al Gore won the popular vote by .5%, George W. Bush carried the Electoral College by 271 to 267 and became the 43rd president. (*Source: The Gazette,* January 18, 2001.) In Exercise 43 of Section 5.5, we determine the political affiliations of Americans using the concepts of this chapter.

5.1 Solving Systems of Linear Equations by Graphing

Objectives

1. Decide whether a given ordered pair is a solution of a system.
2. Solve linear systems by graphing.
3. Solve special systems by graphing.

1 Fill in the blanks, and decide whether the given ordered pair is a solution of the system.

(a) (2, 5)
$3x - 2y = -4$
$5x + y = 15$

$3x - 2y = -4$
$3(\_\_\_) - 2(\_\_\_) = -4$

$5x + y = 15$
$5(2) + \_\_\_ = \_\_\_$

(2, 5) ______ a solution.
(is/is not)

(b) (1, −2)
$x - 3y = 7$
$4x + y = 5$

(1, −2) ______ a solution.
(is/is not)

Answers
1. (a) 2; 5; 5; 15; is **(b)** is not

A **system of linear equations** consists of two or more linear equations with the same variables. Examples of systems of two linear equations include

$$\begin{aligned} 2x + 3y &= 4 \\ 3x - y &= -5 \end{aligned} \qquad \begin{aligned} x + 3y &= 1 \\ -y &= 4 - 2x \end{aligned} \qquad \begin{aligned} x - y &= 1 \\ y &= 3. \end{aligned}$$

In the system on the right, think of $y = 3$ as an equation in two variables by writing it as $0x + y = 3$.

1 Decide whether a given ordered pair is a solution of a system. A **solution of a system** of linear equations is an ordered pair that makes both equations true *at the same time*. A solution of an equation is said to *satisfy* the equation.

Example 1 Determining Whether an Ordered Pair Is a Solution

Is (4, −3) a solution of each system?

(a) $x + 4y = -8$
$3x + 2y = 6$

To decide whether or not (4, −3) is a solution of the system, substitute 4 for x and −3 for y in each equation.

$$\begin{aligned} x + 4y &= -8 \\ 4 + 4(-3) &= -8 \quad ? \\ 4 + (-12) &= -8 \quad ? \quad \text{Multiply.} \\ -8 &= -8 \quad \text{True} \end{aligned} \qquad \begin{aligned} 3x + 2y &= 6 \\ 3(4) + 2(-3) &= 6 \quad ? \\ 12 + (-6) &= 6 \quad ? \quad \text{Multiply.} \\ 6 &= 6 \quad \text{True} \end{aligned}$$

Because (4, −3) satisfies both equations, it is a solution of the system.

(b) $2x + 5y = -7$
$3x + 4y = 2$

Again, substitute 4 for x and −3 for y in both equations.

$$\begin{aligned} 2x + 5y &= -7 \\ 2(4) + 5(-3) &= -7 \quad ? \\ 8 + (-15) &= -7 \quad ? \quad \text{Multiply.} \\ -7 &= -7 \quad \text{True} \end{aligned} \qquad \begin{aligned} 3x + 4y &= 2 \\ 3(4) + 4(-3) &= 2 \quad ? \\ 12 + (-12) &= 2 \quad ? \quad \text{Multiply.} \\ 0 &= 2 \quad \text{False} \end{aligned}$$

The ordered pair (4, −3) is not a solution of this system because it does not satisfy the second equation.

Work Problem 1 at the Side.

We discuss several methods of solving a system of two linear equations in two variables in this chapter.

2 Solve linear systems by graphing. The set of all ordered pairs that are solutions of a system is the **solution set** of the system. One way to find the solution set of a system of two linear equations is to graph both equations on the same axes. The graph of each line shows points whose coordinates satisfy the equation of that line. Any intersection point would be on both lines and would therefore be a solution of both equations. Thus, the coordinates of any point where the lines intersect give a solution of the system. Because two different straight lines can intersect at no more than one point, there can never be more than one solution for such a system. The graph in Figure 1 shows that the solution of the system in Example 1(a) is the intersection point $(4, -3)$.

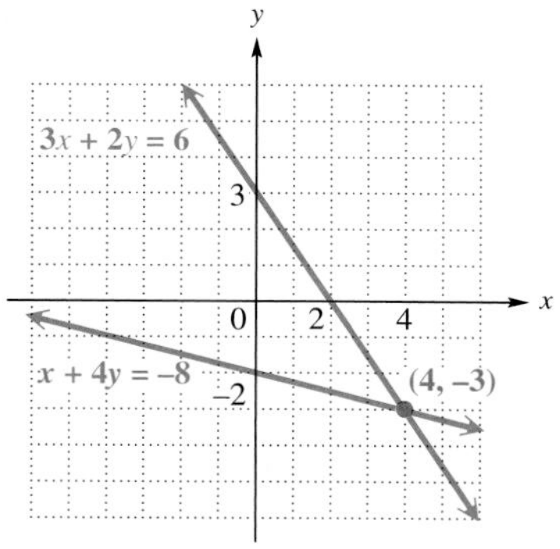

Figure 1

Example 2 Solving a System by Graphing

Solve the system of equations by graphing both equations on the same axes.

$$2x + 3y = 4$$
$$3x - y = -5$$

As shown in Chapter 4, we graph these two equations by plotting several points for each line. Recall from Section 4.2 that we can choose *any* number for either x or y to get an ordered pair. The intercepts are often convenient choices. It is a good idea to use a third ordered pair as a check.

$2x + 3y = 4$

x	y
0	$\frac{4}{3}$
2	0
-2	$\frac{8}{3}$

$3x - y = -5$

x	y
0	5
$-\frac{5}{3}$	0
-2	-1

The lines in Figure 2 suggest that the graphs intersect at the point $(-1, 2)$. We check this by substituting -1 for x and 2 for y in both equations. Because $(-1, 2)$ satisfies both equations, the solution set of this system is $\{(-1, 2)\}$.

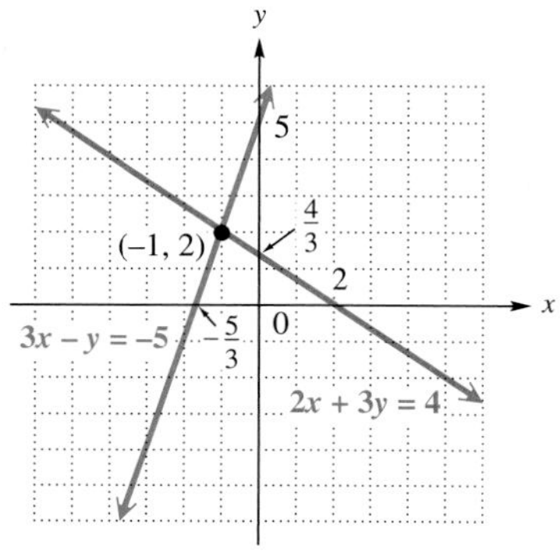

Figure 2

Work Problem 2 at the Side.

2 Solve each system of equations by graphing both equations on the same axes. Check your answers.

(a) $5x - 3y = 9$
$x + 2y = 7$
(One of the lines is already graphed.)

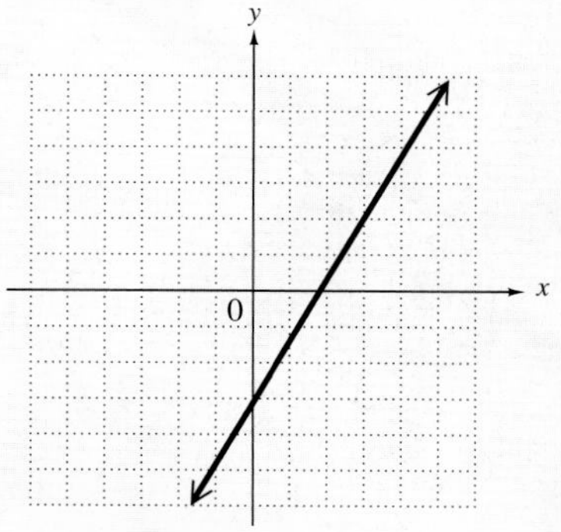

(b) $x + y = 4$
$2x - y = -1$

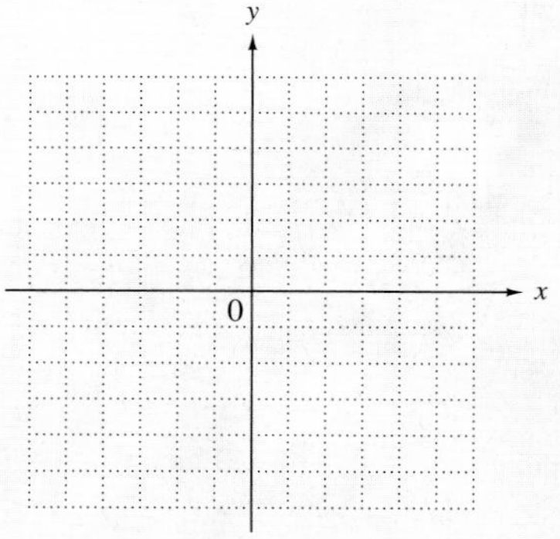

ANSWERS
2. **(a)** $\{(3, 2)\}$ **(b)** $\{(1, 3)\}$

CAUTION

A difficulty with the graphing method of solution is that it may not be possible to determine from the graph the exact coordinates of the point that represents the solution, particularly if these coordinates are not integers. For this reason, algebraic methods of solution are explained later in this chapter. The graphing method does, however, show geometrically how solutions are found and is useful when approximate answers will do.

3 Solve special systems by graphing. Sometimes the graphs of the two equations in a system either do not intersect at all or are the same line, as in the systems in Example 3.

Example 3 Solving Special Systems

Solve each system by graphing.

(a) $2x + y = 2$

$2x + y = 8$

The graphs of these lines are shown in Figure 3. The two lines are parallel and have no points in common. For such a system, there is no solution; we write the solution set as $\emptyset$.

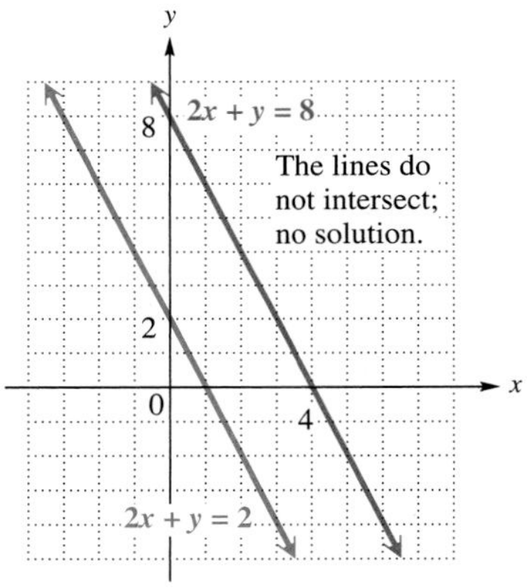

Figure 3

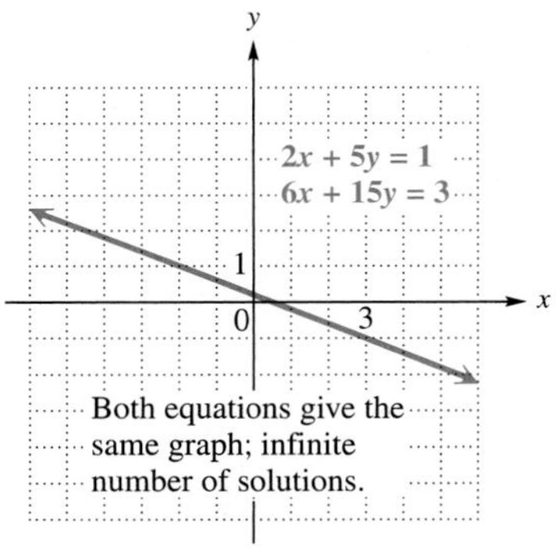

Figure 4

(b) $2x + 5y = 1$

$6x + 15y = 3$

The graphs of these two equations are the same line. See Figure 4. The second equation can be obtained by multiplying each side of the first equation by 3. In this case, every point on the line is a solution of the system, and the solution set contains an infinite number of ordered pairs. We write the solution set as

$$\{(x, y) \mid 2x + 5y = 1\}.$$

NOTE

When a system has an infinite number of solutions, as in Example 3(b), either equation of the system could be used to write the solution set. We prefer to use the equation (in standard form) with coefficients that are integers ($A > 0$) having no common factor (except 1). Other texts may express such solutions differently.

The system in Example 2 has exactly one solution. A system with at least one solution is called a **consistent system.** A system of equations with no solutions, such as the one in Example 3(a), is called an **inconsistent system.** The equations in Example 2 are **independent equations** with different graphs. The equations of the system in Example 3(b) have the same graph and are equivalent. Because they are different forms of the same equation, these equations are called **dependent equations.**

Work Problem **3** at the Side.

Examples 2 and 3 show the three cases that may occur when solving a system of two equations with two variables.

Possible Types of Solutions

1. The graphs intersect at exactly one point, which gives the (single) solution of the system. The **system is consistent,** and the **equations are independent.**

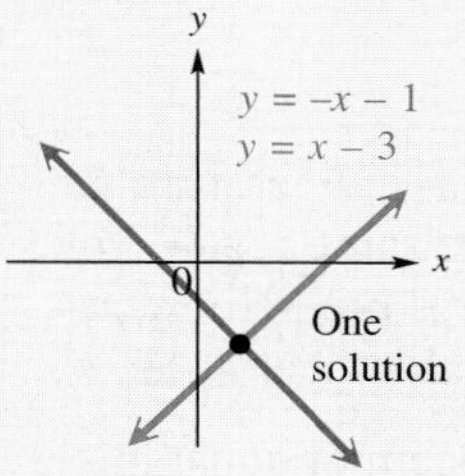

2. The graphs are parallel lines, so there is no solution and the solution set is $\emptyset$. The **system is inconsistent.**

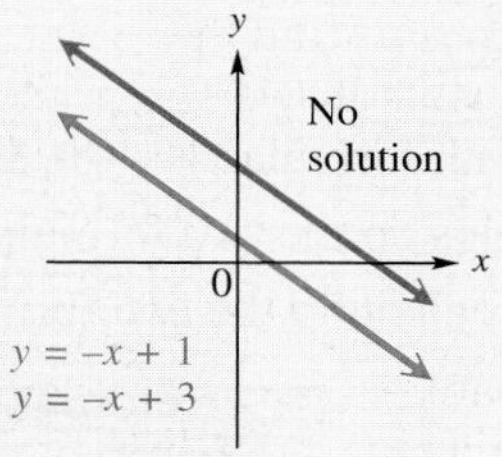

3. The graphs are the same line. The solution set contains an infinite number of ordered pairs. The **equations are dependent.**

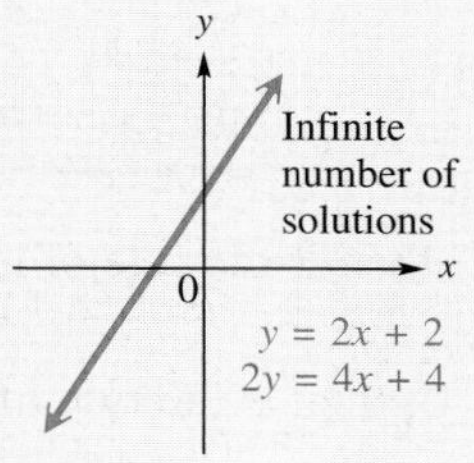

3 Solve each system of equations by graphing both equations on the same axes.

(a) $3x - y = 4$
$6x - 2y = 12$
(One of the lines is already graphed.)

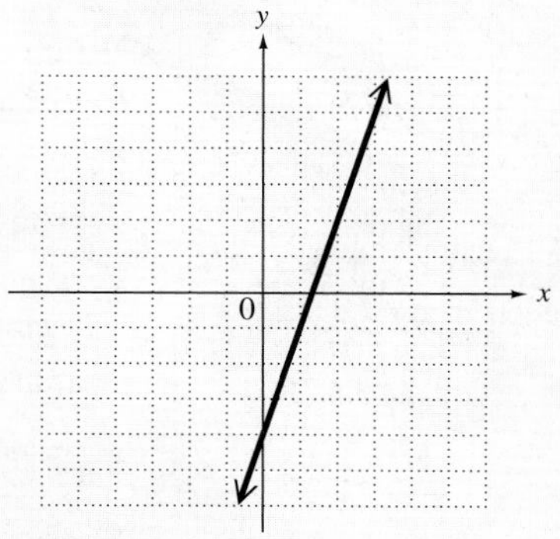

(b) $-x + 3y = 2$
$2x - 6y = -4$

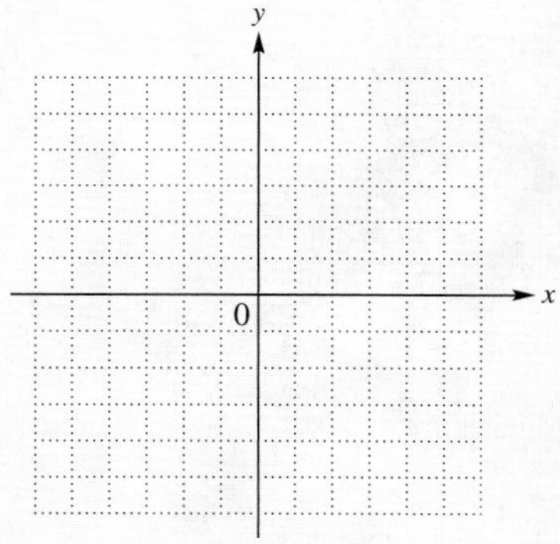

ANSWERS

3. (a) $\emptyset$

(b) $\{(x, y) | x - 3y = -2\}$ (*Note:* To write the solution set, we multiplied the equation $-x + 3y = 2$ by -1 to get $A > 0$.)

Focus on Real-Data Applications

Estimating Fahrenheit Temperature

When traveling in countries other than the United States, you will hear the daily high and low temperatures reported in degrees Celsius, instead of degrees Fahrenheit. The following information may help you.

- The linear equation to convert degrees Celsius to degrees Fahrenheit is $F = \frac{9}{5}C + 32$.
- Travel books advise you to use a *rule of thumb* to estimate Fahrenheit temperature that says "*Double the temperature (degrees Celsius) and add 30.*" This rule of thumb is written mathematically as $F = 2C + 30$.

For Group Discussion

Suppose you are interested in knowing for what temperature the rule of thumb and the actual formulas give the same result. You also want to know if the rule of thumb formula is predicting temperatures that are lower or higher than the actual temperature.

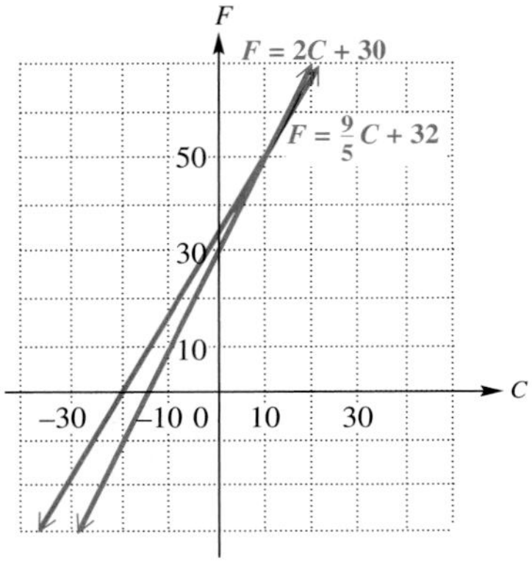

1. The two formulas can be written as the system of equations

$$F = \frac{9}{5}C + 32$$
$$F = 2C + 30.$$

(a) Use the graph of the system of equations to find the point of intersection. (*Hint:* To check your answer, use substitution to see if it satisfies both formulas.) **(10, 50)**

(b) For what temperature in degrees Celsius do the two formulas agree? **10°C**

(c) For what temperature in degrees Fahrenheit do the two formulas agree? **50°F**

2. (a) Complete the table of values to compare the *actual* and the *rule of thumb* formulas for temperature conversion.

°C	°F (*Actual*)	°F (*Rule of Thumb*)
0	**32**	**30**
5	**41**	**40**
10	**50**	**50**
15	**59**	**60**
20	**68**	**70**
30	**86**	**90**

(b) If the daily low is predicted to be 5°C, then is the rule of thumb estimate too high or too low? **low**

(c) If the daily high is predicted to be 20°C, then is the rule of thumb estimate too high or too low? **high**

(d) If the daily high is predicted to be 30°C, then is the rule of thumb estimate too high or too low? **high**

(e) How many degrees "off" is the rule of thumb estimate for the boiling point of water? **+18°**

(f) Comment on the accuracy of using the rule of thumb as an estimate of the actual Fahrenheit temperature. **The rule of thumb is fairly accurate for temperatures less than 20°C, but quickly becomes too high an estimate for higher temperatures.**

Teaching notes and an extension for this activity are provided in the *Printed Test Bank and Instructor's Resource Guide.*

5.1 EXERCISES

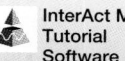

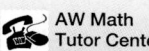

FOR EXTRA HELP: Student's Solutions Manual; MyMathLab.com; InterAct Math Tutorial Software; AW Math Tutor Center; www.mathxl.com; Digital Video Tutor CD 4, Videotape 9

1. Which ordered pair could be a solution of the system graphed? Why is it the only valid choice?

A. (2, 2)
B. (−2, 2)
C. (−2, −2)
D. (2, −2)

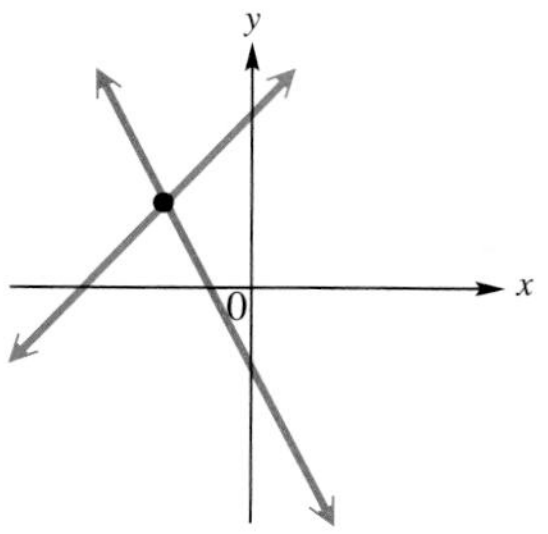

B, because the ordered pair must be in quadrant II.

2. Which ordered pair could be a solution of the system graphed? Why is it the only valid choice?

A. (2, 0)
B. (0, 2)
C. (−2, 0)
D. (0, −2)

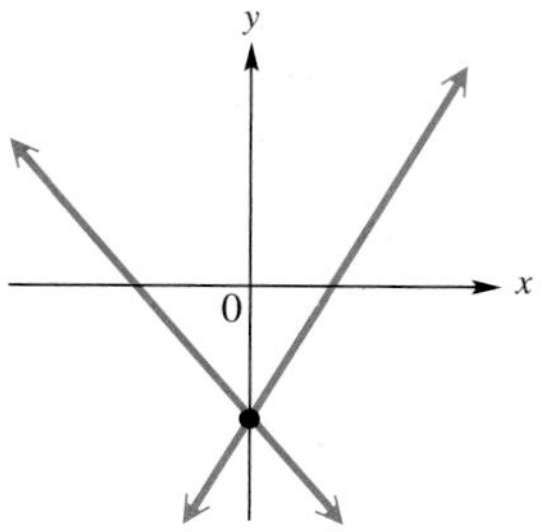

D, because the ordered pair must be on the y-axis, with $y < 0$.

3. How can you tell without graphing that this system has no solution?

$$x + y = 2$$
$$x + y = 4$$

There is no way that the sum of two numbers can be both 2 and 4 at the same time.

4. Explain why a system of two linear equations cannot have exactly two solutions.

Two lines will intersect in at most one point (if they are distinct) or infinitely many points (if they are the same) or no points (if they are parallel). They cannot intersect in exactly two points.

Decide whether the given ordered pair is a solution of the given system. See Example 1.

5. (2, −3)
$$x + y = -1$$
$$2x + 5y = 19$$
no

6. (4, 3)
$$x + 2y = 10$$
$$3x + 5y = 3$$
no

7. (−1, −3)
$$3x + 5y = -18$$
$$4x + 2y = -10$$
yes

8. (−9, −2)
$$2x - 5y = -8$$
$$3x + 6y = -39$$
yes

9. (7, −2)
$$4x = 26 - y$$
$$3x = 29 + 4y$$
yes

10. (9, 1)
$$2x = 23 - 5y$$
$$3x = 24 + 3y$$
yes

11. (6, −8)
$$-2y = x + 10$$
$$3y = 2x + 30$$
no

12. (−5, 2)
$$5y = 3x + 20$$
$$3y = -2x - 4$$
no

Solve each system of equations by graphing both equations on the same axes. See Example 2.

13. $x - y = 2$
$x + y = 6$

14. $x - y = 3$
$x + y = -1$

15. $x + y = 4$
$y - x = 4$

We show the graphs here only for Exercises 13–18.

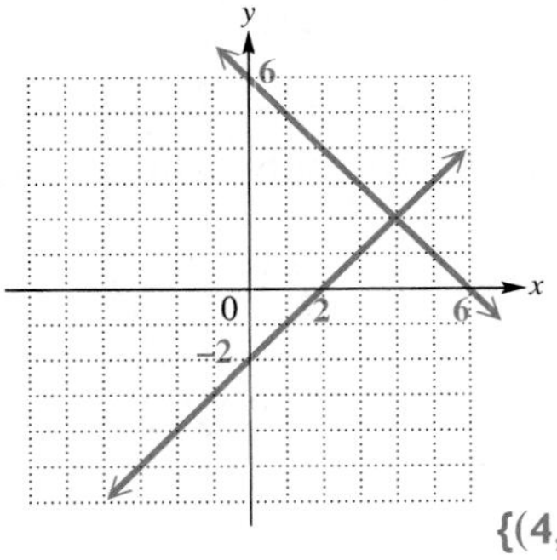

{(4, 2)}

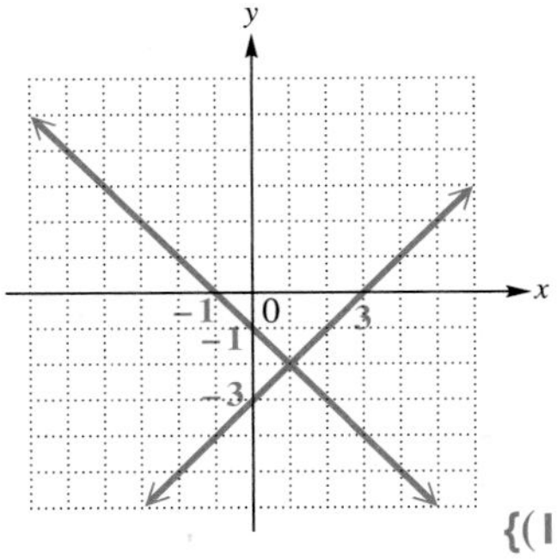

{(1, −2)}

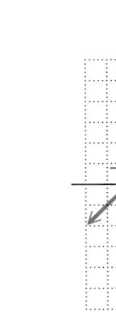

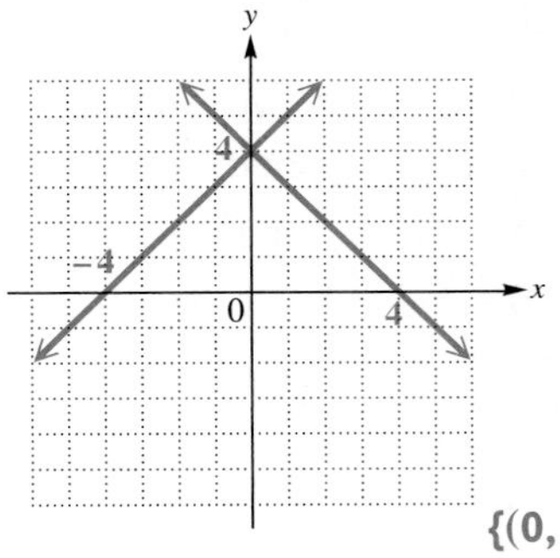

{(0, 4)}

16. $x + y = -5$
$x - y = 5$

17. $x - 2y = 6$
$x + 2y = 2$

18. $2x - y = 4$
$4x + y = 2$

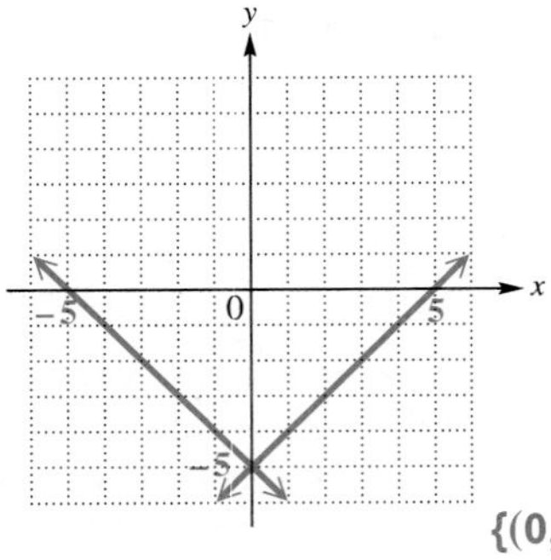

{(0, −5)}

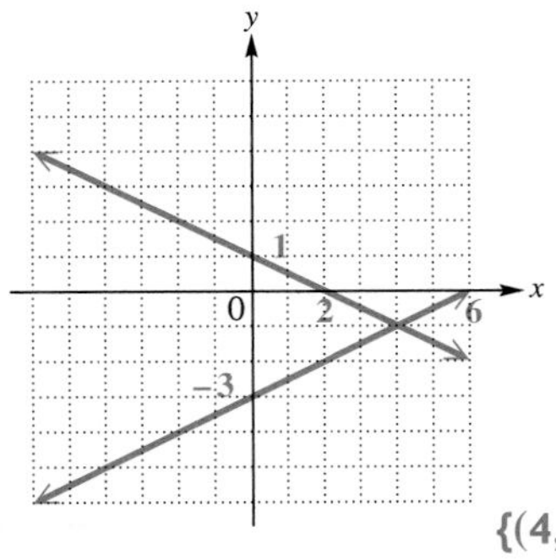

{(4, −1)}

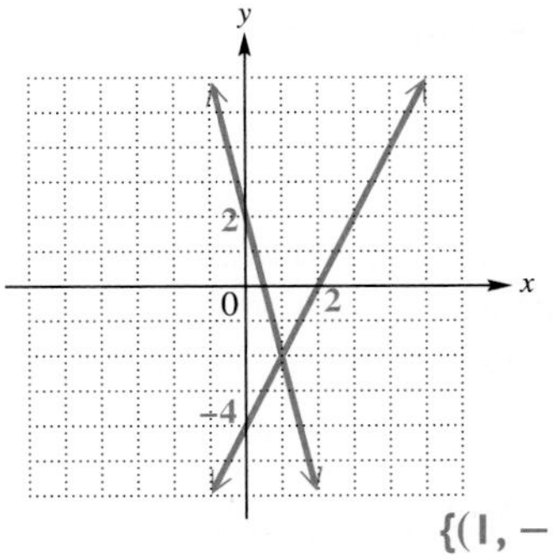

{(1, −2)}

19. $3x - 2y = -3$
$-3x - y = -6$

20. $2x - y = 4$
$2x + 3y = 12$

21. $2x - 3y = -6$
$y = -3x + 2$

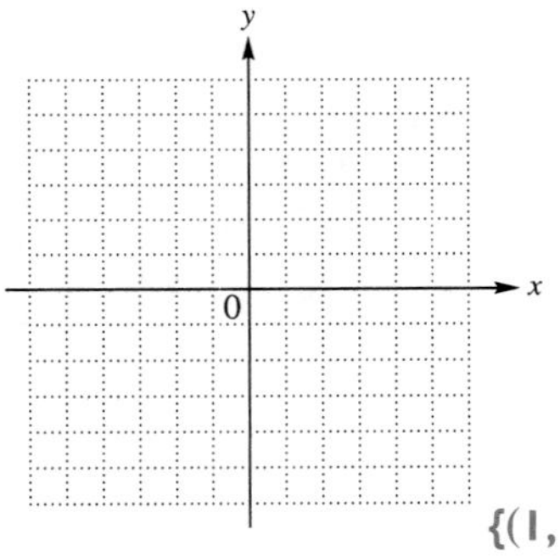

{(1, 3)}

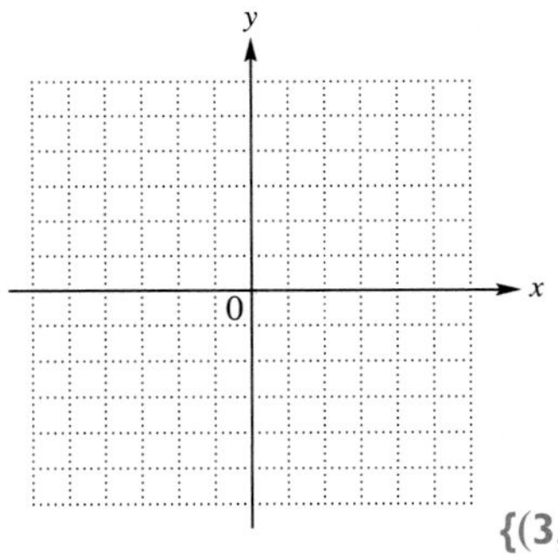

{(3, 2)}

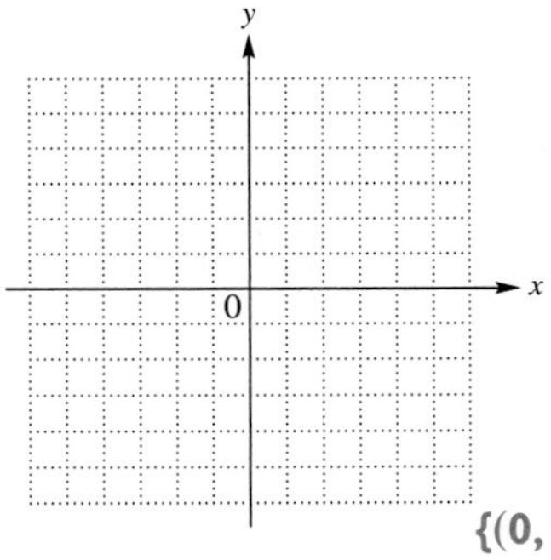

{(0, 2)}

22. $-3x + y = -3$
$y = x - 3$

23. $3x - 4y = 24$
$y = -\frac{3}{2}x + 3$

24. $3x - 2y = 12$
$y = -4x + 5$

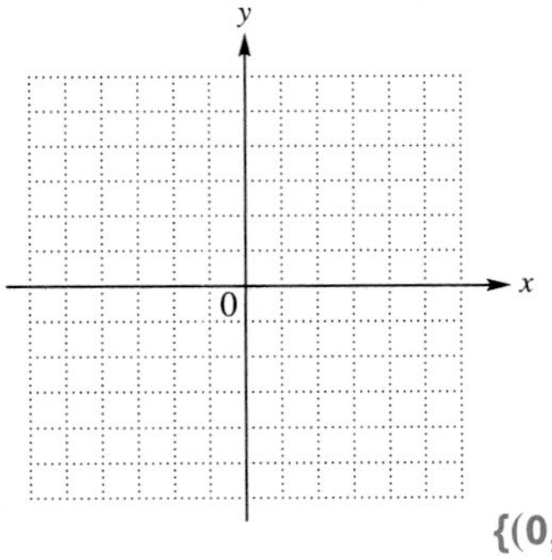

{(0, −3)}

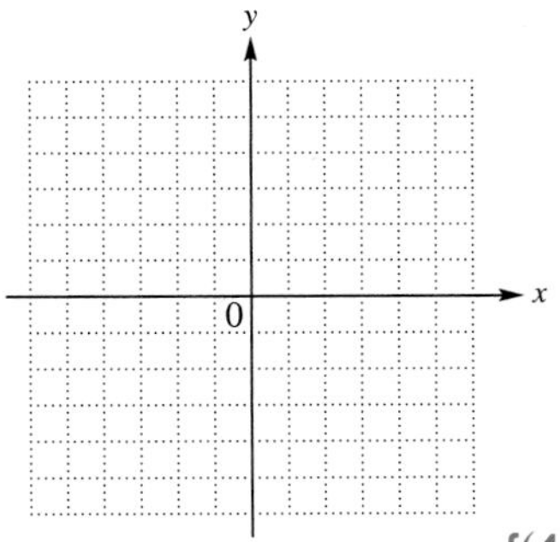

{(4, −3)}

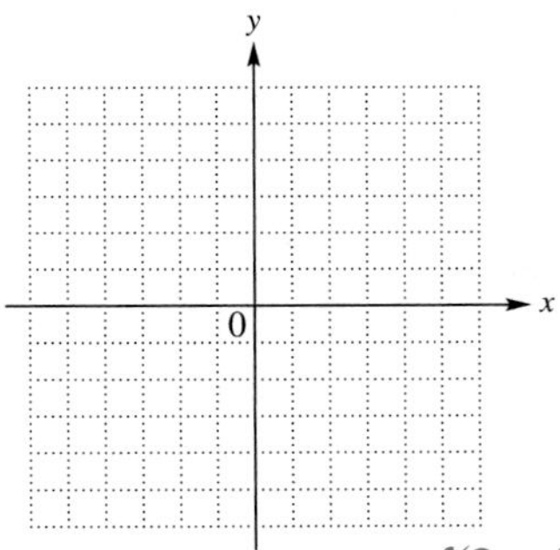

{(2, −3)}

Relating Concepts (Exercises 25–28) For Individual or Group Work

In Exercises 25–27, first write each equation in slope-intercept form. Then use what you learned in Chapter 4 about slope and the y-intercept to describe the graphs of each system of equations. ***Work these exercises in order.***

25. $3x + 2y = 6$
$-2y = 3x - 5$

$y = -\frac{3}{2}x + 3$
$y = -\frac{3}{2}x + \frac{5}{2}$

The graphs are parallel lines.

26. $2x - y = 4$
$x = .5y + 2$

$y = 2x - 4$
$y = 2x - 4$

The graphs are the same line.

27. $x - 3y = 5$
$2x + y = 8$

$y = \frac{1}{3}x - \frac{5}{3}$
$y = -2x + 8$

The graphs are intersecting lines.

28. Use the results of Exercises 25–27 to determine the number of solutions of each system.

Exercise 25: no solution; Exercise 26: infinite number of solutions; Exercise 27: one solution

---

Solve each system by graphing. If the system is inconsistent or the equations are dependent, say so. See Example 3.

29. $x + 2y = 6$
$2x + 4y = 8$

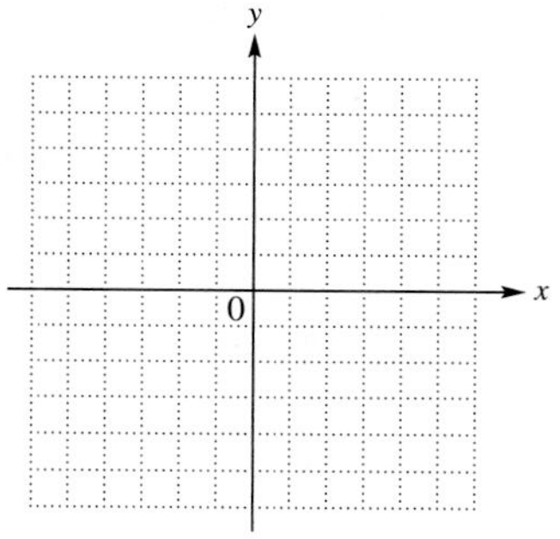

∅; inconsistent system

30. $2x - y = 6$
$6x - 3y = 12$

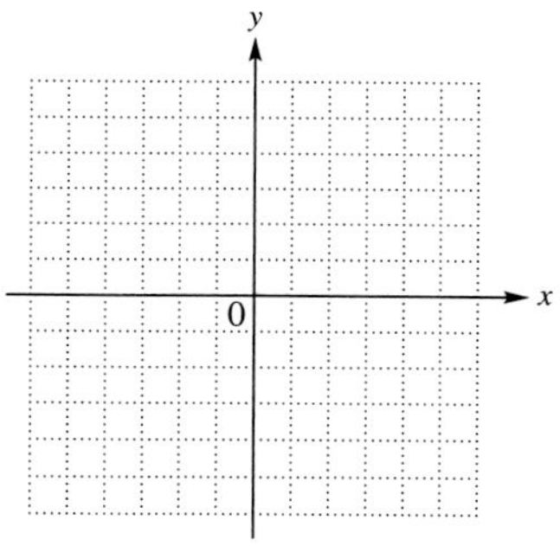

∅; inconsistent system

31. $-2x + y = -4$
$4x = 2y + 8$

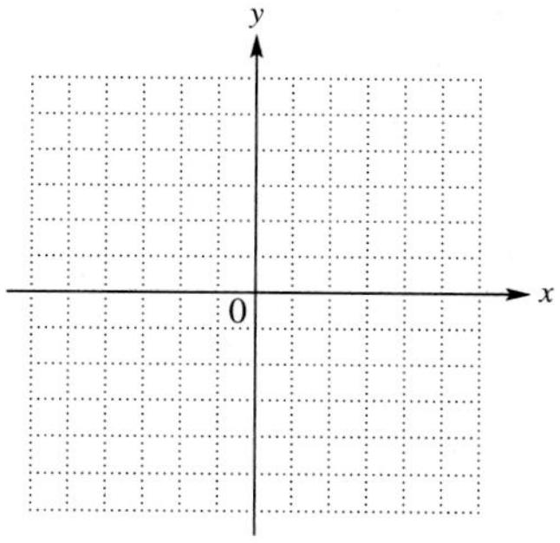

$\{(x, y) | 2x - y = 4\}$; dependent equations

32. $3x + y = 5$
$6x = 10 - 2y$

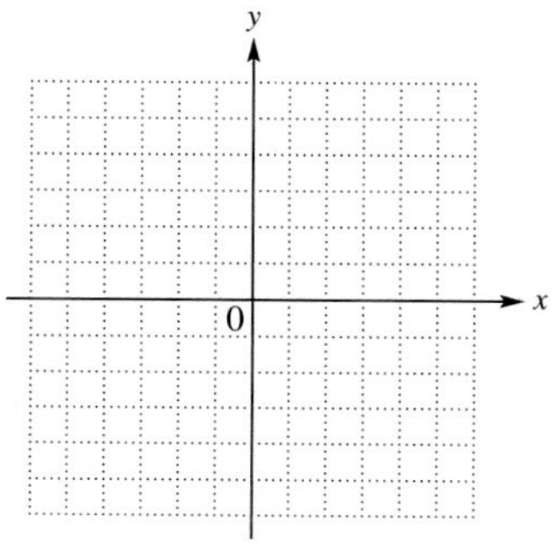

$\{(x, y) | 3x + y = 5\}$; dependent equations

33. $3x = y + 5$
$6x - 5 = 2y$

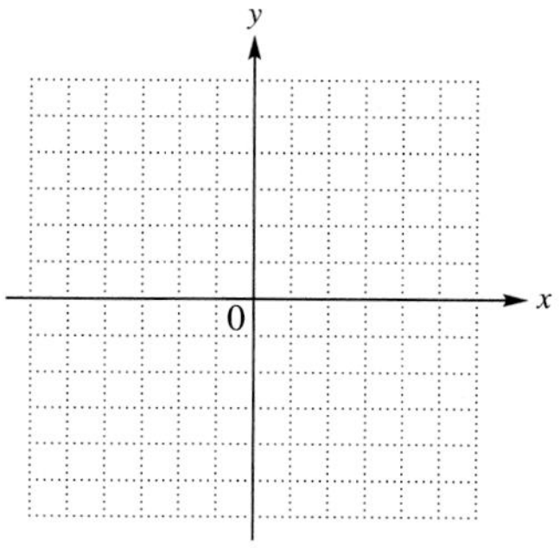

∅; inconsistent system

34. $2x = y - 4$
$4x - 2y = -4$

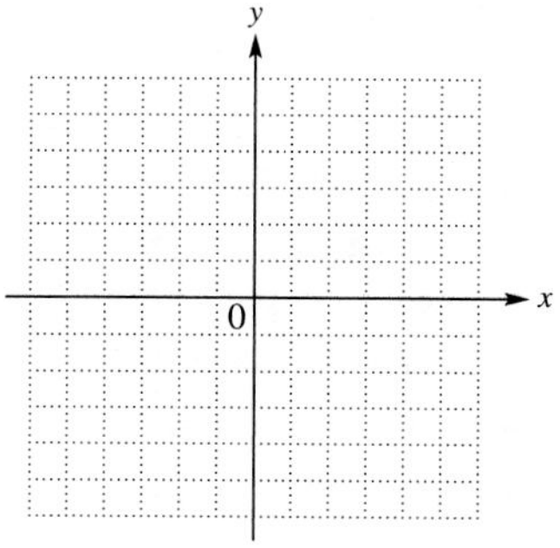

∅; inconsistent system

35. Explain one of the drawbacks of solving a system of equations graphically.

If the coordinates of the point of intersection are not integers, the solution will be difficult to determine from a graph.

36. If the two lines that are the graphs of the equations in a system are parallel, how many solutions does the system have? If the two lines coincide, how many solutions does the system have?

no solution; infinitely many solutions

Answer the questions in Exercises 37–38 by observing the graphs provided.

37. Eboni Perkins compared the monthly payments she would incur for two types of mortgages: fixed-rate and variable-rate. Her observations led to the following graphs.

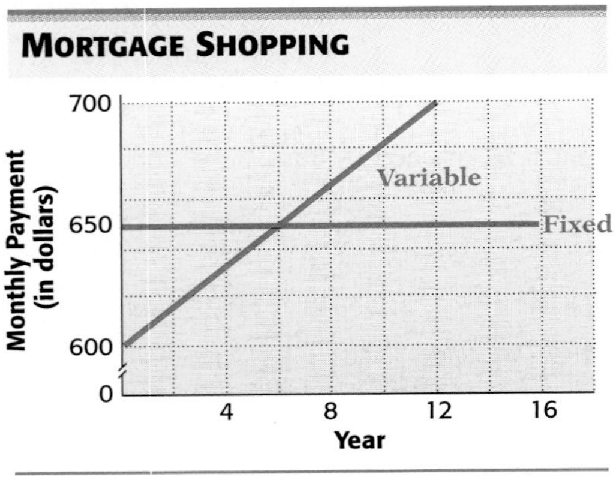

(a) For which years would the monthly payment be more for the fixed-rate mortgage than for the variable-rate mortgage?

years 0 to 6

(b) In what year would the payments be the same, and what would those payments be?

year 6; about $650

38. The figure shows graphs that represent supply and demand for a certain brand of low-fat frozen yogurt at various prices per half-gallon (in dollars).

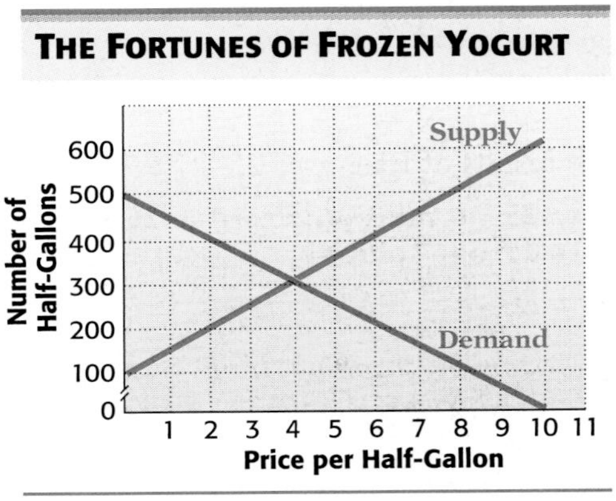

(a) At what price does supply equal demand?

$4

(b) For how many half-gallons does supply equal demand?

300 half-gallons

(c) What are the supply and demand at a price of $2 per half-gallon?

supply: 200 half-gallons; demand: 400 half-gallons

The graph shows how production levels of vinyl LPs, cassettes, and CDs changed from 1986 to 1998. Use the graph to respond to the questions in Exercises 39–42.

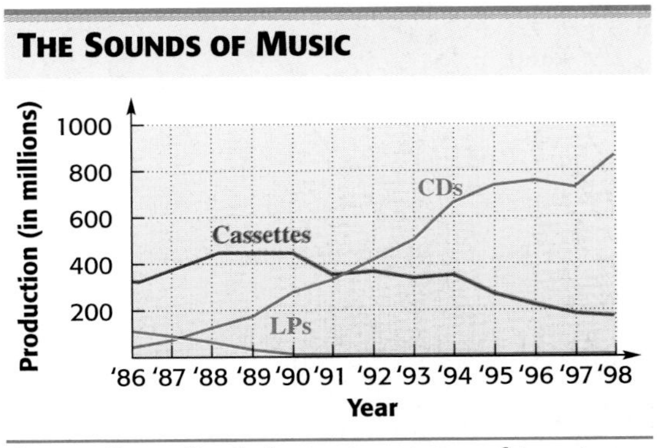

Source: Recording Industry Association of America.

39. In what year did cassette production and CD production reach an equal level? What was that production level?

1991; about 350 million

40. For which years was the production of CDs less than the production of LPs?

from 1986 to 1987

41. Between which two nonconsecutive years was the production of cassettes approximately constant?

between 1988 and 1990

42. If a straight line were used to approximate the graph of CD production from 1986 to 1998, would its slope be positive, negative, or 0?

positive

5.2 Solving Systems of Linear Equations by Substitution

Objectives

1. Solve linear systems by substitution.
2. Solve special systems.
3. Solve linear systems with fractions.

1 Solve linear systems by substitution. Graphing to solve a system of equations has a serious drawback: It is difficult to accurately find a solution such as $\left(\frac{1}{3}, -\frac{5}{6}\right)$ from a graph. One algebraic method for solving a system of equations is the **substitution method.** This method is particularly useful for solving systems where one equation is already solved, or can be solved quickly, for one of the variables.

Example 1 Using the Substitution Method

Solve the system

$$3x + 5y = 26$$
$$y = 2x.$$

The second equation is already solved for y. This equation says that $y = 2x$. Substituting $2x$ for y in the first equation gives

$$\begin{aligned} 3x + 5y &= 26 && \\ 3x + 5(2x) &= 26 && \text{Let } y = 2x. \\ 3x + 10x &= 26 && \text{Multiply.} \\ 13x &= 26 && \text{Combine terms.} \\ x &= 2. && \text{Divide by 13.} \end{aligned}$$

Because $x = 2$, we find y from the equation $y = 2x$ by substituting 2 for x.

$$y = 2(2) = 4 \qquad \text{Let } x = 2.$$

Check that the solution of the given system is (2, 4) by substituting 2 for x and 4 for y in *both* equations. The solution set is $\{(2, 4)\}$.

Work Problem 1 at the Side.

1 Fill in the blanks to solve by the substitution method. Check your solution.

$$3x + 5y = 69$$
$$y = 4x$$

$$\begin{aligned} 3x + 5(\_\_\_\_) &= 69 \\ \_\_\_\_ &= 69 \\ x &= \_\_\_\_ \\ y = 4(\_\_\_\_) &= \_\_\_\_ \end{aligned}$$

The solution set is ____.

Example 2 Using the Substitution Method

Solve the system

$$2x + 5y = 7$$
$$x = -1 - y.$$

The second equation gives x in terms of y. Substitute $-1 - y$ for x in the first equation.

$$\begin{aligned} 2x + 5y &= 7 && \\ 2(-1 - y) + 5y &= 7 && \text{Let } x = -1 - y. \\ -2 - 2y + 5y &= 7 && \text{Distributive property} \\ -2 + 3y &= 7 && \text{Combine terms.} \\ 3y &= 9 && \text{Add 2.} \\ y &= 3 && \text{Divide by 3.} \end{aligned}$$

To find x, substitute 3 for y in the equation $x = -1 - y$ to get $x = -1 - 3 = -4$. Check that the solution set of the given system is $\{(-4, 3)\}$.

Work Problem 2 at the Side.

2 Solve by the substitution method. Check your solution.

$$2x + 7y = -12$$
$$x = 3 - 2y$$

Answers

1. $4x$; $23x$; 3; 3; 12; $\{(3, 12)\}$
2. $\{(15, -6)\}$

3 Solve each system by substitution. Check each solution.

(a) Fill in the blanks to solve

$$x + 4y = -1$$
$$2x - 5y = 11.$$

Solve the first equation for x.

$$x = -1 - \_\_\_\_$$

Substitute into the second equation.

$$2(\_\_\_\_) - 5y = 11$$
$$\_\_\_\_ y = \_\_\_\_$$
$$y = \_\_\_\_$$
$$x = -1 - \_\_\_\_$$
$$x = \_\_\_\_$$

The solution set is ____.

(b) $2x + 5y = 4$
$x + y = -1$

ANSWERS
3. (a) $4y$; $-1 - 4y$; -13; 13; -1; -4; 3; $\{(3, -1)\}$
(b) $\{(-3, 2)\}$

Example 3 Using the Substitution Method

Use substitution to solve the system

$$2x + 3y = 10$$
$$-3x - 2y = 0.$$

To use the substitution method, one of the equations must be solved for one of the variables. We choose the first equation of the system, $2x + 3y = 10$, and solve for x.

$$2x + 3y = 10$$
$$2x = 10 - 3y \qquad \text{Subtract } 3y.$$
$$x = 5 - \frac{3}{2}y \qquad \text{Divide by 2.}$$

Substitute this expression for x in the second equation of the system.

$$-3x - 2y = 0$$
$$-3\left(5 - \frac{3}{2}y\right) - 2y = 0 \qquad \text{Let } x = 5 - \frac{3}{2}y.$$
$$-15 + \frac{9}{2}y - 2y = 0 \qquad \text{Distributive property}$$
$$-15 + \frac{5}{2}y = 0 \qquad \text{Combine terms.}$$
$$\frac{5}{2}y = 15 \qquad \text{Add 15.}$$
$$y = \frac{30}{5} = 6 \qquad \text{Multiply by } \frac{2}{5}.$$

Find x by substituting 6 for y in $x = 5 - \frac{3}{2}y$.

$$x = 5 - \frac{3}{2}(6) = -4$$

Check:

$2x + 3y = 10$		$-3x - 2y = 0$	
$2(-4) + 3(6) = 10$	?	$-3(-4) - 2(6) = 0$	?
$-8 + 18 = 10$	?	$12 - 12 = 0$	?
$10 = 10$	True	$0 = 0$	True

The solution checks, so the solution set of the system is $\{(-4, 6)\}$.

NOTE

In Example 3, we could have started the solution by solving the second equation for either x or y and then substituting the result into the first equation. The solution would be the same.

Work Problem 3 at the Side.

Example 4 **Using the Substitution Method**

Use substitution to solve the system

$$2x = 4 - y \qquad (1)$$
$$6 + 3y + 4x = 16 - x. \qquad (2)$$

Start by simplifying the second equation by adding x and subtracting 6 on each side. This gives the simplified system

$$2x = 4 - y \qquad (1)$$
$$5x + 3y = 10. \qquad (3)$$

For the substitution method, one of the equations must be solved for either x or y. Because the coefficient of y in equation (1) is -1, we avoid fractions by solving this equation for y.

$$2x = 4 - y \qquad (1)$$
$$2x - 4 = -y \qquad \text{Subtract 4.}$$
$$-2x + 4 = y \qquad \text{Multiply by } -1.$$

Now substitute $-2x + 4$ for y in equation (3).

$$5x + 3y = 10$$
$$5x + 3(-2x + 4) = 10 \qquad \text{Let } y = -2x + 4.$$
$$5x - 6x + 12 = 10 \qquad \text{Distributive property}$$
$$-x + 12 = 10 \qquad \text{Combine like terms.}$$
$$-x = -2 \qquad \text{Subtract 12.}$$
$$x = 2 \qquad \text{Multiply by } -1.$$

Since $y = -2x + 4$ and $x = 2$,

$$y = -2(2) + 4 = 0,$$

and the solution is (2, 0).

Check:

$$2x = 4 - y \qquad (1)$$
$$2(2) = 4 - 0 \quad ?$$
$$4 = 4 \qquad \text{True}$$

$$6 + 3y + 4x = 16 - x \qquad (2)$$
$$6 + 3(0) + 4(2) = 16 - 2 \quad ?$$
$$6 + 0 + 8 = 14 \quad ?$$
$$14 = 14 \qquad \text{True}$$

The solution set of the system is $\{(2, 0)\}$.

Work Problem 4 at the Side.

2 Solve special systems. In the previous section we solved inconsistent systems with graphs that are parallel lines and systems of dependent equations with graphs that are the same line. We can also solve these special systems with the substitution method.

4 Solve each system by substitution. First simplify where necessary.

(a) $x = 5 - 3y$
$2x + 3 = 5x - 4y + 14$

(b) $5x - y = -14 + 2x + y$
$7x + 9y + 4 = 3x + 8y$

ANSWERS

4. (a) $\{(-1, 2)\}$ **(b)** $\{(-2, 4)\}$

Example 5 **Solving an Inconsistent System by Substitution**

Use substitution to solve the system

$$x = 5 - 2y \quad (1)$$
$$2x + 4y = 6. \quad (2)$$

Substitute $5 - 2y$ for x in equation (2).

$$2x + 4y = 6$$
$$2(5 - 2y) + 4y = 6 \quad \text{Let } x = 5 - 2y.$$
$$10 - 4y + 4y = 6 \quad \text{Distributive property}$$
$$10 = 6 \quad \textbf{False}$$

This false result means that the equations in the system have graphs that are parallel lines. The system is inconsistent and has solution set $\emptyset$. See Figure 5.

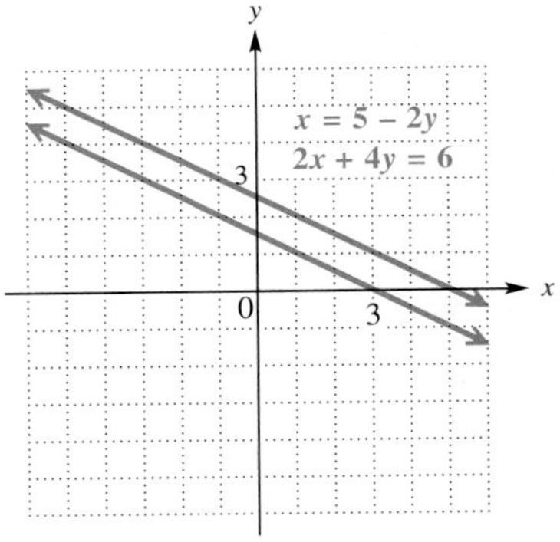

Figure 5

CAUTION

It is a common error to give "false" as the answer to an inconsistent system. The correct response is $\emptyset$.

Example 6 **Solving a System with Dependent Equations by Substitution**

Solve the system by the substitution method.

$$3x - y = 4 \quad (1)$$
$$-9x + 3y = -12 \quad (2)$$

Begin by solving equation (1) for y to get $y = 3x - 4$. Substitute $3x - 4$ for y in equation (2) and solve the resulting equation.

$$-9x + 3y = -12$$
$$-9x + 3(3x - 4) = -12 \quad \text{Let } y = 3x - 4.$$
$$-9x + 9x - 12 = -12 \quad \text{Distributive property}$$
$$0 = 0 \quad \text{Add 12; combine terms.}$$

Continued on Next Page

This true result means that every solution of one equation is also a solution of the other, so the system has an infinite number of solutions: all the ordered pairs corresponding to points that lie on the common graph. The solution set is $\{(x, y) | 3x - y = 4\}$. A graph of the equations of this system is shown in Figure 6.

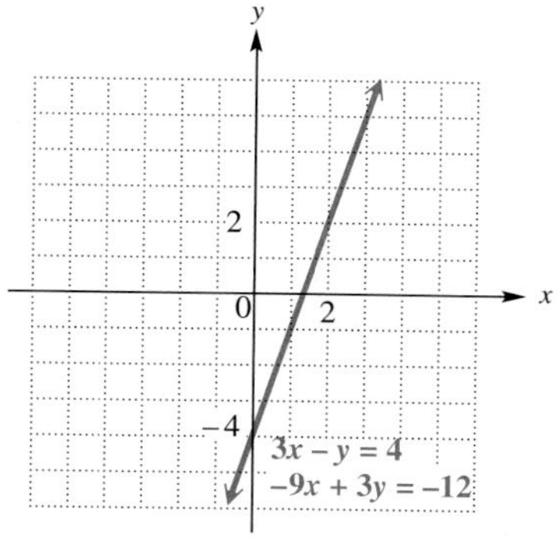

Figure 6

CAUTION

It is a common error to give "true" as the answer to a system of dependent equations. Instead, remember that such a system has an infinite number of solutions.

Work Problem 5 at the Side.

5 Solve each system by substitution.

(a) $8x - y = 4$
$y = 8x + 4$

(b) $7x - 6y = 10$
$-14x + 20 = -12y$

3 Solve linear systems with fractions. When a system includes an equation with fractions as coefficients, eliminate the fractions by multiplying each side of the equation by a common denominator. Then solve the resulting system.

Example 7 Using the Substitution Method with Fractions as Coefficients

Solve the system by the substitution method.

$$3x + \frac{1}{4}y = 2 \qquad (1)$$

$$\frac{1}{2}x + \frac{3}{4}y = -\frac{5}{2} \qquad (2)$$

Clear equation (1) of fractions by multiplying each side by 4.

$$4\left(3x + \frac{1}{4}y\right) = 4(2) \qquad \text{Multiply by 4.}$$

$$4(3x) + 4\left(\frac{1}{4}y\right) = 4(2) \qquad \text{Distributive property}$$

$$12x + y = 8 \qquad (3)$$

Now clear equation (2) of fractions by multiplying each side by the common denominator 4.

Continued on Next Page

ANSWERS

5. (a) $\emptyset$
(b) $\{(x, y) | 7x - 6y = 10\}$

6 Solve the system by the substitution method. First clear all fractions.

$$\frac{2}{3}x + \frac{1}{2}y = 6$$
$$\frac{1}{2}x - \frac{3}{4}y = 0$$

$$4\left(\frac{1}{2}x + \frac{3}{4}y\right) = 4\left(-\frac{5}{2}\right) \quad \text{Multiply by 4.}$$
$$4\left(\frac{1}{2}x\right) + 4\left(\frac{3}{4}y\right) = 4\left(-\frac{5}{2}\right) \quad \text{Distributive property}$$
$$2x + 3y = -10 \quad (4)$$

The given system of equations has been simplified as

$$12x + y = 8 \quad (3)$$
$$2x + 3y = -10. \quad (4)$$

Solve this system by the substitution method. Equation (3) can be solved for y by subtracting $12x$ from each side.

$$12x + y = 8$$
$$y = -12x + 8 \quad \text{Subtract } 12x.$$

Now substitute the result for y in equation (4).

$$2x + 3(-12x + 8) = -10 \quad \text{Let } y = -12x + 8.$$
$$2x - 36x + 24 = -10 \quad \text{Distributive property}$$
$$-34x = -34 \quad \text{Combine terms; subtract 24.}$$
$$x = 1 \quad \text{Divide by } -34.$$

Substitute 1 for x in $y = -12x + 8$ to get $y = -12(1) + 8 = -4$. The solution is $(1, -4)$. Check by substituting 1 for x and -4 for y in both of the original equations. The solution set is $\{(1, -4)\}$.

Work Problem 6 at the Side.

ANSWERS

6. $\{(6, 4)\}$

5.2 EXERCISES

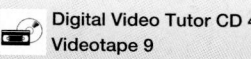

FOR EXTRA HELP — Student's Solutions Manual — MyMathLab.com — InterAct Math Tutorial Software — AW Math Tutor Center — www.mathxl.com — Digital Video Tutor CD 4 Videotape 9

1. A student solves the system

$$5x - y = 15$$
$$7x + y = 21$$

and finds that $x = 3$, which is the correct value for x. The student gives the solution set as $\{3\}$. Is this correct? Explain.

No, it is not correct, because the solution set is $\{(3, 0)\}$. The y-value must also be determined.

2. A student solves the system

$$x + y = 4$$
$$2x + 2y = 8$$

and obtains the equation $0 = 0$. The student gives the solution set as $\{(0, 0)\}$. Is this correct? Explain.

No. Obtaining $0 = 0$ means that the system has infinitely many solutions. In this system, $(0, 0)$ is not a solution.

3. Professor Brandsma gave the following item on a test in algebra:
Use the substitution method to solve the system

$$3x - y = 13$$
$$2x + 5y = 20.$$

One student worked the problem by solving first for y in the first equation. Another student worked it by solving first for x in the second equation. Both students got the correct solution, $(5, 2)$. Which student, do you think, had less work to do? Explain.

The first student had less work to do, because the coefficient of y in the first equation is -1. The second student had to divide by 2, introducing fractions into the expression for x.

4. When you use the substitution method, how can you tell that a system has

(a) no solution?

A false statement, such as $0 = 3$, occurs.

(b) an infinite number of solutions?

A true statement, such as $0 = 0$, occurs.

Solve each system by the substitution method. Check each solution. See Examples 1–3, 5, and 6.

5. $3x + 2y = 27$
$x = y + 4$

$\{(7, 3)\}$

6. $4x + 3y = -5$
$x = y - 3$

$\{(-2, 1)\}$

7. $3x + 5y = 14$
$x - 2y = -10$

$\{(-2, 4)\}$

8. $5x + 2y = -1$
$2x - y = -13$
$\{(-3, 7)\}$

9. $3x + 4 = -y$
$2x + y = 0$
$\{(-4, 8)\}$

10. $2x - 5 = -y$
$x + 3y = 0$
$\{(3, -1)\}$

11. $7x + 4y = 13$
$x + y = 1$
$\{(3, -2)\}$

12. $3x - 2y = 19$
$x + y = 8$
$\{(7, 1)\}$

13. $3x - y = 5$
$y = 3x - 5$
$\{(x, y) | 3x - y = 5\}$

14. $4x - y = -3$
$y = 4x + 3$
$\{(x, y) | 4x - y = -3\}$

15. $6x - 8y = 6$
$2y = -2 + 3x$
$\left\{\left(\frac{1}{3}, -\frac{1}{2}\right)\right\}$

16. $3x + 2y = 6$
$6x = 8 + 4y$
$\left\{\left(\frac{5}{3}, \frac{1}{2}\right)\right\}$

17. $2x + 8y = 3$
$x = 8 - 4y$
$\emptyset$

18. $2x + 10y = 3$
$x = 1 - 5y$
$\emptyset$

19. $12x - 16y = 8$
$3x = 4y + 2$
$\{(x, y) | 3x - 4y = 2\}$

20. $6x + 9y = 6$
$2x = 2 - 3y$
$\{(x, y) | 2x + 3y = 2\}$

Solve each system by the substitution method. First simplify equations where necessary. Check each solution. See Example 4.

21. $4 + 4x - 3y = 34 + x$
$4x = -y - 2 + 3x$
$\{(4, -6)\}$

22. $5x - 4y = 42 - 8y - 2$
$2x + y = x + 1$
$\{(36, -35)\}$

23. $2x - 8y + 3y + 2 = 5y + 16$
$8x - 2y = 4x + 28$
$\{(7, 0)\}$

24. $7x - 9 + 2y - 8 = -3y + 4x + 13$
$4y - 8x = -8 + 9x + 32$
$\{(0, 6)\}$

25.
$$\begin{aligned} -2x + 3y &= 12 + 2y \\ 2x - 5y + 4 &= -8 - 4y \end{aligned}$$
$\{(x, y) | 2x - y = -12\}$

26.
$$\begin{aligned} 2x + 5y &= 7 + 4y - x \\ 5x + 3y + 8 &= 22 - x + y \end{aligned}$$
$\{(x, y) | 3x + y = 7\}$

27.
$$\begin{aligned} 5x + y &= 12 - x - 7y \\ 3x + 2y &= 10 - 6x - 10y \end{aligned}$$
$\emptyset$

28.
$$\begin{aligned} -2x + 3y &= 7 - 5x - y \\ -4x + 2y &= 1 - 10x - 6y \end{aligned}$$
$\emptyset$

29. Solve each system.

(a) $5x - 4y = 7$, $x = 3$ **(b)** $5x - 4y = 7$, $y = -3$

Why are these systems easier to solve than the examples in this section?

(a) $\{(3, 2)\}$ (b) $\{(-1, -3)\}$; In each case, only one step is needed to find the solution because the value of one variable is known.

30. One student solved the system

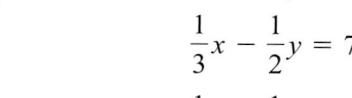

$$\begin{aligned} \frac{1}{3}x - \frac{1}{2}y &= 7 \\ \frac{1}{6}x + \frac{1}{3}y &= 0 \end{aligned}$$

and wrote $\{12\}$ as the solution set. Another solved it and wrote $\{-6\}$ as the solution set. Who, if either, was correct? Why?

Neither was correct, because the solution set is $\{(12, -6)\}$.

Solve each system by the substitution method. First clear all fractions. Check each solution. See Example 7.

31.
$$\begin{aligned} x + \frac{1}{3}y &= y - 2 \\ \frac{1}{4}x + y &= x + y \end{aligned}$$
$\{(0, 3)\}$

32.
$$\begin{aligned} \frac{5}{3}x + 2y &= \frac{1}{3} + y \\ 3x - 3 + \frac{y}{3} &= -2 + 2x \end{aligned}$$
$\{(2, -3)\}$

33.
$$\begin{aligned} \frac{x}{6} + \frac{y}{6} &= 2 \\ -\frac{1}{2}x - \frac{1}{3}y &= -8 \end{aligned}$$
$\{(24, -12)\}$

34.
$$\begin{aligned} \frac{x}{2} - \frac{y}{3} &= 9 \\ \frac{x}{5} - \frac{y}{4} &= 5 \end{aligned}$$
$\{(10, -12)\}$

35.
$$\begin{aligned} \frac{x}{3} - \frac{3y}{4} &= -\frac{1}{2} \\ \frac{x}{6} + \frac{y}{8} &= \frac{3}{4} \end{aligned}$$
$\{(3, 2)\}$

36.
$$\begin{aligned} \frac{x}{5} + 2y &= \frac{16}{5} \\ \frac{3x}{5} + \frac{y}{2} &= -\frac{7}{5} \end{aligned}$$
$\{(-4, 2)\}$

RELATING CONCEPTS (Exercises 37–40) FOR INDIVIDUAL OR GROUP WORK

A system of linear equations can be used to model the cost and the revenue of a business.
Work Exercises 37–40 in order.

37. Suppose that you start a business manufacturing and selling bicycles, and it costs you \$5000 to get started. You determine that each bicycle will cost \$400 to manufacture. Explain why the linear equation $y_1 = 400x + 5000$ gives your *total* cost to manufacture x bicycles (y_1 in dollars).

To find the total cost, multiply the number of bicycles (x) by the cost per bicycle (400 dollars) and add the fixed cost (5000 dollars). Thus, $y_1 = 400x + 5000$ gives this total cost (in dollars).

38. You decide to sell each bike for \$600. What expression in x represents the revenue you will take in if you sell x bikes? Write an equation using y_2 to express your revenue when you sell x bikes (y_2 in dollars). **$y_2 = 600x$**

39. Form a system from the two equations in Exercises 37 and 38, and then solve the system, assuming $y_1 = y_2$, that is, cost = revenue.

$y_1 = 400x + 5000$
$y_2 = 600x$;
solution set: {(25, 15,000)}

40. The value of x from Exercise 39 is the number of bikes it takes to *break even.* Fill in the blanks: When ______ bikes are sold, the break-even point is reached. At that point, you have spent ______ dollars and taken in ______ dollars.

25; 15,000; 15,000

Work each problem.

41. During the period from 1991 to 1996, average ticket prices rose in the National Football League from \$25.21 to \$35.74. If we let $x = 1$ represent 1991, $x = 2$ represent 1992, and so on, the linear equation $y = 2.1x + 22.8$ gives a good approximation for this average price, where y is in dollars. To determine the year in which the average ticket price was \$28.68, solve the system

$$y = 2.1x + 22.8$$
$$y = 28.68.$$

The rounded x-value will then give us the year. Solve this system by substitution to determine the year. (*Hint:* After finding the value of x, you must then determine which year it represents.) (*Source:* Team Marketing Report, Chicago.) **1993**

42. During the period from 1991 to 1996, the average price of a ticket to a National Basketball Association game rose from \$23.24 to \$34.08. If we let $x = 1$ represent the 1991–1992 season, $x = 2$ represent 1992–1993, and so on, the linear equation $y = 2.14x + 20.81$ gives a good approximation for this average price, where y is in dollars. To determine the period in which the average ticket price was \$28.63, solve the system

$$y = 2.14x + 20.81$$
$$y = 28.63.$$

The rounded x-value will then give us the first year of the period. Solve this system by substitution to determine the period. See the hint in Exercise 41. (*Source:* Team Marketing Report, Chicago.) **1994**

5.3 SOLVING SYSTEMS OF LINEAR EQUATIONS BY ELIMINATION

OBJECTIVES

1. Solve linear systems by elimination.
2. Multiply when using the elimination method.
3. Use an alternative method to find the second value in a solution.
4. Use the elimination method to solve special systems.

1 Solve linear systems by elimination. An algebraic method that depends on the addition property of equality can be used to solve systems. As mentioned earlier, adding the same quantity to each side of an equation results in equal sums.

$$\text{If} \quad A = B, \quad \text{then} \quad A + C = B + C.$$

This addition can be taken a step further. Adding *equal* quantities, rather than the *same* quantity, to both sides of an equation also results in equal sums.

$$\text{If} \quad A = B \quad \text{and} \quad C = D, \quad \text{then} \quad A + C = B + D.$$

Using the addition property to solve systems is called the **elimination method.** When using this method, the idea is to *eliminate* one of the variables. To do this, one of the variables in the two equations must have coefficients that are opposites.

Example 1 Using the Elimination Method

Use the elimination method to solve the system

$$x + y = 5$$
$$x - y = 3.$$

Each equation in this system is a statement of equality, so the sum of the right sides equals the sum of the left sides. Adding in this way gives

$$(x + y) + (x - y) = 5 + 3.$$

Combine terms and simplify to get

$$2x = 8$$
$$x = 4. \quad \text{Divide by 2.}$$

Notice that y has been eliminated. The result, $x = 4$, gives the x-value of the solution of the given system. To find the y-value of the solution, substitute 4 for x in either of the two equations of the system.

Work Problem 1 at the Side.

The solution found at the side, (4, 1), can be checked by substituting 4 for x and 1 for y in both equations of the given system.

Check:

$x + y = 5$	$x - y = 3$
$4 + 1 = 5$?	$4 - 1 = 3$?
$5 = 5$ True	$3 = 3$ True

Since both results are true, the solution set of the system is $\{(4, 1)\}$.

CAUTION

A system is not completely solved until values for *both* x and y are found. Do not stop after finding the value of only one variable. Remember to write the solution set as a set containing an ordered pair.

1 **(a)** Substitute 4 for x in the equation $x + y = 5$ to find the value of y.

(b) Give the solution set of the system.

ANSWERS

1. (a) $y = 1$ **(b)** $\{(4, 1)\}$

2 Solve each system by the elimination method. Check each solution.

(a) Fill in the blanks to find the solution.

$$\begin{aligned} x + y &= 8 \\ x - y &= 2 \\ \hline \_\_\_\_ + \_\_\_\_ &= 10 \quad \text{Add.} \\ x &= \_\_\_\_ \\ \_\_\_\_ - y &= 2 \\ -y &= \_\_\_\_ \\ y &= \_\_\_\_ \end{aligned}$$

The solution set is ____.

(b) $3x - y = 7$
$2x + y = 3$

Answers
2. (a) $2x$; 0; 5; 5; -3; 3; $\{(5, 3)\}$
(b) $\{(2, -1)\}$

Work Problem 2 at the Side.

In general, we use the following steps to solve a linear system of equations by the elimination method.

Solving Linear Systems by Elimination

Step 1 **Write in standard form.** Write both equations of the system in standard form $Ax + By = C$.

Step 2 **Multiply.** Multiply one or both equations by appropriate numbers (if necessary) so that the coefficients of x (or y) are opposites of each other.

Step 3 **Add.** Add the two equations to get an equation with only one variable (or no variable).

Step 4 **Solve.** Solve the equation from Step 3.

Step 5 **Substitute.** Substitute the solution from Step 4 into either of the original equations to find the value of the remaining variable.

Step 6 **Check.** Check the solution in both of the original equations. Then write the solution set.

It does not matter which variable is eliminated first. Usually we choose the one that is more convenient to work with.

Example 2 Using the Elimination Method

Solve the system

$$\begin{aligned} y + 11 &= 2x \\ 4 + 5x + y &= 2y + 30. \end{aligned}$$

Step 1 Rewrite both equations in the form $Ax + By = C$ to get the system

$$\begin{aligned} -2x + y &= -11 && \text{Subtract } 2x \text{ and } 11. \\ 5x - y &= 26. && \text{Subtract 4 and } 2y. \end{aligned}$$

Step 2 Because the coefficients of y are 1 and -1, adding will eliminate y. It is not necessary to multiply either equation by a number.

Step 3 Add the two equations. This time we use vertical addition.

$$\begin{aligned} -2x + y &= -11 \\ 5x - y &= 26 \\ \hline 3x &= 15 \qquad \text{Add in columns.} \end{aligned}$$

Step 4 Solve the equation.

$$\begin{aligned} 3x &= 15 \\ x &= 5 && \text{Divide by 3.} \end{aligned}$$

Step 5 Find the value of y by substituting 5 for x in either of the original equations. Choosing the first gives

$$\begin{aligned} y + 11 &= 2x \\ y + 11 &= 2(5) && \text{Let } x = 5. \\ y &= 10 - 11 && \text{Subtract 11.} \\ y &= -1. \end{aligned}$$

Continued on Next Page

Step 6 Check the solution by substitution into both of the original equations. Let $x = 5$ and $y = -1$.

$$y + 11 = 2x \qquad\qquad 4 + 5x + y = 2y + 30$$
$$(-1) + 11 = 2(5) \ ? \qquad\qquad 4 + 5(5) + (-1) = 2(-1) + 30 \ ?$$
$$10 = 10 \quad \text{True} \qquad\qquad 28 = 28 \quad \text{True}$$

The solution $(5, -1)$ is correct, so the solution set is $\{(5, -1)\}$.

Work Problem 3 at the Side.

3 Solve each system by the elimination method. Check each solution.

(a) $2x - y = 2$
$4x + y = 10$

(b) $8x - 5y = 32$
$4x + 5y = 4$

2 Multiply when using the elimination method. In both of the preceding examples, a variable was eliminated by adding the equations. Sometimes we need to multiply each side of one or both equations in a system by some number before adding the equations will eliminate a variable.

Example 3 Multiplying Both Equations When Using the Elimination Method

Solve the system

$$2x + 3y = -15 \qquad (1)$$
$$5x + 2y = 1. \qquad (2)$$

Adding the two equations gives $7x + 5y = -14$, which does not eliminate either variable. However, we can multiply each equation by a suitable number so that the coefficients of one of the two variables are opposites. For example, to eliminate x, multiply each side of equation (1) by 5, and each side of equation (2) by -2.

$$10x + 15y = -75 \qquad \text{Multiply equation (1) by 5.}$$
$$-10x - 4y = -2 \qquad \text{Multiply equation (2) by } -2.$$
$$11y = -77 \qquad \text{Add.}$$
$$y = -7$$

Substituting -7 for y in either equation (1) or (2) gives $x = 3$. Check that the solution set of the system is $\{(3, -7)\}$.

Work Problem 4 at the Side.

4 **(a)** Solve the system in Example 3 by first eliminating the variable y. Check your solution.

(b) Solve

$$6x + 7y = 4$$
$$5x + 8y = -1,$$

and check your solution.

3 Use an alternative method to find the second value in a solution. Sometimes it is easier to find the value of the second variable in a solution by using the elimination method twice. The next example shows this approach.

Example 4 Finding the Second Value Using an Alternative Method

Solve the system

$$4x = 9 - 3y \qquad (1)$$
$$5x - 2y = 8. \qquad (2)$$

Rearrange the terms in equation (1) so that like terms are aligned in columns. Add $3y$ to each side to get the following system.

$$4x + 3y = 9 \qquad (3)$$
$$5x - 2y = 8 \qquad (2)$$

Continued on Next Page

ANSWERS

3. **(a)** $\{(2, 2)\}$ **(b)** $\left\{\left(3, -\frac{8}{5}\right)\right\}$
4. **(a)** $\{(3, -7)\}$ **(b)** $\{(3, -2)\}$

5 Solve each system of equations.

(a) $5x = 7 + 2y$
$5y = 5 - 3x$

(b) $3y = 8 + 4x$
$6x = 9 - 2y$

One way to proceed is to eliminate y by multiplying each side of equation (3) by 2 and each side of equation (2) by 3, and then adding.

$$\begin{aligned} 8x + 6y &= 18 && \text{Multiply equation (3) by 2.} \\ 15x - 6y &= 24 && \text{Multiply equation (2) by 3.} \\ \hline 23x \quad &= 42 && \text{Add.} \\ x &= \frac{42}{23} && \text{Divide by 23.} \end{aligned}$$

Substituting $\frac{42}{23}$ for x in one of the given equations would give y, but the arithmetic involved would be messy. Instead, solve for y by starting again with the original equations and eliminating x. Multiply each side of equation (3) by 5 and each side of equation (2) by -4, and then add.

$$\begin{aligned} 20x + 15y &= 45 && \text{Multiply equation (3) by 5.} \\ -20x + 8y &= -32 && \text{Multiply equation (2) by } -4. \\ \hline 23y &= 13 && \text{Add.} \\ y &= \frac{13}{23} && \text{Divide by 23.} \end{aligned}$$

Check that the solution set is $\{(\frac{42}{23}, \frac{13}{23})\}$.

When the value of the first variable is a fraction, the method used in Example 4 helps avoid arithmetic errors. Of course, this method could be used to solve any system of equations.

Work Problem 5 at the Side.

4 Use the elimination method to solve special systems. The next example shows the elimination method when a system is inconsistent or the equations of the system are dependent. To contrast the elimination method with the substitution method, in part (b) we use the same system solved in Example 6 of the previous section.

Example 5 Using the Elimination Method for an Inconsistent System or Dependent Equations

Solve each system by the elimination method.

(a) $2x + 4y = 5$
$4x + 8y = -9$

Multiply each side of $2x + 4y = 5$ by -2; then add to $4x + 8y = -9$.

$$\begin{aligned} -4x - 8y &= -10 \\ 4x + 8y &= -9 \\ \hline 0 &= -19 && \textbf{False} \end{aligned}$$

The false statement $0 = -19$ shows that the given system has solution set $\emptyset$.

Continued on Next Page

Answers

5. (a) $\left\{\left(\frac{45}{31}, \frac{4}{31}\right)\right\}$ (b) $\left\{\left(\frac{11}{26}, \frac{42}{13}\right)\right\}$

(b) $3x - y = 4$

$-9x + 3y = -12$

Multiply each side of the first equation by 3; then add the two equations.

$$\begin{aligned} 9x - 3y &= 12 \\ -9x + 3y &= -12 \\ \hline 0 &= 0 \quad \text{True} \end{aligned}$$

As before, this result indicates that every solution of one equation is also a solution of the other; there are an infinite number of solutions. The solution set is $\{(x, y) | 3x - y = 4\}$.

Work Problem 6 at the Side.

6 Solve each system by the elimination method.

(a) $4x + 3y = 10$

$2x + \frac{3}{2}y = 12$

(b) $4x - 6y = 10$

$-10x + 15y = -25$

NOTE

A good way to decide whether two linear equations are equivalent is to write them both in slope-intercept form (solved for y). The resulting equations should be the same.

Summary of Situations That May Occur

One of three situations may occur when the elimination method is used to solve a linear system of equations.

1. The result of the addition step is a statement such as $x = 2$ or $y = -3$. The solution will be exactly one ordered pair. The graphs of the equations of the system will intersect at exactly one point. The system is *consistent*, and the equations are *independent.* See Examples 1–4.

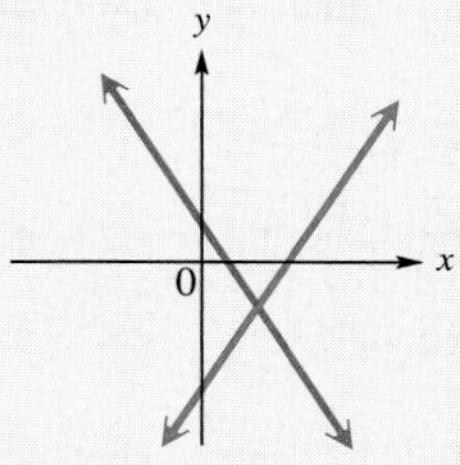

One solution

2. The result of the addition step is a false statement, such as $0 = 4$. In this case, the graphs are parallel lines, and the solution set is $\emptyset$. The system is *inconsistent.* See Example 5(a).

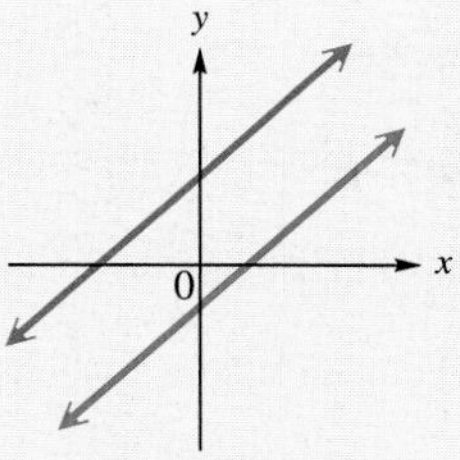

No solution

3. The result of the addition step is a true statement, such as $0 = 0$. The graphs of the equations of the system are the same line, and an infinite number of ordered pairs are solutions. These ordered pairs must satisfy the equation of the line. The equations are *dependent.* See Example 5(b).

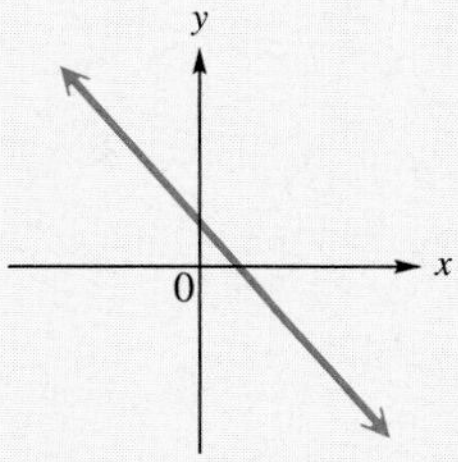

Infinite number of solutions

ANSWERS

6. (a) $\emptyset$

(b) $\{(x, y) | 2x - 3y = 5\}$

When no method of solution of a system is specified and a choice of substitution or elimination is allowed, use the following guidelines.

1. If one of the equations of the system is already solved for one of the variables, such as

$$\begin{aligned} 3x + 4y &= 9 \\ y &= 2x - 6 \end{aligned} \quad \text{or} \quad \begin{aligned} -5x + 3y &= 9 \\ x &= 3y - 7, \end{aligned}$$

the substitution method is the better choice.

2. If both equations are in standard $Ax + By = C$ form, such as

$$\begin{aligned} 4x - 11y &= 3 \\ -2x + 3y &= 4, \end{aligned}$$

and none of the variables has coefficient -1 or 1, the elimination method is the better choice.

3. If one or both of the equations are in standard form and the coefficient of one of the variables is -1 or 1, such as

$$\begin{aligned} 3x + y &= -2 \\ -5x + 2y &= 4 \end{aligned} \quad \text{or} \quad \begin{aligned} -x + 3y &= -4 \\ 3x - 2y &= 8, \end{aligned}$$

choose the elimination method, or solve for the variable with coefficient -1 or 1 and then use the substitution method.

Work Problem 7 at the Side.

7 Use the guidelines to decide whether to use substitution or elimination to solve each system. (Do not actually solve the system.)

(a) $\begin{aligned} 6x - y &= 5 \\ y &= 11x \end{aligned}$

(b) $\begin{aligned} 3x - 5y &= 7 \\ 2x + 3y &= 30 \end{aligned}$

(c) $\begin{aligned} 2x + 3y &= 10 \\ 3x + y &= 18 \end{aligned}$

Answers

7. (a) substitution **(b)** elimination
(c) Either method is appropriate.

5.3 Exercises

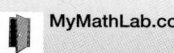

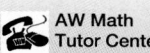

FOR EXTRA HELP: Student's Solutions Manual; MyMathLab.com; InterAct Math Tutorial Software; AW Math Tutor Center; www.mathxl.com; Digital Video Tutor CD 4 Videotape 9

In Exercises 1–4, answer true *or* false *for each statement. If* false, *tell why.*

1. The ordered pair (0, 0) *must* be a solution of a system of the form

$$Ax + By = 0$$
$$Cx + Dy = 0.$$

true

2. To eliminate the y-terms in the system

$$2x + 12y = 7$$
$$3x + 4y = 1,$$

we should multiply the bottom equation by 3 and then add.

False; multiply by -3.

3. The system

$$x + y = 1$$
$$x + y = 2$$

has $\emptyset$ as its solution set.

true

4. Which one of the following systems would be easier to solve using the substitution method? Why?

$$5x - 3y = 7 \qquad 7x + 2y = 4$$
$$2x + 8y = 3 \qquad y = -3x$$

The system on the right is easier to solve by substitution, because the second equation is already solved for y.

Solve each system by the elimination method. Check each solution. See Examples 1 and 2.

5. $x + y = 2$
$2x - y = -5$

$\{(-1, 3)\}$

6. $3x - y = -12$
$x + y = 4$

$\{(-2, 6)\}$

7. $2x + y = -5$
$x - y = 2$

$\{(-1, -3)\}$

8. $2x + y = -15$
$-x - y = 10$

$\{(-5, -5)\}$

9. $3x + 2y = 0$
$-3x - y = 3$

$\{(-2, 3)\}$

10. $5x - y = 5$
$-5x + 2y = 0$

$\{(2, 5)\}$

11. $6x - y = -1$
$-8x + 6y = 17 - 2x + y$

$\left\{\left(\frac{1}{2}, 4\right)\right\}$

12. $3x + 2y = 9 - 3x + y$
$-6x + 3y = 15$

$\left\{\left(\frac{1}{2}, 6\right)\right\}$

Solve each system by the elimination method. Check each solution. See Example 3.

13. $2x - y = 12$
$3x + 2y = -3$

$\{(3, -6)\}$

14. $x + y = 3$
$-3x + 2y = -19$

$\{(5, -2)\}$

15. $x + 3y = 19$
$2x - y = 10$

$\{(7, 4)\}$

16. $4x - 3y = -19$
$2x + y = 13$

$\{(2, 9)\}$

17. $x + 4y = 16$
$3x + 5y = 20$

$\{(0, 4)\}$

18. $2x + y = 8$
$5x - 2y = -16$

$\{(0, 8)\}$

19. $5x - 3y = -20$
$-3x + 6y = 12$

$\{(-4, 0)\}$

20. $4x + 3y = -28$
$5x - 6y = -35$

$\{(-7, 0)\}$

21. $2x - 8y = 0$
$4x + 5y = 0$

$\{(0, 0)\}$

22. $3x - 15y = 0$
$6x + 10y = 0$

$\{(0, 0)\}$

Solve each system by the elimination method. Check each solution. See Example 4.

23. $3x - 7 = -5y$
$5x + 4y = -10$

$\{(-6, 5)\}$

24. $2x + 3y = 13$
$6 + 2y = -5x$

$\{(-4, 7)\}$

25. $2x + 3y = 0$
$4x + 12 = 9y$

$\left\{\left(-\frac{6}{5}, \frac{4}{5}\right)\right\}$

26. $-4x + 3y = 2$
$5x + 3 = -2y$
$\left\{\left(-\frac{13}{23}, -\frac{2}{23}\right)\right\}$

27. $24x + 12y = -7$
$16x - 17 = 18y$
$\left\{\left(\frac{1}{8}, -\frac{5}{6}\right)\right\}$

28. $9x + 4y = -3$
$6x + 7 = -6y$
$\left\{\left(\frac{1}{3}, -\frac{3}{2}\right)\right\}$

29. $3x = 3 + 2y$
$-\frac{4}{3}x + y = \frac{1}{3}$
$\{(11, 15)\}$

30. $3x = 27 + 2y$
$x - \frac{7}{2}y = -25$
$\{(17, 12)\}$

Use the elimination method to solve each system. See Example 5.

31. $x + y = 7$
$x + y = -3$
$\emptyset$

32. $x - y = 4$
$x - y = -3$
$\emptyset$

33. $-x + 3y = 4$
$-2x + 6y = 8$
$\{(x, y) | x - 3y = -4\}$

34. $6x - 2y = 24$
$-3x + y = -12$
$\{(x, y) | 3x - y = 12\}$

35. $5x - 2y = 3$
$10x - 4y = 5$
$\emptyset$

36. $3x - 5y = 1$
$6x - 10y = 4$
$\emptyset$

37. $2x + y = 0$
$-18x - 9y = 0$
$\{(x, y) | 2x + y = 0\}$

38. $3x - 5y = 0$
$9x - 15y = 0$
$\{(x, y) | 3x - 5y = 0\}$

Relating Concepts (Exercises 39–44) For Individual or Group Work

Attending the movies is one of America's favorite forms of entertainment. The graph shows how attendance gradually increased from 1991 to 1996. In 1991, attendance was 1141 *million, as represented by the point* $P(1991, 1141)$. *In 1996, attendance was* 1339 *million, as represented by the point* $Q(1996, 1339)$. *We can find an equation of line segment PQ using a system of equations, and then we can use the equation to approximate the attendance in any of the years between 1991 and 1996.* ***Work Exercises 39–44 in order.***

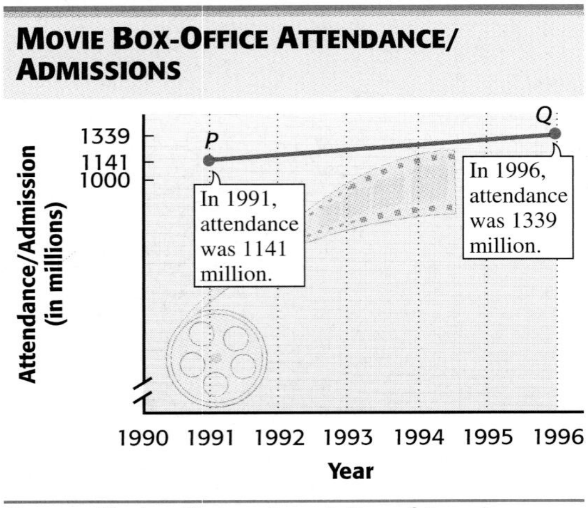

Source: Motion Picture Association of America.

39. The line segment has an equation that can be written in the form $y = ax + b$. Using the coordinates of point P with $x = 1991$ and $y = 1141$, write an equation in the variables a and b. **$1141 = 1991a + b$**

40. Using the coordinates of point Q with $x = 1996$ and $y = 1339$, write a second equation in the variables a and b. **$1339 = 1996a + b$**

41. Write the system of equations formed from the two equations in Exercises 39 and 40, and solve the system using the elimination method.

$1991a + b = 1141$
$1996a + b = 1339$;
solution set: $\{(39.6, -77{,}702.6)\}$

42. What is the equation of the segment PQ?

$y = 39.6x - 77{,}702.6$

43. Let $x = 1993$ in the equation of Exercise 42, and solve for y. How does the result compare with the actual figure of 1244 million?

1220.2 (million); This is slightly less than the actual figure.

44. The data points for the years 1991 through 1996 do not lie in a perfectly straight line. Explain the pitfalls of relying too heavily on using the equation in Exercise 42 to predict attendance.

It is not realistic to expect the data to lie in a perfectly straight line; as a result, the quantity obtained from an equation determined in this way will probably be "off" a bit. We cannot put too much faith in models such as this one, because not all sets of data points are linear in nature.

5.4 Linear Systems of Equations in Three Variables

Objectives

1. Understand the geometry of systems of three equations in three variables.
2. Solve linear systems by elimination.
3. Solve linear systems where some of the equations have missing terms.
4. Solve special systems.

A solution of an equation in three variables, such as

$$2x + 3y - z = 4,$$

is called an **ordered triple** and is written (x, y, z). For example, the ordered triple $(0, 1, -1)$ is a solution of the equation, because

$$2(0) + 3(1) - (-1) = 0 + 3 + 1 = 4.$$

Verify that another solution of this equation is $(10, -3, 7)$.

In the rest of this chapter, the term *linear equation* is extended to equations of the form

$$Ax + By + Cz + \ldots + Dw = K,$$

where not all the coefficients $A, B, C, \ldots, D$ equal 0. For example,

$$2x + 3y - 5z = 7 \quad \text{and} \quad x - 2y - z + 3u - 2w = 8$$

are linear equations, the first with three variables and the second with five variables.

1 **Understand the geometry of systems of three equations in three variables.** In this section, we discuss the solution of a system of linear equations in three variables, such as

$$\begin{aligned} 4x + 8y + z &= 2 \\ x + 7y - 3z &= -14 \\ 2x - 3y + 2z &= 3. \end{aligned}$$

Theoretically, a system of this type can be solved by graphing. However, the graph of a linear equation with three variables is a *plane,* not a line. Since the graph of each equation of the system is a plane, which requires three-dimensional graphing, this method is not practical. However, it does illustrate the number of solutions possible for such systems, as shown in Figure 7.

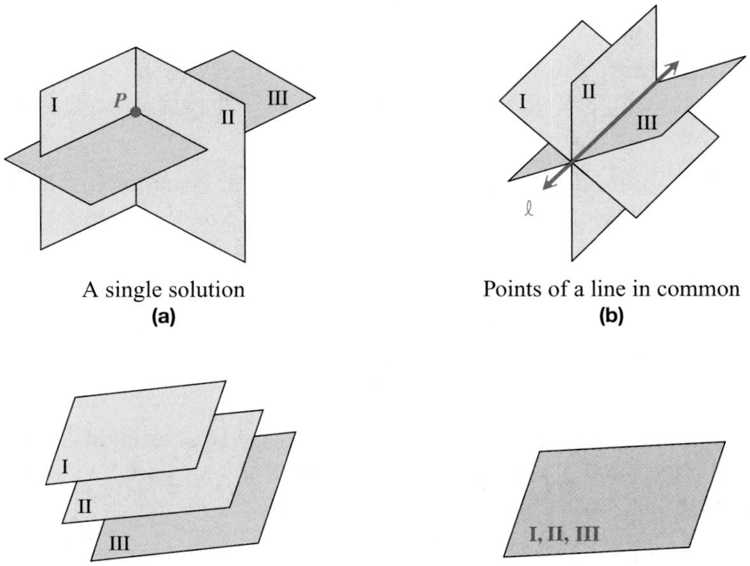

A single solution
(a)

Points of a line in common
(b)

No points in common
(c)

All points in common
(d)

Figure 7

Figure 7 illustrates the following cases.

Graphs of Linear Systems in Three Variables

1. The three planes may meet at a single, common point that is the solution of the system. See Figure 7(a).
2. The three planes may have the points of a line in common so that the infinite set of points that satisfy the equation of the line is the solution of the system. See Figure 7(b).
3. The planes may have no points common to all three so that there is no solution of the system. See Figure 7(c).
4. The three planes may coincide so that the solution of the system is the set of all points on a plane. See Figure 7(d).

NOTE

There are other illustrations of these cases. For example, two of the planes might intersect in a line, while the third plane is parallel to one of these planes, again resulting in no points common to all three planes. We give only one example of each case in Figure 7.

2 **Solve linear systems by elimination.** Since graphing to find the solution set of a system of three equations in three variables is impractical, these systems are solved with an extension of the elimination method, summarized as follows.

Solving a Linear System in Three Variables

Step 1 **Eliminate a variable.** Use the elimination method to eliminate any variable from any two of the original equations. The result is an equation in two variables.

Step 2 **Eliminate the same variable again.** Eliminate the *same* variable from any *other* two equations. The result is an equation in the same two variables as in Step 1.

Step 3 **Eliminate a different variable and solve.** Use the elimination method to eliminate a second variable from the two equations in two variables that result from Steps 1 and 2. The result is an equation in one variable that gives the value of that variable.

Step 4 **Find a second value.** Substitute the value of the variable found in Step 3 into either of the equations in two variables to find the value of the second variable.

Step 5 **Find a third value.** Use the values of the two variables from Steps 3 and 4 to find the value of the third variable by substituting into any of the original equations.

Step 6 **Check.** Check the solution in all of the original equations. Then write the solution set.

Example 1 Solving a System in Three Variables

Solve the system.

$$\begin{aligned} 4x + 8y + z &= 2 && (1)\\ x + 7y - 3z &= -14 && (2)\\ 2x - 3y + 2z &= 3 && (3) \end{aligned}$$

Step 1 As before, the elimination method involves eliminating a variable from the sum of two equations. The choice of which variable to eliminate is arbitrary. Suppose we decide to begin by eliminating z. To do this, we multiply equation (1) by 3 and then add the result to equation (2).

$$\begin{aligned} 12x + 24y + 3z &= 6 && \text{Multiply each side of (1) by 3.}\\ x + 7y - 3z &= -14 && (2)\\ \hline 13x + 31y \qquad &= -8 && \text{Add.} \quad (4) \end{aligned}$$

Step 2 Equation (4) has only two variables. To get another equation without z, we multiply equation (1) by -2 and add the result to equation (3). It is essential at this point to *eliminate the same variable, z.*

$$\begin{aligned} -8x - 16y - 2z &= -4 && \text{Multiply each side of (1) by } -2.\\ 2x - 3y + 2z &= 3 && (3)\\ \hline -6x - 19y \qquad &= -1 && \text{Add.} \quad (5) \end{aligned}$$

Step 3 Now we solve the system of equations (4) and (5) for x and y. This step is possible only if the *same* variable is eliminated in Steps 1 and 2.

$$\begin{aligned} 78x + 186y &= -48 && \text{Multiply each side of (4) by 6.}\\ -78x - 247y &= -13 && \text{Multiply each side of (5) by 13.}\\ \hline -61y &= -61 && \text{Add.}\\ y &= 1 \end{aligned}$$

Step 4 Now we substitute 1 for y in either equation (4) or (5). Choosing (5) gives

$$\begin{aligned} -6x - 19y &= -1 && (5)\\ -6x - 19(1) &= -1 && \text{Let } y = 1.\\ -6x - 19 &= -1\\ -6x &= 18\\ x &= -3. \end{aligned}$$

Step 5 We substitute -3 for x and 1 for y in any one of the three original equations to find z. Choosing (1) gives

$$\begin{aligned} 4x + 8y + z &= 2 && (1)\\ 4(-3) + 8(1) + z &= 2 && \text{Let } x = -3 \text{ and } y = 1.\\ -4 + z &= 2\\ z &= 6. \end{aligned}$$

Continued on Next Page

Step 6 It appears that the ordered triple $(-3, 1, 6)$ is the only solution of the system. We must check that the solution satisfies all three equations of the system. For equation (1),

$$\begin{aligned} 4x + 8y + z &= 2 & &(1) \\ 4(-3) + 8(1) + 6 &= 2 & &? \\ -12 + 8 + 6 &= 2 & &? \\ 2 &= 2. & &\text{True} \end{aligned}$$

Work Problem 1 at the Side.

Because $(-3, 1, 6)$ also satisfies equations (2) and (3), the solution set is $\{(-3, 1, 6)\}$.

Work Problem 2 at the Side.

3 **Solve linear systems where some of the equations have missing terms.** When this happens, one elimination step can be omitted.

Example 2 Solving a System of Equations with Missing Terms

Solve the system.

$$\begin{aligned} 6x - 12y &= -5 & &(1) \\ 8y + z &= 0 & &(2) \\ 9x - z &= 12 & &(3) \end{aligned}$$

Since equation (3) is missing the variable y, a good way to begin the solution is to eliminate y again using equations (1) and (2).

$$\begin{aligned} 12x - 24y &= -10 & &\text{Multiply each side of (1) by 2.} \\ 24y + 3z &= 0 & &\text{Multiply each side of (2) by 3.} \\ \hline 12x + 3z &= -10 & &\text{Add. (4)} \end{aligned}$$

Use this result, together with equation (3), to eliminate z. Multiply equation (3) by 3. This gives

$$\begin{aligned} 27x - 3z &= 36 & &\text{Multiply each side of (3) by 3.} \\ 12x + 3z &= -10 & &(4) \\ \hline 39x &= 26 & &\text{Add.} \\ x &= \frac{26}{39} = \frac{2}{3}. \end{aligned}$$

Substituting into equation (3) gives

$$\begin{aligned} 9x - z &= 12 & &(3) \\ 9\left(\frac{2}{3}\right) - z &= 12 & &\text{Let } x = \tfrac{2}{3}. \\ 6 - z &= 12 \\ z &= -6. \end{aligned}$$

Continued on Next Page

1 Check that the solution $(-3, 1, 6)$ satisfies equations (2) and (3) of Example 1.

(a) $x + 7y - 3z = -14$ (2)

Does the solution satisfy equation (2)?

(b) $2x - 3y + 2z = 3$ (3)

Does the solution satisfy equation (3)?

2 Solve each system.

(a)
$$\begin{aligned} x + y + z &= 2 \\ x - y + 2z &= 2 \\ -x + 2y - z &= 1 \end{aligned}$$

(b)
$$\begin{aligned} 2x + y + z &= 9 \\ -x - y + z &= 1 \\ 3x - y + z &= 9 \end{aligned}$$

ANSWERS
1. **(a)** yes **(b)** yes
2. **(a)** $\{(-1, 1, 2)\}$ **(b)** $\{(2, 1, 4)\}$

Substituting -6 for z in equation (2) gives

$$
\begin{aligned}
8y + z &= 0 && (2)\\
8y - 6 &= 0 && \text{Let } z = -6.\\
8y &= 6\\
y &= \frac{3}{4}.
\end{aligned}
$$

Check in each of the original equations of the system to verify that the solution set of the system is $\{(\frac{2}{3}, \frac{3}{4}, -6)\}$.

Work Problem 3 at the Side.

4 Solve special systems. Linear systems with three variables may be inconsistent or may include dependent equations. The next examples illustrate these cases.

Example 3 Solving an Inconsistent System with Three Variables

Solve the system.

$$
\begin{aligned}
2x - 4y + 6z &= 5 && (1)\\
-x + 3y - 2z &= -1 && (2)\\
x - 2y + 3z &= 1 && (3)
\end{aligned}
$$

Eliminate x by adding equations (2) and (3) to get the equation

$$y + z = 0.$$

Now, *eliminate x again,* using equations (1) and (3).

$$
\begin{aligned}
-2x + 4y - 6z &= -2 && \text{Multiply each side of (3) by } -2.\\
2x - 4y + 6z &= 5 && (1)\\
\hline
0 &= 3 && \textbf{False}
\end{aligned}
$$

The resulting false statement indicates that equations (1) and (3) have no common solution. Thus, the system is inconsistent and the solution set is $\emptyset$. The graph of this system would show these two planes parallel to one another.

NOTE

If you get a false statement when adding as in Example 3, you do not need to go any further with the solution. Since two of the three planes are parallel, it is not possible for the three planes to have any common points.

Work Problem 4 at the Side.

3 Solve each system.

(a)
$$
\begin{aligned}
x - y &= 6\\
2y + 5z &= 1\\
3x - 4z &= 8
\end{aligned}
$$

(b)
$$
\begin{aligned}
5x - y &= 26\\
4y + 3z &= -4\\
x + z &= 5
\end{aligned}
$$

4 Solve each system.

(a)
$$
\begin{aligned}
3x - 5y + 2z &= 1\\
5x + 8y - z &= 4\\
-6x + 10y - 4z &= 5
\end{aligned}
$$

(b)
$$
\begin{aligned}
7x - 9y + 2z &= 0\\
y + z &= 0\\
8x - z &= 0
\end{aligned}
$$

ANSWERS

3. (a) $\{(4, -2, 1)\}$ **(b)** $\{(5, -1, 0)\}$
4. (a) $\emptyset$ **(b)** $\{(0, 0, 0)\}$

5 Solve the system.

$$\begin{aligned} x - y + z &= 4 \\ -3x + 3y - 3z &= -12 \\ 2x - 2y + 2z &= 8 \end{aligned}$$

Example 4 **Solving a System of Dependent Equations with Three Variables**

Solve the system.

$$2x - 3y + 4z = 8 \qquad (1)$$

$$-x + \frac{3}{2}y - 2z = -4 \qquad (2)$$

$$6x - 9y + 12z = 24 \qquad (3)$$

Multiplying each side of equation (1) by 3 gives equation (3). Multiplying each side of equation (2) by -6 also gives equation (3). Because of this, the equations are dependent. All three equations have the same graph, as illustrated in Figure 7(d). The solution set is written

$$\{(x, y, z) \mid 2x - 3y + 4z = 8\}.$$

Although any one of the three equations could be used to write the solution set, we use the equation with coefficients that are integers ($A > 0$) with no common factor (except 1), as we did in Section 5.1.

Work Problem 5 at the Side.

ANSWERS

5. $\{(x, y, z) \mid x - y + z = 4\}$

5.4 EXERCISES

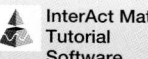

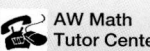

FOR EXTRA HELP: Student's Solutions Manual | MyMathLab.com | InterAct Math Tutorial Software | AW Math Tutor Center | www.mathxl.com | Digital Video Tutor CD 4 Videotape 10

1. Explain what the following statement means: The solution set of the system

$$\begin{aligned} 2x + y + z &= 3 \\ 3x - y + z &= -2 \\ 4x - y + 2z &= 0 \end{aligned}$$

is $\{(-1, 2, 3)\}$.

The statement means that when -1 is substituted for x, 2 is substituted for y, and 3 is substituted for z in the three equations, the resulting three statements are true.

2. The two equations

$$\begin{aligned} x + y + z &= 6 \\ 2x - y + z &= 3 \end{aligned}$$

have a common solution of $(1, 2, 3)$. Which equation would complete a system of three linear equations in three variables having solution set $\{(1, 2, 3)\}$?

A. $3x + 2y - z = 1$ **B.** $3x + 2y - z = 4$

C. $3x + 2y - z = 5$ **D.** $3x + 2y - z = 6$

B

Solve each system of equations. See Example 1.

3. $$\begin{aligned} 2x - 5y + 3z &= -1 \\ x + 4y - 2z &= 9 \\ x - 2y - 4z &= -5 \end{aligned}$$

$\{(3, 2, 1)\}$

4. $$\begin{aligned} x + 3y - 6z &= 7 \\ 2x - y + z &= 1 \\ x + 2y + 2z &= -1 \end{aligned}$$

$\{(1, 0, -1)\}$

5. $$\begin{aligned} 3x + 2y + z &= 8 \\ 2x - 3y + 2z &= -16 \\ x + 4y - z &= 20 \end{aligned}$$

$\{(1, 4, -3)\}$

6. $$\begin{aligned} -3x + y - z &= -10 \\ -4x + 2y + 3z &= -1 \\ 2x + 3y - 2z &= -5 \end{aligned}$$

$\{(2, -1, 3)\}$

7. $$\begin{aligned} -x + 2y + 6z &= 2 \\ 3x + 2y + 6z &= 6 \\ x + 4y - 3z &= 1 \end{aligned}$$

$\left\{\left(1, \frac{3}{10}, \frac{2}{5}\right)\right\}$

8. $$\begin{aligned} 2x + y + 2z &= 1 \\ x + 2y + z &= 2 \\ x - y - z &= 0 \end{aligned}$$

$\left\{\left(\frac{1}{2}, 1, -\frac{1}{2}\right)\right\}$

9. $2x + 5y + 2z = 0$
$4x - 7y - 3z = 1$
$3x - 8y - 2z = -6$

$\{(0, 2, -5)\}$

10. $5x - 2y + 3z = -9$
$4x + 3y + 5z = 4$
$2x + 4y - 2z = 14$

$\{(0, 3, -1)\}$

11. $x + y - z = -2$
$2x - y + z = -5$
$-x + 2y - 3z = -4$

$\left\{\left(-\frac{7}{3}, \frac{22}{3}, 7\right)\right\}$

12. $x + 2y + 3z = 1$
$-x - y + 3z = 2$
$-6x + y + z = -2$

$\left\{\left(\frac{20}{59}, -\frac{33}{59}, \frac{35}{59}\right)\right\}$

Solve each system of equations. See Example 2.

13. $2x - 3y + 2z = -1$
$x + 2y + z = 17$
$2y - z = 7$

$\{(4, 5, 3)\}$

14. $2x - y + 3z = 6$
$x + 2y - z = 8$
$2y + z = 1$

$\{(5, 1, -1)\}$

15. $4x + 2y - 3z = 6$
$x - 4y + z = -4$
$-x + 2z = 2$

$\{(2, 2, 2)\}$

16. $2x + 3y - 4z = 4$
$x - 6y + z = -16$
$-x + 3z = 8$

$\{(4, 4, 4)\}$

17. $2x + y = 6$
$3y - 2z = -4$
$3x - 5z = -7$

$\left\{\left(\frac{8}{3}, \frac{2}{3}, 3\right)\right\}$

18. $4x - 8y = -7$
$4y + z = 7$
$-8x + z = -4$

$\left\{\left(\frac{3}{4}, \frac{5}{4}, 2\right)\right\}$

19. Using your immediate surroundings, give an example of three planes that

(a) intersect in a single point;

(b) do not intersect;

(c) intersect in infinitely many points.

Answers will vary. Some possible answers are (a) two perpendicular walls and the ceiling in a normal room, (b) the floors of three different levels of an office building, and (c) three pages of this book (since they intersect in the spine).

20. Suppose that a system has infinitely many ordered triple solutions of the form (x, y, z) such that

$$x + y + 2z = 1.$$

Give three specific ordered triples that are solutions of the system.

Answers will vary. Three possibilities are $\left(1, 1, -\frac{1}{2}\right)$, $\left(0, 0, \frac{1}{2}\right)$, **and** $(2, 5, -3)$.

Solve each system of equations. See Examples 1, 3, and 4.

21.
$$\begin{aligned} 2x + 2y - 6z &= 5 \\ -3x + y - z &= -2 \\ -x - y + 3z &= 4 \end{aligned}$$

$\emptyset$

22.
$$\begin{aligned} -2x + 5y + z &= -3 \\ 5x + 14y - z &= -11 \\ 7x + 9y - 2z &= -5 \end{aligned}$$

$\emptyset$

23.
$$\begin{aligned} -5x + 5y - 20z &= -40 \\ x - y + 4z &= 8 \\ 3x - 3y + 12z &= 24 \end{aligned}$$

$\{(x, y, z) \mid x - y + 4z = 8\}$

24.
$$\begin{aligned} x + 4y - z &= 3 \\ -2x - 8y + 2z &= -6 \\ 3x + 12y - 3z &= 9 \end{aligned}$$

$\{(x, y, z) \mid x + 4y - z = 3\}$

25.
$$\begin{aligned} 2x + y - z &= 6 \\ 4x + 2y - 2z &= 12 \\ -x - \frac{1}{2}y + \frac{1}{2}z &= -3 \end{aligned}$$

$\{(x, y, z) \mid 2x + y - z = 6\}$

26.
$$\begin{aligned} 2x - 8y + 2z &= -10 \\ -x + 4y - z &= 5 \\ \frac{1}{8}x - \frac{1}{2}y + \frac{1}{8}z &= -\frac{5}{8} \end{aligned}$$

$\{(x, y, z) \mid x - 4y + z = -5\}$

27.
$$\begin{aligned} x + y - 2z &= 0 \\ 3x - y + z &= 0 \\ 4x + 2y - z &= 0 \end{aligned}$$

$\{(0, 0, 0)\}$

28.
$$\begin{aligned} 2x + 3y - z &= 0 \\ x - 4y + 2z &= 0 \\ 3x - 5y - z &= 0 \end{aligned}$$

$\{(0, 0, 0)\}$

Relating Concepts (Exercises 29–36) For Individual or Group Work

Suppose that on a distant planet a function of the form

$$f(x) = ax^2 + bx + c \quad (a \neq 0)$$

describes the height in feet of a projectile x seconds after it has been projected upward. ***Work Exercises 29–36 in order*** *to see how this can be related to a system of three equations in three variables a, b, and c.*

29. After 1 sec, the height of a certain projectile is 128 ft. Thus, $f(1) = 128$. Use this information to find one equation in the variables a, b, and c. (*Hint:* Substitute 1 for x and 128 for $f(x)$.)

$128 = a + b + c$

30. After 1.5 sec, the height is 140 ft. Find a second equation in a, b, and c.

$140 = 2.25a + 1.5b + c$

31. After 3 sec, the height is 80 ft. Find a third equation in a, b, and c.

$80 = 9a + 3b + c$

32. Write a system of three equations in a, b, and c, based on your answers in Exercises 29–31. Solve the system.

$$\begin{aligned} a + b + c &= 128 \\ 2.25a + 1.5b + c &= 140 \\ 9a + 3b + c &= 80; \{(-32, 104, 56)\} \end{aligned}$$

33. What is the function f for this particular projectile?

$f(x) = -32x^2 + 104x + 56$

34. In the function f written in Exercise 33, the __height__ of the projectile is a function of the __time__ elapsed since it was projected.

35. What was the initial height of the projectile? (*Hint:* Find $f(0)$.)

56 ft

36. The projectile reaches its maximum height in 1.625 sec. Find its maximum height.

140.5 ft

5.5 Applications of Linear Systems of Equations

Objectives

1. Solve problems using two variables.
2. Solve money problems using two variables.
3. Solve mixture problems using two variables.
4. Solve distance-rate-time problems using two variables.
5. Solve problems with three variables using a system of three equations.

Many applied problems involve more than one unknown quantity. Although some problems with two unknowns can be solved using just one variable, it is often easier to use two variables. To solve a problem with two unknowns, we must write two equations that relate the unknown quantities. The system formed by the pair of equations can then be solved using the methods of this chapter.

Problems that can be solved by writing a system of equations have been of interest historically. The following problem, which is given in the exercises for this section, first appeared in a Hindu work that dates back to about A.D. 850.

> The mixed price of 9 citrons [a lemonlike fruit shown in the photo] and 7 fragrant wood apples is 107; again, the mixed price of 7 citrons and 9 fragrant wood apples is 101. O you arithmetician, tell me quickly the price of a citron and the price of a wood apple here, having distinctly separated those prices well.

The following steps, based on the six-step problem-solving method first introduced in Chapter 2, give a strategy for solving applied problems using more than one variable.

Solving an Applied Problem by Writing a System of Equations

Step 1 **Read** the problem carefully until you understand what is given and what is to be found.

Step 2 **Assign variables** to represent the unknown values, using diagrams or tables as needed. *Write down* what each variable represents.

Step 3 **Write a system of equations** that relates the unknowns.

Step 4 **Solve** the system of equations.

Step 5 **State the answer** to the problem. Does it seem reasonable?

Step 6 **Check** the answer in the words of the original problem.

1 Solve problems using two variables. Problems about the perimeter of a geometric figure often involve two unknowns and can be solved using systems of equations.

Example 1 Finding the Dimensions of a Soccer Field

Unlike football, where the dimensions of a playing field cannot vary, a rectangular soccer field may have a width between 50 and 100 yd and a length between 50 and 100 yd. Suppose that one particular field has a perimeter of 320 yd. Its length measures 40 yd more than its width. What are the dimensions of this field? (*Source: Microsoft Encarta Encyclopedia 2000.*)

Step 1 **Read** the problem again. We are asked to find the dimensions of the field.

Continued on Next Page

1 Solve the problem.

The length of the foundation of a rectangular house is to be 6 m more than its width. Find the length and width of the house if the perimeter must be 48 m.

Step 2 **Assign variables.** Let L = the length and W = the width. Figure 8 shows a soccer field with the length labeled L and the width labeled W.

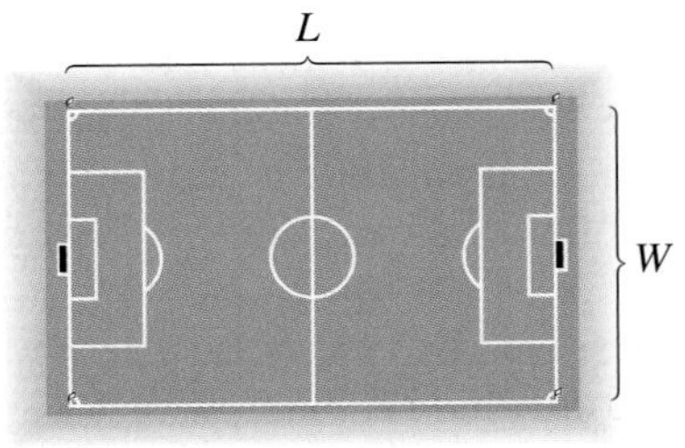

Figure 8

Step 3 **Write a system of equations.** Because the perimeter is 320 yd, we find one equation by using the perimeter formula:

$$2L + 2W = 320.$$

Because the length is 40 yd more than the width, we have

$$L = W + 40.$$

The system is, therefore,

$$2L + 2W = 320 \quad (1)$$
$$L = W + 40. \quad (2)$$

Step 4 **Solve** the system of equations. Since equation (2) is solved for L, we can use the substitution method. We substitute $W + 40$ for L in equation (1), and solve for W.

$$\begin{aligned} 2L + 2W &= 320 && (1) \\ 2(W + 40) + 2W &= 320 && \text{Let } L = W + 40. \\ 2W + 80 + 2W &= 320 && \text{Distributive property} \\ 4W + 80 &= 320 && \text{Combine terms.} \\ 4W &= 240 && \text{Subtract 80.} \\ W &= 60 && \text{Divide by 4.} \end{aligned}$$

Let $W = 60$ in the equation $L = W + 40$ to find L.

$$L = 60 + 40 = 100$$

Step 5 **State the answer.** The length is 100 yd, and the width is 60 yd. Both dimensions are within the ranges given in the problem.

Step 6 **Check.** The perimeter of this soccer field is

$$2(100) + 2(60) = 320 \text{ yd},$$

and the length, 100 yd, is indeed 40 yd more than the width, since

$$100 - 40 = 60.$$

The answer is correct.

Work Problem 1 at the Side.

2 Solve money problems using two variables. Professional sport ticket prices increase annually. Average per-ticket prices in three of the four major sports (football, basketball, and hockey) now exceed $30.00.

ANSWERS

1. length: 15 m; width: 9 m

Example 2 Solving a Problem about Ticket Prices

During recent National Hockey League and National Basketball Association seasons, two hockey tickets and one basketball ticket purchased at their average prices would have cost \$110.40. One hockey ticket and two basketball tickets would have cost \$106.32. What were the average ticket prices for the two sports? (*Source:* Team Marketing Report, Chicago.)

Step 1 **Read** the problem again. There are two unknowns.

Step 2 **Assign variables.** Let h represent the average price for a hockey ticket and b represent the average price for a basketball ticket.

Step 3 **Write a system of equations.** Because two hockey tickets and one basketball ticket cost a total of \$110.40, one equation for the system is

$$2h + b = 110.40.$$

By similar reasoning, the second equation is

$$h + 2b = 106.32.$$

Therefore, the system is

$$2h + b = 110.40 \quad (1)$$
$$h + 2b = 106.32. \quad (2)$$

Step 4 **Solve** the system of equations. To eliminate h, multiply equation (2) by -2 and add.

$$2h + b = 110.40 \quad (1)$$
$$-2h - 4b = -212.64 \quad \text{Multiply each side of (2) by } -2.$$
$$-3b = -102.24 \quad \text{Add.}$$
$$b = 34.08 \quad \text{Divide by } -3.$$

To find the value of h, let $b = 34.08$ in equation (2).

$$h + 2b = 106.32 \quad (2)$$
$$h + 2(34.08) = 106.32 \quad \text{Let } b = 34.08.$$
$$h + 68.16 = 106.32 \quad \text{Multiply.}$$
$$h = 38.16 \quad \text{Subtract 68.16.}$$

Step 5 **State the answer.** The average price for one basketball ticket was \$34.08. For one hockey ticket, the average price was \$38.16.

Step 6 **Check** that these values satisfy the conditions stated in the problem.

Work Problem 2 at the Side.

3 Solve mixture problems using two variables. Mixture problems involving rates of concentration can be solved using more than one variable and a system of equations.

Example 3 Solving a Mixture Problem

How many ounces each of 5% hydrochloric acid and 20% hydrochloric acid must be combined to get 10 oz of solution that is 12.5% hydrochloric acid?

Continued on Next Page

2 Solve the problem.

For recent Major League Baseball and National Football League seasons, based on average ticket prices, three baseball tickets and two football tickets would have cost \$105.05, while two baseball tickets and one football ticket would have cost \$58.12. What were the average ticket prices for the two sports? (*Source:* Team Marketing Report, Chicago.)

Answers

2. baseball: \$11.19; football: \$35.74

3 Solve each problem.

(a) A grocer has some \$4 per lb coffee and some \$8 per lb coffee, which he will mix to make 50 lb of \$5.60 per lb coffee. How many pounds of each should be used?

(b) Some 40% ethyl alcohol solution is to be mixed with some 80% solution to get 200 L of a 50% solution. How many liters of each should be used?

Step 1 **Read** the problem. Two solutions of different strengths are being mixed together to get a specific amount of a solution with an "in-between" strength.

Step 2 **Assign variables.** Let x represent the number of ounces of 5% solution and y represent the number of ounces of 20% solution. Use a table to summarize the information from the problem.

Percent (as a Decimal)	Ounces of Solution	Ounces of Pure Acid
$5\% = .05$	x	$.05x$
$20\% = .20$	y	$.20y$
$12.5\% = .125$	10	$(.125)10$

Figure 9 also illustrates what is happening in the problem.

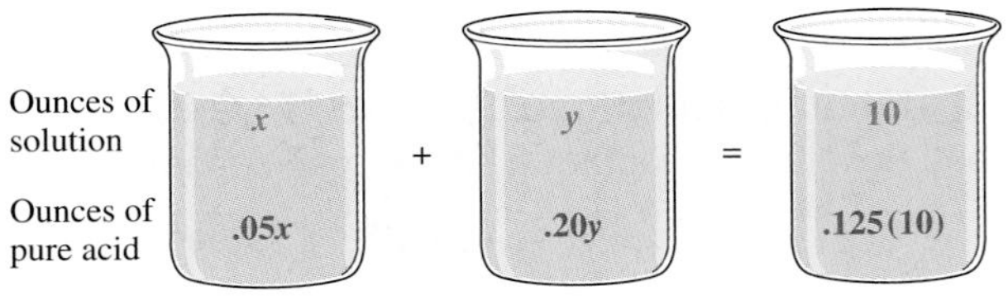

Figure 9

Step 3 **Write a system of equations.** When the x ounces of 5% solution and the y ounces of 20% solution are combined, the total number of ounces is 10, so

$$x + y = 10. \qquad (1)$$

The ounces of acid in the 5% solution $(.05x)$ plus the ounces of acid in the 20% solution $(.20y)$ should equal the total ounces of acid in the mixture, which is $(.125)10$, or 1.25. That is,

$$.05x + .20y = 1.25. \qquad (2)$$

Notice that these equations can be quickly determined by reading down in the table or using the labels in Figure 9.

Step 4 **Solve** the system of equations (1) and (2). Eliminate x by first multiplying equation (2) by 100 to clear it of decimals and then multiplying equation (1) by -5.

$$\begin{aligned} 5x + 20y &= 125 && \text{Multiply each side of (2) by 100.} \\ -5x - 5y &= -50 && \text{Multiply each side of (1) by } -5. \\ \hline 15y &= 75 && \text{Add.} \\ y &= 5 \end{aligned}$$

Because $y = 5$ and $x + y = 10$, x is also 5.

Step 5 **State the answer.** The desired mixture will require 5 oz of the 5% solution and 5 oz of the 20% solution.

Step 6 **Check** that these values satisfy both equations of the system.

Work Problem 3 at the Side.

4 Solve distance-rate-time problems using two variables. Motion problems require the distance formula, $d = rt$, where d is distance, r is rate (or speed), and t is time. These applications often lead to systems of equations, as in the next example.

ANSWERS

3. (a) 30 lb of \$4; 20 lb of \$8
(b) 150 L of 40%; 50 L of 80%

Example 4 Solving a Motion Problem

A car travels 250 km in the same time that a truck travels 225 km. If the speed of the car is 8 km per hr faster than the speed of the truck, find both speeds.

Step 1 **Read** the problem again. Given the distances traveled, you need to find the speed of each vehicle.

Step 2 **Assign variables.**

Let x = the speed of the car
and y = the speed of the truck.

As in Example 3, a table helps organize the information. Fill in the given information for each vehicle (in this case, distance) and use the assigned variables for the unknown speeds (rates).

	d	r	t
Car	250	x	
Truck	225	y	

The table shows nothing about time. To get an expression for time, solve the distance formula, $d = rt$, for t.

$$\frac{d}{r} = t$$

The two times can be written as $\frac{250}{x}$ and $\frac{225}{y}$.

Step 3 **Write a system of equations.** The problem states that the car travels 8 km per hr faster than the truck. Since the two speeds are x and y,

$$x = y + 8.$$

Both vehicles travel for the same time, so from the table

$$\frac{250}{x} = \frac{225}{y}.$$

This is not a linear equation. However, multiplying each side by xy gives

$$250y = 225x,$$

which is linear. The system is

$$x = y + 8 \quad (1)$$
$$250y = 225x. \quad (2)$$

Step 4 **Solve** the system of equations by substitution. Replace x with $y + 8$ in equation (2).

$$250y = 225x \quad (2)$$
$$250y = 225(y + 8) \quad \text{Let } x = y + 8.$$
$$250y = 225y + 1800 \quad \text{Distributive property}$$
$$25y = 1800 \quad \text{Subtract } 225y.$$
$$y = 72 \quad \text{Divide by 25.}$$

Because $x = y + 8$, the value of x is $72 + 8 = 80$.

Continued on Next Page

Step 5 **State the answer.** The car's speed is 80 km per hr, and the truck's speed is 72 km per hr.

Step 6 **Check.** This is especially important since one of the equations had variable denominators.

$$\text{Car: } t = \frac{d}{r} = \frac{250}{80} = 3.125$$

$$\text{Truck: } t = \frac{d}{r} = \frac{225}{72} = 3.125$$

Times are equal.

Since $80 - 72 = 8$, the conditions of the problem are satisfied.

Work Problem 4 at the Side.

4 Solve the problem.

A train travels 600 mi in the same time that a truck travels 520 mi. Find the speed of each vehicle if the train's average speed is 8 mph faster than the truck's.

5 Solve problems with three variables using a system of three equations.

To solve such problems, we extend the method used for two unknowns. Since three variables are used, three equations are necessary to find a solution.

Example 5 Solving a Problem Involving Prices

At Panera Bread, a loaf of honey wheat bread costs \$2.40, a loaf of pumpernickel bread costs \$3.35, and a loaf of French bread costs \$2.10. On a recent day, three times as many loaves of honey wheat were sold as pumpernickel. The number of loaves of French bread sold was 5 less than the number of loaves of honey wheat sold. Total receipts for these breads were \$56.90. How many loaves of each type of bread were sold? (*Source:* Panera Bread menu.)

Step 1 **Read** the problem again. There are three unknowns in this problem.

Step 2 **Assign variables** to represent the three unknowns.

Let x = the number of loaves of honey wheat,

y = the number of loaves of pumpernickel,

and z = the number of loaves of French bread.

Step 3 **Write a system of three equations** using the information in the problem. Since three times as many loaves of honey wheat were sold as pumpernickel,

$$x = 3y, \quad \text{or} \quad x - 3y = 0. \quad (1)$$

Also,

Number of loaves of French bread	equals	5 less than the number of loaves of honey wheat.
↓	↓	↓
z	$=$	$x - 5$,

so

$$x - z = 5. \quad (2)$$

Multiplying the cost of a loaf of each kind of bread by the number of loaves of that kind sold and adding gives the total receipts.

$$2.40x + 3.35y + 2.10z = 56.90$$

Multiply each side of this equation by 100 to clear it of decimals.

$$240x + 335y + 210z = 5690 \quad (3)$$

Step 4 **Solve** the system of three equations using the method shown in Section 5.4.

Work Problem 5 at the Side.

Continued on Next Page

5 Solve the system of equations from Example 5.

$$x - 3y = 0 \quad (1)$$
$$x - z = 5 \quad (2)$$
$$240x + 335y + 210z = 5690 \quad (3)$$

ANSWERS

4. train: 60 mph; truck: 52 mph

5. (12, 4, 7)

Step 5 **State the answer.** The solution is (12, 4, 7), so 12 loaves of honey wheat, 4 loaves of pumpernickel, and 7 loaves of French bread were sold.

Step 6 **Check.** Since $12 = 3 \cdot 4$, the number of loaves of honey wheat is three times the number of loaves of pumpernickel. Also, $12 - 7 = 5$, so the number of loaves of French bread is 5 less than the number of loaves of honey wheat. Multiply the appropriate cost per loaf by the number of loaves sold and add the results to check that total receipts were \$56.90.

Work Problem 6 at the Side.

6 Solve the problem.

A department store has three kinds of perfume: cheap, better, and best. It has 10 more bottles of cheap than better, and 3 fewer bottles of best than better. Each bottle of cheap costs \$8, better costs \$15, and best costs \$32. The total value of all the perfume is \$589. How many bottles of each are there?

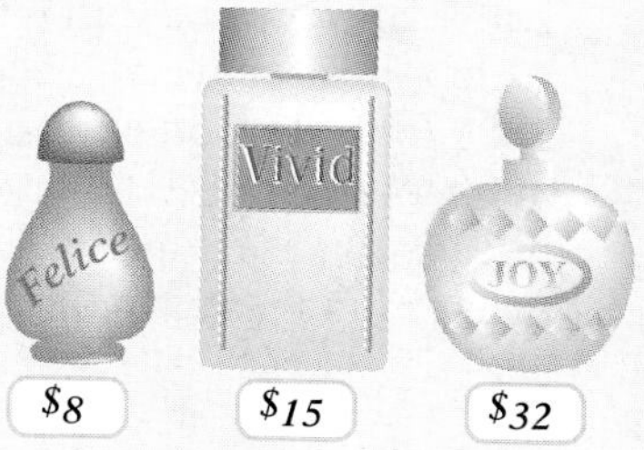

Example 6 Solving a Business Production Problem

A company produces three color television sets, models X, Y, and Z. Each model X set requires 2 hr of electronics work, 2 hr of assembly time, and 1 hr of finishing time. Each model Y requires 1, 3, and 1 hr of electronics, assembly, and finishing time, respectively. Each model Z requires 3, 2, and 2 hr of the same work, respectively. There are 100 hr available for electronics, 100 hr available for assembly, and 65 hr available for finishing per week. How many of each model should be produced each week if all available time must be used?

Step 1 **Read** the problem again. There are three unknowns.

Step 2 **Assign variables.**

Let x = the number of model X produced per week,
y = the number of model Y produced per week,
and z = the number of model Z produced per week.

Organize the information in a table.

	Each Model X	Each Model Y	Each Model Z	Totals
Hours of Electronics Work	2	1	3	100
Hours of Assembly Time	2	3	2	100
Hours of Finishing Time	1	1	2	65

Step 3 **Write a system of three equations.** The x model X sets require $2x$ hr of electronics, the y model Y sets require $1y$ (or y) hr of electronics, and the z model Z sets require $3z$ hr of electronics. Since 100 hr are available for electronics,

$$2x + y + 3z = 100. \quad (1)$$

Similarly, from the fact that 100 hr are available for assembly,

$$2x + 3y + 2z = 100, \quad (2)$$

and the fact that 65 hr are available for finishing leads to the equation

$$x + y + 2z = 65. \quad (3)$$

Again, notice the advantage of setting up a table. By reading across, we can easily determine the coefficients and constants in the equations of the system.

Continued on Next Page

ANSWERS

6. 21 bottles of cheap; 11 of better; 8 of best

Step 4 **Solve** the system

$$2x + y + 3z = 100$$
$$2x + 3y + 2z = 100$$
$$x + y + 2z = 65$$

to find $x = 15$, $y = 10$, and $z = 20$.

Step 5 **State the answer.** The company should produce 15 model X, 10 model Y, and 20 model Z sets per week.

Step 6 **Check** that these values satisfy the conditions of the problem.

Work Problem 7 at the Side.

7 Solve the problem.

A paper mill makes newsprint, bond, and copy machine paper. Each ton of newsprint requires 3 tons of recycled paper and 1 ton of wood pulp. Each ton of bond requires 2 tons of recycled paper, 4 tons of wood pulp, and 3 tons of rags. A ton of copy machine paper requires 2 tons of recycled paper, 3 tons of wood pulp, and 2 tons of rags. The mill has 4200 tons of recycled paper, 5800 tons of wood pulp, and 3900 tons of rags. How much of each kind of paper can be made from these supplies?

ANSWERS

7. 400 tons of newsprint; 900 tons of bond; 600 tons of copy machine paper

5.5 Exercises

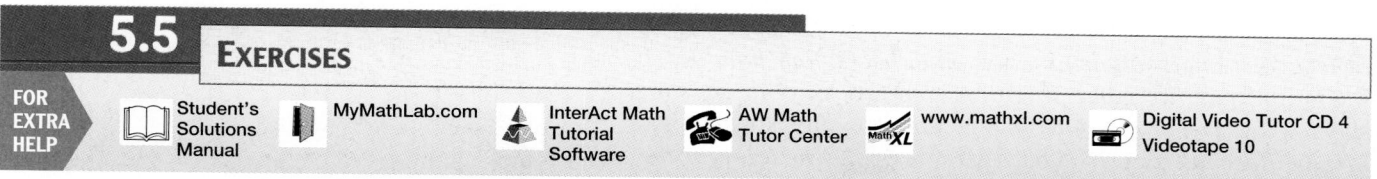

FOR EXTRA HELP: Student's Solutions Manual; MyMathLab.com; InterAct Math Tutorial Software; AW Math Tutor Center; www.mathxl.com; Digital Video Tutor CD 4 Videotape 10

Solve each problem. See Example 1.

1. During the 1999–2000 Major League Baseball regular season, the St. Louis Cardinals played 162 games. They won 28 more games than they lost. What was their win–loss record that year?

wins: 95; losses: 67

2. Refer to Exercise 1. During the same 162-game season, the Chicago Cubs lost 32 more games than they won. What was the team's win–loss record?

wins: 65; losses: 97

2000 MLB Final Standings
National League Central

Team	W	L
St. Louis	___	___
Cincinnati	85	77
Milwaukee	73	89
Houston	72	90
Pittsburgh	69	93
Chicago	___	___

Source: www.mlb.com

3. Venus and Serena measured a tennis court and found that it was 42 ft longer than it was wide and had a perimeter of 228 ft. What were the length and the width of the tennis court?

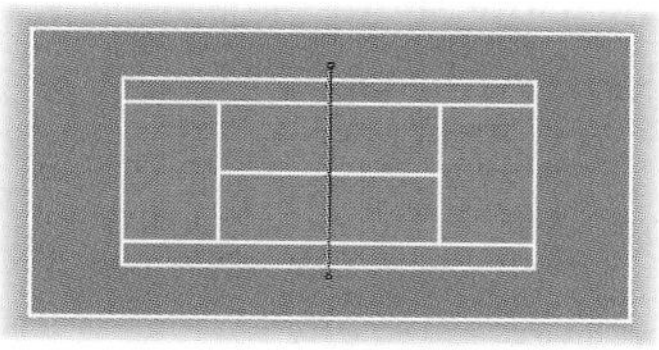

length: 78 ft; width: 36 ft

4. Shaq and Kobe found that the width of their basketball court was 44 ft less than the length. If the perimeter was 288 ft, what were the length and the width of their court?

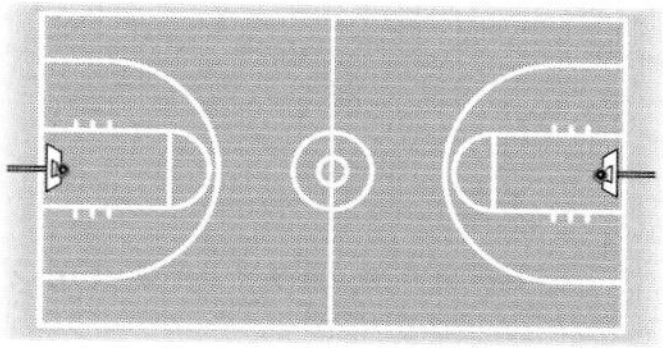

length: 94 ft; width: 50 ft

5. The two biggest U.S. companies in terms of revenue in 2000 were ExxonMobil and General Motors. ExxonMobil's revenue was \$29 billion more than that of General Motors. Total revenue for the two companies was \$399 billion. What was the revenue for each company? (*Source:* Bridge News, MarketGuide.com)

ExxonMobil: \$214 billion; General Motors: \$185 billion

6. The top two U.S. trading partners during the first four months of 2000 were Canada and Mexico. Exports and imports with Mexico were \$57 billion less than those with Canada. Total exports and imports involving these two countries were \$211 billion. How much were U.S. exports and imports with each country? (*Source:* U.S. Bureau of the Census.)

Canada: \$134 billion; Mexico: \$77 billion

In Exercises 7 and 8, find the measures of the angles marked x and y. Remember that (1) *the sum of the measures of the angles of a triangle is* 180°, (2) *supplementary angles have a sum of* 180°, *and* (3) *vertical angles have equal measures.*

7.

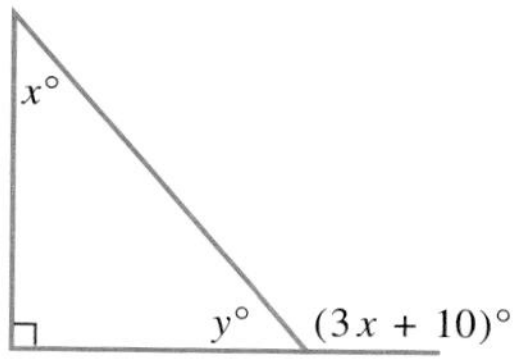

$x = 40$ and $y = 50$, so the angles measure 40° and 50°.

8.

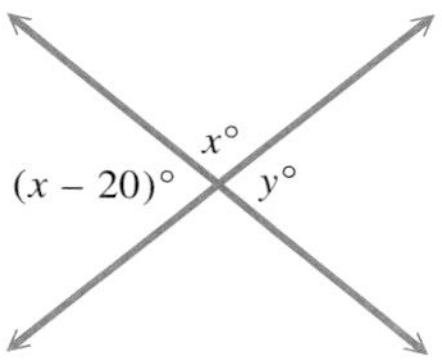

$x = 100$ and $y = 80$, so the angles measure 100° and 80°.

The Fan Cost Index (FCI) represents the cost of four average-price tickets, four small soft drinks, two small beers, four hot dogs, parking for one car, two game programs, and two souvenir caps to a sporting event. For example, in a recent year, the FCI for Major League Baseball was $105.63. This was by far the least for the four major professional sports. (*Source:* Team Marketing Report, Chicago.)

Use the concept of FCI in Exercises 9 and 10. See Example 2.

9. The FCI prices for the National Hockey League and the National Basketball Association totaled $423.12. The hockey FCI was $16.36 more than that of basketball. What were the FCIs for these sports?

NHL: $219.74; NBA: $203.38

10. The FCI prices for Major League Baseball and the National Football League totaled $311.03. The football FCI was $105.87 more than that of baseball. What were the FCIs for these sports?

MLB: $102.58; NFL: $208.45

Solve each problem. See Example 2.

11. Andrew McGinnis works at Wendy's Old Fashioned Hamburgers. During one particular lunch hour, he sold 15 single hamburgers and 10 double hamburgers, totaling $63.25. Another lunch hour, he sold 30 singles and 5 doubles, totaling $78.65. How much did each type of burger cost? (*Source:* Wendy's Old Fashioned Hamburgers menu.)

single: $2.09; double: $3.19

12. Tokyo and New York are among the most expensive cities worldwide for business travelers. Using average costs per day for each city (which includes room, meals, laundry, and two taxi fares), 2 days in Tokyo and 3 days in New York cost $2015. Four days in Tokyo and 2 days in New York cost $2490. What is the average cost per day for each city? (*Source:* ECA International.)

Tokyo: $430; New York: $385

The formulas $p = br$ *(percentage = base* $\times$ *rate) and* $I = prt$ *(simple interest = principal* $\times$ *rate* $\times$ *time) are used in the applications in Exercises 17–24. To prepare to use these formulas, answer the questions in Exercises 13 and 14.*

13. If a container of liquid contains 60 oz of solution, what is the number of ounces of pure acid if the given solution contains the following acid concentrations?

(a) 10% **6 oz** **(b)** 25% **15 oz** **(c)** 40% **24 oz** **(d)** 50% **30 oz**

14. If $5000 is invested in an account paying simple annual interest, how much interest will be earned during the first year at the following rates?

(a) 2% **$100** **(b)** 3% **$150** **(c)** 4% **$200** **(d)** 3.5% **$175**

15. If a pound of turkey costs $.99, how much will x pounds cost? **$.99x**

16. If a ticket to the movie *Pearl Harbor* costs $8 and y tickets are sold, how much is collected from the sale? **$8y**

Solve each problem. See Example 3.

17. How many gallons each of 25% alcohol and 35% alcohol should be mixed to get 20 gal of 32% alcohol?

Percent (as a Decimal)	Gallons of Solution	Gallons of Pure Alcohol
25% = .25	x	
35% = .35	y	
32% =	20	

6 gal of 25%; 14 gal of 35%

18. How many liters each of 15% acid and 33% acid should be mixed to get 120 L of 21% acid?

Percent (as a Decimal)	Liters of Solution	Liters of Pure Acid
15% = .15	x	
33% =	y	
21% =	120	

80 L of 15%; 40 L of 33%

19. Pure acid is to be added to a 10% acid solution to obtain 54 L of a 20% acid solution. What amounts of each should be used?

6 L of pure acid; 48 L of 10% acid

20. A truck radiator holds 36 L of fluid. How much pure antifreeze must be added to a mixture that is 4% antifreeze to fill the radiator with a mixture that is 20% antifreeze?

6 L of pure antifreeze

21. A party mix is made by adding nuts that sell for \$2.50 per kg to a cereal mixture that sells for \$1 per kg. How much of each should be added to get 30 kg of a mix that will sell for \$1.70 per kg?

	Price per Kilogram	Number of Kilograms	Value
Nuts	2.50	x	
Cereal	1.00	y	
Mixture	1.70		

14 kg of nuts; 16 kg of cereal

22. A popular fruit drink is made by mixing fruit juices. Such a drink with 50% juice is to be mixed with another drink that is 30% juice to get 200 L of a drink that is 45% juice. How much of each should be used?

	Percent (as a Decimal)	Liters of Drink	Liters of Pure Juice
50% Juice	.50	x	
30% Juice	.30	y	
Mixture	.45		

150 L of 50% juice; 50 L of 30% juice

23. A total of \$3000 is invested, part at 2% simple interest and part at 4%. If the total annual return from the two investments is \$100, how much is invested at each rate?

Rate (as a Decimal)	Principal	Interest
.02	x	$.02x$
.04	y	$.04y$
	3000	100

\$1000 at 2%; \$2000 at 4%

24. An investor must invest a total of \$15,000 in two accounts, one paying 4% annual simple interest, and the other 3%. If he wants to earn \$550 annual interest, how much should he invest at each rate?

Rate (as a Decimal)	Principal	Interest
.04	x	
.03	y	
	15,000	

\$10,000 at 4%; \$5000 at 3%

The formula $d = rt$ (distance = rate × time) is used in the applications in Exercises 27–30. To prepare to use this formula, answer the questions in Exercises 25 and 26.

25. If the speed of a killer whale is 25 mph and the whale swims for y hr, how many miles does the whale travel?

25y

26. If the speed of a boat in still water is 10 mph, and the speed of the current of a river is x mph, what is the speed of the boat

(a) going upstream (that is, against the current);

$10 - x$ mph

(b) going downstream (that is, with the current)?

$10 + x$ mph

Solve each problem. See Example 4.

27. A freight train and an express train leave towns 390 km apart, traveling toward one another. The freight train travels 30 km per hr slower than the express train. They pass one another 3 hr later. What are their speeds?

	r	t	d
Freight Train	x	3	
Express Train	y	3	

freight train: 50 km per hr; express train: 80 km per hr

28. A train travels 150 km in the same time that a plane covers 400 km. If the speed of the plane is 20 km per hr less than 3 times the speed of the train, find both speeds.

train: 60 km per hr; plane: 160 km per hr

29. In his motorboat, Bill Ruhberg travels upstream at top speed to his favorite fishing spot, a distance of 36 mi, in 2 hr. Returning, he finds that the trip downstream, still at top speed, takes only 1.5 hr. Find the speed of Bill's boat and the speed of the current.

	r	t	d
Upstream	$x - y$	2	
Downstream	$x + y$		

boat: 21 mph; current: 3 mph

30. Traveling for 3 hr into a steady headwind, a plane flies 1650 mi. The pilot determines that flying *with* the same wind for 2 hr, he could make a trip of 1300 mi. Find the speed of the plane and the speed of the wind.

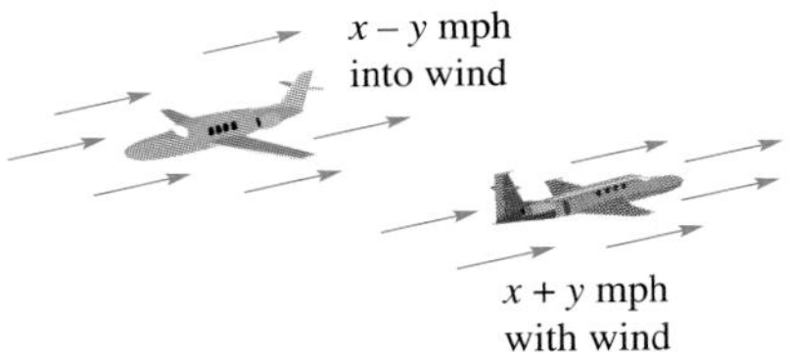

plane: 600 mph; wind: 50 mph

Use the problem-solving techniques of this section to solve each problem with two unknowns. See Examples 1–6.

31. At age 61, rock icon Tina Turner generated the most revenue on the concert circuit in 2000. Turner and second-place 'N Sync together took in $157 million from ticket sales. If 'N Sync took in $3.8 million less than Turner, how much did each generate? (*Source:* Pollstar.)

Turner: $80.4 million; 'N Sync: $76.6 million

32. Carol Britz plans to mix pecan clusters that sell for $3.60 per lb with chocolate truffles that sell for $7.20 per lb to get a mixture that she can sell in Valentine boxes for $4.95 per lb. How much of the $3.60 clusters and the $7.20 truffles should she use to create 80 lb of the mix?

	Price per Pound	Number of Pounds	Value
Pecan Clusters		x	
Chocolate Truffles		y	
Valentine Mixture		80	

50 lb of $3.60 clusters; 30 lb of $7.20 truffles

33. Tickets to a production of *King Lear* at Cape Fear Community College cost $5 for general admission or $4 with a student ID. If 184 people paid to see a performance and $812 was collected, how many of each type of ticket were sold?

76 general admission; 108 with student ID

34. At a business meeting at Panera Bread, the bill for two cappuccinos and three house lattes was $10.95. At another table, the bill for one cappuccino and two house lattes was $6.65. How much did each type of beverage cost? (*Source:* Panera Bread menu.)

cappuccino: $1.95; house latte: $2.35

35. The mixed price of 9 citrons and 7 fragrant wood apples is 107; again, the mixed price of 7 citrons and 9 fragrant wood apples is 101. O you arithmetician, tell me quickly the price of a citron and the price of a wood apple here, having distinctly separated those prices well. (*Source:* Hindu work, A.D. 850.) (*Hint:* "Mixed price" refers to the price of a mixture of the two fruits.)

8 for a citron; 5 for a wood apple

36. Braving blizzard conditions on the planet Hoth, Luke Skywalker sets out at top speed in his snow speeder for a rebel base 4800 mi away. He travels into a steady headwind and makes the trip in 3 hr. Returning, he finds that the trip back, still at top speed but now with a tailwind, takes only 2 hr. Find the top speed of Luke's snow speeder and the speed of the wind.

	r	*t*	*d*
Into Headwind			
With Tailwind			

top speed: 2000 mph; wind speed: 400 mph

Solve each problem involving three unknowns. See Examples 5 and 6. (In Exercises 37–40, remember that the sum of the measures of the angles of a triangle is 180°.*)*

37. In the figure, $z = x + 10$ and $x + y = 100$. Determine a third equation involving x, y, and z, and then find the measures of the three angles.

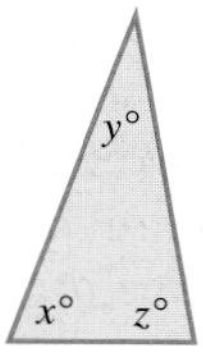

$x + y + z = 180$;
angle measures: 70°, 30°, 80°

38. In the figure, x is 10 less than y and 20 less than z. Write a system of equations and find the measures of the three angles.

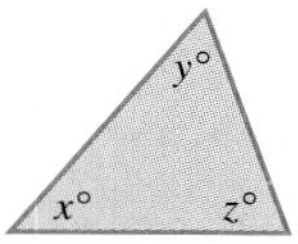

$x = y - 10, x = z - 20,$
$x + y + z = 180$; 50°, 60°, 70°

39. In a certain triangle, the measure of the second angle is 10° more than three times the first. The third angle measure is equal to the sum of the measures of the other two. Find the measures of the three angles.

first: 20°; second: 70°; third: 90°

40. The measure of the largest angle of a triangle is 12° less than the sum of the measures of the other two. The smallest angle measures 58° less than the largest. Find the measures of the angles.

largest: 84°; middle: 70°; smallest: 26°

41. The perimeter of a triangle is 70 cm. The longest side is 4 cm less than the sum of the other two sides. Twice the shortest side is 9 cm less than the longest side. Find the length of each side of the triangle.

shortest: 12 cm; middle: 25 cm; longest: 33 cm

42. The perimeter of a triangle is 56 in. The longest side measures 4 in. less than the sum of the other two sides. Three times the shortest side is 4 in. more than the longest side. Find the lengths of the three sides.

shortest: 10 in.; middle: 20 in.; longest: 26 in.

43. In a random sample of 100 Americans of voting age, 10 more Americans identify themselves as Independents than Republicans. Six fewer Americans identify themselves as Republicans than Democrats. Assuming that all of those sampled are Republican, Democrat, or Independent, how many of those in the sample identify themselves with each political affiliation? (*Source:* The Gallop Organization.)

Independent: 38; Democrat: 34; Republican: 28

44. In the 2000 Summer Olympics in Sydney, Australia, the United States earned 14 more gold medals than silver. The number of bronze medals earned was 17 less than twice the number of silver medals. The United States earned a total of 97 medals. How many of each kind of medal did the United States earn? (*Source: The Gazette,* October 2, 2000.)

gold: 39; silver: 25; bronze: 33

45. Tickets for one show on the Harlem Globetrotters' 75th Anniversary Tour cost \$10, \$18, or, for VIP seats, \$30. So far, five times as many \$18 tickets have been sold as VIP tickets. The number of \$10 tickets equals the number of \$18 tickets plus twice the number of VIP tickets. Sales of these tickets total \$9500. How many of each kind of ticket have been sold? (*Source:* www.ticketmaster.com)

\$10 tickets: 350; \$18 tickets: 250; \$30 tickets: 50

46. Three kinds of tickets are available for a Green Day concert: "up close," "in the middle," and "far out." "Up close" tickets cost \$10 more than "in the middle" tickets, while "in the middle" tickets cost \$10 more than "far out" tickets. Twice the cost of an "up close" ticket is \$20 more than 3 times the cost of a "far out" ticket. Find the price of each kind of ticket.

"up close": \$40; "in the middle": \$30; "far out": \$20

47. A hardware supplier manufactures three kinds of clamps, types A, B, and C. Production restrictions require it to make 10 units more type C clamps than the total of the other types and twice as many type B clamps as type A. The shop must produce a total of 490 units of clamps per day. How many units of each type can be made per day?

type A: 80; type B: 160; type C: 250

48. A Mardi Gras trinket manufacturer supplies three wholesalers, A, B, and C. The output from a day's production is 320 cases of trinkets. She must send wholesaler A three times as many cases as she sends B, and she must send wholesaler C 160 cases less than she provides A and B together. How many cases should she send to each wholesaler to distribute the entire day's production to them?

A: 180 cases; B: 60 cases; C: 80 cases

5.6 Solving Linear Systems of Equations by Matrix Methods

Objectives

1. Define a matrix.
2. Write the augmented matrix for a system.
3. Use row operations to solve a system with two equations.
4. Use row operations to solve a system with three equations.
5. Use row operations to solve special systems.

1 Define a matrix. An ordered array of numbers such as

Columns

$$\text{Rows}\quad \begin{bmatrix} 2 & 3 & 5 \\ 7 & 1 & 2 \end{bmatrix}$$

is called a **matrix.** The numbers are called **elements** of the matrix. Matrices (the plural of *matrix*) are named according to the number of **rows** and **columns** they contain. The rows are read horizontally, and the columns are read vertically. For example, the first row in the preceding matrix is 2 3 5 and the first column is $\begin{matrix} 2 \\ 7 \end{matrix}$. This matrix is a 2×3 (read "two by three") matrix because it has 2 rows and 3 columns. The number of rows is given first, and then the number of columns. Two other examples follow.

$$\begin{bmatrix} -1 & 0 \\ 1 & -2 \end{bmatrix} \quad \begin{matrix} 2 \times 2 \\ \text{matrix} \end{matrix} \qquad \begin{bmatrix} 8 & -1 & -3 \\ 2 & 1 & 6 \\ 0 & 5 & -3 \\ 5 & 9 & 7 \end{bmatrix} \quad \begin{matrix} 4 \times 3 \\ \text{matrix} \end{matrix}$$

A **square matrix** is one that has the same number of rows as columns. The 2×2 matrix is a square matrix.

Calculator Tip Figure 10 shows how a graphing calculator displays the preceding two matrices. Work with matrices is made much easier by using technology when available. Consult your owner's manual for details.

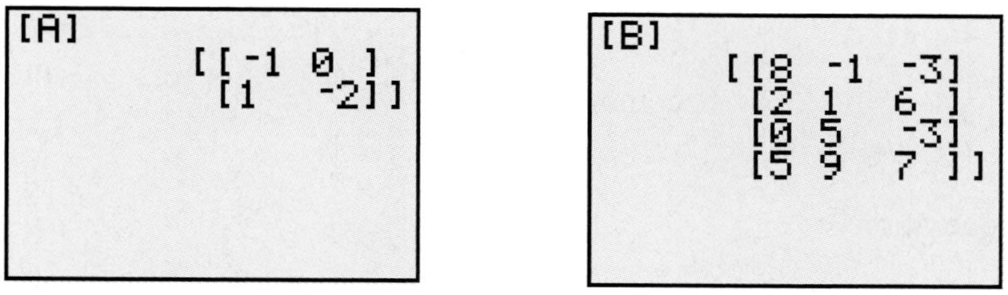

Figure 10

In this section, we discuss a method of solving linear systems that uses matrices. This method is really just a very structured way of using the elimination method to solve a linear system. The advantage of this new method is that it can be done by a graphing calculator or a computer, allowing large systems of equations to be solved easily.

2 Write the augmented matrix for a system. To begin, we write an *augmented matrix* for the system. An **augmented matrix** has a vertical bar that separates the columns of the matrix into two groups. For example, to solve the system

$$\begin{aligned} x - 3y &= 1 \\ 2x + y &= -5, \end{aligned}$$

start with the augmented matrix

$$\left[\begin{array}{cc|c} 1 & -3 & 1 \\ 2 & 1 & -5 \end{array}\right].$$

Place the coefficients of the variables to the left of the bar, and the constants to the right. The bar separates the coefficients from the constants. The matrix is just a shorthand way of writing the system of equations, so the rows of the augmented matrix can be treated the same as the equations of a system of equations.

We know that exchanging the position of two equations in a system does not change the system. Also, multiplying any equation in a system by a nonzero number does not change the system. Comparable changes to the augmented matrix of a system of equations produce new matrices that correspond to systems with the same solutions as the original system.

The following **row operations** produce new matrices that lead to systems having the same solutions as the original system.

Matrix Row Operations

1. Any two rows of the matrix may be interchanged.
2. The numbers in any row may be multiplied by any nonzero real number.
3. Any row may be changed by adding to the numbers of the row the product of a real number and the corresponding numbers of another row.

Examples of these row operations follow.

Row operation 1:

$$\begin{bmatrix} 2 & 3 & 9 \\ 4 & 8 & -3 \\ 1 & 0 & 7 \end{bmatrix} \text{ becomes } \begin{bmatrix} 1 & 0 & 7 \\ 4 & 8 & -3 \\ 2 & 3 & 9 \end{bmatrix}.$$

Interchange row 1 and row 3.

Row operation 2:

$$\begin{bmatrix} 2 & 3 & 9 \\ 4 & 8 & -3 \\ 1 & 0 & 7 \end{bmatrix} \text{ becomes } \begin{bmatrix} 6 & 9 & 27 \\ 4 & 8 & -3 \\ 1 & 0 & 7 \end{bmatrix}.$$

Multiply the numbers in row 1 by 3.

Row operation 3:

$$\begin{bmatrix} 2 & 3 & 9 \\ 4 & 8 & -3 \\ 1 & 0 & 7 \end{bmatrix} \text{ becomes } \begin{bmatrix} 0 & 3 & -5 \\ 4 & 8 & -3 \\ 1 & 0 & 7 \end{bmatrix}.$$

Multiply the numbers in row 3 by -2; add them to the corresponding numbers in row 1.

The third row operation corresponds to the way we eliminated a variable from a pair of equations in the previous sections.

3 **Use row operations to solve a system with two equations.** Row operations can be used to rewrite a matrix until it is the matrix of a system where the solution is easy to find. The goal is a matrix in the form

$$\left[\begin{array}{cc|c} 1 & a & b \\ 0 & 1 & c \end{array}\right] \quad \text{or} \quad \left[\begin{array}{ccc|c} 1 & a & b & c \\ 0 & 1 & d & e \\ 0 & 0 & 1 & f \end{array}\right]$$

for systems with two or three equations, respectively. Notice that there are 1s down the diagonal from upper left to lower right and 0s below the 1s. A matrix written this way is said to be in **row echelon form.** When these matrices are rewritten as systems of equations, the value of one variable is known, and the rest can be found by substitution. The following examples illustrate this method.

Example 1 Using Row Operations to Solve a System with Two Variables

Use row operations to solve the system.

$$\begin{aligned} x - 3y &= 1 \\ 2x + y &= -5 \end{aligned}$$

We start with the augmented matrix of the system.

$$\left[\begin{array}{rr|r} 1 & -3 & 1 \\ 2 & 1 & -5 \end{array}\right]$$

Now we use the various row operations to change this matrix into one that leads to a system that is easier to solve.

It is best to work by columns. We start with the first column and make sure that there is a 1 in the first row, first column position. There is already a 1 in this position. Next, we get 0 in every position below the first. To get a 0 in row two, column one, we use the third row operation and add to the numbers in row two the result of multiplying each number in row one by -2. (We abbreviate this as $-2R_1 + R_2$.) Row one remains unchanged.

$$\left[\begin{array}{cc|c} 1 & -3 & 1 \\ 2 + 1(-2) & 1 + -3(-2) & -5 + 1(-2) \end{array}\right]$$

↑ Original number from row two ↑ -2 times number from row one

$$\left[\begin{array}{rr|r} 1 & -3 & 1 \\ 0 & 7 & -7 \end{array}\right] \quad -2R_1 + R_2$$

The matrix now has a 1 in the first position of column one, with 0 in every position below the first.

Now we go to column two. A 1 is needed in row two, column two. We get this 1 by using the second row operation, multiplying each number of row two by $\frac{1}{7}$.

$$\left[\begin{array}{rr|r} 1 & -3 & 1 \\ 0 & 1 & -1 \end{array}\right] \quad \tfrac{1}{7}R_2$$

This augmented matrix leads to the system of equations

$$\begin{aligned} 1x - 3y &= 1 \\ 0x + 1y &= -1 \end{aligned} \quad \text{or} \quad \begin{aligned} x - 3y &= 1 \\ y &= -1. \end{aligned}$$

From the second equation, $y = -1$. We substitute -1 for y in the first equation to get

$$\begin{aligned} x - 3y &= 1 \\ x - 3(-1) &= 1 \\ x + 3 &= 1 \\ x &= -2. \end{aligned}$$

The solution set of the system is $\{(-2, -1)\}$. Check this solution by substitution in both equations of the system.

Work Problem 1 at the Side.

1 Use row operations to solve the system.

$$\begin{aligned} x - 2y &= 9 \\ 3x + y &= 13 \end{aligned}$$

ANSWERS

1. $\{(5, -2)\}$

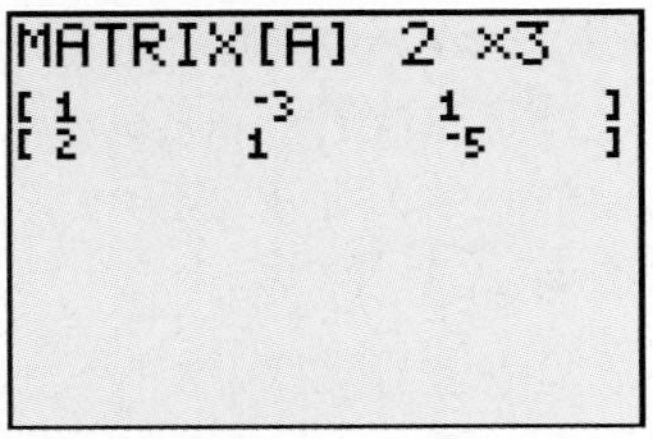

(a)

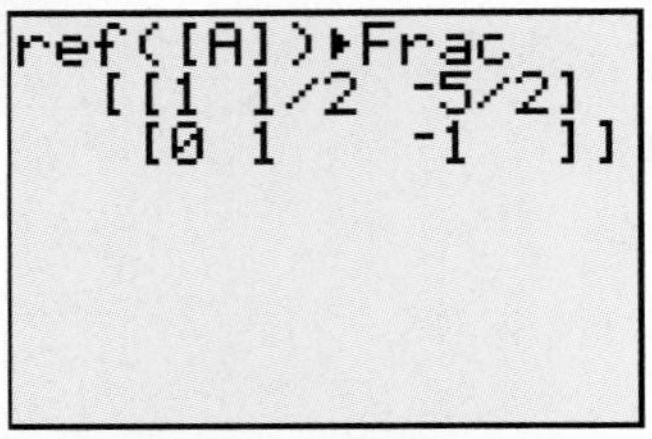

(b)

Figure 11

Calculator Tip If the augmented matrix of the system in Example 1 is entered as matrix A in a graphing calculator (Figure 11(a)) and the row echelon form of the matrix is found (Figure 11(b)), the system becomes

$$x + \frac{1}{2}y = -\frac{5}{2}$$
$$y = -1.$$

While this system looks different from the one we obtained in Example 1, it is equivalent, since its solution set is also $\{(-2, -1)\}$.

4 Use row operations to solve a system with three equations. A linear system with three equations is solved in a similar way. We use row operations to get 1s down the diagonal from left to right and all 0s below each 1.

Example 2 Using Row Operations to Solve a System with Three Variables

Use row operations to solve the system.

$$\begin{aligned} x - y + 5z &= -6 \\ 3x + 3y - z &= 10 \\ x + 3y + 2z &= 5 \end{aligned}$$

Start by writing the augmented matrix of the system.

$$\left[\begin{array}{ccc|c} 1 & -1 & 5 & -6 \\ 3 & 3 & -1 & 10 \\ 1 & 3 & 2 & 5 \end{array}\right]$$

This matrix already has 1 in row one, column one. Next get 0s in the rest of column one. First, add to row two the results of multiplying each number of row one by -3. This gives the matrix

$$\left[\begin{array}{ccc|c} 1 & -1 & 5 & -6 \\ 0 & 6 & -16 & 28 \\ 1 & 3 & 2 & 5 \end{array}\right]. \qquad -3R_1 + R_2$$

Now add to the numbers in row three the results of multiplying each number of row one by -1.

$$\left[\begin{array}{ccc|c} 1 & -1 & 5 & -6 \\ 0 & 6 & -16 & 28 \\ 0 & 4 & -3 & 11 \end{array}\right] \qquad -1R_1 + R_3$$

Get 1 in row two, column two by multiplying each number in row two by $\frac{1}{6}$.

$$\left[\begin{array}{ccc|c} 1 & -1 & 5 & -6 \\ 0 & 1 & -\frac{8}{3} & \frac{14}{3} \\ 0 & 4 & -3 & 11 \end{array}\right] \qquad \tfrac{1}{6}R_2$$

Get 0 in row three, column two by adding to row three the results of multiplying each number in row two by -4.

$$\left[\begin{array}{ccc|c} 1 & -1 & 5 & -6 \\ 0 & 1 & -\frac{8}{3} & \frac{14}{3} \\ 0 & 0 & \frac{23}{3} & -\frac{23}{3} \end{array}\right] \qquad -4R_2 + R_3$$

Continued on Next Page

Finally, get 1 in row three, column three by multiplying each number in row three by $\frac{3}{23}$.

$$\left[\begin{array}{ccc|c} 1 & -1 & 5 & -6 \\ 0 & 1 & -\frac{8}{3} & \frac{14}{3} \\ 0 & 0 & 1 & -1 \end{array}\right] \quad \tfrac{3}{23}R_3$$

This final matrix gives the system of equations

$$\begin{aligned} x - y + 5z &= -6 \\ y - \frac{8}{3}z &= \frac{14}{3} \\ z &= -1. \end{aligned}$$

Substitute -1 for z in the second equation, $y - \frac{8}{3}z = \frac{14}{3}$, to get $y = 2$. Finally, substitute 2 for y and -1 for z in the first equation, $x - y + 5z = -6$, to get $x = 1$. The solution set of the original system is $\{(1, 2, -1)\}$. Check by substitution in the original system.

Work Problem 2 at the Side.

5 Use row operations to solve special systems. In the final example we show how to recognize inconsistent systems or systems with dependent equations when solving these systems with row operations.

Example 3 Recognizing Inconsistent Systems or Dependent Equations

Use row operations to solve each system.

(a) $2x - 3y = 8$
$-6x + 9y = 4$

$$\left[\begin{array}{cc|c} 2 & -3 & 8 \\ -6 & 9 & 4 \end{array}\right] \quad \text{Write the augmented matrix.}$$

$$\left[\begin{array}{cc|c} 1 & -\frac{3}{2} & 4 \\ -6 & 9 & 4 \end{array}\right] \quad \tfrac{1}{2}R_1$$

$$\left[\begin{array}{cc|c} 1 & -\frac{3}{2} & 4 \\ \mathbf{0} & \mathbf{0} & \mathbf{28} \end{array}\right] \quad 6R_1 + R_2$$

The corresponding system of equations is

$$\begin{aligned} x - \frac{3}{2}y &= 4 \\ 0 &= 28, \quad \textbf{False} \end{aligned}$$

which has no solution and is inconsistent. The solution set is $\emptyset$.

(b) $-10x + 12y = 30$
$5x - 6y = -15$

$$\left[\begin{array}{cc|c} -10 & 12 & 30 \\ 5 & -6 & -15 \end{array}\right] \quad \text{Write the augmented matrix.}$$

$$\left[\begin{array}{cc|c} 1 & -\frac{6}{5} & -3 \\ 5 & -6 & -15 \end{array}\right] \quad -\tfrac{1}{10}R_1$$

$$\left[\begin{array}{cc|c} 1 & -\frac{6}{5} & -3 \\ \mathbf{0} & \mathbf{0} & \mathbf{0} \end{array}\right] \quad -5R_1 + R_2$$

Continued on Next Page

2 Use row operations to solve the system.

$$\begin{aligned} 2x - y + z &= 7 \\ x - 3y - z &= 7 \\ -x + y - 5z &= -9 \end{aligned}$$

Answers

2. $\{(2, -2, 1)\}$

The corresponding system is

$$x - \frac{6}{5}y = -3$$

$$0 = 0, \quad \text{True}$$

which has dependent equations. Using the second equation of the original system, we write the solution set as

$$\{(x, y) \mid 5x - 6y = -15\}.$$

Work Problem 3 at the Side.

3 Use row operations to solve each system.

(a)
$$\begin{aligned} x - y &= 2 \\ -2x + 2y &= 2 \end{aligned}$$

(b)
$$\begin{aligned} x - y &= 2 \\ -2x + 2y &= -4 \end{aligned}$$

ANSWERS

3. **(a)** $\emptyset$ **(b)** $\{(x, y) \mid x - y = 2\}$

5.6 EXERCISES

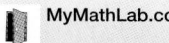

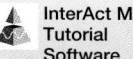

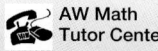

FOR EXTRA HELP: Student's Solutions Manual | MyMathLab.com | InterAct Math Tutorial Software | AW Math Tutor Center | www.mathxl.com | Digital Video Tutor CD 4 Videotape 10

1. Consider the matrix $\begin{bmatrix} -2 & 3 & 1 \\ 0 & 5 & -3 \\ 1 & 4 & 8 \end{bmatrix}$, and answer the following.

(a) What are the elements of the second row? **0, 5, −3**

(b) What are the elements of the third column? **1, −3, 8**

(c) Is this a square matrix? Explain. **yes; The number of rows is the same as the number of columns (three).**

(d) Give the matrix obtained by interchanging the first and third rows.

(e) Give the matrix obtained by multiplying the first row by $-\frac{1}{2}$.

(f) Give the matrix obtained by multiplying the third row by 3 and adding to the first row.

(d) $\begin{bmatrix} 1 & 4 & 8 \\ 0 & 5 & -3 \\ -2 & 3 & 1 \end{bmatrix}$ (e) $\begin{bmatrix} 1 & -\frac{3}{2} & -\frac{1}{2} \\ 0 & 5 & -3 \\ 1 & 4 & 8 \end{bmatrix}$ (f) $\begin{bmatrix} 1 & 15 & 25 \\ 0 & 5 & -3 \\ 1 & 4 & 8 \end{bmatrix}$

2. Give the dimensions of each matrix.

(a) $\begin{bmatrix} 3 & -7 \\ 4 & 5 \\ -1 & 0 \end{bmatrix}$ **(b)** $\begin{bmatrix} 4 & 9 & 0 \\ -1 & 2 & -4 \end{bmatrix}$ **(c)** $\begin{bmatrix} 6 & 3 \\ -2 & 5 \\ 4 & 10 \\ 1 & -11 \end{bmatrix}$

3 × 2 **2 × 3** **4 × 2**

Complete the steps in the matrix solution of each system by filling in the blanks. Give the final system and the solution set. See Example 1.

3. $4x + 8y = 44$
$2x - y = -3$

$\left[\begin{array}{cc|c} 4 & 8 & 44 \\ 2 & -1 & -3 \end{array}\right]$

$\left[\begin{array}{cc|c} 1 & \underline{2} & \underline{11} \\ 2 & -1 & -3 \end{array}\right]$ $\frac{1}{4}R_1$

$\left[\begin{array}{cc|c} 1 & 2 & 11 \\ 0 & \underline{-5} & \underline{-25} \end{array}\right]$ $-2R_1 + R_2$

$\left[\begin{array}{cc|c} 1 & 2 & 11 \\ 0 & 1 & \underline{5} \end{array}\right]$ $-\frac{1}{5}R_2$

$x + 2y = 11$
$y = 5$; $\{(1, 5)\}$

4. $2x - 5y = -1$
$3x + y = 7$

$\left[\begin{array}{cc|c} 2 & -5 & -1 \\ 3 & 1 & 7 \end{array}\right]$

$\left[\begin{array}{cc|c} 1 & -\frac{5}{2} & \underline{-\frac{1}{2}} \\ 3 & 1 & 7 \end{array}\right]$ $\frac{1}{2}R_1$

$\left[\begin{array}{cc|c} 1 & -\frac{5}{2} & -\frac{1}{2} \\ 0 & \underline{\frac{17}{2}} & \underline{\frac{17}{2}} \end{array}\right]$ $-3R_1 + R_2$

$\left[\begin{array}{cc|c} 1 & -\frac{5}{2} & -\frac{1}{2} \\ 0 & 1 & \underline{1} \end{array}\right]$ $\frac{2}{17}R_2$

$x - \frac{5}{2}y = -\frac{1}{2}$
$y = 1$; $\{(2, 1)\}$

Use row operations to solve each system. See Examples 1 and 3.

5. $x + y = 5$
$x - y = 3$
{(4, 1)}

6. $x + 2y = 7$
$x - y = -2$
{(1, 3)}

7. $2x + 4y = 6$
$3x - y = 2$
{(1, 1)}

8. $4x + 5y = -7$
$x - y = 5$
{(2, −3)}

9. $3x + 4y = 13$
$2x - 3y = -14$
{(−1, 4)}

10. $5x + 2y = 8$
$3x - y = 7$
{(2, −1)}

11. $-4x + 12y = 36$
$x - 3y = 9$
∅

12. $2x - 4y = 8$
$-3x + 6y = 5$
∅

Complete the steps in the matrix solution of each system by filling in the blanks. Give the final system and the solution set. See Example 2.

13. $x + y - z = -3$
$2x + y + z = 4$
$5x - y + 2z = 23$

$$\left[\begin{array}{ccc|c} 1 & 1 & -1 & -3 \\ 2 & 1 & 1 & 4 \\ 5 & -1 & 2 & 23 \end{array}\right]$$

$$\left[\begin{array}{ccc|c} 1 & 1 & -1 & -3 \\ 0 & \underline{-1} & \underline{3} & \underline{10} \\ 0 & \underline{-6} & \underline{7} & \underline{38} \end{array}\right] \quad \begin{array}{l} \\ -2R_1 + R_2 \\ -5R_1 + R_3 \end{array}$$

$$\left[\begin{array}{ccc|c} 1 & 1 & -1 & -3 \\ 0 & 1 & \underline{-3} & \underline{-10} \\ 0 & -6 & 7 & 38 \end{array}\right] \quad -1R_2$$

$$\left[\begin{array}{ccc|c} 1 & 1 & -1 & -3 \\ 0 & 1 & -3 & -10 \\ 0 & 0 & \underline{-11} & \underline{-22} \end{array}\right] \quad 6R_2 + R_3$$

$$\left[\begin{array}{ccc|c} 1 & 1 & -1 & -3 \\ 0 & 1 & -3 & -10 \\ 0 & 0 & 1 & \underline{2} \end{array}\right] \quad -\tfrac{1}{11}R_3$$

$x + y - z = -3$
$y - 3z = -10$
$z = 2$;
$\{(3, -4, 2)\}$

14. $2x + y + 2z = 11$
$2x - y - z = -3$
$3x + 2y + z = 9$

$$\left[\begin{array}{ccc|c} 2 & 1 & 2 & 11 \\ 2 & -1 & -1 & -3 \\ 3 & 2 & 1 & 9 \end{array}\right]$$

$$\left[\begin{array}{ccc|c} 1 & \underline{\tfrac{1}{2}} & \underline{1} & \underline{\tfrac{11}{2}} \\ 2 & -1 & -1 & -3 \\ 3 & 2 & 1 & 9 \end{array}\right] \quad \tfrac{1}{2}R_1$$

$$\left[\begin{array}{ccc|c} 1 & \tfrac{1}{2} & 1 & \tfrac{11}{2} \\ 0 & \underline{-2} & \underline{-3} & \underline{-14} \\ 0 & \underline{\tfrac{1}{2}} & \underline{-2} & \underline{-\tfrac{15}{2}} \end{array}\right] \quad \begin{array}{l} \\ -2R_1 + R_2 \\ -3R_1 + R_3 \end{array}$$

$$\left[\begin{array}{ccc|c} 1 & \tfrac{1}{2} & 1 & \tfrac{11}{2} \\ 0 & 1 & \underline{\tfrac{3}{2}} & \underline{7} \\ 0 & \tfrac{1}{2} & -2 & -\tfrac{15}{2} \end{array}\right] \quad -\tfrac{1}{2}R_2$$

$$\left[\begin{array}{ccc|c} 1 & \tfrac{1}{2} & 1 & \tfrac{11}{2} \\ 0 & 1 & \tfrac{3}{2} & 7 \\ 0 & 0 & \underline{-\tfrac{11}{4}} & \underline{-11} \end{array}\right] \quad -\tfrac{1}{2}R_2 + R_3$$

$$\left[\begin{array}{ccc|c} 1 & \tfrac{1}{2} & 1 & \tfrac{11}{2} \\ 0 & 1 & \tfrac{3}{2} & 7 \\ 0 & 0 & 1 & \underline{4} \end{array}\right] \quad -\tfrac{4}{11}R_3$$

$x + \frac{1}{2}y + z = \frac{11}{2}$
$y + \frac{3}{2}z = 7$
$z = 4$; $\{(1, 1, 4)\}$

Use row operations to solve each system. See Examples 2 and 3.

15. $x + y - 3z = 1$
$2x - y + z = 9$
$3x + y - 4z = 8$
$\{(4, 0, 1)\}$

16. $2x + 4y - 3z = -18$
$3x + y - z = -5$
$x - 2y + 4z = 14$
$\{(0, -3, 2)\}$

17. $x + y - z = 6$
$2x - y + z = -9$
$x - 2y + 3z = 1$
$\{(-1, 23, 16)\}$

18. $x + 3y - 6z = 7$
$2x - y + 2z = 0$
$x + y + 2z = -1$
$\{(1, 0, -1)\}$

19. $x - y = 1$
$y - z = 6$
$x + z = -1$
$\{(3, 2, -4)\}$

20. $x + y = 1$
$2x - z = 0$
$y + 2z = -2$
$\{(-1, 2, -2)\}$

21. $x - 2y + z = 4$
$3x - 6y + 3z = 12$
$-2x + 4y - 2z = -8$
$\{(x, y) \mid x - 2y + z = 4\}$

22. $4x + 8y + 4z = 9$
$x + 3y + 4z = 10$
$5x + 10y + 5z = 12$
$\emptyset$

Solve each problem by first setting up a system of equations. Use row operations.

23. The manager of a small company deposits some money in a bank account paying 5% per yr. He uses additional money, amounting to $\frac{1}{3}$ the amount placed in the bank, to buy bonds paying 6% per yr. With the balance of funds he buys an 8% certificate of deposit. The first year his investments earn \$690. If the total investment is \$10,000, how much is invested at each rate?

Rate (as a Decimal)	Amount Invested	Annual Interest
.05	x	$.05x$
.06		
.08		
		690

\$3000 at 5%; \$1000 at 6%; \$6000 at 8%

24. A small company took out three loans totaling \$25,000. The company was able to borrow some of the money at 8%. It borrowed \$2000 more than $\frac{1}{2}$ the amount of the 8% loan at 10%, and the rest at 9%. The total annual interest was \$2220. How much did the company borrow at each rate?

Rate (as a Decimal)	Amount Borrowed	Annual Interest
	x	
.10		
.09		
		2220

\$10,000 at 8%; \$7000 at 10%; \$8000 at 9%

Chapter 5

Summary

Key Terms

5.1	**system of linear equations**	A system of linear equations consists of two or more linear equations with the same variables.
	solution of a system	The solution of a system of linear equations is on the ordered pair that makes all the equations of the system true at the same time.
	solution set of a system	The set of all ordered pairs that are solutions of a system forms its solution set.
	consistent system	A system of equations with at least one solution is a consistent system.
	inconsistent system	An inconsistent system of equations is a system with no solution.
	independent equations	Equations of a system that have different graphs are called independent equations.
	dependent equations	Equations of a system that have the same graph (because they are different forms of the same equation) are called dependent equations.
5.6	**matrix**	A matrix is a rectangular array of numbers, consisting of horizontal **rows** and vertical **columns.**
	elements of a matrix	The numbers in a matrix are its elements.
	square matrix	A square matrix is a matrix that has the same number of rows as columns.
	augmented matrix	An augmented matrix is a matrix that has a vertical bar that separates the columns of the matrix into two groups.
	row echelon form	If a matrix is written with 1s down the diagonal from upper left to lower right and 0s below the 1s, it is said to be in row echelon form.

New Symbols

(x, y, z) ordered triple

$\begin{bmatrix} a & b \\ c & d \end{bmatrix}$ 2×2 matrix

Test Your Word Power

See how well you have learned the vocabulary in this chapter. Answers follow the Quick Review.

1. A **system of linear equations** consists of
- **(a)** at least two linear equations with different variables
- **(b)** two or more linear equations that have an infinite number of solutions
- **(c)** two or more linear equations with the same variables
- **(d)** two or more linear inequalities.

2. A **solution of a system** of linear equations is
- **(a)** an ordered pair that makes one equation of the system true
- **(b)** an ordered pair that makes all the equations of the system true at the same time
- **(c)** any ordered pair that makes one or the other or both equations of the system true
- **(d)** the set of values that make all the equations of the system false.

3. An **inconsistent system** is a system of equations
- **(a)** with one solution
- **(b)** with no solution
- **(c)** with an infinite number of solutions
- **(d)** that have the same graph.

4. Dependent equations
- **(a)** have different graphs
- **(b)** have no solution
- **(c)** have one solution
- **(d)** are different forms of the same equation.

Quick Review

Concepts	*Examples*
5.1 Solving Systems of Linear Equations by Graphing An ordered pair is a solution of a system if it makes all equations of the system true at the same time.	Is $(4, -1)$ a solution of the following system? $x + y = 3$, $2x - y = 9$. Yes; $4 + (-1) = 3$ and $2(4) - (-1) = 9$ are both true.
If the graphs of the equations of a system are both sketched on the same axes, the points of intersection, if any, are solutions of the system.	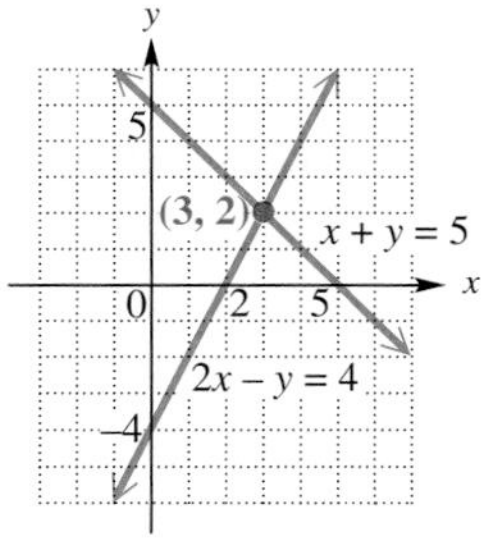 $\{(3, 2)\}$ is the solution set of the system $x + y = 5$, $2x - y = 4$.
5.2 Solving Systems of Linear Equations by Substitution Solve one equation for one variable, and substitute the expression into the other equation to get an equation in one variable. Solve the equation, and then substitute the solution into either of the original equations to obtain the value of the other variable. Check the solution of the system.	Solve by substitution. $x + 2y = -5$ (1); $y = -2x - 1$ (2). Substitute $-2x - 1$ for y in equation (1). $x + 2(-2x - 1) = -5$; $x - 4x - 2 = -5$; $-3x - 2 = -5$; $-3x = -3$; $x = 1$. To find y, let $x = 1$ in equation (2): $y = -2(1) - 1 = -3$. The solution set is $\{(1, -3)\}$.
5.3 Solving Systems of Linear Equations by Elimination	Solve by elimination. $x + 3y = 7$ (1); $3x - y = 1$ (2)
Step 1 Write both equations in standard form $Ax + By = C$.	
Step 2 If necessary, multiply one or both equations by appropriate numbers so that the coefficients of x (or y) are opposites of each other.	Multiply equation (1) by -3 to eliminate the x-terms. $-3x - 9y = -21$; $3x - y = 1$
Step 3 Add the equations to get an equation with only one variable (or no variable).	$-10y = -20$ Add.
Step 4 Solve the equation from Step 3.	$y = 2$ Divide by -10.
Step 5 Substitute the solution from Step 4 into either of the original equations to find the value of the remaining variable.	Substitute 2 for y in equation (1). $x + 3(2) = 7$ (1); $x + 6 = 7$; $x = 1$
Step 6 Check the solution in both of the original equations. Write the solution as an ordered pair.	Since $1 + 3(2) = 7$ and $3(1) - 2 = 1$, the solution $(1, 2)$ checks. The solution set is $\{(1, 2)\}$.

Concepts	*Examples*
5.4 Linear Systems of Equations in Three Variables **Solving a Linear System in Three Variables**	Solve the system.
Step 1 Use the elimination method to eliminate any variable from any two of the original equations.	$x + 2y - z = 6$ (1) $x + y + z = 6$ (2) $2x + y - z = 7$ (3) Add equations (1) and (2); z is eliminated and the result is $2x + 3y = 12$.
Step 2 Eliminate the *same* variable from any *other* two equations.	Eliminate z again by adding equations (2) and (3) to get $3x + 2y = 13$. Now solve the system $2x + 3y = 12$ (4) $3x + 2y = 13.$ (5)
Step 3 Eliminate a second variable from the two equations in two variables that result from Steps 1 and 2. The result is an equation in one variable that gives the value of that variable.	To eliminate x, multiply equation (4) by -3 and equation (5) by 2. $-6x - 9y = -36$ $6x + 4y = 26$ $-5y = -10$ $y = 2$
Step 4 Substitute the value of the variable found in Step 3 into either of the equations in two variables to find the value of the second variable.	Let $y = 2$ in equation (4). $2x + 3(2) = 12$ $2x + 6 = 12$ $2x = 6$ $x = 3$
Step 5 Use the values of the two variables from Steps 3 and 4 to find the value of the third variable by substituting into any of the original equations.	Let $y = 2$ and $x = 3$ in any of the original equations to find $z = 1$.
Step 6 Check the solution in all of the original equations. Then write the solution set.	Check. The solution set is $\{(3, 2, 1)\}$.
5.5 Applications of Linear Systems of Equations Use the six-step problem-solving method. *Step 1* **Read** the problem carefully. *Step 2* **Assign variables.** *Step 3* **Write a system of equations** that relates the unknowns. *Step 4* **Solve** the system. *Step 5* **State the answer.** *Step 6* **Check.**	The perimeter of a rectangle is 18 ft. The length is 3 ft more than twice the width. What are the dimensions of the rectangle? Let x represent the length and y represent the width. From the perimeter formula, one equation is $2x + 2y = 18$. From the problem, another equation is $x = 3 + 2y$. Solve the system $2x + 2y = 18$ $x = 3 + 2y$ to get $x = 7$ and $y = 2$. The length is 7 ft, and the width is 2 ft. Since the perimeter is $2(7) + 2(2) = 18,$ and $3 + 2(2) = 7,$ the solution checks.

Concepts	*Examples*
5.6 Solving Linear Systems of Equations by Matrix Methods **Matrix Row Operations** **1.** Any two rows of the matrix may be interchanged.	$\begin{bmatrix} 1 & 5 & 7 \\ 3 & 9 & -2 \\ 0 & 6 & 4 \end{bmatrix}$ becomes $\begin{bmatrix} 3 & 9 & -2 \\ 1 & 5 & 7 \\ 0 & 6 & 4 \end{bmatrix}$ Interchange R_1 and R_2.
2. The numbers in any row may be multiplied by any nonzero real number.	$\begin{bmatrix} 1 & 5 & 7 \\ 3 & 9 & -2 \\ 0 & 6 & 4 \end{bmatrix}$ becomes $\begin{bmatrix} 1 & 5 & 7 \\ 1 & 3 & -\frac{2}{3} \\ 0 & 6 & 4 \end{bmatrix}$ $\frac{1}{3}R_2$
3. Any row may be changed by adding to the numbers of the row the product of a real number and the numbers of another row.	$\begin{bmatrix} 1 & 5 & 7 \\ 3 & 9 & -2 \\ 0 & 6 & 4 \end{bmatrix}$ becomes $\begin{bmatrix} 1 & 5 & 7 \\ 0 & -6 & -23 \\ 0 & 6 & 4 \end{bmatrix}$ $-3R_1 + R_2$
A system can be solved by matrix methods. Write the augmented matrix, and use row operations to obtain a matrix in row echelon form.	Solve using row operations. $x + 3y = 7$ $2x + y = 4$ $\left[\begin{array}{cc\|c} 1 & 3 & 7 \\ 2 & 1 & 4 \end{array}\right]$ Augmented matrix $\left[\begin{array}{cc\|c} 1 & 3 & 7 \\ 0 & -5 & -10 \end{array}\right]$ $-2R_1 + R_2$ $\left[\begin{array}{cc\|c} 1 & 3 & 7 \\ 0 & 1 & 2 \end{array}\right]$ $-\frac{1}{5}R_2$ $x + 3y = 7$ $y = 2$ When $y = 2$, $x + 3(2) = 7$, so $x = 1$. The solution set is $\{(1, 2)\}$.

Answers to Test Your Word Power

1. (c) *Example:* $2x + y = 7$, $3x - y = 3$ **2. (b)** *Example:* The ordered pair (2, 3) satisfies both equations of the system in the Item 1 example, so it is a solution of the system. **3. (b)** *Example:* The equations of two parallel lines make up an inconsistent system; their graphs never intersect, so there is no solution to the system. **4. (d)** *Example:* The equations $4x - y = 8$ and $8x - 2y = 16$ are dependent because their graphs are the same line.

Chapter 5 Review Exercises

[5.1] *Decide whether the given ordered pair is a solution of the given system.*

1. $(3, 4)$

$$\begin{aligned} 4x - 2y &= 4 \\ 5x + y &= 19 \end{aligned}$$

yes

2. $(-5, 2)$

$$\begin{aligned} x - 4y &= -13 \\ 2x + 3y &= 4 \end{aligned}$$

no

Solve each system by graphing.

3.

$$\begin{aligned} x + y &= 4 \\ 2x - y &= 5 \end{aligned}$$

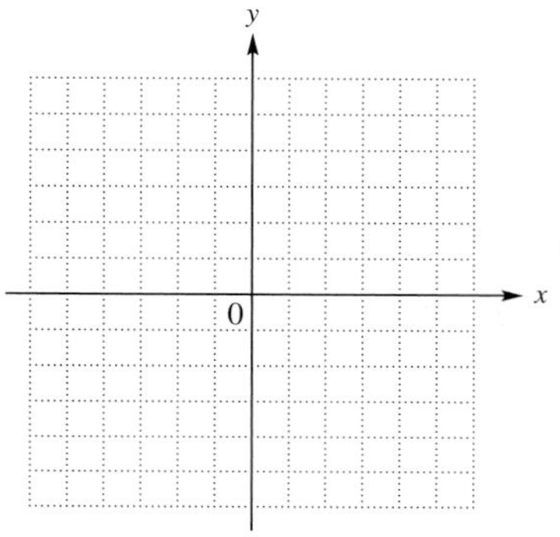

$\{(3, 1)\}$

4.

$$\begin{aligned} x - 2y &= 4 \\ 2x + y &= -2 \end{aligned}$$

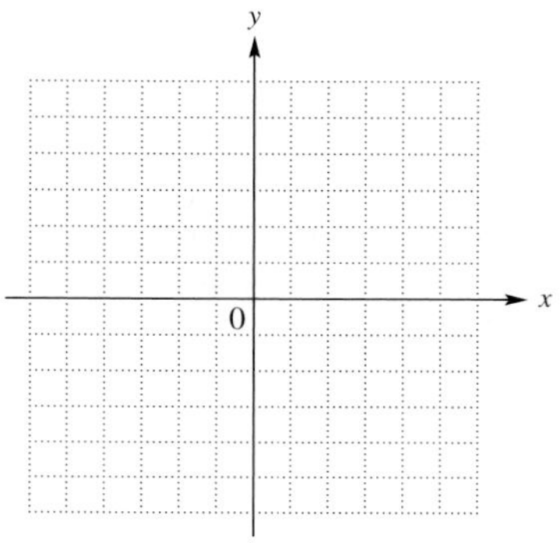

$\{(0, -2)\}$

5.

$$\begin{aligned} x - 2 &= 2y \\ 2x - 4y &= 4 \end{aligned}$$

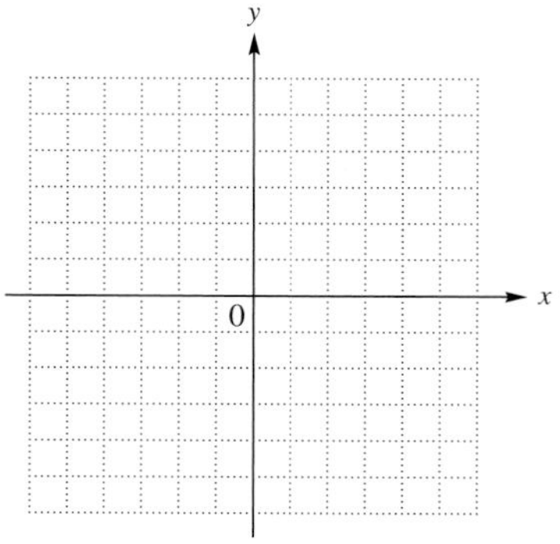

$\{(x, y) \mid x - 2y = 2\}$

6.

$$\begin{aligned} 2x + 4 &= 2y \\ y - x &= -3 \end{aligned}$$

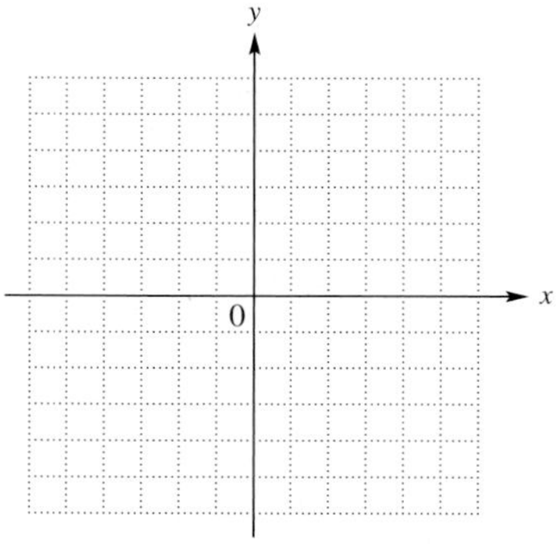

$\emptyset$

7. When a student was asked to determine whether the ordered pair $(1, -2)$ is a solution of the system

$$\begin{aligned} x + y &= -1 \\ 2x + y &= 4, \end{aligned}$$

he answered "yes." His reasoning was that the ordered pair satisfies the equation $x + y = -1$; that is, $1 + (-2) = -1$ is true. Why is the student's answer wrong?

It is not a solution of the system because it is not a solution of the second equation, $2x + y = 4$.

[5.2] *Solve each system by the substitution method.*

8. $3x + y = 7$
$x = 2y$

$\{(2, 1)\}$

9. $2x - 5y = -19$
$y = x + 2$

$\{(3, 5)\}$

10. $4x + 5y = 44$
$x + 2 = 2y$

$\{(6, 4)\}$

11. $5x + 15y = 3$
$x + 3y = 2$

$\emptyset$

[5.3] *Solve each system by the elimination method.*

12. $2x - y = 13$
$x + y = 8$

$\{(7, 1)\}$

13. $3x - y = -13$
$x - 2y = -1$

$\{(-5, -2)\}$

14. $-4x + 3y = 25$
$6x - 5y = -39$

$\{(-4, 3)\}$

15. $3x - 4y = 9$
$6x - 8y = 18$

$\{(x, y) \mid 3x - 4y = 9\}$

16. For the system

$$\begin{aligned} 2x + 12y &= 7 \\ 3x + 4y &= 1, \end{aligned}$$

if we were to multiply the first (top) equation by -3, by what number would we have to multiply the second (bottom) equation in order to

(a) eliminate the x-terms when solving by the elimination method? 2

(b) eliminate the y-terms when solving by the elimination method? 9

Solve each system by any method. First simplify equations, and clear them of fractions where necessary.

17. $2x + y - x = 3y + 5$
$y + 2 = x - 5$

$\{(9, 2)\}$

18. $5x - 3 + y = 4y + 8$
$2y + 1 = x - 3$

$\left\{\left(\frac{10}{7}, -\frac{9}{7}\right)\right\}$

19. $\frac{x}{2} + \frac{y}{3} = 7$
$\frac{x}{4} + \frac{2y}{3} = 8$

$\{(8, 9)\}$

[5.4] *Solve each system of equations.*

20. $2x + 3y - z = -16$
$x + 2y + 2z = -3$
$-3x + y + z = -5$

$\{(1, -5, 3)\}$

21. $3x - y - z = -8$
$4x + 2y + 3z = 15$
$-6x + 2y + 2z = 10$

$\emptyset$

22. $4x - y = 2$
$3y + z = 9$
$x + 2z = 7$

$\{(1, 2, 3)\}$

[5.5] *Solve each problem using a system of equations.*

23. A regulation National Hockey League ice rink has perimeter 570 ft. The length is 30 ft longer than twice the width. What are the dimensions of an NHL ice rink? (*Source: Microsoft Encarta Encyclopedia 2000.*) length: 200 ft; width: 85 ft

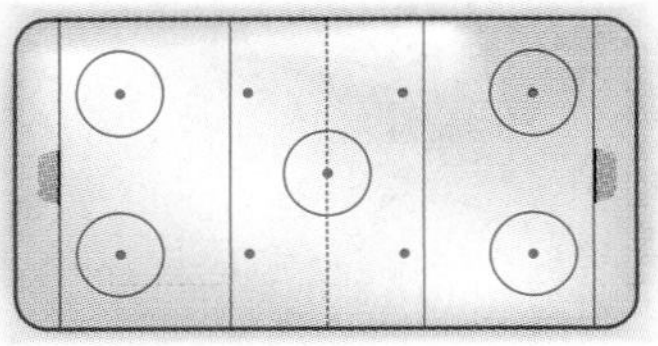

24. On a 6-day business trip, Todd Hall rented a car for \$53 per day at weekday rates and \$35 per day at weekend rates. If his total rental bill was \$264, how many days did he rent at each rate? (*Source:* Enterprise.) 3 weekend days; 3 weekdays

25. A plane flies 560 mi in 1.75 hr traveling with the wind. The return trip later against the same wind takes the plane 2 hr. Find the speed of the plane and the speed of the wind.

	r	*t*	*d*
With Wind	$x + y$	1.75	
Against Wind		2	

plane: 300 mph; wind: 20 mph

26. Sweet's Candy Store is offering a special mix for Valentine's Day. Ms. Sweet will mix some \$2 per lb nuts with some \$1 per lb chocolate candy to get 100 lb of mix, which she will sell at \$1.30 per lb. How many pounds of each should she use?

	Price per Pound	Number of Pounds	Value
Nuts		x	
Chocolate		y	
Mixture		100	

30 lb of nuts; 70 lb of candy

27. A biologist wants to grow two types of algae, green and brown. She has 15 kg of nutrient X and 26 kg of nutrient Y. A vat of green algae needs 2 kg of nutrient X and 3 kg of nutrient Y, while a vat of brown algae needs 1 kg of nutrient X and 2 kg of nutrient Y. How many vats of each type of algae should she grow in order to use all the nutrients?

4 vats of green algae; 7 vats of brown algae

28. The sum of the measures of the angles of a triangle is 180°. The largest angle measures 10° less than the sum of the other two. The measure of the middle-sized angle is the average of the other two. Find the measures of the three angles.

85°, 60°, 35°

29. How many liters each of 8%, 10%, and 20% hydrogen peroxide should be mixed together to get 8 L of 12.5% solution, if the amount of 8% solution used must be 2 L more than the amount of 20% solution used?

5 L of 8%; 3 L of 20%; none of 10%

30. In the great baseball year of 1961, Yankee teammates Mickey Mantle, Roger Maris, and John Blanchard combined for 136 home runs. Mantle hit 7 fewer than Maris. Maris hit 40 more than Blanchard. What were the home run totals for each player? (*Source:* Neft, David S. and Richard M. Cohen, *The Sports Encyclopedia: Baseball 1997.*)

Mantle: 54; Maris: 61; Blanchard: 21

[5.6] *Solve each system using row operations.*

31. $2x + 5y = -4$
$4x - y = 14$

{(3, −2)}

32. $6x + 3y = 9$
$-7x + 2y = 17$

{(−1, 5)}

33. $x + 2y - z = 1$
$3x + 4y + 2z = -2$
$-2x - y + z = -1$

{(0, 0, −1)}

Mixed Review Exercises

Solve by any method.

34. $\frac{2}{3}x + \frac{1}{6}y = \frac{19}{2}$
$\frac{1}{3}x - \frac{2}{9}y = 2$

{(12, 9)}

35. $2x - 5y = 8$
$3x + 4y = 10$

$\left\{\left(\frac{82}{23}, -\frac{4}{23}\right)\right\}$

36. $x = 7y + 10$
$2x + 3y = 3$

{(3, −1)}

37. $x + 4y = 17$
$-3x + 2y = -9$

$\{(5, 3)\}$

38. $-7x + 3y = 12$
$5x + 2y = 8$

$\{(0, 4)\}$

39. $2x + 5y - z = 12$
$-x + y - 4z = -10$
$-8x - 20y + 4z = 31$

$\emptyset$

40. To make a 10% acid solution for chemistry class, Xavier wants to mix some 5% solution with 10 L of 20% solution. How many liters of 5% solution should he use?

Percent (as a Decimal)	Liters of Solution	Liters of Pure Acid

20 L

41. In the 2000 Summer Olympics in Sydney, Australia, the top three medal-winning countries were the United States, Russia, and China, with a combined total of 244 medals. The United States won 9 more medals than Russia, while China won 29 fewer medals than Russia. How many medals did each country win? (*Source: The Gazette,* October 2, 2000.)

U.S.: 97; Russia: 88; China: 59

Relating Concepts (Exercises 42–46) For Individual or Group Work

Thus far in this text we have studied only linear *equations. In later chapters we will study the graphs of other kinds of equations. One such graph is a* circle, *which has an equation of the form*

$$x^2 + y^2 + ax + by + c = 0.$$

It is a fact from geometry that given three noncollinear *points (that is, points that do not all lie on the same straight line), there will be a circle that contains them. For example, the points* (4, 2), (−5, −2), *and* (0, 3) *lie on the circle whose equation is shown in the figure.* ***Work Exercises 42–46 in order*** *to find an equation of the circle passing through the points* (2, 1), (−1, 0), *and* (3, 3).

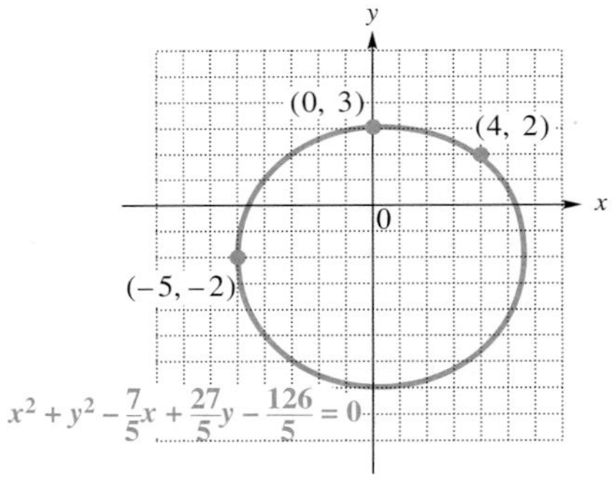

42. Let $x = 2$ and $y = 1$ in the equation $x^2 + y^2 + ax + by + c = 0$ to find an equation in a, b, and c.

$2a + b + c = -5$

43. Let $x = -1$ and $y = 0$ to find a second equation in a, b, and c.

$-a + c = -1$

44. Let $x = 3$ and $y = 3$ to find a third equation in a, b, and c.

$3a + 3b + c = -18$

45. Solve the system of equations formed by your answers in Exercises 42–44 to find the values of a, b, and c. What is the equation of the circle?

$a = 1, b = -7, c = 0; x^2 + y^2 + x - 7y = 0$

46. Explain why the relation whose graph is a circle is not a function.

The relation is not a function because a vertical line intersects its graph more than once.

Chapter 5 TEST

Study Skills Workbook
Activity 12

1. Use a graph to solve the system.

$$x + y = 7$$
$$x - y = 5$$

1. {(6, 1)}

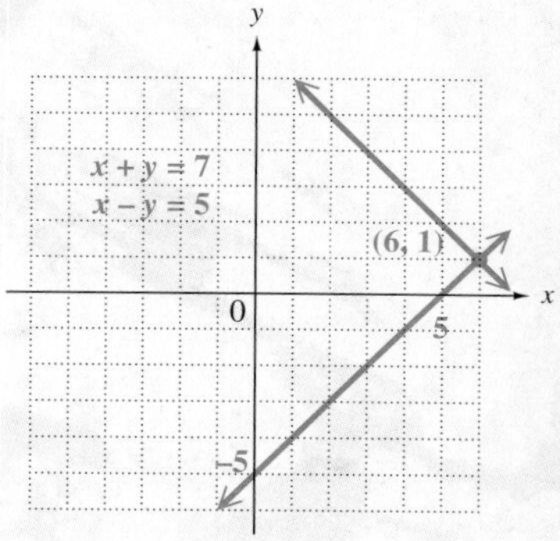

Solve each system using substitution.

2. $2x - 3y = 24$
$y = -\frac{2}{3}x$

2. {(6, −4)}

3. $12x - 5y = 8$
$3x = \frac{5}{4}y + 2$

3. $\{(x, y) | 12x - 5y = 8\}$

4. $3x - y = -8$
$2x + 6y = 3$

4. $\left\{\left(-\frac{9}{4}, \frac{5}{4}\right)\right\}$

Solve each system using elimination.

5. $3x + y = 12$
$2x - y = 3$

5. {(3, 3)}

6. $-5x + 2y = -4$
$6x + 3y = -6$

6. {(0, −2)}

7. $3x + 4y = 8$
$8y = 7 - 6x$

7. ∅

8. $3x + 5y + 3z = 2$
$6x + 5y + z = 0$
$3x + 10y - 2z = 6$

8. $\left\{\left(-\frac{2}{3}, \frac{4}{5}, 0\right)\right\}$

9. $4x + y + z = 11$
$x - y - z = 4$
$y + 2z = 0$

9. {(3, −2, 1)}

10. *Pretty Woman:* $178.4 million; *Runaway Bride:* $152.3 million

11. 45 mph, 75 mph

12. 4 L of 20%; 8 L of 50%

13. AC adaptor: $8; rechargeable flashlight: $15

14. 60 oz of Orange Pekoe; 30 oz of Irish Breakfast; 10 oz of Earl Grey

15. $\left\{\left(\frac{2}{5}, \frac{7}{5}\right)\right\}$

16. $\{(-1, 2, 3)\}$

Solve each problem using a system of equations.

10. Julia Roberts is one of the biggest box-office stars in Hollywood. As of July 2001, her two top-grossing domestic films, *Pretty Woman* and *Runaway Bride,* together earned $330.7 million. If *Runaway Bride* grossed $26.1 million less than *Pretty Woman,* how much did each film gross? (*Source:* ACNielsen EDI.)

11. Two cars start from points 420 mi apart and travel toward each other. They meet after 3.5 hr. Find the average speed of each car if one travels 30 mph slower than the other.

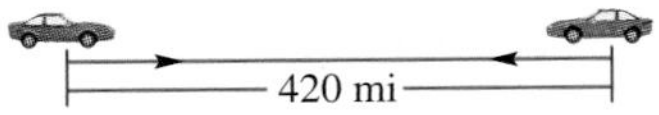

12. A chemist needs 12 L of a 40% alcohol solution. She must mix a 20% solution and a 50% solution. How many liters of each will be required to obtain what she needs?

13. A local electronics store will sell 7 AC adaptors and 2 rechargeable flashlights for $86, or 3 AC adaptors and 4 rechargeable flashlights for $84. What is the price of a single AC adaptor and a single rechargeable flashlight?

14. The owner of a tea shop wants to mix three kinds of tea to make 100 oz of a mixture that will sell for $.83 per oz. He uses Orange Pekoe, which sells for $.80 per oz, Irish Breakfast, for $.85 per oz, and Earl Grey, for $.95 per oz. If he wants to use twice as much Orange Pekoe as Irish Breakfast, how much of each kind of tea should he use?

Solve each system using row operations.

15. $3x + 2y = 4$
$5x + 5y = 9$

16. $x + 3y + 2z = 11$
$3x + 7y + 4z = 23$
$5x + 3y - 5z = -14$

Cumulative Review Exercises CHAPTERS R–5

Evaluate.

1. $(-3)^4$

81

2. -3^4

-81

3. $-(-3)^4$

-81

4. $|-13|$

13

5. $-|-13|$

-13

6. $-|13|$

-13

Evaluate if $x = -4$, $y = 3$, *and* $z = 6$.

7. $|2x| + y^2 - z^3$

-199

8. $-5(x^3 - y^3)$

455

9. $\dfrac{2x^2 - x + z}{y^2 - z}$

14

Solve each equation.

10. $7(2x + 3) - 4(2x + 1) = 2(x + 1)$

$\left\{-\dfrac{15}{4}\right\}$

11. $.04x + .06(x - 1) = 1.04$

$\{11\}$

12. $ax + by = cx + d$ for x

$x = \dfrac{d - by}{a - c}$ or $x = \dfrac{by - d}{c - a}$

13. $|6x - 8| = 4$

$\left\{\dfrac{2}{3}, 2\right\}$

Solve each inequality.

14. $\dfrac{2}{3}y + \dfrac{5}{12}y \leq 20$

$\left(-\infty, \dfrac{240}{13}\right]$

15. $|3x + 2| \leq 4$

$\left[-2, \dfrac{2}{3}\right]$

16. $|12t + 7| \geq 0$

$(-\infty, \infty)$

17. A recent survey measured public recognition of the most popular contemporary advertising slogans. Complete the results shown in the table if 2500 people were surveyed.

Slogan (product or company)	Percent Recognition (nearest tenth of a percent)	Actual Number Who Recognized Slogan (nearest whole number)
Please Don't Squeeze the . . . (Charmin)	80.4%	2010
The Breakfast of Champions (Wheaties)	72.5%	1813
The King of Beers (Budweiser)	62.8%	1570
Like a Good Neighbor (State Farm)	57.2%	1430

(Other slogans included "You're in Good Hands" (Allstate), "Snap, Crackle, Pop" (Rice Krispies), and "The Un-Cola" (7-Up).)
Source: Department of Integrated Marketing Communications, Northwestern University.

Solve each problem.

18. On February 12, 1999, the U.S. Senate voted to acquit William Jefferson Clinton on both counts of impeachment (perjury and obstruction of justice). Of the 200 votes cast that day, there were 10 more "not guilty" votes than "guilty" votes. How many of each vote were there? (*Source:* MSNBC Web site, February 13, 1999.)

not guilty: 105; guilty: 95

19. Two angles of a triangle have the same measure. The measure of the third angle is 4° less than twice the measure of each of the equal angles. Find the measures of the three angles.

46°, 46°, 88°

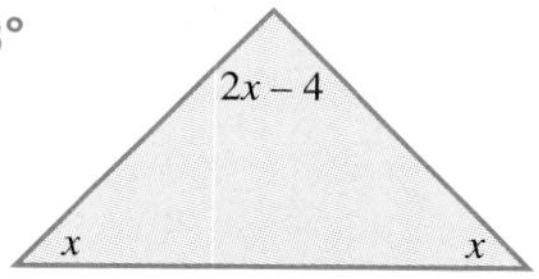

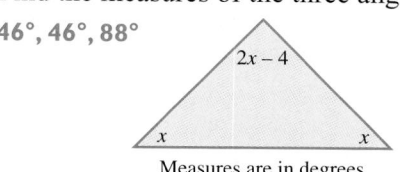

Measures are in degrees.

In Exercises 20–25, point A has coordinates $(-2, 6)$ *and point B has coordinates* $(4, -2)$.

20. What is the equation of the horizontal line through A?

$y = 6$

21. What is the equation of the vertical line through B?

$x = 4$

22. What is the slope of AB?

$-\frac{4}{3}$

23. What is the slope of a line perpendicular to line AB?

$\frac{3}{4}$

24. What is the standard form of the equation of line AB?

$4x + 3y = 10$

25. Write the equation of the line in the form of a linear function.

$f(x) = -\frac{4}{3}x + \frac{10}{3}$

26. Graph the linear function whose graph has slope $\frac{2}{3}$ and passes through the point $(-1, -3)$.

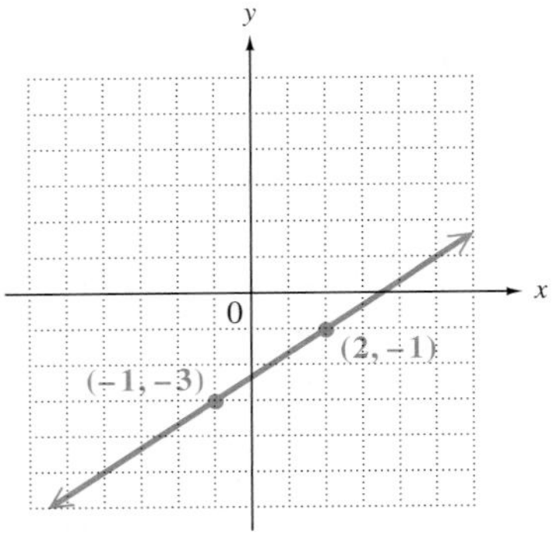

27. Graph the inequality $-3x - 2y \leq 6$.

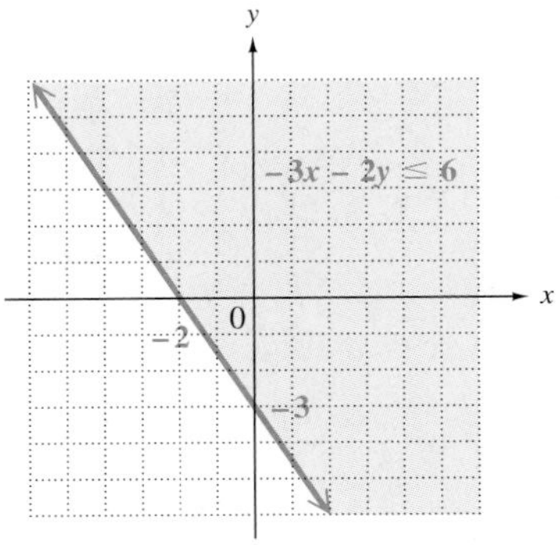

Solve by any method.

28. $-2x + 3y = -15$
$4x - y = 15$

$\{(3, -3)\}$

29. $x + y + z = 10$
$x - y - z = 0$
$-x + y - z = -4$

$\{(5, 3, 2)\}$

Solve each problem using a system of equations.

30. Two of the best-selling toys of 1996 were Tickle Me Elmo and Snacktime Kid. Based on their average retail prices, Elmo cost \$8.63 less than Kid, and together they cost \$63.89. What was the average retail price for each toy? (*Source:* NPD Group, Inc.)

Tickle Me Elmo: \$27.63; Snacktime Kid: \$36.26

31. A grocer plans to mix candy that sells for \$1.20 per lb with candy that sells for \$2.40 per lb to get a mixture that he plans to sell for \$1.65 per lb. How much of the \$1.20 and \$2.40 candy should he use if he wants 80 lb of the mix?

50 lb of \$1.20 candy; 30 lb of \$2.40 candy

The graph shows a company's costs to produce computer parts and the revenue from the sale of those parts.

32. At what production level does the cost equal the revenue? What is the revenue at that point?

$x = 8$ or 800 parts; \$3000

33. Profit is revenue less cost. Estimate the profit on the sale of 1100 parts.

about \$400

COMPUTER PARTS

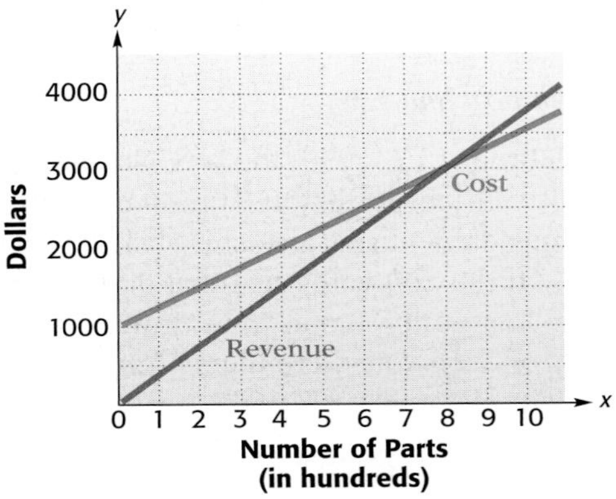

6 Exponents and Polynomials

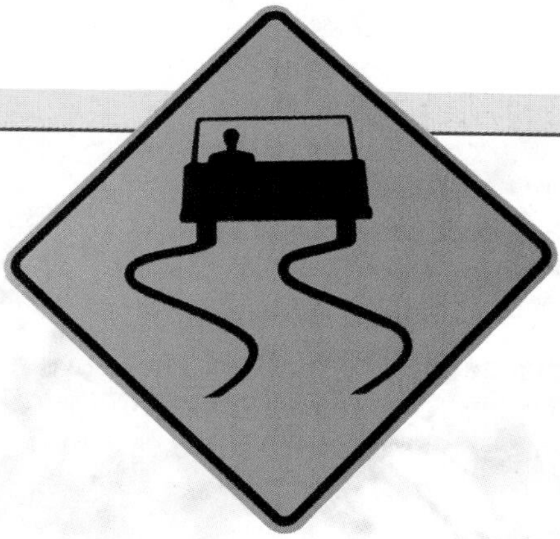

The expression $100t - 13t^2$ gives the distance in feet a car going approximately 68 mph will skid in t sec. This expression in t is an example of a *polynomial,* the topic of this chapter. Accident investigators use polynomials like this to determine the length of a skid or the elapsed time during a skid. See Exercises 43 and 44 of Section 6.1 where we use this polynomial to approximate skidding distance.

6.1 Adding and Subtracting Polynomials

Objectives

1. Review combining like terms.
2. Know the vocabulary for polynomials.
3. Evaluate polynomials.
4. Add polynomials.
5. Subtract polynomials.
6. Add and subtract polynomials with more than one variable.

1 Add like terms.

(a) $5x^4 + 7x^4$

(b) $9pq + 3pq - 2pq$

(c) $r^2 + 3r + 5r^2$

(d) $8t + 6w$

2 Choose all descriptions that apply for each of the expressions in parts (a)–(d).

A. Polynomial
B. Polynomial written in descending powers
C. Not a polynomial

(a) $3m^5 + 5m^2 - 2m + 1$

(b) $2p^4 + p^6$

(c) $\frac{1}{x} + 2x^2 + 3$

(d) $x - 3$

Answers
1. (a) $12x^4$ (b) $10pq$ (c) $6r^2 + 3r$ (d) cannot be added—unlike terms
2. (a) A and B (b) A (c) C (d) A and B

Recall from Section 1.8 that in an expression such as

$$4x^3 + 6x^2 + 5x + 8,$$

the quantities that are added, $4x^3$, $6x^2$, $5x$, and 8 are called *terms*. In the term $4x^3$, the number 4 is called the *numerical coefficient*, or simply the *coefficient*, of x^3. In the same way, 6 is the coefficient of x^2 in the term $6x^2$, 5 is the coefficient of x in the term $5x$, and 8 is the constant term.

1 Review combining like terms. In Section 1.8, we saw that *like terms* are terms with exactly the same variables, with the same exponents on the variables. Only the coefficients may differ. Like terms are combined, or *added*, by adding their coefficients using the distributive property.

Example 1 Adding Like Terms

Simplify each expression by adding like terms.

(a) $-4x^3 + 6x^3 = (-4 + 6)x^3$ Distributive property
$= 2x^3$

(b) $9x^6 - 14x^6 + x^6 = (9 - 14 + 1)x^6 = -4x^6$

(c) $12m^2 + 5m + 4m^2 = (12 + 4)m^2 + 5m$
$= 16m^2 + 5m$

(d) $3x^2y + 4x^2y - x^2y = (3 + 4 - 1)x^2y = 6x^2y$

In Example 1(c), we cannot add $16m^2$ and $5m$. These two terms are unlike because the exponents on the variables are different. *Unlike terms* have different variables or different exponents on the same variables.

Work Problem 1 at the Side.

2 Know the vocabulary for polynomials. A **polynomial in x** is a term or the sum of a finite number of terms of the form ax^n, for any real number a and any whole number n. For example,

$$16x^8 - 7x^6 + 5x^4 - 3x^2 + 4$$

is a polynomial in x. This polynomial is written in **descending powers**, because the exponents on x decrease from left to right. On the other hand,

$$2x^3 - x^2 + \frac{4}{x}$$

is not a polynomial, since a variable appears in a denominator. Of course, we could define a *polynomial* using any variable, not just x, as in Example 1(c). In fact, polynomials may have terms with more than one variable, as in Example 1(d).

Work Problem 2 at the Side.

The **degree of a term** is the sum of the exponents on the variables. A constant term has degree 0. For example, $3x^4$ has degree 4, while $6x^{17}$ has degree 17. The term $5x$ has degree 1, -7 has degree 0, and $2x^2y$ has degree $2 + 1 = 3$ (y has an exponent of 1). The **degree of a polynomial** is the highest degree of any nonzero term of the polynomial. For example, $3x^4 - 5x^2 + 6$ is of degree 4, the polynomial $5x + 7$ is of degree 1, 3 is of degree 0, and $x^2y + xy - 5xy^2$ is of degree 3.

Three types of polynomials are very common and are given special names. A polynomial with only one term is called a **monomial**. (*Mon(o)-* means "one," as in *mono*rail.) Examples are

$$9m, \quad -6y^5, \quad a^2, \quad \text{and} \quad 6. \qquad \text{Monomials}$$

A polynomial with exactly two terms is called a **binomial**. (*Bi-* means "two," as in *bi*cycle.) Examples are

$$-9x^4 + 9x^3, \quad 8m^2 + 6m, \quad \text{and} \quad 3m^5 - 9m^2. \qquad \text{Binomials}$$

A polynomial with exactly three terms is called a **trinomial**. (*Tri-* means "three," as in *tri*angle.) Examples are

$$9m^3 - 4m^2 + 6, \quad \frac{19}{3}y^2 + \frac{8}{3}y + 5, \quad \text{and} \quad -3m^5 - 9m^2 + 2. \qquad \text{Trinomials}$$

Example 2 **Classifying Polynomials**

For each polynomial, first simplify if possible by combining like terms. Then give the degree and tell whether the polynomial is a monomial, a binomial, a trinomial, or none of these.

(a) $2x^3 + 5$

The polynomial cannot be simplified. The degree is 3. The polynomial is a binomial.

(b) $4x - 5x + 2x$

Add like terms to simplify: $4x - 5x + 2x = x$. The degree is 1 (since $x = x^1$). The simplified polynomial is a monomial.

Work Problem 3 at the Side.

3 **Evaluate polynomials.** A polynomial usually represents different numbers for different values of the variable, as shown in the next example.

Example 3 **Evaluating a Polynomial**

Find the value of $3x^4 + 5x^3 - 4x - 4$ when $x = -2$ and when $x = 3$.

First, substitute -2 for x.

$$\begin{aligned} 3x^4 + 5x^3 - 4x - 4 &= 3(-2)^4 + 5(-2)^3 - 4(-2) - 4 \\ &= 3 \cdot 16 + 5(-8) - 4(-2) - 4 && \text{Apply exponents.} \\ &= 48 - 40 + 8 - 4 && \text{Multiply.} \\ &= 12 && \text{Add and subtract.} \end{aligned}$$

Next, replace x with 3.

$$\begin{aligned} 3x^4 + 5x^3 - 4x - 4 &= 3(3)^4 + 5(3)^3 - 4(3) - 4 \\ &= 3 \cdot 81 + 5 \cdot 27 - 4(3) - 4 \\ &= 243 + 135 - 12 - 4 \\ &= 362 \end{aligned}$$

3 For each polynomial, first simplify if possible. Then give the degree and tell whether the polynomial is a monomial, binomial, trinomial, or none of these.

(a) $3x^2 + 2x - 4$

(b) $x^3 + 4x^3$

(c) $x^8 - x^7 + 2x^8$

Answers

3. (a) degree 2; trinomial
(b) degree 3; monomial (simplify to $5x^3$)
(c) degree 8; binomial (simplify to $3x^8 - x^7$)

4 Find the value of $2y^3 + 8y - 6$ in each case.

(a) when $y = -1$

(b) when $y = 4$

5 Add each pair of polynomials.

(a)
$$\begin{array}{r} 4x^3 - 3x^2 + 2x \\ \underline{6x^3 + 2x^2 - 3x} \end{array}$$

(b)
$$\begin{array}{r} x^2 - 2x + 5 \\ \underline{4x^2 \qquad\quad - 2} \end{array}$$

CAUTION

Notice the use of parentheses around the numbers that are substituted for the variable in Example 3. This is particularly important when substituting a negative number for a variable that is raised to a power, so the sign of the product is correct.

Work Problem 4 at the Side.

4 **Add polynomials.** Polynomials may be added, subtracted, multiplied, and divided.

Adding Polynomials

To add two polynomials, add like terms.

Example 4 Adding Polynomials Vertically

(a) Add $6x^3 - 4x^2 + 3$ and $-2x^3 + 7x^2 - 5$.
Write like terms in columns.

$$\begin{array}{r} 6x^3 - 4x^2 + 3 \\ \underline{-2x^3 + 7x^2 - 5} \end{array}$$

Now add, column by column.

$$\begin{array}{rrr} 6x^3 & -4x^2 & 3 \\ \underline{-2x^3} & \underline{7x^2} & \underline{-5} \\ 4x^3 & 3x^2 & -2 \end{array}$$

Add the three sums together.

$$4x^3 + 3x^2 + (-2) = 4x^3 + 3x^2 - 2$$

(b) Add $2x^2 - 4x + 3$ and $x^3 + 5x$.
Write like terms in columns and add column by column.

$$\begin{array}{rrrr} & 2x^2 & - 4x & + 3 \\ \underline{x^3} & & \underline{+ 5x} & \\ x^3 & + 2x^2 & + x & + 3 \end{array}$$

Leave spaces for missing terms.

Work Problem 5 at the Side.

The polynomials in Example 4 also could be added horizontally by combining like terms, as shown in the next example.

Example 5 Adding Polynomials Horizontally

(a) Add $6x^3 - 4x^2 + 3$ and $-2x^3 + 7x^2 - 5$.
Combine like terms.

$$(6x^3 - 4x^2 + 3) + (-2x^3 + 7x^2 - 5)$$

Continued on Next Page

ANSWERS
4. (a) -16 (b) 154
5. (a) $10x^3 - x^2 - x$ (b) $5x^2 - 2x + 3$

The sum is

$$4x^3 + 3x^2 - 2,$$

the same answer found in Example 4(a).

(b) Add $2x^2 - 4x + 3$ and $x^3 + 5x$.

$$\begin{aligned}(2x^2 - 4x + 3) + (x^3 + 5x) &= 2x^2 - 4x + 3 + x^3 + 5x \\ &= x^3 + 2x^2 + x + 3 \quad \text{Combine like terms.}\end{aligned}$$

Work Problem 6 at the Side.

5 Subtract polynomials. Earlier, the difference $x - y$ was defined as $x + (-y)$. (We find the difference $x - y$ by adding x and the opposite of y.) For example,

$$7 - 2 = 7 + (-2) = 5 \quad \text{and} \quad -8 - (-2) = -8 + 2 = -6.$$

A similar method is used to subtract polynomials.

Subtracting Polynomials

To subtract two polynomials, change all the signs of the second polynomial and add the result to the first polynomial.

Example 6 Subtracting Polynomials

(a) Perform the subtraction $(5x - 2) - (3x - 8)$.

Change the signs in the second polynomial and add like terms.

$$\begin{aligned}(5x - 2) - (3x - 8) &= (5x - 2) + (-3x + 8) \\ &= 2x + 6\end{aligned}$$

(b) Subtract $6x^3 - 4x^2 + 2$ from $11x^3 + 2x^2 - 8$.

Write the problem.

$$(11x^3 + 2x^2 - 8) - (6x^3 - 4x^2 + 2)$$

Change all the signs in the second polynomial and add the two polynomials.

$$(11x^3 + 2x^2 - 8) + (-6x^3 + 4x^2 - 2) = 5x^3 + 6x^2 - 10$$

To check a subtraction problem, use the fact that if $a - b = c$, then $a = b + c$. For example, $6 - 2 = 4$, so we check by writing $6 = 2 + 4$, which is correct. Check the polynomial subtraction above by adding $6x^3 - 4x^2 + 2$ and $5x^3 + 6x^2 - 10$. Since the sum is $11x^3 + 2x^2 - 8$, the subtraction was performed correctly.

Work Problem 7 at the Side.

Subtraction also can be done in columns. We will use vertical subtraction in Section 6.7 when we study polynomial division.

Example 7 Subtracting Polynomials Vertically

Use the method of subtracting by columns to find

$$(14y^3 - 6y^2 + 2y - 5) - (2y^3 - 7y^2 - 4y + 6).$$

Continued on Next Page

6 Find each sum.

(a) $(2x^4 - 6x^2 + 7)$
$+ (-3x^4 + 5x^2 + 2)$

(b) $(3x^2 + 4x + 2)$
$+ (6x^3 - 5x - 7)$

7 Subtract, and check your answers by addition.

(a) $(14y^3 - 6y^2 + 2y - 5)$
$- (2y^3 - 7y^2 - 4y + 6)$

(b) $\left(\frac{7}{2}y^2 - \frac{11}{3}y + 8\right)$
$- \left(-\frac{3}{2}y^2 + \frac{4}{3}y + 6\right)$

ANSWERS

6. (a) $-x^4 - x^2 + 9$
(b) $6x^3 + 3x^2 - x - 5$

7. (a) $12y^3 + y^2 + 6y - 11$
(b) $5y^2 - 5y + 2$

Arrange like terms in columns.

$$\begin{array}{r} 14y^3 - 6y^2 + 2y - 5 \\ 2y^3 - 7y^2 - 4y + 6 \\ \hline \end{array}$$

Change all signs in the second row, and then add.

$$\begin{array}{rl} 14y^3 - 6y^2 + 2y - 5 & \\ -2y^3 + 7y^2 + 4y - 6 & \text{Change signs.} \\ \hline 12y^3 + y^2 + 6y - 11 & \text{Add.} \end{array}$$

Work Problem 8 at the Side.

Either the horizontal or the vertical method may be used for adding or subtracting polynomials.

Example 8 **Adding and Subtracting More Than Two Polynomials**

Perform the indicated operations to simplify the expression

$$(4 - x + 3x^2) - (2 - 3x + 5x^2) + (8 + 2x - 4x^2).$$

Rewrite, changing the subtraction to adding the opposite.

$$\begin{aligned} &(4 - x + 3x^2) - (2 - 3x + 5x^2) + (8 + 2x - 4x^2) \\ &\quad = (4 - x + 3x^2) + (-2 + 3x - 5x^2) + (8 + 2x - 4x^2) \\ &\quad = (2 + 2x - 2x^2) + (8 + 2x - 4x^2) \qquad \text{Combine like terms.} \\ &\quad = 10 + 4x - 6x^2 \qquad \text{Combine like terms.} \end{aligned}$$

Work Problem 9 at the Side.

6 **Add and subtract polynomials with more than one variable.** Polynomials in more than one variable are added and subtracted by combining like terms, just as with single-variable polynomials.

Example 9 **Adding and Subtracting Multivariable Polynomials**

Add or subtract as indicated.

(a) $(4a + 2ab - b) + (3a - ab + b)$

$$\begin{aligned} &(4a + 2ab - b) + (3a - ab + b) \\ &\quad = 4a + 2ab - b + 3a - ab + b \\ &\quad = 7a + ab \qquad \text{Combine like terms.} \end{aligned}$$

(b) $(2x^2y + 3xy + y^2) - (3x^2y - xy - 2y^2)$

$$\begin{aligned} &(2x^2y + 3xy + y^2) - (3x^2y - xy - 2y^2) \\ &\quad = 2x^2y + 3xy + y^2 - 3x^2y + xy + 2y^2 \\ &\quad = -x^2y + 4xy + 3y^2 \end{aligned}$$

Work Problem 10 at the Side.

8 Subtract, using the method of subtracting by columns.

$(4y^3 - 16y^2 + 2y)$
$- (12y^3 - 9y^2 + 16)$

9 Perform the indicated operations.

$(6p^4 - 8p^3 + 2p - 1)$
$- (-7p^4 + 6p^2 - 12)$
$+ (p^4 - 3p + 8)$

10 Add or subtract.

(a) $(3mn + 2m - 4n)$
$+ (-mn + 4m + n)$

(b) $(5p^2q^2 - 4p^2 + 2q)$
$- (2p^2q^2 - p^2 - 3q)$

ANSWERS

8. $-8y^3 - 7y^2 + 2y - 16$

9. $14p^4 - 8p^3 - 6p^2 - p + 19$

10. **(a)** $2mn + 6m - 3n$

(b) $3p^2q^2 - 3p^2 + 5q$

6.1 EXERCISES

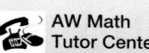

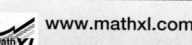

FOR EXTRA HELP: Student's Solutions Manual; MyMathLab.com; InterAct Math Tutorial Software; AW Math Tutor Center; www.mathxl.com; Digital Video Tutor CD 5 Videotape 11

Fill in each blank with the correct response.

1. In the term $7x^5$, the coefficient is 7 and the exponent is 5.

2. The expression $5x^3 - 4x^2$ has two term(s). (how many?)

3. The degree of the term $-4x^8$ is 8.

4. The polynomial $4x^2 - y^2$ is not an example of a trinomial. (is/is not)

5. When $x^2 + 10$ is evaluated for $x = 4$, the result is 26.

6. $5x^9$ is an example of a monomial with coefficient 5, in the variable x, having degree 9.

For each polynomial, determine the number of terms, and name the coefficient of each term.

7. $6x^4$
   1; 6

8. $-9y^5$
   1; −9

9. t^4
   1; 1

10. s^7
    1; 1

11. $-19r^2 - r$
    2; −19, −1

12. $2y^3 - y$
    2; 2, −1

13. $x + 8x^2$
    2; 1, 8

14. $v - 2v^3$
    2; 1, −2

In each polynomial, combine like terms whenever possible. Write the result with descending powers.

15. $-3m^5 + 5m^5$
    $2m^5$

16. $-4y^3 + 3y^3$
    $-y^3$

17. $2r^5 + (-3r^5)$
    $-r^5$

18. $-19y^2 + 9y^2$
    $-10y^2$

19. $.2m^5 - .5m^2$
    cannot be simplified; $.2m^5 - .5m^2$

20. $-.9y + .9y^2$
    cannot be simplified; $.9y^2 - .9y$

21. $-3x^5 + 2x^5 - 4x^5$
    $-5x^5$

22. $6x^3 - 8x^3 + 9x^3$
    $7x^3$

23. $-4p^7 + 8p^7 + 5p^9$
    $5p^9 + 4p^7$

24. $-3a^8 + 4a^8 - 3a^2$
    $a^8 - 3a^2$

25. $-4y^2 + 3y^2 - 2y^2 + y^2$
    $-2y^2$

26. $3r^5 - 8r^5 + r^5 + 2r^5$
    $-2r^5$

For each polynomial, first simplify, if possible, and write it with descending powers. Then give the degree of the resulting polynomial, and tell whether it is a monomial, binomial, trinomial, *or* none of these. *See Example 2.*

27. $6x^4 - 9x$
    already simplified; 4; binomial

28. $7t^3 - 3t$
    already simplified; 3; binomial

29. $5m^4 - 3m^2 + 6m^5 - 7m^3$
    already simplified; $6m^5 + 5m^4 - 7m^3 - 3m^2$**; 5; none of these**

30. $6p^5 + 4p^3 - 8p^4 + 10p^2$

already simplified; $6p^5 - 8p^4 + 4p^3 + 10p^2$; 5; none of these

31. $\frac{5}{3}x^4 - \frac{2}{3}x^4 + \frac{1}{3}x^2 - 4$

$x^4 + \frac{1}{3}x^2 - 4$; 4; trinomial

32. $\frac{4}{5}r^6 + \frac{1}{5}r^6 - r^4 + \frac{2}{5}r$

$r^6 - r^4 + \frac{2}{5}r$; 6; trinomial

33. $.8x^4 - .3x^4 - .5x^4 + 7$

7; 0; monomial

34. $1.2t^3 - .9t^3 - .3t^3 + 9$

9; 0; monomial

Find the value of each polynomial **(a)** *when* $x = 2$ *and* **(b)** *when* $x = -1$. *See Example 3.*

35. $-2x + 3$

(a) -1 (b) 5

36. $5x - 4$

(a) 6 (b) -9

37. $2x^2 + 5x + 1$

(a) 19 (b) -2

38. $-3x^2 + 14x - 2$

(a) 14 (b) -19

39. $2x^5 - 4x^4 + 5x^3 - x^2$

(a) 36 (b) -12

40. $x^4 - 6x^3 + x^2 + 1$

(a) -27 (b) 9

41. $-4x^5 + x^2$

(a) -124 (b) 5

42. $2x^6 - 4x$

(a) 120 (b) 6

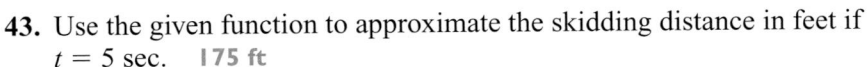

RELATING CONCEPTS (Exercises 43–46) FOR INDIVIDUAL OR GROUP WORK

In the introduction to this chapter, we gave a polynomial that models the distance in feet that a car going approximately 68 *mph will skid in t seconds. If we let D represent this distance, then using function notation from Section 4.6, we have*

$$D(t) = 100t - 13t^2.$$

Each time we evaluate this function (called a polynomial function*) for a value of t, we get one and only one output value D(t). Exercises 43–46 illustrate this idea.* ***Work them in order.***

43. Use the given function to approximate the skidding distance in feet if $t = 5$ sec. 175 ft

44. Use $D(t) = 100t - 13t^2$ to find the distance the car will skid in 1 sec. Write an ordered pair of the form $(t, D(t))$. 87 ft; (1, 87)

45. If gasoline costs \$1.60 per gal, then the function defined by $C(x) = 1.60x$ gives the cost, in dollars, of x gal. How much would 4 gal cost? \$6.40

46. If it costs \$15 plus \$2 per day to rent a chain saw, then $C(x) = 2x + 15$ gives the cost in dollars to rent the chain saw for x days. How much would it cost to rent the saw for 6 days? \$27

Add or subtract as indicated. See Examples 4 and 7.

47. Add.

$$\begin{array}{r} 3m^2 + 5m \\ \underline{2m^2 - 2m} \end{array}$$

$5m^2 + 3m$

48. Add.

$$\begin{array}{r} 4a^3 - 4a^2 \\ \underline{6a^3 + 5a^2} \end{array}$$

$10a^3 + a^2$

49. Subtract.

$$\begin{array}{r} 12x^4 - x^2 \\ \underline{8x^4 + 3x^2} \end{array}$$

$4x^4 - 4x^2$

50. Subtract.

$$\begin{array}{r} 13y^5 - y^3 \\ \underline{7y^5 + 5y^3} \end{array}$$

$6y^5 - 6y^3$

51. Add.

$$\begin{array}{r} \frac{2}{3}x^2 + \frac{1}{5}x + \frac{1}{6} \\ \underline{\frac{1}{2}x^2 - \frac{1}{3}x + \frac{2}{3}} \end{array}$$

$\frac{7}{6}x^2 - \frac{2}{15}x + \frac{5}{6}$

52. Add.

$$\begin{array}{r} \frac{4}{7}y^2 - \frac{1}{5}y + \frac{7}{9} \\ \underline{\frac{1}{3}y^2 - \frac{1}{3}y + \frac{2}{5}} \end{array}$$

$\frac{19}{21}y^2 - \frac{8}{15}y + \frac{53}{45}$

53. Subtract.

$$\begin{array}{r} 12m^3 - 8m^2 + 6m + 7 \\ \underline{+ 5m^2 - 4} \end{array}$$

$12m^3 - 13m^2 + 6m + 11$

54. Subtract.

$$\begin{array}{r} 5a^4 - 3a^3 + 2a^2 - a + 6 \\ \underline{-6a^4 - a^2 + a - 1} \end{array}$$

$11a^4 - 3a^3 + 3a^2 - 2a + 7$

Perform the indicated operations. See Examples 5, 6, and 8.

55. $(2r^2 + 3r - 12) + (6r^2 + 2r)$

$8r^2 + 5r - 12$

56. $(3r^2 + 5r - 6) + (2r - 5r^2)$

$-2r^2 + 7r - 6$

57. $(8m^2 - 7m) - (3m^2 + 7m - 6)$

$5m^2 - 14m + 6$

58. $(x^2 + x) - (3x^2 + 2x - 1)$

$-2x^2 - x + 1$

59. $(16x^3 - x^2 + 3x) + (-12x^3 + 3x^2 + 2x)$

$4x^3 + 2x^2 + 5x$

60. $(-2b^6 + 3b^4 - b^2) + (b^6 + 2b^4 + 2b^2)$

$-b^6 + 5b^4 + b^2$

61. $(7y^4 + 3y^2 + 2y) - (18y^5 - 5y^3 + y)$

$-18y^5 + 7y^4 + 5y^3 + 3y^2 + y$

62. $(8t^5 + 3t^3 + 5t) - (19t^4 - 6t^2 + t)$

$8t^5 - 19t^4 + 3t^3 + 6t^2 + 4t$

63. $[(8m^2 + 4m - 7) - (2m^3 - 5m + 2)] - (m^2 + m)$

$-2m^3 + 7m^2 + 8m - 9$

64. $[(9b^3 - 4b^2 + 3b + 2) - (-2b^3 + b)] - (8b^3 + 6b + 4)$

$3b^3 - 4b^2 - 4b - 2$

Find the perimeter of each geometric figure.

65.

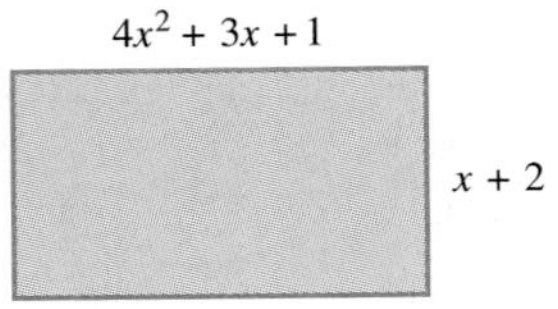

$8x^2 + 8x + 6$

66.

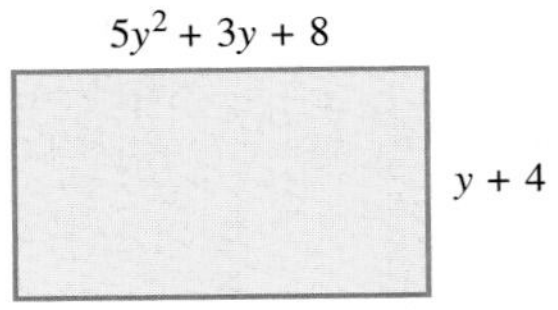

$10y^2 + 8y + 24$

67.

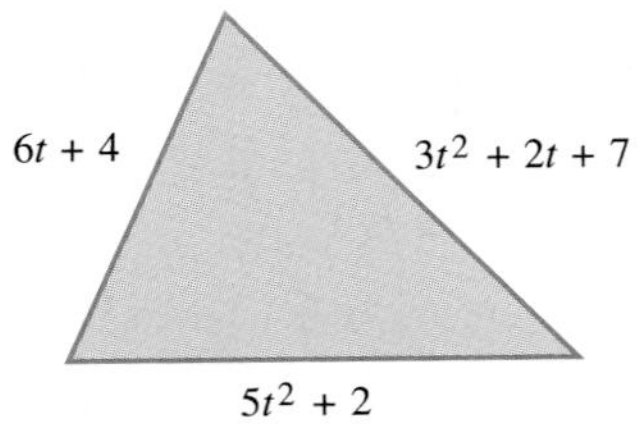

$8t^2 + 8t + 13$

68.

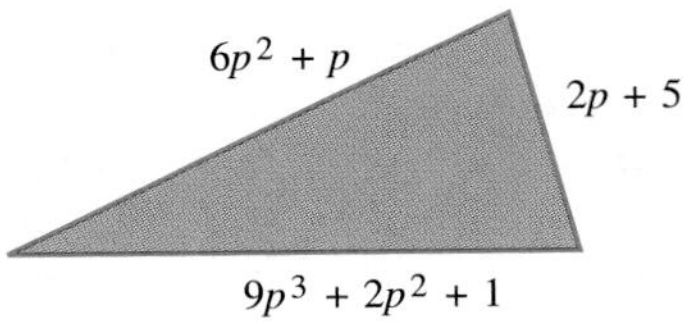

$9p^3 + 8p^2 + 3p + 6$

69. Subtract $9x^2 - 3x + 7$ from $-2x^2 - 6x + 4$.
$-11x^2 - 3x - 3$

70. Subtract $-5w^3 + 5w^2 - 7$ from $6w^3 + 8w + 5$.
$11w^3 - 5w^2 + 8w + 12$

71. Explain why the degree of the term 3^4 is not 4. What is its degree?
The degree of a term is determined by the exponents on the *variables*, but 3 is not a variable. The degree of $3^4 = 3^4x^0$ is 0.

72. Can the sum of two polynomials in x, both of degree 3, be of degree 2? If so, give an example.
yes; $-4x^3 + 3x^2 + x - 1$ and $4x^3 + x^2 + x + 8$, for example

Add or subtract as indicated. See Example 9.

73. $(9a^2b - 3a^2 + 2b) + (4a^2b - 4a^2 - 3b)$
$13a^2b - 7a^2 - b$

74. $(4xy^3 - 3x + y) + (5xy^3 + 13x - 4y)$
$9xy^3 + 10x - 3y$

75. $(2c^4d + 3c^2d^2 - 4d^2) - (c^4d + 8c^2d^2 - 5d^2)$
$c^4d - 5c^2d^2 + d^2$

76. $(3k^2h^3 + 5kh + 6k^3h^2) - (2k^2h^3 - 9kh + k^3h^2)$
$k^2h^3 + 14kh + 5k^3h^2$

77. Subtract.
$$\begin{array}{r} 9m^3n - 5m^2n^2 + 4mn^2 \\ \underline{-3m^3n + 6m^2n^2 + 8mn^2} \\ 12m^3n - 11m^2n^2 - 4mn^2 \end{array}$$

78. Subtract.
$$\begin{array}{r} 12r^5t + 11r^4t^2 - 7r^3t^3 \\ \underline{-8r^5t + 10r^4t^2 + 3r^3t^3} \\ 20r^5t + r^4t^2 - 10r^3t^3 \end{array}$$

6.2 The Product Rule and Power Rules for Exponents

Objectives

1. Use exponents.
2. Use the product rule for exponents.
3. Use the rule $(a^m)^n = a^{mn}$.
4. Use the rule $(ab)^m = a^m b^m$.
5. Use the rule $\left(\frac{a}{b}\right)^m = \frac{a^m}{b^m}$.
6. Use combinations of the rules for exponents.

1 Use exponents. In Chapter 1 we used exponents to write repeated products. Recall that in the expression 5^2, the number 5 is called the *base* and 2 is called the *exponent* or *power*. The expression 5^2 is called an *exponential expression*. Usually we do not write a quantity with an exponent of 1, but sometimes it is convenient to do so. In general, for any quantity a, $a = a^1$.

Example 1 **Using Exponents**

Write $3 \cdot 3 \cdot 3 \cdot 3 \cdot 3$ in exponential form, and evaluate the exponential expression.

Since 3 occurs as a factor five times, the base is 3 and the exponent is 5. The exponential expression is 3^5, read "3 to the fifth power" or simply "3 to the fifth." The value is

$$3^5 = 3 \cdot 3 \cdot 3 \cdot 3 \cdot 3 = 243.$$

Work Problem 1 at the Side.

1 Write $2 \cdot 2 \cdot 2 \cdot 2$ in exponential form, and evaluate.

Example 2 **Evaluating Exponential Expressions**

Evaluate each exponential expression. Name the base and the exponent.

	Base	Exponent
(a) $5^4 = 5 \cdot 5 \cdot 5 \cdot 5 = 625$	5	4
(b) $-5^4 = -1 \cdot 5^4 = -1 \cdot (5 \cdot 5 \cdot 5 \cdot 5) = -625$	5	4
(c) $(-5)^4 = (-5)(-5)(-5)(-5) = 625$	-5	4

CAUTION

It is important to understand the difference between parts (b) and (c) of Example 2. In -5^4 the lack of parentheses shows that the exponent 4 applies only to the base 5, and not -5; in $(-5)^4$ the parentheses show that the exponent 4 applies to the base -5. In summary, $-a^n$ and $(-a)^n$ are not always the same.

Expression	Base	Exponent	Example
$-a^n$	a	n	$-3^2 = -(3 \cdot 3) = -9$
$(-a)^n$	$-a$	n	$(-3)^2 = (-3)(-3) = 9$

Work Problem 2 at the Side.

2 Evaluate each exponential expression. Name the base and the exponent.

(a) $(-2)^5$ **(b)** -2^5

(c) -4^2 **(d)** $(-4)^2$

2 Use the product rule for exponents. To develop the product rule, we use the definition of an exponential expression.

$$2^4 \cdot 2^3 = \underbrace{(2 \cdot 2 \cdot 2 \cdot 2)}_{\text{4 factors}}\underbrace{(2 \cdot 2 \cdot 2)}_{\text{3 factors}}$$
$$= \underbrace{2 \cdot 2 \cdot 2 \cdot 2 \cdot 2 \cdot 2 \cdot 2}_{4 + 3 = 7 \text{ factors}}$$
$$= 2^7$$

Answers
1. $2^4 = 16$
2. (a) $-32; -2; 5$ (b) $-32; 2; 5$ (c) $-16; 4; 2$ (d) $16; -4; 2$

Also,

$$6^2 \cdot 6^3 = (6 \cdot 6)(6 \cdot 6 \cdot 6)$$
$$= 6 \cdot 6 \cdot 6 \cdot 6 \cdot 6$$
$$= 6^5.$$

Generalizing from these examples, $2^4 \cdot 2^3 = 2^{4+3} = 2^7$ and $6^2 \cdot 6^3 = 6^{2+3} = 6^5$. In each case, adding the exponents gives the exponent of the product, suggesting the **product rule for exponents.**

Product Rule for Exponents

For any positive integers m and n, $a^m \cdot a^n = a^{m+n}$.
(Keep the same base and add the exponents.)

Example: $6^2 \cdot 6^5 = 6^{2+5} = 6^7$.

CAUTION

Avoid the common error of multiplying the bases when using the product rule.

$$6^2 \cdot 6^5 \neq 36^7$$

Keep the *same* base and add the exponents.

Example 3 **Using the Product Rule**

Use the product rule for exponents to find each product, if possible.

(a) $6^3 \cdot 6^5 = 6^{3+5} = 6^8$ by the product rule.

(b) $(-4)^7(-4)^2 = (-4)^{7+2} = (-4)^9$ by the product rule.

(c) $x^2 \cdot x = x^2 \cdot x^1 = x^{2+1} = x^3$

(d) $m^4 \cdot m^3 = m^{4+3} = m^7$

(e) $2^3 \cdot 3^2$

The product rule does not apply to the product $2^3 \cdot 3^2$ because the bases are different.

$$2^3 \cdot 3^2 = 8 \cdot 9 = 72$$

(f) $2^3 + 2^4$

The product rule does not apply to $2^3 + 2^4$ because it is a *sum*, not a *product.*

$$2^3 + 2^4 = 8 + 16 = 24$$

CAUTION

The bases must be the same before we can apply the product rule for exponents.

Work Problem 3 at the Side.

3 Find each product by the product rule, if possible.

(a) $8^2 \cdot 8^5$

(b) $(-7)^5 \cdot (-7)^3$

(c) $y^3 \cdot y$

(d) $4^2 \cdot 3^5$

(e) $6^4 + 6^2$

ANSWERS

3. (a) 8^7 **(b)** $(-7)^8$ **(c)** y^4
(d) cannot use the product rule (product: 3888) **(e)** cannot use the product rule

Example 4 **Using the Product Rule**

Multiply $2x^3$ and $3x^7$.

Since $2x^3$ means $2 \cdot x^3$ and $3x^7$ means $3 \cdot x^7$, we use the associative and commutative properties and the product rule to get

$$2x^3 \cdot 3x^7 = 2 \cdot 3 \cdot x^3 \cdot x^7 = 6x^{10}.$$

CAUTION

Be sure you understand the difference between *adding* and *multiplying* exponential expressions. For example,

$$8x^3 + 5x^3 = (8 + 5)x^3 = 13x^3,$$

but

$$(8x^3)(5x^3) = (8 \cdot 5)x^{3+3} = 40x^6.$$

Work Problem 4 at the Side.

3 **Use the rule $(a^m)^n = a^{mn}$.** We can simplify an expression such as $(8^3)^2$ with the product rule for exponents, as follows.

$$(8^3)^2 = (8^3)(8^3) = 8^{3+3} = 8^6$$

The product of the exponents in $(8^3)^2$, 3 and 2, gives the exponent in 8^6. As another example,

$$\begin{aligned} (5^2)^4 &= 5^2 \cdot 5^2 \cdot 5^2 \cdot 5^2 && \text{Definition of exponent} \\ &= 5^{2+2+2+2} && \text{Product rule} \\ &= 5^8, \end{aligned}$$

and $2 \cdot 4 = 8$. These examples suggest **power rule (a) for exponents.**

Power Rule (a) for Exponents

For any positive integers m and n, $(a^m)^n = a^{mn}$.
(Raise a power to a power by multiplying exponents.)

Example: $(3^2)^4 = 3^{2 \cdot 4} = 3^8$.

Example 5 **Using Power Rule (a)**

Use power rule (a) for exponents to simplify each expression.

(a) $(2^5)^3 = 2^{5 \cdot 3} = 2^{15}$ **(b)** $(5^7)^2 = 5^{7 \cdot 2} = 5^{14}$

(c) $(x^2)^5 = x^{2 \cdot 5} = x^{10}$ **(d)** $(n^3)^2 = n^{3 \cdot 2} = n^6$

Work Problem 5 at the Side.

4 **Use the rule $(ab)^m = a^m b^m$.** The properties studied in Chapter 1 can be used to develop two more rules for exponents. Using the definition of an exponential expression and the commutative and associative properties, we can rewrite the expression $(4x)^3$ as shown below.

$$\begin{aligned} (4x)^3 &= (4x)(4x)(4x) && \text{Definition of exponent} \\ &= 4 \cdot 4 \cdot 4 \cdot x \cdot x \cdot x && \text{Commutative and associative properties} \\ &= 4^3x^3 && \text{Definition of exponent} \end{aligned}$$

This example suggests **power rule (b) for exponents.**

4 Multiply.

(a) $5m^2 \cdot 2m^6$

(b) $3p^5 \cdot 9p^4$

(c) $-7p^5 \cdot (3p^8)$

5 Simplify each expression.

(a) $(5^3)^4$

(b) $(6^2)^5$

(c) $(3^2)^4$

(d) $(a^6)^5$

ANSWERS

4. (a) $10m^8$ **(b)** $27p^9$ **(c)** $-21p^{13}$

5. (a) 5^{12} **(b)** 6^{10} **(c)** 3^8 **(d)** a^{30}

6 Simplify.

(a) $5(mn)^3$

(b) $(3a^2b^4)^5$

(c) $(-5m^2)^3$

Power Rule (b) for Exponents

For any positive integer m, $(ab)^m = a^m b^m$.
(Raise a product to a power by raising each factor to the power.)

Example: $(2p)^5 = 2^5 p^5$.

Example 6 Using Power Rule (b)

Use power rule (b) to simplify each expression.

(a) $(3xy)^2 = 3^2x^2y^2$ Power rule (b)
$= 9x^2y^2$

(b) $9(pq)^2 = 9(p^2q^2)$ Power rule (b)
$= 9p^2q^2$

(c) $5(2m^2p^3)^4 = 5[2^4(m^2)^4(p^3)^4]$ Power rule (b)
$= 5(2^4m^8p^{12})$ Power rule (a)
$= 5 \cdot 2^4m^8p^{12}$
$= 80m^8p^{12}$ $5 \cdot 2^4 = 5 \cdot 16 = 80$

(d) $(-5^6)^3 = (-1 \cdot 5^6)^3$ $-a = -1 \cdot a$
$= (-1)^3(5^6)^3$ Power rule (b)
$= -1 \cdot 5^{18}$ Power rule (a)
$= -5^{18}$

CAUTION

Power rule (b) *does not* apply to a *sum*.

$$(x + 4)^2 \neq x^2 + 4^2$$

Work Problem 6 at the Side.

5 **Use the rule $\left(\frac{a}{b}\right)^m = \frac{a^m}{b^m}$.** Since the quotient $\frac{a}{b}$ can be written as $a \cdot \frac{1}{b}$, we can use power rule (b), together with some of the properties of real numbers, to get **power rule (c) for exponents.**

Power Rule (c) for Exponents

For any positive integer m, $\left(\frac{a}{b}\right)^m = \frac{a^m}{b^m}$ $(b \neq 0)$.

(Raise a quotient to a power by raising both the numerator and the denominator to the power.)

Example: $\left(\frac{5}{3}\right)^2 = \frac{5^2}{3^2}$.

ANSWERS
6. (a) $5m^3n^3$ **(b)** $3^5a^{10}b^{20}$ **(c)** -5^3m^6

Example 7 **Using Power Rule (c)**

Simplify each expression.

(a) $\left(\frac{2}{3}\right)^5 = \frac{2^5}{3^5}$

(b) $\left(\frac{m}{n}\right)^4 = \frac{m^4}{n^4}, n \neq 0$

Work Problem 7 at the Side.

Next we list the rules for exponents discussed in this section. These rules are basic to the study of algebra and should be *memorized.*

Rules for Exponents

For positive integers m and n:

			Examples
Product rule		$a^m \cdot a^n = a^{m+n}$	$6^2 \cdot 6^5 = 6^{2+5} = 6^7$
Power rules	**(a)**	$(a^m)^n = a^{mn}$	$(3^2)^4 = 3^{2\cdot 4} = 3^8$
	(b)	$(ab)^m = a^m b^m$	$(2p)^5 = 2^5p^5$
	(c)	$\left(\frac{a}{b}\right)^m = \frac{a^m}{b^m} \quad (b \neq 0)$	$\left(\frac{5}{3}\right)^2 = \frac{5^2}{3^2}$

6 **Use combinations of the rules for exponents.** As shown in the next example, more than one rule may be needed to simplify an expression.

Example 8 **Using Combinations of Rules**

Simplify each expression.

(a) $\left(\frac{2}{3}\right)^2 \cdot 2^3 = \frac{2^2}{3^2} \cdot \frac{2^3}{1}$ Power rule (c)

$= \frac{2^2 \cdot 2^3}{3^2 \cdot 1}$ Multiply fractions.

$= \frac{2^5}{3^2}$ Product rule

(b) $(5x)^3(5x)^4 = (5x)^7$ Product rule

$= 5^7x^7$ Power rule (b)

(c) $(2x^2y^3)^4(3xy^2)^3 = 2^4(x^2)^4(y^3)^4 \cdot 3^3x^3(y^2)^3$ Power rule (b)

$= 2^4 \cdot x^8 \cdot y^{12} \cdot 3^3 \cdot x^3 \cdot y^6$ Power rule (a)

$= 2^4 \cdot 3^3x^8x^3y^{12}y^6$ Commutative and associative properties

$= 16 \cdot 27x^{11}y^{18}$ Product rule

$= 432x^{11}y^{18}$

Continued on Next Page

7 Simplify. Assume all variables represent nonzero real numbers.

(a) $\left(\frac{5}{2}\right)^4$

(b) $\left(\frac{p}{q}\right)^2$

(c) $\left(\frac{r}{t}\right)^3$

ANSWERS

7. (a) $\frac{5^4}{2^4}$ **(b)** $\frac{p^2}{q^2}$ **(c)** $\frac{r^3}{t^3}$

(d) $(-x^3y)^2(-x^5y^4)^3$

Think of the negative sign in each factor as -1.

$$\begin{aligned}(-1x^3y)^2(-1x^5y^4)^3 &= (-1)^2(x^3)^2y^2 \cdot (-1)^3(x^5)^3(y^4)^3 && \text{Power rule (b)}\\ &= (-1)^2(x^6)(y^2)(-1)^3(x^{15})(y^{12}) && \text{Power rule (a)}\\ &= (-1)^5(x^{21})(y^{14}) && \text{Product rule}\\ &= -1x^{21}y^{14}\\ &= -x^{21}y^{14}\end{aligned}$$

CAUTION

Refer to Example 8(c). Notice that

$$(2x^2y^3)^4 = 2^4x^{2\cdot 4}y^{3\cdot 4}, \quad \textbf{not} \quad (2\cdot 4)x^{2\cdot 4}y^{3\cdot 4}.$$

Do not multiply the coefficient 2 and the exponent 4.

Work Problem 8 at the Side.

8 Simplify.

(a) $(2m)^3(2m)^4$

(b) $\left(\frac{5k^3}{3}\right)^2$

(c) $\left(\frac{1}{5}\right)^4(2x)^2$

(d) $(-3xy^2)^3(x^2y)^4$

ANSWERS

8. **(a)** 2^7m^7 **(b)** $\frac{5^2k^6}{3^2}$ **(c)** $\frac{2^2x^2}{5^4}$

(d) $-3^3x^{11}y^{10}$

6.2 EXERCISES

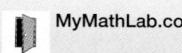

FOR EXTRA HELP: Student's Solutions Manual · MyMathLab.com · InterAct Math Tutorial Software · AW Math Tutor Center · www.mathxl.com · Digital Video Tutor CD 5 Videotape 11

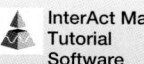

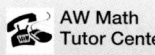

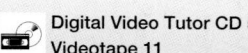

1. What exponent is understood on the base x in the expression xy^2? **1**

2. How are the expressions 3^2, 5^3, and 7^4 read? **three squared; five cubed; seven to the fourth power**

Decide whether each statement is true *or* false.

3. $3^3 = 9$ **false**

4. $(-2)^4 = 2^4$ **true**

5. $(a^2)^3 = a^5$ **false**

6. $\left(\frac{1}{4}\right)^2 = \frac{1}{4^2}$ **true**

Write each expression using exponents. See Example 1.

7. $(-2)(-2)(-2)(-2)(-2)$ **$(-2)^5$**

8. $w \cdot w \cdot w \cdot w \cdot w \cdot w$ **w^6**

9. $\left(\frac{1}{2}\right)\left(\frac{1}{2}\right)\left(\frac{1}{2}\right)\left(\frac{1}{2}\right)\left(\frac{1}{2}\right)\left(\frac{1}{2}\right)$ **$\left(\frac{1}{2}\right)^6$**

10. $\left(-\frac{1}{4}\right)\left(-\frac{1}{4}\right)\left(-\frac{1}{4}\right)\left(-\frac{1}{4}\right)\left(-\frac{1}{4}\right)$ **$\left(-\frac{1}{4}\right)^5$**

11. $(-8p)(-8p)$ **$(-8p)^2$**

12. $(-7x)(-7x)(-7x)(-7x)$ **$(-7x)^4$**

13. Explain how the expressions $(-3)^4$ and -3^4 are different.
The expression $(-3)^4 = (-3)(-3)(-3)(-3) = 81$, while $-3^4 = -(3 \cdot 3 \cdot 3 \cdot 3) = -81$.

14. Explain how the expressions $(5x)^3$ and $5x^3$ are different.
The expression $(5x)^3 = (5x)(5x)(5x) = 125x^3$, while $5x^3 = 5x \cdot x \cdot x \neq 125x^3$.

Identify the base and the exponent for each exponential expression. In Exercises 15–18, also evaluate the expression. See Example 2.

15. 3^5 **base: 3; exponent: 5; 243**

16. 2^7 **base: 2; exponent: 7; 128**

17. $(-3)^5$ **base: -3; exponent: 5; -243**

18. $(-2)^7$ **base: -2; exponent: 7; -128**

19. $(-6x)^4$ **base: $-6x$; exponent: 4**

20. $(-8x)^4$ **base: $-8x$; exponent: 4**

21. $-6x^4$ **base: x; exponent: 4**

22. $-8x^4$ **base: x; exponent: 4**

23. Explain why the product rule does not apply to the expression $5^2 + 5^3$. Then evaluate the expression by finding the individual powers and adding the results.
The product rule does not apply to $5^2 + 5^3$ because it is a *sum*, not a product. $5^2 + 5^3 = 25 + 125 = 150$

24. Explain why the product rule does not apply to the expression $3^2 \cdot 4^3$. Then evaluate the expression by finding the individual powers and multiplying the results.
The product rule applies only to exponential expressions with the same base. $3^2 \cdot 4^3 = 9 \cdot 64 = 576$

Use the product rule to simplify each expression. Write each answer in exponential form. See Examples 3 and 4.

25. $5^2 \cdot 5^6$ **5^8**

26. $3^6 \cdot 3^7$ **3^{13}**

27. $4^2 \cdot 4^7 \cdot 4^3$ **4^{12}**

28. $5^3 \cdot 5^8 \cdot 5^2$ **5^{13}**

29. $(-7)^3(-7)^6$ **$(-7)^9$**

30. $(-9)^8(-9)^5$ **$(-9)^{13}$**

31. $t^3 \cdot t^8 \cdot t^{13}$ **t^{24}**

32. $n^5 \cdot n^6 \cdot n^9$ **n^{20}**

33. $(-8r^4)(7r^3)$ **$-56r^7$**

34. $(10a^7)(-4a^3)$ **$-40a^{10}$**

35. $(-6p^5)(-7p^5)$ **$42p^{10}$**

36. $(-5w^8)(-9w^8)$ **$45w^{16}$**

For each group of terms, first add the given terms. Then start over and multiply them.

37. $5x^4, 9x^4$ $\quad 14x^4; 45x^8$

38. $8t^5, 3t^5$ $\quad 11t^5; 24t^{10}$

39. $-7a^2, 2a^2, 10a^2$ $\quad 5a^2; -140a^6$

40. $6x^3, 9x^3, -2x^3$ $\quad 13x^3; -108x^9$

Use the power rules for exponents to simplify each expression. Write each answer in exponential form. See Examples 5–7.

41. $(4^3)^2$ $\quad 4^6$

42. $(8^3)^6$ $\quad 8^{18}$

43. $(t^4)^5$ $\quad t^{20}$

44. $(y^6)^5$ $\quad y^{30}$

45. $(7r)^3$ $\quad 7^3r^3$

46. $(11x)^4$ $\quad 11^4x^4$

47. $(5xy)^5$ $\quad 5^5x^5y^5$

48. $(9pq)^6$ $\quad 9^6p^6q^6$

49. $8(qr)^3$ $\quad 8q^3r^3$

50. $4(vw)^5$ $\quad 4v^5w^5$

51. $\left(\frac{1}{2}\right)^3$ $\quad \frac{1}{2^3}$

52. $\left(\frac{1}{3}\right)^5$ $\quad \frac{1}{3^5}$

53. $\left(\frac{a}{b}\right)^3 \ (b \neq 0)$ $\quad \frac{a^3}{b^3}$

54. $\left(\frac{r}{t}\right)^4 \ (t \neq 0)$ $\quad \frac{r^4}{t^4}$

55. $\left(\frac{9}{5}\right)^8$ $\quad \frac{9^8}{5^8}$

56. $\left(\frac{12}{7}\right)^3$ $\quad \frac{12^3}{7^3}$

57. $(-2x^2y)^3$ $\quad (-2)^3x^6y^3$

58. $(-5m^4p^2)^3$ $\quad (-5)^3m^{12}p^6$

59. $(3a^3b^2)^2$ $\quad 3^2a^6b^4$

60. $(4x^3y^5)^4$ $\quad 4^4x^{12}y^{20}$

Find the area of each figure. Use the formulas found on the inside covers. (The small squares in the figures indicate 90° right angles.)

61. 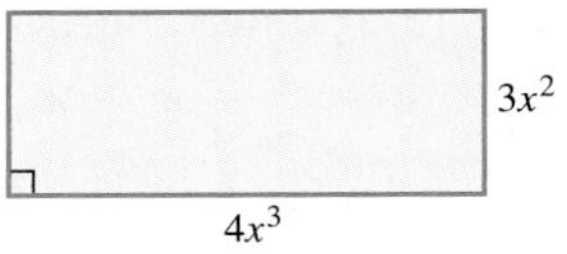

$12x^5$

62. 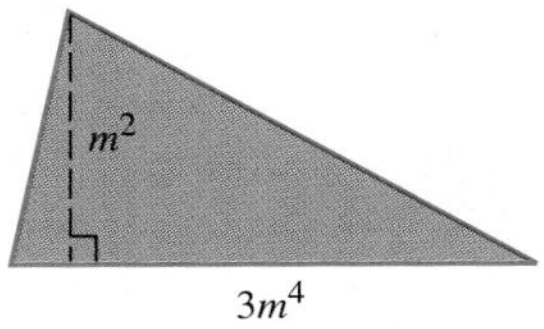

$\frac{3}{2}m^6$

Use a combination of the rules for exponents introduced in this section to simplify each expression. See Example 8.

63. $\left(\frac{5}{2}\right)^3 \cdot \left(\frac{5}{2}\right)^2$ $\quad \frac{5^5}{2^5}$

64. $\left(\frac{3}{4}\right)^5 \cdot \left(\frac{3}{4}\right)^6$ $\quad \frac{3^{11}}{4^{11}}$

65. $\left(\frac{9}{8}\right)^3 \cdot 9^2$ $\quad \frac{9^5}{8^3}$

66. $\left(\frac{8}{5}\right)^4 \cdot 8^3$ $\quad \frac{8^7}{5^4}$

67. $(2x)^9(2x)^3$ $\quad 2^{12}x^{12}$

68. $(6y)^5(6y)^8$ $\quad 6^{13}y^{13}$

69. $(-6p)^4(-6p)$ $\quad (-6)^5p^5$

70. $(-13q)^3(-13q)$ $\quad (-13)^4q^4$

71. $(6x^2y^3)^5$ $\quad 6^5x^{10}y^{15}$

72. $(5r^5t^6)^7$ $\quad 5^7r^{35}t^{42}$

73. $(x^2)^3(x^3)^5$ $\quad x^{21}$

74. $(y^4)^5(y^3)^5$ $\quad y^{35}$

75. $(2w^2x^3y)^2(x^4y)^5$ $\quad 2^2w^4x^{26}y^7$

76. $(3x^4y^2z)^3(yz^4)^5$ $\quad 3^3x^{12}y^{11}z^{23}$

77. $(-r^4s)^2(-r^2s^3)^5$ $\quad -r^{18}s^{17}$

78. $(-ts^6)^4(-t^3s^5)^3$ $\quad -t^{13}s^{39}$

79. $\left(\frac{5a^2b^5}{c^6}\right)^3 \ (c \neq 0)$ $\quad \frac{5^3a^6b^{15}}{c^{18}}$

80. $\left(\frac{6x^3y^9}{z^5}\right)^4 \ (z \neq 0)$ $\quad \frac{6^4x^{12}y^{36}}{z^{20}}$

81. $(-5m^3p^4q)^2(p^2q)^3$ $\quad 25m^6p^{14}q^5$

82. $(-a^4b^5)(-6a^3b^3)^2$ $\quad -36a^{10}b^{11}$

83. $(2x^2y^3z)^4(xy^2z^3)^2$ $\quad 16x^{10}y^{16}z^{10}$

6.3 Multiplying Polynomials

Objectives

1. Multiply a monomial and a polynomial.
2. Multiply two polynomials.
3. Multiply binomials by the FOIL method.

1 Multiply a monomial and a polynomial. As shown earlier, we find the product of two monomials by using the rules for exponents and the commutative and associative properties. For example,

$$(-8m^6)(-9n^6) = (-8)(-9)(m^6)(n^6) = 72m^6n^6.$$

CAUTION

Do not confuse *addition* of terms with *multiplication* of terms. For example,

$$7q^5 + 2q^5 = 9q^5, \quad \text{but} \quad (7q^5)(2q^5) = 7 \cdot 2q^{5+5} = 14q^{10}.$$

To find the product of a monomial and a polynomial with more than one term, we use the distributive property and multiplication of monomials.

Example 1 **Multiplying a Monomial and a Polynomial**

Use the distributive property to find each product.

(a) $4x^2(3x + 5)$

$$4x^2(3x+5) = 4x^2(3x) + 4x^2(5) \qquad \text{Distributive property}$$
$$= 12x^3 + 20x^2 \qquad \text{Multiply monomials.}$$

(b) $-8m^3(4m^3 + 3m^2 + 2m - 1)$

$$= -8m^3(4m^3) + (-8m^3)(3m^2)$$
$$+ (-8m^3)(2m) + (-8m^3)(-1) \qquad \text{Distributive property}$$
$$= -32m^6 - 24m^5 - 16m^4 + 8m^3 \qquad \text{Multiply monomials.}$$

Work Problem 1 at the Side.

1 Find each product.

(a) $5m^3(2m + 7)$

(b) $2x^4(3x^2 + 2x - 5)$

(c) $-4y^2(3y^3 + 2y^2 - 4y + 8)$

2 Multiply two polynomials. We can use the distributive property repeatedly to find the product of any two polynomials. For example, to find the product of the polynomials $x^2 + 3x + 5$ and $x - 4$, think of $x - 4$ as a single quantity and use the distributive property as follows.

$$(x^2 + 3x + 5)(x - 4) = x^2(x - 4) + 3x(x - 4) + 5(x - 4)$$

Now use the distributive property three times to find $x^2(x - 4)$, $3x(x - 4)$, and $5(x - 4)$.

$$x^2(x-4) + 3x(x-4) + 5(x-4)$$
$$= x^2(x) + x^2(-4) + 3x(x) + 3x(-4) + 5(x) + 5(-4)$$
$$= x^3 - 4x^2 + 3x^2 - 12x + 5x - 20 \qquad \text{Multiply monomials.}$$
$$= x^3 - x^2 - 7x - 20 \qquad \text{Combine terms.}$$

This example suggests the following rule.

Answers

1. (a) $10m^4 + 35m^3$ (b) $6x^6 + 4x^5 - 10x^4$ (c) $-12y^5 - 8y^4 + 16y^3 - 32y^2$

2 Multiply.

(a) $(m^3 - 2m + 1) \cdot (2m^2 + 4m + 3)$

(b) $(6p^2 + 2p - 4)(3p^2 - 5)$

ANSWERS
2. (a) $2m^5 + 4m^4 - m^3 - 6m^2 - 2m + 3$
(b) $18p^4 + 6p^3 - 42p^2 - 10p + 20$

Multiplying Polynomials

To multiply two polynomials, multiply each term of the second polynomial by each term of the first polynomial and add the products.

Example 2 Multiplying Two Polynomials

Multiply $(m^2 + 5)(4m^3 - 2m^2 + 4m)$.

Multiply each term of the second polynomial by each term of the first.

$$(m^2 + 5)(4m^3 - 2m^2 + 4m)$$
$$= m^2(4m^3) + m^2(-2m^2) + m^2(4m) + 5(4m^3) + 5(-2m^2) + 5(4m)$$
$$= 4m^5 - 2m^4 + 4m^3 + 20m^3 - 10m^2 + 20m$$

Now combine like terms.

$$= 4m^5 - 2m^4 + 24m^3 - 10m^2 + 20m$$

Work Problem 2 at the Side.

When at least one of the factors in a product of polynomials has three or more terms, the multiplication can be simplified by writing one polynomial above the other vertically.

Example 3 Multiplying Polynomials Vertically

Multiply $(x^3 + 2x^2 + 4x + 1)(3x + 5)$ using the vertical method.

Write the polynomials as follows.

$$\begin{array}{r} x^3 + 2x^2 + 4x + 1 \\ 3x + 5 \\ \hline \end{array}$$

It is not necessary to line up terms in columns, because any terms may be multiplied (not just like terms). Begin by multiplying each of the terms in the top row by 5.

$$\begin{array}{rl} x^3 + 2x^2 + 4x + 1 & \\ 3x + 5 & \\ \hline 5x^3 + 10x^2 + 20x + 5 & \quad 5(x^3 + 2x^2 + 4x + 1) \end{array}$$

Notice how this process is similar to multiplication of whole numbers. Now multiply each term in the top row by $3x$. Be careful to place like terms in columns, since the final step will involve addition (as in multiplying two whole numbers).

$$\begin{array}{rrrrrl} & x^3 & + 2x^2 & + 4x & + 1 & \\ & & & 3x & + 5 & \\ \hline & 5x^3 & + 10x^2 & + 20x & + 5 & \\ 3x^4 & + 6x^3 & + 12x^2 & + 3x & & \quad 3x(x^3 + 2x^2 + 4x + 1) \end{array}$$

Continued on Next Page

Add like terms.

$$\begin{array}{r} x^3 + 2x^2 + 4x + 1 \\ 3x + 5 \\ \hline 5x^3 + 10x^2 + 20x + 5 \\ 3x^4 + 6x^3 + 12x^2 + 3x \quad\; \\ \hline 3x^4 + 11x^3 + 22x^2 + 23x + 5 \end{array}$$

The product is $3x^4 + 11x^3 + 22x^2 + 23x + 5$.

Work Problem 3 at the Side.

Example 4 Multiplying Polynomials Vertically

Find the product of $4m^3 - 2m^2 + 4m$ and $\frac{1}{2}m^2 + \frac{5}{2}$.

$$\begin{array}{rl} 4m^3 - 2m^2 + 4m & \\ \frac{1}{2}m^2 + \frac{5}{2} & \\ \hline 10m^3 - 5m^2 + 10m & \text{Terms of top row multiplied by } \tfrac{5}{2} \\ 2m^5 - m^4 + 2m^3 \qquad\qquad\quad & \text{Terms of top row multiplied by } \tfrac{1}{2}m^2 \\ \hline 2m^5 - m^4 + 12m^3 - 5m^2 + 10m & \text{Add.} \end{array}$$

Work Problem 4 at the Side.

We can use a rectangle to model polynomial multiplication. For example, to find the product

$$(2x + 1)(3x + 2),$$

label a rectangle with each term as shown here.

	$3x$	2
$2x$		
1		

Now put the product of each pair of monomials in the appropriate box.

	$3x$	2
$2x$	$6x^2$	$4x$
1	$3x$	2

The product of the original binomials is the sum of these four monomial products.

$$\begin{aligned} (2x + 1)(3x + 2) &= 6x^2 + 4x + 3x + 2 \\ &= 6x^2 + 7x + 2 \end{aligned}$$

Work Problem 5 at the Side.

3 Multiply binomials by the FOIL method.

In algebra, many of the polynomials to be multiplied are both binomials (with just two terms). For these products, the **FOIL method** reduces the rectangle method to a systematic approach without the rectangle. To develop the FOIL method, we use the distributive property to find $(x + 3)(x + 5)$.

$$\begin{aligned} (x + 3)(x + 5) &= (x + 3)x + (x + 3)5 \\ &= x(x) + 3(x) + x(5) + 3(5) \\ &= x^2 + 3x + 5x + 15 \\ &= x^2 + 8x + 15 \end{aligned}$$

3 Find the product.

$$\begin{array}{r} 3x^2 + 4x - 5 \\ x + 4 \\ \hline \end{array}$$

4 Find each product.

(a) $$\begin{array}{r} k^3 - k^2 + k + 1 \\ \frac{2}{3}k - \frac{1}{3} \\ \hline \end{array}$$

(b) $$\begin{array}{r} a^3 + 3a - 4 \\ 2a^2 + 6a + 5 \\ \hline \end{array}$$

5 Use the rectangle method to find each product.

(a) $(4x + 3)(x + 2)$

	x	2
$4x$	$4x^2$	
3		

(b) $(x + 5)(x^2 + 3x + 1)$

ANSWERS

3. $3x^3 + 16x^2 + 11x - 20$

4. (a) $\frac{2}{3}k^4 - k^3 + k^2 + \frac{1}{3}k - \frac{1}{3}$
(b) $2a^5 + 6a^4 + 11a^3 + 10a^2 - 9a - 20$

5. (a) $4x^2 + 11x + 6$ **(b)** $x^3 + 8x^2 + 16x + 5$

Here is where the letters of the word FOIL originate.

$(x + 3)(x + 5)$	Multiply the **First** terms: $x(x)$.	F
$(x + 3)(x + 5)$	Multiply the **Outer** terms: $x(5)$. This is the **outer product**.	O
$(x + 3)(x + 5)$	Multiply the **Inner** terms: $3(x)$. This is the **inner product**.	I
$(x + 3)(x + 5)$	Multiply the **Last terms**: $3(5)$.	L

The inner product and the outer product should be added mentally so that the three terms of the answer can be written without extra steps as

$$(x + 3)(x + 5) = x^2 + 8x + 15.$$

Work Problem 6 at the Side.

A summary of the steps in the FOIL method follows.

Multiplying Binomials by the FOIL Method

Step 1 Multiply the two First terms of the binomials to get the first term of the answer.

Step 2 Find the Outer product and the Inner product and add them (when possible) to get the middle term of the answer.

Step 3 Multiply the two Last terms of the binomials to get the last term of the answer.

$$\text{F} = x^2 \qquad \text{L} = 15$$

$$(x + 3)(x + 5)$$

$$\text{I} = 3x$$
$$\underline{\text{O} = 5x}$$
$$8x \quad \text{Add.}$$

Example 5 Using the FOIL Method

Use the FOIL method to find the product $(x + 8)(x - 6)$.

Step 1 F Multiply the **first** terms.

$$x(x) = x^2$$

Step 2 O Find the **outer** product.

$$x(-6) = -6x$$

I Find the **inner** product.

$$8(x) = 8x$$

Add the outer and inner products mentally.

$$-6x + 8x = 2x$$

Step 3 L Multiply the **last** terms.

$$8(-6) = -48$$

Continued on Next Page

6 For the product $(2p - 5)(3p + 7)$, find the following.

(a) Product of first terms

(b) Outer product

(c) Inner product

(d) Product of last terms

(e) Complete product in simplified form

ANSWERS

6. **(a)** $2p(3p) = 6p^2$ **(b)** $2p(7) = 14p$ **(c)** $-5(3p) = -15p$ **(d)** $-5(7) = -35$ **(e)** $6p^2 - p - 35$

The product of $x + 8$ and $x - 6$ is the sum of the terms found in the three steps above, so

$$(x + 8)(x - 6) = x^2 + 2x - 48.$$

As a shortcut, this product can be found in the following manner.

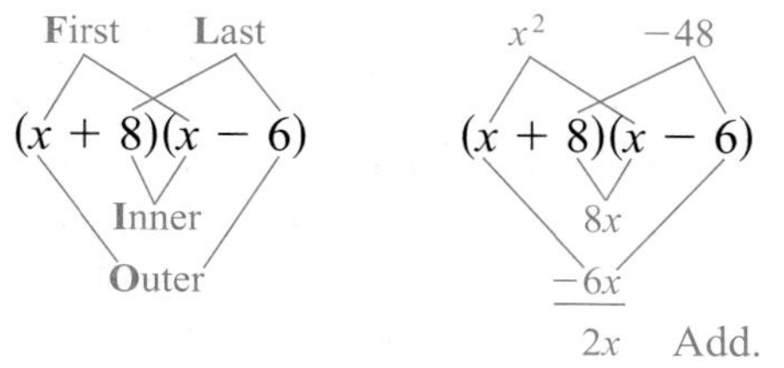

Work Problem 7 at the Side.

It is not possible to add the inner and outer products of the FOIL method if unlike terms result, as shown in the next example.

Example 6 Using the FOIL Method

Multiply $(9x - 2)(3y + 1)$.

First	$(9x - 2)(3y + 1)$	$27xy$	
Outer	$(9x - 2)(3y + 1)$	$9x$	Unlike terms
Inner	$(9x - 2)(3y + 1)$	$-6y$	
Last	$(9x - 2)(3y + 1)$	-2	

F O I L

$$(9x - 2)(3y + 1) = 27xy + 9x - 6y - 2$$

Example 7 Using the FOIL Method

Find each product.

F O I L

(a) $(2k + 5y)(k + 3y) = 2k(k) + 2k(3y) + 5y(k) + 5y(3y)$

$= 2k^2 + 6ky + 5ky + 15y^2$

$= 2k^2 + 11ky + 15y^2$

(b) $(7p + 2q)(3p - q) = 21p^2 - pq - 2q^2$ FOIL

(c) $2x^2(x - 3)(3x + 4) = 2x^2(3x^2 - 5x - 12)$ FOIL

$= 6x^4 - 10x^3 - 24x^2$ Distributive property

Work Problem 8 at the Side.

NOTE

Example 7(c) showed one way to multiply three polynomials. We could have multiplied $2x^2$ and $x - 3$ first, then multiplied that product and $3x + 4$ as follows.

$$2x^2(x - 3)(3x + 4) = (2x^3 - 6x^2)(3x + 4) = 6x^4 - 10x^3 - 24x^2$$

7 Use the FOIL method to find each product.

(a) $(m + 4)(m - 3)$

(b) $(y + 7)(y + 2)$

(c) $(r - 8)(r - 5)$

8 Find each product.

(a) $(4k - 1)(2k + 3)$

(b) $(6m + 5)(m - 4)$

(c) $(3r + 2t)(3r + 4t)$

(d) $y^2(8y + 3)(2y + 1)$

Answers

7. **(a)** $m^2 + m - 12$ **(b)** $y^2 + 9y + 14$ **(c)** $r^2 - 13r + 40$

8. **(a)** $8k^2 + 10k - 3$ **(b)** $6m^2 - 19m - 20$ **(c)** $9r^2 + 18rt + 8t^2$ **(d)** $16y^4 + 14y^3 + 3y^2$

Focus on Real-Data Applications

Algebra as Generalized Arithmetic

The rules of algebra are consistent with those for arithmetic. To learn a method for multiplying binomial factors, such as $(3x + 2)(4x + 1)$, we can observe the method for multiplying two-digit numbers, such as $32 \cdot 41$. The number 32 is shorthand for the expanded number $3 \cdot 10 + 2$, and the number 41 is shorthand for $4 \cdot 10 + 1$. So, multiplying $32 \cdot 41$ is the same as multiplying $(3 \cdot 10 + 2)(4 \cdot 10 + 1)$.

1. An expanded version of the usual algorithm is shown in the first column below. Each partial product, such as 1×2 and 40×30, is shown to clarify how it contributes to the process.
2. In the standard algorithm, it is clear that the 32 represents the sum of 1×2 and 1×30, and 1280 represents the sum of 40×2 and 40×30.
3. When FOIL is used to multiply the numbers, the term $11 \cdot 10$ represents the sum of the partial products 1×30 and 40×2. When we simplify $12 \cdot 10^2 + 11 \cdot 10 + 2$, the result is 1312.
4. When FOIL is used to multiply the binomials, each term exactly matches the corresponding term from the multiplication of the numbers.

Partial Products Multiplication Algorithm	Standard Algorithm	FOIL Method for Numbers	FOIL Method for Variables
32	32	$(3 \cdot 10 + 2)(4 \cdot 10 + 1)$	$(3x + 2)(4x + 1)$
$\times\ 41$	$\times\ 41$	$12 \cdot 10^2 + 3 \cdot 10 + 8 \cdot 10 + 2$	$12x^2 + 3x + 8x + 2$
$2 = 1 \times 2$	32	$12 \cdot 10^2 + 11 \cdot 10 + 2$	$12x^2 + 11x + 2$
$30 = 1 \times 30$	1280	$1200 + 110 + 2$	
$80 = 40 \times 2$	1312	1312	
$1200 = 40 \times 30$			
1312			

For Group Discussion

Use FOIL to compute each binomial product and corresponding arithmetic product. Verify that the results of the arithmetic product are valid. For the numerical problems, write the correct *signed* product for each term.

1. $(2x + 1)(2x - 3)$ and $(2 \cdot 10 + 1)(2 \cdot 10 - 3)$, which is $21 \cdot 17$
   Does the arithmetic FOIL result simplify to the correct answer?
   $4x^2 - 4x - 3$; $4 \cdot 10^2 - 4 \cdot 10 - 3$; $400 - 40 - 3 = 357$; yes
2. $(4x - 2)(2x + 5)$ and $(4 \cdot 10 - 2)(2 \cdot 10 + 5)$, which is $38 \cdot 25$
   Does the arithmetic FOIL result simplify to the correct answer?
   $8x^2 + 16x - 10$; $8 \cdot 10^2 + 16 \cdot 10 - 10$; $800 + 160 - 10 = 950$; yes
3. $(7x - 3)(5x - 4)$ and $(7 \cdot 10 - 3)(5 \cdot 10 - 4)$, which is $67 \cdot 46$
   Does the arithmetic FOIL result simplify to the correct answer?
   $35x^2 - 43x + 12$; $35 \cdot 10^2 - 43 \cdot 10 + 12$; $3500 - 430 + 12 = 3082$; yes
4. A mental trick for multiplying two-digit numbers, such as $27 \cdot 18$, follows: "Multiply the ones ($7 \times 8 = 56$). Write the 6 in the ones place, and carry the 5. Add the inner product (7×1), the outer product (2×8), and the carried 5 ($7 + 16 + 5 = 28$). Write the 8 in the tens place, and carry the 2. Multiply the tens (2×1), and add to the carried 2. Write 4 in the hundreds place. The answer is 486." Why does the trick work? **It is FOIL in reverse order—LIOF.**

Teaching notes for this activity are provided in the *Printed Test Bank and Instructor's Resource Guide.*

6.3 EXERCISES

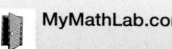

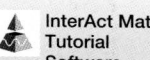

FOR EXTRA HELP: Student's Solutions Manual | MyMathLab.com | InterAct Math Tutorial Software | AW Math Tutor Center | www.mathxl.com | Digital Video Tutor CD 5 Videotape 11

Find each product using the rectangle method shown in the text.

1. $(x + 3)(x + 4)$
$x^2 + 7x + 12$

2. $(x + 5)(x + 2)$
$x^2 + 7x + 10$

3. $(2x + 1)(x^2 + 3x + 2)$
$2x^3 + 7x^2 + 7x + 2$

4. $(x + 4)(3x^2 + 2x + 1)$
$3x^3 + 14x^2 + 9x + 4$

5. In multiplying a monomial by a polynomial, such as in $4x(3x^2 + 7x^3) = 4x(3x^2) + 4x(7x^3)$, the first property that is used is the distributive property.

6. Match each product in parts (a)–(d) with the correct polynomial in choices A–D.

(a) $(x - 5)(x + 3)$ C **(b)** $(x + 5)(x + 3)$ A **(c)** $(x - 5)(x - 3)$ B **(d)** $(x + 5)(x - 3)$ D

A. $x^2 + 8x + 15$ **B.** $x^2 - 8x + 15$ **C.** $x^2 - 2x - 15$ **D.** $x^2 + 2x - 15$

Find each product. See Example 1.

7. $-2m(3m + 2)$
$-6m^2 - 4m$

8. $-5p(6 + 3p)$
$-30p - 15p^2$

9. $\frac{3}{4}p(8 - 6p + 12p^3)$
$6p - \frac{9}{2}p^2 + 9p^4$

10. $\frac{4}{3}x(3 + 2x + 5x^3)$
$4x + \frac{8}{3}x^2 + \frac{20}{3}x^4$

11. $2y^5(3 + 2y + 5y^4)$
$6y^5 + 4y^6 + 10y^9$

12. $2m^4(3m^2 + 5m + 6)$
$6m^6 + 10m^5 + 12m^4$

Find each product. See Examples 2–4.

13. $(6x + 1)(2x^2 + 4x + 1)$
$12x^3 + 26x^2 + 10x + 1$

14. $(9y - 2)(8y^2 - 6y + 1)$
$72y^3 - 70y^2 + 21y - 2$

15. $(4m + 3)(5m^3 - 4m^2 + m - 5)$
$20m^4 - m^3 - 8m^2 - 17m - 15$

16. $(y + 4)(3y^3 - 2y^2 + y + 3)$
$3y^4 + 10y^3 - 7y^2 + 7y + 12$

17. $(2x - 1)(3x^5 - 2x^3 + x^2 - 2x + 3)$
$6x^6 - 3x^5 - 4x^4 + 4x^3 - 5x^2 + 8x - 3$

18. $(2a + 3)(a^4 - a^3 + a^2 - a + 1)$
$2a^5 + a^4 - a^3 + a^2 - a + 3$

19. $(5x^2 + 2x + 1)(x^2 - 3x + 5)$
$5x^4 - 13x^3 + 20x^2 + 7x + 5$

20. $(2m^2 + m - 3)(m^2 - 4m + 5)$
$2m^4 - 7m^3 + 3m^2 + 17m - 15$

Find each binomial product using the FOIL method. See Examples 5–7.

21. $(n - 2)(n + 3)$
$n^2 + n - 6$

22. $(r - 6)(r + 8)$
$r^2 + 2r - 48$

23. $(4r + 1)(2r - 3)$
$8r^2 - 10r - 3$

24. $(5x + 2)(2x - 7)$
$10x^2 - 31x - 14$

25. $(3x + 2)(3x - 2)$
$9x^2 - 4$

26. $(7x + 3)(7x - 3)$
$49x^2 - 9$

27. $(3q + 1)(3q + 1)$
$9q^2 + 6q + 1$

28. $(4w + 7)(4w + 7)$
$16w^2 + 56w + 49$

29. $(3t + 4s)(2t + 5s)$
$6t^2 + 23st + 20s^2$

30. $(8v + 5w)(2v + 3w)$
$16v^2 + 34vw + 15w^2$

31. $(-.3t + .4)(t + .6)$
$-.3t^2 + .22t + .24$

32. $(-.5x + .9)(x - .2)$
$-.5x^2 + x - .18$

33. $\left(x - \frac{2}{3}\right)\left(x + \frac{1}{4}\right)$
$x^2 - \frac{5}{12}x - \frac{1}{6}$

34. $\left(-\frac{8}{3} + 3k\right)\left(-\frac{2}{3} - k\right)$
$\frac{16}{9} + \frac{2}{3}k - 3k^2$

35. $\left(-\frac{5}{4} + 2r\right)\left(-\frac{3}{4} - r\right)$
$\frac{15}{16} - \frac{1}{4}r - 2r^2$

36. $2m^3(4m - 1)(2m + 3)$
$16m^5 + 20m^4 - 6m^3$

37. $3y^3(2y + 3)(y - 5)$
$6y^5 - 21y^4 - 45y^3$

38. $5t^4(t + 3)(3t - 1)$
$15t^6 + 40t^5 - 15t^4$

RELATING CONCEPTS (Exercises 39–44) FOR INDIVIDUAL OR GROUP WORK

Work Exercises 39–44 in order. *(All units are in yards.) Refer to the figure as necessary.*

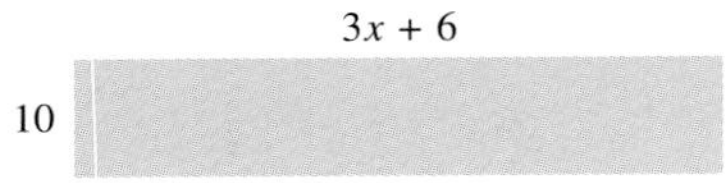

39. Find a polynomial that represents the area of the rectangle. $30x + 60$ yd^2

40. Suppose you know that the area of the rectangle is 600 yd^2. Use this information and the polynomial from Exercise 39 to write an equation in x, and solve it.
$30x + 60 = 600$; 18

41. What are the dimensions of the rectangle?
10 yd by 60 yd

42. Suppose the rectangle represents a lawn and it costs \$3.50 per square yard to lay sod on the lawn. How much will it cost to sod the entire lawn? \$2100

43. Use the result of Exercise 41 to find the perimeter of the lawn. 140 yd

44. Again, suppose the rectangle represents a lawn and it costs \$9.00 per yard to fence the lawn. How much will it cost to fence the lawn? \$1260

---

45. Perform the following multiplications: $(x + 4)(x - 4)$; $(y + 2)(y - 2)$; $(r + 7)(r - 7)$. Observe your answers, and explain the pattern that can be found in the answers.
The answers are $x^2 - 16$, $y^2 - 4$, and $r^2 - 49$. Each product is the difference of the square of the first term and the square of the last term of the binomials.

46. Repeat Exercise 45 for the following: $(x + 4)(x + 4)$; $(y - 2)(y - 2)$; $(r + 7)(r + 7)$.
The answers are $x^2 + 8x + 16$, $y^2 - 4y + 4$, and $r^2 + 14r + 49$. Each product is the sum of the square of the first term, twice the product of the two terms, and the square of the last term of the binomials.

6.4 Special Products

In this section, we develop shortcuts to find certain binomial products that occur frequently.

Objectives

1. Square binomials.
2. Find the product of the sum and difference of two terms.
3. Find higher powers of binomials.

1 Square binomials. The square of a binomial can be found quickly by using the method shown in Example 1.

Example 1 Squaring a Binomial

Find $(m + 3)^2$.

Squaring $m + 3$ by the FOIL method gives

$$(m + 3)(m + 3) = m^2 + 3m + 3m + 9$$
$$= m^2 + 6m + 9.$$

The result has the squares of the first and the last terms of the binomial:

$$m^2 = m^2 \quad \text{and} \quad 3^2 = 9.$$

The middle term is twice the product of the two terms of the binomial, since the outer and inner products are $m(3)$ and $3(m)$, and

$$m(3) + 3(m) = 2(m)(3) = 6m.$$

Work Problem 1 at the Side.

This example suggests the following rules.

Square of a Binomial

The square of a binomial is a trinomial consisting of the square of the first term, plus twice the product of the two terms, plus the square of the last term of the binomial. For a and b,

$$(a + b)^2 = a^2 + 2ab + b^2.$$

Also, $$(a - b)^2 = a^2 - 2ab + b^2.$$

Example 2 Squaring Binomials

Use the rules to square each binomial.

$$(a - b)^2 = a^2 - 2 \cdot a \cdot b + b^2$$

(a) $(5z - 1)^2 = (5z)^2 - 2(5z)(1) + (1)^2$

$= 25z^2 - 10z + 1$ $\qquad (5z)^2 = 5^2z^2 = 25z^2$

(b) $(3b + 5r)^2 = (3b)^2 + 2(3b)(5r) + (5r)^2$

$= 9b^2 + 30br + 25r^2$

(c) $(2a - 9x)^2 = 4a^2 - 36ax + 81x^2$

(d) $\left(4m + \frac{1}{2}\right)^2 = (4m)^2 + 2(4m)\left(\frac{1}{2}\right) + \left(\frac{1}{2}\right)^2$

$= 16m^2 + 4m + \frac{1}{4}$

1 Consider the binomial $x + 4$.

(a) What is the first term of the binomial? Square it.

(b) What is the last term of the binomial? Square it.

(c) Find twice the product of the two terms of the binomial.

(d) Find $(x + 4)^2$.

Answers

1. (a) x; x^2 **(b)** 4; 16 **(c)** $8x$
(d) $x^2 + 8x + 16$

Notice that in the square of a sum all of the terms are positive, as in Examples 2(b) and (d). In the square of a difference, the middle term is negative, as in Examples 2(a) and (c).

CAUTION

A common error when squaring a binomial is to forget the middle term of the product. In general,

$$(a + b)^2 \neq a^2 + b^2.$$

Work Problem 2 at the Side.

2 Find the product of the sum and difference of two terms. Binomial products of the form $(a + b)(a - b)$ also occur frequently. In these products, one binomial is the sum of two terms, and the other is the difference of the same two terms. For example, the product of $x + 2$ and $x - 2$ is

$$\begin{aligned}(x + 2)(x - 2) &= x^2 - 2x + 2x - 4\\ &= x^2 - 4.\end{aligned}$$

As this example suggests, the product of $a + b$ and $a - b$ is the difference between two squares.

Product of the Sum and Difference of Two Terms

$$(a + b)(a - b) = a^2 - b^2$$

Example 3 **Finding the Product of the Sum and Difference of Two Terms**

Find each product.

(a) $(x + 4)(x - 4)$

Use the rule for the product of the sum and difference of two terms.

$$(x + 4)(x - 4) = x^2 - 4^2 = x^2 - 16$$

(b) $\left(\frac{2}{3} - w\right)\left(\frac{2}{3} + w\right)$

By the commutative property, this product is the same as $\left(\frac{2}{3} + w\right)\left(\frac{2}{3} - w\right)$.

$$\left(\frac{2}{3} - w\right)\left(\frac{2}{3} + w\right) = \left(\frac{2}{3} + w\right)\left(\frac{2}{3} - w\right) = \left(\frac{2}{3}\right)^2 - w^2 = \frac{4}{9} - w^2$$

Example 4 **Finding the Product of the Sum and Difference of Two Terms**

Find each product.

$$\begin{matrix}(a & + b) & (a & - b)\\ \downarrow & \downarrow & \downarrow & \downarrow\end{matrix}$$

(a) $(5m + 3)(5m - 3)$

Use the rule for the product of the sum and difference of two terms.

$$\begin{aligned}(5m + 3)(5m - 3) &= (5m)^2 - 3^2\\ &= 25m^2 - 9\end{aligned}$$

Continued on Next Page

2 Find each square by using the rules for the square of a binomial.

(a) $(t + u)^2$

(b) $(2m - p)^2$

(c) $(4p + 3q)^2$

(d) $(5r - 6s)^2$

(e) $\left(3k - \frac{1}{2}\right)^2$

ANSWERS

2. **(a)** $t^2 + 2tu + u^2$
(b) $4m^2 - 4mp + p^2$
(c) $16p^2 + 24pq + 9q^2$
(d) $25r^2 - 60rs + 36s^2$
(e) $9k^2 - 3k + \frac{1}{4}$

(b) $(4x + y)(4x - y) = (4x)^2 - y^2$

$= 16x^2 - y^2$

(c) $\left(z - \frac{1}{4}\right)\left(z + \frac{1}{4}\right) = z^2 - \frac{1}{16}$

Work Problem 3 at the Side.

The product rules of this section will be important later, particularly in Chapters 7 and 8. Therefore, it is important to memorize these rules and practice using them.

3 Find higher powers of binomials. The methods used in the previous section and this section can be combined to find higher powers of binomials.

Example 5 Finding Higher Powers of Binomials

Find each product.

(a) $(x + 5)^3 = (x + 5)^2(x + 5)$ — $a^3 = a^2 \cdot a$

$= (x^2 + 10x + 25)(x + 5)$ — Square the binomial.

$= x^3 + 10x^2 + 25x + 5x^2 + 50x + 125$ — Multiply polynomials.

$= x^3 + 15x^2 + 75x + 125$ — Combine like terms.

(b) $(2y - 3)^4 = (2y - 3)^2(2y - 3)^2$ — $a^4 = a^2 \cdot a^2$

$= (4y^2 - 12y + 9)(4y^2 - 12y + 9)$ — Square each binomial.

$= 16y^4 - 48y^3 + 36y^2 - 48y^3 + 144y^2$ — Multiply polynomials.
$- 108y + 36y^2 - 108y + 81$

$= 16y^4 - 96y^3 + 216y^2 - 216y + 81$ — Combine like terms.

Work Problem 4 at the Side.

3 Find each product by using the rule for the sum and difference of two terms.

(a) $(6a + 3)(6a - 3)$

(b) $(10m + 7)(10m - 7)$

(c) $(7p + 2q)(7p - 2q)$

(d) $\left(3r - \frac{1}{2}\right)\left(3r + \frac{1}{2}\right)$

4 Find each product.

(a) $(m + 1)^3$

(b) $(3k - 2)^4$

Answers

3. (a) $36a^2 - 9$ **(b)** $100m^2 - 49$

(c) $49p^2 - 4q^2$ **(d)** $9r^2 - \frac{1}{4}$

4. (a) $m^3 + 3m^2 + 3m + 1$

(b) $81k^4 - 216k^3 + 216k^2 - 96k + 16$

Focus on

Real-Data Applications

Using a Rule of Thumb

A Dynamic Homes neighborhood features variations of three models of houses. Each buyer has an option to purchase a concrete patio extension, constructed to his or her choice of size. Each of the three models is designed so that the patio will be in the shape of a large square that is missing a corner square, similar to the diagram shown on the left. The size of the removed corner and the length of the patio vary from model to model, as does the size of the entire patio. To determine the dimensions of the patio, the rectangle of size $b \times (a - b)$ in the middle patio diagram can be rotated and repositioned to form the rectangle shown on the right, with length $a + b$ and width $a - b$.

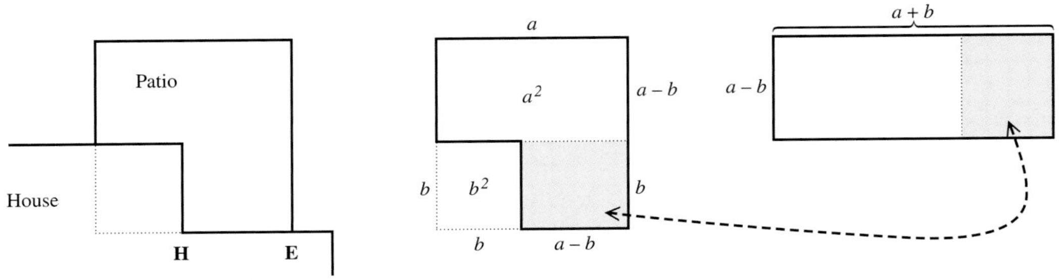

Since every time a house is sold the salesperson must ask the construction supervisor to calculate the cost of the patio extension, the supervisor devises a *rule of thumb* based on the quantity $(a + b)(a - b)$. There are only three possible choices for the value of b, one for each model house. This means that the salesperson needs to know only one additional measurement—the distance from the corner H to the edge of the patio E, which is $a - b$. The thickness of the patio is $\frac{1}{3}$ ft. The cost of concrete is \$58.00 per yd^3. (*Source:* Dunham Price, Inc., Westlake, LA.) There is a 100% markup in price to cover profit as well as costs for ground preparation, building forms, and finishing the concrete, giving a cost factor of \$116.00 per yd^3.

For Group Discussion

1. Why is knowing the values for b and $a - b$ sufficient for finding the quantity $a + b$?

   $(a - b) + 2b = a + b$

2. Explain why the area of the patio can be written both as $(a + b)(a - b)$ and $a^2 - b^2$.

   The area of a rectangle is length × width, which is $(a + b)(a - b)$. The area of the patio is the difference between the large and small squares, or $a^2 - b^2$.

3. Apply the construction supervisor's rule of thumb to the three examples given in the table.

   To calculate the total cost for a patio with long side of length a ft, use the table and work from left to right. The second-to-last column is the volume of concrete needed, and the last column is the total cost of the patio. Round to the next tenth.

						VOLUME	COST
House Model	Corner Length b ft	Corner Length Doubled $2b$	Distance from Corner H to Patio Edge E $a - b$	Add Previous Two Columns $2b + (a - b)$	Multiply Previous Two Columns $(a + b)(a - b)$	Multiply Previous Column by $\frac{1}{3}$ and Divide by 27	Multiply Previous Column by Cost Factor of \$116.00
A	5	10	10	20	200	2.5 yd^3	\$290.00
B	6	12	12	24	288	3.6 yd^3	\$417.60
C	8	16	14	30	420	5.2 yd^3	\$603.20

Teaching notes for this activity are provided in the *Printed Test Bank and Instructor's Resource Guide*.

6.4 EXERCISES

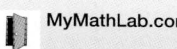

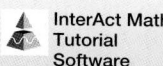

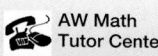

FOR EXTRA HELP: Student's Solutions Manual | MyMathLab.com | InterAct Math Tutorial Software | AW Math Tutor Center | MathXL www.mathxl.com | Digital Video Tutor CD 5 Videotape 11

1. Consider the square $(2x + 3)^2$.

(a) What is the square of the first term, $(2x)^2$? $4x^2$

(b) What is twice the product of the two terms, $2(2x)(3)$? $12x$

(c) What is the square of the last term, 3^2? 9

(d) Write the final product, which is a trinomial, using your results from parts (a)–(c). $4x^2 + 12x + 9$

2. Repeat Exercise 1 for the square $(3x - 2)^2$.

(a) $9x^2$ (b) $-12x$ (c) 4 (d) $9x^2 - 12x + 4$

Find each square. See Examples 1 and 2.

3. $(a - c)^2$
$a^2 - 2ac + c^2$

4. $(p - y)^2$
$p^2 - 2py + y^2$

5. $(p + 2)^2$
$p^2 + 4p + 4$

6. $(r + 5)^2$
$r^2 + 10r + 25$

7. $(4x - 3)^2$
$16x^2 - 24x + 9$

8. $(5y + 2)^2$
$25y^2 + 20y + 4$

9. $(.8t + .7s)^2$
$.64t^2 + 1.12ts + .49s^2$

10. $(.7z - .3w)^2$
$.49z^2 - .42zw + .09w^2$

11. $\left(5x + \frac{2}{5}y\right)^2$
$25x^2 + 4xy + \frac{4}{25}y^2$

12. $\left(6m - \frac{4}{5}n\right)^2$
$36m^2 - \frac{48}{5}mn + \frac{16}{25}n^2$

13. $\left(4a - \frac{3}{2}b\right)^2$
$16a^2 - 12ab + \frac{9}{4}b^2$

14. $x(2x + 5)^2$
$4x^3 + 20x^2 + 25x$

15. $-(4r - 2)^2$
$-16r^2 + 16r - 4$

16. $-(3y - 8)^2$
$-9y^2 + 48y - 64$

17. Consider the product $(7x + 3y)(7x - 3y)$.

(a) What is the product of the first terms, $7x(7x)$? $49x^2$

(b) Multiply the outer terms, $7x(-3y)$. Then multiply the inner terms, $3y(7x)$. Add the results. What is this sum? 0

(c) What is the product of the last terms, $3y(-3y)$? $-9y^2$

(d) Write the complete product using your answers in parts (a) and (c). $49x^2 - 9y^2$
Why is the sum found in part (b) omitted here?

Because 0 is the identity element for addition, it is not necessary to write "+ 0."

18. Repeat Exercise 17 for the product $(5x + 7y)(5x - 7y)$.

(a) $25x^2$ (b) 0 (c) $-49y^2$ (d) $25x^2 - 49y^2$; Because 0 is the identity element for addition, it is not necessary to write "+ 0."

Find each product. See Examples 3 and 4.

19. $(q + 2)(q - 2)$
$q^2 - 4$

20. $(x + 8)(x - 8)$
$x^2 - 64$

21. $(2w + 5)(2w - 5)$
$4w^2 - 25$

22. $(3z + 8)(3z - 8)$
$9z^2 - 64$

23. $(10x + 3y)(10x - 3y)$
$100x^2 - 9y^2$

24. $(13r + 2z)(13r - 2z)$
$169r^2 - 4z^2$

25. $(2x^2 - 5)(2x^2 + 5)$
$4x^4 - 25$

26. $(9y^2 - 2)(9y^2 + 2)$
$81y^4 - 4$

27. $\left(7x + \frac{3}{7}\right)\left(7x - \frac{3}{7}\right)$
$49x^2 - \frac{9}{49}$

28. $\left(9y + \frac{2}{3}\right)\left(9y - \frac{2}{3}\right)$
$81y^2 - \frac{4}{9}$

29. $p(3p + 7)(3p - 7)$
$9p^3 - 49p$

30. $q(5q - 1)(5q + 1)$
$25q^3 - q$

RELATING CONCEPTS (Exercises 31–40) FOR INDIVIDUAL OR GROUP WORK

Special products can be illustrated by using areas of rectangles. Use the figure and ***work Exercises 31–36 in order*** *to justify the special product* $(a + b)^2 = a^2 + 2ab + b^2$.

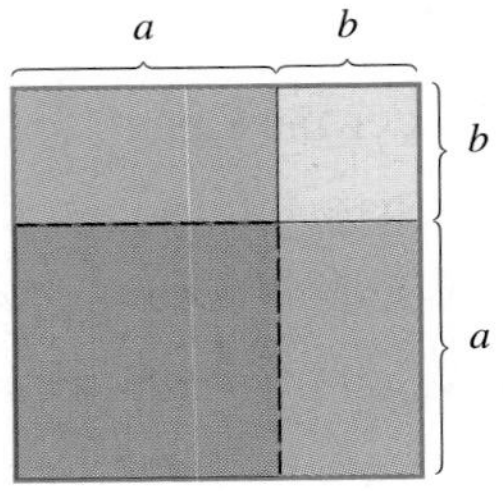

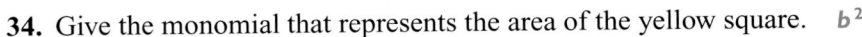

31. Express the area of the large square as the square of a binomial. $(a + b)^2$

32. Give the monomial that represents the area of the red square. a^2

33. Give the monomial that represents the sum of the areas of the blue rectangles.
$2ab$

34. Give the monomial that represents the area of the yellow square. b^2

35. What is the sum of the monomials you obtained in Exercises 32–34?
$a^2 + 2ab + b^2$

36. Explain why the binomial square you found in Exercise 31 must equal the polynomial you found in Exercise 35.
They both represent the area of the entire large square.

To understand how the special product $(a + b)^2 = a^2 + 2ab + b^2$ *can be applied to a purely numerical problem,* ***work Exercises 37–40 in order.***

37. Evaluate 35^2 using either traditional paper-and-pencil methods or a calculator. 1225

38. The number 35 can be written as $30 + 5$. Therefore, $35^2 = (30 + 5)^2$. Use the special product for squaring a binomial with $a = 30$ and $b = 5$ to write an expression for $(30 + 5)^2$. Do not simplify at this time. $30^2 + 2(30)(5) + 5^2$

39. Use the order of operations to simplify the expression you found in Exercise 38. 1225

40. How do the answers in Exercises 37 and 39 compare? They are equal.

Find each product. See Example 5.

41. $(m - 5)^3$
$m^3 - 15m^2 + 75m - 125$

42. $(p + 3)^3$
$p^3 + 9p^2 + 27p + 27$

43. $(2a + 1)^3$
$8a^3 + 12a^2 + 6a + 1$

44. $(3m - 1)^3$
$27m^3 - 27m^2 + 9m - 1$

45. $(3r - 2t)^4$
$81r^4 - 216r^3t + 216r^2t^2 - 96rt^3 + 16t^4$

46. $(2z + 5y)^4$
$16z^4 + 160z^3y + 600z^2y^2 + 1000zy^3 + 625y^4$

47. Explain how the expressions $x^2 + y^2$ and $(x + y)^2$ differ.
$x^2 + y^2$ is the sum of squares, while $(x + y)^2$ is the square of a sum. $(x + y)^2 = x^2 + 2xy + y^2$, and thus contains another term, $2xy$.

48. Does $a^3 + b^3$ equal $(a + b)^3$? Explain your answer.
In general, they are not equal, because $(a + b)^3 = a^3 + 3a^2b + 3ab^2 + b^3$.

In Exercises 49 and 50, refer to the figure shown here.

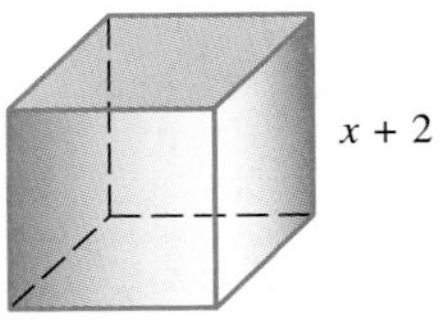

49. Find a polynomial that represents the volume of the cube.
$x^3 + 6x^2 + 12x + 8$

50. If the value of x is 6, what is the volume of the cube?
512 cu. units

6.5 INTEGER EXPONENTS AND THE QUOTIENT RULE

OBJECTIVES

1. Use 0 as an exponent.
2. Use negative numbers as exponents.
3. Use the quotient rule for exponents.
4. Use combinations of rules.

In Section 6.2 we studied the product rule for exponents. In all our earlier work, exponents were positive integers. Now we want to develop meaning for exponents that are not positive integers.

Consider the following list of exponential expressions.

$$2^4 = 16$$
$$2^3 = 8$$
$$2^2 = 4$$

Do you see the pattern in the values? Each time we reduce the exponent by 1, the value is divided by 2 (the base). Using this pattern, we can continue the list to smaller and smaller integer exponents.

$$2^1 = 2$$
$$2^0 = 1$$
$$2^{-1} = \frac{1}{2}$$

Work Problem 1 at the Side.

1 Continue the list of exponentials using -2, -3, and -4 as exponents.

$2^{-2} =$ ______

$2^{-3} =$ ______

$2^{-4} =$ ______

From the preceding list and the answers to Problem 1, it appears that we should define 2^0 as 1 and negative exponents as reciprocals.

1 Use 0 as an exponent. We want the definitions of 0 and negative exponents to satisfy the rules for exponents from Section 6.2. For example, if $6^0 = 1$,

$$6^0 \cdot 6^2 = 1 \cdot 6^2 = 6^2 \quad \text{and} \quad 6^0 \cdot 6^2 = 6^{0+2} = 6^2,$$

so the product rule is satisfied. Check that the power rules are also valid for a 0 exponent. Thus, we define a 0 exponent as follows.

Zero Exponent

For any nonzero real number a, $a^0 = 1$.

Example: $17^0 = 1$.

Example 1 Using Zero Exponents

Evaluate each exponential expression.

(a) $60^0 = 1$

(b) $(-60)^0 = 1$

(c) $-60^0 = -(1) = -1$

(d) $y^0 = 1$, if $y \neq 0$

(e) $6y^0 = 6(1) = 6$, if $y \neq 0$

(f) $(6y)^0 = 1$, if $y \neq 0$

CAUTION

Notice the difference between parts (b) and (c) of Example 1. In Example 1(b) the base is -60 and the exponent is 0. Any nonzero base raised to the exponent zero is 1. But in Example 1(c), the base is 60. Then $60^0 = 1$, and $-60^0 = -1$.

ANSWERS

1. $2^{-2} = \frac{1}{4}$; $2^{-3} = \frac{1}{8}$; $2^{-4} = \frac{1}{16}$

2 Evaluate.

(a) 28^0

(b) $(-16)^0$

(c) -7^0

(d) $m^0, m \neq 0$

(e) $-p^0, p \neq 0$

ANSWERS
2. (a) 1 **(b)** 1 **(c)** -1 **(d)** 1 **(e)** -1

Work Problem 2 at the Side.

2 Use negative numbers as exponents. From the lists at the beginning of this section and margin problem 1, since $2^{-2} = \frac{1}{4}$ and $2^{-3} = \frac{1}{8}$, we can deduce that 2^{-n} should equal $\frac{1}{2^n}$. Is the product rule valid in such cases? For example, if we multiply 6^{-2} by 6^2, we get

$$6^{-2} \cdot 6^2 = 6^{-2+2} = 6^0 = 1.$$

The expression 6^{-2} behaves as if it were the reciprocal of 6^2, because their product is 1. The reciprocal of 6^2 may be written $\frac{1}{6^2}$, leading us to define 6^{-2} as $\frac{1}{6^2}$. This is a particular case of the definition of negative exponents.

Negative Exponents

For any nonzero real number a and any integer n, $$a^{-n} = \frac{1}{a^n}.$$

Example: $3^{-2} = \dfrac{1}{3^2}$.

By definition, a^{-n} and a^n are reciprocals, since

$$a^n \cdot a^{-n} = a^n \cdot \frac{1}{a^n} = 1.$$

Since $1^n = 1$, the definition of a^{-n} can also be written

$$a^{-n} = \frac{1}{a^n} = \frac{1^n}{a^n} = \left(\frac{1}{a}\right)^n.$$

For example,

$$6^{-3} = \left(\frac{1}{6}\right)^3 \quad \text{and} \quad \left(\frac{1}{3}\right)^{-2} = 3^2.$$

Example 2 Using Negative Exponents

Simplify by writing each expression with positive exponents.

(a) $3^{-2} = \dfrac{1}{3^2} = \dfrac{1}{9}$

(b) $5^{-3} = \dfrac{1}{5^3} = \dfrac{1}{125}$

(c) $\left(\dfrac{1}{2}\right)^{-3} = 2^3 = 8$ $\quad$ $\frac{1}{2}$ and 2 are reciprocals.

Notice that we can change the base to its reciprocal if we also change the sign of the exponent.

(d) $\left(\dfrac{2}{5}\right)^{-4} = \left(\dfrac{5}{2}\right)^4$ $\quad$ $\frac{2}{5}$ and $\frac{5}{2}$ are reciprocals.

(e) $\left(\dfrac{4}{3}\right)^{-5} = \left(\dfrac{3}{4}\right)^5$

(f) $4^{-1} - 2^{-1} = \dfrac{1}{4} - \dfrac{1}{2} = \dfrac{1}{4} - \dfrac{2}{4} = -\dfrac{1}{4}$

Apply the exponents first, then subtract.

Continued on Next Page

(g) $p^{-2} = \frac{1}{p^2}, p \neq 0$

(h) $\frac{1}{x^{-4}}, x \neq 0$

$$\frac{1}{x^{-4}} = \frac{1^{-4}}{x^{-4}} \qquad 1^{-4} = 1$$

$$= \left(\frac{1}{x}\right)^{-4} \qquad \text{Power rule (c)}$$

$$= x^4 \qquad \frac{1}{x} \text{ and } x \text{ are reciprocals.}$$

CAUTION

A negative exponent does not indicate a negative number; negative exponents lead to reciprocals.

Expression	**Example**	
a^{-n}	$3^{-2} = \frac{1}{3^2} = \frac{1}{9}$	Not negative
$-a^{-n}$	$-3^{-2} = -\frac{1}{3^2} = -\frac{1}{9}$	Negative

Work Problem 3 at the Side.

The definition of negative exponents allows us to move factors in a fraction if we also change the signs of the exponents. For example,

$$\frac{2^{-3}}{3^{-4}} = \frac{\frac{1}{2^3}}{\frac{1}{3^4}} = \frac{1}{2^3} \cdot \frac{3^4}{1} = \frac{3^4}{2^3},$$

so that

$$\frac{2^{-3}}{3^{-4}} = \frac{3^4}{2^3}.$$

Changing from Negative to Positive Exponents

For any nonzero numbers a and b, and any integers m and n,

$$\frac{a^{-m}}{b^{-n}} = \frac{b^n}{a^m} \quad \text{and} \quad \left(\frac{a}{b}\right)^{-m} = \left(\frac{b}{a}\right)^m.$$

Examples: $\frac{3^{-5}}{2^{-4}} = \frac{2^4}{3^5}$ and $\left(\frac{4}{5}\right)^{-3} = \left(\frac{5}{4}\right)^3$.

3 Write with positive exponents.

(a) 4^{-3}

(b) 6^{-2}

(c) $\left(\frac{2}{3}\right)^{-2}$

(d) $2^{-1} + 5^{-1}$

(e) $m^{-5}, m \neq 0$

(f) $\frac{1}{z^{-4}}, z \neq 0$

ANSWERS

3. (a) $\frac{1}{4^3}$ **(b)** $\frac{1}{6^2}$ **(c)** $\left(\frac{3}{2}\right)^2$

(d) $\frac{1}{2} + \frac{1}{5} = \frac{7}{10}$ **(e)** $\frac{1}{m^5}$ **(f)** z^4

4 Write with only positive exponents. Assume all variables represent nonzero real numbers.

(a) $\dfrac{7^{-1}}{5^{-4}}$

(b) $\dfrac{x^{-3}}{y^{-2}}$

(c) $\dfrac{4h^{-5}}{m^{-2}k}$

(d) p^2q^{-5}

(e) $\left(\dfrac{3m}{p}\right)^{-2}$

ANSWERS

4. (a) $\dfrac{5^4}{7}$ (b) $\dfrac{y^2}{x^3}$ (c) $\dfrac{4m^2}{h^5k}$ (d) $\dfrac{p^2}{q^5}$ (e) $\dfrac{p^2}{3^2m^2}$

Example 3 Changing from Negative to Positive Exponents

Write with only positive exponents. Assume all variables represent nonzero real numbers.

(a) $\dfrac{4^{-2}}{5^{-3}} = \dfrac{5^3}{4^2}$

(b) $\dfrac{m^{-5}}{p^{-1}} = \dfrac{p^1}{m^5} = \dfrac{p}{m^5}$

(c) $\dfrac{a^{-2}b}{3d^{-3}} = \dfrac{bd^3}{3a^2}$

Notice that b in the numerator and 3 in the denominator were not affected.

(d) $x^3y^{-4} = \dfrac{x^3y^{-4}}{1} = \dfrac{x^3}{y^4}$

(e) $\left(\dfrac{x}{2y}\right)^{-4} = \left(\dfrac{2y}{x}\right)^4 = \dfrac{2^4y^4}{x^4}$

Work Problem 4 at the Side.

CAUTION

Be careful. We cannot change negative exponents to positive exponents using this rule if the exponents occur in a sum of terms. For example,

$$\frac{5^{-2} + 3^{-1}}{7 - 2^{-3}}$$

cannot be written with positive exponents using the rule given here. We would have to use the definition of a negative exponent to rewrite this expression with positive exponents, as

$$\frac{\dfrac{1}{5^2} + \dfrac{1}{3}}{7 - \dfrac{1}{2^3}}.$$

3 Use the quotient rule for exponents. What about the quotient of two exponential expressions with the same base? We know that

$$\frac{6^5}{6^3} = \frac{6 \cdot 6 \cdot 6 \cdot 6 \cdot 6}{6 \cdot 6 \cdot 6} = 6^2.$$

Notice that the difference between the exponents, $5 - 3 = 2$, is the exponent in the quotient. Also,

$$\frac{6^2}{6^4} = \frac{6 \cdot 6}{6 \cdot 6 \cdot 6 \cdot 6} = \frac{1}{6^2} = 6^{-2}.$$

Here, $2 - 4 = -2$. These examples suggest the quotient rule for exponents.

Quotient Rule for Exponents

For any nonzero real number a and any integers m and n,

$$\frac{a^m}{a^n} = a^{m-n}.$$

(Keep the base and subtract the exponents.)

Example: $\frac{5^8}{5^4} = 5^{8-4} = 5^4.$

CAUTION

A common **error** is to write $\frac{5^8}{5^4} = 1^{8-4} = 1^4$. Notice that by the quotient rule, the quotient should have the *same base*, 5. That is,

$$\frac{5^8}{5^4} = 5^{8-4} = 5^4.$$

If you are not sure, use the definition of an exponent to write out the factors:

$$5^8 = 5 \cdot 5 \cdot 5 \cdot 5 \cdot 5 \cdot 5 \cdot 5 \cdot 5 \quad \text{and} \quad 5^4 = 5 \cdot 5 \cdot 5 \cdot 5.$$

Then it is clear that the quotient is 5^4.

Example 4 Using the Quotient Rule for Exponents

Simplify, using the quotient rule for exponents. Write answers with positive exponents.

(a) $\frac{5^8}{5^6} = 5^{8-6} = 5^2$

(b) $\frac{4^2}{4^9} = 4^{2-9} = 4^{-7} = \frac{1}{4^7}$

(c) $\frac{5^{-3}}{5^{-7}} = 5^{-3-(-7)} = 5^4$

(d) $\frac{q^5}{q^{-3}} = q^{5-(-3)} = q^8, q \neq 0$

(e) $\frac{3^2x^5}{3^4x^3} = \frac{3^2}{3^4} \cdot \frac{x^5}{x^3} = 3^{2-4} \cdot x^{5-3} = 3^{-2}x^2 = \frac{x^2}{3^2}, x \neq 0$

(f) $\frac{(m+n)^{-2}}{(m+n)^{-4}} = (m+n)^{-2-(-4)} = (m+n)^{-2+4} = (m+n)^2, m \neq -n$

(g) $\frac{7x^{-3}y^2}{2^{-1}x^2y^{-5}} = \frac{7 \cdot 2^1y^2y^5}{x^2x^3} = \frac{14y^7}{x^5}$

Work Problem 5 at the Side.

5 Simplify. Write answers with positive exponents.

(a) $\frac{5^{11}}{5^8}$

(b) $\frac{4^7}{4^{10}}$

(c) $\frac{6^{-5}}{6^{-2}}$

(d) $\frac{8^4m^9}{8^5m^{10}}, m \neq 0$

(e) $\frac{3^{-1}(x+y)^{-3}}{2^{-2}(x+y)^{-4}}, x \neq -y$

ANSWERS

5. **(a)** 5^3 **(b)** $\frac{1}{4^3}$ **(c)** $\frac{1}{6^3}$ **(d)** $\frac{1}{8m}$
(e) $\frac{4}{3}(x+y)$

The definitions and rules for exponents given in this section and Section 6.2 are summarized below.

Definitions and Rules for Exponents

For any integers m and n:		**Examples**
Product rule	$a^m \cdot a^n = a^{m+n}$	$7^4 \cdot 7^5 = 7^9$
Zero exponent	$a^0 = 1 \quad (a \neq 0)$	$(-3)^0 = 1$
Negative exponent	$a^{-n} = \dfrac{1}{a^n} \quad (a \neq 0)$	$5^{-3} = \dfrac{1}{5^3}$
Quotient rule	$\dfrac{a^m}{a^n} = a^{m-n} \quad (a \neq 0)$	$\dfrac{2^2}{2^5} = 2^{2-5} = 2^{-3} = \dfrac{1}{2^3}$
Power rules (a)	$(a^m)^n = a^{mn}$	$(4^2)^3 = 4^6$
(b)	$(ab)^m = a^m b^m$	$(3k)^4 = 3^4 k^4$
(c)	$\left(\dfrac{a}{b}\right)^m = \dfrac{a^m}{b^m} \quad (b \neq 0)$	$\left(\dfrac{2}{3}\right)^2 = \dfrac{2^2}{3^2}$
Negative to positive rules	$\dfrac{a^{-m}}{b^{-n}} = \dfrac{b^n}{a^m} \quad (a \neq 0, b \neq 0)$	$\dfrac{2^{-4}}{5^{-3}} = \dfrac{5^3}{2^4}$
	$\left(\dfrac{a}{b}\right)^{-m} = \left(\dfrac{b}{a}\right)^m$	$\left(\dfrac{4}{7}\right)^{-2} = \left(\dfrac{7}{4}\right)^2$

4 **Use combinations of rules.** As shown in the next example, we may sometimes need to use more than one rule to simplify an expression.

Example 5 **Using a Combination of Rules**

Use a combination of the rules for exponents to simplify each expression. Assume all variables represent nonzero real numbers.

(a) $\dfrac{(4^2)^3}{4^5} = \dfrac{4^6}{4^5}$ Power rule (a)

$= 4^{6-5}$ Quotient rule

$= 4^1 = 4$

(b) $(2x)^3(2x)^2 = (2x)^5$ Product rule

$= 2^5x^5$ or $32x^5$ Power rule (b)

(c) $\left(\dfrac{2x^3}{5}\right)^{-4} = \left(\dfrac{5}{2x^3}\right)^4$ Negative to positive rule

$= \dfrac{5^4}{2^4x^{12}}$ Power rules (a)–(c)

(d) $\left(\dfrac{3x^{-2}}{4^{-1}y^3}\right)^{-3} = \dfrac{3^{-3}x^6}{4^3y^{-9}}$ Power rules (a)–(c)

$= \dfrac{x^6y^9}{4^3 \cdot 3^3}$ Negative to positive rule

Continued on Next Page

(e) $\dfrac{(4m)^{-3}}{(3m)^{-4}} = \dfrac{4^{-3}m^{-3}}{3^{-4}m^{-4}}$ Power rule (b)

$= \dfrac{3^4m^4}{4^3m^3}$ Negative to positive rule

$= \dfrac{3^4m^{4-3}}{4^3}$ Quotient rule

$= \dfrac{3^4m}{4^3}$

NOTE

Since the steps can be done in several different orders, there are many equally correct ways to simplify expressions like Examples 5(d) and 5(e).

Work Problem 6 at the Side.

6 Simplify. Assume all variables represent nonzero real numbers.

(a) $12^5 \cdot 12^{-7} \cdot 12^6$

(b) $y^{-2} \cdot y^5 \cdot y^{-8}$

(c) $\dfrac{(6x)^{-1}}{(3x^2)^{-2}}$

(d) $\dfrac{3^9 \cdot (x^2y)^{-2}}{3^3 \cdot x^{-4}y}$

ANSWERS

6. (a) 12^4 **(b)** $\dfrac{1}{y^5}$ **(c)** $\dfrac{3x^3}{2}$ **(d)** $\dfrac{3^6}{y^3}$

Focus on

Real-Data Applications

Numbers BIG and SMALL

The ancient Egyptians used the *astonished man* symbol to represent a million. We now use exponents to write very big and very small numbers efficiently. Columbia University professor Edward Kasner asked his nine-year-old nephew to think of a name for the exceedingly large number, 10^{100}, which is a 1 followed by 100 zeros. His nephew proclaimed it to be a **googol.** Kasner then called the unimaginably large number, 10^{googol}, a **googolplex.**

> A googol is 10^{100} or
> 10,000,000,000,000,000,000,000,000,000,000,000,
> 000,000,000,000,000,000,000,000,000,000,000,
> 000,000,000,000,000,000,000,000,000,000,000.

Real-world examples of very big and very small numbers are described in Howard Eves's book, *Mathematical Circles Revisited.* A few such examples are listed here.

- The total number of electrons in the universe is, according to an estimate by Sir Arthur Eddington, about 10^{79}.
- The number of grains of sand on the beach at Coney Island, New York, is about 10^{20}.
- The total number of printed words since the Gutenberg Bible appeared is approximately 10^{16}.
- The temperature at the center of an atomic bomb explosion is 2×10^8 degrees Fahrenheit.
- The diameter of a human hair is about 10^{-4} millimeters.
- The diameter of a nucleus of a cell is about 10^{-6} millimeters (1 micron).
- The probability of winning a lottery by choosing 6 numbers from among 50 is about 6.3×10^{-8}.
- The size of a quark is approximately 10^{-18} millimeters.

Interestingly enough, the Web search engine Google is named after a googol. Sergey Brin, president and co-founder of Google, Inc., was a math major. He chose the name Google to describe the vast reach of this search engine. (*Source: The Gazette*, March 2, 2001.)

For Group Discussion

Suppose that you have been offered a new job with "salary negotiable." You present to your new employer the following offer: You will work for 30 days and will be paid 1¢ on day one, 2¢ on day two, 4¢ on day three, 8¢ on day four, and so on, doubling your pay each day for the month. Your employer accepts your proposal, and you begin work on the first day of the next month.

1. On which day will you have received half of your month's wages? **day 29**
2. When will you have received one-fourth of your total month's wages? **day 28**
3. What do you think your approximate monthly salary will be?
   twice day 30 salary, or $\$1.1 \times 10^9$
4. How many days would it take you to become a "googolaire?" **334 days**

Teaching notes and an extension for this activity are provided in the *Printed Test Bank and Instructor's Resource Guide.*

6.5 EXERCISES

FOR EXTRA HELP: Student's Solutions Manual | MyMathLab.com | InterAct Math Tutorial Software | AW Math Tutor Center | www.mathxl.com | Digital Video Tutor CD 5 Videotape 11

Decide whether each expression is positive, negative, or 0.

1. $(-2)^{-3}$
negative

2. $(-3)^{-2}$
positive

3. -2^4
negative

4. -3^6
negative

5. $\left(\frac{1}{4}\right)^{-2}$
positive

6. $\left(\frac{1}{5}\right)^{-2}$
positive

7. $1 - 5^0$
0

8. $1 - 7^0$
0

Each expression is equal to either 0, 1, *or* −1. *Decide which is correct. See Example 1.*

9. $(-4)^0$
1

10. $(-10)^0$
1

11. -9^0
−1

12. -5^0
−1

13. $(-2)^0 - 2^0$
0

14. $(-8)^0 - 8^0$
0

15. $\frac{0^{10}}{10^0}$
0

16. $\frac{0^5}{5^0}$
0

Evaluate each expression. See Examples 1 and 2.

17. $7^0 + 9^0$
2

18. $8^0 + 6^0$
2

19. 4^{-3}
$\frac{1}{64}$

20. 5^{-4}
$\frac{1}{625}$

21. $\left(\frac{1}{2}\right)^{-4}$
16

22. $\left(\frac{1}{3}\right)^{-3}$
27

23. $\left(\frac{6}{7}\right)^{-2}$
$\frac{49}{36}$

24. $\left(\frac{2}{3}\right)^{-3}$
$\frac{27}{8}$

25. $5^{-1} + 3^{-1}$
$\frac{8}{15}$

26. $6^{-1} + 2^{-1}$
$\frac{2}{3}$

27. $-2^{-1} + 3^{-2}$
$-\frac{7}{18}$

28. $(-3)^{-2} + (-4)^{-1}$
$-\frac{5}{36}$

RELATING CONCEPTS (Exercises 29–32) FOR INDIVIDUAL OR GROUP WORK

In Objective 1, we used the product rule to motivate the definition of a 0 *exponent. We can also use the quotient rule. To see this,* ***work Exercises 29–32 in order.***

29. Consider the expression $\frac{25}{25}$. What is its simplest form?
1

30. Write the quotient in Exercise 29 using the fact that $25 = 5^2$.
$\frac{5^2}{5^2}$

31. Apply the quotient rule for exponents to your answer for Exercise 30. Give the answer as a power of 5.
5^0

32. Because your answers for Exercises 29 and 31 both represent $\frac{25}{25}$, they must be equal. Write this equality. What definition does it support?
$5^0 = 1$; This supports the definition of a 0 exponent.

Use the quotient rule to simplify each expression. Write each expression with positive exponents. Assume that all variables represent nonzero real numbers. See Examples 2–4.

33. $\frac{9^4}{9^5}$ $\frac{1}{9}$

34. $\frac{7^3}{7^4}$ $\frac{1}{7}$

35. $\frac{6^{-3}}{6^2}$ $\frac{1}{6^5}$

36. $\frac{4^{-2}}{4^3}$ $\frac{1}{4^5}$

37. $\frac{1}{6^{-3}}$ 6^3

38. $\frac{1}{5^{-2}}$ 5^2

39. $\frac{2}{r^{-4}}$ $2r^4$

40. $\frac{3}{s^{-8}}$ $3s^8$

41. $\frac{4^{-3}}{5^{-2}}$ $\frac{5^2}{4^3}$

42. $\frac{6^{-2}}{5^{-4}}$ $\frac{5^4}{6^2}$

43. p^5q^{-8} $\frac{p^5}{q^8}$

44. $x^{-8}y^4$ $\frac{y^4}{x^8}$

45. $\frac{r^5}{r^{-4}}$ r^9

46. $\frac{a^6}{a^{-4}}$ a^{10}

47. $\frac{6^4x^8}{6^5x^3}$ $\frac{x^5}{6}$

48. $\frac{3^8y^5}{3^{10}y^2}$ $\frac{y^3}{3^2}$

49. $\frac{6y^3}{2y}$ $3y^2$

50. $\frac{5m^2}{m}$ $5m$

51. $\frac{3x^5}{3x^2}$ x^3

52. $\frac{10p^8}{2p^4}$ $5p^4$

Use a combination of the rules for exponents to simplify each expression. Write answers with only positive exponents. Assume that all variables represent nonzero real numbers. See Example 5.

53. $\frac{(7^4)^3}{7^9}$ 7^3

54. $\frac{(5^3)^2}{5^2}$ 5^4

55. $x^{-3} \cdot x^5 \cdot x^{-4}$ $\frac{1}{x^2}$

56. $y^{-8} \cdot y^5 \cdot y^{-2}$ $\frac{1}{y^5}$

57. $\frac{(3x)^{-2}}{(4x)^{-3}}$ $\frac{4^3x}{3^2}$

58. $\frac{(2y)^{-3}}{(5y)^{-4}}$ $\frac{5^4y}{2^3}$

59. $\left(\frac{x^{-1}y}{z^2}\right)^{-2}$ $\frac{x^2z^4}{y^2}$

60. $\left(\frac{p^{-4}q}{r^{-3}}\right)^{-3}$ $\frac{p^{12}}{r^9q^3}$

61. $(6x)^4(6x)^{-3}$ $6x$

62. $(10y)^9(10y)^{-8}$ $10y$

63. $\frac{(m^7n)^{-2}}{m^{-4}n^3}$ $\frac{1}{m^{10}n^5}$

64. $\frac{(m^8n^{-4})^2}{m^{-2}n^5}$ $\frac{m^{18}}{n^{13}}$

65. $\frac{5x^{-3}}{(4x)^2}$ $\frac{5}{16x^5}$

66. $\frac{-3k^5}{(2k)^2}$ $\frac{-3k^3}{4}$

67. $\left(\frac{2p^{-1}q}{3^{-1}m^2}\right)^2$ $\frac{36q^2}{m^4p^2}$

68. $\left(\frac{4xy^2}{x^{-1}y}\right)^{-2}$ $\frac{1}{16x^4y^2}$

6.6 DIVIDING A POLYNOMIAL BY A MONOMIAL

OBJECTIVE

1 Divide a polynomial by a monomial.

1 Divide a polynomial by a monomial. We add two fractions with a common denominator as follows.

$$\frac{a}{c} + \frac{b}{c} = \frac{a + b}{c}$$

Looking at this statement in reverse gives us a rule for dividing a polynomial by a monomial.

Dividing a Polynomial by a Monomial

To divide a polynomial by a monomial, divide each term of the polynomial by the monomial:

$$\frac{a + b}{c} = \frac{a}{c} + \frac{b}{c} \quad (c \neq 0).$$

For example,

$$\frac{2 + 5}{3} = \frac{2}{3} + \frac{5}{3} \quad \text{and} \quad \frac{x + 3z}{2y} = \frac{x}{2y} + \frac{3z}{2y}.$$

The parts of a division problem are named here.

$$\text{Dividend} \rightarrow \frac{12x^2 + 6x}{6x} = 2x + 1 \leftarrow \text{Quotient}$$
$$\text{Divisor} \rightarrow$$

Example 1 **Dividing a Polynomial by a Monomial**

Divide $5m^5 - 10m^3$ by $5m^2$.

Use the preceding rule, with + replaced by −. Then use the quotient rule.

$$\frac{5m^5 - 10m^3}{5m^2} = \frac{5m^5}{5m^2} - \frac{10m^3}{5m^2} = m^3 - 2m$$

Check by multiplying: $5m^2(m^3 - 2m) = 5m^5 - 10m^3$.

Because division by 0 is undefined, the quotient

$$\frac{5m^5 - 10m^3}{5m^2}$$

is undefined if $m = 0$. From now on, we assume that no denominators are 0.

Work Problem 1 at the Side.

1 Divide.

(a) $\frac{6p^4 + 18p^7}{3p^2}$

(b) $\frac{12m^6 + 18m^5 + 30m^4}{6m^2}$

(c) $(18r^7 - 9r^2) \div (3r)$

Example 2 **Dividing a Polynomial by a Monomial**

Divide: $\frac{16a^5 - 12a^4 + 8a^2}{4a^3}$.

Divide each term of $16a^5 - 12a^4 + 8a^2$ by $4a^3$.

$$\frac{16a^5 - 12a^4 + 8a^2}{4a^3} = \frac{16a^5}{4a^3} - \frac{12a^4}{4a^3} + \frac{8a^2}{4a^3}$$

$$= 4a^2 - 3a + \frac{2}{a} \qquad \text{Quotient rule}$$

Continued on Next Page

ANSWERS

1. (a) $2p^2 + 6p^5$ (b) $2m^4 + 3m^3 + 5m^2$ (c) $6r^6 - 3r$

2 Divide.

(a) $\dfrac{20x^4 - 25x^3 + 5x}{5x^2}$

(b) $\dfrac{50m^4 - 30m^3 + 20m}{10m^3}$

3 Divide.

(a) $\dfrac{8y^7 - 9y^6 - 11y - 4}{y^2}$

(b) $\dfrac{12p^5 + 8p^4 + 3p^3 - 5p^2}{3p^3}$

(c) $\dfrac{45x^4y^3 + 30x^3y^2 - 60x^2y}{-15x^2y}$

ANSWERS

2. **(a)** $4x^2 - 5x + \frac{1}{x}$ **(b)** $5m - 3 + \frac{2}{m^2}$

3. **(a)** $8y^5 - 9y^4 - \frac{11}{y} - \frac{4}{y^2}$

(b) $4p^2 + \frac{8p}{3} + 1 - \frac{5}{3p}$

(c) $-3x^2y^2 - 2xy + 4$

The quotient is not a polynomial because of the expression $\frac{2}{a}$, which has a variable in the denominator. While the sum, difference, and product of two polynomials are always polynomials, the quotient of two polynomials may not be.

Again, check by multiplying.

$$4a^3\left(4a^2 - 3a + \frac{2}{a}\right) = 4a^3(4a^2) - 4a^3(3a) + 4a^3\left(\frac{2}{a}\right)$$
$$= 16a^5 - 12a^4 + 8a^2$$

Work Problem 2 at the Side.

Example 3 Dividing a Polynomial by a Monomial

Divide.

$$\frac{12x^4 - 7x^3 + 4x}{4x} = \frac{12x^4}{4x} - \frac{7x^3}{4x} + \frac{4x}{4x}$$
$$= 3x^3 - \frac{7x^2}{4} + 1 \qquad \text{Quotient rule}$$

Check by multiplying.

CAUTION

In Example 3, notice that the quotient $\frac{4x}{4x} = 1$. It is a common error to leave the 1 out of the answer. Multiplying to check will show that the answer $3x^3 - \frac{7}{4}x^2$ is not correct.

Example 4 Dividing a Polynomial by a Monomial

Divide the polynomial

$$180x^4y^{10} - 150x^3y^8 + 120x^2y^6 - 90xy^4 + 100y$$

by the monomial $-30xy^2$.

$$\frac{180x^4y^{10} - 150x^3y^8 + 120x^2y^6 - 90xy^4 + 100y}{-30xy^2}$$
$$= \frac{180x^4y^{10}}{-30xy^2} - \frac{150x^3y^8}{-30xy^2} + \frac{120x^2y^6}{-30xy^2} - \frac{90xy^4}{-30xy^2} + \frac{100y}{-30xy^2}$$
$$= -6x^3y^8 + 5x^2y^6 - 4xy^4 + 3y^2 - \frac{10}{3xy}$$

Work Problem 3 at the Side.

6.6 EXERCISES

FOR EXTRA HELP: Student's Solutions Manual · MyMathLab.com · InterAct Math Tutorial Software · AW Math Tutor Center · www.mathxl.com · Digital Video Tutor CD 5 Videotape 12

Fill in each blank with the correct response.

1. In the statement $\frac{6x^2 + 8}{2} = 3x^2 + 4$, $\underline{6x^2 + 8}$ is the dividend, $\underline{2}$ is the divisor, and $\underline{3x^2 + 4}$ is the quotient.

2. The expression $\frac{3x + 12}{x}$ is undefined if $x = \underline{0}$.

3. To check the division shown in Exercise 1, multiply $\underline{3x^2 + 4}$ by $\underline{2}$ and show that the product is $\underline{6x^2 + 8}$.

4. The expression $5x^2 - 3x + 6 + \frac{2}{x}$ $\underline{\text{is not}}$ (is/is not) a polynomial.

5. Explain why the division problem $\frac{16m^3 - 12m^2}{4m}$ can be performed using the method of this section, while the division problem $\frac{4m}{16m^3 - 12m^2}$ cannot.

To use the method of this section, the divisor must be just one term. This is true of the first problem, but not the second.

6. Evaluate $\frac{5y + 6}{2}$ when $y = 2$. Evaluate $5y + 3$ when $y = 2$. Does $\frac{5y + 6}{2}$ equal $5y + 3$? **8; 13; no**

Perform each division. See Examples 1–4.

7. $\frac{60x^4 - 20x^2 + 10x}{2x}$ **$30x^3 - 10x + 5$**

8. $\frac{120x^6 - 60x^3 + 80x^2}{2x}$ **$60x^5 - 30x^2 + 40x$**

9. $\frac{20m^5 - 10m^4 + 5m^2}{-5m^2}$ **$-4m^3 + 2m^2 - 1$**

10. $\frac{12t^5 - 6t^3 + 6t^2}{-6t^2}$ **$-2t^3 + t - 1$**

11. $\frac{8t^5 - 4t^3 + 4t^2}{2t}$ **$4t^4 - 2t^2 + 2t$**

12. $\frac{8r^4 - 4r^3 + 6r^2}{2r}$ **$4r^3 - 2r^2 + 3r$**

13. $\frac{4a^5 - 4a^2 + 8}{4a}$ **$a^4 - a + \frac{2}{a}$**

14. $\frac{5t^8 + 5t^7 + 15}{5t}$ **$t^7 + t^6 + \frac{3}{t}$**

15. $\frac{12x^5 - 4x^4 + 6x^3}{-6x^2}$ **$-2x^3 + \frac{2x^2}{3} - x$**

16. $\frac{24x^6 - 12x^5 + 30x^4}{-6x^2}$ **$-4x^4 + 2x^3 - 5x^2$**

17. $\frac{4x^2 + 20x^3 - 36x^4}{4x^2}$ **$1 + 5x - 9x^2$**

18. $\frac{5x^2 - 30x^4 + 30x^5}{5x^2}$ **$1 - 6x^2 + 6x^3$**

19. $\frac{4x^4 + 3x^3 + 2x}{3x^2}$ **$\frac{4x^2}{3} + x + \frac{2}{3x}$**

20. $\frac{5x^4 - 6x^3 + 8x}{3x^2}$ **$\frac{5x^2}{3} - 2x + \frac{8}{3x}$**

21. $\frac{27r^4 - 36r^3 - 6r^2 + 3r - 2}{3r}$ **$9r^3 - 12r^2 - 2r + 1 - \frac{2}{3r}$**

22. $\frac{8k^4 - 12k^3 - 2k^2 - 2k - 3}{2k}$ **$4k^3 - 6k^2 - k - 1 - \frac{3}{2k}$**

23. $\frac{2m^5 - 6m^4 + 8m^2}{-2m^3}$ **$-m^2 + 3m - \frac{4}{m}$**

24. $\frac{6r^5 - 8r^4 + 10r^2}{-2r^4}$ **$-3r + 4 - \frac{5}{r^2}$**

25. $(20a^4b^3 - 15a^5b^2 + 25a^3b) \div (-5a^4b)$

$-4b^2 + 3ab - \frac{5}{a}$

26. $(16y^5z - 8y^2z^2 + 12yz^3) \div (-4y^2z^2)$

$-\frac{4y^3}{z} + 2 - \frac{3z}{y}$

27. $(120x^{11} - 60x^{10} + 140x^9 - 100x^8) \div (10x^{12})$

$\frac{12}{x} - \frac{6}{x^2} + \frac{14}{x^3} - \frac{10}{x^4}$

28. $(120x^{12} - 84x^9 + 60x^8 - 36x^7) \div (12x^9)$

$10x^3 - 7 + \frac{5}{x} - \frac{3}{x^2}$

29. The quotient in Exercise 19 is $\frac{4x^2}{3} + x + \frac{2}{3x}$. Notice how the third term is written with x in the denominator. Would $\frac{2}{3}x$ be an acceptable form for this term? Explain why or why not. Is $\frac{4}{3}x^2$ an acceptable form for the first term? Why or why not?

No, $\frac{2}{3}x$ means $\frac{2x}{3}$, which is not the same as $\frac{2}{3x}$. In the first case we multiply by x, in the second case we divide by x. Yes, $\frac{4}{3}x^2 = \frac{4x^2}{3}$. In both cases we are multiplying by x^2.

30. What expression represents the length of the rectangle?

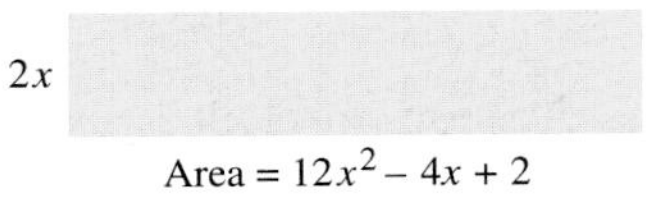

$6x - 2 + \frac{1}{x}$

31. What polynomial, when divided by $5x^3$, yields $3x^2 - 7x + 7$ as a quotient?

$15x^5 - 35x^4 + 35x^3$

32. The quotient of a certain polynomial and $-12y^3$ is $6y^3 - 5y^2 + 2y - 3 + \frac{7}{y}$. Find the polynomial.

$-72y^6 + 60y^5 - 24y^4 + 36y^3 - 84y^2$

RELATING CONCEPTS (Exercises 33–36) FOR INDIVIDUAL OR GROUP WORK

Our system of numeration is called a decimal system. It is based on powers of ten. In a whole number such as 2846, *each digit is understood to represent the number of powers of ten for its place value. The* 2 *represents two thousands* (2×10^3), *the* 8 *represents eight hundreds* (8×10^2), *the* 4 *represents four tens* (4×10^1), *and the* 6 *represents six ones (or units)* (6×10^0). *In expanded form we write*

$$2846 = (2 \times 10^3) + (8 \times 10^2) + (4 \times 10^1) + (6 \times 10^0).$$

Keeping this information in mind, ***work Exercises 33–36 in order.***

33. Divide 2846 by 2, using paper-and-pencil methods: $2\overline{)2846}$.

1423

34. Write your answer in Exercise 33 in expanded form.

$(1 \times 10^3) + (4 \times 10^2) + (2 \times 10^1) + (3 \times 10^0)$

35. Use the methods of this section to divide the polynomial $2x^3 + 8x^2 + 4x + 6$ by 2.

$x^3 + 4x^2 + 2x + 3$

36. Compare your answers in Exercises 34 and 35. How are they similar? How are they different? For what value of x does the answer in Exercise 35 equal the answer in Exercise 34?

They are similar in that the coefficients of the powers of ten are equal to the coefficients of the powers of x. They are different in that one is a number while the other is a polynomial. They are equal if $x = 10$.

6.7 The Quotient of Two Polynomials

Objective

1 Divide a polynomial by a polynomial.

1 Divide a polynomial by a polynomial. We use a method of "long division" to divide a polynomial by a polynomial (other than a monomial). This method is similar to the method of long division used for two whole numbers. For comparison, the division of whole numbers is shown alongside the division of polynomials. Both polynomials must first be written in descending powers.

Dividing Whole Numbers	Dividing Polynomials

Step 1

Dividing Whole Numbers: Divide 6696 by 27.

$$27\overline{)6696}$$

Dividing Polynomials: Divide $8x^3 - 4x^2 - 14x + 15$ by $2x + 3$.

$$2x + 3\overline{)8x^3 - 4x^2 - 14x + 15}$$

Step 2

Dividing Whole Numbers: 66 divided by $27 = 2$; $2 \cdot 27 = 54$.

$$\begin{array}{r} 2 \\ 27\overline{)6696} \\ \underline{54} \end{array}$$

Dividing Polynomials: $8x^3$ divided by $2x = 4x^2$; $4x^2(2x + 3) = 8x^3 + 12x^2$.

$$\begin{array}{r} 4x^2 \qquad\qquad\qquad \\ 2x + 3\overline{)8x^3 - 4x^2 - 14x + 15} \\ \underline{8x^3 + 12x^2} \qquad\qquad\quad \end{array}$$

Step 3

Dividing Whole Numbers: Subtract; then bring down the next digit.

$$\begin{array}{r} 2 \\ 27\overline{)6696} \\ \underline{54}\downarrow \\ 129 \end{array}$$

Dividing Polynomials: Subtract; then bring down the next term.

$$\begin{array}{r} 4x^2 \qquad\qquad\qquad \\ 2x + 3\overline{)8x^3 - 4x^2 - 14x + 15} \\ \underline{8x^3 + 12x^2} \quad \downarrow \qquad \\ -16x^2 - 14x \qquad \end{array}$$

(To subtract two polynomials, change the signs of the second and then add.)

Step 4

Dividing Whole Numbers: 129 divided by $27 = 4$; $4 \cdot 27 = 108$.

$$\begin{array}{r} 24 \\ 27\overline{)6696} \\ \underline{54} \\ 129 \\ \underline{108} \end{array}$$

Dividing Polynomials: $-16x^2$ divided by $2x = -8x$; $-8x(2x + 3) = -16x^2 - 24x$.

$$\begin{array}{r} 4x^2 - 8x \qquad\qquad \\ 2x + 3\overline{)8x^3 - 4x^2 - 14x + 15} \\ \underline{8x^3 + 12x^2} \qquad\qquad\quad \\ -16x^2 - 14x \qquad \\ \underline{-16x^2 - 24x} \qquad \end{array}$$

Step 5

Dividing Whole Numbers: Subtract; then bring down the next digit.

$$\begin{array}{r} 24 \\ 27\overline{)6696} \\ \underline{54} \\ 129 \\ \underline{108}\downarrow \\ 216 \end{array}$$

Dividing Polynomials: Subtract; then bring down the next term.

$$\begin{array}{r} 4x^2 - 8x \qquad\qquad \\ 2x + 3\overline{)8x^3 - 4x^2 - 14x + 15} \\ \underline{8x^3 + 12x^2} \qquad\qquad\quad \\ -16x^2 - 14x \qquad \\ \underline{-16x^2 - 24x} \quad \downarrow \\ 10x + 15 \end{array}$$

(continued)

Step 6

216 divided by 27 = 8;
$8 \cdot 27 = 216$.

$$\begin{array}{r} 248 \\ 27\overline{)6696} \\ \underline{54} \\ 129 \\ \underline{108} \\ 216 \\ \underline{216} \\ 0 \end{array}$$

6696 divided by 27 is 248. There is no remainder.

$10x$ divided by $2x = 5$;
$5(2x + 3) = 10x + 15$.

$$\begin{array}{r} 4x^2 - 8x + 5 \\ 2x + 3\overline{)8x^3 - 4x^2 - 14x + 15} \\ \underline{8x^3 + 12x^2} \qquad\qquad \\ -16x^2 - 14x \qquad \\ \underline{-16x^2 - 24x} \qquad \\ 10x + 15 \\ \underline{10x + 15} \\ 0 \end{array}$$

$8x^3 - 4x^2 - 14x + 15$ divided by $2x + 3$ is $4x^2 - 8x + 5$. There is no remainder.

Step 7

Check by multiplying.

$$27 \cdot 248 = 6696$$

Check by multiplying.

$$(2x + 3)(4x^2 - 8x + 5) = 8x^3 - 4x^2 - 14x + 15$$

Example 1 **Dividing a Polynomial by a Polynomial**

Divide $5x + 4x^3 - 8 - 4x^2$ by $2x - 1$.

Both polynomials must be written with the exponents in descending order. Rewrite the first polynomial as $4x^3 - 4x^2 + 5x - 8$. Then begin the division process.

Divide $4x^3 - 4x^2 + 5x - 8$ by $2x - 1$.

$$\begin{array}{r} 2x^2 - x + 2 \\ 2x - 1\overline{)4x^3 - 4x^2 + 5x - 8} \\ \underline{4x^3 - 2x^2} \qquad\qquad \\ -2x^2 + 5x \qquad \\ \underline{-2x^2 + x} \qquad \\ 4x - 8 \\ \underline{4x - 2} \\ -6 \end{array} \leftarrow \text{Remainder}$$

Step 1 $4x^3$ divided by $2x = 2x^2$; $2x^2(2x - 1) = 4x^3 - 2x^2$.

Step 2 Subtract; bring down the next term.

Step 3 $-2x^2$ divided by $2x = -x$; $-x(2x - 1) = -2x^2 + x$.

Step 4 Subtract; bring down the next term.

Step 5 $4x$ divided by $2x = 2$; $2(2x - 1) = 4x - 2$.

Step 6 Subtract. The remainder is -6. Thus $4x^3 - 4x^2 + 5x - 8$ divided by $2x - 1$ has a quotient of $2x^2 - x + 2$ and a remainder of -6. Write the remainder as the numerator of a fraction that has $2x - 1$ as its denominator. The answer is not a polynomial because of the remainder.

$$\frac{4x^3 - 4x^2 + 5x - 8}{2x - 1} = 2x^2 - x + 2 + \frac{-6}{2x - 1}$$

Continued on Next Page

Step 7 Check by multiplying.

$$(2x-1)\left(2x^2 - x + 2 + \frac{-6}{2x-1}\right)$$
$$= (2x-1)(2x^2) + (2x-1)(-x) + (2x-1)(2)$$
$$+ (2x-1)\left(\frac{-6}{2x-1}\right)$$
$$= 4x^3 - 2x^2 - 2x^2 + x + 4x - 2 - 6$$
$$= 4x^3 - 4x^2 + 5x - 8$$

Work Problem 1 at the Side.

Example 2 **Dividing into a Polynomial with Missing Terms**

Divide $x^3 - 1$ by $x - 1$.

Here the polynomial $x^3 - 1$ is missing the x^2 term and the x term. When terms are missing, use 0 as the coefficient for each missing term. (Zero acts as a placeholder here, just as it does in our number system.)

$$x^3 - 1 = x^3 + 0x^2 + 0x - 1$$

Now divide.

$$\begin{array}{r} x^2 + x + 1 \\ x - 1\overline{)x^3 + 0x^2 + 0x - 1} \\ \underline{x^3 - x^2} \\ x^2 + 0x \\ \underline{x^2 - x} \\ x - 1 \\ \underline{x - 1} \\ 0 \end{array}$$

The remainder is 0. The quotient is $x^2 + x + 1$. Check by multiplying.

$$(x^2 + x + 1)(x - 1) = x^3 - 1$$

Work Problem 2 at the Side.

Example 3 **Dividing by a Polynomial with Missing Terms**

Divide $x^4 + 2x^3 + 2x^2 - x - 1$ by $x^2 + 1$.

Since $x^2 + 1$ has a missing x term, write it as $x^2 + 0x + 1$. Then go through the division process as follows.

$$\begin{array}{r} x^2 + 2x + 1 \\ x^2 + 0x + 1\overline{)x^4 + 2x^3 + 2x^2 - x - 1} \\ \underline{x^4 + 0x^3 + x^2} \\ 2x^3 + x^2 - x \\ \underline{2x^3 + 0x^2 + 2x} \\ x^2 - 3x - 1 \\ \underline{x^2 + 0x + 1} \\ -3x - 2 \leftarrow \text{Remainder} \end{array}$$

Continued on Next Page

1 Divide.

(a) $(x^3 + x^2 + 4x - 6) \div (x - 1)$

(b) $\dfrac{p^3 - 2p^2 - 5p + 9}{p + 2}$

2 Divide.

(a) $\dfrac{r^2 - 5}{r + 4}$

(b) $(x^3 - 8) \div (x - 2)$

Answers

1. **(a)** $x^2 + 2x + 6$

(b) $p^2 - 4p + 3 + \dfrac{3}{p + 2}$

2. **(a)** $r - 4 + \dfrac{11}{r + 4}$

(b) $x^2 + 2x + 4$

3 Divide.

(a) $(2x^4 + 3x^3 - x^2 + 6x + 5) \div (x^2 - 1)$

(b) $\dfrac{2m^5 + m^4 + 6m^3 - 3m^2 - 18}{m^2 + 3}$

4 Divide $3x^3 + 7x^2 + 7x + 10$ by $3x + 6$.

When the result of subtracting ($-3x - 2$, in this case) is a polynomial of smaller degree than the divisor ($x^2 + 0x + 1$), that polynomial is the remainder. Write the answer as

$$x^2 + 2x + 1 + \frac{-3x - 2}{x^2 + 1}.$$

Multiply to check that this is the correct quotient.

Work Problem 3 at the Side.

Example 4 **Dividing a Polynomial with a Quotient That Has Fractional Coefficients**

Divide $4x^3 + 2x^2 + 3x + 1$ by $4x - 4$.

$$\begin{array}{r} x^2 + \frac{3}{2}x + \frac{9}{4} \\ 4x - 4\overline{)4x^3 + 2x^2 + 3x + 1} \\ \underline{4x^3 - 4x^2} \qquad\qquad \\ 6x^2 + 3x \qquad \\ \underline{6x^2 - 6x} \qquad \\ 9x + 1 \\ \underline{9x - 9} \\ 10 \end{array}$$

The quotient is $x^2 + \frac{3}{2}x + \frac{9}{4} + \frac{10}{4x - 4}$.

Work Problem 4 at the Side.

Answers

3. (a) $2x^2 + 3x + 1 + \frac{9x + 6}{x^2 - 1}$

(b) $2m^3 + m^2 - 6$

4. $x^2 + \frac{1}{3}x + \frac{5}{3}$

6.7 EXERCISES

FOR EXTRA HELP: Student's Solutions Manual; MyMathLab.com; InterAct Math Tutorial Software; AW Math Tutor Center; www.mathxl.com; Digital Video Tutor CD 5 Videotape 12

1. In the division problem $(4x^4 + 2x^3 - 14x^2 + 19x + 10) \div (2x + 5) = 2x^3 - 4x^2 + 3x + 2$, which polynomial is the divisor? Which is the quotient?

The divisor is $2x + 5$; the quotient is $2x^3 - 4x^2 + 3x + 2$.

2. When dividing one polynomial by another, how do you know when to stop dividing?

Stop when the degree of the remainder is less than the degree of the divisor, or when the remainder is 0.

3. In dividing $12m^2 - 20m + 3$ by $2m - 3$, what is the first step?

Divide $12m^2$ by $2m$ to get $6m$.

4. In the division in Exercise 3, what is the second step?

Multiply $6m$ by $2m - 3$ to get $12m^2 - 18m$.

Perform each division. See Example 1.

5. $\dfrac{x^2 - x - 6}{x - 3}$ $\quad x + 2$

6. $\dfrac{m^2 - 2m - 24}{m - 6}$ $\quad m + 4$

7. $\dfrac{2y^2 + 9y - 35}{y + 7}$ $\quad 2y - 5$

8. $\dfrac{2y^2 + 9y + 7}{y + 1}$ $\quad 2y + 7$

9. $\dfrac{p^2 + 2p + 20}{p + 6}$ $\quad p - 4 + \dfrac{44}{p + 6}$

10. $\dfrac{x^2 + 11x + 16}{x + 8}$ $\quad x + 3 + \dfrac{-8}{x + 8}$

11. $(r^2 - 8r + 15) \div (r - 3)$ $\quad r - 5$

12. $(t^2 + 2t - 35) \div (t - 5)$ $\quad t + 7$

13. $\dfrac{4a^2 - 22a + 32}{2a + 3}$ $\quad 2a - 14 + \dfrac{74}{2a + 3}$

14. $\dfrac{9w^2 + 6w + 10}{3w - 2}$ $\quad 3w + 4 + \dfrac{18}{3w - 2}$

15. $\dfrac{8x^3 - 10x^2 - x + 3}{2x + 1}$ $\quad 4x^2 - 7x + 3$

16. $\dfrac{12t^3 - 11t^2 + 9t + 18}{4t + 3}$ $\quad 3t^2 - 5t + 6$

RELATING CONCEPTS (Exercises 17–20) FOR INDIVIDUAL OR GROUP WORK

We can find the value of a polynomial in x for a given value of x by substituting that number for x. Surprisingly, we can accomplish the same thing by division. For example, to find the value of $2x^2 - 4x + 3$ for $x = -3$, we would divide $2x^2 - 4x + 3$ by $x - (-3)$. The remainder will give the value of the polynomial for $x = -3$. ***Work Exercises 17–20 in order.***

17. Find the value of $2x^2 - 4x + 3$ for $x = -3$ by substitution. **33**

18. Divide $2x^2 - 4x + 3$ by $x + 3$. Give the remainder. **33**

(continued)

19. Compare your answers to Exercises 17 and 18. What do you notice?

They are the same.

20. Choose another polynomial and evaluate it both ways at some value of the variable. Do the answers agree?

The answers should agree.

Perform each division. See Examples 2–4.

21. $\dfrac{3y^3 + y^2 + 2}{y + 1}$

$3y^2 - 2y + 2$

22. $\dfrac{2r^3 - 6r - 36}{r - 3}$

$2r^2 + 6r + 12$

23. $\dfrac{3k^3 - 4k^2 - 6k + 10}{k^2 - 2}$

$3k - 4 + \dfrac{2}{k^2 - 2}$

24. $\dfrac{5z^3 - z^2 + 10z + 2}{z^2 + 2}$

$5z - 1 + \dfrac{4}{z^2 + 2}$

25. $(x^4 - x^2 - 2) \div (x^2 - 2)$

$x^2 + 1$

26. $(r^4 + 2r^2 - 3) \div (r^2 - 1)$

$r^2 + 3$

27. $\dfrac{6p^4 - 15p^3 + 14p^2 - 5p + 10}{3p^2 + 1}$

$2p^2 - 5p + 4 + \dfrac{6}{3p^2 + 1}$

28. $\dfrac{6r^4 - 10r^3 - r^2 + 15r - 8}{2r^2 - 3}$

$3r^2 - 5r + 4 + \dfrac{4}{2r^2 - 3}$

29. $\dfrac{2x^5 + 9x^4 + 8x^3 + 10x^2 + 14x + 5}{2x^2 + 3x + 1}$

$x^3 + 3x^2 - x + 5$

30. $\dfrac{4t^5 - 11t^4 - 6t^3 + 5t^2 - t + 3}{4t^2 + t - 3}$

$t^3 - 3t^2 - 1$

31. $\dfrac{x^4 - 1}{x^2 - 1}$

$x^2 + 1$

32. $\dfrac{y^3 + 1}{y + 1}$

$y^2 - y + 1$

33. $(10x^3 + 13x^2 + 4x + 1) \div (5x + 5)$

$2x^2 + \dfrac{3}{5}x + \dfrac{1}{5}$

34. $(6x^3 - 19x^2 - 19x - 4) \div (2x - 8)$

$3x^2 + \dfrac{5}{2}x + \dfrac{1}{2}$

Work each problem.

35. Give the length of the rectangle.

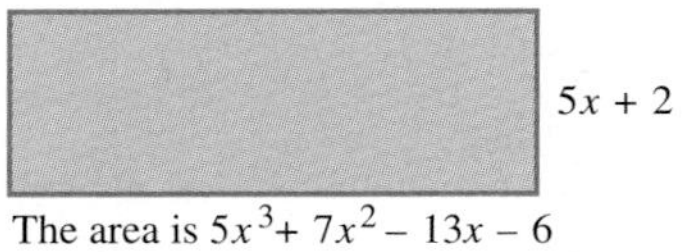

The area is $5x^3 + 7x^2 - 13x - 6$ sq. units.

$x^2 + x - 3$ **units**

36. Find the measure of the base of the parallelogram.

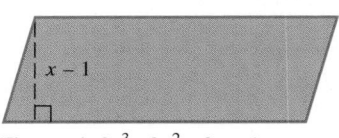

The area is $2x^3 + 2x^2 - 3x - 1$ sq. units.

$2x^2 + 4x + 1$ **units**

6.8 An Application of Exponents: Scientific Notation

Objectives

1. Express numbers in scientific notation.
2. Convert numbers in scientific notation to numbers without exponents.
3. Use scientific notation in calculations.

1 Express numbers in scientific notation. One example of the use of exponents comes from science. The numbers occurring in science are often extremely large (such as the distance from Earth to the sun, 93,000,000 mi) or extremely small (the wavelength of yellow-green light, approximately .0000006 m). Because of the difficulty of working with many zeros, scientists often express such numbers with exponents. Each number is written as $a \times 10^n$, where $1 \le |a| < 10$ and n is an integer. This form is called **scientific notation.** There is always one nonzero digit before the decimal point. For example, 35 is written 3.5×10^1, or 3.5×10; 56,200 is written 5.62×10^4, since

$$56{,}200 = 5.62 \times \mathbf{10{,}000} = 5.62 \times \mathbf{10^4},$$

and .09 is written as 9×10^{-2}.

The steps involved in writing a number in scientific notation are given next. For negative numbers, follow these steps using the absolute value of the number; then make the result negative.

Writing a Number in Scientific Notation

Step 1 Move the decimal point to the right of the first nonzero digit.

Step 2 Count the number of places you moved the decimal point.

Step 3 The number of places in Step 2 is the absolute value of the exponent on 10.

Step 4 The exponent on 10 is positive if the original number is larger than the number in Step 1; the exponent is negative if the original number is smaller than the number in Step 1. If the decimal point is not moved, the exponent is 0.

Example 1 Using Scientific Notation

Write each number in scientific notation.

(a) 93,000,000

Move the decimal point to follow the first nonzero digit. Count the number of places the decimal point was moved.

$$9.3\,000\,000 \quad \text{7 places}$$

The number will be written in scientific notation as 9.3×10^n. To find the value of n, first compare 9.3 with 93,000,000. Since 93,000,000 is *larger* than 9.3, we must multiply by a *positive* power of 10 so the product 9.3×10^n will equal the larger number.

Since the decimal point was moved 7 places, and since n is positive,

$$93{,}000{,}000 = 9.3 \times 10^7.$$

(b) $463{,}000{,}000{,}000{,}000 = 4.63\,000\,000\,000\,000. \quad \text{14 places}$

$= 4.63 \times 10^{14}$

Continued on Next Page

1 Write each number in scientific notation.

(a) 63,000

(b) 5,870,000

(c) .0571

(d) $-.000062$

2 Write without exponents.

(a) 4.2×10^3

(b) 8.7×10^5

(c) 6.42×10^{-3}

3 Simplify, and write without exponents.

(a) $(2.6 \times 10^4)(2 \times 10^{-6})$

(b) $\dfrac{4.8 \times 10^2}{2.4 \times 10^{-3}}$

Answers

1. **(a)** 6.3×10^4 **(b)** 5.87×10^6 **(c)** 5.71×10^{-2} **(d)** -6.2×10^{-5}
2. **(a)** 4200 **(b)** 870,000 **(c)** .00642
3. **(a)** .052 **(b)** 200,000

(c) $3.021 = 3.021 \times 10^0$

(d) .00462

Move the decimal point to the right of the first nonzero digit and count the number of places the decimal point was moved.

$$004.62 \quad \text{3 places}$$

Because .00462 is *smaller* than 4.62, the exponent must be *negative*.

$$.00462 = 4.62 \times 10^{-3}$$

(e) $-.0000762 = -7.62 \times 10^{-5}$

Work Problem 1 at the Side.

2 Convert numbers in scientific notation to numbers without exponents. To convert a number written in scientific notation to a number without exponents, work in reverse. Multiplying a number by a positive power of 10 will make the number larger; multiplying by a negative power of 10 will make the number smaller.

Example 2 Writing Numbers without Exponents

Write each number without exponents.

(a) 6.2×10^3

Since the exponent is positive, make 6.2 larger by moving the decimal point 3 places to the right.

$$6.2 \times 10^3 = 6.200 = 6200$$

(b) $4.283 \times 10^5 = 4.28300 = 428{,}300$ Move 5 places to the right.

(c) $-9.73 \times 10^{-2} = -09.73 = -.0973$ Move 2 places to the left.

As these examples show, the exponent tells the number of places and the direction that the decimal point is moved.

Work Problem 2 at the Side.

3 Use scientific notation in calculations. The next example shows how scientific notation can be used with products and quotients.

Example 3 Multiplying and Dividing with Scientific Notation

Write each product or quotient without exponents.

(a) $(6 \times 10^3)(5 \times 10^{-4})$

$= (6 \times 5)(10^3 \times 10^{-4})$ Commutative and associative properties

$= 30 \times 10^{-1}$ Product rule for exponents

$= 30. = 3$ Write without exponents.

(b) $\dfrac{6 \times 10^{-5}}{2 \times 10^3} = \dfrac{6}{2} \times \dfrac{10^{-5}}{10^3} = 3 \times 10^{-8} = .00000003$

Work Problem 3 at the Side.

Calculator Tip Calculators usually have a key labeled EE or EXP for scientific notation. See An Introduction to Calculators at the front of this book for more information.

Example 4 Applying Scientific Notation

Convert to scientific notation, calculate each computation, then give the result without scientific notation.

(a) In determining helium usage at Kennedy Space Center, the product 70,000(.0283)(1000) must be calculated. (*Source: NASA-AMATYC-NSF Mathematics Explorations II,* Capital Community College, 2000.)

$$\begin{aligned} 70{,}000(.0283)(1000) &= (7 \times 10^4)(2.83 \times 10^{-2})(1 \times 10^3) \\ &= (7 \times 2.83 \times 1)(10^{4-2+3}) \\ &= 19.81 \times 10^5 \\ &= 1{,}981{,}000 \end{aligned}$$

(b) The ratio of the tidal force exerted by the moon compared to that exerted by the sun is given by

$$\frac{73.5 \times 10^{21} \times (1.5 \times 10^8)^3}{1.99 \times 10^{30} \times (3.84 \times 10^5)^3}.$$

(*Source:* Kastner, Bernice, *Space Mathematics*, NASA.)

$$\begin{aligned} \frac{7.35 \times 10^1 \times 10^{21} \times 1.5^3 \times 10^{24}}{1.99 \times 10^{30} \times 3.84^3 \times 10^{15}} &\approx .22 \times 10^{1+21+24-30-15} \\ &= .22 \times 10^1 \\ &= 2.2 \end{aligned}$$

Work Problem 4 at the Side.

4 The speed of light is approximately 3.0×10^5 km per sec. (*Source: World Almanac and Book of Facts*, 2000.) Write answers without exponents.

(a) How far does light travel in 6.0×10^1 sec?

(b) How many seconds does it take light to travel approximately 1.5×10^8 km from the sun to Earth?

ANSWERS

4. (a) 18,000,000 km **(b)** 500 sec

Focus on
Real-Data Applications

Earthquake Intensities Measured by the Richter Scale

Charles F. Richter devised a scale in 1935 to compare the intensities, or relative power, of earthquakes. The **intensity** of an earthquake is measured relative to the intensity of a standard **zero-level** earthquake of intensity I_0. The relationship is equivalent to $I = I_0 \times 10^R$, where R is the **Richter scale** measure. For example, if an earthquake has magnitude 5.0 on the Richter scale, then its intensity is calculated as $I = I_0 \times 10^{5.0} = I_0 \times 100{,}000$, which is 100,000 times as intense as a zero-level earthquake. The following diagram illustrates the intensities of earthquakes and their Richter scale magnitudes.

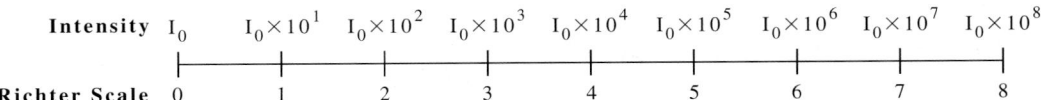

Intensity	I_0	$I_0 \times 10^1$	$I_0 \times 10^2$	$I_0 \times 10^3$	$I_0 \times 10^4$	$I_0 \times 10^5$	$I_0 \times 10^6$	$I_0 \times 10^7$	$I_0 \times 10^8$
Richter Scale	0	1	2	3	4	5	6	7	8

To compare two earthquakes to each other, a ratio of the intensities is calculated. For example, to compare an earthquake that measures 8.0 on the Richter scale to one that measures 5.0, simply find the ratio of the intensities:

$$\frac{\text{intensity } 8.0}{\text{intensity } 5.0} = \frac{I_0 \times 10^{8.0}}{I_0 \times 10^{5.0}} = \frac{10^8}{10^5} = 10^{8-5} = 10^3 = 1000.$$

Therefore an earthquake that measures 8.0 on the Richter Scale is 1000 times as intense as one that measures 5.0.

For Group Discussion

The table gives Richter scale measurements for several earthquakes.

Earthquake		Richter Scale Measurement
1960	Concepción, Chile	9.5
1906	San Francisco, California	8.3
1939	Erzincan, Turkey	8.0
1998	Sumatra, Indonesia	7.0
1998	Adana, Turkey	6.3

Source: World Almanac and Book of Facts, 2000.

1. Compare the intensity of the 1939 Erzincan earthquake to the 1998 Sumatra earthquake.
   Erzincan earthquake was ten times as powerful as the Sumatra earthquake.
2. Compare the intensity of the 1998 Adana earthquake to the 1906 San Francisco earthquake.
   Adana earthquake had one hundredth the power of the San Francisco earthquake.
3. Compare the intensity of the 1939 Erzincan earthquake to the 1998 Adana earthquake.
   Erzincan earthquake was about 50.12 times as powerful as the Adana earthquake.
4. Suppose an earthquake measures 7.2 on the Richter scale. How would the intensity of a second earthquake compare if its Richter scale measure differed by +3.0? By −1.0?
   "+3" corresponds to a factor of 1000 times strength; "−1" corresponds to a factor of one-tenth.

Teaching notes and an extension for this activity are provided in the *Printed Test Bank and Instructor's Resource Guide.*

6.8 EXERCISES

FOR EXTRA HELP: Student's Solutions Manual | MyMathLab.com | InterAct Math Tutorial Software | AW Math Tutor Center | www.mathxl.com (MathXL) | Digital Video Tutor CD 5, Videotape 12

Write the numbers (other than dates) mentioned in the following statements in scientific notation.

1. NASA has budgeted \$13,750,400,000 in each of the years 2003 and 2004 for the international space station. (*Source:* U.S. National Aeronautics and Space Administration.) **1.37504×10^{10}**

2. The mass of Pluto, the smallest planet, is .0021 times that of Earth; the mass of Jupiter, the largest planet, is 317.83 times that of Earth. (*Source: World Almanac and Book of Facts,* 2000.) **2.1×10^{-3}; 3.1783×10^2**

3. In 1998, the federal government spent \$66,636,000,000 on research and development. Industry spent \$143,714,000,000 in that same year. (*Source:* U.S. National Science Foundation.) **6.6636×10^{10}; 1.43714×10^{11}**

4. The risk to industrial workers at the Hansom Landfill at the Kennedy Space Center depends on the reference doses of materials dumped there. For thallium, the reference dose is 700,000 mg/kg per day, and the reference dose for beryllium is 5000 mg/kg per day. (*Source: NASA-AMATYC-NSF Math Explorations I,* Capital Community College, 1999.) **7×10^5; 5×10^3**

Determine whether or not the given number is written in scientific notation as defined in Objective 1. If it is not, write it as such.

5. 4.56×10^3
in scientific notation

6. 7.34×10^5
in scientific notation

7. 5,600,000
not in scientific notation; 5.6×10^6

8. 34,000
not in scientific notation; 3.4×10^4

9. .004
not in scientific notation; 4×10^{-3}

10. .0007
not in scientific notation; 7×10^{-4}

11. $.8 \times 10^2$
not in scientific notation; 8×10^1

12. $.9 \times 10^3$
not in scientific notation; 9×10^2

13. Explain in your own words what it means for a number to be written in scientific notation.

A number is written in scientific notation if it is the product of a number whose absolute value is between 1 and 10 (inclusive of 1) and a power of 10.

14. Explain how to multiply a number by a positive power of ten. Then explain how to multiply a number by a negative power of ten.

To multiply by a positive power of 10, move the decimal point to the right as many places as the exponent on 10. With a negative power of 10, move the decimal point to the left as many places as the exponent on 10.

Write each number in scientific notation. See Example 1.

15. 5,876,000,000
5.876×10^9

16. 9,994,000,000
9.994×10^9

17. 82,350
8.235×10^4

18. 78,330
7.833×10^4

19. .000007
7×10^{-6}

20. .0000004
4×10^{-7}

21. $-.00203$
-2.03×10^{-3}

22. $-.0000578$
-5.78×10^{-5}

Write each number without exponents. See Example 2.

23. 7.5×10^5
750,000

24. 8.8×10^6
8,800,000

25. 5.677×10^{12}
5,677,000,000,000

26. 8.766×10^9
8,766,000,000

27. -6.21×10^0

-6.21

28. -8.56×10^0

-8.56

29. 7.8×10^{-4}

$.00078$

30. 8.9×10^{-5}

$.000089$

31. 5.134×10^{-9}

$.000000005134$

32. 7.123×10^{-10}

$.0000000007123$

Perform the indicated operations, and write the answers in scientific notation and then without exponents. See Example 3.

33. $(2 \times 10^8) \times (3 \times 10^3)$

6×10^{11}; $600{,}000{,}000{,}000$

34. $(4 \times 10^7) \times (3 \times 10^3)$

1.2×10^{11}; $120{,}000{,}000{,}000$

35. $(5 \times 10^4) \times (3 \times 10^2)$

1.5×10^7; $15{,}000{,}000$

36. $(8 \times 10^5) \times (2 \times 10^3)$

1.6×10^9; $1{,}600{,}000{,}000$

37. $(3.15 \times 10^{-4}) \times (2.04 \times 10^8)$

6.426×10^4; $64{,}260$

38. $(4.92 \times 10^{-3}) \times (2.25 \times 10^7)$

1.107×10^5; $110{,}700$

Perform the indicated operations, and write the answers in scientific notation. See Example 3.

39. $\dfrac{9 \times 10^{-5}}{3 \times 10^{-1}}$

3×10^{-4}

40. $\dfrac{12 \times 10^{-4}}{4 \times 10^{-3}}$

3×10^{-1}

41. $\dfrac{8 \times 10^3}{2 \times 10^2}$

4×10^1

42. $\dfrac{5 \times 10^4}{1 \times 10^3}$

5×10^1

43. $\dfrac{2.6 \times 10^{-3} \times 7.0 \times 10^{-1}}{2 \times 10^2 \times 3.5 \times 10^{-3}}$

2.6×10^{-3}

44. $\dfrac{9.5 \times 10^{-1} \times 2.4 \times 10^4}{5 \times 10^3 \times 1.2 \times 10^{-2}}$

3.8×10^2

Work each problem. Give answers without exponents. See Example 4.

45. There are 10^9 social security numbers. The population of the U.S. is about 3×10^8. How many social security numbers are available for each person? (*Source:* U.S. Bureau of the Census.)

about 3.3

46. The number of possible hands in contract bridge is about 6.35×10^{11}. The probability of being dealt one particular hand is $\dfrac{1}{6.35 \times 10^{11}}$. Express this number without scientific notation.

about .0000000000016

47. The top-grossing movie of 1997 was *Titanic*, with box office receipts of about 6×10^8 dollars. That amount represented a fraction of about 9.5×10^{-3} of the total receipts for motion pictures in that year. (*Source:* U.S. Bureau of the Census.) What were the total receipts?

about \$63,000,000,000

48. There were 6.3×10^{10} dollars spent to attend motion pictures in a recent year. Approximately 1.3×10^8 adults attended a motion picture theatre at least once. (*Source:* U.S. National Endowment for the Arts.) What was the average amount spent per person that year?

about \$480

49. The body of a 150-lb person contains about 2.3×10^{-4} lb of copper. How much copper is contained in the bodies of 1200 such people?

about .276 lb

50. It takes about 3.6×10^1 sec at a speed of 3.0×10^5 km per sec for light from the sun to reach Venus. (*Source: World Almanac and Book of Facts,* 2000.) How far is Venus from the sun?

about 10,800,000 km

Chapter 6

Summary

Key Terms

6.1	**polynomial**	A polynomial is a term or the sum of a finite number of terms with whole number exponents.
	descending powers	A polynomial in x is written in descending powers if the exponents on x in its terms are in decreasing order.
	degree of a term	The degree of a term is the sum of the exponents on the variables.
	degree of a polynomial	The degree of a polynomial is the highest degree of any term of the polynomial.
	monomial	A monomial is a polynomial with one term.
	binomial	A binomial is a polynomial with two terms.
	trinomial	A trinomial is a polynomial with three terms.
6.3	**FOIL**	FOIL is a shortcut method for finding the product of two binomials.
	outer product	The outer product of $(2x + 3)(x - 5)$ is $2x(-5)$.
	inner product	The inner product of $(2x + 3)(x - 5)$ is $3x$.
6.7	**scientific notation**	A number written as $a \times 10^n$, where $1 \leq \lvert a \rvert < 10$ and n is an integer, is in scientific notation.

New Symbols

x^{-n} — x to the negative n power

Test Your Word Power

See how well you have learned the vocabulary in this chapter. Answers follow the Quick Review.

1. A **polynomial** is an algebraic expression made up of
- **(a)** a term or a finite product of terms with positive coefficients and exponents
- **(b)** a term or a finite sum of terms with real coefficients and whole number exponents
- **(c)** the product of two or more terms with positive exponents
- **(d)** the sum of two or more terms with whole number coefficients and exponents.

2. The **degree of a term** is
- **(a)** the number of variables in the term
- **(b)** the product of the exponents on the variables
- **(c)** the smallest exponent on the variables
- **(d)** the sum of the exponents on the variables.

3. A **trinomial** is a polynomial with
- **(a)** only one term
- **(b)** exactly two terms
- **(c)** exactly three terms
- **(d)** more than three terms.

4. A **binomial** is a polynomial with
- **(a)** only one term
- **(b)** exactly two terms
- **(c)** exactly three terms
- **(d)** more than three terms.

5. A **monomial** is a polynomial with
- **(a)** only one term
- **(b)** exactly two terms
- **(c)** exactly three terms
- **(d)** more than three terms.

6. **FOIL** is a method for
- **(a)** adding two binomials
- **(b)** adding two trinomials
- **(c)** multiplying two binomials
- **(d)** multiplying two trinomials.

Quick Review

Concepts	*Examples*
6.1 Adding and Subtracting Polynomials **Addition:** Add like terms.	Add: $\begin{array}{r} 2x^2 + 5x - 3 \\ \underline{5x^2 - 2x + 7} \\ 7x^2 + 3x + 4 \end{array}$
Subtraction: Change the signs of the terms in the second polynomial and add to the first polynomial.	$(2x^2 + 5x - 3) - (5x^2 - 2x + 7)$ $= (2x^2 + 5x - 3) + (-5x^2 + 2x - 7)$ $= -3x^2 + 7x - 10$
6.2 The Product Rule and Power Rules for Exponents For any integers m and n: **Product rule** $a^m \cdot a^n = a^{m+n}$	$2^4 \cdot 2^5 = 2^9$
Power rules (a) $(a^m)^n = a^{mn}$	$(3^4)^2 = 3^8$
(b) $(ab)^m = a^m b^m$	$(6a)^5 = 6^5 a^5$
(c) $\left(\frac{a}{b}\right)^m = \frac{a^m}{b^m}$ $(b \neq 0)$.	$\left(\frac{2}{3}\right)^4 = \frac{2^4}{3^4}$
6.3 Multiplying Polynomials Multiply each term of the first polynomial by each term of the second polynomial. Then add like terms.	Multiply: $\begin{array}{rrrrr} & 3x^3 & - 4x^2 & + 2x & - 7 \\ & & & 4x & + 3 \\ \hline & 9x^3 & - 12x^2 & + 6x & - 21 \\ 12x^4 & - 16x^3 & + 8x^2 & - 28x & \\ \hline 12x^4 & - 7x^3 & - 4x^2 & - 22x & - 21 \end{array}$
FOIL Method *Step 1* Multiply the two first terms to get the first term of the answer.	Multiply: $(2x + 3)(5x - 4)$. $2x(5x) = 10x^2$
Step 2 Find the outer product and the inner product and mentally add them, when possible, to get the middle term of the answer.	$2x(-4) + 3(5x) = 7x$
Step 3 Multiply the two last terms to get the last term of the answer.	$3(-4) = -12$ $(2x + 3)(5x - 4) = 10x^2 + 7x - 12$
6.4 Special Products **Square of a Binomial** $(a + b)^2 = a^2 + 2ab + b^2$	$(3x + 1)^2 = 9x^2 + 6x + 1$
$(a - b)^2 = a^2 - 2ab + b^2$	$(2m - 5n)^2 = 4m^2 - 20mn + 25n^2$
Product of the Sum and Difference of Two Terms $(a + b)(a - b) = a^2 - b^2$	$(4a + 3)(4a - 3) = 16a^2 - 9$
6.5 Integer Exponents and the Quotient Rule If $a \neq 0$, for integers m and n: **Zero exponent** $a^0 = 1$	$15^0 = 1$
Negative exponent $a^{-n} = \frac{1}{a^n}$	$5^{-2} = \frac{1}{5^2} = \frac{1}{25}$
Quotient rule $\frac{a^m}{a^n} = a^{m-n}$	$\frac{4^8}{4^3} = 4^5$
Negative to positive rules $\frac{a^{-m}}{b^{-n}} = \frac{b^n}{a^m}$ $\left(\frac{a}{b}\right)^{-m} = \left(\frac{b}{a}\right)^m$.	$\frac{6^{-2}}{7^{-3}} = \frac{7^3}{6^2}$ $\left(\frac{5}{3}\right)^{-4} = \left(\frac{3}{5}\right)^4$

Concepts	*Examples*
6.6 Dividing a Polynomial by a Monomial Divide each term of the polynomial by the monomial: $$\frac{a+b}{c}=\frac{a}{c}+\frac{b}{c}.$$	Divide: $\dfrac{4x^3-2x^2+6x-8}{2x}=\dfrac{4x^3}{2x}-\dfrac{2x^2}{2x}+\dfrac{6x}{2x}-\dfrac{8}{2x}$ $=2x^2-x+3-\dfrac{4}{x}$
6.7 The Quotient of Two Polynomials Use "long division."	$$\begin{array}{r} 2x - 5 + \dfrac{-1}{3x+4} \\ \text{Divide: } 3x+4\overline{)6x^2 - 7x - 21} \\ \underline{6x^2 + 8x} \\ -15x - 21 \\ \underline{-15x - 20} \\ -1 \end{array}$$ ← Remainder
6.8 An Application of Exponents: Scientific Notation To write a number in scientific notation (as $a \times 10^n$), move the decimal point to the right of the first nonzero digit. If the decimal point is moved n places, and this makes the number smaller, n is positive; otherwise, n is negative. If the decimal point is not moved, n is 0.	$247 = 2.47 \times 10^2$ $.0051 = 5.1 \times 10^{-3}$ $4.8 = 4.8 \times 10^0$ $3.25 \times 10^5 = 325{,}000$ $8.44 \times 10^{-6} = .00000844$

ANSWERS TO TEST YOUR WORD POWER

1. (b) *Example:* $5x^3+2x^2-7$ **2. (d)** *Examples:* The term 6 has degree 0, $3x$ has degree 1, $-2x^8$ has degree 8, and $5x^2y^4$ has degree 6. **3. (c)** *Example:* $2a^2-3ab+b^2$ **4. (b)** *Example:* $3t^3+5t$ **5. (a)** *Examples:* -5 and $4xy^5$

6. (c) *Example:* $(m+4)(m-3) = \overset{F}{m(m)} - \overset{O}{3m} + \overset{I}{4m} + \overset{L}{4(-3)} = m^2+m-12$

Focus on

Real-Data Applications

Algebra in Euclid's *Elements*

The word *algebra* is derived from *Al-jabr wa'l muqabalah*, a ninth-century treatise written by the Arabic mathematician, al-Khwarizmi. The notation that we use today, including the use of letters to represent variables and the symbols + for addition and − for subtraction, was introduced in the sixteenth century by François Viète. In Book II of Euclid's *Elements*, algebraic relationships were written in terms of geometric figures. The following proposition is an example.

Proposition 4: "If a straight line is cut at random, the square on the whole equals the squares on the segments plus twice the rectangle contained by the segments."

This proposition can be viewed geometrically. The straight line segment has length $a + b$. The "square on the whole" is the large outer square, $(a + b)^2$. The "squares on the segments" are a^2 and b^2, and the "rectangle contained by the segments" is ab, as shown in the figure. The algebraic statement equivalent to Proposition 4 is $(a + b)^2 = a^2 + b^2 + 2ab$. You should recognize this as the formula for computing the square of a binomial. We usually write it in the form $(a + b)^2 = a^2 + 2ab + b^2$.

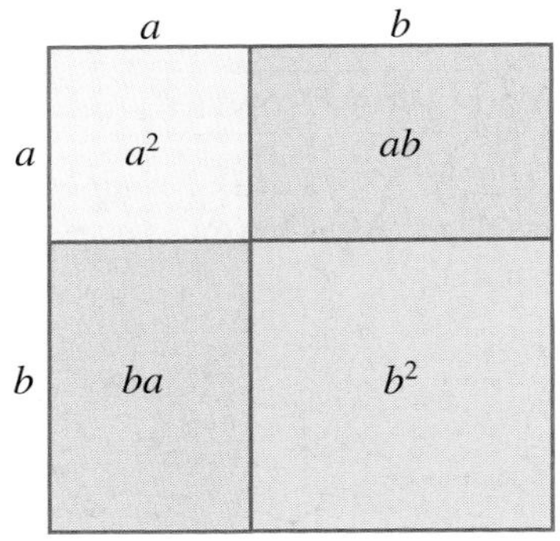

For Group Discussion

Consider the following propositions from Book II of Euclid's *Elements*. An equivalent algebraic statement accompanies each proposition.

Proposition 1: "If there are two straight lines and one of them is cut into any number of segments whatever [2 in the example], then the rectangle contained by the two straight lines equals the sum of the rectangles contained by the uncut straight line and each of the segments."

The equivalent algebraic form is $a(b + c) = ab + ac$.

1. By what name do we know this property? **distributive property**

Proposition 7: "If a straight line is cut at random, then the sum of the square on the whole [a] and that on one of the segments [b] equals twice the rectangle contained by the whole and the said segment plus the square on the remaining segment [$a - b$]."

The equivalent algebraic form is $a^2 + b^2 = 2ab + (a - b)^2$.

2. How is this property written in your textbook? $(a - b)^2 = a^2 - 2ab + b^2$

Proposition 8: An equivalent algebraic form of this proposition is $4ab + (a - b)^2 = (a + b)^2$.

3. Expand both the left and right sides of the formula. Are they the same expression? **yes**

Teaching notes and an extension for this activity are provided in the *Printed Test Bank and Instructor's Resource Guide*.

Chapter 6 Review Exercises

[6.1] *Combine terms where possible in each polynomial. Write the answer in descending powers of the variable. Give the degree of the answer. Identify the polynomial as a* monomial, binomial, trinomial, *or* none of these.

1. $9m^2 + 11m^2 + 2m^2$

$22m^2$; degree 2; monomial

2. $-4p + p^3 - p^2 + 8p + 2$

$p^3 - p^2 + 4p + 2$; degree 3; none of these

3. $12a^5 - 9a^4 + 8a^3 + 2a^2 - a + 3$

already in descending powers; degree 5; none of these

4. $-7y^5 - 8y^4 - y^5 + y^4 + 9y$

$-8y^5 - 7y^4 + 9y$; degree 5; trinomial

Add or subtract as indicated.

5. Add.

$$\begin{array}{r} -2a^3 + 5a^2 \\ \underline{-3a^3 - a^2} \\ -5a^3 + 4a^2 \end{array}$$

6. Add.

$$\begin{array}{r} 4r^3 - 8r^2 + 6r \\ \underline{-2r^3 + 5r^2 + 3r} \\ 2r^3 - 3r^2 + 9r \end{array}$$

7. Subtract.

$$\begin{array}{r} 6y^2 - 8y + 2 \\ \underline{-5y^2 + 2y - 7} \\ 11y^2 - 10y + 9 \end{array}$$

8. Subtract.

$$\begin{array}{r} -12k^4 - 8k^2 + 7k - 5 \\ \underline{k^4 + 7k^2 + 11k + 1} \\ -13k^4 - 15k^2 - 4k - 6 \end{array}$$

9. $(2m^3 - 8m^2 + 4) + (8m^3 + 2m^2 - 7)$

$10m^3 - 6m^2 - 3$

10. $(-5y^2 + 3y + 11) + (4y^2 - 7y + 15)$

$-y^2 - 4y + 26$

11. $(6p^2 - p - 8) - (-4p^2 + 2p + 3)$

$10p^2 - 3p - 11$

12. $(12r^4 - 7r^3 + 2r^2) - (5r^4 - 3r^3 + 2r^2 + 1)$

$7r^4 - 4r^3 - 1$

[6.2] *Use the product rule or power rules to simplify each expression. Write the answer in exponential form.*

13. $4^3 \cdot 4^8$

4^{11}

14. $(-5)^6(-5)^5$

$(-5)^{11}$

15. $(-8x^4)(9x^3)$

$-72x^7$

16. $(2x^2)(5x^3)(x^9)$

$10x^{14}$

17. $(19x)^5$

19^5x^5

18. $(-4y)^7$

$(-4)^7y^7$

19. $5(pt)^4$

$5p^4t^4$

20. $\left(\frac{7}{5}\right)^6$

$\frac{7^6}{5^6}$

21. $(3x^2y^3)^3$

$3^3x^6y^9$

22. $(t^4)^8(t^2)^5$

t^{42}

23. $(6x^2z^4)^2(x^3yz^2)^4$

$6^2x^{16}y^4z^{16}$

24. Explain why the product rule for exponents does not apply to the expression $7^2 + 7^4$.

The product rule for exponents does not apply here because we want the sum of 7^2 and 7^4, not their product.

[6.3] *Find each product.*

25. $5x(2x + 14)$
$10x^2 + 70x$

26. $-3p^3(2p^2 - 5p)$
$-6p^5 + 15p^4$

27. $(3r - 2)(2r^2 + 4r - 3)$
$6r^3 + 8r^2 - 17r + 6$

28. $(2y + 3)(4y^2 - 6y + 9)$
$8y^3 + 27$

29. $(5p^2 + 3p)(p^3 - p^2 + 5)$
$5p^5 - 2p^4 - 3p^3 + 25p^2 + 15p$

30. $(3k - 6)(2k + 1)$
$6k^2 - 9k - 6$

31. $(6p - 3q)(2p - 7q)$
$12p^2 - 48pq + 21q^2$

32. $(m^2 + m - 9)(2m^2 + 3m - 1)$
$2m^4 + 5m^3 - 16m^2 - 28m + 9$

[6.4] *Find each product.*

33. $(a + 4)^2$
$a^2 + 8a + 16$

34. $(3p - 2)^2$
$9p^2 - 12p + 4$

35. $(2r + 5s)^2$
$4r^2 + 20rs + 25s^2$

36. $(r + 2)^3$
$r^3 + 6r^2 + 12r + 8$

37. $(2x - 1)^3$
$8x^3 - 12x^2 + 6x - 1$

38. $(6m - 5)(6m + 5)$
$36m^2 - 25$

39. $(2z + 7)(2z - 7)$
$4z^2 - 49$

40. $(5a + 6b)(5a - 6b)$
$25a^2 - 36b^2$

41. $(2x^2 + 5)(2x^2 - 5)$
$4x^4 - 25$

42. Explain why $(a + b)^2$ is not equal to $a^2 + b^2$.
$(a + b)^2 = (a + b)(a + b) = a^2 + 2ab + b^2$. The term $2ab$ is not in $a^2 + b^2$.

[6.5] *Evaluate each expression.*

43. $5^0 + 8^0$ $\quad 2$

44. 2^{-5} $\quad \frac{1}{32}$

45. $\left(\frac{6}{5}\right)^{-2}$ $\quad \frac{5^2}{6^2}$ or $\frac{25}{36}$

46. $4^{-2} - 4^{-1}$ $\quad -\frac{3}{16}$

Simplify. Write each answer in exponential form, using only positive exponents. Assume all variables are nonzero.

47. $\frac{6^{-3}}{6^{-5}}$ $\quad 6^2$

48. $\frac{x^{-7}}{x^{-9}}$ $\quad x^2$

49. $\frac{p^{-8}}{p^4}$ $\quad \frac{1}{p^{12}}$

50. $\frac{r^{-2}}{r^{-6}}$ $\quad r^4$

51. $(2^4)^2$ $\quad 2^8$

52. $(9^3)^{-2}$ $\quad \frac{1}{9^6}$

53. $(5^{-2})^{-4}$ $\quad 5^8$

54. $(8^{-3})^4$ $\quad \frac{1}{8^{12}}$

55. $\frac{(m^2)^3}{(m^4)^2}$ $\quad \frac{1}{m^2}$

56. $\frac{y^4 \cdot y^{-2}}{y^{-5}}$ $\quad y^7$

57. $\frac{r^9 \cdot r^{-5}}{r^{-2} \cdot r^{-7}}$ $\quad r^{13}$

58. $(-5m^3)^2$ $\quad (-5)^2m^6$

59. $(2y^{-4})^{-3}$
$\frac{y^{12}}{2^3}$

60. $\frac{ab^{-3}}{a^4b^2}$
$\frac{1}{a^3b^5}$

61. $\frac{(6r^{-1})^2 \cdot (2r^{-4})}{r^{-5}(r^2)^{-3}}$
$2 \cdot 6^2 \cdot r^5$

62. $\frac{(2m^{-5}n^2)^3(3m^2)^{-1}}{m^{-2}n^{-4}(m^{-1})^2}$
$\frac{2^3n^{10}}{3m^{13}}$

[6.6] *Perform each division.*

63. $\dfrac{-15y^4}{-9y^2}$

$\dfrac{5y^2}{3}$

64. $\dfrac{-12x^3y^2}{6xy}$

$-2x^2y$

65. $\dfrac{6y^4 - 12y^2 + 18y}{-6y}$

$-y^3 + 2y - 3$

66. $\dfrac{2p^3 - 6p^2 + 5p}{2p^2}$

$p - 3 + \dfrac{5}{2p}$

67. $(5x^{13} - 10x^{12} + 20x^7 - 35x^5) \div (-5x^4)$

$-x^9 + 2x^8 - 4x^3 + 7x$

68. $(-10m^4n^2 + 5m^3n^3 + 6m^2n^4) \div (5m^2n)$

$-2m^2n + mn^2 + \dfrac{6n^3}{5}$

[6.7] *Perform each division.*

69. $(2r^2 + 3r - 14) \div (r - 2)$

$2r + 7$

70. $\dfrac{12m^2 - 11m - 10}{3m - 5}$

$4m + 3 + \dfrac{5}{3m - 5}$

71. $\dfrac{10a^3 + 5a^2 - 14a + 9}{5a^2 - 3}$

$2a + 1 + \dfrac{-8a + 12}{5a^2 - 3}$

72. $\dfrac{2k^4 + 4k^3 + 9k^2 - 8}{2k^2 + 1}$

$k^2 + 2k + 4 + \dfrac{-2k - 12}{2k^2 + 1}$

[6.8] *Write each number in scientific notation.*

73. 48,000,000

4.8×10^7

74. 28,988,000,000

2.8988×10^{10}

75. .000065

6.5×10^{-5}

76. .0000000824

8.24×10^{-8}

Write each number without exponents.

77. 2.4×10^4

24,000

78. 7.83×10^7

78,300,000

79. 8.97×10^{-7}

.000000897

80. 9.95×10^{-12}

.00000000000995

Perform the indicated operations, and write the answers without exponents.

81. $(2 \times 10^{-3}) \times (4 \times 10^5)$

800

82. $\dfrac{8 \times 10^4}{2 \times 10^{-2}}$

4,000,000

83. $\dfrac{12 \times 10^{-5} \times 5 \times 10^4}{4 \times 10^3 \times 6 \times 10^{-2}}$

.025

84. $\dfrac{2.5 \times 10^5 \times 4.8 \times 10^{-4}}{7.5 \times 10^8 \times 1.6 \times 10^{-5}}$

.01

85. There are 13 red balls and 39 black balls in a box. Mix them up and draw 13 out one at a time without returning any ball. The probability that the 13 drawings each will produce a red ball is 1.6×10^{-12}. Write the number given in scientific notation without exponents. (*Source:* Warren Weaver, *Lady Luck*, Doubleday & Company, 1963.)

.0000000000016

86. A Boeing 747 is too big to maneuver with the lively agility required of an Air Force fighter. It performs best when it flies straight and level, as does the worldwide airline industry. That industry has annual revenues that approach \$200 billion. Write this dollar amount in scientific notation. (*Source:* Heppenheimer, T. A., *Turbulent Skies: The History of Commercial Aviation*, John Wiley & Sons, 1995.)

$\mathbf{2 \times 10^{11}}$

Mixed Review Exercises

Perform the indicated operations. Write with positive exponents. Assume that no denominators are equal to 0.

87. $19^0 - 3^0$ $\quad \mathbf{0}$

88. $(3p)^4(3p^{-7})$ $\quad \dfrac{3^5}{p^3}$

89. 7^{-2} $\quad \dfrac{1}{7^2}$

90. $(-7 + 2k)^2$

$49 - 28k + 4k^2$

91. $\dfrac{2y^3 + 17y^2 + 37y + 7}{2y + 7}$

$y^2 + 5y + 1$

92. $\left(\dfrac{6r^2s}{5}\right)^4$

$\dfrac{6^4r^8s^4}{5^4}$

93. $-m^5(8m^2 + 10m + 6)$

$-8m^7 - 10m^6 - 6m^5$

94. $\left(\dfrac{1}{2}\right)^{-5}$

2^5

95. $(25x^2y^3 - 8xy^2 + 15x^3y) \div (5x)$

$5xy^3 - \dfrac{8y^2}{5} + 3x^2y$

96. $(6r^{-2})^{-1}$

$\dfrac{r^2}{6}$

97. $(2x + y)^3$

$8x^3 + 12x^2y + 6xy^2 + y^3$

98. $2^{-1} + 4^{-1}$

$\dfrac{3}{4}$

99. $(a + 2)(a^2 - 4a + 1)$

$a^3 - 2a^2 - 7a + 2$

100. $(5y^3 - 8y^2 + 7) - (-3y^3 + y^2 + 2)$

$8y^3 - 9y^2 + 5$

101. $(2r + 5)(5r - 2)$

$10r^2 + 21r - 10$

102. $(12a + 1)(12a - 1)$

$144a^2 - 1$

103. Find a polynomial that represents the area of the rectangle shown.

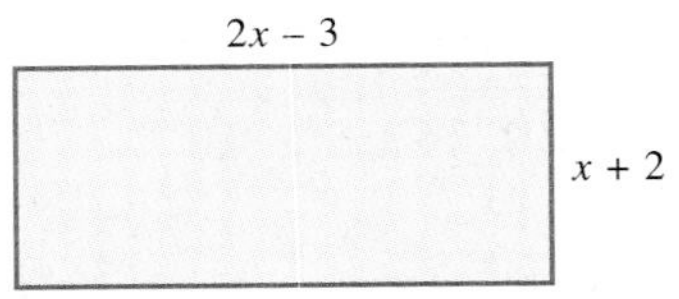

$2x^2 + x - 6$

104. If the side of a square has a measure represented by $5x^4 + 2x^2$, what polynomial represents its area?

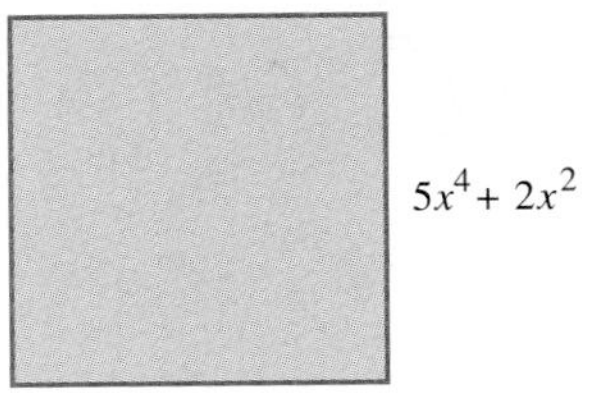

$25x^8 + 20x^6 + 4x^4$

Chapter 6 Test

Study Skills Workbook
Activity 12

Perform the indicated operations.

1. $(5t^4 - 3t^2 + 7t + 3) - (t^4 - t^3 + 3t^2 + 8t + 3)$

1. $4t^4 + t^3 - 6t^2 - t$

2. $(2y^2 - 8y + 8) + (-3y^2 + 2y + 3) - (y^2 + 3y - 6)$

2. $-2y^2 - 9y + 17$

3. Subtract.

$$\begin{array}{r} 9t^3 - 4t^2 + 2t + 2 \\ \underline{9t^3 + 8t^2 - 3t - 6} \end{array}$$

3. $-12t^2 + 5t + 8$

Simplify, and write each answer with only positive exponents.

4. $(-2)^3(-2)^2$

4. $(-2)^5$ or -2^5

5. $\left(\frac{6}{m^2}\right)^3, \quad m \neq 0$

5. $\frac{6^3}{m^6}$

6. $3x^2(-9x^3 + 6x^2 - 2x + 1)$

6. $-27x^5 + 18x^4 - 6x^3 + 3x^2$

7. $(2r - 3)(r^2 + 2r - 5)$

7. $2r^3 + r^2 - 16r + 15$

8. $(t - 8)(t + 3)$

8. $t^2 - 5t - 24$

9. $(4x + 3y)(2x - y)$

9. $8x^2 + 2xy - 3y^2$

10. $(5x - 2y)^2$

10. $25x^2 - 20xy + 4y^2$

11. $(10v + 3w)(10v - 3w)$

11. $100v^2 - 9w^2$

12. $(x + 1)^3$

12. $x^3 + 3x^2 + 3x + 1$

Evaluate each expression.

13. 5^{-4}

13. $\frac{1}{625}$

14. $(-3)^0 + 4^0$

14. 2

15. $4^{-1} + 3^{-1}$

15. $\frac{7}{12}$

Perform the indicated operations. In Exercises 16 and 17, write each answer using only positive exponents. Assume that variables represent nonzero numbers.

16. $\dfrac{8^{-1} \cdot 8^{4}}{8^{-2}}$

16. 8^5

17. $\dfrac{(x^{-3})^{-2}(x^{-1}y)^{2}}{(xy^{-2})^{2}}$

17. x^2y^6

18. $\dfrac{8y^3 - 6y^2 + 4y + 10}{2y}$

18. $4y^2 - 3y + 2 + \dfrac{5}{y}$

19. $(-9x^2y^3 + 6x^4y^3 + 12xy^3) \div (3xy)$

19. $-3xy^2 + 2x^3y^2 + 4y^2$

20. $\dfrac{2x^2 + x - 36}{x - 4}$

20. $2x + 9$

21. $(3x^3 - x + 4) \div (x - 2)$

21. $3x^2 + 6x + 11 + \dfrac{26}{x - 2}$

Write each number in scientific notation.

22. **(a)** 344,000,000,000
(b) .00000557

22. (a) 3.44×10^{11}
(b) 5.57×10^{-6}

Write each number without exponents.

23. **(a)** 2.96×10^{7}
(b) 6.07×10^{-8}

23. (a) 29,600,000
(b) .0000000607

24. What polynomial expression represents the area of this square?

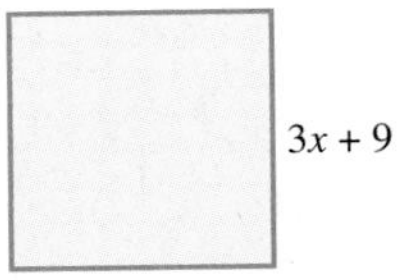

24. $9x^2 + 54x + 81$

25. Give an example of this situation: the sum of two fourth-degree polynomials in x is a third-degree polynomial in x.

25. Answers will vary. One example is $(-4x^4 + 3x^3 + 2x + 1) + (4x^4 - 8x^3 + 2x + 7) = -5x^3 + 4x + 8$.

Cumulative Review Exercises CHAPTERS R–6

Work each problem.

1. $\frac{2}{3} + \frac{1}{8}$

$\frac{19}{24}$

2. $\frac{7}{4} - \frac{9}{5}$

$-\frac{1}{20}$

3. $8.32 - 4.6$

3.72

4. 7.21×8.6

62.006

5. A retailer has \$34,000 invested in her business. She finds that last year she earned 5.4% on this investment. How much did she earn?

\$1836

Find the value of each expression if $x = -2$ and $y = 4$.

6. $\frac{4x - 2y}{x + y}$

-8

7. $x^3 - 4xy$

24

Perform the indicated operations.

8. $\frac{(-13 + 15) - (3 + 2)}{6 - 12}$

$\frac{1}{2}$

9. $-7 - 3[2 + (5 - 8)]$

-4

Decide what property justifies each statement.

10. $(9 + 2) + 3 = 9 + (2 + 3)$

associative property

11. $-7 + 7 = 0$

inverse property

12. $6(4 + 2) = 6(4) + 6(2)$

distributive property

Solve each equation.

13. $2x - 7x + 8x = 30$

$\{10\}$

14. $2 - 3(t - 5) = 4 + t$

$\left\{\frac{13}{4}\right\}$

15. $2(5h + 1) = 10h + 4$

$\emptyset$

16. $d = rt$ for r

$r = \frac{d}{t}$

17. $\frac{x}{5} = \frac{x - 2}{7}$

$\{-5\}$

18. $.05x + .15(50 - x) = 5.50$

$\{20\}$

Solve each problem.

19. A 1-oz mouse takes about 16 times as many breaths as does a 3-ton elephant. (*Source: Dinosaurs, Spitfires, and Sea Dragons*, McGowan, C., Harvard University Press, 1991.) If the two animals take a combined total of 170 breaths per minute, how many breaths does each take during that time period?

mouse: 160; elephant: 10

20. If a number is subtracted from 8 and this difference is tripled, the result is three times the number. Find this number, and you will learn how many times a dolphin rests during a 24-hr period.

4

Solve each equation or inequality.

21. $-8x \le -80$

$[10, \infty)$

22. $-2(x + 4) > 3x + 6$

$\left(-\infty, -\frac{14}{5}\right)$

23. $-3 \le 2x + 5 < 9$

$[-4, 2)$

24. $2x > 4$ and $3x \le 30$

$(2, 10]$

25. $|4x - 7| = 3$

$\left\{1, \frac{5}{2}\right\}$

26. $|2x + 5| > 3$

$(-\infty, -4) \cup (-1, \infty)$

Given $2x - 3y = -6$, find the following.

27. The intercepts and slope of the graph

$(0, 2)$ and $(-3, 0)$; $\frac{2}{3}$

28. The graph

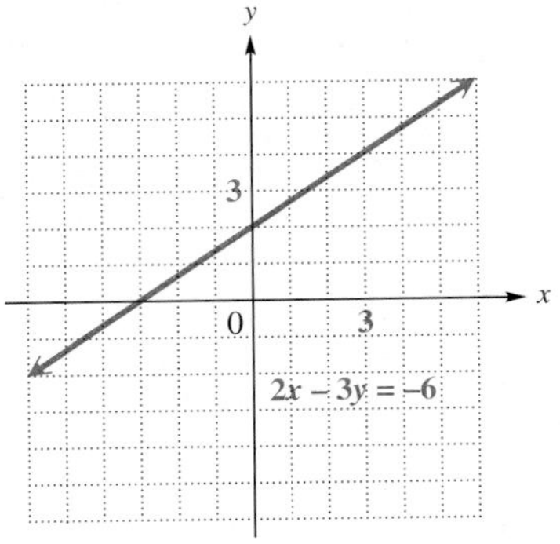

29. Write the given equation using $f(x)$ notation, and find $f(-3)$.

$f(x) = \frac{2}{3}x + 2$; 0

Solve each system of equations.

30. $3x + 8y = 14$
$x - y = 1$

$\{(2, 1)\}$

31. $9x - 3y = -3$
$y = x + 3$

$\{(1, 4)\}$

32. $x + 2y + z = 8$
$2x - y + 3z = 15$
$-x + 3y - 3z = -11$

$\{(2, 1, 4)\}$

Evaluate each expression.

33. $4^{-1} + 3^0$ $\quad \frac{5}{4}$ or $1\frac{1}{4}$

34. $\dfrac{8^{-5} \cdot 8^7}{8^2}$ $\quad 1$

35. Write with positive exponents only: $\dfrac{(a^{-3}b^2)^2}{(2a^{-4}b^{-3})^{-1}}$.

$\frac{2b}{a^{10}}$

36. Write in scientific notation: 34,500.

3.45×10^4

Perform the indicated operations.

37. $(7x^3 - 12x^2 - 3x + 8) + (6x^2 + 4) - (-4x^3 + 8x^2 - 2x - 2)$ $\quad 11x^3 - 14x^2 - x + 14$

38. $(7x + 4)(9x + 3)$

$63x^2 + 57x + 12$

39. $(5x + 8)^2$

$25x^2 + 80x + 64$

40. $\dfrac{y^3 - 3y^2 + 8y - 6}{y - 1}$

$y^2 - 2y + 6$

Factoring and Applications

7

Galileo Galilei, born near Pisa, Italy, in 1564, became a professor of mathematics at the University of Pisa at age 25. He and his students conducted experiments involving the famous Leaning Tower to investigate the relationship between an object's speed of fall and its weight. (*Source: Microsoft Encarta Encyclopedia 2000.*) We will use the concepts of this chapter and the formula Galileo developed from his experiments in Section 7.6.

7.1 Factors; The Greatest Common Factor

Objectives

1. Find the greatest common factor of a list of numbers.
2. Find the greatest common factor of a list of variable terms.
3. Factor out the greatest common factor.
4. Factor by grouping.

Recall from Section R.1 that to **factor** a number means to write it as the product of two or more numbers. The product is called the **factored form** of the number. For example,

$$12 = \underbrace{\overset{\text{Factors}}{6 \cdot 2}}_{\text{Factored form}}.$$

Factoring is a process that "undoes" multiplying. We multiply $6 \cdot 2$ to get 12, but we factor 12 by writing it as $6 \cdot 2$. In this chapter, we extend these ideas to polynomials.

1 Find the greatest common factor of a list of numbers. An integer that is a factor of two or more integers is a **common factor** of those integers. For example, 6 is a common factor of 18 and 24 because 6 is a factor of both 18 and 24. Other common factors of 18 and 24 are 1, 2, and 3. The **greatest common factor (GCF)** of a list of integers is the largest common factor of those integers. This means 6 is the greatest common factor of 18 and 24, since it is the largest of their common factors.

NOTE

Factors of a number are also divisors of the number. The greatest common factor is the same as the greatest common divisor.

Example 1 Finding the Greatest Common Factor for Numbers

Find the greatest common factor for each list of numbers.

(a) 30, 45

First write each number in prime factored form.

$$30 = 2 \cdot 3 \cdot 5$$
$$45 = 3 \cdot 3 \cdot 5$$

Use each prime the *least* number of times it appears in *all* the factored forms. There is no 2 in the prime factored form of 45, so there will be no 2 in the greatest common factor. The least number of times 3 appears in all the factored forms is 1; the least number of times 5 appears is also 1. From this, the

$$\text{GCF} = 3^1 \cdot 5^1 = 3 \cdot 5 = 15.$$

(b) 72, 120, 432

Find the prime factored form of each number.

$$72 = 2 \cdot 2 \cdot 2 \cdot 3 \cdot 3$$
$$120 = 2 \cdot 2 \cdot 2 \cdot 3 \cdot 5$$
$$432 = 2 \cdot 2 \cdot 2 \cdot 2 \cdot 3 \cdot 3 \cdot 3$$

The least number of times 2 appears in all the factored forms is 3, and the least number of times 3 appears is 1. There is no 5 in the prime factored form of either 72 or 432, so the

$$\text{GCF} = 2^3 \cdot 3^1 = 24.$$

Continued on Next Page

(c) 10, 11, 14

Write the prime factored form of each number.

$$10 = 2 \cdot 5$$
$$11 = 11$$
$$14 = 2 \cdot 7$$

There are no primes common to all three numbers, so the GCF is 1.

Work Problem 1 at the Side.

2 Find the greatest common factor of a list of variable terms. The greatest common factor can also be found for a list of variable terms. For example, the terms x^4, x^5, x^6, and x^7 have x^4 as the greatest common factor because the smallest exponent on the variable x is 4.

$$x^4 = 1 \cdot x^4, \quad x^5 = x \cdot x^4, \quad x^6 = x^2 \cdot x^4, \quad x^7 = x^3 \cdot x^4$$

NOTE

The exponent on a variable in the GCF is the *smallest* exponent that appears on that variable in *all* the terms.

Example 2 Finding the Greatest Common Factor for Variable Terms

Find the greatest common factor for each list of terms.

(a) $21m^7$, $-18m^6$, $45m^8$

$$21m^7 = 3 \cdot 7 \cdot m^7$$
$$-18m^6 = -1 \cdot 2 \cdot 3 \cdot 3 \cdot m^6$$
$$45m^8 = 3 \cdot 3 \cdot 5 \cdot m^8$$

First, 3 is the greatest common factor of the coefficients 21, -18, and 45. The smallest exponent on m is 6, so the

$$\text{GCF} = 3m^6.$$

(b) $x^4y^2, x^7y^5, x^3y^7, y^{15}$

$$x^4y^2, \quad x^7y^5, \quad x^3y^7, \quad y^{15}$$

There is no x in the last term, y^{15}, so x will not appear in the greatest common factor. There is a y in each term, however, and 2 is the smallest exponent on y. The GCF is y^2.

(c) $-a^2b, -ab^2$

$$-a^2b = -1a^2b = -1 \cdot 1 \cdot a^2b$$
$$-ab^2 = -1ab^2 = -1 \cdot 1 \cdot ab^2$$

The factors of -1 are -1 and 1. Since $1 > -1$, the GCF is $1ab$ or ab.

NOTE

In a list of negative terms, sometimes a negative common factor is preferable (even though it is not the greatest common factor). In Example 2(c), for instance, we might prefer $-ab$ as the common factor. In factoring exercises, either answer will be acceptable.

1 Find the greatest common factor for each list of numbers.

(a) 30, 20, 15

$30 = 2 \cdot 3 \cdot 5$

$20 = 2 \cdot$ ____ $\cdot$ ____

$15 = 3 \cdot$ ____

GCF = ____

(b) 42, 28, 35

(c) 12, 18, 26, 32

(d) 10, 15, 21

ANSWERS

1. (a) 2; 5; 5; 5 (b) 7 (c) 2 (d) 1

In summary, we find the greatest common factor of a list of terms as follows.

Finding the Greatest Common Factor (GCF)

Step 1 **Factor.** Write each number in prime factored form.

Step 2 **List common factors.** List each prime number or each variable that is a factor of every term in the list. (If a prime does not appear in one of the prime factored forms, it cannot appear in the greatest common factor.)

Step 3 **Choose smallest exponents.** Use as exponents on the common prime factors the *smallest* exponents from the prime factored forms.

Step 4 **Multiply.** Multiply the primes from Step 3. If there are no primes left after Step 3, the greatest common factor is 1.

Work Problem 2 at the Side.

3 Factor out the greatest common factor. The idea of a greatest common factor can be used to write a polynomial in factored form. For example, the polynomial

$$3m + 12$$

has two terms, $3m$ and 12. The greatest common factor of these two terms is 3. We can write $3m + 12$ so that each term is a product with 3 as one factor.

$$3m + 12 = 3 \cdot m + 3 \cdot 4$$

Using the distributive property,

$$3m + 12 = 3 \cdot m + 3 \cdot 4 = 3(m + 4).$$

The factored form of $3m + 12$ is $3(m + 4)$. This process is called **factoring out the greatest common factor.**

CAUTION

The polynomial $3m + 12$ is *not* in factored form when written as the *sum*

$$3 \cdot m + 3 \cdot 4.$$

The *terms* are factored, but the polynomial is not. The factored form of $3m + 12$ is the *product*

$$3(m + 4).$$

Writing a polynomial as a product, that is, in factored form, is called **factoring** the polynomial.

Example 3 **Factoring Out the Greatest Common Factor**

Factor out the greatest common factor.

(a) $5y^2 + 10y = 5y(y) + 5y(2)$ GCF $= 5y$

$= 5y(y + 2)$ Distributive property

Continued on Next Page

2 Find the greatest common factor for each list of terms.

(a) $6m^4, 9m^2, 12m^5$

$6m^4 = 2 \cdot$ ____ $\cdot\, m^4$

$9m^2 = 3 \cdot$ ____ $\cdot$ ____

$12m^5 = 2 \cdot 2 \cdot$ ____ $\cdot$ ____

GCF = ____

(b) $-12p^5, -18q^4$

(c) y^4z^2, y^6z^8, z^9

(d) $12p^{11}, 17q^5$

ANSWERS

2. **(a)** 3; 3; m^2; 3; m^5; $3m^2$ **(b)** 6 **(c)** z^2 **(d)** 1

Check by multiplying: $5y(y + 2) = 5y(y) + 5y(2)$

$= 5y^2 + 10y.$ Original polynomial

(b) $20m^5 + 10m^4 - 15m^3$

The GCF for the terms of this polynomial is $5m^3$.

$20m^5 + 10m^4 - 15m^3$

$= 5m^3(4m^2) + 5m^3(2m) - 5m^3(3)$ Factor each term.

$= 5m^3(4m^2 + 2m - 3)$ Factor out $5m^3$.

Check: $5m^3(4m^2 + 2m - 3) = 20m^5 + 10m^4 - 15m^3$, which is the original polynomial.

(c) $x^5 + x^3 = x^3(x^2) + x^3(1) = x^3(x^2 + 1)$ Don't forget the 1.

(d) $20m^7p^2 - 36m^3p^4 = 4m^3p^2(5m^4) - 4m^3p^2(9p^2)$ GCF $= 4m^3p^2$

$= 4m^3p^2(5m^4 - 9p^2)$

(e) $\frac{1}{6}n^2 + \frac{5}{6}n = \frac{1}{6}n(n) + \frac{1}{6}n(5) = \frac{1}{6}n(n + 5)$

CAUTION

Be sure to include the 1 in a problem like Example 3(c). *Always* check that the factored form can be multiplied out to give the original polynomial.

Work Problem 3 at the Side.

Example 4 **Factoring Out the Greatest Common Factor**

Factor out the greatest common factor.

(a) $a(a + 3) + 4(a + 3)$

The binomial $a + 3$ is the greatest common factor here.

Same

$a(a + 3) + 4(a + 3) = (a + 3)(a + 4)$

(b) $x^2(x + 1) - 5(x + 1) = (x + 1)(x^2 - 5)$ Factor out $x + 1$.

Work Problem 4 at the Side.

4 **Factor by grouping.** When a polynomial has four terms, common factors can sometimes be used to **factor by grouping.**

Example 5 **Factoring by Grouping**

Factor by grouping.

(a) $2x + 6 + ax + 3a$

Group the first two terms and the last two terms, since the first two terms have a common factor of 2 and the last two terms have a common factor of a.

$2x + 6 + ax + 3a = (2x + 6) + (ax + 3a)$

$= 2(x + 3) + a(x + 3)$

The expression is still not in factored form because it is the *sum* of two terms. Now, however, $x + 3$ is a common factor and can be factored out.

$2x + 6 + ax + 3a = 2(x + 3) + a(x + 3)$

$= (x + 3)(2 + a)$

Continued on Next Page

3 Factor out the greatest common factor.

(a) $4x^2 + 6x$

(b) $10y^5 - 8y^4 + 6y^2$

(c) $m^7 + m^9$

(d) $8p^5q^2 + 16p^6q^3 - 12p^4q^7$

(e) $\frac{1}{3}b^2 - \frac{2}{3}b$

(f) $13x^2 - 27$

4 Factor out the greatest common factor.

(a) $r(t - 4) + 5(t - 4)$

(b) $y^2(y + 2) - 3(y + 2)$

(c) $x(x - 1) - 5(x - 1)$

ANSWERS

3. **(a)** $2x(2x + 3)$
(b) $2y^2(5y^3 - 4y^2 + 3)$
(c) $m^7(1 + m^2)$
(d) $4p^4q^2(2p + 4p^2q - 3q^5)$
(e) $\frac{1}{3}b(b - 2)$
(f) no common factor (except 1)

4. **(a)** $(t - 4)(r + 5)$ **(b)** $(y + 2)(y^2 - 3)$
(c) $(x - 1)(x - 5)$

5 Factor by grouping.

(a) $pq + 5q + 2p + 10$

(b) $2a^2 - 4a + 3ab - 6b$

(c) $x^3 + 3x^2 - 5x - 15$

The final result is in factored form because it is a *product.* Note that the goal in factoring by grouping is to get a common factor, $x + 3$ here, so that the last step is possible. Check by multiplying the binomials using the FOIL method from the previous chapter.

Check: $(x + 3)(2 + a) = 2x + ax + 6 + 3a$

$= 2x + 6 + ax + 3a,$ Rearrange terms.

which is the original polynomial.

(b) $2x^2 - 10x + 3xy - 15y = (2x^2 - 10x) + (3xy - 15y)$ Group terms.

$= 2x(x - 5) + 3y(x - 5)$ Factor each group.

$= (x - 5)(2x + 3y)$ Factor out the common factor, $x - 5$.

Check: $(x - 5)(2x + 3y) = 2x^2 + 3xy - 10x - 15y$ FOIL

$= 2x^2 - 10x + 3xy - 15y$ Original polynomial

(c) $t^3 + 2t^2 - 3t - 6 = (t^3 + 2t^2) + (-3t - 6)$ Group terms.

$= t^2(t + 2) - 3(t + 2)$ Factor out -3 so there is a common factor, $t + 2$; $-3(t + 2) = -3t - 6$.

$= (t + 2)(t^2 - 3)$ Factor out $t + 2$.

Check by multiplying.

CAUTION

Be careful with signs when grouping in a problem like Example 5(c). It is wise to check the factoring in the second step, as shown in the example side comment, before continuing.

Work Problem 5 at the Side.

Use these steps to factor a polynomial with four terms by grouping.

Factoring by Grouping

Step 1 **Group terms.** Collect the terms into two groups so that each group has a common factor.

Step 2 **Factor within groups.** Factor out the greatest common factor from each group.

Step 3 **Factor the entire polynomial.** Factor a common binomial factor from the results of Step 2.

Step 4 **If necessary, rearrange terms.** If Step 2 does not result in a common binomial factor, try a different grouping.

ANSWERS

5. (a) $(p + 5)(q + 2)$
(b) $(a - 2)(2a + 3b)$
(c) $(x + 3)(x^2 - 5)$

Example 6 Rearranging Terms Before Factoring by Grouping

Factor by grouping.

(a) $10x^2 - 12y + 15x - 8xy$

Factoring out the common factor of 2 from the first two terms and the common factor of x from the last two terms gives

$$10x^2 - 12y + 15x - 8xy = 2(5x^2 - 6y) + x(15 - 8y).$$

This did not lead to a common factor, so we try rearranging the terms. There is usually more than one way to do this. Let's try

$$10x^2 - 8xy - 12y + 15x,$$

and group the first two terms and the last two terms as follows.

$$\begin{aligned} 10x^2 - 8xy - 12y + 15x &= 2x(5x - 4y) + 3(-4y + 5x) \\ &= 2x(5x - 4y) + 3(5x - 4y) \\ &= (5x - 4y)(2x + 3) \end{aligned}$$

Check: $(5x - 4y)(2x + 3) = 10x^2 + 15x - 8xy - 12y$ FOIL

$= 10x^2 - 12y + 15x - 8xy$ Original polynomial

(b) $2xy + 12 - 3y - 8x$

We need to rearrange these terms to get two groups that each have a common factor. Trial and error suggests the following grouping.

$2xy + 12 - 3y - 8x = (2xy - 3y) + (-8x + 12)$ Group terms.

$= y(2x - 3) - 4(2x - 3)$ Factor each group. Be careful with signs.

$= (2x - 3)(y - 4)$ Factor out the common factor.

Since the quantities in parentheses in the second step must be the same, we factored out -4 rather than 4. Check by multiplying.

CAUTION

Use negative signs carefully when grouping, as in Example 6(b), or a sign error will occur. *Always* check by multiplying.

Work Problem 6 at the Side.

6 Factor by grouping.

(a) $6y^2 - 20w + 15y - 8yw$

(b) $9mn - 4 + 12m - 3n$

ANSWERS

6. (a) $(2y + 5)(3y - 4w)$
(b) $(3m - 1)(3n + 4)$

Focus on **Real-Data Applications**

Idle Prime Time

A positive integer greater than 1 is a prime number if its only factors are 1 and itself. Every positive integer can be written as a product of prime numbers in a unique way, except for the order of the factors. Finding new primes has intrigued people from ancient Greece to modern times. The *Great Internet Mersenne Prime Search* is a consortium headed by George Woltman and Scott Kurowski that has discovered four of the ten largest primes. The prime number $2^{6972593} - 1$ was found during 111 days of idle time on Nayan Hajratwala's home computer. It would take over $4\frac{1}{2}$ miles to actually write this number without commas using a 10-point font. (*Source*: www.utm.edu/research/primes/largest.html)

Prime numbers are essential in the development of unbreakable codes that, in an era of Internet commerce, ensure security in transmitting and storing computer data.

The oldest known method for finding prime numbers is the Sieve of Eratosthenes, similar to the version shown below. Numbers that are not prime (composite numbers) are eliminated and only the prime numbers are left. Begin with 2. Two is prime but multiples of 2 are not, so delete the remaining numbers in Column 2 and all of Columns 4 and 6. Three is prime, but multiples of 3 are not, so delete the remaining numbers in Column 3. Examine the remaining numbers and eliminate any that are composite (such as 25 or 91). The prime numbers are highlighted.

For Group Discussion

1. **Twin primes** occur in pairs that differ by 2. List all the twin primes from the table.

   3 and 5, 5 and 7, 11 and 13, 17 and 19, 29 and 31, 41 and 43, 59 and 61, 71 and 73

2. Observe that all prime numbers larger than 3 are in Columns 1 and 5. Each number in Column 5 is 1 less than a multiple of 6, and therefore has the form $6n - 1$. Each number in Column 1 has a similar structure, $6n + 1$. Show that each of these twin primes, found in the year 2000, has the form $6n + 1$:

$$1693965 \times 2^{66443} \pm 1$$

   and $4648619711505 \times 2^{60000} \pm 1$. (*Hint:* Show that the leading term is divisible by both 2 and 3.)

   Since 2 divides any power of 2, it is only necessary to show that the coefficient is a multiple of 3. The sum of the digits is 39 for the first coefficient and 57 for the second coefficient, so both fit the pattern.

SIEVE OF ERATOSTHENES

Col 1	Col 2	Col 3	Col 4	Col 5	Col 6
1	2	3	4	5	6
7	8	9	10	11	12
13	14	15	16	17	18
19	20	21	22	23	24
25	26	27	28	29	30
31	32	33	34	35	36
37	38	39	40	41	42
43	44	45	46	47	48
49	50	51	52	53	54
55	56	57	58	59	60
61	62	63	64	65	66
67	68	69	70	71	72
73	74	75	76	77	78
79	80	81	82	83	84
85	86	87	88	89	90
91	92	93	94	95	96
97	98	99	100	101	102

3. **Mersenne primes,** named for the 17th century French monk Marin Mersenne, have the form $2^p - 1$, where p is a prime number. Not all such numbers are prime. Show that the number $2^{11} - 1$ is composite and $2^5 - 1$ is prime.

   $2^{11} - 1 = 23 \times 89$; $2^5 - 1 = 31$, which is prime.

4. A **Sophie Germain prime,** named for an 18th century French mathematician, is an odd prime p for which $2p + 1$ is also prime. For example, 5 is a Sophie Germain prime since 11 $(2 \cdot 5 + 1)$ is prime, but 13 is not since 27 $(2 \cdot 13 + 1)$ is composite. List the Sophie Germain primes from the table. **3, 5, 11, 23, 29, 41, 53, 83, 89**

Teaching notes for this activity are provided in the *Printed Test Bank and Instructor's Resource Guide.*

7.1 EXERCISES

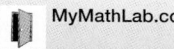

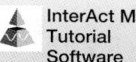

FOR EXTRA HELP: Student's Solutions Manual; MyMathLab.com; InterAct Math Tutorial Software; AW Math Tutor Center; www.mathxl.com; Digital Video Tutor CD 6 Videotape 13

Find the greatest common factor for each list of numbers. See Example 1.

1. 12, 16 **4**

2. 18, 24 **6**

3. 40, 20, 4 **4**

4. 50, 30, 5 **5**

5. 18, 24, 36, 48 **6**

6. 15, 30, 45, 75 **15**

7. 4, 9, 12 **1**

8. 9, 16, 24 **1**

Find the greatest common factor for each list of terms. See Example 2.

9. $16y, 24$ **8**

10. $18w, 27$ **9**

11. $30x^3, 40x^6, 50x^7$ $\mathbf{10x^3}$

12. $60z^4, 70z^8, 90z^9$ $\mathbf{10z^4}$

13. $-x^4y^3, -xy^2$ $\mathbf{xy^2}$

14. $-a^4b^5, -a^3b$ $\mathbf{a^3b}$

15. $42ab^3, -36a, 90b, -48ab$ **6**

16. $45c^3d, 75c, 90d, -105cd$ **15**

Complete each factoring.

17. $9m^4 = 3m^2(\quad)$ $\mathbf{3m^2}$

18. $12p^5 = 6p^3(\quad)$ $\mathbf{2p^2}$

19. $-8z^9 = -4z^5(\quad)$ $\mathbf{2z^4}$

20. $-15k^{11} = -5k^8(\quad)$ $\mathbf{3k^3}$

21. $6m^4n^5 = 3m^3n(\quad)$ $\mathbf{2mn^4}$

22. $27a^3b^2 = 9a^2b(\quad)$ $\mathbf{3ab}$

23. $12y + 24 = 12(\quad)$ $\mathbf{y + 2}$

24. $18p + 36 = 18(\quad)$ $\mathbf{p + 2}$

25. $10a^2 - 20a = 10a(\quad)$ $\mathbf{a - 2}$

26. $15x^2 - 30x = 15x(\quad)$ $\mathbf{x - 2}$

27. $8x^2y + 12x^3y^2 = 4x^2y(\quad)$ $\mathbf{2 + 3xy}$

28. $18s^3t^2 + 10st = 2st(\quad)$ $\mathbf{9s^2t + 5}$

Factor out the greatest common factor. See Examples 3 and 4.

29. $x^2 - 4x$
$\mathbf{x(x - 4)}$

30. $m^2 - 7m$
$\mathbf{m(m - 7)}$

31. $6t^2 + 15t$
$\mathbf{3t(2t + 5)}$

32. $8x^2 + 6x$
$\mathbf{2x(4x + 3)}$

33. $\frac{1}{4}d^2 - \frac{3}{4}d$
$\mathbf{\frac{1}{4}d(d - 3)}$

34. $\frac{1}{5}z^2 + \frac{3}{5}z$
$\mathbf{\frac{1}{5}z(z + 3)}$

35. $12x^3 + 6x^2$
$\mathbf{6x^2(2x + 1)}$

36. $21b^3 - 7b^2$
$\mathbf{7b^2(3b - 1)}$

37. $65y^{10} + 35y^6$
$\mathbf{5y^6(13y^4 + 7)}$

38. $100a^5 + 16a^3$
$\mathbf{4a^3(25a^2 + 4)}$

39. $11w^3 - 100$
no common factor (except 1)

40. $13z^5 - 80$
no common factor (except 1)

41. $8m^2n^3 + 24m^2n^2$
$\mathbf{8m^2n^2(n + 3)}$

42. $19p^2y - 38p^2y^3$
$\mathbf{19p^2y(1 - 2y^2)}$

43. $4x^3 - 10x^2 + 6x$
$\mathbf{2x(2x^2 - 5x + 3)}$

44. $9z^3 - 6z^2 + 12z$
$\mathbf{3z(3z^2 - 2z + 4)}$

45. $13y^8 + 26y^4 - 39y^2$
$\mathbf{13y^2(y^6 + 2y^2 - 3)}$

46. $5x^5 + 25x^4 - 20x^3$

$5x^3(x^2 + 5x - 4)$

47. $45q^4p^5 + 36qp^6 + 81q^2p^3$

$9qp^3(5q^3p^2 + 4p^3 + 9q)$

48. $125a^3z^5 + 60a^4z^4 - 85a^5z^2$

$5a^3z^2(25z^3 + 12az^2 - 17a^2)$

49. $c(x + 2) + d(x + 2)$

$(x + 2)(c + d)$

50. $r(5 - x) + t(5 - x)$

$(5 - x)(r + t)$

51. $a^2(2a + b) - b(2a + b)$

$(2a + b)(a^2 - b)$

52. $3x(x^2 + 5) - y(x^2 + 5)$

$(x^2 + 5)(3x - y)$

Factor by grouping. See Examples 5 and 6.

53. $5m + mn + 20 + 4n$

$(5 + n)(m + 4)$

54. $ts + 5t + 2s + 10$

$(s + 5)(t + 2)$

55. $6xy - 21x + 8y - 28$

$(2y - 7)(3x + 4)$

56. $2mn - 8n + 3m - 12$

$(m - 4)(2n + 3)$

57. $7z^2 + 14z - az - 2a$

$(z + 2)(7z - a)$

58. $2b^2 + 3b - 8ab - 12a$

$(2b + 3)(b - 4a)$

59. $18r^2 + 12ry - 3xr - 2xy$

$(3r + 2y)(6r - x)$

60. $5m^2 + 15mp - 2mp - 6p^2$

$(m + 3p)(5m - 2p)$

61. $w^3 + w^2 + 9w + 9$

$(w + 1)(w^2 + 9)$

62. $y^3 + y^2 + 6y + 6$

$(y + 1)(y^2 + 6)$

63. $3a^3 + 6a^2 - 2a - 4$

$(a + 2)(3a^2 - 2)$

64. $10x^3 + 15x^2 - 8x - 12$

$(2x + 3)(5x^2 - 4)$

65. $16m^3 - 4m^2p^2 - 4mp + p^3$

$(4m - p^2)(4m^2 - p)$

66. $10t^3 - 2t^2s^2 - 5ts + s^3$

$(5t - s^2)(2t^2 - s)$

67. $y^2 + 3x + 3y + xy$

$(y + 3)(y + x)$

68. $m^2 + 14p + 7m + 2mp$

$(m + 7)(m + 2p)$

69. $2z^2 + 6w - 4z - 3wz$

$(z - 2)(2z - 3w)$

70. $2a^2 + 20b - 8a - 5ab$

$(a - 4)(2a - 5b)$

Relating Concepts (Exercises 71–74) For Individual or Group Work

In many cases, the choice of which pairs of terms to group when factoring by grouping can be made in different ways. To see this for Example 6(b), **work Exercises 71–74 in order.**

71. Start with the polynomial from Example 6(b), $2xy + 12 - 3y - 8x$, and rearrange the terms as follows: $2xy - 8x - 3y + 12$. What property from Section 1.7 allows this?

commutative property

72. Group the first two terms and the last two terms of the rearranged polynomial in Exercise 71. Then factor each group.

$2x(y - 4) - 3(y - 4)$

73. Is your result from Exercise 72 in factored form? Explain your answer.

No, because it is not a product. It is the difference between $2x(y - 4)$ and $3(y - 4)$.

74. If your answer to Exercise 73 is *no*, factor the polynomial. Is the result the same as the one shown for Example 6(b)?

$(2x - 3)(y - 4)$; yes

7.2 FACTORING TRINOMIALS

Using FOIL, the product of the binomials $k - 3$ and $k + 1$ is

$$(k - 3)(k + 1) = k^2 - 2k - 3. \quad \text{Multiplying}$$

Suppose instead that we are given the polynomial $k^2 - 2k - 3$ and want to rewrite it as the product $(k - 3)(k + 1)$. That is,

$$k^2 - 2k - 3 = (k - 3)(k + 1). \quad \text{Factoring}$$

Recall from the previous section that this process is called factoring the polynomial. Factoring reverses or "undoes" multiplying.

OBJECTIVES

1. Factor trinomials with a coefficient of 1 for the squared term.
2. Factor trinomials after factoring out the greatest common factor.

1 Factor trinomials with a coefficient of 1 for the squared term. When factoring polynomials with integer coefficients, we use only integers in the factors. For example, we can factor $x^2 + 5x + 6$ by finding integers m and n such that

$$x^2 + 5x + 6 = (x + m)(x + n).$$

To find these integers m and n, we first use FOIL to multiply the two binomials on the right side of the equation:

$$(x + m)(x + n) = x^2 + nx + mx + mn.$$

By the distributive property,

$$x^2 + nx + mx + mn = x^2 + (n + m)x + mn.$$

Comparing this result with $x^2 + 5x + 6$ shows that we must find integers m and n having a sum of 5 and a product of 6.

Product of m and n is 6.

$$x^2 + 5x + 6 = x^2 + (n + m)x + mn$$

Sum of m and n is 5.

Because many pairs of integers have a sum of 5, it is best to begin by listing those pairs of integers whose product is 6. Both 5 and 6 are positive, so we consider only pairs in which both integers are positive.

Work Problem 1 at the Side.

From Problem 1 at the side, we see that the numbers 1 and 6 and the numbers 2 and 3 both have a product of 6, but only the pair 2 and 3 has a sum of 5. So 2 and 3 are the required integers, and

$$x^2 + 5x + 6 = (x + 2)(x + 3).$$

Check by multiplying the binomials using FOIL. *Make sure that the sum of the outer and inner products produces the correct middle term.*

Check: $(x + 2)(x + 3) = x^2 + 5x + 6$

$$\begin{array}{r} 2x \\ 3x \\ \hline 5x \end{array} \quad \text{Add.}$$

This method of factoring can be used only for trinomials that have 1 as the coefficient of the squared term. Methods for factoring other trinomials will be given in the next two sections.

1 **(a)** List all pairs of positive integers whose product is 6.

(b) Find the pair from part (a) whose sum is 5.

ANSWERS

1. (a) 1, 6; 2, 3 (b) 2, 3

2 Factor each trinomial.

(a) $y^2 + 12y + 20$

First complete the given list of numbers.

Factors of 20	Sums of Factors
20, 1	$20 + 1 = 21$
10, ___	$10 +$ ___ $=$ ___
5, ___	$5 +$ ___ $=$ ___

(b) $x^2 + 9x + 18$

3 Factor each trinomial.

(a) $t^2 - 12t + 32$

First complete the given list of numbers.

Factors of 32	Sums of Factors
$-32, -1$	$-32 + (-1) = -33$
$-16,$ ___	$-16 + ($___$) =$ ___
$-8,$ ___	$-8 + ($___$) =$ ___

(b) $y^2 - 10y + 24$

Example 1 Factoring a Trinomial with All Positive Terms

Factor $m^2 + 9m + 14$.

Look for two integers whose product is 14 and whose sum is 9. List the pairs of integers whose products are 14. Then examine the sums. Only positive integers are needed since all signs in $m^2 + 9m + 14$ are positive.

Factors of 14	Sums of Factors	
14, 1	$14 + 1 = 15$	
7, 2	$7 + 2 = 9$	Sum is 9.

From the list, 7 and 2 are the required integers, since $7 \cdot 2 = 14$ and $7 + 2 = 9$. Thus,

$$m^2 + 9m + 14 = (m + 2)(m + 7).$$

Check: $(m + 2)(m + 7) = m^2 + 7m + 2m + 14$
$= m^2 + 9m + 14$

NOTE

In Example 1, the answer also could have been written $(m + 7)(m + 2)$. Because of the commutative property of multiplication, the order of the factors does not matter. *Always* check by multiplying.

Work Problem 2 at the Side.

Example 2 Factoring a Trinomial with a Negative Middle Term

Factor $x^2 - 9x + 20$.

Find two integers whose product is 20 and whose sum is -9. Since the numbers we are looking for have a positive product and a negative sum, we consider only pairs of negative integers.

Factors of 20	Sums of Factors	
$-20, -1$	$-20 + (-1) = -21$	
$-10, -2$	$-10 + (-2) = -12$	
$-5, -4$	$-5 + (-4) = -9$	Sum is -9.

The required integers are -5 and -4, so

$$x^2 - 9x + 20 = (x - 5)(x - 4).$$

Check: $(x - 5)(x - 4) = x^2 - 4x - 5x + 20$
$= x^2 - 9x + 20$

Work Problem 3 at the Side.

ANSWERS
2. (a) 2; 2; 12; 4; 4; 9; $(y + 10)(y + 2)$
(b) $(x + 3)(x + 6)$
3. (a) -2; -2; -18; -4; -4; -12; $(t - 8)(t - 4)$
(b) $(y - 6)(y - 4)$

Example 3 Factoring a Trinomial with Two Negative Terms

Factor $p^2 - 2p - 15$.

Find two integers whose product is -15 and whose sum is -2. If these numbers do not come to mind right away, find them (if they exist) by listing all the pairs of integers whose product is -15. Because the last term, -15, is negative, we need pairs of integers with different signs.

Factors of −15	Sums of Factors	
$15, -1$	$15 + (-1) = 14$	
$-15, 1$	$-15 + 1 = -14$	
$5, -3$	$5 + (-3) = 2$	
$-5, 3$	$-5 + 3 = -2$	Sum is -2.

The required integers are -5 and 3, so

$$p^2 - 2p - 15 = (p - 5)(p + 3).$$

Check: Multiply $(p - 5)(p + 3)$.

NOTE

In Examples 1–3, notice that we listed factors in descending order (disregarding sign) when we were looking for the required pair of integers. This helps avoid skipping the correct combination.

Work Problem 4 at the Side.

As shown in the next example, some trinomials cannot be factored using only integers. We call such trinomials **prime polynomials.**

Example 4 Deciding whether Polynomials Are Prime

Factor each trinomial.

(a) $x^2 - 5x + 12$

As in Example 2, both factors must be negative to give a positive product and a negative sum. First, list all pairs of negative integers whose product is 12. Then examine the sums.

Factors of 12	Sums of Factors
$-12, -1$	$-12 + (-1) = -13$
$-6, -2$	$-6 + (-2) = -8$
$-4, -3$	$-4 + (-3) = -7$

None of the pairs of integers has a sum of -5. Therefore, the trinomial $x^2 - 5x + 12$ *cannot be factored using only integers;* it is a *prime polynomial.*

(b) $k^2 - 8k + 11$

There is no pair of integers whose product is 11 and whose sum is -8, so $k^2 - 8k + 11$ is a prime polynomial.

Work Problem 5 at the Side.

4 Factor each trinomial.

(a) $a^2 - 9a - 22$

(b) $r^2 - 6r - 16$

5 Factor each trinomial, if possible.

(a) $r^2 - 3r - 4$

(b) $m^2 - 2m + 5$

ANSWERS

4. (a) $(a - 11)(a + 2)$ **(b)** $(r - 8)(r + 2)$

5. (a) $(r - 4)(r + 1)$ **(b)** prime

The procedure for factoring a trinomial of the form $x^2 + bx + c$ follows.

Factoring $x^2 + bx + c$

Find two integers whose product is c and whose sum is b.

1. Both integers must be positive if b and c are positive.
2. Both integers must be negative if c is positive and b is negative.
3. One integer must be positive and one must be negative if c is negative.

Example 5 Factoring a Trinomial with Two Variables

Factor $z^2 - 2bz - 3b^2$.

Here, the coefficient of the middle term is $-2b$, so we need to find two expressions whose product is $-3b^2$ and whose sum is $-2b$. The expressions are $-3b$ and b, so

$$z^2 - 2bz - 3b^2 = (z - 3b)(z + b).$$

Check:
$$(z - 3b)(z + b) = z^2 + zb - 3bz - 3b^2$$
$$= z^2 + 1bz - 3bz - 3b^2$$
$$= z^2 - 2bz - 3b^2$$

Work Problem 6 at the Side.

6 Factor each trinomial.

(a) $b^2 - 3ab - 4a^2$

(b) $r^2 - 6rs + 8s^2$

2 Factor trinomials after factoring out the greatest common factor. The trinomial in the next example does not have a coefficient of 1 for the squared term. (In fact, there is no squared term.) However, there may be a common factor.

Example 6 Factoring a Trinomial with a Common Factor

Factor $4x^5 - 28x^4 + 40x^3$.

First, factor out the greatest common factor, $4x^3$.

$$4x^5 - 28x^4 + 40x^3 = 4x^3(x^2 - 7x + 10)$$

Now factor $x^2 - 7x + 10$. The integers -5 and -2 have a product of 10 and a sum of -7. The complete factored form is

$$4x^5 - 28x^4 + 40x^3 = 4x^3(x - 5)(x - 2). \quad \text{Include } 4x^3.$$

Check:
$$4x^3(x - 5)(x - 2) = 4x^3(x^2 - 7x + 10)$$
$$= 4x^5 - 28x^4 + 40x^3$$

7 Factor each trinomial completely.

(a) $2p^3 + 6p^2 - 8p$

(b) $3x^4 - 15x^3 + 18x^2$

CAUTION

When factoring, always look for a common factor first. Remember to include the common factor as part of the answer. As a check, multiplying out the complete factored form should give the original polynomial.

Work Problem 7 at the Side.

ANSWERS

6. (a) $(b - 4a)(b + a)$ **(b)** $(r - 4s)(r - 2s)$

7. (a) $2p(p + 4)(p - 1)$ **(b)** $3x^2(x - 3)(x - 2)$

7.2 EXERCISES

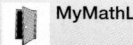

FOR EXTRA HELP: Student's Solutions Manual; MyMathLab.com; InterAct Math Tutorial Software; AW Math Tutor Center; MathXL www.mathxl.com; Digital Video Tutor CD 6 Videotape 13

1. When factoring a trinomial in x as $(x + a)(x + b)$, what must be true of a and b, if the last term of the trinomial is negative?

a and b must have different signs.

2. In Exercise 1, what must be true of a and b if the last term is positive?

a and b must have the same sign.

3. What is meant by a *prime polynomial*?

A prime polynomial is one that cannot be factored using only integers in the factors.

4. How can you check your work when factoring a trinomial? Does the check ensure that the trinomial is completely factored?

To check a factored form, multiply the factors. You should get the trinomial you started with. If you forget to factor out any common factors, the check will not indicate it.

In Exercises 5–8, list all pairs of integers with the given product. Then find the pair whose sum is given. See the tables in Examples 1–4.

5. Product: 12 Sum: 7

1 and 12, −1 and −12, 2 and 6, −2 and −6, 3 and 4, −3 and −4; the pair with a sum of 7 is 3 and 4.

6. Product: 18 Sum: 9

1 and 18, −1 and −18, 2 and 9, −2 and −9, 3 and 6, −3 and −6; the pair with a sum of 9 is 3 and 6.

7. Product: −24 Sum: −5

1 and −24, −1 and 24, 2 and −12, −2 and 12, 3 and −8, −3 and 8, 4 and −6, −4 and 6; the pair with a sum of −5 is 3 and −8.

8. Product: −36 Sum: −16

1 and −36, −1 and 36, 2 and −18, −2 and 18, 3 and −12, −3 and 12, 4 and −9, −4 and 9, 6 and −6; the pair with a sum of −16 is 2 and −18.

9. Which one of the following is the correct factored form of $x^2 - 12x + 32$?

A. $(x - 8)(x + 4)$ **B.** $(x + 8)(x - 4)$

C. $(x - 8)(x - 4)$ **D.** $(x + 8)(x + 4)$

C

10. What would be the first step in factoring $2x^3 + 8x^2 - 10x$?

Factor out the greatest common factor, $2x$.

Complete each factoring.

11. $x^2 + 15x + 44 = (x + 4)(\quad)$

$x + 11$

12. $r^2 + 15r + 56 = (r + 7)(\quad)$

$r + 8$

13. $x^2 - 9x + 8 = (x - 1)(\quad)$

$x - 8$

14. $t^2 - 14t + 24 = (t - 2)(\quad)$

$t - 12$

15. $y^2 - 2y - 15 = (y + 3)(\quad)$

$y - 5$

16. $t^2 - t - 42 = (t + 6)(\quad)$

$t - 7$

17. $x^2 + 9x - 22 = (x - 2)(\quad)$

$x + 11$

18. $x^2 + 6x - 27 = (x - 3)(\quad)$

$x + 9$

19. $y^2 - 7y - 18 = (y + 2)(\quad)$

$y - 9$

20. $y^2 - 2y - 24 = (y + 4)(\quad)$

$y - 6$

Factor completely. If a polynomial cannot be factored, write prime. *See Examples 1–4.*

21. $y^2 + 9y + 8$
$(y + 8)(y + 1)$

22. $a^2 + 9a + 20$
$(a + 4)(a + 5)$

23. $b^2 + 8b + 15$
$(b + 3)(b + 5)$

24. $x^2 + 6x + 8$
$(x + 4)(x + 2)$

25. $m^2 + m - 20$
$(m + 5)(m - 4)$

26. $p^2 + 4p - 5$
$(p + 5)(p - 1)$

27. $x^2 + 3x - 40$
$(x + 8)(x - 5)$

28. $d^2 + 4d - 45$
$(d + 9)(d - 5)$

29. $y^2 - 8y + 15$
$(y - 5)(y - 3)$

30. $y^2 - 6y + 8$
$(y - 4)(y - 2)$

31. $z^2 - 15z + 56$
$(z - 8)(z - 7)$

32. $x^2 - 13x + 36$
$(x - 9)(x - 4)$

33. $r^2 - r - 30$
$(r - 6)(r + 5)$

34. $q^2 - q - 42$
$(q - 7)(q + 6)$

35. $a^2 - 8a - 48$
$(a - 12)(a + 4)$

36. $m^2 - 10m - 24$
$(m - 12)(m + 2)$

37. $x^2 + 4x + 5$
prime

38. $t^2 + 11t + 12$
prime

Factor completely. See Examples 5 and 6.

39. $r^2 + 3ra + 2a^2$
$(r + 2a)(r + a)$

40. $x^2 + 5xa + 4a^2$
$(x + 4a)(x + a)$

41. $x^2 + 4xy + 3y^2$
$(x + y)(x + 3y)$

42. $p^2 + 9pq + 8q^2$
$(p + q)(p + 8q)$

43. $t^2 - tz - 6z^2$
$(t + 2z)(t - 3z)$

44. $a^2 - ab - 12b^2$
$(a + 3b)(a - 4b)$

45. $v^2 - 11vw + 30w^2$
$(v - 5w)(v - 6w)$

46. $v^2 - 11vx + 24x^2$
$(v - 8x)(v - 3x)$

47. $4x^2 + 12x - 40$
$4(x + 5)(x - 2)$

48. $5y^2 - 5y - 30$
$5(y + 2)(y - 3)$

49. $2t^3 + 8t^2 + 6t$
$2t(t + 1)(t + 3)$

50. $3t^3 + 27t^2 + 24t$
$3t(t + 8)(t + 1)$

51. $2x^6 + 8x^5 - 42x^4$
$2x^4(x - 3)(x + 7)$

52. $4y^5 + 12y^4 - 40y^3$
$4y^3(y - 2)(y + 5)$

53. $a^5 + 3a^4b - 4a^3b^2$
$a^3(a + 4b)(a - b)$

54. $z^{10} - 4z^9y - 21z^8y^2$
$z^8(z - 7y)(z + 3y)$

55. $m^3n - 10m^2n^2 + 24mn^3$
$mn(m - 6n)(m - 4n)$

56. $y^3z + 3y^2z^2 - 54yz^3$
$yz(y - 6z)(y + 9z)$

57. Use the FOIL method from Section 6.3 to show that $(2x + 4)(x - 3) = 2x^2 - 2x - 12$. Why, then, is it incorrect to completely factor $2x^2 - 2x - 12$ as $(2x + 4)(x - 3)$?

The factored form $(2x + 4)(x - 3)$ is incorrect because $2x + 4$ has a common factor, which must be factored out for the trinomial to be completely factored.

58. Why is it incorrect to completely factor $3x^2 + 9x - 12$ as the product $(x - 1)(3x + 12)$?

The factored form $(x - 1)(3x + 12)$ is incorrect because $3x + 12$ has a common factor of 3, which must be factored out.

7.3 FACTORING TRINOMIALS BY GROUPING

Trinomials like $2x^2 + 7x + 6$, in which the coefficient of the squared term is *not* 1, are factored with extensions of the methods from the previous sections. One such method uses factoring by grouping from Section 7.1.

OBJECTIVE

1 Factor trinomials by grouping when the coefficient of the squared term is not 1.

1 Factor trinomials by grouping when the coefficient of the squared term is not 1. Recall that a trinomial such as $m^2 + 3m + 2$ is factored by finding two numbers whose product is 2 and whose sum is 3. To factor $2x^2 + 7x + 6$, we look for two integers whose product is $2 \cdot 6 = 12$ and whose sum is 7.

Sum is 7.

$$2x^2 + 7x + 6$$

Product is $2 \cdot 6 = 12$.

By considering pairs of positive integers whose product is 12, the necessary integers are found to be 3 and 4. We use these integers to write the middle term, $7x$, as $7x = 3x + 4x$. The trinomial $2x^2 + 7x + 6$ becomes

$$2x^2 + 7x + 6 = 2x^2 + \underbrace{3x + 4x}_{7x} + 6.$$

$$= (2x^2 + 3x) + (4x + 6) \quad \text{Group terms.}$$

$$= x(2x + 3) + 2(2x + 3) \quad \text{Factor each group.}$$

Must be same

$$2x^2 + 7x + 6 = (2x + 3)(x + 2) \quad \text{Factor out } 2x + 3.$$

Check: $(2x + 3)(x + 2) = 2x^2 + 7x + 6$

In the example above, we could have written $7x$ as $4x + 3x$. Factoring by grouping this way would give the same answer.

Work Problem 1 at the Side.

1 (a) Factor $2x^2 + 7x + 6$ by writing $7x$ as $4x + 3x$. Complete the following.

$2x^2 + 7x + 6$

$= 2x^2 + 4x + 3x + 6$

$= (2x^2 + \_\_\_) + (3x + \_\_\_)$

$= 2x(x + \_\_\_) + 3(x + \_\_\_)$

$= (\_\_\_\_)(2x + 3)$

(b) Is the answer the same? (Remember that the order of the factors does not matter.)

Example 1 Factoring Trinomials by Grouping

Factor each trinomial.

(a) $6r^2 + r - 1$

We must find two integers with a product of $6(-1) = -6$ and a sum of 1.

Sum is 1.

$$6r^2 + r - 1 = 6r^2 + 1r - 1$$

Product is $6(-1) = -6$.

The integers are -2 and 3. We write the middle term, r, as $-2r + 3r$.

$$6r^2 + r - 1 = 6r^2 - 2r + 3r - 1 \quad r = -2r + 3r$$

$$= (6r^2 - 2r) + (3r - 1) \quad \text{Group terms.}$$

$$= 2r(3r - 1) + 1(3r - 1) \quad \text{The binomials must be the same.}$$

$$= (3r - 1)(2r + 1) \quad \text{Factor out } 3r - 1.$$

Check: $(3r - 1)(2r + 1) = 6r^2 + r - 1$

Continued on Next Page

ANSWERS

1. (a) $4x$; 6; 2; 2; $x + 2$ **(b)** yes

(b) $12z^2 - 5z - 2$

Look for two integers whose product is $12(-2) = -24$ and whose sum is -5. The required integers are 3 and -8, so

$$\begin{aligned} 12z^2 - 5z - 2 &= 12z^2 + 3z - 8z - 2 && -5z = 3z - 8z \\ &= (12z^2 + 3z) + (-8z - 2) && \text{Group terms.} \\ &= 3z(4z + 1) - 2(4z + 1) && \text{Factor each group; be careful with signs.} \\ &= (4z + 1)(3z - 2). && \text{Factor out } 4z + 1. \end{aligned}$$

Check: $(4z + 1)(3z - 2) = 12z^2 - 5z - 2$

(c) $10m^2 + mn - 3n^2$

Two integers whose product is $10(-3) = -30$ and whose sum is 1 are -5 and 6. Rewrite the trinomial with four terms.

$$\begin{aligned} 10m^2 + mn - 3n^2 &= 10m^2 - 5mn + 6mn - 3n^2 && mn = -5mn + 6mn \\ &= 5m(2m - n) + 3n(2m - n) && \text{Group terms; factor each group.} \\ &= (2m - n)(5m + 3n) && \text{Factor out } 2m - n. \end{aligned}$$

Check by multiplying.

Work Problem 2 at the Side.

2 Factor each trinomial by grouping.

(a) $2m^2 + 7m + 3$

(b) $5p^2 - 2p - 3$

(c) $15k^2 - km - 2m^2$

Example 2 Factoring a Trinomial with a Common Factor by Grouping

Factor $28x^5 - 58x^4 - 30x^3$.

First factor out the greatest common factor, $2x^3$.

$$28x^5 - 58x^4 - 30x^3 = 2x^3(14x^2 - 29x - 15)$$

To factor $14x^2 - 29x - 15$, find two integers whose product is $14(-15) = -210$ and whose sum is -29. Factoring 210 into prime factors gives

$$210 = 2 \cdot 3 \cdot 5 \cdot 7.$$

Combine these prime factors in pairs in different ways, using one positive and one negative (to get -210). The factors 6 and -35 have the correct sum. Now rewrite the given trinomial and factor it.

$$\begin{aligned} 28x^5 - 58x^4 - 30x^3 &= 2x^3(14x^2 + 6x - 35x - 15) \\ &= 2x^3[(14x^2 + 6x) + (-35x - 15)] \\ &= 2x^3[2x(7x + 3) - 5(7x + 3)] \\ &= 2x^3[(7x + 3)(2x - 5)] \\ &= 2x^3(7x + 3)(2x - 5) \end{aligned}$$

Check by multiplying.

CAUTION

Remember to include the common factor in the final result.

Work Problem 3 at the Side.

3 Factor each trinomial completely.

(a) $4x^2 - 2x - 30$

(b) $18p^4 + 63p^3 + 27p^2$

(c) $6a^2 + 3ab - 18b^2$

ANSWERS

2. **(a)** $(2m + 1)(m + 3)$
(b) $(5p + 3)(p - 1)$
(c) $(5k - 2m)(3k + m)$

3. **(a)** $2(2x + 5)(x - 3)$
(b) $9p^2(2p + 1)(p + 3)$
(c) $3(2a - 3b)(a + 2b)$

7.3 EXERCISES

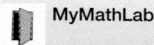

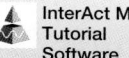

FOR EXTRA HELP: Student's Solutions Manual | MyMathLab.com | InterAct Math Tutorial Software | AW Math Tutor Center | www.mathxl.com | Digital Video Tutor CD 6 Videotape 13

Factor each polynomial by grouping. (The middle term of an equivalent trinomial has already been rewritten.) See Example 1.

1. $m^2 + 6m + 2m + 12$
$(m + 6)(m + 2)$

2. $x^2 + 7x + 2x + 14$
$(x + 7)(x + 2)$

3. $a^2 + 5a - 2a - 10$
$(a + 5)(a - 2)$

4. $y^2 + 4y - 6y - 24$
$(y + 4)(y - 6)$

5. $10t^2 + 5t + 4t + 2$
$(2t + 1)(5t + 2)$

6. $6x^2 + 9x + 4x + 6$
$(2x + 3)(3x + 2)$

7. $15z^2 - 10z - 9z + 6$
$(3z - 2)(5z - 3)$

8. $12p^2 - 9p - 8p + 6$
$(4p - 3)(3p - 2)$

9. $8s^2 - 4st + 6st - 3t^2$
$(2s - t)(4s + 3t)$

10. $3x^2 - 7xy + 6xy - 14y^2$
$(3x - 7y)(x + 2y)$

11. Which pair of integers would be used to rewrite the middle term when factoring $12y^2 + 5y - 2$ by grouping?

A. $-8, 3$ **B.** $8, -3$ **C.** $-6, 4$ **D.** $6, -4$

B

12. Which pair of integers would be used to rewrite the middle term when factoring $20b^2 - 13b + 2$ by grouping?

A. $10, 3$ **B.** $-10, -3$ **C.** $8, 5$ **D.** $-8, -5$

D

Complete the steps to factor each trinomial by grouping.

13. $2m^2 + 11m + 12$

(a) Find two integers whose product is $\underline{2} \cdot \underline{12} = \underline{24}$ and whose sum is $\underline{11}$.

(b) The required integers are $\underline{3}$ and $\underline{8}$. (Order is irrelevant.)

(c) Write the middle term $11m$ as $\underline{3m} + \underline{8m}$.

(d) Rewrite the given trinomial as $\underline{2m^2 + 3m + 8m + 12}$.

(e) Factor the polynomial in part (d) by grouping.
$(2m + 3)(m + 4)$

(f) Check by multiplying.
$(2m + 3)(m + 4) = 2m^2 + 11m + 12$

14. $6y^2 - 19y + 10$

(a) Find two integers whose product is $\underline{6} \cdot \underline{10} = \underline{60}$ and whose sum is $\underline{-19}$.

(b) The required integers are $\underline{-4}$ and $\underline{-15}$. (Order is irrelevant.)

(c) Write the middle term $-19y$ as $\underline{-4y} + \underline{(-15y)}$.

(d) Rewrite the given trinomial as $\underline{6y^2 - 4y - 15y + 10}$.

(e) Factor the polynomial in part (d) by grouping.
$(3y - 2)(2y - 5)$

(f) Check by multiplying.
$(3y - 2)(2y - 5) = 6y^2 - 19y + 10$

Factor each trinomial by grouping. See Examples 1 and 2. **The order of the factors is irrelevant in Exercises 15–38.**

15. $2x^2 + 7x + 3$
$(2x + 1)(x + 3)$

16. $3y^2 + 13y + 4$
$(3y + 1)(y + 4)$

17. $4r^2 + r - 3$
$(4r - 3)(r + 1)$

18. $4r^2 + 3r - 10$
$(4r - 5)(r + 2)$

19. $8m^2 - 10m - 3$
$(4m + 1)(2m - 3)$

20. $20x^2 - 28x - 3$
$(10x + 1)(2x - 3)$

21. $21m^2 + 13m + 2$
$(3m + 1)(7m + 2)$

22. $38x^2 + 23x + 2$
$(2x + 1)(19x + 2)$

23. $6b^2 + 7b + 2$
$(2b + 1)(3b + 2)$

24. $6w^2 + 19w + 10$
$(2w + 5)(3w + 2)$

25. $12y^2 - 13y + 3$
$(4y - 3)(3y - 1)$

26. $15a^2 - 16a + 4$
$(3a - 2)(5a - 2)$

27. $24x^2 - 42x + 9$
$3(4x - 1)(2x - 3)$

28. $48b^2 - 74b - 10$
$2(8b + 1)(3b - 5)$

29. $2m^3 + 2m^2 - 40m$
$2m(m - 4)(m + 5)$

30. $3x^3 + 12x^2 - 36x$
$3x(x - 2)(x + 6)$

31. $32z^5 - 20z^4 - 12z^3$
$4z^3(8z + 3)(z - 1)$

32. $18x^5 + 15x^4 - 75x^3$
$3x^3(2x + 5)(3x - 5)$

33. $12p^2 + 7pq - 12q^2$
$(3p + 4q)(4p - 3q)$

34. $6m^2 - 5mn - 6n^2$
$(3m + 2n)(2m - 3n)$

35. $6a^2 - 7ab - 5b^2$
$(3a - 5b)(2a + b)$

36. $25g^2 - 5gh - 2h^2$
$(5g + h)(5g - 2h)$

37. $5 - 6x + x^2$
$(5 - x)(1 - x)$

38. $7 + 8x + x^2$
$(7 + x)(1 + x)$

39. On a quiz, a student factored $16x^2 - 24x + 5$ by grouping as follows.

$$\begin{aligned} &16x^2 - 24x + 5 \\ &= 16x^2 - 4x - 20x + 5 \\ &= 4x(4x - 1) - 5(4x - 1) \quad \text{His answer} \end{aligned}$$

He thought his answer was correct since it checked by multiplying. Why was the answer marked wrong? What is the correct factored form?

The student stopped too soon. He needs to factor out the common factor $4x - 1$ to get $(4x - 1)(4x - 5)$ as the correct answer.

40. On the same quiz, another student factored $3k^3 - 12k^2 - 15k$ by first factoring out the common factor $3k$ to get $3k(k^2 - 4k - 5)$. Then she wrote

$$\begin{aligned} k^2 - 4k - 5 &= k^2 - 5k + k - 5 \\ &= k(k - 5) + 1(k - 5) \\ &= (k - 5)(k + 1). \quad \text{Her answer} \end{aligned}$$

Why was the answer marked wrong? What is the correct factored form?

The student forgot to include the common factor $3k$ in her answer. The correct answer is $3k(k - 5)(k + 1)$.

7.4 FACTORING TRINOMIALS USING FOIL

1 Factor trinomials using FOIL. This section shows an alternative method of factoring trinomials in which the coefficient of the squared term is not 1. This method uses trial and error.

To factor $2x^2 + 7x + 6$ (the same trinomial factored at the beginning of Section 7.3) by trial and error, we use FOIL backwards. We want to write $2x^2 + 7x + 6$ as the product of two binomials.

$$2x^2 + 7x + 6 = (\qquad)(\qquad)$$

The product of the two first terms of the binomials is $2x^2$. The possible factors of $2x^2$ are $2x$ and x or $-2x$ and $-x$. Since all terms of the trinomial are positive, only positive factors should be considered. Thus, we have

$$2x^2 + 7x + 6 = (2x \qquad)(x \qquad).$$

The product of the two last terms, 6, can be factored as $6 \cdot 1$, $1 \cdot 6$, $2 \cdot 3$, or $3 \cdot 2$. Try each pair to find the pair that gives the correct middle term.

Work Problem 1 at the Side.

In part (b) at the side, since $2x + 6 = 2(x + 3)$, the binomial $2x + 6$ has a common factor of 2, while $2x^2 + 7x + 6$ has no common factor other than 1. The product $(2x + 6)(x + 1)$ cannot be correct. (Part (c) also has one binomial factor with a common factor.)

NOTE

If the original polynomial has no common factor, then none of its binomial factors will either.

Now try the numbers 2 and 3 as factors of 6. Because of the common factor of 2 in $2x + 2$, $(2x + 2)(x + 3)$ will not work. Try $(2x + 3)(x + 2)$.

$$(2x + 3)(x + 2) = 2x^2 + 7x + 6 \quad \text{Correct}$$

$$\begin{array}{r} 3x \\ \underline{4x} \\ 7x \end{array} \quad \text{Add.}$$

Finally, we see that $2x^2 + 7x + 6$ factors as

$$2x^2 + 7x + 6 = (2x + 3)(x + 2).$$

Check by multiplying: $(2x + 3)(x + 2) = 2x^2 + 7x + 6$.

Example 1 **Factoring a Trinomial with All Positive Terms Using FOIL**

Factor $8p^2 + 14p + 5$.

The number 8 has several possible pairs of factors, but 5 has only 1 and 5 or -1 and -5. For this reason, it is easier to begin by considering the factors of 5. Ignore the negative factors since all coefficients in the trinomial are positive. If $8p^2 + 14p + 5$ can be factored, the factors will have the form

$$(\quad + 5)(\quad + 1).$$

Continued on Next Page

OBJECTIVE

1 Factor trinomials using FOIL.

Study Skills Workbook **Activity 5**

1 Multiply to decide whether each factored form is correct or incorrect for $2x^2 + 7x + 6$.

(a) $(2x + 1)(x + 6)$

(b) $(2x + 6)(x + 1)$

(c) $(2x + 2)(x + 3)$

ANSWERS

1. **(a)** incorrect **(b)** incorrect **(c)** incorrect

2 Factor each trinomial.

(a) $2p^2 + 9p + 9$

(b) $6p^2 + 19p + 10$

(c) $8x^2 + 14x + 3$

The possible pairs of factors of $8p^2$ are $8p$ and p, or $4p$ and $2p$. Try various combinations, checking to see if the middle term is $14p$ in each case.

$(8p + 5)(p + 1)$ Incorrect

$5p$
$8p$
$13p$ Add.

$(p + 5)(8p + 1)$ Incorrect

$40p$
p
$41p$ Add.

$(4p + 5)(2p + 1)$ Correct

$10p$
$4p$
$14p$ Add.

Since $14p$ is the correct middle term,

$$8p^2 + 14p + 5 = (4p + 5)(2p + 1).$$

Check: $(4p + 5)(2p + 1) = 8p^2 + 14p + 5$

Work Problem 2 at the Side.

3 Factor each trinomial.

(a) $4y^2 - 11y + 6$

(b) $9x^2 - 21x + 10$

Example 2 Factoring a Trinomial with a Negative Middle Term Using FOIL

Factor $6x^2 - 11x + 3$.

Since 3 has only 1 and 3 or -1 and -3 as factors, it is better here to begin by factoring 3. The last term of the trinomial $6x^2 - 11x + 3$ is positive and the middle term has a negative coefficient, so only negative factors should be considered. Try -3 and -1 as factors of 3:

$$(\quad - 3)(\quad - 1).$$

The factors of $6x^2$ may be either $6x$ and x, or $2x$ and $3x$. Try $2x$ and $3x$.

$(2x - 3)(3x - 1)$ Correct

$-9x$
$-2x$
$-11x$ Add.

These factors give the correct middle term, so

$$6x^2 - 11x + 3 = (2x - 3)(3x - 1).$$

Check by multiplying.

Work Problem 3 at the Side.

ANSWERS

2. **(a)** $(2p + 3)(p + 3)$
(b) $(3p + 2)(2p + 5)$
(c) $(4x + 1)(2x + 3)$

3. **(a)** $(4y - 3)(y - 2)$
(b) $(3x - 5)(3x - 2)$

Example 3 Factoring a Trinomial with a Negative Last Term Using FOIL

Factor $8x^2 + 6x - 9$.

The integer 8 has several possible pairs of factors, as does -9. Since the last term is negative, one positive factor and one negative factor of -9 are needed. Since the coefficient of the middle term is small, it is wise to avoid large factors such as 8 or 9. We try 4 and 2 as factors of 8, and 3 and -3 as factors of -9, and check the middle term.

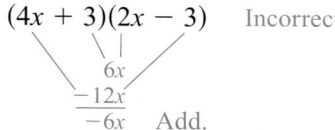

$$(4x + 3)(2x - 3) \quad \text{Incorrect}$$

$6x$
$-12x$
$-6x$ Add.

Now, let's try exchanging 3 and -3, since only the sign of the middle term is incorrect.

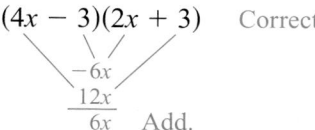

$$(4x - 3)(2x + 3) \quad \text{Correct}$$

$-6x$
$12x$
$6x$ Add.

This combination produces the correct middle term, so

$$8x^2 + 6x - 9 = (4x - 3)(2x + 3).$$

Work Problem 4 at the Side.

Example 4 Factoring a Trinomial with Two Variables

Factor $12a^2 - ab - 20b^2$.

There are several pairs of factors of $12a^2$, including $12a$ and a, $6a$ and $2a$, and $4a$ and $3a$, just as there are many possible pairs of factors of $-20b^2$, including $20b$ and $-b$, $-20b$ and b, $10b$ and $-2b$, $-10b$ and $2b$, $4b$ and $-5b$, and $-4b$ and $5b$. Once again, since the desired middle term is small, avoid the larger factors. Try the factors $6a$ and $2a$ and $4b$ and $-5b$.

$$(6a + 4b)(2a - 5b)$$

This cannot be correct, as mentioned before, since $6a + 4b$ has a common factor while the given trinomial has none. Try $3a$ and $4a$ with $4b$ and $-5b$.

$$(3a + 4b)(4a - 5b) = 12a^2 + ab - 20b^2 \quad \text{Incorrect}$$

Here the middle term has the wrong sign, so change the signs in the factors.

$$(3a - 4b)(4a + 5b) = 12a^2 - ab - 20b^2 \quad \text{Correct}$$

Work Problem 5 at the Side.

4 Factor each trinomial, if possible.

(a) $6x^2 + 5x - 4$

(b) $6m^2 - 11m - 10$

(c) $4x^2 - 3x - 7$

(d) $3y^2 + 8y - 6$

5 Factor each trinomial.

(a) $2x^2 - 5xy - 3y^2$

(b) $8a^2 + 2ab - 3b^2$

ANSWERS

4. (a) $(3x + 4)(2x - 1)$
(b) $(2m - 5)(3m + 2)$
(c) $(4x - 7)(x + 1)$
(d) prime

5. (a) $(2x + y)(x - 3y)$
(b) $(4a + 3b)(2a - b)$

6 Factor each trinomial.

(a) $36z^3 - 6z^2 - 72z$

(b) $-12x^3 + 16x^2y + 3xy^2$

Example 5 Factoring Trinomials with Common Factors

Factor each trinomial.

(a) $15y^3 + 55y^2 + 30y$

First factor out the greatest common factor, $5y$.

$$15y^3 + 55y^2 + 30y = 5y(3y^2 + 11y + 6)$$

Now factor $3y^2 + 11y + 6$. Try $3y$ and y as factors of $3y^2$ and 2 and 3 as factors of 6.

$$(3y + 2)(y + 3) = 3y^2 + 11y + 6 \quad \text{Correct}$$

The complete factored form of $15y^3 + 55y^2 + 30y$ is

$$15y^3 + 55y^2 + 30y = 5y(3y + 2)(y + 3).$$

Check by multiplying.

(b) $-24a^3 - 42a^2 + 45a$

The common factor could be $3a$ or $-3a$. If we factor out $-3a$, the first term of the trinomial will be positive, which makes it easier to factor.

$$\begin{aligned} -24a^3 - 42a^2 + 45a &= -3a(8a^2 + 14a - 15) && \text{Factor out } -3a. \\ &= -3a(4a - 3)(2a + 5) && \text{Use trial and error.} \end{aligned}$$

Check by multiplying.

CAUTION

This caution bears repeating: Remember to include the common factor in the final factored form.

Work Problem 6 at the Side.

ANSWERS

6. (a) $6z(2z - 3)(3z + 4)$
(b) $-x(6x + y)(2x - 3y)$

7.4 EXERCISES

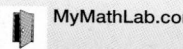

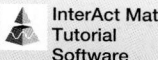

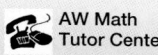

FOR EXTRA HELP: Student's Solutions Manual; MyMathLab.com; InterAct Math Tutorial Software; AW Math Tutor Center; www.mathxl.com; Digital Video Tutor CD 6 Videotape 13

Decide which is the correct factored form of the given polynomial.

1. $2x^2 - x - 1$
A. $(2x - 1)(x + 1)$ **B.** $(2x + 1)(x - 1)$ B

2. $3a^2 - 5a - 2$
A. $(3a + 1)(a - 2)$ **B.** $(3a - 1)(a + 2)$ A

3. $4y^2 + 17y - 15$
A. $(y + 5)(4y - 3)$ **B.** $(2y - 5)(2y + 3)$ A

4. $12c^2 - 7c - 12$
A. $(6c - 2)(2c + 6)$ **B.** $(4c + 3)(3c - 4)$ B

5. $4k^2 + 13mk + 3m^2$
A. $(4k + m)(k + 3m)$ **B.** $(4k + 3m)(k + m)$ A

6. $2x^2 + 11x + 12$
A. $(2x + 3)(x + 4)$ **B.** $(2x + 4)(x + 3)$ A

Complete each factoring.

7. $6a^2 + 7ab - 20b^2 = (3a - 4b)(\quad)$
$2a + 5b$

8. $9m^2 - 3mn - 2n^2 = (3m + n)(\quad)$
$3m - 2n$

9. $2x^2 + 6x - 8 = 2(\quad)$
$= 2(\quad)(\quad)$
$x^2 + 3x - 4$; $x + 4, x - 1$, or $x - 1, x + 4$

10. $3x^2 - 9x - 30 = 3(\quad)$
$= 3(\quad)(\quad)$
$x^2 - 3x - 10$; $x - 5, x + 2$, or $x + 2, x - 5$

11. $4z^3 - 10z^2 - 6z = 2z(\quad)$
$= 2z(\quad)(\quad)$
$2z^2 - 5z - 3$; $2z + 1, z - 3$, or $z - 3, 2z + 1$

12. $15r^3 - 39r^2 - 18r = 3r(\quad)$
$= 3r(\quad)(\quad)$
$5r^2 - 13r - 6$; $5r + 2, r - 3$, or $r - 3, 5r + 2$

13. For the polynomial $12x^2 + 7x - 12$, 2 is not a common factor. Explain why the binomial $2x - 6$, then, cannot be a factor of the polynomial.
The binomial $2x - 6$ cannot be a factor because it has a common factor of 2, but the polynomial does not.

14. Explain how the signs of the last terms of the two binomial factors of a trinomial are determined.
If the first term of the trinomial is positive and the last term is negative, the signs of the last two terms of the factors must be different. The signs are chosen so the middle term has the correct sign. If the first term of the trinomial is positive and the last term is positive, then the signs of the two last terms of the factors must be the same, the sign of the middle term of the trinomial.

Factor each trinomial completely. See Examples 1–5. The order of the factors is irrelevant in Exercises 15–50.

15. $3a^2 + 10a + 7$
$(3a + 7)(a + 1)$

16. $7r^2 + 8r + 1$
$(7r + 1)(r + 1)$

17. $2y^2 + 7y + 6$
$(2y + 3)(y + 2)$

18. $5z^2 + 12z + 4$
$(5z + 2)(z + 2)$

19. $15m^2 + m - 2$
$(3m - 1)(5m + 2)$

20. $6x^2 + x - 1$
$(2x + 1)(3x - 1)$

21. $12s^2 + 11s - 5$
$(3s - 1)(4s + 5)$

22. $20x^2 + 11x - 3$
$(4x + 3)(5x - 1)$

23. $10m^2 - 23m + 12$
$(5m - 4)(2m - 3)$

24. $6x^2 - 17x + 12$
$(3x - 4)(2x - 3)$

25. $8w^2 - 14w + 3$
$(4w - 1)(2w - 3)$

26. $9p^2 - 18p + 8$
$(3p - 2)(3p - 4)$

27. $20y^2 - 39y - 11$
$(4y + 1)(5y - 11)$

28. $10x^2 - 11x - 6$
$(2x - 3)(5x + 2)$

29. $3x^2 - 15x + 16$
prime

30. $2t^2 + 13t - 18$

prime

31. $20x^2 + 22x + 6$

$2(5x + 3)(2x + 1)$

32. $36y^2 + 81y + 45$

$9(4y + 5)(y + 1)$

33. $40m^2q + mq - 6q$

$q(5m + 2)(8m - 3)$

34. $15a^2b + 22ab + 8b$

$b(3a + 2)(5a + 4)$

35. $15n^4 - 39n^3 + 18n^2$

$3n^2(5n - 3)(n - 2)$

36. $24a^4 + 10a^3 - 4a^2$

$2a^2(3a + 2)(4a - 1)$

37. $15x^2y^2 - 7xy^2 - 4y^2$

$y^2(5x - 4)(3x + 1)$

38. $14a^2b^3 + 15ab^3 - 9b^3$

$b^3(7a - 3)(2a + 3)$

39. $5a^2 - 7ab - 6b^2$

$(5a + 3b)(a - 2b)$

40. $6x^2 - 5xy - y^2$

$(6x + y)(x - y)$

41. $12s^2 + 11st - 5t^2$

$(4s + 5t)(3s - t)$

42. $25a^2 + 25ab + 6b^2$

$(5a + 2b)(5a + 3b)$

43. $6m^6n + 7m^5n^2 + 2m^4n^3$

$m^4n(3m + 2n)(2m + n)$

44. $12k^3q^4 - 4k^2q^5 - kq^6$

$kq^4(6k + q)(2k - q)$

If a trinomial has a negative coefficient for the squared term, such as $-2x^2 + 11x - 12$*, it may be easier to factor by first factoring out the common factor* -1*:*

$$\begin{aligned} -2x^2 + 11x - 12 &= -1(2x^2 - 11x + 12) \\ &= -1(2x - 3)(x - 4). \end{aligned}$$

Use this method to factor the trinomials in Exercises 45–50.

45. $-x^2 - 4x + 21$

$-1(x + 7)(x - 3)$

46. $-x^2 + x + 72$

$-1(x + 8)(x - 9)$

47. $-3x^2 - x + 4$

$-1(3x + 4)(x - 1)$

48. $-5x^2 + 2x + 16$

$-1(5x + 8)(x - 2)$

49. $-2a^2 - 5ab - 2b^2$

$-1(a + 2b)(2a + b)$

50. $-3p^2 + 13pq - 4q^2$

$-1(p - 4q)(3p - q)$

RELATING CONCEPTS (Exercises 51–56) FOR INDIVIDUAL OR GROUP WORK

One of the most common problems that beginning algebra students face is this: If an answer obtained doesn't look exactly like the one given in the back of the book, is it necessarily incorrect? Often there are several different equivalent forms of an answer that are all correct. ***Work Exercises 51–56 in order,*** *to see how and why this is possible for factoring problems.*

51. Factor the integer 35 as the product of two prime numbers.

$5 \cdot 7$

52. Factor the integer 35 as the product of the negatives of two prime numbers.

$(-5)(-7)$

53. Verify the following factored form: $6x^2 - 11x + 4 = (3x - 4)(2x - 1)$.

The product of $3x - 4$ and $2x - 1$ is $6x^2 - 11x + 4$.

54. Verify the following factored form: $6x^2 - 11x + 4 = (4 - 3x)(1 - 2x)$.

The product of $4 - 3x$ and $1 - 2x$ is $6x^2 - 11x + 4$.

55. Compare the two valid factored forms in Exercises 53 and 54. How do the factors in each case compare?

The factors in Exercise 53 are the opposites of the factors in Exercise 54.

56. Suppose you know that the correct factored form of a particular trinomial is $(7t - 3)(2t - 5)$. Based on your observations in Exercises 51–55, what is another valid factored form?

$(3 - 7t)(5 - 2t)$

7.5 SPECIAL FACTORING TECHNIQUES

OBJECTIVES

1. Factor a difference of squares.
2. Factor a perfect square trinomial.
3. Factor a difference of cubes.
4. Factor a sum of cubes.

By reversing the rules for multiplication of binomials from the last chapter, we get rules for factoring polynomials in certain forms.

1 Factor a difference of squares. The formula for the product of the sum and difference of the same two terms is

$$(a + b)(a - b) = a^2 - b^2.$$

Reversing this rule leads to the following special factoring rule.

Factoring a Difference of Squares

$$a^2 - b^2 = (a + b)(a - b)$$

For example,

$$m^2 - 16 = m^2 - 4^2 = (m + 4)(m - 4).$$

As the next examples show, the following conditions must be true for a binomial to be a difference of squares.

1. Both terms of the binomial must be squares, such as

$$x^2, \quad 9y^2, \quad 25, \quad 1, \quad m^4.$$

2. The terms must have different signs (one positive and one negative).

Example 1 **Factoring Differences of Squares**

Factor each binomial, if possible.

$$a^2 - b^2 = (a + b)(a - b)$$

(a) $x^2 - 49 = x^2 - 7^2 = (x + 7)(x - 7)$

(b) $y^2 - m^2 = (y + m)(y - m)$

(c) $z^2 - \dfrac{9}{16} = z^2 - \left(\dfrac{3}{4}\right)^2 = \left(z + \dfrac{3}{4}\right)\left(z - \dfrac{3}{4}\right)$

(d) $x^2 - 8$

Because 8 is not the square of an integer, this binomial is not a difference of squares. It is a prime polynomial.

(e) $p^2 + 16$

Since $p^2 + 16$ is a *sum* of squares, it is not equal to $(p + 4)(p - 4)$. Also, using FOIL,

$$(p - 4)(p - 4) = p^2 - 8p + 16 \neq p^2 + 16$$

and

$$(p + 4)(p + 4) = p^2 + 8p + 16 \neq p^2 + 16,$$

so $p^2 + 16$ is a prime polynomial.

1 Factor, if possible.

(a) $p^2 - 100$

(b) $x^2 - \dfrac{25}{36}$

(c) $x^2 + y^2$

(d) $9m^2 - 49$

(e) $64a^2 - 25$

2 Factor completely.

(a) $50r^2 - 32$

(b) $27y^2 - 75$

(c) $25a^2 - 64b^2$

(d) $k^4 - 49$

(e) $81r^4 - 16$

Answers

1. (a) $(p + 10)(p - 10)$
   (b) $\left(x + \frac{5}{6}\right)\left(x - \frac{5}{6}\right)$
   (c) prime
   (d) $(3m + 7)(3m - 7)$
   (e) $(8a + 5)(8a - 5)$
2. (a) $2(5r + 4)(5r - 4)$
   (b) $3(3y + 5)(3y - 5)$
   (c) $(5a + 8b)(5a - 8b)$
   (d) $(k^2 + 7)(k^2 - 7)$
   (e) $(9r^2 + 4)(3r + 2)(3r - 2)$

CAUTION

As Example 1(e) suggests, after any common factor is removed, a *sum* of squares cannot be factored.

Example 2 Factoring Differences of Squares

Factor each difference of squares.

$$a^2 - b^2 = (a + b)(a - b)$$

(a) $25m^2 - 16 = (5m)^2 - 4^2 = (5m + 4)(5m - 4)$

(b) $49z^2 - 64 = (7z)^2 - 8^2 = (7z + 8)(7z - 8)$

NOTE

As in previous sections, you should always check a factored form by multiplying.

Work Problem 1 at the Side.

Example 3 Factoring More Complex Differences of Squares

Factor completely.

(a) $81y^2 - 36$

First factor out the common factor, 9.

$$\begin{aligned} 81y^2 - 36 &= 9(9y^2 - 4) && \text{Factor out 9.} \\ &= 9[(3y)^2 - 2^2] \\ &= 9(3y + 2)(3y - 2) && \text{Difference of squares} \end{aligned}$$

(b) $9x^2 - 4z^2 = (3x)^2 - (2z)^2 = (3x + 2z)(3x - 2z)$

(c) $p^4 - 36 = (p^2)^2 - 6^2 = (p^2 + 6)(p^2 - 6)$

Neither $p^2 + 6$ nor $p^2 - 6$ can be factored further.

(d) $$\begin{aligned} m^4 - 16 &= (m^2)^2 - 4^2 \\ &= (m^2 + 4)(m^2 - 4) && \text{Difference of squares} \\ &= (m^2 + 4)(m + 2)(m - 2) && \text{Difference of squares again} \end{aligned}$$

CAUTION

Remember to factor again when any of the factors is a difference of squares, as in Example 3(d). Check by multiplying.

Work Problem 2 at the Side.

2 **Factor a perfect square trinomial.** The expressions 144, $4x^2$, and $81m^6$ are called *perfect squares* because

$$144 = 12^2, \quad 4x^2 = (2x)^2, \quad \text{and} \quad 81m^6 = (9m^3)^2.$$

A **perfect square trinomial** is a trinomial that is the square of a binomial. For example, $x^2 + 8x + 16$ is a perfect square trinomial because it is the square of the binomial $x + 4$:

$$x^2 + 8x + 16 = (x + 4)(x + 4) = (x + 4)^2.$$

For a trinomial to be a perfect square, *two of its terms must be perfect squares.* For this reason, $16x^2 + 4x + 15$ is not a perfect square trinomial because only the term $16x^2$ is a perfect square.

On the other hand, even if two of the terms are perfect squares, the trinomial may not be a perfect square trinomial. For example, $x^2 + 6x + 36$ has two perfect square terms, but it is not a perfect square trinomial. (Try to find a binomial that can be squared to give $x^2 + 6x + 36$.)

We can multiply to see that the square of a binomial gives one of the following perfect square trinomials.

Factoring Perfect Square Trinomials

$$a^2 + 2ab + b^2 = (a + b)^2$$
$$a^2 - 2ab + b^2 = (a - b)^2$$

The middle term of a perfect square trinomial is always twice the product of the two terms in the squared binomial. (This was shown in Section 6.4.) Use this to check any attempt to factor a trinomial that appears to be a perfect square.

Example 4 Factoring a Perfect Square Trinomial

Factor $x^2 + 10x + 25$.

The term x^2 is a perfect square, and so is 25. Try to factor the trinomial as

$$x^2 + 10x + 25 = (x + 5)^2.$$

To check, take twice the product of the two terms in the squared binomial.

$$2 \cdot x \cdot 5 = 10x$$

Twice — First term of binomial — Last term of binomial

Since $10x$ is the middle term of the trinomial, the trinomial is a perfect square and can be factored as $(x + 5)^2$. Thus,

$$x^2 + 10x + 25 = (x + 5)^2.$$

Work Problem 3 at the Side.

Example 5 Factoring Perfect Square Trinomials

Factor each trinomial.

(a) $x^2 - 22x + 121$

The first and last terms are perfect squares ($121 = 11^2$ or $(-11)^2$). Check to see whether the middle term of $x^2 - 22x + 121$ is twice the product of the first and last terms of the binomial $x - 11$.

Continued on Next Page

3 Factor each trinomial.

(a) $p^2 + 14p + 49$

(b) $m^2 + 8m + 16$

(c) $x^2 + 2x + 1$

ANSWERS

3. **(a)** $(p + 7)^2$ **(b)** $(m + 4)^2$ **(c)** $(x + 1)^2$

$$2 \cdot x \cdot (-11) = -22x$$

(Twice — First term — Last term)

Since twice the product of the first and last terms of the binomial is the middle term, $x^2 - 22x + 121$ is a perfect square trinomial and

$$x^2 - 22x + 121 = (x - 11)^2.$$

Notice that the sign of the second term in the squared binomial is the same as the sign of the middle term in the trinomial.

(b) $9m^2 - 24m + 16 = (3m)^2 + 2(3m)(-4) + (-4)^2 = (3m - 4)^2$

(Twice — First term — Last term)

(c) $25y^2 + 20y + 16$
The first and last terms are perfect squares.

$$25y^2 = (5y)^2 \quad \text{and} \quad 16 = 4^2$$

Twice the product of the first and last terms of the binomial $5y + 4$ is

$$2 \cdot 5y \cdot 4 = 40y,$$

which is not the middle term of $25y^2 + 20y + 16$. This trinomial is not a perfect square. In fact, the trinomial cannot be factored even with the methods of the previous sections; it is a prime polynomial.

(d) $12z^3 + 60z^2 + 75z$
Factor out the common factor, $3z$, first.

$$\begin{aligned} 12z^3 + 60z^2 + 75z &= 3z(4z^2 + 20z + 25) \\ &= 3z[(2z)^2 + 2(2z)(5) + 5^2] \\ &= 3z(2z + 5)^2 \end{aligned}$$

NOTE

As noted in Example 5(a), the sign of the second term in the squared binomial is always the same as the sign of the middle term in the trinomial. Also, the first and last terms of a perfect square trinomial must be *positive,* because they are squares. For example, the polynomial $x^2 - 2x - 1$ cannot be a perfect square because the last term is negative.

Perfect square trinomials can also be factored using grouping or FOIL, although using the method of this section is often easier.

Work Problem 4 at the Side.

3 Factor a difference of cubes. The difference of squares was factored at the beginning of this section; we can also factor the **difference of cubes.** Use the following pattern.

Factoring a Difference of Cubes

$$a^3 - b^3 = (a - b)(a^2 + ab + b^2)$$

4 Factor each trinomial.

(a) $p^2 - 18p + 81$

(b) $16a^2 + 56a + 49$

(c) $121p^2 + 110p + 100$

(d) $64x^2 - 48x + 9$

(e) $27y^3 + 72y^2 + 48y$

ANSWERS

4. (a) $(p - 9)^2$ **(b)** $(4a + 7)^2$ **(c)** prime **(d)** $(8x - 3)^2$ **(e)** $3y(3y + 4)^2$

This pattern *should be memorized.* Multiply on the right to see that the pattern gives the correct factors, as shown in the margin.

$$\begin{array}{r} a^2 + ab + b^2 \\ a - b \\ \hline -a^2b - ab^2 - b^3 \\ a^3 + a^2b + ab^2 \\ \hline a^3 - b^3 \end{array}$$

Notice the pattern of the terms in the factored form of $a^3 - b^3$.

- $a^3 - b^3 =$ (a binomial factor)(a trinomial factor)
- The binomial factor has the difference of the cube roots of the given terms.
- The terms in the trinomial factor are all positive.
- What you write in the binomial factor determines the trinomial factor.

$$a^3 - b^3 = (a - b)(\underbrace{a^2}_{\text{First term squared}} + \underbrace{ab}_{\text{positive product of the terms}} + \underbrace{b^2}_{\text{second term squared}})$$

Example 6 Factoring Differences of Cubes

Factor each difference of cubes.

(a) $m^3 - 125$

Use the pattern for the difference of cubes.

$$\begin{aligned} a^3 - b^3 &= (a - b)(a^2 + ab + b^2) \\ m^3 - 125 = m^3 - 5^3 &= (m - 5)(m^2 + 5m + 5^2) \\ &= (m - 5)(m^2 + 5m + 25) \end{aligned}$$

(b) $8p^3 - 27$

Since $8p^3 = (2p)^3$ and $27 = 3^3$,

$$\begin{aligned} 8p^3 - 27 &= (2p)^3 - 3^3 \\ &= (2p - 3)[(2p)^2 + (2p)3 + 3^2] \\ &= (2p - 3)(4p^2 + 6p + 9). \end{aligned}$$

(c) $4m^3 - 32n^3 = 4(m^3 - 8n^3)$ Factor out the common factor.

$= 4[m^3 - (2n)^3]$ $8n^3 = (2n)^3$

$= 4(m - 2n)[m^2 + m(2n) + (2n)^2]$

$= 4(m - 2n)(m^2 + 2mn + 4n^2)$

CAUTION

A common error in factoring a difference of cubes, such as $a^3 - b^3 = (a - b)(a^2 + ab + b^2)$, is to try to factor $a^2 + ab + b^2$. It is easy to confuse this factor with a perfect square trinomial, $a^2 + 2ab + b^2$. It is unusual to be able to further factor an expression of the form $a^2 + ab + b^2$.

Work Problem 5 at the Side.

4 Factor a sum of cubes. A sum of squares, such as $m^2 + 25$, cannot be factored using real numbers, but a **sum of cubes** can be factored by the following pattern, *which should be memorized.*

5 Factor each difference of cubes.

(a) $t^3 - 64$

(b) $2x^3 - 54$

(c) $8k^3 - y^3$

ANSWERS

5. (a) $(t - 4)(t^2 + 4t + 16)$
(b) $2(x - 3)(x^2 + 3x + 9)$
(c) $(2k - y)(4k^2 + 2ky + y^2)$

6 Factor each sum of cubes.

(a) $x^3 + 8$

(b) $64y^3 + 1$

(c) $27m^3 + 343n^3$

Factoring a Sum of Cubes

$$a^3 + b^3 = (a + b)(a^2 - ab + b^2)$$

Compare the pattern for the *sum* of cubes with the pattern for the *difference* of cubes. The only difference between them is the positive and negative signs.

Positive

$$a^3 - b^3 = (a - b)(a^2 + ab + b^2) \quad \text{Difference of cubes}$$

Same sign Opposite sign

Positive

$$a^3 + b^3 = (a + b)(a^2 - ab + b^2) \quad \text{Sum of cubes}$$

Same sign Opposite sign

Observing these relationships should help you to remember these patterns.

Example 7 **Factoring Sums of Cubes**

Factor each sum of cubes.

(a) $k^3 + 27 = k^3 + 3^3$

$= (k + 3)(k^2 - 3k + 3^2)$

$= (k + 3)(k^2 - 3k + 9)$

(b) $8m^3 + 125p^3 = (2m)^3 + (5p)^3$

$= (2m + 5p)[(2m)^2 - (2m)(5p) + (5p)^2]$

$= (2m + 5p)(4m^2 - 10mp + 25p^2)$

Work Problem 6 at the Side.

The methods of factoring discussed in this section are summarized here.

Special Factoring Rules

Difference of squares	$a^2 - b^2 = (a + b)(a - b)$
Perfect square trinomials	$a^2 + 2ab + b^2 = (a + b)^2$
	$a^2 - 2ab + b^2 = (a - b)^2$
Difference of cubes	$a^3 - b^3 = (a - b)(a^2 + ab + b^2)$
Sum of cubes	$a^3 + b^3 = (a + b)(a^2 - ab + b^2)$

Remember that the *sum of squares* can be factored only if the terms have a common factor.

ANSWERS

6. (a) $(x + 2)(x^2 - 2x + 4)$
(b) $(4y + 1)(16y^2 - 4y + 1)$
(c) $(3m + 7n)(9m^2 - 21mn + 49n^2)$

7.5 EXERCISES

FOR EXTRA HELP Student's Solutions Manual | MyMathLab.com | InterAct Math Tutorial Software | AW Math Tutor Center | www.mathxl.com | Digital Video Tutor CD 6 Videotape 14

1. To help you factor a difference of squares, complete the following list of squares.

$1^2 =$ 1	$2^2 =$ 4	$3^2 =$ 9	$4^2 =$ 16	$5^2 =$ 25
$6^2 =$ 36	$7^2 =$ 49	$8^2 =$ 64	$9^2 =$ 81	$10^2 =$ 100
$11^2 =$ 121	$12^2 =$ 144	$13^2 =$ 169	$14^2 =$ 196	$15^2 =$ 225
$16^2 =$ 256	$17^2 =$ 289	$18^2 =$ 324	$19^2 =$ 361	$20^2 =$ 400

2. To use the factoring techniques described in this section, you will sometimes need to recognize fourth powers of integers. Complete the following list of fourth powers.

$1^4 =$ 1 $\quad 2^4 =$ 16 $\quad 3^4 =$ 81 $\quad 4^4 =$ 256 $\quad 5^4 =$ 625

3. The following powers of x are all perfect squares: $x^2, x^4, x^6, x^8, x^{10}$. Based on this observation, we may make a conjecture (an educated guess) that if the power of a variable is divisible by 2 (with 0 remainder), then it is a perfect square.

4. Which of the following are differences of squares?

A. $x^2 - 4$ **B.** $y^2 + 9$ **C.** $2a^2 - 25$ **D.** $9m^2 - 1$

A, D

Factor each binomial completely. Use your answers in Exercises 1 and 2 as necessary. See Examples 1–3.

5. $y^2 - 25$
$(y + 5)(y - 5)$

6. $t^2 - 16$
$(t + 4)(t - 4)$

7. $9r^2 - 4$
$(3r + 2)(3r - 2)$

8. $4x^2 - 9$
$(2x + 3)(2x - 3)$

9. $36m^2 - \frac{16}{25}$
$\left(6m + \frac{4}{5}\right)\left(6m - \frac{4}{5}\right)$

10. $100b^2 - \frac{4}{49}$
$\left(10b + \frac{2}{7}\right)\left(10b - \frac{2}{7}\right)$

11. $36x^2 - 16$
$4(3x + 2)(3x - 2)$

12. $32a^2 - 8$
$8(2a + 1)(2a - 1)$

13. $196p^2 - 225$
$(14p + 15)(14p - 15)$

14. $361q^2 - 400$
$(19q + 20)(19q - 20)$

15. $16r^2 - 25a^2$
$(4r + 5a)(4r - 5a)$

16. $49m^2 - 100p^2$
$(7m + 10p)(7m - 10p)$

17. $100x^2 + 49$
prime

18. $81w^2 + 16$
prime

19. $p^4 - 49$
$(p^2 + 7)(p^2 - 7)$

20. $r^4 - 25$
$(r^2 + 5)(r^2 - 5)$

21. $x^4 - 1$
$(x^2 + 1)(x + 1)(x - 1)$

22. $y^4 - 16$
$(y^2 + 4)(y + 2)(y - 2)$

23. $p^4 - 256$
$(p^2 + 16)(p + 4)(p - 4)$

24. $16k^4 - 1$
$(4k^2 + 1)(2k + 1)(2k - 1)$

25. When a student was directed to factor $x^4 - 81$ completely, his teacher did not give him full credit when he answered $(x^2 + 9)(x^2 - 9)$. The student argued that because his answer does indeed give $x^4 - 81$ when multiplied out, he should be given full credit. Was the teacher justified in her grading of this item? Why or why not?

The teacher was justified, because it was not factored completely; $x^2 - 9$ can be factored as $(x + 3)(x - 3)$. The complete factored form is $(x^2 + 9)(x + 3)(x - 3)$.

26. The binomial $4x^2 + 16$ is a sum of squares that *can* be factored. How is this binomial factored? When can a sum of squares be factored?

$4x^2 + 16$ is factored as $4(x^2 + 4)$. A sum of squares can be factored if the terms have a common factor.

27. In the polynomial $9y^2 + 14y + 25$, the first and last terms are perfect squares. Can the polynomial be factored? If it can, factor it. If it cannot, explain why it is not a perfect square trinomial.

No, it is not a perfect square because the middle term should be 30y, not 14y.

28. Which of the following are perfect square trinomials?

A. $y^2 - 13y + 36$ **B.** $x^2 + 6x + 9$ **C.** $4z^2 - 4z + 1$ **D.** $16m^2 + 10m + 1$

B, C

Factor each trinomial completely. It may be necessary to factor out the greatest common factor first. See Examples 4 and 5.

29. $w^2 + 2w + 1$
$(w + 1)^2$

30. $p^2 + 4p + 4$
$(p + 2)^2$

31. $x^2 - 8x + 16$
$(x - 4)^2$

32. $x^2 - 10x + 25$
$(x - 5)^2$

33. $t^2 + t + \frac{1}{4}$
$\left(t + \frac{1}{2}\right)^2$

34. $m^2 + \frac{2}{3}m + \frac{1}{9}$
$\left(m + \frac{1}{3}\right)^2$

35. $x^2 - 1.0x + .25$
$(x - .5)^2$

36. $y^2 - 1.4y + .49$
$(y - .7)^2$

37. $2x^2 + 24x + 72$
$2(x + 6)^2$

38. $3y^2 - 48y + 192$
$3(y - 8)^2$

39. $16x^2 - 40x + 25$
$(4x - 5)^2$

40. $36y^2 - 60y + 25$
$(6y - 5)^2$

41. $49x^2 - 28xy + 4y^2$
$(7x - 2y)^2$

42. $4z^2 - 12zw + 9w^2$
$(2z - 3w)^2$

43. $64x^2 + 48xy + 9y^2$
$(8x + 3y)^2$

44. $9t^2 + 24tr + 16r^2$
$(3t + 4r)^2$

45. $50h^3 - 40h^2y + 8hy^2$
$2h(5h - 2y)^2$

46. $18x^3 + 48x^2y + 32xy^2$
$2x(3x + 4y)^2$

47. To help you factor the sum or difference of cubes, complete the following list of cubes.

$1^3 =$ 1 $2^3 =$ 8 $3^3 =$ 27 $4^3 =$ 64 $5^3 =$ 125

$6^3 =$ 216 $7^3 =$ 343 $8^3 =$ 512 $9^3 =$ 729 $10^3 =$ 1000

48. The following powers of x are all perfect cubes: $x^3, x^6, x^9, x^{12}, x^{15}$. Based on this observation, we may make a conjecture that if the power of a variable is divisible by 3 (with 0 remainder), then we have a perfect cube.

49. Which of the following are differences of cubes?

A. $9x^3 - 125$ **B.** $x^3 - 16$ **C.** $x^3 - 1$ **D.** $8x^3 - 27y^3$

C, D

50. Which of the following are sums of cubes?

A. $x^3 + 1$ **B.** $x^3 + 36$ **C.** $12x^3 + 27$ **D.** $64x^3 + 216y^3$

A, D

Factor each binomial completely. Use your answers in Exercises 47 and 48 as necessary. See Examples 6 and 7.

51. $a^3 + 1$

$(a + 1)(a^2 - a + 1)$

52. $m^3 + 8$

$(m + 2)(m^2 - 2m + 4)$

53. $a^3 - 1$

$(a - 1)(a^2 + a + 1)$

54. $m^3 - 8$

$(m - 2)(m^2 + 2m + 4)$

55. $p^3 + q^3$

$(p + q)(p^2 - pq + q^2)$

56. $w^3 + z^3$

$(w + z)(w^2 - wz + z^2)$

57. $y^3 - 216$

$(y - 6)(y^2 + 6y + 36)$

58. $x^3 - 343$

$(x - 7)(x^2 + 7x + 49)$

59. $k^3 + 1000$

$(k + 10)(k^2 - 10k + 100)$

60. $p^3 + 512$

$(p + 8)(p^2 - 8p + 64)$

61. $27x^3 - 1$

$(3x - 1)(9x^2 + 3x + 1)$

62. $64y^3 - 27$

$(4y - 3)(16y^2 + 12y + 9)$

63. $125a^3 + 8$

$(5a + 2)(25a^2 - 10a + 4)$

64. $216b^3 + 125$

$(6b + 5)(36b^2 - 30b + 25)$

65. $y^3 - 8x^3$

$(y - 2x)(y^2 + 2xy + 4x^2)$

66. $w^3 - 216z^3$

$(w - 6z)(w^2 + 6wz + 36z^2)$

67. $27a^3 - 64b^3$

$(3a - 4b)(9a^2 + 12ab + 16b^2)$

68. $125m^3 - 8n^3$

$(5m - 2n)(25m^2 + 10mn + 4n^2)$

69. $8p^3 + 729q^3$

$(2p + 9q)(4p^2 - 18pq + 81q^2)$

70. $27x^3 + 1000y^3$

$(3x + 10y)(9x^2 - 30xy + 100y^2)$

71. $16t^3 - 2$

$2(2t - 1)(4t^2 + 2t + 1)$

72. $3p^3 - 81$

$3(p - 3)(p^2 + 3p + 9)$

73. $40w^3 + 135$

$5(2w + 3)(4w^2 - 6w + 9)$

74. $32z^3 + 500$

$4(2z + 5)(4z^2 - 10z + 25)$

75. $x^3 + y^6$

$(x + y^2)(x^2 - xy^2 + y^4)$

76. $p^9 + q^3$

$(p^3 + q)(p^6 - p^3q + q^2)$

77. $125k^3 - 8m^9$

$(5k - 2m^3)(25k^2 + 10km^3 + 4m^6)$

78. $125c^6 - 216d^3$

$(5c^2 - 6d)(25c^4 + 30c^2d + 36d^2)$

RELATING CONCEPTS (Exercises 79–86) FOR INDIVIDUAL OR GROUP WORK

A binomial may be both *a difference of squares* and *a difference of cubes. One example of such a binomial is $x^6 - 1$. Using the techniques of this section, one factoring method will give the complete factored form, while the other will not.* **Work Exercises 79–86 in order** *to determine the method to use.*

79. Factor $x^6 - 1$ as the difference of two squares.

$(x^3 - 1)(x^3 + 1)$

80. The factored form obtained in Exercise 79 consists of a difference of cubes multiplied by a sum of cubes. Factor each binomial further.

$(x - 1)(x^2 + x + 1)(x + 1)(x^2 - x + 1)$

81. Now start over and factor $x^6 - 1$ as a difference of cubes.

$(x^2 - 1)(x^4 + x^2 + 1)$

82. The factored form obtained in Exercise 81 consists of a binomial that is a difference of squares and a trinomial. Factor the binomial further.

$(x - 1)(x + 1)(x^4 + x^2 + 1)$

83. Compare your results in Exercises 80 and 82. Which one of these is the completely factored form?

The result in Exercise 80 is completely factored.

84. Verify that the trinomial in the factored form in Exercise 82 is the product of the two trinomials in the factored form in Exercise 80.

Show that $x^4 + x^2 + 1 = (x^2 + x + 1)(x^2 - x + 1)$.

85. Use the results of Exercises 79–84 to complete the following statement:

In general, if I must choose between factoring first using the method for a difference of squares or the method for a difference of cubes, I should choose the <u>difference of squares</u> method to eventually obtain the complete factored form.

86. Find the *complete* factored form of $x^6 - 729$ using the knowledge you have gained in Exercises 79–85.

$(x - 3)(x^2 + 3x + 9)(x + 3)(x^2 - 3x + 9)$

Summary Exercises on FACTORING

As you factor a polynomial, ask yourself these questions to decide on a suitable factoring technique.

Factoring a Polynomial

1. Is there a common factor? If so, factor it out.

2. How many terms are in the polynomial?

Two terms: Check to see whether it is a difference of squares or a sum or difference of cubes.

Three terms: Is it a perfect square trinomial? If the trinomial is not a perfect square, check to see whether the coefficient of the squared term is 1. If so, use the method of Section 7.2. If the coefficient of the squared term of the trinomial is not 1, use the general factoring methods of Sections 7.3 and 7.4.

Four terms: Try to factor the polynomial by grouping.

3. Can any factors be factored further? If so, factor them.

Factor each polynomial completely. Remember to check by multiplying.

1. $32m^9 + 16m^5 + 24m^3$
$8m^3(4m^6 + 2m^2 + 3)$

2. $2m^2 - 10m - 48$
$2(m + 3)(m - 8)$

3. $14k^3 + 7k^2 - 70k$
$7k(2k + 5)(k - 2)$

4. $9z^2 + 64$
prime

5. $6z^2 + 31z + 5$
$(6z + 1)(z + 5)$

6. $m^2 - 3mn - 4n^2$
$(m + n)(m - 4n)$

7. $49z^2 - 16y^2$
$(7z + 4y)(7z - 4y)$

8. $100n^2r^2 + 30nr^3 - 50n^2r$
$10nr(10nr + 3r^2 - 5n)$

9. $16x^2 + 20x$
$4x(4x + 5)$

10. $20 + 5m + 12n + 3mn$
$(4 + m)(5 + 3n)$

11. $10y^2 - 7yz - 6z^2$
$(5y - 6z)(2y + z)$

12. $y^4 - 81$
$(y^2 + 9)(y + 3)(y - 3)$

13. $m^2 + 2m - 15$
$(m - 3)(m + 5)$

14. $6y^2 - 5y - 4$
$(2y + 1)(3y - 4)$

15. $32z^3 + 56z^2 - 16z$
$8z(4z - 1)(z + 2)$

16. $15y^2 + 5y$
$5y(3y + 1)$

17. $z^2 - 12z + 36$
$(z - 6)^2$

18. $9m^2 - 64$
$(3m + 8)(3m - 8)$

19. $t^3 + 64$
$(t + 4)(t^2 - 4t + 16)$

20. $16z^2 - 8z + 1$
$(4z - 1)^2$

21. $6y^2 - 6y - 12$
$6(y - 2)(y + 1)$

22. $x^2 + \frac{1}{2}x + \frac{1}{16}$
$\left(x + \frac{1}{4}\right)^2$

23. $p^2 - 17p + 66$
$(p - 6)(p - 11)$

24. $a^2 + 17a + 72$
$(a + 8)(a + 9)$

25. $k^2 + 9$
prime

26. $108m^2 - 36m + 3$
$3(6m - 1)^2$

27. $z^2 - 3za - 10a^2$
$(z + 2a)(z - 5a)$

28. $2a^3 + a^2 - 14a - 7$
$(2a + 1)(a^2 - 7)$

29. $4k^2 - 12k + 9$
$(2k - 3)^2$

30. $64x^3 - 343$
$(4x - 7)(16x^2 + 28x + 49)$

31. $16r^2 + 24rm + 9m^2$
$(4r + 3m)^2$

32. $3k^2 + 4k - 4$
$(3k - 2)(k + 2)$

33. $n^2 - 12n - 35$
prime

34. $a^4 - 625$
$(a^2 + 25)(a + 5)(a - 5)$

35. $16k^2 - 48k + 36$
$4(2k - 3)^2$

36. $8k^2 - 10k - 3$
$(4k + 1)(2k - 3)$

37. $36y^6 - 42y^5 - 120y^4$
$6y^4(3y + 4)(2y - 5)$

38. $5z^3 - 45z^2 + 70z$
$5z(z - 2)(z - 7)$

39. $8p^2 + 23p - 3$
$(8p - 1)(p + 3)$

40. $8k^2 - 2kh - 3h^2$
$(4k - 3h)(2k + h)$

41. $54m^2 - 24z^2$
$6(3m + 2z)(3m - 2z)$

42. $4k^2 - 20kz + 25z^2$
$(2k - 5z)^2$

43. $6a^2 + 10a - 4$
$2(3a - 1)(a + 2)$

44. $15h^2 + 11hg - 14g^2$
$(3h - 2g)(5h + 7g)$

45. $m^2 - 81$
$(m + 9)(m - 9)$

46. $z^3 + 216w^3$
$(z + 6w)(z^2 - 6wz + 36w^2)$

47. $125m^4 - 400m^3n + 195m^2n^2$
$5m^2(5m - 13n)(5m - 3n)$

48. $9y^2 + 12y - 5$
$(3y - 1)(3y + 5)$

49. $m^2 - 4m + 4$
$(m - 2)^2$

50. $36x^2 + 32x + 9$
prime

51. $8p^3 - 1$
$(2p - 1)(4p^2 + 2p + 1)$

52. $10m^2 + 25m - 60$
$5(2m - 3)(m + 4)$

53. $4 - 2q - 6p + 3pq$
$(2 - q)(2 - 3p)$

54. $k^2 - \frac{64}{121}$
$\left(k + \frac{8}{11}\right)\left(k - \frac{8}{11}\right)$

55. $64p^2 - 100m^2$
$4(4p + 5m)(4p - 5m)$

56. $m^3 + 4m^2 - 6m - 24$
$(m + 4)(m^2 - 6)$

57. $100a^2 - 81y^2$
$(10a + 9y)(10a - 9y)$

58. $8a^2 + 23ab - 3b^2$
$(8a - b)(a + 3b)$

59. $a^2 + 8a + 16$
$(a + 4)^2$

60. $4y^2 - 25$
$(2y + 5)(2y - 5)$

7.6 Solving Quadratic Equations by Factoring

Galileo Galilei (1564–1642) developed theories to explain physical phenomena and set up experiments to test his ideas. According to legend, Galileo dropped objects of different weights from the Leaning Tower of Pisa to disprove the belief that heavier objects fall faster than lighter objects. He developed a formula for freely falling objects described by

$$d = 16t^2,$$

where d is the distance in feet that an object falls (disregarding air resistance) in t seconds, regardless of weight. (*Source:* Miller, Charles D., Heeren, Vern E., and Hornsby, John, *Mathematical Ideas,* Ninth Edition, Addison-Wesley Publishing Company, 2001.)

The equation $d = 16t^2$ is a *quadratic equation,* the subject of this section. A quadratic equation contains a squared term and no terms of higher degree.

Quadratic Equation

A **quadratic equation** is an equation that can be written in the form

$$ax^2 + bx + c = 0,$$

where a, b, and c are real numbers, with $a \neq 0$.

The form $ax^2 + bx + c = 0$ is the **standard form** of a quadratic equation. For example,

$$x^2 + 5x + 6 = 0, \quad 2a^2 - 5a = 3, \quad \text{and} \quad y^2 = 4$$

are all quadratic equations, but only $x^2 + 5x + 6 = 0$ is in standard form.

Work Problems 1 and 2 at the Side.

1 Solve quadratic equations by factoring. We use the **zero-factor property** to solve a quadratic equation by factoring.

Zero-Factor Property

If a and b are real numbers and $ab = 0$, then $a = 0$ or $b = 0$.

In words, if the product of two numbers is 0, then at least one of the numbers must be 0. One number *must* be 0, but both *may* be 0.

Example 1 Using the Zero-Factor Property

Solve each equation.

(a) $(x + 3)(2x - 1) = 0$

The product $(x + 3)(2x - 1)$ is equal to 0. By the zero-factor property, the only way that the product of these two factors can be 0 is if at least one of the factors equals 0. Therefore, either $x + 3 = 0$ or $2x - 1 = 0$. Solve each of these two linear equations as in Chapter 2.

$x + 3 = 0$	or	$2x - 1 = 0$	Zero-factor property
$x = -3$		$2x = 1$	Add 1 to each side.
		$x = \frac{1}{2}$	Divide each side by 2.

Continued on Next Page

Objectives

1. Solve quadratic equations by factoring.
2. Solve other equations by factoring.

1 Which of the following equations are quadratic equations?

A. $y^2 - 4y - 5 = 0$

B. $x^3 - x^2 + 16 = 0$

C. $2z^2 + 7z = -3$

D. $x + 2y = -4$

2 Write each quadratic equation in standard form.

(a) $x^2 - 3x = 4$

(b) $y^2 = 9y - 8$

Answers

1. (a) A, C
2. (a) $x^2 - 3x - 4 = 0$
   (b) $y^2 - 9y + 8 = 0$

3 Solve each equation. Check your solutions.

(a) $(x-5)(x+2)=0$

(b) $(3x-2)(x+6)=0$

(c) $z(2z+5)=0$

The given equation, $(x+3)(2x-1)=0$, has two solutions, -3 and $\frac{1}{2}$. Check these solutions by substituting -3 for x in the original equation, $(x+3)(2x-1)=0$. Then start over and substitute $\frac{1}{2}$ for x.

If $x=-3$, then

$$(x+3)(2x-1)=0$$
$$(-3+3)[2(-3)-1]=0 \quad ?$$
$$0(-7)=0. \quad \text{True}$$

If $x=\frac{1}{2}$, then

$$(x+3)(2x-1)=0$$
$$\left(\frac{1}{2}+3\right)\left(2\cdot\frac{1}{2}-1\right)=0 \quad ?$$
$$\frac{7}{2}(1-1)=0 \quad ?$$
$$\frac{7}{2}\cdot 0=0. \quad \text{True}$$

Both -3 and $\frac{1}{2}$ result in true equations, so they are solutions to the original equation. The solution set is $\{-3, \frac{1}{2}\}$.

(b) $y(3y-4)=0$

$$y(3y-4)=0$$
$$y=0 \quad \text{or} \quad 3y-4=0 \quad \text{Zero-factor property}$$
$$3y=4$$
$$y=\frac{4}{3}$$

Check these solutions by substituting each one in the original equation. The solution set is $\{0, \frac{4}{3}\}$.

NOTE

The word *or* as used in Example 1 means "one or the other or both."

Work Problem 3 at the Side.

In Example 1, each equation to be solved was given with the polynomial in factored form. If the polynomial in an equation is not already factored, first make sure that the equation is in standard form. Then factor.

Example 2 Solving Quadratic Equations

Solve each equation.

(a) $x^2-5x=-6$

First, rewrite the equation in standard form by adding 6 to each side.

$$x^2-5x=-6$$
$$x^2-5x+6=0 \quad \text{Add 6.}$$

Now factor x^2-5x+6. Find two numbers whose product is 6 and whose sum is -5. These two numbers are -2 and -3, so the equation becomes

$$(x-2)(x-3)=0. \quad \text{Factor.}$$
$$x-2=0 \quad \text{or} \quad x-3=0 \quad \text{Zero-factor property}$$
$$x=2 \quad \text{or} \quad x=3 \quad \text{Solve each equation.}$$

Continued on Next Page

ANSWERS

3. (a) $\{-2, 5\}$ (b) $\left\{-6, \frac{2}{3}\right\}$ (c) $\left\{-\frac{5}{2}, 0\right\}$

Check: If $x = 2$, then

$$2^2 - 5(2) = -6 \quad ?$$
$$4 - 10 = -6 \quad ?$$
$$-6 = -6. \quad \text{True}$$

If $x = 3$, then

$$3^2 - 5(3) = -6 \quad ?$$
$$9 - 15 = -6 \quad ?$$
$$-6 = -6. \quad \text{True}$$

Both solutions check, so the solution set is {2} and {3}.

(b) $y^2 = y + 20$

Rewrite the equation in standard form.

$$y^2 = y + 20$$
$$y^2 - y - 20 = 0 \qquad \text{Subtract } y \text{ and } 20.$$
$$(y - 5)(y + 4) = 0 \qquad \text{Factor.}$$
$$y - 5 = 0 \quad \text{or} \quad y + 4 = 0 \qquad \text{Zero-factor property}$$
$$y = 5 \quad \text{or} \quad y = -4 \qquad \text{Solve each equation.}$$

Check these solutions by substituting each one in the original equation. The solution set is $\{5, -4\}$.

Work Problem 4 at the Side.

4 Solve each equation. Check your solutions.

(a) $m^2 - 3m - 10 = 0$

(b) $r^2 + 2r = 8$

In summary, follow these steps to solve quadratic equations by factoring.

Solving a Quadratic Equation by Factoring

Step 1 **Write in standard form.** Write the equation so that all terms are on one side of the equals sign in descending powers of the variable, with 0 on the other side.

Step 2 **Factor.** Factor completely.

Step 3 **Use the zero-factor property.** Set each factor with a variable equal to 0, and solve the resulting equations.

Step 4 **Check.** Check each solution in the original equation.

NOTE

Not all quadratic equations can be solved by factoring. A more general method for solving such equations is given in Chapter 10.

Example 3 Solving a Quadratic Equation with a Common Factor

Solve $4p^2 + 40 = 26p$.

Subtract $26p$ from each side and write the equation in standard form to get

$$4p^2 - 26p + 40 = 0.$$
$$2(2p^2 - 13p + 20) = 0 \qquad \text{Factor out 2.}$$
$$2p^2 - 13p + 20 = 0 \qquad \text{Divide each side by 2.}$$
$$(2p - 5)(p - 4) = 0 \qquad \text{Factor.}$$
$$2p - 5 = 0 \quad \text{or} \quad p - 4 = 0 \qquad \text{Zero-factor property}$$
$$2p = 5 \qquad p = 4$$
$$p = \frac{5}{2}$$

Check that the solutions are $\frac{5}{2}$ and 4 by substituting each one in the original equation. The solution set is $\{\frac{5}{2}, 4\}$.

ANSWERS

4. **(a)** $\{-2, 5\}$ **(b)** $\{-4, 2\}$

5 Solve each equation. Check your solutions.

(a) $10a^2 - 5a - 15 = 0$

(b) $4x^2 - 2x = 42$

CAUTION

A common error is to include the common factor 2 as a solution in Example 3. Only factors containing *variables* lead to solutions.

Work Problem 5 at the Side.

Example 4 Solving Quadratic Equations

Solve each equation.

(a) $16m^2 - 25 = 0$

$$16m^2 - 25 = 0$$

$$(4m + 5)(4m - 5) = 0 \qquad \text{Factor.}$$

$$4m + 5 = 0 \quad \text{or} \quad 4m - 5 = 0 \qquad \text{Zero-factor property}$$

$$4m = -5 \quad \text{or} \quad 4m = 5$$

$$m = -\frac{5}{4} \quad \text{or} \quad m = \frac{5}{4}$$

Check the solutions $-\frac{5}{4}$ and $\frac{5}{4}$ in the original equation. The solution set is $\{-\frac{5}{4}, \frac{5}{4}\}$.

(b) $k(2k + 5) = 3$

We need to write this equation in standard form.

$$k(2k + 5) = 3$$

$$2k^2 + 5k = 3 \qquad \text{Multiply.}$$

$$2k^2 + 5k - 3 = 0 \qquad \text{Standard form}$$

$$(2k - 1)(k + 3) = 0 \qquad \text{Factor.}$$

$$2k - 1 = 0 \quad \text{or} \quad k + 3 = 0 \qquad \text{Zero-factor property}$$

$$2k = 1 \qquad k = -3$$

$$k = \frac{1}{2}$$

Check that the solutions are $\frac{1}{2}$ and -3. The solution set is $\{\frac{1}{2}, -3\}$.

(c) $y^2 = 2y$

First write the equation in standard form.

$$y^2 - 2y = 0 \qquad \text{Standard form}$$

$$y(y - 2) = 0 \qquad \text{Factor.}$$

$$y = 0 \quad \text{or} \quad y - 2 = 0 \qquad \text{Zero-factor property}$$

$$y = 2$$

Check that the solutions are 0 and 2. The solution set is $\{0, 2\}$.

ANSWERS

5. **(a)** $\left\{-1, \frac{3}{2}\right\}$ **(b)** $\left\{-3, \frac{7}{2}\right\}$

CAUTION

In Example 4(b), the zero-factor property could not be used to solve the equation as given because of the 3 on the right. Remember that the zero-factor property applies only to a product that equals 0.

In Example 4(c), it is tempting to begin by dividing each side of the equation by y to get $y = 2$. Note that we do not get the other solution, 0, if we divide by a variable. (We *may* divide each side of an equation by a *nonzero* real number, however. For instance, in Example 3 we divided each side by 2.)

Work Problem 6 at the Side.

2 Solve other equations by factoring. We can also use the zero-factor property to solve equations that involve more than two factors with variables, as shown in Examples 5 and 6. (These equations are *not* quadratic equations. Why not?)

Example 5 Solving an Equation with More Than Two Factors

Solve $6z^3 - 6z = 0$.

$$6z^3 - 6z = 0$$
$$6z(z^2 - 1) = 0 \quad \text{Factor out } 6z.$$
$$6z(z + 1)(z - 1) = 0 \quad \text{Factor } z^2 - 1.$$

By an extension of the zero-factor property, this product can equal 0 only if at least one of the factors equals 0. Write and solve three equations, one for each factor with a variable.

$$6z = 0 \quad \text{or} \quad z + 1 = 0 \quad \text{or} \quad z - 1 = 0$$
$$z = 0 \quad \text{or} \quad z = -1 \quad \text{or} \quad z = 1$$

Check by substituting, in turn, 0, -1, and 1 in the original equation. The solution set is $\{0, -1, 1\}$.

Work Problem 7 at the Side.

Example 6 Solving an Equation with a Quadratic Factor

Solve $(2x - 1)(x^2 - 9x + 20) = 0$.

$$(2x - 1)(x^2 - 9x + 20) = 0$$
$$(2x - 1)(x - 5)(x - 4) = 0 \quad \text{Factor } x^2 - 9x + 20.$$
$$2x - 1 = 0 \quad \text{or} \quad x - 5 = 0 \quad \text{or} \quad x - 4 = 0 \quad \text{Zero-factor property}$$
$$x = \frac{1}{2} \quad \text{or} \quad x = 5 \quad \text{or} \quad x = 4$$

Check. The solution set is $\{\frac{1}{2}, 5, 4\}$.

Work Problem 8 at the Side.

CAUTION

In Example 6, it would be unproductive to begin by multiplying the two factors together. Keep in mind that the zero-factor property requires the product of two or more factors to equal 0. Always consider first whether an equation is given in the appropriate form to apply the zero-factor property.

---

6 Solve each equation. Check your solutions.

(a) $49m^2 - 9 = 0$

(b) $p(4p + 7) = 2$

(c) $m^2 = 3m$

7 Solve each equation. Check your solutions.

(a) $r^3 - 16r = 0$

(b) $x^3 - 3x^2 - 18x = 0$

8 Solve each equation. Check your solutions.

(a) $(m + 3)(m^2 - 11m + 10) = 0$

(b) $(2x + 5)(4x^2 - 9) = 0$

ANSWERS

6. (a) $\left\{-\frac{3}{7}, \frac{3}{7}\right\}$ **(b)** $\left\{-2, \frac{1}{4}\right\}$ **(c)** $\{0, 3\}$

7. (a) $\{-4, 0, 4\}$ **(b)** $\{-3, 0, 6\}$

8. (a) $\{-3, 1, 10\}$ **(b)** $\left\{-\frac{5}{2}, -\frac{3}{2}, \frac{3}{2}\right\}$

Focus on Real-Data Applications

Factoring Trinomials Made Easy

FOIL is a memory aid that stands for *First, Outer, Inner, Last* and explains how to multiply binomials such as $(3x - 2)(2x + 1)$. The result of multiplying two binomials is typically a trinomial, $6x^2 - x - 2$ in this case. The ***first*** term of the trinomial, $6x^2$, is the *First* product in FOIL; the ***middle*** term, $-x$, is the sum of the *Outer* and *Inner* products in FOIL; and the ***last*** term, -2, is the *Last* product in FOIL. To factor a trinomial, all we have to do is find the *Outer* and *Inner* coefficients that sum to give the coefficient of the middle term, and then use grouping.

Our approach begins with a **key number,** which is found by multiplying the coefficients of the first and last terms of the trinomial. In our example, the key number is -12 since $6(-2) = -12$. We can display the factors of -12 by entering $Y_1 = -12/X$ in a graphing calculator (Screen 1), and using an automatic table (Screen 2). Factors of -12 are automatically displayed in pairs as $1, -12$; $2, -6$; $3, -4$; $4, -3$; and $6, -2$ (Screen 3). You could scroll up or down to find other factors. Note that $5, -2.4$ and $7, -1.714$ are not factor pairs since -2.4 and -1.714 are not integers.

Screen 1

Screen 2

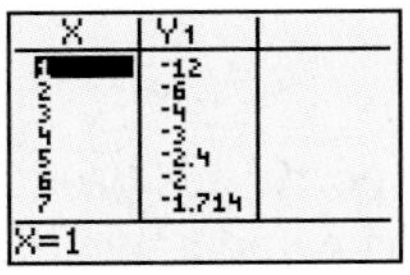

Screen 3

Screen 4

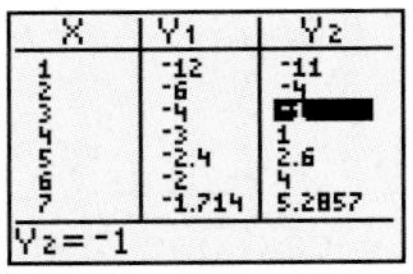

Screen 5

We want to find the pair of factors that sum to the *middle* term coefficient, -1. We can let the calculator do this, too. Enter $Y_2 = X + -12/X$. In this case, X is one of the factors, and $-12/X$ is the other, so Y_2 will give the sum (Screen 4). Look for -1 in the Y_2 column in Screen 5. (You may have to scroll up or down to find it.)

Now we know that the coefficients of the Outer and Inner products are 3 and -4. So we can write $6x^2 - x - 2$ as $6x^2 + 3x - 4x - 2$. Using the grouping method,

$$(6x^2 + 3x) + (-4x - 2) = 3x(2x + 1) - 2(2x + 1) = (3x - 2)(2x + 1).$$

For Group Discussion

Factor each trinomial given in the column heads of the table. First find the key number, and then use a calculator to help you find the coefficients of the Outer and Inner products of FOIL. Then apply the grouping method. (If you do not have a graphing calculator, simply use a regular calculator and create a table similar to that shown in Screen 3. Then add across each row to create a table similar to Screen 5.)

Trinomial	$3x^2 - 2x - 8$	$2x^2 - 11x + 15$	$10x^2 + 11x - 6$	$4x^2 + 5x + 3$
Key Number	-24 (Why?)	30 (*Hint:* Scroll up table.)	-60 (*Hint:* Scroll down table.)	12
Outer, Inner Coefficients	$4, -6$	$-5, -6$	$15, -4$	None
Grouping Method	$(3x^2 + 4x) + (-6x - 8)$ $x(3x + 4) - 2(3x + 4)$ $(x - 2)(3x + 4)$	$(2x^2 - 5x) + (-6x + 15)$ $x(2x - 5) - 3(2x - 5)$ $(x - 3)(2x - 5)$	$(10x^2 + 15x) + (-4x - 6)$ $5x(2x + 3) - 2(2x + 3)$ $(5x - 2)(2x + 3)$	Prime (*Hint:* What does it mean if the middle term coefficient is *not* listed in the Y_2 column?)

Teaching notes and an extension for this activity are provided in the *Printed Test Bank and Instructor's Resource Guide.*

7.6 EXERCISES

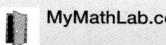

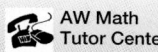

FOR EXTRA HELP: Student's Solutions Manual | MyMathLab.com | InterAct Math Tutorial Software | AW Math Tutor Center | MathXL www.mathxl.com | Digital Video Tutor CD 6 Videotape 14

Solve each equation, and check your solutions. See Example 1.

1. $(x + 5)(x - 2) = 0$ $\{-5, 2\}$

2. $(x - 1)(x + 8) = 0$ $\{-8, 1\}$

3. $(2m - 7)(m - 3) = 0$ $\left\{3, \frac{7}{2}\right\}$

4. $(6k + 5)(k + 4) = 0$ $\left\{-4, -\frac{5}{6}\right\}$

5. $t(6t + 5) = 0$ $\left\{-\frac{5}{6}, 0\right\}$

6. $w(4w + 1) = 0$ $\left\{-\frac{1}{4}, 0\right\}$

7. $2x(3x - 4) = 0$ $\left\{0, \frac{4}{3}\right\}$

8. $6y(4y + 9) = 0$ $\left\{-\frac{9}{4}, 0\right\}$

9. $\left(x + \frac{1}{2}\right)\left(2x - \frac{1}{3}\right) = 0$ $\left\{-\frac{1}{2}, \frac{1}{6}\right\}$

10. $\left(a + \frac{2}{3}\right)\left(5a - \frac{1}{2}\right) = 0$ $\left\{-\frac{2}{3}, \frac{1}{10}\right\}$

11. $(.5z - 1)(2.5z + 2) = 0$ $\{-.8, 2\}$

12. $(.25x + 1)(x - .5) = 0$ $\{-4, .5\}$

13. $(x - 9)(x - 9) = 0$ $\{9\}$

14. $(2y + 1)(2y + 1) = 30$ $\left\{-\frac{1}{2}\right\}$

15. What is wrong with this "solution"?

$$2x(3x - 4) = 0$$
$$x = 2 \quad \text{or} \quad x = 0 \quad \text{or} \quad 3x - 4 = 0$$
$$x = \frac{4}{3}$$

The solutions are 2, 0, and $\frac{4}{3}$.

Set each *variable* factor equal to 0, to get $2x = 0$ or $3x - 4 = 0$. The solutions are 0 and $\frac{4}{3}$.

16. What is wrong with this "solution"?

$$x(7x - 1) = 0$$
$$7x - 1 = 0 \quad \text{Zero-factor property}$$
$$x = \frac{1}{7}$$

The solution is $\frac{1}{7}$.

The variable x is another factor to set equal to 0, so the solutions are 0 and $\frac{1}{7}$.

Solve each equation, and check your solutions. See Examples 2–6.

17. $y^2 + 3y + 2 = 0$ $\{-2, -1\}$

18. $p^2 + 8p + 7 = 0$ $\{-7, -1\}$

19. $y^2 - 3y + 2 = 0$ $\{1, 2\}$

20. $r^2 - 4r + 3 = 0$ $\{1, 3\}$

21. $x^2 = 24 - 5x$ $\{-8, 3\}$

22. $t^2 = 2t + 15$ $\{-3, 5\}$

23. $x^2 = 3 + 2x$ $\{-1, 3\}$

24. $m^2 = 4 + 3m$ $\{-1, 4\}$

25. $z^2 + 3z = -2$ $\{-2, -1\}$

26. $p^2 - 2p = 3$ $\{-1, 3\}$

27. $m^2 + 8m + 16 = 0$ $\{-4\}$

28. $b^2 - 6b + 9 = 0$ $\{3\}$

29. $3x^2 + 5x - 2 = 0$ $\left\{-2, \frac{1}{3}\right\}$

30. $6r^2 - r - 2 = 0$ $\left\{-\frac{1}{2}, \frac{2}{3}\right\}$

31. $6p^2 = 4 - 5p$ $\left\{-\frac{4}{3}, \frac{1}{2}\right\}$

32. $6x^2 = 4 + 5x$
$\left\{-\frac{1}{2}, \frac{4}{3}\right\}$

33. $9s^2 + 12s = -4$
$\left\{-\frac{2}{3}\right\}$

34. $36x^2 + 60x = -25$
$\left\{-\frac{5}{6}\right\}$

35. $y^2 - 9 = 0$
$\{-3, 3\}$

36. $m^2 - 100 = 0$
$\{-10, 10\}$

37. $16k^2 - 49 = 0$
$\left\{-\frac{7}{4}, \frac{7}{4}\right\}$

38. $4w^2 - 9 = 0$
$\left\{-\frac{3}{2}, \frac{3}{2}\right\}$

39. $n^2 = 121$
$\{-11, 11\}$

40. $x^2 = 400$
$\{-20, 20\}$

41. $x^2 = 7x$
$\{0, 7\}$

42. $t^2 = 9t$
$\{0, 9\}$

43. $6r^2 = 3r$
$\left\{0, \frac{1}{2}\right\}$

44. $10y^2 = -5y$
$\left\{-\frac{1}{2}, 0\right\}$

45. $g(g - 7) = -10$
$\{2, 5\}$

46. $r(r - 5) = -6$
$\{2, 3\}$

47. $z(2z + 7) = 4$
$\left\{-4, \frac{1}{2}\right\}$

48. $b(2b + 3) = 9$
$\left\{-3, \frac{3}{2}\right\}$

49. $2(y^2 - 66) = -13y$
$\left\{-12, \frac{11}{2}\right\}$

50. $3(t^2 + 4) = 20t$
$\left\{\frac{2}{3}, 6\right\}$

51. $5x^3 - 20x = 0$
$\{-2, 0, 2\}$

52. $3x^3 - 48x = 0$
$\{-4, 0, 4\}$

53. $9y^3 - 49y = 0$
$\left\{-\frac{7}{3}, 0, \frac{7}{3}\right\}$

54. $16r^3 - 9r = 0$
$\left\{-\frac{3}{4}, 0, \frac{3}{4}\right\}$

55. $(2r + 5)(3r^2 - 16r + 5) = 0$
$\left\{-\frac{5}{2}, \frac{1}{3}, 5\right\}$

56. $(3m + 4)(6m^2 + m - 2) = 0$
$\left\{-\frac{4}{3}, -\frac{2}{3}, \frac{1}{2}\right\}$

57. $(2x + 7)(x^2 + 2x - 3) = 0$
$\left\{-\frac{7}{2}, -3, 1\right\}$

58. $(x + 1)(6x^2 + x - 12) = 0$
$\left\{-\frac{3}{2}, -1, \frac{4}{3}\right\}$

59. Galileo's formula for freely falling objects, $d = 16t^2$, was given at the beginning of this section. The distance d in feet an object falls depends on the time elapsed t in seconds. (This is an example of a function, introduced in Section 4.6.)

(a) Use Galileo's formula and complete the following table. (*Hint:* Substitute each given value into the formula and solve for the unknown value.)

t in seconds	0	1	2	3	4	6
d in feet	0	16	64	144	256	576

(b) When $t = 0$, $d = 0$. Explain this in the context of the problem.

No time has elapsed, so the object hasn't fallen (been released) yet.

(c) When you substituted 256 for d and solved for t, you should have found two solutions, 4 and -4. Why doesn't -4 make sense as an answer?

Time cannot be negative.

7.7 Applications of Quadratic Equations

Objectives

1. Solve problems about geometric figures.
2. Solve problems about consecutive integers.
3. Solve problems using the Pythagorean formula.
4. Solve problems using given quadratic models.

We can now use factoring to solve quadratic equations that arise in application problems. We follow the same six problem-solving steps given in Section 2.4.

Solving an Applied Problem

Step 1 **Read** the problem carefully until you understand what is given and what is to be found.

Step 2 **Assign a variable** to represent the unknown value, using diagrams or tables as needed. Write down what the variable represents. If necessary, express any other unknown values in terms of the variable.

Step 3 **Write an equation** using the variable expression(s).

Step 4 **Solve** the equation.

Step 5 **State the answer.** Does it seem reasonable?

Step 6 **Check** the answer in the words of the original problem.

1 **Solve problems about geometric figures.** Some of the applied problems in this section require one of the formulas given on the inside covers of the text.

Example 1 Solving an Area Problem

The Moens want to plant a rectangular garden in their yard. The width of the garden will be 4 ft less than its length, and they want it to have an area of 96 ft^2. (Recall that ft^2 means square feet.) Find the length and width of the garden.

Step 1 **Read** the problem carefully. We need to find the dimensions of a garden with area 96 ft^2.

Step 2 **Assign a variable.**

Let $x =$ the length of the garden.

Then $x - 4 =$ the width. (The width is 4 ft less than the length.)

See Figure 1.

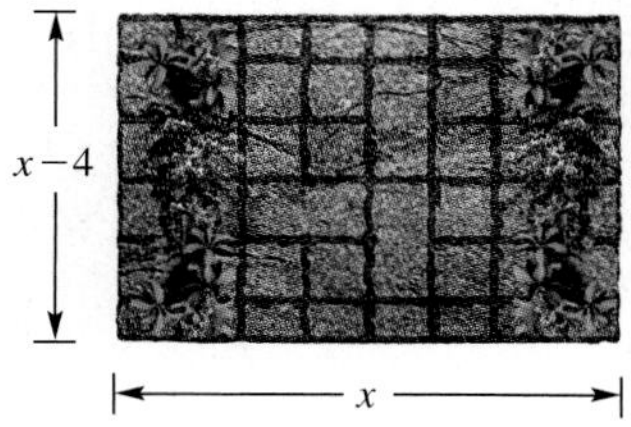

Figure 1

Step 3 **Write an equation.** The area of a rectangle is given by the formula

$$\text{Area} = LW = \text{Length} \times \text{Width}.$$

Substitute 96 for area, x for length, and $x - 4$ for width in the formula.

$$A = LW$$

$$96 = x(x - 4) \qquad \text{Let } A = 96,\ L = x,\ W = x - 4.$$

Continued on Next Page

1 Solve each problem.

(a) The length of a rectangular room is 2 m more than the width. The area of the floor is 48 m^2. Find the length and width of the room.

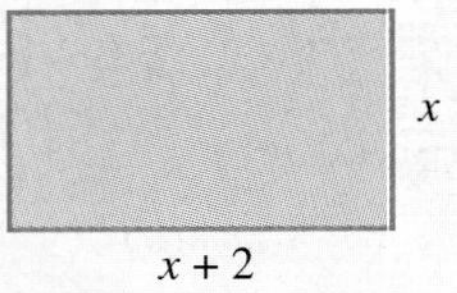

(b) The length of each side of a square is increased by 4 in. The sum of the areas of the original square and the larger square is 106 in^2. What is the length of a side of the original square?

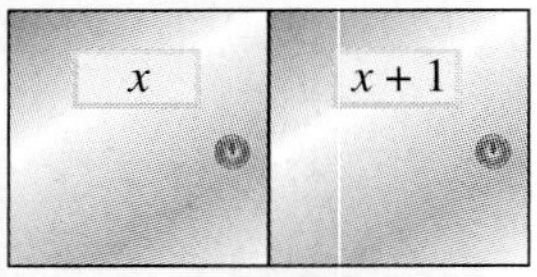

Figure 2

ANSWERS
1. (a) length: 8 m; width: 6 m **(b)** 5 in.

Step 4 **Solve.**

$$96 = x^2 - 4x \quad \text{Distributive property}$$
$$0 = x^2 - 4x - 96 \quad \text{Standard form}$$
$$0 = (x - 12)(x + 8) \quad \text{Factor.}$$
$$x - 12 = 0 \quad \text{or} \quad x + 8 = 0 \quad \text{Zero-factor property}$$
$$x = 12 \quad \text{or} \quad x = -8$$

Step 5 **State the answer.** The solutions are 12 and -8. Because a rectangle cannot have a side of negative length, discard the solution -8. Then the length of the garden will be 12 ft, and the width will be $12 - 4 = 8$ ft.

Step 6 **Check.** The width is 4 ft less than the length, and the area is $12 \cdot 8 = 96$ ft^2.

CAUTION

When solving applied problems, *always* check solutions against physical facts and discard any answers that are not appropriate.

Work Problem 1 at the Side.

2 **Solve problems about consecutive integers.** Recall from our work in Section 2.4 that consecutive integers are integers that are next to each other on a number line, such as 5 and 6, or -11 and -10. Consecutive odd integers are *odd* integers that are next to each other, such as 5 and 7, or -13 and -11. Consecutive *even* integers are defined similarly; for example, 4 and 6 are consecutive even integers, as are -10 and -8. The following list may be helpful.

Consecutive Integers

Let x represent the first of the integers.

Two consecutive integers	$x, x + 1$
Three consecutive integers	$x, x + 1, x + 2$
Two consecutive even or odd integers	$x, x + 2$
Three consecutive even or odd integers	$x, x + 2, x + 4$

Example 2 **Solving a Consecutive Integer Problem**

The product of the numbers on two consecutive post-office boxes is 210. Find the box numbers.

Step 1 **Read** the problem. Note that the boxes are consecutive.

Step 2 **Assign a variable.**

Let x = the first box number.

Then $x + 1$ = the next consecutive box number.

See Figure 2.

Step 3 **Write an equation.** The product of the box numbers is 210, so

$$x(x + 1) = 210.$$

Continued on Next Page

Step 4 **Solve.**

$$x^2 + x = 210$$

$$x^2 + x - 210 = 0 \qquad \text{Standard form}$$

$$(x + 15)(x - 14) = 0 \qquad \text{Factor.}$$

$$x + 15 = 0 \quad \text{or} \quad x - 14 = 0 \qquad \text{Zero-factor property}$$

$$x = -15 \quad \text{or} \quad x = 14$$

Step 5 **State the answer.** The solutions are -15 and 14. Discard the solution -15 since a box number cannot be negative. When $x = 14$, then $x + 1 = 15$, so the post office boxes have the numbers 14 and 15.

Step 6 **Check.** The numbers 14 and 15 are consecutive and $14 \cdot 15 = 210$, as required.

Work Problem 2 at the Side.

2 Solve the problem.

The product of the numbers on two consecutive lockers at a health club is 132. Find the locker numbers.

Example 3 Solving a Consecutive Integer Problem

The product of two consecutive odd integers is 1 less than five times their sum. Find the integers.

Step 1 **Read** carefully. This problem is a little more complicated.

Step 2 **Assign a variable.**

Let s = the smaller integer.

Because the problem mentions consecutive *odd* integers,

$s + 2$ = the next larger odd integer.

Step 3 **Write an equation.** According to the problem, the product is 1 less than five times the sum.

The product	is	five times the sum	less 1.
↓	↓	↓	↓
$s(s + 2)$	$=$	$5(s + s + 2)$	$-\ 1$

Step 4 **Solve.**

$$s^2 + 2s = 5s + 5s + 10 - 1 \qquad \text{Distributive property}$$

$$s^2 + 2s = 10s + 9 \qquad \text{Combine like terms.}$$

$$s^2 - 8s - 9 = 0 \qquad \text{Standard form}$$

$$(s - 9)(s + 1) = 0 \qquad \text{Factor.}$$

$$s - 9 = 0 \quad \text{or} \quad s + 1 = 0 \qquad \text{Zero-factor property}$$

$$s = 9 \quad \text{or} \quad s = -1$$

Step 5 **State the answer.** We need to find two consecutive odd integers.

If $s = 9$ is the first, then $s + 2 = 9 + 2 = 11$ is the second.

If $s = -1$ is the first, then $s + 2 = -1 + 2 = 1$ is the second.

There are two sets of answers here since integers can be positive or negative.

Step 6 **Check.** The product of the first pair of integers is $9 \cdot 11 = 99$. One less than five times their sum is $5(9 + 11) - 1 = 99$. Thus 9 and 11 satisfy the problem. Repeat the check with -1 and 1.

Work Problem 3 at the Side.

3 Solve each problem.

(a) The product of two consecutive even integers is 4 more than two times their sum. Find the integers.

(b) Find three consecutive odd integers such that the product of the smallest and largest is 16 more than the middle integer.

ANSWERS

2. 11 and 12

3. (a) 4 and 6 or -2 and 0 **(b)** 3, 5, 7

CAUTION

Do *not* use x, $x + 1$, $x + 3$, and so on to represent consecutive odd integers. To see why, let $x = 3$. Then $x + 1 = 3 + 1 = 4$ and $x + 3 = 3 + 3 = 6$, and 3, 4, and 6 are not consecutive odd integers.

3 Solve problems using the Pythagorean formula. The next example requires the Pythagorean formula from geometry.

Pythagorean Formula

If a right triangle (a triangle with a 90° angle) has longest side of length c and two other sides of lengths a and b, then

$$a^2 + b^2 = c^2.$$

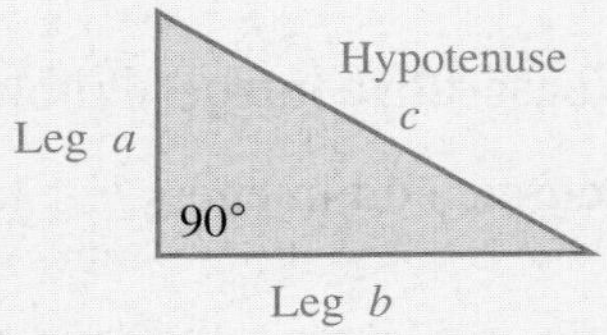

The longest side, the **hypotenuse,** is opposite the right angle. The two shorter sides are the **legs** of the triangle.

Example 4 **Using the Pythagorean Formula**

Ed and Mark leave their office, with Ed traveling north and Mark traveling east. When Mark is 1 mi farther than Ed from the office, the distance between them is 2 mi more than Ed's distance from the office. Find their distances from the office and the distance between them.

Step 1 **Read** the problem again. There will be three answers to this problem.

Step 2 **Assign a variable.** Let x represent Ed's distance from the office, $x + 1$ represent Mark's distance from the office, and $x + 2$ represent the distance between them. Place these on a right triangle, as in Figure 3.

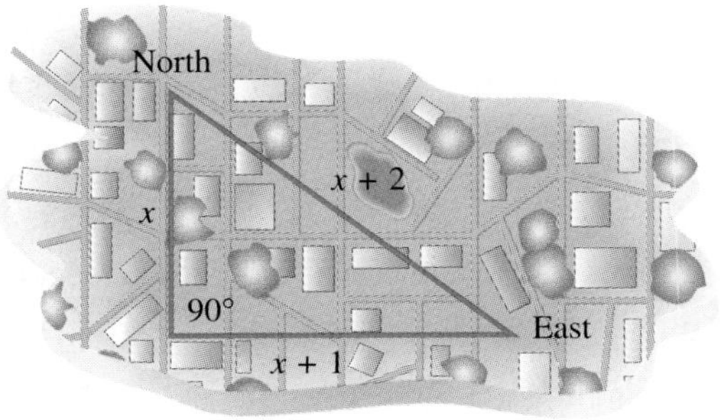

Figure 3

Step 3 **Write an equation.** Substitute into the Pythagorean formula.

$$a^2 + b^2 = c^2$$

$$x^2 + (x + 1)^2 = (x + 2)^2$$

Continued on Next Page

Step 4 **Solve.**

$$x^2 + x^2 + 2x + 1 = x^2 + 4x + 4$$

$$x^2 - 2x - 3 = 0 \quad \text{Standard form}$$

$$(x - 3)(x + 1) = 0 \quad \text{Factor.}$$

$$x - 3 = 0 \quad \text{or} \quad x + 1 = 0 \quad \text{Zero-factor property}$$

$$x = 3 \quad \text{or} \quad x = -1$$

Step 5 **State the answer.** Since -1 cannot represent a distance, 3 is the only possible answer. Ed's distance is 3 mi, Mark's distance is $3 + 1 = 4$ mi, and the distance between them is $3 + 2 = 5$ mi.

Step 6 **Check.** Since $3^2 + 4^2 = 5^2$, the answers are correct.

CAUTION

When solving a problem involving the Pythagorean formula, be sure that the expressions for the sides are properly placed.

$$\textbf{leg}^2 + \textbf{leg}^2 = \textbf{hypotenuse}^2$$

Work Problem 4 at the Side.

4 Solve the problem.

The hypotenuse of a right triangle is 3 in. longer than the longer leg. The shorter leg is 3 in. shorter than the longer leg. Find the lengths of the sides of the triangle.

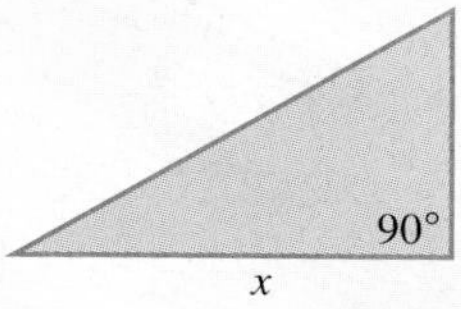

4 Solve problems using given quadratic models. In Examples 1–4, we wrote quadratic equations to model, or mathematically describe, various situations and then solved the equations. In the final examples, you are given the quadratic models and must use them to determine data.

Example 5 Finding the Height of a Ball

A tennis player's serve travels 180 ft per sec (125 mph). If she serves upward, the height h of the ball in feet at time t in seconds is modeled by the quadratic equation

$$h = -16t^2 + 180t + 6.$$

How long will it take for the ball to reach a height of 206 ft?

A height of 206 ft means $h = 206$, so we substitute 206 for h in the equation.

$$\mathbf{206} = -16t^2 + 180t + 6 \quad \text{Let } h = 206.$$

To solve the equation, we first write it in standard form. For convenience, we reverse the sides of the equation.

$$-16t^2 + 180t + 6 = 206$$

$$-16t^2 + 180t - 200 = 0 \quad \text{Standard form}$$

$$4t^2 - 45t + 50 = 0 \quad \text{Divide by } -4.$$

$$(4t - 5)(t - 10) = 0 \quad \text{Factor.}$$

$$4t - 5 = 0 \quad \text{or} \quad t - 10 = 0 \quad \text{Zero-factor property}$$

$$t = \frac{5}{4} \quad \text{or} \quad t = 10$$

Since we found two acceptable answers, the ball will be 206 ft above the ground twice (once on its way up and once on its way down)—at $\frac{5}{4}$ sec and at 10 sec. See Figure 4.

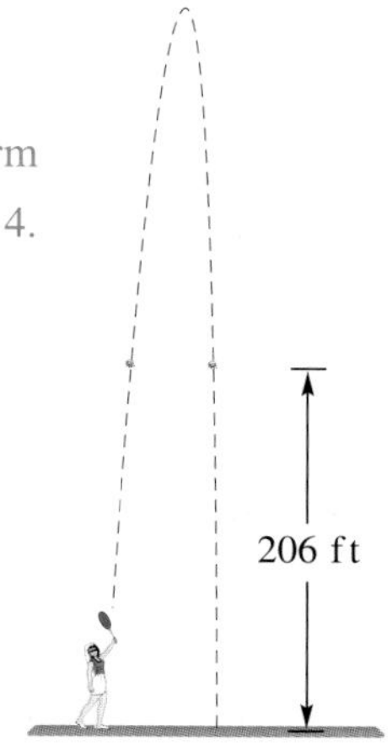

Figure 4

Work Problem 5 at the Side.

5 Solve the problem.

The number of impulses fired after a nerve has been stimulated is modeled by

$$I = -x^2 + 2x + 60,$$

where x is in milliseconds (ms) after the stimulation. When will 45 impulses occur? Do you get two solutions? Why is only one answer given?

ANSWERS

4. 9 in., 12 in., 15 in.

5. After 5 ms; There are two solutions, -3 and 5; Only one answer makes sense here because a negative answer is not appropriate.

6 Use the model in Example 6 to find the annual percent increase in the amount pharmacies paid for drugs in 1995. Give your answer to the nearest tenth. How does it compare to the actual data from the table?

Example 6 Modeling Increases in Drug Prices

The annual percent increase y in the amount pharmacies paid wholesalers for drugs in the years 1990–1999 can be modeled by the quadratic equation

$$y = .23x^2 - 2.6x + 9,$$

where $x = 0$ represents 1990, $x = 1$ represents 1991, and so on. (*Source: IMS Health,* Retail and Provider Perspective.)

(a) Use the model to find the annual percent increase to the nearest tenth in 1997.

In 1997, $x = 1997 - 1990 = 7$. Substitute 7 for x in the equation.

$$y = .23(7)^2 - 2.6(7) + 9 \quad \text{Let } x = 7.$$

$$y = 2.07 \quad \text{Use a calculator.}$$

To the nearest tenth, pharmacies paid about 2.1% more for drugs in 1997.

(b) Repeat part (a) for 1999.

For 1999, $x = 9$.

$$y = .23(\mathbf{9})^2 - 2.6(\mathbf{9}) + 9 \quad \text{Let } x = 1999 - 1990 = 9.$$

$$y = 4.23$$

In 1999, pharmacies paid about 4.2% more for drugs.

(c) The model used in parts (a) and (b) was developed using the data in the table below. How do the results in parts (a) and (b) compare to the actual data from the table?

Year	Percent Increase
1990	8.4
1991	7.2
1992	5.5
1993	3.0
1994	1.7
1995	1.9
1996	1.6
1997	2.5
1998	3.2
1999	4.2

From the table, the actual data for 1997 is 2.5%. Our answer, 2.1%, is a little low. For 1999, the actual data is 4.2%, which is the same as our answer in part (b).

Work Problem 6 at the Side.

NOTE

A graph of the quadratic equation from Example 6 is shown in Figure 5. Notice the basic shape of this graph, which follows the general pattern of the data in the table—it decreases from 1990 to 1996 (with the exception of the data for 1995) and then increases from 1997 to 1999. We will consider such graphs of quadratic equations, called *parabolas*, in more detail in Chapter 10.

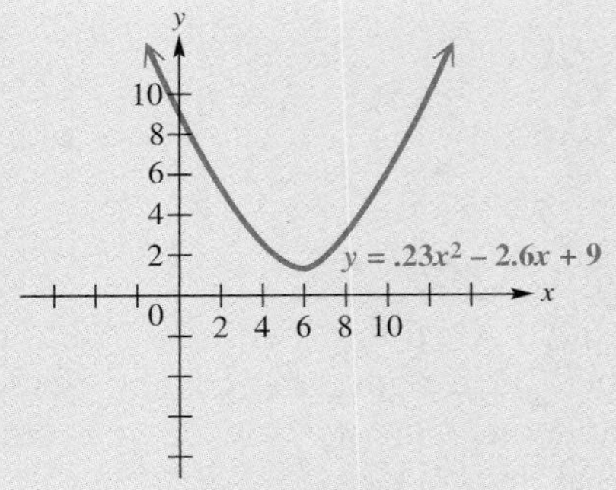

Figure 5

ANSWERS

6. 1.8%; The actual data for 1995 is 1.9%, so our answer using the model is a little low.

7.7 Exercises

FOR EXTRA HELP: Student's Solutions Manual · MyMathLab.com · InterAct Math Tutorial Software · AW Math Tutor Center · www.mathxl.com · Digital Video Tutor CD 6 Videotape 14

1. To review the six problem-solving steps first introduced in Section 2.4, complete each statement.

Step 1: **Read** the problem carefully until you understand what is given and what must be found.

Step 2: Assign a **variable** to represent the unknown value.

Step 3: Write a(n) **equation** using the variable expression(s).

Step 4: **Solve** the equation.

Step 5: State the **answer**.

Step 6: **Check** the answer in the words of the **original** problem.

2. A student solves an applied problem and gets 6 or -3 for the length of the side of a square. Which of these answers is reasonable? Explain.

Only 6 is reasonable since a square cannot have a side of negative length.

In Exercises 3–6, a figure and a corresponding geometric formula are given. Using x as the variable, complete Steps 3–6 for each problem. (Refer to the steps in Exercise 1 as needed.)

3.

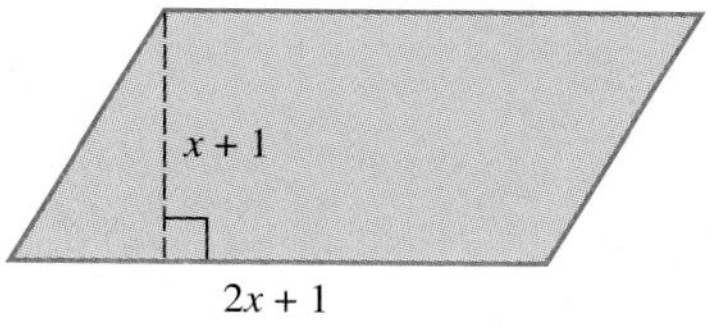

Area of a parallelogram: $A = bh$

The area of this parallelogram is 45 sq. units. Find its base and height.

Step 3: $45 = (2x + 1)(x + 1)$

Step 4: $x = 4$ or $x = -\frac{11}{2}$

Step 5: base: 9 units; height: 5 units

Step 6: $9 \cdot 5 = 45$

4.

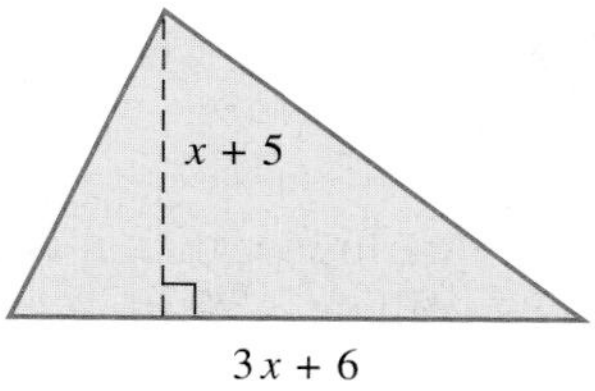

Area of a triangle: $A = \frac{1}{2}bh$

The area of this triangle is 60 sq. units. Find its base and height.

Step 3: $60 = \frac{1}{2}(3x + 6)(x + 5)$

Step 4: $x = 3$ or $x = -10$

Step 5: base: 15 units; height: 8 units

Step 6: $\frac{1}{2}(15)(8) = 60$

5.

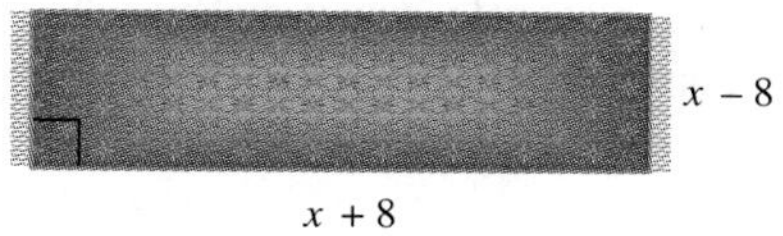

Area of a rectangular rug: $A = LW$

The area of this rug is 80 sq. units. Find its length and width.

Step 3: $80 = (x + 8)(x - 8)$

Step 4: $x = 12$ or $x = -12$

Step 5: length: 20 units; width: 4 units

Step 6: $20 \cdot 4 = 80$

6.

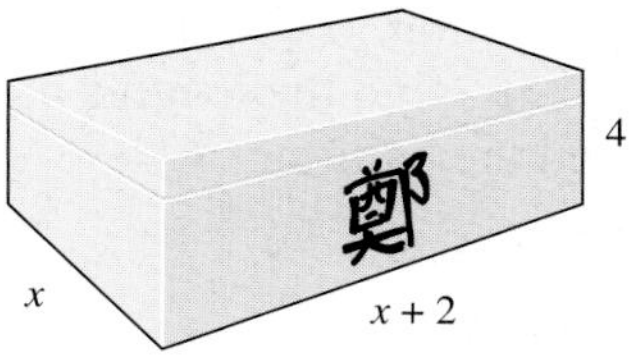

Volume of a rectangular Chinese box: $V = LWH$

The volume of this box is 192 cu. units. Find its length and width.

Step 3: $192 = 4x(x + 2)$

Step 4: $x = 6$ or $x = -8$

Step 5: length: 8 units; width: 6 units

Step 6: $8 \cdot 6 \cdot 4 = 192$

Solve each problem. Check your answers to be sure they are reasonable. Refer to the formulas on the inside covers. See Example 1.

7. The length of a VHS videocassette shell is 3 in. more than its width. The area of the rectangular top side of the shell is 28 in.^{2}. Find the length and width of the videocassette shell.

length: 7 in.; width: 4 in.

8. A plastic box that holds a standard audiocassette has length 4 cm longer than its width. The area of the rectangular top of the box is 77 cm^2. Find the length and width of the box.

length: 11 cm; width: 7 cm

9. The dimensions of a Gateway EV700 computer monitor screen are such that its length is 3 in. more than its width. If the length is increased by 1 in. while the width remains the same, the area is increased by 10 in.^{2}. What are the dimensions of the screen? (*Source:* Author's computer.)

length: 13 in.; width: 10 in.

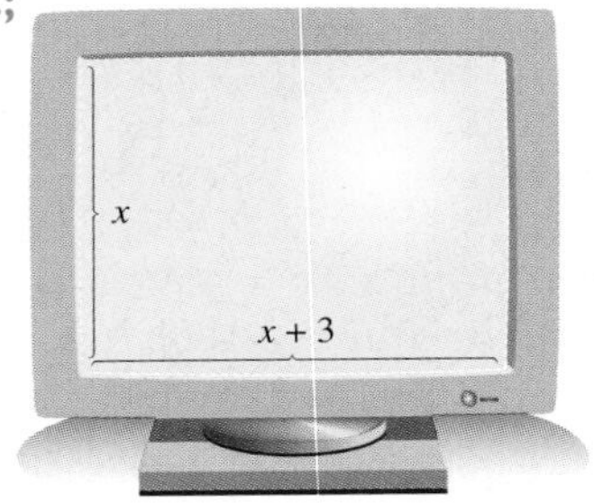

10. The keyboard of the computer in Exercise 9 is 11 in. longer than it is wide. If both its length and width are increased by 2 in., the area of the top of the keyboard is increased by 54 in.^{2}. Find the length and width of the keyboard. (*Source:* Author's computer.)

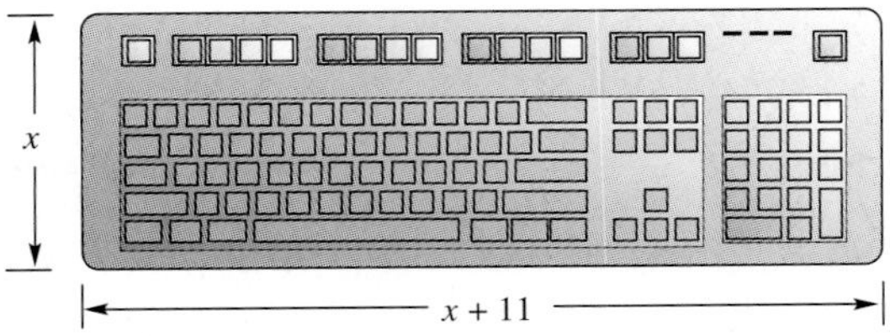

length: 18 in.; width: 7 in.

11. A ten-gallon aquarium is 3 in. higher than it is wide. Its length is 21 in., and its volume is 2730 in.^{3}. What are the height and width of the aquarium?

height: 13 in.; width: 10 in.

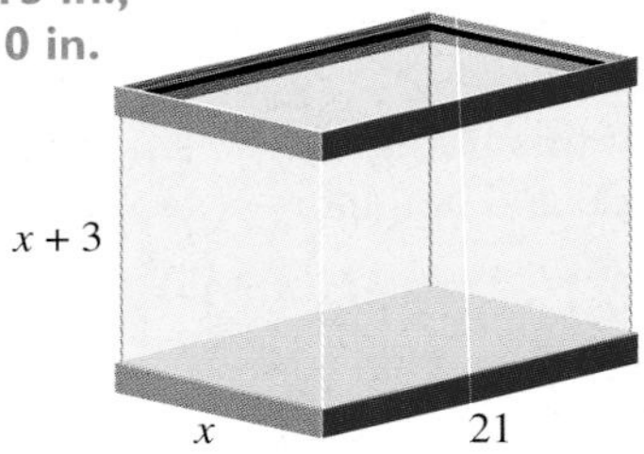

12. A toolbox is 2 ft high, and its width is 3 ft less than its length. If its volume is 80 ft^3, find the length and width of the box.

length: 8 ft; width: 5 ft

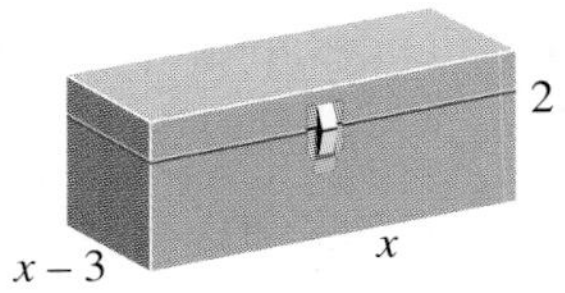

13. A square mirror has sides measuring 2 ft less than the sides of a square painting. If the difference between their areas is 32 ft^2, find the lengths of the sides of the mirror and the painting.

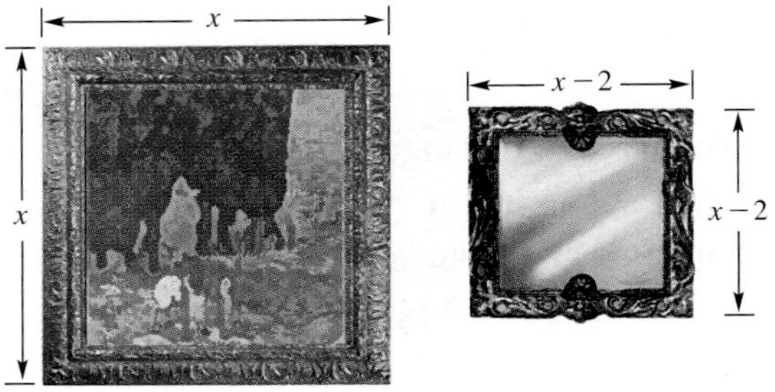

mirror: 7 ft; painting: 9 ft

14. The sides of one square have length 3 m more than the sides of a second square. If the area of the larger square is subtracted from 4 times the area of the smaller square, the result is 36 m^2. What are the lengths of the sides of each square?

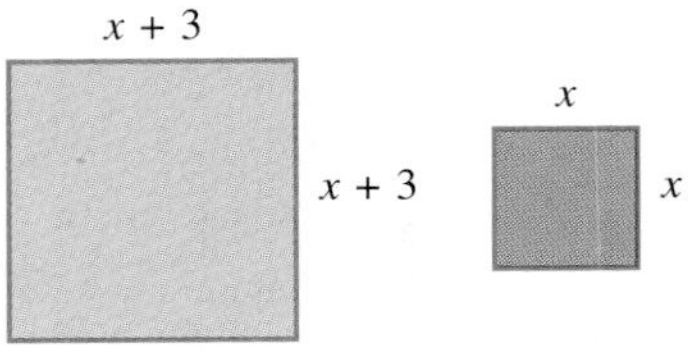

larger square: 8 m; smaller square: 5 m

Solve each problem about consecutive integers. See Examples 2 and 3.

15. The product of the numbers on two consecutive volumes of research data is 420. Find the volume numbers.

20, 21

16. The product of the page numbers on two facing pages of a book is 600. Find the page numbers.

24, 25

17. The product of two consecutive integers is 11 more than their sum. Find the integers.

−3, −2 or 4, 5

18. The product of two consecutive integers is 4 less than four times their sum. Find the integers.

0, 1 or 7, 8

19. Find two consecutive odd integers such that their product is 15 more than three times their sum.

−3, −1 or 7, 9

20. Find two consecutive odd integers such that five times their sum is 23 less than their product.

−3, −1 or 11, 13

21. Find three consecutive even integers such that the sum of the squares of the smaller two is equal to the square of the largest.

−2, 0, 2 or 6, 8, 10

22. Find three consecutive even integers such that the square of the sum of the smaller two is equal to twice the largest.

−2, 0, 2

Use the Pythagorean formula to solve each problem. See Example 4.

23. The hypotenuse of a right triangle is 1 cm longer than the longer leg. The shorter leg is 7 cm shorter than the longer leg. Find the length of the longer leg of the triangle.

12 cm

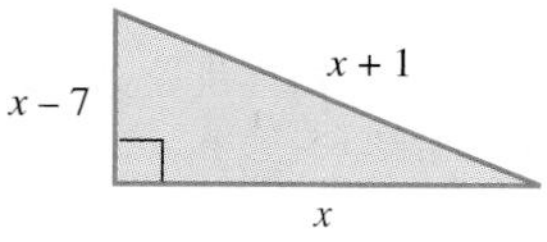

24. The longer leg of a right triangle is 1 m longer than the shorter leg. The hypotenuse is 1 m shorter than twice the shorter leg. Find the length of the shorter leg of the triangle.

3 m

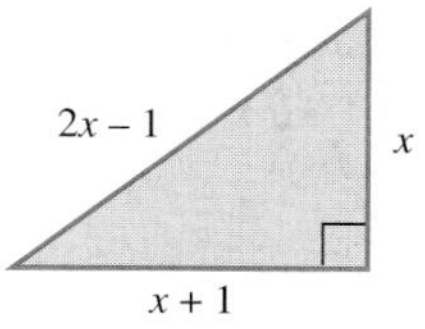

25. Wei-Jen works due north of home. Her husband Alan works due east. They leave for work at the same time. By the time Wei-Jen is 5 mi from home, the distance between them is 1 mi more than Alan's distance from home. How far from home is Alan?

12 mi

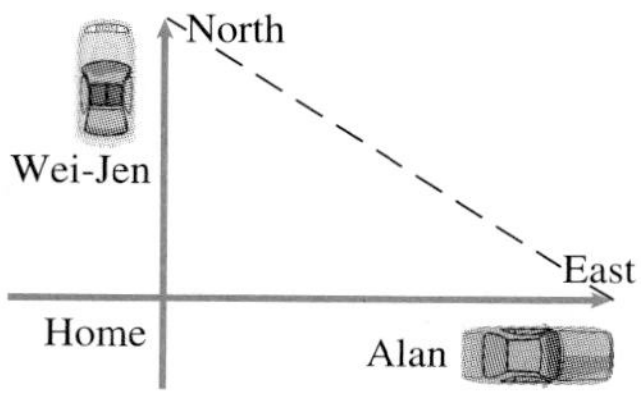

26. Two cars left an intersection at the same time. One traveled north. The other traveled 14 mi farther, but to the east. How far apart were they then, if the distance between them was 4 mi more than the distance traveled east?

34 mi

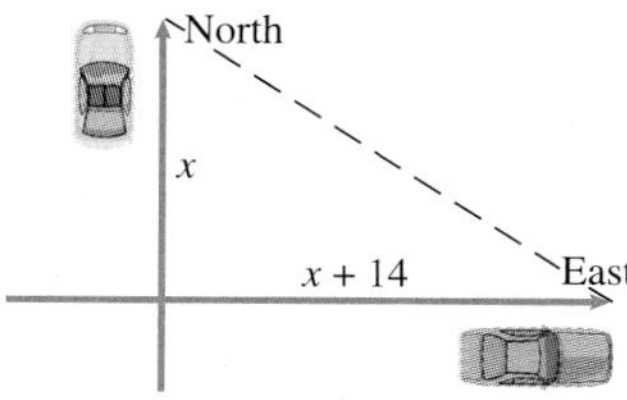

27. A ladder is leaning against a building. The distance from the bottom of the ladder to the building is 4 ft less than the length of the ladder. How high up the side of the building is the top of the ladder if that distance is 2 ft less than the length of the ladder?

8 ft

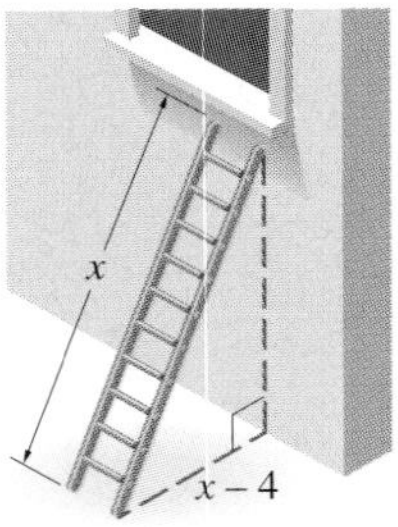

28. A lot has the shape of a right triangle with one leg 2 m longer than the other. The hypotenuse is 2 m less than twice the length of the shorter leg. Find the length of the shorter leg.

6 m

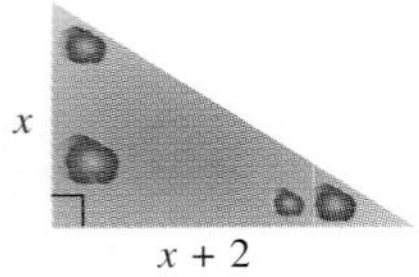

Solve each problem. See Examples 5 and 6.

29. An object propelled from a height of 48 ft with an initial velocity of 32 ft per sec after t seconds has height

$$h = -16t^2 + 32t + 48.$$

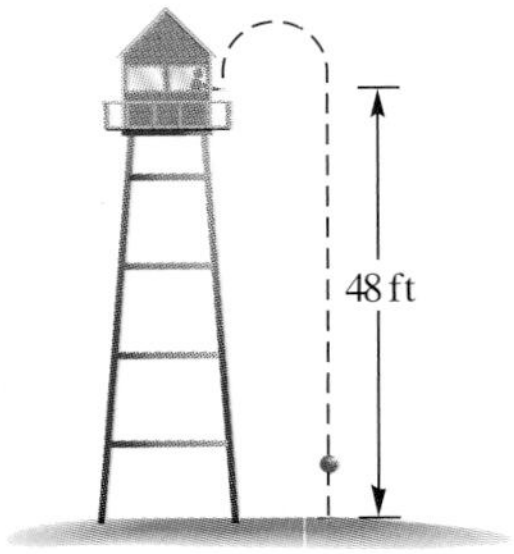

(a) After how many seconds is the height 64 ft? (*Hint:* Let $h = 64$ and solve.)

1 sec

(b) After how many seconds is the height 60 ft?

$\frac{1}{2}$ **sec and** $1\frac{1}{2}$ **sec**

(c) After how many seconds does the object hit the ground? (*Hint:* When the object hits the ground, $h = 0$.)

3 sec

(d) The quadratic equation from part (c) has two solutions, yet only one of them is appropriate for answering the question. Why is this so?

The negative solution, −1, does not make sense since t represents time, which cannot be negative.

30. If an object is propelled upward from ground level with an initial velocity of 64 ft per sec, its height h in feet t seconds later is

$$h = -16t^2 + 64t.$$

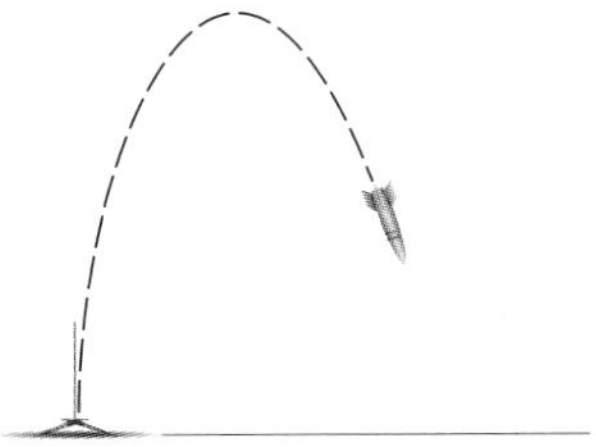

(a) After how many seconds is the height 48 ft?

1 sec and 3 sec

(b) The object reaches its maximum height 2 sec after it is propelled. What is this maximum height?

64 ft

(c) After how many seconds does the object hit the ground?

4 sec

(d) The quadratic equation from part (c) has two solutions, yet only one of them is appropriate for answering the question. Why is this so?

The solution 0 represents the time at which it was propelled.

31. The table shows the number of cellular phones (in millions) owned by Americans.

Year	Cellular Phones (in millions)
1988	2
1990	5
1992	11
1994	24
1996	44
1998	62

Source: Cellular Telecommunications Industry Association.

We used the data to develop the quadratic equation

$$y = .585x^2 + .295x + 1.75,$$

which models the number of cellular phones y (in millions) in the year x, where $x = 0$ represents 1988, $x = 2$ represents 1990, and so on.

(a) Use the model to find the number of cellular phones in 1990. How does the result compare to the actual data in the table?

4.68 million; The result using the model is a little less than 5 million, the actual number for 1990.

(b) What value of x corresponds to 1998?

10

(c) Use the model to find the number of cellular phones in 1998. How does the result compare to the actual data in the table?

63.2 million; The result is a little more than 62 million, the actual number for 1998.

(d) Assuming that the trend in the data continues, use the quadratic equation to predict the number of cellular phones in 2002.

120.54 million

Relating Concepts (Exercises 32–40) For Individual or Group Work

The U.S. trade deficit represents the amount by which exports are less than imports. It provides not only a sign of economic prosperity but also a warning of potential decline. The data in the table shows the U.S. trade deficit for 1995 through 1999.

Year	Deficit (in billions of dollars)
1995	97.5
1996	104.3
1997	104.7
1998	164.3
1999	271.3

Source: U.S. Department of Commerce.

Use the data to ***work Exercises 32–40 in order.***

32. How much did the trade deficit increase from 1998 to 1999? What percent increase is this (to the nearest percent)?

107 billion dollars; 65%

(continued)

33. The U.S. trade deficit for the years shown in the table can be approximated by the linear equation

$$y = 40.8x + 66.9,$$

where y is the deficit in billions of dollars. Here $x = 0$ represents 1995, $x = 1$ represents 1996, and so on. Use this equation to approximate the trade deficits in 1995, 1997, and 1999.

1995: 66.9 billion dollars; 1997: 148.5 billion dollars; 1999: 230.1 billion dollars

34. How do your answers from Exercise 33 compare to the actual data in the table?

The answers using the linear equation are not at all close to the actual data.

35. The trade deficit y (in billions of dollars) can also be approximated by the quadratic equation

$$y = 18.5x^2 - 33.4x + 104,$$

where $x = 0$ again represents 1995, $x = 1$ represents 1996, and so on. Use this equation to approximate the trade deficits in 1995, 1997, and 1999.

1995: 104 billion dollars; 1997: 111.2 billion dollars; 1999: 266.4 billion dollars

36. Compare your answers from Exercise 35 to the actual data in the table. Which equation, the linear or quadratic one, models the data better?

The answers in Exercise 35 are fairly close to the actual data. The quadratic equation models the data better.

37. We can also see graphically why the linear equation is not a very good model for the data. To do so, write the data from the table as a set of ordered pairs (x, y), where x represents the year since 1995 and y represents the trade deficit in billions of dollars.

(0, 97.5), (1, 104.3), (2, 104.7), (3, 164.3), (4, 271.3)

38. Plot the ordered pairs from Exercise 37 on the graph.

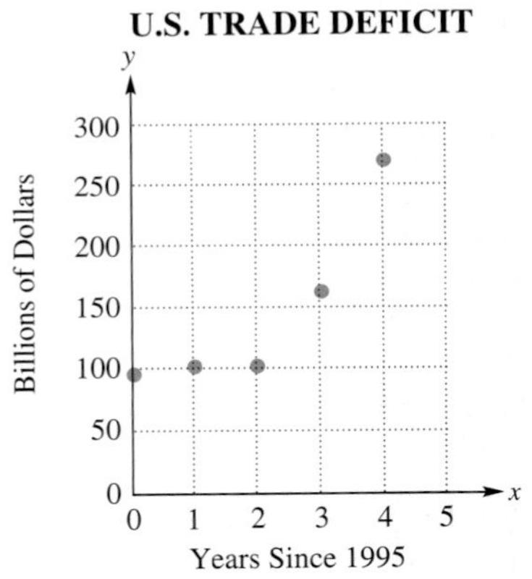

Recall from Chapter 4 that a linear equation has a straight line for its graph. Do the ordered pairs you plotted lie in a linear pattern?

no

39. Assuming that the trend in the data continues and since the quadratic equation models the data fairly well, use the quadratic equation to predict the trade deficit for the year 2000.

399.5 billion dollars

40. The actual trade deficit for 2000 was 369.7 billion dollars. (*Source*: www.census.gov)

(a) How does the actual deficit for 2000 compare to your prediction from Exercise 39?

The actual deficit is about 30 billion dollars less than the prediction.

(b) Should the quadratic equation be used to predict the U.S. trade deficit for years after 2000? Explain.

No, the equation is based on data for the years 1995–1999. Data for later years might not follow the same pattern.

Chapter 7

Summary

Key Terms

7.1	**factor**	An expression A is a factor of an expression B if B can be divided by A with 0 remainder.
	factored form	An expression is in factored form when it is written as a product.
	greatest common factor (GCF)	The greatest common factor is the largest quantity that is a factor of each of a group of quantities.
	factoring	The process of writing a polynomial as a product is called factoring.
7.2	**prime polynomial**	A prime polynomial is a polynomial that cannot be factored using only integers.
7.5	**perfect square trinomial**	A perfect square trinomial is a trinomial that can be factored as the square of a binomial.
7.6	**quadratic equation**	A quadratic equation is an equation that can be written in the form $ax^2 + bx + c = 0$, with $a \neq 0$.
	standard form	The form $ax^2 + bx + c = 0$ is the standard form of a quadratic equation.
7.7	**hypotenuse**	The longest side of a right triangle, opposite the right angle, is the hypotenuse.
	legs	The two shorter sides of a right triangle are the legs.

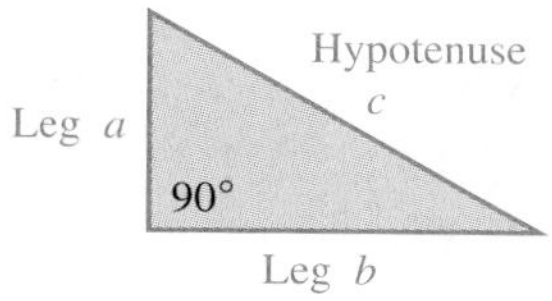

Test Your Word Power

See how well you have learned the vocabulary in this chapter. Answers follow the Quick Review.

1. **Factoring** is
   (a) a method of multiplying polynomials
   (b) the process of writing a polynomial as a product
   (c) the answer in a multiplication problem
   (d) a way to add the terms of a polynomial.
2. A polynomial is in **factored form** when
   (a) it is prime
   (b) it is written as a sum
   (c) the squared term has a coefficient of 1
   (d) it is written as a product.
3. A **perfect square trinomial** is a trinomial
   (a) that can be factored as the square of a binomial
   (b) that cannot be factored
   (c) that is multiplied by a binomial
   (d) where all terms are perfect squares.
4. A **quadratic equation** is an equation that can be written in the form
   (a) $y = mx + b$
   (b) $ax^2 + bx + c = 0$ $(a \neq 0)$
   (c) $Ax + By = C$
   (d) $x = k$.
5. A **hypotenuse** is
   (a) either of the two shorter sides of a triangle
   (b) the shortest side of a right triangle
   (c) the side opposite the right angle in a right triangle
   (d) the longest side in any triangle.

QUICK REVIEW

Concepts | *Examples*

7.1 Factors; The Greatest Common Factor

Finding the Greatest Common Factor (GCF)

Step 1 Write each number in prime factored form.

Step 2 List each prime number or each variable that is a factor of every term in the list.

Step 3 Use as exponents on the common prime factors the smallest exponents from the prime factored forms.

Step 4 Multiply the primes from Step 3.

Find the greatest common factor of $4x^2y$, $-6x^2y^3$, and $2xy^2$.

$$4x^2y = 2 \cdot 2 \cdot x^2 \cdot y$$
$$-6x^2y^3 = -1 \cdot 2 \cdot 3 \cdot x^2 \cdot y^3$$
$$2xy^2 = 2 \cdot x \cdot y^2$$

The greatest common factor is $2xy$.

Factoring by Grouping

Step 1 Group the terms.

Step 2 Factor out the greatest common factor from each group.

Step 3 Factor a common factor from the results of Step 2.

Step 4 If necessary, rearrange terms.

Factor by grouping.

$$\begin{aligned} 2a^2 + 2ab + a + b &= (2a^2 + 2ab) + (a + b) \\ &= 2a(a + b) + 1(a + b) \\ &= (a + b)(2a + 1) \end{aligned}$$

7.2 Factoring Trinomials

To factor $x^2 + bx + c$, find m and n such that $mn = c$ and $m + n = b$.

$mn = c$ (arrow to c)

$$x^2 + bx + c$$

$m + n = b$ (arrow to b)

Then $x^2 + bx + c = (x + m)(x + n)$.

Check by multiplying.

Factor $x^2 + 6x + 8$.

$mn = 8$ (arrow to 8)

$$x^2 + 6x + 8$$

$m + n = 6$ (arrow to 6)

$m = 2$ and $n = 4$

$x^2 + 6x + 8 = (x + 2)(x + 4)$

Check: $(x + 2)(x + 4) = x^2 + 4x + 2x + 8$
$= x^2 + 6x + 8$

7.3 Factoring Trinomials by Grouping

To factor $ax^2 + bx + c$ by grouping:

Find m and n.

$m + n = b$ (arrow to b)

$$ax^2 + bx + c$$

$mn = ac$ (bracket joining a and c)

Then factor $ax^2 + mx + nx + b$ by grouping.

Factor $3x^2 + 14x - 5$.

-15 (bracket joining 3 and -5)

Find two integers with a product of $3(-5) = -15$ and a sum of 14. The integers are -1 and 15.

$$\begin{aligned} 3x^2 + 14x - 5 &= 3x^2 - x + 15x - 5 \\ &= (3x^2 - x) + (15x - 5) \\ &= x(3x - 1) + 5(3x - 1) \\ &= (3x - 1)(x + 5) \end{aligned}$$

Concepts	*Examples*
7.4 Factoring Trinomials Using FOIL To factor $ax^2 + bx + c$ by trial and error: Use FOIL backwards.	By trial and error, $3x^2 + 14x - 5 = (3x - 1)(x + 5).$
7.5 Special Factoring Techniques **Difference of Squares** $a^2 - b^2 = (a + b)(a - b)$	Factor. $4x^2 - 9 = (2x + 3)(2x - 3)$
Perfect Square Trinomials $a^2 + 2ab + b^2 = (a + b)^2$ $a^2 - 2ab + b^2 = (a - b)^2$	$9x^2 + 6x + 1 = (3x + 1)^2$ $4x^2 - 20x + 25 = (2x - 5)^2$
Difference of Cubes $a^3 - b^3 = (a - b)(a^2 + ab + b^2)$	$x^3 - 27 = (x - 3)(x^2 + 3x + 9)$
Sum of Cubes $a^3 + b^3 = (a + b)(a^2 - ab + b^2)$	$x^3 + 343 = (x + 7)(x^2 - 7x + 49)$
7.6 Solving Quadratic Equations by Factoring **Zero-Factor Property** If a and b are real numbers and $ab = 0$, then $a = 0$ or $b = 0$.	If $(x - 2)(x + 3) = 0$, then $x - 2 = 0$ or $x + 3 = 0$.
Solving a Quadratic Equation by Factoring *Step 1* Write the equation in standard form. *Step 2* Factor. *Step 3* Use the zero-factor property.	Solve $2x^2 = 7x + 15$. $2x^2 - 7x - 15 = 0$ $(2x + 3)(x - 5) = 0$ $2x + 3 = 0$ or $x - 5 = 0$ $2x = -3$ $\quad x = 5$ $x = -\frac{3}{2}$
Step 4 Check.	The solutions $-\frac{3}{2}$ and 5 satisfy the original equation. The solution set is $\{-\frac{3}{2}, 5\}$.
7.7 Applications of Quadratic Equations **Pythagorean Formula** In a right triangle, the square of the hypotenuse equals the sum of the squares of the legs. $a^2 + b^2 = c^2$ 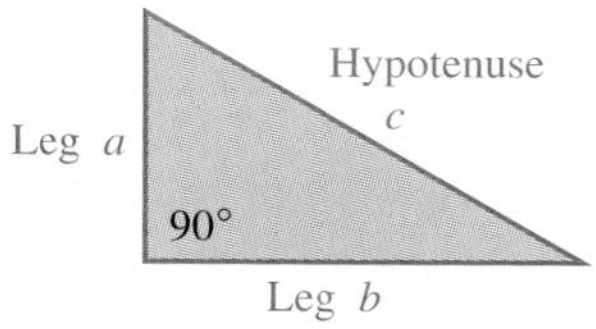	In a right triangle, one leg measures 2 ft longer than the other. The hypotenuse measures 4 ft longer than the shorter leg. Find the lengths of the three sides of the triangle. Let $x =$ the length of the shorter leg. Then $x^2 + (x + 2)^2 = (x + 4)^2.$ Solve this equation to get $x = 6$ or $x = -2$. Discard -2 as a solution. Check that the sides measure 6 ft, $6 + 2 = 8$ ft, and $6 + 4 = 10$ ft.

ANSWERS TO TEST YOUR WORD POWER

1. (b) *Example:* $x^2 - 5x - 14 = (x - 7)(x + 2)$ **2. (d)** *Example:* The factored form of $x^2 - 5x - 14$ is $(x - 7)(x + 2)$. **3. (a)** *Example:* $a^2 + 2a + 1$ is a perfect square trinomial; its factored form is $(a + 1)^2$. **4. (b)** *Examples:* $y^2 - 3y + 2 = 0$, $x^2 - 9 = 0$, $2m^2 = 6m + 8$ **5. (c)** *Example:* See the triangle included in the Quick Review above for Section 7.7.

Focus on **Real-Data Applications**

Stopping Distance

The overall *stopping distance* is the sum of the *thinking distance* (how far the car travels once you realize you have to brake) and the *braking distance* (how far the car travels after you apply the brakes).

The data in the table represents three distinct relationships. The *input* is speed in miles per hour for all three relationships. The *output* is thinking distance in feet for the first relationship, braking distance in feet for the second relationship, and overall stopping distance in feet for the third relationship.

Speed	Thinking Distance	Braking Distance	Overall Stopping Distance
20 mph	20 ft	20 ft	40 ft
30 mph	30 ft	45 ft	75 ft
40 mph	40 ft	80 ft	120 ft
50 mph	50 ft	125 ft	175 ft
60 mph	60 ft	180 ft	240 ft
70 mph	70 ft	245 ft	315 ft

Source: Pass Your Driving Theory Test, British School of Motoring (1996).

For Group Discussion

1. In the relationship between thinking distance and speed, the *output* (y) is numerically the same as the *input* (x).
   - **(a)** Write the equation that expresses this relationship. $y = x$
   - **(b)** When the speed is doubled from 20 mph to 40 mph, how does the thinking distance change? **doubles**
   - **(c)** Does the same pattern hold true if a 30 mph speed is doubled? **yes**
   - **(d)** Is the equation linear or quadratic? Explain. **linear; fits the form** $y = mx + b$
2. The relationship between braking distance and speed is given by the equation $y = \frac{1}{20}x^2$.
   - **(a)** Show that this equation corresponds to the table values for speeds of 20 mph and 40 mph.

     $20 = \frac{1}{20}(20)^2$ **is true;** $80 = \frac{1}{20}(40)^2$ **is true.**
   - **(b)** When the speed is doubled from 20 mph to 40 mph, how does the braking distance change? **quadruples**
   - **(c)** Does the same pattern hold true if a 30 mph speed is doubled? **yes**
   - **(d)** Is the equation linear or quadratic? Explain. **quadratic; fits the form** $y = ax^2 + bx + c$
3. The relationship between overall stopping distance and speed is based on the equations in Problems 1 and 2.
   - **(a)** Use those results to write the equation that expresses the relationship between overall stopping distance and speed. $y = x + \frac{1}{20}x^2$
   - **(b)** Is the equation linear or quadratic? Explain. **quadratic; fits the form** $y = ax^2 + bx + c$
   - **(c)** A *rule of thumb* for calculating overall stopping distance is to take speed in *tens* of miles per hour, divide by 2, add 1, and multiply the result by the speed in miles per hour. For example, at 40 mph, the rule says: $4 \div 2 + 1 = 3$; $3 \times 40 = 120$ ft. Show why this rule of thumb works. [*Hint:* Factor the right side of the equation in part (a).] $y = (\frac{x}{20} + 1)x$

Teaching notes and an extension for this activity are provided in the *Printed Test Bank and Instructor's Resource Guide.*

Chapter 7 REVIEW EXERCISES

[7.1] *Factor out the greatest common factor or factor by grouping.*

1. $7t + 14$
$7(t + 2)$

2. $60z^3 + 30z$
$30z(2z^2 + 1)$

3. $35x^3 + 70x^2$
$35x^2(x + 2)$

4. $100m^2n^3 - 50m^3n^4 + 150m^2n^2$
$50m^2n^2(2n - mn^2 + 3)$

5. $2xy - 8y + 3x - 12$
$(x - 4)(2y + 3)$

6. $6y^2 + 9y + 4xy + 6x$
$(2y + 3)(3y + 2x)$

[7.2] *Factor completely.*

7. $x^2 + 5x + 6$
$(x + 3)(x + 2)$

8. $y^2 - 13y + 40$
$(y - 5)(y - 8)$

9. $q^2 + 6q - 27$
$(q + 9)(q - 3)$

10. $r^2 - r - 56$
$(r - 8)(r + 7)$

11. $r^2 - 4rs - 96s^2$
$(r + 8s)(r - 12s)$

12. $p^2 + 2pq - 120q^2$
$(p + 12q)(p - 10q)$

13. $8p^3 - 24p^2 - 80p$
$8p(p + 2)(p - 5)$

14. $3x^4 + 30x^3 + 48x^2$
$3x^2(x + 2)(x + 8)$

15. $m^2 - 3mn - 18n^2$
$(m + 3n)(m - 6n)$

16. $y^2 - 8yz + 15z^2$
$(y - 3z)(y - 5z)$

17. $p^7 - p^6q - 2p^5q^2$
$p^5(p - 2q)(p + q)$

18. $3r^5 - 6r^4s - 45r^3s^2$
$3r^3(r + 3s)(r - 5s)$

19. $x^2 + x + 1$
prime

20. $3x^2 + 6x + 6$
$3(x^2 + 2x + 2)$

[7.3–7.4]

21. To begin factoring $6r^2 - 5r - 6$, what are the possible first terms of the two binomial factors, if we consider only positive integer coefficients?
r and $6r$, $2r$ and $3r$

22. What is the first step you would use to factor $2z^3 + 9z^2 - 5z$?
Factor out z.

Factor completely.

23. $2k^2 - 5k + 2$

$(2k - 1)(k - 2)$

24. $3r^2 + 11r - 4$

$(3r - 1)(r + 4)$

25. $6r^2 - 5r - 6$

$(3r + 2)(2r - 3)$

26. $10z^2 - 3z - 1$

$(5z + 1)(2z - 1)$

27. $5t^2 - 11t + 12$

prime

28. $24x^5 - 20x^4 + 4x^3$

$4x^3(3x - 1)(2x - 1)$

29. $-6x^2 + 3x + 30$

$-3(x + 2)(2x - 5)$

30. $10r^3s + 17r^2s^2 + 6rs^3$

$rs(5r + 6s)(2r + s)$

[7.5]

31. Which one of the following is a difference of squares?

A. $32x^2 - 1$ **B.** $4x^2y^2 - 25z^2$

C. $x^2 + 36$ **D.** $25y^3 - 1$

B

32. Which one of the following is a perfect square trinomial?

A. $x^2 + x + 1$ **B.** $y^2 - 4y + 9$

C. $4x^2 + 10x + 25$ **D.** $x^2 - 20x + 100$

D

Factor completely.

33. $n^2 - 64$

$(n + 8)(n - 8)$

34. $25b^2 - 121$

$(5b + 11)(5b - 11)$

35. $49y^2 - 25w^2$

$(7y + 5w)(7y - 5w)$

36. $144p^2 - 36q^2$

$36(2p + q)(2p - q)$

37. $x^2 + 100$

prime

38. $z^2 + 10z + 25$

$(z + 5)^2$

39. $r^2 - 12r + 36$

$(r - 6)^2$

40. $9t^2 - 42t + 49$

$(3t - 7)^2$

41. $16m^2 + 40mn + 25n^2$

$(4m + 5n)^2$

42. $125x^3 - 1$

$(5x - 1)(25x^2 + 5x + 1)$

43. $1000p^3 + 27$

$(10p + 3)(100p^2 - 30p + 9)$

44. $8z^3 + 64y^3$

$8(z + 2y)(z^2 - 2yz + 4y^2)$

[7.6] *Solve each equation, and check the solutions.*

45. $(4t + 3)(t - 1) = 0$

$\left\{-\frac{3}{4}, 1\right\}$

46. $(x + 7)(x - 4)(x + 3) = 0$

$\{-7, -3, 4\}$

47. $x(2x - 5) = 0$

$\left\{0, \frac{5}{2}\right\}$

48. $z^2 + 4z + 3 = 0$

$\{-3, -1\}$

49. $m^2 - 5m + 4 = 0$

$\{1, 4\}$

50. $x^2 = -15 + 8x$

$\{3, 5\}$

51. $3z^2 - 11z - 20 = 0$

$\left\{-\frac{4}{3}, 5\right\}$

52. $81t^2 - 64 = 0$

$\left\{-\frac{8}{9}, \frac{8}{9}\right\}$

53. $y^2 = 8y$

$\{0, 8\}$

54. $n(n - 5) = 6$

$\{-1, 6\}$

55. $t^2 - 14t + 49 = 0$

$\{7\}$

56. $t^2 = 12(t - 3)$

$\{6\}$

57. $(5z + 2)(z^2 + 3z + 2) = 0$

$\left\{-\frac{2}{5}, -2, -1\right\}$

58. $x^2 = 9$

$\{-3, 3\}$

[7.7] *Solve each problem.*

59. The length of a rug is 6 ft more than the width. The area is 40 ft^2. Find the length and width of the rug. **length: 10 ft; width: 4 ft**

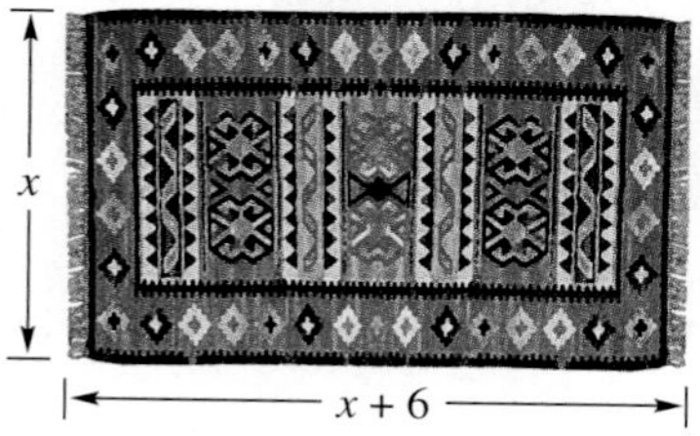

60. The surface area S of a box is given by

$$S = 2WH + 2WL + 2LH.$$

A treasure chest from a sunken galleon has dimensions as shown in the figure. Its surface area is 650 ft^2. Find its width. **5 ft**

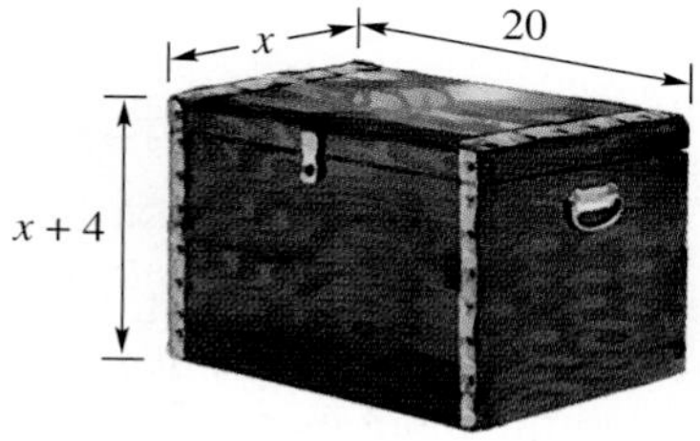

61. The length of a rectangle is three times the width. If the width were increased by 3 m while the length remained the same, the new rectangle would have an area of 30 m^2. Find the length and width of the original rectangle.

length: 6 m; width: 2 m

62. The volume of a rectangular box is 120 m^3. The width of the box is 4 m, and the height is 1 m less than the length. Find the length and height of the box.

length: 6 m; height: 5 m

63. The product of two consecutive integers is 29 more than their sum. What are the integers?

6, 7 or −5, −4

64. Two cars left an intersection at the same time. One traveled west, and the other traveled 14 mi less, but to the south. How far apart were they then, if the distance between them was 16 mi more than the distance traveled south?

26 mi

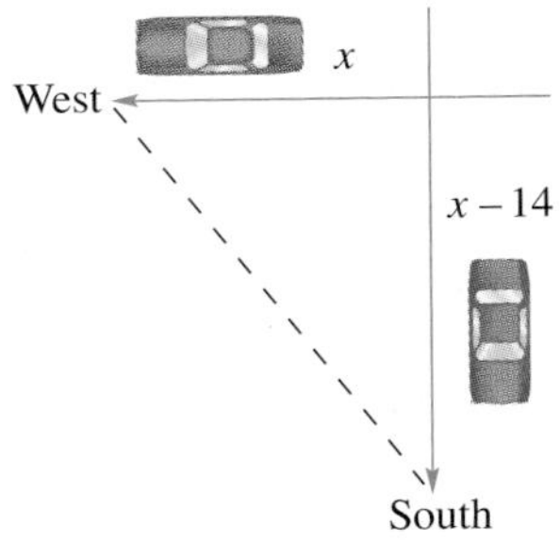

If an object is propelled upward with an initial velocity of 128 *ft per sec, its height h after t seconds is*

$$h = 128t - 16t^2.$$

Find the height of the object after each period of time.

65. 1 sec

112 ft

66. 2 sec

192 ft

67. 4 sec

256 ft

68. For the object described above, when does it return to the ground?

after 8 sec

69. Annual revenue in millions of dollars for eBay is shown in the table.

Year	Annual Revenue (in millions of dollars)
1997	5.1
1998	47.4
1999	224.7

Source: eBay.

Using the data, we developed the quadratic equation

$$y = 67.5x^2 - 25.2x + 5.1$$

to model eBay revenues y in year x, where $x = 0$ represents 1997, $x = 1$ represents 1998, and so on. Because only three years of data were used to determine the model, we must be careful about using it to predict revenue for years beyond 1999.

(a) Use the model to predict annual revenue for eBay in 2000.

$537 million

(b) The revenue for eBay through the first half of 2000 was $183.2 million. Given this information, do you think your prediction in part (a) is reliable? Explain.

No, the prediction seems high. If eBay revenues in the last half of 2000 are comparable to those for the first half of the year, annual revenue in 2000 would be about $366 million.

MIXED REVIEW EXERCISES

70. Which of the following is *not* factored completely?

A. $3(7t)$ **B.** $3x(7t + 4)$ **C.** $(3 + x)(7t + 4)$ **D.** $3(7t + 4) + x(7t + 4)$

D

71. Although $(2x + 8)(3x - 4) = 6x^2 + 16x - 32$ is a true statement, the polynomial is not factored completely. Explain why and give the complete factored form.

The factor $2x + 8$ has a common factor of 2. The complete factored form is $2(x + 4)(3x - 4)$.

Factor completely.

72. $z^2 - 11zx + 10x^2$

$(z - x)(z - 10x)$

73. $3k^2 + 11k + 10$

$(3k + 5)(k + 2)$

74. $15m^2 + 20mp - 12m - 16p$

$(3m + 4p)(5m - 4)$

75. $y^4 - 625$

$(y^2 + 25)(y + 5)(y - 5)$

76. $6m^3 - 21m^2 - 45m$

$3m(2m + 3)(m - 5)$

77. $24ab^3c^2 - 56a^2bc^3 + 72a^2b^2c$

$8abc(3b^2c - 7ac^2 + 9ab)$

78. $25a^2 + 15ab + 9b^2$

prime

79. $1000x^3 - y^3$

$(10x - y)(100x^2 + 10xy + y^2)$

80. $2a^5 - 8a^4 - 24a^3$

$2a^3(a + 2)(a - 6)$

81. $12r^2 + 8rq - 15q^2$

$(2r + 3q)(6r - 5q)$

82. $100a^2 - 9$

$(10a + 3)(10a - 3)$

83. $49t^2 + 56t + 16$

$(7t + 4)^2$

Solve.

84. $t(t - 7) = 0$

$\{0, 7\}$

85. $x^2 + 3x = 10$

$\{-5, 2\}$

86. $25x^2 + 20x + 4 = 0$

$\left\{-\frac{2}{5}\right\}$

Solve each problem.

87. A lot is shaped like a right triangle. The hypotenuse is 3 m longer than the longer leg. The longer leg is 6 m longer than twice the length of the shorter leg. Find the lengths of the sides of the lot.

15 m, 36 m, 39 m

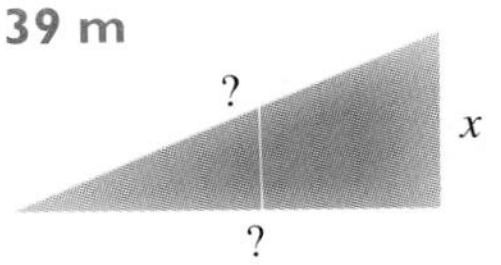

88. A pyramid has a rectangular base with a length that is 2 m more than the width. The height of the pyramid is 6 m, and its volume is 48 m^3. Find the length and width of the base.

length: 6 m; width: 4 m

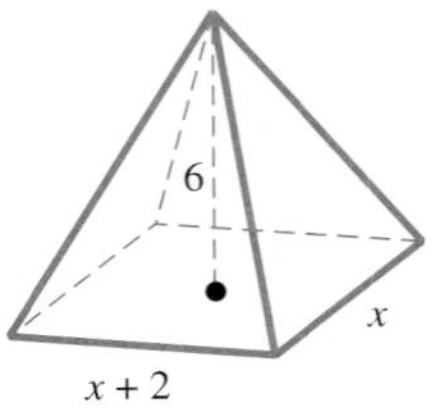

89. The product of the smaller two of three consecutive integers is equal to 23 plus the largest. Find the integers.

−5, −4, −3 or 5, 6, 7

90. If an object is dropped, the distance d in feet it falls in t seconds (disregarding air resistance) is given by the quadratic equation

$$d = 16t^2.$$

Find the distance an object would fall in the following times.

(a) 4 sec **256 ft** **(b)** 8 sec **1024 ft**

91. The floor plan for a house is a rectangle with length 7 m more than its width. The area is 170 m^2. Find the width and length of the house. **width: 10 m; length: 17 m**

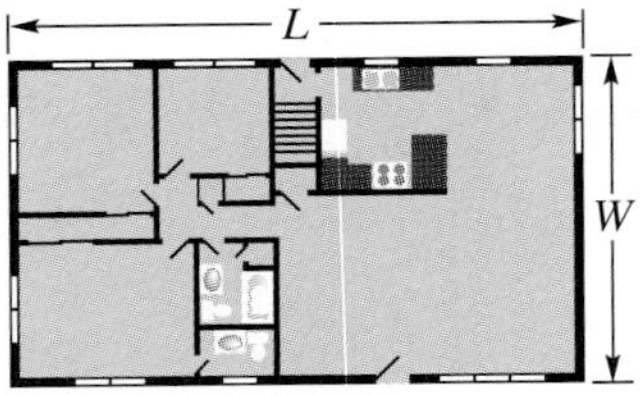

92. The triangular sail of a schooner has an area of 30 m^2. The height of the sail is 4 m more than the base. Find the base of the sail. **6 m**

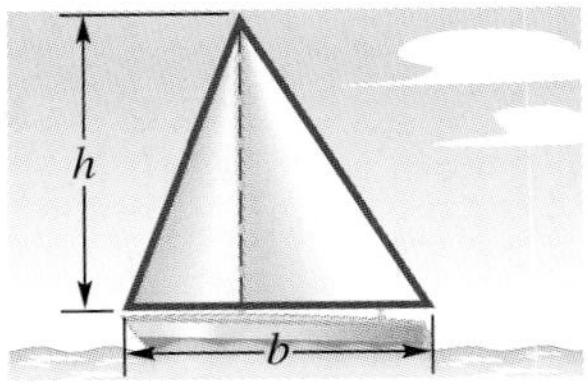

Chapter 7 Test

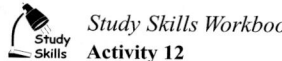

Study Skills Workbook
Activity 12

1. Which one of the following is the correct, completely factored form of $2x^2 - 2x - 24$?

   A. $(2x + 6)(x - 4)$ B. $(x + 3)(2x - 8)$

   C. $2(x + 4)(x - 3)$ D. $2(x + 3)(x - 4)$

Factor each polynomial completely.

2. $12x^2 - 30x$
3. $2m^3n^2 + 3m^3n - 5m^2n^2$
4. $2ax - 2bx + ay - by$
5. $x^2 - 9x + 14$
6. $6x^2 - 19x - 7$
7. $3x^2 - 12x - 15$
8. $10z^2 - 17z + 3$
9. $t^2 + 2t + 3$
10. $x^2 + 36$
11. $y^2 - 49$
12. $9y^2 - 64$
13. $x^2 + 16x + 64$
14. $4x^2 - 28xy + 49y^2$
15. $x^3 - 512$
16. $8k^3 + 64$
17. $-2x^2 - 4x - 2$
18. $6t^4 + 3t^3 - 108t^2$

1. D
2. $6x(2x - 5)$
3. $m^2n(2mn + 3m - 5n)$
4. $(2x + y)(a - b)$
5. $(x - 7)(x - 2)$
6. $(3x + 1)(2x - 7)$
7. $3(x + 1)(x - 5)$
8. $(5z - 1)(2z - 3)$
9. prime
10. prime
11. $(y + 7)(y - 7)$
12. $(3y + 8)(3y - 8)$
13. $(x + 8)^2$
14. $(2x - 7y)^2$
15. $(x - 8)(x^2 + 8x + 64)$
16. $8(k + 2)(k^2 - 2k + 4)$
17. $-2(x + 1)^2$
18. $3t^2(2t + 9)(t - 4)$

19. $4t(t + 4)^2$

20. $(x^2 + 9)(x + 3)(x - 3)$

21. $(p + 3)(p + 3) = p^2 + 6p + 9 \neq p^2 + 9$

22. $\{-3, 9\}$

23. $\left\{\frac{1}{2}, 6\right\}$

24. $\left\{-\frac{2}{5}, \frac{2}{5}\right\}$

25. $\{10\}$

26. $\{0, 3\}$

27. 6 ft by 9 ft

28. $-2, -1$

29. 17 ft

30. 181

19. $4t^3 + 32t^2 + 64t$

20. $x^4 - 81$

21. Why is $(p + 3)(p + 3)$ *not* the correct factored form of $p^2 + 9$?

Solve each equation.

22. $(x + 3)(x - 9) = 0$

23. $2r^2 - 13r + 6 = 0$

24. $25x^2 - 4 = 0$

25. $x(x - 20) = -100$

26. $t^2 = 3t$

Solve each problem.

27. The length of a rectangular flower bed is 3 ft less than twice its width. The area of the bed is 54 ft^2. Find the dimensions of the flower bed.

28. Find two consecutive integers such that the square of the sum of the two integers is 11 more than the smaller integer.

29. A carpenter needs to cut a brace to support a wall stud, as shown in the figure. The brace should be 7 ft less than three times the length of the stud. If the brace will be anchored on the floor 15 ft away from the stud, how long should the brace be?

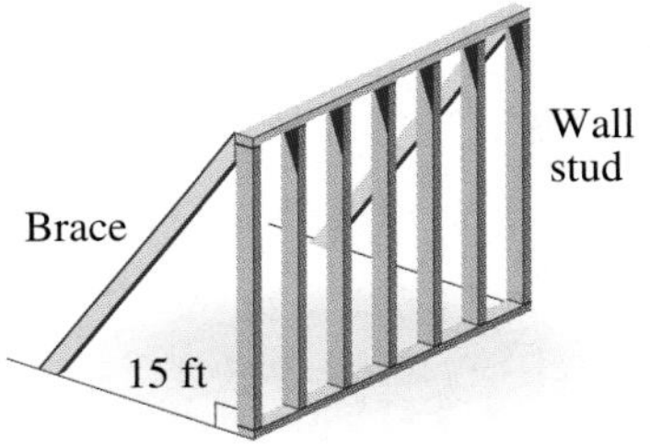

30. TV viewers have more choices than ever. The number of cable TV channels y from 1984 through 1999 can be approximated by the quadratic equation

$$y = .57x^2 + .31x + 48,$$

where $x = 0$ represents 1984, $x = 1$ represents 1985, and so on. (*Source:* National Cable Television Association.) Use the model to estimate the number of cable TV channels in 1999. Round your answer to the nearest whole number.

Cumulative Review Exercises

CHAPTERS R–7

Solve each equation or inequality.

1. $3x + 2(x - 4) = 4(x - 2)$

0

2. $\frac{2}{3}y - \frac{1}{2}(y - 4) = 3$

6

3. $x + 4(2x - 1) \geq x$

$\left[\frac{1}{2}, \infty\right)$

4. Solve for P: $A = P + Prt$

$P = \frac{A}{1 + rt}$

5. From a list of "everyday items" often taken for granted, adults were recently surveyed as to those items they wouldn't want to live without. Complete the results shown in the table if 500 adults were surveyed.

Item	Percent That Wouldn't Want to Live Without	Number That Wouldn't Want to Live Without
Toilet paper	69%	345
Zipper	42%	210
Frozen foods	38%	190
Self-stick note pads	15%	75

(Other items included tape, hairspray, pantyhose, paper clips, and Velcro.)
Source: Market Facts for Kleenex Cottonelle.

Solve each problem.

6. At the 1998 Winter Olympics in Nagano, Japan, the top medal winner was Germany with 29. Germany won 1 more silver medal than bronze and 3 more gold medals than silver. Find the number of each type of medal won. (*Source: The World Almanac and Book of Facts,* 2000.)

gold: 12; silver: 9; bronze: 8

7. In July 2000, roughly 144 million people surfed the Web from home. This was a 35% increase from the same month the previous year. How many people, to the nearest million, surfed the Web from home in July 1999? (*Source: The Gazette,* September 3, 2000.)

107 million

8. Find the measures of the marked angles.

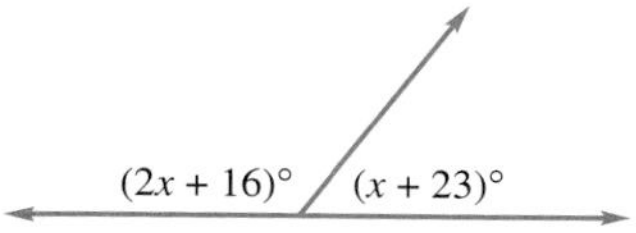

110° and 70°

9. Fill in each blank with *positive* or *negative.* The point with coordinates (a, b) is in

(a) quadrant II if a is <u>negative</u> and b is <u>positive</u>.

(b) quadrant III if a is <u>negative</u> and b is <u>negative</u>.

Consider the equation $y = 12x + 3$. Find the following.

10. The x- and y-intercepts

$\left(-\frac{1}{4}, 0\right)$, $(0, 3)$

11. The slope

12

12. The graph

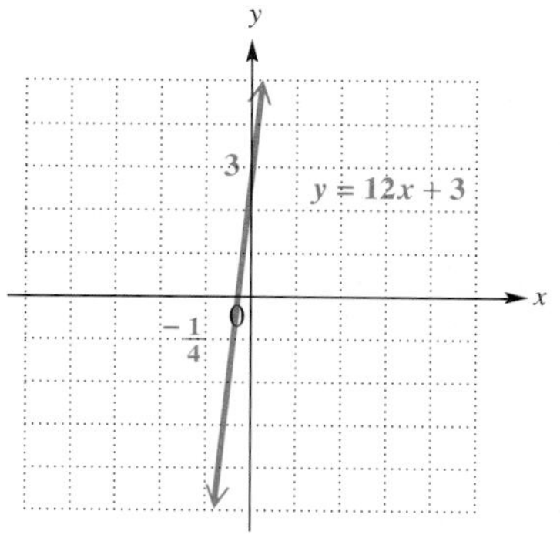

13. The points on the graph show the number of U.S. radio stations in the years 1993–1999, along with the graph of a linear equation that models the data. Use the ordered pairs shown on the graph to find the slope of the line to the nearest whole number. Interpret the slope.

103; A slope of 103 means that the number of radio stations increased by about 103 stations per year.

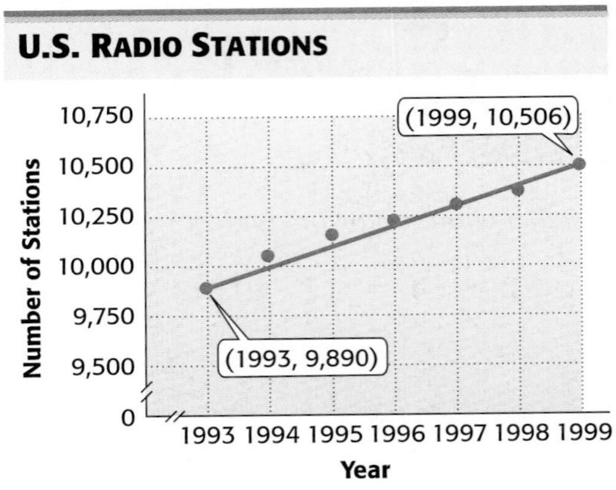

Source: M Street Corporation.

Solve each system.

14. $4x - 3y = -19$
$2x + y = 13$

{(2, 9)}

15. $4x + 8y + z = 2$
$3x + 4y - z = -11$
$2x - 3y + 2z = 3$

{(−3, 1, 6)}

16. Tickets to a production of *Othello* at Nicholls State University cost \$2.50 for general admission or \$2.00 with a student ID. If 184 people paid to see a performance and \$406 was collected, how many of each type of ticket were sold?

76 general admission; 108 with student ID

17. Simplify $\dfrac{(p^2)^3p^{-4}}{(p^{-3})^{-1}p}$ and write the answer using only positive exponents. Assume $p \neq 0$.

$\dfrac{1}{p^2}$

Perform the indicated operations.

18. $(2k^2 + 4k - 2) - (k^2 + 8k - 6)$

$k^2 - 4k + 4$

19. $(9x + 6)(5x - 3)$

$45x^2 + 3x - 18$

20. $\dfrac{8x^4 + 12x^3 - 6x^2 + 20x}{2x}$

$4x^3 + 6x^2 - 3x + 10$

21. To make a pound of honey, bees may travel 55,000 mi and visit more than 2,000,000 flowers. (*Source: Home & Garden* magazine.) Write the two given numbers in scientific notation.

5.5×10^4; 2.0×10^6

Factor completely.

22. $2a^2 + 7a - 4$

$(2a - 1)(a + 4)$

23. $10m^2 + 19m + 6$

$(2m + 3)(5m + 2)$

24. $8t^2 + 10tv + 3v^2$

$(4t + 3v)(2t + v)$

25. $4p^2 - 12p + 9$

$(2p - 3)^2$

26. $25r^2 - 81t^2$

$(5r + 9t)(5r - 9t)$

27. $2pq + 6p^3q + 8p^2q$

$2pq(3p + 1)(p + 1)$

Solve each equation.

28. $6m^2 + m - 2 = 0$

$\left\{-\dfrac{2}{3}, \dfrac{1}{2}\right\}$

29. $8x^2 = 64x$

{0, 8}

30. The length of the hypotenuse of a right triangle is twice the length of the shorter leg, plus 3 m. The longer leg is 7 m longer than the shorter leg. Find the lengths of the sides. **5 m, 12 m, 13 m**

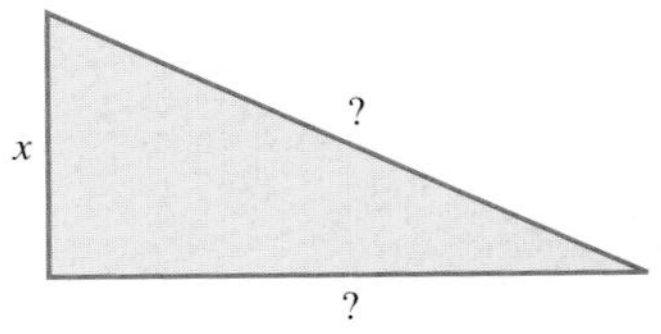

Rational Expressions and Applications

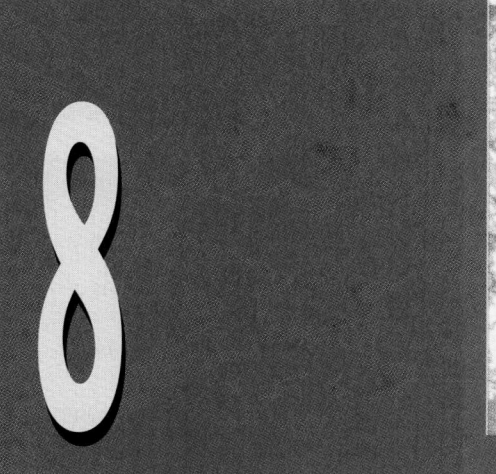

8

At the 2000 Olympic games in Sydney, Australia, Dutch swimmer Inge de Bruijn won three events, the last of which was the women's 50-m freestyle. She completed the race in 24.32 sec. In Example 5(c) of Section 8.5, we use a rational expression to find de Bruijn's rate.

8.1 Rational Expressions and Functions; Multiplying and Dividing

Objectives

1. Define rational expressions.
2. Define rational functions and describe their domains.
3. Write rational expressions in lowest terms.
4. Multiply rational expressions.
5. Find reciprocals for rational expressions.
6. Divide rational expressions.

1 Define rational expressions. In arithmetic, a rational number is the quotient of two integers, with the denominator not 0. In algebra, a **rational expression** or *algebraic fraction* is the quotient of two polynomials, again with the denominator not 0. For example,

$$\frac{x}{y}, \quad \frac{-a}{4}, \quad \frac{m+4}{m-2}, \quad \frac{8x^2-2x+5}{4x^2+5x}, \quad \text{and} \quad x^5\left(\text{or } \frac{x^5}{1}\right)$$

are all rational expressions. In other words, rational expressions are the elements of the set

$$\left\{\frac{P}{Q} \,\middle|\, P, Q \text{ polynomials, with } Q \neq 0\right\}.$$

2 Define rational functions and describe their domains. A function that is defined by a rational expression is called a **rational function** and has the form

$$f(x) = \frac{P(x)}{Q(x)},$$

where $Q(x) \neq 0$.

The domain of a rational function includes all real numbers except those that make $Q(x)$, that is, the denominator, equal to 0. For example, the domain of

$$f(x) = \frac{2}{x-5}$$

includes all real numbers except 5, because 5 would make the denominator equal to 0.

Figure 1 shows a graph of the function defined by $f(x) = \frac{2}{x-5}$. Notice that the graph does not exist when $x = 5$. It does not intersect the dashed vertical line whose equation is $x = 5$. This line is an *asymptote*. We will discuss graphs of rational functions in more detail in Section 8.4.

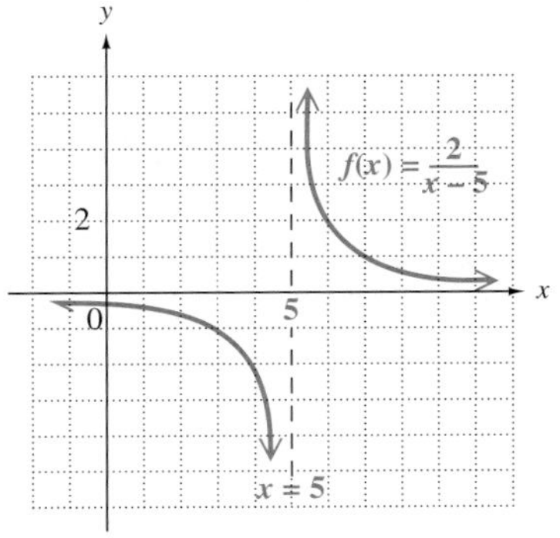

Figure 1

Example 1 Finding Numbers That Are Not in the Domains of Rational Functions

Find all numbers that are not in the domain of each rational function.

(a) $f(x) = \dfrac{3}{7x - 14}$

Continued on Next Page

The only values that cannot be used are those that make the denominator 0. To find these values, set the denominator equal to 0 and solve the resulting equation.

$$7x - 14 = 0$$
$$7x = 14 \qquad \text{Add 14.}$$
$$x = 2 \qquad \text{Divide by 7.}$$

The number 2 cannot be used as a replacement for x; the domain of f includes all real numbers except 2.

(b) $g(x) = \dfrac{3 + x}{x^2 - 4x + 3}$

Set the denominator equal to 0, and solve the equation.

$$x^2 - 4x + 3 = 0$$
$$(x - 3)(x - 1) = 0 \qquad \text{Factor.}$$
$$x - 3 = 0 \quad \text{or} \quad x - 1 = 0 \qquad \text{Zero-factor property}$$
$$x = 3 \quad \text{or} \quad x = 1$$

The domain of g includes all real numbers except 3 and 1.

(c) $h(x) = \dfrac{8x + 2}{3}$

The denominator, 3, can never be 0, so the domain includes all real numbers.

(d) $f(x) = \dfrac{2}{x^2 + 4}$

Setting $x^2 + 4$ equal to 0 leads to $x^2 = -4$. There is no real number whose square is -4. Therefore, any real number can be used, and as in part (c), the domain includes all real numbers.

Work Problem 1 at the Side.

1 Find all numbers that are not in the domain of each rational function.

(a) $f(x) = \dfrac{x + 4}{x - 6}$

(b) $f(x) = \dfrac{x + 6}{x^2 - x - 6}$

(c) $f(x) = \dfrac{3 + 2x}{5}$

(d) $f(x) = \dfrac{2}{x^2 + 1}$

3 Write rational expressions in lowest terms. In arithmetic, we write the fraction $\frac{15}{20}$ in lowest terms by dividing the numerator and denominator by 5 to get $\frac{3}{4}$. We write rational expressions in lowest terms in a similar way, using the **fundamental property of rational numbers.**

Fundamental Property of Rational Numbers

If $\frac{a}{b}$ is a rational number and if c is any nonzero real number, then

$$\frac{a}{b} = \frac{ac}{bc}.$$

In words, the numerator and denominator of a rational number may either be multiplied or divided by the same nonzero number without changing the value of the rational number.

Since $\frac{c}{c}$ is equivalent to 1, the fundamental property is based on the identity property of multiplication.

A rational expression is a quotient of two polynomials. Since the value of a polynomial is a real number for every value of the variable for which it is defined, any statement that applies to rational numbers will also apply to rational expressions. We use the following steps to write rational expressions in lowest terms.

ANSWERS

1. **(a)** 6 **(b)** -2, 3
(c) none (The domain includes all real numbers.)
(d) none (The domain includes all real numbers.)

Writing a Rational Expression in Lowest Terms

Step 1 **Factor.** Factor both numerator and denominator to find their greatest common factor (GCF).

Step 2 **Apply the fundamental property.**

Example 2 Writing Rational Expressions in Lowest Terms

Write each rational expression in lowest terms.

(a) $\frac{8k}{16} = \frac{k \cdot 8}{2 \cdot 8} = \frac{k}{2} \cdot 1 = \frac{k}{2}$

Here, the GCF of the numerator and denominator is 8. We then applied the fundamental property.

(b) $\frac{8 + k}{16}$

The numerator cannot be factored, so this expression cannot be simplified further and is in lowest terms.

(c) $\frac{a^2 - a - 6}{a^2 + 5a + 6} = \frac{(a - 3)(a + 2)}{(a + 3)(a + 2)}$ Factor the numerator and the denominator.

$= \frac{a - 3}{a + 3} \cdot 1$ $\quad \frac{a + 2}{a + 2} = 1$

$= \frac{a - 3}{a + 3}$ Lowest terms

(d) $\frac{y^2 - 4}{2y + 4} = \frac{(y + 2)(y - 2)}{2(y + 2)} = \frac{y - 2}{2}$

(e) $\frac{x^3 - 27}{x - 3} = \frac{(x - 3)(x^2 + 3x + 9)}{x - 3}$ Factor the difference of cubes.

$= x^2 + 3x + 9$ Lowest terms

(f) $\frac{pr + qr + ps + qs}{pr + qr - ps - qs} = \frac{(pr + qr) + (ps + qs)}{(pr + qr) - (ps + qs)}$ Group terms.

$= \frac{r(p + q) + s(p + q)}{r(p + q) - s(p + q)}$ Factor within groups.

$= \frac{(p + q)(r + s)}{(p + q)(r - s)}$ Factor by grouping.

$= \frac{r + s}{r - s}$ Lowest terms

CAUTION

Be careful! When using the fundamental property of rational numbers, only common *factors* may be divided. For example,

$$\frac{y - 2}{2} \neq y \quad \text{and} \quad \frac{y - 2}{2} \neq y - 1$$

because the 2 in $y - 2$ is not a *factor* of the numerator. Remember to *factor* before writing a fraction in lowest terms.

Work Problem 2 at the Side.

In the rational expression from Example 2(c),

$$\frac{a^2 - a - 6}{a^2 + 5a + 6}, \quad \text{or} \quad \frac{(a - 3)(a + 2)}{(a + 3)(a + 2)},$$

a can take any value except -3 or -2 since these values make the denominator 0. In the simplified rational expression

$$\frac{a - 3}{a + 3},$$

a cannot equal -3. Because of this,

$$\frac{a^2 - a - 6}{a^2 + 5a + 6} = \frac{a - 3}{a + 3}$$

for all values of a except -3 or -2. From now on such statements of equality will be made with the understanding that they apply only for those real numbers that make neither denominator equal 0. We will no longer state such restrictions.

Example 3 **Writing Rational Expressions in Lowest Terms**

Write each rational expression in lowest terms.

(a) $\dfrac{m - 3}{3 - m}$

In this rational expression, the numerator and denominator are opposites. The given expression can be written in lowest terms by writing the denominator as $-1(m - 3)$, giving

$$\frac{m - 3}{3 - m} = \frac{m - 3}{-1(m - 3)} = \frac{1}{-1} = -1.$$

The numerator could have been rewritten instead to get the same result.

(b) $\dfrac{r^2 - 16}{4 - r} = \dfrac{(r + 4)(r - 4)}{4 - r}$

$= \dfrac{(r + 4)(r - 4)}{-1(r - 4)}$ Write $4 - r$ as $-1(r - 4)$.

$= \dfrac{r + 4}{-1}$ Fundamental property

$= -(r + 4)$ or $-r - 4$ Lowest terms

As shown in Examples 3(a) and (b), the quotient

$$\frac{a}{-a} \quad (a \neq 0)$$

can be simplified as

$$\frac{a}{-a} = \frac{a}{-1(a)} = \frac{1}{-1} = -1.$$

The following statement summarizes this result.

In general, if the numerator and the denominator of a rational expression are opposites, the expression equals -1.

2 Write each rational expression in lowest terms.

(a) $\dfrac{y^2 + 2y - 3}{y^2 - 3y + 2}$

(b) $\dfrac{3y + 9}{y^2 - 9}$

(c) $\dfrac{y + 2}{y^2 + 4}$

(d) $\dfrac{1 + p^3}{1 + p}$

(e) $\dfrac{3x + 3y + rx + ry}{5x + 5y - rx - ry}$

Answers

2. (a) $\dfrac{y + 3}{y - 2}$ **(b)** $\dfrac{3}{y - 3}$

(c) already in lowest terms

(d) $1 - p + p^2$ **(e)** $\dfrac{3 + r}{5 - r}$

3 Write each rational expression in lowest terms.

(a) $\dfrac{y-2}{2-y}$

(b) $\dfrac{8-b}{8+b}$

(c) $\dfrac{p-2}{4-p^2}$

ANSWERS

3. (a) -1 **(b)** already in lowest terms

(c) $\dfrac{-1}{2+p}$

Based on this result,

$$\frac{q-7}{7-q} = -1 \quad \text{and} \quad \frac{-5a+2b}{5a-2b} = -1.$$

However,

$$\frac{r-2}{r+2}$$

cannot be simplified further since the numerator and the denominator are *not* opposites.

Work Problem 3 at the Side.

4 **Multiply rational expressions.** To multiply rational expressions, follow these steps. (In practice, we usually simplify before multiplying.)

Multiplying Rational Expressions

Step 1 **Factor.** Factor all numerators and denominators as completely as possible.

Step 2 **Apply the fundamental property.**

Step 3 **Multiply.** Multiply remaining factors in the numerator and remaining factors in the denominator. Leave the denominator in factored form.

Step 4 **Check.** Check to be sure the product is in lowest terms.

Example 4 Multiplying Rational Expressions

Multiply.

(a) $\dfrac{5p-5}{p} \cdot \dfrac{3p^2}{10p-10} = \dfrac{5(p-1)}{p} \cdot \dfrac{3p \cdot p}{2 \cdot 5(p-1)}$ Factor.

$= \dfrac{1}{1} \cdot \dfrac{3p}{2}$ Lowest terms

$= \dfrac{3p}{2}$ Multiply.

(b) $\dfrac{k^2+2k-15}{k^2-4k+3} \cdot \dfrac{k^2-k}{k^2+k-20} = \dfrac{(k+5)(k-3)}{(k-3)(k-1)} \cdot \dfrac{k(k-1)}{(k+5)(k-4)}$

$= \dfrac{k}{k-4}$

(c) $(p-4) \cdot \dfrac{3}{5p-20} = \dfrac{p-4}{1} \cdot \dfrac{3}{5p-20}$ Write $p-4$ as $\dfrac{p-4}{1}$.

$= \dfrac{p-4}{1} \cdot \dfrac{3}{5(p-4)}$ Factor.

$= \dfrac{3}{5}$

Continued on Next Page

(d) $\dfrac{x^2+2x}{x+1} \cdot \dfrac{x^2-1}{x^3+x^2} = \dfrac{x(x+2)}{x+1} \cdot \dfrac{(x+1)(x-1)}{x^2(x+1)}$ Factor.

$= \dfrac{(x+2)(x-1)}{x(x+1)}$ Multiply; lowest terms.

(e) $\dfrac{x-6}{x^2-12x+36} \cdot \dfrac{x^2-3x-18}{x^2+7x+12} = \dfrac{x-6}{(x-6)^2} \cdot \dfrac{(x+3)(x-6)}{(x+3)(x+4)}$ Factor.

$= \dfrac{1}{x+4}$ Lowest terms

Remember to include 1 in the numerator when all other factors are eliminated using the fundamental property.

Work Problem 4 at the Side.

5 Find reciprocals for rational expressions. The rational numbers $\frac{a}{b}$ and $\frac{c}{d}$ are reciprocals of each other if they have a product of 1. The **reciprocal** of a rational expression is defined in the same way: Two rational expressions are reciprocals of each other if they have a product of 1. Recall that 0 has no reciprocal. The table shows several rational expressions and their reciprocals. In the first two cases, check that the product of the rational expression and its reciprocal is 1.

Rational Expression	Reciprocal
$\frac{5}{k}$	$\frac{k}{5}$
$\frac{m^2-9m}{2}$	$\frac{2}{m^2-9m}$
$\frac{0}{4}$	undefined

The examples in the table suggest the following procedure.

Finding the Reciprocal

To find the reciprocal of a nonzero rational expression, invert the rational expression.

Work Problem 5 at the Side.

6 Divide rational expressions. Dividing rational expressions is like dividing rational numbers.

Dividing Rational Expressions

To divide two rational expressions, *multiply* the first by the reciprocal of the second.

4 Multiply.

(a) $\dfrac{2r+4}{5r} \cdot \dfrac{3r}{5r+10}$

(b) $\dfrac{c^2+2c}{c^2-4} \cdot \dfrac{c^2-4c+4}{c^2-c}$

(c) $\dfrac{m^2-16}{m+2} \cdot \dfrac{1}{m+4}$

(d) $\dfrac{x-3}{x^2+2x-15} \cdot \dfrac{x^2-25}{x^2+3x-40}$

5 Find each reciprocal.

(a) $\dfrac{-3}{r}$

(b) $\dfrac{7}{y+8}$

(c) $\dfrac{a^2+7a}{2a-1}$

(d) $\dfrac{0}{-5}$

Answers

4. (a) $\frac{6}{25}$ **(b)** $\frac{c-2}{c-1}$ **(c)** $\frac{m-4}{m+2}$ **(d)** $\frac{1}{x+8}$

5. (a) $\frac{r}{-3}$ **(b)** $\frac{y+8}{7}$ **(c)** $\frac{2a-1}{a^2+7a}$

(d) There is no reciprocal.

6 Divide.

(a) $\dfrac{16k^2}{5} \div \dfrac{3k}{10}$

(b) $\dfrac{5p+2}{6} \div \dfrac{15p+6}{5}$

(c) $\dfrac{y^2-2y-3}{y^2+4y+4} \div \dfrac{y^2-1}{y^2+y-2}$

ANSWERS

6. (a) $\dfrac{32k}{3}$ **(b)** $\dfrac{5}{18}$ **(c)** $\dfrac{y-3}{y+2}$

Example 5 **Dividing Rational Expressions**

Divide.

(a) $\dfrac{2z}{9} \div \dfrac{5z^2}{18} = \dfrac{2z}{9} \cdot \dfrac{18}{5z^2}$ Multiply by the reciprocal of the divisor.

$= \dfrac{2z}{9} \cdot \dfrac{2 \cdot 9}{5z^2}$ Factor.

$= \dfrac{4}{5z}$ Multiply; lowest terms

(b) $\dfrac{8k-16}{3k} \div \dfrac{3k-6}{4k^2} = \dfrac{8k-16}{3k} \cdot \dfrac{4k^2}{3k-6}$ Multiply by the reciprocal.

$= \dfrac{8(k-2)}{3k} \cdot \dfrac{4k^2}{3(k-2)}$ Factor.

$= \dfrac{32k}{9}$ Multiply; lowest terms

(c) $\dfrac{5m^2+17m-12}{3m^2+7m-20} \div \dfrac{5m^2+2m-3}{15m^2-34m+15}$

$= \dfrac{5m^2+17m-12}{3m^2+7m-20} \cdot \dfrac{15m^2-34m+15}{5m^2+2m-3}$ Definition of division

$= \dfrac{(5m-3)(m+4)}{(m+4)(3m-5)} \cdot \dfrac{(3m-5)(5m-3)}{(5m-3)(m+1)}$ Factor.

$= \dfrac{5m-3}{m+1}$ Lowest terms

Work Problem 6 at the Side.

8.1 EXERCISES

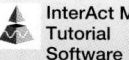

FOR EXTRA HELP: Student's Solutions Manual · MyMathLab.com · InterAct Math Tutorial Software · AW Math Tutor Center · www.mathxl.com · Digital Video Tutor CD 6 Videotape 15

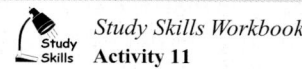

Study Skills Workbook **Activity 11**

Rational expressions can often be written in lowest terms in seemingly *different ways. For example,*

$$\frac{y-3}{-5} \quad \textit{and} \quad \frac{-y+3}{5}$$

look different, but we get the second expression by multiplying the first by -1 in both the numerator and denominator. To practice recognizing equivalent rational expressions, match the expressions in Exercises 1–6 with their equivalents in Choices A–F.

1. $\frac{x-3}{x+4}$ C **2.** $\frac{x+3}{x-4}$ A **3.** $\frac{x-3}{x-4}$ D **4.** $\frac{x+3}{x+4}$ B **5.** $\frac{3-x}{x+4}$ E **6.** $\frac{x+3}{4-x}$ F

A. $\frac{-x-3}{4-x}$ **B.** $\frac{-x-3}{-x-4}$ **C.** $\frac{3-x}{-x-4}$ **D.** $\frac{-x+3}{-x+4}$ **E.** $\frac{x-3}{-x-4}$ **F.** $\frac{-x-3}{x-4}$

7. In Example 1(a), we showed that the domain of the rational function defined by $f(x)=\frac{3}{7x-14}$ does not include 2. Explain in your own words why this is so. In general, how do we find the value or values excluded from the domain of a rational function?

Replacing x with 2 makes the denominator 0 and the value of the expression undefined. To find the values excluded from the domain, set the denominator equal to 0 and solve the equation. All solutions of the equation are excluded from the domain.

8. The domain of the rational function defined by $g(x)=\frac{x+1}{x^2+3}$ includes all real numbers. Explain.

There is no number that makes the denominator 0. In fact, the denominator is greater than or equal to 3 for any replacement of x. Thus, the domain includes all real numbers.

Find all numbers that are not in the domain of each function. See Example 1.

9. $f(x)=\frac{x}{x-7}$ 7

10. $f(x)=\frac{x}{x+3}$ -3

11. $f(x)=\frac{6x-5}{7x+1}$ $-\frac{1}{7}$

12. $f(x)=\frac{8x-3}{2x+7}$ $-\frac{7}{2}$

13. $f(x)=\frac{12x+3}{x}$ 0

14. $f(x)=\frac{9x+8}{x}$ 0

15. $f(x)=\frac{3x+1}{2x^2+x-6}$ $-2, \frac{3}{2}$

16. $f(x)=\frac{2x+4}{3x^2+11x-42}$ $-6, \frac{7}{3}$

17. $f(x)=\frac{x+2}{14}$ none

18. $f(x)=\frac{x-9}{26}$ none

19. $f(x)=\frac{2x^2-3x+4}{3x^2+8}$ none

20. $f(x)=\frac{9x^2-8x+3}{4x^2+1}$ none

21. **(a)** Identify the two *terms* in the numerator and the two *terms* in the denominator of the rational expression $\dfrac{x^2 + 4x}{x + 4}$.

numerator: x^2, $4x$; denominator: x, 4

(b) Describe the steps you would use to write this rational expression in lowest terms. (*Hint:* It simplifies to x.)

First factor the numerator, getting $x(x + 4)$, then divide the numerator and denominator by the common factor of $x + 4$ to get $\dfrac{x}{1}$ or x.

22. Only one of the following rational expressions can be simplified. Which one is it?

A. $\dfrac{x^2 + 2}{x^2}$ **B.** $\dfrac{x^2 + 2}{2}$

C. $\dfrac{x^2 + y^2}{y^2}$ **D.** $\dfrac{x^2 - 5x}{x}$

D

23. Only one of the following rational expressions is *not* equivalent to $\dfrac{x - 3}{4 - x}$. Which one is it?

A. $\dfrac{3 - x}{x - 4}$ **B.** $\dfrac{x + 3}{4 + x}$

C. $-\dfrac{3 - x}{4 - x}$ **D.** $-\dfrac{x - 3}{x - 4}$

B

24. Which two of the following rational expressions equal -1?

A. $\dfrac{2x + 3}{2x - 3}$ **B.** $\dfrac{2x - 3}{3 - 2x}$

C. $\dfrac{2x + 3}{3 + 2x}$ **D.** $\dfrac{2x + 3}{-2x - 3}$

B, D

Write each rational expression in lowest terms. See Example 2.

25. $\dfrac{x^2(x + 1)}{x(x + 1)}$

x

26. $\dfrac{y^3(y - 4)}{y^2(y - 4)}$

y

27. $\dfrac{(x + 4)(x - 3)}{(x + 5)(x + 4)}$

$\dfrac{x - 3}{x + 5}$

28. $\dfrac{(2x + 7)(x - 1)}{(2x + 3)(2x + 7)}$

$\dfrac{x - 1}{2x + 3}$

29. $\dfrac{4x(x + 3)}{8x^2(x - 3)}$

$\dfrac{x + 3}{2x(x - 3)}$

30. $\dfrac{5y^2(y + 8)}{15y(y - 8)}$

$\dfrac{y(y + 8)}{3(y - 8)}$

31. $\dfrac{3x + 7}{3}$

already in lowest terms

32. $\dfrac{4x - 9}{4}$

already in lowest terms

33. $\dfrac{6m + 18}{7m + 21}$

$\dfrac{6}{7}$

34. $\dfrac{5r - 20}{3r - 12}$

$\dfrac{5}{3}$

35. $\dfrac{3z^2 + z}{18z + 6}$

$\dfrac{z}{6}$

36. $\dfrac{2x^2 - 5x}{16x - 40}$

$\dfrac{x}{8}$

37. $\dfrac{2t + 6}{t^2 - 9}$

$\dfrac{2}{t - 3}$

38. $\dfrac{5s - 25}{s^2 - 25}$

$\dfrac{5}{s + 5}$

39. $\dfrac{x^2 + 2x - 15}{x^2 + 6x + 5}$

$\dfrac{x - 3}{x + 1}$

40. $\dfrac{y^2 - 5y - 14}{y^2 + y - 2}$

$\dfrac{y - 7}{y - 1}$

41. $\dfrac{8x^2 - 10x - 3}{8x^2 - 6x - 9}$

$\dfrac{4x + 1}{4x + 3}$

42. $\dfrac{12x^2 - 4x - 5}{8x^2 - 6x - 5}$

$\dfrac{6x - 5}{4x - 5}$

43. $\dfrac{a^3 + b^3}{a + b}$

$a^2 - ab + b^2$

44. $\dfrac{r^3 - s^3}{r - s}$

$r^2 + rs + s^2$

45. $\dfrac{2c^2 + 2cd - 60d^2}{2c^2 - 12cd + 10d^2}$

$\dfrac{c + 6d}{c - d}$

46. $\dfrac{3s^2 - 9st - 54t^2}{3s^2 - 6st - 72t^2}$

$\dfrac{s + 3t}{s + 4t}$

47. $\dfrac{ac - ad + bc - bd}{ac - ad - bc + bd}$

$\dfrac{a + b}{a - b}$

48. $\dfrac{2xy + 2xw + y + w}{2xy + y - 2xw - w}$

$\dfrac{y + w}{y - w}$

Write each rational expression in lowest terms. See Example 3.

49. $\dfrac{7 - b}{b - 7}$

-1

50. $\dfrac{r - 13}{13 - r}$

-1

51. $\dfrac{x^2 - y^2}{y - x}$

52. $\dfrac{m^2 - n^2}{n - m}$

In Exercises 51–56, there are other acceptable ways to express each answer.

51. $-(x + y)$

52. $-(m + n)$

53. $\dfrac{(a - 3)(x + y)}{(3 - a)(x - y)}$

$-\dfrac{x + y}{x - y}$

54. $\dfrac{(8 - p)(x + 2)}{(p - 8)(x - 2)}$

$-\dfrac{x + 2}{x - 2}$

55. $\dfrac{5k - 10}{20 - 10k}$

$-\dfrac{1}{2}$

56. $\dfrac{7x - 21}{63 - 21x}$

$-\dfrac{1}{3}$

57. $\dfrac{a^2 - b^2}{a^2 + b^2}$

already in lowest terms

58. $\dfrac{p^2 + q^2}{p^2 - q^2}$

already in lowest terms

Multiply or divide as indicated. See Examples 4 and 5.

59. $\dfrac{(x + 2)(x + 1)}{(x + 3)(x - 2)} \cdot \dfrac{(x + 3)(x + 4)}{(x + 2)(x + 1)}$

$\dfrac{x + 4}{x - 2}$

60. $\dfrac{(x + 3)(x - 4)}{(x - 4)(x + 2)} \cdot \dfrac{(x + 5)(x - 6)}{(x + 3)(x - 6)}$

$\dfrac{x + 5}{x + 2}$

61. $\dfrac{(2x + 3)(x - 4)}{(x + 8)(x - 4)} \div \dfrac{(x - 4)(x + 2)}{(x - 4)(x + 8)}$

$\dfrac{2x + 3}{x + 2}$

62. $\dfrac{(6x + 5)(x - 3)}{(x + 9)(x - 1)} \div \dfrac{(x - 3)(2x + 7)}{(x - 1)(x + 9)}$

$\dfrac{6x + 5}{2x + 7}$

63. $\dfrac{7t+7}{-6} \div \dfrac{4t+4}{15}$

$-\dfrac{35}{8}$

64. $\dfrac{8z-16}{-20} \div \dfrac{3z-6}{40}$

$-\dfrac{16}{3}$

65. $\dfrac{4x}{8x+4} \cdot \dfrac{14x+7}{6}$

$\dfrac{7x}{6}$

66. $\dfrac{12x-20}{5x} \cdot \dfrac{6}{9x-15}$

$\dfrac{8}{5x}$

67. $\dfrac{p^2-25}{4p} \cdot \dfrac{2}{5-p}$

$-\dfrac{p+5}{2p}$ (There are other ways.)

68. $\dfrac{a^2-1}{4a} \cdot \dfrac{2}{1-a}$

$-\dfrac{a+1}{2a}$ (There are other ways.)

69. $\dfrac{m^2-49}{m+1} \div \dfrac{7-m}{m}$

$\dfrac{-m(m+7)}{m+1}$ (There are other ways.)

70. $\dfrac{k^2-4}{3k^2} \div \dfrac{2-k}{11k}$

$\dfrac{-11(k+2)}{3k}$ (There are other ways.)

71. $\dfrac{12x-10y}{3x+2y} \cdot \dfrac{6x+4y}{10y-12x}$

-2

72. $\dfrac{9s-12t}{2s+2t} \cdot \dfrac{3s+3t}{4t-3s}$

$-\dfrac{9}{2}$

73. $\dfrac{x^2-25}{x^2+x-20} \cdot \dfrac{x^2+7x+12}{x^2-2x-15}$

$\dfrac{x+4}{x-4}$

74. $\dfrac{t^2-49}{t^2+4t-21} \cdot \dfrac{t^2+8t+15}{t^2-2t-35}$

$\dfrac{t+3}{t-3}$

75. $\dfrac{6x^2+5xy-6y^2}{12x^2-11xy+2y^2} \div \dfrac{4x^2-12xy+9y^2}{8x^2-14xy+3y^2}$

$\dfrac{2x+3y}{2x-3y}$

76. $\dfrac{8a^2-6ab-9b^2}{6a^2-5ab-6b^2} \div \dfrac{4a^2+11ab+6b^2}{9a^2+12ab+4b^2}$

$\dfrac{3a+2b}{a+2b}$

77. $\dfrac{3k^2+17kp+10p^2}{6k^2+13kp-5p^2} \div \dfrac{6k^2+kp-2p^2}{6k^2-5kp+p^2}$

$\dfrac{k+5p}{2k+5p}$

78. $\dfrac{16c^2+24cd+9d^2}{16c^2-16cd+3d^2} \div \dfrac{16c^2-9d^2}{16c^2-24cd+9d^2}$

$\dfrac{4c+3d}{4c-d}$

79. $\left(\dfrac{6k^2-13k-5}{k^2+7k} \div \dfrac{2k-5}{k^3+6k^2-7k}\right) \cdot \dfrac{k^2-5k+6}{3k^2-8k-3}$

$(k-1)(k-2)$

80. $\left(\dfrac{2x^3+3x^2-2x}{3x-15} \div \dfrac{2x^3-x^2}{x^2-3x-10}\right) \cdot \dfrac{5x^2-10x}{3x^2+12x+12}$

$\dfrac{5(x-2)}{9}$

8.2 Adding and Subtracting Rational Expressions

Objectives

1. Add and subtract rational expressions with the same denominator.
2. Find a least common denominator.
3. Add and subtract rational expressions with different denominators.

1 **Add and subtract rational expressions with the same denominator.** The following steps, used to add or subtract rational numbers, are also used to add or subtract rational expressions.

Adding or Subtracting Rational Expressions

Step 1 **If the denominators are the same,** add or subtract the numerators. Place the result over the common denominator.

If the denominators are different, first find the least common denominator. Write all rational expressions with this LCD, and then add or subtract the numerators. Place the result over the common denominator.

Step 2 **Simplify.** Write all answers in lowest terms.

Example 1 Adding and Subtracting Rational Expressions with the Same Denominator

Add or subtract as indicated.

(a) $\dfrac{3y}{5} + \dfrac{x}{5} = \dfrac{3y + x}{5}$

The denominators of these rational expressions are the same, so just add the numerators, and place the sum over the common denominator.

(b) $\dfrac{7}{2r^2} - \dfrac{11}{2r^2} = \dfrac{7 - 11}{2r^2} = \dfrac{-4}{2r^2} = -\dfrac{2}{r^2}$ Lowest terms

Subtract the numerators since the denominators are the same, and keep the common denominator.

(c) $\dfrac{m}{m^2 - p^2} + \dfrac{p}{m^2 - p^2} = \dfrac{m + p}{m^2 - p^2}$ Add the numerators; keep the common denominator.

$= \dfrac{m + p}{(m + p)(m - p)}$ Factor.

$= \dfrac{1}{m - p}$ Lowest terms

(d) $\dfrac{4}{x^2 + 2x - 8} + \dfrac{x}{x^2 + 2x - 8} = \dfrac{4 + x}{x^2 + 2x - 8}$

$= \dfrac{4 + x}{(x - 2)(x + 4)}$

$= \dfrac{1}{x - 2}$

Work Problem 1 at the Side.

1 Add or subtract.

(a) $\dfrac{3m}{8} + \dfrac{5n}{8}$

(b) $\dfrac{7}{3a} + \dfrac{10}{3a}$

(c) $\dfrac{2}{y^2} - \dfrac{5}{y^2}$

(d) $\dfrac{a}{a + b} + \dfrac{b}{a + b}$

(e) $\dfrac{2y - 1}{y^2 + y - 2} - \dfrac{y}{y^2 + y - 2}$

Answers

1. (a) $\dfrac{3m + 5n}{8}$ **(b)** $\dfrac{17}{3a}$ **(c)** $-\dfrac{3}{y^2}$ **(d)** 1 **(e)** $\dfrac{1}{y + 2}$

2 Find the LCD for each pair of denominators.

(a) $5k^3s, \quad 10ks^4$

(b) $3 - x, \quad 9 - x^2$

(c) $z, \quad z + 6$

(d) $2y^2 - 3y - 2,$
$2y^2 + 3y + 1$

2 **Find a least common denominator.** We add or subtract rational expressions with different denominators by first writing them with a common denominator, usually the **least common denominator (LCD).**

Finding the Least Common Denominator

Step 1 **Factor.** Factor each denominator.

Step 2 **Find the least common denominator.** The LCD is the product of all different factors from each denominator, with each factor raised to the *greatest* power that occurs in any denominator.

Example 2 Finding Least Common Denominators

Assume that the given expressions are denominators of two fractions. Find the LCD for each pair.

(a) $5xy^2, \quad 2x^3y$

Each denominator is already factored.

$$5xy^2 = 5 \cdot x \cdot y^2$$
$$2x^3y = 2 \cdot x^3 \cdot y$$

Greatest exponent on x is 3.

$$\text{LCD} = 5 \cdot 2 \cdot x^3 \cdot y^2 \quad \leftarrow \text{Greatest exponent on } y \text{ is 2.}$$
$$= 10x^3y^2$$

(b) $k - 3, \quad k$

Each denominator is already factored. The LCD, an expression divisible by *both* $k - 3$ and k, is

$$k(k - 3).$$

It is usually best to leave a least common denominator in factored form.

(c) $y^2 - 2y - 8, \quad y^2 + 3y + 2$

Factor the denominators.

$$\left.\begin{aligned} y^2 - 2y - 8 &= (y - 4)(y + 2) \\ y^2 + 3y + 2 &= (y + 2)(y + 1) \end{aligned}\right\} \text{Factor.}$$

The LCD, divisible by both polynomials, is

$$(y - 4)(y + 2)(y + 1).$$

(d) $8z - 24, \quad 5z^2 - 15z$

$$\left.\begin{aligned} 8z - 24 &= 8(z - 3) \\ 5z^2 - 15z &= 5z(z - 3) \end{aligned}\right\} \text{Factor.}$$

The LCD is $8 \cdot 5z \cdot (z - 3) = 40z(z - 3)$.

Work Problem 2 at the Side.

ANSWERS

2. **(a)** $10k^3s^4$ **(b)** $(3 + x)(3 - x)$
(c) $z(z + 6)$ **(d)** $(y - 2)(2y + 1)(y + 1)$

3 Add and subtract rational expressions with different denominators. Before adding or subtracting two rational expressions, we write each expression with the least common denominator by multiplying its numerator and denominator by the factors needed to get the LCD. This procedure is valid because we are multiplying each rational expression by a form of 1, the identity element for multiplication.

Adding or subtracting rational expressions follows the same procedure as that used for rational numbers. Consider the sum $\frac{7}{15} + \frac{5}{12}$. The LCD for 15 and 12 is 60. Multiply $\frac{7}{15}$ by $\frac{4}{4}$ (a form of 1) and multiply $\frac{5}{12}$ by $\frac{5}{5}$ so that each fraction has denominator 60, and then add the numerators.

$$\frac{7}{15} + \frac{5}{12} = \frac{7 \cdot 4}{15 \cdot 4} + \frac{5 \cdot 5}{12 \cdot 5} \quad \text{Fundamental property}$$
$$= \frac{28}{60} + \frac{25}{60}$$
$$= \frac{28 + 25}{60} \quad \text{Add the numerators.}$$
$$= \frac{53}{60}$$

Example 3 Adding and Subtracting Rational Expressions with Different Denominators

Add or subtract as indicated.

(a) $\dfrac{5}{2p} + \dfrac{3}{8p}$

The LCD for $2p$ and $8p$ is $8p$. To write the first rational expression with a denominator of $8p$, multiply by $\frac{4}{4}$.

$$\frac{5}{2p} + \frac{3}{8p} = \frac{5 \cdot 4}{2p \cdot 4} + \frac{3}{8p} \quad \text{Fundamental property}$$
$$= \frac{20}{8p} + \frac{3}{8p}$$
$$= \frac{20 + 3}{8p} \quad \text{Add the numerators.}$$
$$= \frac{23}{8p}$$

(b) $\dfrac{6}{r} - \dfrac{5}{r - 3}$

The LCD is $r(r - 3)$. Rewrite each rational expression with this denominator.

$$\frac{6}{r} - \frac{5}{r-3} = \frac{6(r-3)}{r(r-3)} - \frac{r \cdot 5}{r(r-3)} \quad \text{Fundamental property}$$
$$= \frac{6r - 18}{r(r-3)} - \frac{5r}{r(r-3)} \quad \text{Distributive and commutative properties}$$
$$= \frac{6r - 18 - 5r}{r(r-3)} \quad \text{Subtract the numerators.}$$
$$= \frac{r - 18}{r(r-3)} \quad \text{Combine terms in the numerator.}$$

Work Problem 3 at the Side.

3 Add or subtract.

(a) $\dfrac{6}{7} + \dfrac{1}{5}$

(b) $\dfrac{8}{3k} - \dfrac{2}{9k}$

(c) $\dfrac{2}{y} - \dfrac{1}{y + 4}$

ANSWERS

3. (a) $\dfrac{37}{35}$ **(b)** $\dfrac{22}{9k}$ **(c)** $\dfrac{y + 8}{y(y + 4)}$

4 Subtract.

(a) $\dfrac{5x+7}{2x+7} - \dfrac{-x-14}{2x+7}$

(b) $\dfrac{2}{r-2} - \dfrac{r}{r-1}$

CAUTION

One of the most common sign errors in algebra occurs when a rational expression with two or more terms in the numerator is being subtracted. Remember that in this situation, the subtraction sign must be distributed to *every* term in the numerator of the fraction that follows it. Study Example 4 carefully to see how this is done.

Example 4 Using the Distributive Property When Subtracting Rational Expressions

Subtract.

(a) $\dfrac{7x}{3x+1} - \dfrac{x-2}{3x+1}$

The denominators are the same for both rational expressions. The subtraction sign must be applied to *both* terms in the numerator of the second rational expression. Notice the careful use of the distributive property here.

$$\frac{7x}{3x+1} - \frac{x-2}{3x+1} = \frac{7x-(x-2)}{3x+1} \quad \text{Write as a single rational expression.}$$

$$= \frac{7x-x+2}{3x+1} \quad \text{Distributive property; be careful with signs.}$$

$$= \frac{6x+2}{3x+1} \quad \text{Combine terms in the numerator.}$$

$$= \frac{2(3x+1)}{3x+1} \quad \text{Factor the numerator.}$$

$$= 2 \quad \text{Lowest terms}$$

(b) $\dfrac{1}{q-1} - \dfrac{1}{q+1}$

$$= \frac{1(q+1)}{(q-1)(q+1)} - \frac{1(q-1)}{(q+1)(q-1)} \quad \text{Fundamental property}$$

$$= \frac{(q+1)-(q-1)}{(q-1)(q+1)} \quad \text{Subtract.}$$

$$= \frac{q+1-q+1}{(q-1)(q+1)} \quad \text{Distributive property}$$

$$= \frac{2}{(q-1)(q+1)} \quad \text{Combine terms in the numerator.}$$

Work Problem 4 at the Side.

In some problems, rational expressions to be added or subtracted have denominators that are opposites of each other. The next example illustrates how to proceed in such a problem.

Answers

4. **(a)** 3 **(b)** $\dfrac{-r^2+4r-2}{(r-2)(r-1)}$

Example 5 **Adding Rational Expressions with Denominators That Are Opposites**

Add.

$$\frac{y}{y-2}+\frac{8}{2-y}$$

To get a common denominator of $y-2$, multiply the second expression by -1 in both the numerator and the denominator.

$$\begin{aligned}\frac{y}{y-2}+\frac{8}{2-y} &= \frac{y}{y-2}+\frac{8(-1)}{(2-y)(-1)}\\ &= \frac{y}{y-2}+\frac{-8}{y-2}\\ &= \frac{y-8}{y-2} && \text{Add the numerators.}\end{aligned}$$

Work Problem 5 at the Side.

The next example illustrates addition and subtraction involving more than two rational expressions.

Example 6 **Adding and Subtracting Three Rational Expressions**

Add and subtract as indicated.

$$\frac{3}{x-2}+\frac{5}{x}-\frac{6}{x^2-2x}$$

The denominator of the third rational expression factors as $x(x-2)$, which is the LCD for the three rational expressions.

$$\begin{aligned}&\frac{3}{x-2}+\frac{5}{x}-\frac{6}{x^2-2x}\\ &= \frac{3x}{x(x-2)}+\frac{5(x-2)}{x(x-2)}-\frac{6}{x(x-2)} && \text{Fundamental property}\\ &= \frac{3x+5(x-2)-6}{x(x-2)} && \text{Add and subtract the numerators.}\\ &= \frac{3x+5x-10-6}{x(x-2)} && \text{Distributive property}\\ &= \frac{8x-16}{x(x-2)} && \text{Combine terms in the numerator.}\\ &= \frac{8(x-2)}{x(x-2)} && \text{Factor the numerator.}\\ &= \frac{8}{x} && \text{Lowest terms}\end{aligned}$$

Work Problem 6 at the Side.

5 Add or subtract as indicated.

(a) $\frac{8}{x-4}+\frac{2}{4-x}$

(b) $\frac{9}{2x-9}-\frac{4}{9-2x}$

6 Add and subtract as indicated.

$$\frac{4}{x-5}+\frac{-2}{x}-\frac{10}{x^2-5x}$$

ANSWERS

5. **(a)** $\frac{6}{x-4}$ or $\frac{-6}{4-x}$ **(b)** $\frac{13}{2x-9}$ or $\frac{-13}{9-2x}$

6. $\frac{2}{x-5}$

7 Subtract.

$$\frac{-a}{a^2 + 3a - 4} - \frac{4a}{a^2 + 7a + 12}$$

Example 7 **Subtracting Rational Expressions**

Subtract.

$$\frac{m + 4}{m^2 - 2m - 3} - \frac{2m - 3}{m^2 - 5m + 6}$$

$$= \frac{m + 4}{(m - 3)(m + 1)} - \frac{2m - 3}{(m - 3)(m - 2)}$$ Factor each denominator.

The LCD is $(m - 3)(m + 1)(m - 2)$.

$$= \frac{(m + 4)(m - 2)}{(m - 3)(m + 1)(m - 2)} - \frac{(2m - 3)(m + 1)}{(m - 3)(m - 2)(m + 1)}$$ Fundamental property

$$= \frac{(m + 4)(m - 2) - (2m - 3)(m + 1)}{(m - 3)(m + 1)(m - 2)}$$ Subtract.

$$= \frac{m^2 + 2m - 8 - (2m^2 - m - 3)}{(m - 3)(m + 1)(m - 2)}$$ Multiply in the numerator.

$$= \frac{m^2 + 2m - 8 - 2m^2 + m + 3}{(m - 3)(m + 1)(m - 2)}$$ Distributive property; be careful with signs.

$$= \frac{-m^2 + 3m - 5}{(m - 3)(m + 1)(m - 2)}$$ Combine terms in the numerator.

If we try to factor the numerator, we find that this rational expression is in lowest terms.

Work Problem 7 at the Side.

Answers

7. $\frac{-5a^2 + a}{(a + 4)(a - 1)(a + 3)}$

8.2 EXERCISES

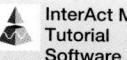

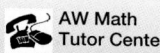

FOR EXTRA HELP: Student's Solutions Manual; MyMathLab.com; InterAct Math Tutorial Software; AW Math Tutor Center; www.mathxl.com; Digital Video Tutor CD 7 Videotape 15

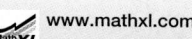

1. Write an explanation for adding or subtracting rational expressions that have a common denominator.

To add or subtract rational expressions that have a common denominator, first add or subtract the numerators. Then place the result over the common denominator. Write the answer in lowest terms.

2. Write an explanation for adding or subtracting rational expressions that have different denominators.

To add or subtract rational expressions that have different denominators, first write each expression as an equivalent expression with the least common denominator. Then follow the procedure described in the answer to Exercise 1.

Add or subtract as indicated. Write all answers in lowest terms. See Example 1.

3. $\frac{7}{t}+\frac{2}{t}$ $\quad\frac{9}{t}$

4. $\frac{5}{r}+\frac{9}{r}$ $\quad\frac{14}{r}$

5. $\frac{11}{5x}-\frac{1}{5x}$ $\quad\frac{2}{x}$

6. $\frac{7}{4y}-\frac{3}{4y}$ $\quad\frac{1}{y}$

7. $\frac{5x+4}{6x+5}+\frac{x+1}{6x+5}$ $\quad 1$

8. $\frac{6y+12}{4y+3}+\frac{2y-6}{4y+3}$ $\quad 2$

9. $\frac{x^2}{x+5}-\frac{25}{x+5}$ $\quad x-5$

10. $\frac{y^2}{y+6}-\frac{36}{y+6}$ $\quad y-6$

11. $\frac{4}{p^2+7p+12}+\frac{p}{p^2+7p+12}$ $\quad\frac{1}{p+3}$

12. $\frac{5}{x^2+x-20}+\frac{x}{x^2+x-20}$ $\quad\frac{1}{x-4}$

13. $\frac{a^3}{a^2+ab+b^2}-\frac{b^3}{a^2+ab+b^2}$ $\quad a-b$

14. $\frac{p^3}{p^2-pq+q^2}+\frac{q^3}{p^2-pq+q^2}$ $\quad p+q$

Assume that the expressions given are denominators of fractions. Find the least common denominator (LCD) for each group. See Example 2.

15. $18x^2y^3,\quad 24x^4y^5$ $\quad 72x^4y^5$

16. $24a^3b^4,\quad 18a^5b^2$ $\quad 72a^5b^4$

17. $z-2,\quad z$ $\quad z(z-2)$

18. $k+3,\quad k$ $\quad k(k+3)$

19. $2y+8,\quad y+4$ $\quad 2(y+4)$

20. $3r-21,\quad r-7$ $\quad 3(r-7)$

21. $x^2-81,\quad x^2+18x+81$ $\quad (x+9)^2(x-9)$

22. $y^2-16,\quad y^2-8y+16$ $\quad (y-4)^2(y+4)$

23. $m+n,\quad m-n,\quad m^2-n^2$ $\quad (m+n)(m-n)$

24. $r+s,\quad r-s,\quad r^2-s^2$ $\quad (r+s)(r-s)$

25. $x^2-3x-4,\quad x+x^2$ $\quad x(x-4)(x+1)$

26. $y^2-8y+12,\quad y^2-6y$ $\quad y(y-2)(y-6)$

27. $2t^2+7t-15,\quad t^2+3t-10$ $\quad (t+5)(t-2)(2t-3)$

28. $s^2-3s-4,\quad 3s^2+s-2$ $\quad (s+1)(s-4)(3s-2)$

29. $2y+6,\quad y^2-9,\quad y$ $\quad 2y(y+3)(y-3)$

30. $9x+18,\quad x^2-4,\quad x$ $\quad 9x(x+2)(x-2)$

31. One student added two rational expressions and obtained the answer $\frac{3}{5-y}$. Another student obtained the answer $\frac{-3}{y-5}$ for the same problem. Is it possible that both answers are correct? Explain.

Yes, they could both be correct because the expressions are equivalent. Multiplying $\frac{3}{5-y}$ by 1 in the form $\frac{-1}{-1}$ gives $\frac{-3}{y-5}$.

32. What is *wrong* with the following work?

$$\frac{x}{x+2} - \frac{4x-1}{x+2} = \frac{x-4x-1}{x+2} = \frac{-3x-1}{x+2}$$

The expression $\frac{x-4x-1}{x+2}$ is incorrect. The third term in the numerator should be $+1$, since the $-$ sign should be distributed to both $4x$ and -1. The answer should be $\frac{-3x+1}{x+2}$.

Add or subtract as indicated. Write all answers in lowest terms. See Examples 3–7.

33. $\frac{8}{t} + \frac{7}{3t}$ — **$\frac{31}{3t}$**

34. $\frac{5}{x} + \frac{9}{4x}$ — **$\frac{29}{4x}$**

35. $\frac{5}{12x^2y} - \frac{11}{6xy}$ — **$\frac{5-22x}{12x^2y}$**

36. $\frac{7}{18a^3b^2} - \frac{2}{9ab}$ — **$\frac{7-4a^2b}{18a^3b^2}$**

37. $\frac{1}{x-1} - \frac{1}{x}$ — **$\frac{1}{x(x-1)}$**

38. $\frac{3}{x-3} - \frac{1}{x}$ — **$\frac{2x+3}{x(x-3)}$**

39. $\frac{3a}{a+1} + \frac{2a}{a-3}$ — **$\frac{5a^2-7a}{(a+1)(a-3)}$**

40. $\frac{2x}{x+4} + \frac{3x}{x-7}$ — **$\frac{5x^2-2x}{(x+4)(x-7)}$**

41. $\frac{17y+3}{9y+7} - \frac{-10y-18}{9y+7}$ — **3**

42. $\frac{7x+8}{3x+2} - \frac{x+4}{3x+2}$ — **2**

43. $\frac{2}{4-x} + \frac{5}{x-4}$ — **$\frac{3}{x-4}$ or $\frac{-3}{4-x}$**

44. $\frac{3}{2-t} + \frac{1}{t-2}$ — **$\frac{2}{2-t}$ or $\frac{-2}{t-2}$**

45. $\frac{w}{w-z} - \frac{z}{z-w}$ — **$\frac{w+z}{w-z}$ or $\frac{-w-z}{z-w}$**

46. $\frac{a}{a-b} - \frac{b}{b-a}$ — **$\frac{a+b}{a-b}$ or $\frac{-a-b}{b-a}$**

47. $\frac{5}{12+4x} - \frac{7}{9+3x}$ — **$\frac{-13}{12(3+x)}$**

48. $\frac{3}{10x+15} - \frac{8}{12x+18}$ — **$\frac{-11}{15(2x+3)}$**

49. $\frac{4x}{x-1} - \frac{2}{x+1} - \frac{4}{x^2-1}$ — **$\frac{2(2x-1)}{x-1}$**

50. $\frac{4}{x+3} - \frac{x}{x-3} - \frac{18}{x^2-9}$ — **$\frac{-x^2+x-30}{(x+3)(x-3)}$**

51. $\dfrac{15}{y^2 + 3y} + \dfrac{2}{y} + \dfrac{5}{y + 3}$

$\dfrac{7}{y}$

52. $\dfrac{7}{t - 2} - \dfrac{6}{t^2 - 2t} - \dfrac{3}{t}$

$\dfrac{4}{t - 2}$

53. $\dfrac{5}{x - 2} + \dfrac{1}{x} + \dfrac{2}{x^2 - 2x}$

$\dfrac{6}{x - 2}$

54. $\dfrac{5x}{x - 3} + \dfrac{2}{x} + \dfrac{6}{x^2 - 3x}$

$\dfrac{5x + 2}{x - 3}$

55. $\dfrac{3x}{x + 1} + \dfrac{4}{x - 1} - \dfrac{6}{x^2 - 1}$

$\dfrac{3x - 2}{x - 1}$

56. $\dfrac{5x}{x + 3} + \dfrac{x + 2}{x} - \dfrac{6}{x^2 + 3x}$

$\dfrac{6x + 5}{x + 3}$

57. $\dfrac{4}{x + 1} + \dfrac{1}{x^2 - x + 1} - \dfrac{12}{x^3 + 1}$

$\dfrac{4x - 7}{x^2 - x + 1}$

58. $\dfrac{5}{x + 2} + \dfrac{2}{x^2 - 2x + 4} - \dfrac{60}{x^3 + 8}$

$\dfrac{5x - 18}{x^2 - 2x + 4}$

59. $\dfrac{2x + 4}{x + 3} + \dfrac{3}{x} - \dfrac{6}{x^2 + 3x}$

$\dfrac{2x + 1}{x}$

60. $\dfrac{4x + 1}{x + 5} - \dfrac{2}{x} + \dfrac{10}{x^2 + 5x}$

$\dfrac{4x - 1}{x + 5}$

61. $\dfrac{5x}{x^2 + xy - 2y^2} - \dfrac{3x}{x^2 + 5xy - 6y^2}$

$\dfrac{2x(x + 12y)}{(x + 2y)(x - y)(x + 6y)}$

62. $\dfrac{6x}{6x^2 + 5xy - 4y^2} - \dfrac{2y}{9x^2 - 16y^2}$

$\dfrac{18x^2 - 28xy + 2y^2}{(3x + 4y)(2x - y)(3x - 4y)}$

A concours d'elegance *is a competition in which a maximum of* 100 *points is awarded to a car based on its general attractiveness. The function defined by the rational expression*

$$c(x) = \frac{1010}{49(101 - x)} - \frac{10}{49}$$

approximates the cost, in thousands of dollars, of restoring a car so that it will win x points.

Use this information to work Exercises 63 and 64.

63. Simplify the expression for $c(x)$ by performing the indicated subtraction.

$c(x) = \dfrac{10x}{49(101 - x)}$

64. Use the simplified expression to determine how much it would cost to win 95 points.

approximately 3.23 thousand dollars

RELATING CONCEPTS (Exercises 65–70) FOR INDIVIDUAL OR GROUP WORK

In Example 6 we showed that

$$\frac{3}{x-2}+\frac{5}{x}-\frac{6}{x^2-2x}$$

is equal to $\frac{8}{x}$. *Algebra is, in a sense, a generalized form of arithmetic.* ***Work Exercises 65–70 in order,*** *to see how the algebra in this example is related to the arithmetic of common fractions.*

65. Perform the following operations, and express your answer in lowest terms.

$$\frac{3}{7}+\frac{5}{9}-\frac{6}{63}$$

$\frac{8}{9}$

66. Substitute 9 for x in the given problem from Example 6. Compare this problem to the one given in Exercise 65. What do you notice?

$\frac{3}{7}+\frac{5}{9}-\frac{6}{63}$; They are the same.

67. Now substitute 9 for x in the answer given in Example 6. Do your results agree with the result you obtained in Exercise 65?

$\frac{8}{9}$; yes

68. Replace x in the problem from Example 6 with the number of letters in your last name, assuming that this number is not 2. If your last name has two letters, let $x = 3$. Now predict the answer to your problem. Verify that your prediction is correct.

Answers will vary. Suppose the name is Bush, so that $x = 4$. The problem is $\frac{3}{2}+\frac{5}{4}-\frac{6}{8}$. The predicted answer is $\frac{8}{4} = 2$, which is correct.

69. Why will $x = 2$ not work for the problem from Example 6?

It causes $\frac{3}{x-2}$ and $\frac{6}{x^2-2x}$ to be undefined, since 0 appears in the denominators.

70. What other value of x is not allowed in the problem given from Example 6?

0

8.3 Complex Fractions

A **complex fraction** is an expression having a fraction in the numerator, denominator, or both. Examples of complex fractions include

$$\frac{1+\frac{1}{x}}{2},\quad \frac{\frac{4}{y}}{6-\frac{3}{y}},\quad \text{and}\quad \frac{\frac{m^2-9}{m+1}}{\frac{m+3}{m^2-1}}.$$

Objectives

1. Simplify complex fractions by simplifying the numerator and denominator. (Method 1)
2. Simplify complex fractions by multiplying by a common denominator. (Method 2)
3. Compare the two methods of simplifying complex fractions.
4. Simplify rational expressions with negative exponents.

1 Simplify complex fractions by simplifying the numerator and denominator. (Method 1) There are two different methods for simplifying complex fractions.

Simplifying a Complex Fraction: Method 1

Step 1 Simplify the numerator and denominator separately.

Step 2 Divide by multiplying the numerator by the reciprocal of the denominator.

Step 3 Simplify the resulting fraction, if possible.

In Step 2, we are treating the complex fraction as a quotient of two rational expressions and dividing. Before performing this step, be sure that both the numerator and denominator are single fractions.

Example 1 **Simplifying Complex Fractions by Method 1**

Use Method 1 to simplify each complex fraction.

(a) $\dfrac{\frac{x+1}{x}}{\frac{x-1}{2x}}$

Both the numerator and the denominator are already simplified, so divide by multiplying the numerator by the reciprocal of the denominator.

$$\frac{\frac{x+1}{x}}{\frac{x-1}{2x}} = \frac{x+1}{x} \div \frac{x-1}{2x} \qquad \text{Write as a division problem.}$$

$$= \frac{x+1}{x} \cdot \frac{2x}{x-1} \qquad \text{Reciprocal of } \frac{x-1}{2x}$$

$$= \frac{2(x+1)}{x-1} \qquad \text{Multiply and simplify.}$$

Continued on Next Page

1 Use Method 1 to simplify each complex fraction.

(a) $\dfrac{\dfrac{a+2}{5a}}{\dfrac{a-3}{7a}}$

(b) $\dfrac{2+\dfrac{1}{k}}{2-\dfrac{1}{k}}$

(c) $\dfrac{\dfrac{r^2-4}{4}}{1+\dfrac{2}{r}}$

(b) $\dfrac{2+\dfrac{1}{y}}{3-\dfrac{2}{y}} = \dfrac{\dfrac{2y}{y}+\dfrac{1}{y}}{\dfrac{3y}{y}-\dfrac{2}{y}}$

$= \dfrac{\dfrac{2y+1}{y}}{\dfrac{3y-2}{y}}$ Simplify the numerator and denominator.

$= \dfrac{2y+1}{y} \cdot \dfrac{y}{3y-2}$ Reciprocal of $\frac{3y-2}{y}$

$= \dfrac{2y+1}{3y-2}$

Work Problem 1 at the Side.

2 Simplify complex fractions by multiplying by a common denominator. (Method 2) The second method for simplifying complex fractions uses the identity property of multiplication.

Simplifying a Complex Fraction: Method 2

Step 1 Multiply the numerator and denominator of the complex fraction by the least common denominator of the fractions in the numerator and the fractions in the denominator of the complex fraction.

Step 2 Simplify the resulting fraction, if possible.

Example 2 Simplifying Complex Fractions by Method 2

Use Method 2 to simplify each complex fraction.

(a) $\dfrac{2+\dfrac{1}{y}}{3-\dfrac{2}{y}}$

Multiply the numerator and denominator by the LCD of all the fractions in the numerator and denominator of the complex fraction. (This is the same as multiplying by 1.) Here the LCD is y.

$\dfrac{2+\dfrac{1}{y}}{3-\dfrac{2}{y}} = \dfrac{2+\dfrac{1}{y}}{3-\dfrac{2}{y}} \cdot 1 = \dfrac{\left(2+\dfrac{1}{y}\right)\cdot y}{\left(3-\dfrac{2}{y}\right)\cdot y}$ Multiply the numerator and denominator by y, since $\frac{y}{y} = 1$.

$= \dfrac{2\cdot y + \dfrac{1}{y}\cdot y}{3\cdot y - \dfrac{2}{y}\cdot y}$ Distributive property

$= \dfrac{2y+1}{3y-2}$

Compare this method with that used in Example 1(b).

Continued on Next Page

ANSWERS

1. (a) $\dfrac{7(a+2)}{5(a-3)}$ (b) $\dfrac{2k+1}{2k-1}$ (c) $\dfrac{r(r-2)}{4}$

(b) $\dfrac{2p + \dfrac{5}{p-1}}{3p - \dfrac{2}{p}}$

The LCD is $p(p - 1)$.

$$\frac{2p + \dfrac{5}{p-1}}{3p - \dfrac{2}{p}} = \frac{\left(2p + \dfrac{5}{p-1}\right) \cdot p(p-1)}{\left(3p - \dfrac{2}{p}\right) \cdot p(p-1)}$$ Multiply the numerator and denominator by the LCD.

$$= \frac{2p[p(p-1)] + \dfrac{5}{p-1} \cdot p(p-1)}{3p[p(p-1)] - \dfrac{2}{p} \cdot p(p-1)}$$ Distributive property

$$= \frac{2p[p(p-1)] + 5p}{3p[p(p-1)] - 2(p-1)}$$

$$= \frac{2p^3 - 2p^2 + 5p}{3p^3 - 3p^2 - 2p + 2}$$

This rational expression is in lowest terms.

Work Problem 2 at the Side.

3 Compare the two methods of simplifying complex fractions. Choosing whether to use Method 1 or Method 2 to simplify a complex fraction is usually a matter of preference. Some students prefer one method over the other, while other students feel comfortable with both methods and rely on practice with many examples to determine which method they will use on a particular problem. In the next example, we illustrate how to simplify a complex fraction using both methods so that you can observe the processes and decide for yourself the pros and cons of each method.

Example 3 Simplifying Complex Fractions Using Both Methods

Use both Method 1 and Method 2 to simplify each complex fraction.

Method 1

(a) $\dfrac{\dfrac{2}{x-3}}{\dfrac{5}{x^2-9}}$

$$= \frac{\dfrac{2}{x-3}}{\dfrac{5}{(x-3)(x+3)}}$$

$$= \frac{2}{x-3} \div \frac{5}{(x-3)(x+3)}$$

$$= \frac{2}{x-3} \cdot \frac{(x-3)(x+3)}{5}$$

$$= \frac{2(x+3)}{5}$$

Method 2

(a) $\dfrac{\dfrac{2}{x-3}}{\dfrac{5}{x^2-9}}$

$$= \frac{\dfrac{2}{x-3} \cdot (x-3)(x+3)}{\dfrac{5}{(x-3)(x+3)} \cdot (x-3)(x+3)}$$

$$= \frac{2(x+3)}{5}$$

Continued on Next Page

2 Use Method 2 to simplify each complex fraction.

(a) $\dfrac{\dfrac{5}{y} + 6}{\dfrac{8}{3y} - 1}$

(b) $\dfrac{\dfrac{1}{y} + \dfrac{1}{y-1}}{\dfrac{1}{y} - \dfrac{2}{y-1}}$

ANSWERS

2. (a) $\dfrac{15 + 18y}{8 - 3y}$ **(b)** $\dfrac{2y - 1}{-y - 1}$ or $\dfrac{1 - 2y}{y + 1}$

3 Use both methods to simplify each complex fraction.

(a) $\dfrac{\dfrac{5}{y+2}}{\dfrac{-3}{y^2-4}}$

(b) $\dfrac{\dfrac{1}{a}-\dfrac{1}{b}}{\dfrac{1}{a^2}-\dfrac{1}{b^2}}$

4 Simplify each expression, using only positive exponents in the answer.

(a) $\dfrac{r^{-2}-s^{-1}}{4r^{-1}+s^{-2}}$

(b) $\dfrac{b^{-4}}{b^{-5}+2}$

ANSWERS

3. (Both methods give the same answers.)
(a) $\dfrac{5(y-2)}{-3}$ (b) $\dfrac{ab}{b+a}$

4. (a) $\dfrac{s^2-r^2s}{4rs^2+r^2}$ (b) $\dfrac{b}{1+2b^5}$

Method 1

(b) $\dfrac{\dfrac{1}{x}+\dfrac{1}{y}}{\dfrac{1}{x^2}-\dfrac{1}{y^2}}$

$$= \dfrac{\dfrac{y}{xy}+\dfrac{x}{xy}}{\dfrac{y^2}{x^2y^2}-\dfrac{x^2}{x^2y^2}}$$

$$= \dfrac{\dfrac{y+x}{xy}}{\dfrac{y^2-x^2}{x^2y^2}}$$

$$= \dfrac{y+x}{xy} \div \dfrac{y^2-x^2}{x^2y^2}$$

$$= \dfrac{y+x}{xy} \cdot \dfrac{x^2y^2}{(y-x)(y+x)}$$

$$= \dfrac{xy}{y-x}$$

Method 2

(b) $\dfrac{\dfrac{1}{x}+\dfrac{1}{y}}{\dfrac{1}{x^2}-\dfrac{1}{y^2}}$

$$= \dfrac{\left(\dfrac{1}{x}+\dfrac{1}{y}\right)\cdot x^2y^2}{\left(\dfrac{1}{x^2}-\dfrac{1}{y^2}\right)\cdot x^2y^2}$$

$$= \dfrac{xy^2+x^2y}{y^2-x^2}$$

$$= \dfrac{xy(y+x)}{(y+x)(y-x)}$$

$$= \dfrac{xy}{y-x}$$

Work Problem 3 at the Side.

4 **Simplify rational expressions with negative exponents.** Rational expressions and complex fractions sometimes involve negative exponents. To simplify such expressions, we begin by rewriting the expressions with only positive exponents.

Example 4 Simplifying a Rational Expression with Negative Exponents

Simplify $\dfrac{m^{-1}+p^{-2}}{2m^{-2}-p^{-1}}$, using only positive exponents in the answer.

First write the expression with only positive exponents using the definition of a negative exponent.

$$\frac{m^{-1}+p^{-2}}{2m^{-2}-p^{-1}} = \frac{\dfrac{1}{m}+\dfrac{1}{p^2}}{\dfrac{2}{m^2}-\dfrac{1}{p}}$$

Note that the 2 in $2m^{-2}$ is not raised to the -2 power, so $2m^{-2} = \dfrac{2}{m^2}$. Simplify the complex fraction using Method 2, multiplying numerator and denominator by the LCD, m^2p^2.

$$\frac{\dfrac{1}{m}+\dfrac{1}{p^2}}{\dfrac{2}{m^2}-\dfrac{1}{p}} = \frac{m^2p^2\cdot\dfrac{1}{m}+m^2p^2\cdot\dfrac{1}{p^2}}{m^2p^2\cdot\dfrac{2}{m^2}-m^2p^2\cdot\dfrac{1}{p}}$$

$$= \frac{mp^2+m^2}{2p^2-m^2p} \quad \text{Lowest terms}$$

Work Problem 4 at the Side.

8.3 EXERCISES

FOR EXTRA HELP

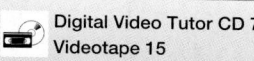

Student's Solutions Manual | MyMathLab.com | InterAct Math Tutorial Software | AW Math Tutor Center | www.mathxl.com | Digital Video Tutor CD 7 Videotape 15

1. Explain in your own words Method 1 for simplifying complex fractions.

Begin by simplifying the numerator. Then simplify the denominator. Write as a division problem, and proceed.

2. Method 2 for simplifying complex fractions says that we can multiply both the numerator and the denominator of the complex fraction by the same nonzero expression. What property of real numbers from Section 1.4 justifies this method?

identity property of multiplication

Use either method to simplify each complex fraction. See Examples 1–3.

3. $\dfrac{\frac{12}{x-1}}{\frac{6}{x}}$ $\quad \dfrac{2x}{x-1}$

4. $\dfrac{\frac{24}{t+4}}{\frac{6}{t}}$ $\quad \dfrac{4t}{t+4}$

5. $\dfrac{\frac{k+1}{2k}}{\frac{3k-1}{4k}}$ $\quad \dfrac{2(k+1)}{3k-1}$

6. $\dfrac{\frac{1-r}{4r}}{\frac{-1-r}{8r}}$ $\quad \dfrac{2(1-r)}{-1-r}$

7. $\dfrac{\frac{4z^2x^4}{9}}{\frac{12x^2z^5}{15}}$ $\quad \dfrac{5x^2}{9z^3}$

8. $\dfrac{\frac{3y^2x^3}{8}}{\frac{9y^3x^4}{16}}$ $\quad \dfrac{2}{3yx}$

9. $\dfrac{\frac{1}{x}+1}{-\frac{1}{x}+1}$ $\quad \dfrac{1+x}{-1+x}$

10. $\dfrac{\frac{2}{k}-1}{\frac{2}{k}+1}$ $\quad \dfrac{2-k}{2+k}$

11. $\dfrac{\frac{3}{x}+\frac{3}{y}}{\frac{3}{x}-\frac{3}{y}}$ $\quad \dfrac{y+x}{y-x}$

12. $\dfrac{\frac{4}{t}-\frac{4}{s}}{\frac{4}{t}+\frac{4}{s}}$ $\quad \dfrac{s-t}{s+t}$

13. $\dfrac{\frac{8x-24y}{10}}{\frac{x-3y}{5x}}$ $\quad 4x$

14. $\dfrac{\frac{10x-5y}{12}}{\frac{2x-y}{6y}}$ $\quad \dfrac{5y}{2}$

15. $\dfrac{\frac{x^2-16y^2}{xy}}{\frac{1}{y}-\frac{4}{x}}$ $\quad x+4y$

16. $\dfrac{\frac{2}{s}-\frac{3}{t}}{\frac{4t^2-9s^2}{st}}$ $\quad \dfrac{1}{2t+3s}$

17. $\dfrac{y-\frac{y-3}{3}}{\frac{4}{9}+\frac{2}{3y}}$ $\quad \dfrac{3y}{2}$

18. $\dfrac{p - \dfrac{p+2}{4}}{\dfrac{3}{4} - \dfrac{5}{2p}}$

$\dfrac{3p^2 - 2p}{3p - 10}$

19. $\dfrac{\dfrac{x+2}{x} + \dfrac{1}{x+2}}{\dfrac{5}{x} + \dfrac{x}{x+2}}$

$\dfrac{x^2 + 5x + 4}{x^2 + 5x + 10}$

20. $\dfrac{\dfrac{y+3}{y} - \dfrac{4}{y-1}}{\dfrac{y}{y-1} + \dfrac{1}{y}}$

$\dfrac{y^2 - 2y - 3}{y^2 + y - 1}$

RELATING CONCEPTS (Exercises 21–26) FOR INDIVIDUAL OR GROUP WORK

Simplifying a complex fraction by Method 1 is a good way to review the methods of adding, subtracting, multiplying, and dividing rational expressions. Method 2 gives a good review of the fundamental property of rational expressions. Refer to the following complex fraction, and **work Exercises 21–26 in order.**

$$\frac{\dfrac{4}{m} + \dfrac{m+2}{m-1}}{\dfrac{m+2}{m} - \dfrac{2}{m-1}}$$

21. Add the fractions in the numerator.

$\dfrac{m^2 + 6m - 4}{m(m-1)}$

22. Subtract as indicated in the denominator.

$\dfrac{m^2 - m - 2}{m(m-1)}$

23. Divide your answer from Exercise 21 by your answer from Exercise 22.

$\dfrac{m^2 + 6m - 4}{m^2 - m - 2}$

24. Go back to the original complex fraction and find the least common denominator of all denominators.

$m(m-1)$

25. Multiply the numerator and denominator of the complex fraction by your answer from Exercise 24.

$\dfrac{m^2 + 6m - 4}{m^2 - m - 2}$

26. Your answers for Exercises 23 and 25 should be the same. Write an explanation comparing the two methods. Which method do you prefer? Explain why.

Method 1 involves simplifying the numerator and the denominator separately and then performing a division. Method 2 involves multiplying the fraction by a form of 1, the identity element for multiplication. (Preferences will vary.)

Simplify each expression, using only positive exponents in the answer. See Example 4.

27. $\dfrac{1}{x^{-2} + y^{-2}}$

$\dfrac{x^2y^2}{y^2 + x^2}$

28. $\dfrac{1}{p^{-2} - q^{-2}}$

$\dfrac{p^2q^2}{q^2 - p^2}$ or $\dfrac{p^2q^2}{(q-p)(q+p)}$

29. $\dfrac{x^{-2} + y^{-2}}{x^{-1} + y^{-1}}$

$\dfrac{y^2 + x^2}{xy^2 + x^2y}$ or $\dfrac{y^2 + x^2}{xy(y+x)}$

30. $\dfrac{x^{-1} - y^{-1}}{x^{-2} - y^{-2}}$

$\dfrac{xy}{y + x}$

31. $\dfrac{x^{-1} + 2y^{-1}}{2y + 4x}$

$\dfrac{1}{2xy}$

32. $\dfrac{a^{-2} - 4b^{-2}}{3b - 6a}$

$\dfrac{b + 2a}{3a^2b^2}$

8.4 Graphs and Equations with Rational Expressions

Objectives

1. Recognize the graph of a rational function.
2. Determine the domain of a rational equation.
3. Solve rational equations.

1 Recognize the graph of a rational function. As we saw in Section 8.1, one or more values of x may be excluded from the domain of some rational functions. As a result, the graph of a rational function is often *discontinuous.* That is, there will be one or more breaks in the graph. For example, we use point plotting and observing the domain to graph the simple rational function defined by

$$f(x) = \frac{1}{x}.$$

The domain of this function includes all real numbers except 0. Thus, there will be no point on the graph with $x = 0$. The vertical line with equation $x = 0$ is called a **vertical asymptote** of the graph. We show some typical ordered pairs in the table for both negative and positive x-values.

x	−3	−2	−1	−.5	−.25	−.1	.1	.25	.5	1	2	3
y	$-\frac{1}{3}$	$-\frac{1}{2}$	−1	−2	−4	−10	10	4	2	1	$\frac{1}{2}$	$\frac{1}{3}$

Notice that the closer positive values of x are to 0, the larger y is. Similarly, the closer negative values of x are to 0, the smaller (more negative) y is. Using this observation, excluding 0 from the domain, and plotting the points in the table, we obtain the graph in Figure 2.

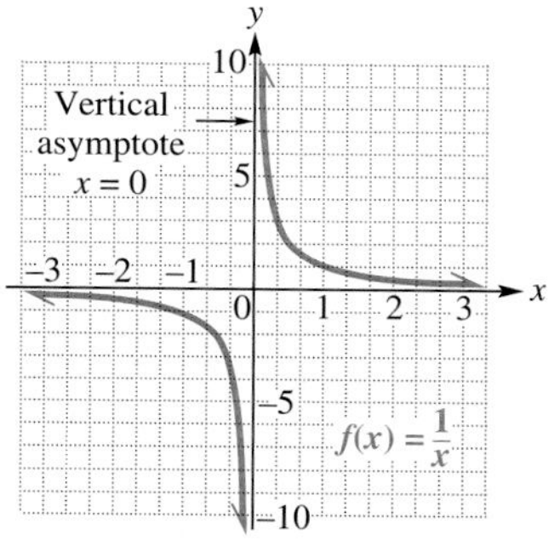

Figure 2

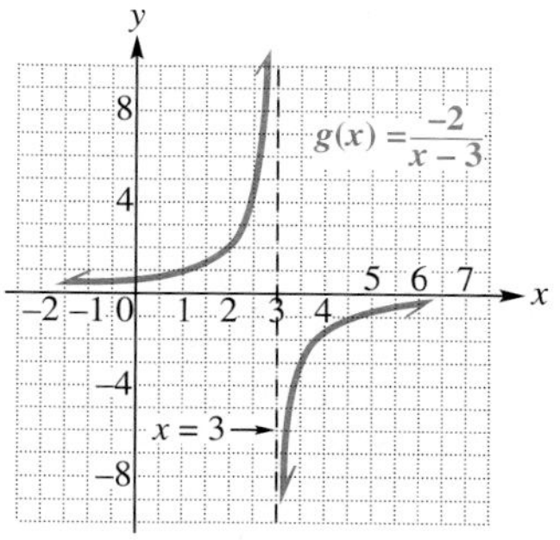

Figure 3

The graph of

$$g(x) = \frac{-2}{x - 3}$$

is shown in Figure 3. Some ordered pairs are shown in the table.

x	−2	−1	0	1	2	2.5	2.75	3.25	3.5	4	5	6
y	$\frac{2}{5}$	$\frac{1}{2}$	$\frac{2}{3}$	1	2	4	8	−8	−4	−2	−1	$-\frac{2}{3}$

There is no point on the graph for $x = 3$ because 3 is excluded from the domain. The dashed line $x = 3$ represents the asymptote and is not part of the graph. As suggested by the points from the table, the graph gets closer to the vertical asymptote as the x-values get closer to 3.

Work Problem 1 at the Side.

The domain of a *rational expression* is the set of all possible values of the variable. Any value that makes the denominator 0 is excluded.

1 Graph each rational function, and give the equation of the vertical asymptote.

(a) $f(x) = -\frac{1}{x}$

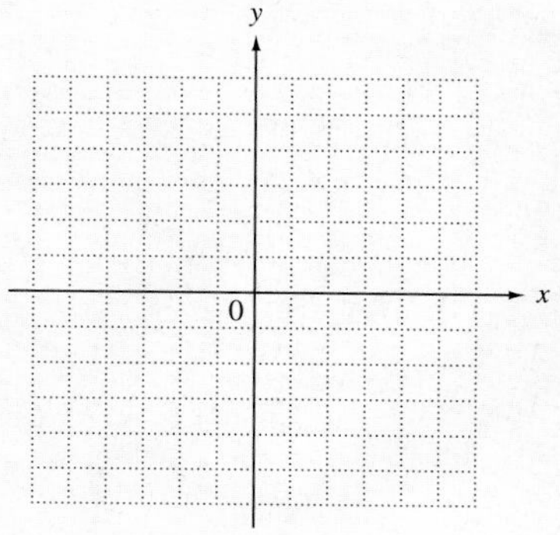

(b) $f(x) = \frac{2}{x + 3}$

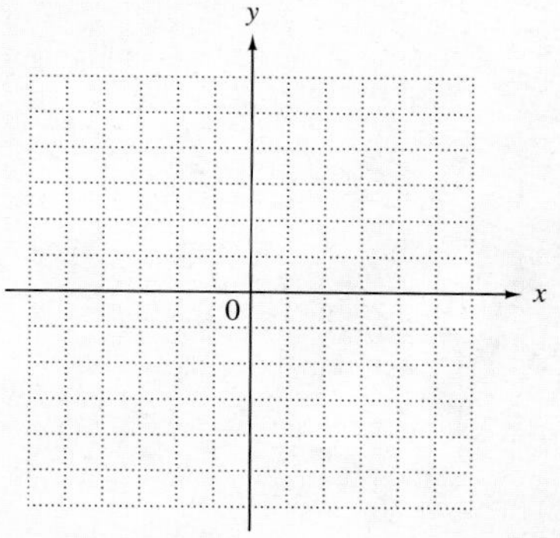

Answers

1. (a) asymptote: $x = 0$

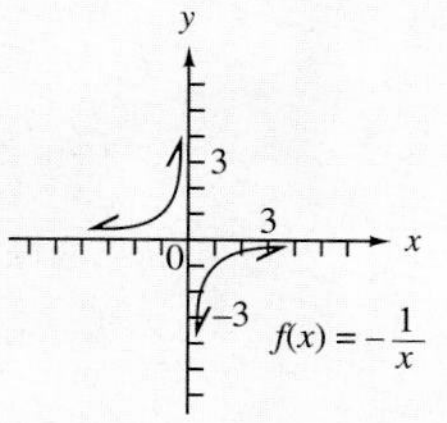

(b) asymptote: $x = -3$

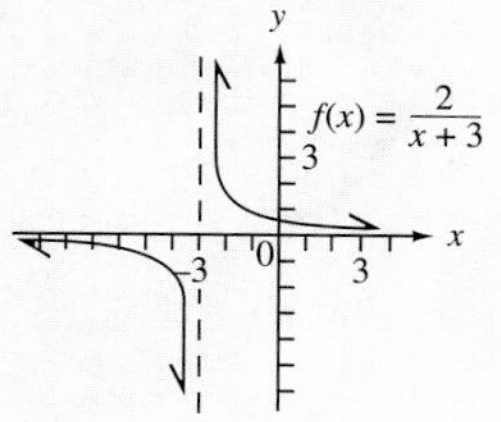

2 Find the domain of each equation.

(a) $\frac{3}{x}+\frac{1}{2}=\frac{5}{6x}$

(b)

$$\frac{4}{x-5}-\frac{2}{x+5}=\frac{1}{x^2-25}$$

ANSWERS
2. **(a)** $\{x|x \neq 0\}$ **(b)** $\{x|x \neq \pm 5\}$

2 Determine the domain of a rational equation. The **domain of a rational equation** is the intersection (overlap) of the domains of the rational expressions in the equation.

Example 1 Determining the Domains of Rational Equations

Find the domain of each equation.

(a) $\frac{2}{x}-\frac{3}{2}=\frac{7}{2x}$

The domains of the three rational terms of the equation are, in order, $\{x|x \neq 0\}$, $(-\infty, \infty)$, and $\{x|x \neq 0\}$. The intersection of these three domains is all real numbers except 0, which may be written $\{x|x \neq 0\}$.

(b) $\frac{2}{x-3}-\frac{3}{x+3}=\frac{12}{x^2-9}$

The domains of these three terms are, respectively, $\{x|x \neq 3\}$, $\{x|x \neq -3\}$ and $\{x|x \neq \pm 3\}$. The domain of the equation is the intersection of the three domains, all real numbers except 3 and -3, written $\{x|x \neq \pm 3\}$.

Work Problem 2 at the Side.

3 Solve rational equations. The easiest way to solve most equations involving rational expressions is to multiply all terms in the equation by the least common denominator. This step will clear the equation of all denominators, as the next examples show. *We can do this only with equations, not expressions.*

Because the first step in solving a rational equation is to multiply each side of the equation by a common denominator, it is *necessary* to either check the solutions or verify that the solutions are in the domain.

CAUTION

When each side of an equation is multiplied by a *variable* expression, the resulting "solutions" may not satisfy the original equation. You *must* either determine and observe the domain or check all potential solutions in the original equation. *It is wise to do both.*

Example 2 Solving an Equation with Rational Expressions

Solve $\frac{2}{x}-\frac{3}{2}=\frac{7}{2x}$.

The domain, which excludes 0, was found in Example 1(a). Multiply each side of the equation by the LCD, $2x$.

$$2x\left(\frac{2}{x}-\frac{3}{2}\right)=2x\left(\frac{7}{2x}\right)$$

$$2x\left(\frac{2}{x}\right)-2x\left(\frac{3}{2}\right)=2x\left(\frac{7}{2x}\right) \quad \text{Distributive property}$$

$$4-3x=7 \quad \text{Multiply.}$$

$$-3x=3 \quad \text{Subtract 4.}$$

$$x=-1 \quad \text{Divide by } -3.$$

Continued on Next Page

To check, replace x with -1 in the original equation.

$$\frac{2}{x} - \frac{3}{2} = \frac{7}{2x}$$

$$\frac{2}{-1} - \frac{3}{2} \stackrel{?}{=} \frac{7}{2(-1)} \quad \text{Let } x = -1.$$

$$-2 - \frac{3}{2} \stackrel{?}{=} -\frac{7}{2}$$

$$-\frac{7}{2} = -\frac{7}{2} \quad \text{True}$$

The solution set is $\{-1\}$.

Work Problem 3 at the Side.

3 Solve $-\frac{3}{20} + \frac{2}{x} = \frac{5}{4x}$.

Example 3 Solving an Equation with No Solution

Solve $\frac{2}{x-3} - \frac{3}{x+3} = \frac{12}{x^2-9}$.

Using the result from Example 1(b), we know that the domain excludes 3 and -3. Multiply each side by the LCD, $(x+3)(x-3)$.

$$(x+3)(x-3)\left(\frac{2}{x-3} - \frac{3}{x+3}\right) = (x+3)(x-3)\left(\frac{12}{x^2-9}\right)$$

$$2(x+3) - 3(x-3) = 12 \quad \text{Distributive property}$$

$$2x + 6 - 3x + 9 = 12 \quad \text{Distributive property}$$

$$-x + 15 = 12 \quad \text{Combine terms.}$$

$$-x = -3 \quad \text{Subtract 15.}$$

$$x = 3 \quad \text{Divide by } -1.$$

Since 3 is not in the domain, it cannot be a solution of the equation. Substitute 3 in the original equation.

$$\frac{2}{x-3} - \frac{3}{x+3} = \frac{12}{x^2-9}$$

$$\frac{2}{3-3} - \frac{3}{3+3} \stackrel{?}{=} \frac{12}{3^2-9} \quad \text{Let } x = 3.$$

$$\frac{2}{0} - \frac{3}{6} \stackrel{?}{=} \frac{12}{0}$$

Since division by 0 is undefined, the given equation has no solution, and the solution set is $\emptyset$.

Work Problem 4 at the Side.

4 Solve each equation.

(a) $\frac{3}{x+1} = \frac{1}{x-1} - \frac{2}{x^2-1}$

(b) $\frac{1}{x-3} + \frac{1}{x+3} = \frac{6}{x^2-9}$

Example 4 Solving an Equation with Rational Expressions

Solve $\frac{3}{p^2+p-2} - \frac{1}{p^2-1} = \frac{7}{2(p^2+3p+2)}$.

Factor each denominator to find the LCD, $2(p-1)(p+2)(p+1)$.

Continued on Next Page

ANSWERS

3. $\{5\}$

4. (a) $\emptyset$ **(b)** $\emptyset$

The domain excludes 1, -2, and -1. Multiply each side by the LCD.

$$2(p-1)(p+2)(p+1)\left(\frac{3}{(p+2)(p-1)} - \frac{1}{(p+1)(p-1)}\right)$$
$$= 2(p-1)(p+2)(p+1)\left(\frac{7}{2(p+2)(p+1)}\right)$$

$$2 \cdot 3(p+1) - 2(p+2) = 7(p-1) \quad \text{Distributive property}$$
$$6p + 6 - 2p - 4 = 7p - 7 \quad \text{Distributive property}$$
$$4p + 2 = 7p - 7 \quad \text{Combine terms.}$$
$$9 = 3p$$
$$3 = p$$

Note that 3 is in the domain; substitute 3 for p in the original equation to check that the solution set is $\{3\}$.

Work Problem 5 at the Side.

5 Solve

$$\frac{4}{x^2 + x - 6} - \frac{1}{x^2 - 4} = \frac{2}{x^2 + 5x + 6}.$$

Example 5 Solving an Equation That Leads to a Quadratic Equation

Solve $\dfrac{2}{3x+1} = \dfrac{1}{x} - \dfrac{6x}{3x+1}$.

Since the denominator $3x + 1$ cannot equal 0, $-\frac{1}{3}$ is excluded from the domain, as is 0. Multiply each side by the LCD, $x(3x + 1)$.

$$x(3x+1)\left(\frac{2}{3x+1}\right) = x(3x+1)\left[\frac{1}{x} - \frac{6x}{3x+1}\right]$$
$$2x = 3x + 1 - 6x^2$$

Since this equation is quadratic, write it in standard form with 0 on the right side.

$$6x^2 - 3x + 2x - 1 = 0$$
$$6x^2 - x - 1 = 0 \quad \text{Standard form}$$
$$(3x+1)(2x-1) = 0 \quad \text{Factor.}$$
$$3x + 1 = 0 \quad \text{or} \quad 2x - 1 = 0 \quad \text{Zero-factor property}$$
$$x = -\frac{1}{3} \quad \text{or} \quad x = \frac{1}{2}$$

Because $-\frac{1}{3}$ is not in the domain of the equation, it is not a solution. Check that the solution set is $\{\frac{1}{2}\}$.

Work Problem 6 at the Side.

6 Solve

$$\frac{1}{x+4} + \frac{x}{x-4} = \frac{-8}{x^2 - 16}.$$

ANSWERS
5. $\{-9\}$
6. $\{-1\}$

8.4 EXERCISES

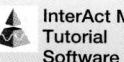

FOR EXTRA HELP: Student's Solutions Manual · MyMathLab.com · InterAct Math Tutorial Software · AW Math Tutor Center · www.mathxl.com · Digital Video Tutor CD 7 Videotape 16

Graph each rational function. Give the equation of the vertical asymptote. See Figures 1 and 2.

1. $f(x) = \dfrac{2}{x}$

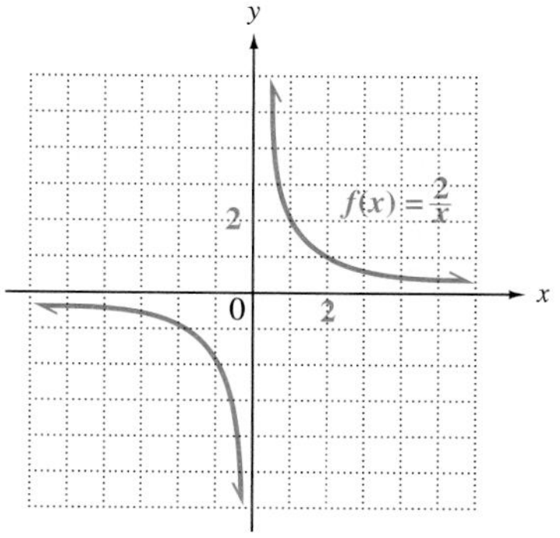

$x = 0$

2. $f(x) = \dfrac{3}{x}$

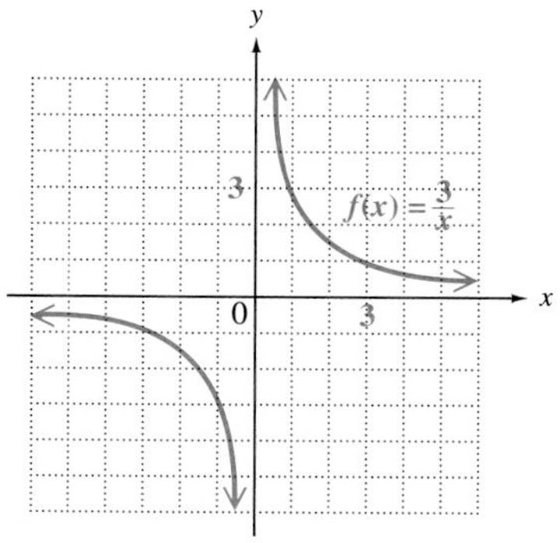

$x = 0$

3. $f(x) = \dfrac{1}{x - 2}$

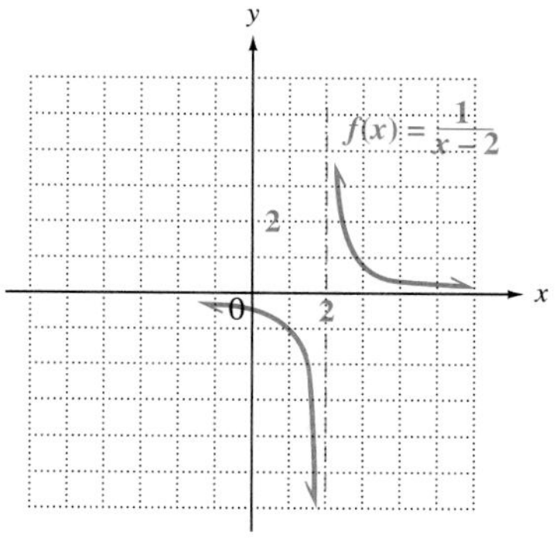

$x = 2$

4. $f(x) = \dfrac{1}{x + 2}$

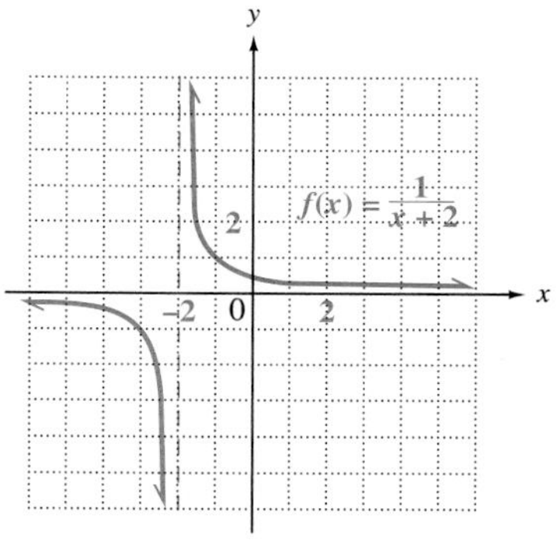

$x = -2$

As explained in this section, any values that would cause a denominator to equal 0 must be excluded from the domain and consequently as solutions of an equation that has variable expressions in the denominators. ***(a)*** *Without actually solving the equation, list all possible numbers that would have to be rejected if they appeared as potential solutions.* ***(b)*** *Then give the domain using set notation. See Example 1.*

5. $\dfrac{1}{x + 1} - \dfrac{1}{x - 2} = 0$

(a) $-1, 2$

(b) $\{x \mid x \neq -1, 2\}$

6. $\dfrac{3}{x + 4} - \dfrac{2}{x - 9} = 0$

(a) $-4, 9$

(b) $\{x \mid x \neq -4, 9\}$

7. $\dfrac{5}{3x + 5} - \dfrac{1}{x} = \dfrac{1}{2x + 3}$

(a) $-\dfrac{5}{3}, 0, -\dfrac{3}{2}$

(b) $\left\{x \mid x \neq -\dfrac{5}{3}, 0, -\dfrac{3}{2}\right\}$

8. $\dfrac{6}{4x+7} - \dfrac{3}{x} = \dfrac{5}{6x-13}$

(a) $-\frac{7}{4}, 0, \frac{13}{6}$

(b) $\left\{x \mid x \neq -\frac{7}{4}, 0, \frac{13}{6}\right\}$

9. $\dfrac{1}{3x} + \dfrac{1}{2x} = \dfrac{x}{3}$

(a) 0

(b) $\{x \mid x \neq 0\}$

10. $\dfrac{5}{6x} - \dfrac{8}{2x} = \dfrac{x}{4}$

(a) 0

(b) $\{x \mid x \neq 0\}$

11. $\dfrac{3x+1}{x-4} = \dfrac{6x+5}{2x-7}$

(a) $4, \frac{7}{2}$

(b) $\left\{x \mid x \neq 4, \frac{7}{2}\right\}$

12. $\dfrac{4x-1}{2x+3} = \dfrac{12x-25}{6x-2}$

(a) $-\frac{3}{2}, \frac{1}{3}$

(b) $\left\{x \mid x \neq -\frac{3}{2}, \frac{1}{3}\right\}$

13. $\dfrac{2}{x^2-x} + \dfrac{1}{x+3} = \dfrac{4}{x-2}$

(a) $0, 1, -3, 2$

(b) $\{x \mid x \neq 0, 1, -3, 2\}$

14. Is it possible that any potential solutions to the equation

$$\frac{x+7}{4} - \frac{x+3}{3} = \frac{x}{12}$$

would have to be rejected? Explain.

Since there are no variables in denominators, there are no potential solutions that would have to be rejected.

Solve each equation. See Examples 2–5.

15. $\dfrac{-5}{2x} + \dfrac{3}{4x} = \dfrac{-7}{4}$

$\{1\}$

16. $\dfrac{6}{5x} - \dfrac{2}{3x} = \dfrac{-8}{45}$

$\{-3\}$

17. $x - \dfrac{24}{x} = -2$

$\{-6, 4\}$

18. $p + \dfrac{15}{p} = -8$

$\{-5, -3\}$

19. $\dfrac{x-4}{x+6} = \dfrac{2x+3}{2x-1}$

$\left\{-\frac{7}{12}\right\}$

20. $\dfrac{5x-8}{x+2} = \dfrac{5x-1}{x+3}$

$\{-11\}$

21. $\dfrac{3x+1}{x-4} = \dfrac{6x+5}{2x-7}$

$\emptyset$

22. $\dfrac{4x-1}{2x+3} = \dfrac{12x-25}{6x-2}$

$\emptyset$

23. $\dfrac{1}{y-1} + \dfrac{5}{12} = \dfrac{-2}{3y-3}$

$\{-3\}$

24. $\dfrac{4}{m+2} - \dfrac{11}{9} = \dfrac{1}{3m+6}$

$\{1\}$

25. $\dfrac{-2}{3t-6} - \dfrac{1}{36} = \dfrac{-3}{4t-8}$

$\{5\}$

26. $\dfrac{3}{4m+2} = \dfrac{17}{2} - \dfrac{7}{2m+1}$

$\{0\}$

27. $\dfrac{3}{k+2} - \dfrac{2}{k^2-4} = \dfrac{1}{k-2}$

$\{5\}$

28. $\dfrac{3}{x-2} + \dfrac{21}{x^2-4} = \dfrac{14}{x+2}$

$\{5\}$

29. $\dfrac{1}{y+2} + \dfrac{3}{y+7} = \dfrac{5}{y^2+9y+14}$

$\varnothing$

30. $\dfrac{1}{t+3} + \dfrac{4}{t+5} = \dfrac{2}{t^2+8t+15}$

$\varnothing$

31. $\dfrac{9}{x} + \dfrac{4}{6x-3} = \dfrac{2}{6x-3}$

$\left\{\dfrac{27}{56}\right\}$

32. $\dfrac{5}{n} + \dfrac{4}{6-3n} = \dfrac{2n}{6-3n}$

$\left\{-\dfrac{15}{2}\right\}$

33. $\dfrac{6}{w+3} + \dfrac{-7}{w-5} = \dfrac{-48}{w^2-2w-15}$

$\varnothing$

34. $\dfrac{2}{r-5} + \dfrac{3}{2r+1} = \dfrac{22}{2r^2-9r-5}$

$\varnothing$

35. $\dfrac{x}{x-3} + \dfrac{4}{x+3} = \dfrac{18}{x^2-9}$

$\{-10\}$

36. $\dfrac{2x}{x-3} + \dfrac{4}{x+3} = \dfrac{-24}{x^2-9}$

$\{-2\}$

37. $\dfrac{6}{x-4} + \dfrac{5}{x} = \dfrac{-20}{x^2-4x}$

$\varnothing$

38. $\dfrac{7}{x-4} + \dfrac{3}{x} = \dfrac{-12}{x^2-4x}$

$\varnothing$

39. $\dfrac{2}{4x+7} + \dfrac{x}{3} = \dfrac{6}{12x+21}$

$\{0\}$

40. $\dfrac{5x+14}{x^2-9} = \dfrac{-2x^2-5x+2}{x^2-9} + \dfrac{2x+4}{x-3}$

$\{x \mid x \neq -3, 3\}$

41. $\dfrac{4x-7}{4x^2-9} = \dfrac{-2x^2+5x-4}{4x^2-9} + \dfrac{x+1}{2x+3}$

$\left\{x \mid x \neq -\dfrac{3}{2}, \dfrac{3}{2}\right\}$

42. What is wrong with the following problem? "Solve $\dfrac{2x+1}{3x-4} + \dfrac{1}{2x+3}$."

"Solve" refers to finding the solution set of an equation. What appears here is not an equation, but an operation. "Solve" should be replaced by "Simplify" or "Add."

Relating Concepts (Exercises 43–46) For Individual or Group Work

An equation of the form

$$\frac{A}{x+B}+\frac{x}{x-B}=\frac{C}{x^2-B^2}$$

will have one rejected solution if the relationship $C = -2AB$ holds true. (This can be proved using methods not covered in intermediate algebra.) For example, if $A = 1$ and $B = 2$, then $C = -2AB = -2(1)(2) = -4$, and the equation becomes

$$\frac{1}{x+2}+\frac{x}{x-2}=\frac{-4}{x^2-4}.$$

This equation has solution set $\{-1\}$; the potential solution -2 must be rejected. To further understand this idea, ***work Exercises 43–46 in order.***

43. Show that the second equation does indeed have solution set $\{-1\}$ and -2 must be rejected.

Substituting -1 for x gives a true statement, $\frac{4}{3}=\frac{4}{3}$. Substituting -2 for x leads to 0 in the first and third denominators.

44. Let $A = 2$ and let $B = 1$. What is the corresponding value of C? Solve the equation determined by A, B, and C. What is the solution set? What value must be rejected?

$C = -4$; $\{-2\}$; -1 is rejected.

45. Let $A = 4$ and let $B = -3$. What is the corresponding value of C? Solve the equation determined by A, B, and C. What is the solution set? What value must be rejected?

$C = 24$; $\{-4\}$; 3 is rejected.

46. Choose two numbers of your own, letting one be A and the other be B. Repeat the process described in Exercises 44 and 45.

Answers will vary. However, in every case, $-B$ will be the rejected solution, and $\{-A\}$ will be the solution set.

Solve each problem.

47. The average number of vehicles waiting in line to enter a sports arena parking area is modeled by the rational function defined by

$$w(x)=\frac{x^2}{2(1-x)},$$

where x is a quantity between 0 and 1 known as the *traffic intensity.* (*Source:* Mannering, F. and W. Kilareski, *Principles of Highway Engineering and Traffic Control*, John Wiley and Sons, 1990.) To the nearest tenth, find the average number of vehicles waiting if the traffic intensity is

(a) .1 **(b)** .8 **(c)** .9.

0 **1.6** **4.1**

(d) What happens to waiting time as traffic intensity increases?

The waiting time also increases.

48. The percent of deaths caused by smoking is modeled by the rational function defined by

$$p(x)=\frac{x-1}{x},$$

where x is the number of times a smoker is more likely to die of lung cancer than a nonsmoker. This is called the *incidence rate.* (*Source:* Walker, A., *Observation and Inference: An Introduction to the Methods of Epidemiology*, Epidemiology Resources Inc., 1991.) For example, $x = 10$ means that a smoker is 10 times more likely than a nonsmoker to die of lung cancer.

(a) Find $p(x)$ if x is 10.

90%

(b) For what value of x is $p(x) = 80\%$? (*Hint:* Change 80% to a decimal.)

5

Summary Exercises on OPERATIONS AND EQUATIONS WITH RATIONAL EXPRESSIONS

A common student error is to confuse an equation, *such as* $\frac{x}{2} + \frac{x}{3} = -5$, *with an* operation, *such as* $\frac{x}{2} + \frac{x}{3}$. *Look for the equals sign to distinguish between them. Equations are solved for a numerical answer, while problems involving* operations *result in simplified* expressions, *as shown below.*

Solving an Equation

Solve: $\frac{x}{2} + \frac{x}{3} = -5.$

Multiply each side by the LCD, 6.

$$6\left(\frac{x}{2} + \frac{x}{3}\right) = 6(-5)$$

$$3x + 2x = -30$$

$$5x = -30$$

$$x = -6$$

Check that the solution set is $\{-6\}$.

Performing an Operation

Add: $\frac{x}{2} + \frac{x}{3}$.

Write both fractions with the LCD, 6.

$$\frac{x}{2} + \frac{x}{3} = \frac{x \cdot 3}{2 \cdot 3} + \frac{x \cdot 2}{3 \cdot 2}$$

$$= \frac{3x}{6} + \frac{2x}{6}$$

$$= \frac{3x + 2x}{6}$$

$$= \frac{5x}{6}$$

In each exercise, identify as an equation *or an* operation. *Then perform the indicated operation or solve the given equation, as appropriate.*

1. $\frac{x}{2} - \frac{x}{4} = 5$

equation; $\{20\}$

2. $\frac{4x - 20}{x^2 - 25} \cdot \frac{(x + 5)^2}{10}$

operation; $\frac{2(x + 5)}{5}$

3. $\frac{6}{7x} - \frac{4}{x}$

operation; $-\frac{22}{7x}$

4. $\dfrac{\frac{1}{x} + \frac{1}{y}}{\frac{1}{x} - \frac{1}{y}}$

operation; $\frac{y + x}{y - x}$

5. $\frac{5}{7t} = \frac{52}{7} - \frac{3}{t}$

equation; $\left\{\frac{1}{2}\right\}$

6. $\frac{x - 5}{3} + \frac{1}{3} = \frac{x - 2}{5}$

equation; $\{7\}$

7. $\frac{7}{6x} + \frac{5}{8x}$

operation; $\frac{43}{24x}$

8. $\frac{4}{x} - \frac{8}{x + 1} = 0$

equation; $\{1\}$

9. $\dfrac{\frac{6}{x + 1} - \frac{1}{x}}{\frac{2}{x} - \frac{4}{x + 1}}$

operation; $\frac{5x - 1}{-2x + 2}$ or $\frac{5x - 1}{-2(x - 1)}$

10. $\frac{8}{r + 2} - \frac{7}{4r + 8}$

operation; $\frac{25}{4(r + 2)}$

11. $\frac{x}{x + y} + \frac{2y}{x - y}$

operation; $\frac{x^2 + xy + 2y^2}{(x + y)(x - y)}$

12. $\frac{3p^2 - 6p}{p + 5} \div \frac{p^2 - 4}{8p + 40}$

operation; $\frac{24p}{p + 2}$

13. $\dfrac{x-2}{9} \cdot \dfrac{5}{8-4x}$

operation; $-\dfrac{5}{36}$

14. $\dfrac{a-4}{3} + \dfrac{11}{6} = \dfrac{a+1}{2}$

equation; $\{0\}$

15. $\dfrac{b^2+b-6}{b^2+2b-8} \cdot \dfrac{b^2+8b+16}{3b+12}$

operation; $\dfrac{b+3}{3}$

16. $\dfrac{10z^2-5z}{3z^3-6z^2} \div \dfrac{2z^2+5z-3}{z^2+z-6}$

operation; $\dfrac{5}{3z}$

17. $\dfrac{5}{x^2-2x} - \dfrac{3}{x^2-4}$

operation; $\dfrac{2x+10}{x(x-2)(x+2)}$

18. $\dfrac{6}{t+1} + \dfrac{4}{5t+5} = \dfrac{34}{15}$

equation; $\{2\}$

19. $\dfrac{\dfrac{5}{x}-\dfrac{3}{y}}{\dfrac{9x^2-25y^2}{x^2y}}$

operation; $\dfrac{-x}{3x+5y}$

20. $\dfrac{-2}{a^2+2a-3} - \dfrac{5}{3-3a} = \dfrac{4}{3a+9}$

equation; $\{-13\}$

21. $\dfrac{4y^2-13y+3}{2y^2-9y+9} \div \dfrac{4y^2+11y-3}{6y^2-5y-6}$

operation; $\dfrac{3y+2}{y+3}$

22. $\dfrac{8}{3k+9} - \dfrac{8}{15} = \dfrac{2}{5k+15}$

equation; $\left\{\dfrac{5}{4}\right\}$

23. $\dfrac{3r}{r-2} = 1 + \dfrac{6}{r-2}$

equation; $\emptyset$

24. $\dfrac{6z^2-5z-6}{6z^2+5z-6} \cdot \dfrac{12z^2-17z+6}{12z^2-z-6}$

operation; $\dfrac{2z-3}{2z+3}$

25. $\dfrac{-1}{3-x} - \dfrac{2}{x-3}$

operation; $\dfrac{-1}{x-3}$ or $\dfrac{1}{3-x}$

26. $\dfrac{\dfrac{t}{4}-\dfrac{1}{t}}{1+\dfrac{t+4}{t}}$

operation; $\dfrac{t-2}{8}$

27. $\dfrac{2}{y+1} - \dfrac{3}{y^2-y-2} = \dfrac{3}{y-2}$

equation; $\{-10\}$

28. $\dfrac{7}{2x^2-8x} + \dfrac{3}{x^2-16}$

operation; $\dfrac{13x+28}{2x(x+4)(x-4)}$

29. $\dfrac{3}{y-3} - \dfrac{3}{y^2-5y+6} = \dfrac{2}{y-2}$

equation; $\emptyset$

30. $\dfrac{2k+\dfrac{5}{k-1}}{3k-\dfrac{2}{k}}$

operation; $\dfrac{k(2k^2-2k+5)}{(k-1)(3k^2-2)}$

8.5 APPLICATIONS OF RATIONAL EXPRESSIONS

OBJECTIVES

1. Find the value of an unknown variable in a formula.
2. Solve a formula for a specified variable.
3. Solve applications using proportions.
4. Solve applications about distance, rate, and time.
5. Solve applications about work rates.

1 Find the value of an unknown variable in a formula. Formulas may contain rational expressions, as does $t = \frac{d}{r}$. We now show how to work with formulas of this type.

Example 1 Finding the Value of a Variable in a Formula

In physics, the focal length, f, of a lens is given by the formula

$$\frac{1}{f} = \frac{1}{p} + \frac{1}{q},$$

where p is the distance from the object to the lens and q is the distance from the lens to the image. See Figure 4. Find q if $p = 20$ cm and $f = 10$ cm.

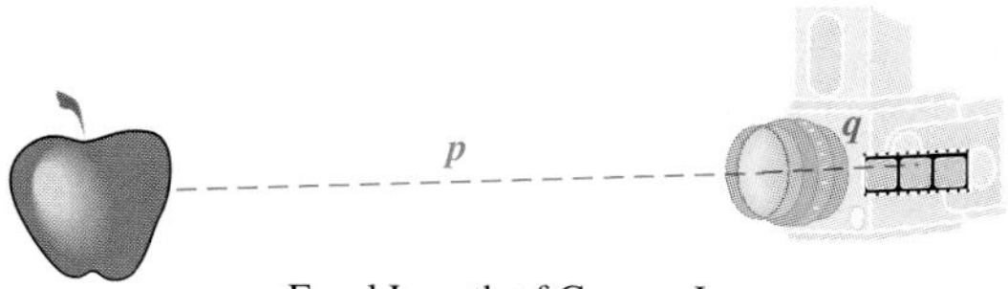

Focal Length of Camera Lens

Figure 4

Replace f with 10 and p with 20.

$$\frac{1}{f} = \frac{1}{p} + \frac{1}{q}$$

$$\frac{1}{10} = \frac{1}{20} + \frac{1}{q} \qquad \text{Let } f = 10, p = 20.$$

$$20q \cdot \frac{1}{10} = 20q\left(\frac{1}{20} + \frac{1}{q}\right) \qquad \text{Multiply by the LCD, } 20q.$$

$$2q = q + 20$$

$$q = 20$$

The distance from the lens to the image is 20 cm.

Work Problem 1 at the Side.

1 Use the formula given in Example 1 to answer each part.

(a) Find p if $f = 15$ and $q = 25$.

(b) Find f if $p = 6$ and $q = 9$.

(c) Find q if $f = 12$ and $p = 16$.

2 Solve a formula for a specified variable. The goal in solving for a specified variable is to isolate it on one side of the equals sign.

Example 2 Solving a Formula for a Specified Variable

Solve $\frac{1}{f} = \frac{1}{p} + \frac{1}{q}$ for p.

$$fpq \cdot \frac{1}{f} = fpq\left(\frac{1}{p} + \frac{1}{q}\right) \qquad \text{Multiply by the LCD, } fpq.$$

$$pq = fq + fp \qquad \text{Distributive property}$$

Transform the equation so that the terms with p (the specified variable) are on the same side. One way to do this is to subtract fp from each side.

Continued on Next Page

ANSWERS

1. (a) $\frac{75}{2}$ (b) $\frac{18}{5}$ (c) 48

$$pq - fp = fq \quad \text{Subtract } fp.$$
$$p(q - f) = fq \quad \text{Factor out } p.$$
$$p = \frac{fq}{q - f} \quad \text{Divide by } q - f.$$

Work Problem 2 at the Side.

2 Solve

$$\frac{3}{p} + \frac{3}{q} = \frac{5}{r}$$

for q.

Example 3 Solving a Formula for a Specified Variable

Solve $I = \dfrac{nE}{R + nr}$ for n.

$$(R + nr)I = (R + nr)\frac{nE}{R + nr} \quad \text{Multiply by } R + nr.$$
$$RI + nrI = nE$$
$$RI = nE - nrI \quad \text{Subtract } nrI.$$
$$RI = n(E - rI) \quad \text{Factor out } n.$$
$$\frac{RI}{E - rI} = n \quad \text{Divide by } E - rI.$$

CAUTION

Refer to the steps in Examples 2 and 3 that factor out the desired variable. This is a step that often gives students difficulty. Remember that the variable for which you are solving *must* be a factor on only one side of the equation, so each side can be divided by the remaining factor in the last step.

Work Problem 3 at the Side.

3 Solve

$$A = \frac{Rr}{R + r}$$

for R.

We can now solve problems that translate into equations with rational expressions. To do so, we continue to use the six-step problem-solving method from Chapter 2.

3 Solve applications using proportions. Recall from Section 2.6 that a **ratio** is a comparison of two quantities. The ratio of a to b may be written in any of the following ways:

$$a \text{ to } b, \quad a:b, \quad \text{or} \quad \frac{a}{b}.$$

Ratios are usually written as quotients in algebra. A **proportion** is a statement that two ratios are equal. Since proportions are a useful and important type of rational equation, we review solving an application using a proportion in the next example.

Example 4 Solving a Proportion

In 1998, 16 of every 100 Americans had no health insurance coverage. The population at that time was about 227 million. How many million had no health insurance? (*Source*: U.S. Bureau of the Census.)

Step 1 **Read** the problem.

Step 2 **Assign a variable.** Let $x =$ the number (in millions) who had no health insurance.

Continued on Next Page

ANSWERS

2. $q = \dfrac{3rp}{5p - 3r}$ or $q = \dfrac{-3rp}{3r - 5p}$

3. $R = \dfrac{-Ar}{A - r}$ or $R = \dfrac{Ar}{r - A}$

Step 3 **Write an equation.** To get an equation, set up a proportion. The ratio x to 227 should equal the ratio 16 to 100. Write the proportion and solve the equation.

$$\frac{16}{100} = \frac{x}{227}$$

Step 4 **Solve.**

$$22{,}700\left(\frac{16}{100}\right) = 22{,}700\left(\frac{x}{227}\right) \quad \text{Multiply by a common denominator.}$$

$$3632 = 100x \quad \text{Simplify.}$$

$$x = 36.32$$

Step 5 **State the answer.** There were 36.32 million Americans with no health insurance in 1998.

Step 6 **Check** that the ratio of this number to 227 million is equivalent to $\frac{16}{100}$.

Work Problem 4 at the Side.

4 Solve applications about distance, rate, and time. If an automobile travels at an average rate of 50 mph for 2 hr, then it travels $50 \times 2 = 100$ mi. This is an example of the basic relationship between distance, rate, and time:

$$\text{distance} = \text{rate} \times \text{time},$$

given by the formula $d = rt$. By solving, in turn, for r and t in the formula, we obtain two other equivalent forms of the formula that involve ratios. The three forms are given below.

Distance, Rate, and Time Relationship

$$d = rt \qquad r = \frac{d}{t} \qquad t = \frac{d}{r}$$

Example 5 **Finding Distance, Rate, or Time**

(a) The speed of sound is 1088 ft per sec at sea level at 32°F. In 5 sec under these conditions, sound travels

$$\underset{\text{Rate}}{1088} \times \underset{\text{Time}}{5} = \underset{\text{Distance}}{5440 \text{ ft.}}$$

Here, we found distance given rate and time, using $d = rt$.

(b) The winner of the first Indianapolis 500 race (in 1911) was Ray Harroun, driving a Marmon Wasp at an average speed of 74.59 mph. (*Source: The Universal Almanac,* 1997.) To complete the 500 mi, it took him

$$\frac{500 \leftarrow \text{Distance}}{74.59 \leftarrow \text{Rate}} = 6.70 \text{ hr (rounded).} \leftarrow \text{Time}$$

Here, we found time given rate and distance using $t = \frac{d}{r}$. To convert .70 hr to minutes, multiply by 60 to get $.70(60) = 42$. It took Harroun about 6 hr, 42 min to complete the race.

(c) At the 2000 Olympic Games in Sydney, Australia, Dutch swimmer Inge de Bruijn won the women's 50-m freestyle swimming event in 24.32 sec. (*Source:* www.olympics.com) Her rate was

$$\text{Rate} = \frac{\text{Distance}}{\text{Time}} \rightarrow \frac{50}{24.32} = 2.06 \text{ m per sec (rounded).}$$

Work Problem 5 at the Side.

4 Solve the problem.

In 1998, approximately 15% of the 11,073,000 children in the United States had no health insurance. How many children were uninsured? (*Source:* U. S. Bureau of the Census.)

5 Solve each problem.

(a) The world record in the men's 100-m dash was set in 1999 by Maurice Green, who ran it in 9.79 sec. What was his speed in meters per second? (*Source:* http://english.sydneylink.com)

(b) The world record for the women's 3000-m run was set by Junxia Wang in 1993. Her speed was 6.173 m per sec. What was her time in seconds?

(c) A small plane flew from Warsaw to Rome averaging 164 mph. The trip took 2 hr. What is the distance between Warsaw and Rome?

ANSWERS
4. 1,660,950
5. (a) 10.21 m per sec (b) 486 sec (c) 328 mi

6 Solve the problem.
A plane travels 100 mi against the wind in the same time that it takes to travel 120 mi with the wind. The wind speed is 20 mph.

(a) Complete this table.

	d	r	t
Against Wind	100	$x - 20$	
With Wind	120	$x + 20$	

(b) Find the speed of the plane in still air.

ANSWERS

6. (a) $\frac{100}{x-20}$; $\frac{120}{x+20}$ **(b)** 220 mph

Example 6 Solving a Problem about Distance, Rate, and Time

A tour boat goes 10 mi against the current in a small river in the same time that it goes 15 mi with the current. If the speed of the current is 3 mph, find the speed of the boat in still water.

Step 1 **Read** the problem. We must find the speed of the boat in still water.

Step 2 **Assign a variable.**

Let x = the speed of the boat in still water; then

$x - 3$ = the speed of the boat against the current;

$x + 3$ = the speed of the boat with the current.

Because the time is the same going against the current as with the current, find time in terms of distance and rate (speed) for each situation.

Start with the distance formula, $d = rt$, and divide each side by r to get

$$t = \frac{d}{r}.$$

Going against the current, the distance is 10 mi and the rate is $x - 3$, giving

$$t = \frac{d}{r} = \frac{10}{x-3}.$$

Going with the current, the distance is 15 mi and the rate is $x + 3$, so

$$t = \frac{d}{r} = \frac{15}{x+3}.$$

This information is summarized in the following table.

	Distance	Rate	Time
Against Current	10	$x - 3$	$\frac{10}{x-3}$
With Current	15	$x + 3$	$\frac{15}{x+3}$

Times are equal.

Step 3 **Write an equation.** Because the times are equal,

$$\frac{10}{x-3} = \frac{15}{x+3}.$$

This is the equation to be solved.

Step 4 **Solve.** The LCD is $(x + 3)(x - 3)$.

$$(x+3)(x-3)\left(\frac{10}{x-3}\right) = (x+3)(x-3)\left(\frac{15}{x+3}\right) \quad \text{Multiply by the LCD.}$$

$$10(x+3) = 15(x-3)$$

$$10x + 30 = 15x - 45 \quad \text{Distributive property}$$

$$30 = 5x - 45 \quad \text{Subtract } 10x.$$

$$75 = 5x \quad \text{Add 45.}$$

$$15 = x \quad \text{Divide by 5.}$$

Step 5 **State the answer.** The speed of the boat in still water is 15 mph.

Step 6 **Check** the answer: $\frac{10}{15-3} = \frac{15}{15+3}$ is true.

Work Problem 6 at the Side.

Example 7 Solving a Problem about Distance, Rate, and Time

At O'Hare Airport, Cheryl and Bill are walking to the gate (at the same speed) to catch their flight to Akron, Ohio. Since Bill wants a window seat, he steps onto the moving sidewalk and continues to walk while Cheryl uses the stationary sidewalk. If the sidewalk moves at 1 m per sec and Bill saves 50 sec covering the 300-m distance, what is their walking speed?

Step 1 **Read** the problem. We must find their walking speed.

Step 2 **Assign a variable.** Let x represent their walking speed in meters per second. Thus Cheryl travels at x m per sec and Bill travels at $x + 1$ m per sec. Since Bill's time is 50 sec less than Cheryl's time, express their times in terms of the known distances and the variable rates. As in Example 6, start with $d = rt$ and divide each side by r to get

$$t = \frac{d}{r}.$$

For Cheryl, the distance is 300 m and the rate is x. Cheryl's time is

$$t = \frac{d}{r} = \frac{300}{x}.$$

Bill travels 300 m at a rate of $x + 1$, so his time is

$$t = \frac{d}{r} = \frac{300}{x+1}.$$

This information is summarized in the following table.

	Distance	Rate	Time
Cheryl	300	x	$\frac{300}{x}$
Bill	300	$x + 1$	$\frac{300}{x+1}$

Step 3 **Write an equation** using the times from the table.

Bill's time is Cheryl's time less 50 seconds.

$$\frac{300}{x+1} = \frac{300}{x} - 50$$

Step 4 **Solve.**

$$x(x+1)\left(\frac{300}{x+1}\right) = x(x+1)\left(\frac{300}{x} - 50\right) \quad \text{Multiply by the LCD, } x(x+1).$$

$$300x = 300(x+1) - 50x(x+1)$$

$$300x = 300x + 300 - 50x^2 - 50x \quad \text{Distributive property}$$

$$0 = 50x^2 + 50x - 300 \quad \text{Standard form}$$

$$0 = x^2 + x - 6 \quad \text{Divide by 50.}$$

$$0 = (x+3)(x-2) \quad \text{Factor.}$$

$$x + 3 = 0 \quad \text{or} \quad x - 2 = 0 \quad \text{Zero-factor property}$$

$$x = -3 \quad \text{or} \quad x = 2$$

Discard the negative answer, since speed cannot be negative.

Step 5 **State the answer.** Their walking speed is 2 m per sec.

Step 6 **Check** the solution in the words of the original problem.

Work Problem 7 at the Side.

7 Solve the problem.

Dona Kenly drove 300 mi north from San Antonio, mostly on the freeway. She usually averaged 55 mph, but an accident slowed her speed through Dallas to 15 mph. If her trip took 6 hr, how many miles did she drive at reduced speed?

	d	r	t
Normal Speed	$300 - x$	55	
Reduced Speed	x	15	

ANSWERS

7. $11\frac{1}{4}$ mi

5 Solve applications about work rates. Problems about work are closely related to distance problems.

Problem Solving

People work at different rates. If the letters r, t, and A represent the rate at which the work is done, the time required, and the amount of work accomplished, respectively, then $A = rt$. Notice the similarity to the distance formula, $d = rt$. Amount of work can be measured in terms of jobs accomplished. Thus, if 1 job is completed, $A = 1$, and the formula gives the rate as

$$1 = rt$$
$$r = \frac{1}{t}.$$

Rate of Work

If a job can be accomplished in t units of time, then the rate of work is

$$\frac{1}{t} \text{ job per unit of time.}$$

To solve a work problem, we begin by using this fact to express all rates of work. See if you can identify the six steps used in the following example.

Example 8 **Solving a Problem about Work**

Letitia and Kareem are working on a neighborhood cleanup. Kareem can clean up all the trash in the area in 7 hr, while Letitia can do the same job in 5 hr. How long will it take them if they work together?

Let x = the number of hours it will take the two people working together. Just as we made a table for the distance formula, $d = rt$, make a table here for $A = rt$, with $A = 1$. Since $A = 1$, the rate for each person will be $\frac{1}{t}$, where t is the time it takes the person to complete the job alone. For example, since Kareem can clean up all the trash in 7 hr, his rate is $\frac{1}{7}$ of the job per hour. Similarly, Letitia's rate is $\frac{1}{5}$ of the job per hour. Fill in the table as shown.

	Rate	Time Working Together	Fractional Part of the Job Done
Kareem	$\frac{1}{7}$	x	$\frac{1}{7}x$
Letitia	$\frac{1}{5}$	x	$\frac{1}{5}x$

Since together they complete 1 job, the sum of the fractional parts accomplished by them should equal 1.

Part done by Kareem	+	Part done by Letitia	is	1 whole job.
$\frac{1}{7}x$	+	$\frac{1}{5}x$	=	1

Continued on Next Page

Solve this equation. The LCD is 35.

$$35\left(\frac{1}{7}x + \frac{1}{5}x\right) = 35 \cdot 1$$

$$5x + 7x = 35$$

$$12x = 35$$

$$x = \frac{35}{12}$$

Working together, Kareem and Letitia can do the entire job in $\frac{35}{12}$ hr, or 2 hr and 55 min. Check this result in the original problem.

Work Problem 8 at the Side.

There is another way to approach problems about work. For instance, in Example 8, x represents the number of hours it will take the two people working together to complete the entire job. In one hour, $\frac{1}{x}$ of the entire job will be completed. Kareem completes $\frac{1}{7}$ of the job in one hour, and Letitia completes $\frac{1}{5}$ of the job, so the sum of their rates should equal $\frac{1}{x}$. This gives the equation

$$\frac{1}{7} + \frac{1}{5} = \frac{1}{x}.$$

When each side of this equation is multiplied by $35x$, the result is $5x + 7x = 35$. Notice that this is the same equation we got in Example 8 in the third line from the bottom. Thus the solution of the equation is the same using either approach.

8 Solve each problem.

(a) Stan needs 45 min to do the dishes, while Deb can do them in 30 min. How long will it take them if they work together?

	Rate	Time Working Together	Fractional Part of the Job Done
Stan	$\frac{1}{45}$	x	
Deb	$\frac{1}{30}$	x	

(b) Suppose it takes Stan 35 min to do the dishes, and together they can do them in 15 min. How long will it take Deb to do them alone?

ANSWERS

8. (a) 18 min **(b)** $26\frac{1}{4}$ min

Focus on Real-Data Applications

It Depends on What You Mean by "Average"

Finding an average seems to be a simple process. Don't we just add the values and divide by the number of values? Well, for rational expressions, it all depends on what you mean by "average."

- To find the average of two fractions, say $\frac{1}{3}$ and $\frac{3}{4}$, add the two fractions and divide by 2.

$$\frac{\frac{1}{3}+\frac{3}{4}}{2}=\frac{\left(\frac{1}{3}+\frac{3}{4}\right)\cdot 12}{2\cdot 12}=\frac{4+9}{24}=\frac{13}{24}$$

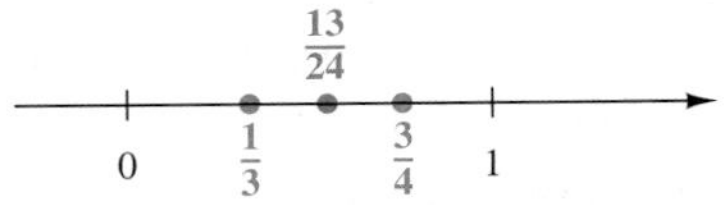

On a number line, the fraction $\frac{13}{24}$ is the **arithmetic mean,** which is exactly halfway between the fractions $\frac{1}{3}$ and $\frac{3}{4}$.

- Suppose you travel one direction at 60 mph and return at 30 mph. To find your average rate, you have to calculate the total distance divided by the total time. Recall that $d = rt$, so the total distance is $2d$, the time going is $\frac{d}{60}$, and the time returning is $\frac{d}{30}$. Since $r = \frac{d}{t}$,

$$\frac{2d}{\frac{d}{60}+\frac{d}{30}}=\frac{2d\cdot 60}{\left(\frac{d}{60}+\frac{d}{30}\right)\cdot 60}=\frac{120d}{d+2d}=\frac{120d}{3d}=40\text{ mph.}$$

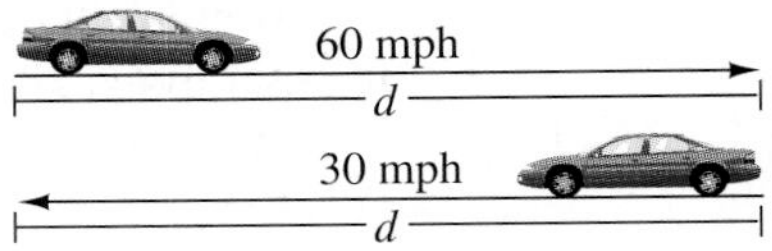

The average rate is 40 mph. This is the *harmonic mean* of 60 and 30. The **harmonic mean** of two numbers a and b is defined as $\frac{2ab}{a+b}$. Note that

$$\frac{2\cdot 60\cdot 30}{60+30}=\frac{3600}{90}=40.$$

- To calculate a batting average, you find the **ratio** of the number of hits to the number of "at bats." Suppose a baseball player has 72 hits in 364 "at bats." His batting average would be $\frac{72}{364} \approx .198$. If the same player gets an additional 3 hits from 8 more "at bats" during the next week, then his revised batting average would be

$$\frac{72+3}{364+8}=\frac{75}{372}\approx .202.$$

For Group Discussion

A carpenter builds wine racks. For each situation, find the appropriate "average" quantity.

1. The carpenter told his helper to cut $\frac{1}{2}$ ft pieces from a dowel. The helper could not find a measuring tape, but he did recall that the distance from the tip of his middle finger to the tip of his thumb was approximately 6 in., so he estimated the lengths. When the carpenter checked his work, he found that the helper had actually cut two pieces that were $\frac{5}{12}$ and $\frac{1}{2}$ ft long. What was the average length of the two pieces?

   1. $\frac{11}{24}$ ft

2. Once the pieces are cut, the carpenter can assemble and finish a wine rack in 2 hr, working alone. His helper takes 4 hr to accomplish the same task, working alone. If the carpenter and the helper work together, what is their average time to assemble and finish a wine rack?

   2. $\frac{4}{3}$ hr or 1 hr 20 min

3. Of 115 wine racks built, 112 passed a quality control check. What was the acceptance rate? During the next week, the carpenter built 35 additional wine racks, of which 28 were acceptable. What was the revised acceptance rate? Round answers to the nearest thousandth.

   3. .974; .933

Teaching notes for this activity are provided in the *Printed Test Bank and Instructor's Resource Guide.*

8.5 EXERCISES

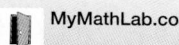

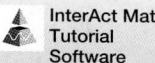

FOR EXTRA HELP: Student's Solutions Manual · MyMathLab.com · InterAct Math Tutorial Software · AW Math Tutor Center · www.mathxl.com · Digital Video Tutor CD 7 Videotape 16

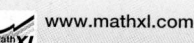

In Exercises 1–4, a familiar formula is given. Give the letter of the choice that is an equivalent form of the given formula.

1. $p = br$ (percent)

A. $b = \dfrac{p}{r}$ **B.** $r = \dfrac{b}{p}$

C. $b = \dfrac{r}{p}$ **D.** $p = \dfrac{r}{b}$

A

2. $V = LWH$ (geometry)

A. $H = \dfrac{LW}{V}$ **B.** $L = \dfrac{V}{WH}$

C. $L = \dfrac{WH}{V}$ **D.** $W = \dfrac{H}{VL}$

B

3. $m = \dfrac{F}{a}$ (physics)

A. $a = mF$ **B.** $F = \dfrac{m}{a}$

C. $F = \dfrac{a}{m}$ **D.** $F = ma$

D

4. $I = \dfrac{E}{R}$ (electricity)

A. $R = \dfrac{I}{E}$ **B.** $R = IE$

C. $E = \dfrac{I}{R}$ **D.** $E = RI$

D

Solve each problem. See Example 1.

5. A gas law in chemistry says that

$$\frac{PV}{T} = \frac{pv}{t}.$$

Suppose that $T = 300$, $t = 350$, $V = 9$, $P = 50$, and $v = 8$. Find p.

65.625

6. In work with electric circuits, the formula

$$\frac{1}{a} = \frac{1}{b} + \frac{1}{c}$$

occurs. Find b if $a = 8$ and $c = 12$.

24

7. A formula from anthropology says that

$$c = \frac{100b}{L}.$$

Find L if $c = 80$ and $b = 5$.

$\dfrac{25}{4}$

8. The gravitational force between two masses is given by

$$F = \frac{GMm}{d^2}.$$

Find M if $F = 10$, $G = 6.67 \times 10^{-11}$, $m = 1$, and $d = 3 \times 10^{-6}$.

1.349

Solve each formula for the specified variable. See Examples 2 and 3.

9. $F = \dfrac{GMm}{d^2}$ for G (physics)

$G = \dfrac{Fd^2}{Mm}$

10. $F = \dfrac{GMm}{d^2}$ for M (physics)

$M = \dfrac{Fd^2}{Gm}$

11. $\frac{1}{a} = \frac{1}{b} + \frac{1}{c}$ for a (electricity)

$a = \frac{bc}{c + b}$

12. $\frac{1}{a} = \frac{1}{b} + \frac{1}{c}$ for b (electricity)

$b = \frac{ac}{c - a}$ or $b = \frac{-ac}{a - c}$

13. $\frac{PV}{T} = \frac{pv}{t}$ for v (chemistry)

$v = \frac{PVt}{pT}$

14. $\frac{PV}{T} = \frac{pv}{t}$ for T (chemistry)

$T = \frac{PVt}{pv}$

15. $I = \frac{nE}{R + nr}$ for r (engineering)

$r = \frac{nE - IR}{In}$

16. $a = \frac{V - v}{t}$ for V (physics)

$V = at + v$

17. $A = \frac{1}{2}h(B + b)$ for b (mathematics)

$b = \frac{2A}{h} - B$ or $b = \frac{2A - Bh}{h}$

18. $S = \frac{n}{2}(a + \ell)d$ for n (mathematics)

$n = \frac{2S}{(a + \ell)d}$

19. $\frac{E}{e} = \frac{R + r}{r}$ for r (engineering)

$r = \frac{eR}{E - e}$

20. $y = \frac{x + z}{a - x}$ for x

$x = \frac{ay - z}{1 + y}$

21. To solve the equation $m = \frac{ab}{a - b}$ for a, what is the first step?

Multiply each side by $a - b$.

22. Suppose you are asked to solve the equation

$$rp - rq = p + q$$

for r. What is the first step?

Factor out r on the left.

Use the bar graph to answer Exercises 23–26.

23. In which year was the ratio of truck accidents to car accidents the least?

1996

24. In which year was the ratio of truck accidents to car accidents the greatest?

1998

25. In which year was the ratio of car accidents to truck accidents closest to 3 to 1?

1996

26. In which year was the ratio of car accidents to truck accidents less than 2 to 1?

1998

MOTOR VEHICLE ACCIDENTS INVOLVING CARS AND TRUCKS

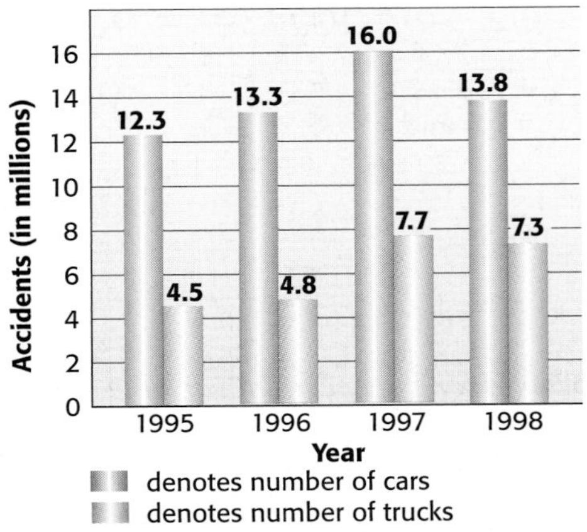

Source: National Safety Council.

Use a proportion to solve each problem. See Example 4.

27. During the 1997–1998 academic year, the ratio of teachers to students in private high schools was approximately 1 to 24. If a private high school had 554 students, how many teachers would be at the school if this ratio was valid for that school? Round your answer to the nearest whole number. (*Source:* U.S. National Center for Education Statistics, *Private School Universe Survey,* 1997–98.)

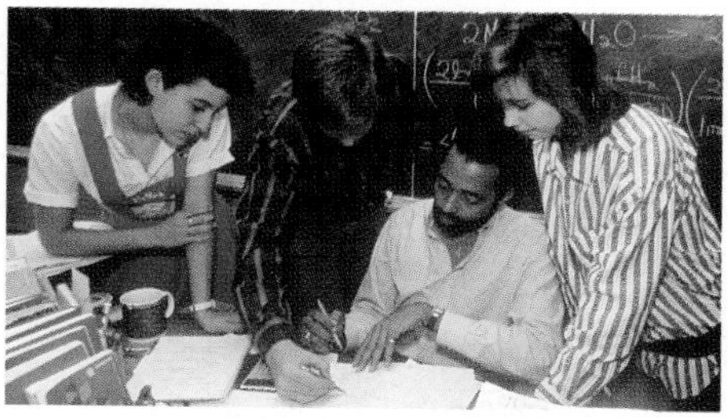

23 teachers

28. During the 1998–1999 National Basketball Association season, Shaquille O'Neal of the Los Angeles Lakers played in 49 games for a total of 1705 min. If he had played in all 50 of the team's games, how many minutes would he have played, assuming that the ratio of games to minutes stayed the same? Round your answer to the nearest whole number. (*Source: Sports Illustrated 2000 Sports Almanac.*)

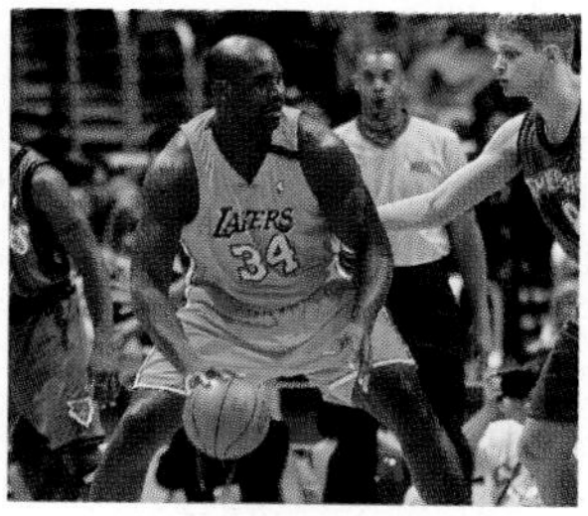

1740 min

29. In a recent year, 50 shares of common stock in Merck Company earned \$191.50. How much more would 75 shares of the stock have earned? (*Source:* Merck & Co., Inc., 1997 annual report.)

\$95.75

30. Seligman Communications and Information Fund, Inc. produced income of \$22,950 on an investment of \$100,000 in a recent year. If the investment had been increased to \$260,000, how much more income would have been produced? (*Source:* Seligman Communications and Information Fund, Inc.)

\$36,720

In geometry, it is shown that two triangles with corresponding angle measures equal, called similar triangles, *have corresponding sides proportional. For example, in the figure, angle A = angle D, angle B = angle E, and angle C = angle F, so the triangles are similar. Then the following ratios of corresponding sides are equal.*

$$\frac{4}{6} = \frac{6}{9} = \frac{2x + 1}{2x + 5}$$

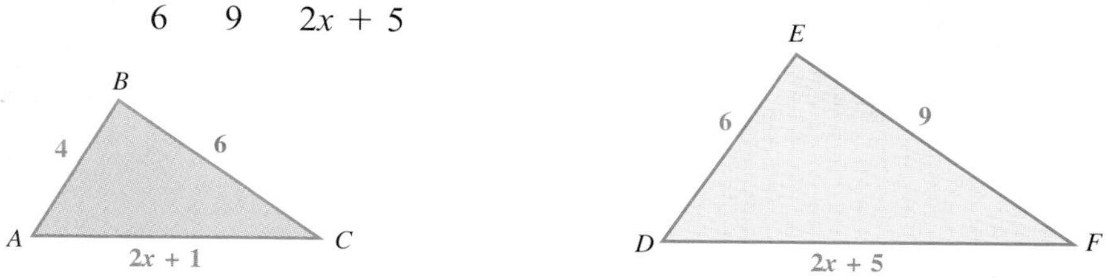

31. Solve for x using the given proportion to find the lengths of the third sides of the triangles.

$x = \frac{7}{2}$; $AC = 8$; $DF = 12$

32. Suppose the following triangles are similar. Find y and the lengths of the two longest sides of each triangle.

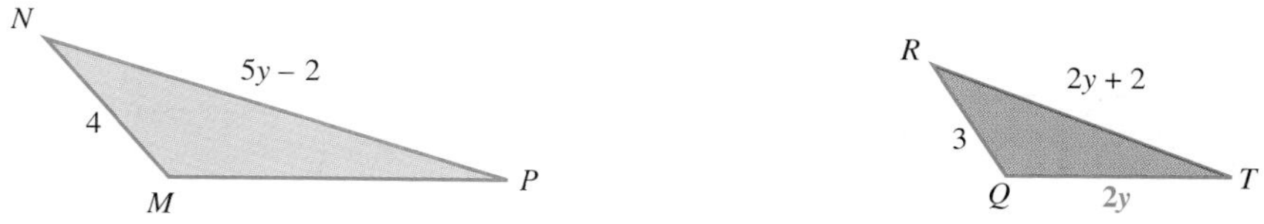

$y = 2$; side $NP = 8$; side $MP = \frac{16}{3}$; side $RT = 6$; side $QT = 4$

Solve each problem. See Example 5.

33. In the 1998 World Championships, Amy Van Dyken of the United States won the 50-m freestyle swimming event for women in 25.15 sec. What was her rate? (*Source: Sports Illustrated 2000 Sports Almanac.*)

1.99 m per sec

34. In the 1998 Winter Games, Catriona LeMay Doan of Canada won the 500-m speed skating event for women. Her rate was 13.0856 m per sec. What was her time (to the nearest hundredth of a second)? (*Source: Sports Illustrated 2000 Sports Almanac.*)

38.21 sec

35. The winner of the 1998 Charlotte 500 (mile) race was Mark Martin, who drove his Ford to victory with a rate of 123.188 mph. What was his time? (*Source: Sports Illustrated 2000 Sports Almanac.*)

4.059 hr

36. In 1998, Jeff Gordon drove his Chevrolet to victory in the North Carolina 400 (mile) race. His rate was 128.423 mph. What was his time? (*Source: Sports Illustrated 2000 Sports Almanac.*)

3.115 hr

37. The winner of the women's 1500-m race in the 2000 Olympics was Nouria Merah-Benida of Algeria with a time of 4.085 min. What was her rate? (*Source:* www.olympics.com)

367.197 m per min

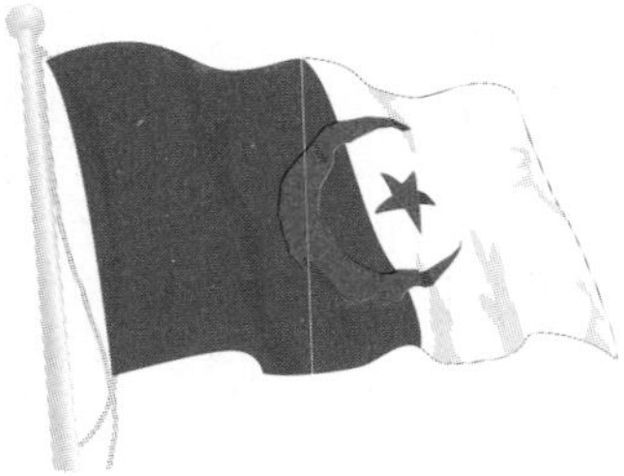

38. Gabriela Szabo of Romania won the women's 5000-m race in the 2000 Olympics with a time of 14.680 min. What was her rate? (*Source:* www.olympics.com)

340.599 m per min

Set up the equation you would use to solve each problem. Do not actually solve the equation. See Examples 6 and 7.

39. Julio flew his airplane 500 mi against the wind in the same time it took him to fly it 600 mi with the wind. If the speed of the wind was 10 mph, what was the average speed of his plane? (Let x = speed of the plane in still air.)

	Distance	Rate	Time
Against the wind	500	$x - 10$	
With the wind	600	$x + 10$	

$$\frac{500}{x - 10} = \frac{600}{x + 10}$$

40. Luvenia can row 4 mph in still water. It takes as long to row 8 mi upstream as 24 mi downstream. How fast is the current? (Let x = speed of the current.)

	Distance	Rate	Time
Upstream	8	$4 - x$	
Downstream	24	$4 + x$	

$$\frac{8}{4 - x} = \frac{24}{4 + x}$$

Solve each problem. See Examples 6 and 7.

41. Kellen's boat goes 12 mph. Find the rate of the current of the river if she can go 6 mi upstream in the same amount of time she can go 10 mi downstream.

	Distance	Rate	Time
Downstream	10	$12 + x$	
Upstream	6	$12 - x$	

3 mph

42. Kasey can travel 8 mi upstream in the same time it takes her to go 12 mi downstream. Her boat goes 15 mph in still water. What is the rate of the current?

	Distance	Rate	Time
Downstream			
Upstream			

3 mph

43. Driving from Tulsa to Detroit, Jeff averaged 50 mph. He figured that if he had averaged 60 mph, his driving time would have decreased 3 hr. How far is it from Tulsa to Detroit?

900 mi

44. If Dr. Dawson rides his bike to his office, he averages 12 mph. If he drives his car, he averages 36 mph. His time driving is $\frac{1}{4}$ hr less than his time riding his bike. How far is his office from home?

$4\frac{1}{2}$ mi

45. A private plane traveled from San Francisco to a secret rendezvous. It averaged 200 mph. On the return trip, the average speed was 300 mph. If the total traveling time was 4 hr, how far from San Francisco was the secret rendezvous?

480 mi

46. Johnny averages 30 mph when he drives on the old highway to his favorite fishing hole, and he averages 50 mph when most of his route is on the interstate. If both routes are the same length, and he saves 2 hr by traveling on the interstate, how far away is the fishing hole?

150 mi

47. On the first part of a trip to Carmel traveling on the freeway, Marge averaged 60 mph. On the rest of the trip, which was 10 mi longer than the first part, she averaged 50 mph. Find the total distance to Carmel if the second part of the trip took 30 min more than the first part.

190 mi

48. While on vacation, Jim and Annie decided to drive all day. During the first part of their trip on the highway, they averaged 60 mph. When they got to Houston, traffic caused them to average only 30 mph. The distance they drove in Houston was 100 mi less than their distance on the highway. What was their total driving distance if they spent 50 min more on the highway than they did in Houston?

200 mi

Solve each problem. See Example 8.

49. Butch and Peggy want to pick up the mess that their grandson, Grant, has made in his playroom. Butch could do it in 15 min working alone. Peggy, working alone, could clean it in 12 min. How long will it take them if they work together?

	Rate	Time Working Together	Fractional Part of the Job Done
Butch	$\frac{1}{15}$	x	
Peggy	$\frac{1}{12}$	x	

$6\frac{2}{3}$ min

50. Lou can groom Jay Beckenstein's dogs in 8 hr, but it takes his business partner, Janet, only 5 hr to groom the same dogs. How long will it take them to groom Jay's dogs if they work together?

	Rate	Time Working Together	Fractional Part of the Job Done
Lou	$\frac{1}{8}$	x	
Janet	$\frac{1}{5}$	x	

$3\frac{1}{13}$ hr

51. Ron Wood can paint a room in 6 hr working alone. If his son, Jason, helps him, the job takes 4 hr. How long would it take Jason to do the job if he worked alone?

12 hr

52. Sandi and Cary Goldstein are refinishing a table. Working alone, Cary could do the job in 7 hr. If the two work together, the job takes 5 hr. How long will it take Sandi to refinish the table working alone?

$17\frac{1}{2}$ hr

53. If a vat of acid can be filled by an inlet pipe in 10 hr and emptied by an outlet pipe in 20 hr, how long will it take to fill the vat if both pipes are open?

20 hr

54. A winery has a vat to hold chardonnay. An inlet pipe can fill the vat in 9 hr, while an outlet pipe can empty it in 12 hr. How long will it take to fill the vat if both the outlet and the inlet pipes are open?

36 hr

55. Suppose that Hortense and Mort can clean their entire house in 7 hr, while their toddler, Mimi, just by being around, can completely mess it up in only 2 hr. If Hortense and Mort clean the house while Mimi is at her grandma's, and then start cleaning up after Mimi the minute she gets home, how long does it take from the time Mimi gets home until the whole place is a shambles?

$2\frac{4}{5}$ hr

56. An inlet pipe can fill an artificial lily pond in 60 min, while an outlet pipe can empty it in 80 min. Through an error, both pipes are left open. How long will it take for the pond to fill?

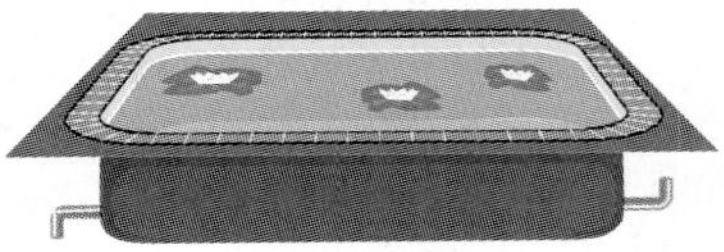

240 min or 4 hr

8.6 VARIATION

OBJECTIVES

1. Write an equation expressing direct variation.
2. Find the constant of variation, and solve direct variation problems.
3. Solve inverse variation problems.
4. Solve joint variation problems.
5. Solve combined variation problems.

Certain types of functions are very common, especially in business and the physical sciences. These are functions where y depends on a multiple of x, or y depends on a number divided by x. In such situations, y is said to *vary directly as x* (in the first case) or *vary inversely as x* (in the second case). For example, by the distance formula, the distance traveled varies directly as the rate (or speed) and the time. The simple interest formula and the formulas for area and volume are other familiar examples of *direct variation.*

On the other hand, the force required to keep a car from skidding on a curve varies inversely as the radius of the curve. Other examples of *inverse variation* are how travel time is inversely proportional to rate or speed and how, for a predetermined gain, principal is inversely proportional to the length of time the amount is invested.

1 Write an equation expressing direct variation. The circumference of a circle is given by the formula $C = 2\pi r$, where r is the radius of the circle. As the formula shows, the circumference is always a constant multiple of the radius. (C is always found by multiplying r by the constant 2π.) Because of this, the circumference is said to *vary directly* as the radius.

Direct Variation

y* varies directly as *x if there exists some constant k such that

$$y = kx.$$

Also, y is said to be **proportional to** x. The number k is called the **constant of variation.** In direct variation, for $k > 0$, as the value of x increases, the value of y also increases. Similarly, as x decreases, y decreases.

2 Find the constant of variation, and solve direct variation problems. The direct variation equation defines a linear function. In applications, functions are often defined by variation equations. For example, if Tom earns \$8 per hour, his wages vary directly as, or are proportional to, the number of hours he works. If y represents his total wages and x the number of hours he has worked, then

$$y = 8x.$$

Here k, the constant of variation, is 8.

Example 1 Finding the Constant of Variation and the Variation Equation

Steven Hidalgo is paid an hourly wage. One week he worked 43 hr and was paid \$795.50. How much does he earn per hour?

Let h represent the number of hours he works and P represent his corresponding pay. Then, P **varies directly as** h, so

$$P = kh.$$

Continued on Next Page

Here k represents Steven's hourly wage. Since $P = 795.50$ when $h = 43$,

$$795.50 = 43k$$
$$k = 18.50. \quad \text{Use a calculator.}$$

His hourly wage is \$18.50, and P and h are related by

$$P = 18.50h.$$

Work Problem 1 at the Side.

1 Find the constant of variation, and write a direct variation equation.

(a) Suzanne Alley is paid a daily wage. One month she worked 17 days and earned \$1334.50.

(b) Distance varies directly as time (at a constant speed). A car travels 100 mi at a constant speed in 2 hr.

Example 2 Solving a Direct Variation Problem

Hooke's law for an elastic spring states that the distance a spring stretches is proportional to the force applied. If a force of 150 newtons* stretches a certain spring 8 cm, how much will a force of 400 newtons stretch the spring? See Figure 5.

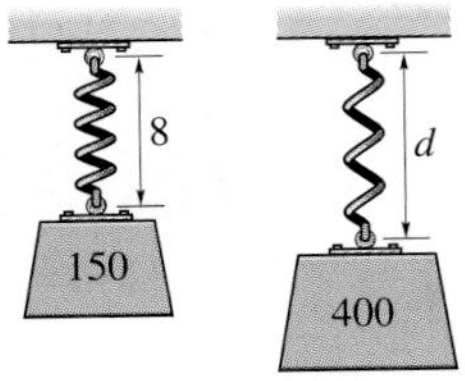

Figure 5

If d is the distance the spring stretches and f is the force applied, then $d = kf$ for some constant k. Since a force of 150 newtons stretches the spring 8 cm, we can use these values to find k.

$$d = kf \quad \text{Variation equation}$$
$$8 = k \cdot 150 \quad \text{Let } d = 8 \text{ and } f = 150.$$
$$k = \frac{8}{150} \quad \text{Find } k.$$
$$k = \frac{4}{75}$$

Substitute $\frac{4}{75}$ for k in the variation equation $d = kf$ to get

$$d = \frac{4}{75}f.$$

For a force of 400 newtons,

$$d = \frac{4}{75}(400) \quad \text{Let } f = 400.$$
$$= \frac{64}{3}.$$

The spring will stretch $\frac{64}{3}$ cm if a force of 400 newtons is applied.

Work Problem 2 at the Side.

2 The charge (in dollars) to customers for electricity (in kilowatt-hours) varies directly as the number of kilowatt-hours used. It costs \$52 to use 800 kilowatt-hours. Find the cost to use 1000 kilowatt-hours.

In summary, use the following steps to solve a variation problem.

ANSWERS

1. (a) $k = 78.50$; Let E represent her earnings for d days. Then $E = 78.50d$. (b) $k = 50$; Let d represent the distance traveled in h hours. Then $d = 50h$.
2. \$65

* A newton is a unit of measure of force used in physics.

Solving a Variation Problem

Step 1 Write the variation equation.

Step 2 Substitute the initial values and solve for k.

Step 3 Rewrite the variation equation with the value of k from Step 2.

Step 4 Substitute the remaining values, solve for the unknown, and find the required answer.

The direct variation equation $y = kx$ is a linear equation. However, other kinds of variation involve other types of equations. For example, one variable can be proportional to a power of another variable.

Direct Variation as a Power

y varies directly as the nth power of x if there exists a real number k such that

$$y = kx^n.$$

An example of direct variation as a power is the formula for the area of a circle, $A = \pi r^2$. Here, π is the constant of variation, and the area varies directly as the square of the radius.

Example 3 Solving a Direct Variation Problem

The distance a body falls from rest varies directly as the square of the time it falls (disregarding air resistance). If a skydiver falls 64 ft in 2 sec, how far will she fall in 8 sec?

Step 1 If d represents the distance the skydiver falls and t the time it takes to fall, then d is a function of t, and

$$d = kt^2$$

for some constant k.

Step 2 To find the value of k, use the fact that the skydiver falls 64 ft in 2 sec.

$$d = kt^2 \quad \text{Variation equation}$$
$$64 = k(2)^2 \quad \text{Let } d = 64 \text{ and } t = 2.$$
$$k = 16 \quad \text{Find } k.$$

Step 3 Using 16 for k, the variation equation becomes

$$d = 16t^2.$$

Step 4 Now let $t = 8$ to find the number of feet the skydiver will fall in 8 sec.

$$d = 16(8)^2 \quad \text{Let } t = 8.$$
$$= 1024$$

The skydiver will fall 1024 ft in 8 sec.

Work Problem 3 at the Side.

3 Solve inverse variation problems. In direct variation, where $k > 0$, as x increases, y increases. Similarly, as x decreases, y decreases. Another type of variation is *inverse variation.* With inverse variation, where $k > 0$, as one variable increases, the other variable decreases. For example, in a closed

3 The area of a circle varies directly as the square of its radius. A circle with radius 3 in. has area 28.278 in.^{2}.

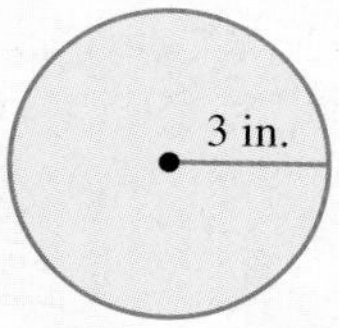

(a) Write a variation equation and give the value of k.

(b) What is the area of a circle with radius 4.1 in.?

ANSWERS

3. (a) $A = kr^2$; 3.142
(b) 52.817 in.^{2} (to the nearest thousandth)

space, volume decreases as pressure increases, as illustrated by a trash compactor. See Figure 6. As the compactor presses down, the pressure on the trash increases; in turn, the trash occupies a smaller space.

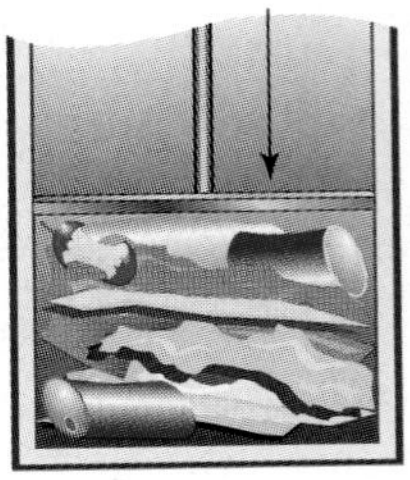
As pressure
on trash
increases,
volume of
trash
decreases.

Figure 6

Inverse Variation

y* varies inversely as *x if there exists a real number k such that

$$y = \frac{k}{x}.$$

Also, ***y* varies inversely as the *n*th power of *x*** if there exists a real number k such that

$$y = \frac{k}{x^n}.$$

Notice that the inverse variation equation also defines a function. Since x is in the denominator, these functions are rational functions. Another example of inverse variation can be found by looking at the formula for the area of a parallelogram. In its usual form, the formula is

$$A = bh.$$

Dividing each side by b gives

$$h = \frac{A}{b}.$$

Here, h (height) varies inversely as b (base), with A (the area) serving as the constant of variation. For example, if a parallelogram has an area of 72 in.^{2}, the values of b and h might be any of the following.

$$\left.\begin{aligned} b = 2,\ h = 36 \\ b = 3,\ h = 24 \\ b = 4,\ h = 18 \end{aligned}\right\} \text{ As } b \text{ increases, } h \text{ decreases.} \qquad \left.\begin{aligned} b = 12,\ h = 6 \\ b = 9,\ \ h = 8 \\ b = 8,\ \ h = 9 \end{aligned}\right\} \text{ As } b \text{ decreases, } h \text{ increases.}$$

Example 4 **Solving an Inverse Variation Problem**

The weight of an object above Earth varies inversely as the square of its distance from the center of Earth. A space shuttle in an elliptical orbit has a maximum distance from the center of Earth (apogee) of 6700 mi. Its minimum distance from the center of Earth (perigee) is 4090 mi. See Figure 7. If an astronaut in the shuttle weighs 57 lb at its apogee, what does the astronaut weigh at its perigee?

Continued on Next Page

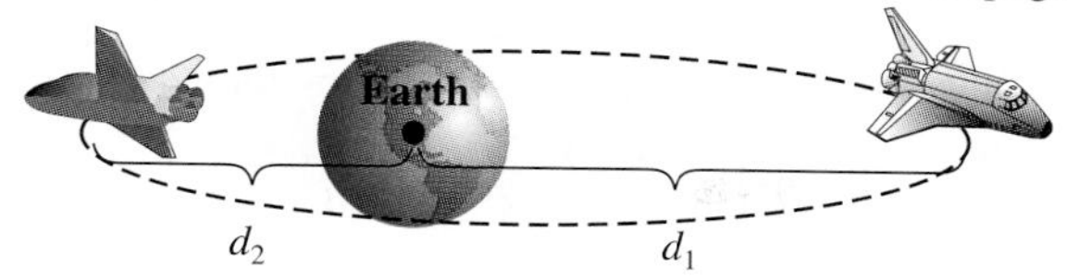

Figure 7

If w is the weight and d is the distance from the center of Earth, then

$$w = \frac{k}{d^2}$$

for some constant k. At the apogee the astronaut weighs 57 lb, and the distance from the center of Earth is 6700 mi. Use these values to find k.

$$57 = \frac{k}{(6700)^2} \quad \text{Let } w = 57 \text{ and } d = 6700.$$

$$k = 57(6700)^2$$

Then the weight at the perigee with $d = 4090$ mi is

$$w = \frac{57(6700)^2}{(4090)^2} \approx 153 \text{ lb.} \quad \text{Use a calculator.}$$

Work Problem 4 at the Side.

4 Solve joint variation problems. It is common for one variable to depend on several others. If one variable varies directly as the *product* of several other variables (perhaps raised to powers), the first variable is said to **vary jointly** as the others.

CAUTION

Note that *and* in the expression "y varies directly as ***m and n***" translates as the product

$$y = kmn.$$

The word *and* does not indicate addition here.

Example 5 **Solving a Joint Variation Problem**

The interest on a loan or an investment is given by the formula $I = prt$. Here, for a given principal p, the interest earned I varies jointly as the interest rate r and the time t the principal is left at interest. If an investment earns \$100 interest at 5% for 2 yr, how much interest will the same principal earn at 4.5% for 3 yr?

We use the formula $I = prt$, where p is the constant of variation because it is the same for both investments. For the first investment, we have $I = 100$, $r = .05$, and $t = 2$, so

$$I = prt$$

$$100 = p(.05)(2) \quad \text{Let } I = 100, r = .05, \text{ and } t = 2.$$

$$100 = .1p$$

$$\frac{100}{.1} = p$$

$$p = 1000.$$

Continued on Next Page

4 If the temperature is constant, the volume of a gas varies inversely as the pressure. For a certain gas, the volume is 10 cm^3 when the pressure is 6 kg per cm^2.

(a) Find the variation equation.

(b) Find the volume when the pressure is 12 kg per cm^2.

ANSWERS

4. (a) $V = \frac{60}{P}$ **(b)** 5 cm^3

5 The volume of a rectangular box of a given height is proportional to its width and length. A box with width 2 ft and length 4 ft has volume 12 ft^3. Find the volume of a box with the same height that is 3 ft wide and 5 ft long.

6 The maximum load that a cylindrical column with a circular cross section can hold varies directly as the fourth power of the diameter of the cross section and inversely as the square of the height. A 9-m column 1 m in diameter will support 8 metric tons. How many metric tons can be supported by a column 12 m high and $\frac{2}{3}$ m in diameter?

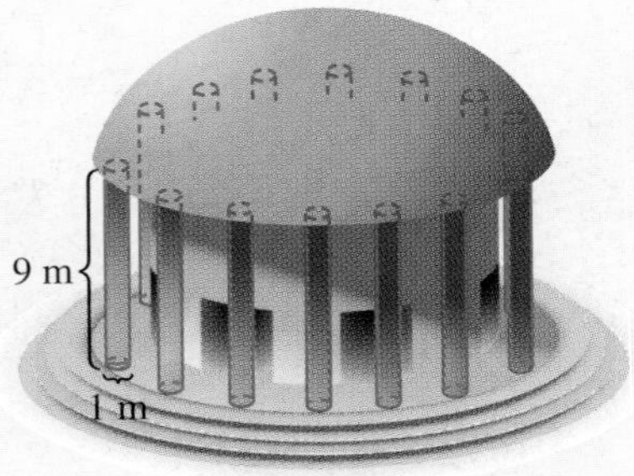

Load = 8 metric tons

Answers

5. 22.5 ft^3

6. $\frac{8}{9}$ metric ton

Now we find I when $p = 1000$, $r = .045$, and $t = 3$ by substituting into $I = prt$.

$$I = 1000(.045)(3) \qquad \text{Let } p = 1000,\ r = .045, \text{ and } t = 3.$$

$$I = 135$$

The interest will be \$135.

Work Problem 5 at the Side.

5 Solve combined variation problems. There are many combinations of direct and inverse variation. Example 6 shows a typical **combined variation** problem.

Example 6 Solving a Combined Variation Problem

Body mass index, or BMI, is used by physicians to assess a person's level of fatness. A BMI from 19 through 25 is considered desirable. BMI varies directly as an individual's weight in pounds and inversely as the square of the individual's height in inches. A person who weighs 118 lb and is 64 in. tall has a BMI of 20. (The BMI is rounded to the nearest whole number.) Find the BMI of a person who weighs 165 lb with a height of 70 in.

Let B represent the BMI, w the weight, and h the height. Then

$$B = \frac{kw}{h^2}. \qquad \begin{array}{l}\leftarrow \text{BMI varies directly as the weight.}\\ \leftarrow \text{BMI varies inversely as the square of the height.}\end{array}$$

To find k, let $B = 20$, $w = 118$, and $h = 64$.

$$20 = \frac{k(118)}{64^2}$$

$$k = \frac{20(64^2)}{118} \qquad \text{Multiply by } 64^2\text{; divide by 118.}$$

$$k \approx 694 \qquad \text{Use a calculator.}$$

Now find B when $k = 694$, $w = 165$, and $h = 70$.

$$B = \frac{694(165)}{70^2} \approx 23 \qquad \text{Nearest whole number}$$

The person's BMI is 23.

Work Problem 6 at the Side.

8.6 EXERCISES

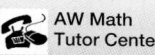

FOR EXTRA HELP: Student's Solutions Manual | MyMathLab.com | InterAct Math Tutorial Software | AW Math Tutor Center | www.mathxl.com | Digital Video Tutor CD 7 Videotape 16

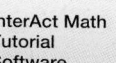

Use personal experience or intuition to determine whether the situation suggests direct *or* inverse *variation.*

1. The number of different lottery tickets you buy and your probability of winning that lottery

direct

2. The amount of pressure put on the accelerator of a car and the speed of the car

direct

3. The number of days from now until December 25 and the magnitude of the frenzy of Christmas shopping

inverse

4. The number of days until the end of the baseball season and the number of home runs that Sammy Sosa has

inverse

5. Your age and the probability that you believe in Santa Claus

inverse

6. The amount of gasoline you pump and the amount you will pay

direct

Determine whether each equation represents direct, inverse, joint, *or* combined *variation.*

7. $y = \frac{3}{x}$

inverse

8. $y = \frac{8}{x}$

inverse

9. $y = 10x^2$

direct

10. $y = 2x^3$

direct

11. $y = 3xz^4$

joint

12. $y = 6x^3z^2$

joint

13. $y = \frac{4x}{wz}$

combined

14. $y = \frac{6x}{st}$

combined

Solve each problem. See Examples 2–5.

15. If x varies directly as y, and $x = 9$ when $y = 3$, find x when $y = 12$.

36

16. If x varies directly as y, and $x = 10$ when $y = 7$, find y when $x = 50$.

35

17. If z varies inversely as w, and $z = 10$ when $w = .5$, find z when $w = 8$.

.625

18. If t varies inversely as s, and $t = 3$ when $s = 5$, find s when $t = 5$.

3

19. p varies jointly as q and r^2, and $p = 200$ when $q = 2$ and $r = 3$. Find p when $q = 5$ and $r = 2$.

$222\frac{2}{9}$

20. f varies jointly as g^2 and h, and $f = 50$ when $g = 4$ and $h = 2$. Find f when $g = 3$ and $h = 6$.

$84\frac{3}{8}$

21. For $k > 0$, if y varies directly as x, when x increases, y <u>increases</u>, and when x decreases, y <u>decreases</u>.

22. For $k > 0$, if y varies inversely as x, when x increases, y <u>decreases</u>, and when x decreases, y <u>increases</u>.

23. Explain the difference between inverse variation and direct variation.

If y varies inversely as x, x is in the denominator; however, if y varies directly as x, x is in the numerator. Also, for $k > 0$, with inverse variation, as x increases, y decreases. With direct variation, y increases as x increases.

24. What is meant by the constant of variation in a direct variation problem? If you were to graph the linear equation $y = kx$ for some constant k, what role would the value of k play in the graph?

The constant of variation is the coefficient of x. In the graph of the linear equation $y = kx$, k represents the slope of the line.

Solve each problem involving variation. See Examples 1–6.

25. Todd bought 8 gal of gasoline and paid \$13.59. To the nearest tenth of a cent, what is the price of gasoline per gallon?

$\$1.69\frac{9}{10}$

26. Melissa gives horseback rides at Shadow Mountain Ranch. A 2.5-hr ride costs \$50.00. What is the price per hour?

\$20

27. The volume of a can of tomatoes is proportional to the height of the can. If the volume of the can is 300 cm^3 when its height is 10.62 cm, find the volume of a can with height 15.92 cm.

about 450 cm^3

28. The weight of an object on Earth is directly proportional to the weight of that same object on the moon. A 200-lb astronaut would weigh 32 lb on the moon. How much would a 50-lb dog weigh on the moon? **8 lb**

29. A large federally funded research project at the University of Michigan's Institute for Social Research indicated that the higher a woman's BMI (see Example 6) in late middle age, the lower her net worth. That is, her BMI varies inversely as her net worth. This was not true for men. (*Source: Sacramento Bee,* December 13, 2000.) Suppose such a woman with a BMI of 35 has a net worth of \$10,000. According to the study results, what would be the net worth of a woman with a BMI of 38?

about \$9211

30. The frequency (number of vibrations per second) of a vibrating guitar string varies inversely as its length. That is, a longer string vibrates fewer times in a second than a shorter string. Suppose a guitar string .65 m long vibrates 4.3 times per sec. What frequency would a string .5 m long have?

5.59 vibrations per sec

31. The amount of light (measured in foot-candles) produced by a light source varies inversely as the square of the distance from the source. If the illumination produced 1 m from a light source is 768 foot-candles, find the illumination produced 6 m from the same source.

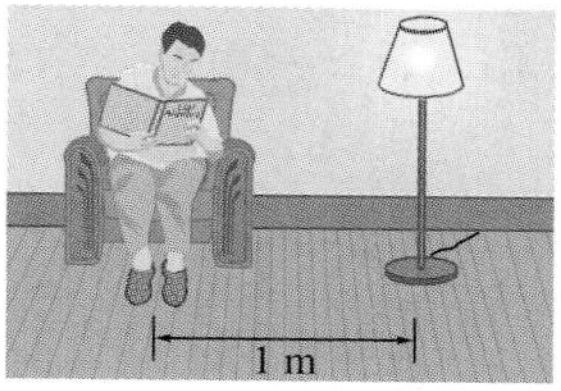

$21\frac{1}{3}$ foot-candles

32. The current in a simple electrical circuit is inversely proportional to the resistance. If the current is 20 amperes (an *ampere* is a unit for measuring current) when the resistance is 5 ohms, find the current when the resistance is 7.5 ohms.

$13\frac{1}{3}$ amperes

33. For a given interest rate, simple interest varies jointly as principal and time. If $2000 left in an account for 4 yr earned interest of $280, how much interest would be earned in 6 yr?

$420

34. The collision impact of an automobile varies jointly as its mass and the square of its speed. Suppose a 2000-lb car traveling at 55 mph has a collision impact of 6.1. What is the collision impact of the same car at 65 mph?

approximately 8.5

35. The force needed to keep a car from skidding on a curve varies inversely as the radius of the curve and jointly as the weight of the car and the square of the speed. If 242 lb of force keep a 2000-lb car from skidding on a curve of radius 500 ft at 30 mph, what force would keep the same car from skidding on a curve of radius 750 ft at 50 mph?

448.1 lb

36. Natural gas provides 35.8% of U.S. energy. (*Source:* U.S. Energy Department.) The volume of gas varies inversely as the pressure and directly as the temperature. (Temperature must be measured in *Kelvin* (K), a unit of measurement used in physics.) If a certain gas occupies a volume of 1.3 L at 300 K and a pressure of 18 newtons per cm^2, find the volume at 340 K and a pressure of 24 newtons per cm^2.

1.105 L

37. The number of long-distance phone calls between two cities in a certain time period varies jointly as the populations of the cities, p_1 and p_2, and inversely as the distance between them. If 80,000 calls are made between two cities 400 mi apart, with populations of 70,000 and 100,000, how many calls are made between cities with populations of 50,000 and 75,000 that are 250 mi apart?

approximately 68,600 calls

38. A body mass index from 27 through 29 carries a slight risk of weight-related health problems, while one of 30 or more indicates a great increase in risk. Use your own height and weight and the information in Example 6 to determine whether you are at risk.

Answers will vary.

Exercises 39 and 40 describe weight-estimation formulas that fishermen have used over the years. Girth *is the distance around the body of the fish.* (*Source: Sacramento Bee,* November 9, 2000.)

39. The weight of a bass varies jointly as its girth and the square of its length. A prize-winning bass weighed in at 22.7 lb and measured 36 in. long with 21 in. girth. How much would a bass 28 in. long with 18 in. girth weigh?

11.8 lb

40. The weight of a trout varies jointly as its length and the square of its girth. One angler caught a trout that weighed 10.5 lb and measured 26 in. long with 18 in. girth. Find the weight of a trout that is 22 in. long with 15 in. girth.

6.2 lb

RELATING CONCEPTS (Exercises 41–46) FOR INDIVIDUAL OR GROUP WORK

A routine activity such as pumping gasoline can be related to many of the concepts studied in this chapter. Suppose that premium unleaded costs \$1.75 *per gal.* ***Work Exercises 41–46 in order.***

41. 0 gal of gasoline cost \$0.00, while 1 gal costs \$1.75. Represent these two pieces of information as ordered pairs of the form (gallons, price).

(0, 0), (1, 1.75)

42. Use the information from Exercise 41 to find the slope of the line on which the two points lie.

1.75

43. Write the slope-intercept form of the equation of the line on which the two points lie.

$y = 1.75x + 0$ or $y = 1.75x$

44. Using function notation, if $f(x) = ax + b$ represents the line from Exercise 43, what are the values of a and b?

$a = 1.75, b = 0$

45. How does the value of a from Exercise 44 relate to gasoline in this situation? With relationship to the line, what do we call this number?

It is the price per gallon and the slope of the line.

46. Why does the equation from Exercise 44 satisfy the conditions for direct variation? In the context of variation, what do we call the value of a?

It can be written in the form $y = kx$ (where $k = a$). The value of a is called the constant of variation.

Chapter 8

SUMMARY

KEY TERMS

8.1	**rational expression**	A rational expression (algebraic fraction) is the quotient of two polynomials with denominator not 0.
	rational function	A rational function is a function that is defined by a rational expression in the form $$f(x) = \frac{P(x)}{Q(x)},$$ where $Q(x) \neq 0$.
8.2	**least common denominator (LCD)**	The least common denominator in a group of denominators is the product of all different factors from each denominator, with each factor raised to the greatest power that occurs in any denominator.
8.3	**complex fraction**	A complex fraction is an expression having a fraction in the numerator, denominator, or both.
8.4	**vertical asymptote**	A rational function of the form $f(x) = \frac{P(x)}{x - a}$ has the line $x = a$ as a vertical asymptote; the graph approaches the line on each side but does not intersect it.
	domain of a rational equation	The domain of a rational equation is the intersection (overlap) of the domains of the rational expressions in the equation.
8.5	**ratio**	A ratio is a comparison of two quantities using a quotient.
	proportion	A proportion is a statement that two ratios are equal.
8.6	**variation equation**	A variation equation describes how a dependent variable varies with respect to the corresponding independent variable.

TEST YOUR WORD POWER

See how well you have learned the vocabulary in this chapter. Answers follow the Quick Review.

1. A **rational expression** is
- **(a)** an algebraic expression made up of a term or the sum of a finite number of terms with real coefficients and integer exponents
- **(b)** a polynomial equation of degree 2
- **(c)** an expression with one or more fractions in the numerator, denominator, or both
- **(d)** the quotient of two polynomials with denominator not zero.

2. In a given set of fractions, the **least common denominator** is
- **(a)** the smallest denominator of all the denominators
- **(b)** the smallest expression that is divisible by all the denominators
- **(c)** the largest integer that evenly divides the numerator and denominator of all the fractions
- **(d)** the largest denominator of all the denominators.

3. A **complex fraction** is
- **(a)** an algebraic expression made up of a term or the sum of a finite number of terms with real coefficients and integer exponents
- **(b)** a polynomial equation of degree 2
- **(c)** an expression with one or more fractions in the numerator, denominator, or both
- **(d)** the quotient of two polynomials with denominator not zero.

4. A **ratio**
- **(a)** compares two quantities using a quotient
- **(b)** says that two quotients are equal
- **(c)** is a product of two quantities
- **(d)** is a difference between two quantities.

5. A **proportion**
- **(a)** compares two quantities using a quotient
- **(b)** says that two quotients are equal
- **(c)** is a product of two quantities
- **(d)** is a difference between two quantities.

QUICK REVIEW

Concepts	Examples
8.1 Rational Expressions and Functions; Multiplying and Dividing	
Fundamental Property of Rational Numbers If $\frac{a}{b}$ is a rational number and if c is any nonzero real number, then $$\frac{a}{b} = \frac{ac}{bc}.$$	$$\frac{3}{4} = \frac{3 \cdot 5}{4 \cdot 5} = \frac{15}{20}$$
Writing a Rational Expression in Lowest Terms Factor the numerator and the denominator completely. Then apply the fundamental property.	Write in lowest terms. $$\frac{2x + 8}{x^2 - 16} = \frac{2(x + 4)}{(x - 4)(x + 4)} = \frac{2}{x - 4}$$
Multiplying Rational Expressions Factor numerators and denominators. Apply the fundamental property and replace all pairs of common factors in numerators and denominators by 1. Multiply the remaining factors in the numerator and in the denominator.	Multiply. $$\frac{x^2 + 2x + 1}{x^2 - 1} \cdot \frac{5}{3x + 3} = \frac{(x + 1)^2}{(x - 1)(x + 1)} \cdot \frac{5}{3(x + 1)} = \frac{5}{3(x - 1)}$$
Dividing Rational Expressions Multiply the first rational expression by the reciprocal of the second.	Divide. $$\frac{2x + 5}{x - 3} \div \frac{2x^2 + 3x - 5}{x^2 - 9} = \frac{2x + 5}{x - 3} \cdot \frac{(x + 3)(x - 3)}{(2x + 5)(x - 1)} = \frac{x + 3}{x - 1}$$
8.2 Adding and Subtracting Rational Expressions	
Adding or Subtracting Rational Expressions If the denominators are the same, add or subtract the numerators. Place the result over the common denominator. If the denominators are different, write all rational expressions with the LCD. Then add or subtract the numerators, and place the result over the common denominator. Be sure the answer is in lowest terms.	Subtract. $$\frac{1}{x + 6} - \frac{3}{x + 2} = \frac{x + 2}{(x + 6)(x + 2)} - \frac{3(x + 6)}{(x + 6)(x + 2)} = \frac{x + 2 - 3(x + 6)}{(x + 6)(x + 2)} = \frac{x + 2 - 3x - 18}{(x + 6)(x + 2)} = \frac{-2x - 16}{(x + 6)(x + 2)}$$

Concepts | *Examples*

8.3 Complex Fractions

Simplifying a Complex Fraction

Method 1 Simplify the numerator and denominator separately, as much as possible. Then multiply the numerator by the reciprocal of the denominator. Write the answer in lowest terms.

Simplify the complex fraction.

Method 1

$$\frac{\frac{1}{x^2}-\frac{1}{y^2}}{\frac{1}{x}+\frac{1}{y}}=\frac{\frac{y^2}{x^2y^2}-\frac{x^2}{x^2y^2}}{\frac{y}{xy}+\frac{x}{xy}}$$

$$=\frac{\frac{y^2-x^2}{x^2y^2}}{\frac{y+x}{xy}}$$

$$=\frac{y^2-x^2}{x^2y^2}\div\frac{y+x}{xy}$$

$$=\frac{(y+x)(y-x)}{x^2y^2}\cdot\frac{xy}{x+y}$$

$$=\frac{y-x}{xy}$$

Method 2 Multiply the numerator and denominator of the complex fraction by the least common denominator of all fractions appearing in the complex fraction. Then simplify the result.

Method 2

$$\frac{\frac{1}{x^2}-\frac{1}{y^2}}{\frac{1}{x}+\frac{1}{y}}=\frac{x^2y^2\left(\frac{1}{x^2}-\frac{1}{y^2}\right)}{x^2y^2\left(\frac{1}{x}+\frac{1}{y}\right)}$$

$$=\frac{y^2-x^2}{xy^2+x^2y}$$

$$=\frac{(y-x)(y+x)}{xy(y+x)}$$

$$=\frac{y-x}{xy}$$

8.4 Graphs and Equations with Rational Expressions

The graph of a simple rational function may have one or more breaks. At such points, the graph will approach an asymptote.

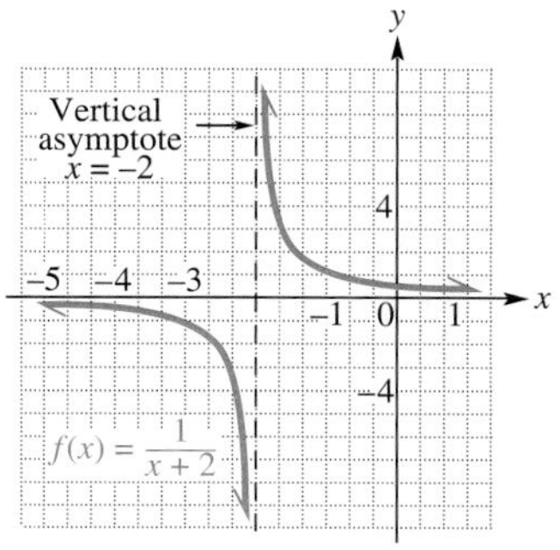

To solve an equation involving rational expressions, first determine the domain. Then multiply all the terms in the equation by the least common denominator. Solve the resulting equation. Each potential solution *must* be checked to see that it is in the domain of the equation.

Solve.

$$\frac{1}{x}+x=\frac{26}{5}$$

Note that 0 is excluded from the domain.

$$5+5x^2=26x \quad \text{Multiply by } 5x.$$

$$5x^2-26x+5=0$$

$$(5x-1)(x-5)=0$$

$$x=\frac{1}{5} \quad \text{or} \quad x=5$$

Both check. The solution set is $\{\frac{1}{5}, 5\}$.

Concepts	Examples
8.5 Applications of Rational Expressions To solve a formula for a particular variable, isolate that variable on one side.	Solve for L. $c = \frac{100b}{L}$ $cL = 100b$ Multiply by L. $L = \frac{100b}{c}$ Divide by c.
To solve a motion problem, use the formula $d = rt$ or one of its equivalents, $t = \frac{d}{r}$ or $r = \frac{d}{t}$.	A canal has a current of 2 mph. Find the speed of Amy's boat in still water if it goes 11 mi downstream in the same time that it goes 8 mi upstream. Let x represent the speed of the boat in still water. (see table below) Because the times are the same, the equation is $\frac{11}{x+2} = \frac{8}{x-2}$. Use $t = \frac{d}{r}$. $11(x-2) = 8(x+2)$ Multiply by the LCD. $11x - 22 = 8x + 16$ Distributive property $3x = 38$ Subtract $8x$ and add 22. $x = 12\frac{2}{3}$ Divide by 3. The speed in still water is $12\frac{2}{3}$ mph.
To solve a work problem, use the fact that if a complete job is done in t units of time, the rate of work is $\frac{1}{t}$ job per unit of time.	
8.6 Variation If there is some constant k such that: $y = kx^n$, then y varies directly as, or is proportional to, x^n; $y = \frac{k}{x^n}$, then y varies inversely as x^n.	The area of a circle **varies directly as** the square of the radius. $A = kr^2$ Pressure **varies inversely as** volume. $P = \frac{k}{V}$

	Distance	Rate	Time
Downstream	11	$x + 2$	$\frac{11}{x+2}$
Upstream	8	$x - 2$	$\frac{8}{x-2}$

ANSWERS TO TEST YOUR WORD POWER

1. **(d)** *Examples:* $-\frac{3}{4y^2}, \frac{5x^3}{x+2}, \frac{a+3}{a^2-4a-5}$
2. **(b)** *Example:* The LCD of $\frac{1}{x}, \frac{2}{3}$, and $\frac{5}{x+1}$ is $3x(x+1)$.
3. **(c)** *Examples:* $\frac{\frac{2}{3}}{\frac{4}{7}}, \frac{x-\frac{1}{x}}{x+\frac{1}{y}}, \frac{\frac{2}{a+1}}{a^2-1}$
4. **(a)** *Example:* $\frac{7 \text{ in.}}{12 \text{ in.}}$ compares two quantities.
5. **(b)** *Example:* The proportion $\frac{2}{3} = \frac{8}{12}$ states that the two ratios are equal.

Chapter 8 Review Exercises

[8.1] ***(a)*** *Find all real numbers that are excluded from the domain.* ***(b)*** *Give the domain using set notation.*

1. $f(x) = \dfrac{-7}{3x + 18}$

(a) -6
(b) $\{x \mid x \neq -6\}$

2. $f(x) = \dfrac{5x + 17}{x^2 - 7x + 10}$

(a) 2, 5
(b) $\{x \mid x \neq 2, 5\}$

3. $f(x) = \dfrac{9}{x^2 - 18x + 81}$

(a) 9
(b) $\{x \mid x \neq 9\}$

Write in lowest terms.

4. $\dfrac{12x^2 + 6x}{24x + 12}$

$\dfrac{x}{2}$

5. $\dfrac{25m^2 - n^2}{25m^2 - 10mn + n^2}$

$\dfrac{5m + n}{5m - n}$

6. $\dfrac{r - 2}{4 - r^2}$

$\dfrac{-1}{2 + r}$

7. What is meant by the reciprocal of a rational expression?

The reciprocal of a rational expression is another rational expression such that the two rational expressions have a product of 1.

Multiply or divide. Write the answer in lowest terms.

8. $\dfrac{(2y + 3)^2}{5y} \cdot \dfrac{15y^3}{4y^2 - 9}$

$\dfrac{3y^2(2y + 3)}{2y - 3}$

9. $\dfrac{w^2 - 16}{w} \cdot \dfrac{3}{4 - w}$

$\dfrac{-3(w + 4)}{w}$

10. $\dfrac{z^2 - z - 6}{z - 6} \cdot \dfrac{z^2 - 6z}{z^2 + 2z - 15}$

$\dfrac{z(z + 2)}{z + 5}$

11. $\dfrac{m^3 - n^3}{m^2 - n^2} \div \dfrac{m^2 + mn + n^2}{m + n}$

1

[8.2] *Assume that each expression is the denominator of a rational expression. Find the least common denominator for each group.*

12. $32b^3$, $24b^5$

$96b^5$

13. $9r^2$, $3r + 1$

$9r^2(3r + 1)$

14. $6x^2 + 13x - 5$, $9x^2 + 9x - 4$

$(3x - 1)(2x + 5)(3x + 4)$

Add or subtract as indicated.

15. $\dfrac{8}{z} - \dfrac{3}{2z^2}$

$\dfrac{16z - 3}{2z^2}$

16. $\dfrac{5y + 13}{y + 1} - \dfrac{1 - 7y}{y + 1}$

12

17. $\dfrac{6}{5a + 10} + \dfrac{7}{6a + 12}$

$\dfrac{71}{30(a + 2)}$

18. $\dfrac{3r}{10r^2 - 3rs - s^2} + \dfrac{2r}{2r^2 + rs - s^2}$

$\dfrac{13r^2 + 5rs}{(5r + s)(2r - s)(r + s)}$

[8.3] *Simplify each complex fraction.*

19. $\dfrac{\dfrac{3}{t}+2}{\dfrac{4}{t}-7}$

$\dfrac{3+2t}{4-7t}$

20. $\dfrac{\dfrac{2}{m-3n}}{\dfrac{1}{3n-m}}$

-2

21. $\dfrac{\dfrac{3}{p}-\dfrac{2}{q}}{\dfrac{9q^2-4p^2}{qp}}$

$\dfrac{1}{3q+2p}$

22. $\dfrac{x^{-2}-y^{-2}}{x^{-1}-y^{-1}}$

$\dfrac{y+x}{xy}$

[8.4]

23. Which is the graph of a rational function? What is the equation of its vertical asymptote?

A.

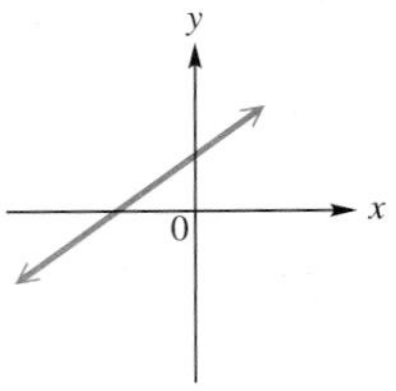

B.

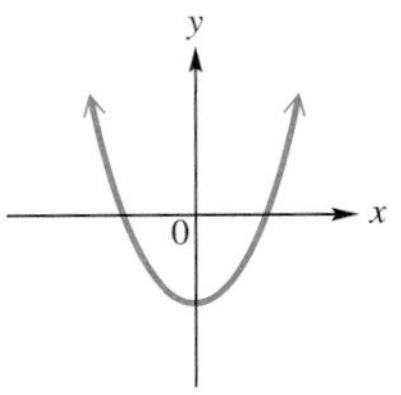

C.

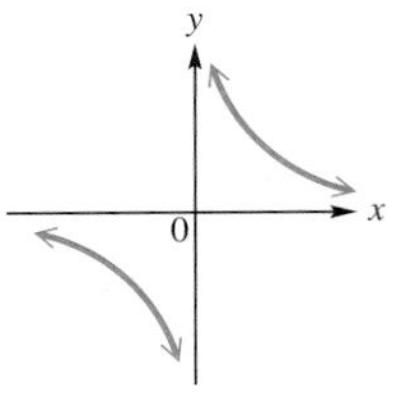

D.

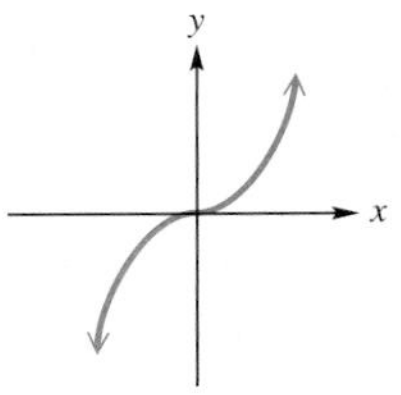

C; $x = 0$

Solve each equation.

24. $\dfrac{1}{t+4}+\dfrac{1}{2}=\dfrac{3}{2t+8}$

$\{-3\}$

25. $\dfrac{-5m}{m+1}+\dfrac{m}{3m+3}=\dfrac{56}{6m+6}$

$\{-2\}$

26. $\dfrac{2}{k-1}-\dfrac{4k+1}{k^2-1}=\dfrac{-1}{k+1}$

$\{0\}$

27. $\dfrac{5}{x+2}+\dfrac{3}{x+3}=\dfrac{x}{x^2+5x+6}$

$\emptyset$

28. After solving the equation

$$\frac{3}{x-3}-\frac{2}{x-2}=\frac{3}{x^2-5x+6},$$

a student got $x = 3$ as her final step. She could not understand why the answer in the back of the book was "$\emptyset$," because she checked her algebra several times and was sure that all her algebraic work was correct. Was she wrong or was the answer in the back of the book wrong? Explain.

Although her algebra was correct, 3 is not a solution because it is not in the domain of the equation. Thus, $\emptyset$ is correct.

29. Explain the difference between simplifying the expression

$$\frac{4}{x}+\frac{1}{2}-\frac{1}{3}$$

and solving the equation

$$\frac{4}{x}+\frac{1}{2}=\frac{1}{3}.$$

In simplifying the expression, we are combining terms to get a single fraction with a denominator of $6x$, while in solving the equation, we are finding a value for x that makes the equation true.

[8.5]

30. According to a law from physics, $\dfrac{1}{A}=\dfrac{1}{B}+\dfrac{1}{C}$. Find A if $B = 30$ and $C = 10$.

$\dfrac{15}{2}$

Solve each formula for the specified variable.

31. $F = \dfrac{GMm}{d^2}$ for m (physics)

$m = \dfrac{Fd^2}{GM}$

32. $\mu = \dfrac{Mv}{M + m}$ for M (electronics)

$M = \dfrac{m\mu}{v - \mu}$

Solve each problem.

33. An article in *Scientific American* predicts that, in the year 2050, 23,200 of the 58,000 passenger-km per day in North America will be provided by high-speed trains. If the traffic volume in a typical region of North America is 15,000, how many passenger-kilometers per day will high-speed trains provide there? (*Source:* Schafer, Andreas and David Victor, "The Past and Future of Global Mobility," *Scientific American*, October, 1997.)

6000 passenger-km per day

34. A river has a current of 4 km per hr. Find the speed of Lynn McTernan's boat in still water if it goes 40 km downstream in the same time that it takes to go 24 km upstream.

	d	r	t
Upstream	24	$x - 4$	
Downstream	40		

16 km per hr

35. A sink can be filled by a cold-water tap in 8 min, and filled by the hot-water tap in 12 min. How long would it take to fill the sink with both taps open?

$4\frac{4}{5}$ **min**

36. Jane Estrella and Jason Jordan need to sort a pile of bottles at the recycling center. Working alone, Jane could do the entire job in 9 hr, while Jason could do the entire job in 6 hr. How long will it take them if they work together?

$3\frac{3}{5}$ **hr**

[8.6] *Solve each variation problem.*

37. The amount of water emptied by a pipe varies directly as the square of the diameter of the pipe. For a certain constant water flow, a pipe emptying into a canal will allow 200 gal of water to escape in an hour. The diameter of the pipe is 6 in. How much water would a 12-in. pipe empty into the canal in an hour, assuming the same water flow? **800 gal**

38. For the subject in a photograph to appear in the same perspective in the photograph as in real life, the viewing distance must be properly related to the amount of enlargement. For a particular camera, the viewing distance varies directly as the amount of enlargement. A picture taken with this camera that is enlarged 5 times should be viewed from a distance of 250 mm. Suppose a print 8.6 times the size of the negative is made. From what distance should it be viewed? **430 mm**

39. The force with which Earth attracts an object above Earth's surface varies inversely with the square of the object's distance from the center of Earth. If an object 4000 mi from the center of Earth is attracted with a force of 160 lb, find the force of attraction on an object 6000 mi from the center of Earth.

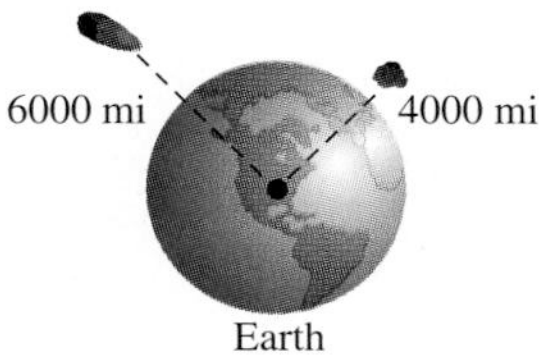

$71\frac{1}{9}$ **lb**

40. For a constant area, the length of a rectangle varies inversely as the width. The length of a rectangle is 27 ft when the width is 10 ft. Find the width of a rectangle with the same area if the length is 18 ft. **15 ft**

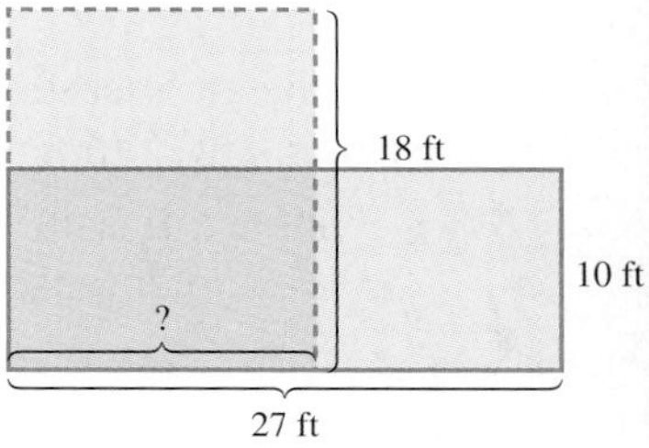

Mixed Review Exercises

Write in lowest terms.

41. $\dfrac{x + 2y}{x^2 - 4y^2}$

$\dfrac{1}{x - 2y}$

42. $\dfrac{x^2 + 2x - 15}{x^2 - x - 6}$

$\dfrac{x + 5}{x + 2}$

Perform the indicated operations.

43. $\dfrac{2}{m} + \dfrac{5}{3m^2}$

$\dfrac{6m + 5}{3m^2}$

44. $\dfrac{k^2 - 6k + 9}{1 - 216k^3} \cdot \dfrac{6k^2 + 17k - 3}{9 - k^2}$

$\dfrac{k - 3}{36k^2 + 6k + 1}$

45. $\dfrac{\dfrac{3}{x} - 5}{6 + \dfrac{1}{x}}$

$\dfrac{3 - 5x}{6x + 1}$

46. $\dfrac{9}{3 - x} - \dfrac{2}{x - 3}$

$\dfrac{11}{3 - x}$ or $\dfrac{-11}{x - 3}$

47. $\dfrac{4y + 16}{30} \div \dfrac{2y + 8}{5}$

$\dfrac{1}{3}$

48. $\dfrac{4a}{a^2 - ab - 2b^2} - \dfrac{6b - a}{a^2 + 4ab + 3b^2}$

$\dfrac{5a^2 + 4ab + 12b^2}{(a + 3b)(a - 2b)(a + b)}$

Solve.

49. $\dfrac{x + 3}{x^2 - 5x + 4} - \dfrac{1}{x} = \dfrac{2}{x^2 - 4x}$

$\left\{\dfrac{1}{3}\right\}$

50. $A = \dfrac{Rr}{R + r}$ for r

$r = \dfrac{AR}{R - A}$ or $r = \dfrac{-AR}{A - R}$

51. $1 - \dfrac{5}{r} = \dfrac{-4}{r^2}$

$\{1, 4\}$

52. The strength of a contact lens is given in units called diopters, and also in millimeters of arc. As the diopters increase, the millimeters of arc decrease. The rational function defined by

$$a = \frac{337}{d}$$

relates the arc measurement a to the diopter measurement d. (*Source:* Bausch and Lomb.)

(a) What arc measurement will correspond to 40.5-diopter lenses?

8.32

(b) A lens with an arc measurement of 7.51 will provide what diopter strength?

44.9

53. The hot-water tap can fill a tub in 20 min. The cold-water tap takes 15 min to fill the tub. How long would it take to fill the tub with both taps open?

$8\frac{4}{7}$ min

Chapter 8 TEST

1. Find all real numbers excluded from the domain of $f(x) = \dfrac{x+3}{3x^2+2x-8}$. Then give the domain using set notation.

1. $-2, \frac{4}{3}; \left\{x \middle| x \neq -2, \frac{4}{3}\right\}$

2. Write $\dfrac{6x^2 - 13x - 5}{9x^3 - x}$ in lowest terms.

2. $\dfrac{2x-5}{x(3x-1)}$

Multiply or divide.

3. $\dfrac{(x+3)^2}{4} \cdot \dfrac{6}{2x+6}$

4. $\dfrac{y^2-16}{y^2-25} \cdot \dfrac{y^2+2y-15}{y^2-7y+12}$

5. $\dfrac{x^2-9}{x^3+3x^2} \div \dfrac{x^2+x-12}{x^3+9x^2+20x}$

3. $\dfrac{3(x+3)}{4}$

4. $\dfrac{y+4}{y-5}$

5. $\dfrac{x+5}{x}$

6. Find the least common denominator for the following group of denominators: $t^2+t-6, \quad t^2+3t, \quad t^2$.

6. $t^2(t+3)(t-2)$

Add or subtract as indicated.

7. $\dfrac{7}{6t^2} - \dfrac{1}{3t}$

8. $\dfrac{9}{x-7} + \dfrac{4}{x+7}$

9. $\dfrac{6}{x+4} + \dfrac{1}{x+2} - \dfrac{3x}{x^2+6x+8}$

7. $\dfrac{7-2t}{6t^2}$

8. $\dfrac{13x+35}{(x-7)(x+7)}$

9. $\dfrac{4}{x+2}$

Simplify each complex fraction.

10. $\dfrac{\dfrac{12}{r+4}}{\dfrac{11}{6r+24}}$

11. $\dfrac{\dfrac{1}{a}-\dfrac{1}{b}}{\dfrac{a}{b}-\dfrac{b}{a}}$

12. $\dfrac{\dfrac{2}{x^2}+\dfrac{1}{y^2}}{\dfrac{1}{x}-\dfrac{1}{y}}$

10. $\dfrac{72}{11}$

11. $-\dfrac{1}{a+b}$

12. $\dfrac{2y^2+x^2}{xy(y-x)}$

13. Sketch the graph of the function defined by $f(x) = \dfrac{-2}{x+1}$. Give the equation of its vertical asymptote.

13. $x = -1$

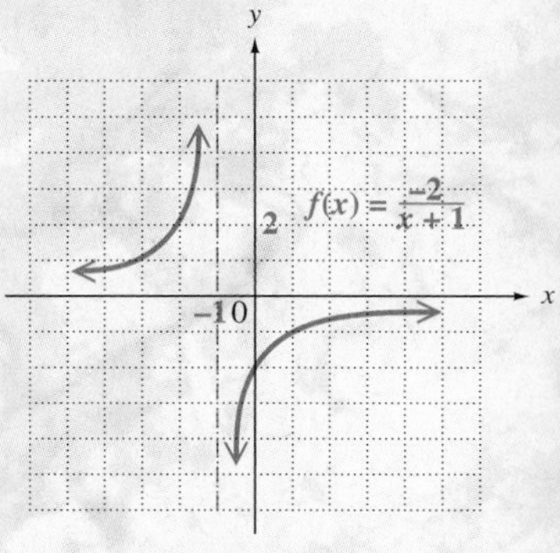

14. (a) operation; $\frac{11(x-6)}{12}$

(b) equation; {6}

15. $\left\{\frac{1}{2}\right\}$

16. {5}

17. $\ell = \frac{2S}{n} - a$ or $\ell = \frac{2S - na}{n}$

18. $3\frac{3}{14}$ hr

19. 15 mph

20. (a) 3 units

(b) 0

21. 256 ft

22. .8 lb

14. One of the following is an expression to be simplified by algebraic operations, and the other is an equation to be solved. Simplify the one that requires operations, and solve the one that is an equation.

(a) $\frac{2x}{3} + \frac{x}{4} - \frac{11}{2}$ **(b)** $\frac{2x}{3} + \frac{x}{4} = \frac{11}{2}$

Solve each equation.

15. $\frac{1}{x} - \frac{4}{3x} = \frac{1}{x-2}$

16. $\frac{y}{y+2} - \frac{1}{y-2} = \frac{8}{y^2-4}$

17. Solve for the variable ℓ in this formula from mathematics:

$$S = \frac{n}{2}(a + \ell).$$

Solve each problem.

18. Wayne can do the job in 9 hr, while Susan can do the same job in 5 hr. How long would it take them to do the job if they worked together?

19. The rate of the current in a stream is 3 mph. Nana's boat can go 36 mi downstream in the same time that it takes to go 24 mi upstream. Find the rate of her boat in still water.

20. In biology, the function defined by

$$g(x) = \frac{5x}{2 + x}$$

gives the growth rate of a population for x units of available food. (*Source:* Smith, J. Maynard, *Models in Ecology*, Cambridge University Press, 1974.)

(a) What amount of food (in appropriate units) would produce a growth rate of 3 units of growth per unit of food?

(b) What is the growth rate if no food is available?

21. For a body falling freely from rest (disregarding air resistance), the distance the body falls varies directly as the square of the time. If an object is dropped from the top of a tower 576 ft high and hits the ground in 6 sec, how far did it fall in the first 4 sec?

22. The force of the wind blowing on a vertical surface varies jointly as the area of the surface and the square of the velocity. If a wind blowing at 40 mph exerts a force of 50 lb on a surface of 500 ft^2, how much force will a wind of 80 mph place on a surface of 2 ft^2?

Cumulative Review Exercises CHAPTERS R–8

Evaluate if $x = -4$, $y = 3$, and $z = 6$.

1. $|2x| + 3y - z^3$

-199

2. $\dfrac{x(2x - 1)}{3y - z}$

12

Solve each equation.

3. $7(2x + 3) - 4(2x + 1) = 2(x + 1)$

$\left\{-\frac{15}{4}\right\}$

4. $|6x - 8| - 4 = 0$

$\left\{\frac{2}{3}, 2\right\}$

5. $ax + by = cx + d$ for x

$x = \frac{d - by}{a - c}$ or $x = \frac{by - d}{c - a}$

Solve each inequality.

6. $\frac{2}{3}x + \frac{5}{12}x \leq 20$

$\left(-\infty, \frac{240}{13}\right]$

7. $|3x + 2| \geq 4$

$(-\infty, -2] \cup \left[\frac{2}{3}, \infty\right)$

Solve each problem.

8. Otis Taylor invested some money at 4% interest and twice as much at 3% interest. His interest for the first year was \$400. How much did he invest at each rate?

\$4000 at 4%; \$8000 at 3%

9. A triangle has an area of 42 m^2. The base is 14 m long. Find the height of the triangle.

6 m

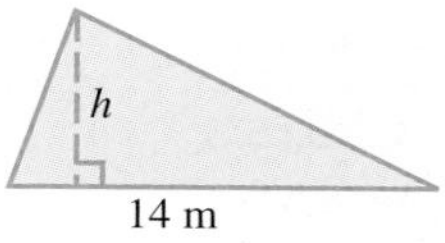

10. Graph $-4x + 2y = 8$ and give the intercepts.

x-intercept: $(-2, 0)$; y-intercept: $(0, 4)$

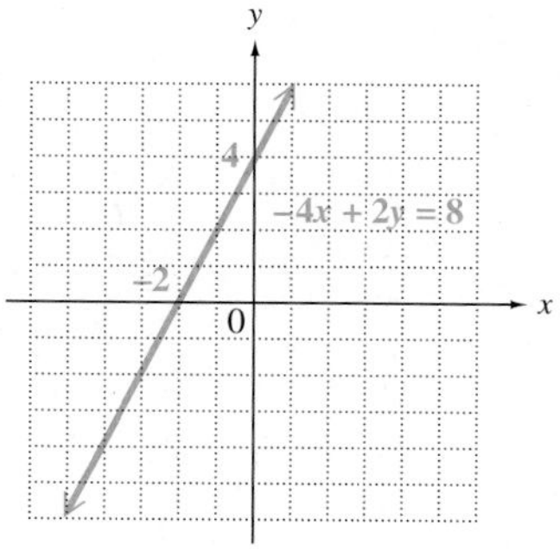

Find the slope of each line described in Exercises 11 and 12.

11. Through $(-5, 8)$ and $(-1, 2)$

$-\frac{3}{2}$

12. Perpendicular to $4x - 3y = 12$

$-\frac{3}{4}$

13. Write an equation of the line in Exercise 11 in the form $y = mx + b$.

$y = -\frac{3}{2}x + \frac{1}{2}$

Graph the solution set of each inequality.

14. $2x + 5y > 10$

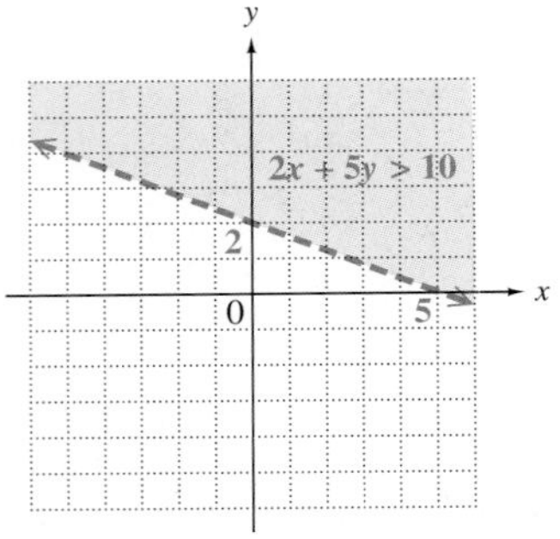

15. $x - y \geq 3$ and $3x + 4y \leq 12$

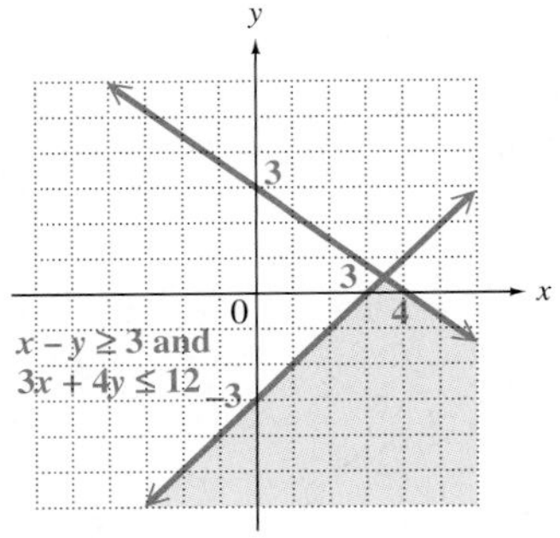

Decide whether each relation defined in Exercises 16–18 defines a function, and give its domain and range.

16. AVERAGE HOURLY WAGES IN MEXICO

Year	Wage (in dollars)
1990	1.25
1992	1.61
1994	1.80
1996	1.21
1998	1.94
2000	2.26

Source: John Christman, CIEMEX-WEFA.

function; domain: {1990, 1992, 1994, 1996, 1998, 2000}; range: {1.25, 1.61, 1.80, 1.21, 1.94, 2.26}

17.

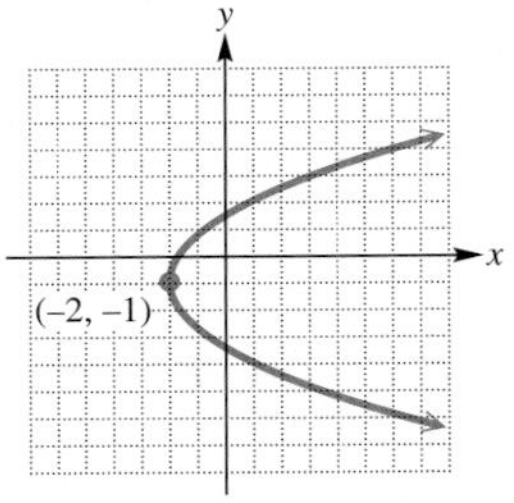

not a function; domain: $[-2, \infty)$; range: $(-\infty, \infty)$

18. $y = -x + 2$

function; domain: $(-\infty, \infty)$; range: $(-\infty, \infty)$

19. Given the equation $5x - 3y = 8$,

(a) write it with function notation $f(x)$;

$f(x) = \dfrac{5x - 8}{3}$ or $f(x) = \dfrac{5}{3}x - \dfrac{8}{3}$

(b) find $f(1)$.

-1

20. If $f(x) = 3x + 6$, what is $f(x + 3)$?

$3x + 15$

Solve each system.

21. $4x - y = -7$
$5x + 2y = 1$

$\{(-1, 3)\}$

22. $x + y - 2z = -1$
$2x - y + z = -6$
$3x + 2y - 3z = -3$

$\{(-2, 3, 1)\}$

23. $x + 2y + z = 5$
$x - y + z = 3$
$2x + 4y + 2z = 11$

$\emptyset$

24. Taking traffic into account, an automobile can travel on the average 7 km in the same time that an airplane can travel 100 km. The average speed of an airplane is 558 km per hr greater than that of an automobile. Find both speeds. (*Source:* Schafer, Andreas, and David Victor, "The Past and Future of Global Mobility," *Scientific American*, October 1997.)

automobile: 42 km per hr; airplane: 600 km per hr

Simplify. Write the answer with only positive exponents. Assume that all variables represent nonzero real numbers.

25. $\left(\dfrac{a^{-3}b^{4}}{a^{2}b^{-1}}\right)^{-2}$

$\dfrac{a^{10}}{b^{10}}$

26. $\left(\dfrac{m^{-4}n^{2}}{m^{2}n^{-3}}\right) \cdot \left(\dfrac{m^{5}n^{-1}}{m^{-2}n^{5}}\right)$

$\dfrac{m}{n}$

Perform the indicated operations.

27. $(3y^2 - 2y + 6) - (-y^2 + 5y + 12)$

$4y^2 - 7y - 6$

28. $-6x^4(x^2 - 3x + 2)$

$-6x^6 + 18x^5 - 12x^4$

29. $(4f + 3)(3f - 1)$

$12f^2 + 5f - 3$

30. $(7t^3 + 8)(7t^3 - 8)$

$49t^6 - 64$

31. $\left(\dfrac{1}{4}x + 5\right)^2$

$\dfrac{1}{16}x^2 + \dfrac{5}{2}x + 25$

32. $(3x^3 + 13x^2 - 17x - 7) \div (3x + 1)$

$x^2 + 4x - 7$

33. **(a)** Write .000076 in scientific notation.

7.6×10^{-5}

(b) Write 5.6×10^9 without scientific notation.

5,600,000,000

Factor each polynomial completely.

34. $2x^2 - 13x - 45$

$(2x + 5)(x - 9)$

35. $100t^4 - 25$

$25(2t^2 + 1)(2t^2 - 1)$

36. $8p^3 + 125$

$(2p + 5)(4p^2 - 10p + 25)$

37. Solve the equation $3x^2 + 4x = 7$.

$\left\{-\dfrac{7}{3}, 1\right\}$

Write each rational expression in lowest terms.

38. $\dfrac{y^2 - 16}{y^2 - 8y + 16}$

$\dfrac{y + 4}{y - 4}$

39. $\dfrac{8x^2 - 18}{8x^2 + 4x - 12}$

$\dfrac{2x - 3}{2(x - 1)}$

Perform the indicated operations. Express the answer in lowest terms.

40. $\dfrac{2a^2}{a + b} \cdot \dfrac{a - b}{4a}$

$\dfrac{a(a - b)}{2(a + b)}$

41. $\dfrac{x + 4}{x - 2} + \dfrac{2x - 10}{x - 2}$

3

42. $\dfrac{2x}{2x - 1} + \dfrac{4}{2x + 1} + \dfrac{8}{4x^2 - 1}$

$\dfrac{2(x + 2)}{2x - 1}$

43. Solve the equation

$$\frac{-3x}{x + 1} + \frac{4x + 1}{x} = \frac{-3}{x^2 + x}.$$

$\{-4\}$

44. Solve the formula

$$\frac{1}{f} = \frac{1}{p} + \frac{1}{q}$$

for q.

$q = \dfrac{fp}{p - f}$ or $q = \dfrac{-fp}{f - p}$

Solve each problem.

45. Lucinda can fly her plane 200 mi against the wind in the same time it takes her to fly 300 mi with the wind. The wind blows at 30 mph. Find the speed of her plane in still air.

150 mph

46. Machine A can complete a certain job in 2 hr. To speed up the work, Machine B, which could complete the job alone in 3 hr, is brought in to help. How long will it take the two machines to complete the job working together?

$1\frac{1}{5}$ hr

Roots and Radicals

9

Many real-life situations are modeled by equations of the form $y = ax^2 + bx + c$. Some common examples are the height of an object thrown upward after a given amount of time and data that change at an increasing rate, such as the number of U.S. cell-phone subscribers discussed in the exercises for Section 9.6. In such cases, if y is known and we want to find the corresponding value of x, we must solve an equation with radicals. In this chapter we will learn to work with radical expressions and solve radical equations.

9.1 Radical Expressions and Graphs

Objectives

1. Find square roots.
2. Decide whether a given root is rational, irrational, or not a real number.
3. Find higher roots.
4. Graph functions defined by radical expressions.
5. Find nth roots of nth powers.
6. Use a calculator to find roots.

In Section 1.1, we discussed the idea of the *square* of a number. Recall that squaring a number means multiplying the number by itself.

$$\text{If } a = 8, \quad \text{then} \quad a^2 = 8 \cdot 8 = 64.$$
$$\text{If } a = -4, \quad \text{then} \quad a^2 = (-4)(-4) = 16.$$
$$\text{If } a = -\frac{1}{2}, \quad \text{then} \quad a^2 = \left(-\frac{1}{2}\right)\left(-\frac{1}{2}\right) = \frac{1}{4}.$$

In this chapter, the opposite process is considered.

$$\text{If } a^2 = 49, \quad \text{then} \quad a = ?$$
$$\text{If } a^2 = 100, \quad \text{then} \quad a = ?$$
$$\text{If } a^2 = 25, \quad \text{then} \quad a = ?$$

1 Find square roots. To find a in the three preceding statements, we must find a number that when multiplied by itself results in the given number. The number a is called a **square root** of the number a^2.

Example 1 Finding All Square Roots of a Number

Find all square roots of 49.

To find a square root of 49, think of a number that when multiplied by itself gives 49. One square root is 7 because $7 \cdot 7 = 49$. Another square root of 49 is -7 because $(-7)(-7) = 49$. The number 49 has two square roots, 7 and -7; one is positive, and one is negative.

Work Problem 1 at the Side.

The **positive** or **principal square root** of a number is written with the symbol $\sqrt{}$. For example, the positive square root of 121 is 11, written

$$\sqrt{121} = 11.$$

The symbol $-\sqrt{}$ is used for the **negative square root** of a number. For example, the negative square root of 121 is -11, written

$$-\sqrt{121} = -11.$$

The symbol $\sqrt{}$, called a **radical sign,** always represents the positive square root (except that $\sqrt{0} = 0$). The number inside the radical sign is called the **radicand,** and the entire expression, radical sign and radicand, is called a **radical.**

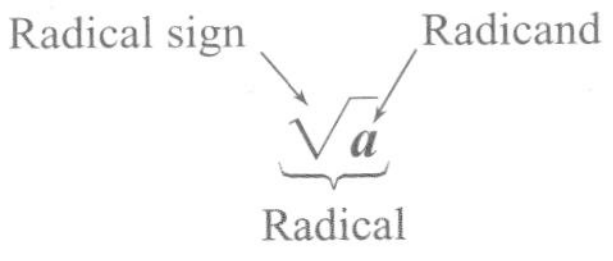

Radicals have a long mathematical history. The radical sign $\sqrt{}$ has been used since sixteenth-century Germany and was probably derived from the letter *R*. The radical symbol in the margin comes from the Latin word for root, *radix*. It was first used by Leonardo da Pisa (Fibonnaci) in 1220. (*Source:* Miller, Charles D., Heeren, Vern E., and Hornsby, John, *Mathematical Ideas*, Ninth Edition, Addison-Wesley, 2001.)

1 Find all square roots.

(a) 100

(b) 25

(c) 36

(d) $\frac{25}{36}$

Early radical symbol

Answers

1. (a) $10, -10$ **(b)** $5, -5$ **(c)** $6, -6$ **(d)** $\frac{5}{6}, -\frac{5}{6}$

Our discussion of square roots is summarized as follows.

Square Roots of *a*

If a is a positive real number,

$\sqrt{a}$ is the positive or principal square root of a,

and $-\sqrt{a}$ is the negative square root of a.

For nonnegative a,

$$\sqrt{a} \cdot \sqrt{a} = (\sqrt{a})^2 = a \quad \text{and} \quad -\sqrt{a} \cdot -\sqrt{a} = (-\sqrt{a})^2 = a.$$

Also, $\sqrt{0} = 0$.

Calculator Tip Most calculators have a square root key, usually labeled $\sqrt{x}$, that allows us to find the square root of a number. On some models, the square root key must be used in conjunction with the key marked INV or 2nd.

Example 2 Finding Square Roots

Find each square root.

(a) $\sqrt{144}$

The radical $\sqrt{144}$ represents the positive or principal square root of 144. Think of a positive number whose square is 144.

$$12^2 = 144, \quad \text{so} \quad \sqrt{144} = 12.$$

(b) $-\sqrt{1024}$

This symbol represents the negative square root of 1024. A calculator with a square root key can be used to find $\sqrt{1024} = 32$. Then, $-\sqrt{1024} = -32$.

(c) $\sqrt{\frac{4}{9}} = \frac{2}{3}$ **(d)** $-\sqrt{\frac{16}{49}} = -\frac{4}{7}$

Work Problem 2 at the Side.

2 **Decide whether a given root is rational, irrational, or not a real number.** All numbers with square roots that are rational are called **perfect squares.** For example, 144 and $\frac{4}{9}$ are perfect squares since their respective square roots, 12 and $\frac{2}{3}$, are rational numbers.

A number that is not a perfect square has a square root that is not a rational number. For example, $\sqrt{5}$ is not a rational number because it cannot be written as the ratio of two integers. Its decimal equivalent (or approximation) neither terminates nor repeats. However, $\sqrt{5}$ is a real number and corresponds to a point on the number line. As mentioned in Chapter 1, a real number that is not rational is called an *irrational number.* The number $\sqrt{5}$ is irrational. Many square roots of integers are irrational.

If a is a positive real number that is not a perfect square, then $\sqrt{a}$ is irrational.

Not every number has a *real number* square root. For example, there is no real number that can be squared to get -36. (The square of a real number can never be negative.) Because of this, $\sqrt{-36}$ is not a real number.

If a is a negative real number, $\sqrt{a}$ is not a real number.

2 Find each square root.

(a) $\sqrt{16}$

(b) $-\sqrt{169}$

(c) $-\sqrt{225}$

(d) $\sqrt{729}$

(e) $\sqrt{\frac{36}{25}}$

ANSWERS

2. **(a)** 4 **(b)** -13 **(c)** -15 **(d)** 27 **(e)** $\frac{6}{5}$

3 Tell whether each square root is *rational*, *irrational*, or *not a real number*.

(a) $\sqrt{9}$

(b) $\sqrt{7}$

(c) $\sqrt{\frac{4}{9}}$

(d) $\sqrt{72}$

(e) $\sqrt{-43}$

CAUTION

Be careful not to confuse $\sqrt{-36}$ and $-\sqrt{36}$. $\sqrt{-36}$ is not a real number since there is no real number that can be squared to get -36. However, $-\sqrt{36}$ is the negative square root of 36, which is -6.

Example 3 **Identifying Types of Square Roots**

Tell whether each square root is *rational*, *irrational*, or *not a real number*.

(a) $\sqrt{17}$

Because 17 is not a perfect square, $\sqrt{17}$ is irrational.

(b) $\sqrt{64}$

The number 64 is a perfect square, 8^2, so $\sqrt{64} = 8$, a rational number.

(c) $\sqrt{-25}$

There is no real number whose square is -25. Therefore, $\sqrt{-25}$ is not a real number.

Work Problem 3 at the Side.

3 Find higher roots. Finding the square root of a number is the inverse (reverse) of squaring a number. In a similar way, there are inverses to finding the cube of a number, or finding the fourth or higher power of a number. These inverses are the **cube root,** written $\sqrt[3]{a}$, and the **fourth root,** written $\sqrt[4]{a}$. Similar symbols are used for higher roots. In general, we have the following.

$\sqrt[n]{a}$

The *n*th root of *a*, written $\sqrt[n]{a}$, is a number whose *n*th power equals *a*. That is,

$$\sqrt[n]{a} = b \quad \text{means} \quad b^n = a.$$

In $\sqrt[n]{a}$, the number *n* is the **index** or **order** of the radical. It is possible to write $\sqrt[2]{a}$ instead of $\sqrt{a}$, but the simpler symbol $\sqrt{a}$ is customary since the square root is the most commonly used root.

Calculator Tip A calculator that has a key marked $\sqrt[x]{y}$, x^y, or y^x (again perhaps in conjunction with the INV or 2nd key) can be used to find higher roots.

When working with cube roots or fourth roots, it is helpful to memorize the first few *perfect cubes* ($2^3 = 8$, $3^3 = 27$, and so on) and the first few perfect fourth powers ($2^4 = 16$, $3^4 = 81$, and so on).

Example 4 **Finding Cube Roots**

Find each cube root.

(a) $\sqrt[3]{8}$

Look for a number that can be cubed to give 8. Because $2^3 = 8$, $\sqrt[3]{8} = 2$.

(b) $\sqrt[3]{-8} = -2$ because $(-2)^3 = -8$.

(c) $\sqrt[3]{216} = 6$ because $6^3 = 216$.

ANSWERS

3. **(a)** rational **(b)** irrational **(c)** rational **(d)** irrational **(e)** not a real number

Notice in Example 4(b) that we can find the cube root of a negative number. (Contrast this with the square root of a negative number, which is not real.) In fact, the cube root of a positive number is positive, and the cube root of a negative number is negative. *There is only one real number cube root for each real number.*

Work Problem 4 at the Side.

When the index of the radical is even (square root, fourth root, and so on), *the radicand must be nonnegative* to get a real number root. Also, for even indexes, the symbols $\sqrt{\ }$, $\sqrt[4]{\ }$, $\sqrt[6]{\ }$, and so on are used for the positive or principal roots. The symbols $-\sqrt{\ }$, $-\sqrt[4]{\ }$, $-\sqrt[6]{\ }$, and so on are used for the negative roots.

Example 5 Finding Higher Roots

Find each root.

(a) $\sqrt[4]{16}$

$\sqrt[4]{16} = 2$ because 2 is positive and $2^4 = 16$.

(b) $-\sqrt[4]{16}$

From part (a), $\sqrt[4]{16} = 2$, so the negative root $-\sqrt[4]{16} = -2$.

(c) $\sqrt[4]{-16}$

For a real number fourth root, the radicand must be nonnegative. There is no real number that equals $\sqrt[4]{-16}$.

(d) $-\sqrt[5]{32}$

First find $\sqrt[5]{32}$. Because 2 is the number whose fifth power is 32, $\sqrt[5]{32} = 2$. If $\sqrt[5]{32} = 2$, then

$$-\sqrt[5]{32} = -2.$$

(e) $\sqrt[5]{-32}$

Because $(-2)^5 = -32$, $\sqrt[5]{-32} = -2$.

Work Problem 5 at the Side.

4 Graph functions defined by radical expressions. A **radical expression** is an algebraic expression that contains radicals. For example,

$$3 - \sqrt{x}, \quad \sqrt[3]{x}, \quad \text{and} \quad \sqrt{2x - 1}$$

are radical expressions.

In earlier chapters we graphed functions defined by linear and rational expressions. Now we examine the graphs of functions defined by the radical expressions $f(x) = \sqrt{x}$ and $f(x) = \sqrt[3]{x}$.

Figure 1 shows the graph of the **square root function** with a table of selected points.

x	$f(x) = \sqrt{x}$
0	0
1	1
4	2
9	3

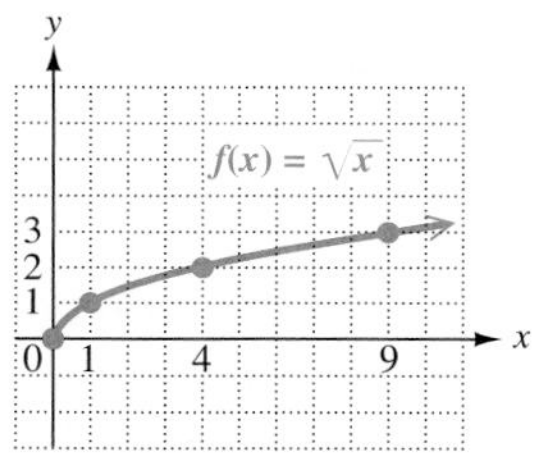

Figure 1

Only nonnegative values can be used for x, so the domain is $[0, \infty)$. Because $\sqrt{x}$ is the principal square root of x, it always has a nonnegative value, so the range is also $[0, \infty)$.

4 Find each cube root.

(a) $\sqrt[3]{27}$

(b) $\sqrt[3]{64}$

(c) $\sqrt[3]{-125}$

5 Find each root.

(a) $\sqrt[4]{81}$

(b) $\sqrt[4]{-81}$

(c) $-\sqrt[4]{625}$

(d) $\sqrt[5]{243}$

(e) $\sqrt[5]{-243}$

ANSWERS

4. **(a)** 3 **(b)** 4 **(c)** -5

5. **(a)** 3 **(b)** not a real number **(c)** -5 **(d)** 3 **(e)** -3

6 Graph each function by creating a table of values. Give the domain and range.

(a) $f(x) = \sqrt{x} + 2$

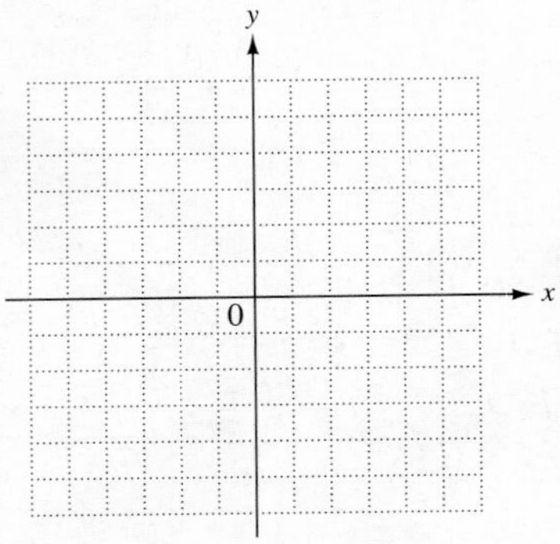

(b) $f(x) = \sqrt[3]{x} - 1$

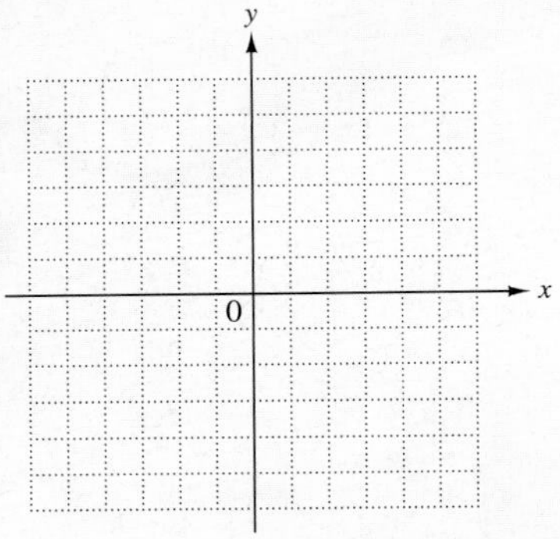

ANSWERS

6. (a) domain: $[0, \infty)$; range: $[2, \infty)$

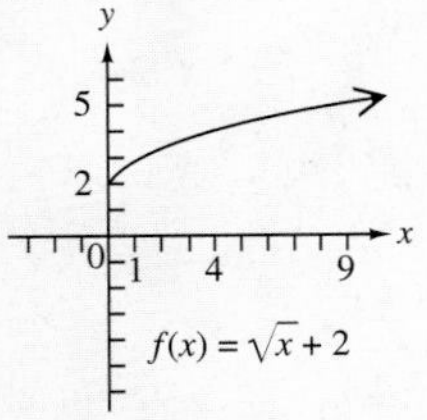

(b) domain: $(-\infty, \infty)$; range: $(-\infty, \infty)$

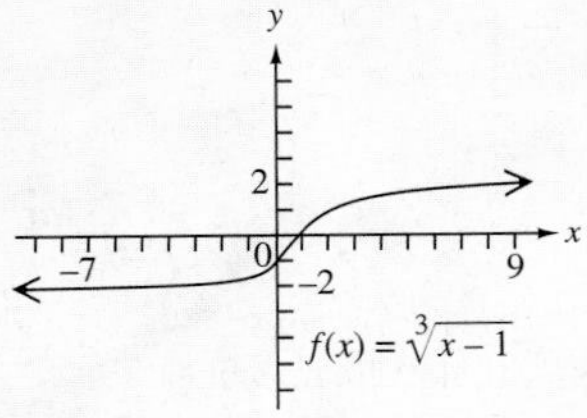

Figure 2 shows the graph of the **cube root function** and a table of selected points.

x	$f(x) = \sqrt[3]{x}$
-8	-2
-1	-1
0	0
1	1
8	2

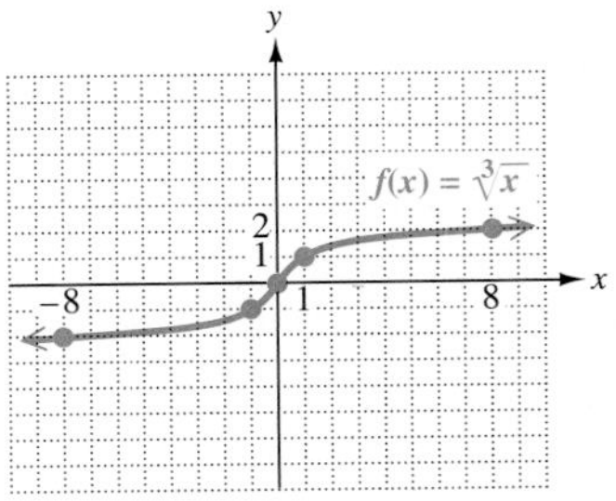

Figure 2

Since any real number (positive, negative, or 0) can be used for x in the cube root function, $\sqrt[3]{x}$ can be positive, negative, or 0. Thus both the domain and the range of the cube root function are $(-\infty, \infty)$.

Example 6 Graphing Functions Defined with Radicals

Graph each function by creating a table of values. Give the domain and the range.

(a) $f(x) = \sqrt{x - 3}$

A table of values is shown. The x-values were chosen in such a way that the function values are all integers. For the radicand to be nonnegative, we must have $x - 3 \geq 0$, or $x \geq 3$. Therefore, the domain is $[3, \infty)$. Again, function values are positive or 0, so the range is $[0, \infty)$. The graph is shown in Figure 3.

x	$f(x) = \sqrt{x - 3}$
3	$\sqrt{3 - 3} = 0$
4	$\sqrt{4 - 3} = 1$
7	$\sqrt{7 - 3} = 2$

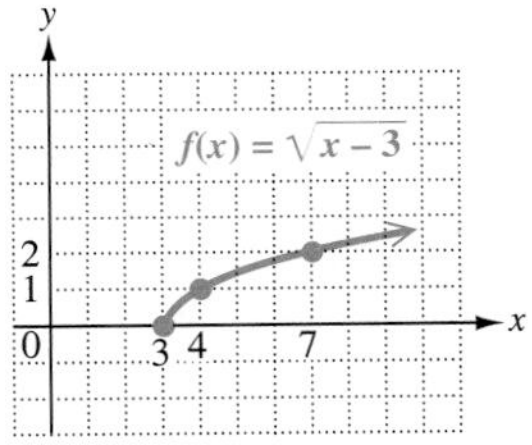

Figure 3

(b) $f(x) = \sqrt[3]{x} + 2$

See the table and Figure 4. Both the domain and the range are $(-\infty, \infty)$.

x	$f(x) = \sqrt[3]{x} + 2$
-8	$\sqrt[3]{-8} + 2 = 0$
-1	$\sqrt[3]{-1} + 2 = 1$
0	$\sqrt[3]{0} + 2 = 2$
1	$\sqrt[3]{1} + 2 = 3$
8	$\sqrt[3]{8} + 2 = 4$

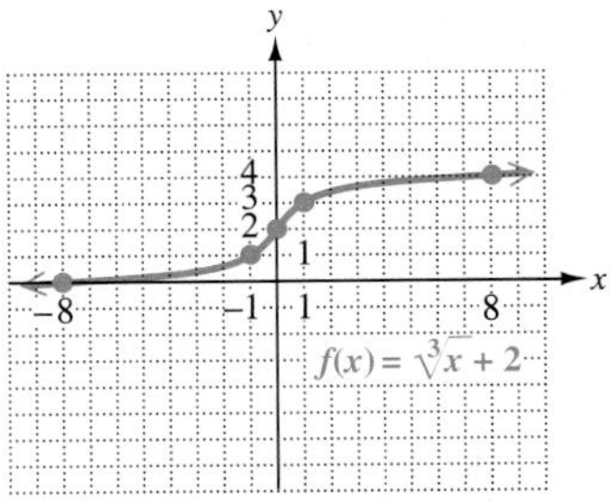

Figure 4

Work Problem 6 at the Side.

5 Find *n*th roots of *n*th powers. A square root of a^2 (where $a \neq 0$) is a number that can be squared to give a^2. This number is either a or $-a$. Since the symbol $\sqrt{a^2}$ represents the *nonnegative* square root, we must write $\sqrt{a^2}$ with absolute value bars, as $|a|$, because a may be a negative number.

$\sqrt{a^2}$

For any real number a, $\sqrt{a^2} = |a|$.

Example 7 **Simplifying Square Roots Using Absolute Value**

Find each square root that is a real number.

(a) $\sqrt{7^2} = |7| = 7$

(b) $\sqrt{(-7)^2} = |-7| = 7$

(c) $\sqrt{k^2} = |k|$

(d) $\sqrt{(-k)^2} = |-k| = |k|$

Work Problem 7 at the Side.

We can generalize this idea to any *n*th root.

$\sqrt[n]{a^n}$

If n is an *even* positive integer, $\sqrt[n]{a^n} = |a|$,

and if n is an *odd* positive integer, $\sqrt[n]{a^n} = a$.

In words, use absolute value when n is even; do not use absolute value when n is odd.

Example 8 **Simplifying Higher Roots Using Absolute Value**

Simplify each root.

(a) $\sqrt[6]{(-3)^6} = |-3| = 3$ n is even; use absolute value.

(b) $\sqrt[5]{(-4)^5} = -4$ n is odd.

(c) $-\sqrt[4]{(-9)^4} = -|-9| = -9$

(d) $-\sqrt{m^4} = -|m^2| = -m^2$

No absolute value bars are needed here because m^2 is nonnegative for any real number value of m.

(e) $\sqrt[3]{a^{12}} = a^4$, because $a^{12} = (a^4)^3$.

(f) $\sqrt[4]{x^{12}} = |x^3|$

We use absolute value bars to guarantee that the result is not negative (because x^3 can be either positive or negative, depending on x). If desired, $|x^3|$ can be written as $x^2 \cdot |x|$.

Work Problem 8 at the Side.

6 **Use a calculator to find roots.** While numbers such as $\sqrt{9}$ and $\sqrt[3]{-8}$ are rational, radicals are often irrational numbers. To find approximations of roots such as $\sqrt{15}$, $\sqrt[3]{10}$, and $\sqrt[4]{2}$, we usually use scientific or graphing calculators. Using a calculator, we find

$$\sqrt{15} \approx 3.872983346, \quad \sqrt[3]{10} \approx 2.15443469, \quad \text{and} \quad \sqrt[4]{2} \approx 1.189207115,$$

where the symbol $\approx$ means "is approximately equal to." In this book we will usually show approximations rounded to three decimal places. Thus, we would write

$$\sqrt{15} \approx 3.873, \quad \sqrt[3]{10} \approx 2.154, \quad \text{and} \quad \sqrt[4]{2} \approx 1.189.$$

Calculator Tip The methods for finding approximations differ among makes and models, and you should always consult your owner's manual for keystroke instructions. Be aware that graphing calculators often differ from scientific calculators in the order in which keystrokes are made.

7 Find each square root that is a real number.

(a) $\sqrt{6^2}$

(b) $\sqrt{(-6)^2}$

(c) $\sqrt{(-r)^2}$

(d) $\sqrt{r^2}$

8 Simplify.

(a) $\sqrt[6]{(-2)^6}$

(b) $-\sqrt[4]{2^4}$

(c) $\sqrt[5]{(-3)^5}$

(d) $\sqrt[3]{a^6}$

(e) $\sqrt[6]{(-p)^6}$

(f) $-\sqrt[6]{y^{24}}$

ANSWERS

7. **(a)** 6 **(b)** 6 **(c)** $|r|$ **(d)** $|r|$

8. **(a)** 2 **(b)** -2 **(c)** -3 **(d)** a^2 **(e)** $|p|$ **(f)** $-y^4$

9 Use a calculator to approximate each radical to three decimal places.

(a) $\sqrt{17}$

(b) $-\sqrt{362}$

(c) $\sqrt[3]{9482}$

(d) $\sqrt[4]{6825}$

ANSWERS

9. (a) 4.123 **(b)** -19.026 **(c)** 21.166 **(d)** 9.089

There is a simple way to check that a calculator approximation is "in the ballpark." Because 16 is a little larger than 15, $\sqrt{16} = 4$ should be a little larger than $\sqrt{15}$. Thus, 3.873 is a reasonable approximation for $\sqrt{15}$.

Example 9 **Finding Approximations for Roots**

Use a calculator to verify that each approximation is correct.

(a) $\sqrt{39} \approx 6.245$ **(b)** $-\sqrt{72} \approx -8.485$

(c) $\sqrt[3]{93} \approx 4.531$ **(d)** $\sqrt[4]{39} \approx 2.499$

Work Problem 9 at the Side.

9.1 EXERCISES

FOR EXTRA HELP: Student's Solutions Manual; MyMathLab.com; InterAct Math Tutorial Software; AW Math Tutor Center; www.mathxl.com; Digital Video Tutor CD 7 Videotape 17

Decide whether each statement is true *or* false. *If* false, *tell why.*

1. Every positive number has two real square roots.

true

2. A negative number has negative square roots.

False. A negative number has no real square roots.

3. Every nonnegative number has two real square roots.

False. Zero has only one square root.

4. The positive square root of a positive number is its principal square root.

true

5. The cube root of every real number has the same sign as the number itself.

true

6. Every positive number has three real cube roots.

False. A positive number has just one real cube root.

Match each expression with the equivalent choice from A–F. Answers may be used more than once.

7. $-\sqrt{16}$ E **8.** $\sqrt{-16}$ F **9.** $\sqrt[3]{-27}$ D **10.** $\sqrt[5]{-32}$ B **11.** $\sqrt[4]{81}$ A **12.** $\sqrt[3]{8}$ C

A. 3 **B.** -2 **C.** 2 **D.** -3 **E.** -4 **F.** Not a real number

Choose the closest approximation of each square root.

13. $\sqrt{123.5}$

A. 9 **B.** 10 **C.** 11 **D.** 12

C

14. $\sqrt{67.8}$

A. 7 **B.** 8 **C.** 9 **D.** 10

B

Refer to the figure to answer the questions in Exercises 15–16.

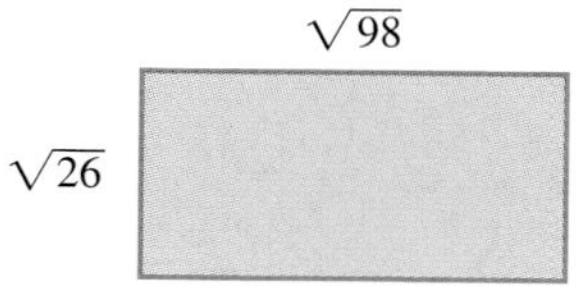

15. Which one of the following is the best estimate of its area?

A. 2500 **B.** 250 **C.** 50 **D.** 100

C

16. Which one of the following is the best estimate of its perimeter?

A. 15 **B.** 250 **C.** 100 **D.** 30

D

17. Consider the expression $-\sqrt{-a}$. Decide whether it is positive, negative, 0, or not a real number if

(a) $a > 0$, **(b)** $a < 0$, **(c)** $a = 0$.

(a) not a real number (b) negative (c) 0

18. If n is odd, under what conditions is $\sqrt[n]{a}$

(a) positive, **(b)** negative, **(c)** 0?

(a) a must be positive ($a > 0$). (b) a must be negative ($a < 0$). (c) a must be 0 ($a = 0$).

Find all square roots of each number. See Example 1.

19. 9
$-3, 3$

20. 16
$-4, 4$

21. 64
$-8, 8$

22. 100
$-10, 10$

23. 144
$-12, 12$

24. 225
$-15, 15$

25. $\frac{25}{196}$
$-\frac{5}{14}, \frac{5}{14}$

26. $\frac{81}{400}$
$-\frac{9}{20}, \frac{9}{20}$

27. 900
$-30, 30$

28. 1600
$-40, 40$

Find each square root. See Examples 2 and 3(c).

29. $\sqrt{1}$
1

30. $\sqrt{4}$
2

31. $\sqrt{49}$
7

32. $\sqrt{81}$
9

33. $-\sqrt{121}$
-11

34. $-\sqrt{196}$
-14

35. $-\sqrt{\frac{144}{121}}$
$-\frac{12}{11}$

36. $-\sqrt{\frac{49}{36}}$
$-\frac{7}{6}$

37. $\sqrt{-121}$
not a real number

38. $\sqrt{-64}$
not a real number

Write rational, irrational, *or* not a real number *for each number. If a number is rational, give its exact value. If a number is irrational, give a decimal approximation to the nearest thousandth. Use a calculator as necessary. See Examples 3 and 9.*

39. $\sqrt{25}$
rational; 5

40. $\sqrt{169}$
rational; 13

41. $\sqrt{29}$
irrational; 5.385

42. $\sqrt{33}$
irrational; 5.745

43. $-\sqrt{64}$
rational; -8

44. $-\sqrt{81}$
rational; -9

45. $-\sqrt{300}$
irrational; -17.321

46. $-\sqrt{500}$
irrational; -22.361

47. $\sqrt{-29}$
not a real number

48. $\sqrt{-47}$
not a real number

49. $\sqrt{1200}$
irrational; 34.641

50. $\sqrt{1500}$
irrational; 38.730

Find each root that is a real number. Use a calculator as necessary. See Examples 4, 5, and 8.

51. $\sqrt[3]{1}$
1

52. $\sqrt[3]{8}$
2

53. $\sqrt[3]{216}$
6

54. $\sqrt[3]{343}$
7

55. $\sqrt[3]{-64}$
-4

56. $\sqrt[3]{-125}$
-5

57. $-\sqrt[3]{512}$
-8

58. $-\sqrt[3]{1000}$
-10

59. $\sqrt[4]{1296}$
6

60. $\sqrt[4]{625}$
5

61. $-\sqrt[4]{81}$
-3

62. $-\sqrt[4]{256}$
-4

63. $\sqrt[4]{-16}$
not a real number

64. $\sqrt[4]{-81}$
not a real number

65. $\sqrt[6]{(-2)^6}$
2

66. $\sqrt[6]{(-4)^6}$
4

67. $\sqrt[5]{(-9)^5}$
-9

68. $\sqrt[5]{(-8)^5}$
-8

69. $\sqrt{\frac{64}{81}}$
$\frac{8}{9}$

70. $\sqrt{\frac{100}{9}}$
$\frac{10}{3}$

71. $\sqrt[3]{\frac{8}{27}}$
$\frac{2}{3}$

72. $\sqrt[4]{\frac{81}{16}}$
$\frac{3}{2}$

73. $\sqrt[6]{\frac{1}{64}}$
$\frac{1}{2}$

74. $\sqrt[5]{\frac{1}{32}}$
$\frac{1}{2}$

Graph each function and give its domain and range. See Example 6.

75. $f(x) = \sqrt{x+3}$

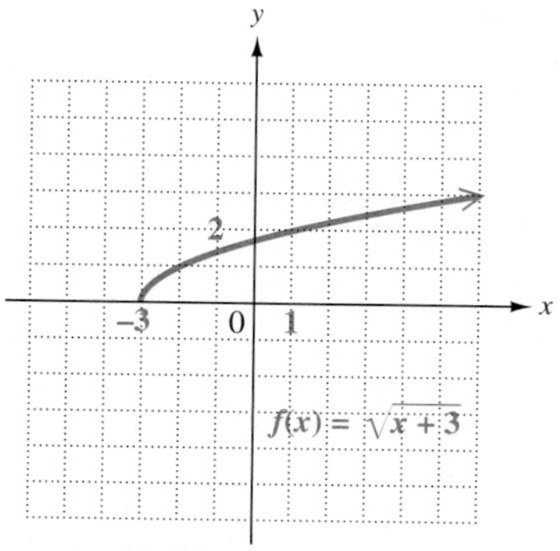

$[-3, \infty); [0, \infty)$

76. $f(x) = \sqrt{x-5}$

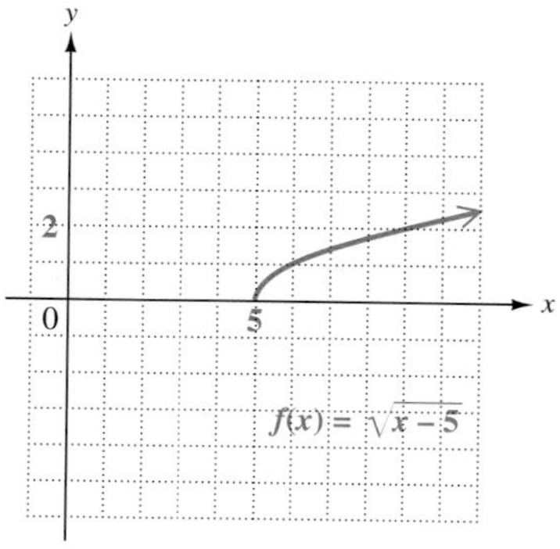

$[5, \infty); [0, \infty)$

77. $f(x) = \sqrt{x} - 2$

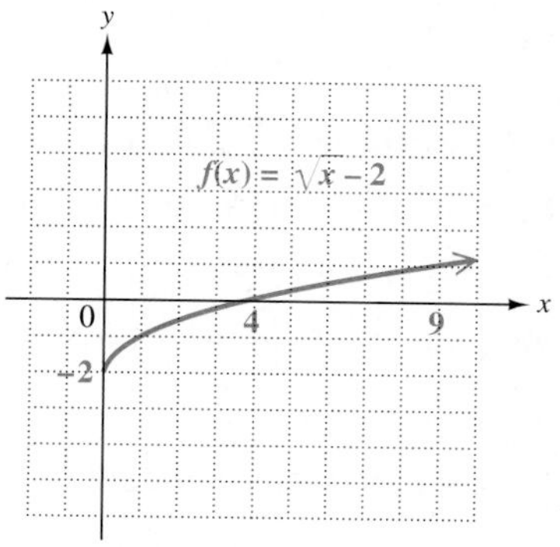

$[0, \infty); [-2, \infty)$

78. $f(x) = \sqrt{x} + 4$

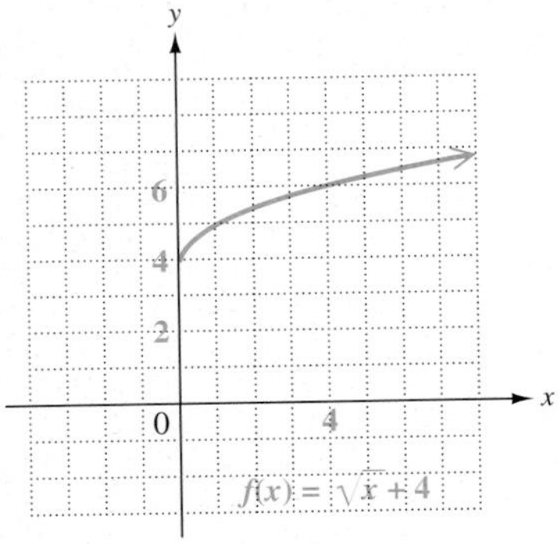

$[0, \infty); [4, \infty)$

79. $f(x) = \sqrt[3]{x} - 3$

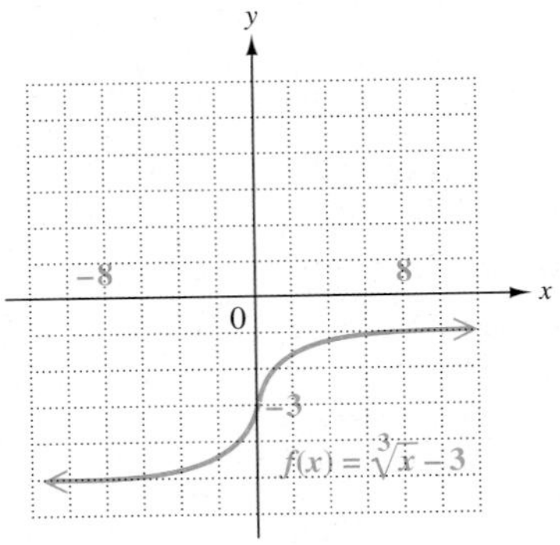

$(-\infty, \infty); (-\infty, \infty)$

80. $f(x) = \sqrt[3]{x} + 1$

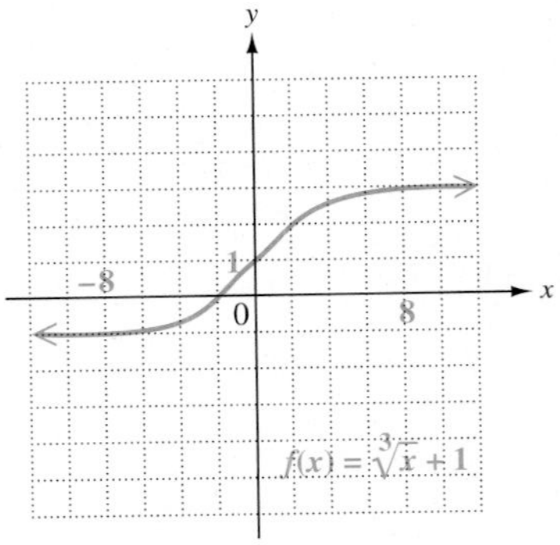

$(-\infty, \infty); (-\infty, \infty)$

Simplify each root. See Examples 7 and 8.

81. $\sqrt{x^2}$
$|x|$

82. $-\sqrt{x^2}$
$-|x|$

83. $\sqrt[3]{x^3}$
x

84. $-\sqrt[3]{x^3}$
$-x$

85. $\sqrt[3]{x^{15}}$
x^5

86. $\sqrt[4]{k^{20}}$
$|k^5|$

87. $\sqrt{x^6}$
$|x^3|$

88. $\sqrt[4]{x^{12}}$
$|x^3|$

Use a calculator to find a decimal approximation for each radical. Round answers to three decimal places if necessary. See Example 9.

89. $\sqrt{9483}$
97.381

90. $\sqrt{6825}$
82.614

91. $\sqrt{284.361}$
16.863

92. $\sqrt{846.104}$
29.088

93. $\sqrt[4]{19.4481}$
2.1

94. $\sqrt[4]{39.0625}$
2.5

95. $\sqrt[3]{3.375}$
1.5

96. $\sqrt[3]{238.328}$
6.2

RELATING CONCEPTS (Exercises 97–102) FOR INDIVIDUAL OR GROUP WORK

Every positive number has two even nth roots, the principal (positive) root and a negative root. ***Work Exercises 97–102 in order,*** *to explore connections between these roots.*

97. Find the square roots of 16.
−4 and 4

98. Find the principal square root of 16.
4

99. Find $\sqrt{16}$ and $-\sqrt{16}$.
4, −4

100. What is the solution set of $x^2 = 16$?
$\{-4, 4\}$

101. Explain what is meant by $\pm\sqrt{16}$.
$\pm\sqrt{16}$ represents the two numbers $\sqrt{16} = 4$ and $-\sqrt{16} = -4$.

102. Explain why $\sqrt{x^2}$ is simplified as $|x|$.
$\sqrt{x^2}$ is always nonnegative, so it must be simplified as $|x|$ because x may be negative.

9.2 RATIONAL EXPONENTS

1 Use exponential notation for *n*th roots. In mathematics we often formulate definitions so that previous rules remain valid. In Chapter 6 we defined 0 as an exponent in such a way that the rules for products, quotients, and powers would still be valid. Now we look at exponents that are rational numbers of the form $\frac{1}{n}$, where n is a natural number.

For the rules of exponents to remain valid, the product $(3^{1/2})^2 = 3^{1/2} \cdot 3^{1/2}$ should be found by adding exponents.

$$\begin{aligned}(3^{1/2})^2 &= 3^{1/2} \cdot 3^{1/2} \\ &= 3^{1/2 + 1/2} \\ &= 3^1 \\ &= 3\end{aligned}$$

However, by definition $(\sqrt{3})^2 = \sqrt{3} \cdot \sqrt{3} = 3$. Since both $(3^{1/2})^2$ and $(\sqrt{3})^2$ are equal to 3, we must have

$$3^{1/2} = \sqrt{3}.$$

This suggests the following generalization.

$a^{1/n}$

If $\sqrt[n]{a}$ is a real number, then

$$a^{1/n} = \sqrt[n]{a}.$$

Example 1 Evaluating Exponentials of the Form $a^{1/n}$

Evaluate each expression.

(a) $64^{1/3} = \sqrt[3]{64} = 4$

(b) $100^{1/2} = \sqrt{100} = 10$

(c) $-256^{1/4} = -\sqrt[4]{256} = -4$

(d) $(-256)^{1/4} = \sqrt[4]{-256}$ is not a real number because the radicand, -256, is negative and the index is even.

(e) $(-32)^{1/5} = \sqrt[5]{-32} = -2$

(f) $\left(\frac{1}{8}\right)^{1/3} = \sqrt[3]{\frac{1}{8}} = \frac{1}{2}$

CAUTION

Notice the difference between parts (c) and (d) in Example 1. The radical in part (c) is the *negative fourth root* of a positive number, while the radical in part (d) is the *principal fourth root of a negative number*, which is not a real number.

Work Problem 1 at the Side.

OBJECTIVES

1. Use exponential notation for *n*th roots.
2. Define $a^{m/n}$.
3. Convert between radicals and rational exponents.
4. Use the rules for exponents with rational exponents.

1 Evaluate each exponential.

(a) $8^{1/3}$

(b) $9^{1/2}$

(c) $-81^{1/4}$

(d) $(-16)^{1/4}$

(e) $64^{1/3}$

(f) $\left(\frac{1}{32}\right)^{1/5}$

ANSWERS

1. (a) 2 **(b)** 3 **(c)** -3 **(d)** not a real number **(e)** 4 **(f)** $\frac{1}{2}$

2 Evaluate each exponential.

(a) $64^{2/3}$

(b) $100^{3/2}$

(c) $-16^{3/4}$

(d) $(-16)^{3/4}$

ANSWERS
2. (a) 16 (b) 1000 (c) −8
(d) not a real number

2 Define $a^{m/n}$. How should we define a number like $8^{2/3}$? For past rules of exponents to be valid,

$$8^{2/3} = 8^{(1/3)2} = (8^{1/3})^2.$$

Since $8^{1/3} = \sqrt[3]{8}$,

$$8^{2/3} = (\sqrt[3]{8})^2 = 2^2 = 4.$$

Generalizing from this example, we define $a^{m/n}$ as follows.

$a^{m/n}$

If m and n are positive integers with m/n in lowest terms, then

$$a^{m/n} = (a^{1/n})^m,$$

provided that $a^{1/n}$ is a real number. If $a^{1/n}$ is not a real number, then $a^{m/n}$ is not a real number.

Example 2 Evaluating Exponentials of the Form $a^{m/n}$

Evaluate each exponential.

(a) $36^{3/2} = (36^{1/2})^3 = 6^3 = 216$

(b) $125^{2/3} = (125^{1/3})^2 = 5^2 = 25$

(c) $-4^{5/2} = -(4^{5/2}) = -(4^{1/2})^5 = -(2)^5 = -32$

(d) $(-27)^{2/3} = [(-27)^{1/3}]^2 = (-3)^2 = 9$

Notice how the − sign is used in parts (c) and (d). In part (c), we first evaluate the exponential and then find its negative. In part (d), the − sign is part of the base, −27.

(e) $(-100)^{3/2}$ is not a real number, since $(-100)^{1/2}$ is not a real number.

Work Problem 2 at the Side.

Example 3 Evaluating Exponentials with Negative Rational Exponents

Evaluate each exponential.

(a) $16^{-3/4}$

By the definition of a negative exponent,

$$16^{-3/4} = \frac{1}{16^{3/4}}.$$

Since $16^{3/4} = (\sqrt[4]{16})^3 = 2^3 = 8$,

$$16^{-3/4} = \frac{1}{16^{3/4}} = \frac{1}{8}.$$

(b) $25^{-3/2} = \frac{1}{25^{3/2}} = \frac{1}{(\sqrt{25})^3} = \frac{1}{5^3} = \frac{1}{125}$

(c) $\left(\frac{8}{27}\right)^{-2/3} = \frac{1}{\left(\frac{8}{27}\right)^{2/3}} = \frac{1}{\left(\sqrt[3]{\frac{8}{27}}\right)^2} = \frac{1}{\left(\frac{2}{3}\right)^2} = \frac{1}{\frac{4}{9}} = \frac{9}{4}$

Continued on Next Page

We could also use the rule $\left(\frac{b}{a}\right)^{-m} = \left(\frac{a}{b}\right)^{m}$ here, as follows.

$$\left(\frac{8}{27}\right)^{-2/3} = \left(\frac{27}{8}\right)^{2/3} = \left(\sqrt[3]{\frac{27}{8}}\right)^{2} = \left(\frac{3}{2}\right)^{2} = \frac{9}{4}$$

CAUTION

When using the rule in Example 3(c), we take the reciprocal only of the base, *not* the exponent. Also, be careful to distinguish between exponential expressions like $-16^{1/4}$, $16^{-1/4}$, and $-16^{-1/4}$.

$$-16^{1/4} = -2, \quad 16^{-1/4} = \frac{1}{2}, \quad \text{and} \quad -16^{-1/4} = -\frac{1}{2}.$$

Work Problem 3 at the Side.

We get an alternative definition of $a^{m/n}$ by using the power rule for exponents a little differently than in the earlier definition. If all indicated roots are real numbers,

$$a^{m/n} = a^{m(1/n)} = (a^m)^{1/n},$$

so

$$a^{m/n} = (a^m)^{1/n}.$$

$a^{m/n}$

If all indicated roots are real numbers, then

$$a^{m/n} = (a^{1/n})^m = (a^m)^{1/n}.$$

We can now evaluate an expression such as $27^{2/3}$ in two ways:

$$27^{2/3} = (27^{1/3})^2 = 3^2 = 9$$

or

$$27^{2/3} = (27^2)^{1/3} = 729^{1/3} = 9.$$

In most cases, it is easier to use $(a^{1/n})^m$.

This rule can also be expressed with radicals as follows.

Radical Form of $a^{m/n}$

If all indicated roots are real numbers, then

$$a^{m/n} = \sqrt[n]{a^m} = (\sqrt[n]{a})^m.$$

In words, we can raise to the power and then take the root, or take the root and then raise to the power.

For example,

$$8^{2/3} = \sqrt[3]{8^2} = \sqrt[3]{64} = 4, \quad \text{and} \quad 8^{2/3} = (\sqrt[3]{8})^2 = 2^2 = 4,$$

so

$$8^{2/3} = \sqrt[3]{8^2} = (\sqrt[3]{8})^2.$$

3 Convert between radicals and rational exponents. Using the definition of rational exponents, we can simplify many problems involving radicals by converting the radicals to numbers with rational exponents. After simplifying, we convert the answer back to radical form.

3 Evaluate each exponential.

(a) $36^{-3/2}$

(b) $32^{-4/5}$

(c) $\left(\frac{4}{9}\right)^{-5/2}$

ANSWERS

3. (a) $\frac{1}{216}$ **(b)** $\frac{1}{16}$ **(c)** $\frac{243}{32}$

4 Write each exponential as a radical. Assume all variables represent positive real numbers. Use the definition that takes the root first.

(a) $5^{2/3}$

(b) $4k^{3/5}$

(c) $(7r)^{4/3}$

(d) $(m^3 + n^3)^{1/3}$

5 Write each radical as an exponential and simplify. Assume all variables represent positive real numbers.

(a) $\sqrt{y^{10}}$

(b) $\sqrt[3]{27y^9}$

(c) $\sqrt[4]{t^4}$

Example 4 Converting between Rational Exponents and Radicals

Write each exponential as a radical. Assume that all variables represent positive real numbers. Use the definition that takes the root first.

(a) $13^{1/2} = \sqrt{13}$ **(b)** $6^{3/4} = (\sqrt[4]{6})^3$

(c) $9m^{5/8} = 9(\sqrt[8]{m})^5$ **(d)** $6x^{2/3} - (4x)^{3/5} = 6(\sqrt[3]{x})^2 - (\sqrt[5]{4x})^3$

(e) $r^{-2/3} = \dfrac{1}{r^{2/3}} = \dfrac{1}{(\sqrt[3]{r})^2}$

(f) $(a^2 + b^2)^{1/2} = \sqrt{a^2 + b^2}$ Note that $\sqrt{a^2 + b^2} \neq a + b$.

In (g)–(i), write each radical as an exponential. Simplify. Assume that all variables represent positive real numbers.

(g) $\sqrt{10} = 10^{1/2}$ **(h)** $\sqrt[4]{3^8} = 3^{8/4} = 3^2 = 9$

(i) $\sqrt[6]{z^6} = z$, since z is positive.

Work Problems 4 and 5 at the Side.

4 Use the rules for exponents with rational exponents. The definition of rational exponents allows us to apply the rules for exponents first introduced in Chapter 6.

Rules for Rational Exponents

Let r and s be rational numbers. For all real numbers a and b for which the indicated expressions exist:

$$a^r \cdot a^s = a^{r+s} \qquad a^{-r} = \frac{1}{a^r} \qquad \frac{a^r}{a^s} = a^{r-s} \qquad \left(\frac{a}{b}\right)^{-r} = \frac{b^r}{a^r}$$

$$(a^r)^s = a^{rs} \qquad (ab)^r = a^r b^r \qquad \left(\frac{a}{b}\right)^r = \frac{a^r}{b^r} \qquad a^{-r} = \left(\frac{1}{a}\right)^r.$$

Example 5 Applying Rules for Rational Exponents

Write with only positive exponents. Assume that all variables represent positive real numbers.

(a) $2^{1/2} \cdot 2^{1/4} = 2^{1/2+1/4} = 2^{3/4}$ Product rule

(b) $\dfrac{5^{2/3}}{5^{7/3}} = 5^{2/3-7/3} = 5^{-5/3} = \dfrac{1}{5^{5/3}}$ Quotient rule

(c) $\dfrac{(x^{1/2}y^{2/3})^4}{y} = \dfrac{(x^{1/2})^4(y^{2/3})^4}{y}$ Power rule

$= \dfrac{x^2y^{8/3}}{y^1}$ Power rule

$= x^2y^{8/3-1}$ Quotient rule

$= x^2y^{5/3}$

Continued on Next Page

ANSWERS

4. (a) $(\sqrt[3]{5})^2$ **(b)** $4(\sqrt[5]{k})^3$ **(c)** $(\sqrt[3]{7r})^4$ **(d)** $\sqrt[3]{m^3 + n^3}$

5. (a) y^5 **(b)** $3y^3$ **(c)** t

(d) $m^{3/4}(m^{5/4} - m^{1/4}) = m^{3/4} \cdot m^{5/4} - m^{3/4} \cdot m^{1/4}$ Distributive property

$= m^{3/4+5/4} - m^{3/4+1/4}$ Product rule

$= m^{8/4} - m^{4/4}$

$= m^2 - m$

Do not make the common mistake of multiplying exponents in the first step.

Work Problem 6 at the Side.

CAUTION

Use the rules of exponents in problems like those in Example 5. Do not convert the expressions to radical form.

Example 6 Applying Rules for Rational Exponents

Rewrite all radicals as exponentials, and then apply the rules for rational exponents. Leave answers in exponential form. Assume that all variables represent positive real numbers.

(a) $\sqrt[3]{x^2} \cdot \sqrt[4]{x} = x^{2/3} \cdot x^{1/4}$ Convert to rational exponents.

$= x^{2/3 + 1/4}$ Product rule

$= x^{8/12 + 3/12}$ Write exponents with a common denominator.

$= x^{11/12}$

(b) $\dfrac{\sqrt{x^3}}{\sqrt[3]{x^2}} = \dfrac{x^{3/2}}{x^{2/3}} = x^{3/2 - 2/3} = x^{5/6}$

(c) $\sqrt{\sqrt[4]{z}} = \sqrt{z^{1/4}} = (z^{1/4})^{1/2} = z^{1/8}$

Work Problem 7 at the Side.

6 Write with only positive exponents. Assume that all variables represent positive real numbers.

(a) $11^{3/4} \cdot 11^{5/4}$

(b) $\dfrac{7^{3/4}}{7^{7/4}}$

(c) $\dfrac{9^{2/3}(x^{1/3})^4}{9^{-1/3}}$

(d) $a^{2/3}(a^{7/3} + a^{1/3})$

7 Simplify using the rules for rational exponents. Assume that all variables represent positive real numbers. Leave answers in exponential form.

(a) $\sqrt[5]{m^3} \cdot \sqrt{m}$

(b) $\dfrac{\sqrt[3]{p^5}}{\sqrt{p^3}}$

(c) $\sqrt[4]{\sqrt[3]{x}}$

ANSWERS

6. (a) 11^2 or 121 **(b)** $\dfrac{1}{7}$ **(c)** $9x^{4/3}$

(d) $a^3 + a$

7. (a) $m^{11/10}$ **(b)** $p^{1/6}$ **(c)** $x^{1/12}$

Focus on Real-Data Applications

Windchill—A Radical Idea

When the wind blows, the air feels much colder than the actual temperature. The **windchill factor** measures the cooling effect that the wind has on one's skin. The formula that the National Weather Service uses to compute windchill is $T_{wc} = .0817(3.71\sqrt{V} + 5.81 - .25V)(T - 91.4) + 91.4$, where T_{wc} is windchill, V is wind speed in miles per hour (mph), and T is air temperature in degrees Fahrenheit. The windchill for various wind speeds and temperatures is shown in the table.

WINDCHILL FACTOR

Wind Speed (mph)	Air Temperature (°Fahrenheit) 35	30	25	20	15	10	5	0	−5	−10	−15	−20	−25	−30	−35
4	35	30	25	20	15	10	5	0	−5	−10	−15	−20	−25	−30	−35
5	32	27	22	16	11	6	0	−5	−10	−15	−21	−26	−31	−36	−42
10	22	16	10	3	−3	−9	−15	−22	−27	−34	−40	−46	−52	−58	−64
15	16	9	2	−5	−11	−18	−25	−31	−38	−45	−51	−58	−65	−72	−78
20	12	4	−3	−10	−17	−24	−31	−39	−46	−53	−60	−67	−74	−81	−88
25	8	1	−7	−15	−22	−29	−36	−44	−51	−59	−66	−74	−81	−88	−96
30	6	−2	−10	−18	−25	−33	−41	−49	−56	−64	−71	−79	−86	−93	−101
35	4	−4	−12	−20	−27	−35	−43	−52	−58	−67	−74	−82	−89	−97	−105
40	3	−5	−13	−21	−29	−37	−45	−53	−60	−69	−76	−84	−92	−100	−107
45	2	−6	−14	−22	−30	−38	−46	−54	−62	−70	−78	−85	−93	−102	−109

Source: USA Today.

If you consider the vertical columns of numbers in the table, the data represents the relationships of windchill versus wind speed for a constant air temperature. For example, if you choose one measure of air temperature to keep constant, such as 10°F, then the following data gives wind speed (V) as the *input* and windchill T_{wc} as the *output*. Wind speed is measured in miles per hour (mph).

V	4	5	10	15	20	25	30	35	40	45
T_{wc}	10	6	−9	−18	−24	−29	−33	−35	−37	−38

For Group Discussion

1. Choose a temperature of 10°F. Use the formula to calculate the windchill for wind speeds of 4, 10, 25, and 40 mph. Round the results to the nearest degree. Do your results match those in the tables? **10.1 ≈ 10; −8.6 ≈ −9; −29.0 ≈ −29; −36.8 ≈ −37; Yes.**

2. On a sheet of graph paper, sketch a graph of windchill, T_{wc}, versus wind speed, V, data for the temperature 10°F. Describe the resulting graph. Is the graph a line or a parabola, for example? **See graph shown in teacher's notes.**

3. For four representative pairs of points, calculate $\dfrac{\text{change in windchill}}{\text{change in wind speed}}$. For example, using the ordered pairs (4, 10) and (5, 6), $\dfrac{\text{change in windchill}}{\text{change in wind speed}} = \dfrac{6 - 10}{5 - 4} = -4.$

   Recall that if this ratio is constant, then the data is linearly related. Is it approximately constant? **Answers will vary depending upon pairs of points chosen. The ratio is not constant, so data is not linearly related.**

Teaching notes and an extension for this activity are provided in the *Printed Test Bank and Instructor's Resource Guide.*

9.2 EXERCISES

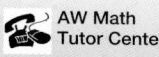

FOR EXTRA HELP — Student's Solutions Manual — MyMathLab.com — InterAct Math Tutorial Software — AW Math Tutor Center — www.mathxl.com MathXL — Digital Video Tutor CD 7 Videotape 17

Evaluate each exponential. See Example 1.

1. $169^{1/2}$ 13

2. $121^{1/2}$ 11

3. $729^{1/3}$ 9

4. $512^{1/3}$ 8

5. $16^{1/4}$ 2

6. $625^{1/4}$ 5

7. $-\left(\frac{64}{81}\right)^{1/2}$ $-\frac{8}{9}$

8. $-\left(\frac{8}{27}\right)^{1/3}$ $-\frac{2}{3}$

9. $(-27)^{1/3}$ -3

10. $(-64)^{1/3}$ -4

11. $(-100)^{1/2}$ not a real number

12. $(-81)^{1/2}$ not a real number

Match each expression with the equivalent choice from A–D.

13. $-6^{1/2}$ D

14. $-36^{.5}$ B

15. $\sqrt[4]{6^2}$ C

16. $\frac{3}{4}(4^{3/2})$ A

A. 6 **B.** -6 **C.** $\sqrt{6}$ **D.** $-\sqrt{6}$

17. Which one of the following is a positive number?

A. $(-27)^{2/3}$ **B.** $(-64)^{5/3}$ **C.** $(-100)^{1/2}$ **D.** $(-32)^{1/5}$

A

18. Explain why $(-64)^{1/2}$ is not a real number, while $-64^{1/2}$ is a real number.

$(-64)^{1/2} = \sqrt{-64}$ is not a real number because there is no real number with a negative square. However, $-64^{1/2} = -\sqrt{64} = -8$, which is a real number.

Evaluate each exponential. See Examples 2 and 3.

19. $100^{5/2}$ 100,000

20. $64^{3/2}$ 512

21. $64^{4/3}$ 256

22. $100^{7/2}$ 10,000,000

23. $64^{-3/2}$ $\frac{1}{512}$

24. $81^{-3/2}$ $\frac{1}{729}$

25. $\left(\frac{625}{16}\right)^{-1/4}$ $\frac{2}{5}$

26. $\left(\frac{36}{25}\right)^{-3/2}$ $\frac{125}{216}$

27. $\left(-\frac{8}{27}\right)^{-2/3}$ $\frac{9}{4}$

28. $\left(-\frac{64}{125}\right)^{-2/3}$ $\frac{25}{16}$

29. $\left(-\frac{4}{9}\right)^{-1/2}$ not a real number

30. $\left(-\frac{16}{25}\right)^{-1/2}$ not a real number

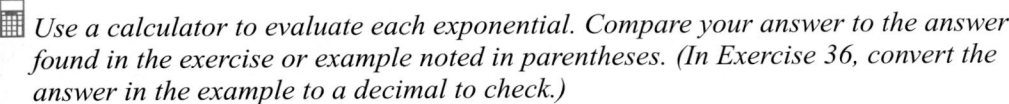

Use a calculator to evaluate each exponential. Compare your answer to the answer found in the exercise or example noted in parentheses. (In Exercise 36, convert the answer in the example to a decimal to check.)

31. $169^{1/2}$ (Exercise 1) 13

32. $121^{1/2}$ (Exercise 2) 11

33. $100^{5/2}$ (Exercise 19) 100,000

34. $64^{3/2}$ (Exercise 20) 512

35. $125^{2/3}$ (Example 2(b)) 25

36. $16^{-3/4}$ (Example 3(a)) .125, which is equal to $\frac{1}{8}$

Write with radicals. Assume that all variables represent positive real numbers. See Examples 4(a)–(f).

37. $12^{1/2}$ $\sqrt{12}$

38. $3^{1/2}$ $\sqrt{3}$

39. $8^{3/4}$ $(\sqrt[4]{8})^3$

40. $7^{2/3}$ $(\sqrt[3]{7})^2$

41. $(9q)^{5/8} - (2x)^{2/3}$ $(\sqrt[8]{9q})^5 - (\sqrt[3]{2x})^2$

42. $(3p)^{3/4} + (4x)^{1/3}$ $(\sqrt[4]{3p})^3 + \sqrt[3]{4x}$

43. $(2m)^{-3/2}$ $\frac{1}{(\sqrt{2m})^3}$

44. $(5y)^{-3/5}$ $\frac{1}{(\sqrt[5]{5y})^3}$

45. $(2y + x)^{2/3}$ $(\sqrt[3]{2y + x})^2$

46. $(r + 2z)^{3/2}$ $(\sqrt{r + 2z})^3$

47. $(3m^4 + 2k^2)^{-2/3}$ $\frac{1}{(\sqrt[3]{3m^4 + 2k^2})^2}$

48. $(5x^2 + 3z^3)^{-5/6}$ $\frac{1}{(\sqrt[6]{5x^2 + 3z^3})^5}$

Simplify each radical by rewriting it with a rational exponent. Assume that all variables represent positive real numbers. See Examples 4(g)–(i).

49. $\sqrt{2^{12}}$ 64

50. $\sqrt{5^{10}}$ 3125

51. $\sqrt[3]{4^9}$ 64

52. $\sqrt[4]{6^8}$ 36

53. $\sqrt{x^{20}}$ x^{10}

54. $\sqrt{r^{50}}$ r^{25}

55. $\sqrt[3]{a^{18}}$ a^6

56. $\sqrt[5]{k^{25}}$ k^5

Use the rules of exponents to simplify each expression. Write all answers with positive exponents. Assume that all variables represent positive real numbers. See Example 5.

57. $3^{1/2} \cdot 3^{3/2}$

9

58. $6^{4/3} \cdot 6^{2/3}$

36

59. $\dfrac{64^{5/3}}{64^{4/3}}$

4

60. $\dfrac{125^{7/3}}{125^{5/3}}$

25

61. $y^{7/3} \cdot y^{-4/3}$

y

62. $r^{-8/9} \cdot r^{17/9}$

r

63. $\dfrac{k^{1/3}}{k^{2/3} \cdot k^{-1}}$

$k^{2/3}$

64. $\dfrac{z^{3/4}}{z^{5/4} \cdot z^{-2}}$

$z^{3/2}$

65. $a^{5/6}a^{-1/3}$

$a^{1/2}$

66. $k^{-4/3}k^{2/5}$

$\dfrac{1}{k^{14/15}}$

67. $(2x^{-1/5}y^{3})^{-4}$

$\dfrac{x^{4/5}}{16y^{12}}$

68. $(64a^{3/2}b^{6})^{-2/3}$

$\dfrac{1}{16ab^4}$

69. $(27x^{12}y^{15})^{2/3}$

$9x^8y^{10}$

70. $(64p^4q^6)^{3/2}$

$512p^6q^9$

71. $\dfrac{(x^{2/3})^2}{(x^2)^{7/3}}$

$\dfrac{1}{x^{10/3}}$

72. $\dfrac{(p^3)^{1/4}}{(p^{5/4})^2}$

$\dfrac{1}{p^{7/4}}$

73. $\dfrac{m^{3/4}n^{-1/4}}{(m^2n)^{1/2}}$

$\dfrac{1}{m^{1/4}n^{3/4}}$

74. $\dfrac{(a^2b^5)^{-1/4}}{(a^{-3}b^2)^{1/6}}$

$\dfrac{1}{b^{19/12}}$

75. $x^{1/2}(2x^{1/2} - x^{-1/2} - 2x)$

$2x - 1 - 2x^{3/2}$

76. $m^{2/3}(3m^{1/3} + m^{-1/3} - 2m)$

$3m + m^{1/3} - 2m^{5/3}$

Write each expression with rational exponents. Then apply the rules for exponents. Write answers in radical form. Assume that all variables represent positive real numbers. See Example 6.

77. $\sqrt[3]{x} \cdot \sqrt{x}$

$\sqrt[6]{x^5}$

78. $\sqrt[4]{y} \cdot \sqrt[5]{y^2}$

$\sqrt[20]{y^{13}}$

79. $\sqrt[4]{49y^6}$

$y\sqrt{7y}$

80. $\sqrt[4]{100y^{10}}$

$y^2\sqrt{10y}$

81. $\dfrac{\sqrt[3]{t^4}}{\sqrt[5]{t^4}}$

$\sqrt[15]{t^8}$

82. $\dfrac{\sqrt[4]{w^3}}{\sqrt[6]{w}}$

$\sqrt[12]{w^7}$

83. $\sqrt[4]{\sqrt{m}}$

$\sqrt[8]{m}$

84. $\sqrt[3]{\sqrt[3]{k}}$

$\sqrt[9]{k}$

RELATING CONCEPTS (Exercises 85–90) FOR INDIVIDUAL OR GROUP WORK

Earlier, we factored expressions like $x^4 - x^5$ by factoring out the greatest common factor to get $x^4 - x^5 = x^4(1 - x)$. We can adapt this approach to factor expressions with rational exponents. When one or more of the exponents is negative or a fraction, we use order on the number line discussed in Chapter 1 to decide on the common factor. In this type of factoring, we want the binomial factor to have only positive exponents, so we always factor out the variable with the least *exponent. A positive exponent is greater than a negative exponent, so in $7z^{5/8} + z^{-3/4}$, we factor out $z^{-3/4}$, because $-3/4$ is less than $5/8$.*

Work Exercises 85–90 in order.

Find the appropriate common factor in each expression.

85. $3x^{-1/2} - 4x^{1/2}$

$x^{-1/2}$

86. $m^3 - 3m^{5/2}$

$m^{5/2}$

87. $9k^{-3/4} + 2k^{-1/4}$

$k^{-3/4}$

Factor each expression.

88. $3x^{-1/2} - 4x^{1/2}$

$x^{-1/2}(3 - 4x)$

89. $m^3 - 3m^{5/2}$

$m^{5/2}(m^{1/2} - 3)$

90. $9k^{-3/4} + 2k^{-1/4}$

$k^{-3/4}(9 + 2k^{1/2})$

Solve each problem.

91. Meteorologists can determine the duration of a storm by using the function defined by

$$T(D) = .07D^{3/2},$$

where D is the diameter of the storm in miles and T is the time in hours. Find the duration of a storm with a diameter of 16 mi. Round your answer to the nearest tenth of an hour.

4.5 hr

92. The threshold weight T, in pounds, for a person is the weight above which the risk of death increases greatly. The threshold weight in pounds for men aged 40–49 is related to height in inches by the function defined by

$$h(T) = 12.3T^{1/3}.$$

What height corresponds to a threshold weight of 216 lb for a 43-yr-old man? Round your answer to the nearest inch, and then to the nearest tenth of a foot.

74 in.; 6.2 ft

9.3 Simplifying Radical Expressions

1 Use the product rule for radicals. We now develop rules for multiplying and dividing radicals that have the same index. For example, is the product of two *n*th-root radicals equal to the *n*th root of the product of the radicands? Is $\sqrt{36 \cdot 4} = \sqrt{36} \cdot \sqrt{4}$? To find out, we simply do the computations:

$$\sqrt{36 \cdot 4} = \sqrt{144} = 12$$
$$\sqrt{36} \cdot \sqrt{4} = 6 \cdot 2 = 12.$$

Notice that in both cases the result is the same. This is an example of the **product rule for radicals.**

Product Rule for Radicals

If $\sqrt[n]{a}$ and $\sqrt[n]{b}$ are real numbers and n is a natural number,

$$\sqrt[n]{a} \cdot \sqrt[n]{b} = \sqrt[n]{ab}.$$

In words, the product of two radicals is the radical of the product.

We justify the product rule using the rules for rational exponents. Since $\sqrt[n]{a} = a^{1/n}$ and $\sqrt[n]{b} = b^{1/n}$,

$$\sqrt[n]{a} \cdot \sqrt[n]{b} = a^{1/n} \cdot b^{1/n} = (ab)^{1/n} = \sqrt[n]{ab}.$$

CAUTION

Use the product rule only when the radicals have the *same* indexes.

Example 1 Using the Product Rule

Multiply. Assume that all variables represent positive real numbers.

(a) $\sqrt{5} \cdot \sqrt{7} = \sqrt{5 \cdot 7} = \sqrt{35}$

(b) $\sqrt{2} \cdot \sqrt{19} = \sqrt{2 \cdot 19} = \sqrt{38}$

(c) $\sqrt{11} \cdot \sqrt{p} = \sqrt{11p}$

(d) $\sqrt{7} \cdot \sqrt{11xyz} = \sqrt{77xyz}$

Work Problem 1 at the Side.

Example 2 Using the Product Rule

Multiply. Assume that all variables represent positive real numbers.

(a) $\sqrt[3]{3} \cdot \sqrt[3]{12} = \sqrt[3]{3 \cdot 12} = \sqrt[3]{36}$

(b) $\sqrt[4]{8y} \cdot \sqrt[4]{3r^2} = \sqrt[4]{24yr^2}$

(c) $\sqrt[6]{10m^4} \cdot \sqrt[6]{5m} = \sqrt[6]{50m^5}$

(d) $\sqrt[4]{2} \cdot \sqrt[5]{2}$ cannot be simplified using the product rule for radicals, because the indexes (4 and 5) are different.

Work Problem 2 at the Side.

Objectives

1. Use the product rule for radicals.
2. Use the quotient rule for radicals.
3. Simplify radicals.
4. Simplify products and quotients of radicals with different indexes.
5. Use the Pythagorean formula.
6. Use the distance formula.

1 Multiply. Assume that all variables represent positive real numbers.

(a) $\sqrt{5} \cdot \sqrt{13}$

(b) $\sqrt{10y} \cdot \sqrt{3k}$

(c) $\sqrt{\frac{5}{a}} \cdot \sqrt{\frac{11}{z}}$

2 Multiply. Assume that all variables represent positive real numbers.

(a) $\sqrt[3]{2} \cdot \sqrt[3]{7}$

(b) $\sqrt[6]{8r^2} \cdot \sqrt[6]{2r^3}$

(c) $\sqrt[5]{9y^2x} \cdot \sqrt[5]{8xy^2}$

(d) $\sqrt{7} \cdot \sqrt[3]{5}$

Answers

1. (a) $\sqrt{65}$ **(b)** $\sqrt{30yk}$ **(c)** $\sqrt{\frac{55}{az}}$

2. (a) $\sqrt[3]{14}$ **(b)** $\sqrt[6]{16r^5}$ **(c)** $\sqrt[5]{72y^4x^2}$
(d) cannot be simplified using the product rule

3 Simplify. Assume that all variables represent positive real numbers.

(a) $\sqrt{\dfrac{100}{81}}$

(b) $\sqrt{\dfrac{11}{25}}$

(c) $\sqrt[3]{\dfrac{18}{125}}$

(d) $\sqrt{\dfrac{y^8}{16}}$

(e) $\sqrt[3]{\dfrac{x^2}{r^{12}}}$

ANSWERS

3. (a) $\dfrac{10}{9}$ (b) $\dfrac{\sqrt{11}}{5}$ (c) $\dfrac{\sqrt[3]{18}}{5}$ (d) $\dfrac{y^4}{4}$ (e) $\dfrac{\sqrt[3]{x^2}}{r^4}$

2 Use the quotient rule for radicals. The quotient rule for radicals is similar to the product rule.

Quotient Rule for Radicals

If $\sqrt[n]{a}$ and $\sqrt[n]{b}$ are real numbers, $b \neq 0$, and n is a natural number, then

$$\sqrt[n]{\frac{a}{b}} = \frac{\sqrt[n]{a}}{\sqrt[n]{b}}.$$

In words, the radical of a quotient is the quotient of the radicals.

Example 3 Using the Quotient Rule

Simplify. Assume that all variables represent positive real numbers.

(a) $\sqrt{\dfrac{16}{25}} = \dfrac{\sqrt{16}}{\sqrt{25}} = \dfrac{4}{5}$

(b) $\sqrt{\dfrac{7}{36}} = \dfrac{\sqrt{7}}{\sqrt{36}} = \dfrac{\sqrt{7}}{6}$

(c) $\sqrt[3]{-\dfrac{8}{125}} = \sqrt[3]{\dfrac{-8}{125}} = \dfrac{\sqrt[3]{-8}}{\sqrt[3]{125}} = \dfrac{-2}{5} = -\dfrac{2}{5}$

(d) $\sqrt[3]{\dfrac{7}{216}} = \dfrac{\sqrt[3]{7}}{\sqrt[3]{216}} = \dfrac{\sqrt[3]{7}}{6}$

(e) $\sqrt[5]{\dfrac{x}{32}} = \dfrac{\sqrt[5]{x}}{\sqrt[5]{32}} = \dfrac{\sqrt[5]{x}}{2}$

(f) $\sqrt[3]{\dfrac{m^6}{125}} = \dfrac{\sqrt[3]{m^6}}{\sqrt[3]{125}} = \dfrac{m^2}{5}$

Work Problem 3 at the Side.

3 Simplify radicals. We use the product and quotient rules to simplify radicals. A radical is **simplified** if the following four conditions are met.

Simplified Radical

1. The radicand has no factor raised to a power greater than or equal to the index.
2. The radicand has no fractions.
3. No denominator contains a radical.
4. Exponents in the radicand and the index of the radical have no common factor (except 1).

Example 4 Simplifying Roots of Numbers

Simplify.

(a) $\sqrt{24}$

Check to see whether 24 is divisible by a perfect square (the square of a natural number) such as 4, 9, ... Choose the largest perfect square that divides into 24. The largest such number is 4. Write 24 as the product of 4 and 6, and then use the product rule.

$$\sqrt{24} = \sqrt{4 \cdot 6} = \sqrt{4} \cdot \sqrt{6} = 2\sqrt{6}$$

Continued on Next Page

(b) $\sqrt{108}$

The number 108 is divisible by the perfect square 36: $\sqrt{108} = \sqrt{36 \cdot 3}$. If this is not obvious, try factoring 108 into its prime factors.

$$\begin{aligned}\sqrt{108} &= \sqrt{2^2 \cdot 3^3} \\ &= \sqrt{2^2 \cdot 3^2 \cdot 3} \\ &= 2 \cdot 3 \cdot \sqrt{3} \qquad \text{Product rule} \\ &= 6\sqrt{3}\end{aligned}$$

(c) $\sqrt{10}$

No perfect square (other than 1) divides into 10, so $\sqrt{10}$ cannot be simplified further.

(d) $\sqrt[3]{16}$

Look for the largest perfect *cube* that divides into 16. The number 8 satisfies this condition, so write 16 as $8 \cdot 2$ (or factor 16 into prime factors).

$$\sqrt[3]{16} = \sqrt[3]{8 \cdot 2} = \sqrt[3]{8} \cdot \sqrt[3]{2} = 2\sqrt[3]{2}$$

(e) $$\begin{aligned}\sqrt[4]{162} &= \sqrt[4]{81 \cdot 2} \qquad \text{81 is a perfect 4th power.} \\ &= \sqrt[4]{81} \cdot \sqrt[4]{2} \qquad \text{Product rule} \\ &= 3\sqrt[4]{2}\end{aligned}$$

CAUTION

In simplifying an expression like that in Example 4(b), be careful with which factors belong *outside* the radical sign and which belong *inside*. Note how $2 \cdot 3$ is written outside because $\sqrt{2^2} = 2$ and $\sqrt{3^2} = 3$, while the remaining 3 is left inside the radical.

Work Problem 4 at the Side.

4 Simplify.

(a) $\sqrt{32}$

(b) $\sqrt{45}$

(c) $\sqrt{300}$

(d) $\sqrt{35}$

(e) $\sqrt[3]{54}$

(f) $\sqrt[4]{243}$

Example 5 Simplifying Radicals Involving Variables

Simplify. Assume that all variables represent positive real numbers.

(a) $$\begin{aligned}\sqrt{16m^3} &= \sqrt{16m^2 \cdot m} \\ &= \sqrt{16m^2} \cdot \sqrt{m} \\ &= 4m\sqrt{m}\end{aligned}$$

No absolute value bars are needed around the m in color because of the assumption that all the variables represent *positive* real numbers.

(b) $$\begin{aligned}\sqrt{200k^7q^8} &= \sqrt{10^2 \cdot 2 \cdot (k^3)^2 \cdot k \cdot (q^4)^2} \qquad \text{Factor.} \\ &= 10k^3q^4\sqrt{2k} \qquad \text{Remove perfect square factors.}\end{aligned}$$

(c) $$\begin{aligned}\sqrt[3]{8x^4y^5} &= \sqrt[3]{(8x^3y^3)(xy^2)} \qquad 8x^3y^3 \text{ is the largest perfect cube that divides } 8x^4y^5. \\ &= \sqrt[3]{8x^3y^3} \cdot \sqrt[3]{xy^2} \\ &= 2xy\sqrt[3]{xy^2}\end{aligned}$$

(d) $$\begin{aligned}\sqrt[4]{32y^9} &= \sqrt[4]{(16y^8)(2y)} \qquad 16y^8 \text{ is the largest 4th power that divides } 32y^9. \\ &= \sqrt[4]{16y^8} \cdot \sqrt[4]{2y} \\ &= 2y^2\sqrt[4]{2y}\end{aligned}$$

ANSWERS

4. **(a)** $4\sqrt{2}$ **(b)** $3\sqrt{5}$ **(c)** $10\sqrt{3}$ **(d)** cannot be simplified further **(e)** $3\sqrt[3]{2}$ **(f)** $3\sqrt[4]{3}$

5 Simplify. Assume that all variables represent positive real numbers.

(a) $\sqrt{25p^7}$

(b) $\sqrt{72y^3x}$

(c) $\sqrt[3]{y^7x^5z^6}$

(d) $\sqrt[4]{32a^5b^7}$

6 Simplify. Assume that all variables represent positive real numbers.

(a) $\sqrt[12]{2^3}$

(b) $\sqrt[6]{t^2}$

7 Simplify $\sqrt{5} \cdot \sqrt[3]{4}$.

ANSWERS

5. **(a)** $5p^3\sqrt{p}$ **(b)** $6y\sqrt{2yx}$ **(c)** $y^2xz^2\sqrt[3]{yx^2}$ **(d)** $2ab\sqrt[4]{2ab^3}$

6. **(a)** $\sqrt[4]{2}$ **(b)** $\sqrt[3]{t}$

7. $\sqrt[6]{2000}$

NOTE

From Example 5 we see that if a variable is raised to a power with an exponent divisible by 2, it is a perfect square. If it is raised to a power with an exponent divisible by 3, it is a perfect cube. In general, if it is raised to a power with an exponent divisible by n, it is a perfect nth power.

Work Problem 5 at the Side.

The conditions for a simplified radical given earlier state that an exponent in the radicand and the index of the radical should have no common factor (except 1). The next example shows how to simplify radicals with such common factors.

Example 6 Simplifying Radicals by Using Smaller Indexes

Simplify. Assume that all variables represent positive real numbers.

(a) $\sqrt[9]{5^6}$

We can write this radical using rational exponents and then write the exponent in lowest terms. We then express the answer as a radical.

$$\sqrt[9]{5^6} = 5^{6/9} = 5^{2/3} = \sqrt[3]{5^2} \quad \text{or} \quad \sqrt[3]{25}$$

(b) $\sqrt[4]{p^2} = p^{2/4} = p^{1/2} = \sqrt{p}$ (Recall the assumption that $p > 0$.)

These examples suggest the following rule.

If m is an integer, n and k are natural numbers, and all indicated roots exist,

$$\sqrt[kn]{a^{km}} = \sqrt[n]{a^m}.$$

Work Problem 6 at the Side.

4 **Simplify products and quotients of radicals with different indexes.** Since the product and quotient rules for radicals apply only when they have the same index, we multiply and divide radicals with different indexes by using rational exponents.

Example 7 Multiplying Radicals with Different Indexes

Simplify $\sqrt{7} \cdot \sqrt[3]{2}$.

Because the different indexes, 2 and 3, have a least common index of 6, use rational exponents to write each radical as a sixth root.

$$\sqrt{7} = 7^{1/2} = 7^{3/6} = \sqrt[6]{7^3} = \sqrt[6]{343}$$

$$\sqrt[3]{2} = 2^{1/3} = 2^{2/6} = \sqrt[6]{2^2} = \sqrt[6]{4}$$

Therefore,

$$\sqrt{7} \cdot \sqrt[3]{2} = \sqrt[6]{343} \cdot \sqrt[6]{4} = \sqrt[6]{1372}. \quad \text{Product rule}$$

Work Problem 7 at the Side.

5 **Use the Pythagorean formula.** The **Pythagorean formula** relates the lengths of the three sides of a right triangle.

Pythagorean Formula

If c is the length of the longest side of a right triangle and a and b are the lengths of the shorter sides, then

$$c^2 = a^2 + b^2.$$

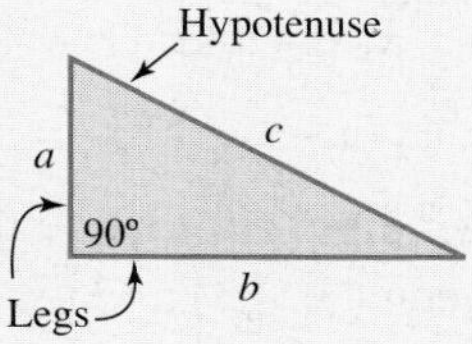

The longest side is the **hypotenuse** and the two shorter sides are the **legs** of the triangle. The hypotenuse is the side opposite the right angle.

Example 8 Using the Pythagorean Formula

Use the Pythagorean formula to find the length of the hypotenuse in the triangle in Figure 5.

To find the length of the hypotenuse c, let $a = 4$ and $b = 6$. Then, use the formula.

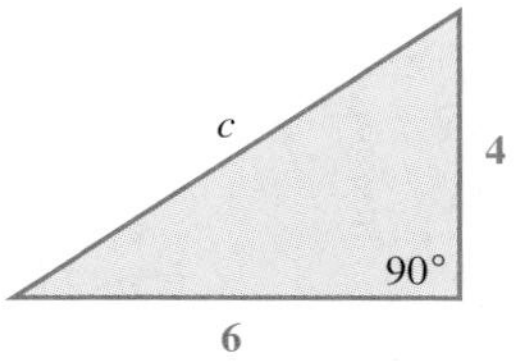

Figure 5

$$c^2 = a^2 + b^2$$
$$c^2 = 4^2 + 6^2 \quad \text{Let } a = 4 \text{ and } b = 6.$$
$$c^2 = 52$$
$$c = \sqrt{52} \quad \text{Choose the principal root.}$$
$$c = \sqrt{4 \cdot 13} \quad \text{Factor.}$$
$$c = \sqrt{4} \cdot \sqrt{13} \quad \text{Product rule}$$
$$c = 2\sqrt{13}$$

The length of the hypotenuse is $2\sqrt{13}$.

Work Problem 8 at the Side.

6 **Use the distance formula.** An important result in algebra is derived by using the Pythagorean formula. The **distance formula** allows us to find the distance between two points in the coordinate plane, or the length of the line segment joining those two points. Figure 6 on the next page shows the points $(3, -4)$ and $(-5, 3)$. The vertical line through $(-5, 3)$ and the horizontal line through $(3, -4)$ intersect at the point $(-5, -4)$. Thus, the point $(-5, -4)$ becomes the vertex of the right angle in a right triangle. By the Pythagorean formula, the square of the length of the hypotenuse, d, of the right triangle in Figure 6 is equal to the sum of the squares of the lengths of the two legs a and b:

$$d^2 = a^2 + b^2.$$

The length a is the difference between the y-coordinates of the endpoints. Since the x-coordinate of both points is -5, the side is vertical, and we can find a by finding the difference between the y-coordinates. We subtract -4 from 3 to get a positive value for a.

$$a = 3 - (-4) = 7$$

8 Find the length of the unknown side in each triangle.

(a)

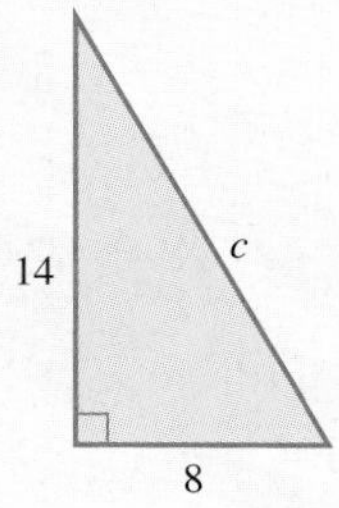

(b)

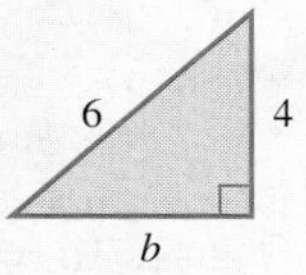

(*Hint:* Write the Pythagorean formula as $b^2 = c^2 - a^2$ here.)

ANSWERS

8. **(a)** $2\sqrt{65}$ **(b)** $2\sqrt{5}$

9 Find the distance between each pair of points.

(a) $(2, -1)$ and $(5, 3)$

(b) $(-3, 2)$ and $(0, -4)$

Similarly, we find b by subtracting -5 from 3.

$$b = 3 - (-5) = \mathbf{8}$$

Substituting these values into the formula, we have

$$d^2 = a^2 + b^2$$
$$d^2 = 7^2 + \mathbf{8}^2 \quad \text{Let } a = 7 \text{ and } \mathbf{b = 8}.$$
$$d^2 = 49 + 64$$
$$d^2 = 113$$
$$d = \sqrt{113}.$$

We choose the principal root since distance cannot be negative. Therefore, the distance between $(-5, 3)$ and $(3, -4)$ is $\sqrt{113}$.

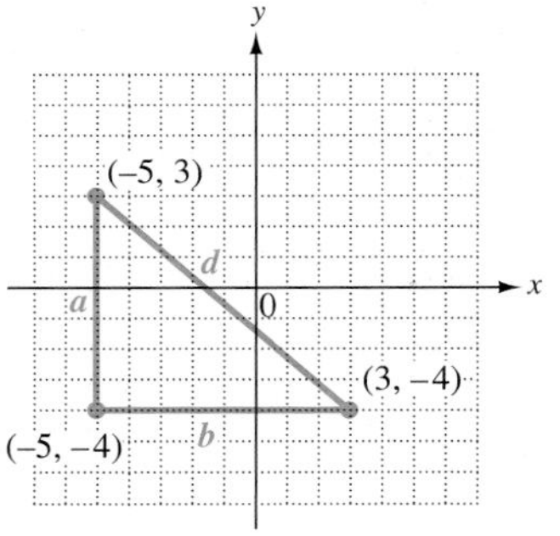

Figure 6

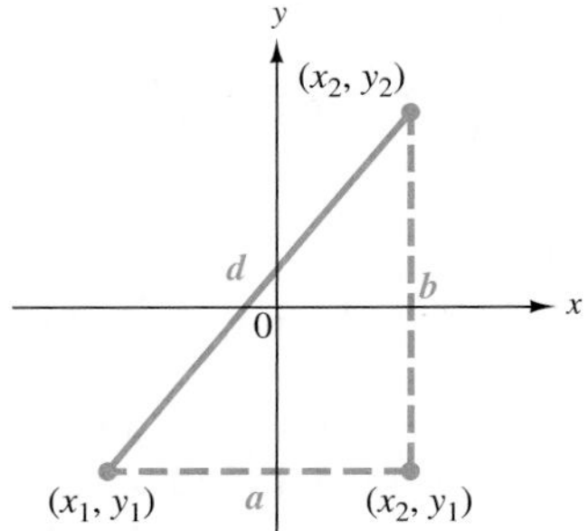

Figure 7

This result can be generalized. Figure 7 shows the two points (x_1, y_1) and (x_2, y_2). To find a formula for the distance d between these two points, notice that the distance between (x_1, y_1) and (x_2, y_1) is given by

$$a = x_2 - x_1,$$

and the distance between (x_2, y_2) and (x_2, y_1) is given by

$$b = y_2 - y_1.$$

From the Pythagorean formula,

$$d^2 = a^2 + b^2$$
$$= (x_2 - x_1)^2 + (y_2 - y_1)^2.$$

Choosing the principal square root gives the **distance formula.**

Distance Formula

The distance between the points (x_1, y_1) and (x_2, y_2) is

$$d = \sqrt{(x_2 - x_1)^2 + (y_2 - y_1)^2}.$$

Example 9 Using the Distance Formula

Find the distance between $(-3, 5)$ and $(6, 4)$.

When using the distance formula to find the distance between two points, designating the points as (x_1, y_1) and (x_2, y_2) is arbitrary. Let us choose $(x_1, y_1) = (-3, 5)$ and $(x_2, y_2) = (6, 4)$.

$$d = \sqrt{(x_2 - x_1)^2 + (y_2 - y_1)^2}$$
$$= \sqrt{(6 - (-3))^2 + (4 - 5)^2} \quad x_2 = 6, y_2 = 4, x_1 = -3, y_1 = 5$$
$$= \sqrt{9^2 + (-1)^2}$$
$$= \sqrt{82}$$

Work Problem 9 at the Side.

Answers

9. **(a)** 5 **(b)** $\sqrt{45}$ or $3\sqrt{5}$

9.3 EXERCISES

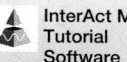

FOR EXTRA HELP: Student's Solutions Manual; MyMathLab.com; InterAct Math Tutorial Software; AW Math Tutor Center; www.mathxl.com; Digital Video Tutor CD 8 Videotape 17

Decide whether each statement is true *or* false *by using the product rule explained in this section. Then support your answer by finding a calculator approximation for each expression.*

1. $2\sqrt{12} = \sqrt{48}$

True; both are equal to $4\sqrt{3}$ and approximately 6.92820323.

2. $\sqrt{72} = 2\sqrt{18}$

True; both are equal to $6\sqrt{2}$ and approximately 8.485281374.

3. $3\sqrt{8} = 2\sqrt{18}$

True; both are equal to $6\sqrt{2}$ and approximately 8.485281374.

4. $5\sqrt{72} = 6\sqrt{50}$

True; both are equal to $30\sqrt{2}$ and approximately 42.42640687.

5. Explain why $\sqrt[3]{x} \cdot \sqrt[3]{x}$ is not equal to x. What is it equal to?

Because there are only two factors of $\sqrt[3]{x}$, $\sqrt[3]{x} \cdot \sqrt[3]{x} = (\sqrt[3]{x})^2$ or $\sqrt[3]{x^2}$.

6. Explain why $\sqrt[4]{x} \cdot \sqrt[4]{x}$ is not equal to x, but *is* equal to $\sqrt{x}$, for $x \geq 0$.

Because there are just two factors, $\sqrt[4]{x} \cdot \sqrt[4]{x} = (\sqrt[4]{x})^2 = x^{2/4} = x^{1/2} = \sqrt{x}$, for $x \geq 0$.

Multiply. See Examples 1 and 2.

7. $\sqrt{5} \cdot \sqrt{6}$

$\sqrt{30}$

8. $\sqrt{10} \cdot \sqrt{3}$

$\sqrt{30}$

9. $\sqrt[3]{7x} \cdot \sqrt[3]{2y}$

$\sqrt[3]{14xy}$

10. $\sqrt[3]{9x} \cdot \sqrt[3]{4y}$

$\sqrt[3]{36xy}$

11. $\sqrt[4]{12} \cdot \sqrt[4]{3}$

$\sqrt[4]{36}$

12. $\sqrt[4]{6} \cdot \sqrt[4]{9}$

$\sqrt[4]{54}$

Simplify each radical. Assume that all variables represent positive real numbers. See Example 3.

13. $\sqrt{\dfrac{64}{121}}$

$\dfrac{8}{11}$

14. $\sqrt{\dfrac{16}{49}}$

$\dfrac{4}{7}$

15. $\sqrt{\dfrac{3}{25}}$

$\dfrac{\sqrt{3}}{5}$

16. $\sqrt{\dfrac{13}{49}}$

$\dfrac{\sqrt{13}}{7}$

17. $\sqrt{\dfrac{x}{25}}$

$\dfrac{\sqrt{x}}{5}$

18. $\sqrt{\dfrac{k}{100}}$

$\dfrac{\sqrt{k}}{10}$

19. $\sqrt{\dfrac{p^6}{81}}$

$\dfrac{p^3}{9}$

20. $\sqrt{\dfrac{w^{10}}{36}}$

$\dfrac{w^5}{6}$

21. $\sqrt[3]{\dfrac{27}{64}}$

$\dfrac{3}{4}$

22. $\sqrt[3]{\dfrac{216}{125}}$

$\dfrac{6}{5}$

23. $\sqrt[3]{-\dfrac{r^2}{8}}$

$-\dfrac{\sqrt[3]{r^2}}{2}$

24. $\sqrt[3]{-\dfrac{t}{125}}$

$-\dfrac{\sqrt[3]{t}}{5}$

Express each radical in simplified form. See Example 4.

25. $\sqrt{12}$ — $2\sqrt{3}$

26. $\sqrt{18}$ — $3\sqrt{2}$

27. $\sqrt{288}$ — $12\sqrt{2}$

28. $\sqrt{72}$ — $6\sqrt{2}$

29. $-\sqrt{32}$ — $-4\sqrt{2}$

30. $-\sqrt{48}$ — $-4\sqrt{3}$

31. $-\sqrt{28}$ — $-2\sqrt{7}$

32. $-\sqrt{24}$ — $-2\sqrt{6}$

33. $\sqrt{-300}$ — not a real number

34. $\sqrt{-150}$ — not a real number

35. $\sqrt[3]{128}$ — $4\sqrt[3]{2}$

36. $\sqrt[3]{24}$ — $2\sqrt[3]{3}$

37. $\sqrt[3]{-16}$ — $-2\sqrt[3]{2}$

38. $\sqrt[3]{-250}$ — $-5\sqrt[3]{2}$

39. $\sqrt[3]{40}$ — $2\sqrt[3]{5}$

40. $\sqrt[3]{375}$ — $5\sqrt[3]{3}$

41. $-\sqrt[4]{512}$ — $-4\sqrt[4]{2}$

42. $-\sqrt[4]{1250}$ — $-5\sqrt[4]{2}$

43. $\sqrt[5]{64}$ — $2\sqrt[5]{2}$

44. $\sqrt[5]{128}$ — $2\sqrt[5]{4}$

45. A student claimed that $\sqrt[3]{14}$ is not in simplified form, since $14 = 8 + 6$, and 8 is a perfect cube. Was his reasoning correct? Why or why not?

His reasoning was incorrect. Here 8 is a term, not a factor.

46. Explain in your own words why $\sqrt[3]{k^4}$ is not a simplified radical.

It is not simplified because the power of k is greater than the index of the radical. The simplified form is $k\sqrt[3]{k}$.

Express each radical in simplified form. Assume that all variables represent positive real numbers. See Example 5.

47. $\sqrt{72k^2}$ — $6k\sqrt{2}$

48. $\sqrt{18m^2}$ — $3m\sqrt{2}$

49. $\sqrt[3]{\dfrac{81}{64}}$ — $\dfrac{3\sqrt[3]{3}}{4}$

50. $\sqrt[3]{\dfrac{32}{216}}$ — $\dfrac{\sqrt[3]{4}}{3}$

51. $\sqrt{121x^6}$ — $11x^3$

52. $\sqrt{256z^{12}}$ — $16z^6$

53. $-\sqrt[3]{27t^{12}}$ — $-3t^4$

54. $-\sqrt[3]{64y^{18}}$ — $-4y^6$

55. $-\sqrt{100m^8z^4}$ — $-10m^4z^2$

56. $-\sqrt{25t^6s^{20}}$ — $-5t^3s^{10}$

57. $-\sqrt[3]{-125a^6b^9c^{12}}$ — $5a^2b^3c^4$

58. $-\sqrt[3]{-216y^{15}x^6z^3}$ — $6y^5x^2z$

59. $\sqrt[4]{\frac{1}{16}r^8t^{20}}$ $\quad \frac{1}{2}r^2t^5$

60. $\sqrt[4]{\frac{81}{256}t^{12}u^8}$ $\quad \frac{3}{4}t^3u^2$

61. $\sqrt{50x^3}$ $\quad 5x\sqrt{2x}$

62. $\sqrt{300z^3}$ $\quad 10z\sqrt{3z}$

63. $-\sqrt{500r^{11}}$ $\quad -10r^5\sqrt{5r}$

64. $-\sqrt{200p^{13}}$ $\quad -10p^6\sqrt{2p}$

65. $\sqrt{13x^7y^8}$ $\quad x^3y^4\sqrt{13x}$

66. $\sqrt{23k^9p^{14}}$ $\quad k^4p^7\sqrt{23k}$

67. $\sqrt[3]{8z^6w^9}$ $\quad 2z^2w^3$

68. $\sqrt[3]{64a^{15}b^{12}}$ $\quad 4a^5b^4$

69. $\sqrt[3]{-16z^5t^7}$ $\quad -2zt^2\sqrt[3]{2z^2t}$

70. $\sqrt[3]{-81m^4n^{10}}$ $\quad -3mn^3\sqrt[3]{3mn}$

71. $\sqrt[4]{81x^{12}y^{16}}$ $\quad 3x^3y^4$

72. $\sqrt[4]{81t^8u^{28}}$ $\quad 3t^2u^7$

73. $-\sqrt[4]{162r^{15}s^{10}}$ $\quad -3r^3s^2\sqrt[4]{2r^3s^2}$

74. $-\sqrt[4]{32k^5m^{10}}$ $\quad -2km^2\sqrt[4]{2km^2}$

75. $\sqrt{\frac{y^{11}}{36}}$ $\quad \frac{y^5\sqrt{y}}{6}$

76. $\sqrt{\frac{v^{13}}{49}}$ $\quad \frac{v^6\sqrt{v}}{7}$

77. $\sqrt[3]{\frac{x^{16}}{27}}$ $\quad \frac{x^5\sqrt[3]{x}}{3}$

78. $\sqrt[3]{\frac{y^{17}}{125}}$ $\quad \frac{y^5\sqrt[3]{y^2}}{5}$

Simplify each radical. Assume that $x \geq 0$. See Example 6.

79. $\sqrt[4]{48^2}$ $\quad 4\sqrt{3}$

80. $\sqrt[4]{50^2}$ $\quad 5\sqrt{2}$

81. $\sqrt[10]{x^{25}}$ $\quad x^2\sqrt{x}$

82. $\sqrt[12]{x^{44}}$ $\quad x^3\sqrt[3]{x^2}$

Simplify by first writing the radicals with the same index. Then multiply. See Example 7.

83. $\sqrt[3]{4} \cdot \sqrt{3}$ $\quad \sqrt[6]{432}$

84. $\sqrt[3]{5} \cdot \sqrt{6}$ $\quad \sqrt[6]{5400}$

85. $\sqrt[4]{3} \cdot \sqrt[3]{4}$ $\quad \sqrt[12]{6912}$

86. $\sqrt[5]{7} \cdot \sqrt[7]{5}$ $\quad \sqrt[35]{2,573,571,875}$

Find the unknown length in each right triangle. Simplify the answer if necessary. See Example 8.

87.

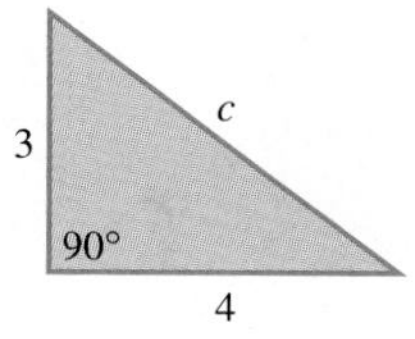

5

88.

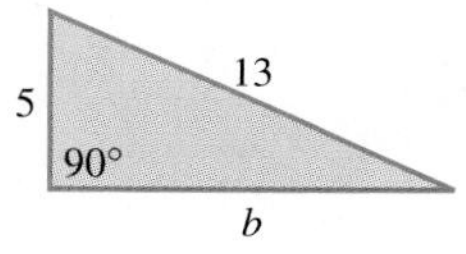

12

89.

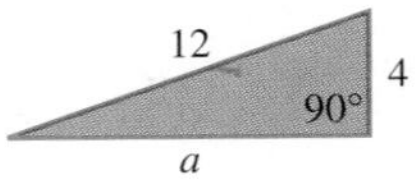

$8\sqrt{2}$

90.

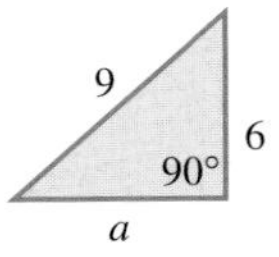

$3\sqrt{5}$

Find the distance between each pair of points. See Example 9.

91. $(5, 3)$ and $(-1, 2)$

$\sqrt{37}$

92. $(-1, 4)$ and $(5, 3)$

$\sqrt{37}$

93. $(-1, 5)$ and $(-7, 7)$

$2\sqrt{10}$

94. $(4, 5)$ and $(-8, 4)$

$\sqrt{145}$

95. $(\sqrt{2}, \sqrt{6})$ and $(-2\sqrt{2}, 4\sqrt{6})$

$6\sqrt{2}$

96. $(\sqrt{7}, 9\sqrt{3})$ and $(-\sqrt{7}, 4\sqrt{3})$

$\sqrt{103}$

97. $(x + y, y)$ and $(x - y, x)$

$\sqrt{5y^2 - 2xy + x^2}$

98. $(c, c - d)$ and $(d, c + d)$

$\sqrt{c^2 - 2cd + 5d^2}$

Solve each problem.

99. A Sanyo color television, model AVM-2755, has a rectangular screen with a 21.7-in. width. Its height is 16 in. What is the diameter of the screen to the nearest tenth of an inch? (*Source:* Actual measurements of the author's television.)

27.0 in.

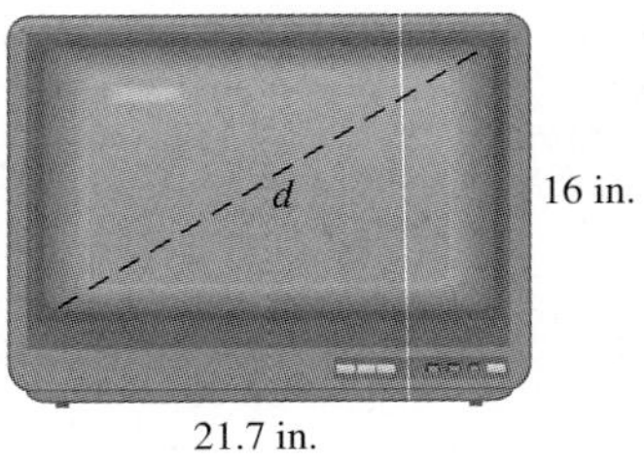

100. The length of the diagonal of a box is given by

$$D = \sqrt{L^2 + W^2 + H^2},$$

where L, W, and H are the length, width, and height of the box. Find the length of the diagonal, D, of a box that is 4 ft long, 3 ft high, and 2 ft wide. Give the exact value, then round to the nearest tenth of a foot.

$\sqrt{29}$ **ft; 5.4 ft**

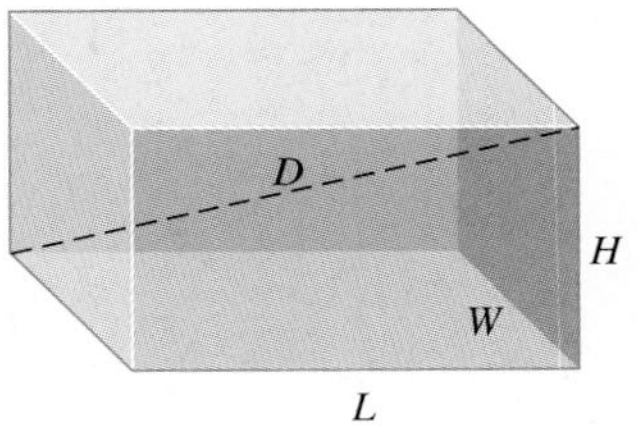

9.4 Adding and Subtracting Radical Expressions

The examples in the preceding section discussed simplifying radical expressions that involve multiplication and division. Now we show how to simplify radical expressions that involve addition and subtraction.

Objectives

1 Simplify radical expressions involving addition and subtraction.

1 Simplify radical expressions involving addition and subtraction. An expression such as $4\sqrt{2} + 3\sqrt{2}$ can be simplified by using the distributive property.

$$4\sqrt{2} + 3\sqrt{2} = (4 + 3)\sqrt{2} = 7\sqrt{2}$$

As another example, $2\sqrt{3} - 5\sqrt{3} = (2 - 5)\sqrt{3} = -3\sqrt{3}$. This is similar to simplifying $2x + 3x$ to $5x$ or $5y - 8y$ to $-3y$.

CAUTION

Only radical expressions with the *same index* and the *same radicand* may be combined. Expressions such as $5\sqrt{3} + 2\sqrt{2}$ or $3\sqrt{3} + 2\sqrt[3]{3}$ cannot be simplified by combining terms.

Example 1 Adding and Subtracting Radicals

Add or subtract to simplify each radical expression.

(a) $3\sqrt{24} + \sqrt{54}$

Begin by simplifying each radical; then use the distributive property to combine terms.

$$\begin{aligned} 3\sqrt{24} + \sqrt{54} &= 3\sqrt{4} \cdot \sqrt{6} + \sqrt{9} \cdot \sqrt{6} && \text{Product rule} \\ &= 3 \cdot 2\sqrt{6} + 3\sqrt{6} \\ &= 6\sqrt{6} + 3\sqrt{6} \\ &= 9\sqrt{6} && \text{Combine terms.} \end{aligned}$$

(b) $$\begin{aligned} 2\sqrt{20x} - \sqrt{45x} &= 2\sqrt{4} \cdot \sqrt{5x} - \sqrt{9} \cdot \sqrt{5x} && \text{Product rule} \\ &= 2 \cdot 2\sqrt{5x} - 3\sqrt{5x} \\ &= 4\sqrt{5x} - 3\sqrt{5x} \\ &= \sqrt{5x} && \text{Combine terms.} \end{aligned}$$

Because the radicand is $5x$, we must have $x \geq 0$.

(c) $2\sqrt{3} - 4\sqrt{5}$

Here the radicals differ and are already simplified, so $2\sqrt{3} - 4\sqrt{5}$ cannot be simplified further.

Work Problem 1 at the Side.

1 Add or subtract to simplify each radical expression.

(a) $3\sqrt{5} + 7\sqrt{5}$

(b) $2\sqrt{11} - \sqrt{11} + 3\sqrt{44}$

(c) $5\sqrt{12y} + 6\sqrt{75y}, \quad y \geq 0$

(d) $3\sqrt{8} - 6\sqrt{50} + 2\sqrt{200}$

(e) $9\sqrt{5} - 4\sqrt{10}$

CAUTION

Do not confuse the product rule with combining like terms. The root of a sum ***does not equal*** the sum of the roots. For example,

$$\sqrt{9 + 16} \neq \sqrt{9} + \sqrt{16}, \text{ since}$$

$$\sqrt{9 + 16} = \sqrt{25} = 5, \quad \text{but} \quad \sqrt{9} + \sqrt{16} = 3 + 4 = 7.$$

Answers

1. (a) $10\sqrt{5}$ (b) $7\sqrt{11}$ (c) $40\sqrt{3y}$ (d) $-4\sqrt{2}$ (e) cannot be simplified further

2 Add or subtract to simplify each radical expression. Assume that all variables represent positive real numbers.

(a) $7\sqrt[3]{81} + 3\sqrt[3]{24}$

(b) $-2\sqrt[4]{32} - 7\sqrt[4]{162}$

(c) $\sqrt[3]{p^4q^7} - \sqrt[3]{64pq}$

3 Add. Assume that all variables represent positive real numbers.

$$\sqrt{\frac{80}{y^4}} + \sqrt{\frac{81}{y^{10}}}$$

ANSWERS

2. **(a)** $27\sqrt[3]{3}$ **(b)** $-25\sqrt[4]{2}$ **(c)** $(pq^2 - 4)\sqrt[3]{pq}$

3. $\dfrac{4y^3\sqrt{5} + 9}{y^5}$

Example 2 **Adding and Subtracting Radicals with Higher Indexes**

Add or subtract to simplify each radical expression. Assume that all variables represent positive real numbers.

(a)
$$\begin{aligned} 2\sqrt[3]{16} - 5\sqrt[3]{54} &= 2\sqrt[3]{8 \cdot 2} - 5\sqrt[3]{27 \cdot 2} && \text{Factor.} \\ &= 2\sqrt[3]{8} \cdot \sqrt[3]{2} - 5\sqrt[3]{27} \cdot \sqrt[3]{2} && \text{Product rule} \\ &= 2 \cdot 2 \cdot \sqrt[3]{2} - 5 \cdot 3 \cdot \sqrt[3]{2} \\ &= 4\sqrt[3]{2} - 15\sqrt[3]{2} \\ &= -11\sqrt[3]{2} && \text{Combine terms.} \end{aligned}$$

(b)
$$\begin{aligned} 2\sqrt[3]{x^2y} + \sqrt[3]{8x^5y^4} &= 2\sqrt[3]{x^2y} + \sqrt[3]{(8x^3y^3)x^2y} && \text{Factor.} \\ &= 2\sqrt[3]{x^2y} + 2xy\sqrt[3]{x^2y} && \text{Product rule} \\ &= (2 + 2xy)\sqrt[3]{x^2y} && \text{Distributive property} \end{aligned}$$

CAUTION

Remember to write the index when working with cube roots, fourth roots, and so on.

Work Problem 2 at the Side.

Example 3 **Adding and Subtracting Radicals with Fractions**

Perform the indicated operations. Assume that all variables represent positive real numbers.

(a)
$$\begin{aligned} 2\sqrt{\frac{75}{16}} + 4\frac{\sqrt{8}}{\sqrt{32}} &= 2\frac{\sqrt{25 \cdot 3}}{\sqrt{16}} + 4\frac{\sqrt{4 \cdot 2}}{\sqrt{16 \cdot 2}} && \text{Quotient rule} \\ &= 2\left(\frac{5\sqrt{3}}{4}\right) + 4\left(\frac{2\sqrt{2}}{4\sqrt{2}}\right) && \text{Product rule} \\ &= \frac{5\sqrt{3}}{2} + 2 && \text{Multiply; } \tfrac{\sqrt{2}}{\sqrt{2}} = 1. \\ &= \frac{5\sqrt{3}}{2} + \frac{4}{2} && \text{Write with a common denominator.} \\ &= \frac{5\sqrt{3} + 4}{2} \end{aligned}$$

(b)
$$\begin{aligned} 10\sqrt[3]{\frac{5}{x^6}} - 3\sqrt[3]{\frac{4}{x^9}} &= 10\frac{\sqrt[3]{5}}{\sqrt[3]{x^6}} - 3\frac{\sqrt[3]{4}}{\sqrt[3]{x^9}} && \text{Quotient rule} \\ &= \frac{10\sqrt[3]{5}}{x^2} - \frac{3\sqrt[3]{4}}{x^3} \\ &= \frac{10x\sqrt[3]{5}}{x^3} - \frac{3\sqrt[3]{4}}{x^3} && \text{Write with a common denominator.} \\ &= \frac{10x\sqrt[3]{5} - 3\sqrt[3]{4}}{x^3} \end{aligned}$$

Work Problem 3 at the Side.

9.4 EXERCISES

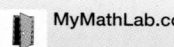

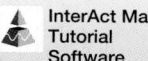

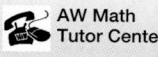

FOR EXTRA HELP: Student's Solutions Manual | MyMathLab.com | InterAct Math Tutorial Software | AW Math Tutor Center | www.mathxl.com | Digital Video Tutor CD 8 Videotape 17

1. Which one of the following sums could be simplified without first simplifying the individual radical expressions?

   A. $\sqrt{50} + \sqrt{32}$ **B.** $3\sqrt{6} + 9\sqrt{6}$ **C.** $\sqrt[3]{32} - \sqrt[3]{108}$ **D.** $\sqrt[5]{6} - \sqrt[5]{192}$ **B**

2. Let $a = 1$ and $b = 64$.

   (a) Evaluate $\sqrt{a} + \sqrt{b}$. Then find $\sqrt{a + b}$. Are they equal? **9; $\sqrt{65}$; no**

   (b) Evaluate $\sqrt[3]{a} + \sqrt[3]{b}$. Then find $\sqrt[3]{a + b}$. Are they equal? **5; $\sqrt[3]{65}$; no**

   (c) Complete the following: In general, $\sqrt[n]{a} + \sqrt[n]{b} \neq$ ________, based on the observations in parts (a) and (b) of this exercise. **$\sqrt[n]{a + b}$**

3. Even though the indexes of the terms are not equal, the sum $\sqrt{64} + \sqrt[3]{125} + \sqrt[4]{16}$ can be simplified quite easily. What is this sum? Why can these terms be combined so easily?

   15; each radicand is a whole number power corresponding to the index of the radical.

4. Explain why $28 - 4\sqrt{2}$ is not equal to $24\sqrt{2}$. (This error is a common one among algebra students.)

   We cannot group 28 − 4 here. Multiplication must take place before subtraction, according to the order of operations. (Only like terms can be combined.)

Add or subtract. Assume that all variables represent positive real numbers. See Examples 1–3.

5. $\sqrt{36} - \sqrt{100}$ **-4**

6. $\sqrt{25} - \sqrt{81}$ **-4**

7. $-2\sqrt{48} + 3\sqrt{75}$ **$7\sqrt{3}$**

8. $4\sqrt{32} - 2\sqrt{8}$ **$12\sqrt{2}$**

9. $6\sqrt{18} - \sqrt{32} + 2\sqrt{50}$ **$24\sqrt{2}$**

10. $5\sqrt{8} + 3\sqrt{72} - 3\sqrt{50}$ **$13\sqrt{2}$**

11. $-2\sqrt{63} + 2\sqrt{28} + 2\sqrt{7}$ **0**

12. $-\sqrt{27} + 2\sqrt{48} - \sqrt{75}$ **0**

13. $2\sqrt{5} + 3\sqrt{20} + 4\sqrt{45}$ **$20\sqrt{5}$**

14. $5\sqrt{54} - 2\sqrt{24} - 2\sqrt{96}$ **$3\sqrt{6}$**

15. $8\sqrt{2x} - \sqrt{8x} + \sqrt{72x}$ **$12\sqrt{2x}$**

16. $4\sqrt{18k} - \sqrt{72k} + \sqrt{50k}$ **$11\sqrt{2k}$**

17. $3\sqrt{72m^2} - 5\sqrt{32m^2} - 3\sqrt{18m^2}$ **$-11m\sqrt{2}$**

18. $9\sqrt{27p^2} - 14\sqrt{108p^2} + 2\sqrt{48p^2}$ **$-49p\sqrt{3}$**

19. $-\sqrt[3]{54} + 2\sqrt[3]{16}$ **$\sqrt[3]{2}$**

20. $15\sqrt[3]{81} - 4\sqrt[3]{24}$ **$37\sqrt[3]{3}$**

21. $2\sqrt[3]{27x} - 2\sqrt[3]{8x}$ **$2\sqrt[3]{x}$**

22. $6\sqrt[3]{128m} + 3\sqrt[3]{16m}$ **$30\sqrt[3]{2m}$**

23. $5\sqrt[4]{32} + 3\sqrt[4]{162}$ **$19\sqrt[4]{2}$**

24. $2\sqrt[4]{512} + 4\sqrt[4]{32}$ **$16\sqrt[4]{2}$**

25. $3\sqrt[4]{x^5y} - 2x\sqrt[4]{xy}$ **$x\sqrt[4]{xy}$**

26. $2\sqrt[4]{m^9p^6} - 3m^2p\sqrt[4]{mp^2}$

$-m^2p\sqrt[4]{mp^2}$

27. $\sqrt[3]{64xy^2} + \sqrt[3]{27x^4y^5}$

$(4 + 3xy)\sqrt[3]{xy^2}$

28. $\sqrt[4]{625s^3t} - \sqrt[4]{81s^7t^5}$

$(5 - 3st)\sqrt[4]{s^3t}$

29. $\sqrt{\frac{8}{9}} + \sqrt{\frac{18}{36}}$

$\frac{7\sqrt{2}}{6}$

30. $\sqrt{\frac{12}{16}} + \sqrt{\frac{48}{64}}$

$\sqrt{3}$

31. $\frac{\sqrt{32}}{3} + \frac{2\sqrt{2}}{3} - \frac{\sqrt{2}}{\sqrt{9}}$

$\frac{5\sqrt{2}}{3}$

32. $\frac{\sqrt{27}}{2} - \frac{3\sqrt{3}}{2} + \frac{\sqrt{3}}{\sqrt{4}}$

$\frac{\sqrt{3}}{2}$

In Example 1(a) we show that $3\sqrt{24} + \sqrt{54} = 9\sqrt{6}$. *To support this result, we can find a calculator approximation of* $3\sqrt{24}$, *then find a calculator approximation of* $\sqrt{54}$, *and add these two approximations. Then, we find a calculator approximation of* $9\sqrt{6}$. *It should correspond to the sum that we just found. (For this example, both approximations are* 22.04540769. *Due to rounding procedures, there may be a discrepancy in the final digit if you try to duplicate this work.) Follow this procedure to support the statements in Exercises 33–36.*

33. $3\sqrt{32} - 2\sqrt{8} = 8\sqrt{2}$

Both are approximately 11.3137085.

34. $4\sqrt{12} - 7\sqrt{27} = -13\sqrt{3}$

Both are approximately −22.5166605.

35. $2\sqrt{40} + 6\sqrt{90} - 3\sqrt{160} = 10\sqrt{10}$

Both are approximately 31.6227766.

36. $5\sqrt{28} - 3\sqrt{63} + 2\sqrt{112} = 9\sqrt{7}$

Both are approximately 23.8117618.

37. A rectangular yard has a length of $\sqrt{192}$ m and a width of $\sqrt{48}$ m. Choose the best estimate of its dimensions. Then estimate the perimeter.

A. 14 m by 7 m **B.** 5 m by 7 m

C. 14 m by 8 m **D.** 15 m by 8 m

A; 42 m

38. If the sides of a triangle are $\sqrt{65}$ in., $\sqrt{35}$ in., and $\sqrt{26}$ in., which one of the following is the best estimate of its perimeter?

A. 20 in. **B.** 26 in.

C. 19 in. **D.** 24 in.

C

Solve each problem. Give answers as simplified radical expressions.

39. Find the perimeter of the triangle.

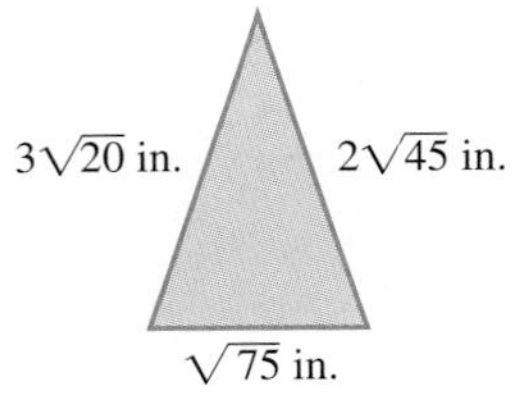

$12\sqrt{5} + 5\sqrt{3}$ in.

40. Find the perimeter of the rectangle.

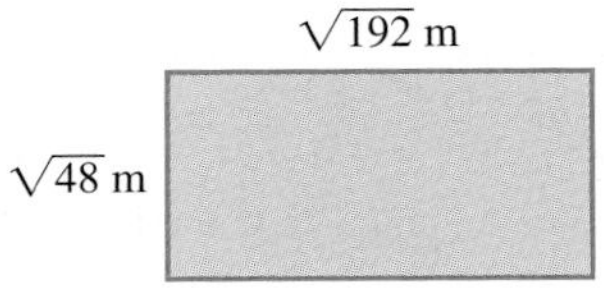

$24\sqrt{3}$ m

41. What is the perimeter of the computer graphic?

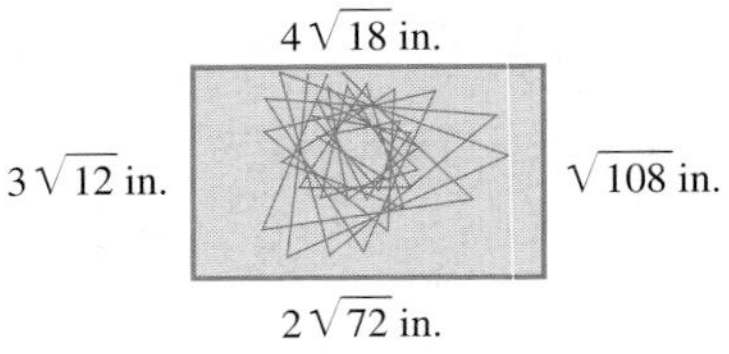

$24\sqrt{2} + 12\sqrt{3}$ in.

42. Find the area of the trapezoid.

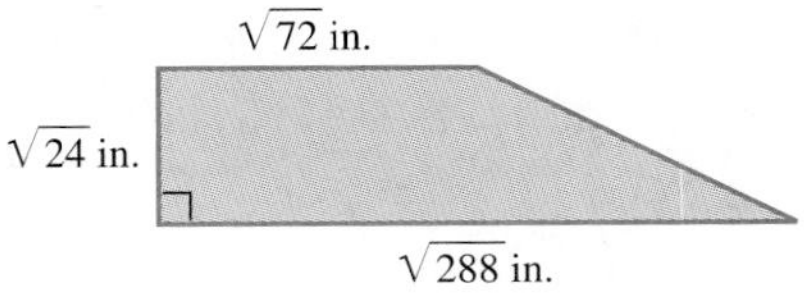

$36\sqrt{3}$ in.^{2}

9.5 MULTIPLYING AND DIVIDING RADICAL EXPRESSIONS

OBJECTIVES

1. Multiply radical expressions.
2. Rationalize denominators with one radical term.
3. Rationalize denominators with binomials involving radicals.
4. Write radical quotients in lowest terms.

1 Multiply radical expressions. We multiply binomial expressions involving radicals by using the FOIL (First, Outer, Inner, Last) method. For example, we find the product of the binomials $\sqrt{5} + 3$ and $\sqrt{6} + 1$ as follows.

$$(\sqrt{5} + 3)(\sqrt{6} + 1) = \underbrace{\sqrt{5} \cdot \sqrt{6}}_{\text{First}} + \underbrace{\sqrt{5} \cdot 1}_{\text{Outer}} + \underbrace{3 \cdot \sqrt{6}}_{\text{Inner}} + \underbrace{3 \cdot 1}_{\text{Last}}$$
$$= \sqrt{30} + \sqrt{5} + 3\sqrt{6} + 3$$

This result cannot be simplified further.

Example 1 Multiplying Binomials Involving Radical Expressions

Multiply using FOIL.

(a) $(7 - \sqrt{3})(\sqrt{5} + \sqrt{2}) = \overset{F}{7\sqrt{5}} + \overset{O}{7\sqrt{2}} - \overset{I}{\sqrt{3} \cdot \sqrt{5}} - \overset{L}{\sqrt{3} \cdot \sqrt{2}}$

$= 7\sqrt{5} + 7\sqrt{2} - \sqrt{15} - \sqrt{6}$

(b) $(\sqrt{10} + \sqrt{3})(\sqrt{10} - \sqrt{3})$

$= \sqrt{10} \cdot \sqrt{10} - \sqrt{10} \cdot \sqrt{3} + \sqrt{10} \cdot \sqrt{3} - \sqrt{3} \cdot \sqrt{3}$

$= 10 - 3$

$= 7$

Notice that this is the kind of product that results in the difference of squares:

$$(a + b)(a - b) = a^2 - b^2.$$

Here, $a = \sqrt{10}$ and $b = \sqrt{3}$.

(c) $(\sqrt{7} - 3)^2 = (\sqrt{7} - 3)(\sqrt{7} - 3)$

$= \sqrt{7} \cdot \sqrt{7} - 3\sqrt{7} - 3\sqrt{7} + 3 \cdot 3$

$= 7 - 6\sqrt{7} + 9$

$= 16 - 6\sqrt{7}$

(d) $(5 - \sqrt[3]{3})(5 + \sqrt[3]{3}) = 5 \cdot 5 + 5\sqrt[3]{3} - 5\sqrt[3]{3} - \sqrt[3]{3} \cdot \sqrt[3]{3}$

$= 25 - \sqrt[3]{3^2}$

$= 25 - \sqrt[3]{9}$

1 Multiply using FOIL.

(a) $(2 + \sqrt{3})(1 + \sqrt{5})$

(b) $(2\sqrt{3} + \sqrt{5})(\sqrt{6} - 3\sqrt{5})$

(c) $(4 + \sqrt{3})(4 - \sqrt{3})$

(d) $(\sqrt{6} - \sqrt{5})^2$

(e) $(4 + \sqrt[3]{7})(4 - \sqrt[3]{7})$

NOTE

In Example 1(c) we could have used the formula for the square of a binomial,

$$(a - b)^2 = a^2 - 2ab + b^2,$$

to get the same result.

$$\begin{aligned}(\sqrt{7} - 3)^2 &= (\sqrt{7})^2 - 2(\sqrt{7})(3) + 3^2 \\ &= 7 - 6\sqrt{7} + 9 \\ &= 16 - 6\sqrt{7}\end{aligned}$$

Work Problem 1 at the Side.

2 Rationalize denominators with one radical term. As defined earlier, a simplified radical expression will have no radical in the denominator. The origin of this agreement no doubt occurred before the days of high-speed calculation, when computation was a tedious process performed by hand. To see this, consider the radical expression $\frac{1}{\sqrt{2}}$. To find a decimal approximation by hand, it would be necessary to divide 1 by a decimal approximation for $\sqrt{2}$, such as 1.414. It would be much easier if the divisor were a whole number. This can be accomplished by multiplying $\frac{1}{\sqrt{2}}$ by 1 in the form $\frac{\sqrt{2}}{\sqrt{2}}$:

$$\frac{1}{\sqrt{2}} \cdot \frac{\sqrt{2}}{\sqrt{2}} = \frac{\sqrt{2}}{2}.$$

Now the computation would require dividing 1.414 by 2 to obtain .707, a much easier task.

With current technology, either form of this fraction can be approximated with the same number of keystrokes. See Figure 8, which shows how a calculator gives the same approximation for both forms of the expression.

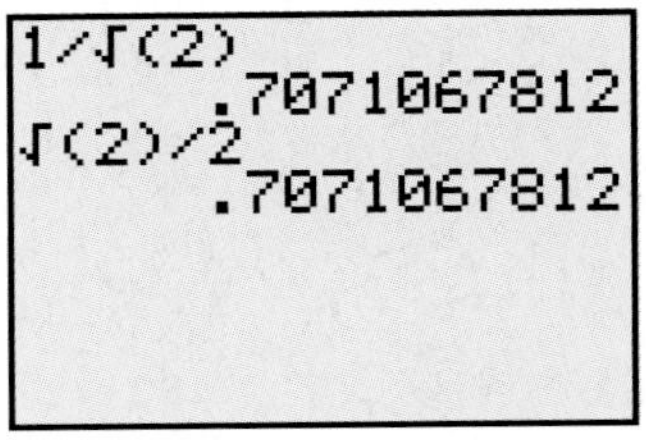

Figure 8

It is still important to be able to find equivalent forms of radical expressions. A common way of "standardizing" the form of a radical expression is to have the denominator contain no radicals. The process of removing radicals from a denominator so that the denominator contains only rational numbers is called **rationalizing the denominator.**

Example 2 Rationalizing Denominators with Square Roots

Rationalize each denominator.

(a) $\dfrac{3}{\sqrt{7}}$

Multiply the numerator and denominator by $\sqrt{7}$. This is, in effect, multiplying by 1.

Continued on Next Page

ANSWERS

1. (a) $2 + 2\sqrt{5} + \sqrt{3} + \sqrt{15}$
(b) $6\sqrt{2} - 6\sqrt{15} + \sqrt{30} - 15$
(c) 13 (d) $11 - 2\sqrt{30}$
(e) $16 - \sqrt[3]{49}$

$$\frac{3}{\sqrt{7}} = \frac{3 \cdot \sqrt{7}}{\sqrt{7} \cdot \sqrt{7}}$$

In the denominator, since $\sqrt{7} \cdot \sqrt{7} = \sqrt{7 \cdot 7} = \sqrt{49} = 7$,

$$\frac{3}{\sqrt{7}} = \frac{3\sqrt{7}}{7}.$$

The denominator is now a rational number.

(b) $\frac{5\sqrt{2}}{\sqrt{5}} = \frac{5\sqrt{2} \cdot \sqrt{5}}{\sqrt{5} \cdot \sqrt{5}} = \frac{5\sqrt{10}}{5} = \sqrt{10}$

(c) $\frac{6}{\sqrt{12}}$

Less work is involved if the radical in the denominator is simplified first.

$$\frac{6}{\sqrt{12}} = \frac{6}{\sqrt{4 \cdot 3}} = \frac{6}{2\sqrt{3}} = \frac{3}{\sqrt{3}}$$

Now rationalize the denominator by multiplying the numerator and denominator by $\sqrt{3}$.

$$\frac{3 \cdot \sqrt{3}}{\sqrt{3} \cdot \sqrt{3}} = \frac{3\sqrt{3}}{3} = \sqrt{3}$$

Work Problem 2 at the Side.

2 Rationalize each denominator.

(a) $\frac{8}{\sqrt{3}}$

(b) $\frac{\sqrt{3}}{\sqrt{7}}$

(c) $\frac{3}{\sqrt{48}}$

(d) $\frac{-16}{\sqrt{32}}$

Example 3 Rationalizing Denominators in Roots of Fractions

Simplify each radical.

(a) $\sqrt{\frac{18}{125}}$

$$\sqrt{\frac{18}{125}} = \frac{\sqrt{18}}{\sqrt{125}} \quad \text{Quotient rule}$$

$$= \frac{\sqrt{9 \cdot 2}}{\sqrt{25 \cdot 5}} \quad \text{Factor.}$$

$$= \frac{3\sqrt{2}}{5\sqrt{5}} \quad \text{Product rule}$$

$$= \frac{3\sqrt{2} \cdot \sqrt{5}}{5\sqrt{5} \cdot \sqrt{5}} \quad \text{Multiply by } \frac{\sqrt{5}}{\sqrt{5}}.$$

$$= \frac{3\sqrt{10}}{5 \cdot 5} \quad \text{Product rule}$$

$$= \frac{3\sqrt{10}}{25}$$

Continued on Next Page

ANSWERS

2. **(a)** $\frac{8\sqrt{3}}{3}$ **(b)** $\frac{\sqrt{21}}{7}$ **(c)** $\frac{\sqrt{3}}{4}$ **(d)** $-2\sqrt{2}$

3 Simplify. Assume that all variables represent positive real numbers.

(a) $\sqrt{\frac{8}{45}}$

(b) $\sqrt{\frac{72}{y}}$

(c) $\sqrt{\frac{200k^6}{y^7}}$

4 Simplify.

(a) $\sqrt[3]{\frac{15}{32}}$

(b) $\sqrt[3]{\frac{m^{12}}{n}}, \quad n \neq 0$

(c) $\sqrt[4]{\frac{6y}{w^2}}, \quad y \geq 0, w \neq 0$

ANSWERS

3. (a) $\frac{2\sqrt{10}}{15}$ **(b)** $\frac{6\sqrt{2y}}{y}$ **(c)** $\frac{10k^3\sqrt{2y}}{y^4}$

4. (a) $\frac{\sqrt[3]{30}}{4}$ **(b)** $\frac{m^4\sqrt[3]{n^2}}{n}$ **(c)** $\frac{\sqrt[4]{6yw^2}}{w}$

(b) $\sqrt{\frac{50m^4}{p^5}}, \quad p > 0$

$$\begin{aligned}
\sqrt{\frac{50m^4}{p^5}} &= \frac{\sqrt{50m^4}}{\sqrt{p^5}} && \text{Quotient rule}\\
&= \frac{5m^2\sqrt{2}}{p^2\sqrt{p}} && \text{Product rule}\\
&= \frac{5m^2\sqrt{2}\cdot\sqrt{p}}{p^2\sqrt{p}\cdot\sqrt{p}} && \text{Multiply by } \frac{\sqrt{p}}{\sqrt{p}}.\\
&= \frac{5m^2\sqrt{2p}}{p^2\cdot p} && \text{Product rule}\\
&= \frac{5m^2\sqrt{2p}}{p^3}
\end{aligned}$$

Work Problem **3** at the Side.

Example 4 Rationalizing Denominators with Cube Roots

Simplify.

(a) $\sqrt[3]{\frac{27}{16}}$

Use the quotient rule and simplify the numerator and denominator.

$$\sqrt[3]{\frac{27}{16}} = \frac{\sqrt[3]{27}}{\sqrt[3]{16}} = \frac{3}{\sqrt[3]{8}\cdot\sqrt[3]{2}} = \frac{3}{2\sqrt[3]{2}}$$

To get a rational denominator, multiply the numerator and denominator by a number that will result in a perfect cube in the radicand in the denominator. Since $2 \cdot 4 = 8$, a perfect cube, multiply the numerator and denominator by $\sqrt[3]{4}$.

$$\sqrt[3]{\frac{27}{16}} = \frac{3}{2\sqrt[3]{2}} = \frac{3\cdot\sqrt[3]{4}}{2\sqrt[3]{2}\cdot\sqrt[3]{4}} = \frac{3\sqrt[3]{4}}{2\sqrt[3]{8}} = \frac{3\sqrt[3]{4}}{2\cdot 2} = \frac{3\sqrt[3]{4}}{4}$$

(b) $\sqrt[4]{\frac{5x}{z}}, \quad x \geq 0,\ z > 0$

$$\sqrt[4]{\frac{5x}{z}} = \frac{\sqrt[4]{5x}}{\sqrt[4]{z}}\cdot\frac{\sqrt[4]{z^3}}{\sqrt[4]{z^3}} = \frac{\sqrt[4]{5xz^3}}{\sqrt[4]{z^4}} = \frac{\sqrt[4]{5xz^3}}{z}$$

CAUTION

It is easy to make mistakes in problems like the one in Example 4(a). A typical error is to multiply the numerator and denominator by $\sqrt[3]{2}$, forgetting that

$$\sqrt[3]{2}\cdot\sqrt[3]{2} \neq 2.$$

You need *three* factors of 2 to get 2^3 under the radical. As implied in Example 4(a),

$$\sqrt[3]{2}\cdot\sqrt[3]{2}\cdot\sqrt[3]{2} = 2.$$

Work Problem **4** at the Side.

3 Rationalize denominators with binomials involving radicals. Recall the special product

$$(a + b)(a - b) = a^2 - b^2.$$

To rationalize a denominator that contains a binomial expression (one that contains exactly two terms) involving radicals, such as

$$\frac{3}{1 + \sqrt{2}},$$

we must use conjugates. The conjugate of $1 + \sqrt{2}$ is $1 - \sqrt{2}$. In general, $a + b$ and $a - b$ are **conjugates.**

Rationalizing Binomial Denominators

Whenever a radical expression has a sum or difference with square root radicals in the denominator, we rationalize the denominator by multiplying both the numerator and denominator by the conjugate of the denominator.

For the expression $\frac{3}{1 + \sqrt{2}}$, we rationalize the denominator by multiplying both the numerator and denominator by $1 - \sqrt{2}$, the conjugate of the denominator.

$$\frac{3}{1 + \sqrt{2}} = \frac{3(1 - \sqrt{2})}{(1 + \sqrt{2})(1 - \sqrt{2})}$$

Then $(1 + \sqrt{2})(1 - \sqrt{2}) = 1^2 - (\sqrt{2})^2 = 1 - 2 = -1$. Placing -1 in the denominator gives

$$= \frac{3(1 - \sqrt{2})}{-1}$$

$$= \frac{3}{-1}(1 - \sqrt{2})$$

$$= -3(1 - \sqrt{2}) \quad \text{or} \quad -3 + 3\sqrt{2}.$$

Example 5 **Rationalizing Binomial Denominators**

Rationalize each denominator.

(a) $\frac{5}{4 - \sqrt{3}}$

To rationalize the denominator, multiply both the numerator and denominator by the conjugate of the denominator, $4 + \sqrt{3}$.

$$\frac{5}{4 - \sqrt{3}} = \frac{5(4 + \sqrt{3})}{(4 - \sqrt{3})(4 + \sqrt{3})}$$

$$= \frac{5(4 + \sqrt{3})}{16 - 3}$$

$$= \frac{5(4 + \sqrt{3})}{13}$$

Notice that the numerator is left in factored form. This makes it easier to determine whether the expression is written in lowest terms.

Continued on Next Page

5 Rationalize each denominator.

(a) $\dfrac{-4}{\sqrt{5}+2}$

(b) $\dfrac{15}{\sqrt{7}+\sqrt{2}}$

(c) $\dfrac{\sqrt{3}+\sqrt{5}}{\sqrt{2}-\sqrt{7}}$

(d) $\dfrac{2}{\sqrt{k}+\sqrt{z}}$
$(k \neq z, k > 0, z > 0)$

6 Write each quotient in lowest terms.

(a) $\dfrac{15-5\sqrt{3}}{5}$

(b) $\dfrac{24-36\sqrt{7}}{16}$

ANSWERS

5. (a) $-4(\sqrt{5}-2)$ **(b)** $3(\sqrt{7}-\sqrt{2})$

(c) $\dfrac{-(\sqrt{6}+\sqrt{21}+\sqrt{10}+\sqrt{35})}{5}$

(d) $\dfrac{2(\sqrt{k}-\sqrt{z})}{k-z}$

6. (a) $3-\sqrt{3}$ **(b)** $\dfrac{6-9\sqrt{7}}{4}$

(b) $\dfrac{\sqrt{2}-\sqrt{3}}{\sqrt{5}+\sqrt{3}}$

Multiply the numerator and denominator by $\sqrt{5}-\sqrt{3}$ to rationalize the denominator.

$$\frac{\sqrt{2}-\sqrt{3}}{\sqrt{5}+\sqrt{3}} = \frac{(\sqrt{2}-\sqrt{3})(\sqrt{5}-\sqrt{3})}{(\sqrt{5}+\sqrt{3})(\sqrt{5}-\sqrt{3})}$$
$$= \frac{\sqrt{10}-\sqrt{6}-\sqrt{15}+3}{5-3}$$
$$= \frac{\sqrt{10}-\sqrt{6}-\sqrt{15}+3}{2}$$

(c) $$\frac{3}{\sqrt{5m}-\sqrt{p}} = \frac{3(\sqrt{5m}+\sqrt{p})}{(\sqrt{5m}-\sqrt{p})(\sqrt{5m}+\sqrt{p})}$$
$$= \frac{3(\sqrt{5m}+\sqrt{p})}{5m-p} \quad (5m \neq p, m > 0, p > 0)$$

Work Problem 5 at the Side.

4 Write radical quotients in lowest terms.

Example 6 Writing Radical Quotients in Lowest Terms

Write each quotient in lowest terms.

(a) $\dfrac{6+2\sqrt{5}}{4}$

Factor the numerator and denominator, then write in lowest terms.

$$\frac{6+2\sqrt{5}}{4} = \frac{2(3+\sqrt{5})}{2\cdot 2} = \frac{3+\sqrt{5}}{2}$$

Here is an alternative method for writing this expression in lowest terms.

$$\frac{6+2\sqrt{5}}{4} = \frac{6}{4}+\frac{2\sqrt{5}}{4} = \frac{3}{2}+\frac{\sqrt{5}}{2} = \frac{3+\sqrt{5}}{2}$$

(b) $$\frac{5y-\sqrt{8y^2}}{6y} = \frac{5y-2y\sqrt{2}}{6y},\ y > 0 \qquad \text{Product rule}$$
$$= \frac{y(5-2\sqrt{2})}{6y} \qquad \text{Factor the numerator.}$$
$$= \frac{5-2\sqrt{2}}{6}$$

Note that the final fraction cannot be simplified further because there is no common factor of 2 in the numerator.

CAUTION

Be careful to factor *before* writing a quotient in lowest terms.

Work Problem 6 at the Side.

9.5 EXERCISES

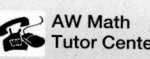

FOR EXTRA HELP: Student's Solutions Manual; MyMathLab.com; InterAct Math Tutorial Software; AW Math Tutor Center; www.mathxl.com; Digital Video Tutor CD 8 Videotape 18

Match each part of a rule for a special product in Column I with the part it equals in Column II.

I		II
1. $(x + \sqrt{y})(x - \sqrt{y})$	E	A. $x - y$
2. $(\sqrt{x} + y)(\sqrt{x} - y)$	C	B. $x + 2y\sqrt{x} + y^2$
3. $(\sqrt{x} + \sqrt{y})(\sqrt{x} - \sqrt{y})$	A	C. $x - y^2$
4. $(\sqrt{x} + \sqrt{y})^2$	F	D. $x - 2\sqrt{xy} + y$
5. $(\sqrt{x} - \sqrt{y})^2$	D	E. $x^2 - y$
6. $(\sqrt{x} + y)^2$	B	F. $x + 2\sqrt{xy} + y$

Multiply, then simplify each product. Assume that all variables represent positive real numbers. See Example 1.

7. $\sqrt{3}(\sqrt{12} - 4)$
   $6 - 4\sqrt{3}$

8. $\sqrt{5}(\sqrt{125} - 6)$
   $25 - 6\sqrt{5}$

9. $\sqrt{2}(\sqrt{18} - \sqrt{3})$
   $6 - \sqrt{6}$

10. $\sqrt{5}(\sqrt{15} + \sqrt{5})$
    $5\sqrt{3} + 5$

11. $(\sqrt{6} + 2)(\sqrt{6} - 2)$
    2

12. $(\sqrt{7} + 8)(\sqrt{7} - 8)$
    -57

13. $(\sqrt{12} - \sqrt{3})(\sqrt{12} + \sqrt{3})$
    9

14. $(\sqrt{18} + \sqrt{8})(\sqrt{18} - \sqrt{8})$
    10

15. $(\sqrt{3} + 2)(\sqrt{6} - 5)$
    $3\sqrt{2} - 5\sqrt{3} + 2\sqrt{6} - 10$

16. $(\sqrt{7} + 1)(\sqrt{2} - 4)$
    $\sqrt{14} - 4\sqrt{7} + \sqrt{2} - 4$

17. $(\sqrt{3x} + 2)(\sqrt{3x} - 2)$
    $3x - 4$

18. $(\sqrt{6y} - 4)(\sqrt{6y} + 4)$
    $6y - 16$

19. $(2\sqrt{x} + \sqrt{y})(2\sqrt{x} - \sqrt{y})$
    $4x - y$

20. $(\sqrt{p} + 5\sqrt{s})(\sqrt{p} - 5\sqrt{s})$
    $p - 25s$

21. $(4\sqrt{x} + 3)^2$
    $16x + 24\sqrt{x} + 9$

22. $(5\sqrt{p} - 6)^2$
    $25p - 60\sqrt{p} + 36$

23. $(9 - \sqrt[3]{2})(9 + \sqrt[3]{2})$
    $81 - \sqrt[3]{4}$

24. $(7 + \sqrt[3]{6})(7 - \sqrt[3]{6})$
    $49 - \sqrt[3]{36}$

25. The correct answer to Exercise 7 is $6 - 4\sqrt{3}$. Explain why this is not equal to $2\sqrt{3}$.

$6 - 4\sqrt{3}$ is not equal to $2\sqrt{3}$ because 6 and $4\sqrt{3}$ are not like terms, so they cannot be combined.

26. When we rationalize the denominator in the radical expression $\frac{1}{\sqrt{2}}$, we multiply both the numerator and denominator by $\sqrt{2}$. What property of real numbers covered in Section 1.4 justifies this procedure?

identity property for multiplication

Rationalize the denominator in each expression. Assume that all variables represent positive real numbers. See Example 2.

27. $\frac{7}{\sqrt{7}}$ **$\sqrt{7}$**

28. $\frac{11}{\sqrt{11}}$ **$\sqrt{11}$**

29. $\frac{15}{\sqrt{3}}$ **$5\sqrt{3}$**

30. $\frac{12}{\sqrt{6}}$ **$2\sqrt{6}$**

31. $\frac{\sqrt{3}}{\sqrt{2}}$ **$\frac{\sqrt{6}}{2}$**

32. $\frac{\sqrt{7}}{\sqrt{6}}$ **$\frac{\sqrt{42}}{6}$**

33. $\frac{9\sqrt{3}}{\sqrt{5}}$ **$\frac{9\sqrt{15}}{5}$**

34. $\frac{3\sqrt{2}}{\sqrt{11}}$ **$\frac{3\sqrt{22}}{11}$**

35. $\frac{-6}{\sqrt{18}}$ **$-\sqrt{2}$**

36. $\frac{-5}{\sqrt{24}}$ **$\frac{-5\sqrt{6}}{12}$**

37. $\frac{-8\sqrt{3}}{\sqrt{k}}$ **$\frac{-8\sqrt{3k}}{k}$**

38. $\frac{-4\sqrt{13}}{\sqrt{m}}$ **$\frac{-4\sqrt{13m}}{m}$**

39. $\frac{6\sqrt{3y}}{\sqrt{y^3}}$ **$\frac{6\sqrt{3}}{y}$**

40. $\frac{-8\sqrt{5y}}{\sqrt{y^5}}$ **$\frac{-8\sqrt{5}}{y^2}$**

41. Look again at the expression in Exercise 39. Start by multiplying both the numerator and the denominator by $\sqrt{y}$, to obtain the final answer. Then start over, multiplying both the numerator and denominator by $\sqrt{y^3}$, to obtain the same answer. Which method do you prefer? Why?

Both methods lead to the same result, $\frac{6\sqrt{3}}{y}$, but multiplying the numerator and denominator by $\sqrt{y}$ produces this result more directly, with less simplification required.

42. Explain why $\frac{1}{\sqrt[3]{2}}$ would not be written with the denominator rationalized if you begin by multiplying both the numerator and denominator by $\sqrt[3]{2}$. By what should you multiply them both to achieve the desired result?

To rationalize a cube root, three factors of the quantity under the radical sign are needed. We must multiply by $\sqrt[3]{2^2}$ or $\sqrt[3]{4}$ to rationalize $\sqrt[3]{2}$.

Simplify. Assume that all variables represent positive real numbers. See Examples 3 and 4.

43. $\sqrt{\frac{7}{2}}$ **$\frac{\sqrt{14}}{2}$**

44. $\sqrt{\frac{10}{3}}$ **$\frac{\sqrt{30}}{3}$**

45. $-\sqrt{\frac{7}{50}}$ **$-\frac{\sqrt{14}}{10}$**

46. $-\sqrt{\frac{13}{75}}$ **$-\frac{\sqrt{39}}{15}$**

47. $\sqrt{\frac{24}{x}}$ **$\frac{2\sqrt{6x}}{x}$**

48. $\sqrt{\frac{52}{y}}$ **$\frac{2\sqrt{13y}}{y}$**

49. $-\sqrt{\frac{98r^3}{s}}$ **$-\frac{7r\sqrt{2rs}}{s}$**

50. $-\sqrt{\frac{150m^5}{n}}$ **$-\frac{5m^2\sqrt{6mn}}{n}$**

51. $\sqrt{\frac{288x^7}{y^9}}$ **$\frac{12x^3\sqrt{2xy}}{y^5}$**

52. $\sqrt{\frac{242t^9}{u^{11}}}$ **$\frac{11t^4\sqrt{2tu}}{u^6}$**

53. $\sqrt[3]{\frac{2}{3}}$ $\frac{\sqrt[3]{18}}{3}$

54. $\sqrt[3]{\frac{4}{5}}$ $\frac{\sqrt[3]{100}}{5}$

55. $\sqrt[3]{\frac{4}{9}}$ $\frac{\sqrt[3]{12}}{3}$

56. $\sqrt[3]{\frac{5}{16}}$ $\frac{\sqrt[3]{20}}{4}$

57. $-\sqrt[3]{\frac{2p}{r^2}}$ $-\frac{\sqrt[3]{2pr}}{r}$

58. $-\sqrt[3]{\frac{6x}{y^2}}$ $-\frac{\sqrt[3]{6xy}}{y}$

59. $\sqrt[4]{\frac{16}{x}}$ $\frac{2\sqrt[4]{x^3}}{x}$

60. $\sqrt[4]{\frac{81}{y}}$ $\frac{3\sqrt[4]{y^3}}{y}$

61. Explain the procedure you will use to rationalize the denominator of the expression in Exercise 63:

$$\frac{2}{4+\sqrt{3}}.$$

Multiply the numerator and denominator by $4-\sqrt{3}$, so the denominator becomes $(4+\sqrt{3})(4-\sqrt{3}) = 16 - 3 = 13$, a rational number.

62. Would multiplying both the numerator and denominator of $\frac{2}{4+\sqrt{3}}$ by $4+\sqrt{3}$ lead to a rationalized denominator? Why or why not?

No, because $(4+\sqrt{3})(4+\sqrt{3}) = 16 + 8\sqrt{3} + 3 = 19 + 8\sqrt{3}$, which is not a rational number.

Rationalize the denominator in each expression. Assume that all variables represent positive real numbers and that no denominators are 0. See Example 5.

63. $\frac{2}{4+\sqrt{3}}$ $\frac{2(4-\sqrt{3})}{13}$

64. $\frac{6}{5+\sqrt{2}}$ $\frac{6(5-\sqrt{2})}{23}$

65. $\frac{6}{\sqrt{5}+\sqrt{3}}$ $3(\sqrt{5}-\sqrt{3})$

66. $\frac{12}{\sqrt{6}+\sqrt{3}}$ $4(\sqrt{6}-\sqrt{3})$

67. $\frac{-4}{\sqrt{3}-\sqrt{7}}$ $\sqrt{3}+\sqrt{7}$

68. $\frac{-3}{\sqrt{2}+\sqrt{5}}$ $\sqrt{2}-\sqrt{5}$

69. $\frac{1-\sqrt{2}}{\sqrt{7}+\sqrt{6}}$ $\sqrt{7}-\sqrt{6}-\sqrt{14}+2\sqrt{3}$

70. $\frac{-1-\sqrt{3}}{\sqrt{6}+\sqrt{5}}$ $-\sqrt{6}+\sqrt{5}-3\sqrt{2}+\sqrt{15}$

71. $\frac{4\sqrt{x}}{\sqrt{x}-2\sqrt{y}}$ $\frac{4\sqrt{x}(\sqrt{x}+2\sqrt{y})}{x-4y}$

72. $\frac{5\sqrt{r}}{3\sqrt{r}+\sqrt{s}}$ $\frac{5\sqrt{r}(3\sqrt{r}-\sqrt{s})}{9r-s}$

73. $\frac{\sqrt{x}-\sqrt{y}}{\sqrt{2x}+\sqrt{3y}}$ $\frac{x\sqrt{2}-\sqrt{3xy}-\sqrt{2xy}+y\sqrt{3}}{2x-3y}$

74. $\frac{\sqrt{a}+\sqrt{b}}{\sqrt{5a}-\sqrt{2b}}$ $\frac{a\sqrt{5}+\sqrt{2ab}+\sqrt{5ab}+b\sqrt{2}}{5a-2b}$

75. If a and b are both positive numbers and $a^2 = b^2$, then $a = b$. Use this fact to show that

$$\frac{\sqrt{6}-\sqrt{2}}{4} = \frac{\sqrt{2-\sqrt{3}}}{2}.$$

Square each side to show that each square is equal to $\frac{2-\sqrt{3}}{4}$.

76. Use a calculator approximation to support the result in Exercise 75.

Each original expression is approximately equal to .2588190451.

Write each quotient in lowest terms. Assume that all variables represent positive real numbers. See Example 6.

77. $\dfrac{25+10\sqrt{6}}{20}$ **$\dfrac{5+2\sqrt{6}}{4}$**

78. $\dfrac{12-6\sqrt{2}}{24}$ **$\dfrac{2-\sqrt{2}}{4}$**

79. $\dfrac{16+4\sqrt{8}}{12}$ **$\dfrac{4+2\sqrt{2}}{3}$**

80. $\dfrac{12+9\sqrt{72}}{18}$ **$\dfrac{2+9\sqrt{2}}{3}$**

81. $\dfrac{6x+\sqrt{24x^3}}{3x}$ **$\dfrac{6+2\sqrt{6x}}{3}$**

82. $\dfrac{11y+\sqrt{242y^5}}{22y}$ **$\dfrac{1+y\sqrt{2y}}{2}$**

RELATING CONCEPTS (Exercises 83–86) FOR INDIVIDUAL OR GROUP WORK

Sometimes it is desirable to rationalize the numerator *in an expression. The procedure is similar to rationalizing the denominator. For example, to rationalize the numerator of*

$$\frac{6-\sqrt{2}}{3},$$

we multiply both the numerator and denominator by the conjugate of the numerator, $6+\sqrt{2}$.

$$\frac{6-\sqrt{2}}{3} = \frac{(6-\sqrt{2})(6+\sqrt{2})}{3(6+\sqrt{2})} = \frac{36-2}{3(6+\sqrt{2})} = \frac{34}{3(6+\sqrt{2})}$$

In the final expression, the numerator is rationalized. ***Work Exercises 83–86 in order.***

83. Rationalize the numerator of $\dfrac{8\sqrt{5}-1}{6}$. **$\dfrac{319}{6(8\sqrt{5}+1)}$**

84. Rationalize the numerator of $\dfrac{3\sqrt{a}+\sqrt{b}}{\sqrt{b}-\sqrt{a}}$. Assume a and b are positive and $a \neq b$. **$\dfrac{9a-b}{(\sqrt{b}-\sqrt{a})(3\sqrt{a}-\sqrt{b})}$**

85. Rationalize the denominator of the expression in Exercise 84. **$\dfrac{(3\sqrt{a}+\sqrt{b})(\sqrt{b}+\sqrt{a})}{b-a}$**

86. Describe the difference in the procedures used in Exercises 84 and 85.

In Exercise 84, we multiplied the numerator and denominator by the conjugate of the numerator, while in Exercise 85 we multiplied by the conjugate of the denominator.

9.6 Equations with Radical Expressions

An equation that includes one or more radical expressions with a variable is called a **radical equation.** Some examples of radical equations are

$$\sqrt{x-4}=8, \quad \sqrt{5x+12}=3\sqrt{2x-1}, \quad \text{and} \quad \sqrt[3]{6+x}=27.$$

OBJECTIVES

1. Solve radical equations using the power rule.
2. Solve radical equations that require additional steps.
3. Solve radical equations with indexes greater than 2.

1 Solve radical equations using the power rule. The equation $x = 1$ has only one solution. Its solution set is $\{1\}$. If we square both sides of this equation, we get $x^2 = 1$. This new equation has two solutions: -1 and 1. Notice that the solution of the original equation is also a solution of the squared equation. However, the squared equation has another solution, -1, that is *not* a solution of the original equation. When solving equations with radicals, we use this idea of raising both sides to a power. It is an application of the *power rule.*

Power Rule for Solving Equations with Radicals

If both sides of an equation are raised to the same power, all solutions of the original equation are also solutions of the new equation.

Read the power rule carefully; it does *not* say that all solutions of the new equation are solutions of the original equation. They may or may not be. Solutions that do not satisfy the original equation are called **extraneous solutions;** they must be discarded.

CAUTION

When the power rule is used to solve an equation, ***every solution of the new equation* must *be checked in the original equation.***

Example 1 **Using the Power Rule**

Solve $\sqrt{3x+4}=8$.

Use the power rule and square both sides to get

$$(\sqrt{3x+4})^2 = 8^2$$
$$3x+4=64$$
$$3x=60$$
$$x=20.$$

To check, substitute the potential solution in the *original* equation.

$$\sqrt{3x+4}=8$$
$$\sqrt{3\cdot 20+4}=8 \quad ? \quad \text{Let } x=20.$$
$$\sqrt{64}=8 \quad ?$$
$$8=8 \quad \text{True}$$

Since 20 satisfies the *original* equation, the solution set is $\{20\}$.

Work Problem 1 at the Side.

The solution of the equation in Example 1 can be generalized to give a method for solving equations with radicals.

1 Solve.

(a) $\sqrt{r}=3$

(b) $\sqrt{5x+1}=4$

ANSWERS
1. (a) $\{9\}$ **(b)** $\{3\}$

2 Solve.

(a) $\sqrt{k} + 4 = -3$

(b) $\sqrt{x-9} - 3 = 0$

Solving an Equation with Radicals

Step 1 **Isolate the radical.** Make sure that one radical term is alone on one side of the equation.

Step 2 **Apply the power rule.** Raise both sides of the equation to a power that is the same as the index of the radical.

Step 3 **Solve.** Solve the resulting equation; if it still contains a radical, repeat Steps 1 and 2.

Step 4 **Check.** It is essential that all potential solutions be checked in the original equation.

CAUTION

Remember Step 4 or you may get an incorrect solution set.

Example 2 Using the Power Rule

Solve $\sqrt{5q-1} + 3 = 0$.

Step 1 To get the radical alone on one side, subtract 3 from each side.

$$\sqrt{5q-1} = -3$$

Step 2 Now square both sides.

$$(\sqrt{5q-1})^2 = (-3)^2$$

Step 3

$$5q - 1 = 9$$
$$5q = 10$$
$$q = 2$$

Step 4 Check the potential solution, 2, by substituting it in the original equation.

$$\sqrt{5q-1} + 3 = 0$$
$$\sqrt{5 \cdot 2 - 1} + 3 = 0 \quad ? \quad \text{Let } q = 2.$$
$$3 + 3 = 0 \quad \text{False}$$

This false result shows that 2 is *not* a solution of the original equation; it is extraneous. The solution set is $\emptyset$.

NOTE

We could have determined after Step 1 that the equation in Example 2 has no solution because the expression on the left cannot be negative.

Work Problem 2 at the Side.

2 Solve radical equations that require additional steps. The next examples involve finding the square of a binomial. Recall that

$$(x + y)^2 = x^2 + 2xy + y^2.$$

ANSWERS

2. (a) $\emptyset$ **(b)** $\{18\}$

Example 3 **Using the Power Rule; Squaring a Binomial**

Solve $\sqrt{4 - x} = x + 2$.

Step 1 The radical is alone on the left side of the equation.

Step 2 Square both sides; the square of $x + 2$ is $(x + 2)^2 = x^2 + 4x + 4$.

$$(\sqrt{4 - x})^2 = (x + 2)^2$$
$$4 - x = x^2 + 4x + 4$$

Twice the product of 2 and x

Step 3 The new equation is quadratic, so get 0 on one side.

$$0 = x^2 + 5x \qquad \text{Subtract 4 and add } x.$$
$$0 = x(x + 5) \qquad \text{Factor.}$$
$$x = 0 \quad \text{or} \quad x + 5 = 0 \qquad \text{Zero-factor property}$$
$$x = -5$$

Step 4 Check each potential solution in the original equation.

If $x = 0$, then

$$\sqrt{4 - x} = x + 2$$
$$\sqrt{4 - 0} = 0 + 2 \quad ?$$
$$\sqrt{4} = 2 \quad ?$$
$$2 = 2. \quad \text{True}$$

If $x = -5$, then

$$\sqrt{4 - x} = x + 2$$
$$\sqrt{4 - (-5)} = -5 + 2 \quad ?$$
$$\sqrt{9} = -3 \quad ?$$
$$3 = -3. \quad \text{False}$$

The solution set is $\{0\}$. The other potential solution, -5, is extraneous.

CAUTION

When a radical equation requires squaring a binomial as in Example 3, remember to include the middle term.

$(x + 2)^2 \neq x^2 + 4$	$(x + 2)^2 = x^2 + 4x + 4$
INCORRECT	**CORRECT**

Work Problem 3 at the Side.

3 Solve.

(a) $\sqrt{3z - 5} = z - 1$

(b) $x + 1 = \sqrt{-2x - 2}$

Example 4 **Using the Power Rule; Squaring a Binomial**

Solve $\sqrt{m^2 - 4m + 9} = m - 1$.

Squaring both sides gives $(m - 1)^2 = m^2 - 2(m)(1) + 1^2$ on the right.

$$(\sqrt{m^2 - 4m + 9})^2 = (m - 1)^2$$
$$m^2 - 4m + 9 = m^2 - 2m + 1$$

Twice the product of m and -1

Subtract m^2 and 1 from each side, then add $4m$ to each side to get

$$8 = 2m$$
$$4 = m.$$

Check this potential solution in the original equation.

$$\sqrt{m^2 - 4m + 9} = m - 1$$
$$\sqrt{4^2 - 4 \cdot 4 + 9} = 4 - 1 \quad ? \qquad \text{Let } m = 4.$$
$$3 = 3 \qquad \text{True}$$

The solution set of the original equation is $\{4\}$.

Work Problem 4 at the Side.

4 Solve

$\sqrt{4a^2 + 2a - 3} = 2a + 7$.

ANSWERS

3. **(a)** $\{2, 3\}$ **(b)** $\{-1\}$

4. $\{-2\}$

5 Solve
$\sqrt{p+1} - \sqrt{p-4} = 1.$

6 Solve each equation.

(a) $\sqrt[3]{p^2 + 3p + 12} = \sqrt[3]{p^2}$

(b) $\sqrt[4]{2k+5} + 1 = 0$

ANSWERS
5. $\{8\}$
6. **(a)** $\{-4\}$ **(b)** $\emptyset$

Example 5 Using the Power Rule; Squaring Twice

Solve $\sqrt{5m+6} + \sqrt{3m+4} = 2$.

Start by getting one radical alone on one side of the equation by subtracting $\sqrt{3m+4}$ from each side.

$$\sqrt{5m+6} = 2 - \sqrt{3m+4}$$

Now square both sides.

$$(\sqrt{5m+6})^2 = (2 - \sqrt{3m+4})^2$$
$$5m + 6 = 4 - 4\sqrt{3m+4} + (3m+4)$$

Twice the product of 2 and $-\sqrt{3m+4}$

This equation still contains a radical, so square both sides again. Before doing this, isolate the radical term on the right.

$$5m + 6 = 8 + 3m - 4\sqrt{3m+4}$$
$$2m - 2 = -4\sqrt{3m+4} \quad \text{Subtract 8 and } 3m.$$
$$m - 1 = -2\sqrt{3m+4} \quad \text{Divide by 2.}$$
$$(m-1)^2 = (-2\sqrt{3m+4})^2 \quad \text{Square both sides again.}$$
$$m^2 - 2m + 1 = (-2)^2(\sqrt{3m+4})^2 \quad (ab)^2 = a^2b^2$$
$$m^2 - 2m + 1 = 4(3m+4)$$
$$m^2 - 2m + 1 = 12m + 16 \quad \text{Distributive property}$$
$$m^2 - 14m - 15 = 0 \quad \text{Standard form}$$
$$(m-15)(m+1) = 0 \quad \text{Factor.}$$
$$m - 15 = 0 \quad \text{or} \quad m + 1 = 0 \quad \text{Zero-factor property}$$
$$m = 15 \quad \text{or} \quad m = -1$$

Check each of these potential solutions in the original equation. Only -1 works, so the solution set, $\{-1\}$, has only one element.

Work Problem 5 at the Side.

3 Solve radical equations with indexes greater than 2.

The power rule also works for powers greater than 2.

Example 6 Using the Power Rule for a Power Greater than 2

Solve $\sqrt[3]{z+5} = \sqrt[3]{2z-6}$.

Raise both sides to the third power.

$$(\sqrt[3]{z+5})^3 = (\sqrt[3]{2z-6})^3$$
$$z + 5 = 2z - 6$$
$$11 = z$$

Check this result in the original equation.

$$\sqrt[3]{z+5} = \sqrt[3]{2z-6}$$
$$\sqrt[3]{11+5} = \sqrt[3]{2 \cdot 11 - 6} \quad ? \quad \text{Let } z = 11.$$
$$\sqrt[3]{16} = \sqrt[3]{16} \quad \text{True}$$

The solution set is $\{11\}$.

Work Problem 6 at the Side.

9.6 EXERCISES

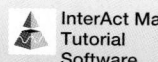

FOR EXTRA HELP — Student's Solutions Manual; MyMathLab.com; InterAct Math Tutorial Software; AW Math Tutor Center; www.mathxl.com; Digital Video Tutor CD 8 Videotape 18

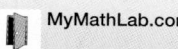

1. Is 9 a solution of the equation $\sqrt{x} = -3$? If not, what is the solution of this equation?

No; there is no solution.

2. Before even attempting to solve $\sqrt{3x + 18} = x$, how can you be sure that the equation cannot have a negative solution?

The radical on the left-hand side cannot be negative, and it must equal x, so x cannot be negative.

Solve each equation. See Examples 1 and 2.

3. $\sqrt{x - 3} = 4$

{19}

4. $\sqrt{y + 2} = 5$

{23}

5. $\sqrt{3k - 2} = 6$

$\left\{\frac{38}{3}\right\}$

6. $\sqrt{4t + 7} = 9$

$\left\{\frac{37}{2}\right\}$

7. $\sqrt{x} + 9 = 0$

$\emptyset$

8. $\sqrt{w} + 4 = 0$

$\emptyset$

9. $\sqrt{3x - 6} - 3 = 0$

{5}

10. $\sqrt{7y + 11} - 5 = 0$

{2}

11. $\sqrt{6x + 2} - \sqrt{5x + 3} = 0$

{1}

12. $\sqrt{3 + 5x} - \sqrt{x + 11} = 0$

{2}

13. $3\sqrt{x} = \sqrt{8x + 9}$

{9}

14. $6\sqrt{p} = \sqrt{30p + 24}$

{4}

15. Explain what is wrong with this step in the solution process for $\sqrt{3x + 4} = 8 - x$.

$$3x + 4 = 64 + x^2$$

You cannot just square each term. The right-hand side should be $(8 - x)^2 = 64 - 16x + x^2$.

16. Explain what is wrong with this step in the solution process for $\sqrt{5y + 6} = \sqrt{y + 3} - 3$.

$$5y + 6 = (y + 3) - 9$$

You cannot just square each term. The right-hand side should be $(\sqrt{y + 3} - 3)^2 = y + 3 - 6\sqrt{y + 3} + 9$.

Solve each equation. See Examples 3 and 4.

17. $\sqrt{3x + 4} = 8 - x$

{4}

18. $\sqrt{5x + 1} = 2x - 2$

{3}

19. $\sqrt{13 + 4t} = t + 4$

$\{-3, -1\}$

20. $\sqrt{50 + 7k} = k + 8$

$\{-7, -2\}$

21. $\sqrt{r^2 - 15r + 15} + 5 = r$

$\emptyset$

22. $\sqrt{p^2 + 12p - 4} + 4 = p$

$\emptyset$

23. $\sqrt{3x + 7} - 3x = 5$

$\{-1\}$

24. $\sqrt{4x + 13} - 2x = -1$

$\{3\}$

25. $\sqrt{4x + 2} - 4x = 0$

$\left\{\frac{1}{2}\right\}$

26. $\sqrt{4 - 2x} - 8 = 2x$

$\left\{-\frac{5}{2}\right\}$

Solve each equation. See Example 5.

27. $\sqrt{r + 4} - \sqrt{r - 4} = 2$

$\{5\}$

28. $\sqrt{m + 1} - \sqrt{m - 2} = 1$

$\{3\}$

29. $\sqrt{11 + 2q} + 1 = \sqrt{5q + 1}$

$\{7\}$

30. $\sqrt{6 + 5y} - 3 = \sqrt{y + 3}$

$\{6\}$

31. $\sqrt{3 - 3p} - \sqrt{3p + 2} = 3$

$\emptyset$

32. $\sqrt{3x + 4} - \sqrt{2x - 4} = 2$

$\{4, 20\}$

33. What is the smallest power to which you can raise both sides of the radical equation

$$\sqrt[3]{x+3} = \sqrt[3]{5+4x}$$

so that the radicals are eliminated?

3

34. What is the smallest power to which you can raise both sides of the radical equation

$$\sqrt{x+3} = \sqrt[3]{10x+14}$$

so that the radicals are eliminated?

6

Solve each equation. See Example 6.

35. $\sqrt[3]{2x^2+3x-7} = \sqrt[3]{2x^2+4x+6}$

$\{-13\}$

36. $\sqrt[3]{3y^2-4y+6} = \sqrt[3]{3y^2-2y+8}$

$\{-1\}$

37. $\sqrt[3]{1-2k} - \sqrt[3]{-k-13} = 0$

$\{14\}$

38. $\sqrt[3]{11-2t} - \sqrt[3]{-1-5t} = 0$

$\{-4\}$

39. $\sqrt[4]{x-1} + 2 = 0$

$\emptyset$

40. $\sqrt[4]{2k+3} + 1 = 0$

$\emptyset$

41. $\sqrt[4]{x+7} = \sqrt[4]{2x}$

$\{7\}$

42. $\sqrt[4]{y+8} = \sqrt[4]{3y}$

$\{4\}$

For each equation, rewrite the expressions with rational exponents as radical expressions. Then solve using the procedures explained in this section.

43. $(5r-6)^{1/2} = 2 + (3r-6)^{1/2}$

$\{2, 14\}$

44. $(3w+7)^{1/2} = 1 + (w+2)^{1/2}$

$\{-2, -1\}$

45. $(2w - 1)^{2/3} - w^{1/3} = 0$

$\left\{\frac{1}{4}, 1\right\}$

46. $(x^2 - 2x)^{1/3} - x^{1/3} = 0$

$\{0, 3\}$

If x represents the number of years since 1985, the equation $y = .4x^2$ *approximates the number of U.S. cell-phone subscribers, in millions. For example,* $x = 5$ *represents 1990,* $x = 10$ *represents 1995, and so on.*

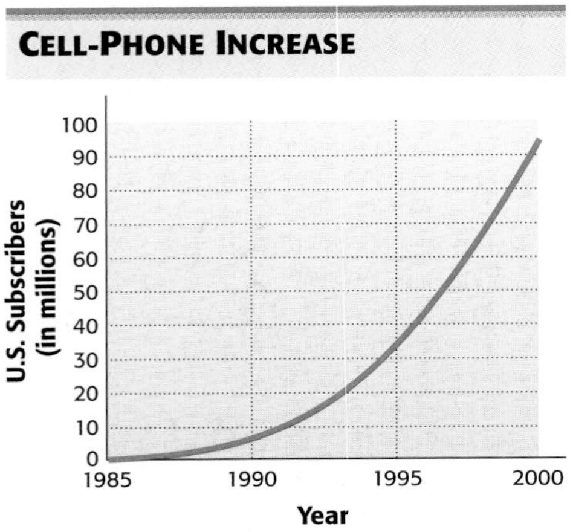

Source: Cellular Telecommunications Industry Association.

47. Replace x in the equation for each year shown in the figure, and give the value of y.

1985: 0; 1990: 10 million; 1995: 40 million; 2000: 90 million

48. Use the figure to estimate the number of subscribers for each year shown.

1985: 0; 1990: 6 million; 1995: 34 million; 2000: 95 million

49. Compare the values found from the equation with your estimates from the figure. Does the equation give a good approximation of the data from the figure? To the nearest million, in which year after 1985 is the approximation closest?

The approximation is reasonably good; 1990.

50. Use the equation to approximate the year when the number of cell-phone subscribers reached 70 million.

1998

9.7 Complex Numbers

As we saw in Chapter 1, the set of real numbers includes many other number sets (the rational numbers, integers, and natural numbers, for example). In this section a new set of numbers is introduced that includes the set of real numbers, as well as numbers that are even roots of negative numbers, like $\sqrt{-2}$.

Objectives

1. Simplify numbers of the form $\sqrt{-b}$, where $b > 0$.
2. Recognize imaginary complex numbers.
3. Add and subtract complex numbers.
4. Multiply complex numbers.
5. Divide complex numbers.
6. Find powers of i.

1 Simplify numbers of the form $\sqrt{-b}$, where $b > 0$. The equation $x^2 + 1 = 0$ has no real number solution since any solution must be a number whose square is -1. In the set of real numbers, all squares are nonnegative numbers because the product of two positive numbers or two negative numbers is positive and $0^2 = 0$. To provide a solution for the equation $x^2 + 1 = 0$, a new number i is defined so that

$$i^2 = -1.$$

That is, i is a number whose square is -1, so $i = \sqrt{-1}$. This definition of i makes it possible to define any square root of a negative number as follows.

For any positive number b,

$$\sqrt{-b} = i\sqrt{b}.$$

Example 1 **Simplifying Square Roots of Negative Numbers**

Write each number as a product of a real number and i.

(a) $\sqrt{-100} = i\sqrt{100} = 10i$ **(b)** $-\sqrt{-36} = -i\sqrt{36} = -6i$

(c) $\sqrt{-2} = i\sqrt{2}$

CAUTION

It is easy to mistake $\sqrt{2}i$ for $\sqrt{2i}$, with the i under the radical. For this reason, we usually write $\sqrt{2}i$ as $i\sqrt{2}$, as in the definition of $\sqrt{-b}$.

Work Problem 1 at the Side.

When finding a product such as $\sqrt{-4} \cdot \sqrt{-9}$, we cannot use the product rule for radicals because it applies only to nonnegative radicands. For this reason, we change $\sqrt{-b}$ to the form $i\sqrt{b}$ before performing any multiplications or divisions. For example,

$$\begin{aligned}\sqrt{-4} \cdot \sqrt{-9} &= i\sqrt{4} \cdot i\sqrt{9} \\ &= i \cdot 2 \cdot i \cdot 3 \\ &= 6i^2 \\ &= 6(-1) \quad \text{Substitute: } i^2 = -1. \\ &= -6.\end{aligned}$$

1 Write each number as a product of a real number and i.

(a) $\sqrt{-16}$

(b) $-\sqrt{-81}$

(c) $\sqrt{-7}$

Answers

1. (a) $4i$ **(b)** $-9i$ **(c)** $i\sqrt{7}$

2 Multiply.

(a) $\sqrt{-7} \cdot \sqrt{-7}$

(b) $\sqrt{-5} \cdot \sqrt{-10}$

(c) $\sqrt{-15} \cdot \sqrt{2}$

3 Divide.

(a) $\dfrac{\sqrt{-32}}{\sqrt{-2}}$

(b) $\dfrac{\sqrt{-27}}{\sqrt{-3}}$

(c) $\dfrac{\sqrt{-40}}{\sqrt{10}}$

ANSWERS

2. **(a)** -7 **(b)** $-5\sqrt{2}$ **(c)** $i\sqrt{30}$

3. **(a)** 4 **(b)** 3 **(c)** $2i$

CAUTION

Using the product rule for radicals *before* using the definition of $\sqrt{-b}$ gives a *wrong* answer. The preceding example shows that

$$\sqrt{-4} \cdot \sqrt{-9} = -6, \text{ but}$$

$$\sqrt{-4(-9)} = \sqrt{36} = 6,$$

so $$\sqrt{-4} \cdot \sqrt{-9} \neq \sqrt{-4(-9)}.$$

Example 2 **Multiplying Square Roots of Negative Numbers**

Multiply.

(a) $\sqrt{-3} \cdot \sqrt{-7} = i\sqrt{3} \cdot i\sqrt{7}$

$= i^2\sqrt{3 \cdot 7}$

$= (-1)\sqrt{21}$ Substitute: $i^2 = -1$.

$= -\sqrt{21}$

(b) $\sqrt{-2} \cdot \sqrt{-8} = i\sqrt{2} \cdot i\sqrt{8}$

$= i^2\sqrt{2 \cdot 8}$

$= (-1)\sqrt{16}$

$= (-1)4$

$= -4$

(c) $\sqrt{-5} \cdot \sqrt{6} = i\sqrt{5} \cdot \sqrt{6} = i\sqrt{30}$

Work Problem 2 at the Side.

The methods used to find products also apply to quotients.

Example 3 **Dividing Square Roots of Negative Numbers**

Divide.

(a) $\dfrac{\sqrt{-75}}{\sqrt{-3}} = \dfrac{i\sqrt{75}}{i\sqrt{3}} = \sqrt{\dfrac{75}{3}} = \sqrt{25} = 5$

(b) $\dfrac{\sqrt{-32}}{\sqrt{8}} = \dfrac{i\sqrt{32}}{\sqrt{8}} = i\sqrt{\dfrac{32}{8}} = i\sqrt{4} = 2i$

Work Problem

2 **Recognize imaginary complex numbers.** With the imaginary number i and the real numbers, a new set of numbers can be formed that includes the real numbers as a subset. The *complex numbers* are defined as follows.

Complex Number

If a and b are real numbers, then any number of the form $a + bi$ is called a **complex number.**

In the complex number $a + bi$, the number a is called the **real part** and b is called the **imaginary part.** When $b = 0$, $a + bi$ is a real number, so the real numbers are a subset of the complex numbers. Complex numbers with $b \neq 0$ are called **imaginary numbers.*** In spite of their name, imaginary numbers are very useful in applications, particularly in work with electricity.

The relationships among the various sets of numbers discussed in this book are shown in Figure 9.

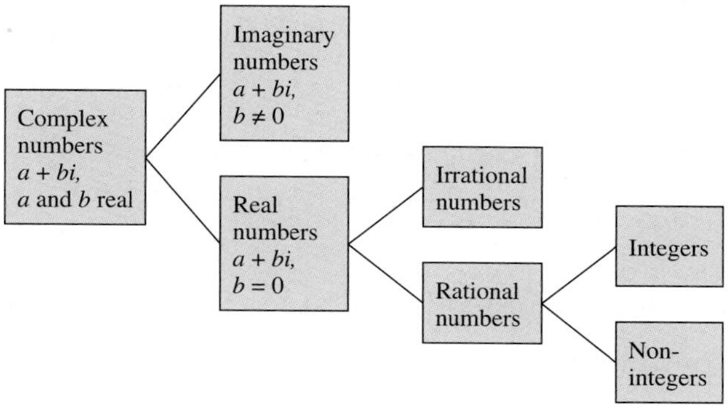

Figure 9

3 **Add and subtract complex numbers.** The commutative, associative, and distributive properties for real numbers are also valid for complex numbers. Thus, to add complex numbers, we add their real parts and add their imaginary parts.

Example 4 Adding Complex Numbers

Add.

(a) $(2 + 3i) + (6 + 4i)$

$= (2 + 6) + (3 + 4)i$ Commutative, associative, and distributive properties

$= 8 + 7i$

(b) $5 + (9 - 3i) = (5 + 9) - 3i$

$= 14 - 3i$

Work Problem 4 at the Side.

We subtract complex numbers by subtracting their real parts and subtracting their imaginary parts.

Example 5 Subtracting Complex Numbers

Subtract.

(a) $(6 + 5i) - (3 + 2i) = (6 - 3) + (5 - 2)i$

$= 3 + 3i$

(b) $(7 - 3i) - (8 - 6i) = (7 - 8) + [-3 - (-6)]i$

$= -1 + 3i$

(c) $(-9 + 4i) - (-9 + 8i) = (-9 + 9) + (4 - 8)i$

$= 0 - 4i$

$= -4i$

Work Problem 5 at the Side.

* Some texts define bi as the imaginary part of the complex number $a + bi$. Also, imaginary numbers are sometimes defined as complex numbers with $a = 0$ and $b \neq 0$.

4 Add.

(a) $(4 + 6i) + (-3 + 5i)$

(b) $(-1 + 8i) + (9 - 3i)$

5 Subtract.

(a) $(7 + 3i) - (4 + 2i)$

(b) $(-6 - i) - (-5 - 4i)$

(c) $8 - (3 - 2i)$

ANSWERS

4. (a) $1 + 11i$ **(b)** $8 + 5i$

5. (a) $3 + i$ **(b)** $-1 + 3i$ **(c)** $5 + 2i$

6 Multiply.

(a) $6i(4 + 3i)$

(b) $(6 - 4i)(2 + 4i)$

(c) $(3 - 2i)(3 + 2i)$

In Example 5(c), the answer was written as $0 - 4i$ and then as just $-4i$. A complex number written in the form $a + bi$, like $0 - 4i$, is in **standard form.** In this section, most answers will be given in standard form, but if a or b is 0, we consider answers such as a or bi to be in standard form.

4 Multiply complex numbers. We multiply complex numbers as we multiply polynomials. Complex numbers of the form $a + bi$ have the same form as binomials, so we multiply two complex numbers in standard form by using the FOIL method for multiplying binomials. (Recall that FOIL stands for *First, Outer, Inner, Last.*)

Example 6 Multiplying Complex Numbers

Multiply.

(a) $4i(2 + 3i)$

Use the distributive property.

$$\begin{aligned} 4i(2 + 3i) &= 4i(2) + 4i(3i) \\ &= 8i + 12i^2 \\ &= 8i + 12(-1) \quad \text{Substitute: } i^2 = -1. \\ &= -12 + 8i \end{aligned}$$

(b) $(3 + 5i)(4 - 2i)$

Use the FOIL method.

$$\begin{aligned} (3 + 5i)(4 - 2i) &= \underbrace{3(4)}_{\text{First}} + \underbrace{3(-2i)}_{\text{Outer}} + \underbrace{5i(4)}_{\text{Inner}} + \underbrace{5i(-2i)}_{\text{Last}} \\ &= 12 - 6i + 20i - 10i^2 \\ &= 12 + 14i - 10(-1) \quad \text{Substitute: } i^2 = -1. \\ &= 12 + 14i + 10 \\ &= 22 + 14i \end{aligned}$$

(c)
$$\begin{aligned} (2 + 3i)(1 - 5i) &= 2(1) + 2(-5i) + 3i(1) + 3i(-5i) \quad \text{FOIL} \\ &= 2 - 10i + 3i - 15i^2 \\ &= 2 - 7i - 15(-1) \\ &= 2 - 7i + 15 \\ &= 17 - 7i \end{aligned}$$

Work Problem 6 at the Side.

The two complex numbers $a + bi$ and $a - bi$ are called *conjugates* of each other. The product of a complex number and its conjugate is always a real number, as shown here.

$$\begin{aligned} (a + bi)(a - bi) &= a^2 - abi + abi - b^2i^2 \\ &= a^2 - b^2(-1) \\ (a + bi)(a - bi) &= a^2 + b^2 \end{aligned}$$

For example, $(3 + 7i)(3 - 7i) = 3^2 + 7^2 = 9 + 49 = 58$.

5 Divide complex numbers. The quotient of two complex numbers should be a complex number. To write the quotient as a complex number, we need to eliminate i in the denominator. We use conjugates to do this.

Answers

6. (a) $-18 + 24i$ **(b)** $28 + 16i$ **(c)** 13

Example 7 Dividing Complex Numbers

Find each quotient.

(a) $\dfrac{8 + 9i}{5 + 2i}$

Multiply both the numerator and denominator by the conjugate of the denominator. The conjugate of $5 + 2i$ is $5 - 2i$.

$$\begin{aligned}\frac{8 + 9i}{5 + 2i} &= \frac{(8 + 9i)(5 - 2i)}{(5 + 2i)(5 - 2i)}\\ &= \frac{40 - 16i + 45i - 18i^2}{5^2 + 2^2}\\ &= \frac{58 + 29i}{29} && \text{Substitute: } i^2 = -1; \text{ combine terms.}\\ &= \frac{29(2 + i)}{29} && \text{Factor the numerator.}\\ &= 2 + i && \text{Lowest terms}\end{aligned}$$

Notice that this is just like rationalizing a denominator. The final result is in standard form.

(b) $\dfrac{1 + i}{i}$

The conjugate of i is $-i$. Multiply both the numerator and denominator by $-i$.

$$\begin{aligned}\frac{1 + i}{i} &= \frac{(1 + i)(-i)}{i(-i)}\\ &= \frac{-i - i^2}{-i^2}\\ &= \frac{-i - (-1)}{-(-1)} && \text{Substitute: } i^2 = -1.\\ &= \frac{-i + 1}{1}\\ &= 1 - i\end{aligned}$$

Work Problem 7 at the Side.

Calculator Tip In Examples 4–7, we showed how complex numbers can be added, subtracted, multiplied, and divided using algebraic methods. Many current models of graphing calculators can perform these operations. Figure 10 shows how the computations in parts of Examples 4–7 are carried out by a TI-83 calculator. It is important to use parentheses as shown.

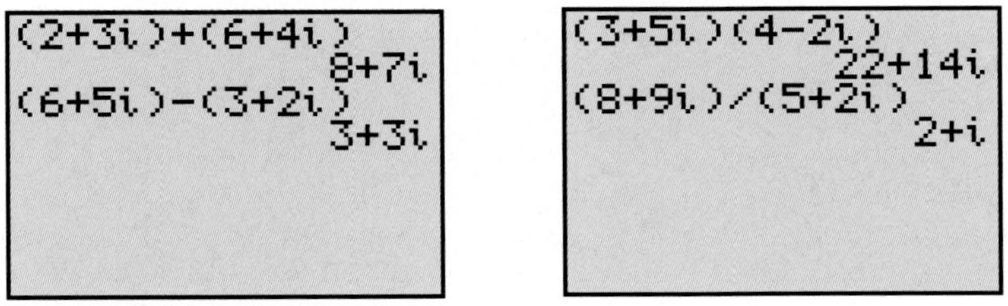

Figure 10

7 Find each quotient.

(a) $\dfrac{2 + i}{3 - i}$

(b) $\dfrac{6 + 2i}{4 - 3i}$

(c) $\dfrac{5}{3 - 2i}$

(d) $\dfrac{5 - i}{i}$

Answers

7. (a) $\frac{1}{2} + \frac{1}{2}i$ **(b)** $\frac{18}{25} + \frac{26}{25}i$ **(c)** $\frac{15}{13} + \frac{10}{13}i$ **(d)** $-1 - 5i$

8 Find each power of i.

(a) i^{21}

(b) i^{36}

(c) i^{50}

(d) i^{-9}

6 Find powers of *i*. Because i^2 is defined to be -1, we can find higher powers of i as shown in the following examples.

$$i^3 = i \cdot i^2 = i(-1) = -i \qquad i^6 = i^2 \cdot i^4 = (-1) \cdot 1 = -1$$

$$i^4 = i^2 \cdot i^2 = (-1)(-1) = 1 \qquad i^7 = i^3 \cdot i^4 = (-i) \cdot 1 = -i$$

$$i^5 = i \cdot i^4 = i \cdot 1 = i \qquad i^8 = i^4 \cdot i^4 = 1 \cdot 1 = 1$$

As these examples suggest, the powers of i rotate through the four numbers i, -1, $-i$, and 1. Larger powers of i can be simplified by using the fact that $i^4 = 1$. For example,

$$i^{75} = (i^4)^{18} \cdot i^3 = 1^{18} \cdot i^3 = 1 \cdot i^3 = i^3 = -i.$$

This example suggests a quick method for simplifying larger powers of i.

Example 8 Simplifying Powers of *i*

Find each power of i.

(a) $i^{12} = (i^4)^3 = 1^3 = 1$

(b)
$$\begin{aligned} i^{39} &= i^{36} \cdot i^3 \\ &= (i^4)^9 \cdot i^3 \\ &= 1^9 \cdot (-i) \\ &= -i \end{aligned}$$

(c) $i^{-2} = \dfrac{1}{i^2} = \dfrac{1}{-1} = -1$

(d) $i^{-1} = \dfrac{1}{i}$

To simplify this quotient, multiply both the numerator and denominator by $-i$, the conjugate of i.

$$\begin{aligned} \frac{1}{i} &= \frac{1(-i)}{i(-i)} \\ &= \frac{-i}{-i^2} \\ &= \frac{-i}{-(-1)} \\ &= \frac{-i}{1} \\ &= -i \end{aligned}$$

Work Problem 8 at the Side.

ANSWERS

8. **(a)** i **(b)** 1 **(c)** -1 **(d)** $-i$

9.7 EXERCISES

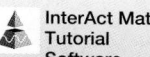

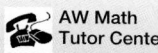

FOR EXTRA HELP: Student's Solutions Manual | MyMathLab.com | InterAct Math Tutorial Software | AW Math Tutor Center | MathXL www.mathxl.com | Digital Video Tutor CD 8 Videotape 18

Decide whether each expression is equal to 1, −1, i, or −i.

1. $\sqrt{-1}$ i

2. $-i^2$ 1

3. $\frac{1}{i}$ $-i$

4. $(-i)^2$ -1

5. Every real number is a complex number. Explain why this is so.
$a + bi$ is a complex number if a and b are real numbers and i is the imaginary unit. Therefore, for every real number a, if $b = 0$, $a = a + 0i$ is a complex number.

6. Not every complex number is a real number. Give an example of this, and explain why this statement is true.
$7i$ is a complex number that is not a real number. Any complex number $a + bi$ with $b \neq 0$ is not a real number.

Write each number as a product of a real number and i. Simplify all radical expressions. See Example 1.

7. $\sqrt{-169}$ $13i$

8. $\sqrt{-225}$ $15i$

9. $-\sqrt{-144}$ $-12i$

10. $-\sqrt{-196}$ $-14i$

11. $\sqrt{-5}$ $i\sqrt{5}$

12. $\sqrt{-21}$ $i\sqrt{21}$

13. $\sqrt{-48}$ $4i\sqrt{3}$

14. $\sqrt{-96}$ $4i\sqrt{6}$

Multiply or divide as indicated. See Examples 2 and 3.

15. $\sqrt{-15} \cdot \sqrt{-15}$ -15

16. $\sqrt{-19} \cdot \sqrt{-19}$ -19

17. $\sqrt{-4} \cdot \sqrt{-25}$ -10

18. $\sqrt{-9} \cdot \sqrt{-81}$ -27

19. $\frac{\sqrt{-300}}{\sqrt{-100}}$ $\sqrt{3}$

20. $\frac{\sqrt{-40}}{\sqrt{-10}}$ 2

21. $\frac{\sqrt{-75}}{\sqrt{3}}$ $5i$

22. $\frac{\sqrt{-160}}{\sqrt{10}}$ $4i$

Add or subtract as indicated. Write your answers in standard form. See Examples 4 and 5.

23. $(3 + 2i) + (-4 + 5i)$ $-1 + 7i$

24. $(7 + 15i) + (-11 + 14i)$ $-4 + 29i$

25. $(5 - i) + (-5 + i)$ 0

26. $(-2 + 6i) + (2 - 6i)$ 0

27. $(4 + i) - (-3 - 2i)$ $7 + 3i$

28. $(9 + i) - (3 + 2i)$ $6 - i$

29. $(-3 - 4i) - (-1 - 4i)$

-2

30. $(-2 - 3i) - (-5 - 3i)$

3

31. $(-4 + 11i) + (-2 - 4i) + (7 + 6i)$

$1 + 13i$

32. $(-1 + i) + (2 + 5i) + (3 + 2i)$

$4 + 8i$

33. $[(7 + 3i) - (4 - 2i)] + (3 + i)$

$6 + 6i$

34. $[(7 + 2i) + (-4 - i)] - (2 + 5i)$

$1 - 4i$

35. Fill in the blank with the correct response: Because $(4 + 2i) - (3 + i) = 1 + i$, using the definition of subtraction we can check this to find that $(1 + i) + (3 + i) =$ $\underline{4 + 2i}$.

36. Fill in the blank with the correct response: Because $\frac{-5}{2 - i} = -2 - i$, using the definition of division we can check this to find that $(-2 - i)(2 - i) =$ $\underline{-5}$.

Multiply. See Example 6.

37. $(3i)(27i)$

-81

38. $(5i)(125i)$

-625

39. $(-8i)(-2i)$

-16

40. $(-32i)(-2i)$

-64

41. $5i(-6 + 2i)$

$-10 - 30i$

42. $3i(4 + 9i)$

$-27 + 12i$

43. $(4 + 3i)(1 - 2i)$

$10 - 5i$

44. $(7 - 2i)(3 + i)$

$23 + i$

45. $(4 + 5i)^2$

$-9 + 40i$

46. $(3 + 2i)^2$

$5 + 12i$

47. $(12 + 3i)(12 - 3i)$

153

48. $(6 + 7i)(6 - 7i)$

85

49. **(a)** What is the conjugate of $a + bi$? $a - bi$

(b) If we multiply $a + bi$ by its conjugate, we get $\underline{a^2}$ + $\underline{b^2}$, which is always a real number.

50. Explain the procedure you would use to find the quotient

$$\frac{-1 + 5i}{3 + 2i}.$$

Multiply both the numerator and denominator by the complex conjugate of the denominator, $3 - 2i$. Then simplify the result by multiplying in the numerator and denominator and combining like terms. Write the quotient in the form $a + bi$.

Write each quotient in the form a + bi. See Example 7.

51. $\frac{2}{1 - i}$

$1 + i$

52. $\frac{29}{5 + 2i}$

$5 - 2i$

53. $\frac{-7 + 4i}{3 + 2i}$

$-1 + 2i$

54. $\frac{-38 - 8i}{7 + 3i}$

$-5 + i$

55. $\frac{8i}{2 + 2i}$

$2 + 2i$

56. $\frac{-8i}{1 + i}$

$-4 - 4i$

57. $\frac{2 - 3i}{2 + 3i}$

$-\frac{5}{13} - \frac{12}{13}i$

58. $\frac{-1 + 5i}{3 + 2i}$

$\frac{7}{13} + \frac{17}{13}i$

RELATING CONCEPTS (Exercises 59–64) FOR INDIVIDUAL OR GROUP WORK

Consider these expressions:

Binomials	**Complex Numbers**
$x + 2, \quad 3x - 1$	$1 + 2i, \quad 3 - i.$

When we add, subtract, or multiply complex numbers in standard form, the rules are the same as those for the corresponding operations on binomials. That is, we add or subtract like terms, and we use FOIL to multiply. Division, however, is comparable to division by the sum or difference of radicals, where we multiply by the conjugate of the denominator to get a rational denominator. To express the quotient of two complex numbers in standard form, we also multiply by the conjugate of the denominator. ***Work Exercises 59–64 in order,*** *to better understand these ideas.*

59. (a) Add the two binomials.

$4x + 1$

(b) Add the two complex numbers.

$4 + i$

60. (a) Subtract the second binomial from the first.

$-2x + 3$

(b) Subtract the second complex number from the first.

$-2 + 3i$

61. (a) Multiply the two binomials.

$3x^2 + 5x - 2$

(b) Multiply the two complex numbers.

$5 + 5i$

62. (a) Rationalize the denominator: $\frac{\sqrt{3} - 1}{1 + \sqrt{2}}$.

$-\sqrt{3} + \sqrt{6} + 1 - \sqrt{2}$

(b) Write in standard form: $\frac{3 - i}{1 + 2i}$.

$\frac{1}{5} - \frac{7}{5}i$

63. Explain why the answers for parts (a) and (b) in Exercise 61 do not correspond as the answers in Exercises 59 and 60 do.

Because $i^2 = -1$, two pairs of like terms can be combined in Exercise 61(b).

64. Explain why the answers for parts (a) and (b) in Exercise 62 do not correspond as the answers in Exercises 59 and 60 do.

Because $i^2 = -1$, additional terms can be combined in the numerator and denominator.

65. Recall that if $a \neq 0$, $\frac{1}{a}$ is called the reciprocal of a. Use this definition to express the reciprocal of $5 - 4i$ in the form $a + bi$.

$\frac{5}{41} + \frac{4}{41}i$

66. Recall that if $a \neq 0$, a^{-1} is defined to be $\frac{1}{a}$. Use this definition to express $(4 - 3i)^{-1}$ in the form $a + bi$.

$\frac{4}{25} + \frac{3}{25}i$

Find each power of i. See Example 8.

67. i^{18}

-1

68. i^{26}

-1

69. i^{89}

i

70. i^{45}

i

71. i^{96}

1

72. i^{48}

1

73. i^{-5}

$-i$

74. i^{-17}

$-i$

75. A student simplified i^{-18} as follows:

$$i^{-18} = i^{-18} \cdot i^{20} = i^{-18+20} = i^2 = -1.$$

Explain the mathematical justification for this correct work.

Since $i^{20} = (i^4)^5 = 1^5 = 1$, the student multiplied by 1, which is justified by the identity property for multiplication.

76. Explain why

$$(46 + 25i)(3 - 6i) \quad \text{and} \quad (46 + 25i)(3 - 6i)i^{12}$$

must be equal. (Do not actually perform the computation.)

$i^{12} = (i^4)^3 = 1^3 = 1$, so by the identity property for multiplication, the two products must be equal.

Ohm's law for the current I in a circuit with voltage E, resistance R, capacitance reactance X_c, and inductive reactance X_L is

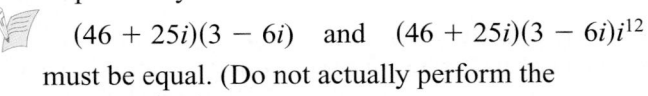

$$I = \frac{E}{R + (X_L - X_c)i}.$$

Use this law to work Exercises 77 and 78.

77. Find I if $E = 2 + 3i$, $R = 5$, $X_L = 4$, and $X_c = 3$.

$\frac{1}{2} + \frac{1}{2}i$

78. Find E if $I = 1 - i$, $R = 2$, $X_L = 3$, and $X_c = 1$.

4

79. Show that $1 + 5i$ is a solution of

$$x^2 - 2x + 26 = 0.$$

$(1 + 5i)^2 - 2(1 + 5i) + 26$ will simplify to 0 when the operations are applied.

80. Show that $3 + 2i$ is a solution of

$$x^2 - 6x + 13 = 0.$$

$(3 + 2i)^2 - 6(3 + 2i) + 13$ will simplify to 0 when the operations are applied.

Chapter 9

Summary

Key Terms

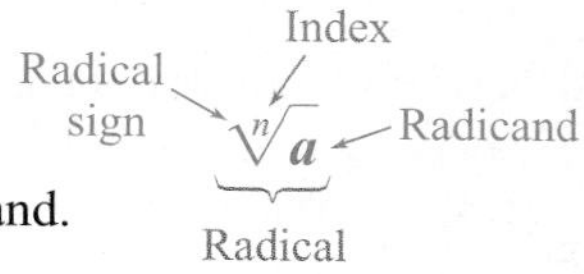

9.1	**square root**	The number b is a square root of a if $b^2 = a$.
	principal square root	The positive square root of a number is its principal square root.
	radicand	The number or expression inside a radical sign is called the radicand.
	radical	A radical sign with a radicand is called a radical.
	perfect square	A number with a rational square root is called a perfect square.
	cube root	The number b is a cube root of a if $b^3 = a$.
	index (order)	In a radical of the form $\sqrt[n]{a}$, the number n is the index or order.
	radical expression	An algebraic expression containing a radical is called a radical expression.
9.5	**rationalizing the denominator**	The process of removing radicals from the denominator so that the denominator contains only rational quantities is called rationalizing the denominator.
	conjugate	The conjugate of $a + b$ is $a - b$.
9.6	**radical equation**	A radical equation is an equation that includes one or more radical expressions with variables.
	extraneous solution	An extraneous solution of a radical equation is a solution of $x = a^2$ that is not a solution of $\sqrt{x} = a$.
9.7	**complex number**	A complex number is a number that can be written in the form $a + bi$, where a and b are real numbers.
	real part	The real part of $a + bi$ is a.
	imaginary part	The imaginary part of $a + bi$ is b.
	imaginary number	A complex number $a + bi$ with $b \neq 0$ is called an imaginary number.
	standard form (of a complex number)	A complex number is in standard form if it is written as $a + bi$.

New Symbols

$\sqrt{}$	radical sign
$\sqrt[n]{a}$	radical; principal nth root of a
$\pm$	positive or negative
$\approx$	is approximately equal to
$a^{1/n}$	a to the power $\frac{1}{n}$
$a^{m/n}$	a to the power $\frac{m}{n}$
i	a number whose square is -1

Test Your Word Power

See how well you have learned the vocabulary in this chapter. Answers follow the Quick Review.

1. A **radicand** is
(a) the index of a radical
(b) the number or expression under the radical sign
(c) the positive root of a number
(d) the radical sign.

2. The **Pythagorean formula** states that, in a right triangle,
(a) the sum of the measures of the angles is 180°
(b) the sum of the lengths of the two shorter sides equals the length of the longest side
(c) the longest side is opposite the right angle
(d) the square of the length of the longest side equals the sum of the squares of the lengths of the two shorter sides.

3. A **hypotenuse** is
(a) either of the two shorter sides of a triangle
(b) the shortest side of a triangle
(c) the side opposite the right angle in a triangle
(d) the longest side in any triangle.

4. Rationalizing the denominator is the process of
(a) eliminating fractions from a radical expression
(b) changing the denominator of a fraction from a radical to a rational number
(c) clearing a radical expression of radicals
(d) multiplying radical expressions.

5. An **extraneous solution** is a solution
(a) that does not satisfy the original equation
(b) that makes an equation true
(c) that makes an expression equal 0
(d) that checks in the original equation.

6. A **complex number** is
(a) a real number that includes a complex fraction
(b) a zero multiple of i
(c) a number of the form $a + bi$, where a and b are real numbers
(d) the square root of -1.

Quick Review

Concepts	*Examples*
9.1 Radical Expressions and Graphs	
$\sqrt[n]{a} = b$ means $b^n = a$. $\sqrt[n]{a}$ is the principal nth root of a. $\sqrt[n]{a^n} = \|a\|$ if n is even. $\sqrt[n]{a^n} = a$ if n is odd.	The two square roots of 64 are $\sqrt{64} = 8$, the principal square root, and $-\sqrt{64} = -8$. $\sqrt[3]{-27} = -3$ $\sqrt[4]{(-2)^4} = \|-2\| = 2$
Functions Defined by Radical Expressions The square root function with $f(x) = \sqrt{x}$ and the cube root function with $f(x) = \sqrt[3]{x}$ are two important functions defined by radical expressions.	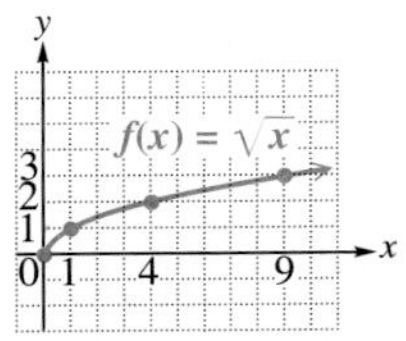 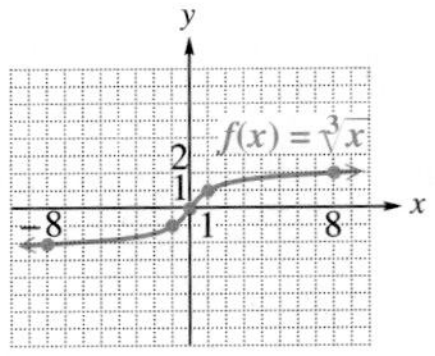
9.2 Rational Exponents $a^{1/n} = \sqrt[n]{a}$ whenever $\sqrt[n]{a}$ exists.	$81^{1/2} = \sqrt{81} = 9$ $-64^{1/3} = -\sqrt[3]{64} = -4$
If m and n are positive integers with m/n in lowest terms, then $a^{m/n} = (a^{1/n})^m$, provided that $a^{1/n}$ is a real number.	$8^{5/3} = (8^{1/3})^5 = 2^5 = 32$
All of the usual definitions and rules for exponents are valid for rational exponents.	$5^{-1/2} \cdot 5^{1/4} = 5^{-1/2+1/4} = 5^{-1/4} = \frac{1}{5^{1/4}}$ $(y^{2/5})^{10} = y^4$ $\frac{x^{-1/3}}{x^{-1/2}} = x^{-1/3-(-1/2)} = x^{-1/3+1/2} = x^{1/6},\quad x > 0$

Concepts	*Examples*

9.3 Simplifying Radical Expressions

Product and Quotient Rules for Radicals

If $\sqrt[n]{a}$ and $\sqrt[n]{b}$ are real numbers and n is a natural number,

$$\sqrt[n]{a} \cdot \sqrt[n]{b} = \sqrt[n]{ab}$$

and

$$\sqrt[n]{\frac{a}{b}} = \frac{\sqrt[n]{a}}{\sqrt[n]{b}}, \qquad b \neq 0.$$

$$\sqrt{3} \cdot \sqrt{7} = \sqrt{21}$$

$$\sqrt[5]{x^3y} \cdot \sqrt[5]{xy^2} = \sqrt[5]{x^4y^3}$$

$$\frac{\sqrt{x^5}}{\sqrt{x^4}} = \sqrt{\frac{x^5}{x^4}} = \sqrt{x}, \quad x > 0$$

Simplified Radical

1. The radicand has no factor raised to a power greater than or equal to the index.
2. The radicand has no fractions.
3. No denominator contains a radical.
4. Exponents in the radicand and the index of the radical have no common factors (except 1).

$$\sqrt{18} = \sqrt{9 \cdot 2} = 3\sqrt{2}$$

$$\sqrt[3]{54x^5y^3} = \sqrt[3]{27x^3y^3 \cdot 2x^2} = 3xy\sqrt[3]{2x^2}$$

$$\sqrt{\frac{7}{4}} = \frac{\sqrt{7}}{\sqrt{4}} = \frac{\sqrt{7}}{2}$$

$$\sqrt[9]{x^3} = x^{3/9} = x^{1/3} \quad \text{or} \quad \sqrt[3]{x}$$

Pythagorean Formula

If c is the length of the longest side of a right triangle and a and b are the lengths of the shorter sides, then $c^2 = a^2 + b^2$. The longest side is the hypotenuse and the two shorter sides are the legs of the triangle. The hypotenuse is opposite the right angle.

Find b for the triangle in the figure.

$$10^2 + b^2 = (2\sqrt{61})^2$$

$$b^2 = 4(61) - 100$$

$$b^2 = 144$$

$$b = 12$$

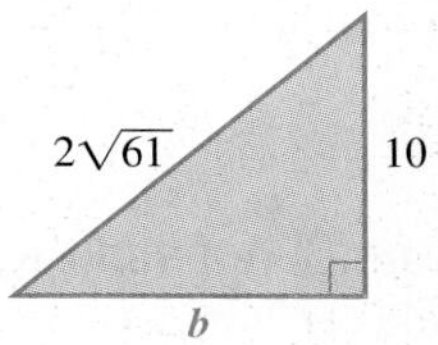

Distance Formula

The distance between (x_1, y_1) and (x_2, y_2) is

$$d = \sqrt{(x_2 - x_1)^2 + (y_2 - y_1)^2}.$$

The distance between $(3, -2)$ and $(-1, 1)$ is

$$\sqrt{(-1 - 3)^2 + [1 - (-2)]^2}$$

$$= \sqrt{(-4)^2 + 3^2} = \sqrt{16 + 9} = \sqrt{25} = 5.$$

9.4 Adding and Subtracting Radical Expressions

Only radical expressions with the same index and the same radicand may be combined.

$$3\sqrt{17} + 2\sqrt{17} - 8\sqrt{17} = (3 + 2 - 8)\sqrt{17}$$

$$= -3\sqrt{17}$$

$$\sqrt[3]{2} - \sqrt[3]{250} = \sqrt[3]{2} - 5\sqrt[3]{2}$$

$$= -4\sqrt[3]{2}$$

$$\left.\begin{matrix}\sqrt{15} + \sqrt{30} \\ \sqrt{3} + \sqrt[3]{9}\end{matrix}\right\} \text{ cannot be simplified further}$$

9.5 Multiplying and Dividing Radical Expressions

Multiply binomial radical expressions by using the FOIL method. Special products from Section 6.3 may apply.

$$(\sqrt{2} + \sqrt{7})(\sqrt{3} - \sqrt{6})$$

$$= \sqrt{6} - 2\sqrt{3} + \sqrt{21} - \sqrt{42} \qquad \sqrt{12} = 2\sqrt{3}$$

$$(\sqrt{5} - \sqrt{10})(\sqrt{5} + \sqrt{10}) = 5 - 10 = -5$$

$$(\sqrt{3} - \sqrt{2})^2 = 3 - 2\sqrt{3} \cdot \sqrt{2} + 2 = 5 - 2\sqrt{6}$$

Rationalize the denominator by multiplying both the numerator and denominator by the same expression.

$$\frac{\sqrt{7}}{\sqrt{5}} = \frac{\sqrt{7} \cdot \sqrt{5}}{\sqrt{5} \cdot \sqrt{5}} = \frac{\sqrt{35}}{5}$$

$$\frac{4}{\sqrt{5} - \sqrt{2}} = \frac{4(\sqrt{5} + \sqrt{2})}{(\sqrt{5} - \sqrt{2})(\sqrt{5} + \sqrt{2})}$$

$$= \frac{4(\sqrt{5} + \sqrt{2})}{5 - 2} = \frac{4(\sqrt{5} + \sqrt{2})}{3}$$

Concepts	*Examples*
9.6 Equations with Radical Expressions **Solving an Equation with Radicals** *Step 1* Isolate one radical on one side of the equation. *Step 2* Raise each side of the equation to a power that is the same as the index of the radical. *Step 3* Solve the resulting equation; if it still contains a radical, repeat Steps 1 and 2. *Step 4* Check all potential solutions in the *original* equation. Potential solutions that do not check are extraneous; they are not part of the solution set.	Solve $\sqrt{2x+3} - x = 0$. $\sqrt{2x+3} = x$ $(\sqrt{2x+3})^2 = x^2$ $2x + 3 = x^2$ $x^2 - 2x - 3 = 0$ $(x-3)(x+1) = 0$ $x - 3 = 0$ or $x + 1 = 0$ $x = 3$ or $x = -1$ A check shows that 3 is a solution, but -1 is extraneous. The solution set is $\{3\}$.
9.7 Complex Numbers $i^2 = -1$, so $i = \sqrt{-1}$. For any positive number b, $\sqrt{-b} = i\sqrt{b}$. To multiply radicals with negative radicands, first change each factor to the form $i\sqrt{b}$, then multiply. The same procedure applies to quotients.	$\sqrt{-25} = i\sqrt{25} = 5i$ $\sqrt{-3} \cdot \sqrt{-27} = i\sqrt{3} \cdot i\sqrt{27}$ $= i^2\sqrt{81}$ $= -1 \cdot 9$ $= -9$ $\frac{\sqrt{-18}}{\sqrt{-2}} = \frac{i\sqrt{18}}{i\sqrt{2}} = \sqrt{\frac{18}{2}} = \sqrt{9} = 3$
Adding and Subtracting Complex Numbers Add (or subtract) the real parts and add (or subtract) the imaginary parts.	$(5 + 3i) + (8 - 7i) = 13 - 4i$ $(5 + 3i) - (8 - 7i) = -3 + 10i$
Multiplying and Dividing Complex Numbers Multiply complex numbers by using the FOIL method.	$(2 + i)(5 - 3i) = 10 - 6i + 5i - 3i^2$ $= 10 - i - 3(-1)$ $= 10 - i + 3$ $= 13 - i$
Divide complex numbers by multiplying the numerator and the denominator by the conjugate of the denominator.	$\frac{2}{3+i} = \frac{2(3-i)}{(3+i)(3-i)} = \frac{2(3-i)}{9-i^2}$ $= \frac{2(3-i)}{10} = \frac{3-i}{5}$

Answers to Test Your Word Power

1. (b) *Example:* In $\sqrt{3xy}$, $3xy$ is the radicand. **2. (d)** *Example:* In a right triangle where $a = 6$, $b = 8$, and $c = 10$, $6^2 + 8^2 = 10^2$. **3. (c)** *Example:* In a right triangle where the sides measure 9, 12, and 15 units, the hypotenuse is the side with measure 15 units. **4. (b)** *Example:* To rationalize the denominator of $\frac{5}{\sqrt{3}+1}$, multiply both the numerator and denominator by $\sqrt{3} - 1$ to get $\frac{5(\sqrt{3}-1)}{2}$. **5. (a)** *Example:* The potential solution 2 is extraneous in $\sqrt{5q-1} + 3 = 0$. **6. (c)** *Examples:* -5 (or $-5 + 0i$), $7i$ (or $0 + 7i$), and $\sqrt{2} - 4i$.

Chapter 9 REVIEW EXERCISES

[9.1] *Find each real number root. Use a calculator as necessary.*

1. $\sqrt{1764}$

42

2. $-\sqrt{289}$

-17

3. $-\sqrt{-841}$

not a real number

4. $\sqrt[3]{216}$

6

5. $\sqrt[5]{-32}$

-2

6. $\sqrt{x^2}$

$|x|$

7. $\sqrt[3]{x^3}$

x

8. $\sqrt[4]{x^{20}}$

$|x|^5$ or $|x^5|$

Graph each function. Give the domain and the range.

9. $f(x) = \sqrt{x - 1}$

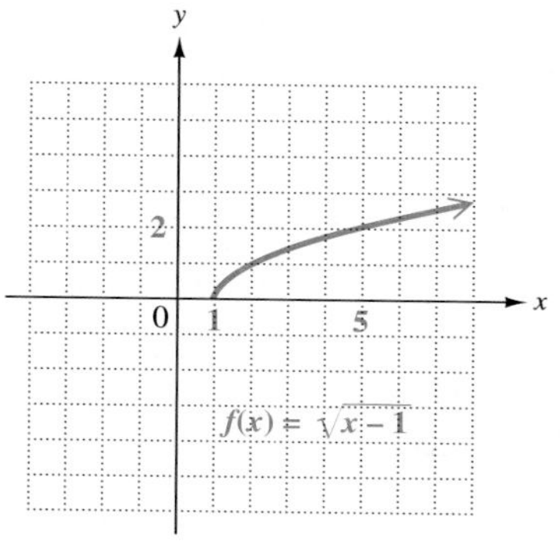

domain: $[1, \infty)$; range: $[0, \infty)$

10. $f(x) = \sqrt[3]{x} + 4$

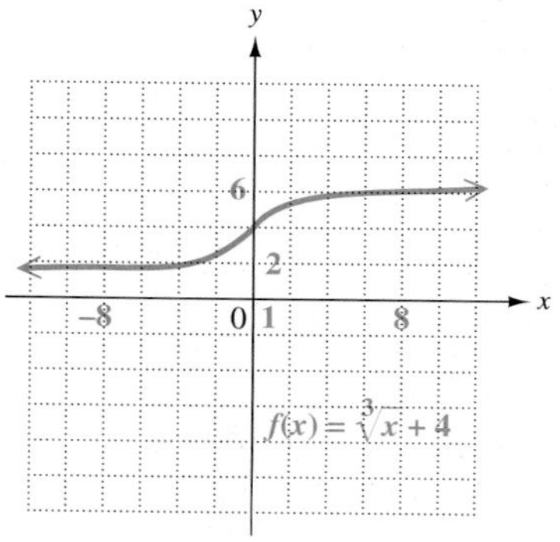

domain: $(-\infty, \infty)$; range: $(-\infty, \infty)$

11. Under what conditions is $\sqrt[n]{a}$ not a real number?

n must be even, and *a* must be negative.

12. If a is negative and n is even, what can be said about $a^{1/n}$?

It is not a real number.

Use a calculator to find a decimal approximation for each radical. Round to the nearest thousandth.

13. $\sqrt{40}$

6.325

14. $\sqrt{77}$

8.775

15. $\sqrt{310}$

17.607

16. According to an article in *The World Scanner Report* (August 1991), the distance D, in miles, to the horizon from an observer's point of view over water or "flat" earth is given by

$$D = \sqrt{2H},$$

where H is the height of the point of view, in feet. If a person whose eyes are 6 ft above ground level is standing at the top of a hill 44 ft above "flat" earth, approximately how far to the horizon will she be able to see?

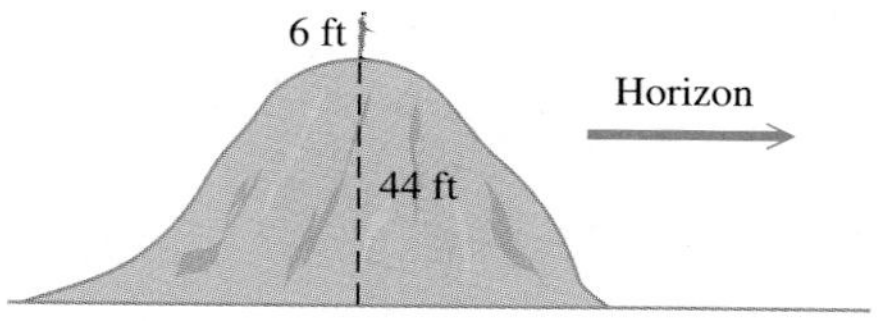

10 mi

17. The time for one complete swing of a simple pendulum is given by

$$t = 2\pi\sqrt{\frac{L}{g}},$$

where t is time in seconds, L is the length of the pendulum in feet, and g, the force due to gravity, is about 32 ft per sec^2. Find the time of a complete swing of a 2-ft pendulum to the nearest tenth of a second.

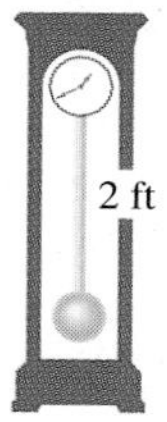

1.6 sec

[9.2] *Find each real number root.*

18. $49^{1/2}$
7

19. $-8^{1/3}$
-2

20. $(-16)^{1/4}$
not a real number

21. Explain the relationship between the expressions $a^{m/n}$ and $\sqrt[n]{a^m}$.

By a power rule for exponents and the definition of $x^{1/n}$, $a^{m/n} = (a^m)^{1/n} = \sqrt[n]{a^m}$.

Use the definitions and rules for exponents to simplify each expression. Assume that all variables represent positive real numbers.

22. $16^{5/4}$
32

23. $-8^{2/3}$
-4

24. $-\left(\frac{36}{25}\right)^{3/2}$
$-\frac{216}{125}$

25. $\left(-\frac{1}{8}\right)^{-5/3}$
-32

26. $\left(\frac{81}{10{,}000}\right)^{-3/4}$
$\frac{1000}{27}$

27. $7^{1/3} \cdot 7^{5/3}$
49

28. $\frac{96^{2/3}}{96^{-1/3}}$
96

29. $\frac{k^{2/3}k^{-1/2}k^{3/4}}{2(k^2)^{-1/4}}$
$\frac{k^{17/12}}{2}$

30. Write $2^{4/5}$ as a radical. $\sqrt[5]{2^4}$ or $\sqrt[5]{16}$

Use the rules of exponents to simplify each expression by first converting to rational exponents. Convert answers to radical form. Assume that all variables represent positive real numbers.

31. $\sqrt{3^{18}}$
3^9

32. $\sqrt{7^9}$
$7^4\sqrt{7}$

33. $\sqrt[3]{m^5} \cdot \sqrt[3]{m^8}$
$m^4\sqrt[3]{m}$

34. $\sqrt[4]{k^2} \cdot \sqrt[4]{k^7}$
$k^2\sqrt[4]{k}$

35. $\sqrt[3]{\sqrt{m}}$
$\sqrt[6]{m}$

36. $\sqrt[4]{16y^5}$
$2y\sqrt[4]{y}$

37. $\sqrt[5]{y} \cdot \sqrt[3]{y}$
$\sqrt[15]{y^8}$

38. $\frac{\sqrt[3]{y^2}}{\sqrt[4]{y}}$
$\sqrt[12]{y^5}$

[9.3] *Simplify each expression. Assume that all variables represent positive real numbers.*

39. $\sqrt{6} \cdot \sqrt{11}$
$\sqrt{66}$

40. $\sqrt{5} \cdot \sqrt{r}$
$\sqrt{5r}$

41. $\sqrt[3]{6} \cdot \sqrt[3]{5}$
$\sqrt[3]{30}$

42. $\sqrt[4]{7} \cdot \sqrt[4]{3}$
$\sqrt[4]{21}$

43. $\sqrt{20}$
$2\sqrt{5}$

44. $-\sqrt{125}$
$-5\sqrt{5}$

45. $\sqrt[3]{-108x^4y}$
$-3x\sqrt[3]{4xy}$

46. $\sqrt[3]{64p^4q^6}$
$4pq^2\sqrt[3]{p}$

47. $\sqrt{\frac{49}{81}}$
$\frac{7}{9}$

48. $\sqrt{\frac{y^3}{144}}$
$\frac{y\sqrt{y}}{12}$

49. $\sqrt[3]{\frac{m^{15}}{27}}$
$\frac{m^5}{3}$

50. $\sqrt[3]{\frac{r^2}{8}}$
$\frac{\sqrt[3]{r^2}}{2}$

51. $\frac{\sqrt[3]{2^4}}{\sqrt[4]{32}}$
$\sqrt[12]{2}$

52. $\frac{\sqrt{x}}{\sqrt[5]{x}}$
$\sqrt[10]{x^3}$

Find the distance between each pair of points.

53. $(2, 7)$ and $(-1, -4)$
$\sqrt{130}$

54. $(-3, -5)$ and $(4, -3)$
$\sqrt{53}$

[9.4] *Perform the indicated operations. Assume that all variables represent positive real numbers.*

55. $2\sqrt{8} - 3\sqrt{50}$
$-11\sqrt{2}$

56. $8\sqrt{80} - 3\sqrt{45}$
$23\sqrt{5}$

57. $-\sqrt{27y} + 2\sqrt{75y}$
$7\sqrt{3y}$

58. $2\sqrt{54m^3} + 5\sqrt{96m^3}$
$26m\sqrt{6m}$

59. $3\sqrt[3]{54} + 5\sqrt[3]{16}$
$19\sqrt[3]{2}$

60. $-6\sqrt[4]{32} + \sqrt[4]{512}$
$-8\sqrt[4]{2}$

[9.5] *Multiply, then simplify the products.*

61. $(\sqrt{3} + 1)(\sqrt{3} - 2)$
$1 - \sqrt{3}$

62. $(\sqrt{7} + \sqrt{5})(\sqrt{7} - \sqrt{5})$
2

63. $(3\sqrt{2} + 1)(2\sqrt{2} - 3)$
$9 - 7\sqrt{2}$

64. $(\sqrt{11} + 3\sqrt{5})(\sqrt{11} + 5\sqrt{5})$
$86 + 8\sqrt{55}$

65. $(\sqrt{13} - \sqrt{2})^2$
$15 - 2\sqrt{26}$

66. $(\sqrt{5} - \sqrt{7})^2$
$12 - 2\sqrt{35}$

Rationalize each denominator. Assume that all variables represent positive real numbers.

67. $\dfrac{-6\sqrt{3}}{\sqrt{2}}$
$-3\sqrt{6}$

68. $\dfrac{3\sqrt{7p}}{\sqrt{y}}$
$\dfrac{3\sqrt{7py}}{y}$

69. $-\sqrt[3]{\dfrac{9}{25}}$
$-\dfrac{\sqrt[3]{45}}{5}$

70. $\sqrt[3]{\dfrac{108m^3}{n^5}}$
$\dfrac{3m\sqrt[3]{4n}}{n^2}$

71. $\dfrac{1}{\sqrt{2} + \sqrt{7}}$
$\dfrac{\sqrt{2} - \sqrt{7}}{-5}$

72. $\dfrac{-5}{\sqrt{6} - \sqrt{3}}$
$\dfrac{-5(\sqrt{6} + \sqrt{3})}{3}$

[9.6] *Solve each equation.*

73. $\sqrt{8y + 9} = 5$
$\{2\}$

74. $\sqrt{2z - 3} - 3 = 0$
$\{6\}$

75. $\sqrt{3m + 1} = -1$
$\emptyset$

76. $\sqrt{7z + 1} = z + 1$
$\{0, 5\}$

77. $3\sqrt{m} = \sqrt{10m - 9}$
$\{9\}$

78. $\sqrt{p^2 + 3p + 7} = p + 2$
$\{3\}$

79. $\sqrt{a + 2} - \sqrt{a - 3} = 1$
$\{7\}$

80. $\sqrt[3]{5m - 1} = \sqrt[3]{3m - 2}$
$\left\{-\dfrac{1}{2}\right\}$

81. $\sqrt[4]{b + 6} = \sqrt[4]{2b}$
$\{6\}$

[9.7] *Write as a product of a real number and i.*

82. $\sqrt{-25}$
$5i$

83. $\sqrt{-200}$
$10i\sqrt{2}$

84. $\sqrt{-160}$
$4i\sqrt{10}$

Perform the indicated operations. Write each imaginary number answer in standard form.

85. $(-2 + 5i) + (-8 - 7i)$
$-10 - 2i$

86. $(5 + 4i) - (-9 - 3i)$
$14 + 7i$

87. $\sqrt{-5} \cdot \sqrt{-7}$
$-\sqrt{35}$

88. $\sqrt{-25} \cdot \sqrt{-81}$
-45

89. $\dfrac{\sqrt{-72}}{\sqrt{-8}}$
3

90. $(2 + 3i)(1 - i)$
$5 + i$

91. $(6 - 2i)^2$

$32 - 24i$

92. $\frac{3 - i}{2 + i}$

$1 - i$

93. $\frac{5 + 14i}{2 + 3i}$

$4 + i$

Find each power of i.

94. i^{11}

$-i$

95. i^{52}

1

96. i^{-13}

$-i$

MIXED REVIEW EXERCISES

Simplify. Assume that all variables represent positive real numbers.

97. $-\sqrt{169a^2b^4}$

$-13ab^2$

98. $1000^{-2/3}$

$\frac{1}{100}$

99. $\frac{y^{-1/3} \cdot y^{5/6}}{y}$

$\frac{1}{y^{1/2}}$

100. $\frac{z^{-1/4}x^{1/2}}{z^{1/2}x^{-1/4}}$

$\frac{x^{3/4}}{z^{3/4}}$

101. $\sqrt[4]{k^{24}}$

k^6

102. $\sqrt[3]{54z^9t^8}$

$3z^3t^2\sqrt[3]{2t^2}$

103. $-5\sqrt{18} + 12\sqrt{72}$

$57\sqrt{2}$

104. $8\sqrt[3]{x^3y^2} - 2x\sqrt[3]{y^2}$

$6x\sqrt[3]{y^2}$

105. $(\sqrt{5} - \sqrt{3})(\sqrt{7} + \sqrt{3})$

$\sqrt{35} + \sqrt{15} - \sqrt{21} - 3$

106. $\frac{-1}{\sqrt{12}}$ $-\frac{\sqrt{3}}{6}$

107. $\sqrt[3]{\frac{12}{25}}$ $\frac{\sqrt[3]{60}}{5}$

108. $\frac{2\sqrt{z}}{\sqrt{z} - 2}$ $\frac{2\sqrt{z}(\sqrt{z} + 2)}{z - 4}$

109. $\sqrt{-49}$

$7i$

110. $(4 - 9i) + (-1 + 2i)$

$3 - 7i$

111. $\frac{\sqrt{50}}{\sqrt{-2}}$

$-5i$

Solve each equation.

112. $\sqrt{x + 4} = x - 2$

$\{5\}$

113. $\sqrt{6 + 2y} - 1 = \sqrt{7 - 2y}$

$\left\{\frac{3}{2}\right\}$

Solve each problem.

114. Carpenters stabilize wall frames with a diagonal brace as shown in the figure. The length of the brace is given by $L = \sqrt{H^2 + W^2}$. If the bottom of the brace is attached 9 ft from the corner and the brace is 12 ft long, how far up the corner post should it be nailed (to the nearest tenth of a foot)?

7.9 ft

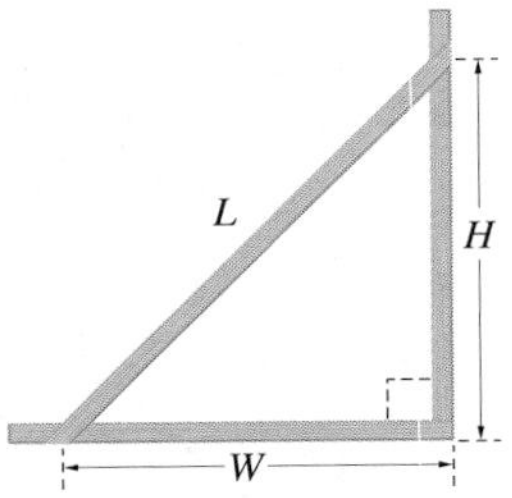

115. The sales in millions of dollars of Intel's flash memory chip are closely approximated by $f(x) = 11x^2 + 100$, where $x = 0$ represents the year 1995, $x = 5$ represents 2000, and so on. (*Source:* Cellular Telecommunications Industry Association, Intel Corp.)

(a) Use this function to approximate sales in 2001. Compare your answer with the company's estimate of \$490 million. **\$496 million, which agrees closely with the estimate.**

(b) According to the function, in what year were sales about \$270 million? Does this agree with the actual year, 1999? **In year 3.9 or late in 1998, which agrees well with the actual year.**

Chapter 9 Test

Find each root. Use a calculator as necessary.

1. $-\sqrt{841}$

2. $125^{1/3}$

3. For $\sqrt{146.25}$, which choice gives the best estimate?

   A. 10 **B.** 11 **C.** 12 **D.** 13

4. Give a calculator approximation of $\sqrt{146.25}$ to the nearest hundredth.

5. Graph the function defined by $f(x) = \sqrt{x + 6}$, and give the domain and the range.

Simplify each expression. Assume that all variables represent positive real numbers.

6. $(-64)^{-4/3}$

7. $\dfrac{3^{2/5}x^{-1/4}y^{2/5}}{3^{-8/5}x^{7/4}y^{1/10}}$

8. $\sqrt{54x^5y^6}$

9. $\sqrt[4]{32a^7b^{13}}$

10. $\sqrt{2} \cdot \sqrt[3]{5}$

11. $3\sqrt{20} - 5\sqrt{80} + 4\sqrt{500}$

12. $(7\sqrt{5} + 4)(2\sqrt{5} - 1)$

Answers

1. -29
2. 5
3. C
4. 12.09
5. domain: $[-6, \infty)$; range: $[0, \infty)$

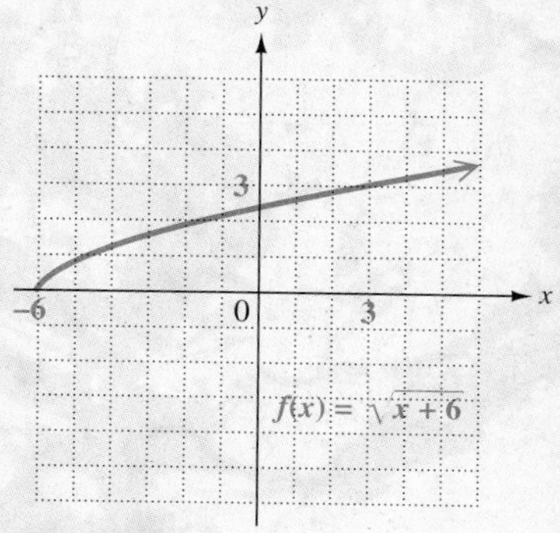

6. $\dfrac{1}{256}$
7. $\dfrac{9y^{3/10}}{x^2}$
8. $3x^2y^3\sqrt{6x}$
9. $2ab^3\sqrt[4]{2a^3b}$
10. $\sqrt[6]{200}$
11. $26\sqrt{5}$
12. $66 + \sqrt{5}$

13. $-2(\sqrt{7}-\sqrt{5})$

13. $\dfrac{-4}{\sqrt{7}+\sqrt{5}}$

14. $\dfrac{-\sqrt{10}}{4}$

14. $\dfrac{-5}{\sqrt{40}}$

15. $\dfrac{2\sqrt[3]{25}}{5}$

15. $\dfrac{2}{\sqrt[3]{5}}$

16. $\sqrt{26}$

16. Find the distance between the points $(-3, 8)$ and $(2, 7)$.

17. $\sqrt{145}$

17. Use the Pythagorean formula to find the exact length of side b in the figure.

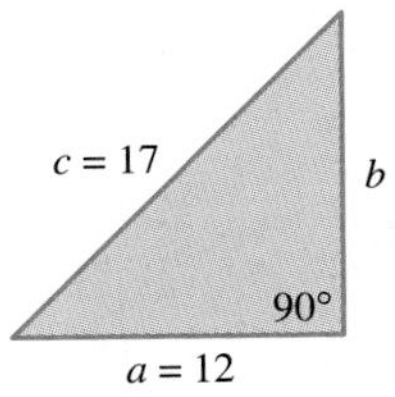

Solve each equation.

18. $\{-1\}$

18. $\sqrt[3]{5x}=\sqrt[3]{2x-3}$

19. $\{6\}$

19. $\sqrt{7-x}+5=x$

Perform the indicated operations. Express answers in the form $a+bi$.

20. $-5-8i$

20. $(-2+5i)-(3+6i)-7i$

21. $3+4i$

21. $\dfrac{7+i}{1-i}$

22. $-i$

22. Simplify i^{35}.

Cumulative Review Exercises CHAPTERS R–9

Solve each equation.

1. $7 - (4 + 3t) + 2t = -6(t - 2) - 5$

$\left\{\frac{4}{5}\right\}$

2. $|6x - 9| = |-4x + 2|$

$\left\{\frac{11}{10}, \frac{7}{2}\right\}$

Solve each inequality.

3. $-5 - 3(m - 2) < 11 - 2(m + 2)$

$(-6, \infty)$

4. $1 + 4x > 5$ and $-2x > -6$

$(1, 3)$

5. $-2 < 1 - 3y < 7$

$(-2, 1)$

6. Write an equation of the line through the points $(-4, 6)$ and $(7, -6)$. $12x + 11y = 18$

7. The lines with equations $2x + 3y = 8$ and $6y = 4x + 16$ are
A. parallel, **B.** perpendicular, **C.** neither. C

8. For the graph of $f(x) = -3x + 6$,

(a) what is the y-intercept? $(0, 6)$

(b) what is the x-intercept? $(2, 0)$

9. For many items, the cost per item to manufacture it varies inversely as the number made. Widgets are this type of item. It costs \$200 each to manufacture 1500 widgets. How much will it cost per widget to make 2500 widgets? \$120

10. Graph the inequality $-2x + y < -6$.

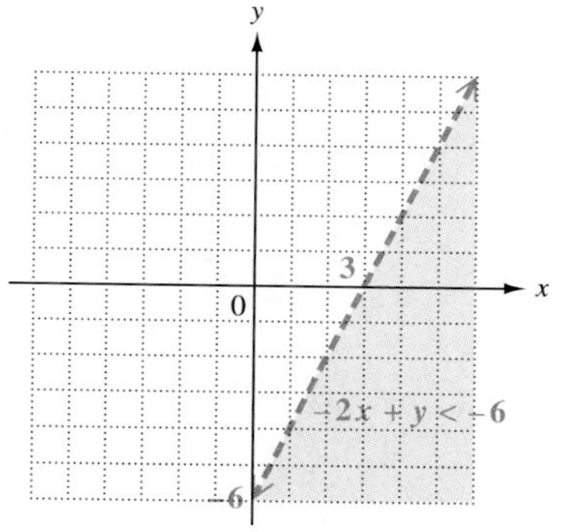

11. Find the measures of the marked angles.

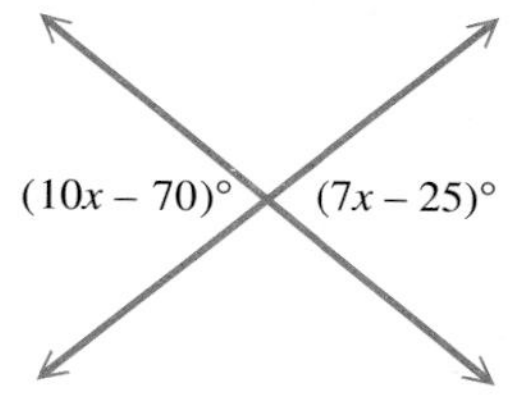

Both angles measure 80°.

Solve each system.

12.
$$\begin{aligned} 3x - y &= 23 \\ 2x + 3y &= 8 \end{aligned}$$

$\{(7, -2)\}$

13.
$$\begin{aligned} 5x + 2y &= 7 \\ 10x + 4y &= 12 \end{aligned}$$

$\emptyset$

14.
$$\begin{aligned} 2x + y - z &= 5 \\ 3x + 2y + z &= 8 \\ 4x + 2y - 2z &= 10 \end{aligned}$$

infinite number of solutions

15. In 1997, if you had sent five 2-oz letters and three 3-oz letters using first-class mail, it would have cost \$5.09. Sending three 2-oz letters and five 3-oz letters would have cost \$5.55. What was the 1997 postage rate for one 2-oz letter and for one 3-oz letter? (*Source:* U.S. Postal Service.)

2-oz letter: \$.55; 3-oz letter: \$.78

Perform the indicated operations.

16. $(3k^3 - 5k^2 + 8k - 2) - (4k^3 + 11k + 7) + (2k^2 - 5k)$

$-k^3 - 3k^2 - 8k - 9$

17. $(8x - 7)(x + 3)$

$8x^2 + 17x - 21$

18. $\dfrac{8z^3 - 16z^2 + 24z}{8z^2}$

$z - 2 + \dfrac{3}{z}$

19. $\dfrac{6y^4 - 3y^3 + 5y^2 + 6y - 9}{2y + 1}$

$3y^3 - 3y^2 + 4y + 1 + \dfrac{-10}{2y + 1}$

Factor each polynomial completely.

20. $2p^2 - 5pq + 3q^2$

$(2p - 3q)(p - q)$

21. $18k^4 + 9k^2 - 20$

$(3k^2 + 4)(6k^2 - 5)$

22. $x^3 + 512$

$(x + 8)(x^2 - 8x + 64)$

Perform each operation and express answers in lowest terms.

23. $\dfrac{y^2 + y - 12}{y^3 + 9y^2 + 20y} \div \dfrac{y^2 - 9}{y^3 + 3y^2}$

$\dfrac{y}{y + 5}$

24. $\dfrac{1}{x + y} + \dfrac{3}{x - y}$

$\dfrac{4x + 2y}{(x + y)(x - y)}$

Simplify each complex fraction.

25. $\dfrac{\dfrac{-6}{x - 2}}{\dfrac{8}{3x - 6}}$

$-\dfrac{9}{4}$

26. $\dfrac{\dfrac{1}{a} - \dfrac{1}{b}}{\dfrac{a}{b} - \dfrac{b}{a}}$

$-\dfrac{1}{a + b}$

Solve by factoring.

27. $2x^2 + 11x + 15 = 0$

$\left\{-3, -\dfrac{5}{2}\right\}$

28. $5t(t - 1) = 2(1 - t)$

$\left\{-\dfrac{2}{5}, 1\right\}$

Simplify.

29. $27^{-5/3}$

$\dfrac{1}{243}$

30. $\dfrac{x^{-2/3}}{x^{-3/4}}, \quad x \neq 0$

$x^{1/12}$

31. $8\sqrt{20} + 3\sqrt{80} - 2\sqrt{500}$

$8\sqrt{5}$

32. $\dfrac{-9}{\sqrt{80}}$

$\dfrac{-9\sqrt{5}}{20}$

33. $\dfrac{4}{\sqrt{6} - \sqrt{5}}$

$4(\sqrt{6} + \sqrt{5})$

34. $\dfrac{12}{\sqrt[3]{2}}$

$6\sqrt[3]{4}$

35. Find the distance between the points $(-4, 4)$ and $(-2, 9)$.

$\sqrt{29}$

36. Solve $\sqrt{8x - 4} - \sqrt{7x + 2} = 0$.

$\{6\}$

Solve each problem.

37. The current of a river runs at 3 mph. Brent's boat can go 36 mi downstream in the same time that it takes to go 24 mi upstream. Find the speed of the boat in still water. **15 mph**

38. How many liters of pure alcohol must be mixed with 40 L of 18% alcohol to obtain a 22% alcohol solution?

$\dfrac{80}{39}$ or $2\dfrac{2}{39}$ L

39. A jar containing only dimes and quarters has 29 coins with a face value of \$4.70. How many of each denomination are there?

17 dimes and 12 quarters

40. Brenda rides her bike 4 mph faster than her husband, Chuck. If Brenda can ride 48 mi in the same time that Chuck can ride 24 mi, what are their speeds?

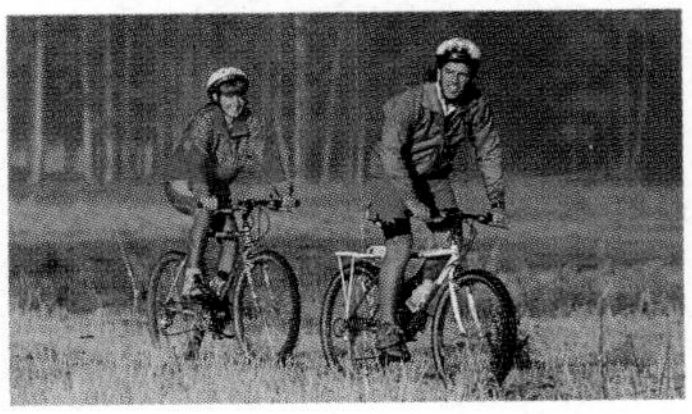

Brenda: 8 mph; Chuck: 4 mph

Quadratic Equations, Inequalities, and Graphs

10

In recent years, the number of U.S. companies filing for bankruptcy has been at its highest level since the recession of the early 1990s. One casualty of this trend is retailer Montgomery Ward. Started in 1872 as a mail-order catalog business, the company grew to include 250 stores in 30 states. After filing for Chapter 11 bankruptcy protection, the retailer closed for good in 2001. (*Source: USA Today,* December 29, 2000.) In Sections 10.5 and 10.6, we use *quadratic functions* to model the number of company bankruptcy filings.

10.1 Solving Quadratic Equations by the Square Root Property

Objectives

1. Solve quadratic equations of the form $x^2 = k$, where $k > 0$.
2. Solve quadratic equations of the form $(ax + b)^2 = k$, where $k > 0$.
3. Solve quadratic equations with imaginary solutions.

We introduced quadratic equations in Section 7.6. Recall that a *quadratic equation* is defined as follows.

Quadratic Equation

An equation that can be written in the form

$$ax^2 + bx + c = 0,$$

where a, b, and c are real numbers, with $a \neq 0$, is a **quadratic equation.** The given form is called **standard form.**

A quadratic equation is a *second-degree equation*, that is, an equation with a squared term and no terms of higher degree. For example,

$$4m^2 + 4m - 5 = 0 \quad \text{and} \quad 3x^2 = 4x - 8$$

are quadratic equations, with the first equation in standard form.

Work Problem 1 at the Side.

In Section 7.6 we used factoring and the zero-factor property to solve quadratic equations.

Zero-Factor Property

If two numbers have a product of 0, then at least one of the numbers must be 0. That is, if $ab = 0$, then $a = 0$ or $b = 0$.

We solved a quadratic equation such as $3x^2 - 5x - 28 = 0$ using the zero-factor property as follows.

$$3x^2 - 5x - 28 = 0$$

$$(3x + 7)(x - 4) = 0 \qquad \text{Factor.}$$

$$3x + 7 = 0 \quad \text{or} \quad x - 4 = 0 \qquad \text{Zero-factor property}$$

$$3x = -7 \quad \text{or} \quad x = 4 \qquad \text{Solve each equation.}$$

$$x = -\frac{7}{3}$$

The solution set is $\{-\frac{7}{3}, 4\}$.

Work Problem 2 at the Side.

1 Solve quadratic equations of the form $x^2 = k$, where $k > 0$. We can solve equations such as $x^2 = 9$ by factoring as follows.

$$x^2 = 9$$

$$x^2 - 9 = 0 \qquad \text{Subtract 9.}$$

$$(x + 3)(x - 3) = 0 \qquad \text{Factor.}$$

$$x + 3 = 0 \quad \text{or} \quad x - 3 = 0 \qquad \text{Zero-factor property}$$

$$x = -3 \quad \text{or} \quad x = 3$$

We might also have solved $x^2 = 9$ by noticing that x must be a number whose square is 9. Thus, $x = \sqrt{9} = 3$ or $x = -\sqrt{9} = -3$. This is generalized as the **square root property of equations.**

---

1 (a) Which of the following are quadratic equations?

A. $x + 2y = 0$

B. $x^2 - 8x + 16 = 0$

C. $2t^2 - 5t = 3$

D. $x^3 + x^2 + 4 = 0$

(b) Which quadratic equation identified in part (a) is in standard form?

2 Solve each equation by factoring.

(a) $x^2 + 3x + 2 = 0$

(b) $3m^2 = 3 - 8m$

(*Hint:* Remember to write the equation in standard form first.)

Answers

1. (a) B, C (b) B

2. (a) $\{-2, -1\}$ (b) $\left\{-3, \frac{1}{3}\right\}$

Square Root Property of Equations

If k is a positive number and if $x^2 = k$, then

$$x = \sqrt{k} \quad \text{or} \quad x = -\sqrt{k}.$$

NOTE

When we solve an equation, we want to find *all* values of the variable that satisfy the equation. Therefore, we want both the positive and negative square roots of k.

Example 1 Solving Quadratic Equations by the Square Root Property

Solve each equation. Write radicals in simplified form.

(a) $x^2 = 16$

By the square root property, if $x^2 = 16$, then

$$x = \sqrt{16} = 4 \quad \text{or} \quad x = -\sqrt{16} = -4.$$

An abbreviation for $x = 4$ or $x = -4$ is written $x = \pm 4$ (read "plus or minus 4"). Check each solution by substituting it for x in the original equation. The solution set is $\{4, -4\}$ or $\{\pm 4\}$.

(b) $r^2 = 5$

By the square root property,

$$r = \sqrt{5} \quad \text{or} \quad r = -\sqrt{5},$$

and the solution set is $\{\sqrt{5}, -\sqrt{5}\}$.

(c) $m^2 - 8 = 0$

$$m^2 = 8 \qquad \text{Add 8.}$$

$$m = \sqrt{8} \quad \text{or} \quad m = -\sqrt{8} \qquad \text{Square root property}$$

$$m = 2\sqrt{2} \quad \text{or} \quad m = -2\sqrt{2} \qquad \text{Simplify } \sqrt{8}.$$

The solution set is $\{2\sqrt{2}, -2\sqrt{2}\}$.

(d) $4x^2 - 48 = 0$

Solve for x^2.

$$4x^2 - 48 = 0$$

$$4x^2 = 48 \qquad \text{Add 48.}$$

$$x^2 = 12 \qquad \text{Divide by 4.}$$

$$x = \sqrt{12} \quad \text{or} \quad x = -\sqrt{12} \qquad \text{Square root property}$$

$$x = 2\sqrt{3} \quad \text{or} \quad x = -2\sqrt{3} \qquad \sqrt{12} = \sqrt{4} \cdot \sqrt{3} = 2\sqrt{3}$$

Check: $4x^2 - 48 = 0$ Original equation

$4(2\sqrt{3})^2 - 48 = 0$?	$4(-2\sqrt{3})^2 - 48 = 0$?
$4(12) - 48 = 0$?	$4(12) - 48 = 0$?
$48 - 48 = 0$?	$48 - 48 = 0$?
$0 = 0$ True	$0 = 0$ True

The solution set is $\{2\sqrt{3}, -2\sqrt{3}\}$.

Work Problem 3 at the Side.

3 Solve each equation. Write radicals in simplified form.

(a) $x^2 = 49$

(b) $x^2 = 11$

(c) $x^2 = 12$

(d) $3x^2 - 54 = 0$

ANSWERS

3. (a) $\{7, -7\}$ **(b)** $\{\sqrt{11}, -\sqrt{11}\}$ **(c)** $\{2\sqrt{3}, -2\sqrt{3}\}$ **(d)** $\{3\sqrt{2}, -3\sqrt{2}\}$

4 Solve the problem.

An expert marksman can hold a silver dollar at forehead level, drop it, draw his gun, and shoot the coin as it passes waist level. If the coin falls about 4 ft, use the formula in Example 2 to find the time that elapses between the dropping of the coin and the shot.

Example 2 **Using the Square Root Property in an Application**

Galileo Galilei (1564–1642) developed a formula for freely falling objects described by

$$d = 16t^2,$$

where d is the distance in feet that an object falls (disregarding air resistance) in t seconds, regardless of weight. Galileo dropped objects from the Leaning Tower of Pisa to develop this formula. If the Leaning Tower is about 180 ft tall, use Galileo's formula to determine how long it would take an object dropped from the tower to fall to the ground. (*Source:* Miller, Charles D., Heeren, Vern E., and Hornsby, John, *Mathematical Ideas, 9th Edition,* Addison-Wesley, 2001; *Microsoft Encarta Encyclopedia 2000.*)

We substitute 180 for d in Galileo's formula.

$$d = 16t^2$$

$$180 = 16t^2 \qquad \text{Let } d = 180.$$

$$11.25 = t^2 \qquad \text{Divide by 16.}$$

$$t = \sqrt{11.25} \quad \text{or} \quad t = -\sqrt{11.25} \qquad \text{Square root property}$$

Since time cannot be negative, we discard the negative solution. In applied problems, we usually prefer approximations to exact values. Using a calculator, $\sqrt{11.25} \approx 3.4$ so $t \approx 3.4$. The object would fall to the ground in about 3.4 sec.

Work Problem 4 at the Side.

2 **Solve quadratic equations of the form $(ax + b)^2 = k$, where $k > 0$.** In each equation in Example 1, the exponent 2 appeared with a single variable as its base. The square root property can be extended to solve equations where the base is a binomial, as shown in the next examples.

Example 3 **Solving Quadratic Equations by the Square Root Property**

Solve each equation.

(a) $(x - 3)^2 = 16$

Apply the square root property, using $x - 3$ as the base.

$$(x - 3)^2 = 16$$

$$x - 3 = \sqrt{16} \quad \text{or} \quad x - 3 = -\sqrt{16}$$

$$x - 3 = 4 \quad \text{or} \quad x - 3 = -4 \qquad \sqrt{16} = 4$$

$$x = 7 \quad \text{or} \quad x = -1 \qquad \text{Add 3.}$$

Check both answers in the original equation.

$$(x - 3)^2 = 16 \qquad \text{Original equation}$$

$$(7 - 3)^2 = 16 \ ? \quad \text{Let } x = 7. \qquad (-1 - 3)^2 = 16 \ ? \quad \text{Let } x = -1.$$

$$4^2 = 16 \ ? \qquad (-4)^2 = 16 \ ?$$

$$16 = 16 \quad \text{True} \qquad 16 = 16 \quad \text{True}$$

The solutions are 7 and -1, so the solution set is $\{7, -1\}$.

Continued on Next Page

ANSWERS

4. .5 sec

(b) $(x + 1)^2 = 6$

By the square root property,

$$x + 1 = \sqrt{6} \quad \text{or} \quad x + 1 = -\sqrt{6}$$

$$x = -1 + \sqrt{6} \quad \text{or} \quad x = -1 - \sqrt{6}.$$

Check:

$$(-1 + \sqrt{6} + 1)^2 = (\sqrt{6})^2 = 6;$$

$$(-1 - \sqrt{6} + 1)^2 = (-\sqrt{6})^2 = 6.$$

The solution set is $\{-1 + \sqrt{6}, -1 - \sqrt{6}\}$.

Work Problem 5 at the Side.

5 Solve each equation.

(a) $(m + 2)^2 = 36$

(b) $(p - 4)^2 = 3$

Example 4 Solving a Quadratic Equation by the Square Root Property

Solve $(3r - 2)^2 = 27$.

$$3r - 2 = \sqrt{27} \quad \text{or} \quad 3r - 2 = -\sqrt{27} \qquad \text{Square root property}$$

Now simplify the radical: $\sqrt{27} = \sqrt{9 \cdot 3} = \sqrt{9} \cdot \sqrt{3} = 3\sqrt{3}$.

$$3r - 2 = 3\sqrt{3} \quad \text{or} \quad 3r - 2 = -3\sqrt{3}$$

$$3r = 2 + 3\sqrt{3} \quad \text{or} \quad 3r = 2 - 3\sqrt{3} \qquad \text{Add 2.}$$

$$r = \frac{2 + 3\sqrt{3}}{3} \quad \text{or} \quad r = \frac{2 - 3\sqrt{3}}{3} \qquad \text{Divide by 3.}$$

We show the check for the first solution. The check for the second solution is similar.

Check:

$$(3r - 2)^2 = 27 \qquad \text{Original equation}$$

$$\left[3\left(\frac{2 + 3\sqrt{3}}{3}\right) - 2\right]^2 = 27 \quad ?$$

$$(2 + 3\sqrt{3} - 2)^2 = 27 \quad ?$$

$$(3\sqrt{3})^2 = 27 \quad ?$$

$$27 = 27 \qquad \text{True}$$

The solution set is $\left\{\frac{2 + 3\sqrt{3}}{3}, \frac{2 - 3\sqrt{3}}{3}\right\}$.

Work Problem 6 at the Side.

6 Solve each equation.

(a) $(2x - 5)^2 = 18$

(b) $(5m + 1)^2 = 7$

3 Solve quadratic equations with imaginary solutions. So far, all the equations we have solved using the square root property have had two real solutions. In the equation $x^2 = k$, if $k < 0$, there will be two imaginary solutions.

Example 5 Solving Quadratic Equations with Imaginary Solutions

Solve each equation.

(a) $x^2 = -15$

$$x = \sqrt{-15} \quad \text{or} \quad x = -\sqrt{-15} \qquad \text{Square root property}$$

$$x = i\sqrt{15} \quad \text{or} \quad x = -i\sqrt{15} \qquad \sqrt{-1} = i$$

The solution set is $\{i\sqrt{15}, -i\sqrt{15}\}$.

Continued on Next Page

Answers

5. (a) $\{-8, 4\}$ **(b)** $\{4 + \sqrt{3}, 4 - \sqrt{3}\}$

6. (a) $\left\{\frac{5 + 3\sqrt{2}}{2}, \frac{5 - 3\sqrt{2}}{2}\right\}$

(b) $\left\{\frac{-1 + \sqrt{7}}{5}, \frac{-1 - \sqrt{7}}{5}\right\}$

(b) $(t + 2)^2 = -16$

$$t + 2 = \sqrt{-16} \quad \text{or} \quad t + 2 = -\sqrt{-16} \qquad \text{Square root property}$$

$$t + 2 = 4i \quad \text{or} \quad t + 2 = -4i \qquad \sqrt{-16} = 4i$$

$$t = -2 + 4i \quad \text{or} \quad t = -2 - 4i$$

The solution set is $\{-2 + 4i, -2 - 4i\}$.

Work Problem 7 at the Side.

7 Solve each equation.

(a) $x^2 = -17$

(b) $(k + 5)^2 = -100$

ANSWERS

7. **(a)** $\{i\sqrt{17}, -i\sqrt{17}\}$
(b) $\{-5 + 10i, -5 - 10i\}$

10.1 EXERCISES

FOR EXTRA HELP: Student's Solutions Manual | MyMathLab.com | InterAct Math Tutorial Software | AW Math Tutor Center | www.mathxl.com | Digital Video Tutor CD 8 Videotape 19

1. A student was asked to solve the quadratic equation $x^2 = 16$ and did not get full credit for the solution set $\{4\}$. Why?

   The equation is also true for $x = -4$.

2. Why can't the zero-factor property be used to solve every quadratic equation?

   Some quadratic equations cannot be easily factored.

3. Give a one-sentence description or explanation of each of the following.

   (a) Zero-factor property

   The zero-factor property states that if a product equals 0, then at least one of the factors equals 0.

   (b) Square root property

   The square root property states that if the square of a quantity equals a number, then the quantity equals the positive or negative square root of the number.

4. What is wrong with the following "solution"?

$$x^2 - x - 2 = 5$$
$$(x - 2)(x + 1) = 5$$
$$x - 2 = 5 \quad \text{or} \quad x + 1 = 5 \qquad \text{Zero-factor property}$$
$$x = 7 \quad \text{or} \quad x = 4$$

   The zero-factor property requires a product equal to 0. In this solution, the first step should have been to rewrite the equation with 0 on one side.

Use the square root property to solve each equation. See Example 1.

5. $x^2 = 81$

   $\{9, -9\}$

6. $z^2 = 225$

   $\{15, -15\}$

7. $t^2 = 17$

   $\{\sqrt{17}, -\sqrt{17}\}$

8. $k^2 = 19$

   $\{\sqrt{19}, -\sqrt{19}\}$

9. $m^2 = 32$

   $\{4\sqrt{2}, -4\sqrt{2}\}$

10. $x^2 = 54$

    $\{3\sqrt{6}, -3\sqrt{6}\}$

11. $r^2 - 3 = 0$

    $\{\sqrt{3}, -\sqrt{3}\}$

12. $x^2 - 13 = 0$

    $\{\sqrt{13}, -\sqrt{13}\}$

13. $t^2 - 20 = 0$

    $\{2\sqrt{5}, -2\sqrt{5}\}$

14. $p^2 - 50 = 0$

    $\{5\sqrt{2}, -5\sqrt{2}\}$

15. $3n^2 - 72 = 0$

    $\{2\sqrt{6}, -2\sqrt{6}\}$

16. $5z^2 - 200 = 0$

    $\{2\sqrt{10}, -2\sqrt{10}\}$

Solve each equation using the square root property. See Examples 3 and 4.

17. $(x + 2)^2 = 25$

    $\{-7, 3\}$

18. $(t + 8)^2 = 9$

    $\{-5, -11\}$

19. $(x - 4)^2 = 3$

    $\{4 + \sqrt{3}, 4 - \sqrt{3}\}$

20. $(x + 3)^2 = 11$

    $\{-3 + \sqrt{11}, -3 - \sqrt{11}\}$

21. $(t + 5)^2 = 48$

    $\{-5 + 4\sqrt{3}, -5 - 4\sqrt{3}\}$

22. $(m - 6)^2 = 27$

    $\{6 + 3\sqrt{3}, 6 - 3\sqrt{3}\}$

23. $(3k + 2)^2 = 49$

    $\left\{-3, \frac{5}{3}\right\}$

24. $(5t + 3)^2 = 36$

    $\left\{-\frac{9}{5}, \frac{3}{5}\right\}$

25. $(3k - 1)^2 = 7$

    $\left\{\frac{1 + \sqrt{7}}{3}, \frac{1 - \sqrt{7}}{3}\right\}$

26. $(2x + 4)^2 = 10$

$\left\{\frac{-4+\sqrt{10}}{2}, \frac{-4-\sqrt{10}}{2}\right\}$

27. $(4p + 1)^2 = 24$

$\left\{\frac{-1+2\sqrt{6}}{4}, \frac{-1-2\sqrt{6}}{4}\right\}$

28. $(5k - 2)^2 = 12$

$\left\{\frac{2+2\sqrt{3}}{5}, \frac{2-2\sqrt{3}}{5}\right\}$

29. $(3k + 1)^2 = 18$

$\left\{\frac{-1+3\sqrt{2}}{3}, \frac{-1-3\sqrt{2}}{3}\right\}$

30. $(5z + 6)^2 = 75$

$\left\{\frac{-6+5\sqrt{3}}{5}, \frac{-6-5\sqrt{3}}{5}\right\}$

Find the imaginary solutions of each equation. See Example 5.

31. $x^2 = -12$

$\{2i\sqrt{3}, -2i\sqrt{3}\}$

32. $y^2 = -18$

$\{3i\sqrt{2}, -3i\sqrt{2}\}$

33. $(r - 5)^2 = -3$

$\{5 + i\sqrt{3}, 5 - i\sqrt{3}\}$

34. $(t + 6)^2 = -5$

$\{-6 + i\sqrt{5}, -6 - i\sqrt{5}\}$

35. $(6k - 1)^2 = -8$

$\left\{\frac{1+2i\sqrt{2}}{6}, \frac{1-2i\sqrt{2}}{6}\right\}$

36. $(4m - 7)^2 = -27$

$\left\{\frac{7+3i\sqrt{3}}{4}, \frac{7-3i\sqrt{3}}{4}\right\}$

Solve Exercises 37 and 38 using Galileo's formula, $d = 16t^2$. Round answers to the nearest tenth. See Example 2.

37. The Gateway Arch in St. Louis, Missouri, is 630 ft tall. How long would it take an object dropped from the top of it to fall to the ground? (*Source: Home & Away*, November/December 2000.)

6.3 sec

38. Mount Rushmore National Memorial in South Dakota features a sculpture of four of America's favorite presidents carved into the rim of the mountain, 500 ft above the valley floor. How long would it take a rock dropped from the top of the sculpture to fall to the ground? (*Source: Microsoft Encarta Encyclopedia 2000.*)

5.6 sec

Solve each problem.

39. The area A of a circle with radius r is given by the formula

$$A = \pi r^2.$$

If a circle has area 81π in.^{2}, what is its radius?

9 in.

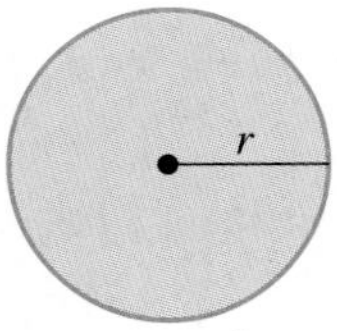

40. The surface area S of a sphere with radius r is given by the formula

$$S = 4\pi r^2.$$

If a sphere has surface area 36π ft^2, what is its radius?

3 ft

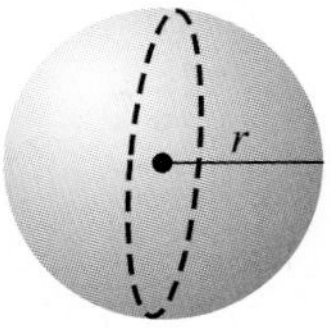

10.2 Solving Quadratic Equations by Completing the Square

Objectives

1. Solve quadratic equations by completing the square when the coefficient of the squared term is 1.
2. Solve quadratic equations by completing the square when the coefficient of the squared term is not 1.
3. Simplify an equation before solving.

1 Solve quadratic equations by completing the square when the coefficient of the squared term is 1. The methods studied so far are not sufficient to solve the equation

$$x^2 + 6x + 7 = 0.$$

If we could write the equation in a form like $(x + 3)^2 = 2$, we could solve it with the square root property discussed in the previous section. To do that, we need to have a perfect square trinomial on one side of the equation. The next example shows how this is done.

Work Problem 1 at the Side.

Example 1 Rewriting an Equation to Use the Square Root Property

Solve $x^2 + 6x + 7 = 0$.

Start by subtracting 7 from each side of the equation.

$$x^2 + 6x = -7$$

The quantity on the left side of $x^2 + 6x = -7$ must be made into a perfect square trinomial. The expression $x^2 + 6x + 9$ is a perfect square, since

$$x^2 + 6x + 9 = (x + 3)^2.$$

Therefore, if 9 is added to each side, the equation will have a perfect square trinomial on the left side, as needed.

$$x^2 + 6x + 9 = -7 + 9 \quad \text{Add 9.}$$
$$(x + 3)^2 = 2 \quad \text{Factor.}$$

Now use the square root property to complete the solution.

$$x + 3 = \sqrt{2} \quad \text{or} \quad x + 3 = -\sqrt{2}$$
$$x = -3 + \sqrt{2} \quad \text{or} \quad x = -3 - \sqrt{2}$$

Check by substituting $-3 + \sqrt{2}$ and $-3 - \sqrt{2}$ for x in the original equation. The solution set is $\{-3 + \sqrt{2}, -3 - \sqrt{2}\}$.

The process of changing the form of the equation in Example 1 from

$$x^2 + 6x + 7 = 0 \quad \text{to} \quad (x + 3)^2 = 2$$

is called **completing the square**. Completing the square changes only the form of the equation. To see this, multiply out the left side of $(x + 3)^2 = 2$ and combine terms. Then subtract 2 from each side to see that the result is $x^2 + 6x + 7 = 0$.

Look again at the original equation,

$$x^2 + 6x + 7 = 0.$$

Note that 9 is the square of half the coefficient of x, 6.

$$\frac{1}{2} \cdot 6 = 3 \quad \text{and} \quad 3^2 = 9$$

↑ Coefficient of x

To complete the square in Example 1, 9 was added to each side.

1 As a review, factor each perfect square trinomial.

(a) $x^2 + 6x + 9$

(b) $q^2 - 20q + 100$

Answers

1. (a) $(x + 3)^2$ **(b)** $(q - 10)^2$

2 Solve by completing the square.

(a) $x^2 + 4x = 1$

(b) $z^2 + 6z - 3 = 0$

ANSWERS

2. (a) $\{-2 + \sqrt{5}, -2 - \sqrt{5}\}$
(b) $\{-3 + 2\sqrt{3}, -3 - 2\sqrt{3}\}$

Example 2 Completing the Square to Solve a Quadratic Equation

Complete the square to solve $x^2 - 8x = 5$.

To complete the square on $x^2 - 8x$, take half the coefficient of x and square it.

$$\frac{1}{2}(-8) = -4 \quad \text{and} \quad (-4)^2 = 16$$

(−8: Coefficient of x)

Add the result, 16, to each side of the equation.

$$x^2 - 8x = 5 \qquad \text{Given equation}$$
$$x^2 - 8x + 16 = 5 + 16 \qquad \text{Add 16.}$$
$$(x - 4)^2 = 21 \qquad \text{Factor the left side as the square of a binomial.}$$

Now apply the square root property.

$$x - 4 = \sqrt{21} \quad \text{or} \quad x - 4 = -\sqrt{21} \qquad \text{Square root property}$$
$$x = 4 + \sqrt{21} \quad \text{or} \quad x = 4 - \sqrt{21} \qquad \text{Add 4.}$$

A check indicates that the solution set is $\{4 + \sqrt{21}, 4 - \sqrt{21}\}$.

In general, to solve an equation of the form

$$x^2 + mx = n$$

by completing the square, we begin by adding $\left(\frac{1}{2}m\right)^2$ to each side.

Work Problem 2 at the Side.

2 Solve quadratic equations by completing the square when the coefficient of the squared term is not 1. Suppose that an equation is of the form $ax^2 + bx + c = 0$, where $a \neq 1$. To get 1 as the coefficient of x^2, first divide each side of the equation by a. The next examples illustrate this approach.

Example 3 Solving a Quadratic Equation by Completing the Square

Solve $4x^2 + 16x = 9$.

Before completing the square, the coefficient of x^2 must be 1. Here the coefficient of x^2 is 4. Make the coefficient 1 by dividing each side of the equation by 4.

$$x^2 + 4x = \frac{9}{4} \qquad \text{Divide by 4.}$$

Next, complete the square by taking half the coefficient of x, or $\frac{1}{2}(4) = 2$, and squaring the result: $2^2 = 4$. Add 4 to each side of the equation, combine terms on the right side, and factor on the left.

$$x^2 + 4x + 4 = \frac{9}{4} + 4 \qquad \text{Add 4.}$$
$$x^2 + 4x + 4 = \frac{25}{4} \qquad \text{Combine terms.}$$
$$(x + 2)^2 = \frac{25}{4} \qquad \text{Factor.}$$

Continued on Next Page

Use the square root property and solve for x.

$$x + 2 = \sqrt{\frac{25}{4}} \quad \text{or} \quad x + 2 = -\sqrt{\frac{25}{4}}$$

$$x + 2 = \frac{5}{2} \quad \text{or} \quad x + 2 = -\frac{5}{2} \qquad \text{Square root property}$$

$$x = -2 + \frac{5}{2} \quad \text{or} \quad x = -2 - \frac{5}{2} \qquad \text{Subtract 2.}$$

$$x = \frac{1}{2} \quad \text{or} \quad x = -\frac{9}{2} \qquad \text{Combine terms.}$$

Check:

$$4x^2 + 16x = 9 \qquad\qquad 4x^2 + 16x = 9$$

$$4\left(\frac{1}{2}\right)^2 + 16\left(\frac{1}{2}\right) = 9 \quad ? \qquad 4\left(-\frac{9}{2}\right)^2 + 16\left(-\frac{9}{2}\right) = 9 \quad ?$$

$$4\left(\frac{1}{4}\right) + 8 = 9 \quad ? \qquad 4\left(\frac{81}{4}\right) - 72 = 9 \quad ?$$

$$1 + 8 = 9 \quad ? \qquad 81 - 72 = 9 \quad ?$$

$$9 = 9 \quad \text{True} \qquad 9 = 9 \quad \text{True}$$

The solution set is $\{\frac{1}{2}, -\frac{9}{2}\}$.

The steps in solving a quadratic equation $ax^2 + bx + c = 0$ $(a \neq 0)$ by completing the square are summarized here.

Solving a Quadratic Equation by Completing the Square

Step 1 **Be sure the squared term has coefficient 1.** If the coefficient of the squared term is 1, proceed to Step 2. If the coefficient of the squared term is not 1 but some other nonzero number a, divide each side of the equation by a. This gives an equation that has 1 as the coefficient of the squared term.

Step 2 **Put in correct form.** Make sure that all terms with variables are on one side of the equals sign and that all constants are on the other side.

Step 3 **Complete the square.** Take half the coefficient of the first-degree term, and square the result. Add the square to each side of the equation. The side containing the variables can now be factored as a perfect square.

Step 4 **Solve.** Apply the square root property to solve the equation.

Work Problem 3 at the Side.

3 Solve by completing the square.

(a) $9x^2 + 18x + 5 = 0$

(b) $4t^2 - 24t + 11 = 0$

ANSWERS

3. (a) $\left\{-\frac{1}{3}, -\frac{5}{3}\right\}$ **(b)** $\left\{\frac{11}{2}, \frac{1}{2}\right\}$

4 Solve by completing the square.

(a) $3x^2 + 5x - 2 = 0$

(b) $2x^2 - 4x - 1 = 0$

ANSWERS

4. (a) $\left\{-2, \frac{1}{3}\right\}$ **(b)** $\left\{\frac{2+\sqrt{6}}{2}, \frac{2-\sqrt{6}}{2}\right\}$

Example 4 Solving a Quadratic Equation by Completing the Square

Solve $2x^2 - 4x - 5 = 0$.

First divide each side of the equation by 2 to get 1 as the coefficient of the squared term.

$$x^2 - 2x - \frac{5}{2} = 0 \qquad \text{Step 1}$$

$$x^2 - 2x = \frac{5}{2} \qquad \text{Step 2}$$

$$\left[\frac{1}{2}(-2)\right]^2 = (-1)^2 = 1 \qquad \text{Step 3}$$

$$x^2 - 2x + 1 = \frac{5}{2} + 1$$

$$(x-1)^2 = \frac{7}{2}$$

$$x - 1 = \sqrt{\frac{7}{2}} \quad \text{or} \quad x - 1 = -\sqrt{\frac{7}{2}} \qquad \text{Step 4}$$

$$x = 1 + \sqrt{\frac{7}{2}} \quad \text{or} \quad x = 1 - \sqrt{\frac{7}{2}}$$

$$x = 1 + \frac{\sqrt{14}}{2} \quad \text{or} \quad x = 1 - \frac{\sqrt{14}}{2} \qquad \text{Rationalize denominators.}$$

Add the two terms in each solution as follows:

$$1 + \frac{\sqrt{14}}{2} = \frac{2}{2} + \frac{\sqrt{14}}{2} = \frac{2+\sqrt{14}}{2}$$

$$1 - \frac{\sqrt{14}}{2} = \frac{2}{2} - \frac{\sqrt{14}}{2} = \frac{2-\sqrt{14}}{2}.$$

Check that the solution set is $\left\{\frac{2+\sqrt{14}}{2}, \frac{2-\sqrt{14}}{2}\right\}$.

Work Problem 4 at the Side.

Example 5 Solving a Quadratic Equation by Completing the Square (Imaginary Solutions)

Solve $4p^2 + 8p + 5 = 0$.

$$p^2 + 2p + \frac{5}{4} = 0 \qquad \text{Divide by 4.}$$

$$p^2 + 2p = -\frac{5}{4} \qquad \text{Subtract } \tfrac{5}{4}.$$

The coefficient of p is 2. Take half of 2, square the result, and add this square to each side. The left side can then be written as a perfect square.

$$p^2 + 2p + 1 = -\frac{5}{4} + 1 \qquad \text{Add 1.}$$

$$(p+1)^2 = -\frac{1}{4} \qquad \text{Factor.}$$

Continued on Next Page

Because the constant on the right side of the equation is negative, this equation will have imaginary solutions.

$$p + 1 = \sqrt{-\frac{1}{4}} \quad \text{or} \quad p + 1 = -\sqrt{-\frac{1}{4}} \qquad \text{Square root property}$$

$$p + 1 = \frac{1}{2}i \quad \text{or} \quad p + 1 = -\frac{1}{2}i \qquad \sqrt{-\tfrac{1}{4}} = \tfrac{1}{2}i$$

$$p = -1 + \frac{1}{2}i \quad \text{or} \quad p = -1 - \frac{1}{2}i \qquad \text{Subtract 1.}$$

Check:

$$4p^2 + 8p + 5 = 0 \qquad \text{Original equation}$$

$$4\left(-1 + \frac{1}{2}i\right)^2 + 8\left(-1 + \frac{1}{2}i\right) + 5 = 0 \quad ?$$

$$4\left[1 + 2(-1)\left(\frac{1}{2}i\right) - \frac{1}{4}\right] - 8 + 4i + 5 = 0 \quad ?$$

$$4\left[\frac{3}{4} - i\right] - 3 + 4i = 0 \quad ?$$

$$3 - 4i - 3 + 4i = 0 \quad ?$$

$$0 = 0 \qquad \text{True}$$

The check of the other solution is similar. The solution set is

$$\left\{-1 + \frac{1}{2}i, -1 - \frac{1}{2}i\right\}.$$

Work Problem 5 at the Side.

5 Solve each equation.

(a) $x^2 + 2x + 7 = 0$

(b) $5t^2 - 15t + 12 = 0$

6 Solve each equation.

(a) $r(r - 3) = -1$

(b) $(x + 2)(x + 1) = 5$

3 Simplify an equation before solving. The next example shows how to simplify a quadratic equation before solving it.

Example 6 Simplifying an Equation before Completing the Square

Solve $(x + 3)(x - 1) = 2$.

$$(x + 3)(x - 1) = 2 \qquad \text{Given equation}$$

$$x^2 + 2x - 3 = 2 \qquad \text{Use FOIL.}$$

$$x^2 + 2x = 5 \qquad \text{Add 3.}$$

$$x^2 + 2x + 1 = 5 + 1 \qquad \text{Add 1 to get a perfect square on the left.}$$

$$(x + 1)^2 = 6 \qquad \text{Factor on the left; add on the right.}$$

$$x + 1 = \sqrt{6} \quad \text{or} \quad x + 1 = -\sqrt{6} \qquad \text{Square root property}$$

$$x = -1 + \sqrt{6} \quad \text{or} \quad x = -1 - \sqrt{6} \qquad \text{Subtract 1.}$$

The solution set is $\{-1 + \sqrt{6}, -1 - \sqrt{6}\}$.

Work Problem 6 at the Side.

ANSWERS

5. **(a)** $\{-1 + i\sqrt{6}, -1 - i\sqrt{6}\}$

(b) $\left\{\frac{15 + i\sqrt{15}}{10}, \frac{15 - i\sqrt{15}}{10}\right\}$

6. **(a)** $\left\{\frac{3 + \sqrt{5}}{2}, \frac{3 - \sqrt{5}}{2}\right\}$

(b) $\left\{\frac{-3 + \sqrt{21}}{2}, \frac{-3 - \sqrt{21}}{2}\right\}$

NOTE

The procedure for completing the square is also used in other areas of mathematics. For example, we will use it in Section 10.7 when we graph quadratic equations and again in Chapter 12 when we work with circles.

10.2 EXERCISES

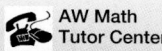

FOR EXTRA HELP: Student's Solutions Manual; MyMathLab.com; InterAct Math Tutorial Software; AW Math Tutor Center; www.mathxl.com; Digital Video Tutor CD 8, Videotape 19

Fill in each blank with the correct response.

1. To solve the equation $x^2 - 8x = 4$ by completing the square, the first step is to add 16 to each side of the equation.

2. To solve the equation $3x^2 - 8x - 1 = 0$ by completing the square, the first step is to divide each side of the equation by 3.

3. To solve $(t + 2)(t - 5) = 18$ by completing the square, we should start by multiplying $(t + 2)(t - 5)$ to get $t^2 - 3t - 10$.

4. It is not possible to solve $x^3 - x - 1 = 0$ by completing the square because it is not a quadratic equation because of the x^3-term.

5. Which step is an appropriate way to begin solving the quadratic equation $2x^2 - 4x = 9$ by completing the square? D

A. Add 4 to each side of the equation.
B. Factor the left side as $2x(x - 2)$.
C. Factor the left side as $x(2x - 4)$.
D. Divide each side by 2.

6. In Example 3 of Section 7.6, we solved the quadratic equation $4p^2 - 26p + 40 = 0$ by factoring. If we were to solve by completing the square, would we get the same solutions, $\frac{5}{2}$ and 4? yes

Find the number that should be added to each expression to make it a perfect square. See Example 2.

7. $x^2 + 14x$ 49

8. $z^2 + 18z$ 81

9. $k^2 - 5k$ $\frac{25}{4}$

10. $m^2 - 9m$ $\frac{81}{4}$

11. $r^2 + \frac{1}{2}r$ $\frac{1}{16}$

12. $s^2 - \frac{1}{3}s$ $\frac{1}{36}$

Solve each equation by completing the square. See Examples 1 and 2.

13. $x^2 - 4x = -3$ $\{1, 3\}$

14. $x^2 - 2x = 8$ $\{-2, 4\}$

15. $x^2 + 5x + 6 = 0$ $\{-3, -2\}$

16. $x^2 + 6x + 5 = 0$ $\{-5, -1\}$

17. $x^2 + 2x - 5 = 0$ $\{-1 + \sqrt{6}, -1 - \sqrt{6}\}$

18. $x^2 + 4x + 1 = 0$ $\{-2 + \sqrt{3}, -2 - \sqrt{3}\}$

19. $x^2 + 10x + 18 = 0$ $\{-5 + \sqrt{7}, -5 - \sqrt{7}\}$

20. $x^2 + 8x + 11 = 0$ $\{-4 + \sqrt{5}, -4 - \sqrt{5}\}$

21. $x^2 + x - 1 = 0$ $\left\{\frac{-1 + \sqrt{5}}{2}, \frac{-1 - \sqrt{5}}{2}\right\}$

22. $x^2 + x - 3 = 0$ $\left\{\frac{-1 + \sqrt{13}}{2}, \frac{-1 - \sqrt{13}}{2}\right\}$

Solve each equation by completing the square. See Examples 3–6.

23. $4x^2 + 4x - 3 = 0$ $\left\{-\frac{3}{2}, \frac{1}{2}\right\}$

24. $9x^2 + 3x - 2 = 0$ $\left\{-\frac{2}{3}, \frac{1}{3}\right\}$

25. $2x^2 - 4x = 5$ $\left\{\frac{2+\sqrt{14}}{2}, \frac{2-\sqrt{14}}{2}\right\}$

26. $2x^2 - 6x = 3$ $\left\{\frac{3+\sqrt{15}}{2}, \frac{3-\sqrt{15}}{2}\right\}$

27. $3r^2 + 2r - 2 = 0$ $\left\{\frac{-1+\sqrt{7}}{3}, \frac{-1-\sqrt{7}}{3}\right\}$

28. $5x^2 - 10x + 2 = 0$ $\left\{\frac{5+\sqrt{15}}{5}, \frac{5-\sqrt{15}}{5}\right\}$

29. $3k^2 + 7k = 4$ $\left\{\frac{-7+\sqrt{97}}{6}, \frac{-7-\sqrt{97}}{6}\right\}$

30. $2k^2 + 5k = 1$ $\left\{\frac{-5+\sqrt{33}}{4}, \frac{-5-\sqrt{33}}{4}\right\}$

31. $(x + 3)(x - 1) = 5$ $\{-4, 2\}$

32. $(y - 8)(y + 2) = 24$ $\{-4, 10\}$

33. $-x^2 + 2x = -5$ $\{1 + \sqrt{6}, 1 - \sqrt{6}\}$

34. $-r^2 + 3r = -2$ $\left\{\frac{3+\sqrt{17}}{2}, \frac{3-\sqrt{17}}{2}\right\}$

Find the imaginary solutions of each equation. See Example 5.

35. $m^2 + 4m + 13 = 0$ $\{-2 + 3i, -2 - 3i\}$

36. $t^2 + 6t + 10 = 0$ $\{-3 + i, -3 - i\}$

37. $3r^2 + 4r + 4 = 0$ $\left\{\frac{-2+2i\sqrt{2}}{3}, \frac{-2-2i\sqrt{2}}{3}\right\}$

38. $4x^2 + 5x + 5 = 0$ $\left\{\frac{-5+i\sqrt{55}}{8}, \frac{-5-i\sqrt{55}}{8}\right\}$

39. $-m^2 - 6m - 12 = 0$ $\{-3 + i\sqrt{3}, -3 - i\sqrt{3}\}$

40. $-k^2 - 5k - 10 = 0$ $\left\{\frac{-5+i\sqrt{15}}{2}, \frac{-5-i\sqrt{15}}{2}\right\}$

RELATING CONCEPTS (Exercises 41–46) FOR INDIVIDUAL OR GROUP WORK

The Greeks had a method of completing the square geometrically in which they literally changed a figure into a square. For example, to complete the square for $x^2 + 6x$, we begin with a square of side x, as in the figure. We add three rectangles of width 1 to the right side and the bottom to get a region with area $x^2 + 6x$. To fill in the corner (complete the square), we must add 9 1-by-1 squares as shown.

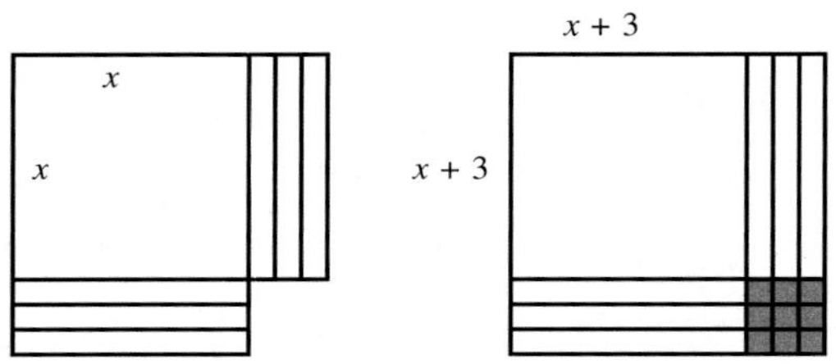

Work Exercises 41–46 in order.

41. What is the area of the original square? x^2

42. What is the area of each strip? x

43. What is the total area of the six strips? $6x$

44. What is the area of each small square in the corner of the second figure? 1

45. What is the total area of the small squares? 9

46. What is the area of the new, larger square? $(x + 3)^2$ or $x^2 + 6x + 9$

10.3 SOLVING QUADRATIC EQUATIONS BY THE QUADRATIC FORMULA

OBJECTIVES

1. Solve quadratic equations using the quadratic formula.
2. Use the discriminant to determine the number and type of solutions.

The examples in the previous section showed that any quadratic equation can be solved by completing the square; however, completing the square can be tedious and time consuming. In this section, we complete the square to solve the general quadratic equation $ax^2 + bx + c = 0$, where a, b, and c are complex numbers and $a \neq 0$. The solution of this general equation gives a formula for finding the solution of any specific quadratic equation.

To solve $ax^2 + bx + c = 0$ by completing the square (assuming $a > 0$ for now), we follow the steps given in Section 10.2.

$$ax^2 + bx + c = 0$$

$$x^2 + \frac{b}{a}x + \frac{c}{a} = 0 \qquad \text{Divide by } a. \text{ (Step 1)}$$

$$x^2 + \frac{b}{a}x = -\frac{c}{a} \qquad \text{Subtract } \tfrac{c}{a}. \text{ (Step 2)}$$

$$\left[\frac{1}{2}\left(\frac{b}{a}\right)\right]^2 = \left(\frac{b}{2a}\right)^2 = \frac{b^2}{4a^2} \qquad \text{(Step 3)}$$

$$x^2 + \frac{b}{a}x + \frac{b^2}{4a^2} = -\frac{c}{a} + \frac{b^2}{4a^2} \qquad \text{Add } \tfrac{b^2}{4a^2} \text{ to each side.}$$

Write the left side as a perfect square, and rearrange the right side.

$$\left(x + \frac{b}{2a}\right)^2 = \frac{b^2}{4a^2} + \frac{-c}{a}$$

$$\left(x + \frac{b}{2a}\right)^2 = \frac{b^2}{4a^2} + \frac{-4ac}{4a^2} \qquad \text{Write with a common denominator.}$$

$$\left(x + \frac{b}{2a}\right)^2 = \frac{b^2 - 4ac}{4a^2} \qquad \text{Add fractions.}$$

$$x + \frac{b}{2a} = \sqrt{\frac{b^2 - 4ac}{4a^2}} \quad \text{or} \quad x + \frac{b}{2a} = -\sqrt{\frac{b^2 - 4ac}{4a^2}} \qquad \text{Square root property (Step 4)}$$

Since

$$\sqrt{\frac{b^2 - 4ac}{4a^2}} = \frac{\sqrt{b^2 - 4ac}}{\sqrt{4a^2}} = \frac{\sqrt{b^2 - 4ac}}{2a},$$

the result can be expressed as

$$x + \frac{b}{2a} = \frac{\sqrt{b^2 - 4ac}}{2a} \quad \text{or} \quad x + \frac{b}{2a} = \frac{-\sqrt{b^2 - 4ac}}{2a}$$

$$x = \frac{-b}{2a} + \frac{\sqrt{b^2 - 4ac}}{2a} \quad \text{or} \quad x = \frac{-b}{2a} - \frac{\sqrt{b^2 - 4ac}}{2a}$$

$$x = \frac{-b + \sqrt{b^2 - 4ac}}{2a} \quad \text{or} \quad x = \frac{-b - \sqrt{b^2 - 4ac}}{2a}.$$

If $a < 0$, the same two solutions are obtained. The result is the **quadratic formula,** often abbreviated as follows.

1 Identify the values of a, b, and c. (*Hint:* If necessary, write the equation in standard form first.) *Do not actually solve.*

(a) $-3q^2 + 9q - 4 = 0$

(b) $3x^2 = 6x + 2$

2 Solve $4x^2 - 11x - 3 = 0$ using the quadratic formula.

ANSWERS
1. (a) $-3; 9; -4$ **(b)** $3; -6; -2$
2. $\left\{-\frac{1}{4}, 3\right\}$

Quadratic Formula

The solutions of $ax^2 + bx + c = 0$ $(a \neq 0)$ are given by

$$x = \frac{-b \pm \sqrt{b^2 - 4ac}}{2a}.$$

CAUTION

In the quadratic formula, the square root is added to or subtracted from the value of $-b$ *before* dividing by $2a$.

1 **Solve quadratic equations using the quadratic formula.** To use the quadratic formula, first write the given equation in standard form $ax^2 + bx + c = 0$; then identify the values of a, b, and c and substitute them into the quadratic formula, as shown in the next examples.

Work Problem 1 at the Side.

Example 1 Using the Quadratic Formula (Rational Solutions)

Solve $6x^2 - 5x - 4 = 0$.

First, identify the values of a, b, and c of the general quadratic equation, $ax^2 + bx + c = 0$. Here a, the coefficient of the second-degree term, is 6, while b, the coefficient of the first-degree term, is -5, and the constant c is -4. Substitute these values into the quadratic formula.

$$x = \frac{-b \pm \sqrt{b^2 - 4ac}}{2a}$$

$$x = \frac{-(-5) \pm \sqrt{(-5)^2 - 4(6)(-4)}}{2(6)} \qquad a = 6, b = -5, c = -4$$

$$x = \frac{5 \pm \sqrt{25 + 96}}{12}$$

$$x = \frac{5 \pm \sqrt{121}}{12}$$

$$x = \frac{5 \pm 11}{12}$$

This last statement leads to two solutions, one from + and one from −.

$$x = \frac{5 + 11}{12} = \frac{16}{12} = \frac{4}{3} \quad \text{or} \quad x = \frac{5 - 11}{12} = \frac{-6}{12} = -\frac{1}{2}$$

Check each solution by substituting it in the original equation. The solution set is $\left\{-\frac{1}{2}, \frac{4}{3}\right\}$.

Work Problem 2 at the Side.

We could have used factoring to solve the equation in Example 1.

$6x^2 - 5x - 4 = 0$		
$(3x - 4)(2x + 1) = 0$		Factor.
$3x - 4 = 0$ or $2x + 1 = 0$		Zero-factor property
$3x = 4$ or $2x = -1$		Solve each equation.
$x = \frac{4}{3}$ or $x = -\frac{1}{2}$		Same solutions as in Example 1

10.3 EXERCISES

FOR EXTRA HELP: Student's Solutions Manual | MyMathLab.com | InterAct Math Tutorial Software | AW Math Tutor Center | www.mathxl.com | Digital Video Tutor CD 9 Videotape 20

1. A student wrote the following as the quadratic formula for solving $ax^2 + bx + c = 0$, $a \neq 0$:

$$x = -b \pm \frac{\sqrt{b^2 - 4ac}}{2a}.$$

Was this correct? Explain.

The student was incorrect, since the fraction bar should extend under the term $-b$.

2. What is wrong with the following "solution" of $5x^2 - 5x + 1 = 0$?

$$x = \frac{5 \pm \sqrt{25 - 4(5)(1)}}{2(5)} \qquad a = 5, b = -5, c = 1$$

$$x = \frac{5 \pm \sqrt{5}}{10}$$

$$x = \frac{1}{2} \pm \sqrt{5}$$

The last step is wrong. Because 5 is not a common factor in the numerator, the fraction cannot be simplified. The solutions are $\frac{5 \pm \sqrt{5}}{10}$.

Use the quadratic formula to solve each equation. (All solutions for these equations are real numbers.) See Examples 1 and 2.

3. $m^2 - 8m + 15 = 0$

$\{3, 5\}$

4. $x^2 + 3x - 28 = 0$

$\{-7, 4\}$

5. $2k^2 + 4k + 1 = 0$

$\left\{\frac{-2 + \sqrt{2}}{2}, \frac{-2 - \sqrt{2}}{2}\right\}$

6. $2w^2 + 3w - 1 = 0$

$\left\{\frac{-3 + \sqrt{17}}{4}, \frac{-3 - \sqrt{17}}{4}\right\}$

7. $2x^2 - 2x = 1$

$\left\{\frac{1 + \sqrt{3}}{2}, \frac{1 - \sqrt{3}}{2}\right\}$

8. $9t^2 + 6t = 1$

$\left\{\frac{-1 + \sqrt{2}}{3}, \frac{-1 - \sqrt{2}}{3}\right\}$

9. $x^2 + 18 = 10x$

$\{5 + \sqrt{7}, 5 - \sqrt{7}\}$

10. $x^2 - 4 = 2x$

$\{1 + \sqrt{5}, 1 - \sqrt{5}\}$

11. $4k^2 + 4k - 1 = 0$

$\left\{\frac{-1 + \sqrt{2}}{2}, \frac{-1 - \sqrt{2}}{2}\right\}$

12. $4r^2 - 4r - 19 = 0$

$\left\{\frac{1 + 2\sqrt{5}}{2}, \frac{1 - 2\sqrt{5}}{2}\right\}$

13. $2 - 2x = 3x^2$

$\left\{\frac{-1 + \sqrt{7}}{3}, \frac{-1 - \sqrt{7}}{3}\right\}$

14. $26r - 2 = 3r^2$

$\left\{\frac{13 + \sqrt{163}}{3}, \frac{13 - \sqrt{163}}{3}\right\}$

15. $\frac{x^2}{4} - \frac{x}{2} = 1$
(*Hint:* First clear the fractions.)

$\{1 + \sqrt{5}, 1 - \sqrt{5}\}$

16. $p^2 + \frac{p}{3} = \frac{1}{6}$
(*Hint:* First clear the fractions.)

$\left\{\frac{-1 + \sqrt{7}}{6}, \frac{-1 - \sqrt{7}}{6}\right\}$

17. $-2t(t + 2) = -3$

$\left\{\frac{-2 + \sqrt{10}}{2}, \frac{-2 - \sqrt{10}}{2}\right\}$

18. $-3x(x + 2) = -4$

$\left\{\frac{-3 + \sqrt{21}}{3}, \frac{-3 - \sqrt{21}}{3}\right\}$

19. $(r - 3)(r + 5) = 2$

$\{-1 + 3\sqrt{2}, -1 - 3\sqrt{2}\}$

20. $(k + 1)(k - 7) = 1$

$\{3 + \sqrt{17}, 3 - \sqrt{17}\}$

Use the quadratic formula to solve each equation. (All solutions for these equations are imaginary numbers.) See Example 3.

21. $x^2 - 3x + 17 = 0$

$\left\{\frac{3 + i\sqrt{59}}{2}, \frac{3 - i\sqrt{59}}{2}\right\}$

22. $x^2 - 5x + 20 = 0$

$\left\{\frac{5 + i\sqrt{55}}{2}, \frac{5 - i\sqrt{55}}{2}\right\}$

23. $r^2 - 6r + 14 = 0$

$\{3 + i\sqrt{5}, 3 - i\sqrt{5}\}$

24. $t^2 + 4t + 11 = 0$

$\{-2 + i\sqrt{7}, -2 - i\sqrt{7}\}$

25. $4x^2 - 4x = -7$

$\left\{\frac{1 + i\sqrt{6}}{2}, \frac{1 - i\sqrt{6}}{2}\right\}$

26. $9x^2 - 6x = -7$

$\left\{\frac{1 + i\sqrt{6}}{3}, \frac{1 - i\sqrt{6}}{3}\right\}$

27. $x(3x + 4) = -2$

$\left\{\frac{-2 + i\sqrt{2}}{3}, \frac{-2 - i\sqrt{2}}{3}\right\}$

28. $p(2p + 3) = -2$

$\left\{\frac{-3 + i\sqrt{7}}{4}, \frac{-3 - i\sqrt{7}}{4}\right\}$

Use the discriminant to determine whether the solutions for each equation are
A. *two rational numbers,* **B.** *one rational number,*
C. *two irrational numbers,* **D.** *two imaginary numbers.*
Do not actually solve. See Example 4.

29. $25x^2 + 70x + 49 = 0$

B

30. $4k^2 - 28k + 49 = 0$

B

31. $x^2 + 4x + 2 = 0$

C

32. $9x^2 - 12x - 1 = 0$

C

33. $3x^2 = 5x + 2$

A

34. $4x^2 = 4x + 3$

A

35. $3m^2 - 10m + 15 = 0$

D

36. $18x^2 + 60x + 82 = 0$

D

37. Using the discriminant, which equations in Exercises 29–36 can be solved by factoring?

The equations in Exercises 29, 30, 33, and 34 can be solved by factoring.

38. Based on your answer in Exercise 37, solve the equation given in each exercise.

(a) Exercise 29

$\left\{-\frac{7}{5}\right\}$

(b) Exercise 33

$\left\{-\frac{1}{3}, 2\right\}$

10.4 EQUATIONS QUADRATIC IN FORM

We have introduced four methods for solving quadratic equations written in standard form $ax^2 + bx + c = 0$. The following table lists some advantages and disadvantages of each method.

METHODS FOR SOLVING QUADRATIC EQUATIONS

Method	Advantages	Disadvantages
Factoring	This is usually the fastest method.	Not all polynomials are factorable; some factorable polynomials are hard to factor.
Square root property	This is the simplest method for solving equations of the form $(ax + b)^2 = k$.	Few equations are given in this form.
Completing the square	This method can always be used, although most people prefer the quadratic formula.	It requires more steps than other methods.
Quadratic formula	This method can always be used.	It is more difficult than factoring because of the square root, although calculators can simplify its use.

OBJECTIVES

1. Solve an equation with fractions by writing it in quadratic form.
2. Use quadratic equations to solve applied problems.
3. Solve an equation with radicals by writing it in quadratic form.
4. Solve an equation that is quadratic in form by substitution.

1 Solve an equation with fractions by writing it in quadratic form. A variety of nonquadratic equations can be written in the form of a quadratic equation and solved by using one of the methods in the table. As you solve the equations in this section, try to decide which method is best for each equation.

Example 1 Solving an Equation with Fractions that Leads to a Quadratic Equation

Solve $\frac{1}{x} + \frac{1}{x-1} = \frac{7}{12}$.

Clear fractions by multiplying each term by the least common denominator, $12x(x - 1)$. (Note that the domain must be restricted to $x \neq 0$ and $x \neq 1$.)

$$12x(x-1)\frac{1}{x} + 12x(x-1)\frac{1}{x-1} = 12x(x-1)\frac{7}{12}$$

$$12(x-1) + 12x = 7x(x-1)$$

$$12x - 12 + 12x = 7x^2 - 7x \quad \text{Distributive property}$$

$$24x - 12 = 7x^2 - 7x \quad \text{Combine terms.}$$

A quadratic equation must be in standard form before it can be solved by factoring or the quadratic formula. Combine and rearrange terms so that one side is 0. Then use factoring to solve the resulting equation.

$$0 = 7x^2 - 31x + 12 \quad \text{Standard form}$$

$$0 = (7x - 3)(x - 4) \quad \text{Factor.}$$

Using the zero-factor property gives the solutions $\frac{3}{7}$ and 4. Check by substituting these solutions in the original equation. The solution set is $\{\frac{3}{7}, 4\}$.

Work Problem 1 at the Side.

1 Solve each equation. Check your solutions.

(a) $\frac{5}{m} + \frac{12}{m^2} = 2$

(b) $\frac{2}{x} + \frac{1}{x-2} = \frac{5}{3}$

(c) $\frac{4}{m-1} + 9 = -\frac{7}{m}$

ANSWERS

1. (a) $\left\{-\frac{3}{2}, 4\right\}$ **(b)** $\left\{\frac{4}{5}, 3\right\}$

(c) $\left\{\frac{7}{9}, -1\right\}$

2 Use quadratic equations to solve applied problems. Earlier we solved distance-rate-time (or motion) problems that led to linear equations or rational equations. Now we can extend that work to motion problems that lead to quadratic equations. We continue to use the six-step problem-solving method from Chapter 2.

Example 2 Solving a Motion Problem

A riverboat for tourists averages 12 mph in still water. It takes the boat 1 hr, 4 min to go 6 mi upstream and return. Find the speed of the current. See Figure 1.

Figure 1

Step 1 **Read** the problem carefully.

Step 2 **Assign a variable.** Let $x =$ the speed of the current. The rate (or speed) upstream is the speed of the boat in still water less the speed of the current, or $12 - x$. Similarly, the speed downstream is $12 + x$. So,

$$12 - x = \text{the rate upstream;}$$
$$12 + x = \text{the rate downstream.}$$

Use the distance formula, $d = rt$, solved for time t.

$$t = \frac{d}{r}$$

This information can be used to complete a table.

	d	r	t
Upstream	6	$12 - x$	$\frac{6}{12 - x}$
Downstream	6	$12 + x$	$\frac{6}{12 + x}$

Times in hours

Step 3 **Write an equation.** The total time, 1 hr and 4 min, can be written as

$$1 + \frac{4}{60} = 1 + \frac{1}{15} = \frac{16}{15} \text{ hr.}$$

Because the time upstream plus the time downstream equals $\frac{16}{15}$ hr,

$$\underbrace{\frac{6}{12 - x}}_{\text{Time upstream}} + \underbrace{\frac{6}{12 + x}}_{\text{Time downstream}} = \underbrace{\frac{16}{15}}_{\text{Total time}}.$$

Step 4 **Solve** the equation. Multiply each side by $15(12 - x)(12 + x)$, the LCD, and solve the resulting quadratic equation.

Continued on Next Page

$$
\begin{aligned}
15(12 + x)6 + 15(12 - x)6 &= 16(12 - x)(12 + x) \\
90(12 + x) + 90(12 - x) &= 16(144 - x^2) \\
1080 + 90x + 1080 - 90x &= 2304 - 16x^2 && \text{Distributive property} \\
2160 &= 2304 - 16x^2 && \text{Combine terms.} \\
16x^2 &= 144 \\
x^2 &= 9 && \text{Divide by 16.} \\
x = 3 \quad \text{or} \quad x &= -3 && \text{Square root property}
\end{aligned}
$$

Step 5 **State the answer.** The speed of the current cannot be -3, so the answer is 3 mph.

Step 6 **Check** that this value satisfies the original problem.

CAUTION

As shown in Example 2, when a quadratic equation is used to solve an applied problem, sometimes only *one* answer satisfies the application. It is *always necessary* to check each answer in the words of the original problem.

Work Problem 2 at the Side.

In Chapter 8 we solved problems about work rates. Recall that a person's work rate is $\frac{1}{t}$ part of the job per hour, where t is the time in hours required to do the complete job. Thus, the part of the job the person will do in x hours is $\frac{1}{t}x$.

Example 3 Solving a Work Problem

It takes two carpet layers 4 hr to carpet a room. If each worked alone, one of them could do the job in 1 hr less time than the other. How long would it take each carpet layer to complete the job alone?

Step 1 **Read** the problem again. There will be two answers.

Step 2 **Assign a variable.** Let x represent the number of hours for the slower carpet layer to complete the job alone. Then the faster carpet layer could do the entire job in $x - 1$ hr. The slower person's rate is $\frac{1}{x}$, and the faster person's rate is $\frac{1}{x-1}$. Together, they do the job in 4 hr. Complete a table as shown.

	Rate	Time Working Together	Fractional Part of the Job Done
Slower Worker	$\frac{1}{x}$	4	$\frac{1}{x}(4)$
Faster Worker	$\frac{1}{x-1}$	4	$\frac{1}{x-1}(4)$

Sum is 1 whole job.

Continued on Next Page

2 Solve each problem.

(a) In 4 hr, Kerrie can go 15 mi upriver and come back. The speed of the current is 5 mph. Complete this table.

	d	r	t
Up			
Down			

(b) Find the speed of the boat from part (a) in still water.

(c) In $1\frac{3}{4}$ hr, Ken rows his boat 5 mi upriver and comes back. The speed of the current is 3 mph. How fast does Ken row?

ANSWERS

2. (a) row 1: 15; $x - 5$; $\frac{15}{x-5}$; row 2: 15; $x + 5$; $\frac{15}{x+5}$

(b) 10 mph **(c)** 7 mph

3 Solve each problem. Round answers to the nearest tenth.

(a) Carlos can complete a certain lab test in 2 hr less time than Jaime can. If they can finish the job together in 2 hr, how long would it take each of them working alone?

	Rate	Time Working Together	Fractional Part of the Job Done
Carlos			
Jaime			

(b) Two chefs are preparing a banquet. One chef could prepare the banquet in 2 hr less time than the other. Together, they complete the job in 5 hr. How long would it take the faster chef working alone?

ANSWERS
3. **(a)** Jaime: 5.2 hr; Carlos: 3.2 hr **(b)** 9.1 hr

Step 3 **Write an equation.** The sum of the fractional parts done by the workers should equal 1 (the whole job).

$$\underset{\downarrow}{\text{Part done by slower worker}} + \underset{\downarrow}{\text{part done by faster worker}} = \underset{\downarrow}{\text{1 whole job.}}$$
$$\frac{4}{x} + \frac{4}{x-1} = 1$$

Step 4 **Solve** the equation. Multiply each side by the LCD, $x(x-1)$.

$$4(x-1) + 4x = x(x-1)$$
$$4x - 4 + 4x = x^2 - x \qquad \text{Distributive property}$$
$$0 = x^2 - 9x + 4 \qquad \text{Standard form}$$

This equation cannot be solved by factoring, so use the quadratic formula.

$$x = \frac{9 \pm \sqrt{81-16}}{2} = \frac{9 \pm \sqrt{65}}{2} \qquad a = 1, b = -9, c = 4$$

To the nearest tenth,

$$x = \frac{9+\sqrt{65}}{2} \approx 8.5 \quad \text{or} \quad x = \frac{9-\sqrt{65}}{2} \approx .5. \qquad \text{Use a calculator.}$$

Step 5 **State the answer.** Only the solution 8.5 makes sense in the original problem. (Why?) Thus, the slower worker can do the job in about 8.5 hr and the faster in about $8.5 - 1 = 7.5$ hr.

Step 6 **Check** that these results satisfy the original problem.

Work Problem 3 at the Side.

3 Solve an equation with radicals by writing it in quadratic form.

Example 4 Solving Radical Equations That Lead to Quadratic Equations

Solve each equation.

(a) $k = \sqrt{6k - 8}$

This equation is not quadratic. However, squaring both sides of the equation gives a quadratic equation that can be solved by factoring.

$$k^2 = 6k - 8 \qquad \text{Square both sides.}$$
$$k^2 - 6k + 8 = 0 \qquad \text{Standard form}$$
$$(k-4)(k-2) = 0 \qquad \text{Factor.}$$
$$k - 4 = 0 \quad \text{or} \quad k - 2 = 0 \qquad \text{Zero-factor property}$$
$$k = 4 \quad \text{or} \quad k = 2 \qquad \text{Potential solutions}$$

Recall from our work with radical equations in Section 9.6 that squaring both sides of an equation can introduce extraneous solutions that do not satisfy the original equation. Therefore, *all potential solutions must be checked in the original (not the squared) equation.*

Check: If $k = 4$, then

$$k = \sqrt{6k-8}$$
$$4 = \sqrt{6(4) - 8} \quad ?$$
$$4 = \sqrt{16} \quad ?$$
$$4 = 4. \qquad \text{True}$$

If $k = 2$, then

$$k = \sqrt{6k-8}$$
$$2 = \sqrt{6(2) - 8} \quad ?$$
$$2 = \sqrt{4} \quad ?$$
$$2 = 2. \qquad \text{True}$$

Both solutions check, so the solution set is $\{2, 4\}$.

Continued on Next Page

(b) $x + \sqrt{x} = 6$

$\sqrt{x} = 6 - x$	Get the radical alone on one side.
$x = 36 - 12x + x^2$	Square both sides.
$0 = x^2 - 13x + 36$	Standard form
$0 = (x - 4)(x - 9)$	Factor.
$x - 4 = 0$ or $x - 9 = 0$	Zero-factor property
$x = 4$ or $x = 9$	Potential solutions

Check both potential solutions in the *original* equation.

If $x = 4$, then

$x + \sqrt{x} = 6$

$4 + \sqrt{4} = 6$?

$6 = 6.$ True

If $x = 9$, then

$x + \sqrt{x} = 6$

$9 + \sqrt{9} = 6$?

$12 = 6.$ False

Only the solution 4 checks, so the solution set is $\{4\}$.

Work Problem 4 at the Side.

4 Solve an equation that is quadratic in form by substitution. A nonquadratic equation that can be written in the form $au^2 + bu + c = 0$, for $a \neq 0$ and an algebraic expression u, is called **quadratic in form.**

Example 5 Solving Equations That Are Quadratic in Form

Solve each equation.

(a) $x^4 - 13x^2 + 36 = 0$

Because $x^4 = (x^2)^2$, we can write this equation in quadratic form with $u = x^2$ and $u^2 = x^4$.

$x^4 - 13x^2 + 36 = 0$	
$(x^2)^2 - 13x^2 + 36 = 0$	$x^4 = (x^2)^2$
$u^2 - 13u + 36 = 0$	Let $u = x^2$.
$(u - 4)(u - 9) = 0$	Factor.
$u - 4 = 0$ or $u - 9 = 0$	Zero-factor property
$u = 4$ or $u = 9$	Solve.

To find x, we substitute x^2 for u.

$x^2 = 4$ or $x^2 = 9$	
$x = \pm 2$ or $x = \pm 3$	Square root property

The equation $x^4 - 13x^2 + 36 = 0$, a fourth-degree equation, has four solutions.* The solution set is $\{-3, -2, 2, 3\}$, which can be verified by substituting into the equation.

(b) $4x^4 + 1 = 5x^2$

Again, use the fact that $x^4 = (x^2)^2$ and let $u = x^2$ and $u^2 = x^4$.

$$4(x^2)^2 + 1 = 5x^2$$

$$4u^2 + 1 = 5u \qquad \text{Let } u = x^2.$$

Continued on Next Page

4 Solve each equation. Check your solutions.

(a) $x = \sqrt{7x - 10}$

(b) $2x = \sqrt{x} + 1$

ANSWERS

4. **(a)** $\{2, 5\}$ **(b)** $\{1\}$

---

* In general, an equation in which an nth-degree polynomial equals 0 has n solutions, although some of them may be repeated.

$$\begin{aligned} 4u^2 - 5u + 1 &= 0 && \text{Standard form} \\ (4u - 1)(u - 1) &= 0 && \text{Factor.} \\ 4u - 1 = 0 \quad \text{or} \quad u - 1 &= 0 && \text{Zero-factor property} \\ u = \frac{1}{4} \quad \text{or} \quad u &= 1 && \text{Solve.} \\ x^2 = \frac{1}{4} \quad \text{or} \quad x^2 &= 1 && \text{Substitute } x^2 \text{ for } u. \\ x = \pm\frac{1}{2} \quad \text{or} \quad x &= \pm 1 && \text{Square root property} \end{aligned}$$

Check that the solution set is $\{-1, -\frac{1}{2}, \frac{1}{2}, 1\}$.

NOTE

Some students prefer to solve equations like those in Example 5 by factoring directly. For example,

$$\begin{aligned} x^4 - 13x^2 + 36 &= 0 && \text{Example 5(a) equation} \\ (x^2 - 9)(x^2 - 4) &= 0 && \text{Factor.} \\ (x + 3)(x - 3)(x + 2)(x - 2) &= 0. && \text{Factor again.} \end{aligned}$$

Using the zero-factor property gives the same solutions obtained in Example 5(a).

Work Problem 5 at the Side.

5 Solve each equation. Check your solutions.

(a) $m^4 - 10m^2 + 9 = 0$

(b) $9k^4 - 37k^2 + 4 = 0$

Example 6 Solving Equations That Are Quadratic in Form

Solve each equation.

(a) $2(4m - 3)^2 + 7(4m - 3) + 5 = 0$

Because of the repeated quantity $4m - 3$, this equation is quadratic in form with $u = 4m - 3$. (Any letter except m could be used instead of u.)

$$\begin{aligned} 2(4m - 3)^2 + 7(4m - 3) + 5 &= 0 \\ 2u^2 + 7u + 5 &= 0 && \text{Let } 4m - 3 = u. \\ (2u + 5)(u + 1) &= 0 && \text{Factor.} \\ 2u + 5 = 0 \quad \text{or} \quad u + 1 &= 0 && \text{Zero-factor property} \\ u = -\frac{5}{2} \quad \text{or} \quad u &= -1 \\ 4m - 3 = -\frac{5}{2} \quad \text{or} \quad 4m - 3 &= -1 && \text{Substitute } 4m - 3 \text{ for } u. \\ 4m = \frac{1}{2} \quad \text{or} \quad 4m &= 2 && \text{Solve for } m. \\ m = \frac{1}{8} \quad \text{or} \quad m &= \frac{1}{2} \end{aligned}$$

Check that the solution set of the original equation is $\{\frac{1}{8}, \frac{1}{2}\}$.

Continued on Next Page

ANSWERS

5. (a) $\{-3, -1, 1, 3\}$ **(b)** $\left\{-2, -\frac{1}{3}, \frac{1}{3}, 2\right\}$

(b) $2a^{2/3} - 11a^{1/3} + 12 = 0$

Let $a^{1/3} = u$; then $a^{2/3} = (a^{1/3})^2 = u^2$. Substitute into the given equation.

$$2u^2 - 11u + 12 = 0 \quad \text{Let } a^{1/3} = u;\ a^{2/3} = u^2.$$

$$(2u - 3)(u - 4) = 0 \quad \text{Factor.}$$

$$2u - 3 = 0 \quad \text{or} \quad u - 4 = 0 \quad \text{Zero-factor property}$$

$$u = \frac{3}{2} \quad \text{or} \quad u = 4$$

$$a^{1/3} = \frac{3}{2} \quad \text{or} \quad a^{1/3} = 4 \quad u = a^{1/3}$$

$$(a^{1/3})^3 = \left(\frac{3}{2}\right)^3 \quad \text{or} \quad (a^{1/3})^3 = 4^3 \quad \text{Cube each side.}$$

$$a = \frac{27}{8} \quad \text{or} \quad a = 64$$

Check that the solution set is $\{\frac{27}{8}, 64\}$.

CAUTION

A common error when solving problems like those in Examples 5 and 6 is to stop too soon. Once you have solved for u, remember to substitute and solve for the values of the *original* variable.

Work Problem 6 at the Side.

6 Solve each equation. Check your solutions.

(a) $5(r + 3)^2 + 9(r + 3) = 2$

(b) $4m^{2/3} = 3m^{1/3} + 1$

ANSWERS

6. (a) $\left\{-5, -\frac{14}{5}\right\}$ **(b)** $\left\{-\frac{1}{64}, 1\right\}$

Focus on *Real-Data Applications*

Smile! You're on Golden Ratio!

The Golden Ratio is the number phi, $\phi = \frac{1 + \sqrt{5}}{2}$. The Rhind Papyrus, dated 1600 B.C., referred to the **sacred ratio** used in building the Great Pyramids at Giza, Egypt. The ancient Greeks used ϕ in art and architecture, striving for a proportion that was the most pleasing to the eye. The Parthenon is the classic illustration of the use of ϕ in achieving that goal.

In a segment of length 1 that is divided into two parts, the Golden Ratio is defined as the proportion that equates the ratio of the whole segment to the larger segment and the ratio of the larger segment to the smaller segment. In the diagram, segment AC has length 1. Point B divides the segment so that AB has length x and BC has length $1 - x$. If x represents the length of the larger segment AB, then ϕ is the ratio $\frac{1}{x}$ and the Golden Proportion is

$$\frac{\text{whole}}{\text{larger}} = \frac{\text{larger}}{\text{smaller}} \quad \text{or} \quad \frac{1}{x} = \frac{x}{1 - x}.$$

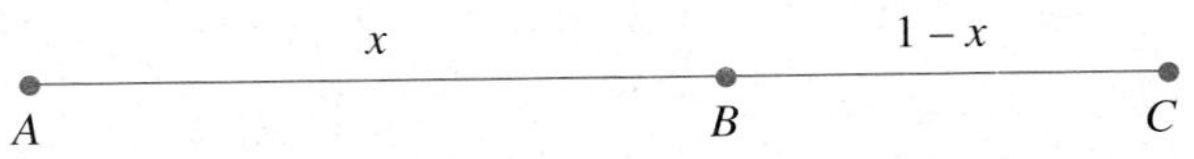

The Golden Ratio is used in dentistry and medicine today. Eddy Levin, an English dentist, became interested in applications of the Golden Ratio, or Golden Proportion, to orthodontia and dentistry in 1978. His work is now a compulsory topic of study in U.S. dental schools. Viewed from the front, the "four front teeth, from central incisor to the premolar are the most significant part of the smile and they are in Golden Proportion to each other." He invented the Golden Mean Gauge, which is a tool that measures the Golden Proportion. (*Source:* www.goldenmeangauge.co.uk)

For Group Discussion

1. Write the Golden Proportion as a quadratic equation. **$x^2 = 1 - x$ or $x^2 + x - 1 = 0$**

(a) Use the quadratic formula to solve this quadratic equation for x. Note that x must be a positive number since it is the length of AB.

(b) The Golden Ratio is $\phi = \frac{1}{x}$. Rationalize the denominator to write ϕ in exact form (using radicals).

(c) Write an approximate value for ϕ, rounded to 6 decimal places.

(a) $x = \frac{-1 + \sqrt{5}}{2}$ (b) $\phi = \frac{1 + \sqrt{5}}{2}$ (c) 1.618034

2. The Golden Ratio is a mathematically curious number. The reciprocal of ϕ is one less than ϕ, and the square of ϕ is one more than ϕ.

(a) Find $\frac{1}{\phi}$ and $\phi - 1$. (*Hint:* You have previously found the quantity $\frac{1}{\phi}$.)

(b) Find ϕ^2 and $\phi + 1$ in exact form.

(a) $\frac{1}{\phi} = x = \frac{-1 + \sqrt{5}}{2} = \phi - 1$

(b) $\phi^2 = \left(\frac{1 + \sqrt{5}}{2}\right)^2 = \frac{3 + \sqrt{5}}{2} = \phi + 1$

Teaching notes and an extension for this activity are provided in the *Printed Test Bank and Instructor's Resource Guide.*

10.4 EXERCISES

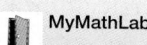

FOR EXTRA HELP: Student's Solutions Manual; MyMathLab.com; InterAct Math Tutorial Software; AW Math Tutor Center; www.mathxl.com; Digital Video Tutor CD 9 Videotape 20

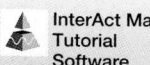

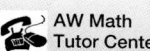

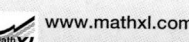

Based on the discussion and examples of this section, write a sentence describing the first step you would take to solve each equation. Do not actually solve.

1. $\dfrac{14}{x} = x - 5$

Multiply by the LCD, x.

2. $\sqrt{1 + x} + x = 5$

Isolate the radical term on one side.

3. $(r^2 + r)^2 - 8(r^2 + r) + 12 = 0$

Substitute a variable for $r^2 + r$.

4. $3t = \sqrt{16 - 10t}$

Square both sides.

5. What is wrong with the following "solution"?

$$\begin{aligned} x &= \sqrt{3x + 4} \\ x^2 &= 3x + 4 \quad \text{Square both sides.} \\ x^2 - 3x - 4 &= 0 \\ (x - 4)(x + 1) &= 0 \\ x - 4 = 0 \quad &\text{or} \quad x + 1 = 0 \\ x = 4 \quad &\text{or} \quad x = -1 \end{aligned}$$

Solution set: $\{4, -1\}$

The potential solution -1 does not check. The solution set is $\{4\}$.

6. What is wrong with the following "solution"?

$$\begin{aligned} 2(m - 1)^2 - 3(m - 1) + 1 &= 0 \\ 2u^2 - 3u + 1 &= 0 \quad \text{Let } u = m - 1. \\ (2u - 1)(u - 1) &= 0 \\ 2u - 1 = 0 \quad &\text{or} \quad u - 1 = 0 \\ u = \frac{1}{2} \quad &\text{or} \quad u = 1 \end{aligned}$$

Solution set: $\left\{\frac{1}{2}, 1\right\}$

The solutions given are for u. Each must be set equal to $m - 1$ and solved for m. The correct solution set is $\left\{\frac{3}{2}, 2\right\}$.

Solve each equation. Check your solutions. See Example 1.

7. $1 - \dfrac{3}{x} - \dfrac{28}{x^2} = 0$

$\{-4, 7\}$

8. $4 - \dfrac{7}{r} - \dfrac{2}{r^2} = 0$

$\left\{-\frac{1}{4}, 2\right\}$

9. $3 - \dfrac{1}{t} = \dfrac{2}{t^2}$

$\left\{-\frac{2}{3}, 1\right\}$

10. $1 + \dfrac{2}{k} = \dfrac{3}{k^2}$

$\{-3, 1\}$

11. $\dfrac{1}{x} + \dfrac{2}{x + 2} = \dfrac{17}{35}$

$\left\{-\frac{14}{17}, 5\right\}$

12. $\dfrac{2}{m} + \dfrac{3}{m + 9} = \dfrac{11}{4}$

$\left\{-8, \frac{9}{11}\right\}$

13. $\dfrac{2}{x + 1} + \dfrac{3}{x + 2} = \dfrac{7}{2}$

$\left\{-\frac{11}{7}, 0\right\}$

14. $\dfrac{4}{3 - p} + \dfrac{2}{5 - p} = \dfrac{26}{15}$

$\left\{0, \frac{59}{13}\right\}$

15. $\dfrac{3}{2x} - \dfrac{1}{2(x + 2)} = 1$

$\left\{\frac{-1 + \sqrt{13}}{2}, \frac{-1 - \sqrt{13}}{2}\right\}$

16. $\dfrac{4}{3x} - \dfrac{1}{2(x + 1)} = 1$

$\left\{\frac{-1 + \sqrt{193}}{12}, \frac{-1 - \sqrt{193}}{12}\right\}$

17. If it takes m hours to grade a set of papers, what is the grader's rate (in job per hour)?

$\frac{1}{m}$ **job per hr**

18. A boat goes 20 mph in still water, and the rate of the current is t mph.

(a) What is the rate of the boat when it travels upstream?

20 − t mph

(b) What is the rate of the boat when it travels downstream?

20 + t mph

Solve each problem. See Examples 2 and 3.

19. On a windy day Yoshiaki found that he could go 16 mi downstream and then 4 mi back upstream at top speed in a total of 48 min. What was the top speed of Yoshiaki's boat if the current was 15 mph?

	d	r	t
Upstream	4	$x - 15$	
Downstream	16		

25 mph

20. Lekesha flew her plane for 6 hr at a constant speed. She traveled 810 mi with the wind, then turned around and traveled 720 mi against the wind. The wind speed was a constant 15 mph. Find the speed of the plane.

	d	r	t
With Wind	810		
Against Wind	720		

255 mph

21. In Canada, Medicine Hat and Cranbrook are 300 km apart. Harry rides his Honda 20 km per hr faster than Yoshi rides his Yamaha. Find Harry's average speed if he travels from Cranbrook to Medicine Hat in $1\frac{1}{4}$ hr less time than Yoshi. (*Source: State Farm Road Atlas.*)

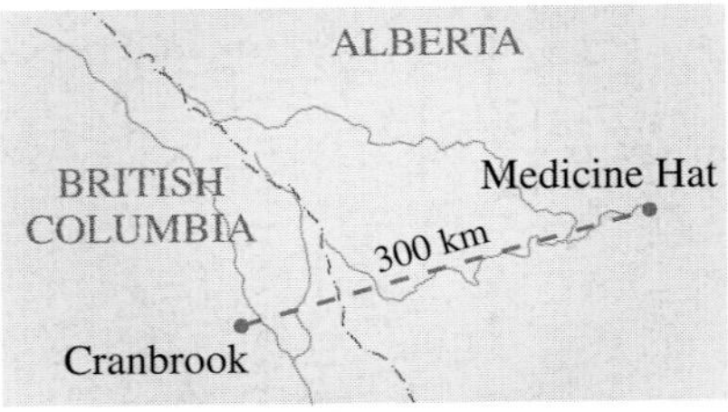

80 km per hr

22. In California, the distance from Jackson to Lodi is about 40 mi, as is the distance from Lodi to Manteca. Rico drove from Jackson to Lodi during the rush hour, stopped in Lodi for a root beer, and then drove on to Manteca at 10 mph faster. Driving time for the entire trip was 88 min. Find his speed from Jackson to Lodi. (*Source: State Farm Road Atlas.*)

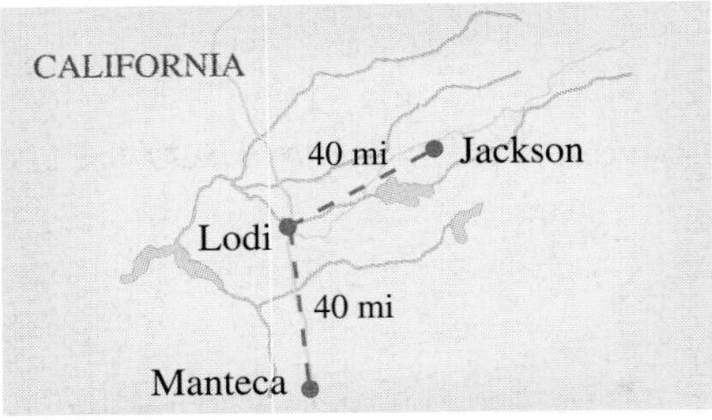

50 mph

23. Working together, two people can cut a large lawn in 2 hr. One person can do the job alone in 1 hr less time than the other. How long (to the nearest tenth) would it take the faster person to do the job? (*Hint:* x is the time of the faster person.)

	Rate	Time Working Together	Fractional Part of the Job Done
Faster Worker	$\frac{1}{x}$	2	
Slower Worker		2	

3.6 hr

24. A janitorial service provides two people to clean an office building. Working together, the two can clean the building in 5 hr. One person is new to the job and would take 2 hr longer than the other person to clean the building alone. How long (to the nearest tenth) would it take the new worker to clean the building alone?

	Rate	Time Working Together	Fractional Part of the Job Done
Faster Worker			
Slower Worker			

11.1 hr

25. A washing machine can be filled in 6 min if both the hot and cold water taps are fully opened. Filling the washer with hot water alone takes 9 min longer than filling it with cold water alone. How long does it take to fill the washer with cold water?

9 min

26. Two pipes together can fill a large tank in 2 hr. One of the pipes, used alone, takes 3 hr longer than the other to fill the tank. How long would each pipe take to fill the tank alone?

3 hr; 6 hr

Solve each equation. Check your solutions. See Example 4.

27. $2x = \sqrt{11x + 3}$

$\{3\}$

28. $4x = \sqrt{6x + 1}$

$\left\{\frac{1}{2}\right\}$

29. $3x = \sqrt{16 - 10x}$

$\left\{\frac{8}{9}\right\}$

30. $4t = \sqrt{8t + 3}$

$\left\{\frac{3}{4}\right\}$

31. $p - 2\sqrt{p} = 8$

$\{16\}$

32. $k + \sqrt{k} = 12$

$\{9\}$

33. $m = \sqrt{\dfrac{6 - 13m}{5}}$

$\left\{\frac{2}{5}\right\}$

34. $r = \sqrt{\dfrac{20 - 19r}{6}}$

$\left\{\frac{5}{6}\right\}$

Solve each equation. Check your solutions. See Examples 5 and 6.

35. $t^4 - 18t^2 + 81 = 0$

$\{-3, 3\}$

36. $x^4 - 8x^2 + 16 = 0$

$\{-2, 2\}$

37. $4k^4 - 13k^2 + 9 = 0$

$\left\{-\frac{3}{2}, -1, 1, \frac{3}{2}\right\}$

38. $9x^4 - 25x^2 + 16 = 0$

$\left\{-\frac{4}{3}, -1, 1, \frac{4}{3}\right\}$

39. $x^4 + 48 = 16x^2$

$\{-2\sqrt{3}, -2, 2, 2\sqrt{3}\}$

40. $z^4 = 17z^2 - 72$

$\{-3, -2\sqrt{2}, 2\sqrt{2}, 3\}$

41. $(x + 3)^2 + 5(x + 3) + 6 = 0$

$\{-6, -5\}$

42. $(k - 4)^2 + (k - 4) - 20 = 0$

$\{-1, 8\}$

43. $(t + 5)^2 + 6 = 7(t + 5)$

$\{-4, 1\}$

44. $3(m + 4)^2 - 8 = 2(m + 4)$

$\left\{-\frac{16}{3}, -2\right\}$

45. $2 + \dfrac{5}{3k - 1} = \dfrac{-2}{(3k - 1)^2}$

$\left\{-\frac{1}{3}, \frac{1}{6}\right\}$

46. $3 - \dfrac{7}{2p + 2} = \dfrac{6}{(2p + 2)^2}$

$\left\{-\frac{4}{3}, \frac{1}{2}\right\}$

47. $x^{2/3} + x^{1/3} - 2 = 0$

$\{-8, 1\}$

48. $x^{2/3} - 2x^{1/3} - 3 = 0$

$\{-1, 27\}$

49. $r^{2/3} + r^{1/3} - 12 = 0$

$\{-64, 27\}$

50. $3x^{2/3} - x^{1/3} - 24 = 0$

$\left\{-\frac{512}{27}, 27\right\}$

51. $2(1 + \sqrt{r})^2 = 13(1 + \sqrt{r}) - 6$

$\{25\}$

52. $(k^2 + k)^2 + 12 = 8(k^2 + k)$

$\{-3, -2, 1, 2\}$

RELATING CONCEPTS (Exercises 53–58) FOR INDIVIDUAL OR GROUP WORK

Consider the following equation, which contains variable expressions in the denominators.

$$\frac{x^2}{(x-3)^2} + \frac{3x}{x-3} - 4 = 0$$

Work Exercises 53–58 in order.

53. Why must 3 be excluded from the domain of this equation?

It would cause both denominators to be 0, and division by 0 is undefined.

54. Multiply each side of the equation by the LCD, $(x - 3)^2$, and solve. There is only one solution—what is it?

$\frac{12}{5}$

55. Write the equation in a different manner so that it is quadratic in form using the expression $\frac{x}{x-3}$.

$\left(\frac{x}{x-3}\right)^2 + 3\left(\frac{x}{x-3}\right) - 4 = 0$

56. In your own words, explain why the expression $\frac{x}{x-3}$ cannot equal 1.

The numerator can never equal the denominator, since the denominator is 3 less than the numerator.

57. Solve the equation from Exercise 55 by making the substitution $t = \frac{x}{x-3}$. You should get two values for t. Why is one of them impossible for this equation?

$\left\{\frac{12}{5}\right\}$**; The values for t are -4 and 1. The value 1 is impossible because it leads to a contradiction $\left(\text{since } \frac{x}{x-3} \text{ is never equal to } 1\right)$.**

58. Solve the equation $x^2(x - 3)^{-2} + 3x(x - 3)^{-1} - 4 = 0$ by letting $s = (x - 3)^{-1}$. You should get two values for s. Why is this impossible for this equation?

$\left\{\frac{12}{5}\right\}$**; The values for s are $\frac{1}{x}$ and $\frac{-4}{x}$. The value $\frac{1}{x}$ is impossible, since $\frac{1}{x} \neq \frac{1}{x-3}$ for all x.**

10.5 Formulas and Further Applications

1 Solve formulas for variables involving squares and square roots. The methods presented earlier in this chapter and the previous one can be used to solve such formulas.

Objectives

1. Solve formulas for variables involving squares and square roots.
2. Solve applied problems using the Pythagorean formula.
3. Solve applied problems using area formulas.
4. Solve applied problems using quadratic functions as models.

Example 1 Solving for Variables Involving Squares or Square Roots

Solve each formula for the given variable.

(a) $w = \dfrac{kFr}{v^2}$ for v

$$w = \frac{kFr}{v^2} \quad \text{Get } v \text{ alone on one side.}$$

$$v^2 w = kFr \qquad \text{Multiply by } v^2.$$

$$v^2 = \frac{kFr}{w} \qquad \text{Divide by } w.$$

$$v = \pm\sqrt{\frac{kFr}{w}} \qquad \text{Square root property}$$

$$v = \frac{\pm\sqrt{kFr}}{\sqrt{w}} \cdot \frac{\sqrt{w}}{\sqrt{w}} = \frac{\pm\sqrt{kFrw}}{w} \qquad \text{Rationalize the denominator.}$$

(b) $d = \sqrt{\dfrac{4A}{\pi}}$ for A

$$d = \sqrt{\frac{4A}{\pi}}$$

$$d^2 = \frac{4A}{\pi} \qquad \text{Square both sides.}$$

$$\pi d^2 = 4A \qquad \text{Multiply by } \pi.$$

$$\frac{\pi d^2}{4} = A \qquad \text{Divide by 4.}$$

Work Problem 1 at the Side.

1 Solve each formula for the given variable.

(a) $A = \pi r^2$ for r

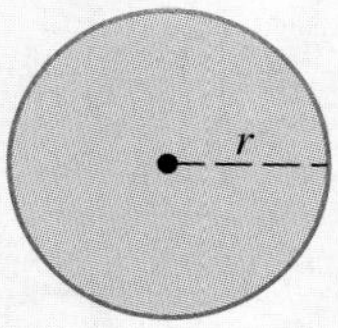

(b) $s = 30\sqrt{\dfrac{a}{p}}$ for a

NOTE

In many formulas like $v = \frac{\pm\sqrt{kFrw}}{w}$ in Example 1(a), we choose the positive value. In our work here, we will include both positive and negative values.

Example 2 Solving for a Squared Variable

Solve $s = 2t^2 + kt$ for t.

Since the equation has terms with t^2 and t, write it in standard form $ax^2 + bx + c = 0$, with t as the variable instead of x.

$$s = 2t^2 + kt$$

$$0 = 2t^2 + kt - s$$

Continued on Next Page

Answers

1. (a) $r = \dfrac{\pm\sqrt{A\pi}}{\pi}$ (b) $a = \dfrac{ps^2}{900}$

2 Solve $2t^2 - 5t + k = 0$ for t.

Now use the quadratic formula with $a = 2$, $b = k$, and $c = -s$.

$$t = \frac{-k \pm \sqrt{k^2 - 4(2)(-s)}}{2(2)} \quad \text{Solve for } t.$$

$$t = \frac{-k \pm \sqrt{k^2 + 8s}}{4}$$

The solutions are $t = \dfrac{-k + \sqrt{k^2 + 8s}}{4}$ and $t = \dfrac{-k - \sqrt{k^2 + 8s}}{4}$.

Work Problem 2 at the Side.

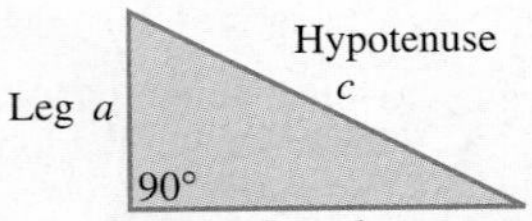

$c^2 = a^2 + b^2$

Pythagorean Formula

2 **Solve applied problems using the Pythagorean formula.** The Pythagorean formula $a^2 + b^2 = c^2$, illustrated by the figure in the margin, was introduced in Chapter 9 and is used to solve applications involving right triangles. Such problems often require solving quadratic equations.

Example 3 Using the Pythagorean Formula

Two cars left an intersection at the same time, one heading due north, the other due west. Some time later, they were exactly 100 mi apart. The car headed north had gone 20 mi farther than the car headed west. How far had each car traveled?

Step 1 **Read** the problem carefully.

Step 2 **Assign a variable.** Let x be the distance traveled by the car headed west. Then $x + 20$ is the distance traveled by the car headed north. See Figure 2. The cars are 100 mi apart, so the hypotenuse of the right triangle equals 100.

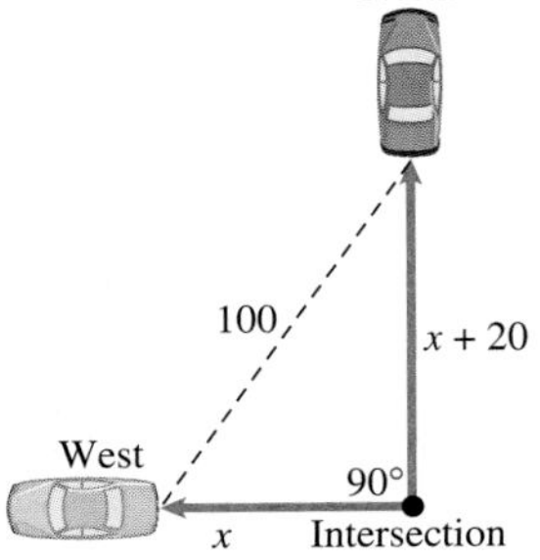

Figure 2

Step 3 **Write an equation.** Use the Pythagorean formula.

$$c^2 = a^2 + b^2$$
$$100^2 = x^2 + (x + 20)^2$$

Step 4 **Solve.**

$$10{,}000 = x^2 + x^2 + 40x + 400 \quad \text{Square the binomial.}$$
$$0 = 2x^2 + 40x - 9600 \quad \text{Standard form}$$
$$0 = x^2 + 20x - 4800 \quad \text{Divide by 2.}$$
$$0 = (x + 80)(x - 60) \quad \text{Factor.}$$
$$x + 80 = 0 \quad \text{or} \quad x - 60 = 0 \quad \text{Zero-factor property}$$
$$x = -80 \quad \text{or} \quad x = 60$$

Step 5 **State the answer.** Since distance cannot be negative, discard the negative solution. The required distances are 60 mi and $60 + 20 = 80$ mi.

Step 6 **Check.** Since $60^2 + 80^2 = 100^2$, the answers are correct.

Work Problem 3 at the Side.

3 Solve the problem.

A 13-ft ladder is leaning against a house. The distance from the bottom of the ladder to the house is 7 ft less than the distance from the top of the ladder to the ground. How far is the bottom of the ladder from the house?

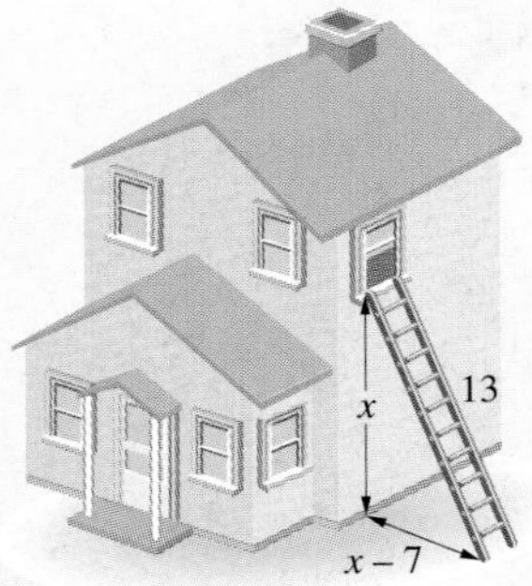

ANSWERS

2. $t = \dfrac{5 + \sqrt{25 - 8k}}{4}, t = \dfrac{5 - \sqrt{25 - 8k}}{4}$

3. 5 ft

3 **Solve applied problems using area formulas.**

Example 4 **Solving an Area Problem**

A rectangular reflecting pool in a park is 20 ft wide and 30 ft long. The park gardener wants to plant a strip of grass of uniform width around the edge of the pool. She has enough seed to cover 336 ft^2. How wide will the strip be?

Step 1 **Read** the problem carefully.

Step 2 **Assign a variable.** The pool is shown in Figure 3. If x represents the unknown width of the grass strip, the width of the large rectangle is given by $20 + 2x$ (the width of the pool plus two grass strips), and the length is given by $30 + 2x$.

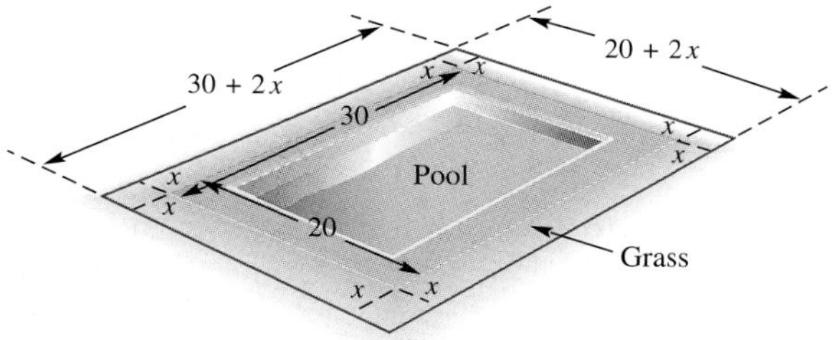

Figure 3

Step 3 **Write an equation.** The area of the large rectangle is given by the product of its length and width, $(30 + 2x)(20 + 2x)$. The area of the pool is $30 \cdot 20 = 600$ ft^2. The area of the large rectangle, minus the area of the pool, should equal the area of the grass strip. Since the area of the grass strip is to be 336 ft^2, the equation is

$$\underset{\text{rectangle}}{\text{Area of}} \quad - \quad \underset{\text{pool}}{\text{area of}} \quad = \quad \underset{\text{grass.}}{\text{area of}}$$

$$(30 + 2x)(20 + 2x) - 600 = 336.$$

Step 4 **Solve.**

$$\begin{aligned} 600 + 100x + 4x^2 - 600 &= 336 && \text{Multiply.} \\ 4x^2 + 100x - 336 &= 0 && \text{Standard form} \\ x^2 + 25x - 84 &= 0 && \text{Divide by 4.} \\ (x + 28)(x - 3) &= 0 && \text{Factor.} \\ x = -28 \quad \text{or} \quad x &= 3 && \text{Zero-factor property} \end{aligned}$$

Step 5 **State the answer.** The width cannot be -28 ft, so the grass strip should be 3 ft wide.

Step 6 **Check.** If $x = 3$, then the area of the large rectangle (which includes the grass strip) is

$$(30 + 2 \cdot 3)(20 + 2 \cdot 3) = 36 \cdot 26 = 936 \text{ ft}^2. \quad \text{Area of pool and strip}$$

The area of the pool is $30 \cdot 20 = 600$ ft^2. So, the area of the grass strip is $936 - 600 = 336$ ft^2, which is the area the gardener had enough seed to cover. The answer is correct.

Work Problem 4 at the Side.

4 **Solve applied problems using quadratic functions as models.** Some applied problems can be modeled by *quadratic functions,* which can be written in the form

$$f(x) = ax^2 + bx + c,$$

for real numbers a, b, and c, $a \neq 0$.

4 Solve the problem.

Suppose the pool in Example 4 is 20 ft by 40 ft and there is enough seed to cover 700 ft^2. How wide should the grass strip be?

ANSWERS

4. 5 ft

5 Solve the problem.

A ball is propelled vertically upward from the ground. Its distance in feet from the ground at t seconds is

$$s(t) = -16t^2 + 64t.$$

At what times will the ball be 32 ft from the ground? Use a calculator and round answers to the nearest tenth. (*Hint:* There are two answers.)

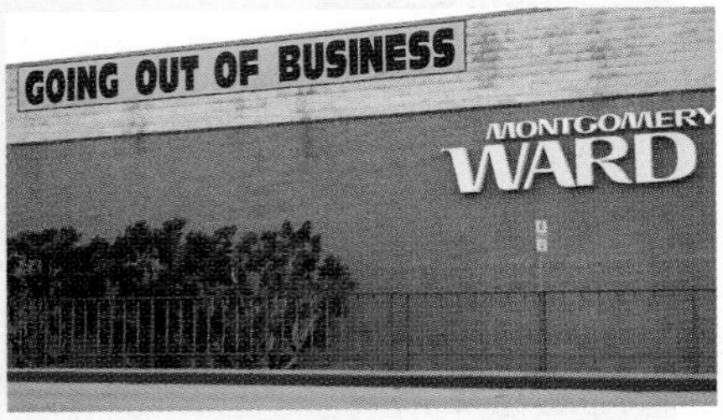

6 Use a calculator to evaluate

$$\frac{24.4 \pm \sqrt{(-24.4)^2 - 4(2.84)(-11)}}{2(2.84)}$$

for both solutions. Round to the nearest tenth. Which solution is valid for this problem?

Answers
5. at .6 sec and at 3.4 sec
6. 9.0, −.4; 9.0

Example 5 Solving an Applied Problem Using a Quadratic Function

If an object is propelled upward from the top of a 144-ft building at 112 ft per sec, its position (in feet above the ground) is given by

$$s(t) = -16t^2 + 112t + 144,$$

where t is time in seconds after it was thrown. When does it hit the ground?

When the object hits the ground, its distance above the ground is 0. We must find the value of t that makes $s(t) = 0$.

$$0 = -16t^2 + 112t + 144 \quad \text{Let } s(t) = 0.$$
$$0 = t^2 - 7t - 9 \quad \text{Divide by } -16.$$
$$t = \frac{7 \pm \sqrt{49 + 36}}{2} \quad \text{Quadratic formula}$$
$$t = \frac{7 \pm \sqrt{85}}{2} \approx \frac{7 \pm 9.2}{2} \quad \text{Use a calculator.}$$

The solutions are $t \approx 8.1$ or $t \approx -1.1$. Since time cannot be negative, discard the negative solution. The object will hit the ground about 8.1 sec after it is thrown.

Work Problem 5 at the Side.

Example 6 Using a Quadratic Function to Model Company Bankruptcy Filings

The number of companies filing for bankruptcy was high in the early 1990s due to an economic recession. The number then declined during the middle 1990s, and in recent years has increased again. The quadratic function defined by

$$f(x) = 2.84x^2 - 24.4x + 129$$

approximates the number of company bankruptcy filings during the years 1990–1999, where x is the number of years since 1990. (*Source:* www.BankruptcyData.com)

(a) Use the model to approximate the number of company bankruptcy filings in 1995.

For 1995, $x = 5$, so find $f(5)$.

$$f(5) = 2.84(5)^2 - 24.4(5) + 129 \quad \text{Let } x = 5.$$
$$= 78$$

There were 78 company bankruptcy filings in 1995.

(b) In what year did company bankruptcy filings reach 140?

Find the value of x that makes $f(x) = 140$.

$$f(x) = 2.84x^2 - 24.4x + 129$$
$$140 = 2.84x^2 - 24.4x + 129 \quad \text{Let } f(x) = 140.$$
$$0 = 2.84x^2 - 24.4x - 11 \quad \text{Standard form}$$

Now use $a = 2.84$, $b = -24.4$, and $c = -11$ in the quadratic formula.

Work Problem 6 at the Side.

The positive solution is $x \approx 9$, so company bankruptcy filings reached 140 in $1990 + 9 = 1999$. (Reject the negative solution since the model is not valid for negative values of x.)

10.5 EXERCISES

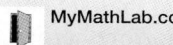

FOR EXTRA HELP Student's Solutions Manual | MyMathLab.com | InterAct Math Tutorial Software | AW Math Tutor Center | www.mathxl.com | Digital Video Tutor CD 9 Videotape 20

1. What is the first step in solving a formula like $gw^2 = 2r$ for w?

Solve for w^2 by dividing each side by g.

2. What is the first step in solving a formula like $gw^2 = kw + 24$ for w?

Write it in standard form (with 0 on one side, in decreasing powers of w).

In Exercises 3 and 4, solve for m in terms of the other variables ($m > 0$).

3.

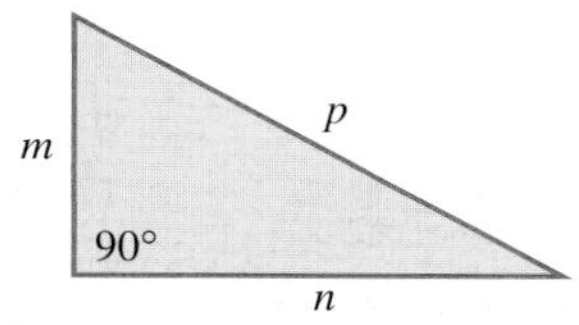

$m = \sqrt{p^2 - n^2}$

4.

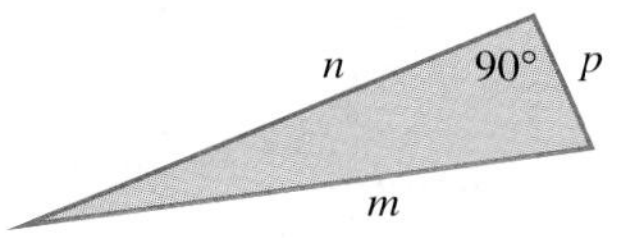

$m = \sqrt{p^2 + n^2}$

Solve each equation for the indicated variable. (Leave ± in your answers.) See Examples 1 and 2.

5. $d = kt^2$ for t

$t = \dfrac{\pm\sqrt{dk}}{k}$

6. $s = kwd^2$ for d

$d = \dfrac{\pm\sqrt{skw}}{kw}$

7. $I = \dfrac{ks}{d^2}$ for d

$d = \dfrac{\pm\sqrt{skI}}{I}$

8. $R = \dfrac{k}{d^2}$ for d

$d = \dfrac{\pm\sqrt{kR}}{R}$

9. $F = \dfrac{kA}{v^2}$ for v

$v = \dfrac{\pm\sqrt{kAF}}{F}$

10. $L = \dfrac{kd^4}{h^2}$ for h

$h = \dfrac{\pm d^2\sqrt{kL}}{L}$

11. $V = \dfrac{1}{3}\pi r^2 h$ for r

$r = \dfrac{\pm\sqrt{3\pi Vh}}{\pi h}$

12. $V = \pi(r^2 + R^2)h$ for r

$r = \dfrac{\pm\sqrt{V\pi h - \pi^2 R^2 h^2}}{\pi h}$

13. $At^2 + Bt = -C$ for t

$t = \dfrac{-B \pm \sqrt{B^2 - 4AC}}{2A}$

14. $S = 2\pi rh + \pi r^2$ for r

$r = \dfrac{-\pi h \pm \sqrt{\pi^2 h^2 + \pi S}}{\pi}$

15. $D = \sqrt{kh}$ for h

$h = \dfrac{D^2}{k}$

16. $F = \dfrac{k}{\sqrt{d}}$ for d

$d = \dfrac{k^2}{F^2}$

17. $p = \sqrt{\dfrac{k\ell}{g}}$ for ℓ

$\ell = \dfrac{p^2 g}{k}$

18. $p = \sqrt{\dfrac{k\ell}{g}}$ for g

$g = \dfrac{k\ell}{p^2}$

Solve each problem. When appropriate, round answers to the nearest tenth. See Example 3.

19. Two ships leave port at the same time, one heading due south and the other heading due east. Several hours later, they are 170 mi apart. If the ship traveling south traveled 70 mi farther than the other, how many miles did they each travel?

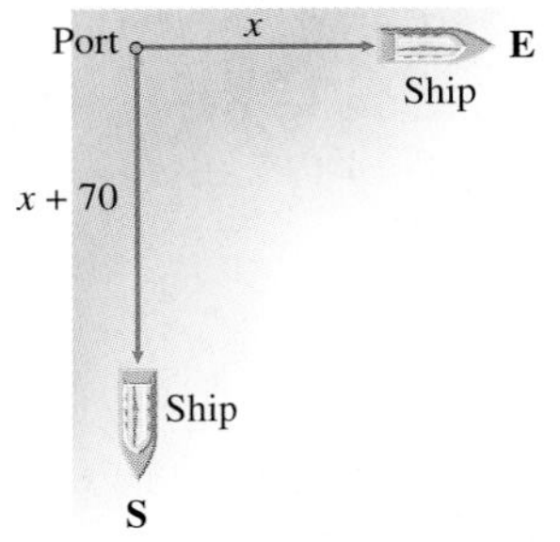

eastbound ship: 80 mi; southbound ship: 150 mi

20. Allyson Pellissier is flying a kite that is 30 ft farther above her hand than its horizontal distance from her. The string from her hand to the kite is 150 ft long. How high is the kite?

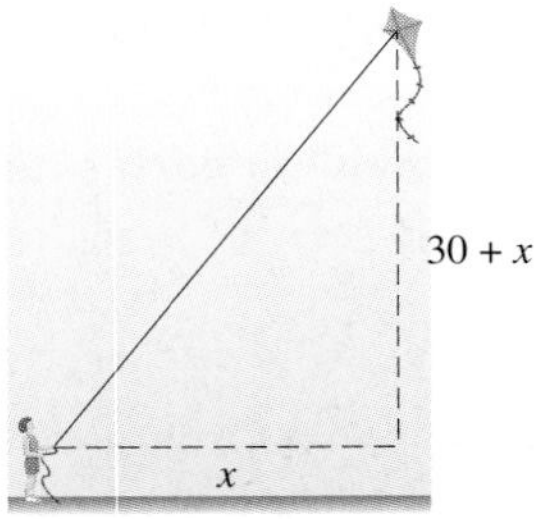

120 ft

21. Find the lengths of the sides of the triangle.

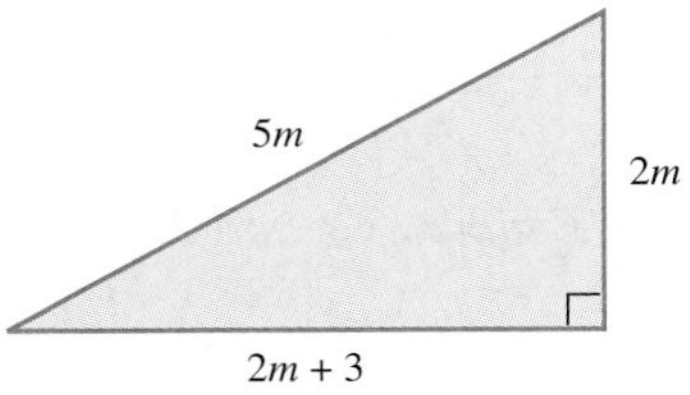

2.3, 5.3, 5.8

22. Find the lengths of the sides of the triangle.

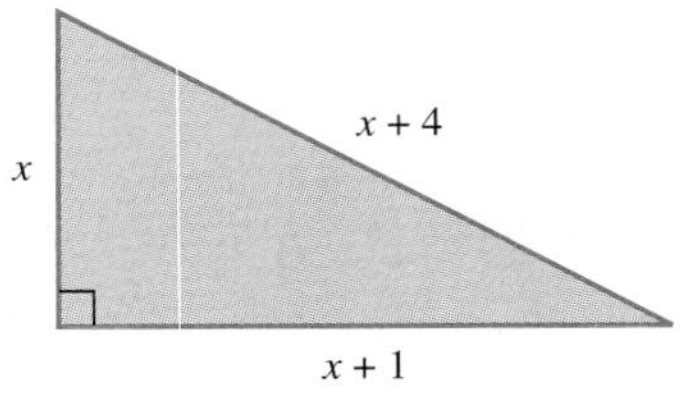

7.9, 8.9, 11.9

Solve each problem. See Example 4.

23. A couple wants to buy a rug for a room that is 20 ft long and 15 ft wide. They want to leave an even strip of flooring uncovered around the edges of the room. How wide a strip will they have if they buy a rug with an area of 234 ft^2?

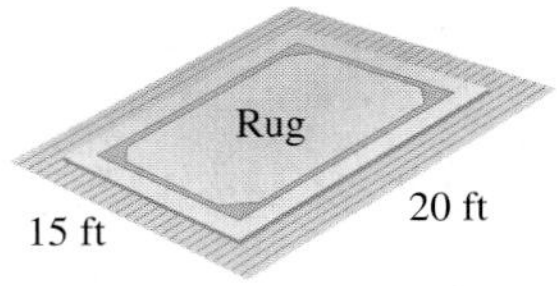

1 ft

24. A club swimming pool is 30 ft wide and 40 ft long. The club members want an exposed aggregate border in a strip of uniform width around the pool. They have enough material for 296 ft^2. How wide can the strip be?

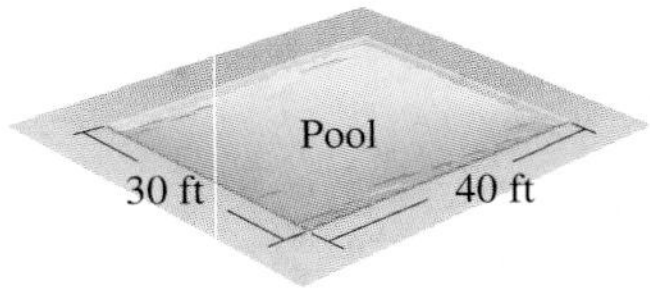

2 ft

25. A rectangular piece of sheet metal has a length that is 4 in. less than twice the width. A square piece 2 in. on a side is cut from each corner. The sides are then turned up to form an uncovered box of volume 256 $in.^3$. Find the length and width of the original piece of metal.

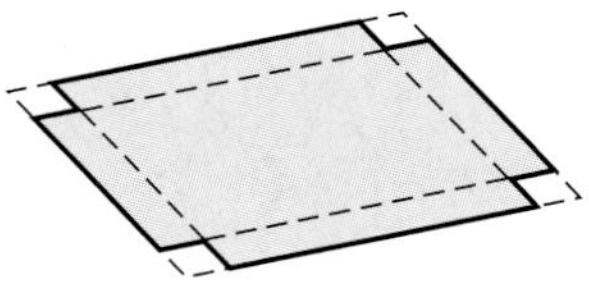

20 in. by 12 in.

26. Another rectangular piece of sheet metal is 2 in. longer than it is wide. A square piece 3 in. on a side is cut from each corner. The sides are then turned up to form an uncovered box of volume 765 $in.^3$. Find the dimensions of the original piece of metal.

21 in. by 23 in.

Solve each problem. Round answers to the nearest tenth. See Example 5.

27. A ball is projected upward from the ground. Its distance in feet from the ground in t seconds is given by

$$s(t) = -16t^2 + 128t.$$

At what times will the ball be 213 ft from the ground?

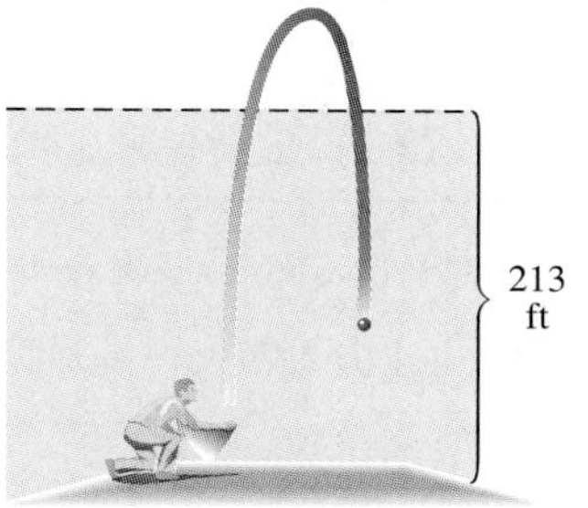

2.4 sec and 5.6 sec

28. A toy rocket is launched from ground level. Its distance in feet from the ground in t seconds is given by

$$s(t) = -16t^2 + 208t.$$

At what times will the rocket be 550 ft from the ground?

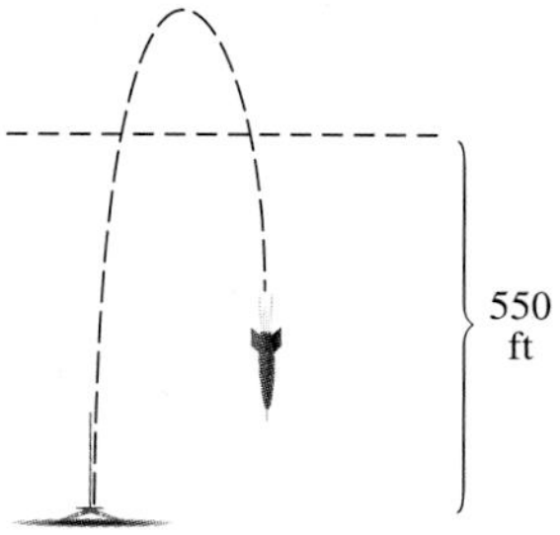

3.7 sec and 9.3 sec

29. The function defined by

$$D(t) = 13t^2 - 100t$$

gives the distance in feet a car going approximately 68 mph will skid in t seconds. Find the time it would take for the car to skid 180 ft.

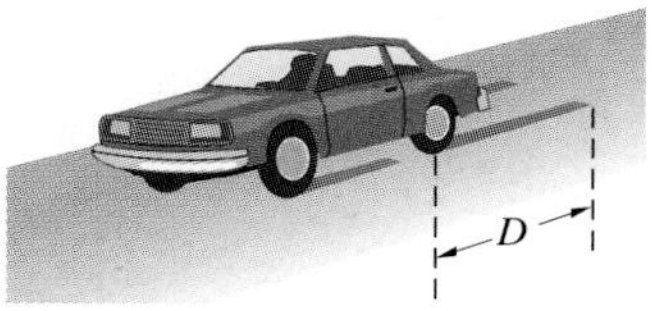

9.2 sec

30. The function given in Exercise 29 becomes

$$D(t) = 13t^2 - 73t$$

for a car going 50 mph. Find the time for this car to skid 218 ft.

7.8 sec

A rock is projected upward from ground level, and its distance in feet from the ground in t seconds is given by $s(t) = -16t^2 + 160t$. Use algebra and a short explanation to answer Exercises 31 and 32.

31. After how many seconds does it reach a height of 400 ft? How would you describe in words its position at this height?

It reaches its *maximum* height at 5 sec because this is the only time it reaches 400 ft.

32. After how many seconds does it reach a height of 425 ft? How would you interpret the mathematical result here?

Because the discriminant is negative, the rock never reaches a height of 425 ft.

Solve each problem using a quadratic equation.

33. A certain bakery has found that the daily demand for bran muffins is $\frac{3200}{p}$, where p is the price of a muffin in cents. The daily supply is $3p - 200$. Find the price at which supply and demand are equal.

$.80

34. In one area the demand for compact discs is $\frac{700}{P}$ per day, where P is the price in dollars per disc. The supply is $5P - 1$ per day. At what price does supply equal demand?

$11.93

Sales of SUVs (sport utility vehicles) in the United States (in millions) for the years 1990–1999 are shown in the bar graph and can be modeled by the quadratic function defined by

$$f(x) = .016x^2 + .124x + .787.$$

Here, $x = 0$ represents 1990, $x = 1$ represents 1991, and so on. Use the graph and the model to work Exercises 35–38. See Example 6.

SALES OF SUVS IN THE UNITED STATES (IN MILLIONS)

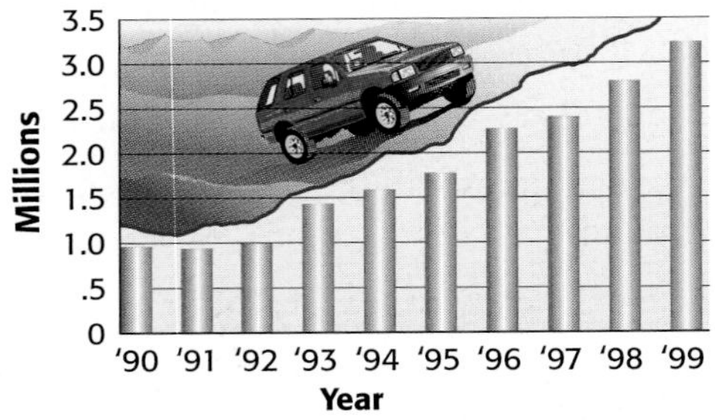

Source: CNW Marketing Research of Bandon, OR, based on automakers' reported sales.

35. (a) Use the graph to estimate sales in 1997 to the nearest tenth.

2.4 million

(b) Use the model to approximate sales in 1997 to the nearest tenth. How does this result compare to your estimate from part (a)?

2.4 million; They are the same.

36. (a) Use the model to estimate sales in 2000 to the nearest tenth.

3.6 million

(b) Sales through October 2000 were about 2.9 million. Based on this, is the sales estimate for 2000 from part (a) reasonable? Explain.

Yes. Sales were about .3 million each month, so at this rate, sales for 2000 would be about 3.6 million.

37. Based on the model, in what year did sales reach 2 million? (Round down to the nearest year.) How does this result compare to the sales shown in the graph?

1995; The graph indicates that sales reached 2 million in 1996.

38. Based on the model, in what year did sales reach 3 million? (Round down to the nearest year.) How does this result compare to the sales shown in the graph?

1998; The graph indicates that sales reached 3 million in 1999.

William Froude was a 19th century naval architect who used the expression

$$\frac{v^2}{g\ell}$$

in shipbuilding. This expression, known as the Froude number, was also used by R. McNeill Alexander in his research on dinosaurs. (Source: *"How Dinosaurs Ran,"* Scientific American, *April 1991.) In Exercises 39 and 40, find the value of v (in meters per second), given that g* = 9.8 m per sec^2.

39. Rhinoceros: $\ell = 1.2$; Froude number = 2.57

5.5 m per sec

40. Triceratops: $\ell = 2.8$; Froude number = .16

2.1 m per sec

Recall from Chapter 8 that corresponding sides of similar triangles are proportional. Use this fact to find the lengths of the indicated sides of each pair of similar triangles. Check all possible solutions in both triangles. Sides of a triangle cannot be negative (and are not drawn to scale here).

41. Side AC

5 or 14

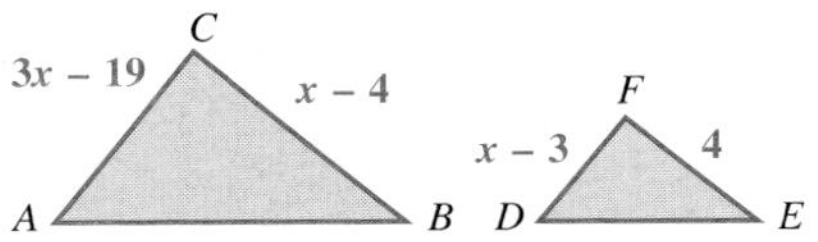

42. Side RQ

4

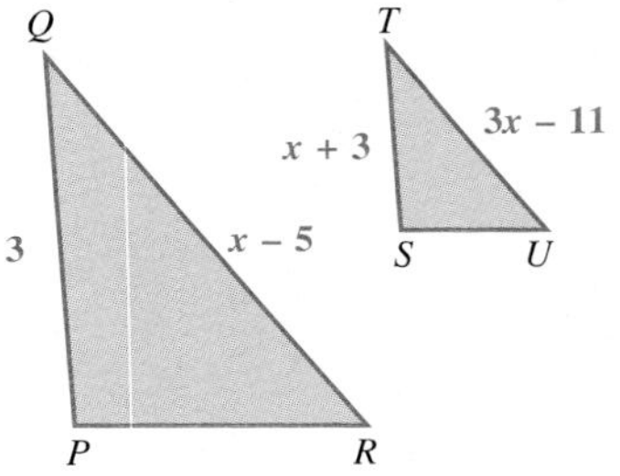

10.6 Graphs of Quadratic Functions

Objectives

1. Graph a quadratic function.
2. Graph parabolas with horizontal and vertical shifts.
3. Predict the shape and direction of a parabola from the coefficient of x^2.
4. Find a quadratic function to model data.

1 Graph a quadratic function. In chapters 8 and 9 we graphed a few simple rational and radical functions by point-plotting. In Figure 4, we give a table of ordered pairs for the simplest quadratic function, defined by $y = x^2$, and the resulting graph.

x	y
−2	4
−1	1
0	0
1	1
2	4

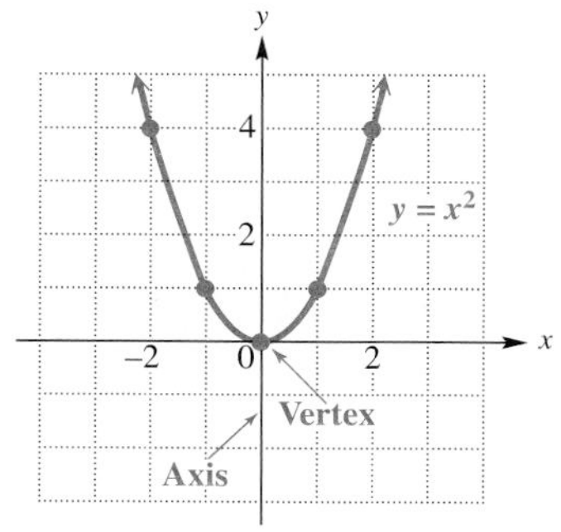

Figure 4

This graph is called a **parabola.** The point (0, 0), the lowest point on the curve, is the **vertex** of this parabola. The vertical line through the vertex is the **axis** of the parabola, here $x = 0$. A parabola is **symmetric about its axis;** that is, if the graph were folded along the axis, the two portions of the curve would coincide. As Figure 4 suggests, x can be any real number, so the domain of the function defined by $y = x^2$ is $(-\infty, \infty)$. Since y is always nonnegative, the range is $[0, \infty)$.

In Section 10.5, we solved applications modeled by quadratic functions. In this section and the next, we consider graphs of more general quadratic functions as defined here.

Quadratic Function

A function that can be written in the form

$$f(x) = ax^2 + bx + c$$

for real numbers a, b, and c, with $a \neq 0$, is a **quadratic function.**

The graph of any quadratic function is a parabola with a vertical axis. We use the variable y and function notation $f(x)$ interchangeably when discussing parabolas. Although we use the letter f most often to name quadratic functions, other letters can be used. We use the capital letter F to distinguish between different parabolas graphed on the same coordinate axes.

Parabolas, which are a type of *conic section* (Chapter 12), have many applications. The large disks seen on the sidelines of televised football games, which are used by television crews to pick up the shouted signals of players on the field, have cross sections that are parabolas. Cross sections of radar dishes and automobile headlights also form parabolas. The cables that are used to support suspension bridges are shaped like parabolas.

2 Graph parabolas with horizontal and vertical shifts. Parabolas need not have their vertices at the origin, as does the graph of $f(x) = x^2$. For example, to graph a parabola of the form $F(x) = x^2 + k$, start by selecting sample values of x like those that were used to graph $f(x) = x^2$. The corresponding values of $F(x)$ in $F(x) = x^2 + k$ differ by k from those of $f(x) = x^2$. For this reason, the graph of $F(x) = x^2 + k$ is *shifted,* or *translated,* k units vertically compared with that of $f(x) = x^2$.

1 Graph each parabola. Give the vertex, domain, and range.

(a) $f(x) = x^2 + 3$

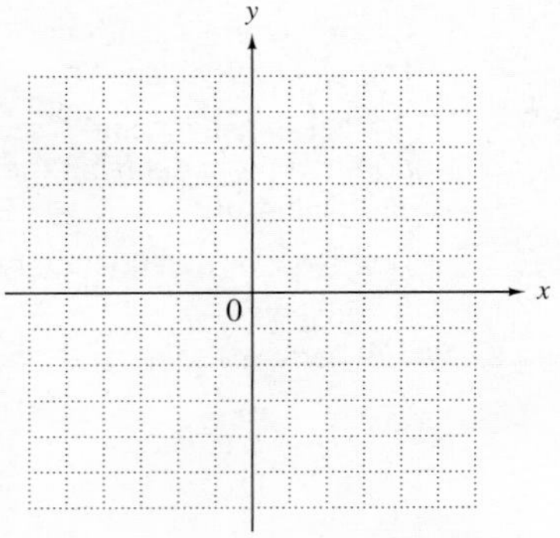

(b) $f(x) = x^2 - 1$

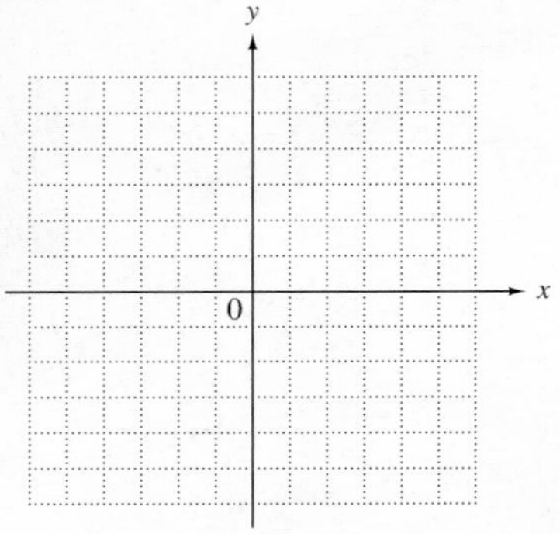

Example 1 Graphing a Parabola with a Vertical Shift

Graph $F(x) = x^2 - 2$.

This graph has the same shape as that of $f(x) = x^2$, but since k here is -2, the graph is shifted 2 units down, with vertex $(0, -2)$. Every function value is 2 less than the corresponding function value of $f(x) = x^2$. Plotting points on both sides of the vertex gives the graph in Figure 5. Notice that since the parabola is symmetric about its axis $x = 0$, the plotted points are "mirror images" of each other. Since x can be any real number, the domain is still $(-\infty, \infty)$; the value of y (or $F(x)$) is always greater than or equal to -2, so the range is $[-2, \infty)$. The graph of $f(x) = x^2$ is shown for comparison.

x	$f(x) = x^2$	$F(x) = x^2 - 2$
-2	4	2
-1	1	-1
0	0	-2
1	1	-1
2	4	2

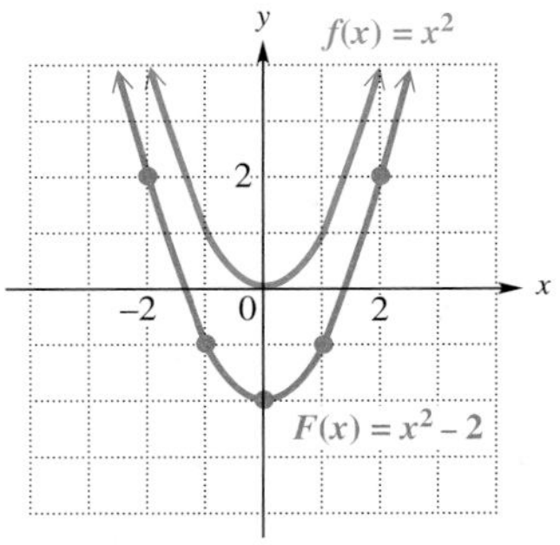

Figure 5

Vertical Shift

The graph of $F(x) = x^2 + k$ is a parabola with the same shape as the graph of $f(x) = x^2$. The parabola is shifted k units up if $k > 0$, and $|k|$ units down if $k < 0$. The vertex is $(0, k)$.

Work Problem 1 at the Side.

The graph of $F(x) = (x - h)^2$ is also a parabola with the same shape as that of $f(x) = x^2$. Because $(x - h)^2 \geq 0$ for all x, the vertex of $F(x) = (x - h)^2$ is the lowest point on the parabola. The lowest point occurs here when $F(x)$ is 0. To get $F(x)$ equal to 0, let $x = h$ so the vertex of $F(x) = (x - h)^2$ is $(h, 0)$. Based on this, the graph of $F(x) = (x - h)^2$ is shifted h units horizontally compared with that of $f(x) = x^2$.

Example 2 Graphing a Parabola with a Horizontal Shift

Graph $F(x) = (x - 2)^2$.

When $x = 2$, then $F(x) = 0$, giving the vertex $(2, 0)$. The graph of $F(x) = (x - 2)^2$ has the same shape as that of $f(x) = x^2$ but is shifted 2 units to the right. Plotting several points on one side of the vertex and using symmetry about the axis $x = 2$ to find corresponding points on the other side of the vertex gives the graph in Figure 6. Again, the domain is $(-\infty, \infty)$; the range is $[0, \infty)$.

Continued on Next Page

ANSWERS

1. (a)

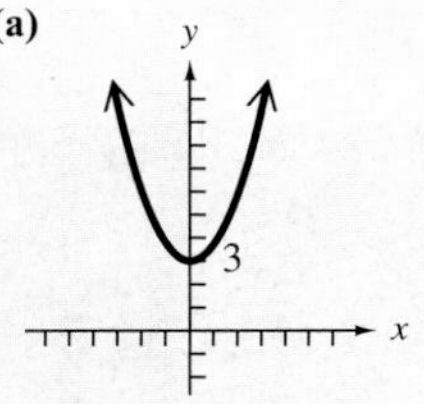

vertex: $(0, 3)$; domain: $(-\infty, \infty)$; range: $[3, \infty)$

(b)

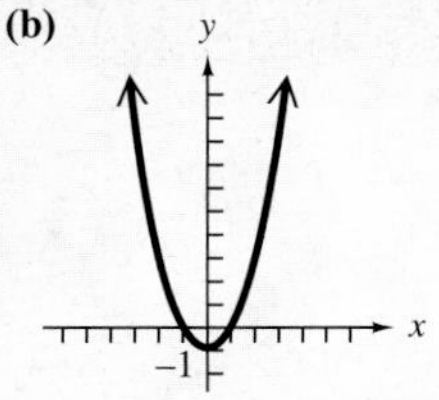

vertex: $(0, -1)$; domain: $(-\infty, \infty)$; range: $[-1, \infty)$

x	$F(x) = (x - 2)^2$
0	4
1	1
2	0
3	1
4	4

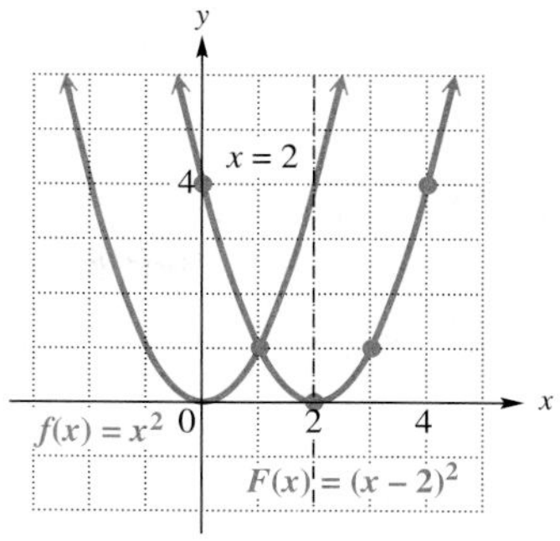

Figure 6

2 Graph each parabola. Give the vertex, axis, domain, and range.

(a) $f(x) = (x - 3)^2$

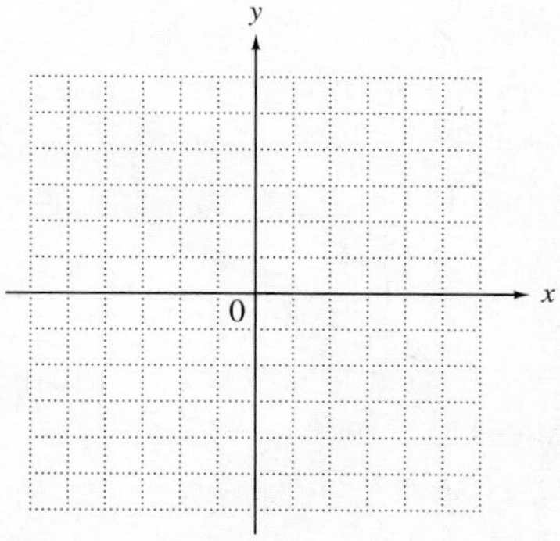

(b) $f(x) = (x + 2)^2$

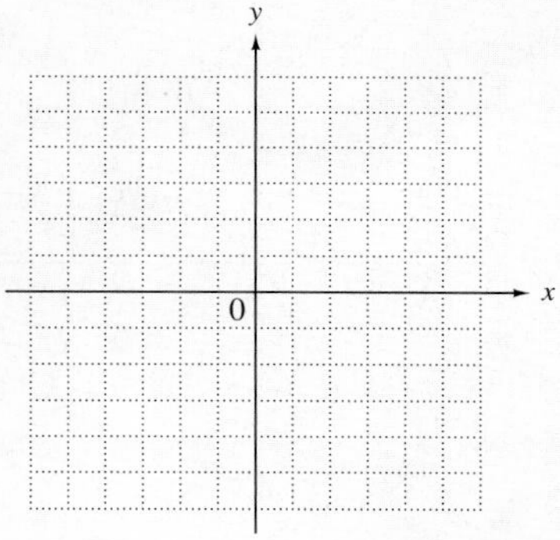

Horizontal Shift

The graph of $F(x) = (x - h)^2$ is a parabola with the same shape as the graph of $f(x) = x^2$. The parabola is shifted h units horizontally: h units to the right if $h > 0$, and $|h|$ units to the left if $h < 0$. The vertex is $(h, 0)$.

CAUTION

Errors frequently occur when horizontal shifts are involved. To determine the direction and magnitude of a horizontal shift, find the value that would cause the expression $x - h$ to equal 0. For example, the graph of $F(x) = (x - 5)^2$ would be shifted 5 units to the *right,* because $+5$ would cause $x - 5$ to equal 0. On the other hand, the graph of $F(x) = (x + 5)^2$ would be shifted 5 units to the *left,* because -5 would cause $x + 5$ to equal 0.

Work Problem 2 at the Side.

A parabola can have both horizontal and vertical shifts.

Example 3 Graphing a Parabola with Horizontal and Vertical Shifts

Graph $F(x) = (x + 3)^2 - 2$.

This graph has the same shape as that of $f(x) = x^2$, but is shifted 3 units to the left (since $x + 3 = 0$ if $x = -3$) and 2 units down (because of the -2). As shown in Figure 7, the vertex is $(-3, -2)$, with axis $x = -3$. This function has domain $(-\infty, \infty)$ and range $[-2, \infty)$.

x	$F(x)$
-5	2
-4	-1
-3	-2
-2	-1
-1	2

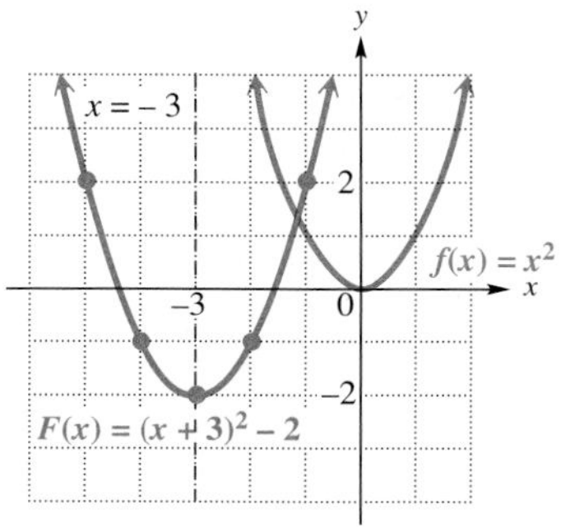

Figure 7

ANSWERS

2. (a)

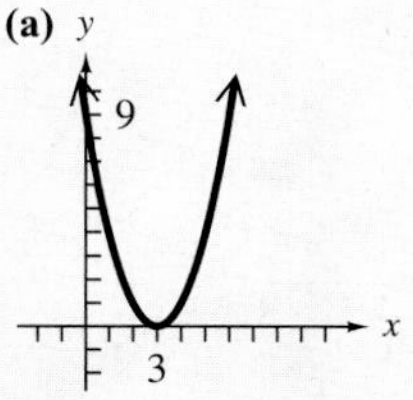

vertex: $(3, 0)$; axis: $x = 3$; domain: $(-\infty, \infty)$; range: $[0, \infty)$

(b)

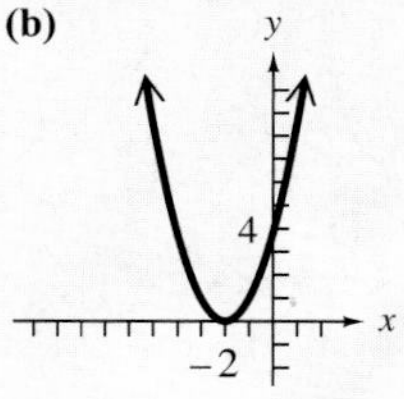

vertex: $(-2, 0)$; axis: $x = -2$; domain: $(-\infty, \infty)$; range: $[0, \infty)$

The characteristics of the graph of a parabola of the form $F(x) = (x - h)^2 + k$ are summarized as follows.

Vertex and Axis

The graph of $F(x) = (x - h)^2 + k$ is a parabola with the same shape as the graph of $f(x) = x^2$ with vertex (h, k). The axis is the vertical line $x = h$.

Work Problem 3 at the Side.

3 Predict the shape and direction of a parabola from the coefficient of x^2. Not all parabolas open up, and not all parabolas have the same shape as the graph of $f(x) = x^2$.

Example 4 Graphing a Parabola That Opens Down

Graph $f(x) = -\dfrac{1}{2}x^2$.

This parabola is shown in Figure 8. The coefficient $-\frac{1}{2}$ affects the shape of the graph; the $\frac{1}{2}$ makes the parabola wider (since the values of $\frac{1}{2}x^2$ increase more slowly than those of x^2), and the negative sign makes the parabola open down. The graph is not shifted in any direction; the vertex is still (0, 0). Unlike the parabolas graphed in Examples 1–3, the vertex here has the *largest* function value of any point on the graph. The domain is $(-\infty, \infty)$; the range is $(-\infty, 0]$.

x	$f(x)$
-2	-2
-1	$-\frac{1}{2}$
0	0
1	$-\frac{1}{2}$
2	-2

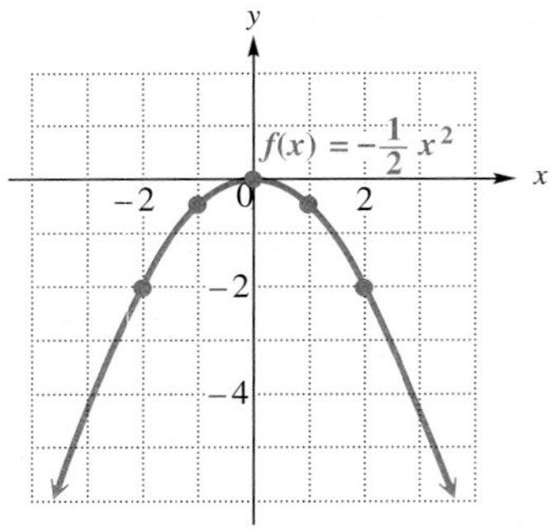

Figure 8

Some general principles concerning the graph of $F(x) = a(x - h)^2 + k$ are summarized as follows.

General Principles

1. The graph of the quadratic function defined by
$$F(x) = a(x - h)^2 + k, \quad a \neq 0$$
is a parabola with vertex (h, k) and the vertical line $x = h$ as axis.
2. The graph opens up if a is positive and down if a is negative.
3. The graph is wider than that of $f(x) = x^2$ if $0 < |a| < 1$. The graph is narrower than that of $f(x) = x^2$ if $|a| > 1$.

3 Graph each parabola. Give the vertex, axis, domain, and range.

(a) $f(x) = (x + 2)^2 - 1$

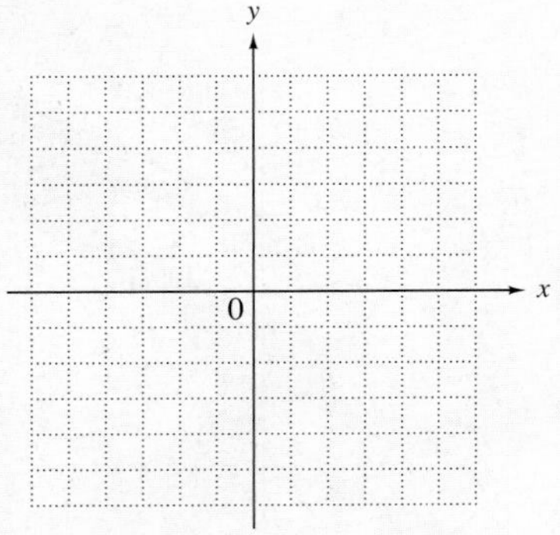

(b) $f(x) = (x - 2)^2 + 5$

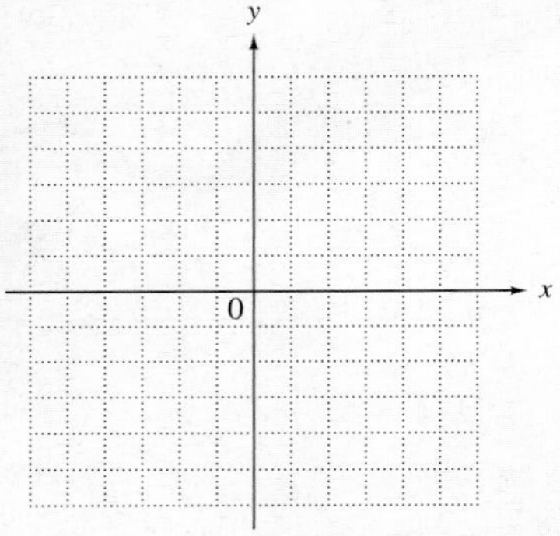

ANSWERS

3. (a)

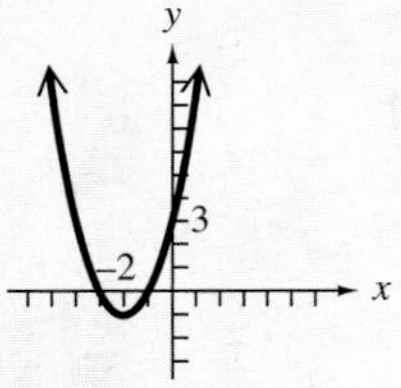

vertex: $(-2, -1)$; axis: $x = -2$; domain: $(-\infty, \infty)$; range: $[-1, \infty)$

(b)

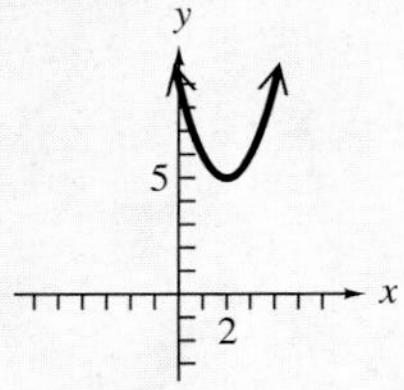

vertex: $(2, 5)$; axis: $x = 2$; domain: $(-\infty, \infty)$; range: $[5, \infty)$

Work Problems 4 and 5 at the Side.

Example 5 Using the General Principles to Graph a Parabola

Graph $F(x) = -2(x + 3)^2 + 4$.

The parabola opens down (because $a < 0$), and is narrower than the graph of $f(x) = x^2$, since $|-2| = 2 > 1$, causing values of $F(x)$ to decrease more quickly than those of $f(x) = -x^2$. This parabola has vertex $(-3, 4)$ as shown in Figure 9. To complete the graph, we plotted the ordered pairs $(-4, 2)$ and, by symmetry, $(-2, 2)$. Symmetry can be used to find additional ordered pairs that satisfy the equation, if desired.

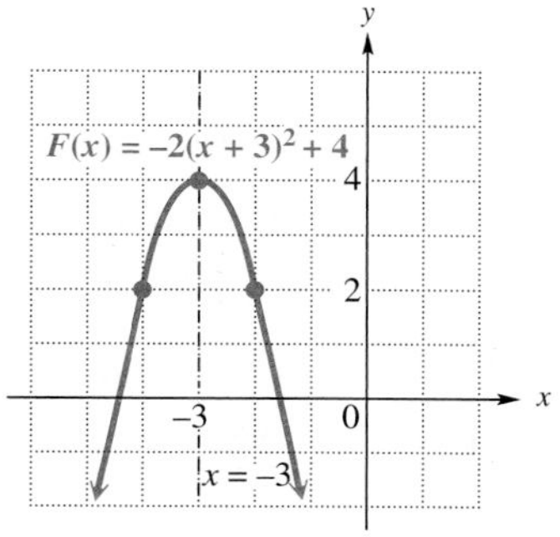

Figure 9

Work Problem 6 at the Side.

4 Find a quadratic function to model data.

Example 6 Finding a Quadratic Function to Model the Rise in Multiple Births

The number of higher-order multiple births in the United States is rising. Let x represent the number of years since 1970 and y represent the rate of higher-order multiples born per 100,000 births since 1971. The data are shown in the following table.

U.S. HIGHER-ORDER MULTIPLE BIRTHS

Year	x	y
1971	1	29.1
1976	6	35.0
1981	11	40.0
1986	16	47.0
1991	21	100.0
1996	26	152.6

Source: National Center for Health Statistics.

Find a quadratic function that models the data.

A scatter diagram of the ordered pairs (x, y) is shown in Figure 10 on the next page. Notice that the graphed points do not follow a linear pattern, so a linear function would not model the data very well. Instead, the general shape suggested by the scatter diagram indicates that a parabola should approximate these points, as shown by the dashed curve in the graph in Figure 11. The equation for such a parabola would have a positive coefficient for x^2 since the graph opens up.

Continued on Next Page

4 Decide whether each parabola opens up or down.

(a) $f(x) = -\frac{2}{3}x^2$

(b) $f(x) = \frac{3}{4}x^2 + 1$

(c) $f(x) = -2x^2 - 3$

(d) $f(x) = 3x^2 + 2$

5 Decide whether each parabola in Problem 4 is wider or narrower than the graph of $f(x) = x^2$.

6 Graph

$f(x) = \frac{1}{2}(x - 2)^2 + 1$.

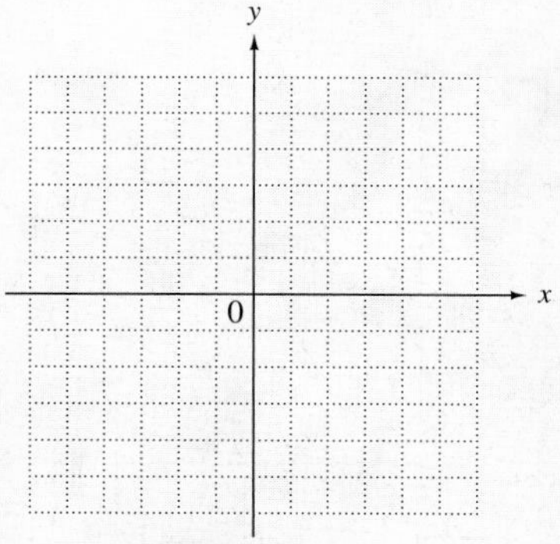

ANSWERS

4. **(a)** down **(b)** up **(c)** down **(d)** up

5. **(a)** wider **(b)** wider **(c)** narrower **(d)** narrower

6.

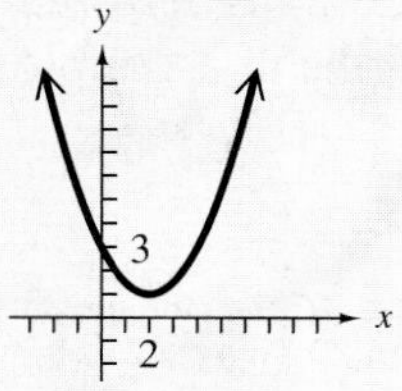

7 Tell whether a linear or quadratic function would be a more appropriate model for each set of graphed data. If linear, tell whether the slope should be positive or negative. If quadratic, tell whether the coefficient a of x^2 should be positive or negative.

(a)

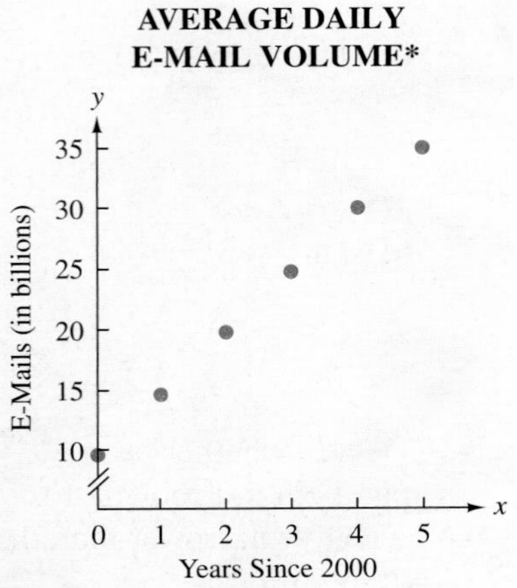

*Projected
Source: General Accounting Office.

(b)

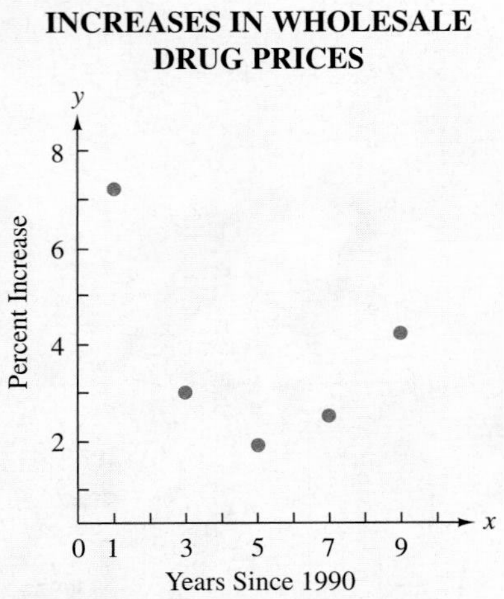

Source: *IMS Health*, Retail and Provider Perspective.

8 Using the points (1, 29.1), (6, 35), and (26, 152.6), find another quadratic model for the data on higher-order multiple births in Example 6.

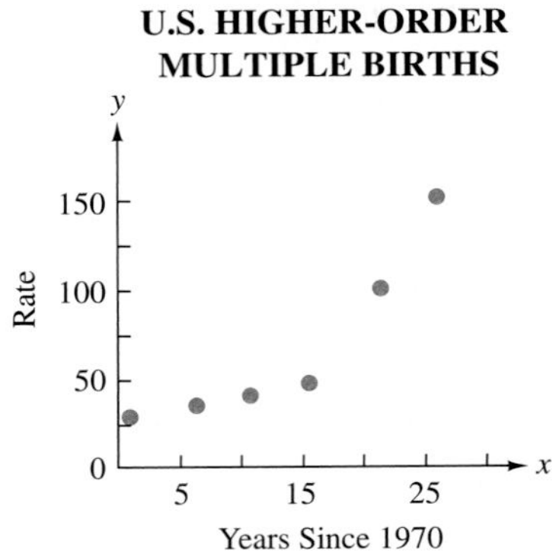

Figure 10

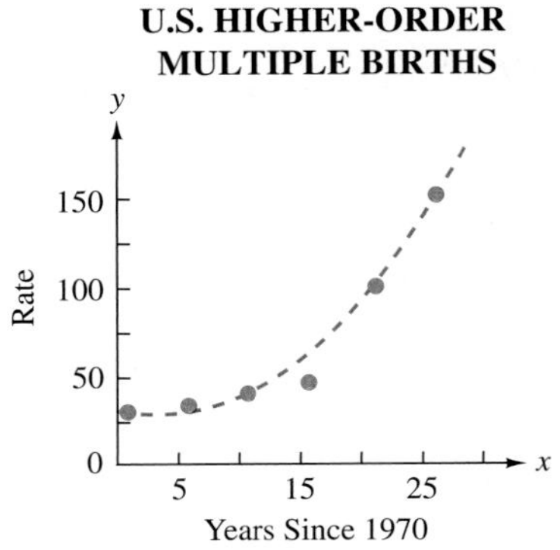

Figure 11

To find a quadratic function of the form

$$y = ax^2 + bx + c$$

that models, or *fits*, these data, we choose three representative ordered pairs and use them to write a system of three equations. Using (1, 29.1), (11, 40), and (21, 100), we substitute the x- and y-values from the ordered pairs into the quadratic form $y = ax^2 + bx + c$ to get the three equations

$$a(\mathbf{1})^2 + b(\mathbf{1}) + c = \mathbf{29.1} \quad \text{or} \quad a + b + c = 29.1 \quad (1)$$
$$a(\mathbf{11})^2 + b(\mathbf{11}) + c = \mathbf{40} \quad \text{or} \quad 121a + 11b + c = 40 \quad (2)$$
$$a(\mathbf{21})^2 + b(\mathbf{21}) + c = \mathbf{100} \quad \text{or} \quad 441a + 21b + c = 100. \quad (3)$$

We can find the values of a, b, and c by solving this system of three equations in three variables using the methods of Section 5.4. Multiplying equation (1) by -1 and adding the result to equation (2) gives

$$120a + 10b = 10.9. \quad (4)$$

Multiplying equation (2) by -1 and adding the result to equation (3) gives

$$320a + 10b = 60. \quad (5)$$

We can eliminate b from this system of equations in two variables by multiplying equation (4) by -1 and adding the result to equation (5) to get

$$200a = 49.1$$
$$a = .2455. \quad \text{Use a calculator.}$$

We substitute .2455 for a in equation (4) or (5) to find that $b = -1.856$. Substituting the values of a and b into equation (1) gives $c = 30.7105$. Using these values of a, b, and c, our model is defined by

$$y = .2455x^2 - 1.856x + 30.7105.$$

Work Problems 7 and 8 at the Side.

Calculator Tip The *quadratic regression* feature on a graphing calculator can be used to generate a quadratic model that fits given data. See your owner's manual for details on how to do this.

ANSWERS
7. **(a)** linear; positive **(b)** quadratic; positive
8. $y = .188x^2 - .136x + 29.05$

10.6 EXERCISES

FOR EXTRA HELP | Student's Solutions Manual | MyMathLab.com | InterAct Math Tutorial Software | AW Math Tutor Center | www.mathxl.com | Digital Video Tutor CD 9 Videotape 21

1. Match each quadratic function with its graph from choices A–D.

(a) $f(x) = (x + 2)^2 - 1$ B

(b) $f(x) = (x + 2)^2 + 1$ C

(c) $f(x) = (x - 2)^2 - 1$ A

(d) $f(x) = (x - 2)^2 + 1$ D

A.

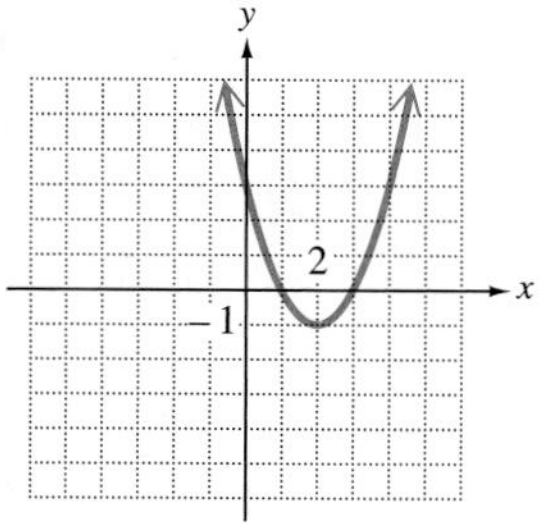

B.

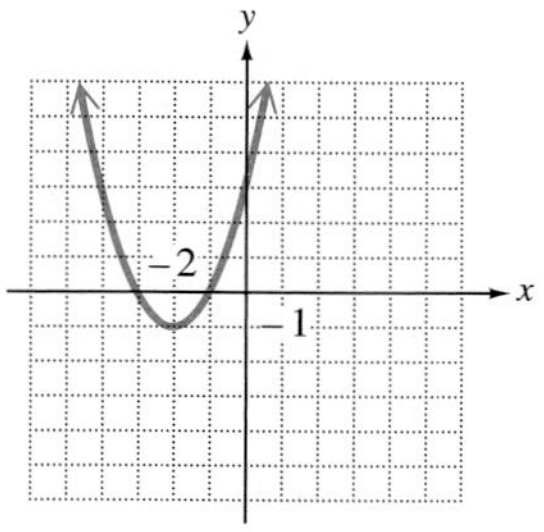

C.

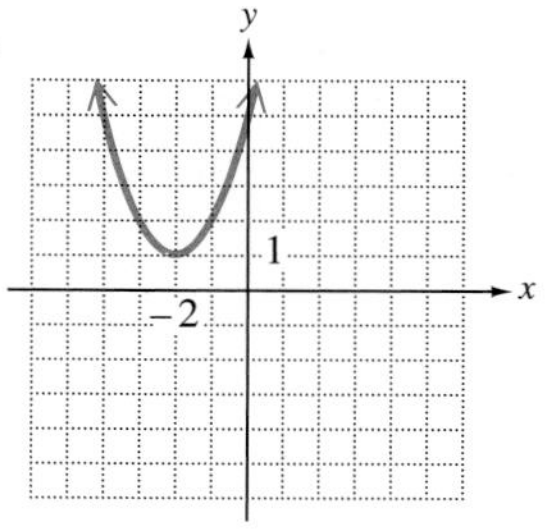

D.

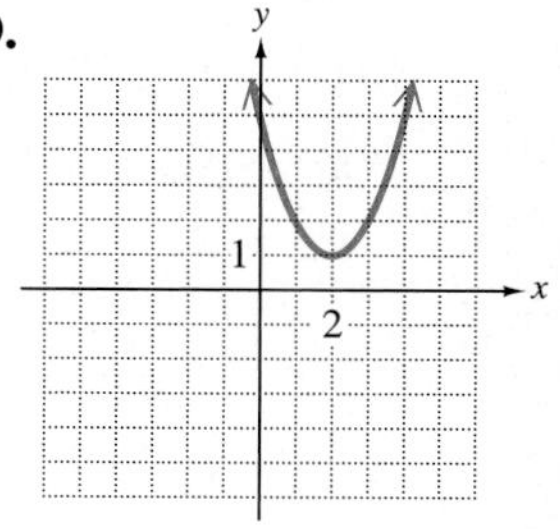

2. Match each quadratic function with its graph from choices A–D.

(a) $f(x) = -x^2 + 2$ D

(b) $f(x) = -x^2 - 2$ C

(c) $f(x) = -(x + 2)^2$ B

(d) $f(x) = -(x - 2)^2$ A

A.

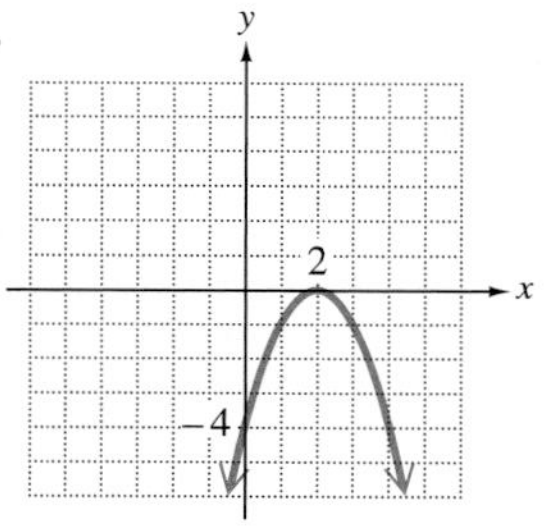

B.

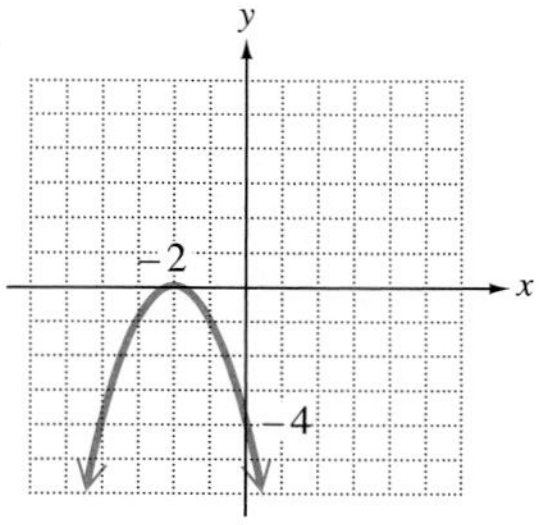

C.

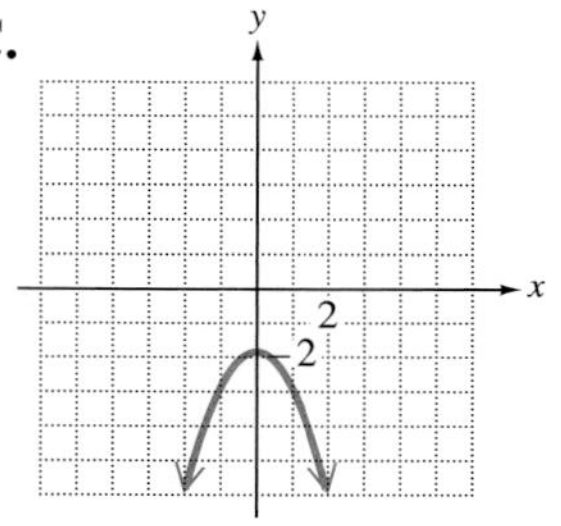

D.

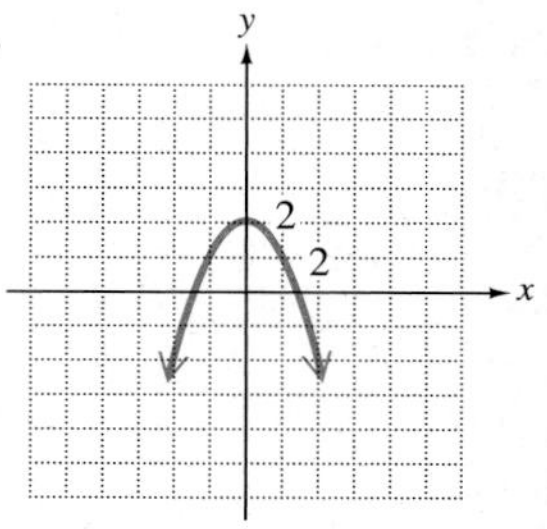

Identify the vertex of each parabola. See Examples 1–4.

3. $f(x) = -3x^2$ **(0, 0)**

4. $f(x) = \frac{1}{2}x^2$ **(0, 0)**

5. $f(x) = x^2 + 4$ **(0, 4)**

6. $f(x) = x^2 - 4$ **(0, −4)**

7. $f(x) = (x - 1)^2$ **(1, 0)**

8. $f(x) = (x + 3)^2$ **(−3, 0)**

9. $f(x) = (x + 3)^2 - 4$ **(−3, −4)**

10. $f(x) = (x - 5)^2 - 8$ **(5, −8)**

11. Describe how each of the parabolas in Exercises 9 and 10 is shifted compared to the graph of $f(x) = x^2$.

In Exercise 9, the parabola is shifted 3 units to the left and 4 units down. The parabola in Exercise 10 is shifted 5 units to the right and 8 units down.

12. What does the value of a in $F(x) = a(x - h)^2 + k$ tell you about the graph of the equation compared to the graph of $f(x) = x^2$?

If $|a| > 1$, the graph of $F(x) = a(x - h)^2 + k$ is narrower than the graph of $f(x) = x^2$. If $0 < |a| < 1$, the graph is wider than the graph of $f(x) = x^2$. If a is negative, the graph opens down; the graph of $f(x) = x^2$ opens up.

For each quadratic function, tell whether the graph opens up or down and whether the graph is wider, narrower, or the same shape as the graph of $f(x) = x^2$. See Examples 4 and 5.

13. $f(x) = -\frac{2}{5}x^2$ down; wider

14. $f(x) = -2x^2$ down; narrower

15. $f(x) = 3x^2 + 1$ up; narrower

16. $f(x) = \frac{2}{3}x^2 - 4$ up; wider

17. For $f(x) = a(x - h)^2 + k$, in what quadrant is the vertex if

(a) $h > 0, k > 0$; I
(b) $h > 0, k < 0$; IV
(c) $h < 0, k > 0$; II
(d) $h < 0, k < 0$? III

18. Match each quadratic function with the description of the parabola that is its graph.

(a) $f(x) = (x - 4)^2 - 2$ D
(b) $f(x) = (x - 2)^2 - 4$ B
(c) $f(x) = -(x - 4)^2 - 2$ C
(d) $f(x) = -(x - 2)^2 - 4$ A

A. Vertex $(2, -4)$, opens down
B. Vertex $(2, -4)$, opens up
C. Vertex $(4, -2)$, opens down
D. Vertex $(4, -2)$, opens up

Sketch the graph of each parabola. Plot at least two points in addition to the vertex. In Exercises 25–32, give the axis, domain, and range of the parabola.

19. $f(x) = -2x^2$

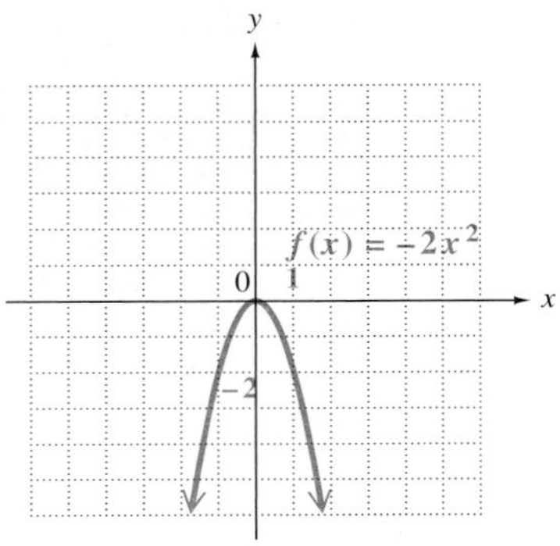

20. $f(x) = \frac{1}{3}x^2$

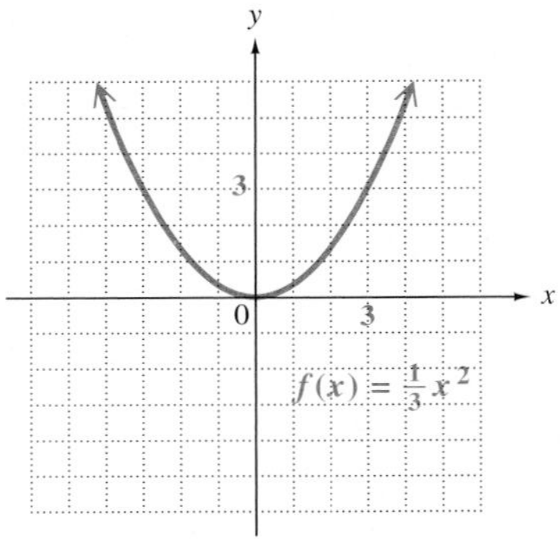

21. $f(x) = x^2 - 1$

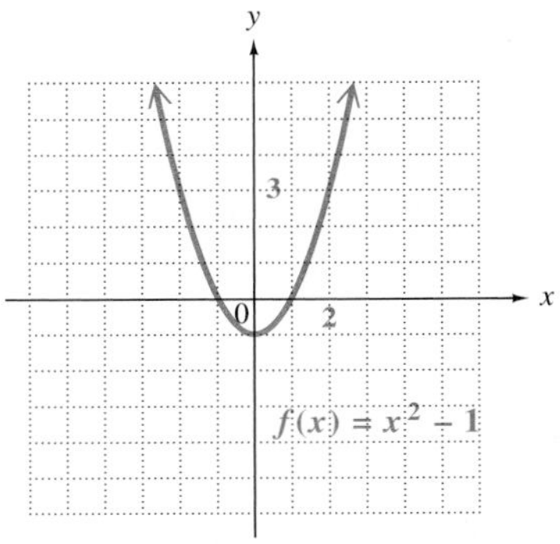

22. $f(x) = x^2 + 3$

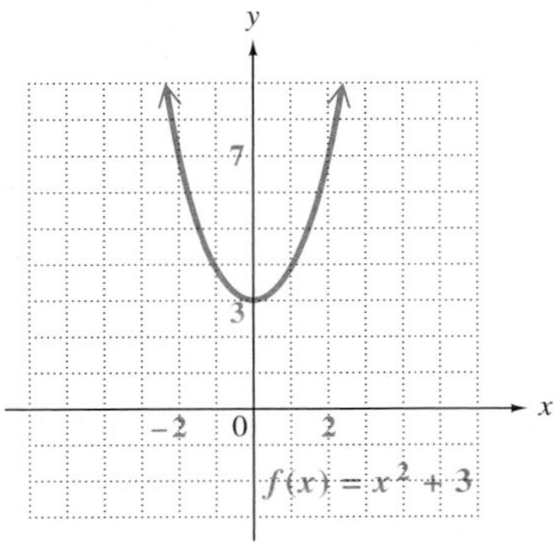

23. $f(x) = -x^2 + 2$

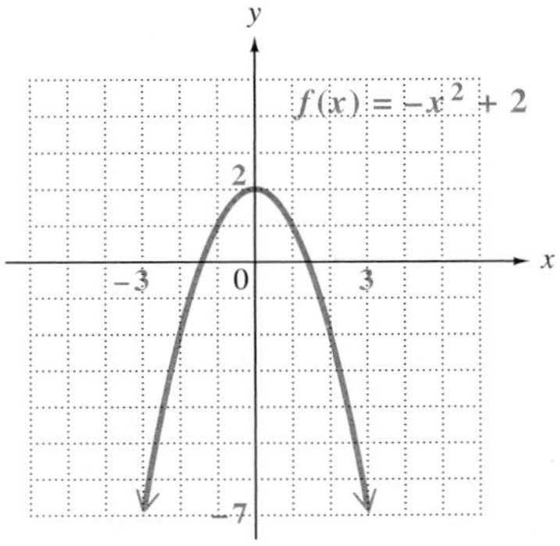

24. $f(x) = 2x^2 - 2$

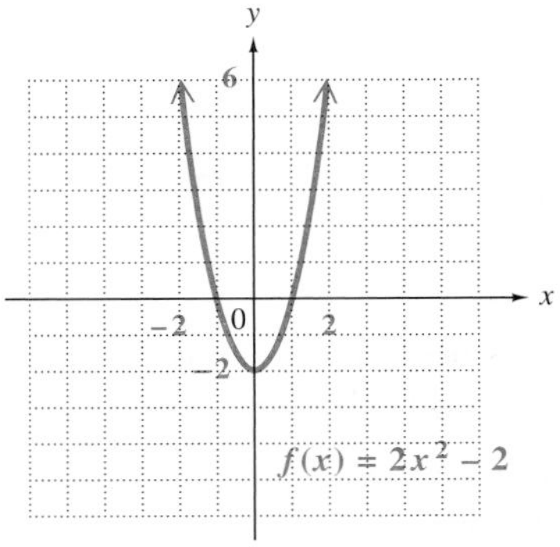

25. $f(x) = \frac{1}{2}(x - 4)^2$

axis: $x = 4$
domain: $(-\infty, \infty)$
range: $[0, \infty)$

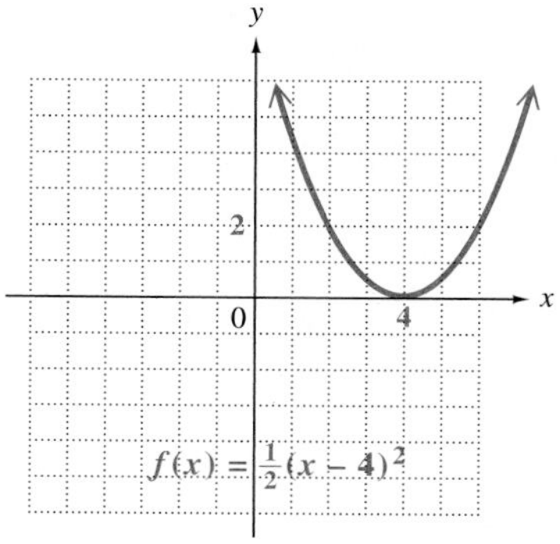

26. $f(x) = -2(x + 1)^2$

axis: $x = -1$
domain: $(-\infty, \infty)$
range: $(-\infty, 0]$

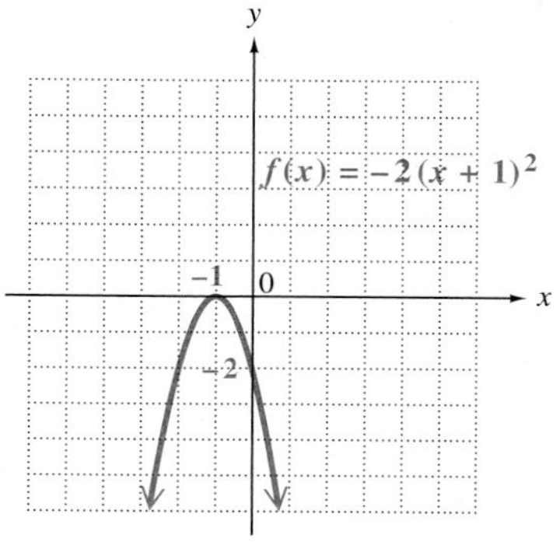

27. $f(x) = (x + 2)^2 - 1$

axis: $x = -2$
domain: $(-\infty, \infty)$
range: $[-1, \infty)$

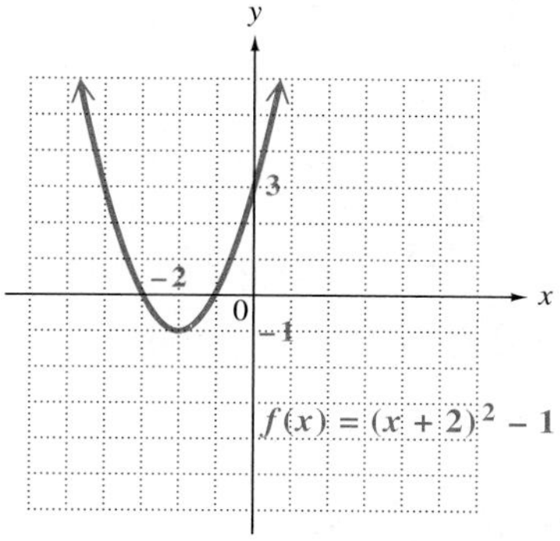

28. $f(x) = (x - 1)^2 + 2$

axis: $x = 1$
domain: $(-\infty, \infty)$
range: $[2, \infty)$

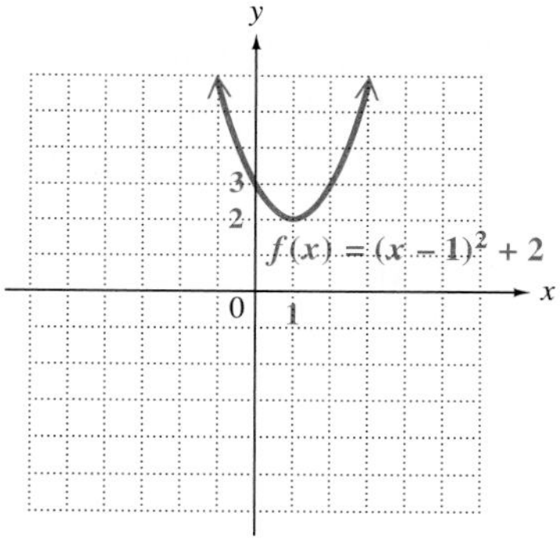

29. $f(x) = -2(x + 3)^2 + 4$

axis: $x = -3$
domain: $(-\infty, \infty)$
range: $(-\infty, 4]$

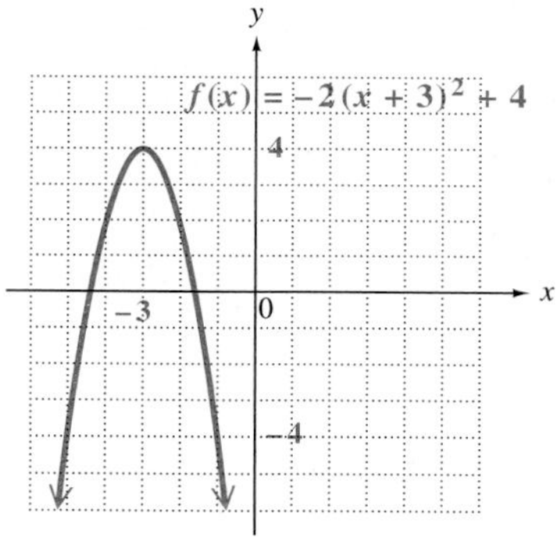

30. $f(x) = 2(x - 2)^2 - 3$

axis: $x = 2$
domain: $(-\infty, \infty)$
range: $[-3, \infty)$

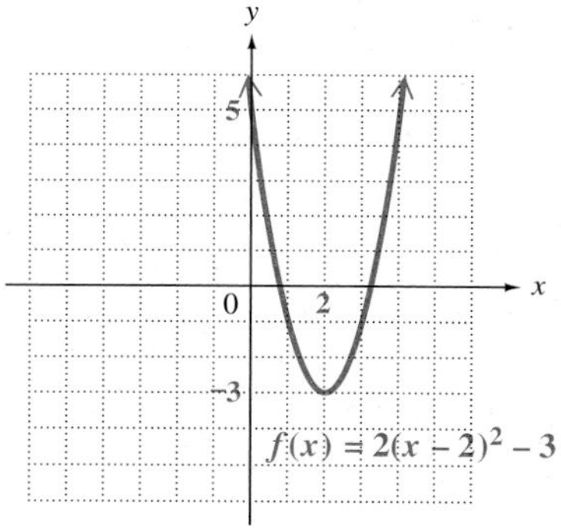

31. $f(x) = -\frac{2}{3}(x + 2)^2 + 1$

axis: $x = -2$
domain: $(-\infty, \infty)$
range: $(-\infty, 1]$

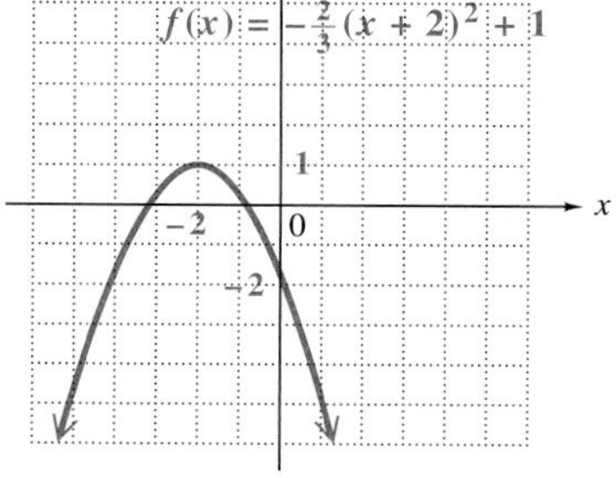

32. $f(x) = -\frac{1}{2}(x + 1)^2 + 2$

axis: $x = -1$
domain: $(-\infty, \infty)$
range: $(-\infty, 2]$

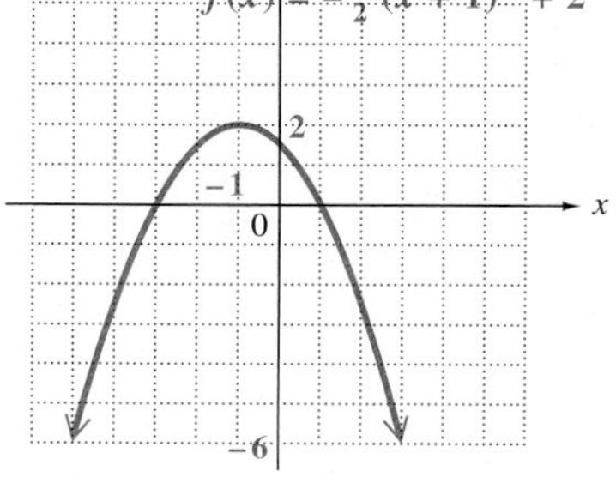

RELATING CONCEPTS (Exercises 33–38) FOR INDIVIDUAL OR GROUP WORK

The procedures described in this section that allow the graph of $f(x) = x^2$ to be shifted vertically and horizontally are applicable to other types of functions. In Section 4.6 we introduced linear functions of the form $g(x) = ax + b$. Consider the graph of the simplest linear function defined by $g(x) = x$, shown here, and then ***work Exercises 33–38 in order.***

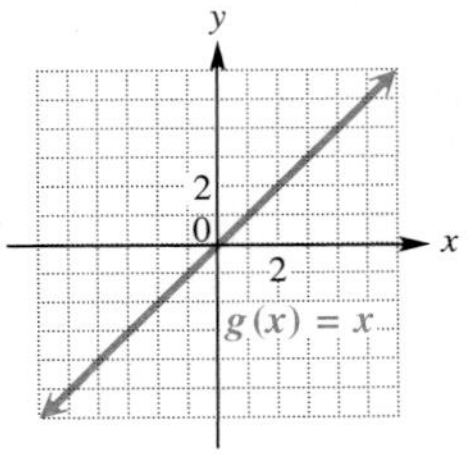

33. Based on the concepts of this section, how does the graph of $F(x) = x^2 + 6$ compare to the graph of $f(x) = x^2$ if a *vertical* shift is considered?

It is shifted 6 units up.

34. Graph the linear function defined by $G(x) = x + 6$.

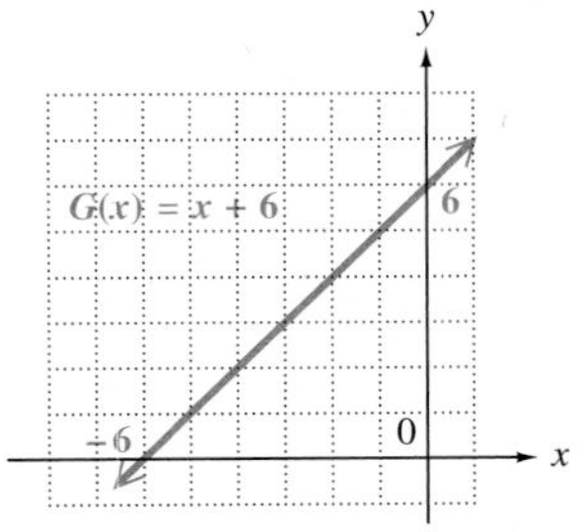

35. Based on the concepts of Chapter 4, how does the graph of $G(x) = x + 6$ compare to the graph of $g(x) = x$ if a *vertical* shift is considered? (*Hint:* Look at the y-intercept.)

It is shifted 6 units up.

36. Based on the concepts of this section, how does the graph of $F(x) = (x - 6)^2$ compare to the graph of $f(x) = x^2$ if a *horizontal* shift is considered?

It is shifted 6 units to the right.

37. Graph the linear function defined by $G(x) = x - 6$.

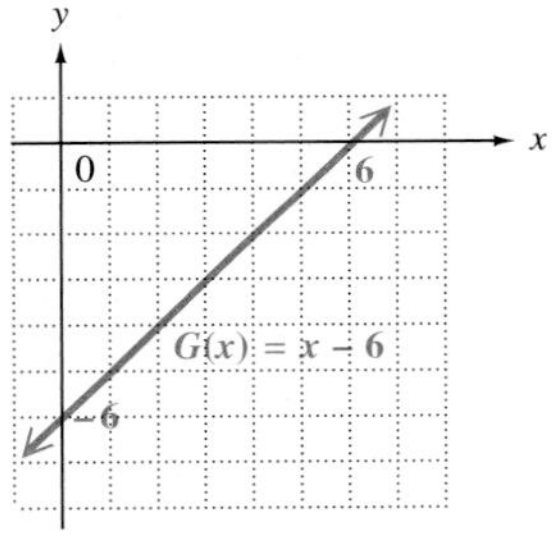

38. Based on the concepts of Chapter 4, how does the graph of $G(x) = x - 6$ compare to the graph of $g(x) = x$ if a *horizontal* shift is considered? (*Hint:* Look at the x-intercept.)

It is shifted 6 units to the right.

In Exercises 39–44, tell whether a linear or quadratic function would be a more appropriate model for each set of graphed data. If linear, tell whether the slope should be positive or negative. If quadratic, tell whether the coefficient a of x^2 should be positive or negative. See Example 6.

39.

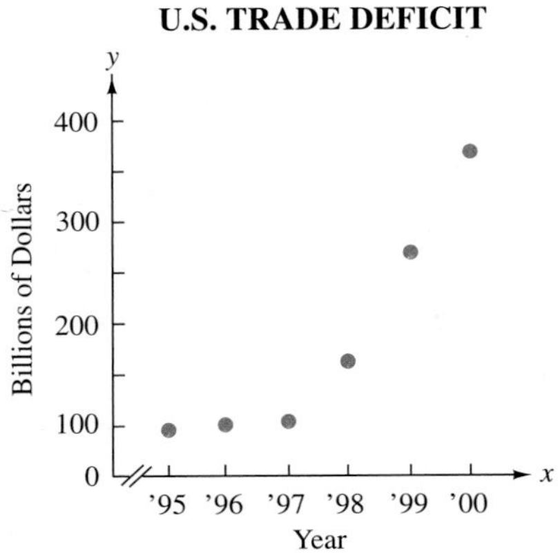

Source: U.S. Department of Commerce.

quadratic; positive

40.

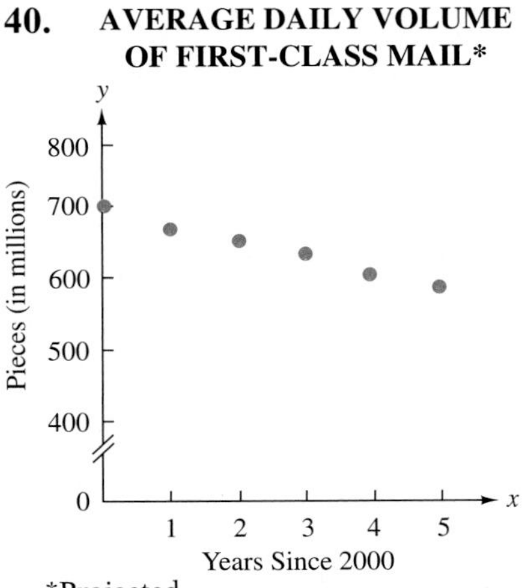

*Projected
Source: General Accounting Office.

linear; negative

41.

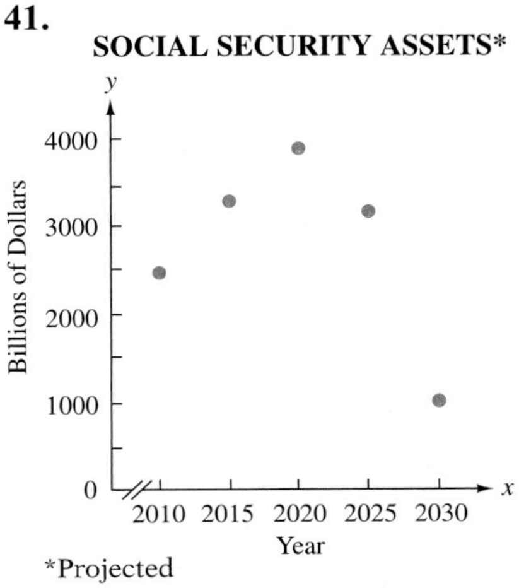

*Projected
Source: Social Security Administration.

quadratic; negative

42. **CEDAR RAPIDS SCHOOLS—GENERAL RESERVE FUND**

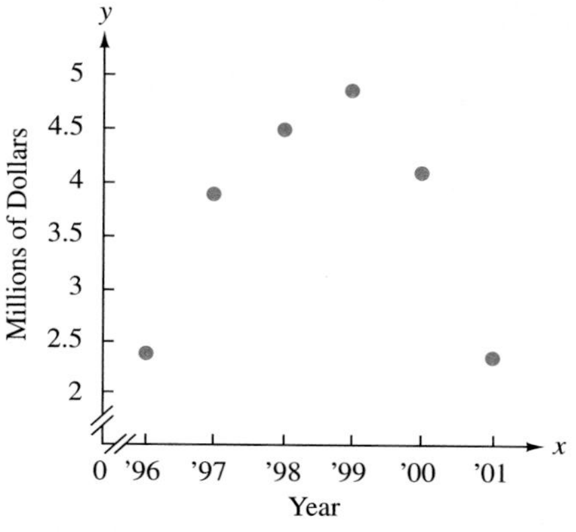

Source: Cedar Rapids School District.

quadratic; negative

43. **CONSUMER DEMAND FOR ELECTRICITY**

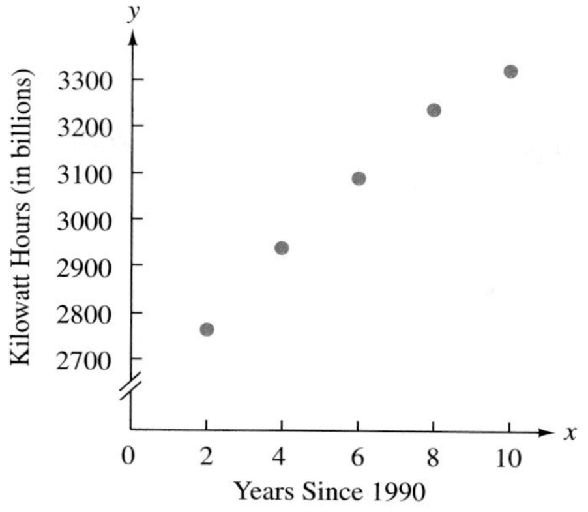

Source: U.S. Department of Energy.

linear; positive

44. **U.S. COMMERCIAL BANK FAILURES**

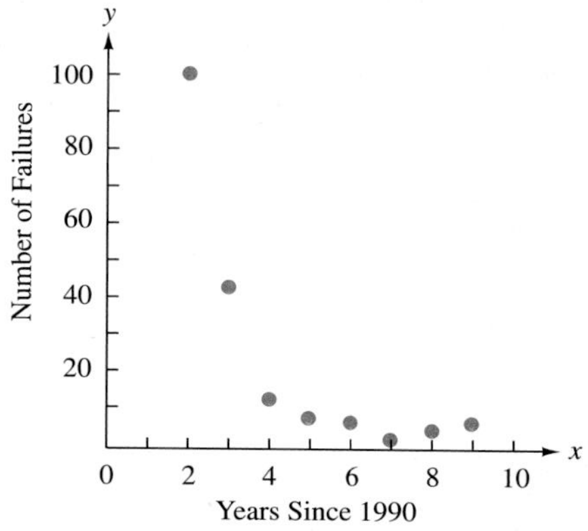

Source: www.ABA.com

quadratic; positive

Solve each problem. See Example 6.

45. The number of company bankruptcy filings for selected years between 1990 and 1999 are shown in the table. In the year column, 0 represents 1990, 2 represents 1992, and so on.

COMPANY BANKRUPTCY FILINGS

Year	Number of Bankruptcies
0	115
2	91
4	70
6	84
8	120
9	145

Source: www.BankruptcyData.com

(a) Use the ordered pairs (year, number of bankruptcies) to make a scatter diagram of the data.

COMPANY BANKRUPTCY FILINGS

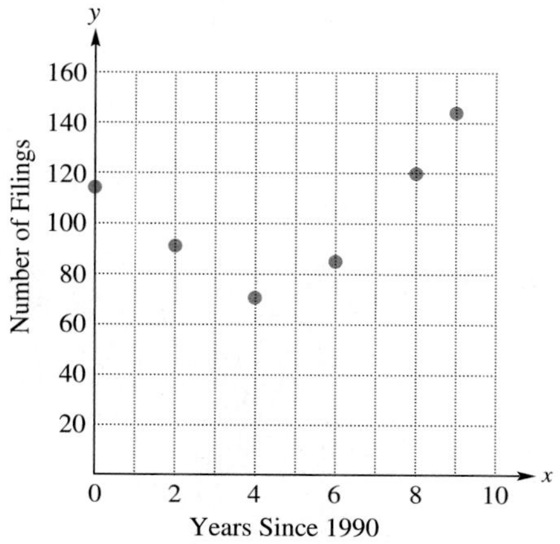

(b) Use the scatter diagram to decide whether a linear or quadratic function would better model the data. If quadratic, should the coefficient a of x^2 be positive or negative?

quadratic; positive

(c) Use the ordered pairs (0, 115), (4, 70), and (8, 120) to find a quadratic function that models the data. Round the values of a, b, and c in your model to three decimal places, as necessary.

$y = 2.969x^2 - 23.125x + 115$

(d) Use your model from part (c) to approximate the number of company bankruptcy filings in 2000. Round your answer to the nearest whole number.

181

(e) The number of company bankruptcy filings through September 8, 2000 was 124. Based on this, is your estimate from part (d) reasonable? Explain.

Yes. About 15 companies filed for bankruptcy each month, so at this rate, filings for 2000 would be about 180.

46. The number of new AIDS patients who survived the first year for the years from 1991 through 1997 are shown in the table. In the year column, 1 represents 1991, 2 represents 1992, and so on.

AIDS PATIENTS WHO SURVIVED THE FIRST YEAR

Year	Number of Patients
1	55
2	130
3	155
4	160
5	155
6	150
7	115

Source: HIV Health Services Planning Council.

(a) Use the ordered pairs (year, number of patients) to make a scatter diagram of the data.

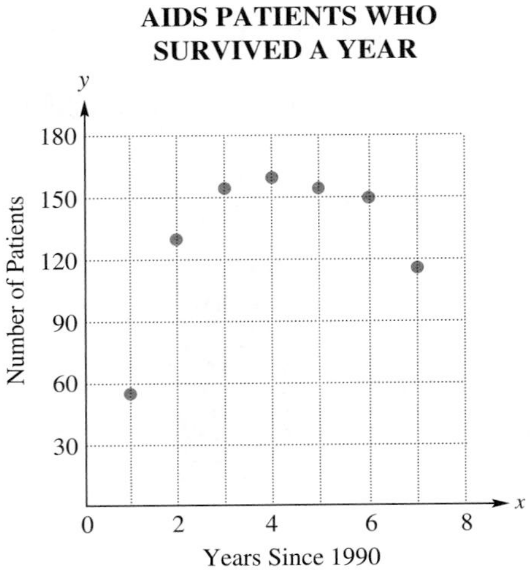

(b) Would a linear or quadratic function better model the data?

quadratic

(c) Should the coefficient a of x^2 in a quadratic model be positive or negative?

negative

(d) Use the ordered pairs (2, 130), (3, 155), and (7, 115) to find a quadratic function that models the data.

$y = -7x^2 + 60x + 38$

(e) Use your model from part (d) to approximate the number of AIDS patients who survived the first year in 1994 and 1996. How well does the model approximate the actual data from the table?

1994: 166; 1996: 146; The model approximates the data reasonably well.

47. In Example 6, we determined that the quadratic function defined by

$$y = .2455x^2 - 1.856x + 30.7105$$

modeled the rate of higher-order multiple births, where x represents the number of years since 1970.

(a) Use this model to approximate the rate of higher-order births in 1998 to the nearest tenth.

171.2

(b) The actual rate of higher-order births in 1998 was 193.5. (*Source:* National Center for Health Statistics.) How does the approximation using the model compare to the actual rate for 1998?

The approximation using the model is low.

48. Should the model from Exercise 47 be used to approximate the rate of higher-order multiple births in years after 1998? Explain.

No; Since the model did not approximate the 1998 rate very closely, it will probably not be valid for later years.

10.7 More about Parabolas; Applications

1 Find the vertex of a vertical parabola. When the equation of a parabola is given in the form $f(x) = ax^2 + bx + c$, we need to locate the vertex in order to sketch an accurate graph. There are two ways to do this: complete the square as shown in Examples 1 and 2, or use a formula derived by completing the square.

Example 1 Completing the Square to Find the Vertex

Find the vertex of the graph of $f(x) = x^2 - 4x + 5$.

To find the vertex, we need to express $x^2 - 4x + 5$ in the form $(x - h)^2 + k$. We do this by completing the square on $x^2 - 4x$, as in Section 10.2. The process is a little different here because we want to keep $f(x)$ alone on one side of the equation. Instead of adding the appropriate number to each side, we *add and subtract* it on the right. This is equivalent to adding 0.

$$f(x) = x^2 - 4x + 5$$

$$= (x^2 - 4x \quad\quad) + 5 \qquad \text{Group the variable terms.}$$

$$\left[\frac{1}{2}(-4)\right]^2 = (-2)^2 = 4$$

$$= (x^2 - 4x + 4 - 4) + 5 \qquad \text{Add and subtract 4.}$$

$$= (x^2 - 4x + 4) - 4 + 5 \qquad \text{Bring } -4 \text{ outside the parentheses.}$$

$$f(x) = (x - 2)^2 + 1 \qquad \text{Factor; combine terms.}$$

The vertex of this parabola is (2, 1).

Work Problem 1 at the Side.

Example 2 Completing the Square to Find the Vertex When $a \neq 1$

Find the vertex of the graph of $f(x) = -3x^2 + 6x - 1$.

We must complete the square on $-3x^2 + 6x$. Because the x^2-term has a coefficient other than 1, we factor that coefficient out of the first two terms and then proceed as in Example 1.

$$f(x) = -3x^2 + 6x - 1$$

$$= -3(x^2 - 2x) - 1 \qquad \text{Factor out } -3.$$

$$\left[\frac{1}{2}(-2)\right]^2 = (-1)^2 = 1$$

$$= -3(x^2 - 2x + 1 - 1) - 1 \qquad \text{Add and subtract 1.}$$

$$= -3(x^2 - 2x + 1) + (-3)(-1) - 1 \qquad \text{Distributive property}$$

$$= -3(x^2 - 2x + 1) + 3 - 1$$

$$f(x) = -3(x - 1)^2 + 2 \qquad \text{Factor; combine terms.}$$

The vertex is (1, 2).

Work Problem 2 at the Side.

Objectives

1. Find the vertex of a vertical parabola.
2. Graph a quadratic function.
3. Use the discriminant to find the number of x-intercepts of a vertical parabola.
4. Use quadratic functions to solve problems involving maximum or minimum value.
5. Graph horizontal parabolas.

1 Find the vertex of each parabola.

(a) $f(x) = x^2 - 6x + 7$

(b) $f(x) = x^2 + 4x - 9$

2 Find the vertex of each parabola.

(a) $f(x) = 2x^2 - 4x + 1$

(b) $f(x) = -\frac{1}{2}x^2 + 2x - 3$

Answers

1. (a) $(3, -2)$ **(b)** $(-2, -13)$
2. (a) $(1, -1)$ **(b)** $(2, -1)$

3 Use the formula to find the vertex of the graph of each quadratic function.

(a) $f(x) = -2x^2 + 3x - 1$

(b) $f(x) = 4x^2 - x + 5$

To derive a formula for the vertex of the graph of the quadratic function $y = ax^2 + bx + c$, complete the square on the standard form of the equation.

$$f(x) = ax^2 + bx + c \quad (a \neq 0) \qquad \text{Standard form}$$

$$= a\left(x^2 + \frac{b}{a}x\right) + c \qquad \text{Factor } a \text{ from the first two terms.}$$

$$\left[\frac{1}{2}\left(\frac{b}{a}\right)\right]^2 = \left(\frac{b}{2a}\right)^2 = \frac{b^2}{4a^2}$$

$$= a\left(x^2 + \frac{b}{a}x + \frac{b^2}{4a^2} - \frac{b^2}{4a^2}\right) + c \qquad \text{Add and subtract } \tfrac{b^2}{4a^2}.$$

$$= a\left(x^2 + \frac{b}{a}x + \frac{b^2}{4a^2}\right) + a\left(-\frac{b^2}{4a^2}\right) + c \qquad \text{Distributive property}$$

$$= a\left(x^2 + \frac{b}{a}x + \frac{b^2}{4a^2}\right) - \frac{b^2}{4a} + c$$

$$= a\left(x + \frac{b}{2a}\right)^2 + \frac{4ac - b^2}{4a} \qquad \text{Factor; combine terms.}$$

$$f(x) = a\Big[x - \underbrace{\left(\frac{-b}{2a}\right)}_{h}\Big]^2 + \underbrace{\frac{4ac - b^2}{4a}}_{k} \qquad f(x) = (x - h)^2 + k$$

This equation shows that the vertex (h, k) can be expressed in terms of a, b, and c. However, it is not necessary to remember this expression for k, since it can be found by replacing x with $\frac{-b}{2a}$. Using function notation, if $y = f(x)$, the y-value of the vertex is $f\left(\frac{-b}{2a}\right)$.

Vertex Formula

The graph of the quadratic function defined by $f(x) = ax^2 + bx + c$ has vertex

$$\left(\frac{-b}{2a}, f\left(\frac{-b}{2a}\right)\right),$$

and the axis of the parabola is the line

$$x = \frac{-b}{2a}.$$

Example 3 **Using the Formula to Find the Vertex**

Use the vertex formula to find the vertex of the graph of

$$f(x) = x^2 - x - 6.$$

For this function, $a = 1$, $b = -1$, and $c = -6$. The x-coordinate of the vertex of the parabola is given by

$$\frac{-b}{2a} = \frac{-(-1)}{2(1)} = \frac{1}{2}.$$

The y-coordinate is $f\left(\frac{-b}{2a}\right) = f\left(\frac{1}{2}\right)$.

$$f\left(\frac{1}{2}\right) = \left(\frac{1}{2}\right)^2 - \frac{1}{2} - 6 = \frac{1}{4} - \frac{1}{2} - 6 = -\frac{25}{4}$$

The vertex is $\left(\frac{1}{2}, -\frac{25}{4}\right)$.

Work Problem 3 at the Side.

ANSWERS

3. (a) $\left(\frac{3}{4}, \frac{1}{8}\right)$ **(b)** $\left(\frac{1}{8}, \frac{79}{16}\right)$

2 **Graph a quadratic function.** We give a general approach for graphing any quadratic function here.

Graphing a Quadratic Function f

Step 1 **Determine whether the graph opens up or down.** If $a > 0$, the parabola opens up; if $a < 0$, it opens down.

Step 2 **Find the vertex.** Use either the vertex formula or completing the square.

Step 3 **Find any intercepts.** To find the x-intercepts (if any), solve $f(x) = 0$. To find the y-intercept, evaluate $f(0)$.

Step 4 **Complete the graph.** Plot the points found so far. Find and plot additional points as needed, using symmetry about the axis.

Example 4 Using the Steps to Graph a Quadratic Function

Graph the quadratic function defined by

$$f(x) = x^2 - x - 6.$$

Step 1 From the equation, $a = 1$, so the graph of the function opens up.

Step 2 The vertex, $(\frac{1}{2}, -\frac{25}{4})$, was found in Example 3 by substituting the values $a = 1$, $b = -1$, and $c = -6$ in the vertex formula.

Step 3 Now find any intercepts. Since the vertex, $(\frac{1}{2}, -\frac{25}{4})$, is in quadrant IV and the graph opens up, there will be two x-intercepts. To find them, let $f(x) = 0$ and solve the equation.

$$f(x) = x^2 - x - 6$$
$$0 = x^2 - x - 6 \quad \text{Let } f(x) = 0.$$
$$0 = (x - 3)(x + 2) \quad \text{Factor.}$$
$$x - 3 = 0 \quad \text{or} \quad x + 2 = 0 \quad \text{Zero-factor property}$$
$$x = 3 \quad \text{or} \quad x = -2$$

The x-intercepts are $(3, 0)$ and $(-2, 0)$. To find the y-intercept, evaluate $f(0)$.

$$f(x) = x^2 - x - 6$$
$$f(0) = 0^2 - 0 - 6 \quad \text{Let } x = 0.$$
$$f(0) = -6$$

The y-intercept is $(0, -6)$.

Step 4 Plot the points found so far and additional points as needed using symmetry about the axis $x = \frac{1}{2}$. The graph is shown in Figure 12. The domain is $(-\infty, \infty)$, and the range is $[-\frac{25}{4}, \infty)$.

x	y
-2	0
-1	-4
0	-6
$\frac{1}{2}$	$-\frac{25}{4}$
2	-4
3	0

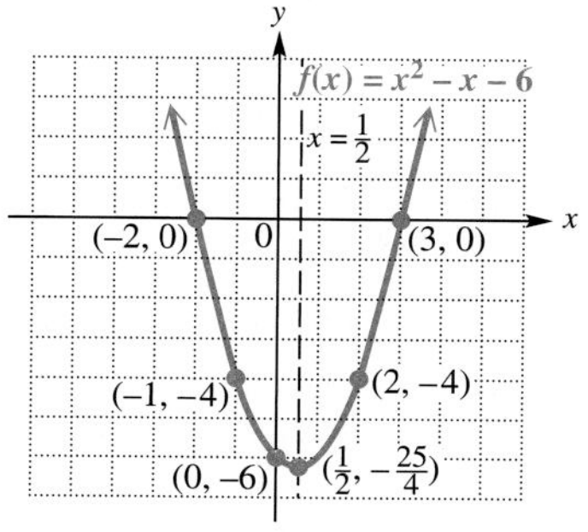

Figure 12

Work Problem 4 at the Side.

4 Graph the quadratic function defined by

$$f(x) = x^2 - 6x + 5.$$

Give the axis, domain, and range.

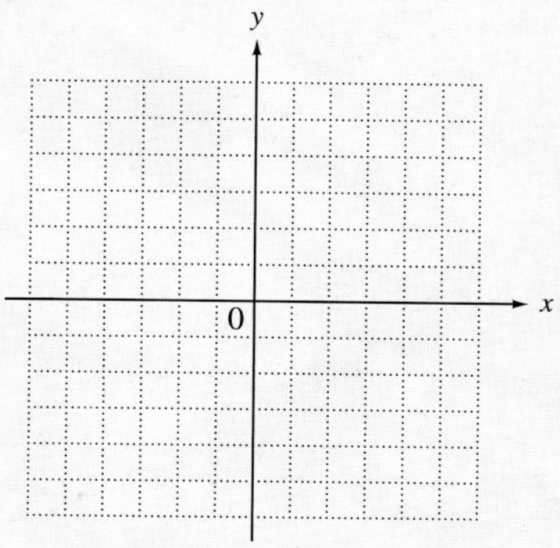

ANSWERS

4.

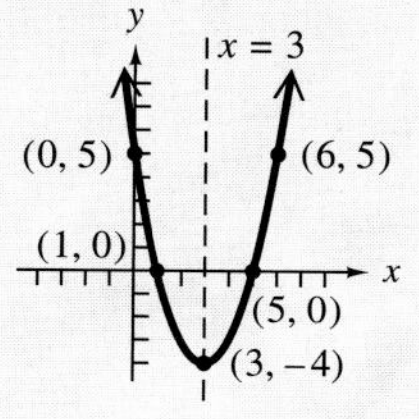

axis: $x = 3$; domain: $(-\infty, \infty)$; range: $[-4, \infty)$

5 Use the discriminant to determine the number of x-intercepts of the graph of each quadratic function.

(a) $f(x) = 4x^2 - 20x + 25$

(b) $f(x) = 2x^2 + 3x + 5$

(c) $f(x) = -3x^2 - x + 2$

3 **Use the discriminant to find the number of x-intercepts of a vertical parabola.** The graph of a quadratic function may have two x-intercepts, one x-intercept, or no x-intercepts, as shown in Figure 13. Recall from Section 10.3 that $b^2 - 4ac$ is called the *discriminant* of the quadratic equation $ax^2 + bx + c = 0$ and that we can use it to determine the number of real solutions of a quadratic equation.

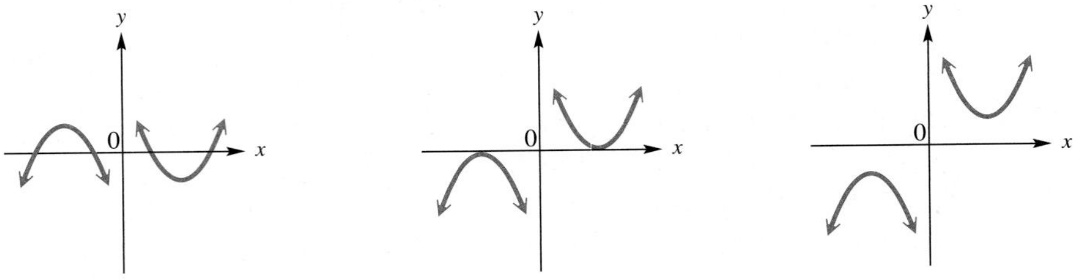

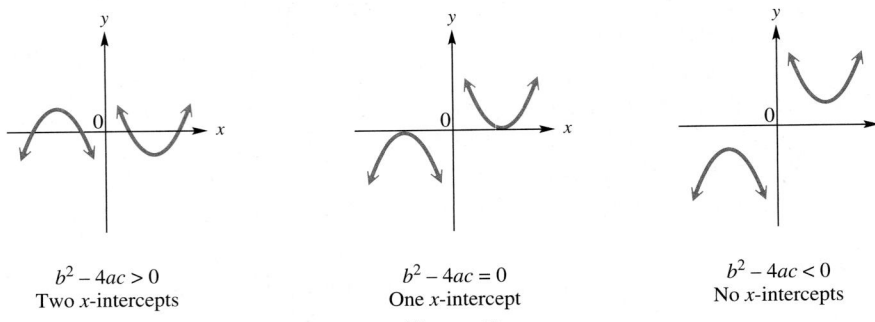

$b^2 - 4ac > 0$ Two x-intercepts | $b^2 - 4ac = 0$ One x-intercept | $b^2 - 4ac < 0$ No x-intercepts

Figure 13

In a similar way, we can use the discriminant of a quadratic *function* to determine the number of x-intercepts of its graph. If the discriminant is positive, the parabola will have two x-intercepts. If the discriminant is 0, there will be only one x-intercept, and it will be the vertex of the parabola. If the discriminant is negative, the graph will have no x-intercepts.

Example 5 Using the Discriminant to Determine the Number of x-Intercepts

Use the discriminant to determine the number of x-intercepts of the graph of each quadratic function.

(a) $f(x) = 2x^2 + 3x - 5$

The discriminant is $b^2 - 4ac$. Here $a = 2$, $b = 3$, and $c = -5$, so

$$b^2 - 4ac = 9 - 4(2)(-5)$$
$$= 49.$$

Since the discriminant is positive, the parabola has two x-intercepts.

(b) $f(x) = -3x^2 - 1$

In this equation, $a = -3$, $b = 0$, and $c = -1$. The discriminant is

$$b^2 - 4ac = 0 - 4(-3)(-1)$$
$$= -12.$$

The discriminant is negative, so the graph has no x-intercepts.

(c) $f(x) = 9x^2 + 6x + 1$

Here, $a = 9$, $b = 6$, and $c = 1$. The discriminant is

$$b^2 - 4ac = 36 - 4(9)(1)$$
$$= 0.$$

The parabola has only one x-intercept (its vertex) because the value of the discriminant is 0.

Work Problem 5 at the Side.

ANSWERS

5. **(a)** discriminant is 0; one x-intercept
(b) discriminant is -31; no x-intercepts
(c) discriminant is 25; two x-intercepts

4 Use quadratic functions to solve problems involving maximum or minimum value. The vertex of a parabola is either the highest or the lowest point on the parabola. The y-value of the vertex gives the maximum or minimum value of y, while the x-value tells where that maximum or minimum occurs.

In many applied problems we must find the largest or smallest value of some quantity. When we can express that quantity as a quadratic function, the value of k in the vertex gives that optimum value.

Example 6 **Finding the Maximum Area of a Rectangular Region**

A farmer has 120 ft of fencing. He wants to put a fence around a rectangular field next to a building. Find the maximum area he can enclose.

Figure 14

Figure 14 shows the field. Let x represent the width of the field. Since he has 120 ft of fencing,

$$x + x + \text{length} = 120 \qquad \text{Sum of the sides is 120 ft.}$$
$$2x + \text{length} = 120 \qquad \text{Combine terms.}$$
$$\text{length} = 120 - 2x. \qquad \text{Subtract } 2x.$$

The area is given by the product of the width and length, so

$$A = x(120 - 2x)$$
$$= 120x - 2x^2.$$

To determine the maximum area, find the vertex of the parabola given by $A = 120x - 2x^2$ using the vertex formula. Writing the equation in standard form as $A = -2x^2 + 120x$ gives $a = -2$, $b = 120$, and $c = 0$, so

$$h = \frac{-b}{2a} = \frac{-120}{2(-2)} = \frac{-120}{-4} = \mathbf{30};$$

$$f(\mathbf{30}) = -2(\mathbf{30})^2 + 120(\mathbf{30}) = -2(900) + 3600 = \mathbf{1800}.$$

The graph is a parabola that opens down, and its vertex is $(\mathbf{30}, \mathbf{1800})$. Thus, the maximum area will be 1800 ft^2. This area will occur if x, the width of the field, is 30 ft.

6 Solve Example 6 if the farmer has only 100 ft of fencing.

CAUTION

Be careful when interpreting the meanings of the coordinates of the vertex. The first coordinate, x, gives the value for which the *function value* is a maximum or a minimum. Be sure to read the problem carefully to determine whether you are asked to find the value of the independent variable, the function value, or both.

Work Problem 6 at the Side.

Example 7 **Finding the Maximum Height Attained by a Projectile**

If air resistance is neglected, a projectile on Earth shot straight upward with an initial velocity of 40 m per sec will be at a height s in meters given by

$$s(t) = -4.9t^2 + 40t,$$

where t is the number of seconds elapsed after projection. After how many seconds will it reach its maximum height, and what is this maximum height?

For this function, $a = -4.9$, $b = 40$, and $c = 0$. Use the vertex formula.

$$h = \frac{-b}{2a} = \frac{-40}{2(-4.9)} \approx \mathbf{4.1} \qquad \text{Use a calculator.}$$

This indicates that the maximum height is attained at 4.1 sec. To find this maximum height, calculate $f(4.1)$.

$$f(\mathbf{4.1}) = -4.9(\mathbf{4.1})^2 + 40(\mathbf{4.1})$$

$$\approx \mathbf{81.6} \qquad \text{Use a calculator.}$$

The projectile will attain a maximum height of approximately 81.6 m.

Work Problem 7 at the Side.

7 Solve the problem.

A toy rocket is launched from the ground so that its distance in feet above the ground after t seconds is

$$s(t) = -16t^2 + 208t.$$

Find the maximum height it reaches and the number of seconds it takes to reach that height.

5 **Graph horizontal parabolas.** If x and y are interchanged in the equation $y = ax^2 + bx + c$, the equation becomes $x = ay^2 + by + c$. Because of the interchange of the roles of x and y, these parabolas are horizontal (with horizontal lines as axes), compared with the vertical ones graphed previously.

Graph of a Horizontal Parabola

The graph of

$$x = ay^2 + by + c \quad \text{or} \quad x = a(y-k)^2 + h$$

is a parabola with vertex (h, k) and the horizontal line $y = k$ as axis. The graph opens to the right if $a > 0$ and to the left if $a < 0$.

Example 8 **Graphing a Horizontal Parabola**

Graph $x = (y-2)^2 - 3$.

This graph has its vertex at $(-3, 2)$, since the roles of x and y are reversed. It opens to the right, the positive x-direction, and has the same shape as $y = x^2$. Plotting a few additional points gives the graph shown in Figure 15. Note that the graph is symmetric about its axis, $y = 2$. The domain is $[-3, \infty)$, and the range is $(-\infty, \infty)$.

Continued on Next Page

ANSWERS

6. The field should be 25 ft by 50 ft with a maximum area of 1250 ft^2.

7. 676 ft; 6.5 sec

x	y
−3	2
−2	3
−2	1
1	4
1	0

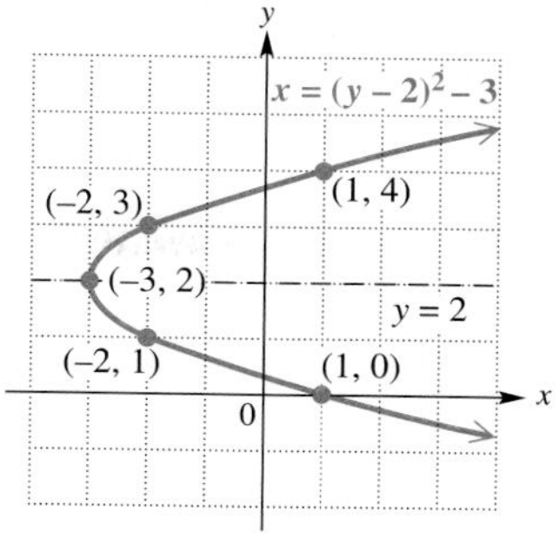

Figure 15

Work Problem 8 at the Side.

When a quadratic equation is given in the form $x = ay^2 + by + c$, completing the square on y will allow us to find the vertex.

Example 9 Completing the Square to Graph a Horizontal Parabola

Graph $x = -2y^2 + 4y - 3$. Give the domain and range of the relation.

$$x = -2y^2 + 4y - 3$$

$$= -2(y^2 - 2y) - 3 \qquad \text{Factor out } -2.$$

$$= -2(y^2 - 2y + 1 - 1) - 3 \qquad \text{Complete the square; add and subtract 1.}$$

$$= -2(y^2 - 2y + 1) + (-2)(-1) - 3 \qquad \text{Distributive property}$$

$$x = -2(y - 1)^2 - 1 \qquad \text{Factor; simplify.}$$

Because of the negative coefficient (−2), the graph opens to the left (the negative x-direction) and is narrower than the graph of $y = x^2$. As shown in Figure 16, the vertex is $(-1, 1)$. The domain is $(-\infty, -1]$, and the range is $(-\infty, \infty)$.

x	y
−3	2
−3	0
−1	1

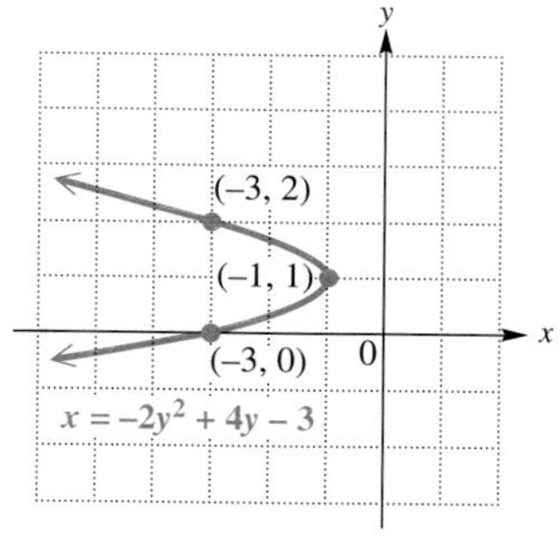

Figure 16

Work Problem 9 at the Side.

CAUTION

Only quadratic equations solved for y (whose graphs are vertical parabolas) are examples of functions. The horizontal parabolas in Examples 8 and 9 are *not* graphs of functions, because they do not satisfy the vertical line test. Furthermore, the vertex formula given earlier does not apply to parabolas with horizontal axes.

8 Graph $x = (y + 1)^2 - 4$. Give the axis, domain, and range.

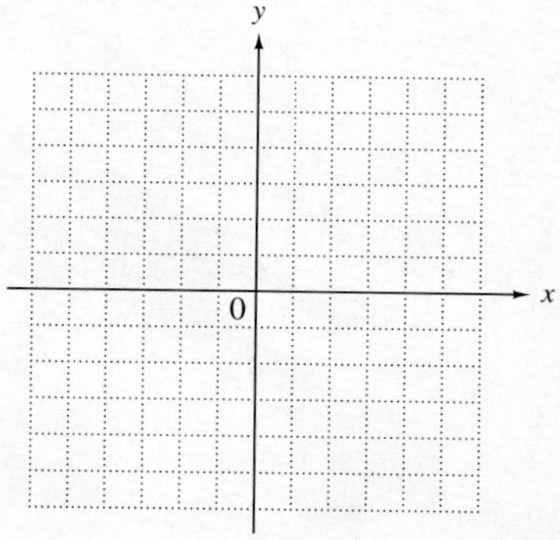

9 Find the vertex of each parabola. Tell whether the graph opens to the right or to the left. Give the domain and range.

(a) $x = 2y^2 - 6y + 5$

(b) $x = -y^2 + 2y + 5$

ANSWERS

8.

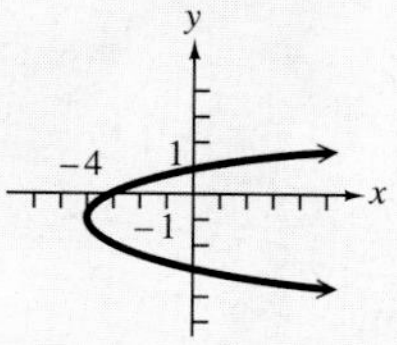

axis: $y = -1$; domain: $[-4, \infty)$; range: $(-\infty, \infty)$

9. **(a)** $\left(\frac{1}{2}, \frac{3}{2}\right)$; right; domain: $\left[\frac{1}{2}, \infty\right)$; range: $(-\infty, \infty)$

(b) $(6, 1)$; left; domain: $(-\infty, 6]$; range: $(-\infty, \infty)$

In summary, the graphs of parabolas studied in this section and the previous one fall into the following categories.

GRAPHS OF PARABOLAS

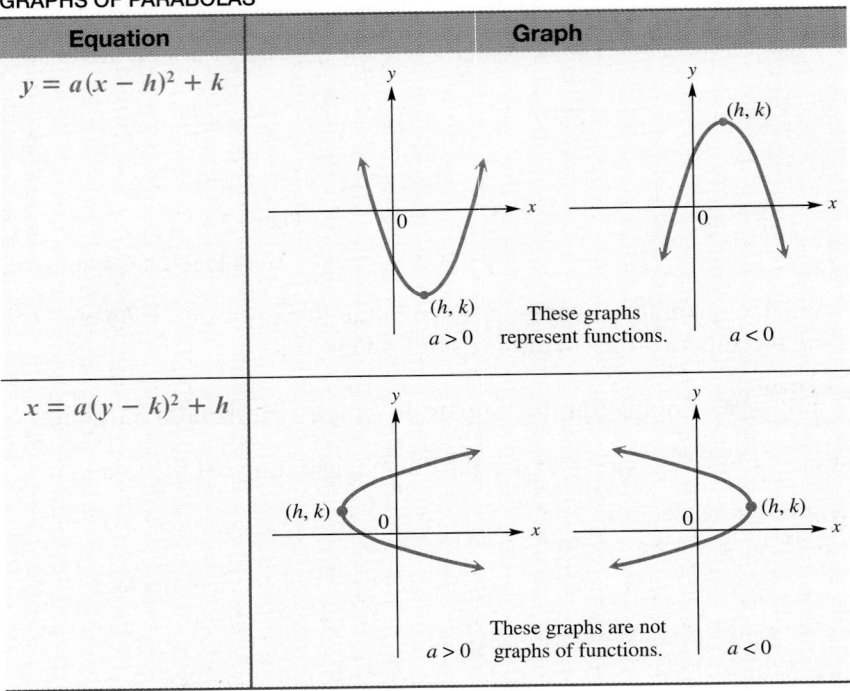

Equation	Graph
$y = a(x - h)^2 + k$	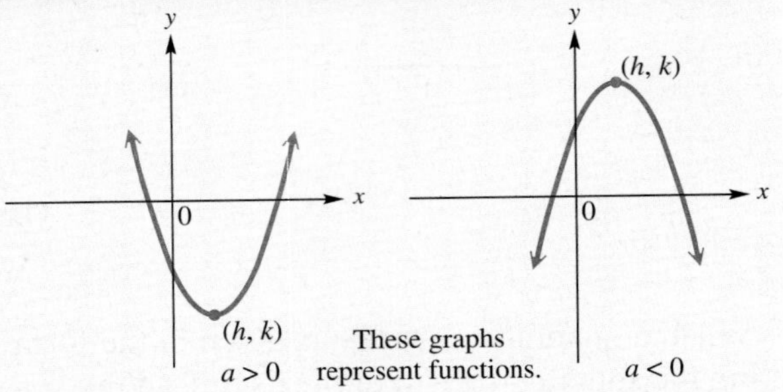
$x = a(y - k)^2 + h$	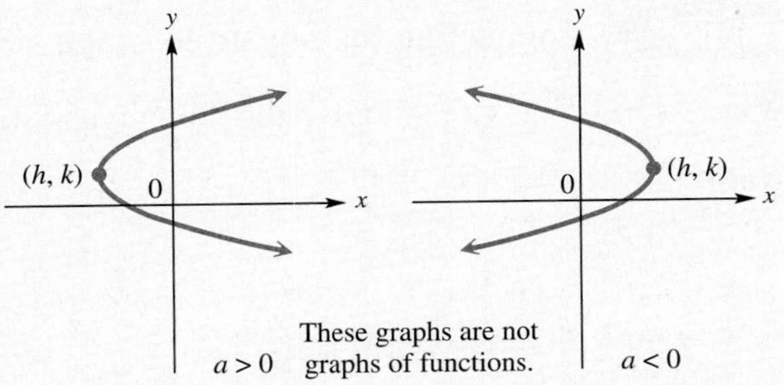

10.7 EXERCISES

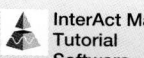

FOR EXTRA HELP: Student's Solutions Manual | MyMathLab.com | InterAct Math Tutorial Software | AW Math Tutor Center | www.mathxl.com | Digital Video Tutor CD 9 Videotape 21

1. How can you determine just by looking at the equation of a parabola whether it has a vertical or a horizontal axis?

If x is squared, it has a vertical axis; if y is squared, it has a horizontal axis.

2. Why can't the graph of a quadratic function be a horizontal parabola?

A horizontal parabola fails the vertical line test.

3. How can you determine the number of x-intercepts of the graph of a quadratic function without graphing the function?

Use the discriminant of the corresponding quadratic equation. If it is positive, there are two x-intercepts. If it is 0, there is just one x-intercept (the vertex), and if it is negative, there are no x-intercepts.

4. If the vertex of the graph of a quadratic function is $(1, -3)$ and the graph opens down, how many x-intercepts does the graph have?

none

Find the vertex of each parabola. For each equation, decide whether the graph opens up, down, to the left, or to the right, and whether it is wider, narrower, or the same shape as the graph of $y = x^2$. If it is a vertical parabola, use the discriminant to determine the number of x-intercepts. See Examples 1–3, 5, 8, and 9.

5. $y = 2x^2 + 4x + 5$

$(-1, 3)$; up; narrower; no x-intercepts

6. $y = 3x^2 - 6x + 4$

$(1, 1)$; up; narrower; no x-intercepts

7. $y = -x^2 + 5x + 3$

$\left(\frac{5}{2}, \frac{37}{4}\right)$; down; same; two x-intercepts

8. $x = -y^2 + 7y - 2$

$\left(\frac{41}{4}, \frac{7}{2}\right)$; to the left; same

9. $x = \frac{1}{3}y^2 + 6y + 24$

$(-3, -9)$; to the right; wider

10. $x = \frac{1}{2}y^2 + 10y - 5$

$(-55, -10)$; to the right; wider

Graph each parabola using the techniques described in this section. Give the domain and range. See Examples 4, 8, and 9.

11. $f(x) = x^2 + 4x + 3$
domain: **$(-\infty, \infty)$**
range: **$[-1, \infty)$**

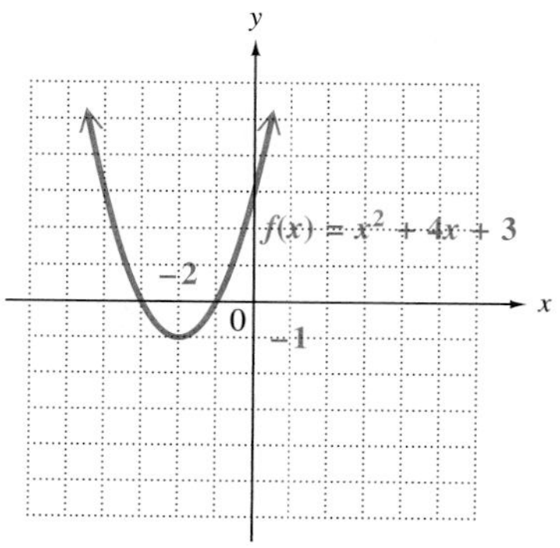

12. $f(x) = x^2 + 2x - 2$
domain: **$(-\infty, \infty)$**
range: **$[-3, \infty)$**

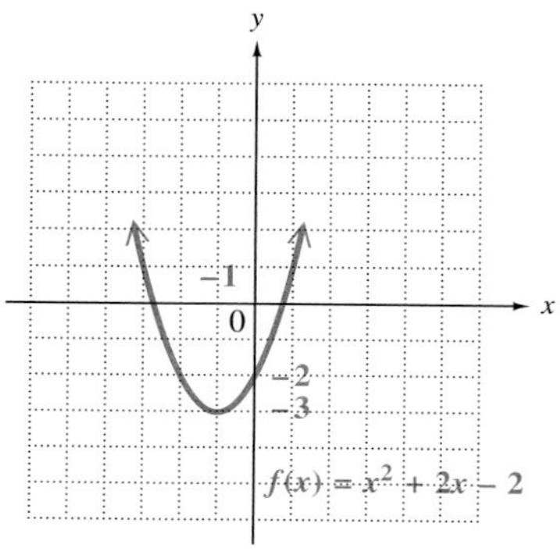

13. $f(x) = -2x^2 + 4x - 5$
domain: **$(-\infty, \infty)$**
range: **$(-\infty, -3]$**

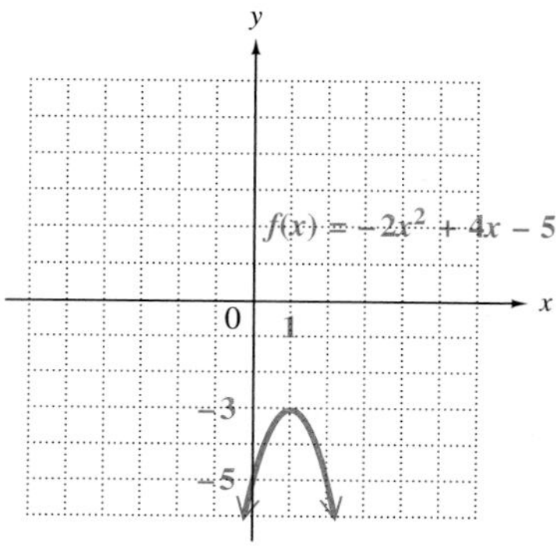

14. $f(x) = -3x^2 + 12x - 8$
domain: $(-\infty, \infty)$
range: $(-\infty, 4]$

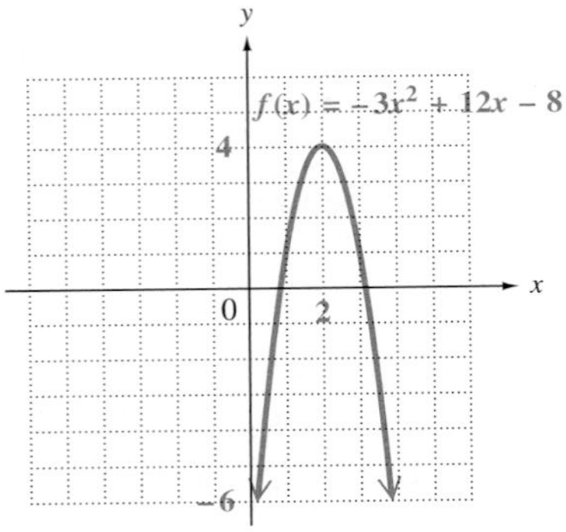

15. $x = -\frac{1}{5}y^2 + 2y - 4$
domain: $(-\infty, 1]$
range: $(-\infty, \infty)$

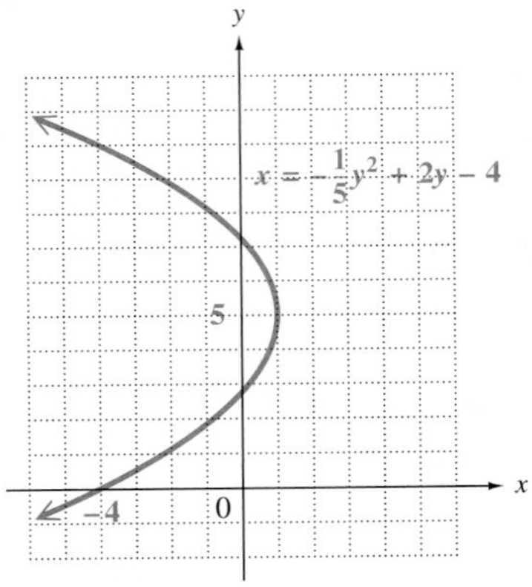

16. $x = -\frac{1}{2}y^2 - 4y - 6$
domain: $(-\infty, 2]$
range: $(-\infty, \infty)$

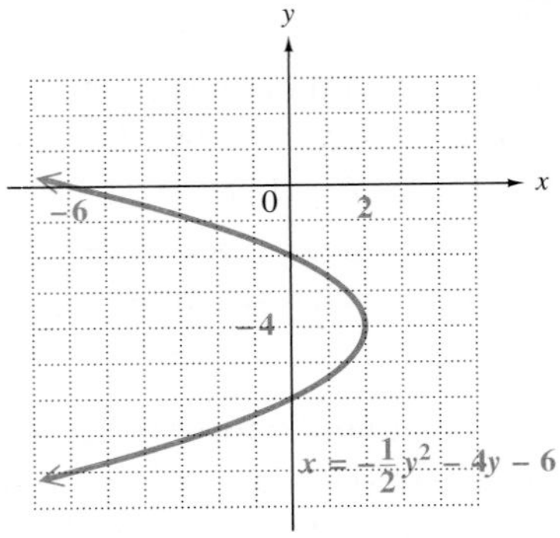

17. $x = 3y^2 + 12y + 5$
domain: $[-7, \infty)$
range: $(-\infty, \infty)$

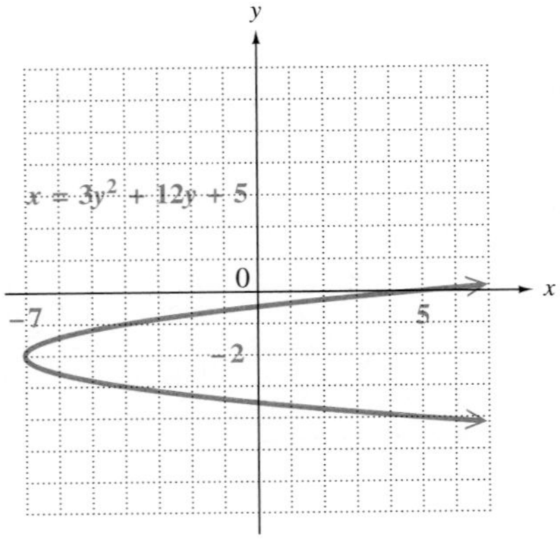

18. $x = 4y^2 + 16y + 11$
domain: $[-5, \infty)$
range: $(-\infty, \infty)$

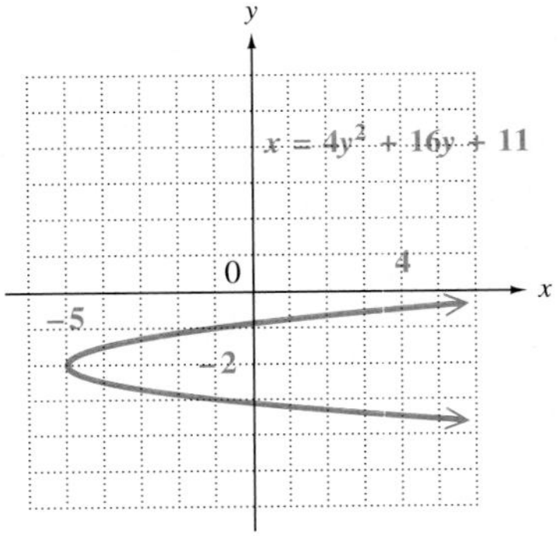

Use the concepts of this section to match each equation with its graph.

A.

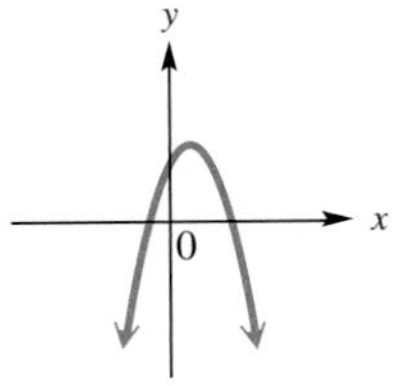

B.

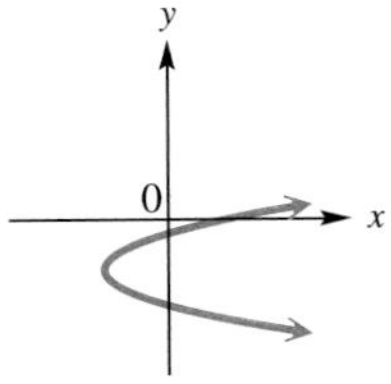

C.

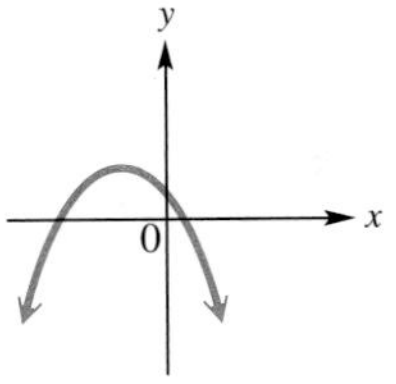

D.

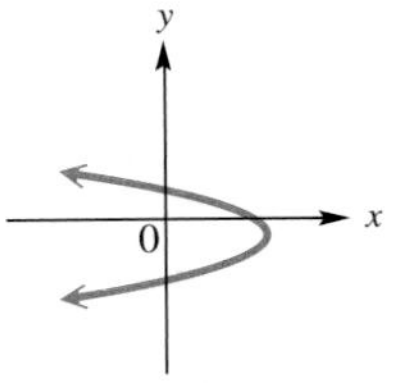

E.

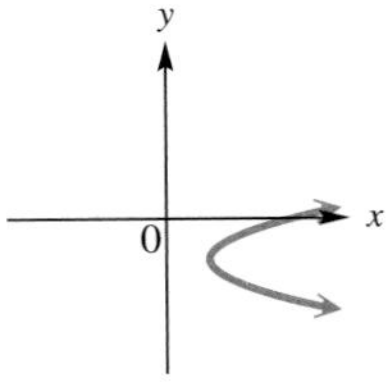

F.

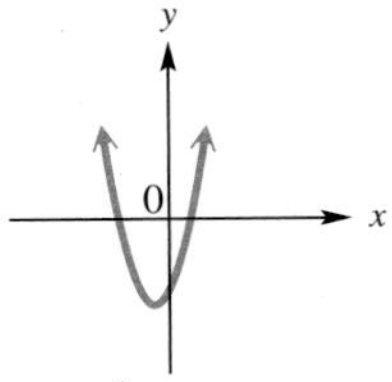

19. $y = 2x^2 + 4x - 3$ F

20. $y = -x^2 + 3x + 5$ A

21. $y = -\frac{1}{2}x^2 - x + 1$ C

22. $x = y^2 + 6y + 3$ B

23. $x = -y^2 - 2y + 4$ D

24. $x = 3y^2 + 6y + 5$ E

Solve each problem. See Examples 6 and 7.

25. Palo Alto College is planning to construct a rectangular parking lot on land bordered on one side by a highway. The plan is to use 640 ft of fencing to fence off the other three sides. What should the dimensions of the lot be if the enclosed area is to be a maximum?

160 ft by 320 ft

26. Keisha Hughes has 100 m of fencing material to enclose a rectangular exercise run for her dog. What width will give the enclosure the maximum area?

25 m

27. Find the pair of numbers whose sum is 60 and whose product is a maximum. (*Hint:* Let x and $60 - x$ represent the two numbers.)

30 and 30

28. Find the pair of numbers whose sum is 10 and whose product is a maximum.

5 and 5

29. If an object on Earth is propelled upward with an initial velocity of 32 ft per sec, then its height (in feet) after t seconds is given by

$$h(t) = 32t - 16t^2.$$

Find the maximum height attained by the object and the number of seconds it takes to hit the ground.

16 ft; 2 sec

30. A projectile on Earth is fired straight upward so that its distance (in feet) above the ground t seconds after firing is given by

$$s(t) = -16t^2 + 400t.$$

Find the maximum height it reaches and the number of seconds it takes to reach that height.

2500 ft; 12.5 sec

31. A charter flight charges a fare of \$200 per person, plus \$4 per person for each unsold seat on the plane. If the plane holds 100 passengers and if x represents the number of unsold seats, find the following.

(a) A function defined by $R(x)$ that describes the total revenue received for the flight (*Hint:* Multiply the number of people flying, $100 - x$, by the price per ticket, $200 + 4x$.)

$R(x) = 20{,}000 + 200x - 4x^2$

(b) The number of unsold seats that will produce the maximum revenue

25

(c) The maximum revenue

\$22,500

32. For a trip to a resort, a charter bus company charges a fare of \$48 per person, plus \$2 per person for each unsold seat on the bus. If the bus has 42 seats and x represents the number of unsold seats, find the following.

(a) A function defined by $R(x)$ that describes the total revenue from the trip (*Hint*: Multiply the total number riding, $42 - x$, by the price per ticket, $48 + 2x$.)

$R(x) = -2x^2 + 36x + 2016$

(b) The number of unsold seats that produces the maximum revenue

9

(c) The maximum revenue

\$2178

33. The annual percent increase in the amount pharmacies paid wholesalers for drugs in the years 1990–1999 can be modeled by the quadratic function with

$$f(x) = .228x^2 - 2.57x + 8.97,$$

where $x = 0$ represents 1990, $x = 1$ represents 1991, and so on. (*Source: IMS Health*, Retail and Provider Perspective.)

(a) Since the coefficient of x^2 in the model is positive, the graph of this quadratic function is a parabola that opens up. Will the y-value of the vertex of this graph be a maximum or minimum?

minimum

(b) In what year was the minimum percent increase? (Round down to the nearest year.) Use the actual x-value of the vertex, to the nearest tenth, to find this increase.

1995; 1.7%

34. The U.S. domestic oyster catch (in millions) for the years 1990–1998 can be approximated by the quadratic function with

$$f(x) = -.566x^2 + 5.08x + 29.2,$$

where $x = 0$ represents 1990, $x = 1$ represents 1991, and so on. (*Source:* National Marine Fisheries Service.)

(a) Since the coefficient of x^2 in the model is negative, the graph of this quadratic function is a parabola that opens down. Will the y-value of the vertex of this graph be a maximum or minimum?

maximum

(b) In what year was the maximum domestic oyster catch? (Round down to the nearest year.) Use the actual x-value of the vertex, to the nearest tenth, to find this catch.

1994; 41 million

35. The graph shows how Social Security assets are expected to change as the number of retirees receiving benefits increases.

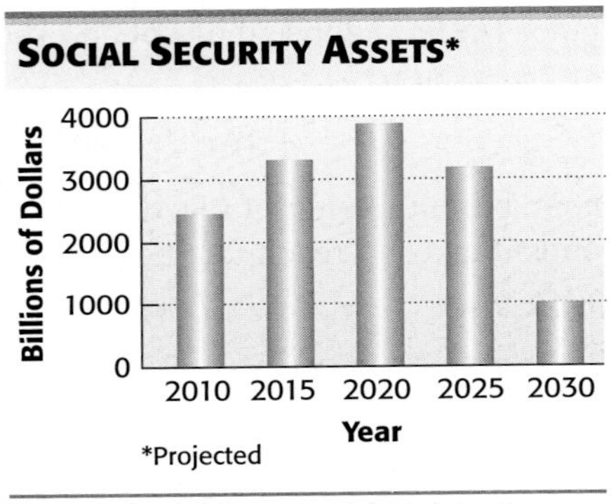

Source: Social Security Administration.

The graph suggests that a quadratic function would be a good fit to the data. The data are approximated by the function with

$$f(x) = -20.57x^2 + 758.9x - 3140.$$

In the model, $x = 10$ represents 2010, $x = 15$ represents 2015, and so on, and $f(x)$ is in billions of dollars.

(a) Explain why the coefficient of x^2 in the model is negative, based on the graph.

The coefficient of x^2 is negative because the parabola opens down.

(b) Algebraically determine the vertex of the graph, with coordinates to four significant digits.

(18.45, 3860)

(c) Interpret the answer to part (b) as it applies to the application.

In 2018 Social Security assets will reach their maximum value of $3860 billion.

36. The graph shows the performance of investment portfolios with different mixtures of U.S. and foreign investments for the period January 1, 1971, to December 31, 1996.

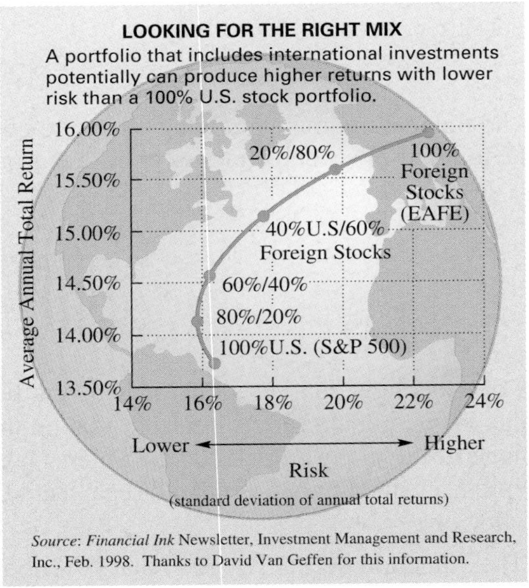

(a) Is this the graph of a function? Explain.

No. It fails the vertical line test.

(b) What investment mixture shown on the graph appears to represent the vertex? What relative amount of risk does this point represent? What return on investment does it provide?

80% U.S. and 20% foreign; about 15.8%; about 14.2%

(c) Which point on the graph represents the riskiest investment mixture? What return on investment does it provide?

the point corresponding to 100% foreign stocks; 16%

10.8 QUADRATIC AND RATIONAL INEQUALITIES

We discussed methods of solving linear inequalities in Chapter 3 and methods of solving quadratic equations in this chapter. Now we combine these ideas to solve *quadratic inequalities.*

OBJECTIVES

1. Solve quadratic inequalities.
2. Solve polynomial inequalities of degree 3 or more.
3. Solve rational inequalities.

Quadratic Inequality

A **quadratic inequality** can be written in the form

$$ax^2 + bx + c < 0 \quad \text{or} \quad ax^2 + bx + c > 0,$$

where a, b, and c are real numbers, with $a \neq 0$.

As before, $<$ and $>$ may be replaced with $\leq$ and $\geq$.

1 Solve quadratic inequalities. One method for solving a quadratic inequality is by graphing the related quadratic function.

Example 1 Solving Quadratic Inequalities by Graphing

Solve each inequality.

(a) $x^2 - x - 12 > 0$

To solve the inequality, we graph the related quadratic function defined by $f(x) = x^2 - x - 12$. We are particularly interested in the x-intercepts, which are found as in Section 10.7 by letting $f(x) = 0$ and solving the quadratic equation

$$x^2 - x - 12 = 0.$$

$$(x - 4)(x + 3) = 0 \qquad \text{Factor.}$$

$$x - 4 = 0 \quad \text{or} \quad x + 3 = 0 \qquad \text{Zero-factor property}$$

$$x = 4 \quad \text{or} \quad x = -3$$

Thus, the x-intercepts are (4, 0), and (−3, 0). The graph, which opens up since the coefficient of x^2 is positive, is shown in Figure 17(a). Notice from this graph that x-values less than −3 or greater than 4 result in y-values *greater than* 0. Therefore, the solution set of $x^2 - x - 12 > 0$, written in interval notation, is

$$(-\infty, -3) \cup (4, \infty).$$

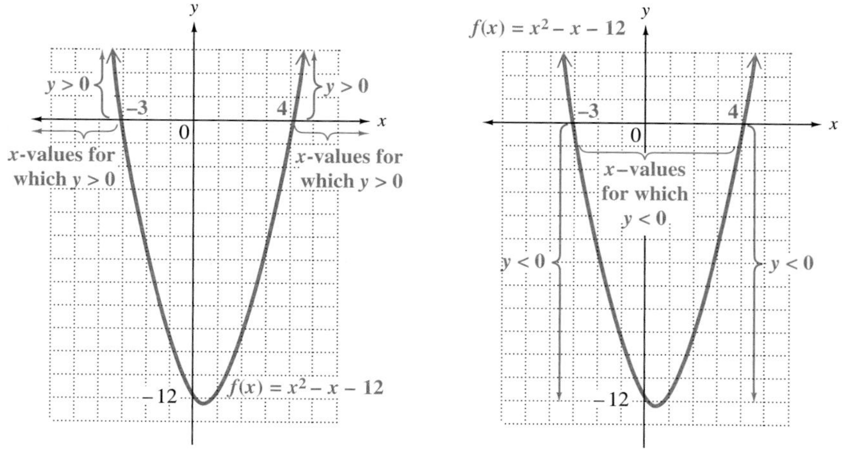

The graph is *above* the x-axis for $(-\infty, -3) \cup (4, \infty)$.

(a)

The graph is *below* the x-axis for $(-3, 4)$.

(b)

Figure 17

Continued on Next Page

(b) $x^2 - x - 12 < 0$

Here we want values of y that are *less than* 0. Referring to Figure 17(b) on the previous page, we notice from the graph that x-values between -3 and 4 result in y-values less than 0. Therefore, the solution set of the inequality $x^2 - x - 12 < 0$, written in interval notation, is $(-3, 4)$.

NOTE

If the inequalities in Example 1 had used $\geq$ and $\leq$, the solution sets would have included the x-values of the intercepts and been written in interval notation as $(-\infty, -3] \cup [4, \infty)$ for Example 1(a) and $[-3, 4]$ for Example 1(b).

Work Problems 1 and 2 at the Side.

In Example 1, we used graphing to divide the x-axis into intervals. Then using the graphs in Figure 17, we determined which x-values resulted in y-values that were either greater than or less than 0. Another method for solving a quadratic inequality uses these basic ideas without actually graphing the related quadratic function.

Example 2 Solving a Quadratic Inequality Using Test Numbers

Solve $x^2 - x - 12 > 0$.

First solve the quadratic equation $x^2 - x - 12 = 0$ by factoring, as in Example 1(a).

$$(x - 4)(x + 3) = 0$$

$$x - 4 = 0 \quad \text{or} \quad x + 3 = 0$$

$$x = 4 \quad \text{or} \quad x = -3$$

The numbers 4 and -3 divide the number line into the three intervals shown in Figure 18. Be careful to put the smaller number on the left. (Notice the similarity between Figure 18 and the x-axis with intercepts $(-3, 0)$ and $(4, 0)$ in Figure 17(a).)

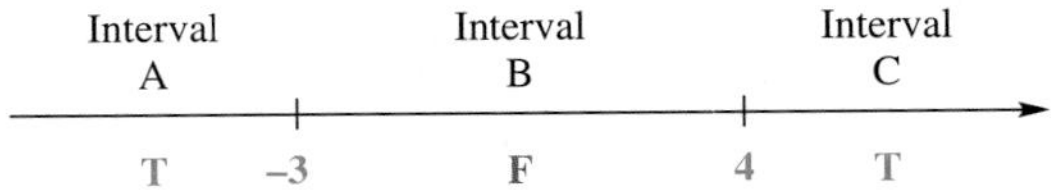

Figure 18

The numbers 4 and -3 are the only numbers that make the expression $x^2 - x - 12$ equal to 0. All other numbers make the expression either positive or negative. The sign of the expression can change from positive to negative or from negative to positive only at a number that makes it 0. Therefore, if one number in an interval satisfies the inequality, then all the numbers in that interval will satisfy the inequality. To see if the numbers in Interval A satisfy the inequality, choose any number from Interval A in Figure 18 (that is, any number less than -3). Substitute this number for x in the original inequality $x^2 - x - 12 > 0$. If the result is *true,* then all numbers in Interval A satisfy the inequality.

Continued on Next Page

1 Use the graph to solve each quadratic inequality.

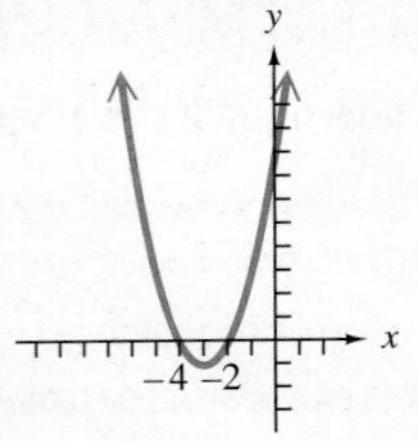

$f(x) = x^2 + 6x + 8$

(a) $x^2 + 6x + 8 > 0$

(b) $x^2 + 6x + 8 < 0$

2 Solve each quadratic inequality by graphing.

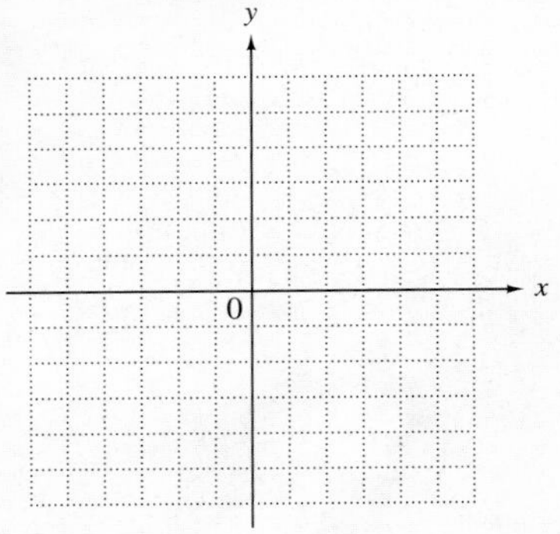

(a) $x^2 + 3x - 4 \geq 0$

(b) $x^2 + 3x - 4 \leq 0$

ANSWERS

1. **(a)** $(-\infty, -4) \cup (-2, \infty)$ **(b)** $(-4, -2)$
2. **(a)** $(-\infty, -4] \cup [1, \infty)$ **(b)** $[-4, 1]$

We choose -5 from Interval A. Substitute -5 for x.

$$x^2 - x - 12 > 0 \qquad \text{Original inequality}$$
$$(-5)^2 - (-5) - 12 > 0 \qquad ?$$
$$25 + 5 - 12 > 0 \qquad ?$$
$$18 > 0 \qquad \text{True}$$

Because -5 from Interval A satisfies the inequality, all numbers from Interval A are solutions.

Try 0 from Interval B. If $x = 0$, then

$$0^2 - 0 - 12 > 0 \qquad ?$$
$$-12 > 0. \qquad \text{False}$$

The numbers in Interval B are *not* solutions.

Work Problem 3 at the Side.

In Problem 3 at the side, the number 5 satisfies the inequality, so the numbers in Interval C are also solutions.

Based on these results (shown by the colored letters in Figure 18), the solution set includes the numbers in Intervals A and C, as shown on the graph in Figure 19. The solution set is written in interval notation as

$$(-\infty, -3) \cup (4, \infty).$$

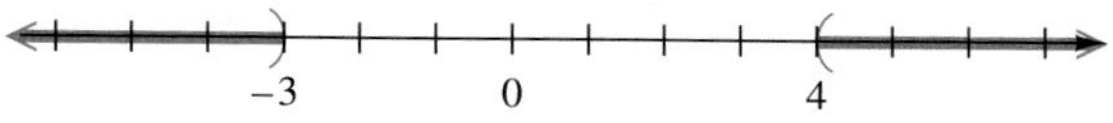

Figure 19

This agrees with the solution set we found by graphing the related quadratic function in Example 1(a).

In summary, a quadratic inequality is solved by following these steps.

Solving a Quadratic Inequality

Step 1 **Write the inequality as an equation and solve it.**

Step 2 **Use the solutions from Step 1 to determine intervals.** Graph the numbers found in Step 1 on a number line. These numbers divide the number line into intervals.

Step 3 **Find the intervals that satisfy the inequality.** Substitute a number from each interval into the original inequality to determine the intervals that satisfy the inequality. All numbers in those intervals are in the solution set. A graph of the solution set will usually look like one of these. (Square brackets might be used instead of parentheses.)

or

Step 4 **Consider the endpoints separately.** The numbers from Step 1 are included in the solution set if the inequality is $\leq$ or $\geq$; they are not included if it is $<$ or $>$.

Work Problem 4 at the Side.

3 Does the number 5 from Interval C satisfy $x^2 - x - 12 > 0$?

4 Solve each inequality, and graph the solution set.

(a) $x^2 + x - 6 > 0$

(b) $3m^2 - 13m - 10 \leq 0$

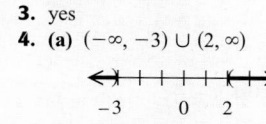

ANSWERS

3. yes

4. (a) $(-\infty, -3) \cup (2, \infty)$

(b) $\left[-\frac{2}{3}, 5\right]$

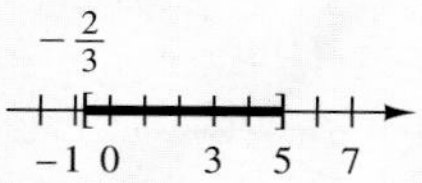

Special cases of quadratic inequalities may occur, as in the next example.

Example 3 **Solving Special Cases**

Solve $(2t - 3)^2 > -1$.

Because $(2t - 3)^2$ is never negative, it is always greater than -1. Thus, the solution is the set of all real numbers, $(-\infty, \infty)$. In the same way, there is no solution for $(2t - 3)^2 < -1$ and the solution set is $\emptyset$.

Work Problem 5 at the Side.

5 Solve each inequality.

(a) $(3k - 2)^2 > -2$

(b) $(5z + 3)^2 < -3$

2 Solve polynomial inequalities of degree 3 or more. Higher-degree polynomial inequalities that can be factored are solved in the same way as quadratic inequalities.

Example 4 **Solving a Third-Degree Polynomial Inequality**

Solve $(x - 1)(x + 2)(x - 4) \leq 0$.

This is a *cubic* (third-degree) inequality rather than a quadratic inequality, but it can be solved using the method shown in the box by extending the zero-factor property to more than two factors. Begin by setting the factored polynomial *equal* to 0 and solving the equation. (Step 1)

$$(x - 1)(x + 2)(x - 4) = 0$$

$$x - 1 = 0 \quad \text{or} \quad x + 2 = 0 \quad \text{or} \quad x - 4 = 0$$

$$x = 1 \quad \text{or} \quad x = -2 \quad \text{or} \quad x = 4$$

Locate the numbers -2, 1, and 4 on a number line, as in Figure 20, to determine the Intervals A, B, C, and D. (Step 2)

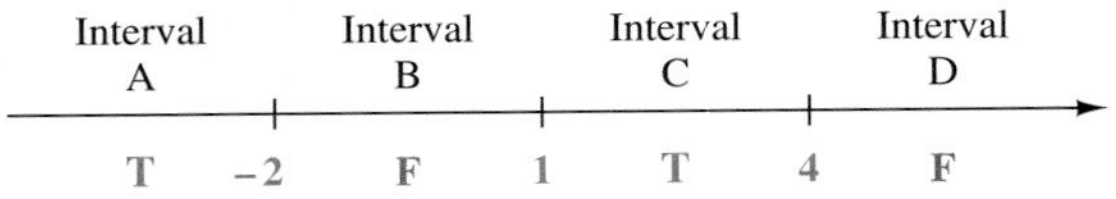

Figure 20

Substitute a number from each interval in the *original* inequality to determine which intervals satisfy the inequality. (Step 3) It is helpful to organize this information in a table.

Interval	Test Number	Test of Inequality	True or False?
A	-3	$-28 \leq 0$	T
B	0	$8 \leq 0$	F
C	2	$-8 \leq 0$	T
D	5	$28 \leq 0$	F

Verify the information given in the table and graphed in Figure 21. The numbers in Intervals A and C are in the solution set, which is written in interval notation as

$$(-\infty, -2] \cup [1, 4].$$

Notice that the three endpoints are included since the inequality symbol is $\leq$. (Step 4)

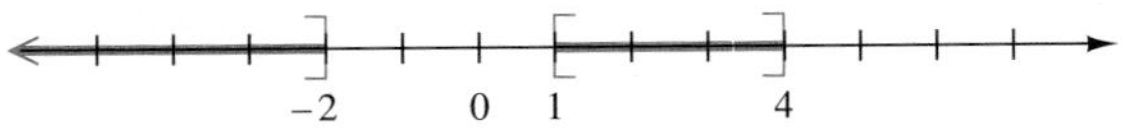

Figure 21

Work Problem 6 at the Side.

6 Solve each inequality, and graph the solution set.

(a) $(x - 3)(x + 2)(x + 1) > 0$

(b) $(k - 5)(k + 1)(k - 3) \leq 0$

ANSWERS

5. (a) $(-\infty, \infty)$ **(b)** $\emptyset$

6. (a) $(-2, -1) \cup (3, \infty)$

(b) $(-\infty, -1] \cup [3, 5]$

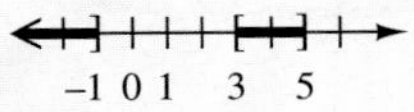

3 **Solve rational inequalities.** Inequalities that involve rational expressions, called **rational inequalities,** are solved similarly using the following steps.

Solving a Rational Inequality

Step 1 **Write the inequality** so that 0 is on one side and there is a single fraction on the other side.

Step 2 **Determine the numbers that make the numerator and denominator equal to 0.**

Step 3 **Divide a number line into intervals.** Use the numbers from Step 2.

Step 4 **Find the intervals that satisfy the inequality.** Test a number from each interval by substituting it into the *original* inequality.

Step 5 **Consider the endpoints separately.** Exclude any values that make the denominator 0.

Example 5 Solving a Rational Inequality

Solve $\dfrac{-1}{p-3} > 1$.

Write the inequality so that 0 is on one side. (Step 1)

$$\frac{-1}{p-3} - 1 > 0 \qquad \text{Subtract 1.}$$

$$\frac{-1}{p-3} - \frac{p-3}{p-3} > 0 \qquad \text{Use } p-3 \text{ as the common denominator.}$$

$$\frac{-1-p+3}{p-3} > 0 \qquad \text{Write the left side as a single fraction; Be careful with signs in the numerator.}$$

$$\frac{-p+2}{p-3} > 0 \qquad \text{Combine terms.}$$

The sign of the rational expression $\frac{-p+2}{p-3}$ will change from positive to negative or negative to positive only at those numbers that make the numerator or denominator 0. The number 2 makes the numerator 0, and 3 makes the denominator 0. (Step 2) These two numbers, 2 and 3, divide a number line into three intervals. See Figure 22. (Step 3)

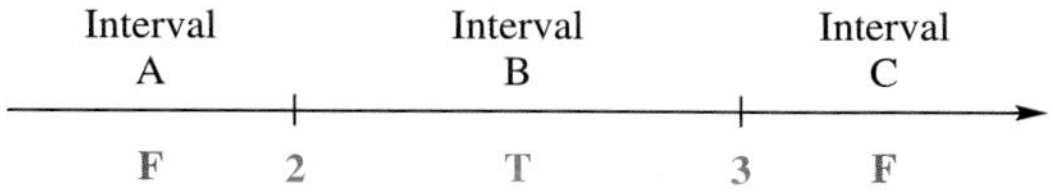

Figure 22

Testing a number from each interval in the *original* inequality, $\frac{-1}{p-3} > 1$, gives the results shown in the table. (Step 4)

Interval	Test Number	Test of Inequality	True or False?
A	0	$\frac{1}{3} > 1$	F
B	2.5	$2 > 1$	T
C	4	$-1 > 1$	F

Continued on Next Page

The solution set is the interval (2, 3). This interval does not include 3 since it would make the denominator of the original inequality 0; 2 is not included either since the inequality symbol is >. (Step 5) A graph of the solution set is given in Figure 23.

Figure 23

Work Problem 7 at the Side.

7 Solve each inequality, and graph the solution set.

(a) $\dfrac{2}{x-4} < 3$

(b) $\dfrac{5}{z+1} > 4$

Example 6 Solving a Rational Inequality

Solve $\dfrac{m-2}{m+2} \le 2$.

Write the inequality so that 0 is on one side. (Step 1)

$$\frac{m-2}{m+2} - 2 \le 0 \qquad \text{Subtract 2.}$$

$$\frac{m-2}{m+2} - \frac{2(m+2)}{m+2} \le 0 \qquad \text{Use } m+2 \text{ as the common denominator.}$$

$$\frac{m-2-2m-4}{m+2} \le 0 \qquad \text{Write as a single fraction.}$$

$$\frac{-m-6}{m+2} \le 0 \qquad \text{Combine terms.}$$

The number -6 makes the numerator 0, and -2 makes the denominator 0. (Step 2) These two numbers determine three intervals (Step 3). Test one number from each interval (Step 4) to see that the solution set is the interval

$$(-\infty, -6] \cup (-2, \infty).$$

The number -6 satisfies the original inequality, but -2 cannot be used as a solution since it makes the denominator 0 (Step 5). A graph of the solution set is shown in Figure 24.

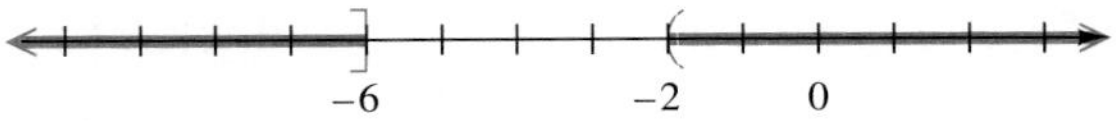

Figure 24

Work Problem 8 at the Side.

8 Solve $\dfrac{k+2}{k-1} \le 5$, and graph the solution set.

Answers

7. (a) $(-\infty, 4) \cup \left(\frac{14}{3}, \infty\right)$

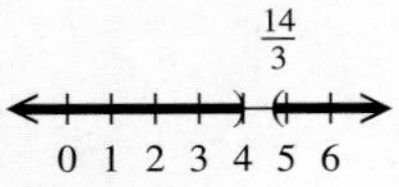

(b) $\left(-1, \frac{1}{4}\right)$

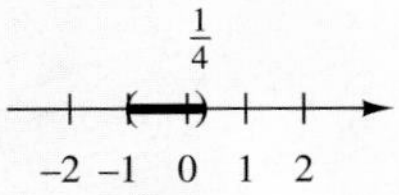

8. $(-\infty, 1) \cup \left[\frac{7}{4}, \infty\right)$

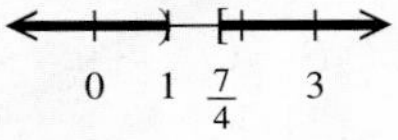

10.8 EXERCISES

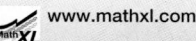

FOR EXTRA HELP Student's Solutions Manual | MyMathLab.com | InterAct Math Tutorial Software | AW Math Tutor Center | www.mathxl.com | Digital Video Tutor CD 9 Videotape 21

In Example 1, we determined the solution sets of the quadratic inequalities $x^2 - x - 12 > 0$ and $x^2 - x - 12 < 0$ by graphing $f(x) = x^2 - x - 12$. The x-intercepts of this graph indicated the solutions of the equation $x^2 - x - 12 = 0$. The x-values of the points on the graph that were **above** the x-axis formed the solution set of $x^2 - x - 12 > 0$, and the x-values of the points on the graph that were **below** the x-axis formed the solution set of $x^2 - x - 12 < 0$.

In Exercises 1–4, the graph of a quadratic function f is given. Use the graph to find the solution set of each equation or inequality. See Example 1.

1. **(a)** $x^2 - 4x + 3 = 0$
(b) $x^2 - 4x + 3 > 0$
(c) $x^2 - 4x + 3 < 0$

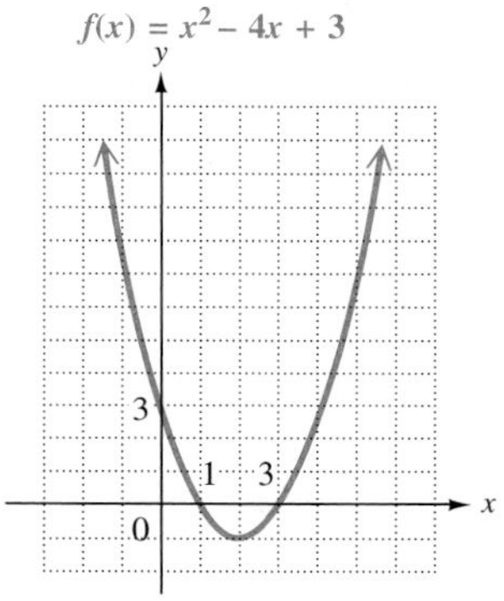

(a) $\{1, 3\}$ (b) $(-\infty, 1) \cup (3, \infty)$ (c) $(1, 3)$

2. **(a)** $3x^2 + 10x - 8 = 0$
(b) $3x^2 + 10x - 8 \geq 0$
(c) $3x^2 + 10x - 8 < 0$

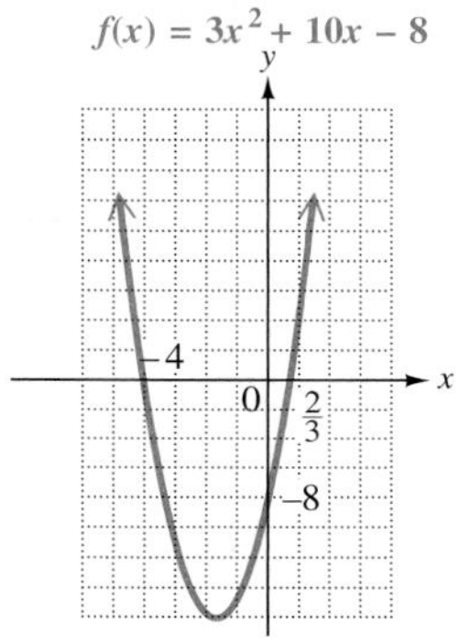

(a) $\left\{-4, \frac{2}{3}\right\}$ (b) $(-\infty, -4] \cup \left[\frac{2}{3}, \infty\right)$ (c) $\left(-4, \frac{2}{3}\right)$

3. **(a)** $-2x^2 - x + 15 = 0$
(b) $-2x^2 - x + 15 \geq 0$
(c) $-2x^2 - x + 15 \leq 0$

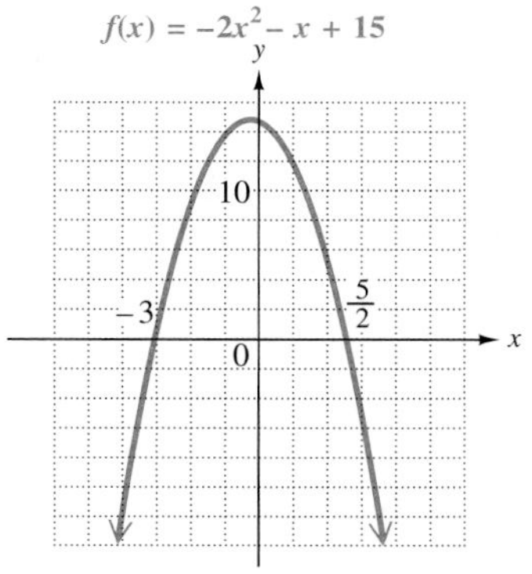

(a) $\left\{-3, \frac{5}{2}\right\}$ (b) $\left[-3, \frac{5}{2}\right]$ (c) $(-\infty, -3] \cup \left[\frac{5}{2}, \infty\right)$

4. **(a)** $-x^2 + 3x + 10 = 0$
(b) $-x^2 + 3x + 10 \geq 0$
(c) $-x^2 + 3x + 10 \leq 0$

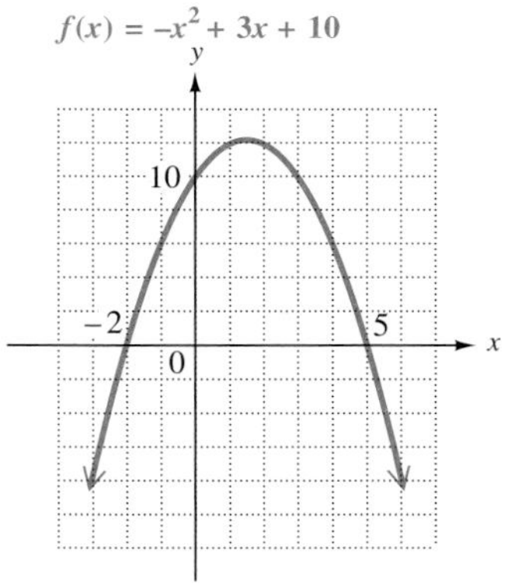

(a) $\{-2, 5\}$ (b) $[-2, 5]$ (c) $(-\infty, -2] \cup [5, \infty)$

5. Explain how you determine whether to include or exclude endpoints when solving a quadratic or higher-degree inequality.

Include the endpoints if the symbol is $\geq$ or $\leq$. Exclude the endpoints if the symbol is $>$ or $<$.

6. The solution set of the inequality $x^2 + x - 12 < 0$ is the interval $(-4, 3)$. Without actually performing any work, give the solution set of the inequality $x^2 + x - 12 \geq 0$.

$(-\infty, -4] \cup [3, \infty)$

Solve each inequality, and graph the solution set. See Example 2.

7. $(x + 1)(x - 5) > 0$

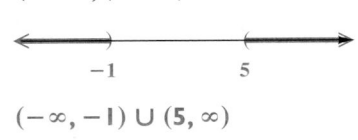

$(-\infty, -1) \cup (5, \infty)$

8. $(m + 6)(m - 2) > 0$

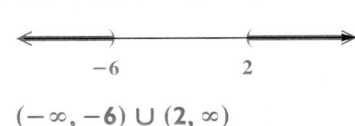

$(-\infty, -6) \cup (2, \infty)$

9. $(r + 4)(r - 6) < 0$

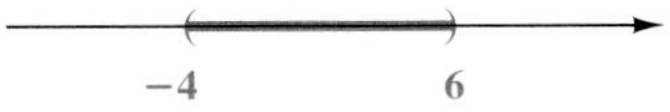

$(-4, 6)$

10. $(x + 4)(x - 8) < 0$

$(-4, 8)$

11. $x^2 - 4x + 3 \geq 0$

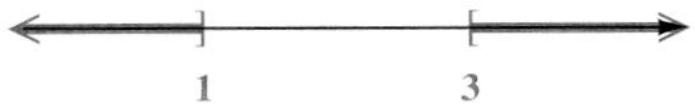

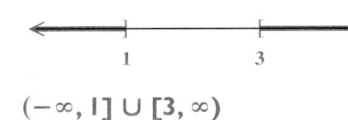

$(-\infty, 1] \cup [3, \infty)$

12. $m^2 - 3m - 10 \geq 0$

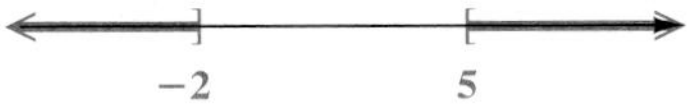

$(-\infty, -2] \cup [5, \infty)$

13. $10t^2 + 9t \geq 9$

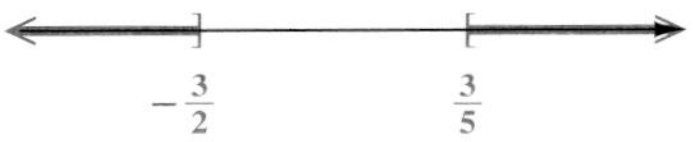

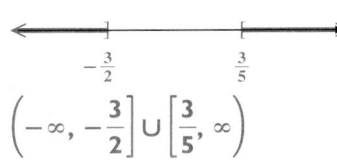

$\left(-\infty, -\frac{3}{2}\right] \cup \left[\frac{3}{5}, \infty\right)$

14. $3r^2 + 10r \geq 8$

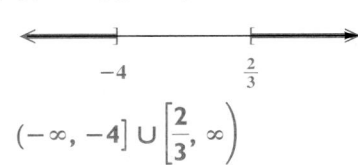

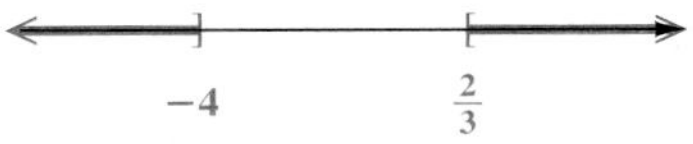

$(-\infty, -4] \cup \left[\frac{2}{3}, \infty\right)$

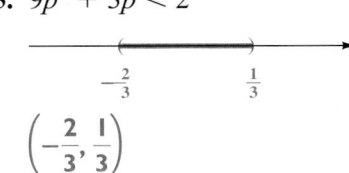

15. $9p^2 + 3p < 2$

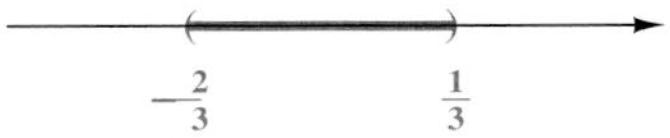

$\left(-\frac{2}{3}, \frac{1}{3}\right)$

16. $2x^2 + x < 15$

$\left(-3, \frac{5}{2}\right)$

17. $6x^2 + x \geq 1$

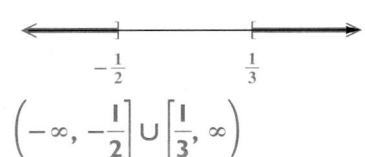

$\left(-\infty, -\frac{1}{2}\right] \cup \left[\frac{1}{3}, \infty\right)$

18. $4m^2 + 7m \geq -3$

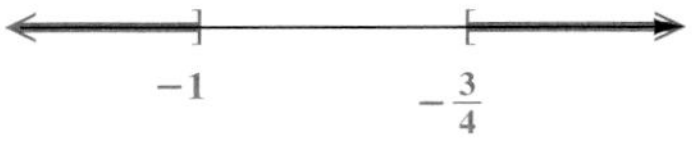

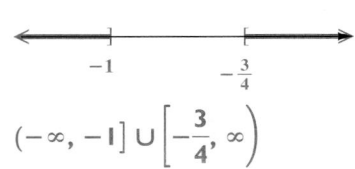

$(-\infty, -1] \cup \left[-\frac{3}{4}, \infty\right)$

19. $x^2 - 6x + 6 \geq 0$
(*Hint:* Use the quadratic formula.)

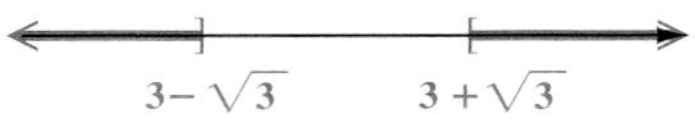

$(-\infty, 3 - \sqrt{3}] \cup [3 + \sqrt{3}, \infty)$

20. $3k^2 - 6k + 2 \leq 0$
(*Hint:* Use the quadratic formula.)

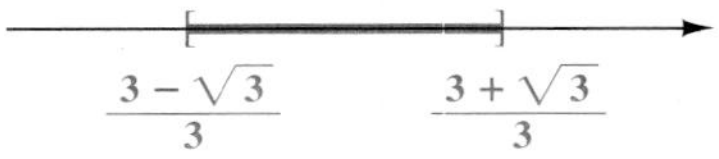

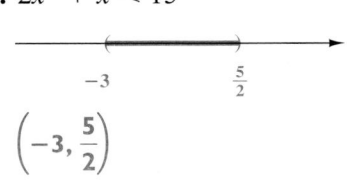

$\left[\frac{3 - \sqrt{3}}{3}, \frac{3 + \sqrt{3}}{3}\right]$

Solve each inequality. See Example 3.

21. $(4 - 3x)^2 \geq -2$

$(-\infty, \infty)$

22. $(6p + 7)^2 \geq -1$

$(-\infty, \infty)$

23. $(3x + 5)^2 \leq -4$

$\emptyset$

24. $(8t + 5)^2 \leq -5$

$\emptyset$

Solve each inequality, and graph the solution set. See Example 4.

25. $(p - 1)(p - 2)(p - 4) < 0$

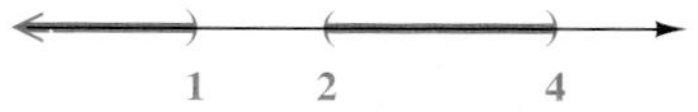

$(-\infty, 1) \cup (2, 4)$

26. $(2r + 1)(3r - 2)(4r + 7) < 0$

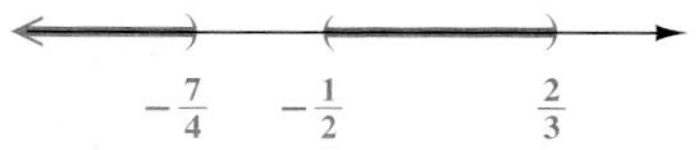

$\left(-\infty, -\frac{7}{4}\right) \cup \left(-\frac{1}{2}, \frac{2}{3}\right)$

27. $(x - 4)(2x + 3)(3x - 1) \geq 0$

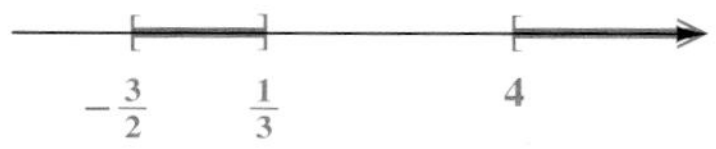

$\left[-\frac{3}{2}, \frac{1}{3}\right] \cup [4, \infty)$

28. $(z + 2)(4z - 3)(2z + 7) \geq 0$

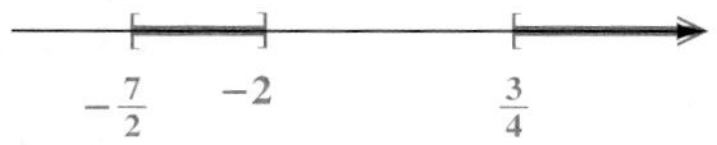

$\left[-\frac{7}{2}, -2\right] \cup \left[\frac{3}{4}, \infty\right)$

Solve each inequality, and graph the solution set. See Examples 5 and 6.

29. $\dfrac{x - 1}{x - 4} > 0$

$(-\infty, 1) \cup (4, \infty)$

30. $\dfrac{x + 1}{x - 5} > 0$

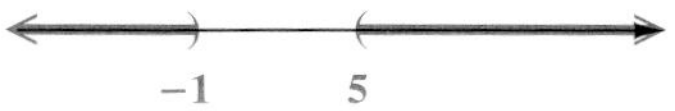

$(-\infty, -1) \cup (5, \infty)$

31. $\dfrac{2n + 3}{n - 5} \leq 0$

$\left[-\frac{3}{2}, 5\right)$

32. $\dfrac{3t + 7}{t - 3} \leq 0$

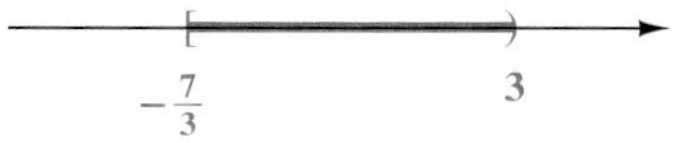

$\left[-\frac{7}{3}, 3\right)$

33. $\dfrac{8}{x - 2} \geq 2$

$(2, 6]$

34. $\dfrac{20}{x - 1} \geq 1$

$(1, 21]$

35. $\dfrac{3}{2t-1} < 2$

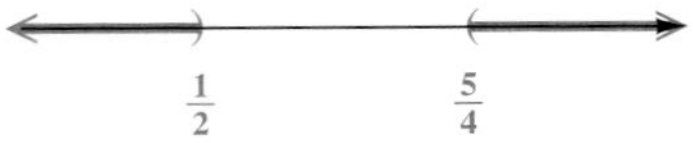

$\left(-\infty, \frac{1}{2}\right) \cup \left(\frac{5}{4}, \infty\right)$

36. $\dfrac{6}{m-1} < 1$

$(-\infty, 1) \cup (7, \infty)$

37. $\dfrac{w}{w+2} \geq 2$

$[-4, -2)$

38. $\dfrac{m}{m+5} \geq 2$

$[-10, -5)$

39. $\dfrac{4k}{2k-1} < k$

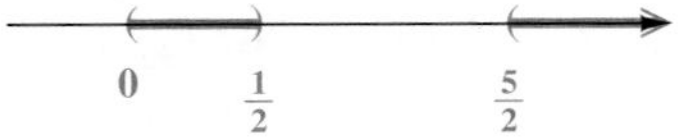

$\left(0, \frac{1}{2}\right) \cup \left(\frac{5}{2}, \infty\right)$

40. $\dfrac{r}{r+2} < 2r$

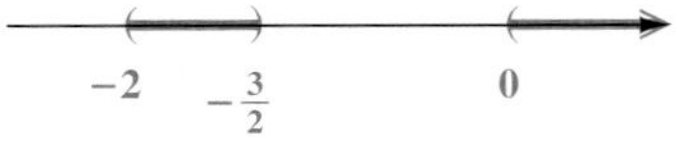

$\left(-2, -\frac{3}{2}\right) \cup (0, \infty)$

Relating Concepts (Exercises 41–44) For Individual or Group Work

A rock is projected vertically upward from the ground. Its distance s in feet above the ground after t seconds is given by the quadratic function defined by

$$s(t) = -16t^2 + 256t.$$

Work Exercises 41–44 in order, *to see how quadratic equations and inequalities are related.*

41. At what times will the rock be 624 ft above the ground? (*Hint:* Let $s(t) = 624$ and solve the quadratic *equation.*)

3 sec and 13 sec

42. At what times will the rock be more than 624 ft above the ground? (*Hint:* Set $s(t) > 624$ and solve the quadratic *inequality.*)

between 3 sec and 13 sec

43. At what times will the rock be at ground level? (*Hint:* Let $s(t) = 0$ and solve the quadratic *equation.*)

at 0 sec (the time when it is initially projected) and at 16 sec (the time when it hits the ground)

44. At what times will the rock be less than 624 ft above the ground? (*Hint:* Set $s(t) < 624$, solve the quadratic *inequality,* and observe the solutions in Exercises 42 and 43 to determine the smallest and largest possible values of t.)

between 0 and 3 sec and between 13 and 16 sec

Chapter 10

SUMMARY

KEY TERMS

10.1	**quadratic equation**	A quadratic equation is an equation that can be written in the form $ax^2 + bx + c = 0$, where a, b, and c are real numbers, with $a \neq 0$. This form is called standard form.
10.3	**quadratic formula**	The quadratic formula is a formula for solving quadratic equations.
	discriminant	The discriminant is the expression under the radical in the quadratic formula.
10.4	**quadratic in form**	A nonquadratic equation that can be written as a quadratic equation is called quadratic in form.
10.6	**parabola**	The graph of a quadratic function is a parabola.
	vertex	The point on a parabola that has the smallest y-value (if the parabola opens up) or the largest y-value (if the parabola opens down) is called the vertex of the parabola.
	axis	The vertical or horizontal line through the vertex of a parabola is its axis.
	quadratic function	A function defined by $f(x) = ax^2 + bx + c$, for real numbers a, b, and c, with $a \neq 0$, is a quadratic function.
10.8	**quadratic inequality**	A quadratic inequality is an inequality that can be written in the form $ax^2 + bx + c < 0$ or $ax^2 + bx + c > 0$, or with $\leq$ or $\geq$, where a, b, and c are real numbers, with $a \neq 0$.
	rational inequality	An inequality that involves a rational expression is a rational inequality.

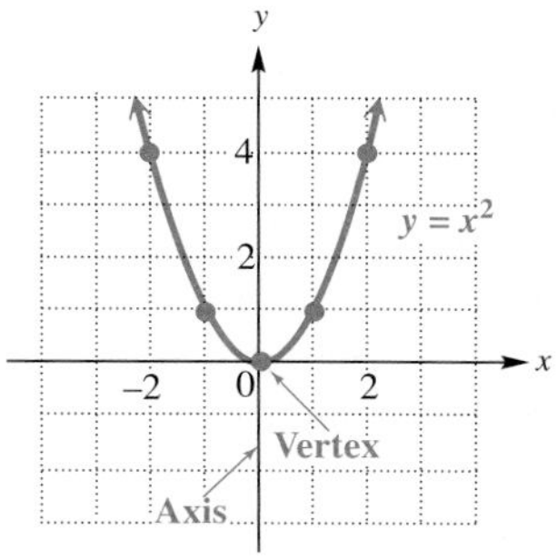

TEST YOUR WORD POWER

See how well you have learned the vocabulary in this chapter. Answers follow the Quick Review.

1. The **quadratic formula** is
   (a) a formula to find the number of solutions of a quadratic equation
   (b) a formula to find the type of solutions of a quadratic equation
   (c) the standard form of a quadratic equation
   (d) a general formula for solving any quadratic equation.

2. A **quadratic function** is a function that can be written in the form
   (a) $f(x) = mx + b$ for real numbers m and b
   (b) $f(x) = \frac{P(x)}{Q(x)}$, where $Q(x) \neq 0$
   (c) $f(x) = ax^2 + bx + c$ for real numbers a, b, and c $(a \neq 0)$
   (d) $f(x) = \sqrt{x}$ for $x \geq 0$.

3. A **parabola** is the graph of
   (a) any equation in two variables
   (b) a linear equation
   (c) an equation of degree 3
   (d) a quadratic equation in 2 variables.

4. The **vertex** of a parabola is
   (a) the point where the graph intersects the y-axis
   (b) the point where the graph intersects the x-axis
   (c) the lowest point on a parabola that opens up or the highest point on a parabola that opens down
   (d) the origin.

5. The **axis** of a parabola is
   (a) either the x-axis or the y-axis
   (b) the vertical line (of a vertical parabola) or the horizontal line (of a horizontal parabola) through the vertex
   (c) the lowest or highest point on the graph of a parabola
   (d) a line through the origin.

6. A parabola is **symmetric about its axis** since
   (a) its graph is near the axis
   (b) its graph is identical on each side of the axis
   (c) its graph looks different on each side of the axis
   (d) its graph intersects the axis.

Quick Review

Concepts	*Examples*
***10.1** Solving Quadratic Equations by the Square Root Property* **Square Root Property** If x and k are complex numbers and $x^2 = k$, then $x = \sqrt{k}$ or $x = -\sqrt{k}$.	Solve $(x-1)^2 = 8$. $x - 1 = \sqrt{8}$ or $x - 1 = -\sqrt{8}$ $x = 1 + 2\sqrt{2}$ or $x = 1 - 2\sqrt{2}$ Solution set: $\{1 + 2\sqrt{2}, 1 - 2\sqrt{2}\}$
***10.2** Solving Quadratic Equations by Completing the Square* **Completing the Square** To solve $ax^2 + bx + c = 0$ $(a \neq 0)$: *Step 1* If $a \neq 1$, divide each side by a. *Step 2* Write the equation with the variable terms on one side and the constant on the other. *Step 3* Take half the coefficient of x and square it. Add the square to each side. Factor the perfect square trinomial, and write it as the square of a binomial. Simplify the other side. *Step 4* Use the square root property to complete the solution.	Solve $2x^2 - 4x - 18 = 0$. $x^2 - 2x - 9 = 0$ Divide by 2. $x^2 - 2x = 9$ Add 9. $\left[\frac{1}{2}(-2)\right]^2 = (-1)^2 = 1$ $x^2 - 2x + 1 = 9 + 1$ $(x-1)^2 = 10$ $x - 1 = \sqrt{10}$ or $x - 1 = -\sqrt{10}$ $x = 1 + \sqrt{10}$ or $x = 1 - \sqrt{10}$ Solution set: $\{1 + \sqrt{10}, 1 - \sqrt{10}\}$
***10.3** Solving Quadratic Equations by the Quadratic Formula* **Quadratic Formula** The solutions of $ax^2 + bx + c = 0$ $(a \neq 0)$ are given by $x = \frac{-b \pm \sqrt{b^2 - 4ac}}{2a}$.	Solve $3x^2 + 5x + 2 = 0$. $x = \frac{-5 \pm \sqrt{5^2 - 4(3)(2)}}{2(3)} = \frac{-5 \pm 1}{6}$ $x = -1$ or $x = -\frac{2}{3}$ Solution set: $\{-1, -\frac{2}{3}\}$
The Discriminant If a, b, and c are integers, then the discriminant, $b^2 - 4ac$, of $ax^2 + bx + c = 0$ determines the number and type of solutions as follows.	For $x^2 + 3x - 10 = 0$, the discriminant is $3^2 - 4(1)(-10) = 49$. Two rational solutions For $4x^2 + x + 1 = 0$, the discriminant is $1^2 - 4(4)(1) = -15$. Two imaginary solutions

Discriminant	Number and Type of Solutions
Positive, the square of an integer	Two rational solutions
Positive, not the square of an integer	Two irrational solutions
Zero	One rational solution
Negative	Two imaginary solutions

Concepts	*Examples*

10.4 Equations Quadratic in Form

A nonquadratic equation that can be written in the form

$$au^2 + bu + c = 0,$$

for $a \neq 0$ and an algebraic expression u, is called quadratic in form. Substitute u for the expression, solve for u, and then solve for the variable in the expression.

Solve $3(x + 5)^2 + 7(x + 5) + 2 = 0$.

$$3u^2 + 7u + 2 = 0 \qquad \text{Let } u = x + 5.$$
$$(3u + 1)(u + 2) = 0$$
$$u = -\frac{1}{3} \quad \text{or} \quad u = -2$$
$$x + 5 = -\frac{1}{3} \quad \text{or} \quad x + 5 = -2 \qquad x + 5 = u$$
$$x = -\frac{16}{3} \quad \text{or} \quad x = -7$$

Solution set: $\{-7, -\frac{16}{3}\}$

10.5 Formulas and Further Applications

To solve a formula for a squared variable, proceed as follows.

(a) The variable appears only to the second power. Isolate the squared variable on one side of the equation, then use the square root property.

Solve $A = \dfrac{2mp}{r^2}$ for r.

$$r^2A = 2mp \qquad \text{Multiply by } r^2.$$
$$r^2 = \frac{2mp}{A} \qquad \text{Divide by } A.$$
$$r = \pm\sqrt{\frac{2mp}{A}} \qquad \text{Square root property}$$
$$r = \frac{\pm\sqrt{2mpA}}{A} \qquad \text{Rationalize the denominator.}$$

(b) The variable appears to the first and second powers. Write the equation in standard form, then use the quadratic formula.

Solve $m^2 + rm = t$ for m.

$$m^2 + rm - t = 0 \qquad \text{Standard form}$$
$$m = \frac{-r \pm \sqrt{r^2 - 4(1)(-t)}}{2(1)} \qquad a = 1, b = r, c = -t$$
$$m = \frac{-r \pm \sqrt{r^2 + 4t}}{2}$$

10.6 Graphs of Quadratic Functions

1. The graph of the quadratic function with $F(x) = a(x - h)^2 + k$, $a \neq 0$, is a parabola with vertex at (h, k) and the vertical line $x = h$ as axis.
2. The graph opens up if a is positive and down if a is negative.
3. The graph is wider than the graph of $f(x) = x^2$ if $0 < |a| < 1$ and narrower if $|a| > 1$.

Graph $f(x) = -(x + 3)^2 + 1$.

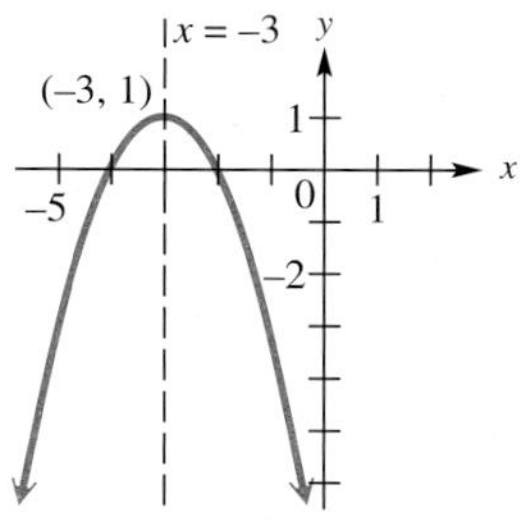

The graph opens down since $a < 0$. It is shifted 3 units left and 1 unit up, so the vertex is $(-3, 1)$, with axis $x = -3$.

10.7 More about Parabolas; Applications

The vertex of the graph of $f(x) = ax^2 + bx + c$, $a \neq 0$, may be found by completing the square. The vertex has coordinates

$$\left(\frac{-b}{2a}, f\left(\frac{-b}{2a}\right)\right).$$

Graphing a Quadratic Function

Step 1 Determine whether the graph opens up or down.
Step 2 Find the vertex.
Step 3 Find the x-intercepts (if any). Find the y-intercept.
Step 4 Find and plot additional points as needed.

Graph $f(x) = x^2 + 4x + 3$.

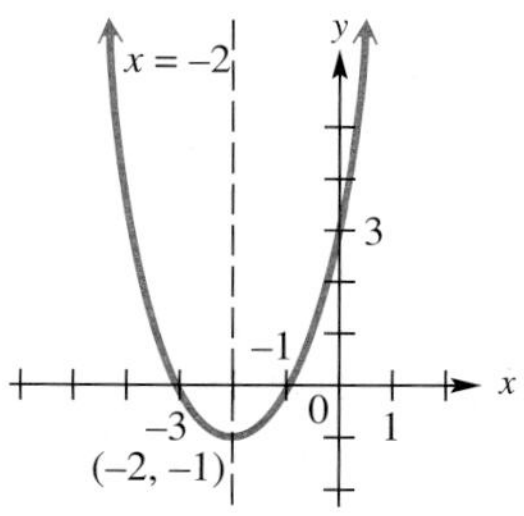

The graph opens up since $a > 0$. The vertex is $(-2, -1)$. The solutions of $x^2 + 4x + 3 = 0$ are -1 and -3, so the x-intercepts are $(-1, 0)$ and $(-3, 0)$. Since $f(0) = 3$, the y-intercept is $(0, 3)$.

Concepts | *Examples*

10.7 More about Parabolas; Applications (continued)

The graph of $x = ay^2 + by + c$ is a horizontal parabola, opening to the right if $a > 0$ or to the left if $a < 0$. Horizontal parabolas do not represent functions.

Graph $x = 2y^2 + 6y + 5$.

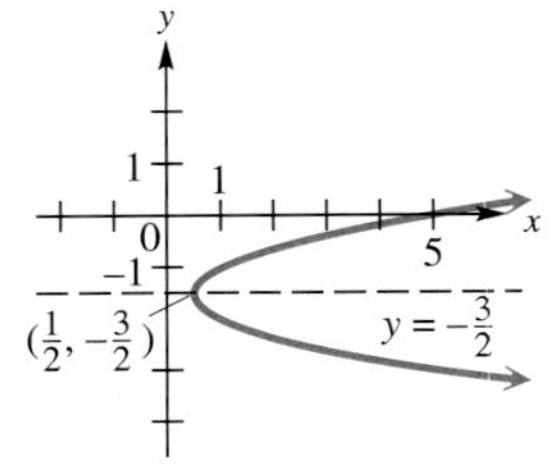

10.8 Quadratic and Rational Inequalities

Solving a Quadratic (or Higher-Degree Polynomial) Inequality

Step 1 Write the inequality as an equation and solve.

Solve $2x^2 + 5x + 2 < 0$.

$$2x^2 + 5x + 2 = 0$$

$$x = -\frac{1}{2} \quad \text{or} \quad x = -2$$

Step 2 Use the numbers found in Step 1 to divide a number line into intervals.

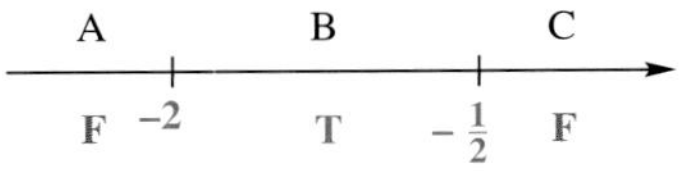

Step 3 Substitute a number from each interval into the original inequality to determine the intervals that belong in the solution set.

$x = -3$ makes the original inequality false; $x = -1$ makes it true; $x = 0$ makes it false.

Step 4 Consider the endpoints separately.

Solution set: $(-2, -\frac{1}{2})$

Solving a Rational Inequality

Solve $\frac{x}{x+2} \geq 4$.

Step 1 Write the inequality so that 0 is on one side and there is a single fraction on the other side.

$$\frac{x}{x+2} - 4 \geq 0$$

$$\frac{x}{x+2} - \frac{4(x+2)}{x+2} \geq 0$$

$$\frac{-3x - 8}{x+2} \geq 0$$

Step 2 Determine the numbers that make the numerator and denominator 0.

$-\frac{8}{3}$ makes the numerator 0; -2 makes the denominator 0.

Step 3 Use the numbers from Step 2 to divide a number line into intervals.

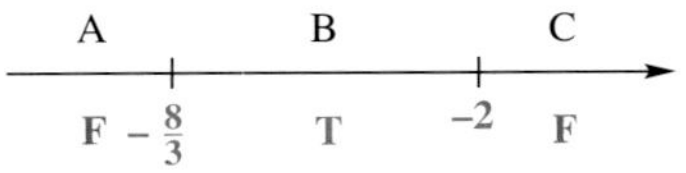

Step 4 Substitute a number from each interval into the original inequality to determine the intervals that belong in the solution set.

-4 makes the original inequality false; $-\frac{7}{3}$ makes it true; 0 makes it false.

Step 5 Consider the endpoints separately.

The solution set is $[-\frac{8}{3}, -2)$, since -2 makes the denominator 0.

ANSWERS TO TEST YOUR WORD POWER

1. (d) *Example:* The solutions of $ax^2 + bx + c = 0$ $(a \neq 0)$ are given by $x = \frac{-b \pm \sqrt{b^2 - 4ac}}{2a}$. **2. (c)** *Examples:* $f(x) = x^2 - 2$, $f(x) = (x + 4)^2 + 1$, $f(x) = x^2 - 4x + 5$ **3. (d)** *Examples:* See the figures in the Quick Review for Sections 10.6 and 10.7. **4. (c)** *Example:* The graph of $y = (x + 3)^2$ has vertex $(-3, 0)$, which is the lowest point on the graph. **5. (b)** *Example:* The axis of $y = (x + 3)^2$ is the vertical line $x = -3$. **6. (b)** *Example:* Since the graph of $y = (x + 3)^2$ is symmetric about its axis $x = -3$, the points $(-2, 1)$ and $(-4, 1)$ are on the graph.

Chapter 10 Review Exercises

*Exercises marked * have imaginary number solutions.*

[10.1] *Solve each equation by using the square root property.*

1. $t^2 = 121$

$\{11, -11\}$

2. $p^2 = 3$

$\{\sqrt{3}, -\sqrt{3}\}$

3. $(r - 3)^2 = 10$

$\{3 + \sqrt{10}, 3 - \sqrt{10}\}$

4. $(2x + 5)^2 = 100$

$\left\{-\frac{15}{2}, \frac{5}{2}\right\}$

5. $(2p + 1)^2 = 14$

$\left\{\frac{-1 + \sqrt{14}}{2}, \frac{-1 - \sqrt{14}}{2}\right\}$

***6.** $(3k - 2)^2 = -25$

$\left\{\frac{2 + 5i}{3}, \frac{2 - 5i}{3}\right\}$

7. A student gave the following "solution" to the equation $x^2 = 12$.

$x^2 = 12$

$x = \sqrt{12}$ Square root property

$x = 2\sqrt{3}$

What is wrong with this solution?

By the square root property, $x = \sqrt{12}$ or $x = -\sqrt{12}$.

8. Navy Pier Center in Chicago, Illinois, features a 150-ft tall Ferris wheel. Use Galileo's formula $d = 16t^2$ to find how long it would take a wallet dropped from the top of the Ferris wheel to fall to the ground. Round your answer to the nearest tenth of a second. (*Source: Microsoft Encarta Encyclopedia 2000.*) **3.1 sec**

[10.2] *Solve each equation by completing the square.*

9. $m^2 + 6m + 5 = 0$

$\{-5, -1\}$

10. $p^2 + 4p = 7$

$\{-2 + \sqrt{11}, -2 - \sqrt{11}\}$

11. $-x^2 + 5 = 2x$

$\{-1 + \sqrt{6}, -1 - \sqrt{6}\}$

12. $2x^2 - 3 = -8x$

$\left\{\frac{-4 + \sqrt{22}}{2}, \frac{-4 - \sqrt{22}}{2}\right\}$

13. $4(x^2 + 7x) + 29 = -20$

$\left\{-\frac{7}{2}\right\}$

***14.** $(4x + 1)(x - 1) = -7$

$\left\{\frac{3 + i\sqrt{87}}{8}, \frac{3 - i\sqrt{87}}{8}\right\}$

[10.3] *Solve each equation using the quadratic formula.*

15. $2x^2 + x - 21 = 0$

$\left\{-\frac{7}{2}, 3\right\}$

16. $k^2 + 5k = 7$

$\left\{\frac{-5 + \sqrt{53}}{2}, \frac{-5 - \sqrt{53}}{2}\right\}$

17. $(t + 3)(t - 4) = -2$

$\left\{\frac{1 + \sqrt{41}}{2}, \frac{1 - \sqrt{41}}{2}\right\}$

*18. $2x^2 + 3x + 4 = 0$

$\left\{\frac{-3 + i\sqrt{23}}{4}, \frac{-3 - i\sqrt{23}}{4}\right\}$

*19. $3p^2 = 2(2p - 1)$

$\left\{\frac{2 + i\sqrt{2}}{3}, \frac{2 - i\sqrt{2}}{3}\right\}$

20. $m(2m - 7) = 3m^2 + 3$

$\left\{\frac{-7 + \sqrt{37}}{2}, \frac{-7 - \sqrt{37}}{2}\right\}$

Use the discriminant to predict whether the solutions to each equation are
A. *two rational numbers;* **B.** *one rational number;*
C. *two irrational numbers;* **D.** *two imaginary numbers.*

21. $x^2 + 5x + 2 = 0$

C

22. $4t^2 = 3 - 4t$

A

23. $4x^2 = 6x - 8$

D

24. $9z^2 + 30z + 25 = 0$

B

[10.4] *Solve each equation.*

25. $\frac{15}{x} = 2x - 1$

$\left\{-\frac{5}{2}, 3\right\}$

26. $\frac{1}{n} + \frac{2}{n + 1} = 2$

$\left\{-\frac{1}{2}, 1\right\}$

27. $-2r = \sqrt{\frac{48 - 20r}{2}}$

$\{-4\}$

28. $8(3x + 5)^2 + 2(3x + 5) - 1 = 0$

$\left\{-\frac{11}{6}, -\frac{19}{12}\right\}$

29. $2x^{2/3} - x^{1/3} - 28 = 0$

$\left\{-\frac{343}{8}, 64\right\}$

30. $p^4 - 5p^2 + 4 = 0$

$\{-2, -1, 1, 2\}$

Solve each problem. Round answers to the nearest tenth, as necessary.

31. Phong paddled his canoe 20 mi upstream, then paddled back. If the speed of the current was 3 mph and the total trip took 7 hr, what was Phong's speed?

7 mph

32. Maureen O'Connor drove 8 mi to pick up her friend Laurie, and then drove 11 mi to a mall at a speed 15 mph faster. If Maureen's total travel time was 24 min, what was her speed on the trip to pick up Laurie?

40 mph

33. An old machine processes a batch of checks in 1 hr more time than a new one. How long would it take the old machine to process a batch of checks that the two machines together process in 2 hr?

4.6 hr

34. Greg Tobin can process a stack of invoices 1 hr faster than Carter Fenton can. Working together, they take 1.5 hr. How long would it take each person working alone?

Greg: 2.6 hr; Carter: 3.6 hr

[10.5] *Solve each formula for the indicated variable. (Give answers with $\pm$.)*

35. $k = \frac{rF}{wv^2}$ for v

$v = \frac{\pm\sqrt{rFkw}}{kw}$

36. $p = \sqrt{\frac{yz}{6}}$ for y

$y = \frac{6p^2}{z}$

37. $mt^2 = 3mt + 6$ for t

$t = \frac{3m \pm \sqrt{9m^2 + 24m}}{2m}$

Solve each problem. Round answers to the nearest tenth, as necessary.

38. A large machine requires a part in the shape of a right triangle with a hypotenuse 9 ft less than twice the length of the longer leg. The shorter leg must be $\frac{3}{4}$ the length of the longer leg. Find the lengths of the three sides of the part.

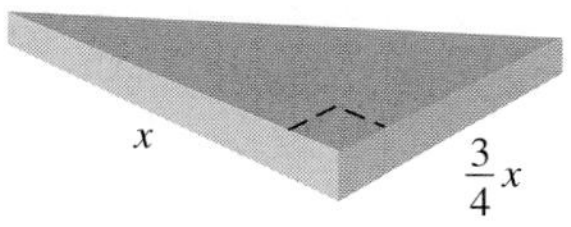

9 ft, 12 ft, 15 ft

39. A square has an area of 256 cm^2. If the same amount is removed from one dimension and added to the other, the resulting rectangle has an area 16 cm^2 less. Find the dimensions of the rectangle.

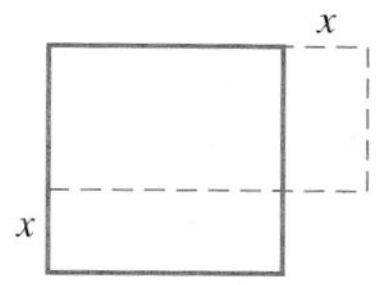

12 cm by 20 cm

40. Nancy wants to buy a mat for a photograph that measures 14 in. by 20 in. She wants to have an even border around the picture when it is mounted on the mat. If the area of the mat she chooses is 352 in.^{2}, how wide will the border be?

1 in.

41. A search light moves horizontally back and forth along a wall with the distance of the light from a starting point at t minutes given by the quadratic function defined by

$$f(t) = 100t^2 - 300t.$$

How long will it take before the light returns to the starting point?

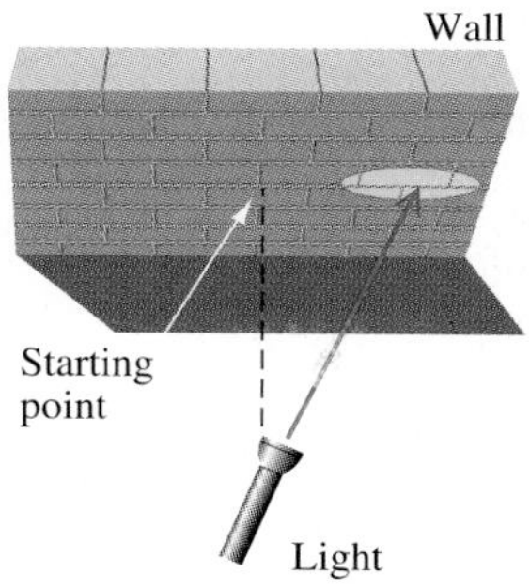

3 min

42. The Mart Hotel in Dallas, Texas, is 400 ft high. Suppose that a ball is projected upward from the top of the Mart, and its position in feet above the ground is given by the quadratic function defined by

$$f(t) = -16t^2 + 45t + 400,$$

where t is the number of seconds elapsed. How long will it take for the ball to reach a height of 200 ft above the ground? (*Source: World Almanac and Book of Facts,* 2000.)

5.2 sec

43. The Toronto Dominion Center in Winnipeg, Manitoba, is 407 ft high. Suppose that a ball is projected upward from the top of the Center, and its position in feet above the ground is given by the quadratic function defined by

$$s(t) = -16t^2 + 75t + 407,$$

where t is the number of seconds elapsed. How long will it take for the ball to reach a height of 450 ft above the ground? (*Source: World Almanac and Book of Facts,* 2000.)

.7 sec and 4.0 sec

44. The manager of a fast-food outlet has determined that the demand for frozen yogurt is $\frac{25}{p}$ units per day, where p is the price (in dollars) per unit. The supply is $70p + 15$ units per day. Find the price at which supply and demand are equal.

\$.50

45. Use the formula $A = P(1 + r)^2$ to find the interest rate r at which a principal P of \$10,000 will increase to \$10,920.25 in 2 yr.

4.5%

46. The number of e-mail boxes in North America (in millions) for the years 1995–2001 are shown in the graph and can be modeled by the quadratic function defined by

$$f(x) = 3.29x^2 - 10.4x + 21.6.$$

In the model, $x = 5$ represents 1995, $x = 10$ represents 2000, and so on.

(a) Use the model to approximate the number of e-mail boxes in 2001 to the nearest whole number. How does this result compare to the number shown in the graph?

305; It is close to the number shown in the graph.

(b) Based on the model, in what year did the number of e-mail boxes reach 200 million? (Round down to the nearest year.) How does this result compare to the number shown in the graph?

$x \approx 9$, which represents 1999; Based on the graph, the number of e-mail boxes did not quite reach 200 million in 1999.

GROWTH OF E-MAIL BOXES IN NORTH AMERICA

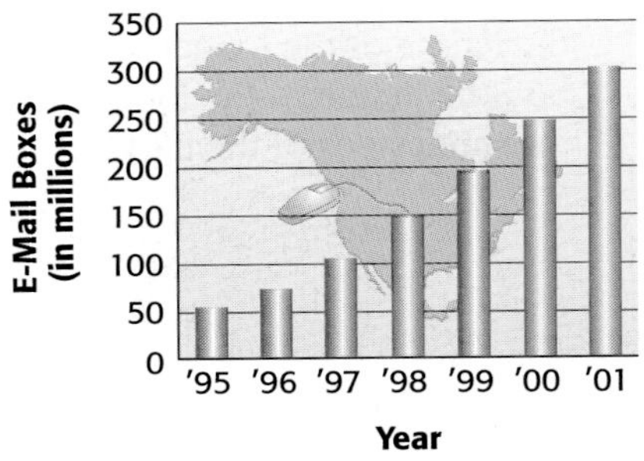

Source: IDC research.

[10.6–10.7] *Identify the vertex of each parabola.*

47. $f(x) = -(x - 1)^2$

$(1, 0)$

48. $f(x) = (x - 3)^2 + 7$

$(3, 7)$

49. $y = -3x^2 + 4x - 2$

$\left(\frac{2}{3}, -\frac{2}{3}\right)$

50. $x = (y - 3)^2 - 4$

$(-4, 3)$

Graph each parabola. Give the domain and range.

51. $y = 2(x - 2)^2 - 3$
domain: $(-\infty, \infty)$
range: $[-3, \infty)$

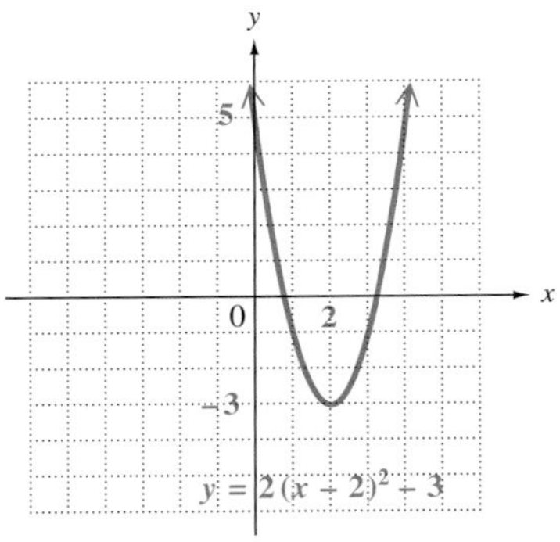

52. $f(x) = -2x^2 + 8x - 5$
domain: $(-\infty, \infty)$
range: $(-\infty, 3]$

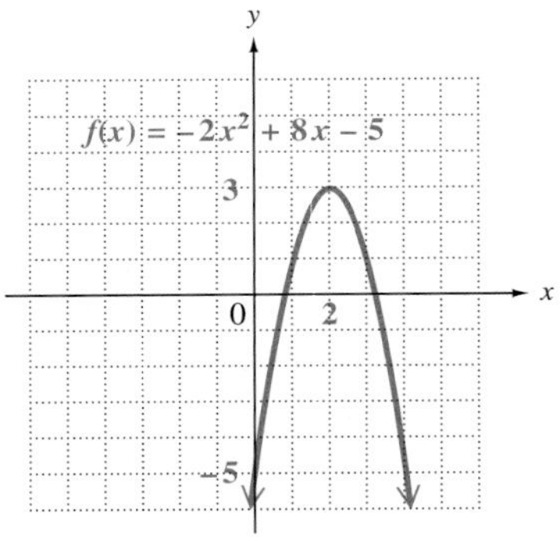

53. $x = 2(y + 3)^2 - 4$
domain: $[-4, \infty)$
range: $(-\infty, \infty)$

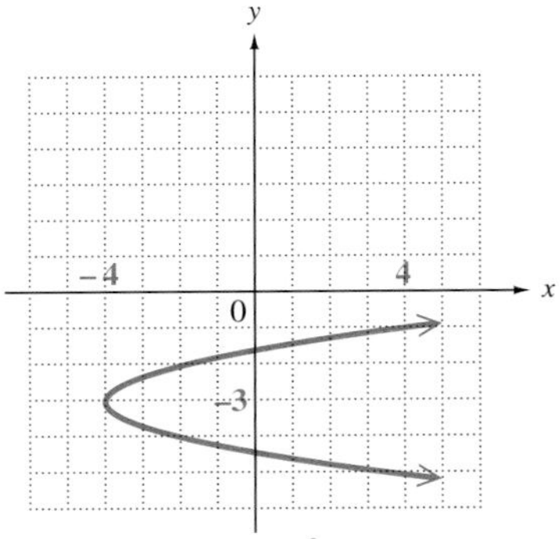

54. $x = -\frac{1}{2}y^2 + 6y - 14$
domain: $(-\infty, 4]$
range: $(-\infty, \infty)$

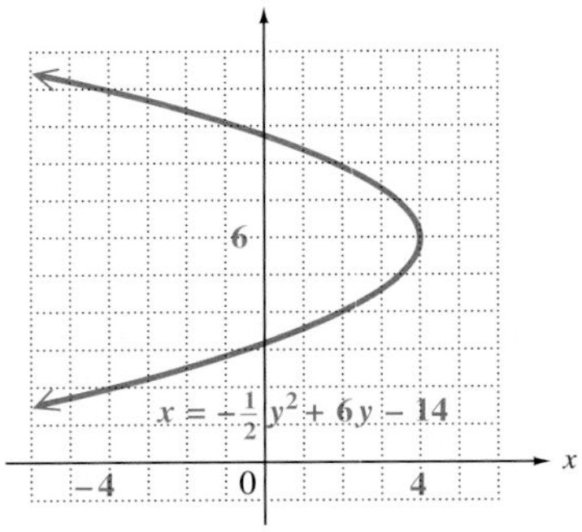

Solve each problem.

55. Consumer spending for home video games in dollars per person per year is given in the table. Let $x = 0$ represent 1990, $x = 2$ represent 1992, and so on.

CONSUMER SPENDING FOR HOME VIDEO GAMES

Year	Dollars
1990	12.39
1992	13.08
1994	15.78
1996	19.43
1997	22.71
1998	24.14
1999	25.08

Source: Statistical Abstract of the United States.

(a) Use the data for 1990, 1994, and 1997 in the quadratic form $ax^2 + bx + c = y$ to write a system of three equations.

$c = 12.39$, $16a + 4b + c = 15.78$, $49a + 7b + c = 22.71$

(b) Solve the system from part (a) to get a quadratic function f that models the data.

$f(x) = .2089x^2 + .0118x + 12.39$

(c) Use the model found in part (b) to approximate consumer spending for home video games in 1998 to the nearest cent. How does your answer compare to the actual data from the table?

\$25.85; The result using the model is a little high.

56. The height (in feet) of a projectile t seconds after being fired from Earth into the air is given by

$$f(t) = -16t^2 + 160t.$$

Find the number of seconds required for the projectile to reach maximum height. What is the maximum height?

5 sec; 400 ft

57. Find the length and width of a rectangle having a perimeter of 200 m if the area is to be a maximum.

length: 50 m; width: 50 m

[10.8] *Solve each inequality, and graph the solution set.*

58. $(x - 4)(2x + 3) > 0$

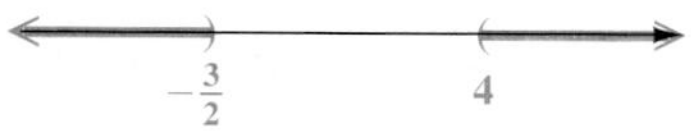

$\left(-\infty, -\frac{3}{2}\right) \cup (4, \infty)$

59. $x^2 + x \leq 12$

$[-4, 3]$

60. $(x + 2)(x - 3)(x + 5) \leq 0$

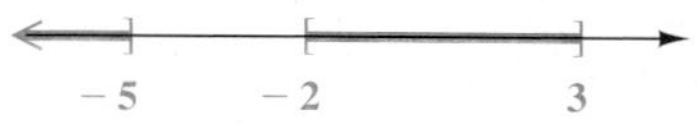

$(-\infty, -5] \cup [-2, 3]$

61. $(4m + 3)^2 \leq -4$

$\emptyset$

62. $\dfrac{6}{2z - 1} < 2$

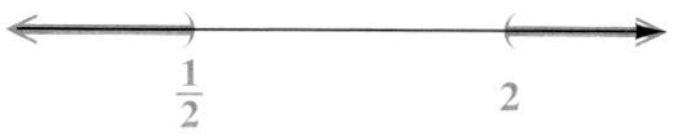

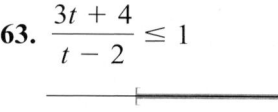

$\left(-\infty, \frac{1}{2}\right) \cup (2, \infty)$

63. $\dfrac{3t + 4}{t - 2} \leq 1$

$[-3, 2)$

Mixed Review Exercises

Solve.

64. $V = r^2 + R^2h$ for R

$R = \frac{\pm\sqrt{Vh - r^2h}}{h}$

***65.** $3t^2 - 6t = -4$

$\left\{\frac{3 + i\sqrt{3}}{3}, \frac{3 - i\sqrt{3}}{3}\right\}$

66. $(x^2 - 2x)^2 = 11(x^2 - 2x) - 24$

$\{-2, -1, 3, 4\}$

67. $(r - 1)(2r + 3)(r + 6) < 0$

$(-\infty, -6) \cup \left(-\frac{3}{2}, 1\right)$

68. $(3k + 11)^2 = 7$

$\left\{\frac{-11 + \sqrt{7}}{3}, \frac{-11 - \sqrt{7}}{3}\right\}$

69. $S = \frac{Id^2}{k}$ for d

$d = \frac{\pm\sqrt{SkI}}{I}$

70. $2x - \sqrt{x} = 6$

$\{4\}$

71. $6 + \frac{15}{s^2} = -\frac{19}{s}$

$\left\{-\frac{5}{3}, -\frac{3}{2}\right\}$

72. $\frac{-2}{x + 5} \leq -5$

$\left(-5, -\frac{23}{5}\right]$

73. Graph $f(x) = 4x^2 + 4x - 2$. Give the domain and range.

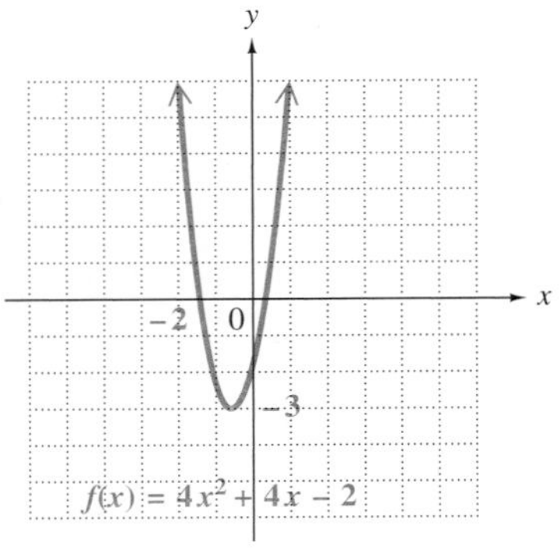

domain: $(-\infty, \infty)$;

range: $[-3, \infty)$

74. Natural gas use in the United States in trillions of cubic feet (ft^3) from 1970 through 1999 can be modeled by the quadratic function defined by

$$f(x) = .014x^2 - .396x + 21.2,$$

where $x = 0$ represents 1970, $x = 5$ represents 1975, and so on. (*Source:* Energy Information Administration.)

(a) Use the model to approximate natural gas use in 2000.

21.92 trillion ft^3

(b) Based on the model, in what year will natural gas use reach 25 trillion ft^3? (Round down to the nearest year.)

2005

Chapter 10 Test

Study Skills Workbook
Activity 12

*Items marked * require knowledge of imaginary numbers.*

Solve by using the square root property.

1. $t^2 = 54$

1. $\{3\sqrt{6}, -3\sqrt{6}\}$

2. $(7x + 3)^2 = 25$

2. $\left\{-\frac{8}{7}, \frac{2}{7}\right\}$

3. Solve $x^2 + 2x = 1$ by completing the square.

3. $\{-1 + \sqrt{2}, -1 - \sqrt{2}\}$

Solve using the quadratic formula.

4. $2x^2 - 3x - 1 = 0$

4. $\left\{\frac{3 + \sqrt{17}}{4}, \frac{3 - \sqrt{17}}{4}\right\}$

***5.** $3t^2 - 4t = -5$

5. $\left\{\frac{2 + i\sqrt{11}}{3}, \frac{2 - i\sqrt{11}}{3}\right\}$

6. $3x = \sqrt{\frac{9x + 2}{2}}$

6. $\left\{\frac{2}{3}\right\}$

***7.** If k is a negative number, then which one of the following equations will have two imaginary solutions?

A. $x^2 = 4k$ **B.** $x^2 = -4k$

C. $(x + 2)^2 = -k$ **D.** $x^2 + k = 0$

7. A

8. What is the discriminant for $2x^2 - 8x - 3 = 0$? How many and what type of solutions does this equation have? (Do not actually solve.)

8. discriminant: 88; There are two irrational solutions.

Solve by any method.

9. $3 - \frac{16}{x} - \frac{12}{x^2} = 0$

9. $\left\{-\frac{2}{3}, 6\right\}$

10. $4x^2 + 7x - 3 = 0$

10. $\left\{\frac{-7 + \sqrt{97}}{8}, \frac{-7 - \sqrt{97}}{8}\right\}$

11. $\left\{-2, -\frac{1}{3}, \frac{1}{3}, 2\right\}$

11. $9x^4 + 4 = 37x^2$

12. $\left\{-\frac{5}{2}, 1\right\}$

12. $12 = (2n + 1)^2 + (2n + 1)$

13. $r = \frac{\pm\sqrt{\pi S}}{2\pi}$

13. Solve for r: $S = 4\pi r^2$. (Leave $\pm$ in your answer.)

14. Maretha: 11.1 hr; Lillaana: 9.1 hr

Solve each problem.

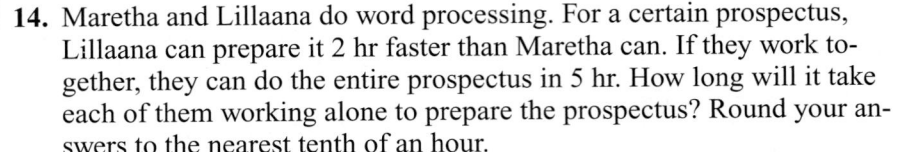

14. Maretha and Lillaana do word processing. For a certain prospectus, Lillaana can prepare it 2 hr faster than Maretha can. If they work together, they can do the entire prospectus in 5 hr. How long will it take each of them working alone to prepare the prospectus? Round your answers to the nearest tenth of an hour.

15. 7 mph

15. Sandi Goldstein paddled her canoe 10 mi upstream, and then paddled back to her starting point. If the rate of the current was 3 mph and the entire trip took $3\frac{1}{2}$ hr, what was Sandi's rate?

16. 2 ft

16. Tyler McGinnis has a pool 24 ft long and 10 ft wide. He wants to construct a concrete walk around the pool. If he plans for the walk to be of uniform width and cover 152 ft^2, what will the width of the walk be?

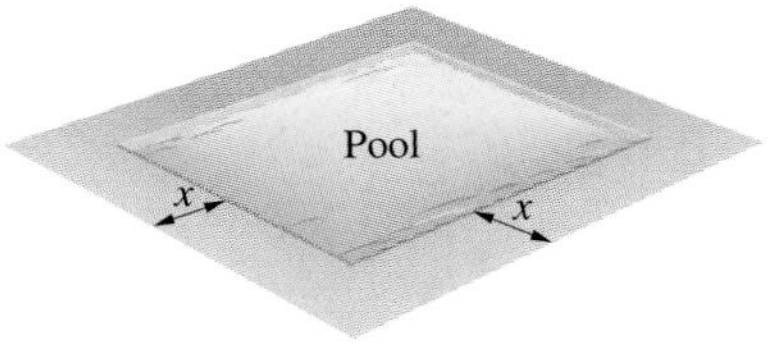

17. 16 m

17. At a point 30 m from the base of a tower, the distance to the top of the tower is 2 m more than twice the height of the tower. Find the height of the tower.

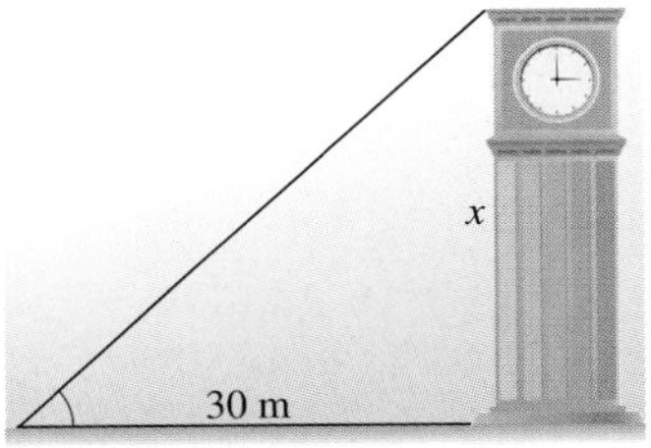

18. The percent increase for in-state tuition at Iowa public universities during the years 1992–2002 can be modeled by the quadratic function defined by

$$f(x) = .156x^2 - 2.05x + 10.2,$$

where $x = 2$ represents 1992, $x = 3$ represents 1993, and so on. (*Source:* Iowa Board of Regents.)

(a) Based on this model, by what percent (to the nearest tenth) did tuition increase in 2001?

(b) In what year was the minimum tuition increase? (Round down to the nearest year.) To the nearest tenth, by what percent did tuition increase that year?

18. (a) 6.5%

(b) 1996; 3.5%

19. Which one of the following most closely resembles the graph of $f(x) = a(x - h)^2 + k$ if $a < 0$, $h > 0$, and $k < 0$?

A.

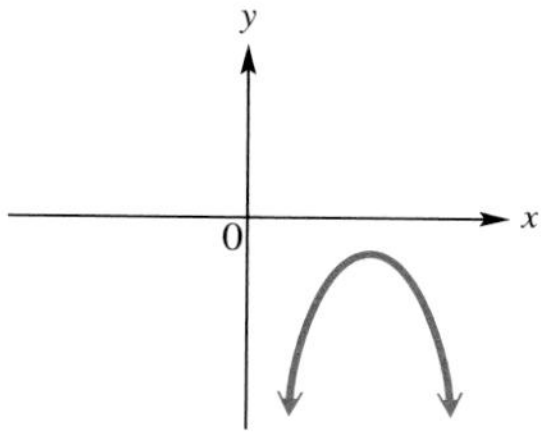

B.

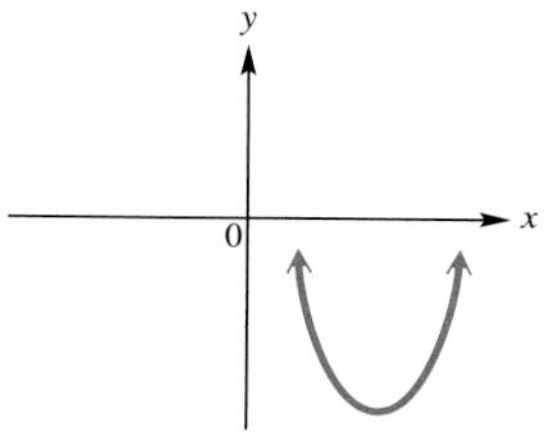

C.

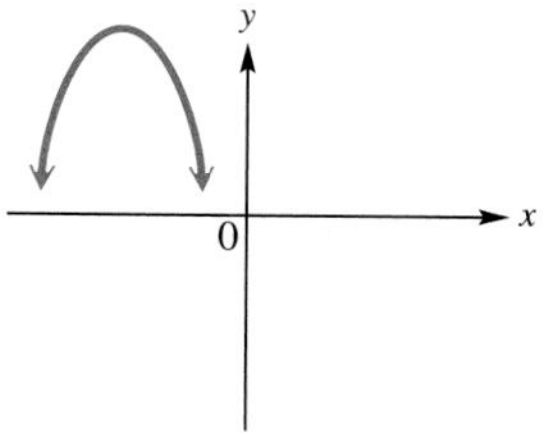

D.

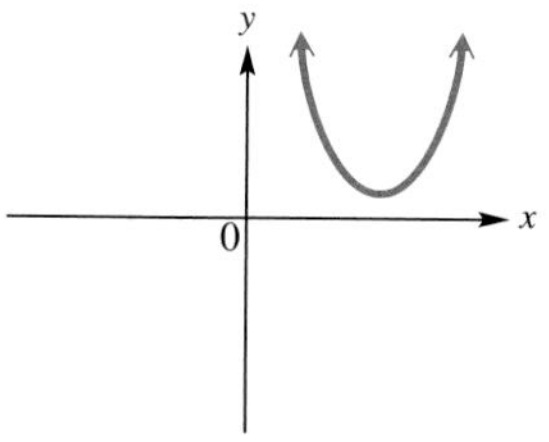

19. A

Graph each parabola.

20. $f(x) = \frac{1}{2}x^2 - 2$

Give the vertex.

20. (0, −2)

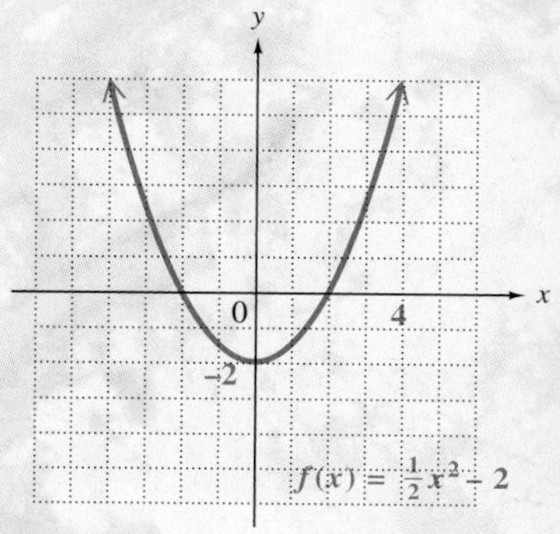

21. **vertex: (2, 3); domain: $(-\infty, \infty)$; range: $(-\infty, 3]$**

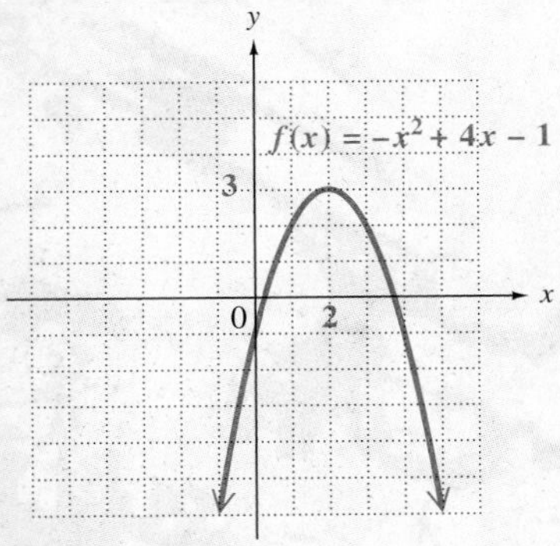

21. $f(x) = -x^2 + 4x - 1$

Give the vertex, domain, and range.

22. **vertex: (−5, −2); domain: $[-5, \infty)$; range: $(-\infty, \infty)$**

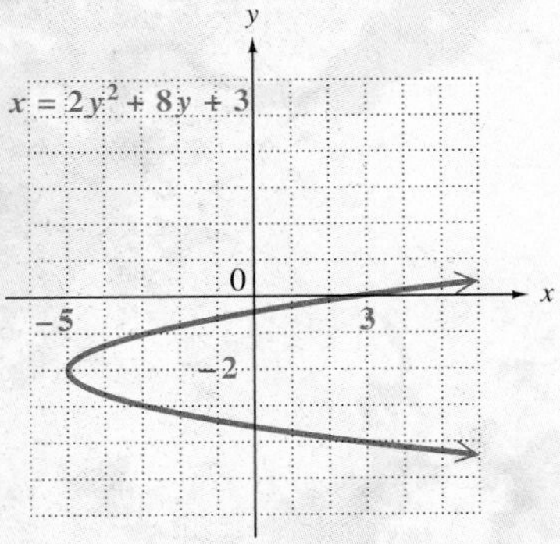

22. $x = 2y^2 + 8y + 3$

Give the vertex, domain, and range.

23. **140 ft by 70 ft; 9800 ft^2**

23. Morgan's Department Store wants to construct a rectangular parking lot on land bordered on one side by a highway. The store has 280 ft of fencing that is to be used to fence off the other three sides. What should be the dimensions of the lot if the enclosed area is to be a maximum? What is the maximum area?

Solve. Graph each solution set.

24. **$(-\infty, -5) \cup \left(\frac{3}{2}, \infty\right)$**

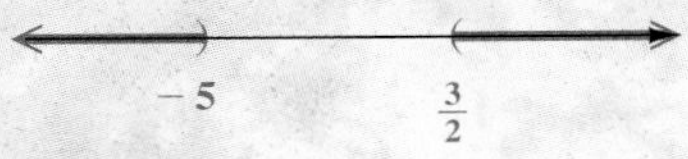

24. $2x^2 + 7x > 15$

25. **$(-\infty, 4) \cup [9, \infty)$**

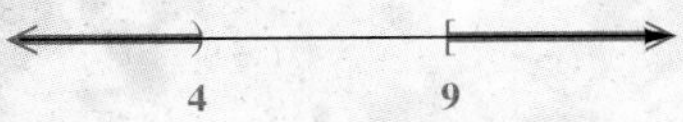

25. $\dfrac{5}{t - 4} \le 1$

Cumulative Review Exercises CHAPTERS R–10

1. Let $S = \{-\frac{7}{3}, -2, -\sqrt{3}, 0, .7, \sqrt{12}, \sqrt{-8}, 7, \frac{32}{3}\}$. List the elements of S that are elements of each set.
   (a) Integers **(b)** Rational numbers **(c)** Real numbers **(d)** Complex numbers

   $-2, 0, 7$ $-\frac{7}{3}, -2, 0, .7, 7, \frac{32}{3}$ all except $\sqrt{-8}$ All are complex numbers.

Simplify each expression.

2. $|-3| + 8 - |-9| - (-7 + 3)$
   6

3. $2(-3)^2 + (-8)(-5) + (-17)$
   41

In this day of Automated Teller Machines (ATMs), people often find themselves doing what they have done for years when faced with a soft drink machine that won't respond: They talk to it. According to one report, the following are percentages of people in the United States, the United Kingdom (UK), and Germany who talk to ATMs and what they say.

	United States	UK	Germany
Thanking the ATM	22%	24%	14%
Cursing the ATM	31%	41%	53%
Telling the ATM to Hurry Up	47%	36%	33%

Source: BMRB International for NCR.

In a random sample of 3000 *people, how many would there be in each category?*

4. People in the United States who curse the ATM
   930

5. People in the UK who thank the ATM
   720

6. People in Germany who tell the ATM to hurry up
   990

7. How many more German cursers would there be than United States thankers?
   930

Solve each equation or inequality.

8. $-2x + 4 = 5(x - 4) + 17$
   $\{1\}$

9. $-2x + 4 \leq -x + 3$
   $[1, \infty)$

10. $|3x - 7| \leq 1$
    $\left[2, \frac{8}{3}\right]$

11. Find the slope and y-intercept of the line with equation $2x - 4y = 7$.
    slope: $\frac{1}{2}$; y-intercept: $\left(0, -\frac{7}{4}\right)$

12. Write the equation in standard form of the line through $(2, -1)$ and perpendicular to $-3x + y = 5$.
    $x + 3y = -1$

Graph each relation. Tell whether or not each is a function, and if it is, give its domain and range.

13. $4x - 5y = 15$

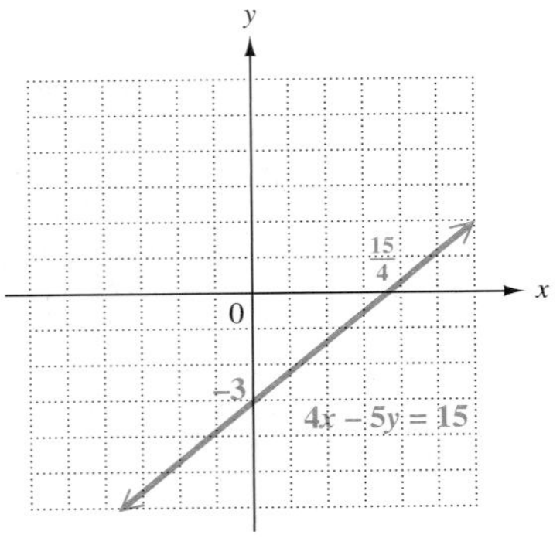

function; domain: $(-\infty, \infty)$; range: $(-\infty, \infty)$

14. $4x - 5y < 15$

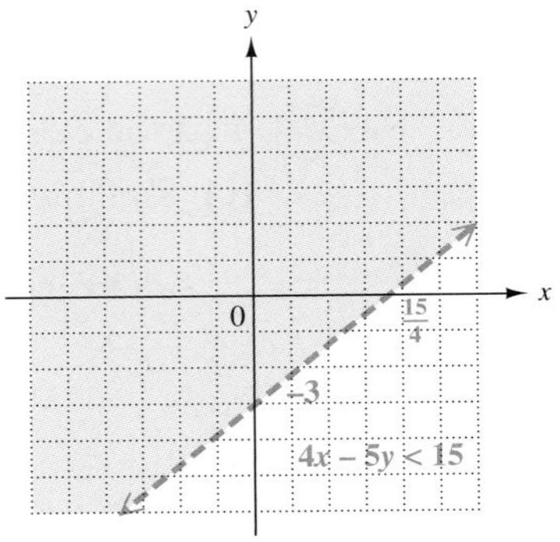

not a function

15. $f(x) = -2(x - 1)^2 + 3$

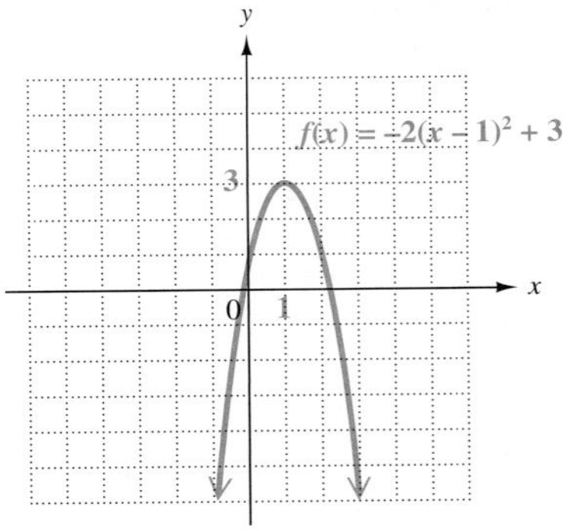

function; domain: $(-\infty, \infty)$; range: $(-\infty, 3]$

16. The record track-qualifying speeds at North Carolina Motor Speedway since Richard Petty captured the first pole in 1965 are given in the table and can be modeled by a linear equation. Let $x = 0$ represent 1965, $x = 10$ represent 1975, and so on.

(a) Use the ordered pairs (0, 116.26) and (20, 141.85) to write a linear equation that models these data.

$y = 1.2795x + 116.26$

(b) Use your model to approximate the record speed for 1998 to the nearest hundredth. How does it compare to the actual value from the table?

158.48; It is a little too high.

QUALIFYING RECORDS

Year	Speed (in mph)
1965	116.26
1975	132.02
1985	141.85
1995	155.38
1998	156.36

Source: NASCAR.

17. Does the relation $x = 5$ define a function? Explain why or why not.

No, because the graph is a vertical line, which is not the graph of a function by the vertical line test.

Solve each system of equations.

18. $2x - 4y = 10$
$9x + 3y = 3$

$\{(1, -2)\}$

19. $x + y + 2z = 3$
$-x + y + z = -5$
$2x + 3y - z = -8$

$\{(3, -4, 2)\}$

20. The recent merger of America Online and Time Warner is the largest in U.S. history. The two companies have combined sales of \$34.2 billion. Sales for AOL are \$.3 billion less than 4 times the sales of Time Warner. What are the sales for each company? (*Source:* Company reports.)

(a) Write a system of equations to solve the problem.

$x + y = 34.2$; $x = 4y - .3$

(b) Solve the problem.

AOL: \$27.3 billion; Time Warner: \$6.9 billion

Write with positive exponents only. Assume variables represent positive real numbers.

21. $\left(\dfrac{x^{-3}y^{2}}{x^{5}y^{-2}}\right)^{-1}$

$\dfrac{x^8}{y^4}$

22. $\dfrac{(4x^{-2})^{2}(2y^{3})}{8x^{-3}y^{5}}$

$\dfrac{4}{xy^2}$

Perform the indicated operations.

23. $\left(\dfrac{2}{3}t + 9\right)^{2}$

$\dfrac{4}{9}t^2 + 12t + 81$

24. $(3t^3 + 5t^2 - 8t + 7) - (6t^3 + 4t - 8)$

$-3t^3 + 5t^2 - 12t + 15$

25. Divide $4x^3 + 2x^2 - x + 26$ by $x + 2$.

$4x^2 - 6x + 11 + \dfrac{4}{x + 2}$

26. According to the Congressional Budget Office, the federal budget surplus is expected to total \$3,100,000,000,000 over the next decade. Write this amount using scientific notation. (*Source: The Gazette,* January 31, 2001.)

$\$3.1 \times 10^{12}$

Factor completely.

27. $16x - x^3$

$x(4 + x)(4 - x)$

28. $24m^2 + 2m - 15$

$(4m - 3)(6m + 5)$

29. $9x^2 - 30xy + 25y^2$

$(3x - 5y)^2$

Perform the operations, and express answers in lowest terms. Assume denominators are nonzero.

30. $\dfrac{5t+2}{-6} \div \dfrac{15t+6}{5}$

$-\dfrac{5}{18}$

31. $\dfrac{3}{2-k} - \dfrac{5}{k} + \dfrac{6}{k^2-2k}$

$-\dfrac{8}{k}$

32. $\dfrac{\dfrac{r}{s} - \dfrac{s}{r}}{\dfrac{r}{s} + 1}$

$\dfrac{r-s}{r}$

Simplify each radical expression.

33. $\sqrt[3]{\dfrac{27}{16}}$

$\dfrac{3\sqrt[3]{4}}{4}$

34. $\dfrac{2}{\sqrt{7}-\sqrt{5}}$

$\sqrt{7}+\sqrt{5}$

Solve each equation.

35. $2x = \sqrt{\dfrac{5x+2}{3}}$

$\left\{\dfrac{2}{3}\right\}$

36. $2x^2 - 4x - 3 = 0$

$\left\{\dfrac{2+\sqrt{10}}{2}, \dfrac{2-\sqrt{10}}{2}\right\}$

37. $z^2 - 2z = 15$

$\{-3, 5\}$

38. $\dfrac{3}{x-3} - \dfrac{2}{x-2} = \dfrac{3}{x^2-5x+6}$

$\emptyset$

39. $p^4 - 10p^2 + 9 = 0$

$\{-3, -1, 1, 3\}$

40. Two cars left an intersection at the same time, one heading due south and the other due east. Later they were exactly 95 mi apart. The car heading east had gone 38 mi less than twice as far as the car heading south. How far had each car traveled?

southbound car: 57 mi; eastbound car: 76 mi

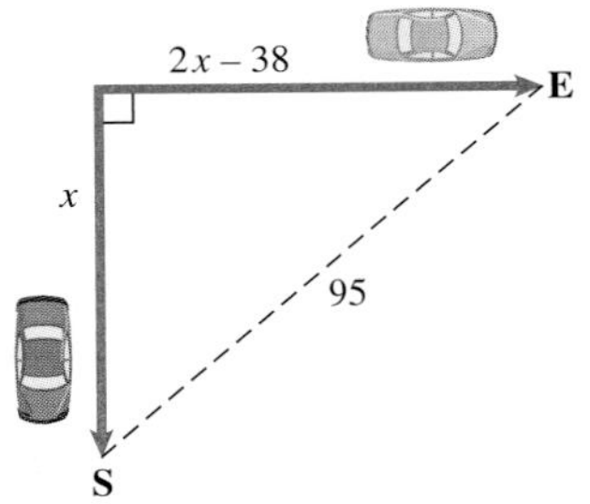

Exponential and Logarithmic Functions

11

The exponential and logarithmic functions introduced in this chapter are used to model a wide variety of situations, including environmental issues, compound interest, earthquake intensity, fossil dating, and sound levels. Recently, there has been concern about the level of sound Americans are subjected to daily. For example, action sequences in *Pearl Harbor, The Movie* reached 107 decibels, while the sound levels of *Lethal Weapon 4* often reached 100 decibels or more, compared to an average of 95 decibels for a motorcycle. In Section 11.5, Exercise 39, we give a logarithmic function to measure sound levels and to find the decibel levels of other recent movies. (*Source: World Almanac and Book of Facts,* 2001, www.lhh.org/noise/)

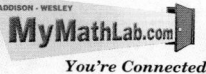

11.1 Inverse Functions

Objectives

1. Decide whether a function is one-to-one and, if it is, find its inverse.
2. Use the horizontal line test to determine whether a function is one-to-one.
3. Find the equation of the inverse of a function.
4. Graph f^{-1} from the graph of f.

In this chapter we will study two important types of functions, *exponential* and *logarithmic*. These functions are related in a special way: They are *inverses* of one another. We begin by discussing inverse functions in general.

Calculator Tip A calculator with the following keys will be essential in this chapter.

y^x, 10^x or LOG, e^x or ln x

We will explain how these keys are used at appropriate places in the chapter.

1 Decide whether a function is one-to-one and, if it is, find its inverse. Suppose we define the function

$$G = \{(-2, 2), (-1, 1), (0, 0), (1, 3), (2, 5)\}.$$

We can form another set of ordered pairs from G by interchanging the x- and y-values of each pair in G. Call this set F, with

$$F = \{(2, -2), (1, -1), (0, 0), (3, 1), (5, 2)\}.$$

To show that these two sets are related, F is called the *inverse* of G. For a function f to have an inverse, f must be *one-to-one.*

One-to-One Function

In a one-to-one function, each x-value corresponds to only one y-value, and each y-value corresponds to just one x-value.

The function shown in Figure 1(a) is not one-to-one because the y-value 7 corresponds to *two* x-values, 2 and 3. That is, the ordered pairs (2, 7) and (3, 7) both appear in the function. The function in Figure 1(b) is one-to-one.

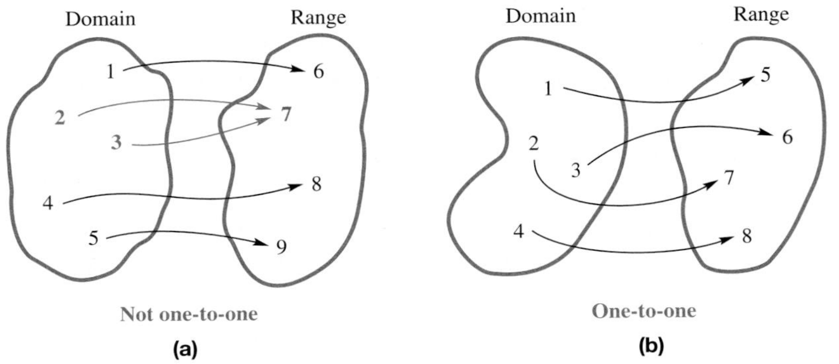

Figure 1

The *inverse* of any one-to-one function f is found by interchanging the components of the ordered pairs of f. The inverse of f is written f^{-1}. Read f^{-1} as "the inverse of f" or "f-inverse."

CAUTION

The symbol $f^{-1}(x)$ does not represent $\dfrac{1}{f(x)}$.

The definition of the inverse of a function follows.

Inverse of a Function

The **inverse** of a one-to-one function f, written f^{-1}, is the set of all ordered pairs of the form (y, x), where (x, y) belongs to f. Since the inverse is formed by interchanging x and y, the domain of f becomes the range of f^{-1} and the range of f becomes the domain of f^{-1}.

For inverses f and f^{-1}, it follows that $f(f^{-1}(x)) = x$ and $f^{-1}(f(x)) = x$.

Example 1 Finding the Inverses of One-to-One Functions

Find the inverse of each one-to-one function.

(a) $F = \{(-2, 1), (-1, 0), (0, 1), (1, 2), (2, 2)\}$

Each x-value in F corresponds to just one y-value. However, the y-value 2 corresponds to two x-values, 1 and 2. Also, the y-value 1 corresponds to both -2 and 0. Because some y-values correspond to more than one x-value, F is not one-to-one and does not have an inverse.

(b) $G = \{(3, 1), (0, 2), (2, 3), (4, 0)\}$

Every x-value in G corresponds to only one y-value, and every y-value corresponds to only one x-value, so G is a one-to-one function. The inverse function is found by interchanging the x- and y-values in each ordered pair.

$$G^{-1} = \{(1, 3), (2, 0), (3, 2), (0, 4)\}$$

Notice how the domain and range of G become the range and domain, respectively, of G^{-1}.

(c) The U.S. Environmental Protection Agency has developed an indicator of air quality called the Pollutant Standard Index (PSI). If the PSI exceeds 100 on a particular day, that day is classified as unhealthy. The table shows the number of unhealthy days in Chicago for the years 1991–1997.

Year	Number of Unhealthy Days
1991	21
1992	4
1993	3
1994	8
1995	21
1996	6
1997	9

Source: U.S. Environmental Protection Agency.

Let f be the function defined in the table, with the years forming the domain and the numbers of unhealthy days forming the range. Then f is not one-to-one, because in two different years (1991 and 1995), the number of unhealthy days was the same, 21.

Work Problem 1 at the Side.

1 Find the inverse of each one-to-one function.

(a) $\{(1, 2), (2, 4), (3, 3), (4, 5)\}$

(b) $\{(0, 3), (-1, 2), (1, 3)\}$

(c) A Norwegian physiologist has developed a rule for predicting running times based on the time to run 5 km (5K). An example for one runner is shown here. (*Source:* Stephen Seiler, Agder College, Kristiansand, Norway.)

Distance	Time
1.5K	4:22
3K	9:18
5K	16:00
10K	33:40

ANSWERS

1. **(a)** $\{(2, 1), (4, 2), (3, 3), (5, 4)\}$
(b) not a one-to-one function
(c)

Time	Distance
4:22	1.5K
9:18	3K
16:00	5K
33:40	10K

2 Use the horizontal line test to determine whether each graph is the graph of a one-to-one function.

(a)

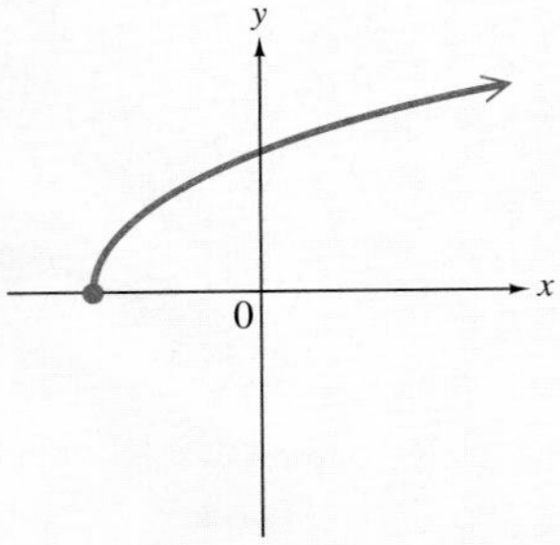

(b)

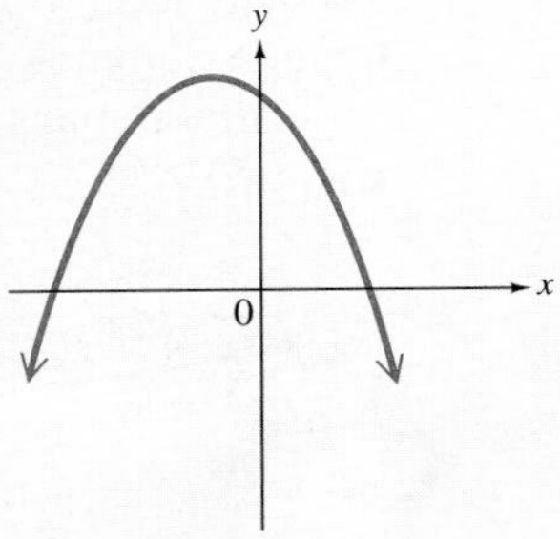

ANSWERS

2. **(a)** one-to-one **(b)** not one-to-one

2 Use the horizontal line test to determine whether a function is one-to-one. It may be difficult to decide whether a function is one-to-one just by looking at the equation that defines the function. However, by graphing the function and observing the graph, we can use the *horizontal line test* to tell whether the function is one-to-one.

Horizontal Line Test

A function is one-to-one if every horizontal line intersects the graph of the function at most once.

The horizontal line test follows from the definition of a one-to-one function. Any two points that lie on the same horizontal line have the same y-coordinate. No two ordered pairs that belong to a one-to-one function may have the same y-coordinate, and therefore no horizontal line will intersect the graph of a one-to-one function more than once.

Example 2 Using the Horizontal Line Test

Use the horizontal line test to determine whether the graphs in Figures 2 and 3 are graphs of one-to-one functions.

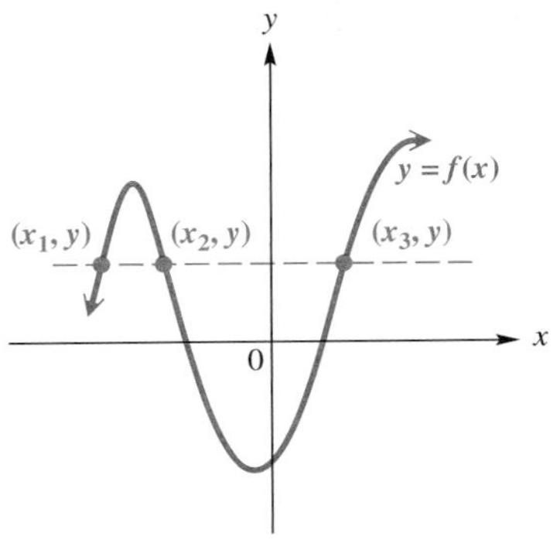

Figure 2

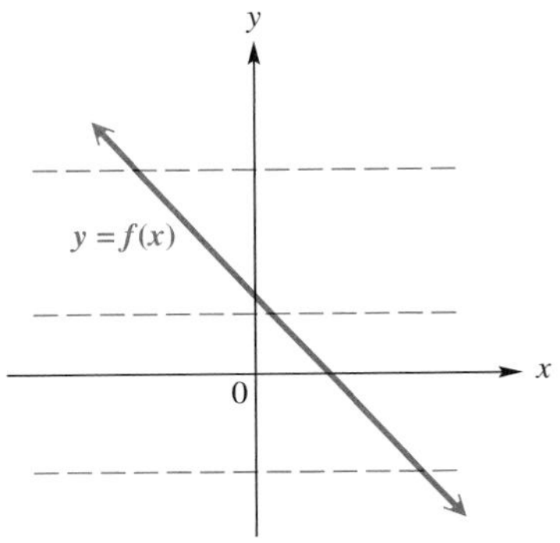

Figure 3

Because the horizontal line shown in Figure 2 intersects the graph in more than one point (actually three points), the function is not one-to-one.

Every horizontal line will intersect the graph in Figure 3 in exactly one point. This function is one-to-one.

Work Problem 2 at the Side.

3 Find the equation of the inverse of a function. By definition, the inverse of a function is found by interchanging the x- and y-values of each of its ordered pairs. The equation of the inverse of a function defined by $y = f(x)$ is found in the same way.

Finding the Equation of the Inverse of $y = f(x)$

For a one-to-one function f defined by an equation $y = f(x)$, find the defining equation of the inverse as follows.

Step 1 Interchange x and y.

Step 2 Solve for y.

Step 3 Replace y with $f^{-1}(x)$.

Example 3 Finding Equations of Inverses

Decide whether each equation defines a one-to-one function. If so, find the equation of the inverse.

(a) $f(x) = 2x + 5$

The graph of $y = 2x + 5$ is a nonvertical line, so by the horizontal line test, f is a one-to-one function. To find the inverse, let $y = f(x)$ so that

$$y = 2x + 5$$

$$x = 2y + 5 \qquad \text{Interchange } x \text{ and } y. \text{ (Step 1)}$$

$$2y = x - 5 \qquad \text{Solve for } y. \text{ (Step 2)}$$

$$y = \frac{x-5}{2}$$

$$f^{-1}(x) = \frac{x-5}{2}. \qquad \text{(Step 3)}$$

Thus, f^{-1} is a linear function. In the function with $y = 2x + 5$, the value of y is found by starting with a value of x, multiplying by 2, and adding 5. The equation for the inverse has us *subtract* 5, and then *divide* by 2. This shows how an inverse is used to "undo" what a function does to the variable x.

(b) $y = x^2 + 2$

This equation has a vertical parabola as its graph, so some horizontal lines will intersect the graph at two points. For example, both $x = 3$ and $x = -3$ correspond to $y = 11$. Because of the x^2-term, there are many pairs of x-values that correspond to the same y-value. This means that the function defined by $y = x^2 + 2$ is not one-to-one and does not have an inverse.

If this is not noticed, following the steps for finding the equation of an inverse leads to

$$y = x^2 + 2$$

$$x = y^2 + 2 \qquad \text{Interchange } x \text{ and } y.$$

$$x - 2 = y^2 \qquad \text{Solve for } y.$$

$$\pm\sqrt{x-2} = y \qquad \text{Square root property}$$

The last step shows that there are two y-values for each choice of $x > 2$, so the given function is not one-to-one and cannot have an inverse.

(c) $f(x) = (x - 2)^3$

Because of the cube, each value of x produces just one value of y, so this is a one-to-one function.

$$y = (x-2)^3 \qquad \text{Replace } f(x) \text{ with } y.$$

$$x = (y-2)^3 \qquad \text{Interchange } x \text{ and } y.$$

$$\sqrt[3]{x} = \sqrt[3]{(y-2)^3} \qquad \text{Take the cube root on each side.}$$

$$\sqrt[3]{x} = y - 2$$

$$\sqrt[3]{x} + 2 = y$$

$$f^{-1}(x) = \sqrt[3]{x} + 2 \qquad \text{Replace } y \text{ with } f^{-1}(x).$$

Work Problem 3 at the Side.

3 Decide whether each equation defines a one-to-one function. If so, find the equation that defines the inverse.

(a) $f(x) = 3x - 4$

(b) $f(x) = x^3 + 1$

(c) $f(x) = (x - 3)^2$

ANSWERS

3. (a) one-to-one function; $f^{-1}(x) = \frac{x+4}{3}$

(b) one-to-one function; $f^{-1}(x) = \sqrt[3]{x-1}$

(c) not a one-to-one function

4 Graph f^{-1} from the graph of f. One way to graph the inverse of a function f whose equation is known is to find some ordered pairs that belong to f, interchange x and y to get ordered pairs that belong to f^{-1}, plot those points, and sketch the graph of f^{-1} through the points. A simpler way is to select points on the graph of f and use symmetry to find corresponding points on the graph of f^{-1}. For example, suppose the point (a, b) shown in Figure 4 belongs to a one-to-one function f. Then the point (b, a) belongs to f^{-1}. The line segment connecting (a, b) and (b, a) is perpendicular to, and cut in half by, the line $y = x$. The points (a, b) and (b, a) are "mirror images" of each other with respect to $y = x$. For this reason we can find the graph of f^{-1} from the graph of f by locating the mirror image of each point in f with respect to the line $y = x$.

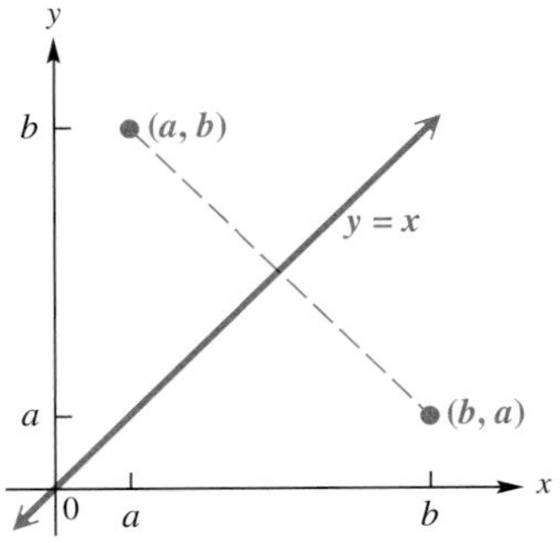

Figure 4

Example 4 Graphing the Inverse

Graph the inverses of the functions shown in Figure 5.

In Figure 5 the graphs of two functions are shown in blue. Their inverses are shown in red. In each case, the graph of f^{-1} is symmetric to the graph of f with respect to the line $y = x$.

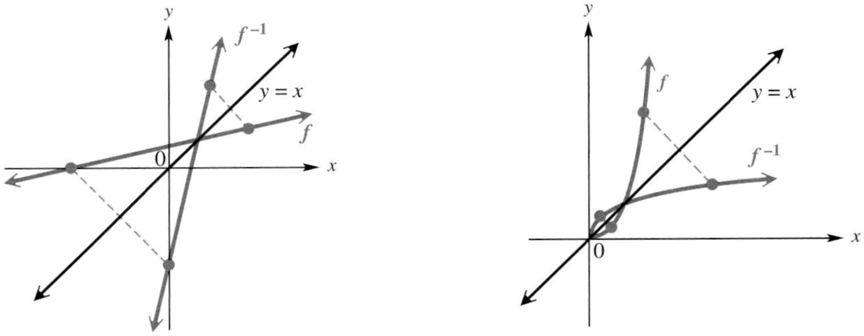

Figure 5

Work Problem 4 at the Side.

4 Use the given graphs to graph each inverse.

(a)

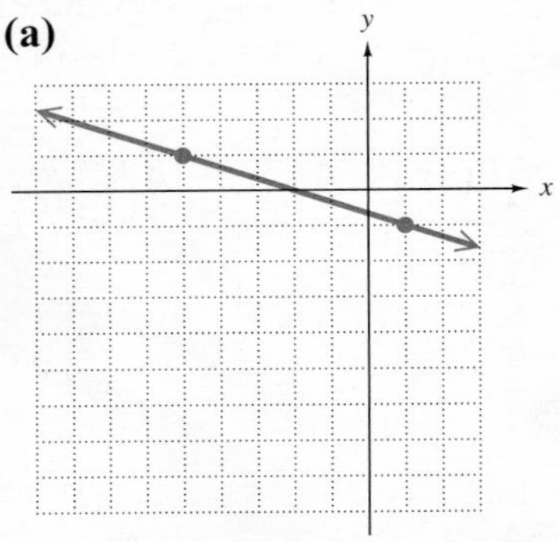

(b)

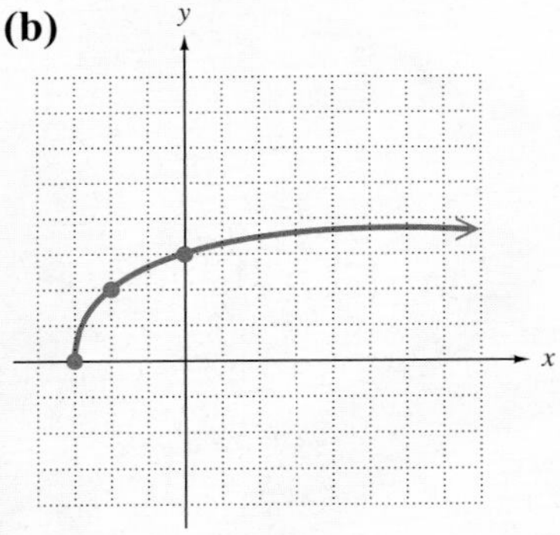

(c)

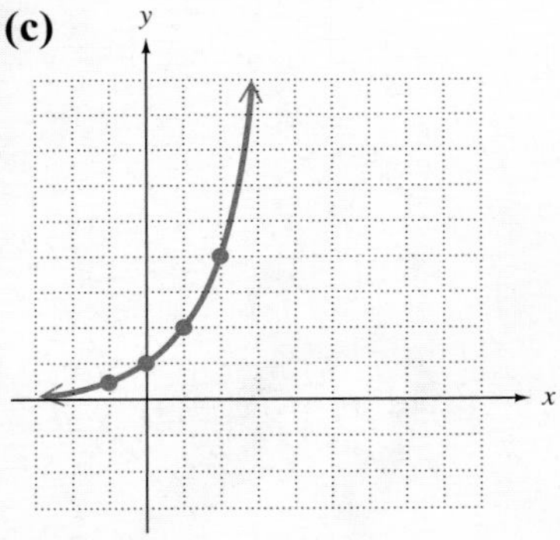

ANSWERS

4. (a)

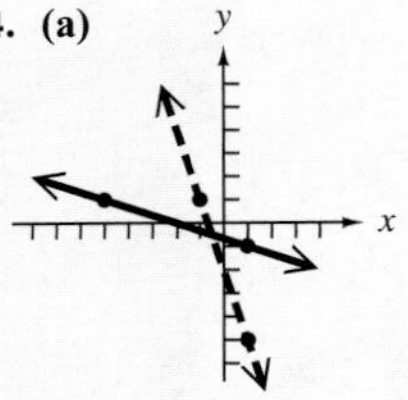

(b)

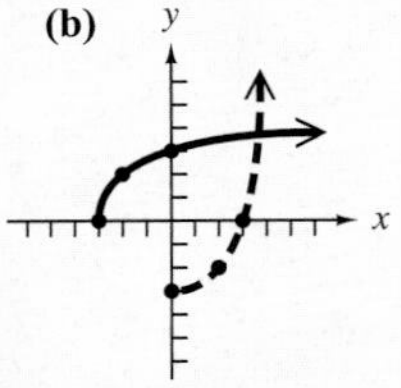

(c)

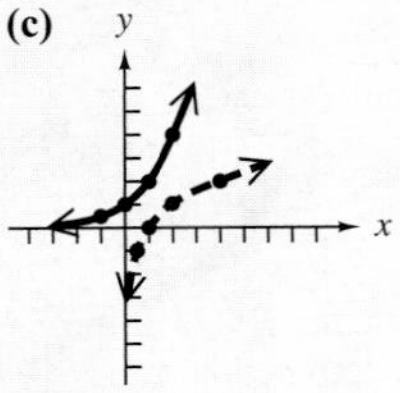

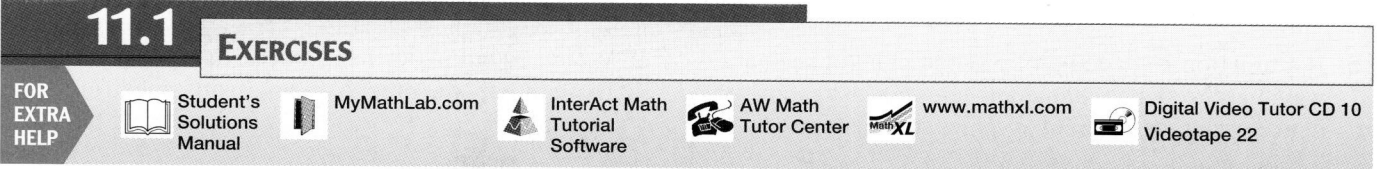

11.1 EXERCISES

FOR EXTRA HELP: Student's Solutions Manual | MyMathLab.com | InterAct Math Tutorial Software | AW Math Tutor Center | www.mathxl.com | Digital Video Tutor CD 10 Videotape 22

1. The table shows the number of uncontrolled hazardous waste sites that require further investigation to determine whether remedies are needed under the Superfund program. The seven states listed are ranked in the top ten in the United States.

If this correspondence is considered to be a function that pairs each state with its number of uncontrolled waste sites, is it one-to-one? If not, explain why.

State	Number of Sites
New Jersey	108
Pennsylvania	101
California	94
New York	79
Florida	53
Illinois	40
Wisconsin	40

Source: U.S. Environmental Protection Agency.

It is not one-to-one because both Illinois and Wisconsin are paired with the same range element, 40.

2. The table shows emissions of a major air pollutant, carbon monoxide, in the United States for the years 1991–1997.

If this correspondence is considered to be a function that pairs each year with its emissions amount, is it one-to-one? If not, explain why.

Year	Amount of Emissions (in thousand short tons)
1991	97,790
1992	94,400
1993	94,526
1994	98,854
1995	89,151
1996	90,611
1997	87,451

Source: U.S. Environmental Protection Agency.

It is one-to-one.

3. Suppose you consider the set of ordered pairs (x, y) such that x represents a person in your mathematics class and y represents that person's mother. Explain how this function might not be a one-to-one function.

Two or more siblings might be in the class. They would be paired with the same mother.

4. The road mileage between Denver, Colorado, and several selected U.S. cities is shown in the table below.

City	Distance to Denver (in miles)
Atlanta	1398
Dallas	781
Indianapolis	1058
Kansas City, MO	600
Los Angeles	1059
San Francisco	1235

If we consider this as a function that pairs each city with a distance, is it a one-to-one function? How could we change the answer to this question by adding 1 mile to one of the distances shown?

Yes. By adding 1 to 1058 two distances would be the same, so the function would not be one-to-one.

Choose the correct response from the given list.

5. If a function is made up of ordered pairs in such a way that the same y-value appears in a correspondence with two different x-values, then

A. the function is one-to-one
B. the function is not one-to-one
C. its graph does not pass the vertical line test
D. it has an inverse function associated with it.

B

6. Which equation defines a one-to-one function? Explain why the others are not, using specific examples.

A. $f(x) = x$ **B.** $f(x) = x^2$
C. $f(x) = |x|$ **D.** $f(x) = -x^2 + 2x - 1$

Choice A is one-to-one. In choice B, $f(1) = f(-1) = 1$, and so $f(x) = x^2$ is not one-to-one. In choice C, $f(2) = f(-2) = 2$, and so $f(x) = |x|$ is not one-to-one. Finally, in choice D, $f(-2) = f(4) = -9$, and so $f(x) = -x^2 + 2x - 1$ is also not one-to-one.

7. Only one of the graphs illustrates a one-to-one function. Which one is it?

A.
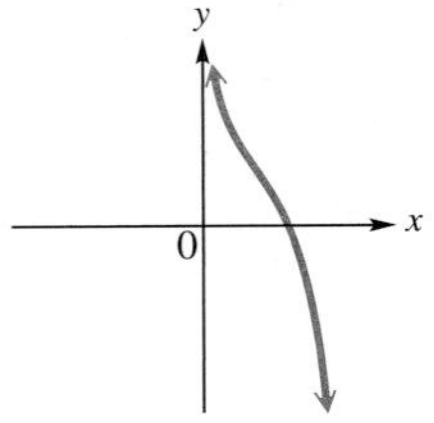

B.
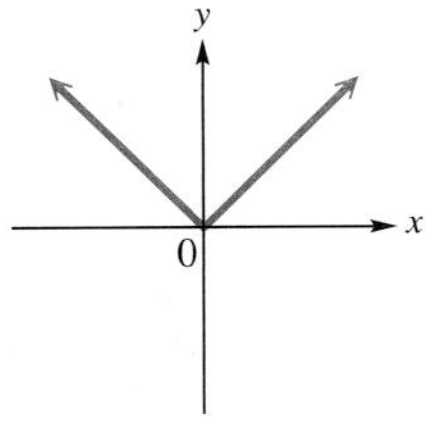

C.
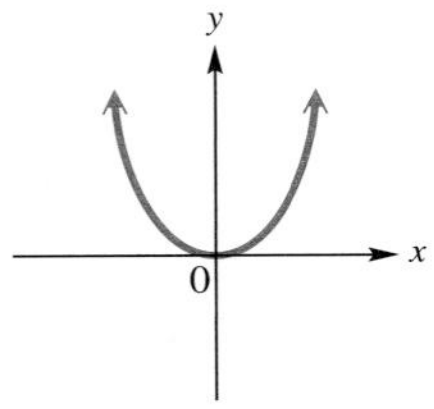

D.
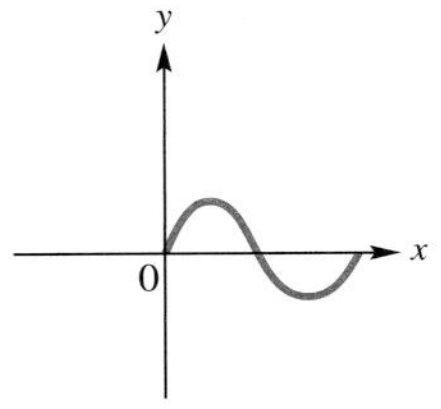

A

8. If a function f is one-to-one and the point (p, q) lies on the graph of f, then which point *must* lie on the graph of f^{-1}?

A. $(-p, q)$ **B.** $(-q, -p)$
C. $(p, -q)$ **D.** (q, p)

D

If the function is one-to-one, find its inverse. See Examples 1–3.

9. $\{(3, 6), (2, 10), (5, 12)\}$

$\{(6, 3), (10, 2), (12, 5)\}$

10. $\{(-1, 3), (0, 5), (5, 0), (7, -\frac{1}{2})\}$

$\left\{(3, -1), (5, 0), (0, 5), \left(-\frac{1}{2}, 7\right)\right\}$

11. $\{(-1, 3), (2, 7), (4, 3), (5, 8)\}$

not one-to-one

12. $\{(-8, 6), (-4, 3), (0, 6), (5, 10)\}$

not one-to-one

13. $f(x) = 2x + 4$

$f^{-1}(x) = \frac{x - 4}{2}$

14. $f(x) = 3x + 1$

$f^{-1}(x) = \frac{x - 1}{3}$

15. $g(x) = \sqrt{x - 3}, x \geq 3$

$g^{-1}(x) = x^2 + 3, x \geq 0$

16. $g(x) = \sqrt{x + 2}, x \geq -2$

$g^{-1}(x) = x^2 - 2, x \geq 0$

17. $f(x) = 3x^2 + 2$

not one-to-one

18. $f(x) = -4x^2 - 1$

not one-to-one

19. $f(x) = x^3 - 4$

$f^{-1}(x) = \sqrt[3]{x + 4}$

20. $f(x) = x^3 - 3$

$f^{-1}(x) = \sqrt[3]{x + 3}$

*Let $f(x) = 2^x$. We will see in the next section that the function f is one-to-one. Find each value, always working part **(a)** before part **(b)**.*

21. **(a)** $f(3)$ 8
(b) $f^{-1}(8)$ 3

22. **(a)** $f(4)$ 16
(b) $f^{-1}(16)$ 4

23. **(a)** $f(0)$ 1
(b) $f^{-1}(1)$ 0

24. **(a)** $f(-2)$ $\frac{1}{4}$
(b) $f^{-1}(\frac{1}{4})$ −2

*The graphs of some functions are given in Exercises 25–30. **(a)** Use the horizontal line test to determine whether each function is one-to-one. **(b)** If the function is one-to-one, graph the inverse of the function with a dashed line (or curve) on the same set of axes. (Remember that if f is one-to-one and $f(a) = b$, then $f^{-1}(b) = a$.) See Example 4.*

25.

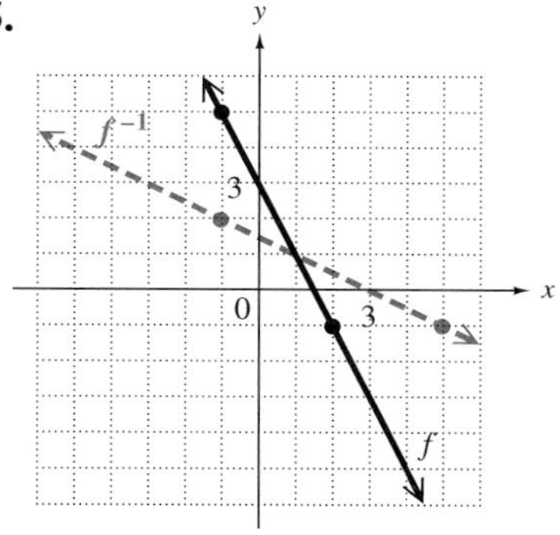

(a) one-to-one

26.

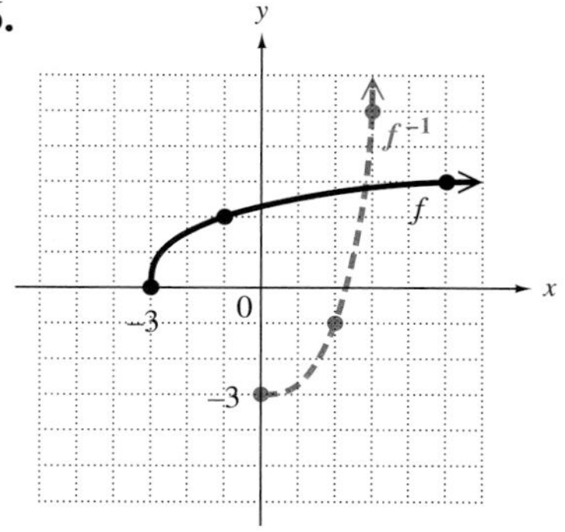

(a) one-to-one

27.

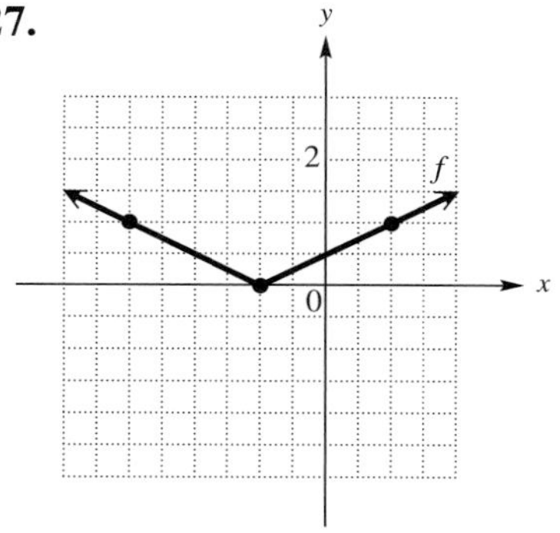

(a) not one-to-one

28.

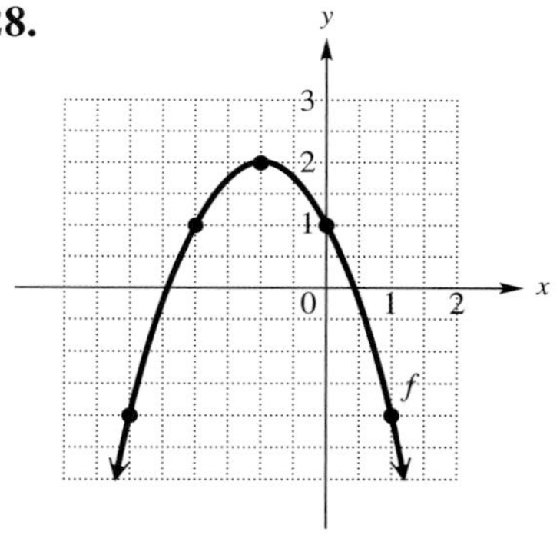

(a) not one-to-one

29.

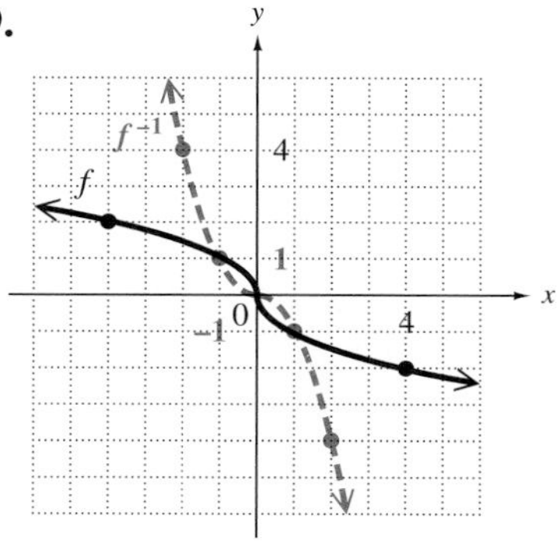

(a) one-to-one

30.

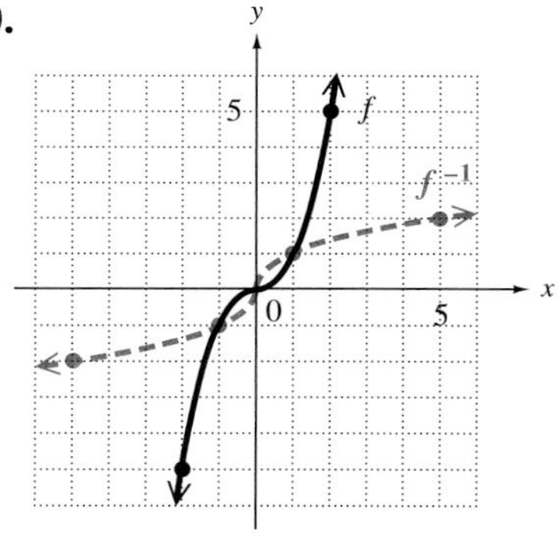

(a) one-to-one

Each function defined in Exercises 31–38 is a one-to-one function. Graph the function as a solid line (or curve), and then graph its inverse on the same set of axes as a dashed line (or curve). In Exercises 37 and 38 you are given a table to complete so that graphing the function will be easier. See Example 4.

31. $f(x) = 2x - 1$

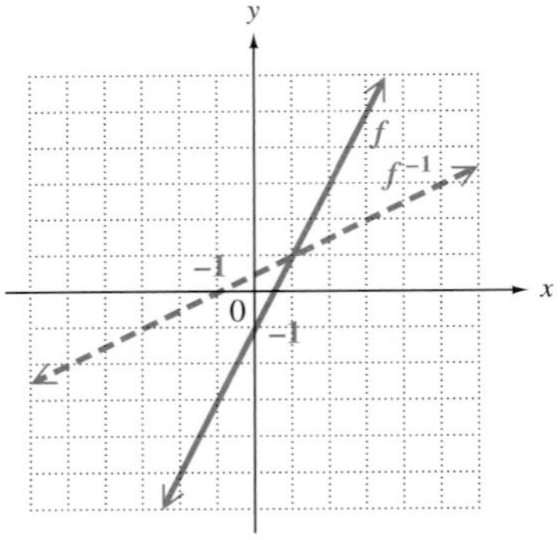

32. $f(x) = 2x + 3$

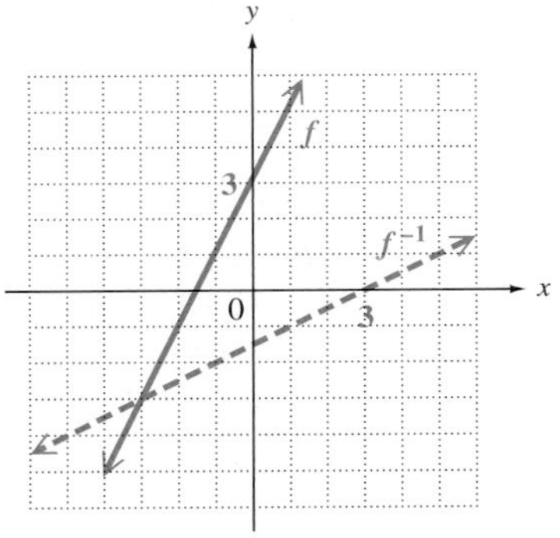

33. $g(x) = -4x$

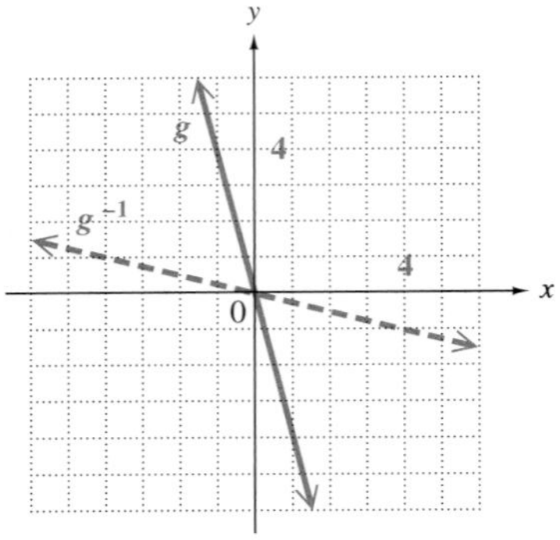

34. $g(x) = -2x$

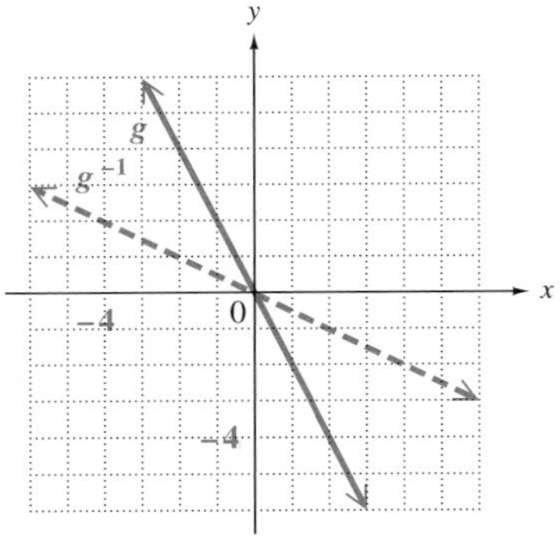

35. $f(x) = \sqrt{x}, x \geq 0$

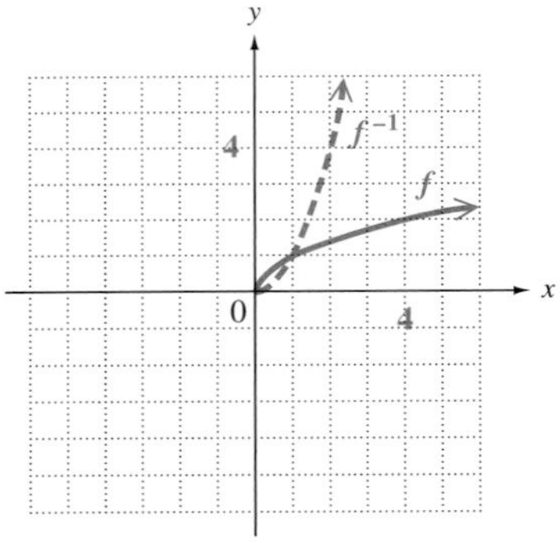

36. $f(x) = -\sqrt{x}, x \geq 0$

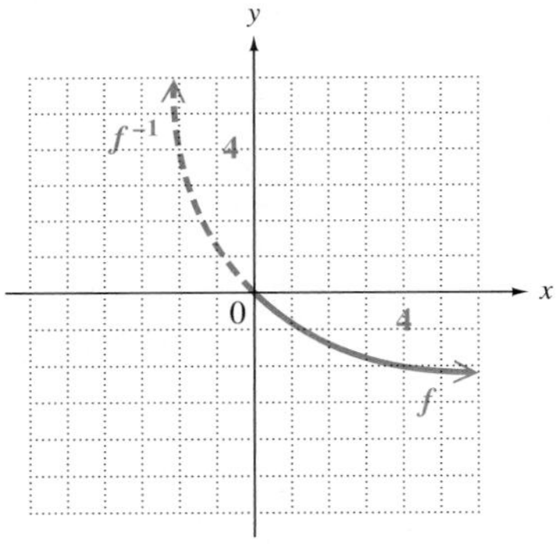

37. $y = x^3 - 2$

x	y
−1	−3
0	−2
1	−1
2	6

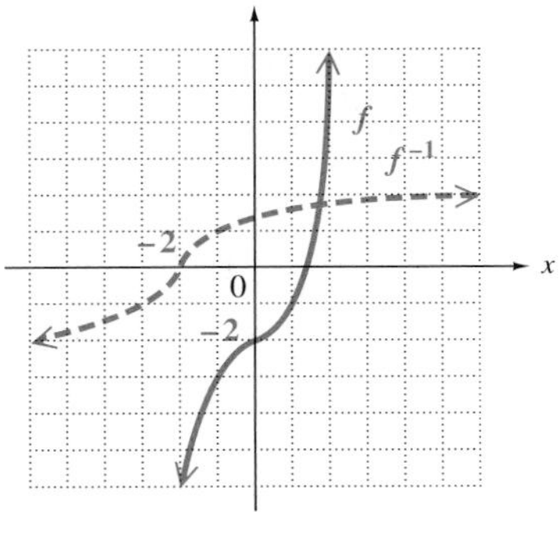

38. $y = x^3 + 3$

x	y
−2	−5
−1	2
0	3
1	4

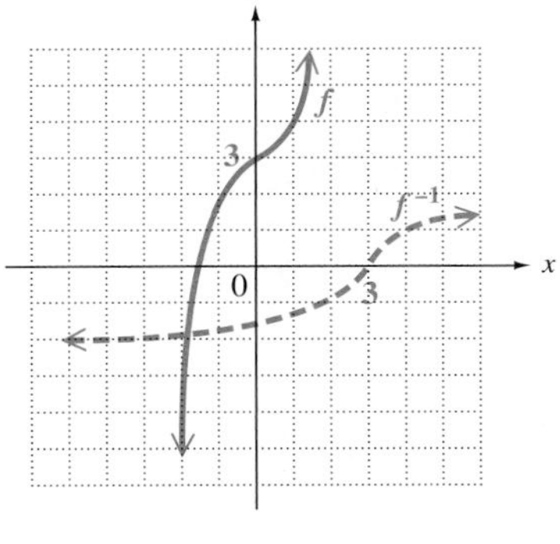

11.2 Exponential Functions

Objectives

1. Define exponential functions.
2. Graph exponential functions.
3. Solve exponential equations of the form $a^x = a^k$ for x.
4. Use exponential functions in applications involving growth or decay.

1 Define exponential functions. In Section 9.2 we showed how to evaluate 2^x for rational values of x. For example,

$$2^3 = 8, \qquad 2^{-1} = \frac{1}{2}, \qquad 2^{1/2} = \sqrt{2}, \qquad 2^{3/4} = \sqrt[4]{2^3} = \sqrt[4]{8}.$$

In more advanced courses it is shown that 2^x exists for all real number values of x, both rational and irrational. (Later in this chapter, we will see how to approximate the value of 2^x for irrational x.) The following definition of an exponential function assumes that a^x exists for all real numbers x.

Exponential Function

For $a > 0$, $a \neq 1$, and all real numbers x,

$$f(x) = a^x$$

defines an **exponential function.**

NOTE

The two restrictions on a in the definition of an exponential function are important. The restriction that a must be positive is necessary so that the function can be defined for all real numbers x. For example, letting a be negative ($a = -2$, for instance) and letting $x = \frac{1}{2}$ would give the expression $(-2)^{1/2}$, which is not real. The other restriction, $a \neq 1$, is necessary because 1 raised to any power is equal to 1, and the function would then be the linear function defined by $f(x) = 1$.

2 Graph exponential functions. We can graph an exponential function by finding several ordered pairs that belong to the function, plotting these points, and connecting them with a smooth curve.

CAUTION

Be sure to plot enough points to see how rapidly the graph rises.

Example 1 Graphing an Exponential Function with $a > 1$

Graph $f(x) = 2^x$.

Choose some values of x, and find the corresponding values of $f(x)$.

x	-3	-2	-1	0	1	2	3	4
$f(x) = 2^x$	$\frac{1}{8}$	$\frac{1}{4}$	$\frac{1}{2}$	1	2	4	8	16

Plotting these points and drawing a smooth curve through them gives the graph shown in Figure 6 on the next page. This graph is typical of the graphs of exponential functions of the form $F(x) = a^x$, where $a > 1$. The larger the value of a, the faster the graph rises. To see this, compare the graph of $F(x) = 5^x$ with the graph of $f(x) = 2^x$ in Figure 6.

Continued on Next Page

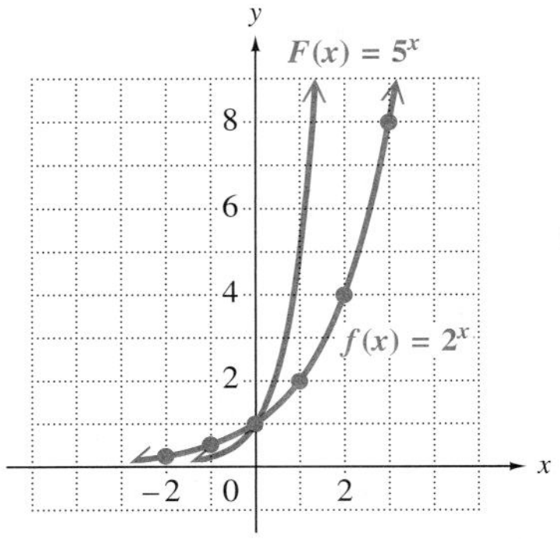

Figure 6

By the vertical line test, the graphs in Figure 6 represent functions. As these graphs suggest, the domain of an exponential function includes all real numbers. Because y is always positive, the range is $(0, \infty)$. Figure 6 also shows an important characteristic of exponential functions where $a > 1$: as x gets larger, y increases at a faster and faster rate.

Example 2 Graphing an Exponential Function with $a < 1$

Graph $g(x) = \left(\frac{1}{2}\right)^x$.

Again, find some points on the graph.

x	-3	-2	-1	0	1	2	3
$g(x) = (\frac{1}{2})^x$	8	4	2	1	$\frac{1}{2}$	$\frac{1}{4}$	$\frac{1}{8}$

The graph, shown in Figure 7, is very similar to that of $f(x) = 2^x$ (Figure 6) with the same domain and range, except that here as x gets larger, *y decreases.* This graph is typical of the graph of a function of the form $F(x) = a^x$, where $0 < a < 1$.

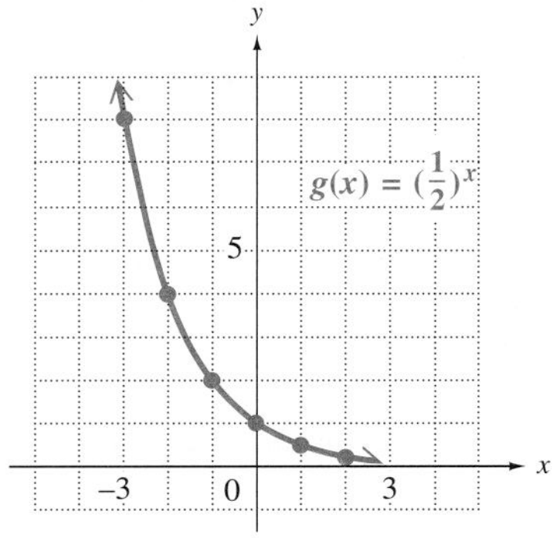

Figure 7

Work Problem 1 at the Side.

Based on Examples 1 and 2, we make the following generalizations about the graphs of exponential functions of the form $F(x) = a^x$.

1 Graph.

(a) $f(x) = 10^x$

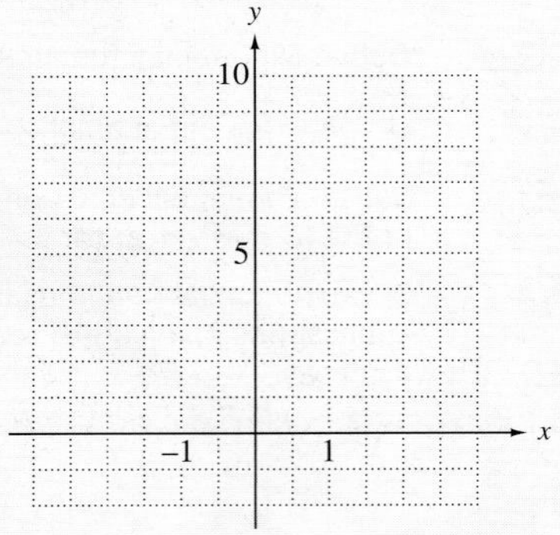

(b) $g(x) = \left(\frac{1}{4}\right)^x$

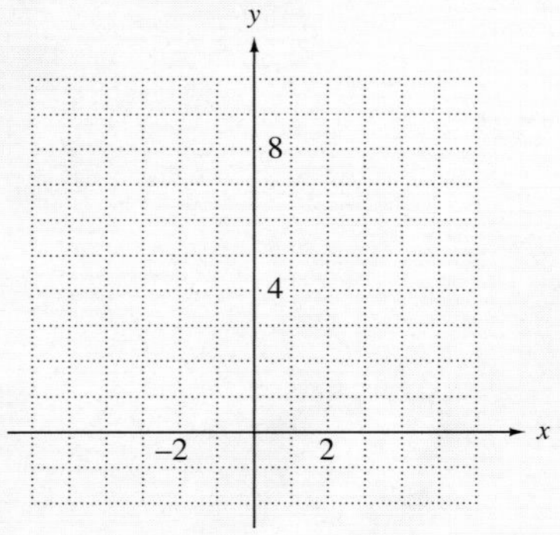

ANSWERS

1. (a)

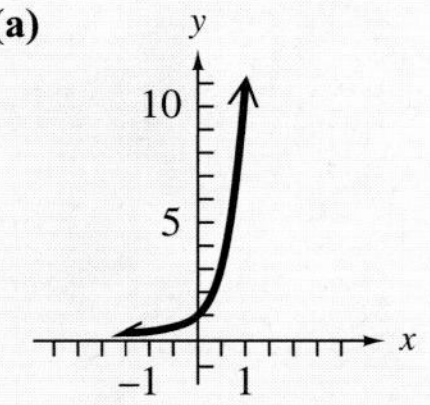

(b)

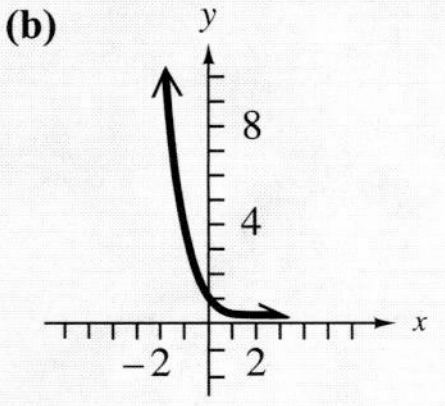

Graph of $F(x) = a^x$

1. The graph will always contain the point $(0, 1)$.
2. When $a > 1$, the graph will *rise* from left to right. When $0 < a < 1$, the graph will *fall* from left to right. In both cases, the graph goes from the second quadrant to the first.
3. The graph will approach the x-axis, but never touch it. (Recall from Chapter 8 that such a line is called an *asymptote*.)
4. The domain is $(-\infty, \infty)$, and the range is $(0, \infty)$.

2 Graph $y = 2^{4x-3}$.

Example 3 **Graphing a More Complicated Exponential Function**

Graph $f(x) = 3^{2x-4}$.

Find some ordered pairs.

$$\text{If } x = 0, \text{ then } y = 3^{2(0)-4} = 3^{-4} = \frac{1}{81}.$$

$$\text{If } x = 2, \text{ then } y = 3^{2(2)-4} = 3^0 = 1.$$

These ordered pairs, $(0, \frac{1}{81})$ and $(2, 1)$, along with the other ordered pairs shown in the table, lead to the graph in Figure 8. The graph is similar to the graph of $f(x) = 3^x$ except that it is shifted to the right and rises more rapidly.

x	y
0	$\frac{1}{81}$
1	$\frac{1}{9}$
2	1
3	9

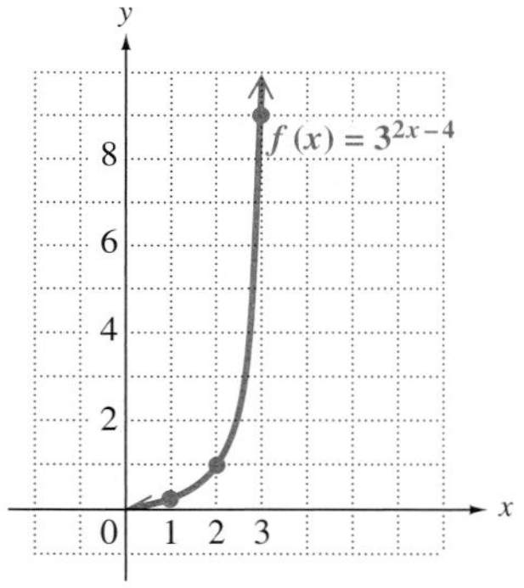

Figure 8

Work Problem 2 at the Side.

3 **Solve exponential equations of the form $a^x = a^k$ for x.** Until this chapter, we have solved only equations that had the variable as a base, like $x^2 = 8$; all exponents have been constants. An **exponential equation** is an equation that has a variable in an exponent, such as

$$9^x = 27.$$

By the horizontal line test, the exponential function defined by $F(x) = a^x$ is a one-to-one function, so we can use the following property to solve many exponential equations.

Property for Solving an Exponential Equation

For $a > 0$ and $a \neq 1$, if $a^x = a^y$ then $x = y$.

This property would not necessarily be true if $a = 1$.

ANSWERS

2.

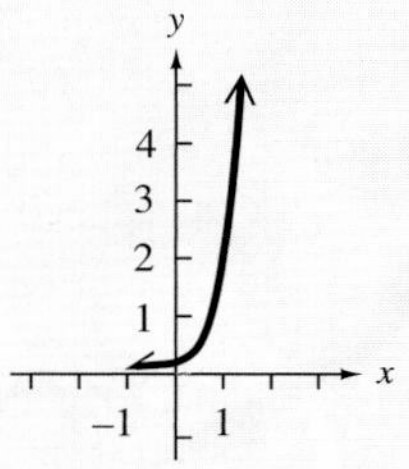

3 Solve. Check your answers.

(a) $25^x = 125$

(b) $4^x = 32$

(c) $81^p = 27$

To solve an exponential equation using this property, follow these steps.

Solving an Exponential Equation

Step 1 **Each side must have the same base.** If the two sides of the equation do not have the same base, express each as a power of the same base.

Step 2 **Simplify exponents.** If necessary, use the rules of exponents to simplify the exponents.

Step 3 **Set exponents equal.** Use the property given in this section to set the exponents equal.

Step 4 **Solve.** Solve the equation obtained in Step 3.

NOTE

These steps cannot be applied to an exponential equation like

$$3^x = 12$$

because Step 1 cannot easily be done. A method for solving such equations is given in Section 11.6.

Example 4 **Solving an Exponential Equation**

Solve the equation $9^x = 27$.

We can use the property given in the box if both sides are written with the same base. Since $9 = 3^2$ and $27 = 3^3$,

$$\begin{aligned} 9^x &= 27 && \\ (3^2)^x &= 3^3 && \text{Write with the same base. (Step 1)} \\ 3^{2x} &= 3^3 && \text{Power rule for exponents (Step 2)} \\ 2x &= 3 && \text{If } a^x = a^y, \text{ then } x = y. \text{ (Step 3)} \\ x &= \frac{3}{2}. && \text{(Step 4)} \end{aligned}$$

Check that the solution set is $\{\frac{3}{2}\}$ by substituting $\frac{3}{2}$ for x in the original equation.

Work Problem 3 at the Side.

Example 5 **Solving Exponential Equations**

Solve each equation.

(a) $4^{3x-1} = 16^{x+2}$

Since $4 = 2^2$ and $16 = 2^4$,

$$\begin{aligned} (2^2)^{3x-1} &= (2^4)^{x+2} && \text{Write with the same base.} \\ 2^{6x-2} &= 2^{4x+8} && \text{Power rule for exponents} \\ 6x - 2 &= 4x + 8 && \text{Set exponents equal.} \\ 2x &= 10 && \text{Subtract } 4x\text{; add 2.} \\ x &= 5. && \text{Divide by 2.} \end{aligned}$$

Verify that the solution set is $\{5\}$.

Continued on Next Page

ANSWERS

3. (a) $\left\{\frac{3}{2}\right\}$ (b) $\left\{\frac{5}{2}\right\}$ (c) $\left\{\frac{3}{4}\right\}$

(b) $6^x = \dfrac{1}{216}$

$$6^x = \frac{1}{216}$$

$$6^x = \frac{1}{6^3} \qquad 216 = 6^3$$

$$6^x = 6^{-3} \qquad \text{Write with the same base; } \frac{1}{6^3} = 6^{-3}.$$

$$x = -3 \qquad \text{Set exponents equal.}$$

Verify that the solution set is $\{-3\}$.

(c) $\left(\dfrac{2}{3}\right)^x = \dfrac{9}{4}$

$$\left(\frac{2}{3}\right)^x = \left(\frac{4}{9}\right)^{-1} \qquad \frac{9}{4} = \left(\frac{4}{9}\right)^{-1}$$

$$\left(\frac{2}{3}\right)^x = \left[\left(\frac{2}{3}\right)^2\right]^{-1} \qquad \text{Write with the same base.}$$

$$\left(\frac{2}{3}\right)^x = \left(\frac{2}{3}\right)^{-2} \qquad \text{Power rule for exponents}$$

$$x = -2 \qquad \text{Set exponents equal.}$$

Check that the solution set is $\{-2\}$.

Work Problem 4 at the Side.

4 **Use exponential functions in applications involving growth or decay.**

Example 6 **Solving an Application Involving Exponential Growth**

One result of the rapidly increasing world population is an increase of carbon dioxide in the air, which scientists believe may be contributing to global warming. Both population and carbon dioxide in the air are increasing exponentially. This means that the growth rate is continually increasing. The graph in Figure 9 shows the concentration of carbon dioxide (in parts per million) in the air.

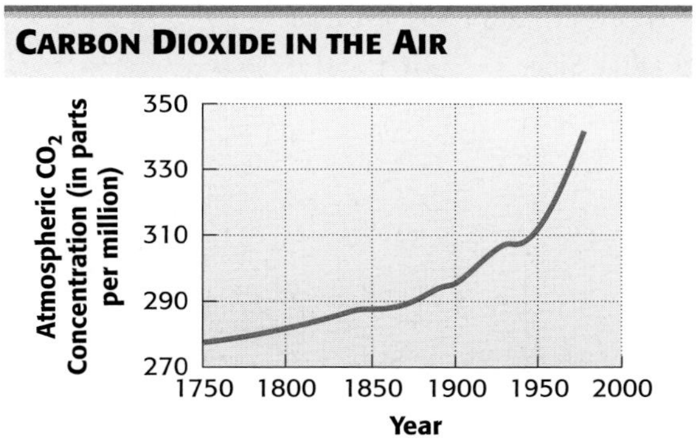

Source: Sacramento Bee, Monday, September 13, 1993.

Figure 9

Continued on Next Page

4 Solve each equation and check the solution.

(a) $25^{x-2} = 125^x$

(b) $4^x = \dfrac{1}{32}$

(c) $\left(\dfrac{3}{4}\right)^x = \dfrac{16}{9}$

ANSWERS

4. **(a)** $\{-4\}$ **(b)** $\left\{-\frac{5}{2}\right\}$ **(c)** $\{-2\}$

The data are approximated by the function with

$$f(x) = 278(1.00084)^x,$$

where x is the number of years since 1750. Use this function and a calculator to approximate the concentration of carbon dioxide in parts per million for each year.

(a) 1900

Since x represents the number of years since 1750, in this case $x = 1900 - 1750 = 150$. Thus, evaluate $f(150)$.

$$f(150) = 278(1.00084)^{150} \quad \text{Let } x = 150.$$
$$\approx 315 \text{ parts per million} \quad \text{Use a calculator.}$$

(b) 1950

Use $x = 1950 - 1750 = 200$: $f(200) \approx 329$ parts per million.

Example 7 **Applying an Exponential Decay Function**

The atmospheric pressure (in millibars) at a given altitude x, in meters, can be approximated by the function defined by

$$f(x) = 1038(1.000134)^{-x},$$

for values of x between 0 and 10,000. Because the base is greater than 1 and the coefficient of x in the exponent is negative, the function values decrease as x increases. This means that as the altitude increases, the atmospheric pressure decreases. (*Source:* Miller, A. and J. Thompson, *Elements of Meteorology,* Fourth Edition, Charles E. Merrill Publishing Company, 1993.)

(a) According to this function, what is the pressure at ground level?

At ground level, $x = 0$, so

$$f(0) = 1038(1.000134)^{-0} = 1038(1) = 1038.$$

The pressure is 1038 millibars.

(b) What is the pressure at 5000 m?

Use a calculator to find $f(5000)$.

$$f(5000) = 1038(1.000134)^{-5000} \approx 531$$

The pressure is approximately 531 millibars.

Work Problem 5 at the Side.

5 Solve each problem.

(a) Use the function in Example 6 to approximate the carbon dioxide concentration in 1925.

(b) Use the function in Example 7 to find the pressure at 8000 m.

ANSWERS

5. (a) 322 parts per million

(b) approximately 355 millibars

11.2 EXERCISES

FOR EXTRA HELP Student's Solutions Manual | MyMathLab.com | InterAct Math Tutorial Software | AW Math Tutor Center | www.mathxl.com | Digital Video Tutor CD 10 Videotape 22

Choose the correct response in Exercises 1–4.

1. Which point lies on the graph of $f(x) = 2^x$? C

A. $(1, 0)$ **B.** $(2, 1)$

C. $(0, 1)$ **D.** $\left(\sqrt{2}, \frac{1}{2}\right)$

2. Which statement is true? C

A. The y-intercept of the graph of $f(x) = 10^x$ is $(0, 10)$.

B. For any $a > 1$, the graph of $f(x) = a^x$ falls from left to right.

C. The point $(\frac{1}{2}, \sqrt{5})$ lies on the graph of $f(x) = 5^x$.

D. The graph of $y = 4^x$ rises at a faster rate than the graph of $y = 10^x$.

3. The asymptote of the graph of $F(x) = a^x$ A

A. is the x-axis. **B.** is the y-axis.

C. has equation $x = 1$. **D.** has equation $y = 1$.

4. Which equation is graphed here? C

A. $y = 1000\left(\frac{1}{2}\right)^{.3x}$

B. $y = 1000\left(\frac{1}{2}\right)^{x}$

C. $y = 1000(2)^{.3x}$

D. $y = 1000^x$

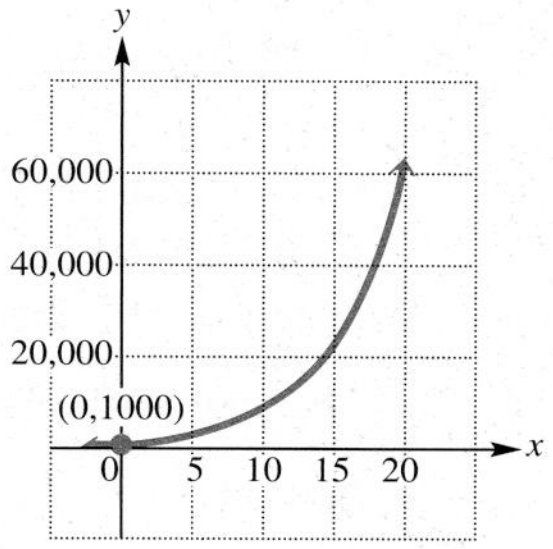

Graph each exponential function. See Examples 1–3.

5. $f(x) = 3^x$

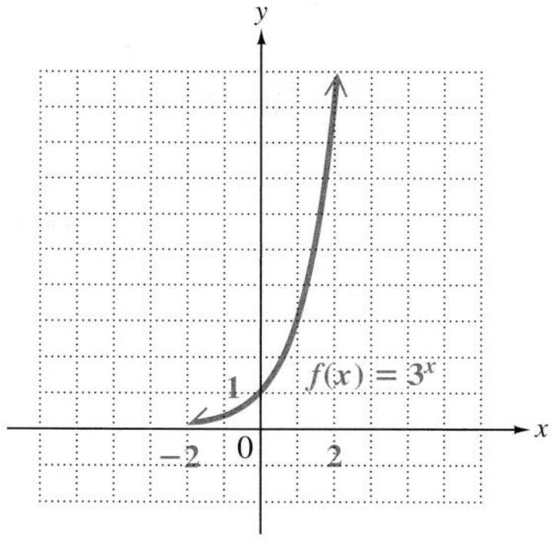

6. $f(x) = 5^x$

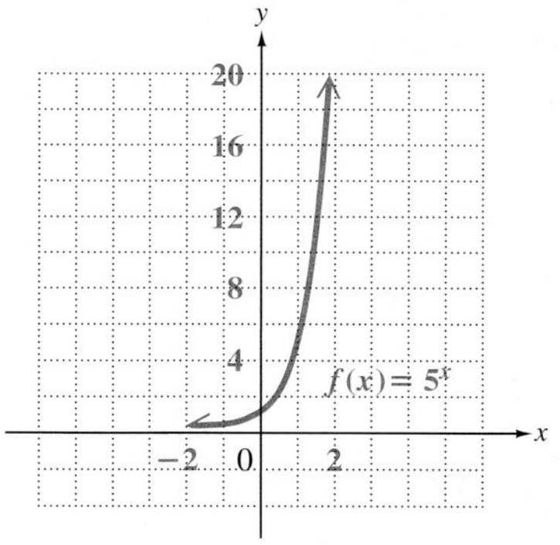

7. $g(x) = \left(\frac{1}{3}\right)^x$

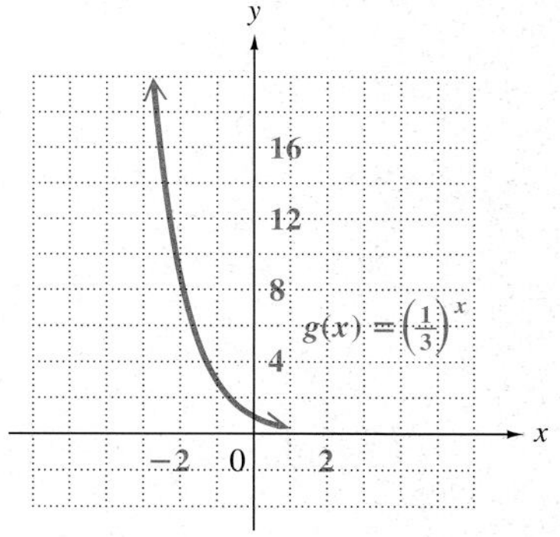

8. $g(x) = \left(\frac{1}{5}\right)^x$

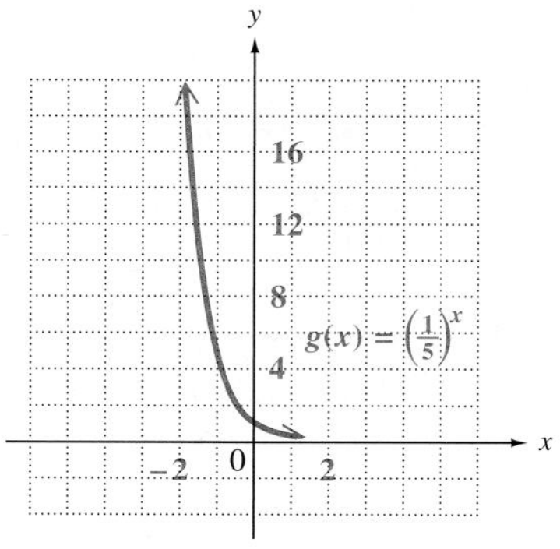

9. $y = 2^{2x-2}$

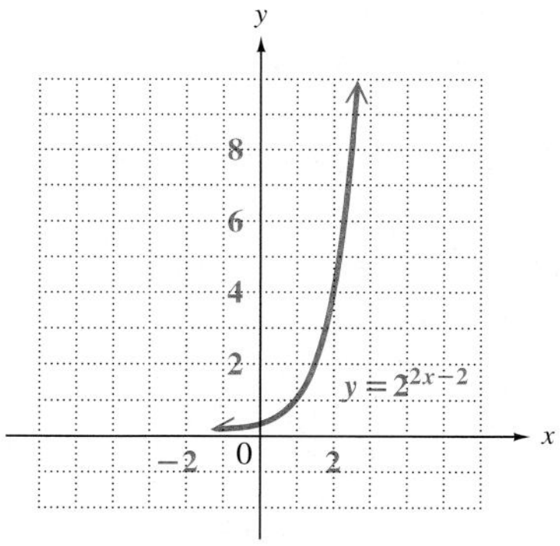

10. $y = 2^{2x+1}$

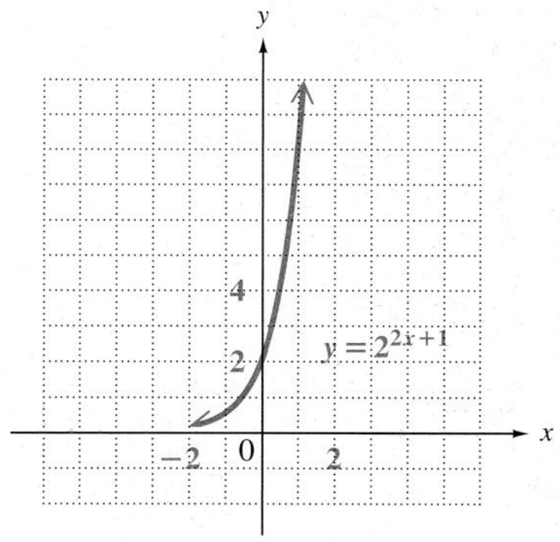

Solve each equation. See Examples 4 and 5.

11. $6^x = 36$ $\{2\}$

12. $8^x = 64$ $\{2\}$

13. $100^x = 1000$ $\left\{\frac{3}{2}\right\}$

14. $8^x = 4$ $\left\{\frac{2}{3}\right\}$

15. $16^{2x+1} = 64^{x+3}$ $\{7\}$

16. $9^{2x-8} = 27^{x-4}$ $\{4\}$

17. $5^x = \frac{1}{125}$ $\{-3\}$

18. $3^x = \frac{1}{81}$ $\{-4\}$

19. $5^x = .2$ $\{-1\}$

20. $10^x = .1$ $\{-1\}$

21. $\left(\frac{3}{2}\right)^x = \frac{8}{27}$ $\{-3\}$

22. $\left(\frac{4}{3}\right)^x = \frac{27}{64}$ $\{-3\}$

23. (a) For an exponential function defined by $f(x) = a^x$, if $a > 1$, the graph **rises** (rises/falls) from left to right. If $0 < a < 1$, the graph **falls** (rises/falls) from left to right.

(b) Based on your answers in part (a), make a conjecture (an educated guess) concerning whether an exponential function defined by $f(x) = a^x$ is one-to-one. Then decide whether it has an inverse based on the concepts of Section 11.1.

It is one-to-one and thus has an inverse.

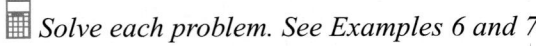

Solve each problem. See Examples 6 and 7.

The figure shown here accompanied the article "Is Our World Warming?" which appeared in the October 1990 issue of National Geographic. *It shows projected temperature increases using two graphs: one an exponential-type curve and the other linear. From the figure, approximate the increase* **(a)** *for the exponential curve, and* **(b)** *for the linear graph for each of the following years.*

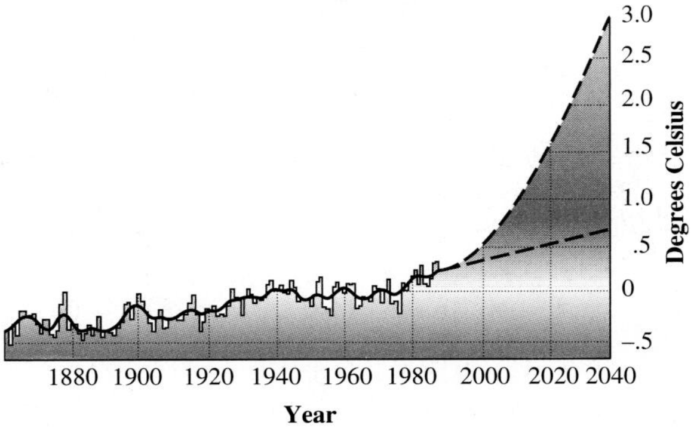

Graph, "Zero Equals Average Global Temperature for the Period 1950–1979." Dale D. Glasgow, © National Geographic Society. Reprinted by permission.

24. 2000 **(a)** .5°C **(b)** .35°C

25. 2010 **(a)** 1.0°C **(b)** .4°C

26. 2020 **(a)** 1.6°C **(b)** .5°C

27. 2040 **(a)** 3.0°C **(b)** .7°C

28. A small business estimates that the value $V(t)$ of a copy machine is decreasing according to the function defined by

$$V(t) = 5000(2)^{-.15t},$$

where t is the number of years that have elapsed since the machine was purchased and $V(t)$ is in dollars.

(a) What was the original value of the machine? **\$5000**

(b) What is the value of the machine 5 yr after purchase? Give your answer to the nearest dollar. **\$2973**

(c) What is the value of the machine 10 yr after purchase? Give your answer to the nearest dollar. **\$1768**

(d) Graph the function.

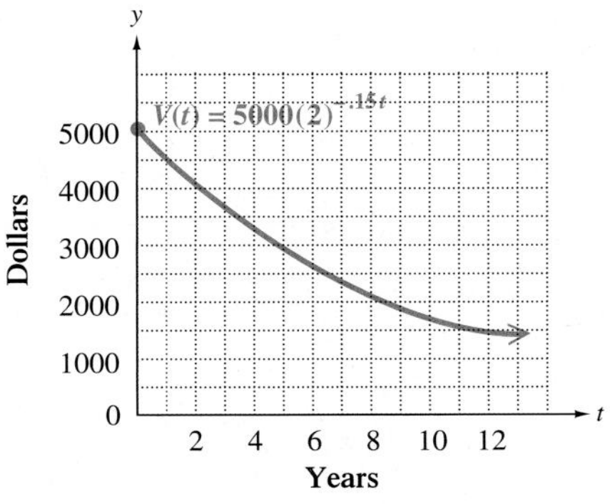

11.3 Logarithmic Functions

The graph of $y = 2^x$ is the curve shown in blue in Figure 10. Because $y = 2^x$ defines a one-to-one function, it has an inverse. Interchanging x and y gives $x = 2^y$, the inverse of $y = 2^x$. As we saw in Section 11.1, the graph of the inverse is found by reflecting the graph of $y = 2^x$ about the line $y = x$. The graph of $x = 2^y$ is shown as a red curve in Figure 10.

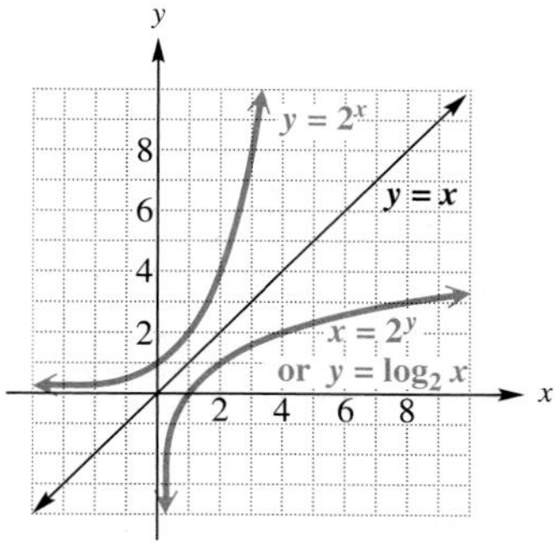

Figure 10

Objectives

1. Define a logarithm.
2. Convert between exponential and logarithmic forms.
3. Solve logarithmic equations of the form $\log_a b = k$ for a, b, or k.
4. Define and graph logarithmic functions.
5. Use logarithmic functions in applications of growth or decay.

1 Define a logarithm. We cannot solve the equation $x = 2^y$ for the dependent variable y with the methods presented up to now. The following definition is used to solve $x = 2^y$ for y.

Logarithm

For all positive numbers a, $a \neq 1$, and all positive numbers x,

$$y = \log_a x \text{ means the same as } x = a^y.$$

This key statement should be memorized. The abbreviation **log** is used for **logarithm.** Read $\log_a x$ as "the logarithm of x to the base a." To remember the location of the base and the exponent in each form, refer to the following diagrams.

Exponent ↓	Exponent ↓
Logarithmic form: $y = \log_a x$	Exponential form: $x = a^y$
↑ Base	↑ Base

In working with logarithmic form and exponential form, remember the following.

Meaning of $\log_a x$

A logarithm is an exponent; $\log_a x$ is the exponent to which the base a must be raised to obtain x.

1 Complete the table.

Exponential Form	Logarithmic Form
$2^5 = 32$	________
$100^{1/2} = 10$	________
________	$\log_8 4 = \frac{2}{3}$
________	$\log_6 \frac{1}{1296} = -4$

2 Convert between exponential and logarithmic forms. We can use the definition of logarithm to write exponential statements in logarithmic form and logarithmic statements in exponential form. The following table shows several pairs of equivalent statements.

Exponential Form	Logarithmic Form
$3^2 = 9$	$\log_3 9 = 2$
$\left(\frac{1}{5}\right)^{-2} = 25$	$\log_{1/5} 25 = -2$
$10^5 = 100{,}000$	$\log_{10} 100{,}000 = 5$
$4^{-3} = \frac{1}{64}$	$\log_4 \frac{1}{64} = -3$

Work Problem 1 at the Side.

3 Solve logarithmic equations of the form $\log_a b = k$ for a, b, or k. A **logarithmic equation** is an equation with a logarithm in at least one term. We solve logarithmic equations of the form $\log_a b = k$ for any of the three variables by first writing the equation in exponential form.

Example 1 Solving Logarithmic Equations

Solve each equation.

(a) $\log_4 x = -2$

By the definition of logarithm, $\log_4 x = -2$ is equivalent to $x = 4^{-2}$. Solve this exponential equation.

$$x = 4^{-2} = \frac{1}{16}$$

The solution set is $\{\frac{1}{16}\}$.

(b) $\log_{1/2} (3x + 1) = 2$

$$3x + 1 = \left(\frac{1}{2}\right)^2 \quad \text{Write in exponential form.}$$

$$3x + 1 = \frac{1}{4}$$

$$12x + 4 = 1 \quad \text{Multiply by 4.}$$

$$12x = -3 \quad \text{Subtract 4.}$$

$$x = -\frac{1}{4} \quad \text{Divide by 12.}$$

The solution set is $\{-\frac{1}{4}\}$.

(c) $\log_x 3 = 2$

$$x^2 = 3 \quad \text{Write in exponential form.}$$

$$x = \pm\sqrt{3} \quad \text{Take square roots.}$$

Notice that only the principal square root satisfies the equation, since the base must be a positive number. The solution set is $\{\sqrt{3}\}$.

Continued on Next Page

ANSWERS

1. $\log_2 32 = 5$; $\log_{100} 10 = \frac{1}{2}$; $8^{2/3} = 4$; $6^{-4} = \frac{1}{1296}$

(d) $\log_{49} \sqrt[3]{7} = x$

$$49^x = \sqrt[3]{7} \quad \text{Write in exponential form.}$$
$$(7^2)^x = 7^{1/3}$$
$$7^{2x} = 7^{1/3} \quad \text{Write with the same base.}$$
$$2x = \frac{1}{3} \quad \text{Set exponents equal.}$$
$$x = \frac{1}{6} \quad \text{Divide by 2.}$$

The solution set is $\{\frac{1}{6}\}$.

Work Problem **2** at the Side.

For any real number b, we know that $b^1 = b$ and $b^0 = 1$. Writing these two statements in logarithmic form gives the following two properties of logarithms.

For any positive real number b, $b \neq 1$,

$$\log_b b = 1 \quad \text{and} \quad \log_b 1 = 0.$$

Example 2 Using Properties of Logarithms

Use the preceding two properties of logarithms to evaluate each logarithm.

(a) $\log_7 7 = 1$

(b) $\log_{\sqrt{2}} \sqrt{2} = 1$

(c) $\log_9 1 = 0$

(d) $\log_{.2} 1 = 0$

Work Problem **3** at the Side.

4 Define and graph logarithmic functions. Now we define the logarithmic function with base a.

Logarithmic Function

If a and x are positive numbers, with $a \neq 1$, then

$$G(x) = \log_a x$$

defines the **logarithmic function with base *a*.**

To graph a logarithmic function, it is helpful to write it in exponential form first. Then plot selected ordered pairs to determine the graph.

Example 3 Graphing a Logarithmic Function

Graph $y = \log_{1/2} x$.

By writing $y = \log_{1/2} x$ in exponential form as $x = (\frac{1}{2})^y$, we can identify ordered pairs that satisfy the equation. Here it is easier to choose values for y and find the corresponding values of x. See the table of ordered pairs.

Continued on Next Page

2 Solve each equation.

(a) $\log_3 27 = x$

(b) $\log_5 p = 2$

(c) $\log_m \frac{1}{16} = -4$

(d) $\log_x 12 = 3$

3 Evaluate each logarithm.

(a) $\log_{2/5} \frac{2}{5}$

(b) $\log_{.4} 1$

ANSWERS

2. (a) $\{3\}$ **(b)** $\{25\}$ **(c)** $\{2\}$ **(d)** $\sqrt[3]{12}$

3. (a) 1 **(b)** 0

4 Graph.

(a) $y = \log_3 x$

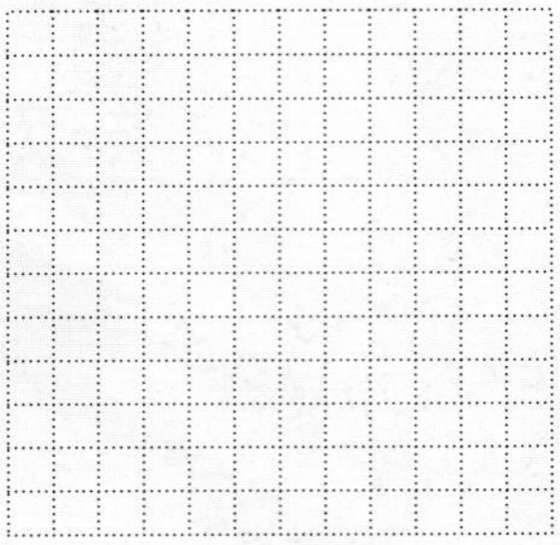

(b) $y = \log_{1/10} x$

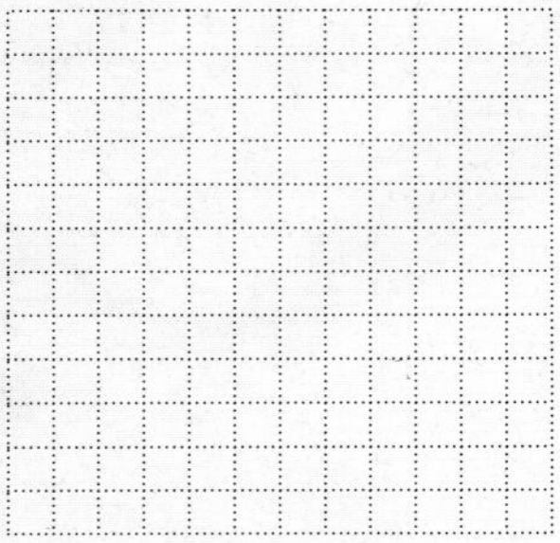

x	y
$\frac{1}{4}$	2
$\frac{1}{2}$	1
1	0
2	−1
4	−2

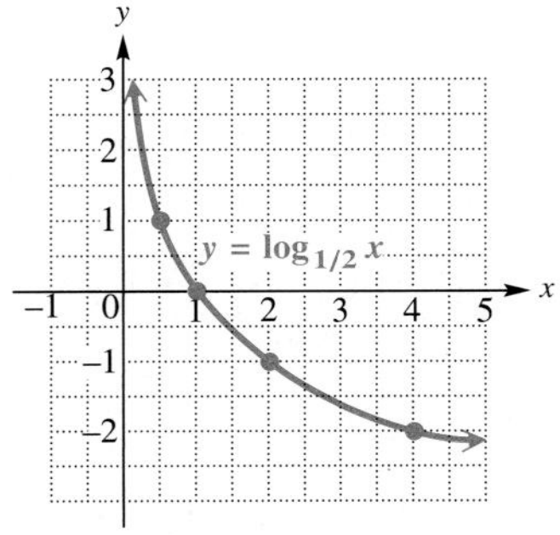

Figure 11

Plotting these points (be careful to get them in the right order) and connecting them with a smooth curve gives the graph in Figure 11. This graph is typical of logarithmic functions with $0 < a < 1$. The graph of $x = 2^y$ in Figure 10, which is equivalent to $y = \log_2 x$, is typical of graphs of logarithmic functions with base $a > 1$.

Work Problem 4 at the Side.

Based on the graphs of the functions defined by $y = \log_2 x$ in Figure 10 and $y = \log_{1/2} x$ in Figure 11, we make the following generalizations about the graphs of logarithmic functions of the form $G(x) = \log_a x$.

Graph of $G(x) = \log_a x$

1. The graph contains the point (1, 0).
2. When $a > 1$, the graph will *rise* from left to right, from the fourth quadrant to the first. When $0 < a < 1$, the graph will *fall* from left to right, from the first quadrant to the fourth.
3. The graph will approach the y-axis, but never touch it. (The y-axis is an asymptote.)
4. The domain is $(0, \infty)$, and the range is $(-\infty, \infty)$.

Compare these generalizations to the similar ones for exponential functions in Section 11.2.

5 Use logarithmic functions in applications of growth or decay. Logarithmic functions, like exponential functions, can be applied to growth or decay of real-world phenomena.

Example 4 Solving an Application of a Logarithmic Function

The function defined by

$$f(x) = 27 + 1.105 \log_{10}(x + 1)$$

approximates the barometric pressure in inches of mercury at a distance of x miles from the eye of a typical hurricane. (*Source:* Miller, A. and R. Anthes, *Meteorology,* Fifth Edition, Charles E. Merrill Publishing Company, 1985.)

Continued on Next Page

ANSWERS

4. (a)

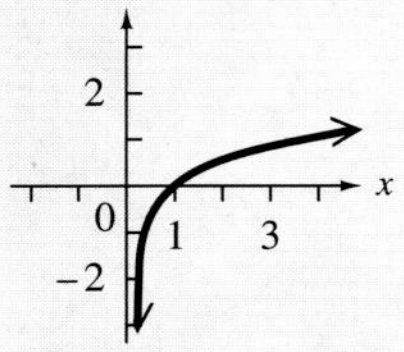

(b)

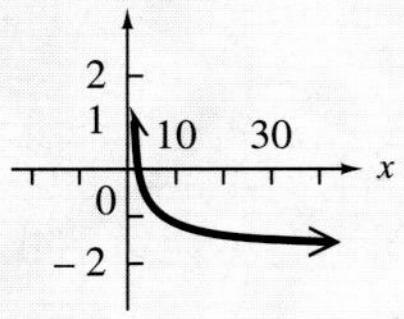

(a) Approximate the pressure 9 mi from the eye of the hurricane.
Let $x = 9$, and find $f(9)$.

$$\begin{aligned} f(9) &= 27 + 1.105 \log_{10}(9 + 1) && \text{Let } x = 9. \\ &= 27 + 1.105 \log_{10} 10 && \text{Add inside parentheses.} \\ &= 27 + 1.105(1) && \log_{10} 10 = 1 \\ &= 28.105 && \text{Add.} \end{aligned}$$

The pressure 9 mi from the eye of the hurricane is 28.105 in.

(b) Approximate the pressure 99 mi from the eye of the hurricane.

$$\begin{aligned} f(99) &= 27 + 1.105 \log_{10}(99 + 1) && \text{Let } x = 99. \\ &= 27 + 1.105 \log_{10} 100 && \text{Add inside parentheses.} \\ &= 27 + 1.105(2) && \log_{10} 100 = 2 \\ &= 29.21 \end{aligned}$$

The pressure 99 mi from the eye of the hurricane is 29.21 in.

Work Problem 5 at the Side.

5 Solve the problem.

A population of mites in a laboratory is growing according to the function with

$$P(t) = 80 \log_{10}(t + 10),$$

where t is the number of days after a study is begun.

(a) Find the number of mites at the beginning of the study.

(b) Find the number present after 90 days.

(c) Find the number present after 990 days.

ANSWERS

5. **(a)** 80 **(b)** 160 **(c)** 240

Focus on

Real-Data Applications

m&m's and Exponential Decay

Exponential functions are important for modeling decay patterns, including the life of a light bulb and radioactive decaying elements, such as carbon-14. You can simulate an exponential decay problem with an m&m experiment.

Use a fun-size or small package of regular m&m's. Before you begin the simulation, check that each candy has the logo "m&m" stamped on one side—you may eat the candies with no logo. Place the m&m's in a cup, shake, and toss them onto a napkin. In the table, record the number of m&m's showing the logo. Discard (or eat) all the candies for which the m&m logo is not showing. Repeat until there are 1 or no candies left. The data from one such simulation using 64 m&m's are shown in the table.

EXPERIMENTAL DATA

Toss	Number of m&m Logos Showing	Your Results
0	64	
1	29	
2	17	
3	6	
4	4	
5	3	
6	2	
7	1	

For Group Discussion

1. In a perfect world, you might expect the number of candies left after each toss in our simulation using 64 m&m's to follow the pattern 64, 32, 16, 8, 4, 2, 1. An exponential model has an equation of the form $y = ab^x$. The constant a represents the initial quantity (value when $x = 0$), and the constant b represents the growth rate factor ($b > 1$) or decay rate factor ($0 < b < 1$). For our perfect-world data, what would be the values of a and b? What would be the model exponential equation?

   $a = 64, b = \frac{1}{2}; y = 64\left(\frac{1}{2}\right)^x$

2. On the grid, plot the points for the experimental data, your results, and the points for the theoretical (perfect-world) model. Use a different color to plot each set of data. How well do the graphs match?

   Answers will vary.

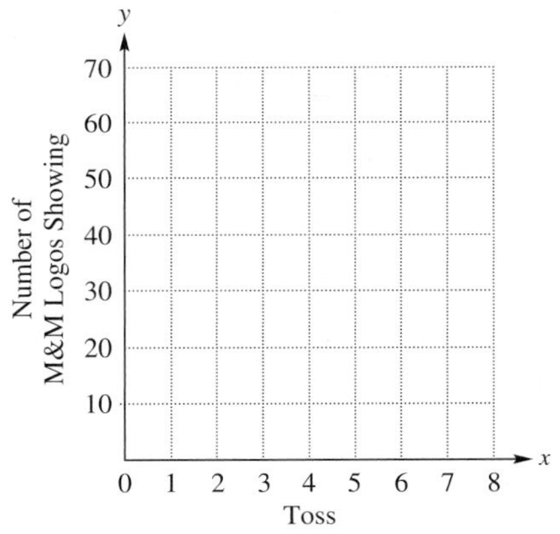

3. You can use a graphing calculator to find the statistical model for the sample experimental data, $y = 50.4(.56)^x$. Develop a table of values for $x = 0, 1, 2, \ldots, 7$ and superimpose the plot of the statistical model on your graph from Problem 2.

   (a) Does the theoretical or the statistical equation better model your experimental data?

   Answers will vary.

   (b) Based on the statistical equation, give an estimate of the initial number of m&m's.

   approximately 50

   (c) Based on the statistical equation, estimate the decay rate factor.

   approximately .56

Teaching notes and an extension for this activity are provided in the *Printed Test Bank and Instructor's Resource Guide.*

11.3 EXERCISES

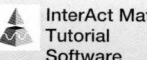

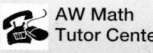

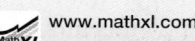

FOR EXTRA HELP: Student's Solutions Manual | MyMathLab.com | InterAct Math Tutorial Software | AW Math Tutor Center | www.mathxl.com | Digital Video Tutor CD 10 Videotape 22

1. By definition, $\log_a x$ is the exponent to which the base a must be raised in order to obtain x. Use this definition to match the logarithm in Column I with its value in Column II. (*Example:* $\log_3 9$ is equal to 2 because 2 is the exponent to which 3 must be raised in order to obtain 9.)

I		II
(a) $\log_4 16$	C	**A.** -2
(b) $\log_3 81$	F	**B.** -1
(c) $\log_3\left(\frac{1}{3}\right)$	B	**C.** 2
(d) $\log_{10} .01$	A	**D.** 0
(e) $\log_5\sqrt{5}$	E	**E.** $\frac{1}{2}$
(f) $\log_{13} 1$	D	**F.** 4

2. Match the logarithmic equation in Column I with the corresponding exponential equation from Column II.

I		II
(a) $\log_{1/3} 3 = -1$	B	**A.** $8^{1/3} = \sqrt[3]{8}$
(b) $\log_5 1 = 0$	E	**B.** $\left(\frac{1}{3}\right)^{-1} = 3$
(c) $\log_2\sqrt{2} = \frac{1}{2}$	D	**C.** $4^1 = 4$
(d) $\log_{10} 1000 = 3$	F	**D.** $2^{1/2} = \sqrt{2}$
(e) $\log_8\sqrt[3]{8} = \frac{1}{3}$	A	**E.** $5^0 = 1$
(f) $\log_4 4 = 1$	C	**F.** $10^3 = 1000$

Write in logarithmic form. See the table in Objective 2.

3. $4^5 = 1024$

$\log_4 1024 = 5$

4. $3^6 = 729$

$\log_3 729 = 6$

5. $\left(\frac{1}{2}\right)^{-3} = 8$

$\log_{1/2} 8 = -3$

6. $\left(\frac{1}{6}\right)^{-3} = 216$

$\log_{1/6} 216 = -3$

7. $10^{-3} = .001$

$\log_{10} .001 = -3$

8. $36^{1/2} = 6$

$\log_{36} 6 = \frac{1}{2}$

9. $\sqrt[4]{625} = 5$

$\log_{625} 5 = \frac{1}{4}$

10. $\sqrt[3]{343} = 7$

$\log_{343} 7 = \frac{1}{3}$

Write in exponential form. See the table in Objective 2.

11. $\log_4 64 = 3$

$4^3 = 64$

12. $\log_2 512 = 9$

$2^9 = 512$

13. $\log_{10}\frac{1}{10{,}000} = -4$

$10^{-4} = \frac{1}{10{,}000}$

14. $\log_{100} 100 = 1$

$100^1 = 100$

15. $\log_6 1 = 0$

$6^0 = 1$

16. $\log_\pi 1 = 0$

$\pi^0 = 1$

17. $\log_9 3 = \frac{1}{2}$

$9^{1/2} = 3$

18. $\log_{64} 2 = \frac{1}{6}$

$64^{1/6} = 2$

19. When a student asked his teacher to explain to him how to evaluate $\log_9 3$ without showing any work, his teacher told him, "Think radically." Explain what the teacher meant by this hint.

Since the radical $\sqrt{9} = 9^{1/2} = 3$, the exponent to which 9 must be raised is 1/2.

20. A student told her teacher "I know that $\log_2 1$ is the exponent to which 2 must be raised in order to obtain 1, but I can't think of any such number." How would you explain to the student that the value of $\log_2 1$ is 0?

Recall that any nonzero number raised to the 0 power equals 1.

Solve each equation for x. See Examples 1 and 2.

21. $x = \log_{27} 3$

$\left\{\frac{1}{3}\right\}$

22. $x = \log_{125} 5$

$\left\{\frac{1}{3}\right\}$

23. $\log_x 9 = \frac{1}{2}$

$\{81\}$

24. $\log_x 5 = \frac{1}{2}$

$\{25\}$

25. $\log_x 125 = -3$

$\left\{\frac{1}{5}\right\}$

26. $\log_x 64 = -6$

$\left\{\frac{1}{2}\right\}$

27. $\log_{12} x = 0$

$\{1\}$

28. $\log_4 x = 0$

$\{1\}$

29. $\log_x x = 1$

$\{x \mid x > 0, x \neq 1\}$

30. $\log_x 1 = 0$

$\{x \mid x > 0, x \neq 1\}$

31. $\log_x \frac{1}{25} = -2$

$\{5\}$

32. $\log_x \frac{1}{10} = -1$

$\{10\}$

33. $\log_8 32 = x$

$\left\{\frac{5}{3}\right\}$

34. $\log_{81} 27 = x$

$\left\{\frac{3}{4}\right\}$

35. $\log_\pi \pi^4 = x$

$\{4\}$

36. $\log_{\sqrt{2}} \sqrt{2^9} = x$

$\{9\}$

37. $\log_6 \sqrt{216} = x$

$\left\{\frac{3}{2}\right\}$

38. $\log_4 \sqrt{64} = x$

$\left\{\frac{3}{2}\right\}$

If the point (p, q) is on the graph of $f(x) = a^x$ (for $a > 0$ and $a \neq 1$), then the point (q, p) is on the graph of $f^{-1}(x) = \log_a x$. Use this fact and refer to the graphs required in Exercises 5–8 in Section 11.2 to graph each logarithmic function. See Example 3.

39. $y = \log_3 x$

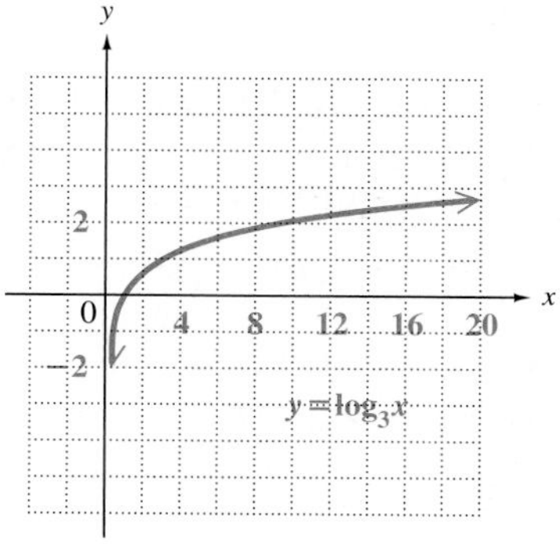

40. $y = \log_5 x$

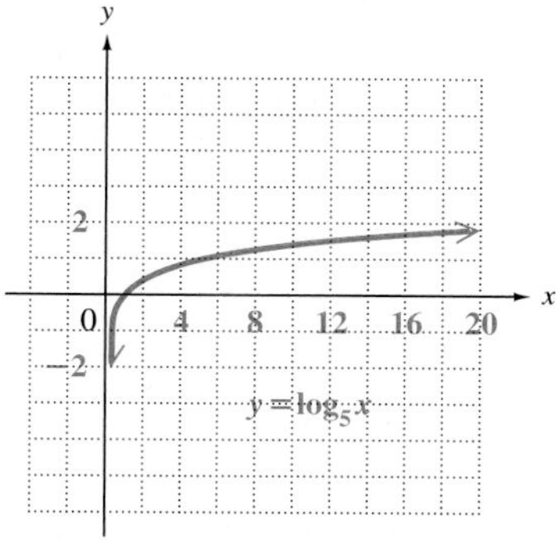

41. $y = \log_{1/3} x$

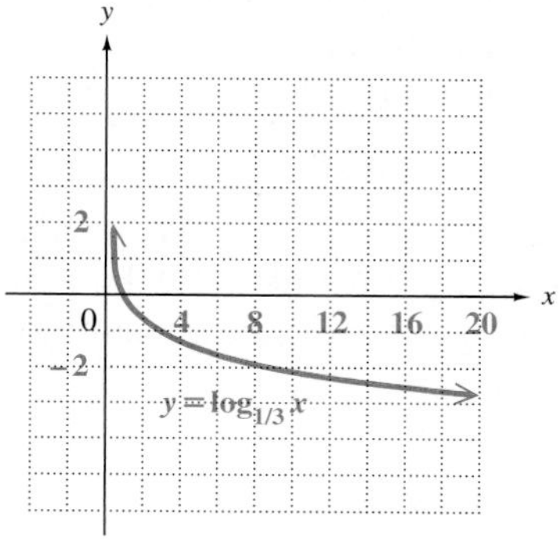

42. $y = \log_{1/5} x$

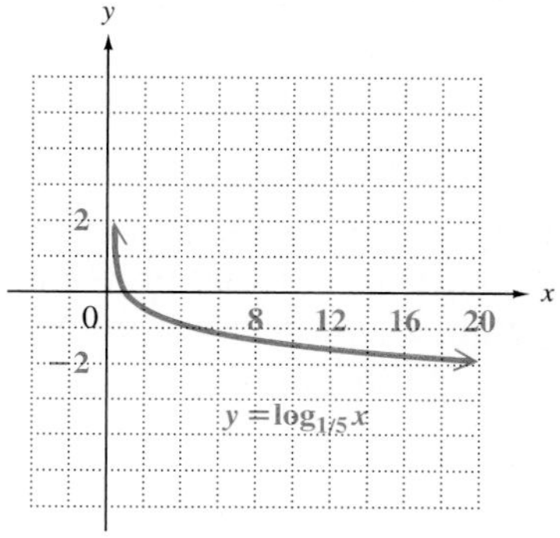

43. Compare the summary of facts about the graph of $F(x) = a^x$ in Section 11.2 with the similar summary of facts about the graph of $G(x) = \log_a x$ in this section. Make a list of the facts that reinforce the concept that F and G are inverse functions.

Answers will vary.

44. The domain of $F(x) = a^x$ is $(-\infty, \infty)$, while the range is $(0, \infty)$. Therefore, since $G(x) = \log_a x$ defines the inverse of F, the domain of G is $\underline{(0, \infty)}$, while the range of G is $\underline{(-\infty, \infty)}$.

Use the graph to predict the value of $f(t)$ for each value of t.

45. $t = 0$

8

46. $t = 10$

16

47. $t = 60$

24

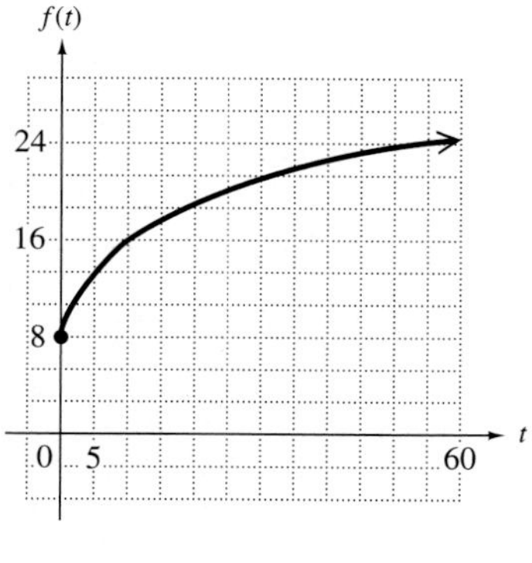

48. Show that the points determined in Exercises 45–47 lie on the graph of $f(t) = 8 \log_5(2t + 5)$.

$f(0) = 8; f(10) = 16; f(60) = 24$

49. Explain why 1 is not allowed as a base for a logarithmic function.

Since every real number power of 1 equals 1, if $y = \log_1 x$, then $x = 1^y$ and so $x = 1$ for every y. This contradicts the definition of a function.

50. Explain why $\log_a 1$ is 0 for any value of a that is allowed as the base of a logarithm. Use a rule of exponents introduced earlier in your explanation.

$x = \log_a 1$ is equivalent to $a^x = 1$. The only value of x that makes $a^x = 1$ is 0. (Recall that $a \neq 1$.)

51. The graphs of both $f(x) = 3^x$ and $g(x) = \log_3 x$ rise from left to right. Which one rises at a faster rate?

$f(x) = 3^x$

52. Use the exponential key of your calculator to find approximations for the expression $(1 + \frac{1}{x})^x$, using x values of 1, 10, 100, 1000, and 10,000. Explain what seems to be happening as x gets larger and larger.

The expression gets closer and closer to a number that is approximately 2.718.

Solve each application of a logarithmic function. See Example 4.

53. According to selected figures from 1981 through 1995, the number of Superfund hazardous waste sites in the United States can be approximated by the function with

$$f(x) = 11.34 + 317.01 \log_2 x,$$

where $x = 1$ corresponds to 1981, $x = 2$ to 1982, and so on. (*Source:* U.S. Environmental Protection Agency.) Use the function to approximate the number of sites in each of the following years.

(a) 1984 **645 sites**

(b) 1988 **962 sites**

(c) 1994 **1218 sites**

54. According to selected figures from 1980 through 1993, the number of trillion cubic feet of dry natural gas consumed worldwide can be approximated by the function with

$$f(x) = 51.47 + 6.044 \log_2 x,$$

where $x = 1$ corresponds to 1980, $x = 2$ to 1981, and so on. (*Source:* Energy Information Administration.) Use the function to approximate consumption in each of the following years.

(a) 1980 **51.47 trillion ft³**

(b) 1987 **69.602 trillion ft³**

(c) 1993 **74.482 trillion ft³**

In the United States, the intensity of an earthquake is rated using the Richter scale. *The Richter scale rating of an earthquake of intensity x is given by*

$$R = \log_{10} \frac{x}{x_0},$$

where x_0 is the intensity of an earthquake of a certain (small) size. The figure shows Richter scale ratings for major Southern California earthquakes since 1920. As the figure indicates, earthquakes "come in bunches" and the 1990s were an especially busy time.

MAJOR SOUTHERN CALIFORNIA EARTHQUAKES

Earthquakes with magnitudes greater than 4.8

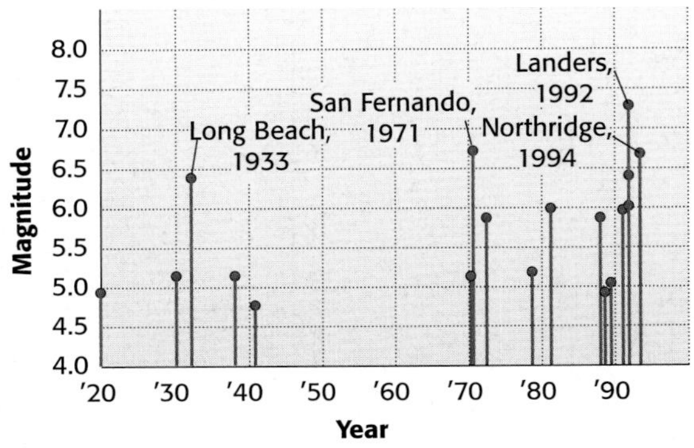

Source: Caltech; U.S. Geological Survey.

55. The 1994 Northridge earthquake had a Richter scale rating of 6.7; the Landers earthquake had a rating of 7.3. How much more powerful was the Landers earthquake than the Northridge earthquake?

about 4 times as powerful

56. Compare the smallest rated earthquake in the figure (at 4.8) with the Landers quake. How much more powerful was the Landers quake?

about 300 times as powerful

11.4 PROPERTIES OF LOGARITHMS

OBJECTIVES

1. Use the product rule for logarithms.
2. Use the quotient rule for logarithms.
3. Use the power rule for logarithms.
4. Use properties to write alternative forms of logarithmic expressions.

Logarithms have been used as an aid to numerical calculation for several hundred years. Today the widespread use of calculators has made the use of logarithms for calculation obsolete. However, logarithms are still very important in applications and in further work in mathematics.

1 Use the product rule for logarithms. One way in which logarithms simplify problems is by changing a problem of multiplication into one of addition. We know that $\log_2 4 = 2$, $\log_2 8 = 3$, and $\log_2 32 = 5$. Since $2 + 3 = 5$,

$$\log_2 32 = \log_2 4 + \log_2 8$$
$$\log_2(4 \cdot 8) = \log_2 4 + \log_2 8.$$

This is true in general.

Product Rule for Logarithms

If x, y, and b are positive real numbers, where $b \neq 1$, then

$$\log_b xy = \log_b x + \log_b y.$$

In words, the logarithm of a product is the sum of the logarithms of the factors.

NOTE

The word statement of the product rule can be restated by replacing "logarithm" with "exponent." The rule then becomes the familiar rule for multiplying exponential expressions: The *exponent* of a product is equal to the sum of the *exponents* of the factors.

To prove this rule, let $m = \log_b x$ and $n = \log_b y$, and recall that

$$\log_b x = m \quad \text{means} \quad b^m = x.$$
$$\log_b y = n \quad \text{means} \quad b^n = y.$$

Now consider the product xy.

$xy = b^m \cdot b^n$	Substitution
$xy = b^{m+n}$	Product rule for exponents
$\log_b xy = m + n$	Convert to logarithmic form.
$\log_b xy = \log_b x + \log_b y$	Substitution

The last statement is the result we wished to prove.

Example 1 Using the Product Rule

Use the product rule to rewrite each expression. Assume $x > 0$.

(a) $\log_5(6 \cdot 9)$
By the product rule,

$$\log_5(6 \cdot 9) = \log_5 6 + \log_5 9.$$

(b) $\log_7 8 + \log_7 12 = \log_7(8 \cdot 12) = \log_7 96$

Continued on Next Page

1 Use the product rule to rewrite each expression.

(a) $\log_6(5 \cdot 8)$

(b) $\log_4 3 + \log_4 7$

(c) $\log_8 8k, \quad k > 0$

(d) $\log_5 m^2, \quad m \neq 0$

2 Use the quotient rule to rewrite each expression.

(a) $\log_7 \frac{9}{4}$

(b) $\log_3 p - \log_3 q, \quad p > 0, \quad q > 0$

(c) $\log_4 \frac{3}{16}$

(c) $\log_3(3x) = \log_3 3 + \log_3 x$

$= 1 + \log_3 x$ $\qquad \log_3 3 = 1$

(d) $\log_4 x^3 = \log_4(x \cdot x \cdot x)$ $\qquad x^3 = x \cdot x \cdot x$

$= \log_4 x + \log_4 x + \log_4 x$ $\qquad$ Product rule

$= 3 \log_4 x$

Work Problem 1 at the Side.

2 Use the quotient rule for logarithms. The rule for division is similar to the rule for multiplication.

Quotient Rule for Logarithms

If x, y, and b are positive real numbers, where $b \neq 1$, then

$$\log_b \frac{x}{y} = \log_b x - \log_b y.$$

In words, the logarithm of a quotient is the difference between the logarithm of the numerator and the logarithm of the denominator.

The proof of this rule is very similar to the proof of the product rule.

Example 2 Using the Quotient Rule

Use the quotient rule to rewrite each logarithm.

(a) $\log_4 \frac{7}{9} = \log_4 7 - \log_4 9$

(b) $\log_5 6 - \log_5 x = \log_5 \frac{6}{x}$, for $x > 0$.

(c) $\log_3 \frac{27}{5} = \log_3 27 - \log_3 5$

$= 3 - \log_3 5$ $\qquad \log_3 27 = 3$

CAUTION

Remember that there is no property of logarithms to rewrite the logarithm of a *sum* or *difference.* For example, we *cannot* write $\log_b(x + y)$ in terms of $\log_b x$ and $\log_b y$. Also, $\log_b \frac{x}{y} \neq \frac{\log_b x}{\log_b y}$.

Work Problem 2 at the Side.

3 Use the power rule for logarithms. The next rule gives a method for evaluating powers and roots such as

$$2^{\sqrt{2}}, \quad (\sqrt{2})^{3/4}, \quad (.032)^{5/8}, \quad \text{and} \quad \sqrt[5]{12}.$$

ANSWERS

1. (a) $\log_6 5 + \log_6 8$ (b) $\log_4 21$ (c) $1 + \log_8 k$ (d) $2 \log_5 m, \quad m > 0$

2. (a) $\log_7 9 - \log_7 4$ (b) $\log_3 \frac{p}{q}$ (c) $\log_4 3 - 2$

This rule makes it possible to find approximations for numbers that could not be evaluated before. By the product rule for logarithms,

$$\begin{aligned}\log_5 2^3 &= \log_5(2 \cdot 2 \cdot 2)\\ &= \log_5 2 + \log_5 2 + \log_5 2\\ &= 3 \log_5 2.\end{aligned}$$

Also,

$$\begin{aligned}\log_2 7^4 &= \log_2(7 \cdot 7 \cdot 7 \cdot 7)\\ &= \log_2 7 + \log_2 7 + \log_2 7 + \log_2 7\\ &= 4 \log_2 7.\end{aligned}$$

Furthermore, we saw in Example 1(d) that $\log_4 x^3 = 3 \log_4 x$. These examples suggest the following rule.

Power Rule for Logarithms

If x and b are positive real numbers, where $b \neq 1$, and if r is any real number, then

$$\log_b x^r = r \log_b x.$$

In words, the logarithm of a number to a power equals the exponent times the logarithm of the number.

As examples of this result,

$$\log_b m^5 = 5 \log_b m \quad \text{and} \quad \log_3 5^4 = 4 \log_3 5.$$

To prove the power rule, let

$\log_b x = m.$	
$b^m = x$	Convert to exponential form.
$(b^m)^r = x^r$	Raise to the power r.
$b^{mr} = x^r$	Power rule for exponents
$\log_b x^r = mr$	Convert to logarithmic form.
$\log_b x^r = rm$	
$\log_b x^r = r \log_b x$	$m = \log_b x$

This is the statement to be proved.

As a special case of the power rule, let $r = \frac{1}{p}$, so

$$\log_b \sqrt[p]{x} = \log_b x^{1/p} = \frac{1}{p} \log_b x.$$

For example, using this result, with $x > 0$,

$$\log_b \sqrt[5]{x} = \log_b x^{1/5} = \frac{1}{5} \log_b x \quad \text{and} \quad \log_b \sqrt[3]{x^4} = \log_b x^{4/3} = \frac{4}{3} \log_b x.$$

Another special case is

$$\log_b \frac{1}{x} = \log_b x^{-1} = -\log_b x.$$

NOTE

For a review of rational exponents, refer to Section 9.2.

3 Use the power rule to rewrite each logarithm. Assume $a > 0, b > 0, x > 0, a \neq 1$, and $b \neq 1$.

(a) $\log_3 5^2$

(b) $\log_a x^4$

(c) $\log_b \sqrt{8}$

(d) $\log_2 \sqrt[3]{2}$

4 Find the value of each logarithmic expression.

(a) $\log_{10} 10^3$

(b) $\log_2 8$

(c) $5^{\log_5 3}$

ANSWERS

3. **(a)** $2 \log_3 5$ **(b)** $4 \log_a x$
(c) $\frac{1}{2} \log_b 8$ **(d)** $\frac{1}{3}$

4. **(a)** 3 **(b)** 3 **(c)** 3

Example 3 Using the Power Rule

Use the power rule to rewrite each logarithm. Assume $b > 0, x > 0$, and $b \neq 1$.

(a) $\log_5 4^2 = 2 \log_5 4$

(b) $\log_b x^5 = 5 \log_b x$

(c) $\log_b \sqrt{7}$
When using the power rule with logarithms of expressions involving radicals, begin by rewriting the radical expression with a rational exponent.

$$\log_b \sqrt{7} = \log_b 7^{1/2} \qquad \sqrt{x} = x^{1/2}$$
$$= \frac{1}{2} \log_b 7 \qquad \text{Power rule}$$

(d) $\log_2 \sqrt[5]{x^2} = \log_2 x^{2/5} \qquad \sqrt[5]{x^2} = x^{2/5}$

$$= \frac{2}{5} \log_2 x$$

Work Problem 3 at the Side.

Two special properties involving both exponential and logarithmic expressions come directly from the fact that logarithmic and exponential functions are inverses of each other.

Special Properties

If $b > 0$ and $b \neq 1$, then

$$b^{\log_b x} = x, \ x > 0 \quad \text{and} \quad \log_b b^x = x.$$

To prove the first statement, let

$$y = \log_b x.$$
$$b^y = x \qquad \text{Convert to exponential form.}$$
$$b^{\log_b x} = x \qquad \text{Replace } y \text{ with } \log_b x.$$

The proof of the second statement is similar.

Example 4 Using the Special Properties

Find the value of each logarithmic expression.

(a) $\log_5 5^4$
Since $\log_b b^x = x$,

$$\log_5 5^4 = 4.$$

(b) $\log_3 9 = \log_3 3^2 = 2$

(c) $4^{\log_4 10} = 10$

Work Problem 4 at the Side.

Here is a summary of the properties of logarithms.

Properties of Logarithms

If x, y, and b are positive real numbers, where $b \neq 1$, and r is any real number, then

Product Rule $\log_b xy = \log_b x + \log_b y$

Quotient Rule $\log_b \dfrac{x}{y} = \log_b x - \log_b y$

Power Rule $\log_b x^r = r \log_b x$

Special Properties $b^{\log_b x} = x$ and $\log_b b^x = x$.

4 **Use properties to write alternative forms of logarithmic expressions.** Applying the properties of logarithms is important for solving equations with logarithms and in calculus.

Example 5 **Writing Logarithms in Alternative Forms**

Use the properties of logarithms to rewrite each expression. Assume all variables represent positive real numbers.

(a) $\log_4 4x^3 = \log_4 4 + \log_4 x^3$ Product rule

$= 1 + 3 \log_4 x$ $\log_4 4 = 1$; Power rule

(b) $\log_7 \sqrt{\dfrac{m}{n}} = \log_7 \left(\dfrac{m}{n}\right)^{1/2}$

$= \dfrac{1}{2} \log_7 \dfrac{m}{n}$ Power rule

$= \dfrac{1}{2} (\log_7 m - \log_7 n)$ Quotient rule

(c) $\log_5 \dfrac{a^2}{bc} = \log_5 a^2 - \log_5 bc$ Quotient rule

$= 2 \log_5 a - \log_5 bc$ Power rule

$= 2 \log_5 a - (\log_5 b + \log_5 c)$ Product rule

$= 2 \log_5 a - \log_5 b - \log_5 c$

Notice the careful use of parentheses in the third step. Since we are subtracting the logarithm of a product and rewriting it as a sum of two terms, we must place parentheses around the sum.

(d) $4 \log_b m - \log_b n = \log_b m^4 - \log_b n$ Power rule

$= \log_b \dfrac{m^4}{n}$ Quotient rule

Continued on Next Page

5 Use the properties of logarithms to rewrite each expression. Assume all variables represent positive real numbers.

(a) $\log_6 36m^5$

(b) $\log_2 \sqrt{9z}$

(c) $\log_q \dfrac{8r^2}{m-1}$, $m \neq 1, q \neq 1$

(d) $2 \log_a x + 3 \log_a y$, $a \neq 1$

(e) $\log_4(3x + y)$

(e) $\log_b(x+1) + \log_b(2x-1) - \dfrac{2}{3}\log_b x$

$= \log_b(x+1) + \log_b(2x-1) - \log_b x^{2/3}$ Power rule

$= \log_b \dfrac{(x+1)(2x-1)}{x^{2/3}}$ Product and quotient rules

$= \log_b \dfrac{2x^2 + x - 1}{x^{2/3}}$

(f) $\log_8(2p + 3r)$ cannot be rewritten by the properties of logarithms.

Work Problem 5 at the Side.

ANSWERS

5. **(a)** $2 + 5 \log_6 m$ **(b)** $\log_2 3 + \dfrac{1}{2}\log_2 z$
(c) $\log_q 8 + 2 \log_q r - \log_q(m-1)$
(d) $\log_a x^2y^3$ **(e)** cannot be rewritten

11.4 EXERCISES

FOR EXTRA HELP: Student's Solutions Manual | MyMathLab.com | InterAct Math Tutorial Software | AW Math Tutor Center | www.mathxl.com | Digital Video Tutor CD 10 Videotape 23

Decide whether each statement of a logarithmic property is true *or* false. *If it is* false, *correct it by changing the right side of the equation.*

1. $\log_b x + \log_b y = \log_b(x + y)$

false: $\log_b x + \log_b y = \log_b xy$

2. $\log_b \frac{x}{y} = \log_b x - \log_b y$

true

3. $\log_b b^x = x$

true

4. $\log_b x^r = \log_b rx$

false: $\log_b x^r = r \log_b x$

Use the properties of logarithms introduced in this section to express each logarithm as a sum or difference of logarithms, or as a single number if possible. Assume that all variables represent positive real numbers. See Examples 1–5.

5. $\log_7 \frac{4}{5}$

$\log_7 4 - \log_7 5$

6. $\log_8 \frac{9}{11}$

$\log_8 9 - \log_8 11$

7. $\log_2 8^{1/4}$

$\frac{1}{4} \log_2 8$ or $\frac{3}{4}$

8. $\log_3 9^{3/4}$

$\frac{3}{4} \log_3 9$ or $\frac{3}{2}$

9. $\log_4 \frac{3\sqrt{x}}{y}$

$\log_4 3 + \frac{1}{2} \log_4 x - \log_4 y$

10. $\log_5 \frac{6\sqrt{z}}{w}$

$\log_5 6 + \frac{1}{2} \log_5 z - \log_5 w$

11. $\log_3 \frac{\sqrt[3]{4}}{x^2 y}$

$\frac{1}{3} \log_3 4 - 2 \log_3 x - \log_3 y$

12. $\log_7 \frac{\sqrt[3]{13}}{pq^2}$

$\frac{1}{3} \log_7 13 - \log_7 p - 2 \log_7 q$

13. $\log_3 \sqrt{\frac{xy}{5}}$

$\frac{1}{2} \log_3 x + \frac{1}{2} \log_3 y - \frac{1}{2} \log_3 5$

14. $\log_6 \sqrt{\frac{pq}{7}}$

$\frac{1}{2} \log_6 p + \frac{1}{2} \log_6 q - \frac{1}{2} \log_6 7$

15. $\log_2 \frac{\sqrt[3]{x} \cdot \sqrt[5]{y}}{r^2}$

$\frac{1}{3} \log_2 x + \frac{1}{5} \log_2 y - 2 \log_2 r$

16. $\log_4 \frac{\sqrt[4]{z} \cdot \sqrt[5]{w}}{s^2}$

$\frac{1}{4} \log_4 z + \frac{1}{5} \log_4 w - 2 \log_4 s$

17. A student erroneously wrote

$$\log_a(x + y) = \log_a x + \log_a y.$$

When his teacher explained that this was wrong, the student claimed he had used the distributive property. Write a few sentences explaining why the distributive property does not apply in this case.

The distributive property tells us that the *product* $a(x + y)$ equals the sum $ax + ay$. In the notation $\log_a(x + y)$, the parentheses do not indicate multiplication. They indicate that $x + y$ is the result of raising a to some power.

18. Write a few sentences explaining how the rules for multiplying and dividing powers of the same base are similar to the rules for finding logarithms of products and quotients.

Logarithms of products and quotients behave exactly as the exponents in products and quotients of exponentials: $a^m \cdot a^n = a^{m+n}$ and $\log_a mn = \log_a m + \log_a n$.

Also, $\frac{a^m}{a^n} = a^{m-n}$ and $\log_a \frac{m}{n} = \log_a m - \log_a n$.

Use the properties of logarithms introduced in this section to rewrite each expression as a single logarithm. Assume all variables are defined in such a way that the variable expressions are positive, and bases are positive numbers not equal to 1. See Examples 1–5.

19. $\log_b x + \log_b y$

$\log_b xy$

20. $\log_b 2 + \log_b z$

$\log_b 2z$

21. $3 \log_a m - \log_a n$

$\log_a \frac{m^3}{n}$

22. $5 \log_b x - \log_b y$

$\log_b \frac{x^5}{y}$

23. $(\log_a r - \log_a s) + 3 \log_a t$

$\log_a \frac{rt^3}{s}$

24. $(\log_a p - \log_a q) + 2 \log_a r$

$\log_a \frac{pr^2}{q}$

25. $3 \log_a 5 - 4 \log_a 3$

$\log_a \frac{125}{81}$

26. $3 \log_a 5 + \frac{1}{2} \log_a 9$

$\log_a 375$

27. $\log_{10}(x + 3) + \log_{10}(x - 3)$

$\log_{10}(x^2 - 9)$

28. $\log_{10}(y + 4) + \log_{10}(y - 4)$

$\log_{10}(y^2 - 16)$

29. $3 \log_p x + \frac{1}{2} \log_p y - \frac{3}{2} \log_p z - 3 \log_p a$

$\log_p \frac{x^3 y^{1/2}}{z^{3/2} a^3}$

30. $\frac{1}{3} \log_b x + \frac{2}{3} \log_b y - \frac{3}{4} \log_b s - \frac{2}{3} \log_b t$

$\log_b \frac{x^{1/3} y^{2/3}}{s^{3/4} t^{2/3}}$

31. Explain why the statement for the power rule for logarithms requires that x be a positive real number.

For the power rule $\log_b x^r = r \log_b x$ to be true, x must be in the domain of $g(x) = \log_b x$, so $x > 0$.

32. What is wrong with the following "proof" that $\log_2 16$ does not exist?

$$\log_2 16 = \log_2(-4)(-4)$$
$$= \log_2(-4) + \log_2(-4)$$

Since the logarithm of a negative number is not defined, the final step cannot be evaluated, and so $\log_2 16$ does not exist.

We cannot apply the product rule as in the first step, since $\log_b xy = \log_b x + \log_b y$ only if x and y are positive numbers.

RELATING CONCEPTS (Exercises 33–38) FOR INDIVIDUAL OR GROUP WORK

Work Exercises 33–38 in order.

33. Evaluate $\log_3 81$.

4

34. Write the *meaning* of the expression $\log_3 81$.

It is the exponent to which 3 must be raised in order to obtain 81.

35. Evaluate $3^{\log_3 81}$.

81

36. Write the *meaning* of the expression $\log_2 19$.

It is the exponent to which 2 must be raised in order to obtain 19.

37. Evaluate $2^{\log_2 19}$.

19

38. Keeping in mind that a logarithm is an exponent, and using the results from Exercises 33–37, what is the simplest form of the expression $k^{\log_k m}$?

m

11.5 COMMON AND NATURAL LOGARITHMS

As mentioned earlier, logarithms are important in many applications of mathematics to everyday problems, particularly in biology, engineering, economics, and social science. In this section we find numerical approximations for logarithms. Traditionally, base 10 logarithms were used most often because our number system is base 10. Logarithms to base 10 are called **common logarithms,** and $\log_{10} x$ is abbreviated as simply $\log x$, where the base is understood to be 10.

OBJECTIVES

1. Evaluate common logarithms using a calculator.
2. Use common logarithms in applications.
3. Evaluate natural logarithms using a calculator.
4. Use natural logarithms in applications.

1 Evaluate common logarithms using a calculator. We use calculators to evaluate common logarithms. In the next example we give the results of evaluating some common logarithms using a calculator with a LOG key. (This may be a second function key on some calculators.) For simple scientific calculators, just enter the number, then press the LOG key. For graphing calculators, these steps are reversed. We will give all logarithms to four decimal places.

Example 1 Evaluating Common Logarithms

Evaluate each logarithm using a calculator.

(a) $\log 327.1 \approx 2.5147$ **(b)** $\log 437{,}000 \approx 5.6405$

(c) $\log .0615 \approx -1.2111$

Notice that $\log .0615 \approx -1.2111$, a negative result. The common logarithm of a number between 0 and 1 is always negative because the logarithm is the exponent on 10 that produces the number. For example,

$$10^{-1.2111} \approx .0615.$$

If the exponent (the logarithm) were positive, the result would be greater than 1 because $10^0 = 1$. See Figure 12.

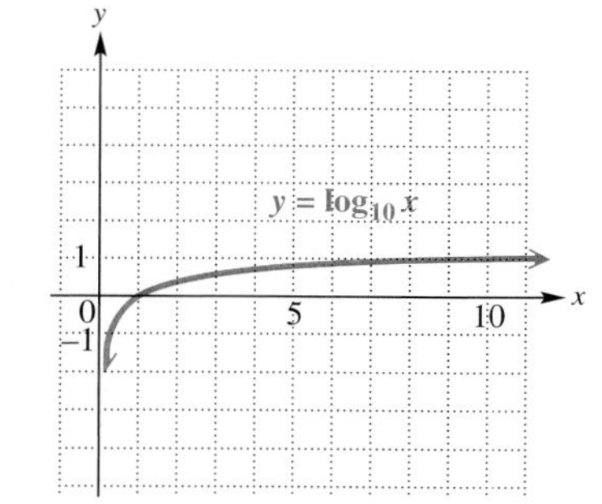

Figure 12

Work Problem 1 at the Side.

1 Evaluate each logarithm to four decimal places using a calculator.

(a) $\log 41{,}600$

(b) $\log 43.5$

(c) $\log .442$

2 Use common logarithms in applications. In chemistry, pH is a measure of the acidity or alkalinity of a solution; water, for example, has pH 7. In general, acids have pH numbers less than 7, and alkaline solutions have pH values greater than 7. The **pH** of a solution is defined as

$$\mathrm{pH} = -\log[\mathrm{H_3O^+}],$$

where $[\mathrm{H_3O^+}]$ is the hydronium ion concentration in moles per liter. It is customary to round pH values to the nearest tenth.

ANSWERS
1. (a) 4.6191 **(b)** 1.6385 **(c)** −.3546

2 Solve the problem.

Find the pH of water with a hydronium ion concentration of 1.2×10^{-3}. If this water had been taken from a wetland, is the wetland a rich fen, a poor fen, or a bog?

3 Find the hydronium ion concentrations of solutions with the following pH values.

(a) 4.6

(b) 7.5

Example 2 Using pH in an Application

Wetlands are classified as *bogs, fens, marshes,* and *swamps.* These classifications are based on pH values. A pH value between 6.0 and 7.5, such as that of Summerby Swamp in Michigan's Hiawatha National Forest, indicates that the wetland is a "rich fen." When the pH is between 4.0 and 6.0, the wetland is a "poor fen," and if the pH falls to 3.0 or less, it is a "bog." (*Source:* Mohlenbrock, R., "Summerby Swamp, Michigan," *Natural History,* March 1994.)

Suppose that the hydronium ion concentration of a sample of water from a wetland is 6.3×10^{-3}. How would this wetland be classified?

Use the definition of pH.

$$\begin{aligned} pH &= -\log(6.3 \times 10^{-3}) \\ &= -(\log 6.3 + \log 10^{-3}) && \text{Product rule} \\ &= -[.7993 - 3(1)] \\ &= -.7993 + 3 \\ &\approx 2.2 \end{aligned}$$

Since the pH is less than 3.0, the wetland is a bog.

Work Problem 2 at the Side.

Example 3 Finding Hydronium Ion Concentration

Find the hydronium ion concentration of drinking water with pH 6.5.

$$\begin{aligned} \mathbf{pH} &= -\log[H_3O^+] \\ \mathbf{6.5} &= -\log[H_3O^+] && \text{Let pH} = 6.5. \\ \log[H_3O^+] &= -6.5 && \text{Multiply by } -1. \end{aligned}$$

Solve for $[H_3O^+]$ by writing the equation in exponential form, remembering that the base is 10.

$$\begin{aligned} [H_3O^+] &= 10^{-6.5} \\ [H_3O^+] &\approx 3.2 \times 10^{-7} && \text{Use a calculator.} \end{aligned}$$

Work Problem 3 at the Side.

3 Evaluate natural logarithms using a calculator. The most important logarithms used in applications are **natural logarithms,** which have as base the number e. The number e is a fundamental number in our universe. For this reason e, like π, is called a *universal constant.* The letter e is used to honor Leonhard Euler, who published extensive results on the number in 1748. Since it is an irrational number, its decimal expansion never

ANSWERS
2. (a) 2.9; bog
3. (a) 2.5×10^{-5} (b) 3.2×10^{-8}

terminates and never repeats. The first few digits of the decimal value of e are 2.7182818285. A calculator key e^x or the two keys INV and ln x are used to approximate powers of e. For example, a calculator gives

$$e^2 \approx 7.389056099,$$
$$e^3 \approx 20.08553692,$$
and
$$e^{.6} \approx 1.8221188.$$

Logarithms to base e are called natural logarithms because they occur in biology and the social sciences in natural situations that involve growth or decay. The base e logarithm of x is written $\ln x$ (read "el en x"). A graph of $y = \ln x$, the equation that defines the natural logarithmic function, is given in Figure 13.

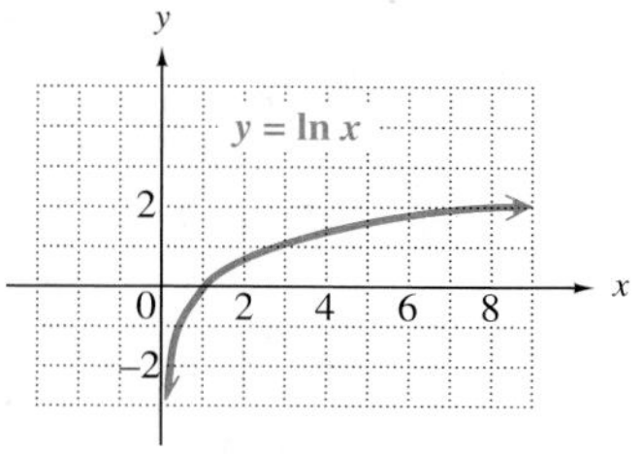

Figure 13

A calculator key labeled ln x is used to evaluate natural logarithms. If your calculator has an e^x key, but not a key labeled ln x, find natural logarithms by entering the number, pressing the INV key, and then pressing the e^x key. This works because $y = e^x$ defines the inverse function of $y = \ln x$ (or $y = \log_e x$).

Example 4 Finding Natural Logarithms

Find each logarithm to four decimal places.

(a) $\ln .5841 \approx -.5377$

As with common logarithms, a number between 0 and 1 has a negative natural logarithm.

(b) $\ln 192.7 \approx 5.2611$

(c) $\ln 10.84 \approx 2.3832$

Work Problem 4 at the Side.

4 **Use natural logarithms in applications.** A common application of natural logarithmic functions is to express growth or decay of a quantity, as in the next example.

Example 5 Applying Natural Logarithms

The altitude in meters that corresponds to an atmospheric pressure of x millibars is given by the logarithmic function with

$$f(x) = 51{,}600 - 7457 \ln x.$$

(*Source:* Miller, A. and J. Thompson, *Elements of Meteorology,* Fourth Edition, Charles E. Merrill Publishing Company, 1993.) Use this function to find the altitude when atmospheric pressure is 400 millibars.

Let $x = 400$ and substitute in the expression for $f(x)$.

$$f(400) = 51{,}600 - 7457 \ln 400$$
$$\approx 6900$$

Atmospheric pressure is 400 millibars at approximately 6900 m.

4 Find each logarithm to four decimal places.

(a) $\ln .01$

(b) $\ln 27$

(c) $\ln 529$

ANSWERS

4. (a) -4.6052 **(b)** 3.2958 **(c)** 6.2710

5 Use the logarithmic function in Example 5 to approximate the altitude at 700 millibars of pressure.

Calculator Tip In Example 5, the final answer was obtained using a calculator *without* rounding the intermediate values. In general, it is best to wait until the final step to round the answer; otherwise, a build-up of round-off error may cause the final answer to have an incorrect final decimal place digit.

Work Problem 5 at the Side.

ANSWERS

5. approximately 2700 m

11.5 EXERCISES

FOR EXTRA HELP: Student's Solutions Manual; MyMathLab.com; InterAct Math Tutorial Software; AW Math Tutor Center; www.mathxl.com; Digital Video Tutor CD 10 Videotape 23

Choose the correct response in Exercises 1–4.

1. What is the base in the expression log x?

A. e **B.** 1 **C.** 10 **D.** x

C

2. What is the base in the expression ln x?

A. e **B.** 1 **C.** 10 **D.** x

A

3. Since $10^0 = 1$ and $10^1 = 10$, between what two consecutive integers is the value of log 5.6?

A. 5 and 6 **B.** 10 and 11 **C.** 0 and 1 **D.** -1 and 0

C

4. Since $e^1 \approx 2.718$ and $e^2 \approx 7.389$, between what two consecutive integers is the value of ln 5.6?

A. 5 and 6 **B.** 2 and 3 **C.** 1 and 2 **D.** 0 and 1

C

5. Without using a calculator, give the value of $\log 10^{19.2}$.

19.2

6. Without using a calculator, give the value of $\ln e^{\sqrt{2}}$.

$\sqrt{2}$

You will need a calculator for the remaining exercises in this set.

Find each logarithm. Give an approximation to four decimal places. See Examples 1 and 4.

7. log 43

1.6335

8. log 98

1.9912

9. log 328.4

2.5164

10. log 457.2

2.6601

11. log .0326

-1.4868

12. log .1741

$-.7592$

13. $\log(4.76 \times 10^9)$

9.6776

14. $\log(2.13 \times 10^4)$

4.3284

15. ln 7.84

2.0592

16. ln 8.32

2.1187

17. ln .0556

-2.8896

18. ln .0217

-3.8304

19. ln 388.1

5.9613

20. ln 942.6

6.8486

21. $\ln(8.59 \times e^2)$

4.1506

22. $\ln(7.46 \times e^3)$

5.0096

23. ln 10

2.3026

24. $\log e$

.4343

25. Let m be the number of letters in your first name, and let n be the number of letters in your last name.

(a) In your own words, explain what $\log_m n$ means.

(b) Use your calculator to find $\log_m n$.

(c) Raise m to the power indicated by the number you found in part (b). What is your result?

Answers will vary. Suppose the name is Paul Bunyan, with $m = 4$ and $n = 6$.
(a) $\log_4 6$ is the exponent to which 4 must be raised in order to obtain 6. (b) 1.29248125
(c) 6 (the value of n)

26. Use your calculator to find approximations of the following logarithms.

(a) log 356.8

2.552424846

(b) log 35.68

1.552424846

(c) log 3.568

.552424846

(d) Observe your answers and make a conjecture concerning the decimal values of the common logarithms of numbers greater than 1 that have the same digits.

The whole number parts will vary but the decimal parts are the same.

27. Try to find $\log(-1)$ using a calculator. (If you have a graphing calculator, it should be in real number mode.) What happens? Explain why this happens.

An error message appears because we cannot find the common logarithm of a negative number.

Refer to Example 2. In Exercises 28 and 29, suppose that water from a wetland area is sampled and found to have the given hydronium ion concentration. Determine whether the wetland is a rich fen, *a* poor fen, *or a* bog.

28. 2.5×10^{-5}

poor fen

29. 2.5×10^{-2}

bog

Use the formula $\text{pH} = -\log[H_3O^+]$ *to find the* pH *of the substance with the given hydronium ion concentration. See Example 2.*

30. Ammonia, 2.5×10^{-12}

11.6

31. Tuna, 1.3×10^{-6}

5.9

Use the formula for pH *to find the hydronium ion concentration of the substance with the given* pH. *See Example 3.*

32. Human blood plasma, 7.4

4.0×10^{-8}

33. Human gastric contents, 2.0

1.0×10^{-2}

34. Spinach, 5.4

4.0×10^{-6}

35. Bananas, 4.6

2.5×10^{-5}

Solve each problem. See Example 5.

36. The number of years, $N(r)$, since two independently evolving languages split off from a common ancestral language is approximated by

$$N(r) = -5000 \ln r,$$

where r is the percent of words (in decimal form) from the ancestral language common to both languages now. Find the number of years since the split for each percent of common words.

(a) 85% (or .85)

800 yr

(b) 35% (or .35)

5200 yr

(c) 10% (or .10)

11,500 yr

37. The time t in years for an amount increasing at a rate of r (in decimal form) to double is given by

$$t = \frac{\ln 2}{\ln(1 + r)}.$$

This is called *doubling time.* Find the doubling time to the nearest tenth for an investment at each interest rate.

(a) 2% = .02

35.0 yr

(b) 5% = .05

14.2 yr

(c) 8% = .08

9.0 yr

38. The concentration of a drug injected into the bloodstream decreases with time. The intervals of time T when the drug should be administered are given by

$$T = \frac{1}{k} \ln \frac{C_2}{C_1},$$

where k is a constant determined by the drug in use, C_2 is the concentration at which the drug is harmful, and C_1 is the concentration below which the drug is ineffective. (*Source:* Horelick, Brindell and Sinan Koont, "Applications of Calculus to Medicine: Prescribing Safe and Effective Dosage," *UMAP Module 202,* 1977.) Thus, if $T = 4$, the drug should be administered every 4 hr. For a certain drug, $k = \frac{1}{3}$, $C_2 = 5$, and $C_1 = 2$. How often should the drug be administered? (*Hint:* Round down.)

every 3 hr

39. The loudness of sounds is measured in a unit called a *decibel,* abbreviated dB. A very faint sound, called the *threshold sound,* is assigned an intensity I_0. If a particular sound has intensity I, then the decibel level of this louder sound is

$$D = 10 \log\left(\frac{I}{I_0}\right).$$

Find the average decibel level for each popular movie with the given intensity I. For comparison, a motorcycle or power saw has a decibel level of about 95 dB, and the sound of a jackhammer or helicopter is about 105 dB. (*Source: World Almanac and Book of Facts,* 2001; www.lhh.org/noise/)

(a) *Armageddon;* $5.012 \times 10^{10} I_0$

107 dB

(b) *Godzilla;* $10^{10} I_0$

100 dB

(c) *Saving Private Ryan;* 6,310,000,000 I_0

98 dB

40. The growth of outpatient surgery as a percent of total surgeries at hospitals is approximated by

$$f(x) = -1317 + 304 \ln x,$$

where x represents the number of years since 1900. (*Source:* American Hospital Association.)

(a) What does this function predict for the percent of outpatient surgeries in 1998?

77%

(b) When did outpatient surgeries reach 50%? (*Hint:* Substitute for y, then write the equation in exponential form to solve it.)

1989

41. In the central Sierra Nevada of California, the percent of moisture p that falls as snow rather than rain is approximated reasonably well by

$$p = 86.3 \ln h - 680,$$

where h is the altitude in feet.

(a) What percent of the moisture at 5000 ft falls as snow?

55%

(b) What percent at 7500 ft falls as snow?

90%

42. The *cost-benefit equation*

$$T = -.642 - 189 \ln(1 - p)$$

describes the approximate tax T, in dollars per ton, that would result in a p% (in decimal form) reduction in carbon dioxide emissions.

(a) What tax will reduce emissions 25%?

$54 per ton

(b) Explain why the equation is not valid for $p = 0$ or $p = 1$.

If $p = 0$, then $\ln(1 - p) = \ln 1 = 0$, so T would be negative. If $p = 1$, then $\ln(1 - p) = \ln 0$, but the domain of $\ln x$ is $(0, \infty)$.

43. The age in years of a female blue whale is approximated by

$$t = -2.57 \ln\left(\frac{87 - L}{63}\right),$$

where L is its length in feet.

(a) How old is a female blue whale that measures 80 ft?

5.6 yr

(b) The equation that defines t has domain $24 < L < 87$. Explain why.

$t > 0$ and $\frac{87 - L}{63}$ is positive and in the domain of the function only if $24 < L < 87$.

11.6 Exponential and Logarithmic Equations; Further Applications

As mentioned earlier, exponential and logarithmic functions are important in many applications of mathematics. Using these functions in applications requires solving exponential and logarithmic equations. Some simple equations were solved in Sections 11.2 and 11.3. More general methods for solving these equations depend on the following properties.

Properties for Solving Exponential and Logarithmic Equations

For all real numbers $b > 0$, $b \neq 1$, and any real numbers x and y:

1. If $x = y$, then $b^x = b^y$.
2. If $b^x = b^y$, then $x = y$.
3. If $x = y$, and $x > 0$, $y > 0$, then $\log_b x = \log_b y$.
4. If $x > 0$, $y > 0$, and $\log_b x = \log_b y$, then $x = y$.

We used Property 2 to solve exponential equations in Section 11.2.

1 Solve equations involving variables in the exponents. The first examples illustrate a general method for solving exponential equations using Property 3.

Example 1 Solving an Exponential Equation

Solve $3^m = 12$.

$$3^m = 12$$
$$\log 3^m = \log 12 \quad \text{Property 3}$$
$$m \log 3 = \log 12 \quad \text{Power rule}$$
$$m = \frac{\log 12}{\log 3} \quad \text{Divide by log 3.}$$

This quotient is the exact solution. To get a decimal approximation for the solution, use a calculator.

$$m \approx 2.262$$

The solution set is $\{2.262\}$. Check that $3^{2.262} \approx 12$.

CAUTION

Be careful: $\frac{\log 12}{\log 3}$ is *not* equal to log 4 because $\log 4 \approx .6021$, but $\frac{\log 12}{\log 3} \approx 2.262$.

Work Problem 1 at the Side.

When an exponential equation has e as the base, it is easiest to use base e logarithms.

Objectives

1. Solve equations involving variables in the exponents.
2. Solve equations involving logarithms.
3. Solve applications of compound interest.
4. Solve applications involving base e exponential growth and decay.
5. Use the change-of-base rule.

1 Solve each equation and give the decimal approximation to three places.

(a) $2^p = 9$

(b) $10^k = 4$

Answers

1. (a) $\{3.170\}$ **(b)** $\{.602\}$

2 Solve $e^{-.01t} = .38$.

Example 2 **Solving an Exponential Equation with Base *e***

Solve $e^{.003x} = 40$.

Take base e logarithms on both sides.

$$\ln e^{.003x} = \ln 40$$

$$.003x \ln e = \ln 40 \quad \text{Power rule}$$

$$.003x = \ln 40 \quad \ln e = \ln e^1 = 1$$

$$x = \frac{\ln 40}{.003} \quad \text{Divide by .003.}$$

$$x \approx 1230 \quad \text{Use a calculator.}$$

The solution set is $\{1230\}$. Check that $e^{.003(1230)} \approx 40$.

Work Problem 2 at the Side.

General Method for Solving an Exponential Equation

Take logarithms to the same base on both sides and then use the power rule of logarithms or the special property $\log_b b^x = x$. (See Examples 1 and 2.)

As a special case, if both sides can be written as exponentials with the same base, do so, and set the exponents equal. (See Section 11.2.)

3 Solve $\log_5 \sqrt{x - 7} = 1$.

2 **Solve equations involving logarithms.** The properties of logarithms from Section 11.4 are useful here, as is using the definition of a logarithm to change the equation to exponential form.

Example 3 **Solving a Logarithmic Equation**

Solve $\log_2(x + 5)^3 = 4$.

$$(x + 5)^3 = 2^4 \quad \text{Convert to exponential form.}$$

$$(x + 5)^3 = 16$$

$$x + 5 = \sqrt[3]{16} \quad \text{Take the cube root on each side.}$$

$$x = -5 + \sqrt[3]{16}$$

$$x = -5 + 2\sqrt[3]{2} \quad \text{Simplify the radical.}$$

Verify that the solution satisfies the equation, so the solution set is $\{-5 + 2\sqrt[3]{2}\}$.

CAUTION

Recall that the domain of $y = \log_b x$ is $(0, \infty)$. For this reason, it is always necessary to check that the solution of an equation with logarithms yields only logarithms of positive numbers in the original equation.

Work Problem 3 at the Side.

ANSWERS
2. $\{96.8\}$
3. $\{32\}$

Example 4 **Solving a Logarithmic Equation**

Solve $\log_2(x + 1) - \log_2 x = \log_2 7$.

$$\log_2(x + 1) - \log_2 x = \log_2 7$$

$$\log_2 \frac{x + 1}{x} = \log_2 7 \quad \text{Quotient rule}$$

$$\frac{x + 1}{x} = 7 \quad \text{Property 4}$$

$$x + 1 = 7x \quad \text{Multiply by } x.$$

$$\frac{1}{6} = x \quad \text{Subtract } x\text{; divide by 6.}$$

Check this solution by substituting in the original equation. Here, both $x + 1$ and x must be positive. If $x = \frac{1}{6}$, this condition is satisfied, so the solution set is $\{\frac{1}{6}\}$.

Work Problem 4 at the Side.

4 Solve
$\log_8(2x + 5) + \log_8 3 = \log_8 33$.

Example 5 **Solving a Logarithmic Equation**

Solve $\log x + \log(x - 21) = 2$.

For this equation, write the left side as a single logarithm. Then write in exponential form and solve the equation.

$$\log x + \log(x - 21) = 2$$

$$\log x(x - 21) = 2 \quad \text{Product rule}$$

$$x(x - 21) = 10^2 \quad \text{Log } x = \log_{10} x\text{; write in exponential form.}$$

$$x^2 - 21x = 100$$

$$x^2 - 21x - 100 = 0 \quad \text{Standard form}$$

$$(x - 25)(x + 4) = 0 \quad \text{Factor.}$$

$$x - 25 = 0 \quad \text{or} \quad x + 4 = 0 \quad \text{Zero-factor property}$$

$$x = 25 \quad \text{or} \quad x = -4$$

The value -4 must be rejected as a solution since it leads to the logarithm of a negative number in the original equation:

$$\log(-4) + \log(-4 - 21) = 2. \quad \text{The left side is undefined.}$$

The only solution, therefore, is 25, and the solution set is $\{25\}$.

5 Solve
$\log_3 2x - \log_3(3x + 15) = -2$.

CAUTION

Do not reject a potential solution just because it is nonpositive. Reject any value that *leads to* the logarithm of a nonpositive number.

Work Problem 5 at the Side.

In summary, we use the following steps to solve a logarithmic equation.

Answers
4. $\{3\}$
5. $\{1\}$

6 Find the value of \$2000 deposited at 5% compounded annually for 10 yr.

Solving a Logarithmic Equation

Step 1 **Get a single logarithm on one side.** Use the product rule or quotient rule of logarithms to do this.

Step 2 **(a) Use property 4.** If $\log_b x = \log_b y$, then $x = y$. (See Example 4.)
(b) Write the equation in exponential form. If $\log_b x = k$, then $x = b^k$. (See Examples 3 and 5.)

3 Solve applications of compound interest. So far in this book, problems involving applications of interest have been limited to simple interest using the formula $I = prt$. In most cases, interest paid or charged is compound interest (interest paid on both principal and interest). The formula for compound interest is an important application of exponential functions.

Compound Interest

If P dollars is deposited in an account paying an annual rate of interest r compounded (paid) n times per year, the account will contain

$$A = P\left(1 + \frac{r}{n}\right)^{nt}$$

dollars after t years.

In this formula, r is expressed as a decimal.

Example 6 **Solving a Compound Interest Problem for A**

How much money will there be in an account at the end of 5 yr if \$1000 is deposited at 6% compounded quarterly? (Assume no withdrawals are made.)

Because interest is compounded quarterly, $n = 4$. The other values given in the problem are $P = 1000$, $r = .06$ (because $6\% = .06$), and $t = 5$. Substitute into the compound interest formula to get the value of A.

$$A = 1000\left(1 + \frac{.06}{4}\right)^{4 \cdot 5}$$

$$A = 1000(1.015)^{20}$$

Now use the y^x key on a calculator, and round the answer to the nearest cent.

$$A = 1346.86$$

The account will contain \$1346.86. (The actual amount of interest earned is \$1346.86 − \$1000 = \$346.86. Why?)

Work Problem 6 at the Side.

Example 7 **Solving a Compound Interest Problem for t**

Suppose inflation is averaging 3% per year. How many years will it take for prices to double?

We want to find the number of years t for \$1 to grow to \$2 at a rate of 3% per year. In the compound interest formula, we let $A = 2$, $P = 1$, $r = .03$, and $n = 1$.

Continued on Next Page

ANSWERS
6. about \$3257.79

$$2 = 1\left(1 + \frac{.03}{1}\right)^{1t}$$

$$2 = (1.03)^t \quad \text{Simplify.}$$

$$\log 2 = \log(1.03)^t \quad \text{Property 3}$$

$$\log 2 = t \log 1.03 \quad \text{Power rule}$$

$$t = \frac{\log 2}{\log 1.03} \quad \text{Divide by log 1.03.}$$

$$t \approx 23.45$$

Prices will double in about 23 yr. (This is called the *doubling time* of the money.) To check, verify that $1.03^{23.45} \approx 2$.

Work Problem 7 at the Side.

7 Find the number of years it will take for \$500 to increase to \$750 in an account paying 4% interest compounded semiannually.

Banks sometimes compute interest based on **continuous compounding.** With this type of compounding, rather than paying interest a finite number of times per year, interest is earned at all times. As a result, the formula for compound interest cannot be applied because n is infinite. The formula used to determine the amount A in an account having initial principal P compounded continuously at an annual rate r for t years is

$$A = Pe^{rt}.$$

Example 8 **Solving a Continuous Interest Problem**

How much will \$1000 grow to in 5 yr at an annual interest rate of 6% compounded continuously?

Use the formula.

$$A = Pe^{rt}$$

$$A = 1000e^{(.06)5} \quad \text{Let } P = 1000,\ r = .06, \text{ and } t = 5.$$

$$A \approx 1349.86 \quad \text{Use a calculator; round to two decimal places.}$$

The account will grow to \$1349.86.

Work Problem 8 at the Side.

8 How much will \$2500 grow to at 4% interest compounded continuously for 3 yr?

4 **Solve applications involving base *e* exponential growth and decay.** We saw some applications involving exponential growth and decay in Section 11.2. In many cases, quantities grow or decay according to a function defined by an exponential expression with base e. You have probably heard of the carbon-14 dating process used to determine the age of fossils. The method used is based on a base e exponential decay function.

ANSWERS
7. about 10.24 yr
8. \$2818.74

9 Radioactive strontium decays according to the function

$$y = y_0 e^{-.0239t},$$

where t is time in years.

(a) If an initial sample contains $y_0 = 12$ g of radioactive strontium, how many grams will be present after 35 yr?

(b) What is the half-life of radioactive strontium?

Answers

9. (a) 5.20 g **(b)** 29 yr

Example 9 **Solving an Exponential Decay Application**

Carbon-14 is a radioactive form of carbon that is found in all living plants and animals. After a plant or animal dies, the radioactive carbon-14 disintegrates according to the function with

$$y = y_0 e^{-.000121t},$$

where t is time in years, y is the amount of the sample at time t, and y_0 is the initial amount present at $t = 0$.

(a) If an initial sample contains $y_0 = 10$ g of carbon-14, how many grams will be present after 3000 yr?

Let $y_0 = 10$ and $t = 3000$ in the formula, and use a calculator.

$$y = 10e^{-.000121(3000)} \approx 6.96 \text{ g}$$

(b) How long would it take for the initial sample to decay to half of its original amount? (This is called the *half-life.*)

Let $y = \frac{1}{2}(10) = 5$, and solve for t.

$$5 = 10e^{-.000121t} \quad \text{Substitute.}$$

$$\frac{1}{2} = e^{-.000121t} \quad \text{Divide by 10.}$$

$$\ln \frac{1}{2} = -.000121t \quad \text{Take natural logarithms; } \ln e^k = k.$$

$$t = \frac{\ln \frac{1}{2}}{-.000121} \quad \text{Divide by } -.000121.$$

$$t \approx 5728 \quad \text{Use a calculator.}$$

The half-life is just over 5700 yr.

Work Problem 9 at the Side.

5 **Use the change-of-base rule.** In the previous section we used a calculator to approximate the values of common logarithms (base 10) or natural logarithms (base e). However, some applications involve logarithms to other bases. For example, for the years 1980–1996, the percentage of women who had a baby in the last year and returned to work is given by

$$y = 38.83 + 4.208 \log_2 x,$$

for year x. (*Source:* U.S. Bureau of the Census.) To use this function, we need to find a base 2 logarithm. The following rule is used to convert logarithms from one base to another.

Change-of-Base Rule

If $a > 0$, $a \neq 1$, $b > 0$, $b \neq 1$, and $x > 0$, then

$$\log_a x = \frac{\log_b x}{\log_b a}.$$

NOTE

As an aid in remembering the change-of-base rule, notice that x is "above" a on both sides of the equation.

Any positive number other than 1 can be used for base b in the change-of-base rule, but usually the only practical bases are e and 10 because calculators give logarithms only for these two bases.

To derive the change-of-base rule, let $\log_a x = m$.

$$\log_a x = m$$

$$a^m = x \quad \text{Change to exponential form.}$$

$$\log_b(a^m) = \log_b x \quad \text{Property 3}$$

$$m \log_b a = \log_b x \quad \text{Power rule}$$

$$(\log_a x)(\log_b a) = \log_b x \quad \text{Substitute for } m.$$

$$\log_a x = \frac{\log_b x}{\log_b a} \quad \text{Divide by } \log_b a.$$

The last step gives the change-of-base rule.

Example 10 Using the Change-of-Base Rule

Find $\log_5 12$.

Use common logarithms and the change-of-base rule.

$$\log_5 12 = \frac{\log 12}{\log 5}$$

$$\approx 1.5440 \quad \text{Use a calculator.}$$

Work Problem 10 at the Side.

Example 11 Using the Change-of-Base Rule in an Application

Use natural logarithms in the change-of-base rule and the equation

$$y = 38.83 + 4.208 \log_2 x$$

(given earlier) to find the percent of women who returned to work after having a baby in 1995. In the equation, $x = 0$ represents 1980.

Substitute $1995 - 1980 = 15$ for x in the equation.

$$y = 38.83 + 4.208 \log_2 15$$

$$= 38.83 + 4.208\left(\frac{\ln 15}{\ln 2}\right) \quad \text{Change-of-base rule}$$

$$\approx 55.3\% \quad \text{Use a calculator.}$$

This is very close to the actual value of 55%.

Work Problem 11 at the Side.

10 Find $\log_3 17$. (Use common logarithms.)

11 In Example 11, what percent of women returned to work after having a baby in 1990?

Answers

10. 2.5789

11. 52.8%; This is very close to the actual value of 53%.

Focus on **Real-Data Applications**

Evaluating Investments: The Rule of 72

The Rule of 72 gives an estimate of the doubling time of an investment. It is a useful tool in evaluating and comparing investments.

- The Rule of 72 is $\frac{72}{100r}$, where r is the annual interest rate. (Since r is the interest rate as a *decimal*, $100r$ is the interest rate as a *percent*.)
- The compound interest formula is $A = P(1 + \frac{r}{n})^{nt}$, for \$$P$ invested at interest rate r (in decimal form), compounded n times per year, that accumulates to \$$A$ after t years.
- The continuous interest formula is $A = Pe^{rt}$, for \$$P$ invested at interest rate r (in decimal form) that accumulates to \$$A$ after t years.

For Group Discussion

1. To investigate how the Rule of 72 works, we will use the Rule of 72 to estimate the doubling time for money invested at 10%.
   (a) What is the estimated doubling time, to the nearest year, for the investment? **7 yr**
   (b) If \$2000 is invested at 10% compounded quarterly, what is its accumulated value after the predicted doubling time? Did the Rule of 72 give a good estimate? **\$3992.99; yes**
   (c) If \$2000 is invested at 10% compounded continuously, what is its accumulated value after the predicted doubling time? Did the Rule of 72 give a good estimate? **\$4027.51; yes**

2. If money is invested at 8%, the Rule of 72 predicts a 9-year doubling time. Sketch a graph to illustrate the doubling effect of an investment of \$2000 over time. The x-axis represents time in years with 0, 9, 18, 27, 36, and 45 representing five doubling-time periods. The y-axis represents the value of the investment in dollars.

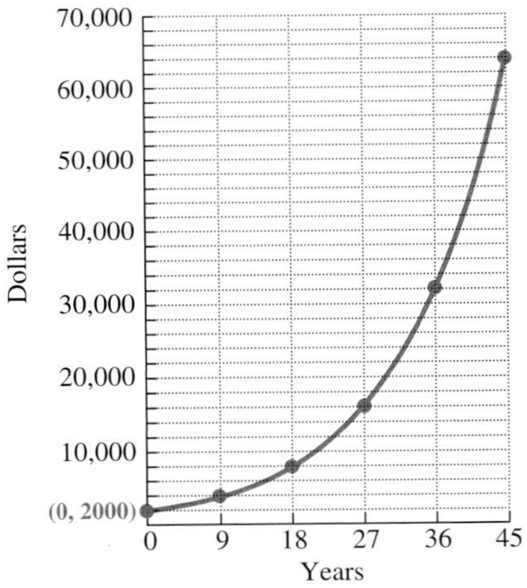

3. Now investigate why the Rule of 72 works. If an investment doubles in value, the continuous interest formula has the form $2P = Pe^{rt}$. Since P is not 0, divide each side of the equation by P to get $2 = e^{rt}$. To solve this equation for t, take the natural logarithm on each side, $\ln 2 = \ln e^{rt}$. Using the power rule, this simplifies to $\ln 2 = rt$. Therefore, $t = \frac{\ln 2}{r}$. Since $\ln 2 \approx .69$, this formula becomes $t = \frac{100 \ln 2}{100r} \approx \frac{69}{100r}$. The number 69 is less useful than 72, which has more factors (i.e., 2, 3, 4, 6, 8, 9, 12, 18, 24, 36), and the doubling time for compound interest will be slightly longer anyway. So, the Rule of 72 estimates this formula as $\frac{72}{100r}$. Does the Rule of 72 underestimate or overestimate the true doubling time for continuously compounded investments? Explain your answer. **Overestimate; 72 > 69.**

Teaching notes and an extension for this activity are provided in the *Printed Test Bank and Instructor's Resource Guide.*

11.6 EXERCISES

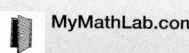

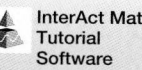

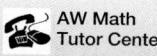

FOR EXTRA HELP: Student's Solutions Manual; MyMathLab.com; InterAct Math Tutorial Software; AW Math Tutor Center; www.mathxl.com; Digital Video Tutor CD 10 Videotape 23

RELATING CONCEPTS (Exercises 1–4) FOR INDIVIDUAL OR GROUP WORK

In Section 11.2 we solved an equation such as $5^x = 125$ by writing each side as a power of the same base, setting exponents equal, and then solving the resulting equation. The equation is solved as follows.

$5^x = 125$	Original equation
$5^x = 5^3$	$125 = 5^3$
$x = 3$	Set exponents equal.

Solution set: $\{3\}$

The method described in this section can also be used to solve this equation.

Work Exercises 1–4 in order, *to see how this is done.*

1. Take common logarithms on both sides, and write this equation.

$\log 5^x = \log 125$

2. Apply the power rule for logarithms on the left.

$x \log 5 = \log 125$

3. Get x alone on the left.

$x = \dfrac{\log 125}{\log 5}$

4. Use a calculator to find the decimal form of the solution. What is the solution set?

$\dfrac{\log 125}{\log 5} = 3; \{3\}$

Many of the problems in the remaining exercises require a scientific calculator.

Solve each equation. Give solutions to three decimal places. See Example 1.

5. $7^x = 5$

$\{.827\}$

6. $4^x = 3$

$\{.792\}$

7. $9^{-x+2} = 13$

$\{.833\}$

8. $6^{-t+1} = 22$

$\{-.725\}$

9. $3^{2x} = 14$

$\{1.201\}$

10. $5^{.3x} = 11$

$\{4.966\}$

11. $2^{y+3} = 5^y$

$\{2.269\}$

12. $6^{m+3} = 4^m$

$\{-13.257\}$

Solve each equation. Use natural logarithms. Give solutions to three decimal places. See Example 2.

13. $e^{.006x} = 30$

$\{566.866\}$

14. $e^{.012x} = 23$

$\{261.291\}$

15. $e^{-.103x} = 7$

$\{-18.892\}$

16. $e^{-.205x} = 9$

$\{-10.718\}$

17. $\ln e^{x} = 4$

$\{4\}$

18. $\ln e^{3x} = 9$

$\{3\}$

19. $\ln e^{.04x} = \sqrt{3}$

$\{43.301\}$

20. $\ln e^{.45x} = \sqrt{7}$

$\{5.879\}$

21. Try solving one of the equations in Exercises 13–16 using common logarithms rather than natural logarithms. (You should get the same solution.) Explain why using natural logarithms is a better choice.

Natural logarithms are a better choice because e is the base.

22. If you were asked to solve $10^{.0025x} = 75$, would natural or common logarithms be a better choice? Explain.

Common logarithms are a better choice because 10 is the base.

Solve each equation. Give the exact solution. See Example 3.

23. $\log_3(6x + 5) = 2$

$\left\{\frac{2}{3}\right\}$

24. $\log_5(12x - 8) = 3$

$\left\{\frac{133}{12}\right\}$

25. $\log_2(2x - 1) = 5$

$\left\{\frac{33}{2}\right\}$

26. $\log_6(4x + 2) = 2$

$\left\{\frac{17}{2}\right\}$

27. $\log_7(x + 1)^3 = 2$

$\{-1 + \sqrt[3]{49}\}$

28. $\log_4(y - 3)^3 = 4$

$\{3 + 4\sqrt[3]{4}\}$

29. Suppose that in solving a logarithmic equation having the term $\log(x - 3)$ you obtain an apparent solution of 2. All algebraic work is correct. Explain why you must reject 2 as a solution of the equation.

2 cannot be a solution because $\log(2 - 3) = \log(-1)$, and -1 is not in the domain of $\log x$.

30. Suppose that in solving a logarithmic equation having the term $\log(3 - x)$ you obtain an apparent solution of -4. All algebraic work is correct. Should you reject -4 as a solution of the equation? Explain why or why not.

No, because $3 - (-4) = 7$ is in the domain of $\log(3 - x)$.

Solve each equation. Give exact solutions. See Examples 4 and 5.

31. $\log(6x + 1) = \log 3$

$\left\{\frac{1}{3}\right\}$

32. $\log(7 - x) = \log 12$

$\{-5\}$

33. $\log_5(3t + 2) - \log_5 t = \log_5 4$

$\{2\}$

34. $\log_2(x + 5) - \log_2(x - 1) = \log_2 3$

$\{4\}$

35. $\log 4x - \log(x - 3) = \log 2$

$\emptyset$

36. $\log(-x) + \log 3 = \log(2x - 15)$

$\emptyset$

37. $\log_2 x + \log_2(x - 7) = 3$

$\{8\}$

38. $\log(2x - 1) + \log 10x = \log 10$

$\{1\}$

39. $\log 5x - \log(2x - 1) = \log 4$

$\left\{\frac{4}{3}\right\}$

40. $\log_3 x + \log_3(2x + 5) = 1$

$\left\{\frac{1}{2}\right\}$

41. $\log_2 x + \log_2(x - 6) = 4$

$\{8\}$

42. $\log_2 x + \log_2(x + 4) = 5$

$\{4\}$

Solve each problem. See Examples 6–8.

43. **(a)** How much money will there be in an account at the end of 6 yr if \$2000 is deposited at 4% compounded quarterly? (Assume no withdrawals are made.)

\$2539.47

(b) To one decimal place, how long will it take for the account to grow to \$3000?

10.2 yr

44. **(a)** How much money will there be in an account at the end of 7 yr if \$3000 is deposited at 3.5% compounded quarterly? (Assume no withdrawals are made.)

\$3828.78

(b) To one decimal place, when will the account grow to \$5000?

14.7 yr

45. What will be the amount A in an account with initial principal \$4000 if interest is compounded continuously at an annual rate of 3.5% for 6 yr?

\$4934.71

46. Refer to Exercise 44. Does the money grow to a larger value under those conditions, or when invested for 7 yr at 3% compounded continuously?

The account described in Exercise 44 will amount to \$127.75 more, so it is a better deal.

47. How long would it take an initial principal P to double if it is invested at 4.5% compounded continuously?

15.4 yr

48. How long would it take \$4000 to grow to \$6000 at 3.25% compounded continuously?

12.5 yr

Solve each problem. See Example 9.

49. A sample of 400 g of lead-210 decays to polonium-210 according to the function with

$$A(t) = 400e^{-.032t},$$

where t is time in years. How much lead will be left in the sample after 25 yr?

about 180 g

50. How long will it take the initial sample of lead in Exercise 49 to decay to half of its original amount?

about 21.66 yr

Use the change-of-base rule (with either common or natural logarithms) to find each logarithm. Give approximations to four decimal places. See Example 10.

51. $\log_6 13$

1.4315

52. $\log_7 19$

1.5131

53. $\log_{\sqrt{2}} \pi$

3.3030

54. $\log_\pi \sqrt{2}$

.3028

55. $\log_{21} .7496$

−.0947

56. $\log_{19} .8325$

−.0623

Work each problem. See Example 11.

One measure of the diversity of the species in an ecological community is the index of diversity, *a logarithmic function defined by*

$$H(x) = -(p_1 \ln p_1 + p_2 \ln p_2 + \ldots + p_n \ln p_n),$$

where $p_1, p_2, \ldots, p_n$ are the proportions of a sample belonging to each of n species in the sample. (Source: Ludwig, John and James Reynolds, Statistical Ecology: A Primer on Methods and Computing, *New York, Wiley, 1988.) Find the index of diversity to three decimal places if a sample of* 100 *from a community produces the following numbers.*

57. 90 of one species, 10 of another

.325

58. 60 of one species, 40 of another

.67

Chapter 11

SUMMARY

KEY TERMS

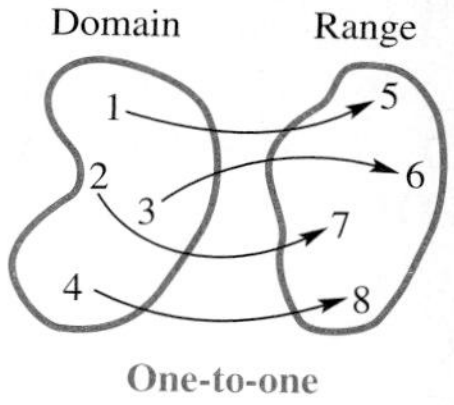

11.1 one-to-one function A one-to-one function is a function in which each x-value corresponds to just one y-value and each y-value corresponds to just one x-value.

inverse of a function f If f is a one-to-one function, the inverse of f is the set of all ordered pairs of the form (y, x), where (x, y) belongs to f.

11.2 exponential equation An equation involving an exponential, where the variable is in the exponent, is an exponential equation.

11.3 logarithm A logarithm is an exponent; $\log_a x$ is the exponent on the base a that gives the number x.

logarithmic equation A logarithmic equation is an equation with a logarithm in at least one term.

11.5 common logarithm A common logarithm is a logarithm to the base 10.

natural logarithm A natural logarithm is a logarithm to the base e.

NEW SYMBOLS

f^{-1}	the inverse of f	$\ln x$	natural (base e) logarithm of x
$\log_a x$	the logarithm of x to the base a	e	a constant, approximately 2.7182818285
$\log x$	common (base 10) logarithm of x		

TEST YOUR WORD POWER

See how well you have learned the vocabulary in this chapter. Answers follow the Quick Review.

1. In a **one-to-one function**
   (a) each x-value corresponds to only one y-value
   (b) each x-value corresponds to one or more y-values
   (c) each x-value is the same as each y-value
   (d) each x-value corresponds to only one y-value and each y-value corresponds to only one x-value.

2. If f is a one-to-one function, then the **inverse** of f is
   (a) the set of all solutions of f
   (b) the set of all ordered pairs formed by interchanging the coordinates of the ordered pairs of f
   (c) an equation involving an exponential expression
   (d) the set of all ordered pairs that are the opposite (negative) of the coordinates of the ordered pairs of f.

3. An **exponential function** is a function defined by an expression of the form
   (a) $f(x) = ax^2 + bx + c$ for real numbers a, b, c $(a \neq 0)$
   (b) $f(x) = \log_a x$, for a and x positive numbers $(a \neq 1)$
   (c) $f(x) = a^x$ for all real numbers x $(a > 0, a \neq 1)$
   (d) $f(x) = \sqrt{x}$ for $x \geq 0$.

4. A **logarithm** is
   (a) an exponent
   (b) a base
   (c) an equation
   (d) a term.

5. A **logarithmic function** is a function that is defined by an expression of the form
   (a) $f(x) = ax^2 + bx + c$ for real numbers a, b, c $(a \neq 0)$
   (b) $f(x) = \log_a x$, for a and x positive numbers $(a \neq 1)$
   (c) $f(x) = a^x$ for all real numbers x $(a > 0, a \neq 1)$
   (d) $f(x) = \sqrt{x}$ for $x \geq 0$.

Quick Review

Concepts	*Examples*

11.1 Inverse Functions

Horizontal Line Test

If a horizontal line intersects the graph of a function in no more than one point, then the function is one-to-one.

Find f^{-1} if $f(x) = 2x - 3$. The graph of f is a straight line, so f is one-to-one by the horizontal line test.

Inverse Functions

For a one-to-one function f defined by an equation $y = f(x)$, the equation that defines the inverse function f^{-1} is found by interchanging x and y, solving for y, and replacing y with $f^{-1}(x)$.

Interchange x and y in the equation $y = 2x - 3$.

$$x = 2y - 3$$

Solve for y to get $\quad y = \dfrac{x+3}{2}.$

Therefore, $\quad f^{-1}(x) = \dfrac{x+3}{2}.$

In general, the graph of f^{-1} is the mirror image of the graph of f with respect to the line $y = x$.

The graphs of a nonlinear function f and its inverse f^{-1} are shown here.

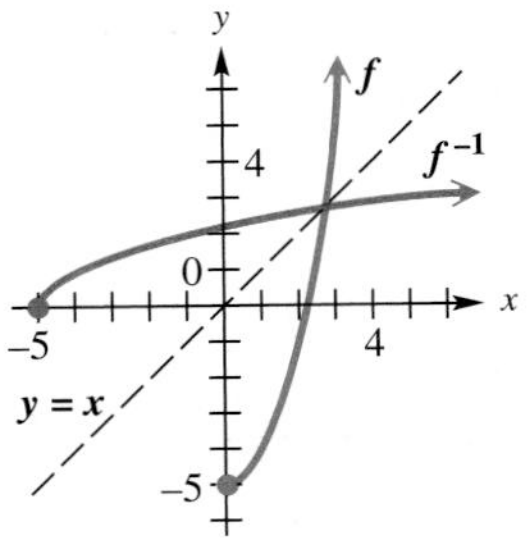

11.2 Exponential Functions

For $a > 0$, $a \neq 1$, $f(x) = a^x$ defines an exponential function with base a.

$F(x) = 3^x$ defines an exponential function with base 3.

Graph of $F(x) = a^x$

1. The graph contains the point $(0, 1)$.
2. When $a > 1$, the graph rises from left to right. When $0 < a < 1$, the graph falls from left to right.
3. The x-axis is an asymptote.
4. The domain is $(-\infty, \infty)$; the range is $(0, \infty)$.

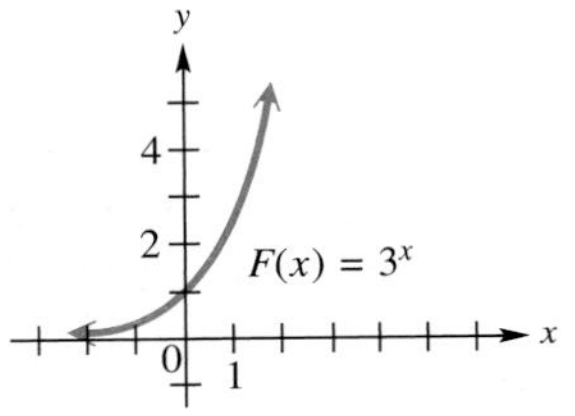

11.3 Logarithmic Functions

$y = \log_a x$ means $x = a^y$.

$y = \log_2 x$ means $x = 2^y$.

For $b > 0$, $b \neq 1$, $\log_b b = 1$ and $\log_b 1 = 0$.

$\log_3 3 = 1 \qquad \log_5 1 = 0$

For $a > 0$, $a \neq 1$, $x > 0$, $G(x) = \log_a x$ defines the logarithmic function with base a.

$G(x) = \log_3 x$ defines the logarithmic function with base 3.

Graph of $G(x) = \log_a x$

1. The graph contains the point $(1, 0)$.
2. When $a > 1$, the graph rises from left to right. When $0 < a < 1$, the graph falls from left to right.
3. The y-axis is an asymptote.
4. The domain is $(0, \infty)$; the range is $(-\infty, \infty)$.

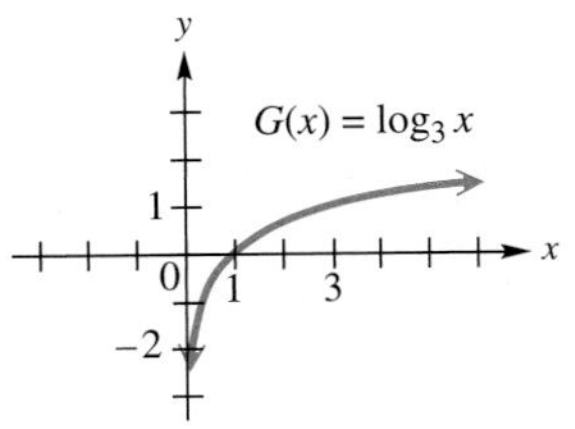

Concepts	*Examples*
11.4 Properties of Logarithms	
Product Rule	
$\log_a xy = \log_a x + \log_a y$	$\log_2 3m = \log_2 3 + \log_2 m$
Quotient Rule	
$\log_a \frac{x}{y} = \log_a x - \log_a y$	$\log_5 \frac{9}{4} = \log_5 9 - \log_5 4$
Power Rule	
$\log_a x^r = r \log_a x$	$\log_{10} 2^3 = 3 \log_{10} 2$
Special Properties	
$b^{\log_b x} = x$ and $\log_b b^x = x$	$6^{\log_6 10} = 10$ $\quad \log_3 3^4 = 4$
11.5 Common and Natural Logarithms	
Common logarithms (base 10) are used in applications such as pH, sound level, and intensity of an earthquake. Use the LOG key of a calculator to evaluate common logarithms.	Use the formula $\text{pH} = -\log [H_3O^+]$ to find the pH (to one decimal place) of grapes with hydronium ion concentration 5.0×10^{-5}. $\text{pH} = -\log(5.0 \times 10^{-5})$ Substitute. $= -(\log 5.0 + \log 10^{-5})$ Property of logarithms ≈ 4.3 Evaluate.
Natural logarithms (base e) are most often used in applications of growth and decay, such as time for money invested to double, decay of chemical compounds, and biological growth. Use the ln x key or both the INV and e^x keys to evaluate natural logarithms.	Use the formula for doubling time (in years) $t = \frac{\ln 2}{\ln(1 + r)}$ to find the doubling time to the nearest tenth at an interest rate of 4%. $t = \frac{\ln 2}{\ln(1 + .04)}$ Substitute. ≈ 17.7 Evaluate. The doubling time is about 17.7 yr.
11.6 Exponential and Logarithmic Equations; Further Applications	
To solve exponential equations, use these properties ($b > 0$, $b \neq 1$).	
1. If $b^x = b^y$, then $x = y$.	Solve $2^{3x} = 2^5$. $3x = 5$ $x = \frac{5}{3}$ The solution set is $\{\frac{5}{3}\}$.
2. If $x = y$ ($x > 0$, $y > 0$), then $\log_b x = \log_b y$.	Solve $5^m = 8$. $\log 5^m = \log 8$ $m \log 5 = \log 8$ $m = \frac{\log 8}{\log 5} \approx 1.2920$ The solution set is $\{1.2920\}$.

(continued)

Concepts	*Examples*
11.6 Exponential and Logarithmic Equations; Further Applications (continued)	
To solve logarithmic equations, use these properties, where $b > 0$, $b \neq 1$, $x > 0$, $y > 0$. First use the properties of Section 11.4, if necessary, to get the equation in the proper form.	
1. If $\log_b x = \log_b y$, then $x = y$.	Solve $\log_3 2x = \log_3(x + 1)$. $$2x = x + 1$$ $$x = 1$$ The solution set is $\{1\}$.
2. If $\log_b x = y$, then $b^y = x$.	Solve $\log_2(3a - 1) = 4$. $$3a - 1 = 2^4$$ $$3a - 1 = 16$$ $$3a = 17$$ $$a = \frac{17}{3}$$ The solution set is $\{\frac{17}{3}\}$.
Change-of-Base Rule If $a > 0$, $a \neq 1$, $b > 0$, $b \neq 1$, $x > 0$, then $$\log_a x = \frac{\log_b x}{\log_b a}.$$	$$\log_3 17 = \frac{\ln 17}{\ln 3} = \frac{\log 17}{\log 3} \approx 2.5789$$

ANSWERS TO TEST YOUR WORD POWER

1. (d) *Example:* The function $f = \{(0, 2), (1, -1), (3, 5), (-2, 3)\}$ is one-to-one. **2. (b)** *Example:* The inverse of the one-to-one function f defined in Answer 1 is $f^{-1} = \{(2, 0), (-1, 1), (5, 3), (3, -2)\}$. **3. (c)** *Examples:* $f(x) = 4^x$, $g(x) = (\frac{1}{2})^x$, $h(x) = 2^{-x+3}$ **4. (a)** *Example:* $\log_a x$ is the exponent to which a must be raised to obtain x; $\log_3 9 = 2$ since $3^2 = 9$. **5. (b)** *Examples:* $y = \log_3 x$, $y = \log_{1/3} x$

Chapter 11 Review Exercises

[11.1] *Determine whether each graph is the graph of a one-to-one function.*

1.

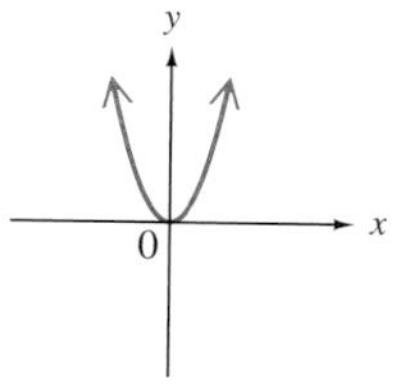

not one-to-one

2.

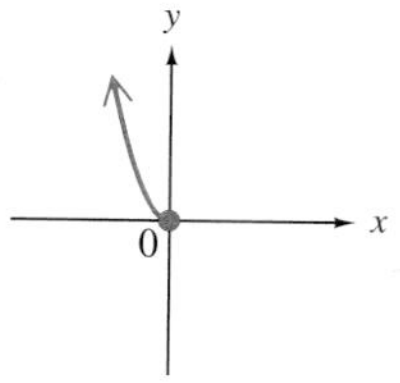

one-to-one

3. The table lists caffeine amounts in several popular 12-oz sodas. If the set of sodas is the domain and the set of caffeine amounts is the range of the function consisting of the six pairs listed, is it a one-to-one function? Why or why not?

Soda	Caffeine (mg)
Mountain Dew	55
Diet Coke	45
Dr. Pepper	41
Sunkist Orange Soda	41
Diet Pepsi-Cola	36
Coca-Cola Classic	34

Source: National Soft Drink Association.

This function is not one-to-one because two sodas in the list have 41 mg of caffeine.

Determine whether each function is one-to-one. If it is, find its inverse.

4. $f(x) = -3x + 7$

$f^{-1}(x) = \frac{x - 7}{-3}$ or $\frac{7 - x}{3}$

5. $f(x) = \sqrt[3]{6x - 4}$

$f^{-1}(x) = \frac{x^3 + 4}{6}$

6. $f(x) = -x^2 + 3$

not one-to-one

Each function graphed is one-to-one. Graph its inverse.

7.

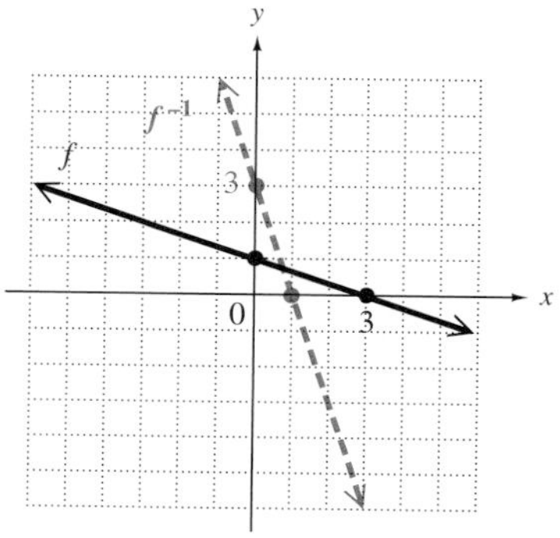

8.

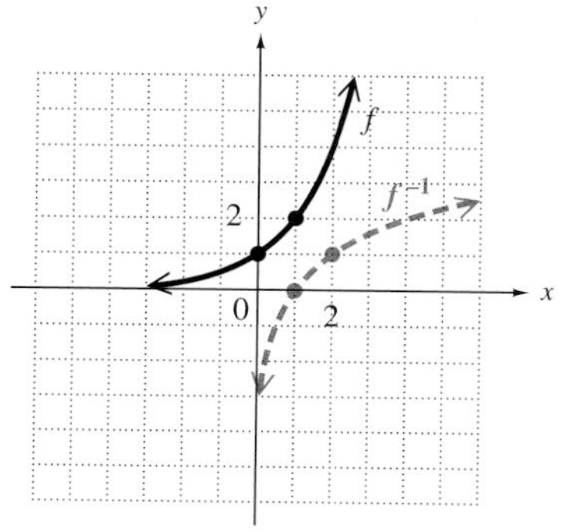

[11.2] *Graph each function.*

9. $f(x) = 3^x$

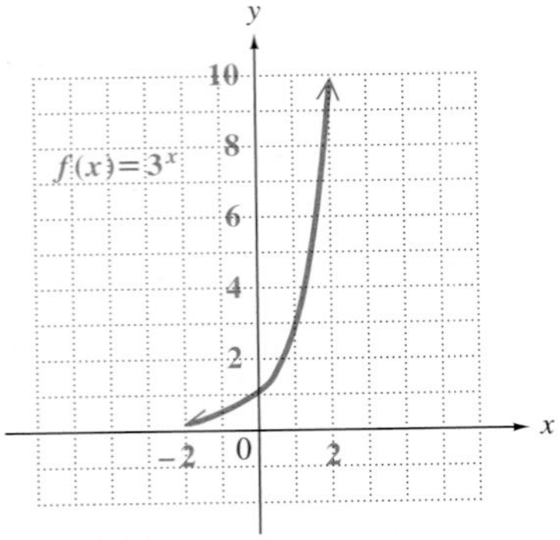

10. $f(x) = \left(\frac{1}{3}\right)^x$

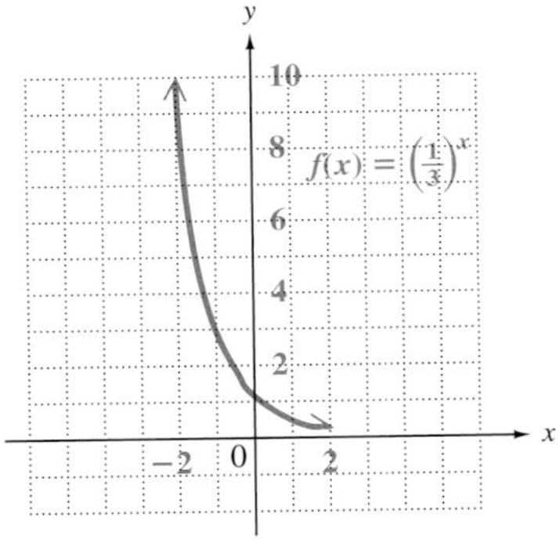

11. $y = 3^{x+1}$

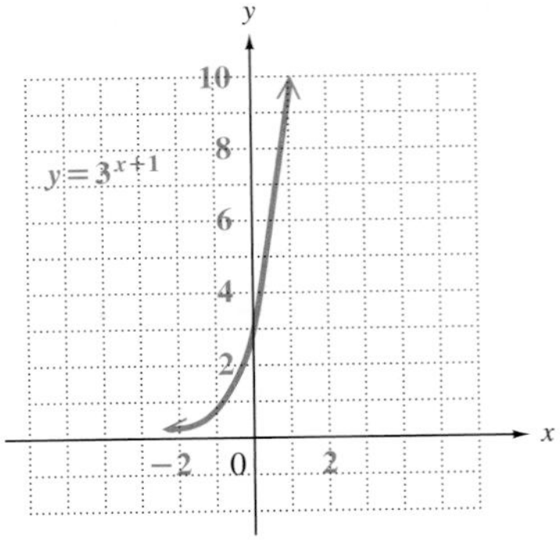

Solve each equation.

12. $4^{3x} = 8^{x+4}$

{4}

13. $\left(\frac{1}{27}\right)^{x-1} = 9^{2x}$

$\left\{\frac{3}{7}\right\}$

14. $5^x = 1$

{0}

In the remainder of the Chapter Review, many exercises will require a scientific calculator. We do not mark each such exercise.

15. The gross wastes generated in plastics, in millions of tons, from 1960 through 1990 can be approximated by the exponential function with

$$W(x) = .67(1.123)^x,$$

where $x = 0$ corresponds to 1960, $x = 5$ to 1965, and so on. Use this function to approximate the plastic waste amounts for the following years. (*Source:* U.S. Environmental Protection Agency, *Characterization of Municipal Solid Waste in the United States: 1994 Update,* 1995.)

(a) 1965 **1.2 million tons**   **(b)** 1975 **3.8 million tons**   **(c)** 1990 **21.8 million tons**

[11.3]

16. (a) Write in exponential form: $\log_5 625 = 4$. $\mathbf{5^4 = 625}$

(b) Write in logarithmic form: $5^{-2} = .04$. $\mathbf{\log_5 .04 = -2}$

17. (a) In your own words, explain the meaning of $\log_b a$. **$\log_b a$ represents the exponent on b that equals a.**

(b) Based on the meaning of $\log_b a$, what is the simplest form of $b^{\log_b a}$? ***a***

Graph each function.

18. $g(x) = \log_3 x$ (*Hint:* See Exercise 9.)

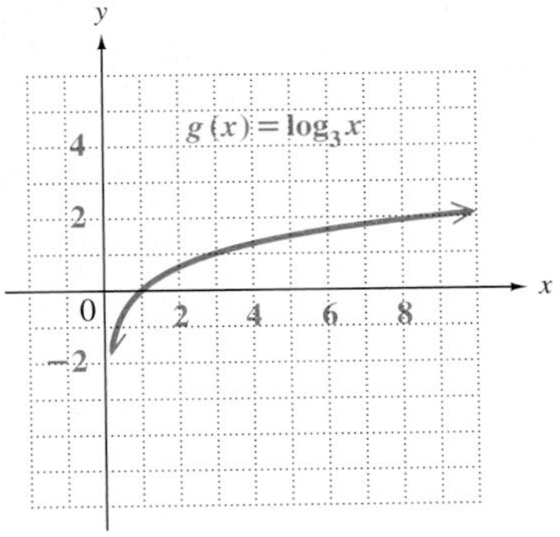

19. $g(x) = \log_{1/3} x$ (*Hint:* See Exercise 10.)

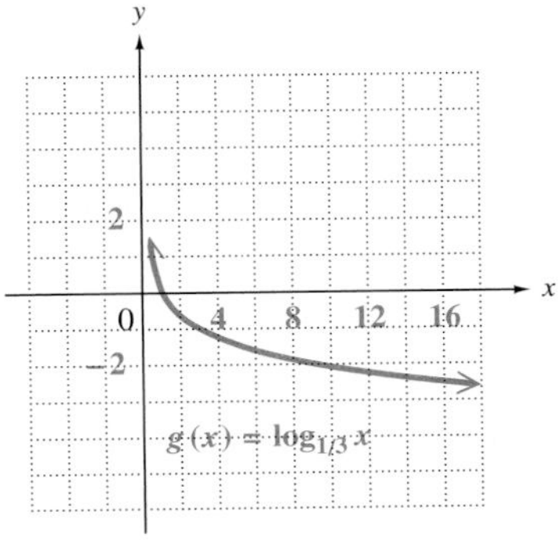

Solve each equation.

20. $\log_8 64 = x$

$\{2\}$

21. $\log_7\left(\frac{1}{49}\right) = x$

$\{-2\}$

22. $\log_4 x = \frac{3}{2}$

$\{8\}$

23. $\log_b b^2 = 2$

$\{b \mid b > 0, b \neq 1\}$

[11.4] *Apply the properties of logarithms to express each logarithm as a sum or difference of logarithms. Assume that all variables represent positive real numbers.*

24. $\log_4 3x^2$ $\log_4 3 + 2 \log_4 x$

25. $\log_2 \frac{p^2 r}{\sqrt{z}}$ $2 \log_2 p + \log_2 r - \frac{1}{2} \log_2 z$

Use the properties of logarithms to write each expression as a single logarithm. Assume that all variables represent positive real numbers, $b \neq 1$.

26. $\log_b 3 + \log_b x - 2 \log_b y$

$\log_b \frac{3x}{y^2}$

27. $\log_3(x + 7) - \log_3(4x + 6)$

$\log_3 \frac{x + 7}{4x + 6}$

[11.5] *Evaluate each logarithm. Give approximations to four decimal places.*

28. log 28.9

1.4609

29. log .257

−.5901

30. ln 28.9

3.3638

31. ln .257

−1.3587

Use the formula $\text{pH} = -\log[\text{H}_3\text{O}^+]$ *to find the* pH *of each substance with the given hydronium ion concentration.*

32. Milk, 4.0×10^{-7}

6.4

33. Crackers, 3.8×10^{-9}

8.4

34. If orange juice has pH 4.6, what is its hydronium ion concentration?

2.5×10^{-5}

Solve each problem.

35. Section 11.5 Exercise 37 introduced the *doubling function* defined by

$$t = \frac{\ln 2}{\ln(1 + r)},$$

that gives the number of years required to double your money when it is invested at interest rate r (in decimal form) compounded annually. How long does it take to double your money at each rate? Round answers to the nearest year.

(a) 4% 18 yr

(b) 6% 12 yr

(c) 10% 7 yr

(d) 12% 6 yr

(e) Compare each answer in parts (a)–(d) with these numbers:

$$\frac{72}{4}, \frac{72}{6}, \frac{72}{10}, \frac{72}{12}.$$

What do you find?

Each comparison shows approximately the same number. For example, in part (a) the doubling time is 18 yr (rounded) and $\frac{72}{4} = 18$. Thus, the formula $t = \frac{72}{100r}$ (called the *rule of 72*) is an excellent approximation of the doubling time formula. (It is used by bankers for that purpose.)

36. The graph shows the percent change in commercial rents in California from 1992 through 1999.

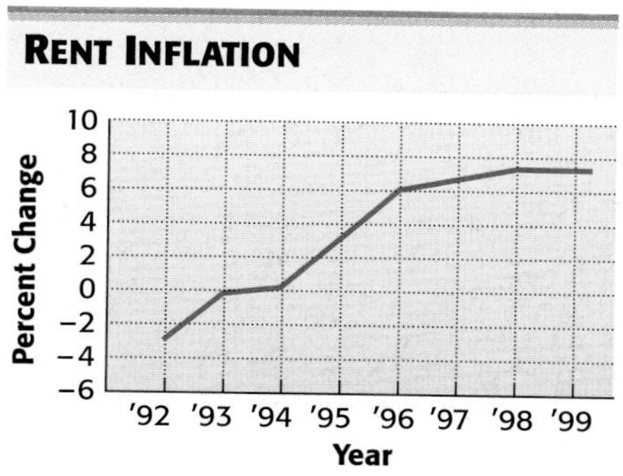

Source: CB Commercial/Torto Wheaton Research.

The percent change in rents is approximated by the logarithmic function with

$$g(x) = -650 + 143 \ln x,$$

where x represents the number of years since 1900.

(a) Find $g(92)$ and $g(99)$.

$g(92) = -3.4$; $g(99) = 7.1$

(b) Compare your results with the corresponding values in the graph. $g(92)$ agrees closely with the y-value from the graph of about -3; $g(99)$ also is reasonably close to the y-value from the graph of about 7.5.

[11.6] *Solve each equation. Give solutions to three decimal places.*

37. $3^x = 9.42$

{2.042}

38. $2^{x-1} = 15$

{4.907}

39. $e^{.06x} = 3$

{18.310}

Solve each equation. Give exact solutions.

40. $\log_3(9x + 8) = 2$

$\left\{\frac{1}{9}\right\}$

41. $\log_5(y + 6)^3 = 2$

$\{-6 + \sqrt[3]{25}\}$

42. $\log_3(p + 2) - \log_3 p = \log_3 2$

{2}

43. $\log(2x + 3) - \log x = 1$

$\left\{\frac{3}{8}\right\}$

44. $\log_4 x + \log_4(8 - x) = 2$

{4}

45. $\log_2 x + \log_2(x + 15) = 4$

{1}

Solve each problem.

46. How much would be in an account after 3 yr if \$6500.00 was invested at 3% annual interest, compounded daily (use $n = 365$)?

\$7112.11

47. Which is a better plan?

Plan A: Invest \$1000.00 at 4% compounded quarterly for 3 yr

Plan B: Invest \$1000.00 at 3.9% compounded monthly for 3 yr

Plan A; it would pay \$2.92 more.

A machine purchased for business use depreciates, *or loses value, over a period of years. The value of the machine at the end of its useful life is called its* scrap value. *By one method of depreciation (where it is assumed a constant percentage of the value depreciates annually), the scrap value, S, is given by*

$$S = C(1 - r)^n,$$

where C is the original cost, n is the useful life in years, and r is the constant percent of depreciation.

48. Find the scrap value of a machine costing \$30,000, having a useful life of 12 yr and a constant annual rate of depreciation of 15%.

\$4267

49. A machine has a "half-life" of 6 yr. Find the constant annual rate of depreciation.

about 11%

Use the change-of-base rule (with either common or natural logarithms) to find each logarithm. Give approximations to four decimal places.

50. $\log_{16} 13$

.9251

51. $\log_4 12$

1.7925

52. $\log_{\sqrt{6}} \sqrt{13}$

1.4315

Mixed Review Exercises

Solve.

53. $\log_3(x + 9) = 4$

{72}

54. $\log_2 32 = x$

{5}

55. $\log_x \frac{1}{81} = 2$

$\left\{\frac{1}{9}\right\}$

56. $27^x = 81$

$\left\{\frac{4}{3}\right\}$

57. $2^{2x-3} = 8$

{3}

58. $\log_3(x + 1) - \log_3 x = 2$

$\left\{\frac{1}{8}\right\}$

59. $\log(3x - 1) = \log 10$

$\left\{\frac{11}{3}\right\}$

60. Find the value of n in the equation for Exercise 48 if the scrap value is \$10,000, the cost is \$30,000, and the depreciation rate is 15%.

6.8 yr

Chapter 11 TEST

Study Skills Workbook
Activity 12

1. Decide whether each function is one-to-one.

(a) $f(x) = x^2 + 9$

(b)

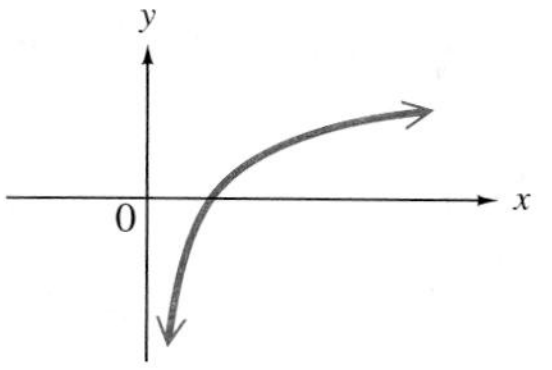

1. (a) not one-to-one
(b) one-to-one

2. Find $f^{-1}(x)$ for the one-to-one function defined by $f(x) = \sqrt[3]{x + 7}$.

2. $f^{-1}(x) = x^3 - 7$

3. Graph the inverse of f, given the graph of f here.

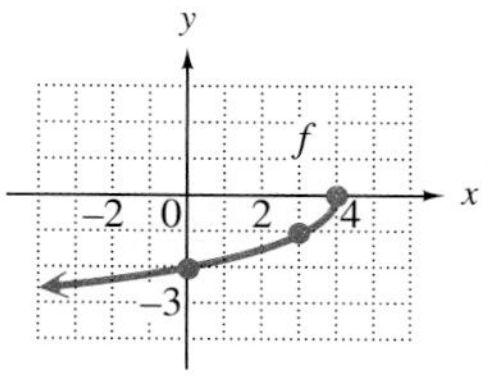

3.

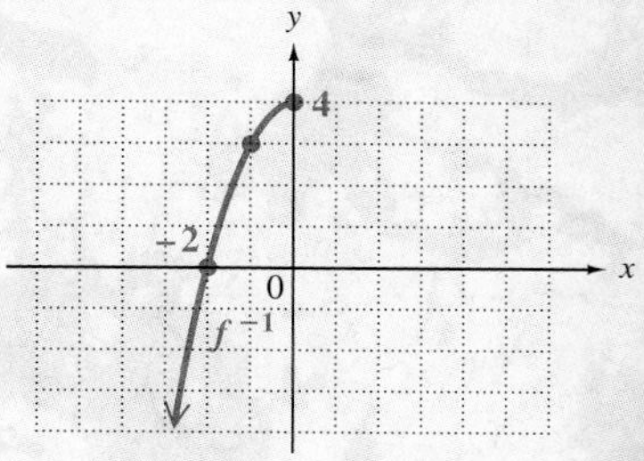

Graph each function.

4. $y = 6^x$

4.

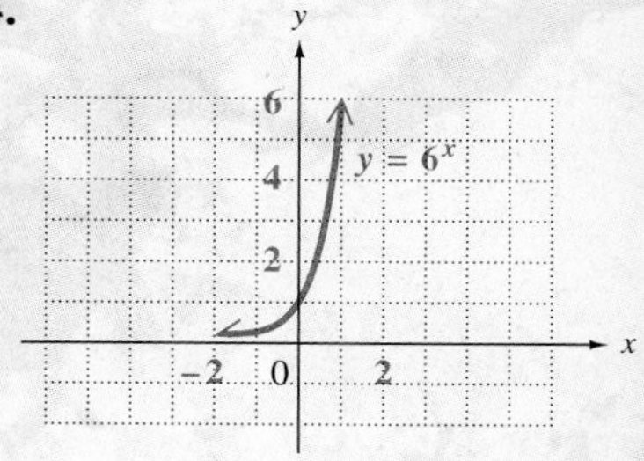

5. $y = \log_6 x$

5.

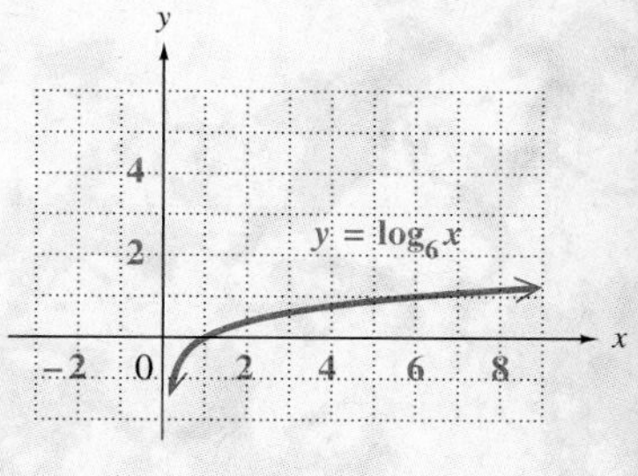

6. Explain how the graph of the function in Exercise 5 can be obtained from the graph of the function in Exercise 4.

6. Interchange the x- and y-values of the ordered pairs, because the functions are inverses.

Solve each equation. Give the exact solution.

7. $5^x = \dfrac{1}{625}$

8. $2^{3x-7} = 8^{2x+2}$

7. $\{-4\}$

8. $\left\{-\dfrac{13}{3}\right\}$

9. 30.0 million; 37.7 million

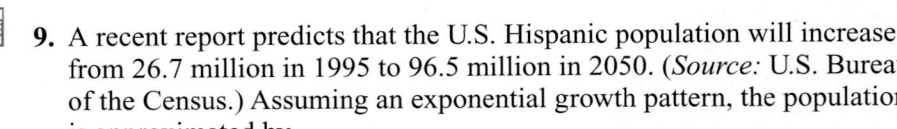

9. A recent report predicts that the U.S. Hispanic population will increase from 26.7 million in 1995 to 96.5 million in 2050. (*Source:* U.S. Bureau of the Census.) Assuming an exponential growth pattern, the population is approximated by

$$f(t) = 26.7e^{.023t},$$

where t represents the number of years since 1995. Use this function to estimate the population in 2000 and 2010.

10. $\log_4 .0625 = -2$

10. Write in logarithmic form: $4^{-2} = .0625$.

11. $7^2 = 49$

11. Write in exponential form: $\log_7 49 = 2$.

Solve each equation.

12. {32}

13. $\left\{\frac{1}{2}\right\}$

14. {2}

12. $\log_{1/2} x = -5$

13. $x = \log_9 3$

14. $\log_x 16 = 4$

15. $2 \log_3 x + \log_3 y$

15. Use properties of logarithms to write $\log_3 x^2y$ as a sum or difference of logarithms. Assume the variables represent positive real numbers.

16. $\log_b \frac{r^{1/4}s^2}{t^{2/3}}$

16. Use properties of logarithms to write $\frac{1}{4}\log_b r + 2\log_b s - \frac{2}{3}\log_b t$ as a single logarithm. Assume the variables represent positive real numbers, $b \neq 1$.

17. (a) 1.3284

(b) −.8440

(c) 2.1245

17. Use a calculator to find an approximation to four decimal places for each logarithm.

(a) log 21.3 **(b)** ln .43 **(c)** $\log_6 45$

18. {3.9656}

18. Solve $3^x = 78$, giving the solution to four decimal places.

19. {3}

19. Solve $\log_8(x + 5) + \log_8(x - 2) = \log_8 8$.

20. (a) $12,507.51

(b) 15.5 yr

20. Suppose that $10,000 is invested at 4.5% annual interest, compounded quarterly.

(a) How much will be in the account in 5 yr if no money is withdrawn?

(b) How long will it take for the initial principal to double?

Let $S = \{-\frac{9}{4}, -2, -\sqrt{2}, 0, .6, \sqrt{11}, \sqrt{-8}, 6, \frac{30}{3}\}$. *List the elements of S that are elements of each set.*

1. Integers

$-2, 0, 6, \frac{30}{3}$ (or 10)

2. Rational numbers

$-\frac{9}{4}, -2, 0, .6, 6, \frac{30}{3}$ (or 10)

3. Irrational numbers

$-\sqrt{2}, \sqrt{11}$

Simplify each expression.

4. $|-8| + 6 - |-2| - (-6 + 2)$

16

5. $2(-5) + (-8)(4) - (-3)$

-39

Solve each equation or inequality.

6. $7 - (3 + 4a) + 2a = -5(a - 1) - 3$

$\left\{-\frac{2}{3}\right\}$

7. $2m + 2 \leq 5m - 1$

$[1, \infty)$

8. $|2x - 5| = 9$

$\{-2, 7\}$

9. $|3p| - 4 = 12$

$\left\{-\frac{16}{3}, \frac{16}{3}\right\}$

10. $|3k - 8| \leq 1$

$\left[\frac{7}{3}, 3\right]$

11. $|4m + 2| > 10$

$(-\infty, -3) \cup (2, \infty)$

Graph each equation or inequality.

12. $y = -2.5x + 5$

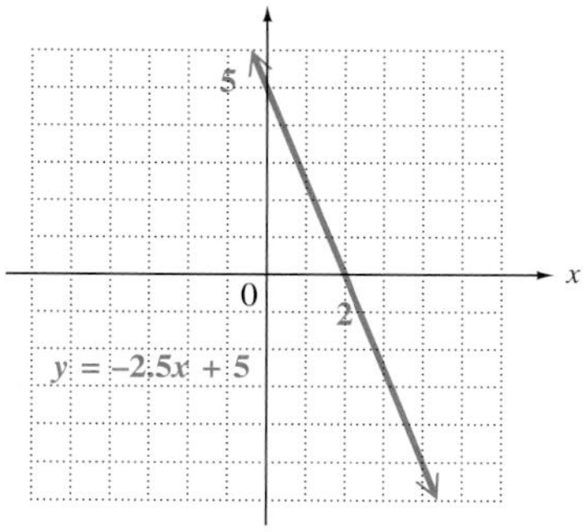

13. $-4x + y \leq 5$

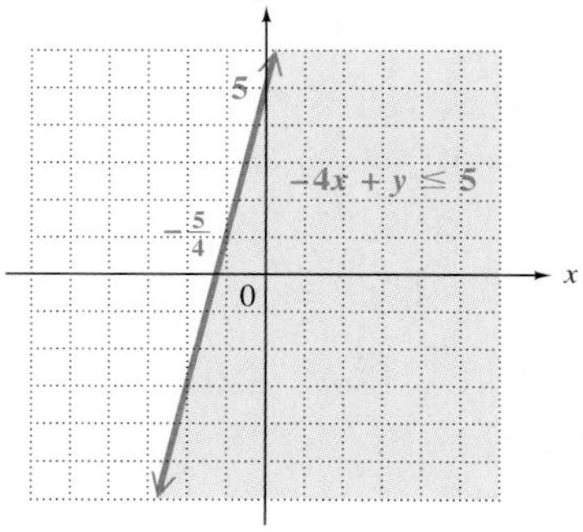

14. The graph indicates that timber harvests by Sierra Pacific Industries dropped from 17,716 acres in 1997 to 9733 acres in 1999.

(a) Is this the graph of a function?

yes

(b) What is the slope of the line in the graph? Interpret the slope in the context of the timber harvests.

−4000; The number of acres harvested decreased by 4000 acres per year during 1997–1999.

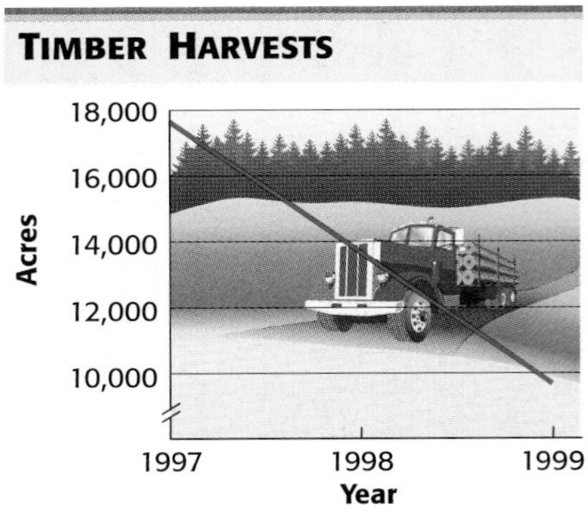

Source: Department of Forestry and Fire Protection.

15. Find the slope-intercept form of the equation of the line through $(5, -1)$ and parallel to the line with equation $3x - 4y = 12$.

$y = \frac{3}{4}x - \frac{19}{4}$

Solve each system of equations.

16. $5x - 3y = 14$
$2x + 5y = 18$

$\{(4, 2)\}$

17. $x + 2y + 3z = 11$
$3x - y + z = 8$
$2x + 2y - 3z = -12$

$\{(1, -1, 4)\}$

18. Candy worth \$1.00 per lb is to be mixed with candy worth \$1.96 per lb to get 16 lb of a mixture that will be sold for \$1.60 per lb. How many pounds of each candy should be used?

6 lb of \$1.00 candy and 10 lb of \$1.96 candy

Price per Pound	Number of Pounds	Value
\$1.00	x	$1x$
	y	
\$1.60		

Perform the indicated operations.

19. $(2p + 3)(3p - 1)$

$6p^2 + 7p - 3$

20. $(4k - 3)^2$

$16k^2 - 24k + 9$

21. $(3m^3 + 2m^2 - 5m) - (8m^3 + 2m - 4)$

$-5m^3 + 2m^2 - 7m + 4$

22. Divide $6t^4 + 17t^3 - 4t^2 + 9t + 4$ by $3t + 1$.

$2t^3 + 5t^2 - 3t + 4$

Factor completely.

23. $8x + x^3$

$x(8 + x^2)$

24. $24y^2 - 7y - 6$

$(3y - 2)(8y + 3)$

25. $5z^3 - 19z^2 - 4z$

$z(5z + 1)(z - 4)$

26. $16a^2 - 25b^4$

$(4a + 5b^2)(4a - 5b^2)$

27. $8c^3 + d^3$

$(2c + d)(4c^2 - 2cd + d^2)$

28. $16r^2 + 56rq + 49q^2$

$(4r + 7q)^2$

Perform the indicated operations.

29. $\dfrac{(5p^3)^4(-3p^7)}{2p^2(4p^4)}$

$-\dfrac{1875p^{13}}{8}$

30. $\dfrac{x^2 - 9}{x^2 + 7x + 12} \div \dfrac{x - 3}{x + 5}$

$\dfrac{x + 5}{x + 4}$

31. $\dfrac{2}{k + 3} - \dfrac{5}{k - 2}$

$\dfrac{-3k - 19}{(k + 3)(k - 2)}$

32. $\dfrac{3}{p^2 - 4p} - \dfrac{4}{p^2 + 2p}$

$\dfrac{22 - p}{p(p - 4)(p + 2)}$

33. Solve $\dfrac{1}{x} - \dfrac{3}{2x} = \dfrac{1}{x + 1}$.

$\left\{-\dfrac{1}{3}\right\}$

Simplify.

34. $\sqrt{288}$

$12\sqrt{2}$

35. $\dfrac{-8^{4/3}}{8^2}$

$-\dfrac{1}{4}$

36. $2\sqrt{32} - 5\sqrt{98}$

$-27\sqrt{2}$

37. Solve $\sqrt{2x + 1} - \sqrt{x} = 1$.

$\{0, 4\}$

38. Multiply $(5 + 4i)(5 - 4i)$.

41

Solve each equation or inequality.

39. $3x^2 = x + 1$

$\left\{\dfrac{1 \pm \sqrt{13}}{6}\right\}$

40. $k^2 + 2k - 8 > 0$

$(-\infty, -4) \cup (2, \infty)$

41. $x^4 - 5x^2 + 4 = 0$

$\{\pm 1, \pm 2\}$

Graph.

42. $y = \frac{1}{3}(x - 1)^2 + 2$

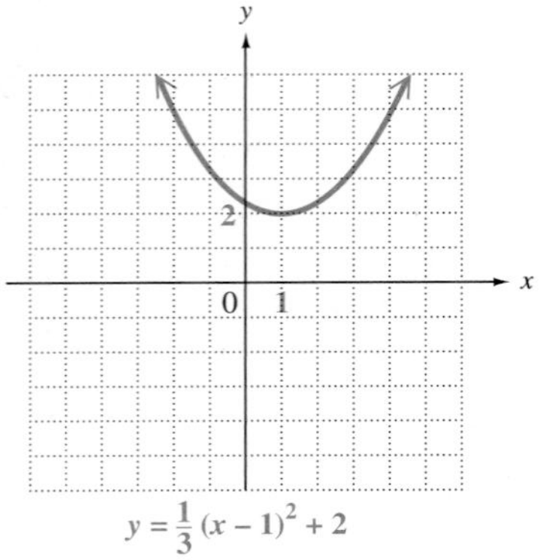

43. $f(x) = 2^x$

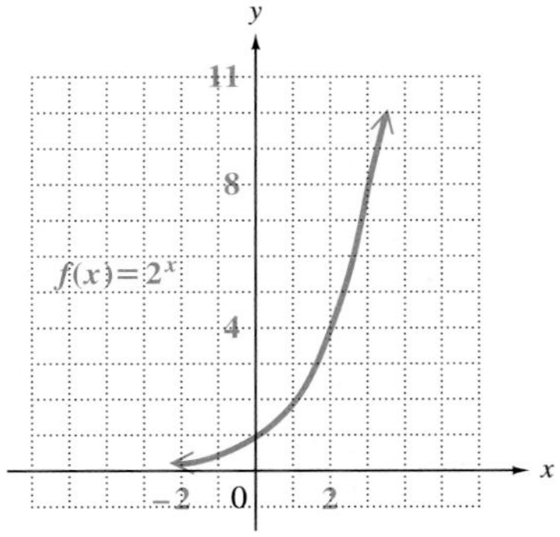

44. $f(x) = \log_3 x$

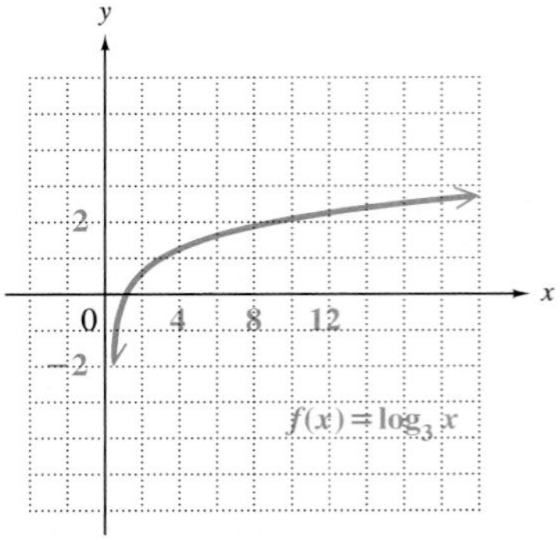

Solve.

45. $5^{x+3} = \left(\frac{1}{25}\right)^{3x+2}$

$\{-1\}$

46. $\log_5 x + \log_5(x + 4) = 1$

$\{1\}$

47. Write $\log_5 125 = 3$ in exponential form.

$5^3 = 125$

48. Rewrite the following using the product, quotient, and power rules for logarithms:

$$\log \frac{x^3\sqrt{y}}{z}.$$

$3 \log x + \frac{1}{2} \log y - \log z$

49. We used the formula for continuous compounding

$$A = Pe^{rt}$$

in Section 11.6. To three decimal places, what growth rate r will triple the value of P in 10 yr?

.110 or 11%

50. Let the number of bacteria present in a certain culture be given by

$$B(t) = 25{,}000e^{.2t},$$

where t is time measured in hours, and $t = 0$ corresponds to noon. Find, to the nearest hundred, the number of bacteria present at:

(a) noon — 25,000

(b) 2 P.M. — 37,300

(c) 5 P.M. — 68,000

Nonlinear Functions, Conic Sections, and Nonlinear Systems

12

When a plane intersects an infinite cone at different angles, it produces curves called **conic sections.** In Chapter 10 we studied one example of conic sections, the *parabola.* In 1609, Johann Kepler (1571–1630) established the importance of another conic section, the *ellipse,* when he discovered that the orbits of the planets around the sun are elliptical, not circular. Exercises 37 and 38 of Section 12.2 involve the equations of the elliptical orbits formed by the planets Mars and Venus.

12.1 Additional Graphs of Functions; Operations and Composition

Objectives

1. Recognize the graphs of the elementary functions defined by $|x|$, $\frac{1}{x}$, and $\sqrt{x}$, and graph their translations.
2. Perform operations on functions.
3. Find the composition of functions.

In earlier chapters we introduced the function defined by $f(x) = x^2$, sometimes called the **squaring function.** This is one of the most important elementary functions in algebra.

1 Recognize the graphs of the elementary functions defined by $|x|$, $\frac{1}{x}$, and $\sqrt{x}$, and graph their translations. Another one of the elementary functions, defined by $f(x) = |x|$, is called the **absolute value function.** Its graph, along with a table of selected ordered pairs, is shown in Figure 1. Its domain is $(-\infty, \infty)$, and its range is $[0, \infty)$.

x	y
0	0
± 1	1
± 2	2
± 3	3

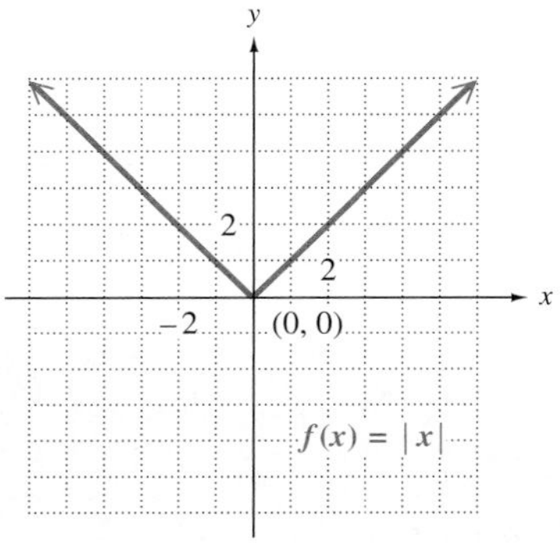

Figure 1

The **reciprocal function,** defined by $f(x) = \frac{1}{x}$, was introduced in Chapter 8. Its graph is shown in Figure 2, along with a table of selected ordered pairs. Notice that x can never equal 0 for this function, and as a result, as x gets closer and closer to 0, the graph approaches either ∞ or $-\infty$. Also, $\frac{1}{x}$ can never equal 0, and as x approaches ∞ or $-\infty$, $\frac{1}{x}$ approaches 0. The axes are called **asymptotes** for the function. (Asymptotes are studied in more detail in college algebra courses.) For the reciprocal function, the domain and the range are both $(-\infty, 0) \cup (0, \infty)$.

x	y
$\frac{1}{3}$	3
$\frac{1}{2}$	2
1	1
2	$\frac{1}{2}$
3	$\frac{1}{3}$

x	y
$-\frac{1}{3}$	-3
$-\frac{1}{2}$	-2
-1	-1
-2	$-\frac{1}{2}$
-3	$-\frac{1}{3}$

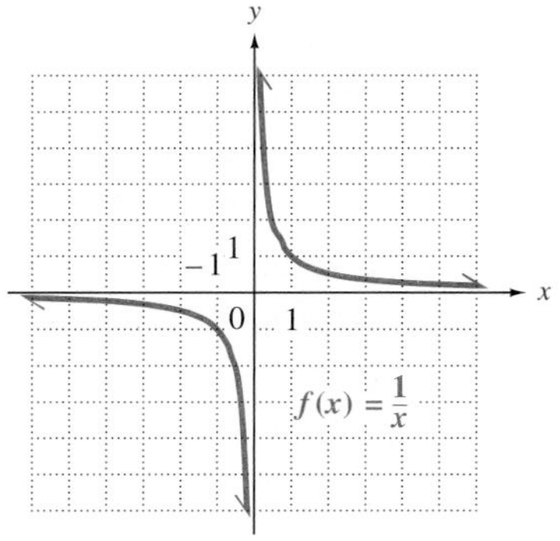

Figure 2

The **square root function,** defined by $f(x) = \sqrt{x}$, was introduced in Chapter 9. Its graph is shown in Figure 3. Notice that since we restrict function values to be real numbers, x cannot take on negative values. Thus, the domain of the square root function is $[0, \infty)$. Because the principal square root is always nonnegative, the range is also $[0, \infty)$. A table of values is shown along with the graph.

x	y
0	0
1	1
4	2

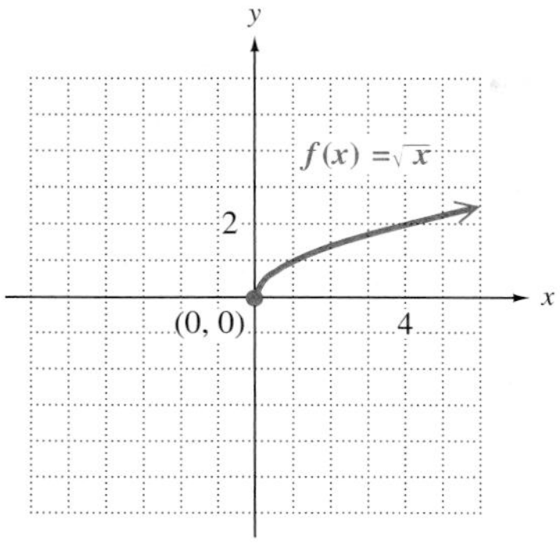

Figure 3

Just as the graph of $f(x) = x^2$ can be shifted, or translated, as we saw in Section 10.6, so can the graphs of these other elementary functions.

Example 1 Applying a Horizontal Shift

Graph $f(x) = |x - 2|$.

The graph of $y = (x - 2)^2$ is obtained by shifting the graph of $y = x^2$ two units to the right. In a similar manner, the graph of $f(x) = |x - 2|$ is found by shifting the graph of $y = |x|$ two units to the right, as shown in Figure 4. The table of ordered pairs accompanying the graph supports this, as you can see by comparing it to the table with Figure 1. The domain of this function is $(-\infty, \infty)$, and its range is $[0, \infty)$.

x	y
0	2
1	1
2	0
3	1
4	2

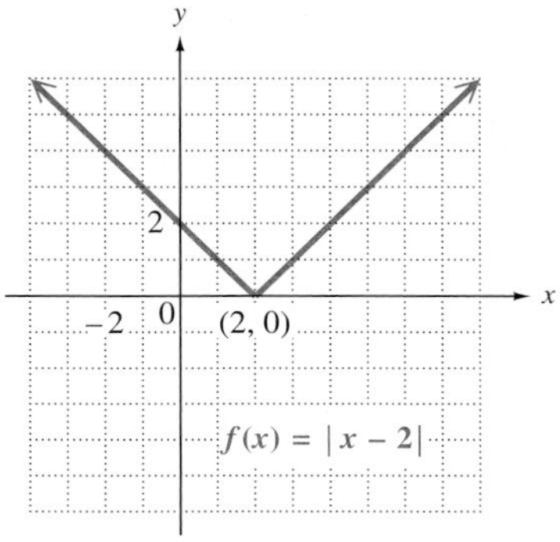

Figure 4

Work Problem 1 at the Side.

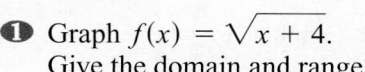

1 Graph $f(x) = \sqrt{x + 4}$. Give the domain and range.

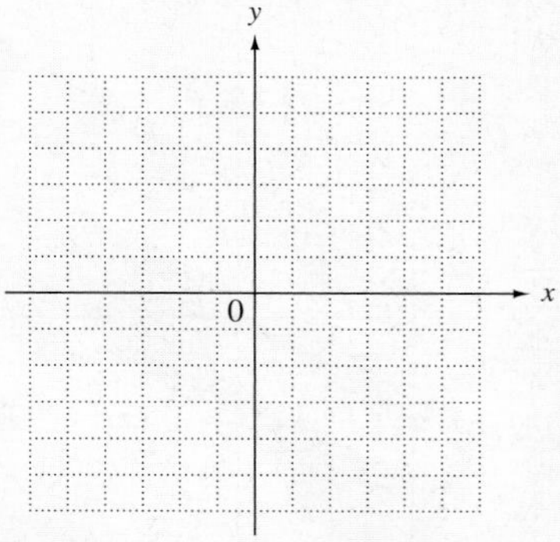

ANSWERS

1.

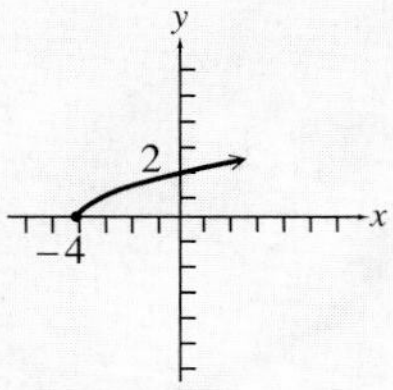

$[-4, \infty)$; $[0, \infty)$

2 Graph $f(x) = \dfrac{1}{x} - 2.$

Give the domain and range.

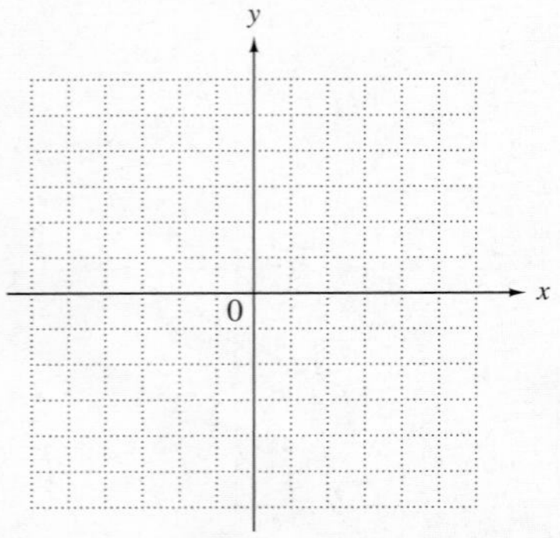

Example 2 Applying a Vertical Shift

Graph $f(x) = \dfrac{1}{x} + 3.$

The graph of this function is found by shifting the graph of $y = \frac{1}{x}$ three units up. See Figure 5. The domain is $(-\infty, 0) \cup (0, \infty)$, and the range is $(-\infty, 3) \cup (3, \infty)$.

x	y
$\frac{1}{3}$	6
$\frac{1}{2}$	5
1	4
2	3.5

x	y
$-\frac{1}{3}$	0
$-\frac{1}{2}$	1
−1	2
−2	2.5

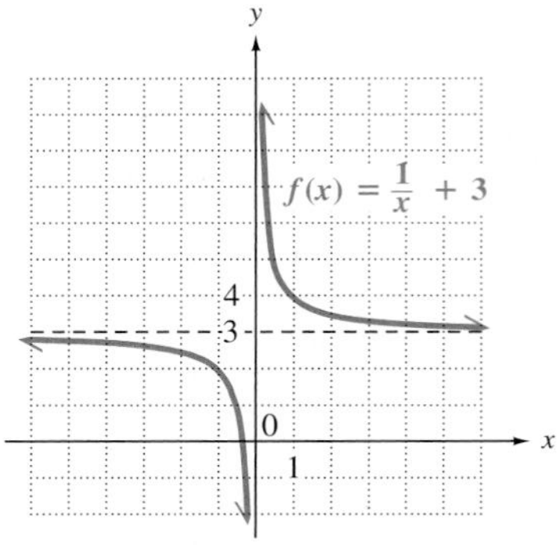

Figure 5

Work Problem 2 at the Side.

3 Graph $f(x) = |x + 2| + 1.$

Give the domain and range.

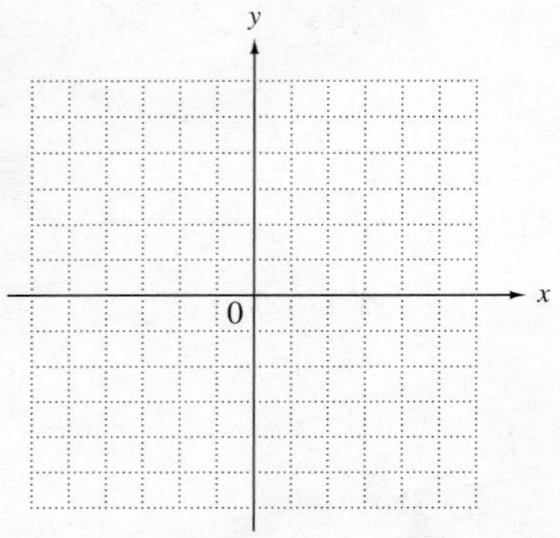

Example 3 Applying Both Horizontal and Vertical Shifts

Graph $f(x) = \sqrt{x + 1} - 4.$

The graph of $y = (x + 1)^2 - 4$ is obtained by shifting the graph of $y = x^2$ one unit to the left and four units down. Following this pattern here, we shift the graph of $y = \sqrt{x}$ one unit to the left and four units down to get the graph of $f(x) = \sqrt{x + 1} - 4$. See Figure 6. The domain is $[-1, \infty)$, and the range is $[-4, \infty)$.

x	y
−1	−4
0	−3
3	−2

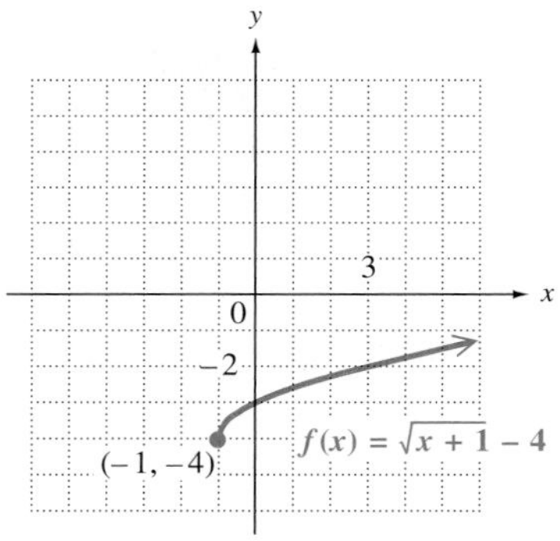

Figure 6

Work Problem 3 at the Side.

2 Perform operations on functions.

Businesses often use the equation "profit equals revenue minus cost," written using function notation as $P(x) = R(x) - C(x)$, where x is the number of items produced and sold. Thus, the profit function is found by subtracting the cost function from the revenue function. New functions can be formed using other operations as well.

ANSWERS

2.

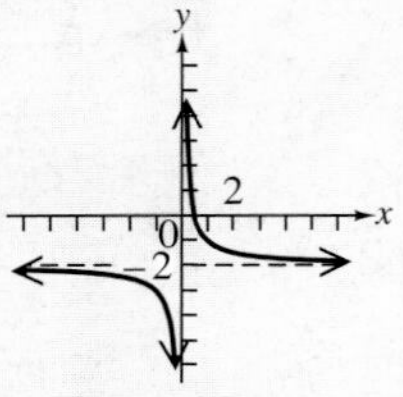

$(-\infty, 0) \cup (0, \infty)$; $(-\infty, -2) \cup (-2, \infty)$

3.

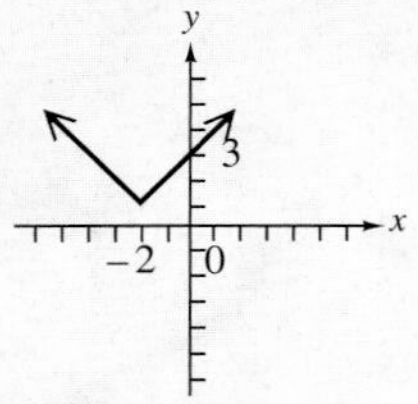

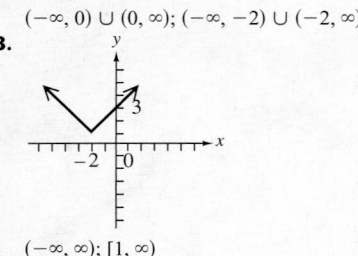

$(-\infty, \infty)$; $[1, \infty)$

We define the following **operations on functions.**

Operations on Functions

If $f(x)$ and $g(x)$ define functions, then

$$(f+g)(x) = f(x) + g(x), \qquad \text{Sum}$$

$$(f-g)(x) = f(x) - g(x), \qquad \text{Difference}$$

$$(fg)(x) = f(x) \cdot g(x), \qquad \text{Product}$$

$$\left(\frac{f}{g}\right)(x) = \frac{f(x)}{g(x)}, \quad g(x) \neq 0. \qquad \text{Quotient}$$

In each case, the domain of the new function is the intersection of the domains of f and g. Additionally, the domain of the quotient function must exclude any values of x for which $g(x) = 0$. (Why?)

Example 4 **Adding, Subtracting, Multiplying, and Dividing Functions**

For the functions defined by

$$f(x) = 10x^2 - 2x \quad \text{and} \quad g(x) = 2x,$$

find each of the following.

(a) $(f+g)(2)$

$$\begin{aligned} (f+g)(2) &= f(2) + g(2) && \text{Use the definition.} \\ &= [10(2)^2 - 2(2)] + 2(2) && \text{Substitute.} \\ &= 40 \end{aligned}$$

Alternatively, we could first find $(f+g)(x)$.

$$\begin{aligned} (f+g)(x) &= f(x) + g(x) && \text{Use the definition.} \\ &= (10x^2 - 2x) + 2x && \text{Add the polynomials.} \\ &= 10x^2 && \text{Combine terms.} \end{aligned}$$

Then,

$$(f+g)(2) = 10(2)^2 = 40. \qquad \text{The result is the same.}$$

(b) $(f-g)(x)$ and $(f-g)(1)$

$$\begin{aligned} (f-g)(x) &= f(x) - g(x) && \text{Use the definition.} \\ &= (10x^2 - 2x) - 2x && \text{Substitute.} \\ &= 10x^2 - 4x && \text{Combine terms.} \end{aligned}$$

Then,

$$(f-g)(1) = 10(1)^2 - 4(1) = 6. \qquad \text{Substitute.}$$

Confirm that $f(1) - g(1)$ gives the same result.

(c)

$$\begin{aligned} (fg)(x) &= f(x) \cdot g(x) && \text{Use the definition.} \\ &= (10x^2 - 2x)2x && \text{Substitute.} \\ &= 20x^3 - 4x^2 && \text{Distributive property} \end{aligned}$$

Continued on Next Page

4 For $f(x) = 18x^2 - 24x$ and $g(x) = 3x$, find each of the following.

(a) $(f + g)(x)$ and $(f + g)(-1)$

(b) $(f - g)(x)$ and $(f - g)(1)$

(c) $(fg)(x)$

(d) $\left(\frac{f}{g}\right)(x)$

(d)
$$\left(\frac{f}{g}\right)(x) = \frac{f(x)}{g(x)}$$
$$= \frac{10x^2 - 2x}{2x}$$
$$= \frac{10x^2}{2x} - \frac{2x}{2x}$$
$$= 5x - 1, \quad x \neq 0$$

Since $g(x)$, in this case $2x$, cannot equal 0, $x \neq 0$.

Work Problem 4 at the Side.

3 **Find the composition of functions.** The diagram in Figure 7 shows a function f that assigns to each element x of set X some element y of set Y. Suppose that a function g takes each element of set Y and assigns a value z of set Z. Using both f and g, then, an element x in X is assigned to an element z in Z. The result of this process is a new function h, which takes an element x in X and assigns an element z in Z.

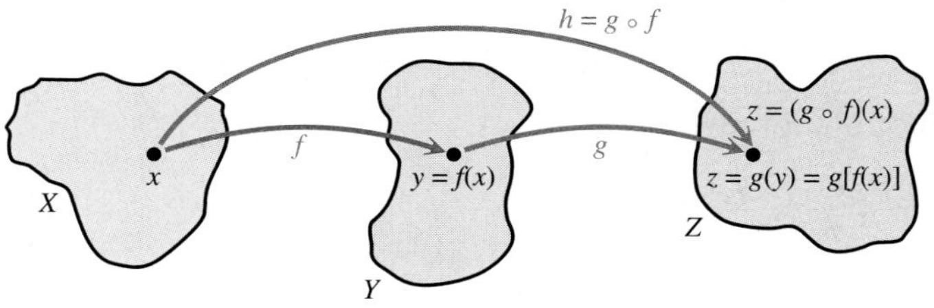

Figure 7

This function h is called the *composition* of functions g and f, written $g \circ f$, and is defined as follows.

Composition of Functions

If f and g are functions, then the **composite function,** or **composition,** of g and f is defined by

$$(g \circ f)(x) = g[f(x)]$$

for all x in the domain of f such that $f(x)$ is in the domain of g.

Read $g \circ f$ as "g of f."

As a real-life example of how composite functions occur, suppose an oil well off the California coast is leaking, with the leak spreading oil in a circular layer over the surface. See Figure 8.

Figure 8

ANSWERS

4. **(a)** $18x^2 - 21x$; 39 **(b)** $18x^2 - 27x$; -9
(c) $54x^3 - 72x^2$ **(d)** $6x - 8$, $x \neq 0$

At any time t, in minutes, after the beginning of the leak, the radius of the circular oil slick is given by $r(t) = 5t$ ft. Since $A(r) = \pi r^2$ gives the area of a circle of radius r, the area can be expressed as a function of time by substituting $5t$ for r in $A(r) = \pi r^2$ to get

$$A(r) = \pi r^2$$
$$A[r(t)] = \pi(5t)^2 = 25\pi t^2.$$

The function $A[r(t)]$ is a composite function of the functions A and r.

Example 5 **Finding a Composite Function**

Let $f(x) = x^2$ and $g(x) = x + 3$. Find $(f \circ g)(4)$.

$(f \circ g)(4) = f[g(4)]$	Definition
$= f(4 + 3)$	Use the rule for $g(x)$; $g(4) = 4 + 3$.
$= f(7)$	Add.
$= 7^2$	Use the rule for $f(x)$; $f(7) = 7^2$.
$= 49$	

Notice in Example 5 that if we reverse the order of the functions, the composition of g and f is defined by $g[f(x)]$. Once again, letting $x = 4$, we have

$(g \circ f)(4) = g[f(4)]$	Definition
$= g(4^2)$	Use the rule for $f(x)$; $f(4) = 4^2$.
$= g(16)$	Square 4.
$= 16 + 3$	Use the rule for $g(x)$; $g(16) = 16 + 3$.
$= 19.$	

Here we see that $(f \circ g)(4) \neq (g \circ f)(4)$ because $49 \neq 19$. In general,

$$(f \circ g)(x) \neq (g \circ f)(x).$$

Example 6 **Finding Composite Functions**

Let $f(x) = 4x - 1$ and $g(x) = x^2 + 5$. Find each of the following.

(a) $(f \circ g)(2)$

$$\begin{aligned}(f \circ g)(2) &= f[g(2)]\\ &= f(2^2 + 5)\\ &= f(9)\\ &= 4(9) - 1\\ &= \mathbf{35}\end{aligned}$$

(b) $(f \circ g)(x)$

Here, use $g(x)$ as the input for the function f.

$(f \circ g)(x) = f[g(x)]$	
$= 4(g(x)) - 1$	Use the rule for $f(x)$; $f(x) = 4x - 1$.
$= 4(x^2 + 5) - 1$	$g(x) = x^2 + 5$
$= 4x^2 + 20 - 1$	Distributive property
$= 4x^2 + 19$	Combine terms.

Continued on Next Page

5 Let $f(x) = 3x + 6$ and $g(x) = x^3$. Find each of the following.

(a) $(f \circ g)(2)$

(b) $(g \circ f)(2)$

(c) $(f \circ g)(x)$

(d) $(g \circ f)(x)$

(c) Find $(f \circ g)(2)$ again, this time using the rule obtained in part (b).

$$(f \circ g)(x) = \mathbf{4x^2 + 19} \quad \text{From part (b)}$$
$$(f \circ g)(2) = 4(2)^2 + 19$$
$$= 4(4) + 19$$
$$= 16 + 19$$
$$= \mathbf{35}$$

The result, 35, is the same as the result in part (a).

Work Problem 5 at the Side.

ANSWERS

5. (a) 30 **(b)** 1728 **(c)** $3x^3 + 6$ **(d)** $(3x + 6)^3$

12.1 EXERCISES

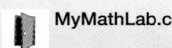

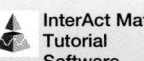

FOR EXTRA HELP: Student's Solutions Manual | MyMathLab.com | InterAct Math Tutorial Software | AW Math Tutor Center | www.mathxl.com | Digital Video Tutor CD 11 Videotape 24

Fill in each blank with the correct response.

1. For the reciprocal function defined by $f(x) = \dfrac{1}{x}$, __0__ is the only real number not in the domain.

2. The range of the square root function, given by $f(x) = \sqrt{x}$, is __$[0, \infty)$__.

3. The lowest point on the graph of $f(x) = |x|$ has coordinates (__0__, __0__).

4. The range of $f(x) = x^2 + 4$, a translation of the squaring function, is __$[4, \infty)$__.

Without actually plotting points, match each function defined by the absolute value expression with its graph. See Example 1.

5. $f(x) = |x - 2| + 2$ B

6. $f(x) = |x + 2| + 2$ C

7. $f(x) = |x - 2| - 2$ A

8. $f(x) = |x + 2| - 2$ D

A.

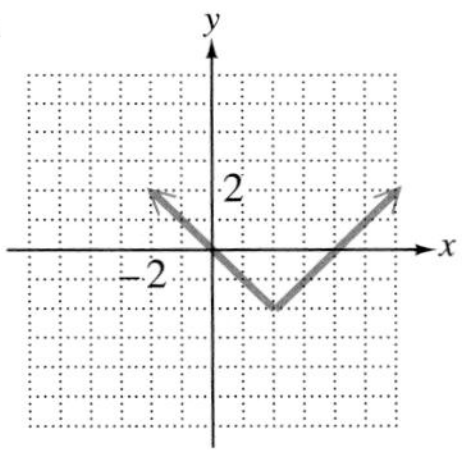

B.

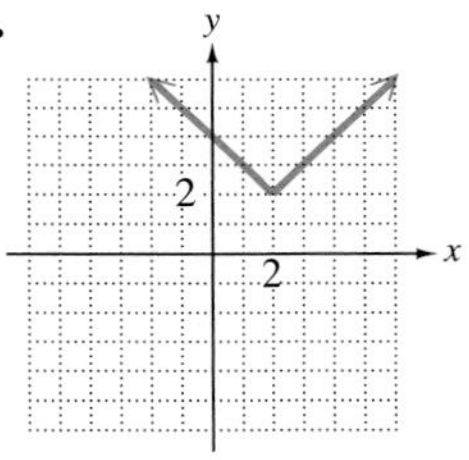

C.

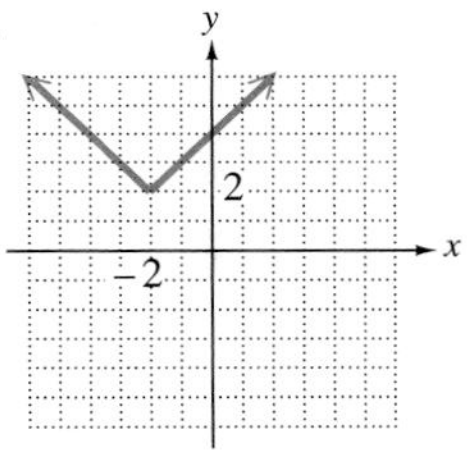

D.

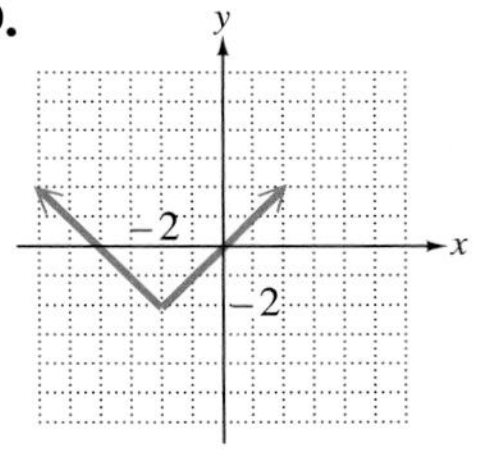

Graph each function. Give the domain and range. See Examples 1–3.

9. $f(x) = |x + 1|$

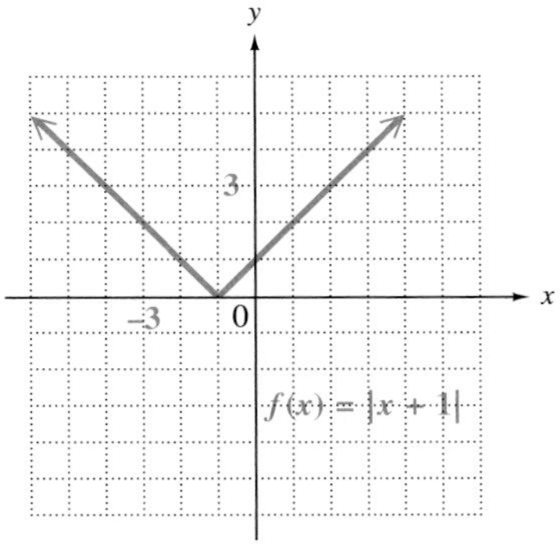

$(-\infty, \infty)$; $[0, \infty)$

10. $f(x) = |x - 1|$

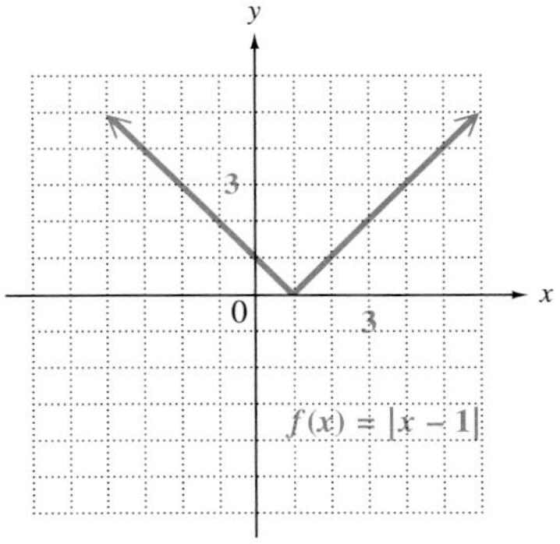

$(-\infty, \infty)$; $[0, \infty)$

11. $f(x) = \dfrac{1}{x} + 1$

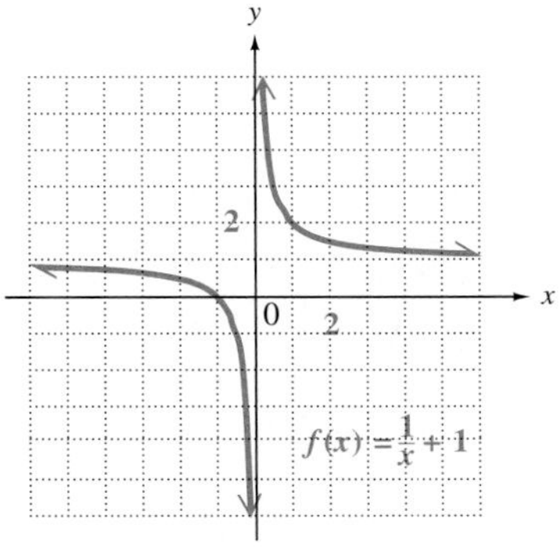

$(-\infty, 0) \cup (0, \infty)$;
$(-\infty, 1) \cup (1, \infty)$

12. $f(x) = \frac{1}{x} - 1$

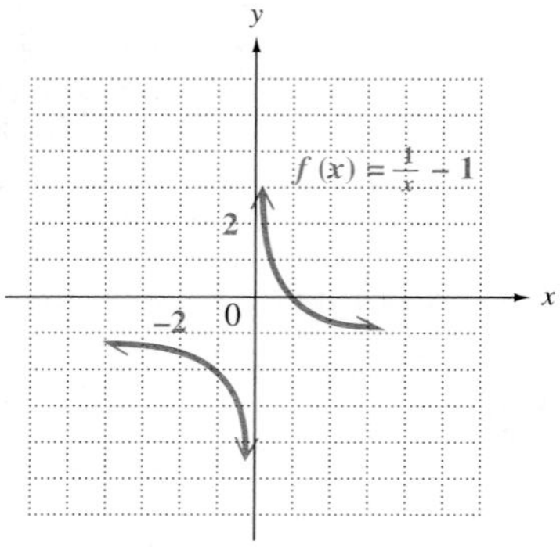

$(-\infty, 0) \cup (0, \infty)$;
$(-\infty, -1) \cup (-1, \infty)$

13. $f(x) = \sqrt{x - 2}$

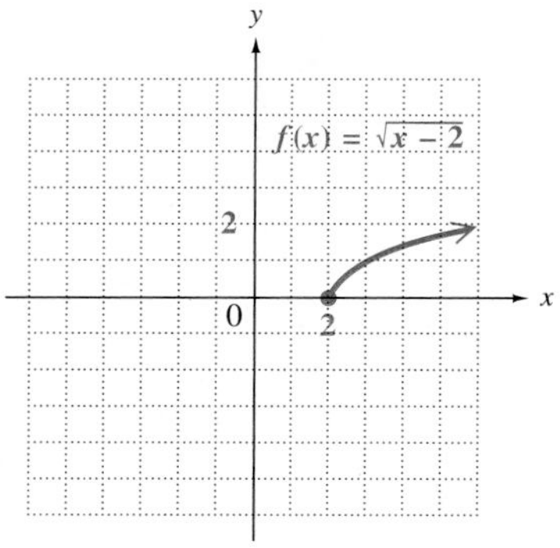

$[2, \infty)$; $[0, \infty)$

14. $f(x) = \sqrt{x + 5}$

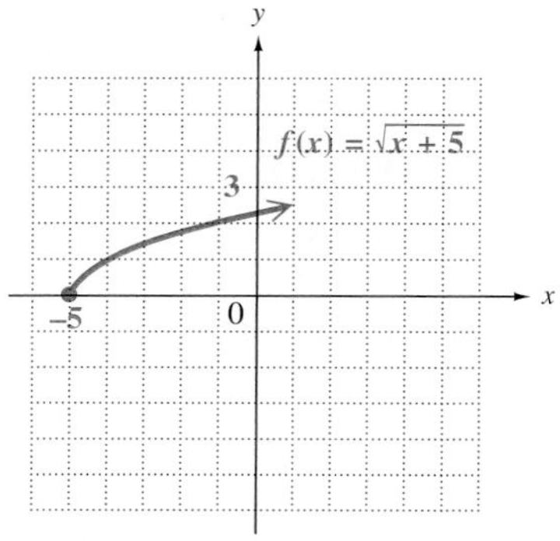

$[-5, \infty)$; $[0, \infty)$

15. $f(x) = \frac{1}{x - 2}$

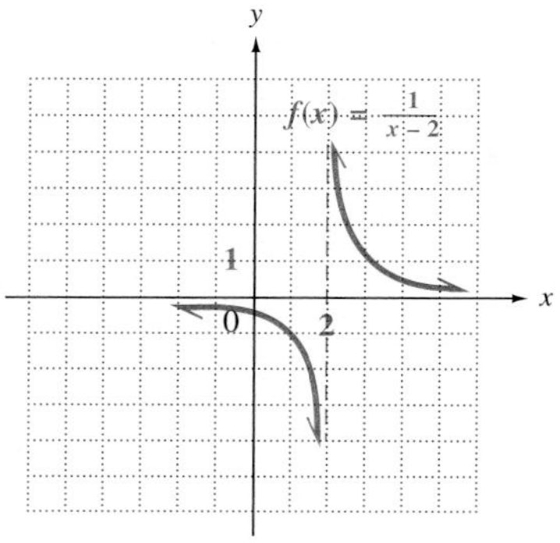

$(-\infty, 2) \cup (2, \infty)$;
$(-\infty, 0) \cup (0, \infty)$

16. $f(x) = \frac{1}{x + 2}$

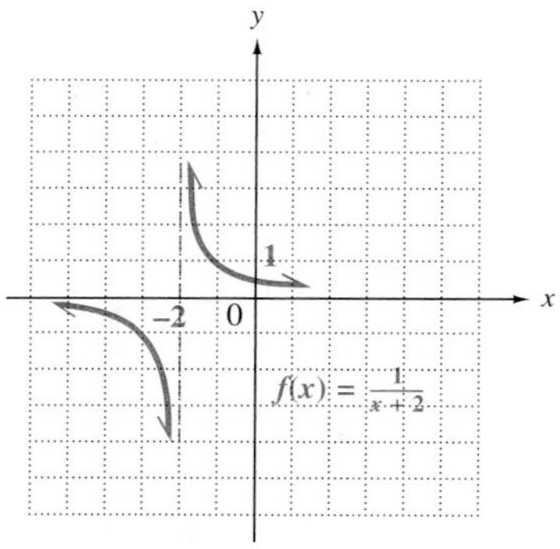

$(-\infty, -2) \cup (-2, \infty)$;
$(-\infty, 0) \cup (0, \infty)$

17. $f(x) = \sqrt{x + 3} - 3$

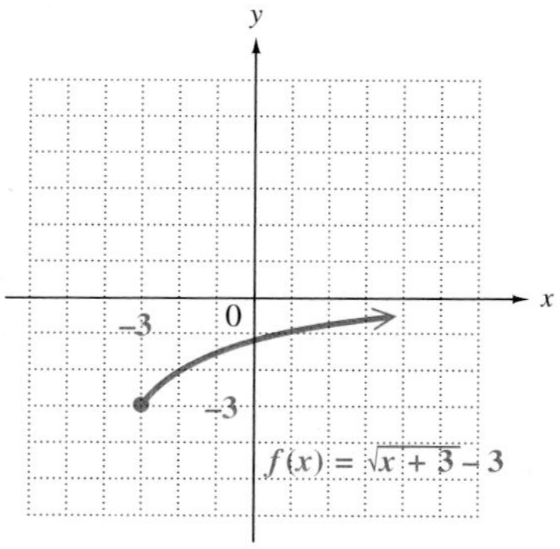

$[-3, \infty)$; $[-3, \infty)$

18. Explain how the graph of $f(x) = \frac{1}{x - 3} + 2$ is obtained from the graph of $g(x) = \frac{1}{x}$.

Shift the graph of $g(x) = \frac{1}{x}$ three units to the right and two units up.

Let $f(x) = x^2 - 9$, $g(x) = 2x$, *and* $h(x) = x - 3$.
Find each of the following. See Example 4.

19. $(f + g)(x)$

$x^2 + 2x - 9$

20. $(f - g)(x)$

$x^2 - 2x - 9$

21. $(fg)(x)$

$2x^3 - 18x$

22. $\left(\frac{f}{g}\right)(x)$

$\frac{x^2 - 9}{2x}, \quad x \neq 0$

23. $(f + g)(3)$

6

24. $(f - g)(-3)$

6

25. $(fg)(2)$

-20

26. $\left(\frac{f}{g}\right)(2)$

$-\frac{5}{4}$

27. $(f - h)(x)$

$x^2 - x - 6$

28. $(f + h)(x)$

$x^2 + x - 12$

29. $\left(\frac{f}{h}\right)(x)$

$x + 3, \quad x \neq 3$

30. $(fh)(x)$

$x^3 - 3x^2 - 9x + 27$

31. $(f - h)(-3)$

6

32. $(f + h)(-2)$

-10

33. $\left(\frac{f}{h}\right)(1)$

4

34. $(fh)(1)$

16

Let $f(x) = x^2 + 4$, $g(x) = 2x + 3$, *and* $h(x) = x + 5$.
Find each value or expression. See Examples 5 and 6.

35. $(h \circ g)(4)$

16

36. $(f \circ g)(4)$

125

37. $(g \circ f)(6)$

83

38. $(h \circ f)(6)$

45

39. $(f \circ h)(-2)$

13

40. $(h \circ g)(-2)$

4

41. $(f \circ g)(x)$

$4x^2 + 12x + 13$

42. $(g \circ h)(x)$

$2x + 13$

43. $(f \circ h)(x)$

$x^2 + 10x + 29$

44. $(g \circ f)(x)$

$2x^2 + 11$

45. $(h \circ g)(x)$

$2x + 8$

46. $(h \circ f)(x)$

$x^2 + 9$

Solve each problem.

47. The function defined by $f(x) = 12x$ computes the number of inches in x ft and the function defined by $g(x) = 5280x$ computes the number of feet in x mi. What is $(f \circ g)(x)$ and what does it compute?

$(f \circ g)(x) = 63{,}360x$; It computes the number of inches in x mi.

48. The perimeter x of a square with sides of length s is given by the formula $x = 4s$.

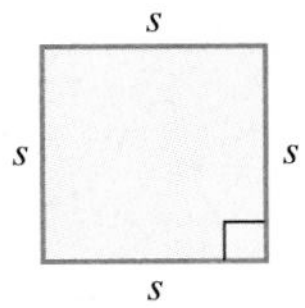

(a) Solve for s in terms of x.

$s = \frac{x}{4}$

(b) If y represents the area of this square, write y as a function of the perimeter x.

$y = \frac{x^2}{16}$

(c) Use the composite function of part (b) to find the area of a square with perimeter 6.

2.25

49. When a thermal inversion layer is over a city (as happens often in Los Angeles), pollutants cannot rise vertically but are trapped below the layer and must disperse horizontally. Assume that a factory smokestack begins emitting a pollutant at 8 A.M. Assume that the pollutant disperses horizontally over a circular area. Suppose that t represents the time, in hours, since the factory began emitting pollutants ($t = 0$ represents 8 A.M.), and assume that the radius of the circle of pollution is $r(t) = 2t$ mi. Let $A(r) = \pi r^2$ represent the area of a circle of radius r. Find and interpret $(A \circ r)(t)$.

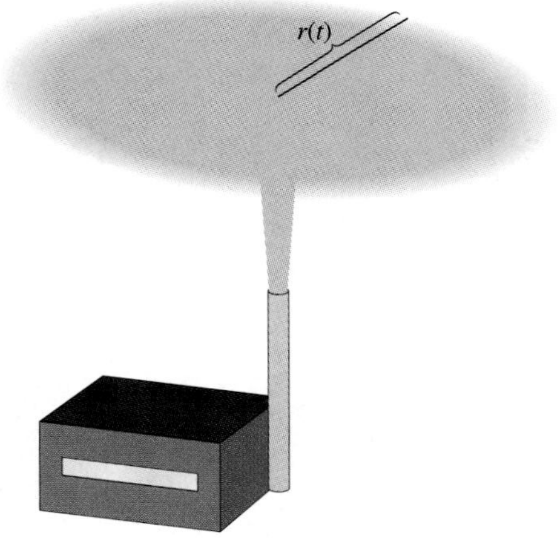

$(A \circ r)(t) = 4\pi t^2$; This is the area of the circular layer as a function of time.

50. An oil well off the Gulf Coast is leaking, with the leak spreading oil over the surface as a circle. At any time t, in minutes, after the beginning of the leak, the radius of the circular oil slick on the surface is $r(t) = 4t$ ft. Let $A(r) = \pi r^2$ represent the area of a circle of radius r. Find and interpret $(A \circ r)(t)$.

$(A \circ r)(t) = 16\pi t^2$; This is the area of the oil slick as a function of time.

12.2 The Circle and the Ellipse

When an infinite cone is intersected by a plane, the resulting figure is called a *conic section.* The parabola is one example of a conic section; circles, ellipses, and hyperbolas may also result. See Figure 9.

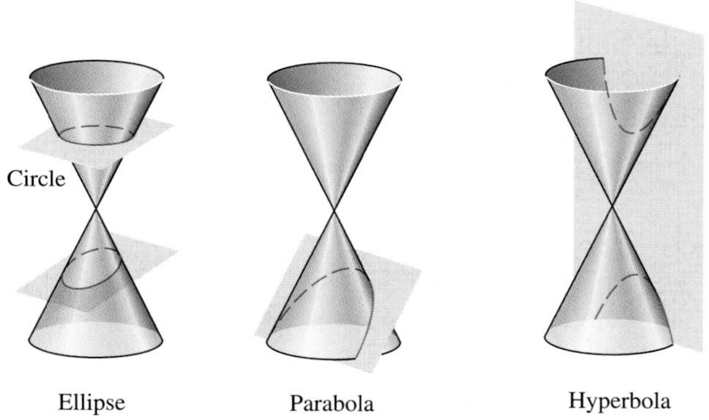

Figure 9

Objectives

1. Find the equation of a circle given the center and radius.
2. Determine the center and radius of a circle given its equation.
3. Recognize the equation of an ellipse.
4. Graph ellipses.

1 Find the equation of a circle given the center and radius. A **circle** is the set of all points in a plane that lie a fixed distance from a fixed point. The fixed point is called the **center,** and the fixed distance is called the **radius.** We use the distance formula to find an equation of a circle.

Example 1 Finding the Equation of a Circle and Graphing It

Find an equation of the circle with radius 3 and center at (0, 0), and graph it.

If the point (x, y) is on the circle, the distance from (x, y) to the center (0, 0) is 3. By the distance formula,

$$\sqrt{(x_2 - x_1)^2 + (y_2 - y_1)^2} = d$$

$$\sqrt{(x - 0)^2 + (y - 0)^2} = 3$$

$$x^2 + y^2 = 9. \quad \text{Square both sides.}$$

An equation of this circle is $x^2 + y^2 = 9$. The graph is shown in Figure 10.

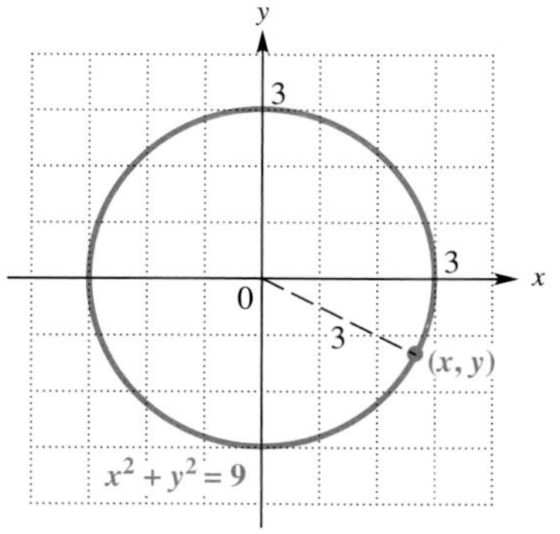

Figure 10

Work Problem 1 at the Side.

A circle may not be centered at the origin, as seen in the next example.

1 Find an equation of the circle with radius 4 and center (0, 0). Sketch its graph.

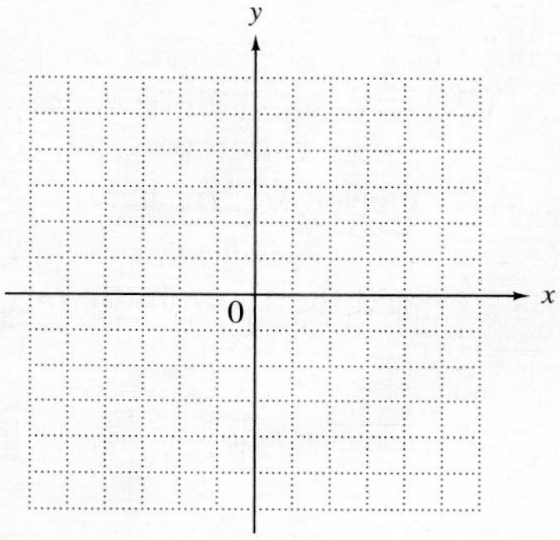

Answers

1. $x^2 + y^2 = 16$

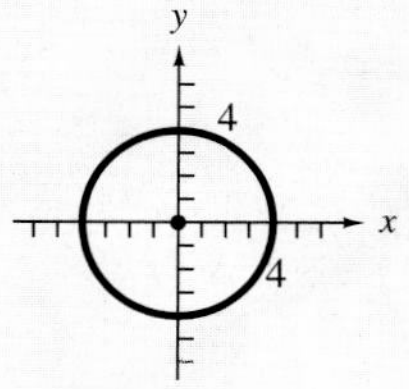

2 **(a)** Find an equation of the circle with center at $(3, -2)$ and radius 4. Graph the circle.

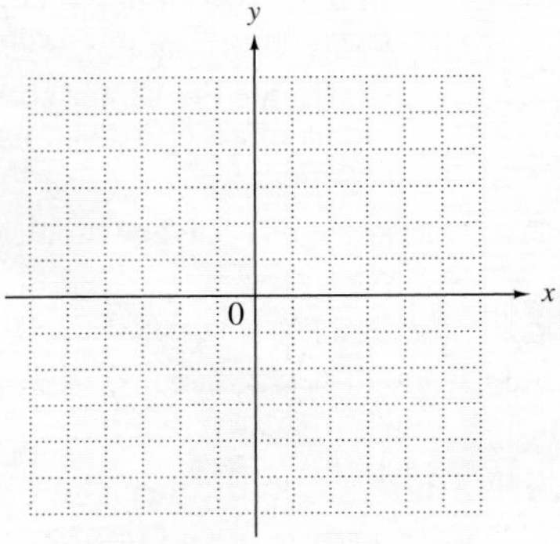

(b) Use the center-radius form to determine the center and radius of $(x - 5)^2 + (y + 2)^2 = 9$, and then graph the circle.

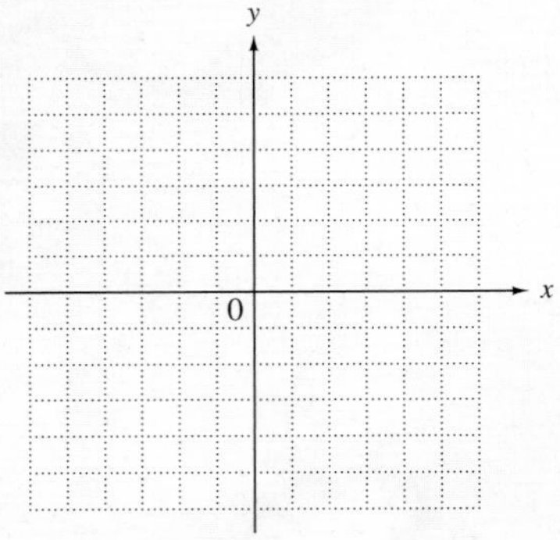

Example 2 Finding an Equation of a Circle and Graphing It

Find an equation of the circle with center at $(4, -3)$ and radius 5, and graph it.

Use the distance formula again.

$$\sqrt{(x-4)^2 + [y-(-3)]^2} = 5$$

$$(x-4)^2 + (y+3)^2 = 25 \quad \text{Square both sides.}$$

To graph the circle, plot the center $(4, -3)$, then move 5 units right, left, up, and down from the center. Draw a smooth curve through these four points, sketching one quarter of the circle at a time. The graph of this circle is shown in Figure 11.

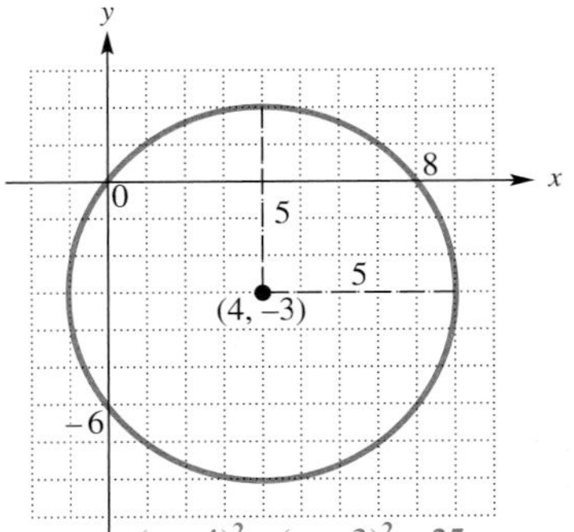

$(x-4)^2 + (y+3)^2 = 25$

Figure 11

Examples 1 and 2 suggest the form of an equation of a circle with radius r and center at (h, k). If (x, y) is a point on the circle, the distance from the center (h, k) to the point (x, y) is r. Then by the distance formula,

$$\sqrt{(x-h)^2 + (y-k)^2} = r.$$

Squaring both sides gives us the following **center-radius form** of the equation of a circle.

Equation of a Circle (Center-Radius Form)

$$(x-h)^2 + (y-k)^2 = r^2$$

is an equation of the circle of radius r with center at (h, k).

Example 3 Using the Center-Radius Form of the Equation of a Circle

Find an equation of the circle with center at $(-1, 2)$ and radius 4.

Use the center-radius form, with $h = -1$, $k = 2$, and $r = 4$.

$$(x-h)^2 + (y-k)^2 = r^2$$

$$[x-(-1)]^2 + (y-2)^2 = 4^2$$

$$(x+1)^2 + (y-2)^2 = 16$$

Work Problem 2 at the Side.

Answers

2. (a) $(x-3)^2 + (y+2)^2 = 16$

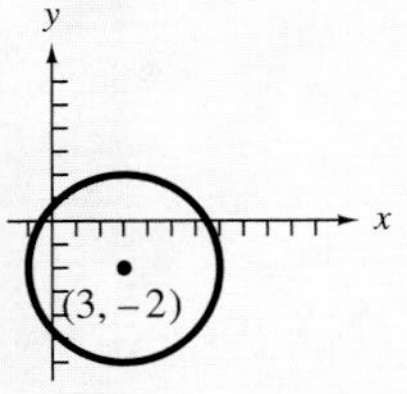

(b) center at $(5, -2)$; radius 3

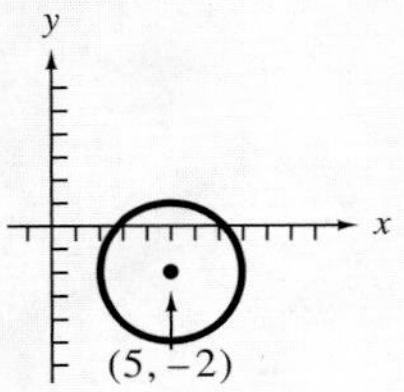

2 Determine the center and radius of a circle given its equation. In the equation found in Example 2, multiplying out $(x - 4)^2$ and $(y + 3)^2$ and then combining like terms gives

$$(x - 4)^2 + (y + 3)^2 = 25$$
$$x^2 - 8x + 16 + y^2 + 6y + 9 = 25$$
$$x^2 + y^2 - 8x + 6y = 0.$$

This general form suggests that an equation with both x^2- and y^2-terms with equal coefficients may represent a circle. The next example shows how to tell, by completing the square. This procedure was introduced in Chapter 10.

Example 4 Completing the Square to Find the Center and Radius

Graph $x^2 + y^2 + 2x + 6y - 15 = 0.$

Since the equation has x^2- and y^2-terms with equal coefficients, its graph might be that of a circle. To find the center and radius, complete the squares on x and y.

$$x^2 + y^2 + 2x + 6y = 15 \quad \text{Get the constant on the right.}$$

$$(x^2 + 2x \quad\quad) + (y^2 + 6y \quad\quad) = 15 \quad \text{Rewrite in anticipation of completing the square.}$$

$$\left[\frac{1}{2}(2)\right]^2 = 1 \qquad \left[\frac{1}{2}(6)\right]^2 = 9 \quad \text{Square half the coefficient of each middle term.}$$

$$(x^2 + 2x + 1) + (y^2 + 6y + 9) = 15 + 1 + 9 \quad \text{Complete the squares on both } x \text{ and } y.$$

$$(x + 1)^2 + (y + 3)^2 = 25 \quad \text{Factor on the left; add on the right.}$$

$$[x - (-1)]^2 + [y - (-3)]^2 = 5^2 \quad \text{Center-radius form}$$

The last equation shows that the graph is a circle with center at $(-1, -3)$ and radius 5. The graph is shown in Figure 12.

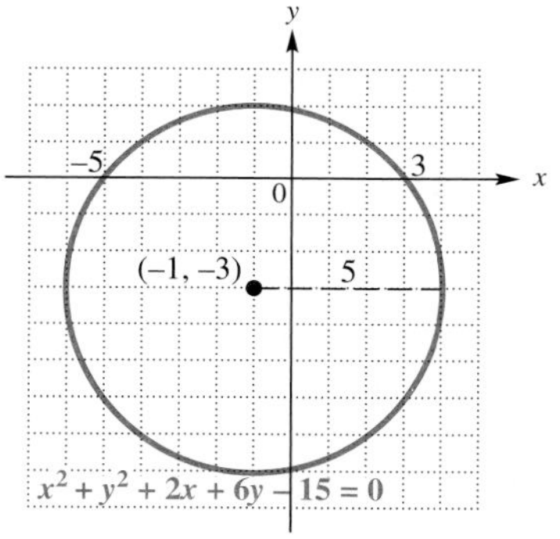

Figure 12

NOTE

If the procedure of Example 4 leads to an equation of the form $(x - h)^2 + (y - k)^2 = 0$, the graph is the single point (h, k). If the constant on the right side is negative, the equation has no graph.

Work Problem 3 at the Side.

3 Find the center and radius of the circle with equation

$$x^2 + y^2 - 6x + 8y - 4 = 0.$$

ANSWERS

3. center at $(3, -4)$; radius $\sqrt{29}$

3 **Recognize the equation of an ellipse.** An **ellipse** is the set of all points in a plane the *sum* of whose distances from two fixed points is constant. These fixed points are called **foci** (singular: *focus*). Figure 13 shows an ellipse whose foci are $(c, 0)$ and $(-c, 0)$, with x-intercepts $(a, 0)$ and $(-a, 0)$ and y-intercepts $(0, b)$ and $(0, -b)$. It can be shown that $c^2 = a^2 - b^2$ for an ellipse of this type. The origin is the **center** of the ellipse.

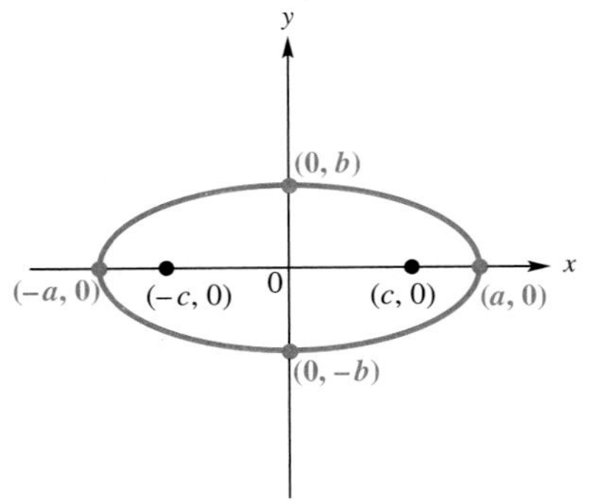

Figure 13

From the preceding definition, it can be shown by the distance formula that an ellipse has the following equation.

Equation of an Ellipse

The ellipse whose x-intercepts are $(a, 0)$ and $(-a, 0)$ and whose y-intercepts are $(0, b)$ and $(0, -b)$ has an equation of the form

$$\frac{x^2}{a^2} + \frac{y^2}{b^2} = 1.$$

A circle is a special case of an ellipse, where $a^2 = b^2$.

The paths of Earth and other planets around the sun are approximately ellipses; the sun is at one focus and a point in space is at the other. The orbits of communication satellites and other space vehicles are elliptical. Elliptical bicycle gears are designed to respond to the legs' natural strengths and weaknesses. At the top and bottom of the powerstroke, where the legs have the least leverage, the gear offers little resistance, but as the gear rotates, the resistance increases. This allows the legs to apply more power where it is most naturally available. See Figure 14.

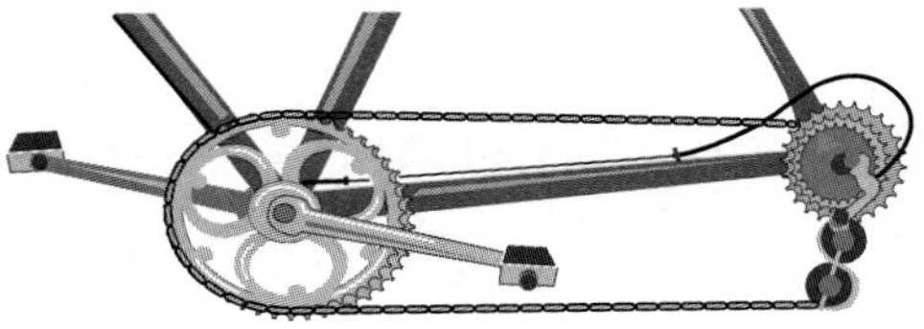

Figure 14

4 **Graph ellipses.** To graph an ellipse centered at the origin, we plot the four intercepts and then sketch the ellipse through those points.

Example 5 Graphing Ellipses

Graph each ellipse.

(a) $\dfrac{x^2}{49} + \dfrac{y^2}{36} = 1$

Here, $a^2 = 49$, so $a = \pm 7$, and the x-intercepts for this ellipse are $(7, 0)$ and $(-7, 0)$. Similarly, $b^2 = 36$, so $b = \pm 6$, and the y-intercepts are $(0, 6)$ and $(0, -6)$. Plotting the intercepts and sketching the ellipse through them gives the graph in Figure 15.

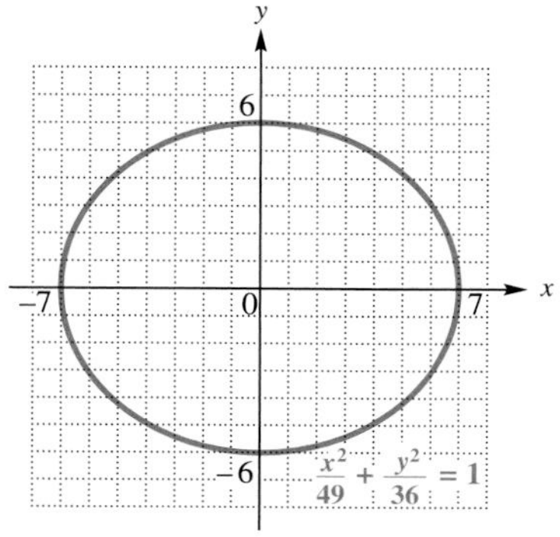

Figure 15

(b) $\dfrac{x^2}{36} + \dfrac{y^2}{121} = 1$

The x-intercepts for this ellipse are $(6, 0)$ and $(-6, 0)$, and the y-intercepts are $(0, 11)$ and $(0, -11)$. Join these with the smooth curve of an ellipse. The graph has been sketched in Figure 16.

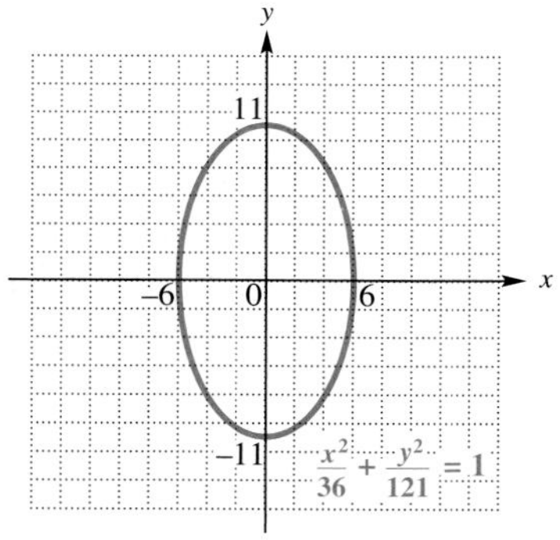

Figure 16

Work Problem 4 at the Side.

As with the graphs of parabolas and circles, the graph of an ellipse may be shifted horizontally and vertically, as in the next example.

4 Graph each ellipse.

(a) $\dfrac{x^2}{4} + \dfrac{y^2}{25} = 1$

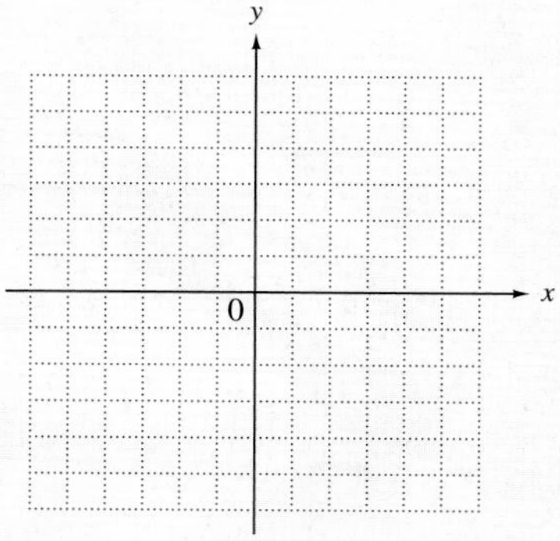

(b) $\dfrac{x^2}{64} + \dfrac{y^2}{49} = 1$

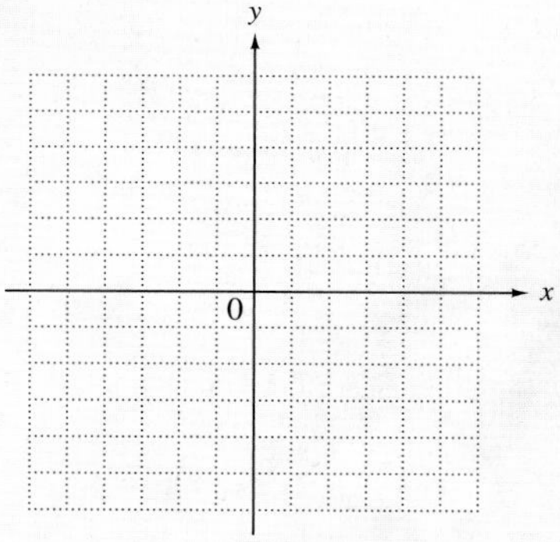

ANSWERS

4. (a)

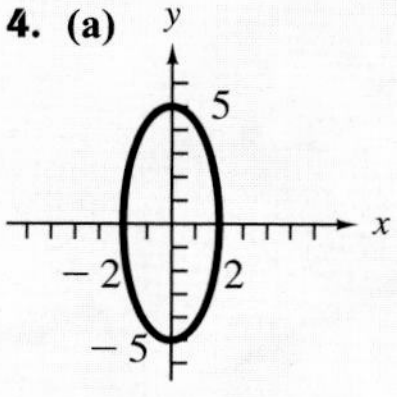

(b)

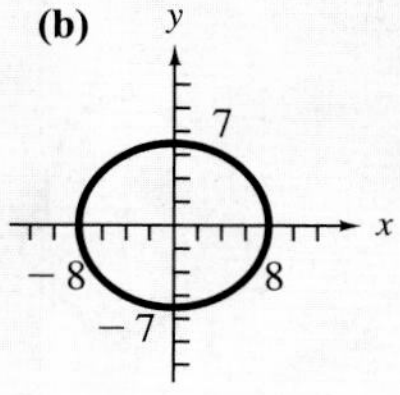

5 Graph

$$\frac{(x+4)^2}{16} + \frac{(y-1)^2}{36} = 1.$$

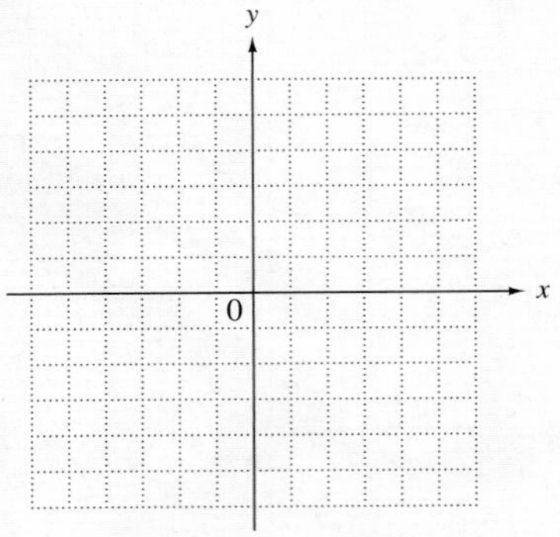

Example 6 Graphing an Ellipse Shifted Horizontally and Vertically

Graph $\dfrac{(x-2)^2}{25} + \dfrac{(y+3)^2}{49} = 1.$

Just as $(x-2)^2$ and $(y+3)^2$ would indicate that the center of a circle would be $(2, -3)$, so it is with this ellipse. Figure 17 shows that the graph goes through the four points $(2, 4)$, $(7, -3)$, $(2, -10)$, and $(-3, -3)$. The x-values of these points are found by adding $\pm a = \pm 5$ to 2, and the y-values come from adding $\pm b = \pm 7$ to -3.

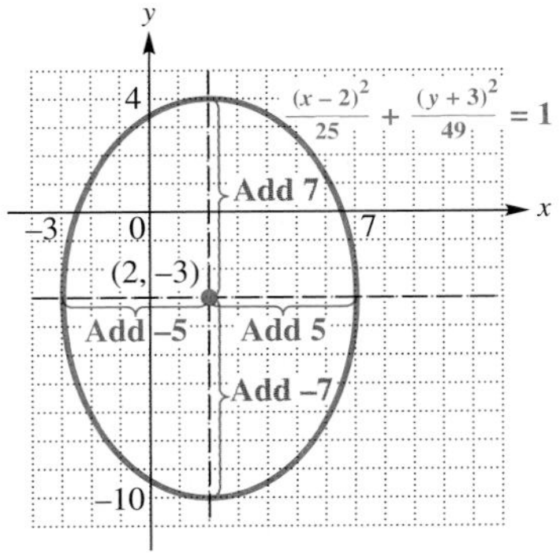

Figure 17

Work Problem 5 at the Side.

Notice that the graphs in this section are not graphs of functions. The only conic section whose graph is a function is the vertical parabola with equation $f(x) = ax^2 + bx + c$.

ANSWERS

5.

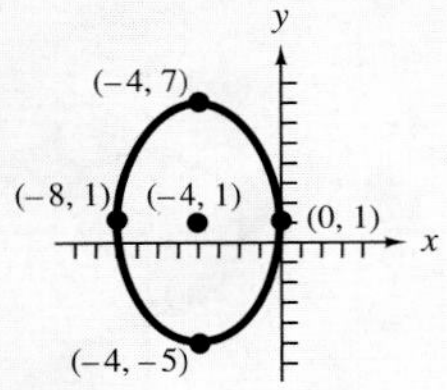

12.2 EXERCISES

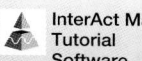

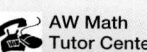

FOR EXTRA HELP: Student's Solutions Manual | MyMathLab.com | InterAct Math Tutorial Software | AW Math Tutor Center | www.mathxl.com | Digital Video Tutor CD 11 Videotape 24

1. See Example 1. Consider the circle whose equation is $x^2 + y^2 = 25$.

(a) What are the coordinates of its center? **(0, 0)**

(b) What is its radius? **5**

(c) Sketch its graph.

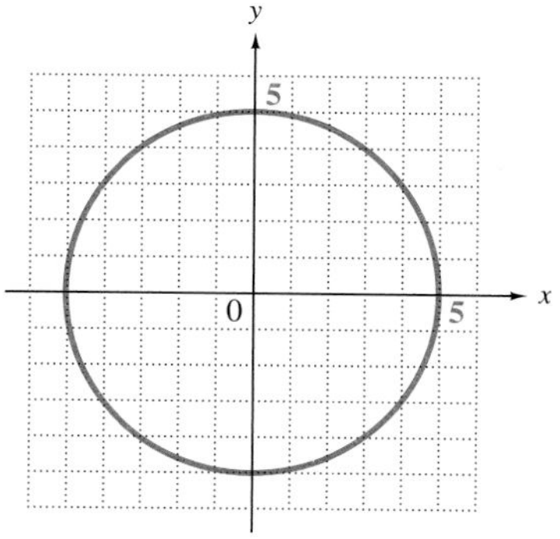

2. Explain why a set of points defined by a circle does not satisfy the definition of a function.

There will always be domain values that yield more than one range value. A circle fails the vertical line test.

Match each equation with the correct graph. See Examples 1–3.

3. $(x - 3)^2 + (y - 2)^2 = 25$ **B**

4. $(x - 3)^2 + (y + 2)^2 = 25$ **C**

5. $(x + 3)^2 + (y - 2)^2 = 25$ **D**

6. $(x + 3)^2 + (y + 2)^2 = 25$ **A**

A.

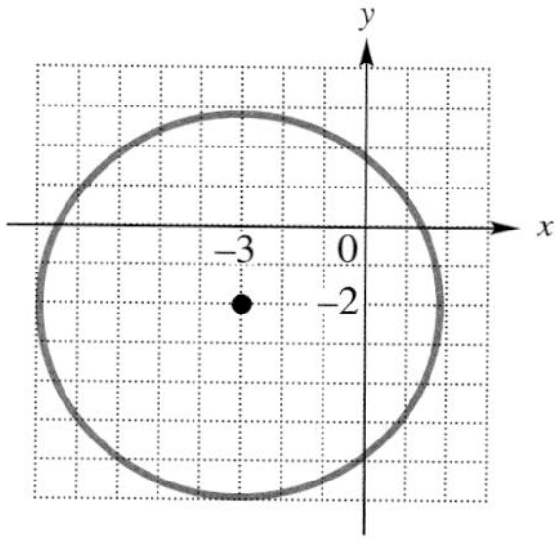

B.

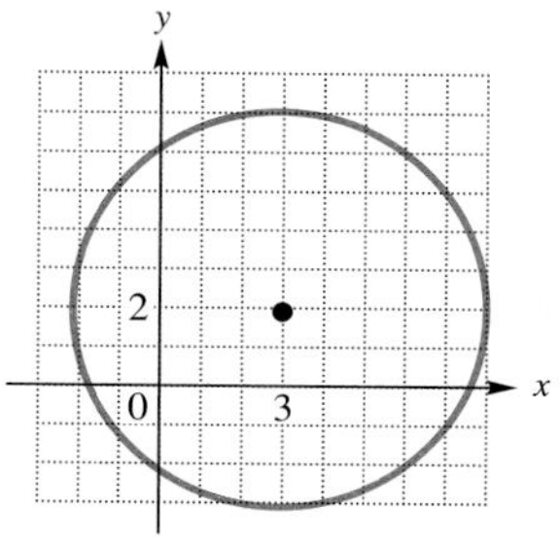

C.

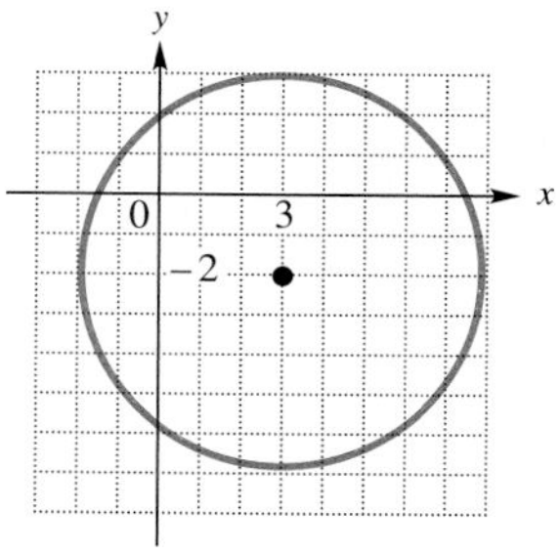

D.

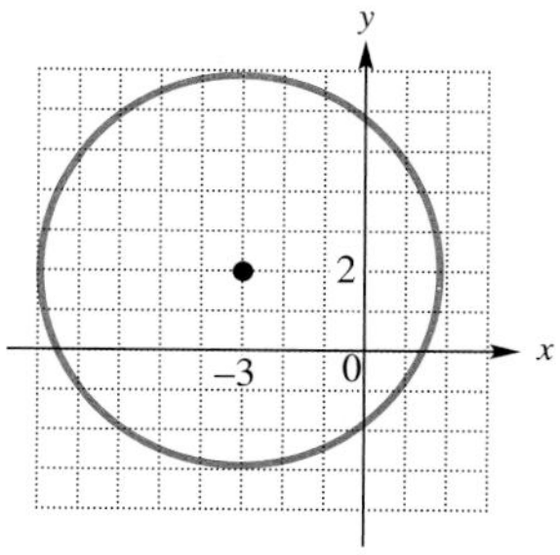

Find the equation of a circle satisfying the given conditions. See Examples 2 and 3.

7. Center: $(-4, 3)$; radius: 2

$(x + 4)^2 + (y - 3)^2 = 4$

8. Center: $(5, -2)$; radius: 4

$(x - 5)^2 + (y + 2)^2 = 16$

9. Center: $(-8, -5)$; radius: $\sqrt{5}$

$(x + 8)^2 + (y + 5)^2 = 5$

10. Center: $(-12, 13)$; radius: $\sqrt{7}$

$(x + 12)^2 + (y - 13)^2 = 7$

Find the center and radius of each circle. (Hint: In Exercises 15 and 16, divide each side by a common factor.) See Example 4.

11. $x^2 + y^2 + 4x + 6y + 9 = 0$

$(-2, -3); r = 2$

12. $x^2 + y^2 - 8x - 12y + 3 = 0$

$(4, 6); r = 7$

13. $x^2 + y^2 + 10x - 14y - 7 = 0$

$(-5, 7); r = 9$

14. $x^2 + y^2 - 2x + 4y - 4 = 0$

$(1, -2); r = 3$

15. $3x^2 + 3y^2 - 12x - 24y + 12 = 0$

$(2, 4); r = 4$

16. $2x^2 + 2y^2 + 20x + 16y + 10 = 0$

$(-5, -4); r = 6$

17. A circle can be drawn on a piece of posterboard by fastening one end of a string with a thumbtack, pulling the string taut with a pencil, and tracing a curve, as shown in the figure. Explain why this method works.

The thumbtack acts as the center and the length of the string acts as the radius.

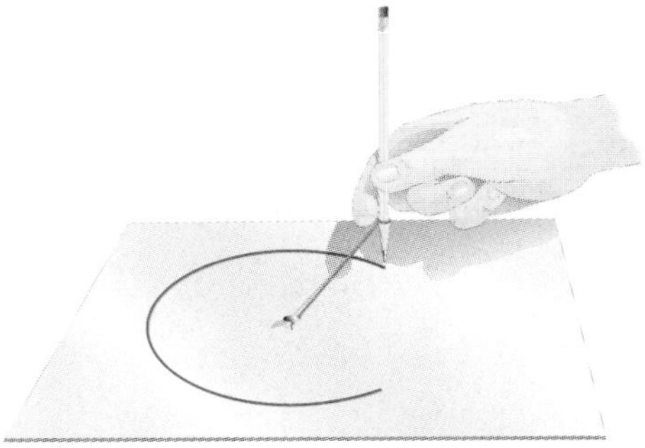

Graph each circle. See Examples 1–4.

18. $x^2 + y^2 = 9$

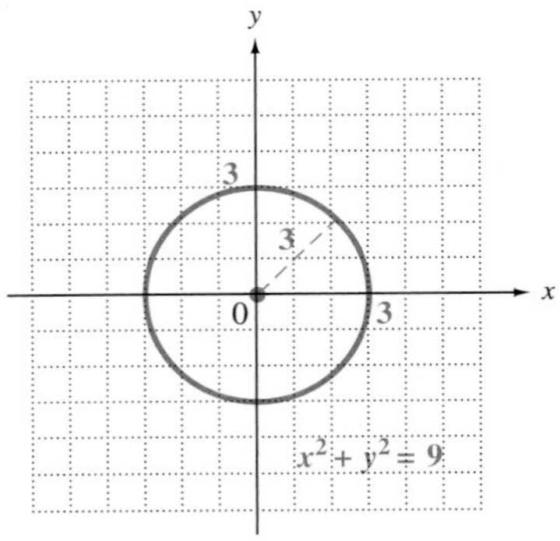

19. $x^2 + y^2 = 4$

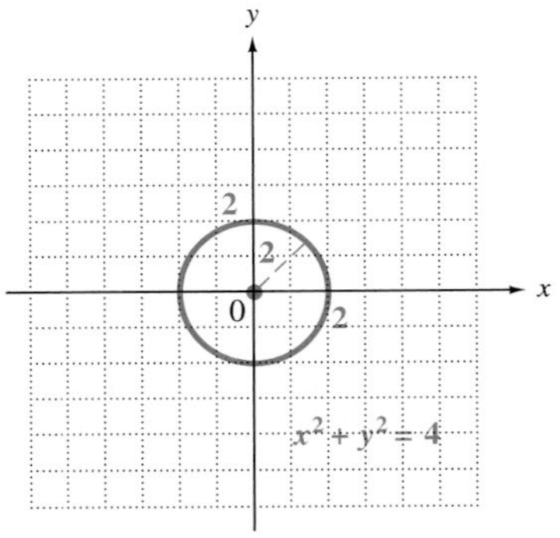

20. $2y^2 = 10 - 2x^2$

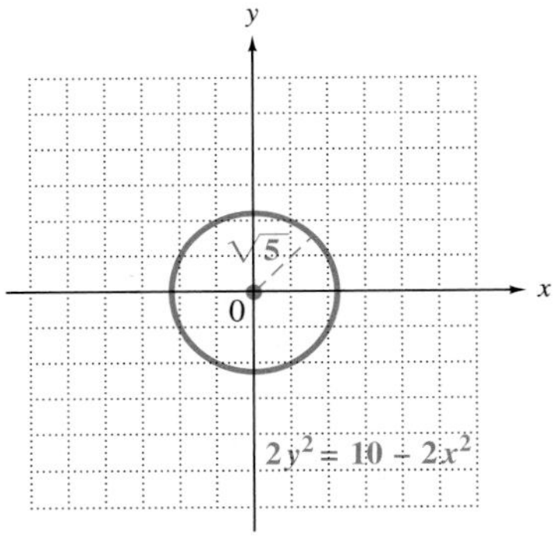

21. $3x^2 = 48 - 3y^2$

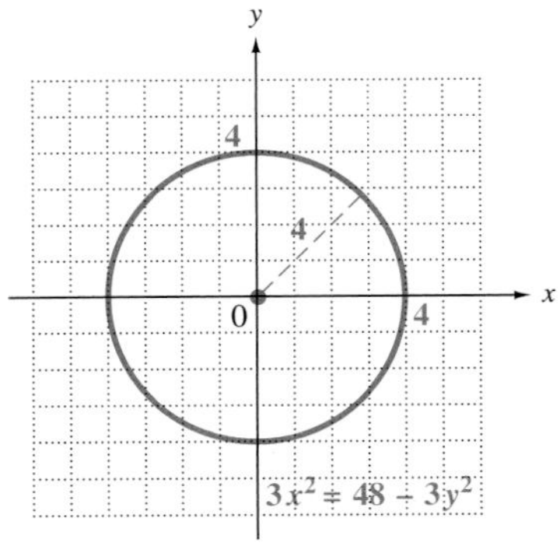

22. $(x + 3)^2 + (y - 2)^2 = 9$

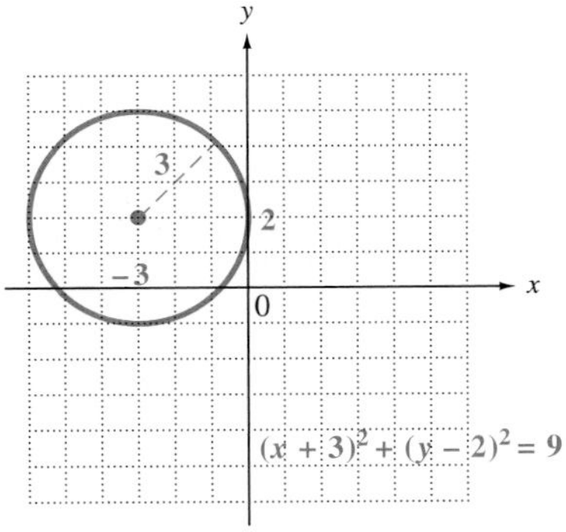

23. $(x - 1)^2 + (y + 3)^2 = 16$

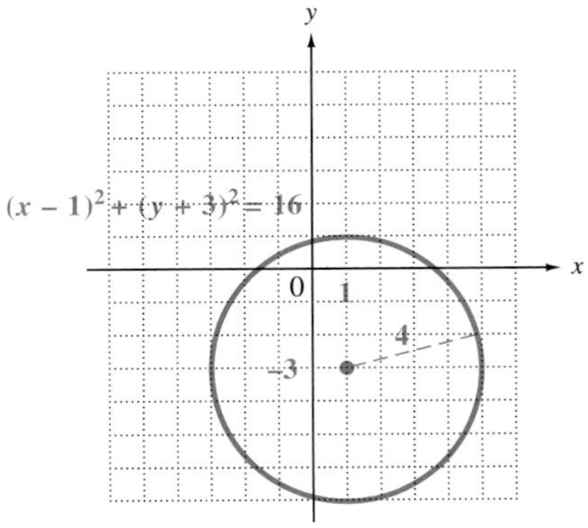

24. $x^2 + y^2 - 4x - 6y + 9 = 0$

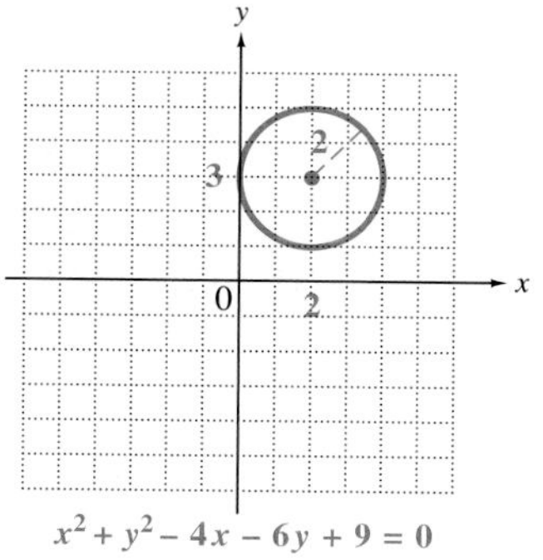

25. $x^2 + y^2 + 8x + 2y - 8 = 0$

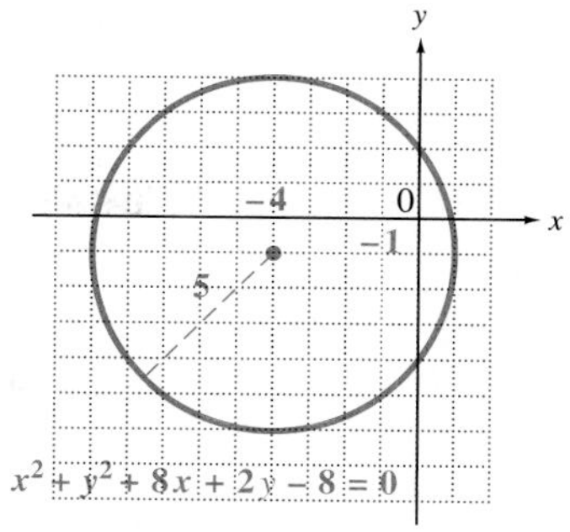

26. An ellipse can be drawn on a piece of posterboard by fastening two ends of a length of string with thumbtacks, pulling the string taut with a pencil, and tracing a curve, as shown in the figure. Explain why this method works.

The two thumbtacks act as foci, and the length of the string is constant, satisfying the requirements of the definition of an ellipse.

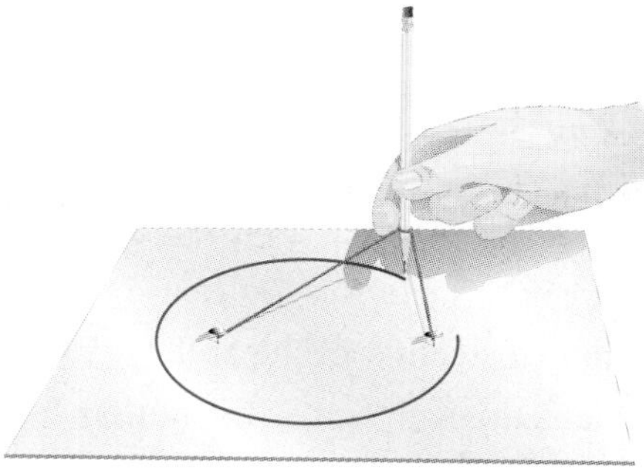

Graph each ellipse. See Examples 5 and 6.

27. $\dfrac{x^2}{9} + \dfrac{y^2}{25} = 1$

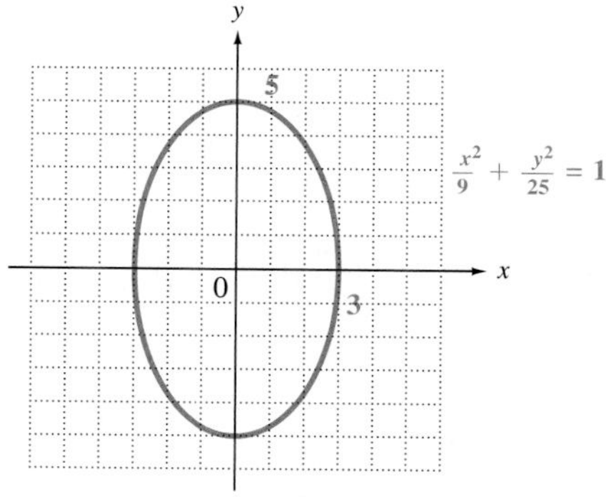

28. $\dfrac{x^2}{9} + \dfrac{y^2}{16} = 1$

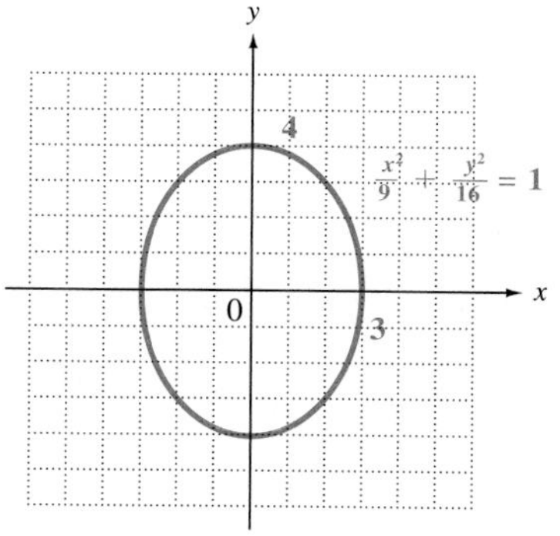

29. $\dfrac{x^2}{36} + \dfrac{y^2}{16} = 1$

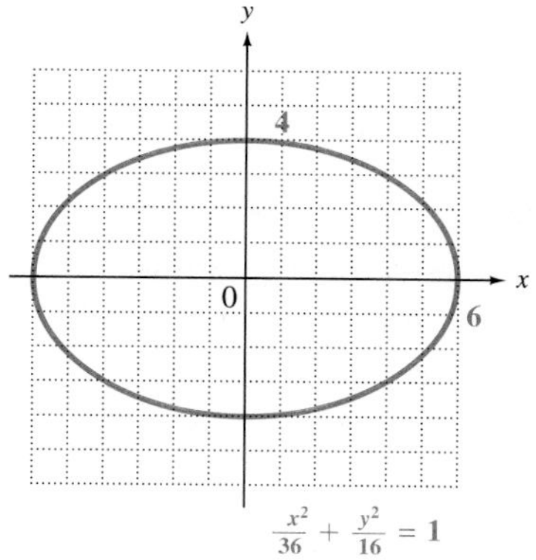

30. $\dfrac{x^2}{9} + \dfrac{y^2}{4} = 1$

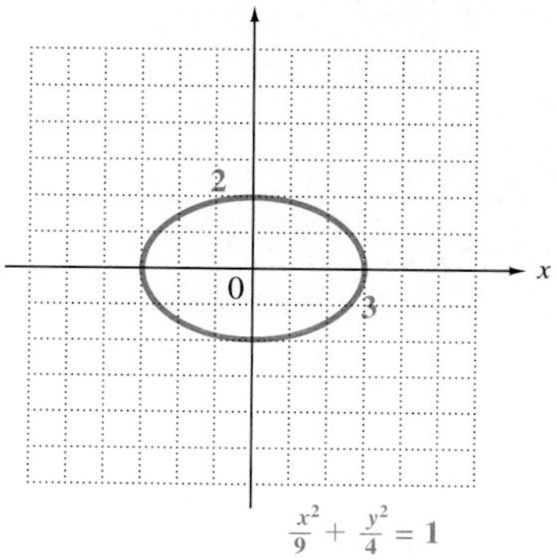

31. $\dfrac{x^2}{49} + \dfrac{y^2}{25} = 1$

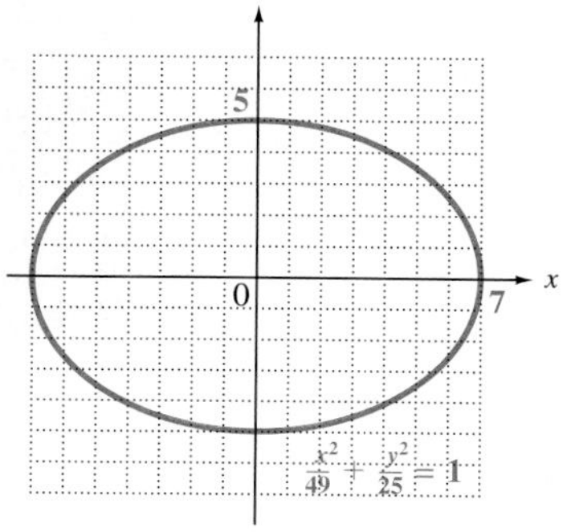

32. $\dfrac{x^2}{16} + \dfrac{y^2}{9} = 1$

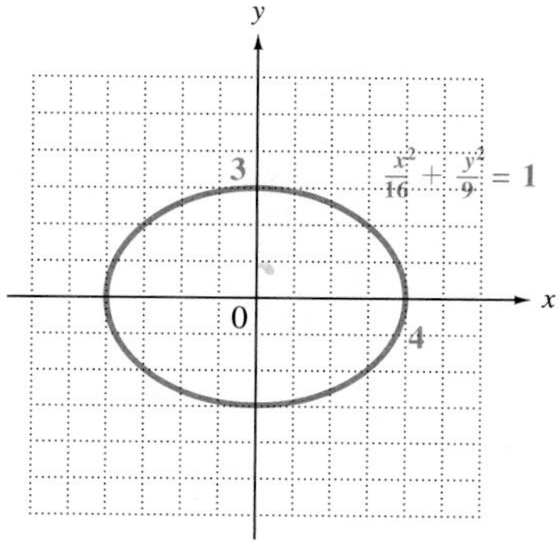

33. $\dfrac{(x-2)^2}{16}+\dfrac{(y-1)^2}{9}=1$

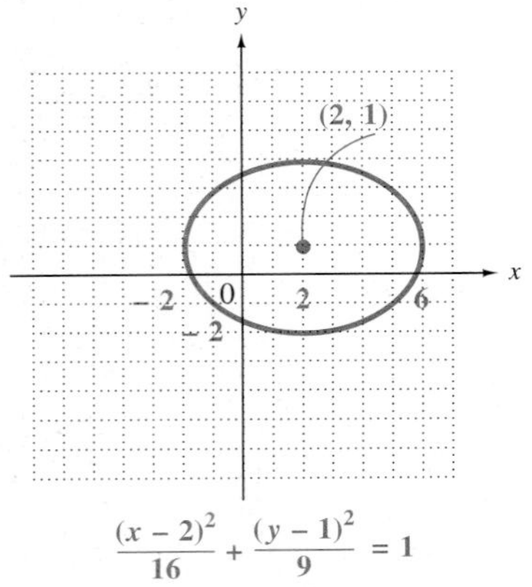

34. $\dfrac{(x-4)^2}{9}+\dfrac{(y+2)^2}{4}=1$

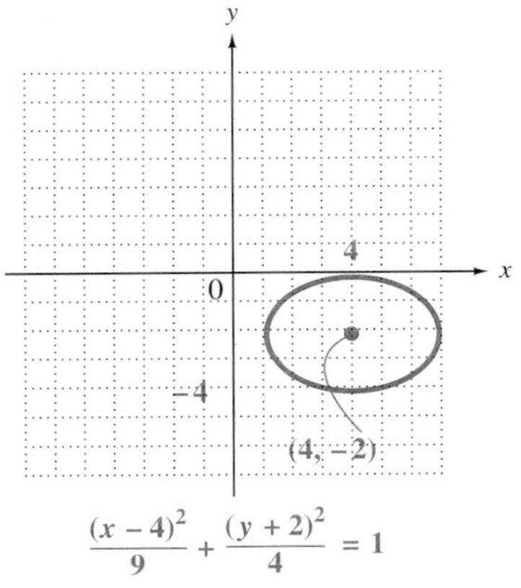

Solve each problem.

35. An arch has the shape of half an ellipse. The equation of the ellipse is $100x^2 + 324y^2 = 32{,}400$, where x and y are in meters.

(a) How high is the center of the arch? **10 m**

(b) How wide is the arch across the bottom? **36 m**

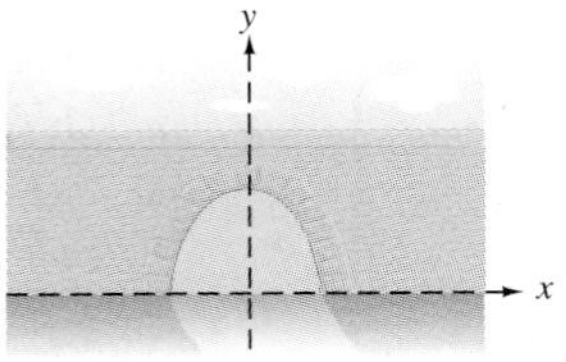

NOT TO SCALE

36. A one-way street passes under an overpass, which is in the form of the top half of an ellipse, as shown in the figure. Suppose that a truck 12 ft wide passes directly under the overpass. What is the maximum possible height of this truck? **12 ft**

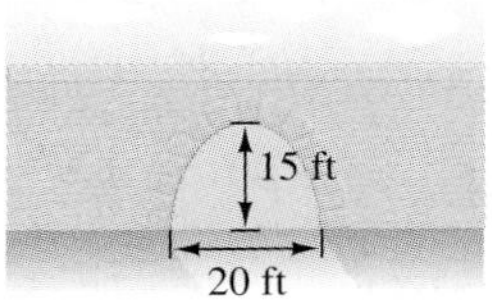

In Exercises 37 and 38, see Figure 13 and use the fact that $c^2 = a^2 - b^2$ where $a^2 > b^2$.

37. The orbit of Mars is an ellipse with the sun at one focus. For x and y in millions of miles, the equation of the orbit is

$$\frac{x^2}{141.7^2}+\frac{y^2}{141.1^2}=1.$$

(*Source:* Kaler, James B., *Astronomy!*, Addison-Wesley, 1997.)

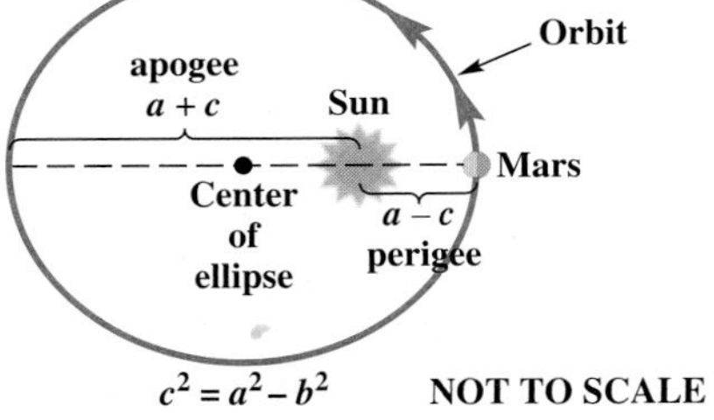

(a) Find the greatest distance (the *apogee*) from Mars to the sun. **154.7 million mi**

(b) Find the smallest distance (the *perigee*) from Mars to the sun. **128.7 million mi (Answers are rounded.)**

38. The orbit of Venus around the sun (one of the foci) is an ellipse with equation

$$\frac{x^2}{5013}+\frac{y^2}{4970}=1,$$

where x and y are measured in millions of miles.

(*Source:* Kaler, James B., *Astronomy!*, Addison-Wesley, 1997.)

(a) Find the greatest distance between Venus and the sun. **77.4 million mi**

(b) Find the smallest distance between Venus and the sun. **64.2 million mi (Answers are rounded.)**

12.3 The Hyperbola and Other Functions Defined by Radicals

Objectives

1. Recognize the equation of a hyperbola.
2. Graph hyperbolas by using asymptotes.
3. Identify conic sections by their equations.
4. Graph certain square root functions.

1 Recognize the equation of a hyperbola. A **hyperbola** is the set of all points in a plane such that the absolute value of the *difference* of the distances from two fixed points (called *foci*) is constant. Figure 18 shows a hyperbola; using the distance formula and the definition above, we can show that this hyperbola has equation $\frac{x^2}{16} - \frac{y^2}{12} = 1$.

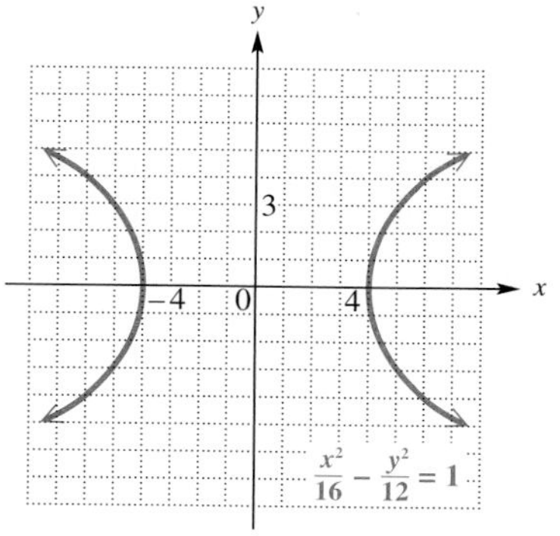

Figure 18

To graph hyperbolas centered at the origin, we need to find their intercepts. For the hyperbola in Figure 18, we proceed as follows.

***x*-Intercepts**

Let $y = 0$.

$$\frac{x^2}{16} - \frac{0^2}{12} = 1 \qquad \text{Let } y = 0.$$

$$\frac{x^2}{16} = 1$$

$$x^2 = 16 \qquad \text{Multiply by 16.}$$

$$x = \pm 4$$

The x-intercepts are (4, 0) and (−4, 0).

***y*-Intercepts**

Let $x = 0$.

$$\frac{0^2}{16} - \frac{y^2}{12} = 1 \qquad \text{Let } x = 0.$$

$$-\frac{y^2}{12} = 1$$

$$y^2 = -12 \qquad \text{Multiply by } -12.$$

Because there are no *real* solutions to $y^2 = -12$, the graph has no y-intercepts.

The graph of $\frac{x^2}{16} - \frac{y^2}{12} = 1$ has no y-intercepts. On the other hand, the hyperbola in Figure 19 has no x-intercepts. Its equation is

$$\frac{y^2}{25} - \frac{x^2}{9} = 1,$$

with y-intercepts (0, 5) and (0, −5).

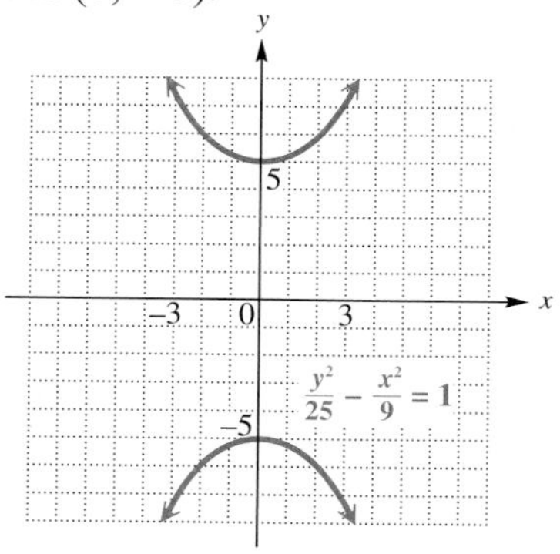

Figure 19

Equations of Hyperbolas

A hyperbola with x-intercepts $(a, 0)$ and $(-a, 0)$ has an equation of the form

$$\frac{x^2}{a^2} - \frac{y^2}{b^2} = 1,$$

and a hyperbola with y-intercepts $(0, b)$ and $(0, -b)$ has an equation of the form

$$\frac{y^2}{b^2} - \frac{x^2}{a^2} = 1.$$

2 **Graph hyperbolas by using asymptotes.** The two branches of the graph of a hyperbola approach a pair of intersecting straight lines, which are its asymptotes. See Figure 20. The asymptotes are useful for sketching the graph of the hyperbola.

Asymptotes of Hyperbolas

The extended diagonals of the rectangle with corners at the points (a, b), $(-a, b)$, $(-a, -b)$, and $(a, -b)$ are the **asymptotes** of the hyperbolas

$$\frac{x^2}{a^2} - \frac{y^2}{b^2} = 1 \quad \text{and} \quad \frac{y^2}{b^2} - \frac{x^2}{a^2} = 1.$$

This rectangle is called the **fundamental rectangle.** Using the methods of Chapter 4, we could show that the equations of these asymptotes are

$$y = \frac{b}{a}x \quad \text{and} \quad y = -\frac{b}{a}x.$$

To graph hyperbolas, follow these steps.

Graphing a Hyperbola

Step 1 **Find the intercepts.** Locate the intercepts at $(a, 0)$ and $(-a, 0)$ if the x^2-term has a positive coefficient, or at $(0, b)$ and $(0, -b)$ if the y^2-term has a positive coefficient.

Step 2 **Find the fundamental rectangle.** Locate the corners of the fundamental rectangle at (a, b), $(-a, b)$, $(-a, -b)$, and $(a, -b)$.

Step 3 **Sketch the asymptotes.** The extended diagonals of the rectangle are the asymptotes of the hyperbola, and they have equations $y = \pm \frac{b}{a}x$.

Step 4 **Draw the graph.** Sketch each branch of the hyperbola through an intercept and approaching (but not touching) the asymptotes.

Example 1 Graphing a Horizontal Hyperbola

Graph $\dfrac{x^2}{16} - \dfrac{y^2}{25} = 1$.

Step 1 Here $a = 4$ and $b = 5$. The x-intercepts are $(4, 0)$ and $(-4, 0)$.

Step 2 The four points $(4, 5)$, $(-4, 5)$, $(-4, -5)$, and $(4, -5)$ are the corners of the fundamental rectangle, as shown in Figure 20.

Steps 3 and 4 The equations of the asymptotes are $y = \pm\frac{5}{4}x$, and the hyperbola approaches these lines as x and y get larger and larger in absolute value.

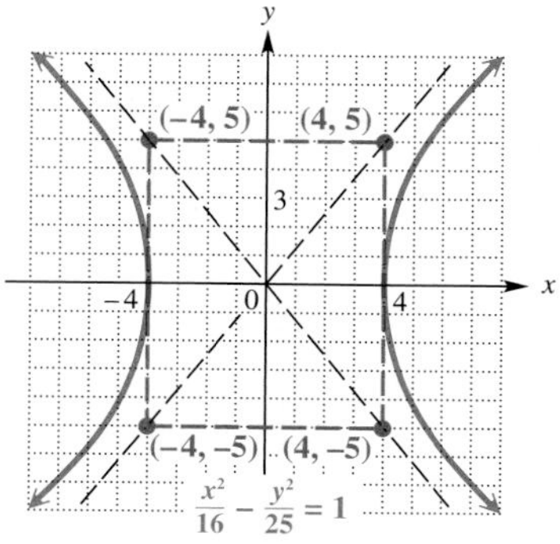

Figure 20

CAUTION

When sketching the graph of a hyperbola, be sure that the branches do not touch the asymptotes.

Work Problem 1 at the Side.

1 Graph $\dfrac{x^2}{4} - \dfrac{y^2}{25} = 1$.

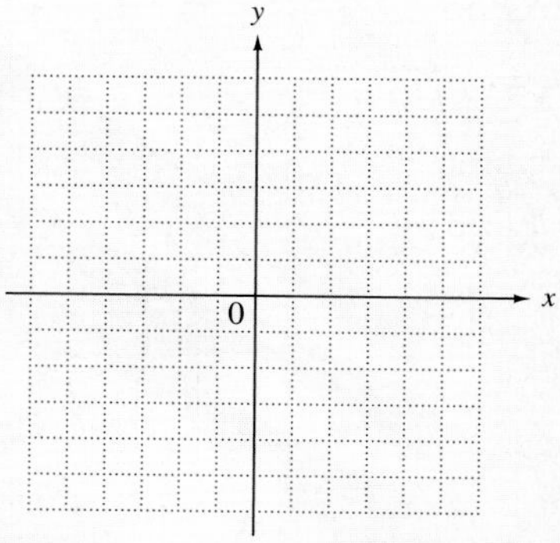

2 Graph $\dfrac{y^2}{81} - \dfrac{x^2}{64} = 1$.

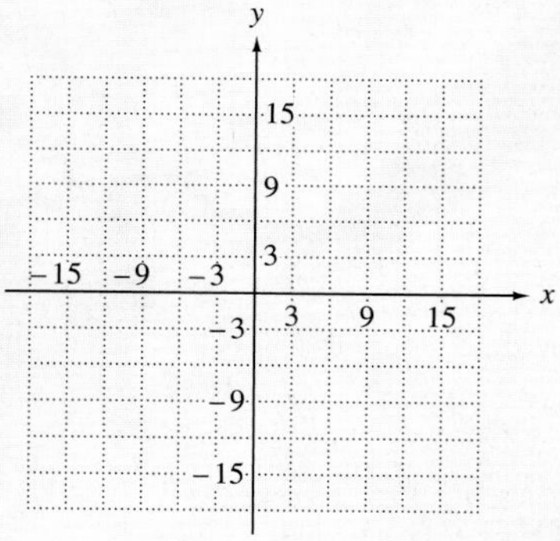

Example 2 Graphing a Vertical Hyperbola

Graph $\dfrac{y^2}{49} - \dfrac{x^2}{16} = 1$.

This hyperbola has y-intercepts $(0, 7)$ and $(0, -7)$. The asymptotes are the extended diagonals of the rectangle with corners at $(4, 7)$, $(-4, 7)$, $(-4, -7)$, and $(4, -7)$. Their equations are $y = \pm\frac{7}{4}x$. See Figure 21.

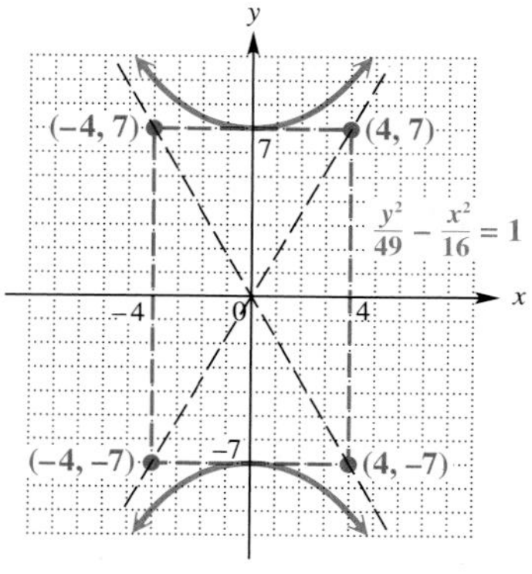

Figure 21

Work Problem 2 at the Side.

ANSWERS

1.

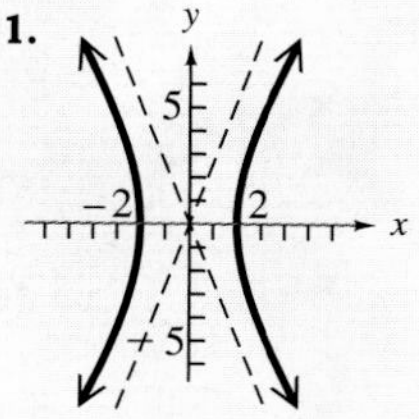

2.

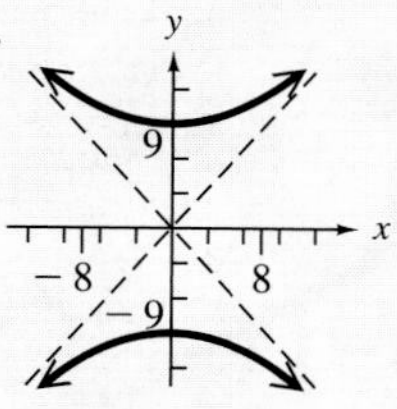

3 Identify conic sections by their equations. Rewriting a second-degree equation in one of the forms given for ellipses, hyperbolas, circles, or parabolas makes it possible to determine when the graph is one of these.

SUMMARY OF CONIC SECTIONS

Equation	Graph	Description	Identification
$y = a(x - h)^2 + k$	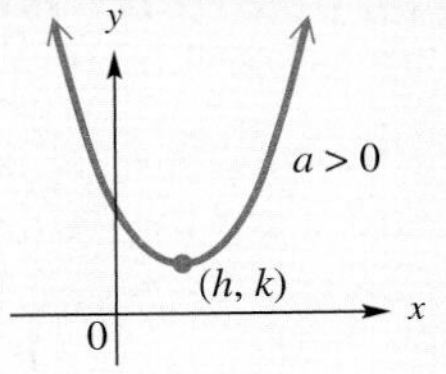 Parabola	It opens up if $a > 0$, down if $a < 0$. The vertex is (h, k).	It has an x^2-term. y is not squared.
$x = a(y - k)^2 + h$	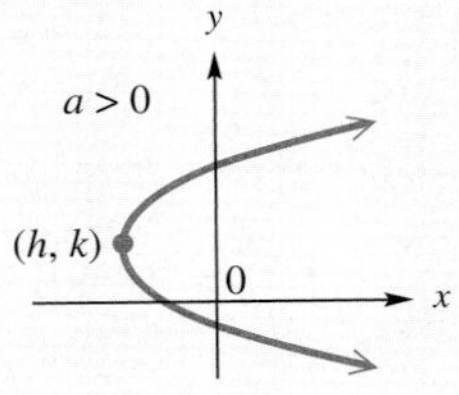 Parabola	It opens to the right if $a > 0$, to the left if $a < 0$. The vertex is (h, k).	It has a y^2-term. x is not squared.
$(x - h)^2 + (y - k)^2 = r^2$	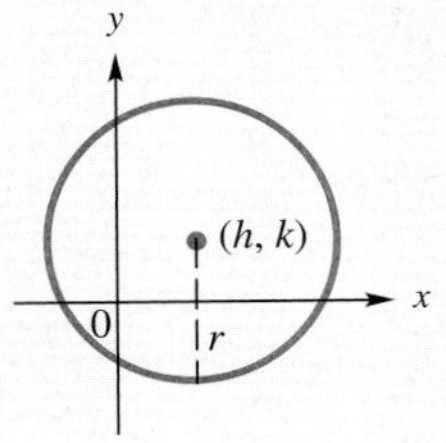 Circle	The center is (h, k), and the radius is r.	x^2- and y^2-terms have the same positive coefficient.
$\frac{x^2}{a^2} + \frac{y^2}{b^2} = 1$	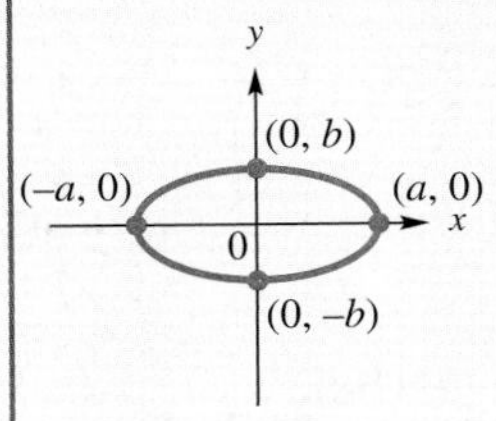 Ellipse	The x-intercepts are $(a, 0)$ and $(-a, 0)$. The y-intercepts are $(0, b)$ and $(0, -b)$.	x^2- and y^2-terms have different positive coefficients.
$\frac{x^2}{a^2} - \frac{y^2}{b^2} = 1$	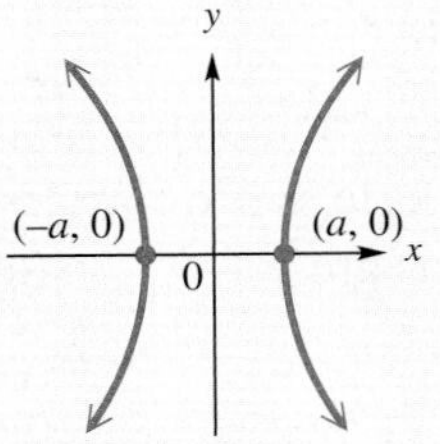 Hyperbola	The x-intercepts are $(a, 0)$ and $(-a, 0)$. The asymptotes are found from (a, b), $(a, -b)$, $(-a, -b)$, and $(-a, b)$.	x^2 has a positive coefficient. y^2 has a negative coefficient.
$\frac{y^2}{b^2} - \frac{x^2}{a^2} = 1$	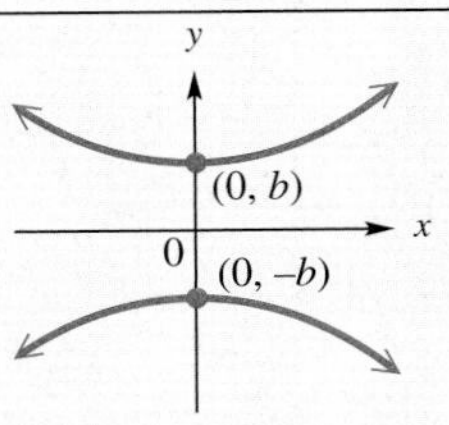 Hyperbola	The y-intercepts are $(0, b)$ and $(0, -b)$. The asymptotes are found from (a, b), $(a, -b)$, $(-a, -b)$, and $(-a, b)$.	y^2 has a positive coefficient. x^2 has a negative coefficient.

Example 3 **Identifying the Graphs of Equations**

Identify the graph of each equation.

(a) $9x^2 = 108 + 12y^2$

Both variables are squared, so the graph is either an ellipse or a hyperbola. (This situation also occurs for a circle, which is a special case of the ellipse.) To see which one it is, rewrite the equation so that the x^2- and y^2-terms are on one side of the equation and 1 is on the other.

$$9x^2 - 12y^2 = 108 \quad \text{Subtract } 12y^2.$$

$$\frac{x^2}{12} - \frac{y^2}{9} = 1 \quad \text{Divide by 108.}$$

Because of the minus sign, the graph of this equation is a hyperbola.

(b) $x^2 = y - 3$

Only one of the two variables, x, is squared, so this is the vertical parabola $y = x^2 + 3$.

(c) $x^2 = 9 - y^2$

Get the variable terms on the same side of the equation.

$$x^2 + y^2 = 9 \quad \text{Add } y^2.$$

The graph of this equation is a circle with center at the origin and radius 3.

Work Problem 3 at the Side.

3 Identify the graph of each equation.

(a) $3x^2 = 27 - 4y^2$

(b) $6x^2 = 100 + 2y^2$

(c) $3x^2 = 27 - 4y$

(d) $3x^2 = 27 - 3y^2$

4 **Graph certain square root functions.** Recall that no vertical line will intersect the graph of a function in more than one point. Thus, horizontal parabolas and all circles, ellipses, and the hyperbolas discussed in this chapter are examples of graphs that do not satisfy the conditions of a function. However, by considering only a part of the graph of each of these we have the graph of a function, as seen in Figure 22.

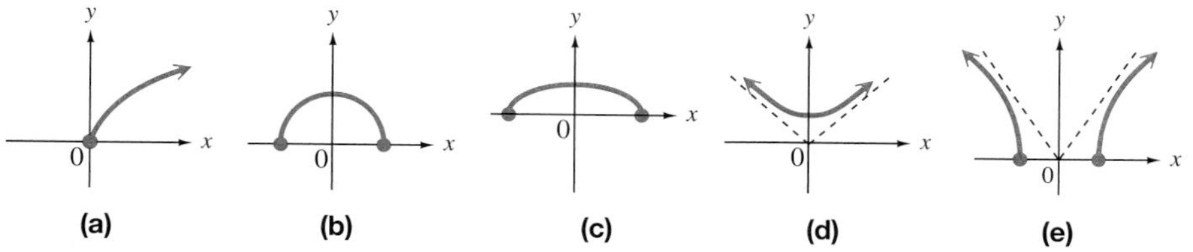

Figure 22

In parts (a), (b), (c), and (d) of Figure 22, the top portion of a conic section is shown (parabola, circle, ellipse, and hyperbola, respectively). In part (e), the top two portions of a hyperbola are shown. In each case, the graph is that of a function since the graph satisfies the conditions of the vertical line test.

In Sections 9.1 and 12.1 we observed the square root function defined by $f(x) = \sqrt{x}$. To find equations for the types of graphs shown in Figure 22, we extend its definition.

Square Root Function

A function of the form

$$f(x) = \sqrt{u}$$

for an algebraic expression u, with $u \geq 0$, is called a **square root function.**

ANSWERS

3. **(a)** ellipse **(b)** hyperbola **(c)** parabola **(d)** circle

4 Graph $f(x) = \sqrt{36 - x^2}$. Give the domain and range.

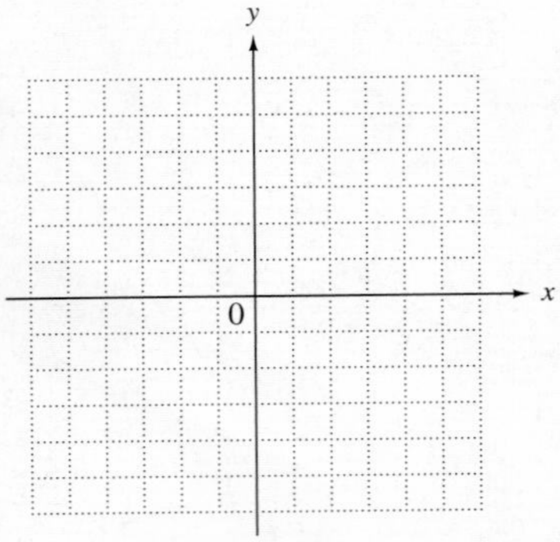

5 Graph

$$\frac{y}{3} = -\sqrt{1 - \frac{x^2}{4}}.$$

Give the domain and range.

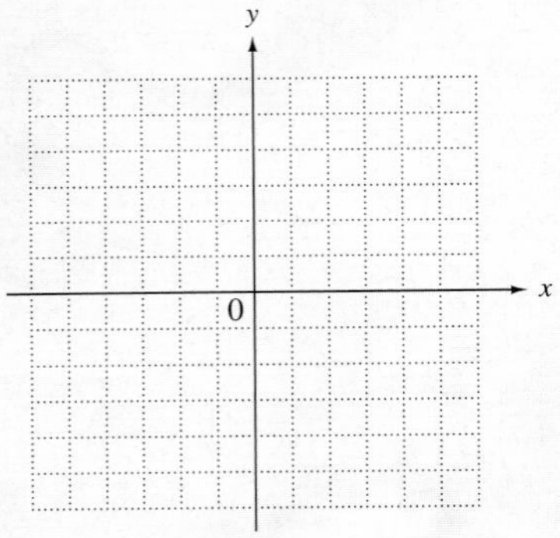

Example 4 Graphing a Semicircle

Graph $f(x) = \sqrt{25 - x^2}$. Give the domain and range.

Replace $f(x)$ with y and square both sides to get the equation

$$y^2 = 25 - x^2, \quad \text{or} \quad x^2 + y^2 = 25.$$

This is the graph of a circle with center at (0, 0) and radius 5. Since $f(x)$, or y, represents a principal square root in the original equation, $f(x)$ must be nonnegative. This restricts the graph to the upper half of the circle, as shown in Figure 23. Use the graph and the vertical line test to verify that it is indeed a function. The domain is $[-5, 5]$, and the range is $[0, 5]$.

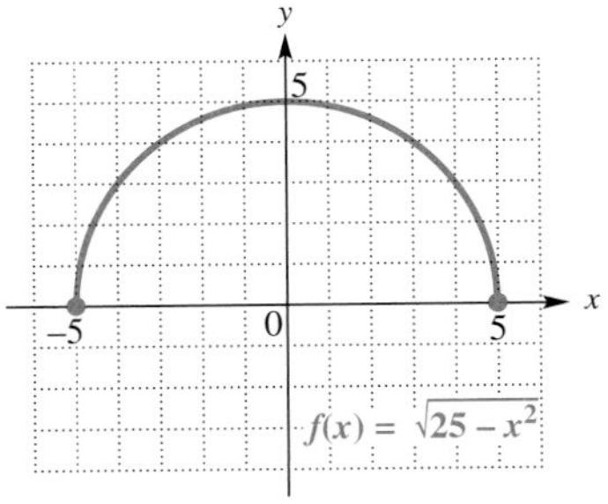

Figure 23

Work Problem 4 at the Side.

Example 5 Graphing a Portion of an Ellipse

Graph $\frac{y}{6} = -\sqrt{1 - \frac{x^2}{16}}$. Give the domain and range.

Square both sides to get an equation whose form is known.

$$\frac{y^2}{36} = 1 - \frac{x^2}{16}$$

$$\frac{x^2}{16} + \frac{y^2}{36} = 1 \qquad \text{Add } \tfrac{x^2}{16}.$$

This is the equation of an ellipse with x-intercepts (4, 0) and $(-4, 0)$ and y-intercepts (0, 6) and $(0, -6)$. Since $\frac{y}{6}$ equals a negative square root in the original equation, y must be nonpositive, restricting the graph to the lower half of the ellipse, as shown in Figure 24. Verify that this is the graph of a function, using the vertical line test. The domain is $[-4, 4]$, and the range is $[-6, 0]$.

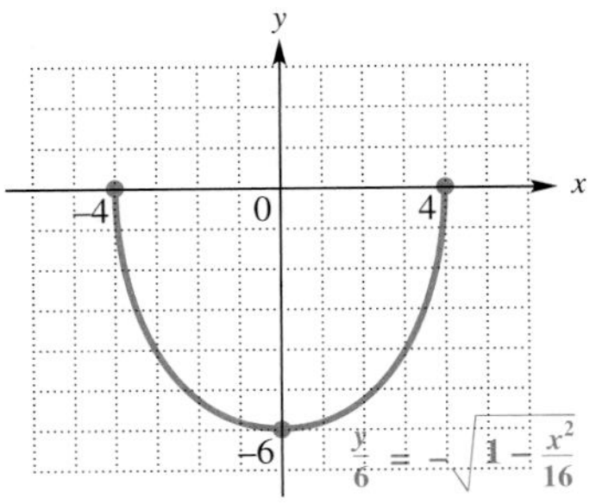

Figure 24

Work Problem 5 at the Side.

Answers

4.

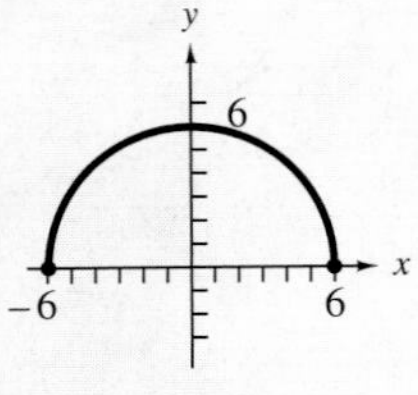

$[-6, 6]$; $[0, 6]$

5.

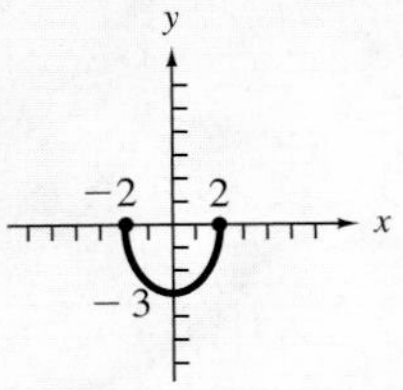

$[-2, 2]$; $[-3, 0]$

12.3 EXERCISES

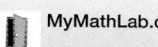

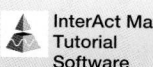

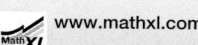

FOR EXTRA HELP Student's Solutions Manual | MyMathLab.com | InterAct Math Tutorial Software | AW Math Tutor Center | www.mathxl.com | Digital Video Tutor CD 11 Videotape 24

Based on the discussions of ellipses in the previous section and of hyperbolas in this section, match each equation with its graph.

1. $\frac{x^2}{25} + \frac{y^2}{9} = 1$ C

2. $\frac{x^2}{9} + \frac{y^2}{25} = 1$ B

3. $\frac{x^2}{9} - \frac{y^2}{25} = 1$ D

4. $\frac{x^2}{25} - \frac{y^2}{9} = 1$ A

A.

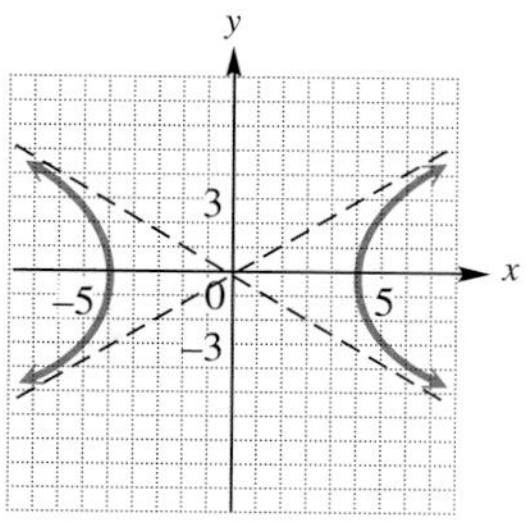

B.

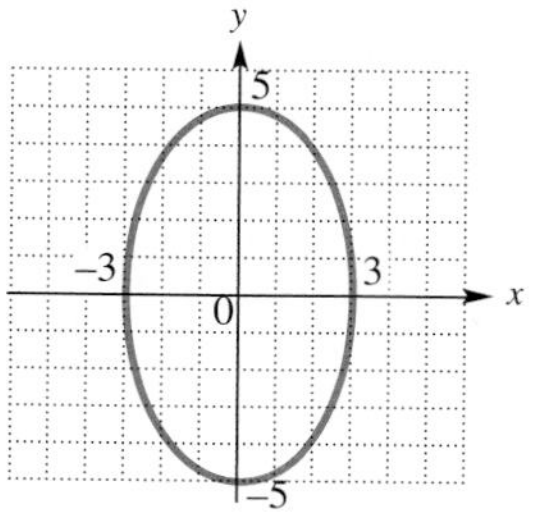

C.

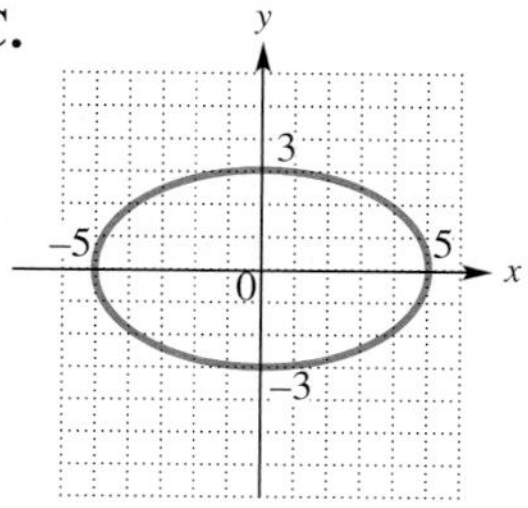

D.

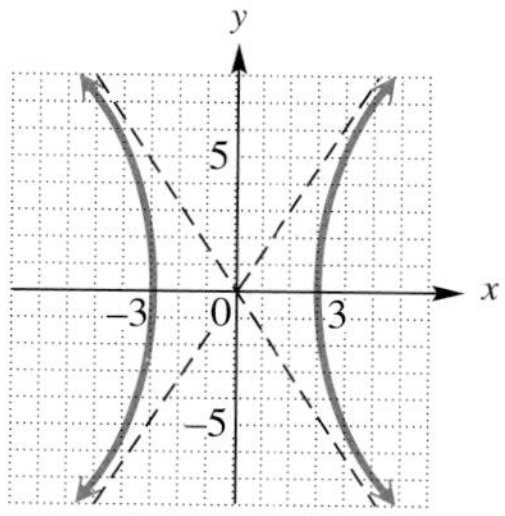

5. Write an explanation of how you can tell from the equation whether the branches of a hyperbola open up and down or left and right.

When written in one of the forms given in the box titled "Equations of Hyperbolas" in this section, it will open up and down if the − sign precedes the x^2-term; it will open left and right if the − sign precedes the y^2-term.

6. Describe how the fundamental rectangle is used to sketch a hyperbola.

The points (a, b), $(a, -b)$, $(-a, -b)$, and $(-a, b)$ are used as corners of a rectangle. The diagonals of the rectangle are drawn, which are the asymptotes for the hyperbola.

Graph each hyperbola. See Examples 1 and 2.

7. $\frac{x^2}{16} - \frac{y^2}{9} = 1$

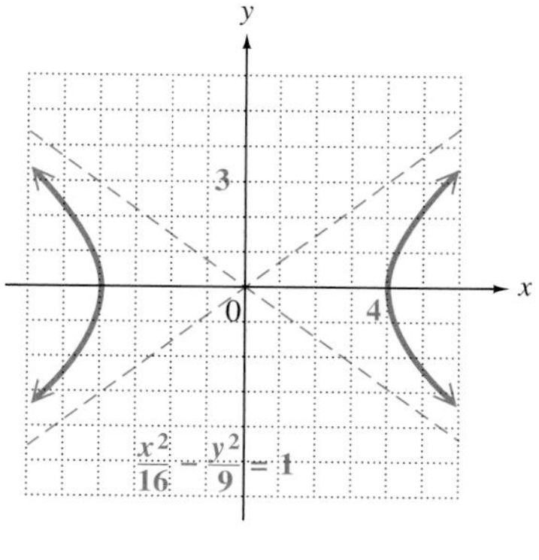

8. $\frac{y^2}{4} - \frac{x^2}{25} = 1$

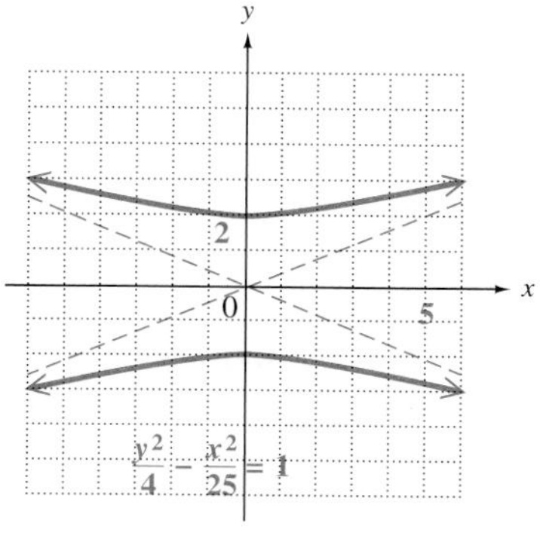

9. $\frac{y^2}{9} - \frac{x^2}{9} = 1$

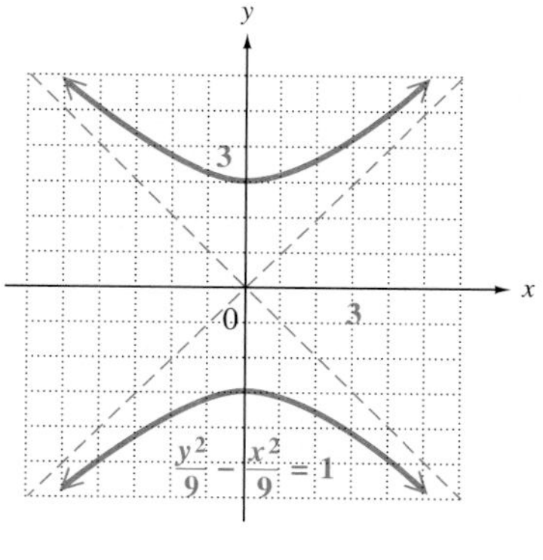

10. $\dfrac{x^2}{49} - \dfrac{y^2}{16} = 1$

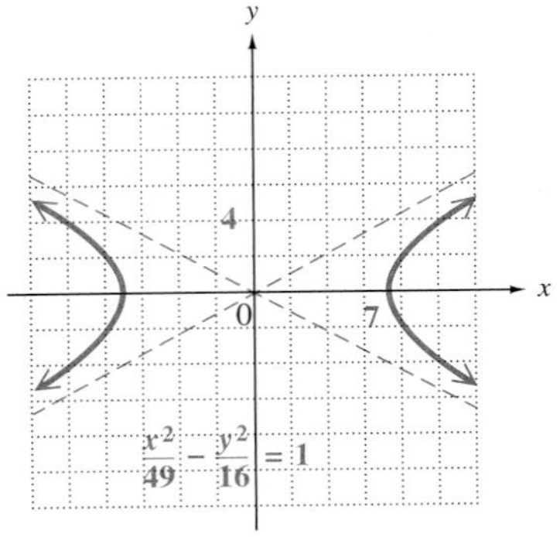

11. $\dfrac{x^2}{25} - \dfrac{y^2}{36} = 1$

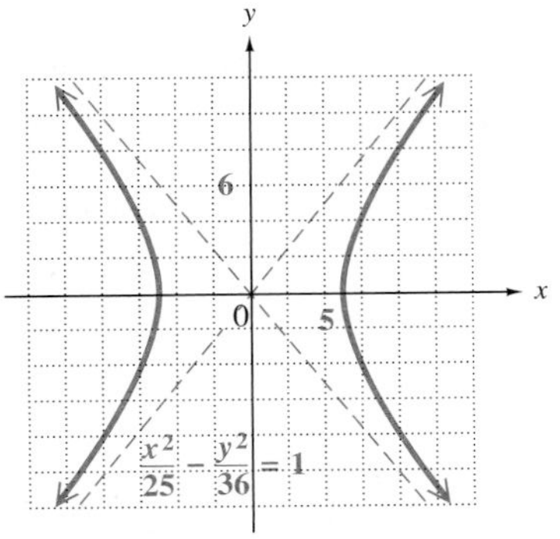

12. $\dfrac{y^2}{9} - \dfrac{x^2}{4} = 1$

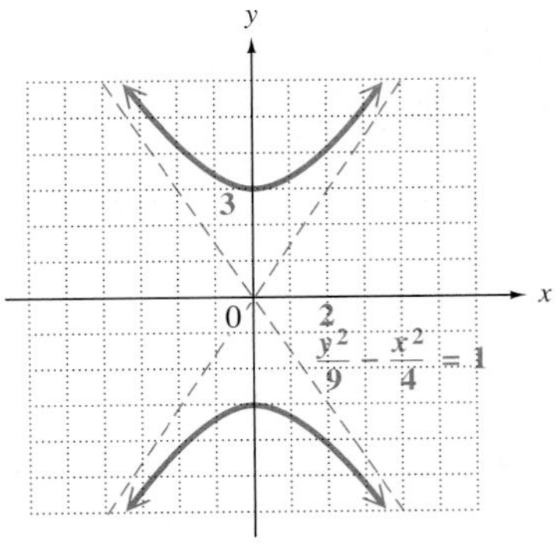

Identify the graph of each equation as a parabola, circle, ellipse, *or* hyperbola, *and sketch it. See Example 3.*

13. $x^2 - y^2 = 16$ **hyperbola**

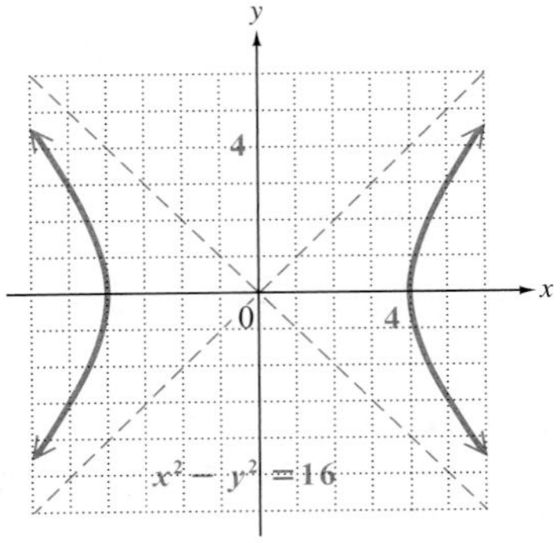

14. $x^2 + y^2 = 16$ **circle**

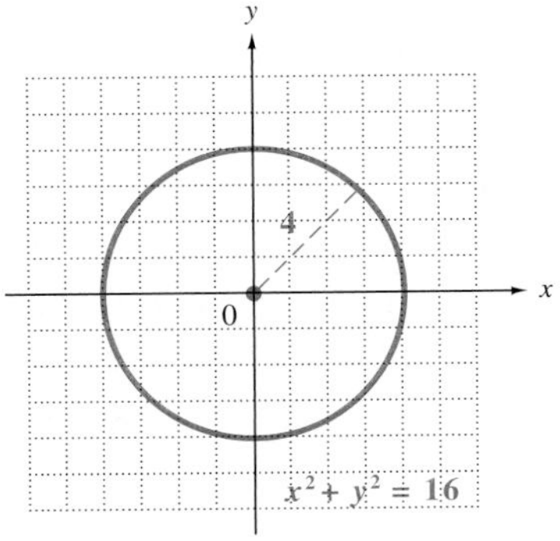

15. $4x^2 + y^2 = 16$ **ellipse**

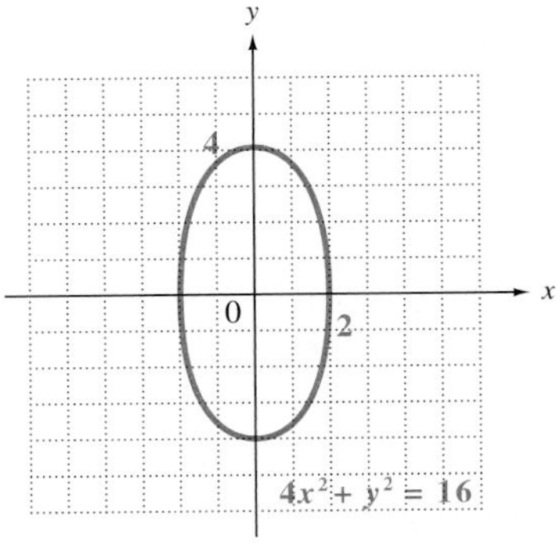

16. $x^2 - 2y = 0$ **parabola**

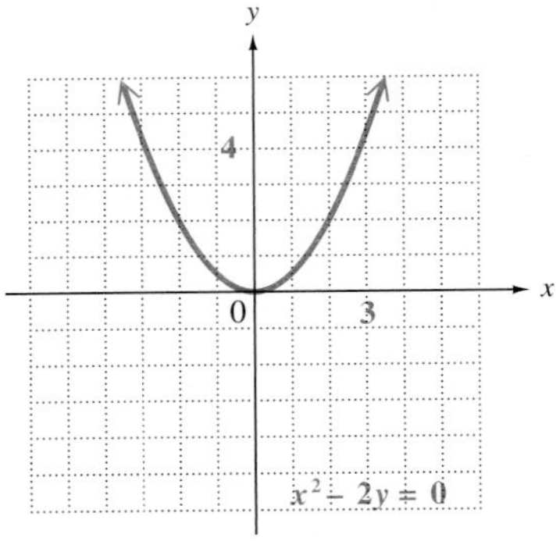

17. $y^2 = 36 - x^2$ **circle**

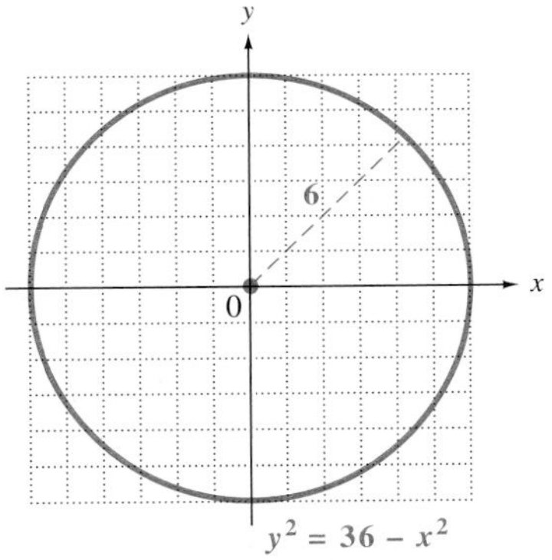

18. $9x^2 + 25y^2 = 225$ **ellipse**

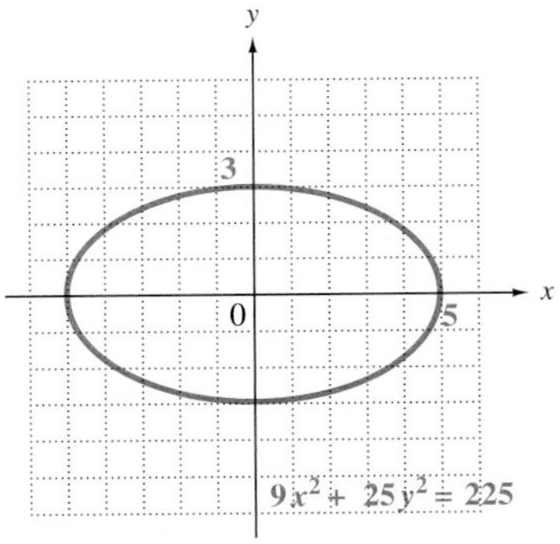

19. $9x^2 = 144 + 16y^2$ **hyperbola**

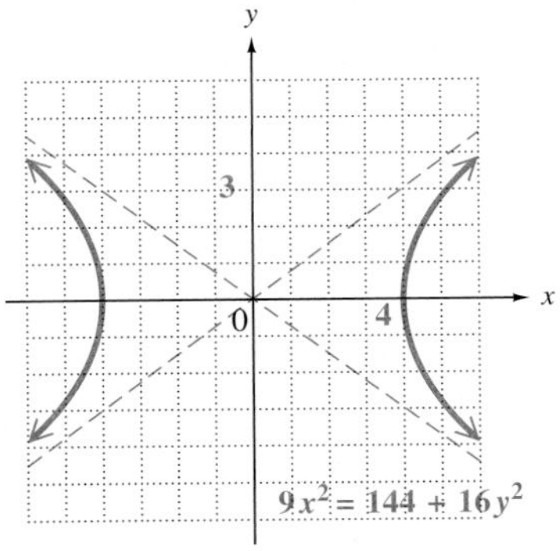

20. $y^2 = 4 + x^2$ **hyperbola**

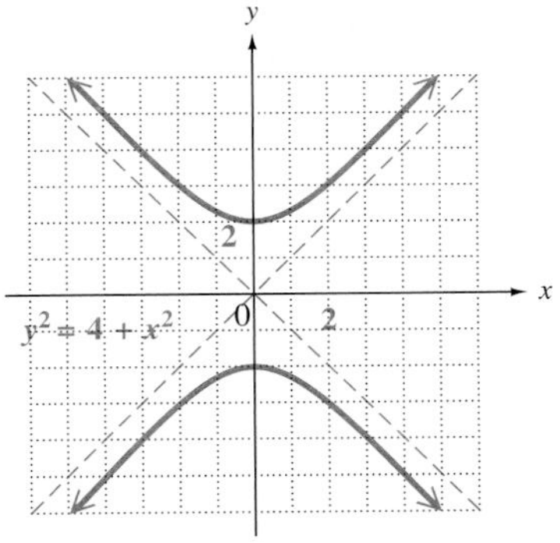

21. $x^2 + 9y^2 = 9$ **ellipse**

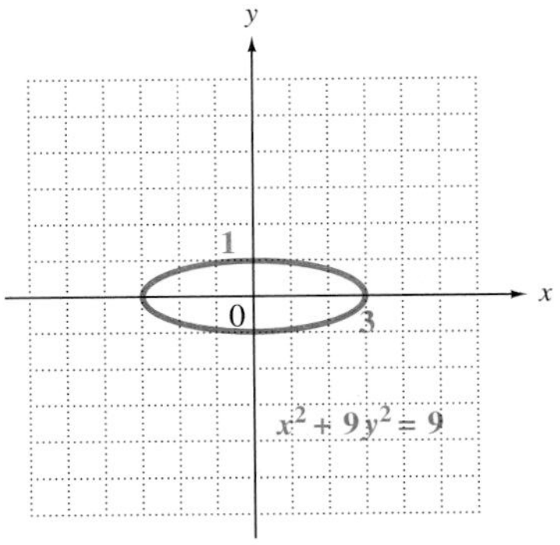

Graph each function defined by a radical expression. Give the domain and range. See Examples 4 and 5.

22. $f(x) = \sqrt{16 - x^2}$

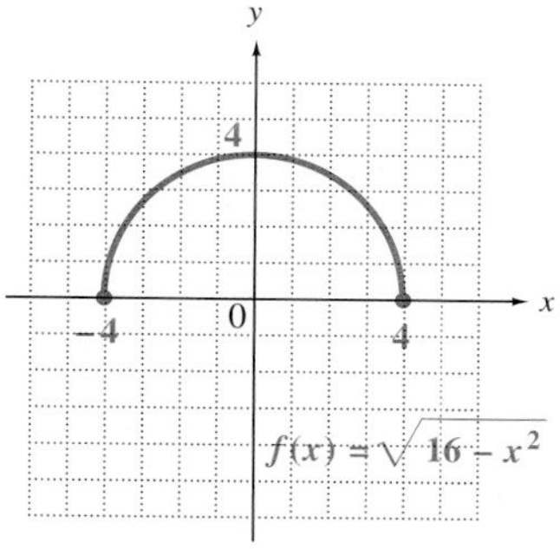

[−4, 4]; [0, 4]

23. $f(x) = \sqrt{9 - x^2}$

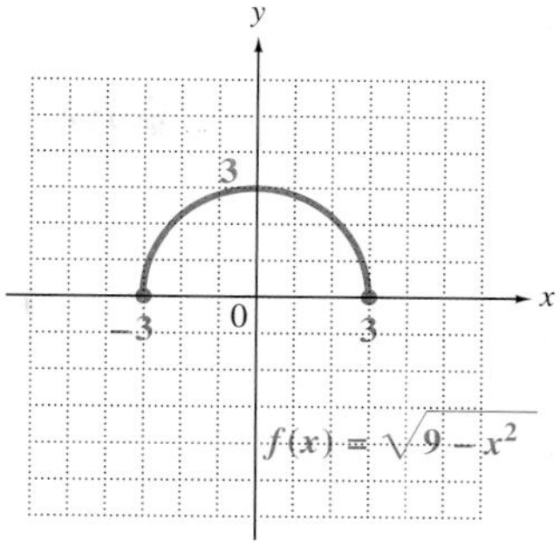

[−3, 3]; [0, 3]

24. $f(x) = -\sqrt{36 - x^2}$

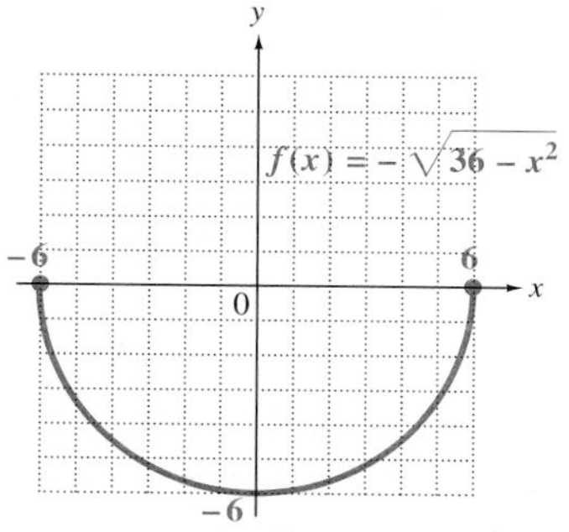

[−6, 6]; [−6, 0]

25. $f(x) = -\sqrt{25 - x^2}$

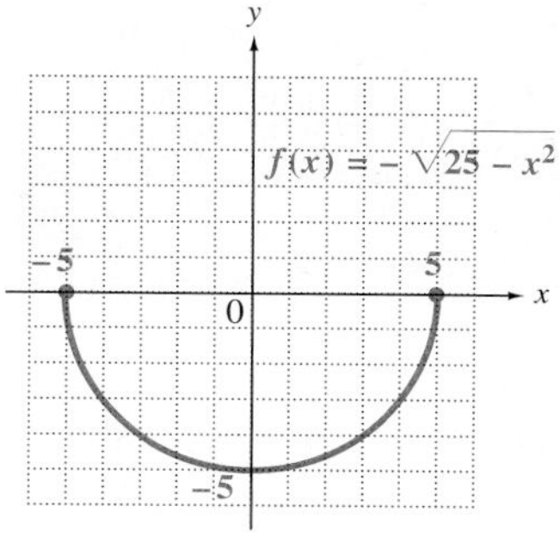

[−5, 5]; [−5, 0]

26. $\frac{y}{3} = \sqrt{1 + \frac{x^2}{9}}$

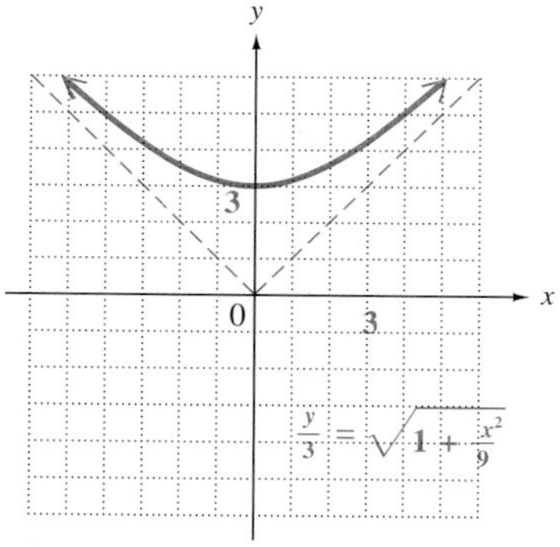

(−∞, ∞); [3, ∞)

27. $y = \sqrt{\frac{x + 4}{2}}$

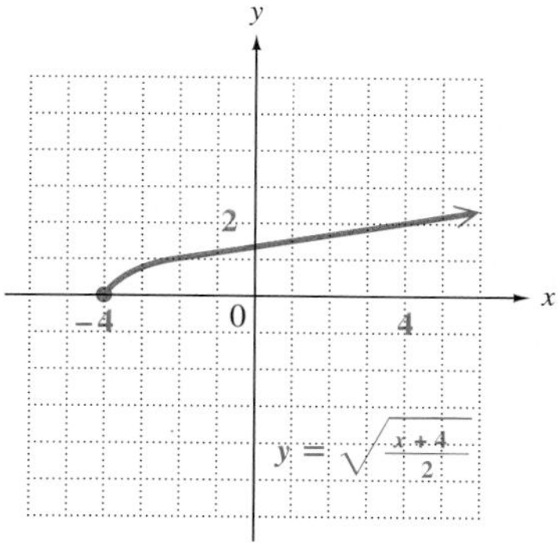

[−4, ∞); [0, ∞)

28. $y = -2\sqrt{\frac{9 - x^2}{9}}$

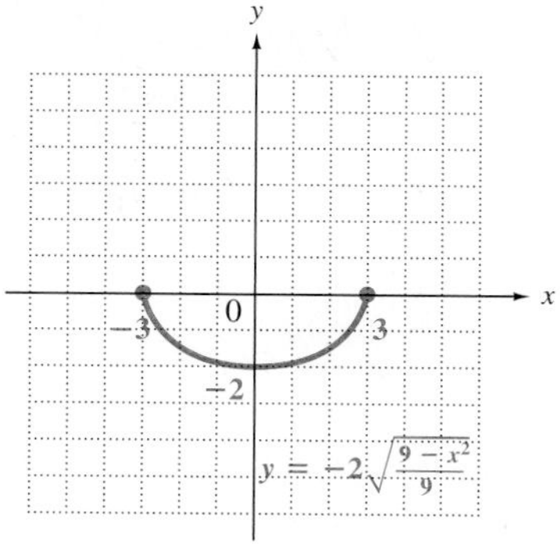

[−3, 3]; [−2, 0]

Solve each problem.

29. Two buildings in a sports complex are shaped and positioned like a portion of the branches of the hyperbola with equation

$$400x^2 - 625y^2 = 250{,}000,$$

where x and y are in meters.

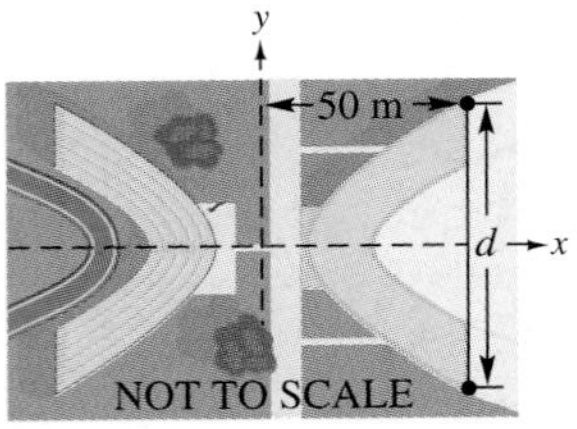

(a) How far apart are the buildings at their closest point? **50 m**

(b) Find the distance d in the figure. **69.3 m**

30. In rugby, after a *try* (similar to a touchdown in American football) the scoring team attempts a kick for extra points. The ball must be kicked from directly behind the point where the try was scored. The kicker can choose the distance but cannot move the ball sideways. It can be shown that the kicker's best choice is on the hyperbola with equation

$$\frac{x^2}{g^2} - \frac{y^2}{g^2} = 1,$$

where $2g$ is the distance between the goal posts. Since the hyperbola approaches its asymptotes, it is easier for the kicker to estimate points on the asymptotes instead of on the hyperbola. What are the asymptotes of this hyperbola? Why is it relatively easy to estimate them? (*Source:* Isaksen, Daniel C., "How to Kick a Field Goal," *The College Mathematics Journal,* September 1996.)

$y = \pm x$; The lines $y = \pm x$ form a 45° angle with the line through the goal posts. Most people can estimate a 45° angle fairly easily.

31. When a satellite is launched into orbit, the shape of its trajectory is determined by its velocity. The trajectory will be hyperbolic if the velocity V, in meters per second, satisfies the inequality

$$V > \frac{2.82 \times 10^7}{\sqrt{D}},$$

where D is the distance, in meters, from the center of Earth. For what values of V will the trajectory be hyperbolic if $D = 4.25 \times 10^7$ m? (*Source:* Kaler, James B., *Astronomy!,* Addison-Wesley, 1997.)

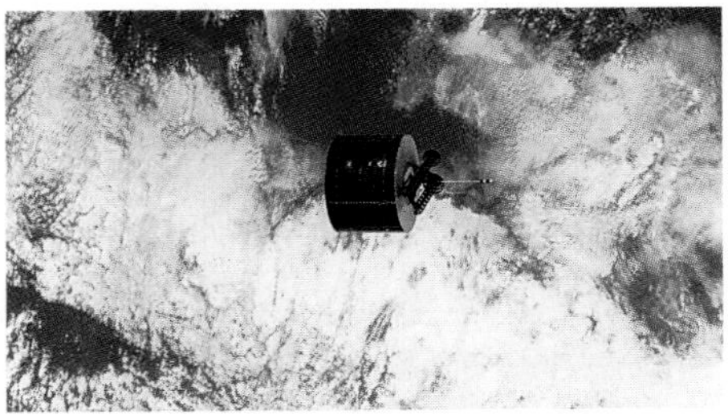

for V greater than 4325.68 m per sec

32. The percent of women in the work force has increased steadily for many years. The line graph shows the change for the period from 1975 to 1999, where $x = 75$ represents 1975, $x = 80$ represents 1980, and so on.

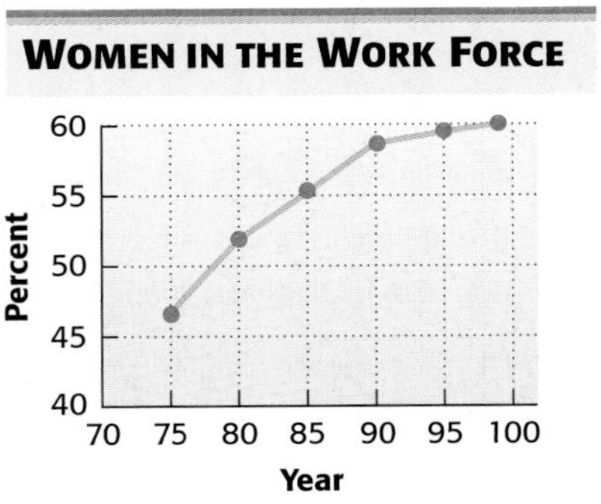

Source: U.S. Bureau of Labor Statistics.

The graph resembles the upper branch of a horizontal hyperbola. Using statistical methods, we found the corresponding square root equation

$$y = .607\sqrt{383.9 + x^2},$$

which closely approximates the line graph.

(a) According to the graph, what percent of women were in the work force in 1985? **about 55%**

(b) According to the equation, what percent of women worked in 1985? (Round to the nearest percent.) **about 53%**

12.4 NONLINEAR SYSTEMS OF EQUATIONS

OBJECTIVES

1. Solve a nonlinear system by substitution.
2. Use the elimination method to solve a system with two second-degree equations.
3. Solve a system that requires a combination of methods.

An equation in which some terms have more than one variable or a variable of degree 2 or greater is called a **nonlinear equation.** A **nonlinear system of equations** includes at least one nonlinear equation.

When solving a nonlinear system, it helps to visualize the types of graphs of the equations of the system to determine the possible number of points of intersection. For example, if a system includes two equations where the graph of one is a parabola and the graph of the other is a line, then there may be 0, 1, or 2 points of intersection, as illustrated in Figure 25.

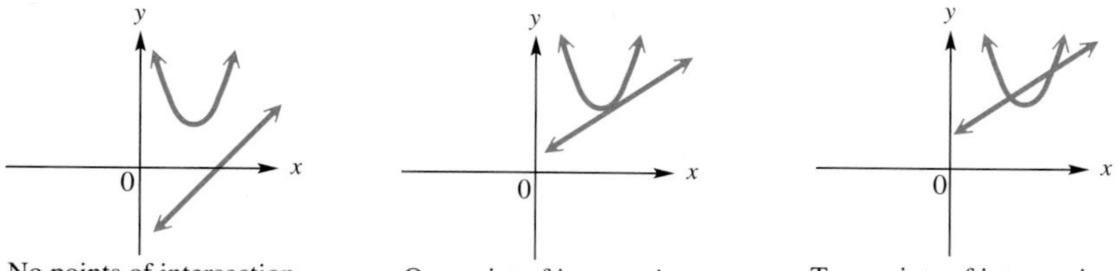

Figure 25

1 Solve a nonlinear system by substitution.

We solve nonlinear systems by the elimination method, the substitution method, or a combination of the two. The substitution method is usually best when one of the equations is linear.

Example 1 Solving a Nonlinear System by Substitution

Solve the system.

$$x^2 + y^2 = 9 \quad (1)$$
$$2x - y = 3 \quad (2)$$

The graph of (1) is a circle and the graph of (2) is a line. Visualizing the possible ways the graphs could intersect indicates that there may be 0, 1, or 2 points of intersection. It is best to solve the linear equation first for one of the two variables; then substitute the resulting expression into the nonlinear equation to obtain an equation in one variable.

$$2x - y = 3 \quad (2)$$
$$y = 2x - 3 \quad (3)$$

Substitute $2x - 3$ for y in equation (1).

$$x^2 + (2x - 3)^2 = 9$$
$$x^2 + 4x^2 - 12x + 9 = 9$$
$$5x^2 - 12x = 0$$
$$x(5x - 12) = 0 \quad \text{GCF is } x.$$
$$x = 0 \quad \text{or} \quad x = \frac{12}{5} \quad \text{Zero-factor property}$$

Let $x = 0$ in equation (3) to get $y = -3$. If $x = \frac{12}{5}$, then $y = \frac{9}{5}$. The solution set of the system is $\{(0, -3), (\frac{12}{5}, \frac{9}{5})\}$. The graph in Figure 26 on the next page confirms the two points of intersection.

Continued on Next Page

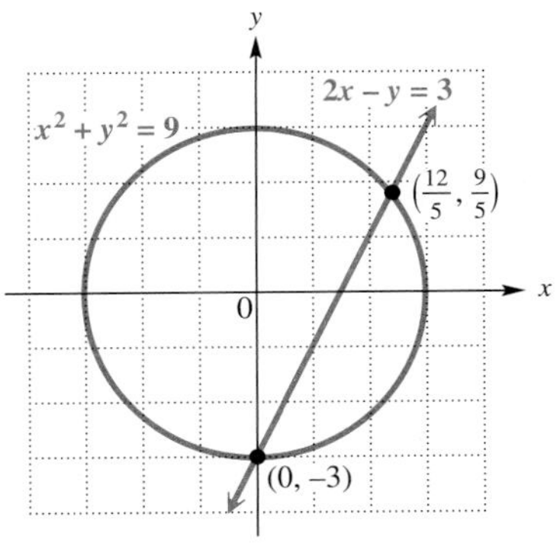

Figure 26

Work Problem 1 at the Side.

1 Solve each system.

(a) $x^2 + y^2 = 10$
$x = y + 2$

(b) $x^2 - 2y^2 = 8$
$y + x = 6$

Example 2 Solving a Nonlinear System by Substitution

Solve the system.

$$6x - y = 5 \quad (1)$$
$$xy = 4 \quad (2)$$

The graph of (1) is a line. We have not specifically mentioned equations like (2); however, it can be shown by plotting points that its graph is a hyperbola. Visualizing a line and a hyperbola indicates that there may be 0, 1, or 2 points of intersection. Since neither equation has a squared term, we can solve either equation for one of the variables and then substitute the result into the other equation. Solving $xy = 4$ for x gives $x = \frac{4}{y}$. Substitute $\frac{4}{y}$ for x in equation (1).

$$6\left(\frac{4}{y}\right) - y = 5 \qquad \text{Let } x = \frac{4}{y}.$$

$$\frac{24}{y} - y = 5$$

$$24 - y^2 = 5y \qquad \text{Multiply by } y\ (y \neq 0).$$

$$0 = y^2 + 5y - 24$$

$$0 = (y - 3)(y + 8) \qquad \text{Factor.}$$

$$y = 3 \quad \text{or} \quad y = -8 \qquad \text{Zero-factor property}$$

We substitute these results into $x = \frac{4}{y}$ to obtain the corresponding values of x.

$$\text{If } y = 3, \text{ then } x = \frac{4}{3}. \qquad \text{If } y = -8, \text{ then } x = -\frac{1}{2}.$$

The solution set of the system is $\{(\frac{4}{3}, 3), (-\frac{1}{2}, -8)\}$. The graph in Figure 27 shows that there are two points of intersection.

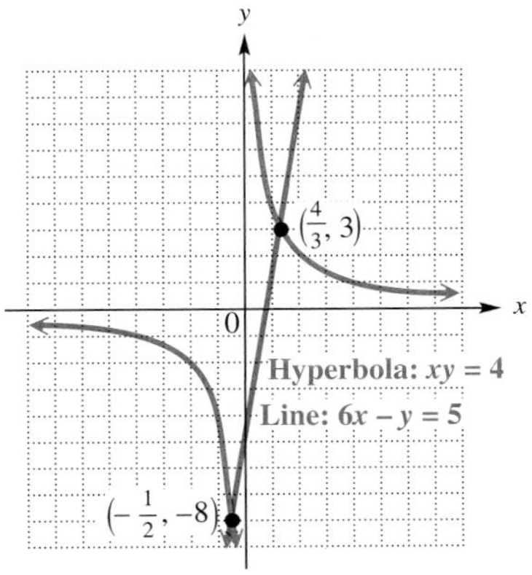

Figure 27

Work Problem 2 at the Side.

2 Solve each system.

(a) $xy = 8$
$x + y = 6$

(b) $xy + 10 = 0$
$4x + 9y = -2$

ANSWERS
1. (a) $\{(3, 1), (-1, -3)\}$
(b) $\{(4, 2), (20, -14)\}$
2. (a) $\{(4, 2), (2, 4)\}$
(b) $\left\{(-5, 2), \left(\frac{9}{2}, -\frac{20}{9}\right)\right\}$

2 Use the elimination method to solve a system with two second-degree equations. The elimination method is often used when both equations are second degree.

Example 3 Solving a Nonlinear System by Elimination

Solve the system.

$$x^2 + y^2 = 9 \quad (1)$$
$$2x^2 - y^2 = -6 \quad (2)$$

The graph of (1) is a circle, while the graph of (2) is a hyperbola. By analyzing the possibilities we conclude that there may be 0, 1, 2, 3, or 4 points of intersection. Adding the two equations will eliminate y, leaving an equation that can be solved for x.

$$\begin{aligned} x^2 + y^2 &= 9 \\ 2x^2 - y^2 &= -6 \\ \hline 3x^2 \qquad &= 3 \\ x^2 &= 1 \end{aligned}$$
$$x = 1 \quad \text{or} \quad x = -1$$

Each value of x gives corresponding values for y when substituted into one of the original equations. Using equation (1) gives the following.

If $x = 1$, then

$$1^2 + y^2 = 9$$
$$y^2 = 8$$
$$y = \sqrt{8} \quad \text{or} \quad y = -\sqrt{8}$$
$$y = 2\sqrt{2} \quad \text{or} \quad y = -2\sqrt{2}.$$

If $x = -1$, then

$$(-1)^2 + y^2 = 9$$
$$y^2 = 8$$
$$y = 2\sqrt{2} \quad \text{or} \quad y = -2\sqrt{2}.$$

The solution set is $\{(1, 2\sqrt{2}), (1, -2\sqrt{2}), (-1, 2\sqrt{2}), (-1, -2\sqrt{2})\}$. Figure 28 shows the four points of intersection.

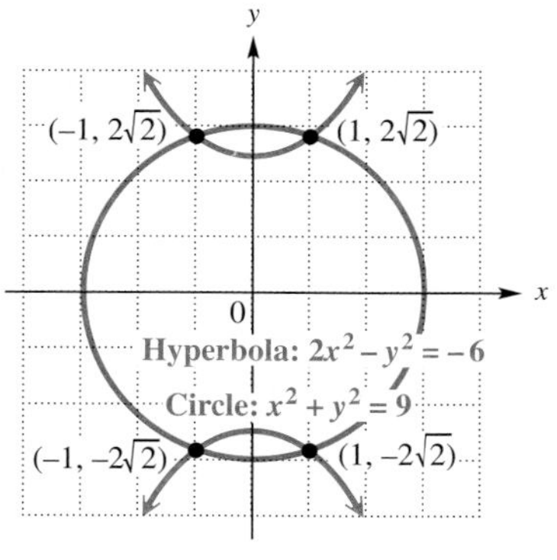

Figure 28

Work Problem 3 at the Side.

3 Solve a system that requires a combination of methods. Solving a system of second-degree equations may require a combination of methods.

---

3 Solve each system.

(a) $x^2 + y^2 = 41$
$x^2 - y^2 = 9$

(b) $x^2 + 3y^2 = 40$
$4x^2 - y^2 = 4$

ANSWERS

3. (a) $\{(5, 4), (5, -4), (-5, 4), (-5, -4)\}$
(b) $\{(2, 2\sqrt{3}), (2, -2\sqrt{3}), (-2, 2\sqrt{3}), (-2, -2\sqrt{3})\}$

Example 4 **Solving a Nonlinear System by a Combination of Methods**

Solve the system.

$$x^2 + 2xy - y^2 = 7 \quad (1)$$
$$x^2 - y^2 = 3 \quad (2)$$

While we have not graphed equations like (1), its graph is a hyperbola. The graph of (2) is also a hyperbola. Two hyperbolas may have 0, 1, 2, 3, or 4 points of intersection. We use the elimination method here in combination with the substitution method. We begin by eliminating the squared terms by multiplying each side of equation (2) by -1 and then adding the result to equation (1).

$$\begin{array}{rl} x^2 + 2xy - y^2 &= 7 \\ -x^2 \qquad\quad + y^2 &= -3 \\ \hline 2xy \qquad\quad &= 4 \end{array}$$

Next, we solve $2xy = 4$ for y. (Either variable would do.)

$$2xy = 4$$
$$y = \frac{2}{x} \quad (3)$$

Now, we substitute $y = \frac{2}{x}$ into one of the original equations. It is easier to do this with equation (2).

$$x^2 - y^2 = 3 \quad (2)$$
$$x^2 - \left(\frac{2}{x}\right)^2 = 3$$
$$x^2 - \frac{4}{x^2} = 3$$
$$x^4 - 4 = 3x^2 \quad \text{Multiply by } x^2, x \neq 0.$$
$$x^4 - 3x^2 - 4 = 0 \quad \text{Subtract } 3x^2.$$
$$(x^2 - 4)(x^2 + 1) = 0 \quad \text{Factor.}$$
$$x^2 - 4 = 0 \quad \text{or} \quad x^2 + 1 = 0$$
$$x^2 = 4 \quad \text{or} \quad x^2 = -1$$
$$x = 2 \quad \text{or} \quad x = -2 \qquad x = i \quad \text{or} \quad x = -i$$

Substituting these four values of x into equation (3) gives the corresponding values for y.

If $x = 2$, then $y = 1$. If $x = i$, then $y = -2i$.
If $x = -2$, then $y = -1$. If $x = -i$, then $y = 2i$.

Note that if we substitute the x-values we found into equation (1) or (2) instead of into equation (3), we get extraneous solutions. It is always wise to check all solutions in both of the given equations. There are four ordered pairs in the solution set, two with real values and two with imaginary values. The solution set is

$$\{(2, 1), (-2, -1), (i, -2i), (-i, 2i)\}.$$

Continued on Next Page

The graph of the system, shown in Figure 29, shows only the two real intersection points because the graph is in the real number plane. The two ordered pairs with imaginary components are solutions of the system, but do not appear on the graph.

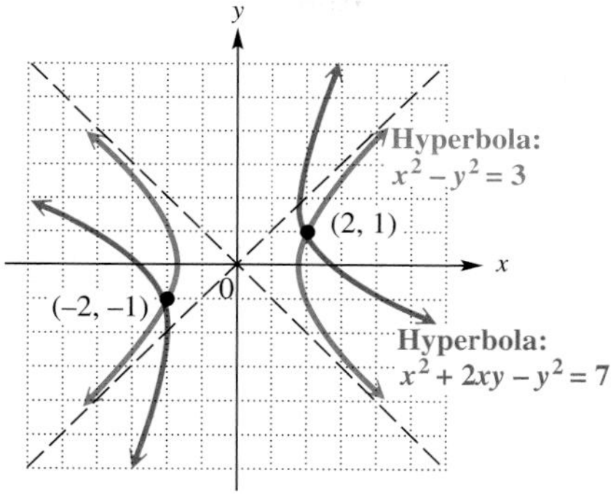

Figure 29

Work Problem 4 at the Side.

NOTE

In the examples of this section, we analyzed the possible number of points of intersection of the graphs in each system. However, in Examples 2 and 4, we worked with equations whose graphs had not been studied. Keep in mind that it is not absolutely essential to visualize the number of points of intersection in order to solve the system. Furthermore, as in Example 4, there are sometimes imaginary solutions to nonlinear systems which do not appear as points of intersection in the real plane. Visualizing the geometry of the graphs is only an aid to solving these systems.

4 Solve each system.

(a) $x^2 + xy + y^2 = 3$
$x^2 + y^2 = 5$

(b) $x^2 + 7xy - 2y^2 = -8$
$-2x^2 + 4y^2 = 16$

ANSWERS

4. (a) $\{(1, -2), (-1, 2), (2, -1), (-2, 1)\}$
(b) $\{(0, 2), (0, -2), (2i\sqrt{2}, 0), (-2i\sqrt{2}, 0)\}$

Focus on

Real-Data Applications

Who Arrived First?

Suppose Vivian, Tommy, Carmen, and Manuel all leave home at 9:00 A.M. to drive to Atlanta, Georgia, along U.S. Interstate 75. The distance between Valdosta, Georgia and Atlanta is 245 mi.

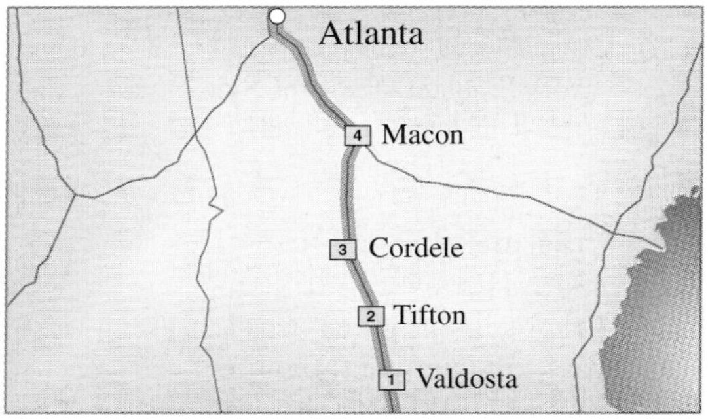

1. Vivian leaves from Valdosta, Georgia. She drives a Miata convertible and cruises at 85 mph.
2. Tommy leaves from Tifton, Georgia, which is 50 mi north of Valdosta. He drives a 1984 Toyota truck averaging 65 mph.
3. Carmen leaves from Cordele, Georgia, which is 40 mi north of Tifton. She drives a 1995 Honda Accord averaging 60 mph.
4. Manuel leaves from Macon, Georgia, which is 65 mi north of Cordele. He is riding a twenty-speed bike at 25 mph.

For Group Discussion

The independent variable is the number of hours traveled after 9:00 A.M. The dependent variable is distance, relative to Valdosta, after t hours. To compare the four trips, distances are measured from a common starting point in Valdosta. Recall that distance equals the product of rate and time. Tommy will have driven a distance of $65t$ mi after t hours, and since he starts 50 mi north of Valdosta, an equation that represents Tommy's distance relative to Valdosta is $d = 65t + 50$.

1. Write equations to represent the distances after t hr (relative to Valdosta) of Vivian, Carmen, and Manuel.

Vivian: $d = 85t$; Carmen: $d = 60t + 90$; Manuel: $d = 25t + 155$

2. On a sheet of graph paper, sketch graphs of the four distance equations. Graph the horizontal line $d = 245$ to represent the distance between Valdosta and Atlanta. Based on your graphs, list the order in which the drivers reach Atlanta.

Carmen, Vivian, Tommy, Manuel

3. Based on your equations from Problem 1, at what time (rounded to the nearest minute) does each driver reach Atlanta? Are the results consistent with your conclusions based on your graphs?

Carmen: 11:35 A.M.; Vivian: 11:53 A.M.; Tommy: 12:00 Noon; Manuel: 12:36 P.M.; yes

4. Use a system of equations to find each time and location (distance from Valdosta). Round times to the nearest minute and distances to the nearest tenth of a mile, as necessary.

(a) Find the time and location at which Vivian passes Tommy. **11:30 A.M.; 212.5 mi**

(b) Find the time and location at which Carmen passes Manuel. **10:51 A.M.; 201.4 mi**

(c) Does Carmen pass any other traveler before reaching Atlanta? **No.**

Teaching notes for this activity are provided in the *Printed Test Bank and Instructor's Resource Guide.*

12.4 EXERCISES

FOR EXTRA HELP Student's Solutions Manual | MyMathLab.com | InterAct Math Tutorial Software | AW Math Tutor Center | www.mathxl.com | Digital Video Tutor CD 11 Videotape 25

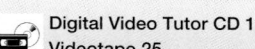

1. Write an explanation of the steps you would use to solve the system

$$x^2 + y^2 = 25$$
$$y = x - 1$$

by the substitution method. Why would the elimination method not be appropriate for this system?

Substitute $x - 1$ for y in the first equation. Then solve for x. Find the corresponding y-values by substituting back into $y = x - 1$. In the first equation, both variables are squared and in the second, both variables are to the first power, so the elimination method is not appropriate.

2. Write an explanation of the steps you would use to solve the system

$$x^2 + y^2 = 12$$
$$x^2 - y^2 = 13$$

by the elimination method.

Add the two equations to eliminate y^2. Solve for the values of x. Then go back to either original equation to solve for the values of y.

Each sketch represents the graphs of a pair of equations in a system. How many points are in each solution set?

3.

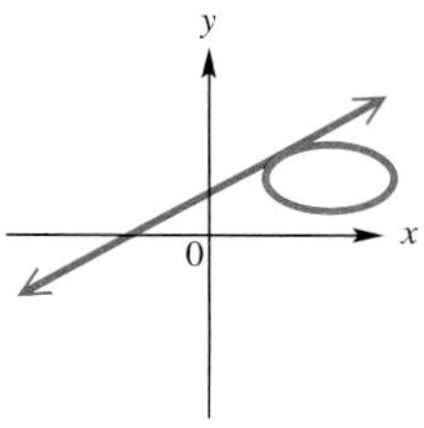

one

4.

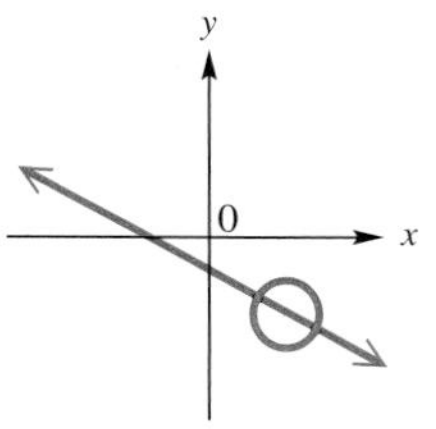

two

5.

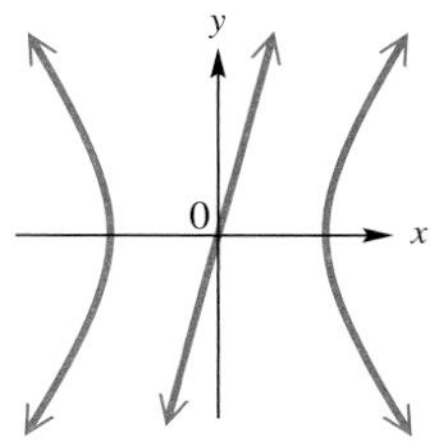

none

6.

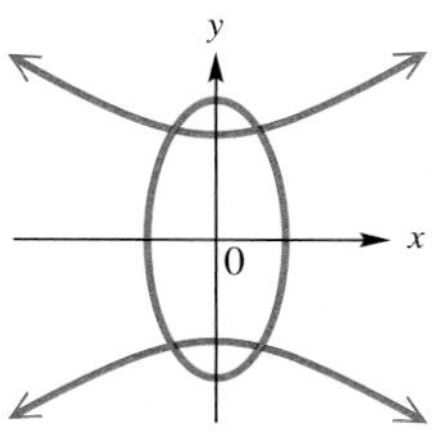

four

Suppose that a nonlinear system is composed of equations whose graphs are those described, and the number of points of intersection of the two graphs is as given. Make a sketch satisfying these conditions. (There may be more than one way to do this.)

7. A line and a circle; no points

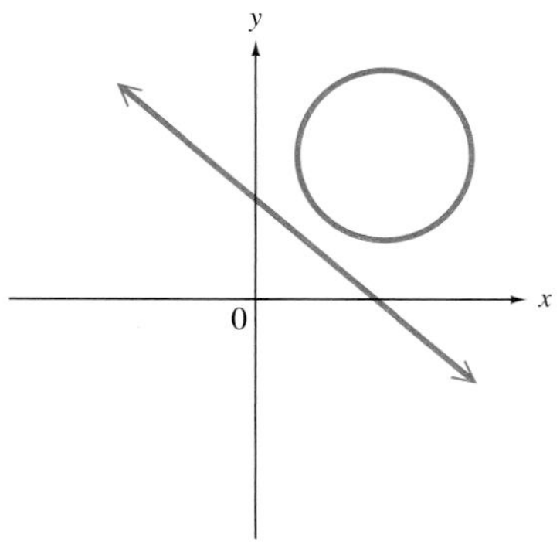

8. A line and a circle; one point

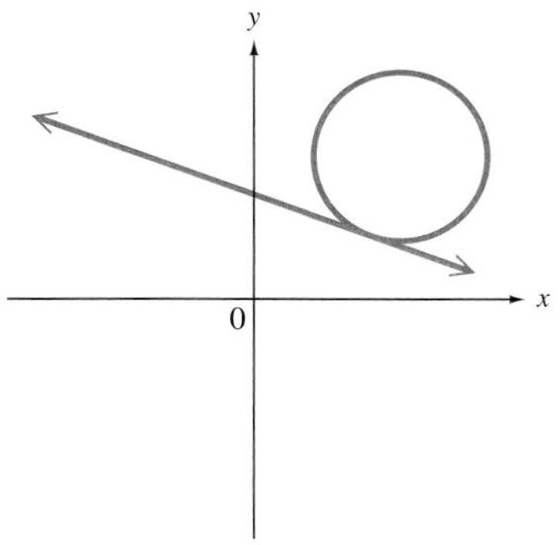

9. A line and an ellipse; two points

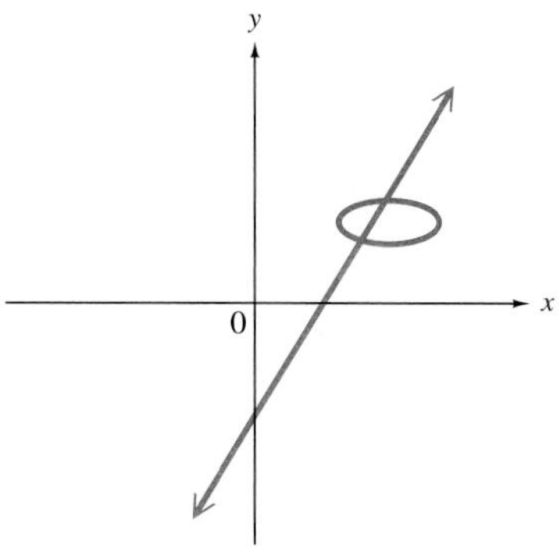

10. A line and a hyperbola; no points

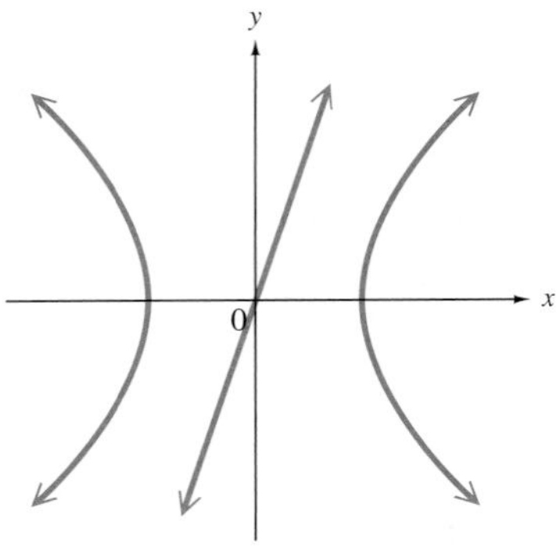

11. A circle and an ellipse; four points

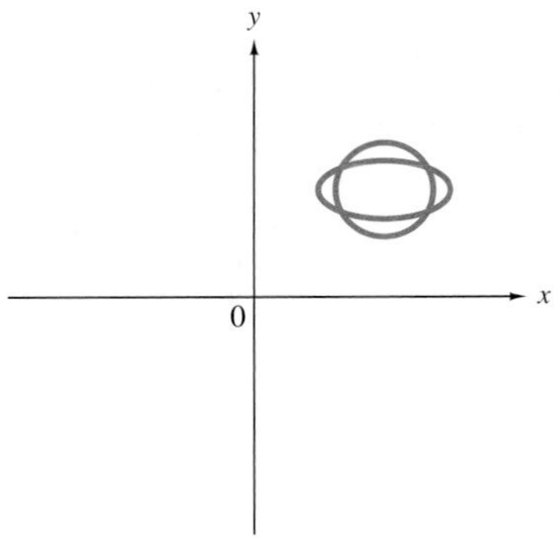

12. A parabola and an ellipse; one point

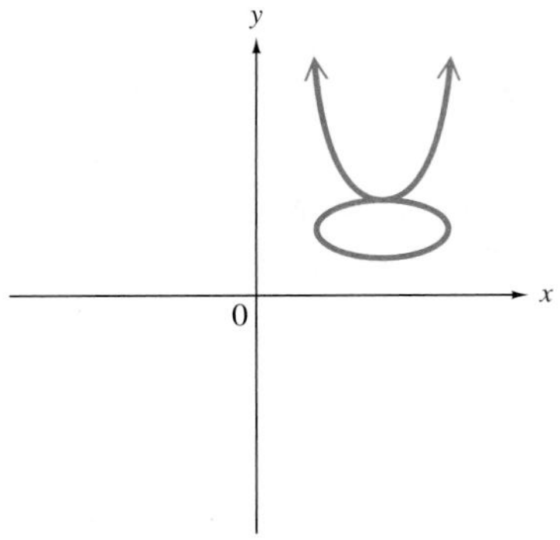

Solve each system by the substitution method. See Examples 1 and 2.

13. $y = 4x^2 - x$
$y = x$

$\left\{(0, 0), \left(\frac{1}{2}, \frac{1}{2}\right)\right\}$

14. $y = x^2 + 6x$
$3y = 12x$

$\{(0, 0), (-2, -8)\}$

15. $y = x^2 + 6x + 9$
$x + y = 3$

$\{(-6, 9), (-1, 4)\}$

16. $y = x^2 + 8x + 16$
$x - y = -4$

$\{(-3, 1), (-4, 0)\}$

17. $x^2 + y^2 = 2$
$2x + y = 1$

$\left\{\left(-\frac{1}{5}, \frac{7}{5}\right), (1, -1)\right\}$

18. $2x^2 + 4y^2 = 4$
$x = 4y$

$\left\{\left(\frac{4}{3}, \frac{1}{3}\right), \left(-\frac{4}{3}, -\frac{1}{3}\right)\right\}$

19. $xy = 4$
$3x + 2y = -10$

$\left\{(-2, -2), \left(-\frac{4}{3}, -3\right)\right\}$

20. $xy = -5$
$2x + y = 3$

$\left\{\left(\frac{5}{2}, -2\right), (-1, 5)\right\}$

21. $xy = -3$
$x + y = -2$

$\{(-3, 1), (1, -3)\}$

22. $xy = 12$
$x + y = 8$

$\{(6, 2), (2, 6)\}$

23. $y = 3x^2 + 6x$
$y = x^2 - x - 6$

$\left\{\left(-\frac{3}{2}, -\frac{9}{4}\right), (-2, 0)\right\}$

24. $y = 2x^2 + 1$
$y = 5x^2 + 2x - 7$

$\left\{\left(\frac{4}{3}, \frac{41}{9}\right), (-2, 9)\right\}$

25. $2x^2 - y^2 = 6$
$y = x^2 - 3$

$\{(-\sqrt{3}, 0), (\sqrt{3}, 0), (-\sqrt{5}, 2), (\sqrt{5}, 2)\}$

26. $x^2 + y^2 = 4$
$y = x^2 - 2$

$\{(0, -2), (\sqrt{3}, 1), (-\sqrt{3}, 1)\}$

Solve each system using the elimination method or a combination of the elimination and substitution methods. See Examples 3 and 4.

27. $3x^2 + 2y^2 = 12$
$x^2 + 2y^2 = 4$

$\{(-2, 0), (2, 0)\}$

28. $2x^2 + y^2 = 28$
$4x^2 - 5y^2 = 28$

$\{(-2\sqrt{3}, -2), (-2\sqrt{3}, 2), (2\sqrt{3}, -2), (2\sqrt{3}, 2)\}$

29. $xy = 6$
$3x^2 - y^2 = 12$

$\{(i\sqrt{2}, -3i\sqrt{2}), (-i\sqrt{2}, 3i\sqrt{2}), (-\sqrt{6}, -\sqrt{6}), (\sqrt{6}, \sqrt{6})\}$

30. $xy = 5$
$2y^2 - x^2 = 5$

$\left\{(\sqrt{5}, \sqrt{5}), (-\sqrt{5}, -\sqrt{5}), \left(i\sqrt{10}, -\frac{i\sqrt{10}}{2}\right), \left(-i\sqrt{10}, \frac{i\sqrt{10}}{2}\right)\right\}$

31. $2x^2 + 2y^2 = 8$
$3x^2 + 4y^2 = 24$

$\{(-2i\sqrt{2}, -2\sqrt{3}), (-2i\sqrt{2}, 2\sqrt{3}), (2i\sqrt{2}, -2\sqrt{3}), (2i\sqrt{2}, 2\sqrt{3})\}$

32. $5x^2 + 5y^2 = 20$
$x^2 + 2y^2 = 2$

$\{(-\sqrt{6}, -i\sqrt{2}), (-\sqrt{6}, i\sqrt{2}), (\sqrt{6}, -i\sqrt{2}), (\sqrt{6}, i\sqrt{2})\}$

33. $x^2 + xy + y^2 = 15$
$x^2 + y^2 = 10$

$\{(-\sqrt{5}, -\sqrt{5}), (\sqrt{5}, \sqrt{5})\}$

34. $2x^2 + 3xy + 2y^2 = 21$
$x^2 + y^2 = 6$

$\{(\sqrt{3}, \sqrt{3}), (-\sqrt{3}, -\sqrt{3})\}$

35. $3x^2 + 2xy - 3y^2 = 5$
$-x^2 - 3xy + y^2 = 3$

$\{(i, 2i), (-i, -2i), (2, -1), (-2, 1)\}$

36. $-2x^2 + 7xy - 3y^2 = 4$
$2x^2 - 3xy + 3y^2 = 4$

$\left\{(\sqrt{2}, \sqrt{2}), (-\sqrt{2}, -\sqrt{2}), \left(\sqrt{3}, \frac{2\sqrt{3}}{3}\right), \left(-\sqrt{3}, -\frac{2\sqrt{3}}{3}\right)\right\}$

Solve each problem by using a nonlinear system.

37. The area of a rectangular rug is 84 ft^2 and its perimeter is 38 ft. Find the length and width of the rug.

length: 12 ft; width: 7 ft

38. Find the length and width of a rectangular room whose perimeter is 50 m and whose area is 100 m^2.

length: 20 m; width: 5 m

39. A company has found that the price p (in dollars) of its scientific calculator is related to the supply x (in thousands) by the equation

$$px = 16.$$

The price is related to the demand x (in thousands) for the calculator by the equation

$$p = 10x + 12.$$

The *equilibrium price* is the value of p where demand equals supply. Find the equilibrium price and the supply/demand at that price by solving a system of equations. (*Hint:* Demand, price, and supply must all be positive.)

\$20; 800 calculators

40. The calculator company in Exercise 39 has also determined that the cost y to make x (thousand) calculators is

$$y = 4x^2 + 36x + 20,$$

while the revenue y from the sale of x (thousand) calculators is

$$36x^2 - 3y = 0.$$

Find the *break-even point,* where cost equals revenue, by solving a system of equations.

5000 calculators; \$300

41. Historically in the United States, the number of bachelor's degrees earned by men has been greater than the number earned by women. In the 1970s, however, this began to change as the number earned by men decreased. It stayed fairly constant in the 1980s, and then in the 1990s slowly began to increase again. Meanwhile, the number of bachelor's degrees earned by women has continued to rise steadily throughout this period. Functions that model the situation are defined by the following equations, where y is the number of degrees (in thousands) granted in year x, with $x = 0$ corresponding to 1970.

Men: $y = .138x^2 + .064x + 451$

Women: $y = 12.1x + 334$

Solve this system of equations to find the year when the same number of bachelor's degrees was awarded to men and women. How many bachelor's degrees were awarded in that year? Give answer to the nearest ten thousand. (*Source:* U.S. National Center for Education Statistics, *Digest of Education Statistics,* annual.)

1981; 470 thousand

42. Andy Grove, chairman of chip maker Intel Corp., recently noted that decreasing prices for computers and stable prices for Internet access implied that the trend lines for these costs either have crossed or soon will. He predicted that the time is not far away when computers, like cell phones, may be given away to sell on-line time. To see this, assume a price of \$1000 for a computer, and let x represent the number of months it will be used. (*Source:* Corcoran, Elizabeth, "Can Free Computers Be That Far Away?", *Washington Post,* from *Sacramento Bee,* February 3, 1999.)

(a) Write an equation for the monthly cost y of the computer over this period.

$y = \dfrac{1000}{x}$

(b) The average monthly on-line cost is about \$20. Assume this will remain constant and write an equation to express this cost.

$y = 20$

(c) Solve the system of equations from parts (a) and (b). Interpret your answer in relation to the situation.

(50, 20); The solution tells us that in 50 months, the monthly cost of the computer will be \$20, the same as the on-line cost.

12.5 Second-Degree Inequalities and Systems of Inequalities

Objectives

1. Graph second-degree inequalities.
2. Graph the solution set of a system of inequalities.

1 Graph second-degree inequalities. The linear inequality $3x + 2y \leq 5$ is graphed by first graphing the boundary line $3x + 2y = 5$. A **second-degree inequality** is an inequality with at least one variable of degree 2 and no variable with degree greater than 2. An example is $x^2 + y^2 \leq 36$. Such inequalities are graphed in the same way. The boundary of the inequality $x^2 + y^2 \leq 36$ is the graph of the equation $x^2 + y^2 = 36$, a circle with radius 6 and center at the origin, as shown in Figure 30. The inequality $x^2 + y^2 \leq 36$ will include either the points outside the circle or the points inside the circle, as well as the boundary. We decide which region to shade by substituting any test point not on the circle, such as (0, 0), into the original inequality. Since $0^2 + 0^2 \leq 36$ is a true statement, the original inequality includes the points inside the circle, the shaded region in Figure 30, and the boundary.

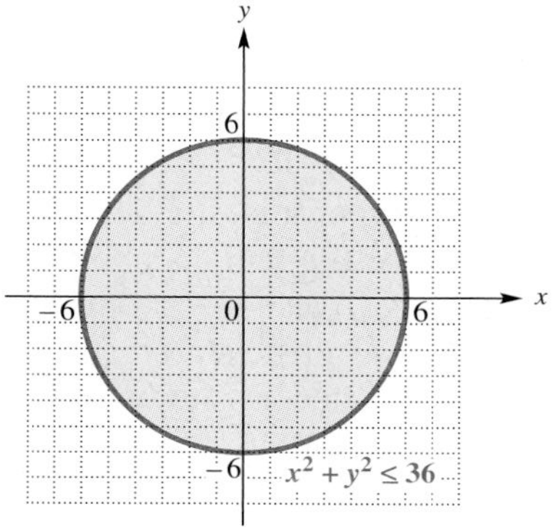

Figure 30

Example 1 Graphing a Second-Degree Inequality

Graph $y < -2(x - 4)^2 - 3$.

The boundary, $y = -2(x - 4)^2 - 3$, is a parabola that opens down with vertex at $(4, -3)$. Using (0, 0) as a test point gives

$$0 < -2(0 - 4)^2 - 3 \quad ?$$
$$0 < -32 - 3 \quad ?$$
$$0 < -35. \qquad \text{False}$$

Because the final inequality is a false statement, the points in the region containing (0, 0) do not satisfy the inequality. Figure 31 shows the final graph; the parabola is drawn as a dashed curve since the points of the parabola itself do not satisfy the inequality, and the region inside (or below) the parabola is shaded.

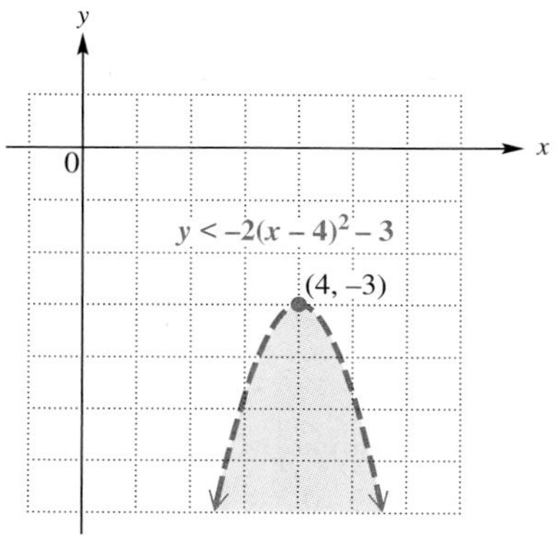

Figure 31

NOTE

Since the substitution is easy, the origin is the test point of choice unless the graph actually passes through (0, 0).

Work Problem 1 at the Side.

Example 2 Graphing a Second-Degree Inequality

Graph $16y^2 \leq 144 + 9x^2$.

First rewrite the inequality as follows.

$$16y^2 - 9x^2 \leq 144 \qquad \text{Subtract } 9x^2.$$

$$\frac{y^2}{9} - \frac{x^2}{16} \leq 1 \qquad \text{Divide by 144.}$$

This form shows that the boundary is the hyperbola given by

$$\frac{y^2}{9} - \frac{x^2}{16} = 1.$$

Since the graph is a vertical hyperbola, the desired region will be either the region between the branches or the regions above the top branch and below the bottom branch. Choose (0, 0) as a test point. Substituting into the original inequality leads to $0 \leq 144$, a true statement, so the region between the branches containing (0, 0) is shaded, as shown in Figure 32.

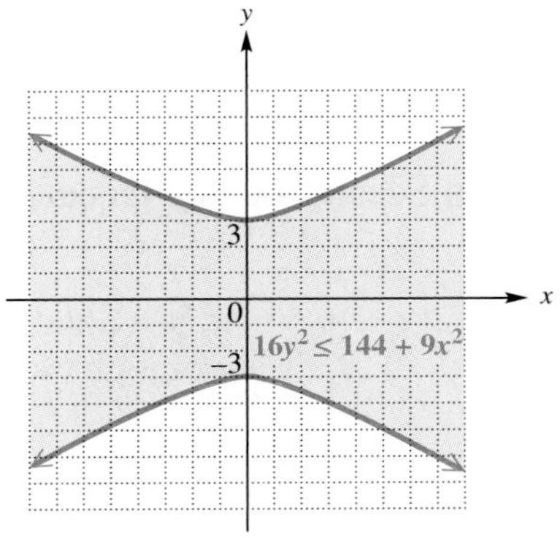

Figure 32

Work Problem 2 at the Side.

2 Graph the solution set of a system of inequalities. If two or more inequalities are considered at the same time, we have a **system of inequalities.** To find the solution set of the system, we find the intersection of the graphs (solution sets) of the inequalities in the system.

Example 3 Graphing a System of Two Inequalities

Graph the solution set of the system.

$$2x + 3y > 6$$
$$x^2 + y^2 < 16$$

Begin by graphing the solution set of $2x + 3y > 6$. The boundary line is the graph of $2x + 3y = 6$ and is a dashed line because of the symbol >. The test point (0, 0) leads to a false statement in the inequality $2x + 3y > 6$,

Continued on Next Page

1 Graph $y \geq (x + 1)^2 - 5$.

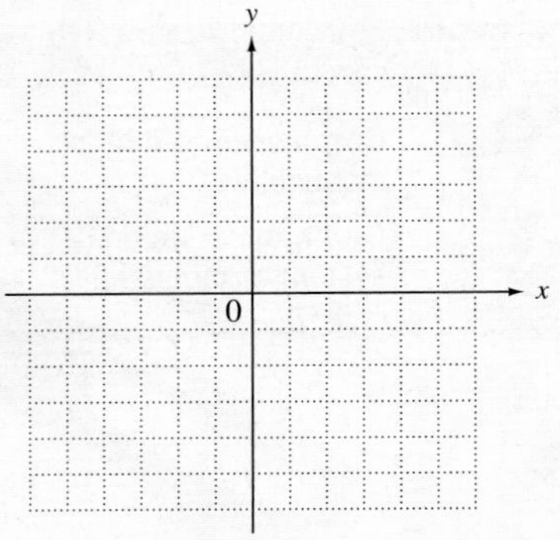

2 Graph $x^2 + 4y^2 > 36$.

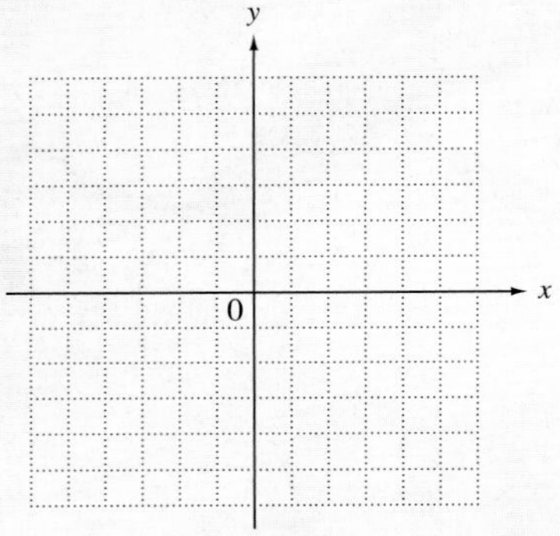

ANSWERS

1.

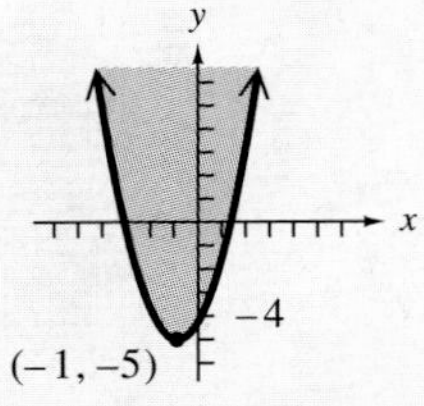

2.

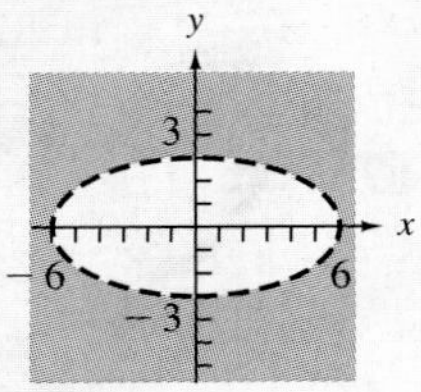

so shade the region above the line, as shown in Figure 33. The graph of $x^2 + y^2 < 16$ is the interior of a dashed circle centered at the origin with radius 4. This is shown in Figure 34.

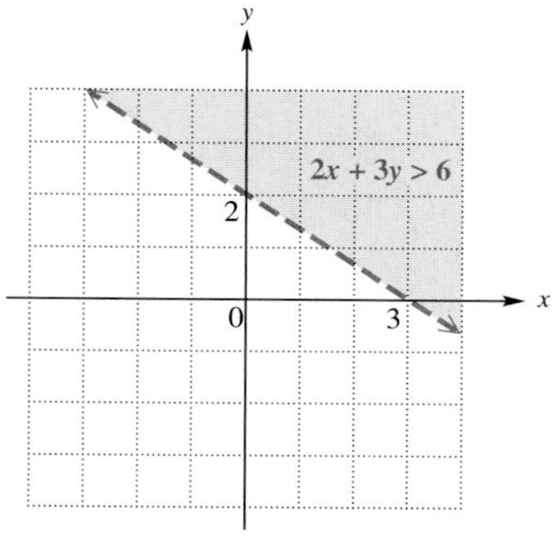

Figure 33

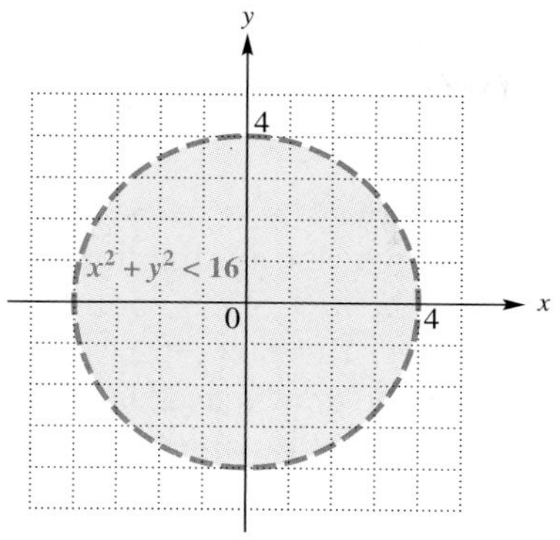

Figure 34

Finally, to get the graph of the solution set of the system, determine the intersection of the graphs of the two inequalities. The overlapping region in Figure 35 is the solution set.

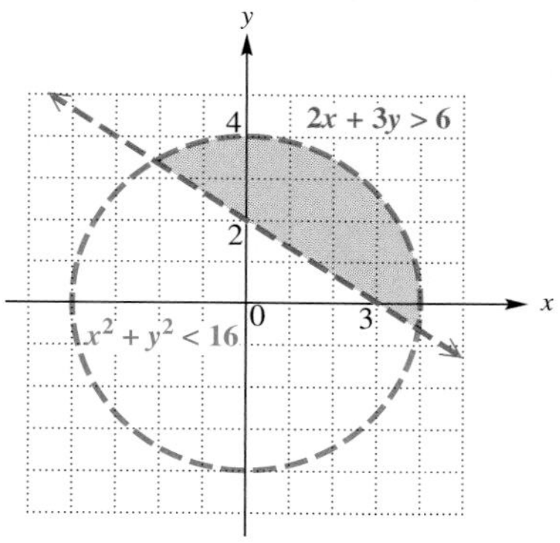

Figure 35

Work Problem 3 at the Side.

Example 4 Graphing a Linear System with Three Inequalities

Graph the solution set of the system.

$$x + y < 1$$
$$y \le 2x + 3$$
$$y \ge -2$$

Graph each inequality separately, on the same axes. The graph of $x + y < 1$ consists of all points below the dashed line $x + y = 1$. The graph of $y \le 2x + 3$ is the region that lies below the solid line $y = 2x + 3$. Finally, the graph of $y \ge -2$ is the region above the solid horizontal line $y = -2$. The graph of the system, the intersection of these three graphs, is the triangular region enclosed by the three boundary lines in Figure 36, including two of its boundaries.

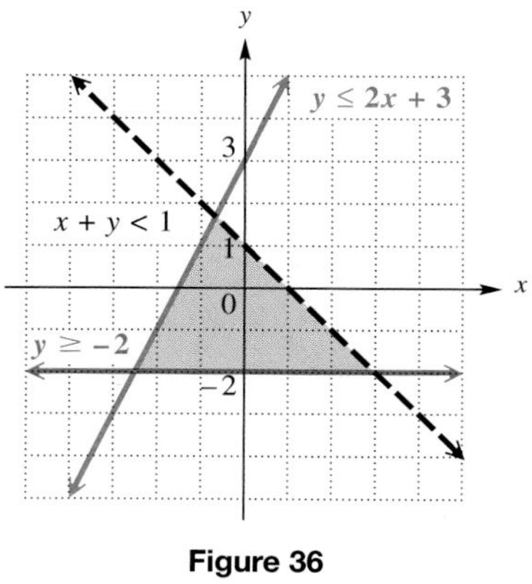

Figure 36

Work Problem 4 at the Side.

3 Graph the solution set of the system.

$$x^2 + y^2 \le 25$$
$$x + y \le 3$$

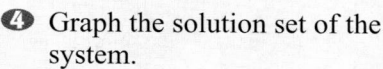

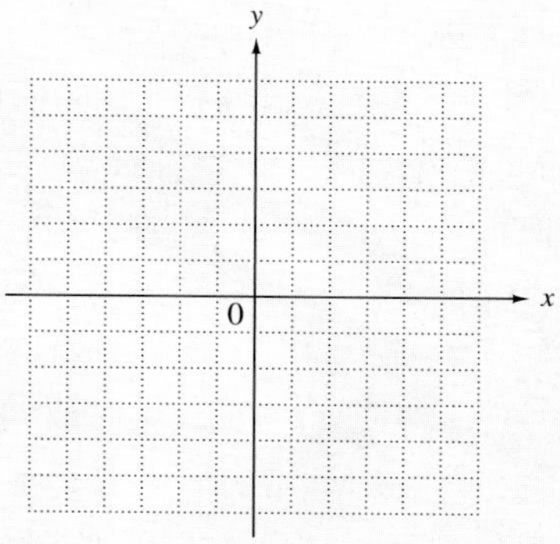

4 Graph the solution set of the system.

$$3x - 4y \ge 12$$
$$x + 3y \ge 6$$
$$y \le 2$$

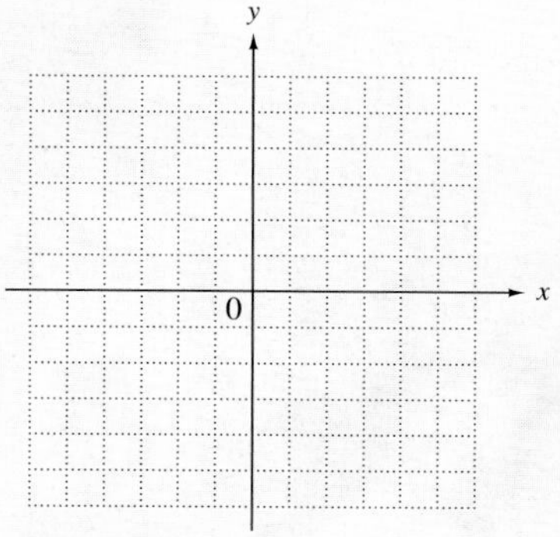

ANSWERS

3.

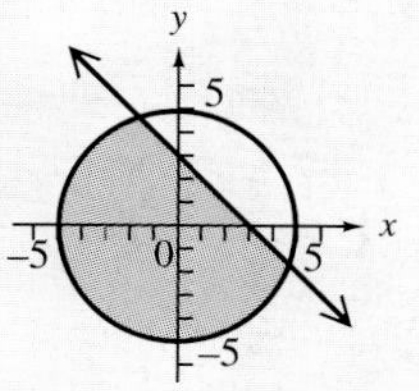

4.

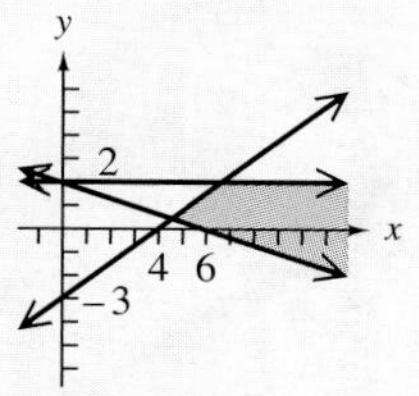

5 Graph the solution set of the system.

$$y \geq x^2 + 1$$
$$\frac{x^2}{9} + \frac{y^2}{4} \geq 1$$
$$y \leq 5$$

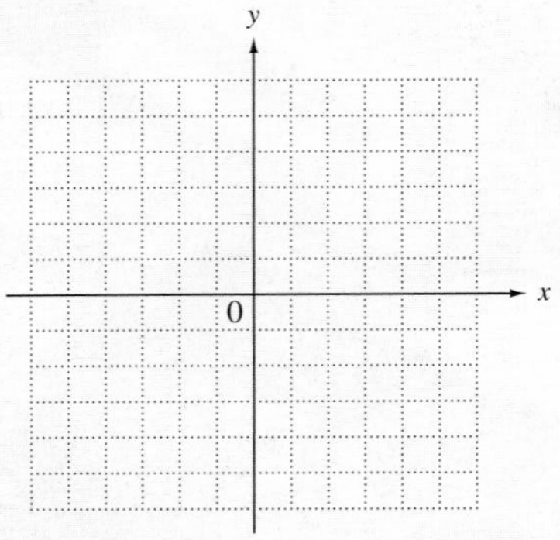

Example 5 Graphing a System with Three Inequalities

Graph the solution set of the system.

$$y \geq x^2 - 2x + 1$$
$$2x^2 + y^2 > 4$$
$$y < 4$$

The graph of $y = x^2 - 2x + 1$ is a parabola with vertex at (1, 0). Those points above (or in the interior of) the parabola satisfy the condition $y > x^2 - 2x + 1$. Thus, points on the parabola or in the interior are in the solution set of $y \geq x^2 - 2x + 1$. The graph of the equation $2x^2 + y^2 = 4$ is an ellipse. We draw it as a dashed curve. To satisfy the inequality $2x^2 + y^2 > 4$, a point must lie outside the ellipse. The graph of $y < 4$ includes all points below the dashed line $y = 4$. Finally, the graph of the system is the shaded region in Figure 37 that lies outside the ellipse, inside or on the boundary of the parabola, and below the line $y = 4$.

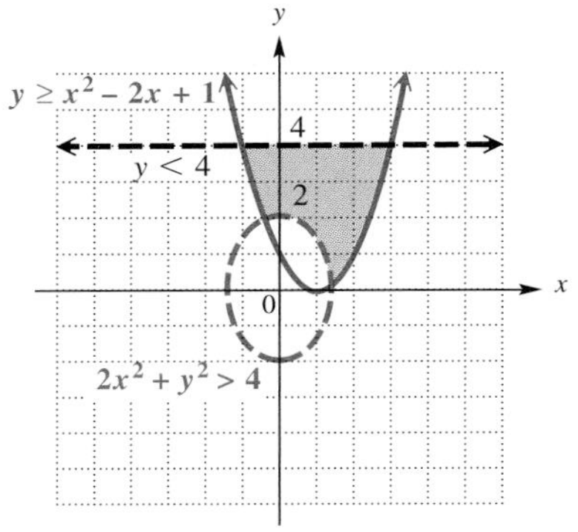

Figure 37

Work Problem 5 at the Side.

ANSWERS

5.

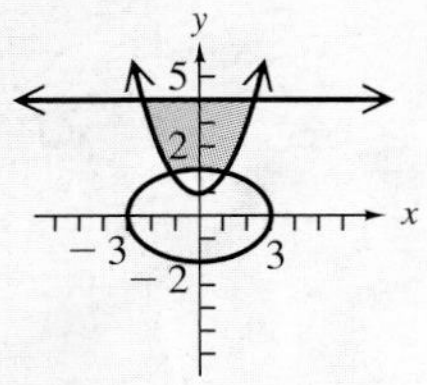

12.5 EXERCISES

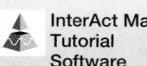

FOR EXTRA HELP: Student's Solutions Manual | MyMathLab.com | InterAct Math Tutorial Software | AW Math Tutor Center | MathXL www.mathxl.com | Digital Video Tutor CD 11 Videotape 25

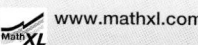

1. Which one of the following is a description of the graph of the solution set of this system?

$$x^2 + y^2 < 25$$
$$y > -2$$

A. All points outside the circle $x^2 + y^2 = 25$ and above the line $y = -2$

B. All points outside the circle $x^2 + y^2 = 25$ and below the line $y = -2$

C. All points inside the circle $x^2 + y^2 = 25$ and above the line $y = -2$

D. All points inside the circle $x^2 + y^2 = 25$ and below the line $y = -2$

C

2. Fill in each blank with the appropriate response. The graph of the system

$$y > x^2 + 1$$
$$\frac{x^2}{9} + \frac{y^2}{4} > 1$$
$$y < 5$$

consists of all points **above** (above/below) the parabola $y = x^2 + 1$, **outside** (inside/outside) the ellipse $\frac{x^2}{9} + \frac{y^2}{4} = 1$, and **below** (above/below) the line $y = 5$.

3. Explain how to graph the solution set of a nonlinear inequality.

Graph the corresponding equation as a solid curve if the inequality is ≤ or ≥, or as a dashed curve if the inequality is < or >. Use a test point to decide which side of the boundary satisfies the inequality, and shade it. The shaded region is the solution set.

4. Explain how to graph the solution set of a system of inequalities.

Graph each inequality separately, and determine the intersection of the shaded regions. This is the solution set of the system.

Graph each inequality. See Examples 1 and 2.

5. $y > x^2 - 1$

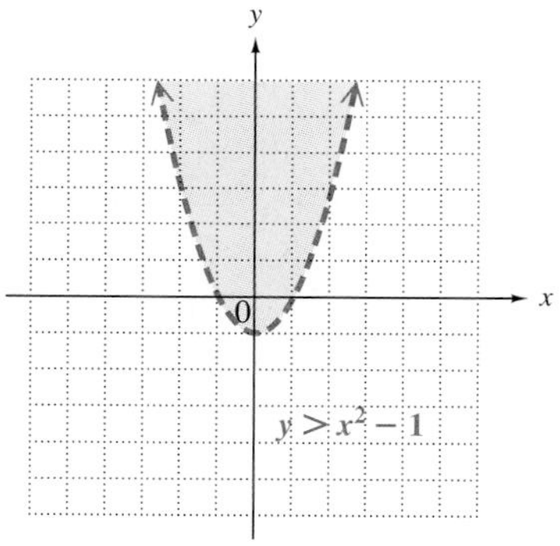

6. $y^2 > 4 + x^2$

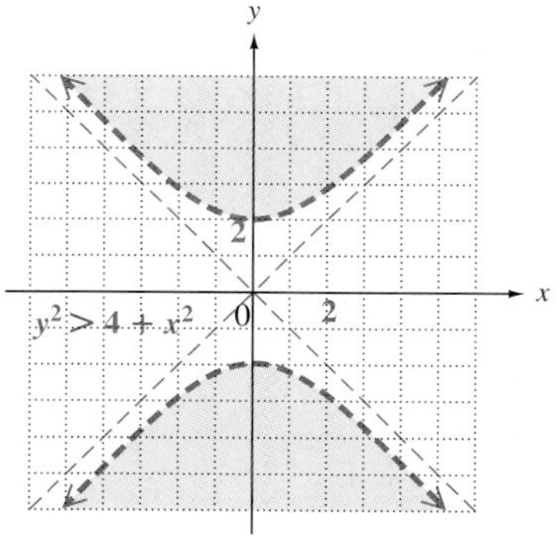

7. $y^2 \leq 4 - 2x^2$

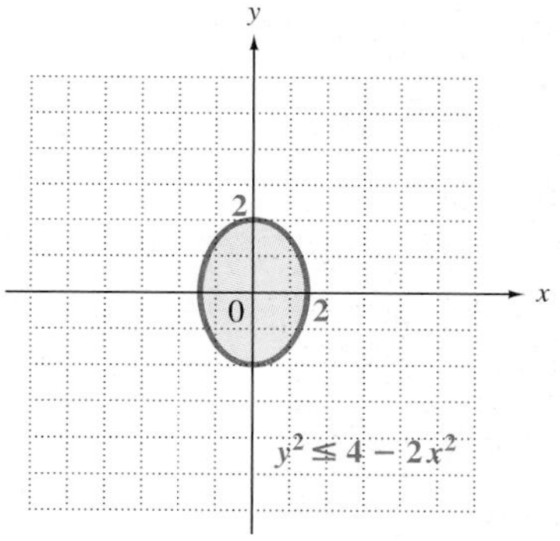

8. $y + 2 \geq x^2$

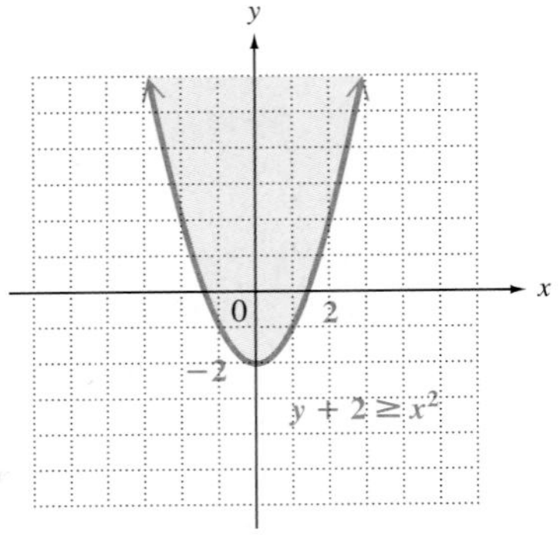

9. $x^2 \leq 16 - y^2$

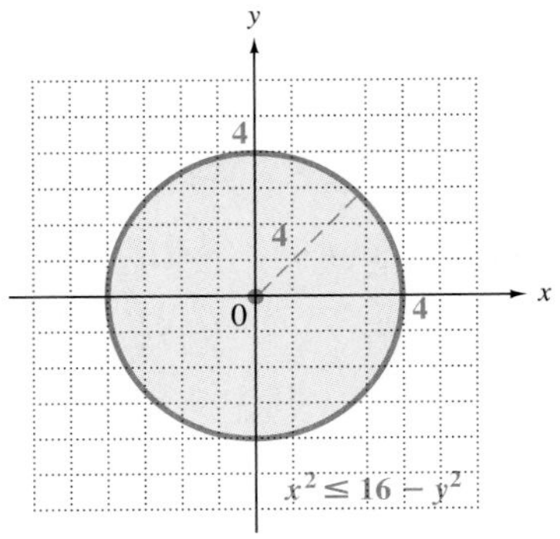

10. $2y^2 \geq 8 - x^2$

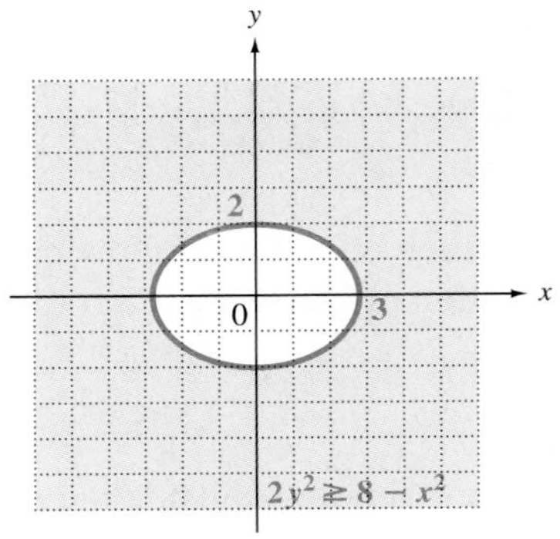

11. $x^2 \leq 16 + 4y^2$

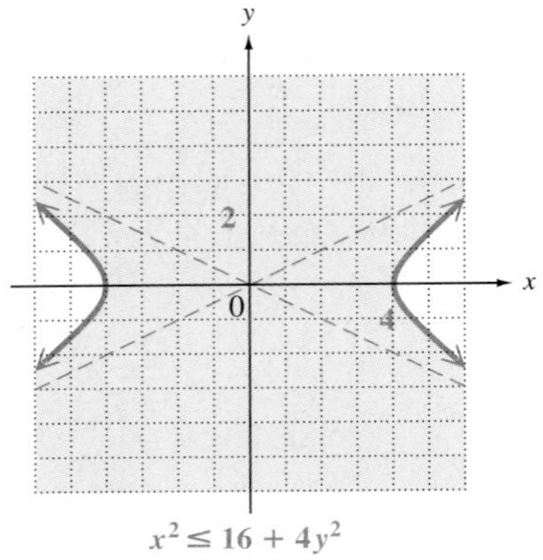

12. $y \leq x^2 + 4x + 2$

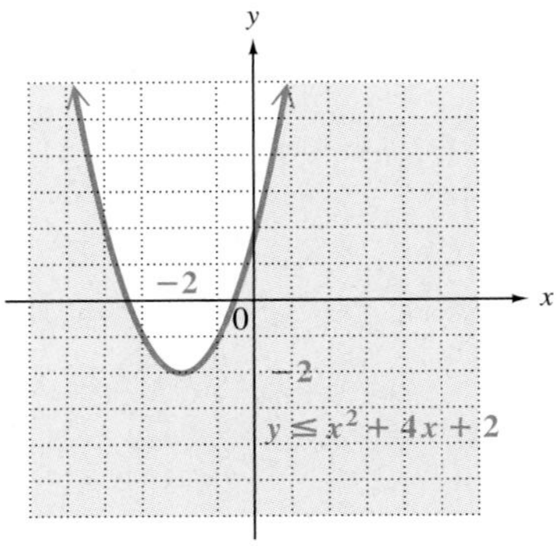

13. $9x^2 < 16y^2 - 144$

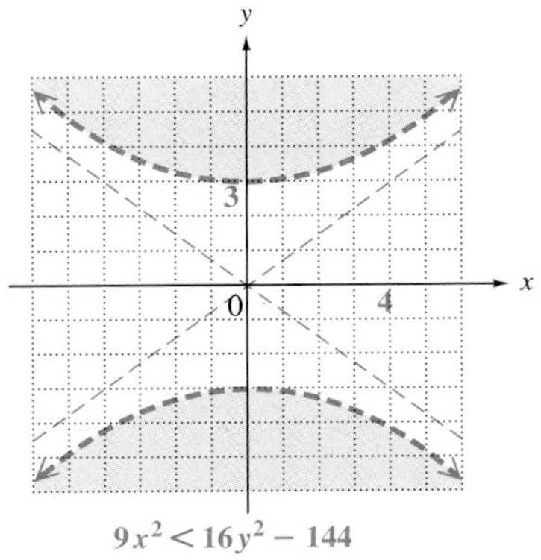

14. $9x^2 > 16y^2 + 144$

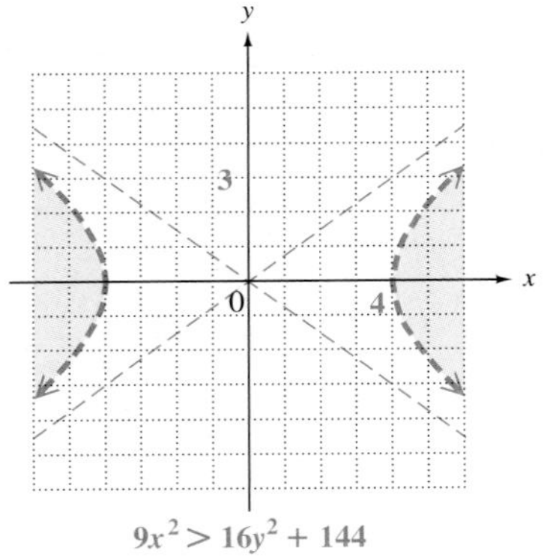

15. $4y^2 \leq 36 - 9x^2$

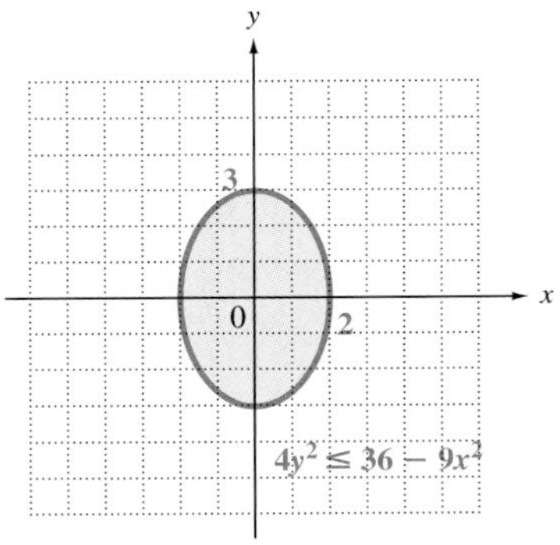

16. $x^2 - 4 \geq -4y^2$

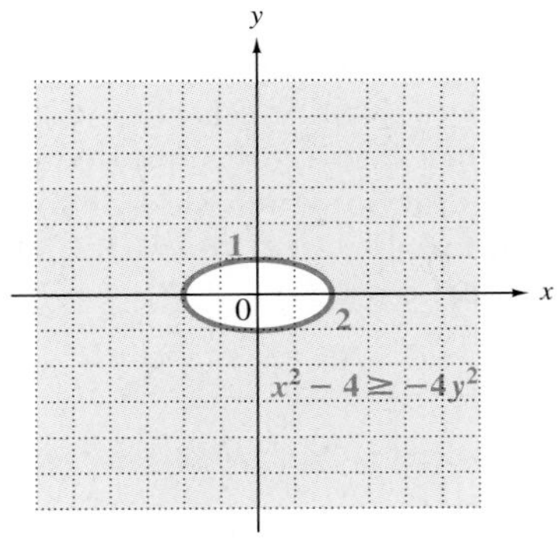

17. $x \geq y^2 - 8y + 14$

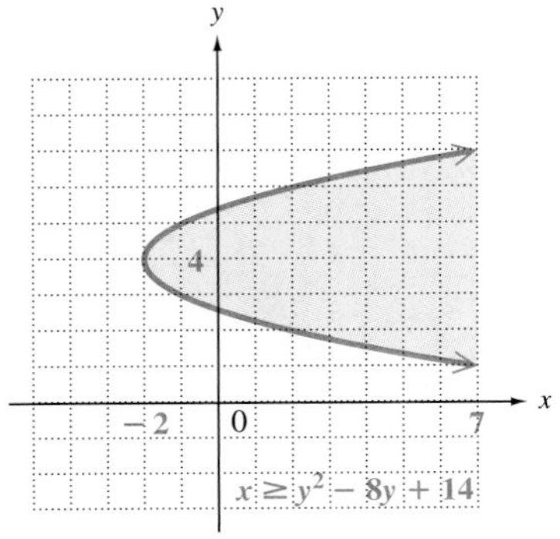

18. $x \leq -y^2 + 6y - 7$

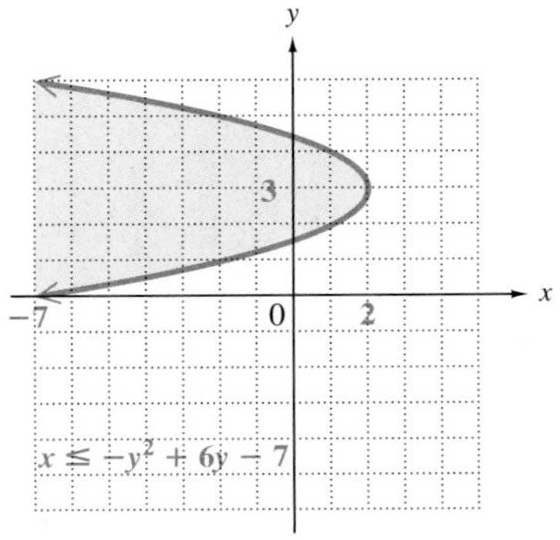

19. $25x^2 \leq 9y^2 + 225$

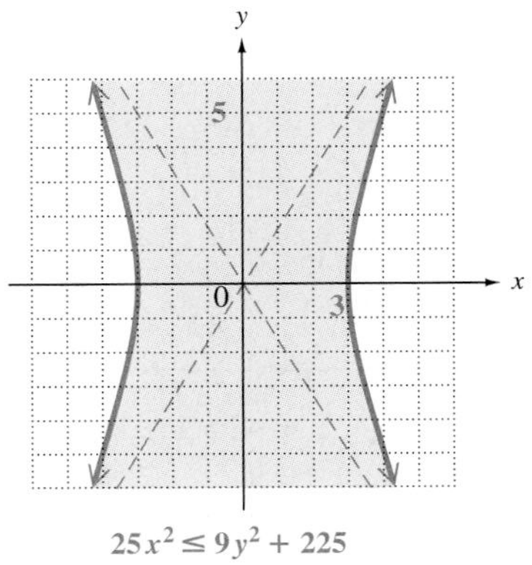

Graph each system of inequalities. See Examples 3–5.

20. $2x + 5y < 10$
$x - 2y < 4$

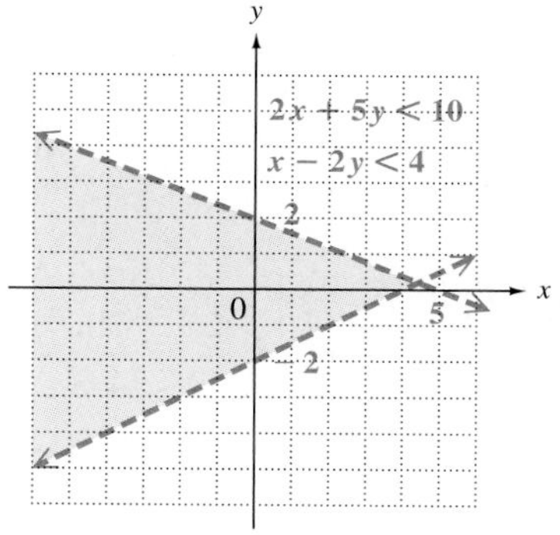

21. $3x - y > -6$
$4x + 3y > 12$

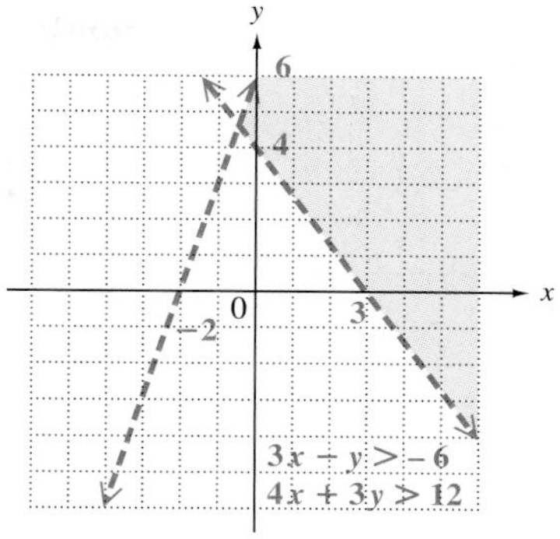

22. $5x - 3y \leq 15$
$4x + y \geq 4$

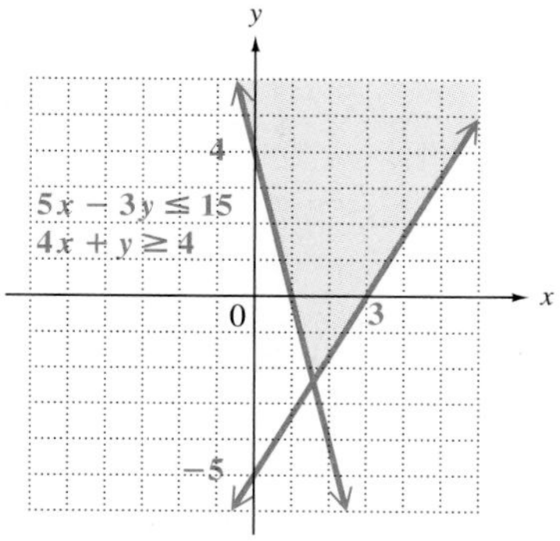

23. $4x - 3y \leq 0$
$x + y \leq 5$

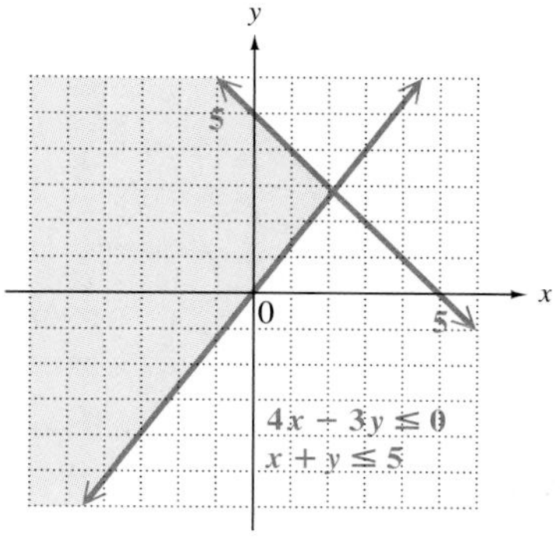

24. $x \leq 5$
$y \leq 4$

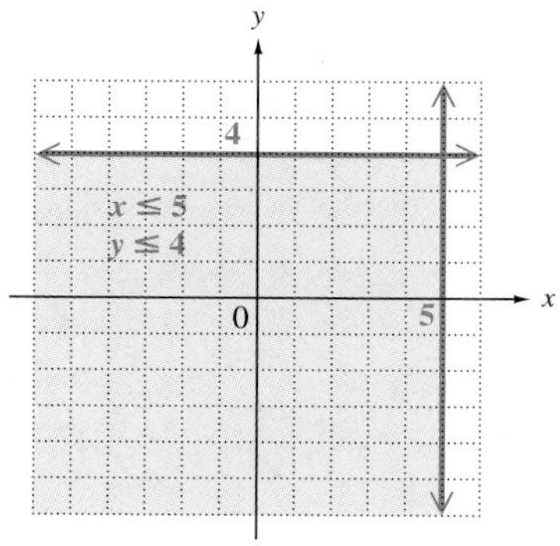

25. $x \geq -2$
$y \leq 4$

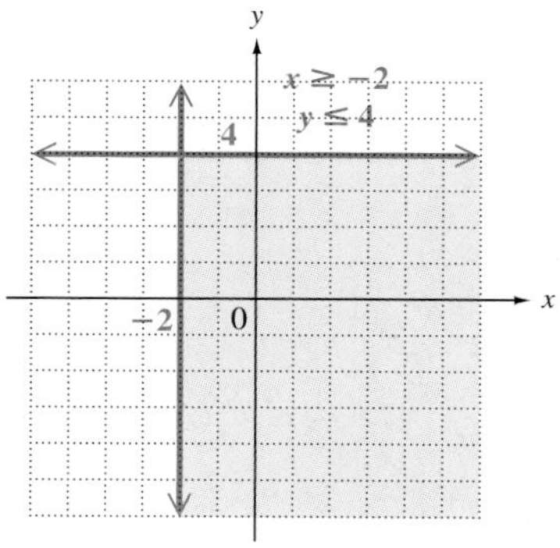

26. $y > x^2 - 4$
$y < -x^2 + 3$

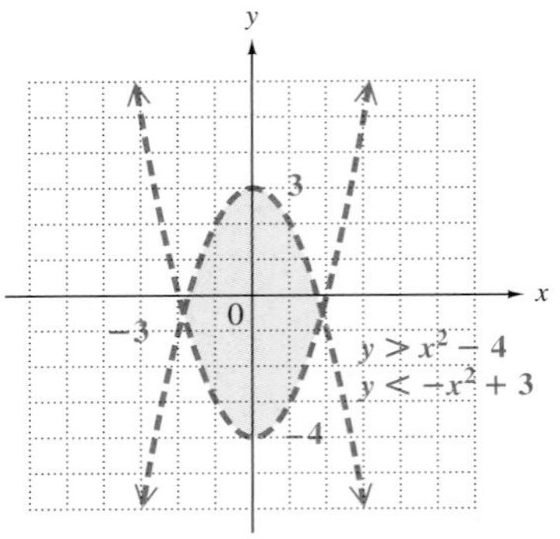

27. $x^2 - y^2 \geq 9$
$\frac{x^2}{16} + \frac{y^2}{9} \leq 1$

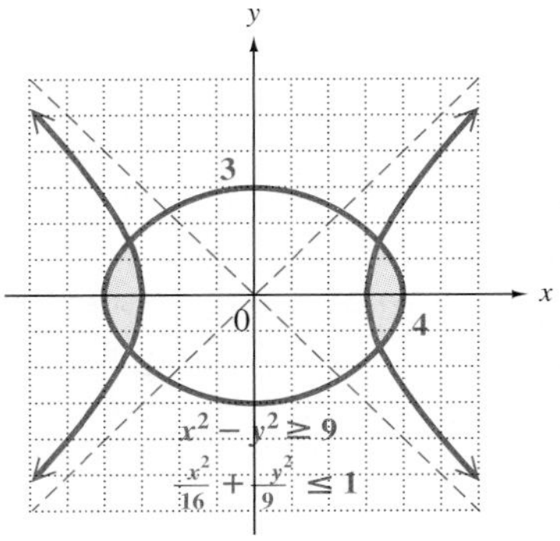

28. $y^2 - x^2 \geq 4$
$-5 \leq y \leq 5$

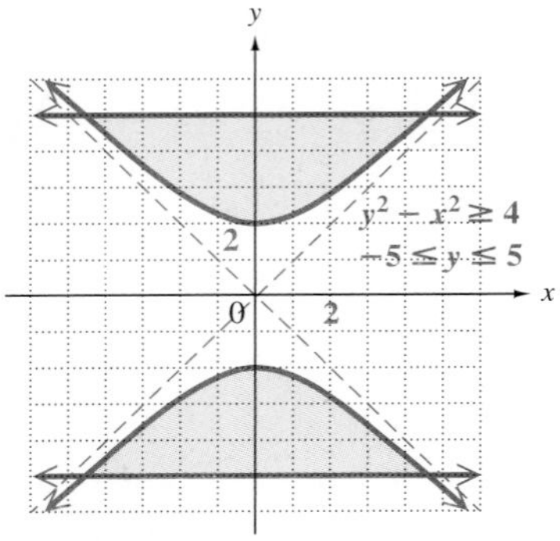

29. $x \geq 0$
$y \geq 0$
$x^2 + y^2 \geq 4$
$x + y \leq 5$

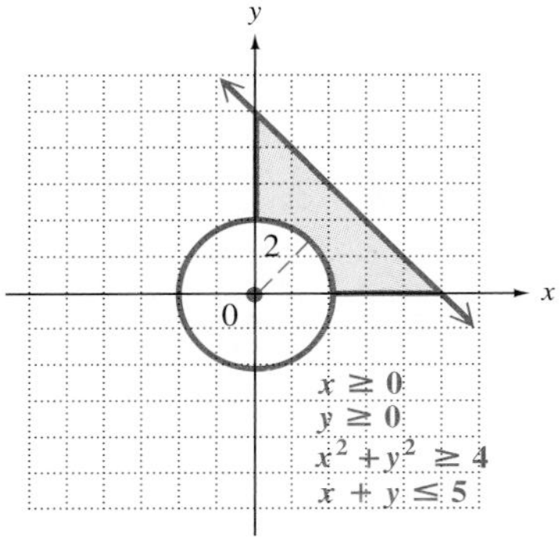

30. $y \leq -x^2$
$y \geq x - 3$
$y \leq -1$
$x < 1$

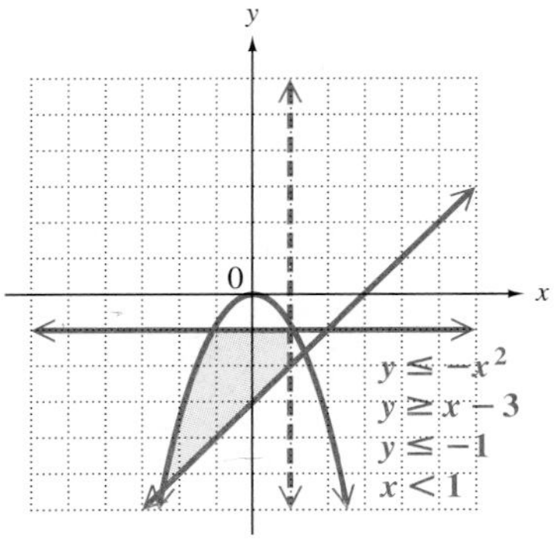

31. $y < x^2$
$y > -2$
$x + y < 3$
$3x - 2y > -6$

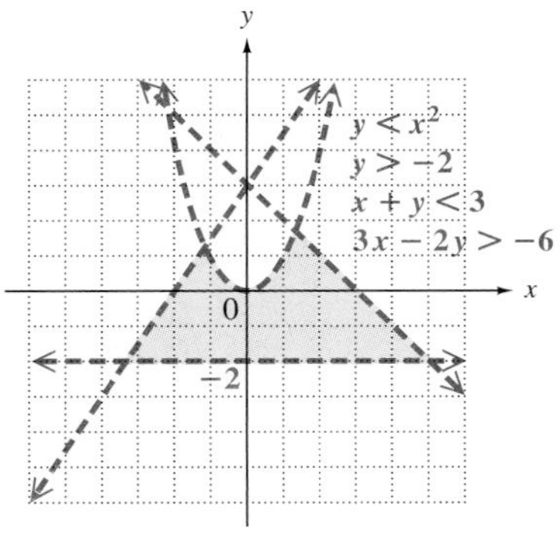

Chapter 12

SUMMARY

KEY TERMS

12.1	**asymptotes**	Lines that a graph approaches, such as the x- and y-axes for the graph of the reciprocal function, are called asymptotes of the graph.
	composition	If f and g are functions, then the composition of g and f is defined by $(g \circ f)(x) = g[f(x)]$ for all x in the domain of f such that $f(x)$ is in the domain of g.
12.2	**circle**	A circle is the set of all points in a plane that lie a fixed distance from a fixed point.
	center	The fixed point discussed in the definition of a circle is the center of the circle.
	radius	The radius of a circle is the fixed distance between the center and any point on the circle.

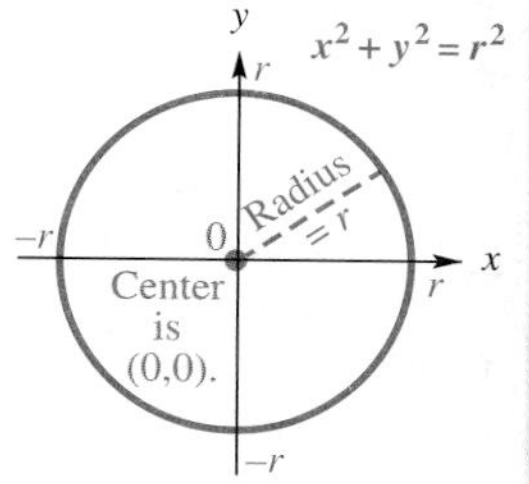

	ellipse	An ellipse is the set of all points in a plane the sum of whose distances from two fixed points is constant.

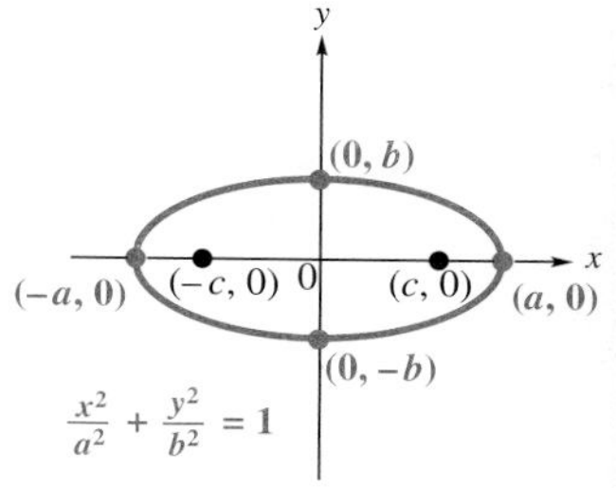

12.3	**hyperbola**	A hyperbola is the set of all points in a plane such that the absolute value of the difference of the distances from two fixed points is constant.
	asymptotes of a hyperbola	The two intersecting lines that the branches of a hyperbola approach are called asymptotes of the hyperbola.
	fundamental rectangle	The asymptotes of a hyperbola are the extended diagonals of its fundamental rectangle.
12.4	**nonlinear equation**	An equation in which some terms have more than one variable or a variable of degree 2 or greater is called a nonlinear equation.
	nonlinear system of equations	A nonlinear system of equations is a system with at least one nonlinear equation.
12.5	**second-degree inequality**	A second-degree inequality is an inequality with at least one variable of degree 2 and no variable with degree greater than 2.
	system of inequalities	A system of inequalities consists of two or more inequalities to be solved at the same time.

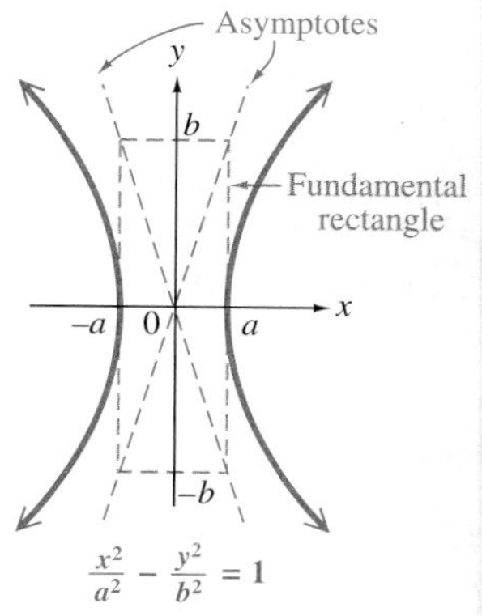

NEW SYMBOLS

$(f \circ g)(x) = f[g(x)]$ composite function

TEST YOUR WORD POWER

See how well you have learned the vocabulary in this chapter. Answers follow the Quick Review.

1. Conic sections are
- **(a)** graphs of first-degree equations
- **(b)** the result of two or more intersecting planes
- **(c)** graphs of first-degree inequalities
- **(d)** figures that result from the intersection of an infinite cone with a plane.

2. A **circle** is the set of all points in a plane
- **(a)** the difference of whose distances from two fixed points is constant
- **(b)** that lie a fixed distance from a fixed point
- **(c)** the sum of whose distances from two fixed points is constant
- **(d)** that make up the graph of any second-degree equation.

3. An **ellipse** is the set of all points in a plane
- **(a)** such that the absolute value of the difference of the distances from two fixed points is constant
- **(b)** that lie a fixed distance from a fixed point
- **(c)** the sum of whose distances from two fixed points is constant
- **(d)** that make up the graph of any second-degree equation.

4. A **hyperbola** is the set of all points in a plane
- **(a)** such that the absolute value of the difference of the distances from two fixed points is constant
- **(b)** that lie a fixed distance from a fixed point
- **(c)** the sum of whose distances from two fixed points is constant
- **(d)** that make up the graph of any second-degree equation.

5. A **nonlinear equation** is an equation
- **(a)** in which some terms have more than one variable or a variable of degree 2 or greater
- **(b)** in which the terms have only one variable
- **(c)** of degree 1
- **(d)** of a linear function.

6. A **nonlinear system of equations** is a system
- **(a)** with at least one linear equation
- **(b)** with two or more inequalities
- **(c)** with at least one nonlinear equation
- **(d)** with at least two linear equations.

QUICK REVIEW

Concepts	*Examples*

12.1 Additional Graphs of Functions; Operations and Composition

Other Functions

In addition to the squaring function, some other important elementary functions in algebra are the absolute value function, defined by $f(x) = |x|$; the reciprocal function, defined by $f(x) = \frac{1}{x}$; and the square root function, defined by $f(x) = \sqrt{x}$.

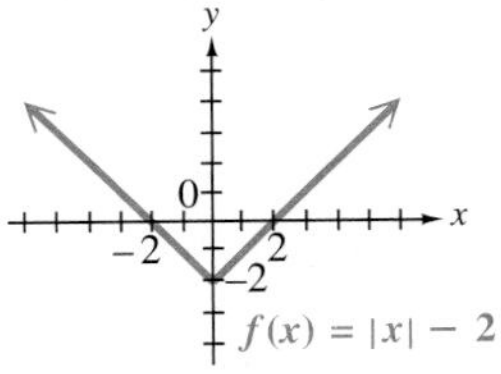

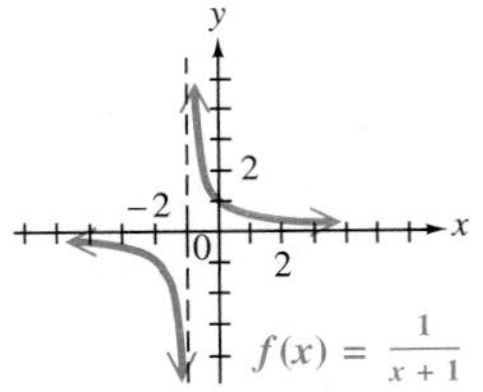

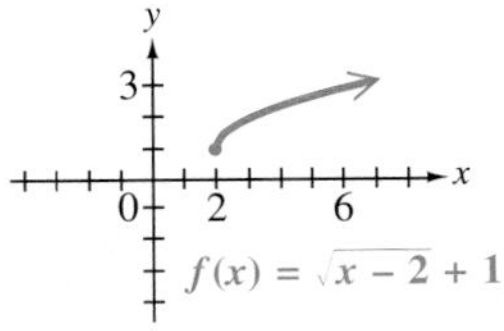

Operations on Functions

If $f(x)$ and $g(x)$ define functions, then

$$(f + g)(x) = f(x) + g(x),$$
$$(f - g)(x) = f(x) - g(x),$$
$$(fg)(x) = f(x) \cdot g(x),$$
$$\left(\frac{f}{g}\right)(x) = \frac{f(x)}{g(x)}, \quad g(x) \neq 0.$$

If $f(x) = x^2$ and $g(x) = 2x + 1$, then

$$(f + g)(x) = f(x) + g(x) = x^2 + 2x + 1,$$
$$(f - g)(x) = f(x) - g(x) = x^2 - 2x - 1,$$
$$(fg)(x) = f(x) \cdot g(x) = 2x^3 + x^2,$$
$$\left(\frac{f}{g}\right)(x) = \frac{f(x)}{g(x)} = \frac{x^2}{2x + 1}, \quad x \neq -\frac{1}{2}.$$

Composition of f and g

$$(f \circ g)(x) = f[g(x)]$$

If $f(x) = x^2$ and $g(x) = 2x + 1$, then

$$(f \circ g)(x) = f[g(x)]$$
$$= (2x + 1)^2 = 4x^2 + 4x + 1.$$

Concepts	*Examples*

12.2 The Circle and the Ellipse

Circle

The circle with radius r and center at (h, k) has an equation of the form

$$(x - h)^2 + (y - k)^2 = r^2.$$

The circle with equation $(x + 2)^2 + (y - 3)^2 = 25$ has center $(-2, 3)$ and radius 5.

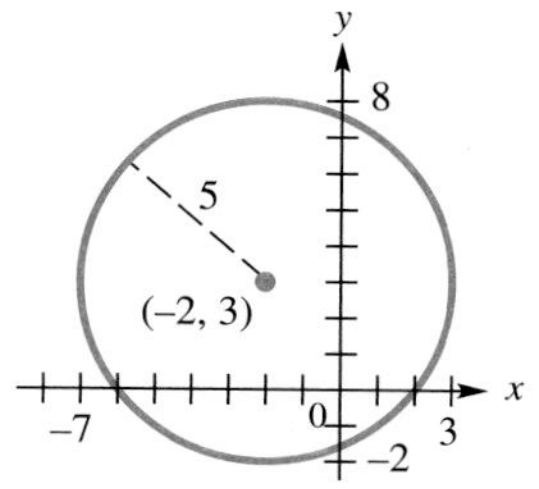

Ellipse

The ellipse whose x-intercepts are $(a, 0)$ and $(-a, 0)$ and whose y-intercepts are $(0, b)$ and $(0, -b)$ has an equation of the form

$$\frac{x^2}{a^2} + \frac{y^2}{b^2} = 1.$$

Graph $\dfrac{x^2}{9} + \dfrac{y^2}{4} = 1.$

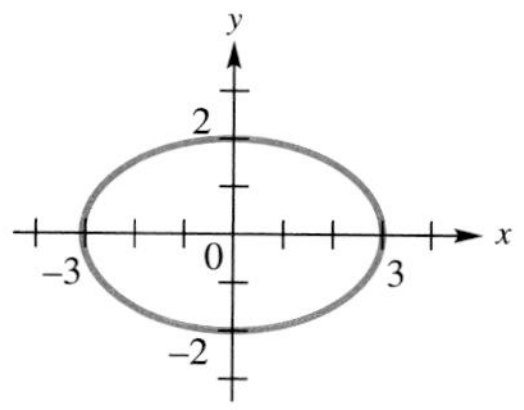

12.3 The Hyperbola and Other Functions Defined by Radicals

Hyperbola

A hyperbola with x-intercepts $(a, 0)$ and $(-a, 0)$ has an equation of the form

$$\frac{x^2}{a^2} - \frac{y^2}{b^2} = 1,$$

and a hyperbola with y-intercepts $(0, b)$ and $(0, -b)$ has an equation of the form

$$\frac{y^2}{b^2} - \frac{x^2}{a^2} = 1.$$

Graph $\dfrac{x^2}{4} - \dfrac{y^2}{4} = 1.$

The graph has x-intercepts $(2, 0)$ and $(-2, 0)$.

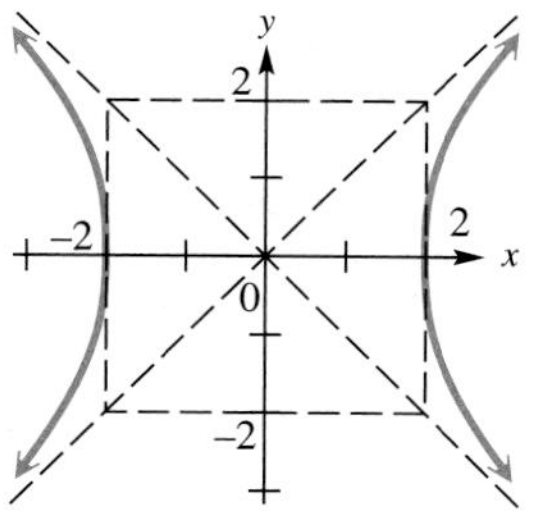

The extended diagonals of the fundamental rectangle with corners at the points (a, b), $(-a, b)$, $(-a, -b)$, and $(a, -b)$ are the asymptotes of these hyperbolas.

The fundamental rectangle has corners at $(2, 2)$, $(-2, 2)$, $(-2, -2)$, and $(2, -2)$.

Graphing a Square Root Function

To graph a square root function, square both sides so that the equation can be easily recognized. Then graph only the part indicated by the original equation.

Graph $y = -\sqrt{4 - x^2}$.

Square both sides and rearrange terms to get

$$x^2 + y^2 = 4.$$

This equation has a circle as its graph. However, graph only the lower half of the circle, since the original equation indicates that y cannot be positive.

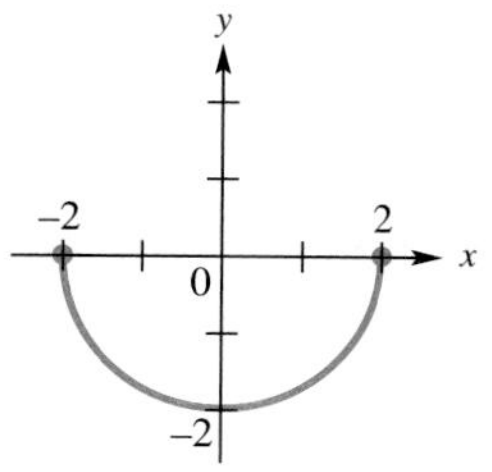

Concepts	*Examples*

12.4 Nonlinear Systems of Equations

Solving a Nonlinear System

A nonlinear system can be solved by the substitution method, the elimination method, or a combination of the two.

Solve the system.

$$x^2 + 2xy - y^2 = 14 \quad (1)$$
$$x^2 - y^2 = -16 \quad (2)$$

Multiply equation (2) by -1 and use elimination.

$$\begin{aligned} x^2 + 2xy - y^2 &= 14 \\ -x^2 \qquad + y^2 &= 16 \\ \hline 2xy \qquad &= 30 \\ xy &= 15 \end{aligned}$$

Solve for y to obtain $y = \frac{15}{x}$, and substitute into equation (2).

$$x^2 - \left(\frac{15}{x}\right)^2 = -16$$

$$x^2 - \frac{225}{x^2} = -16$$

$$x^4 + 16x^2 - 225 = 0 \qquad \text{Multiply by } x^2\text{; add } 16x^2.$$

$$(x^2 - 9)(x^2 + 25) = 0 \qquad \text{Factor.}$$

$$x = \pm 3 \quad \text{or} \quad x = \pm 5i \qquad \text{Zero-factor property}$$

Find corresponding y-values to get the solution set

$$\{(3, 5), (-3, -5), (5i, -3i), (-5i, 3i)\}.$$

12.5 Second-Degree Inequalities and Systems of Inequalities

Graphing a Second-Degree Inequality

To graph a second-degree inequality, graph the corresponding equation as a boundary and use test points to determine which region(s) form the solution set. Shade the appropriate region(s).

Graphing a System of Inequalities

The solution set of a system of inequalities is the intersection of the solution sets of the individual inequalities.

Graph $y \geq x^2 - 2x + 3$.

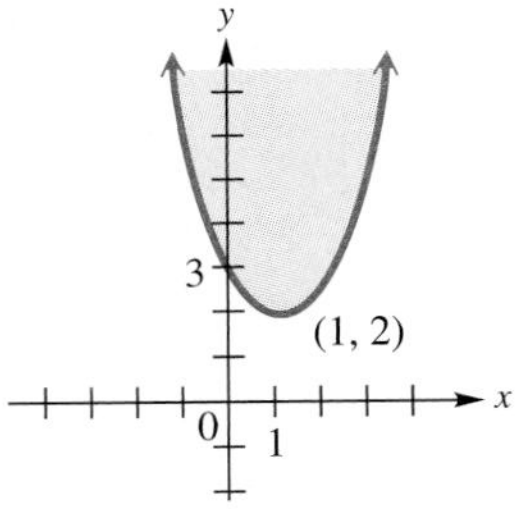

Graph the solution set of the system.

$$3x - 5y > -15$$
$$x^2 + y^2 \leq 25$$

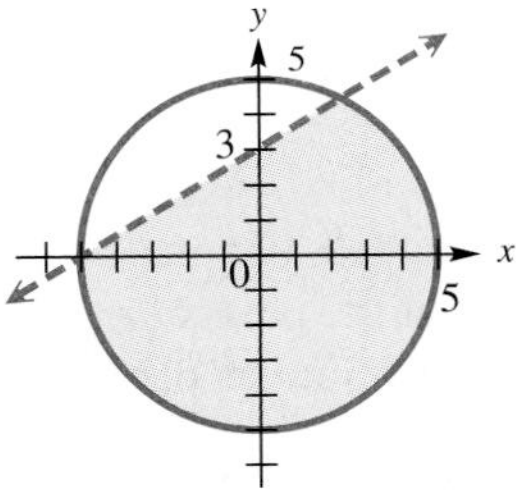

ANSWERS TO TEST YOUR WORD POWER

1. (d) *Example:* Parabolas, circles, ellipses, and hyperbolas are conic sections. **2. (b)** *Example:* See the graph of $x^2 + y^2 = 9$ in Figure 10 of Section 12.2. **3. (c)** *Example:* See the graph of $\frac{x^2}{49} + \frac{y^2}{36} = 1$ in Figure 15 of Section 12.2. **4. (a)** *Example:* See the graph of $\frac{x^2}{16} - \frac{y^2}{12} = 1$ in Figure 18 of Section 12.3. **5. (a)** *Examples:* $y = x^2 + 8x + 16$, $xy = 5$, $2x^2 - y^2 = 6$ **6. (c)** *Example:* $x^2 + y^2 = 2$
$2x + y = 1$

Chapter 12 Review Exercises

[12.1] *Graph each function.*

1. $f(x) = |x + 4|$

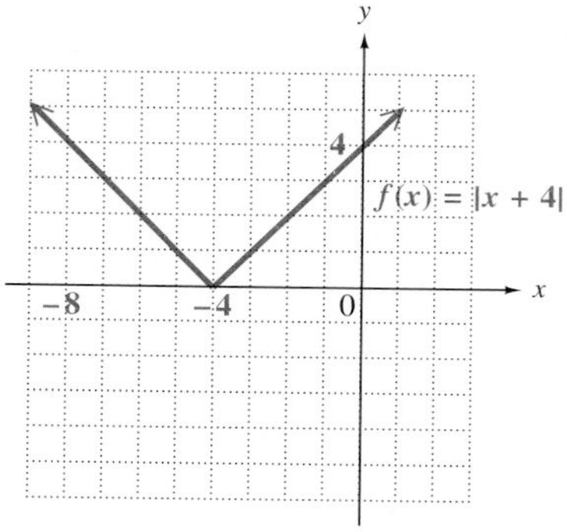

2. $f(x) = \dfrac{1}{x - 4}$

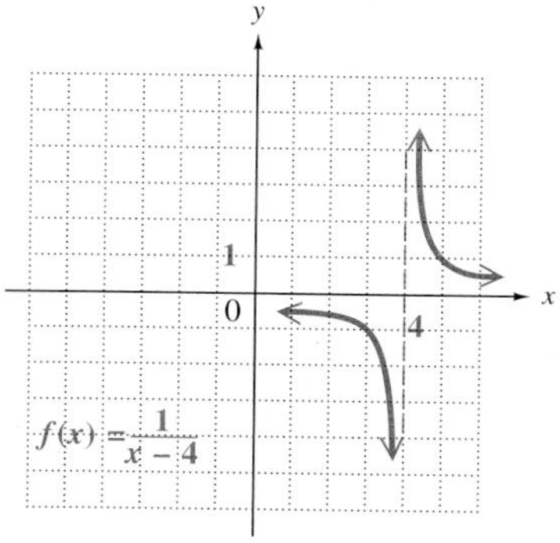

3. $f(x) = \sqrt{x} + 3$

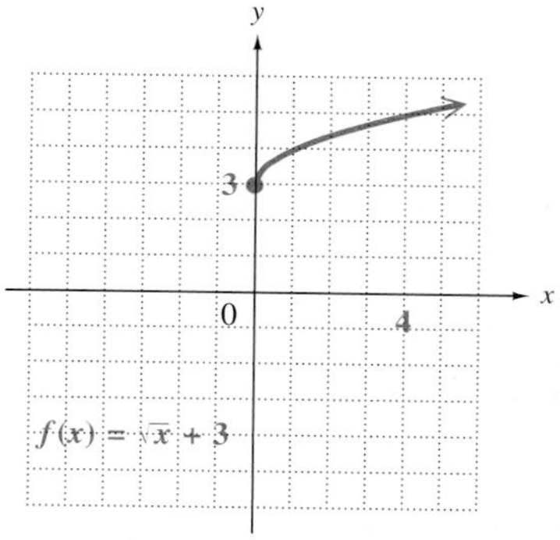

Let $f(x) = 3x^2 + 2x - 1$ *and* $g(x) = 5x + 7$. *Find each of the following.*

4. $(f + g)(x)$

$3x^2 + 7x + 6$

5. $(f - g)(-1)$

-2

6. $(f \circ g)(-2)$

20

7. $(g \circ f)(-2)$

42

8. $(f \circ g)(x)$

$75x^2 + 220x + 160$

9. $(g \circ f)(x)$

$15x^2 + 10x + 2$

10. Based on your answers to Exercises 6–9, discuss whether composition of functions is a commutative operation.

No, composition of functions is not a commutative operation. For example, the results of Exercises 8 and 9 show that $(f \circ g)(x) \neq (g \circ f)(x)$ in this case.

[12.2] *Write an equation for each circle.*

11. Center $(-2, 4)$, $r = 3$

$(x + 2)^2 + (y - 4)^2 = 9$

12. Center $(-1, -3)$, $r = 5$

$(x + 1)^2 + (y + 3)^2 = 25$

13. Center $(4, 2)$, $r = 6$

$(x - 4)^2 + (y - 2)^2 = 36$

Find the center and radius of each circle.

14. $x^2 + y^2 + 6x - 4y - 3 = 0$

$(-3, 2), r = 4$

15. $x^2 + y^2 - 8x - 2y + 13 = 0$

$(4, 1), r = 2$

16. $2x^2 + 2y^2 + 4x + 20y = -34$

$(-1, -5), r = 3$

17. $4x^2 + 4y^2 - 24x + 16y = 48$

$(3, -2), r = 5$

Graph each equation.

18. $x^2 + y^2 = 16$

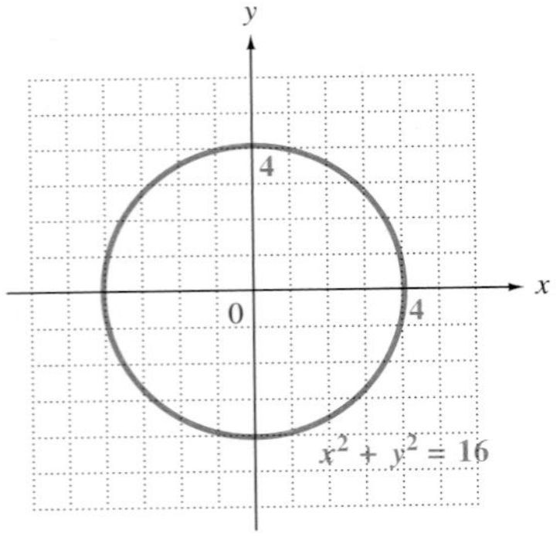

19. $\dfrac{x^2}{16} + \dfrac{y^2}{9} = 1$

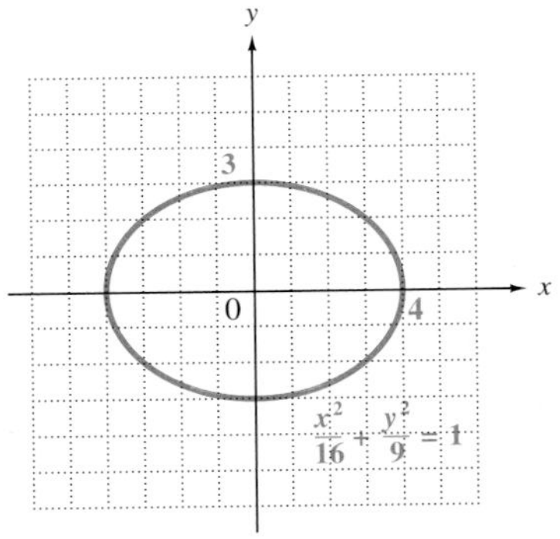

20. $\dfrac{x^2}{49} + \dfrac{y^2}{25} = 1$

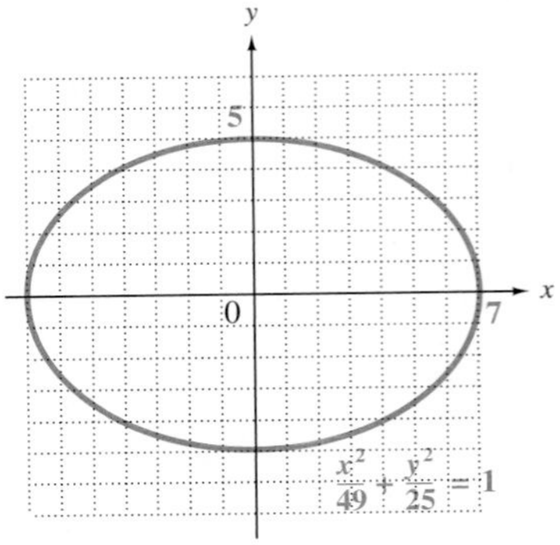

21. A satellite is in an elliptical orbit around Earth with perigee altitude of 160 km and apogee altitude of 16,000 km. See the figure. (*Source:* Kastner, Bernice, *Space Mathematics,* NASA, 1985.) Find the equation of the ellipse.

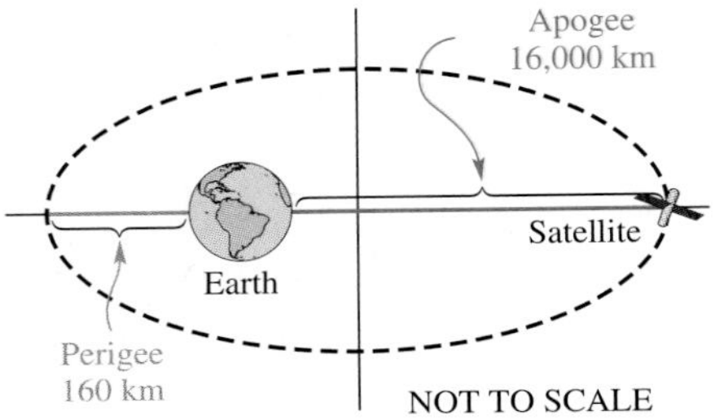

$$\frac{x^2}{65{,}286{,}400} + \frac{y^2}{2{,}560{,}000} = 1$$

22. This figure illustrates how the crawfish race is conducted at the Crawfish Festival in Breaux Bridge, Louisiana. Explain why a circular "racetrack" is appropriate for such a race.

A circular racetrack is most appropriate because the crawfish can move in any direction. Distance from the center determines the winner.

[12.3] *Graph each equation.*

23. $\dfrac{x^2}{16} - \dfrac{y^2}{25} = 1$

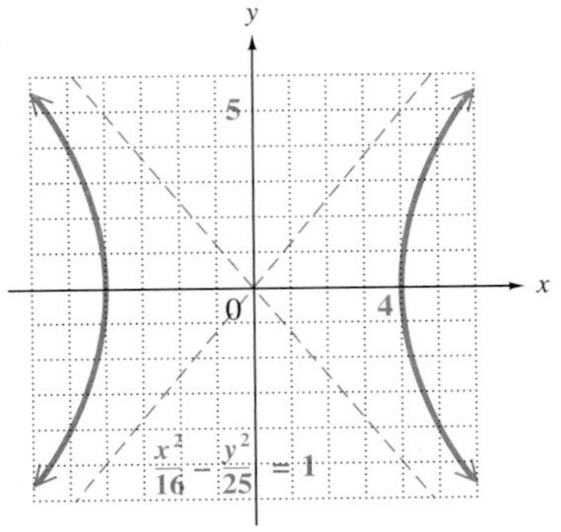

24. $\dfrac{y^2}{25} - \dfrac{x^2}{4} = 1$

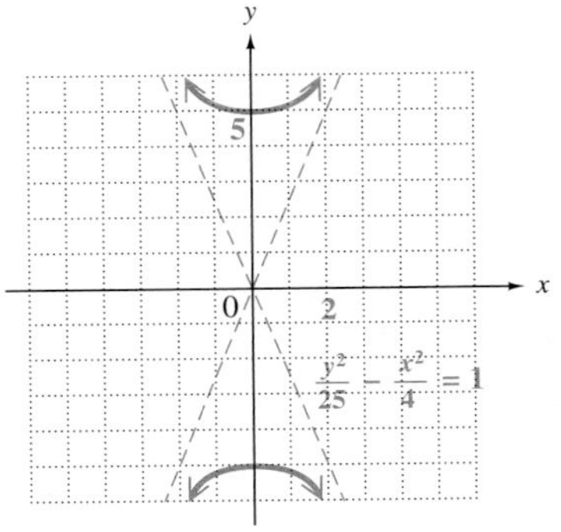

25. $f(x) = -\sqrt{16 - x^2}$

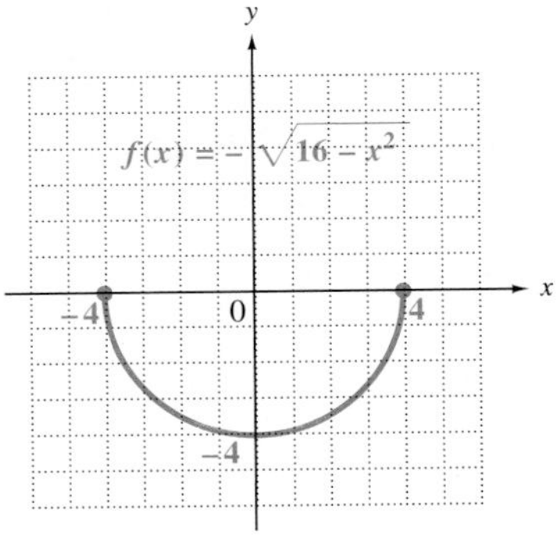

Identify the graph of each equation as a parabola, circle, ellipse, *or* hyperbola.

26. $x^2 + y^2 = 64$
circle

27. $y = 2x^2 - 3$
parabola

28. $y^2 = 2x^2 - 8$
hyperbola

29. $y^2 = 8 - 2x^2$
ellipse

30. $x = y^2 + 4$
parabola

31. $x^2 - y^2 = 64$
hyperbola

32. Ships and planes often use a location-finding system called LORAN. With this system, a radio transmitter at M sends out a series of pulses. (See the figure.) When each pulse is received at transmitter S, it then sends out a pulse. A ship at P receives pulses from both M and S. A receiver on the ship measures the difference in the arrival times of the pulses. A special map gives hyperbolas that correspond to the differences in arrival times (which give the distances d_1 and d_2 in the figure). The ship can then be located as lying on a branch of a particular hyperbola. Suppose $d_1 = 80$ mi and $d_2 = 30$ mi, and the distance between transmitters M and S is 100 mi. Use the definition to find an equation of the hyperbola the ship is located on.

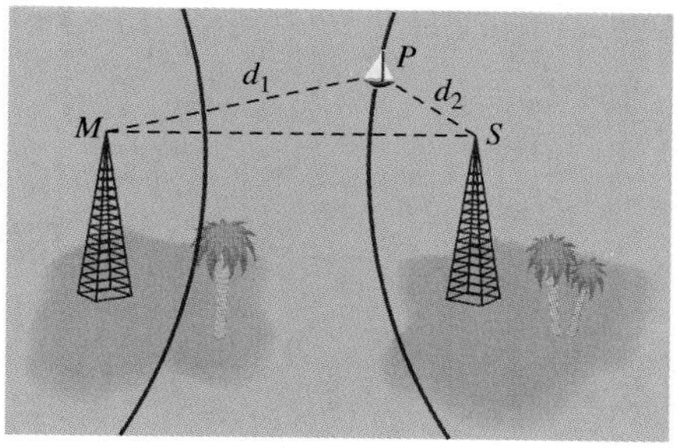

$\dfrac{x^2}{625} - \dfrac{y^2}{1875} = 1$

[12.4] *Solve each system.*

33. $2y = 3x - x^2$
$x + 2y = -12$

$\{(6, -9), (-2, -5)\}$

34. $y + 1 = x^2 + 2x$
$y + 2x = 4$

$\{(1, 2), (-5, 14)\}$

35. $x^2 + 3y^2 = 28$
$y - x = -2$

$\{(4, 2), (-1, -3)\}$

36. $xy = 8$
$x - 2y = 6$

$\{(-2, -4), (8, 1)\}$

37. $x^2 + y^2 = 6$
$x^2 - 2y^2 = -6$

$\{(-\sqrt{2}, 2), (-\sqrt{2}, -2), (\sqrt{2}, -2), (\sqrt{2}, 2)\}$

38. $3x^2 - 2y^2 = 12$
$x^2 + 4y^2 = 18$

$\{(-\sqrt{6}, -\sqrt{3}), (-\sqrt{6}, \sqrt{3}), (\sqrt{6}, -\sqrt{3}), (\sqrt{6}, \sqrt{3})\}$

39. How many solutions are possible for a system of two equations whose graphs are a circle and a line?

0, 1, or 2

40. How many solutions are possible for a system of two equations whose graphs are a parabola and a hyperbola?

0, 1, 2, 3, or 4

[12.5] *Graph each inequality.*

41. $9x^2 \geq 16y^2 + 144$

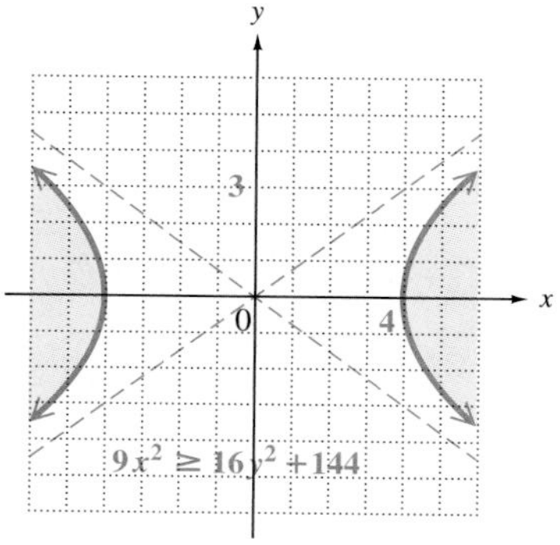

42. $4x^2 + y^2 \geq 16$

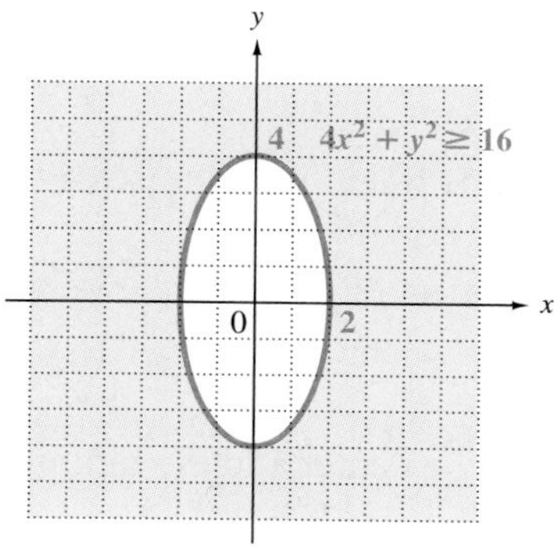

43. $y < -(x + 2)^2 + 1$

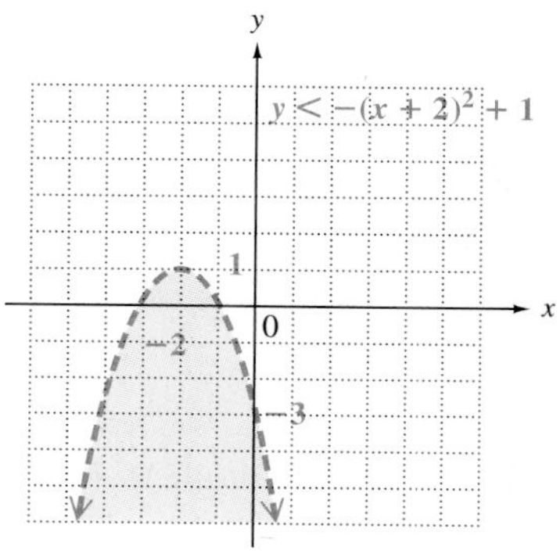

Graph each system of inequalities.

44. $2x + 5y \le 10$
$3x - y \le 6$

45. $|x| \le 2$
$|y| > 1$
$4x^2 + 9y^2 \le 36$

46. $9x^2 \le 4y^2 + 36$
$x^2 + y^2 \le 16$

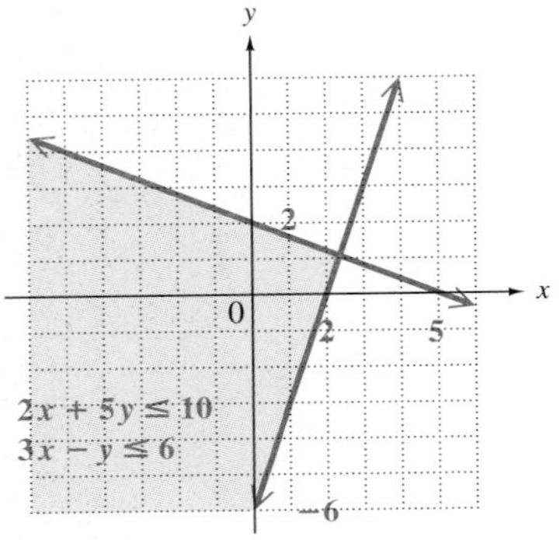

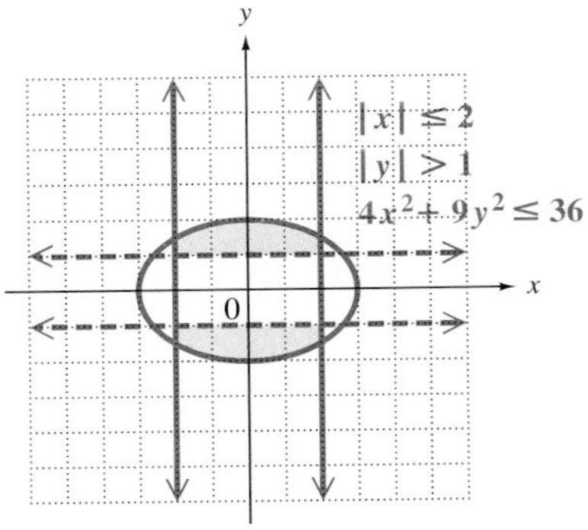

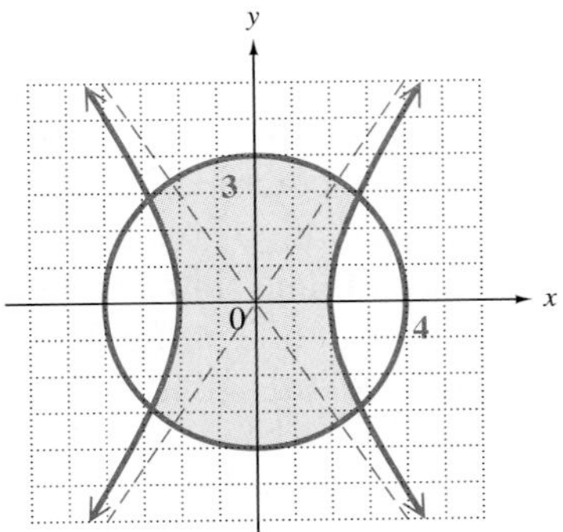

Relating Concepts (Exercises 47–51) For Individual or Group Work

In Chapter 5 we discussed several methods of solving systems of linear equations in three variables. Now these methods can be used to find an equation of a circle through three points in a plane that are not on the same line. The equation of a circle can be written in the form $x^2 + y^2 + ax + by + c = 0$ for some values of a, b, and c. ***Work Exercises 47–51 in order,*** *to find the equation of the circle through the points* (2, 4), (5, 1), *and* (−1, 1).

47. Determine one equation in a, b, and c by letting $x = 2$ and $y = 4$ in the general form given above. Write it with a, b, and c on the left and the constant on the right.

$2a + 4b + c = -20$

48. Repeat Exercise 47 for the point (5, 1).

$5a + b + c = -26$

49. Repeat Exercise 47 for the point (−1, 1).

$-a + b + c = -2$

50. Solve the system formed by the equations found in Exercises 47–49, and give the equation of the circle that satisfies these conditions.

$\{(-4, -2, -4)\}$; $x^2 + y^2 - 4x - 2y - 4 = 0$

51. Use the methods of this chapter to find the center and the radius of the circle in Exercise 50.

center: (2, 1); radius: 3

MIXED REVIEW EXERCISES

Graph.

52. $\dfrac{x^2}{64} + \dfrac{y^2}{25} = 1$

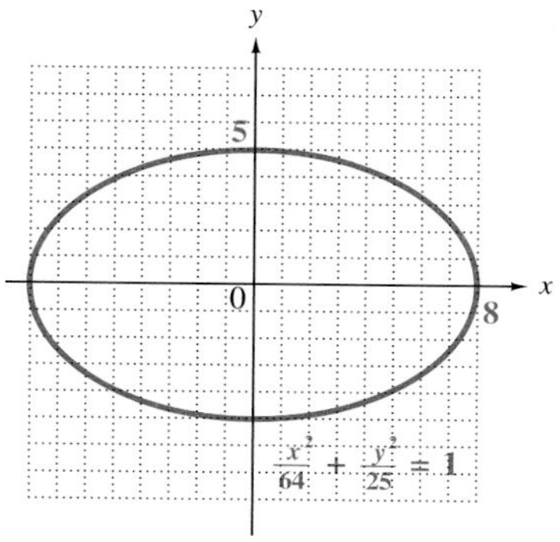

53. $\dfrac{y^2}{4} - 1 = \dfrac{x^2}{9}$

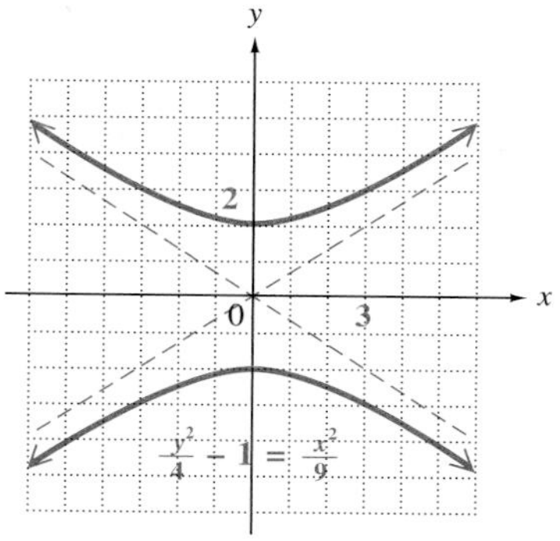

54. $x^2 + y^2 = 25$

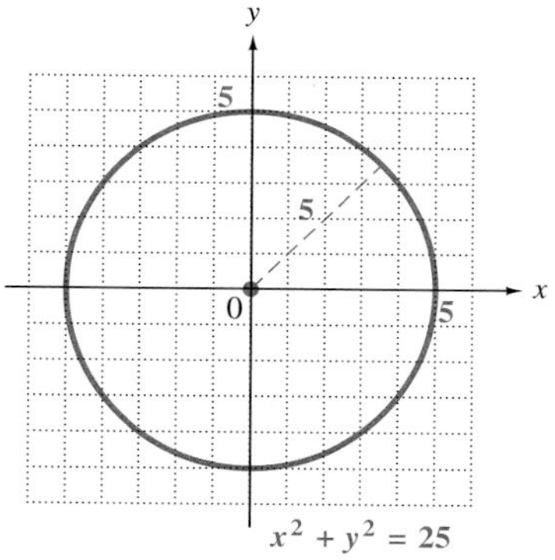

55. $x^2 + 9y^2 = 9$

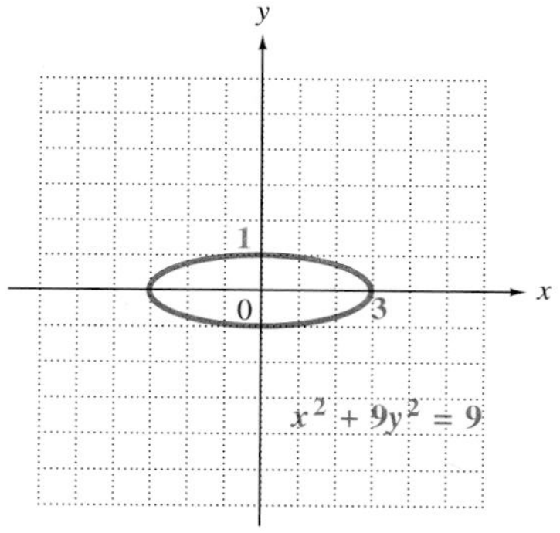

56. $x^2 - 9y^2 = 9$

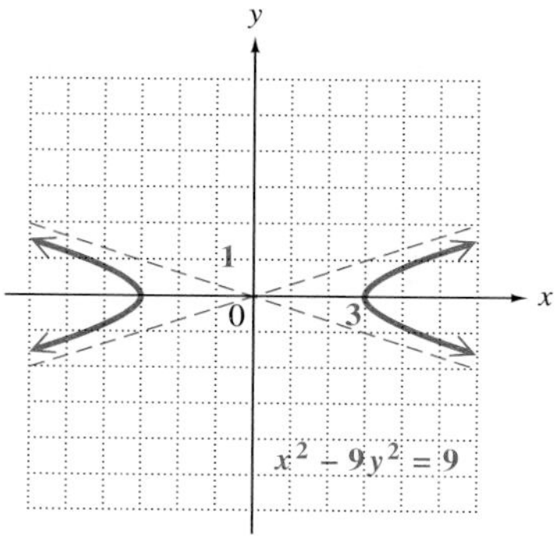

57. $f(x) = \sqrt{4 - x}$

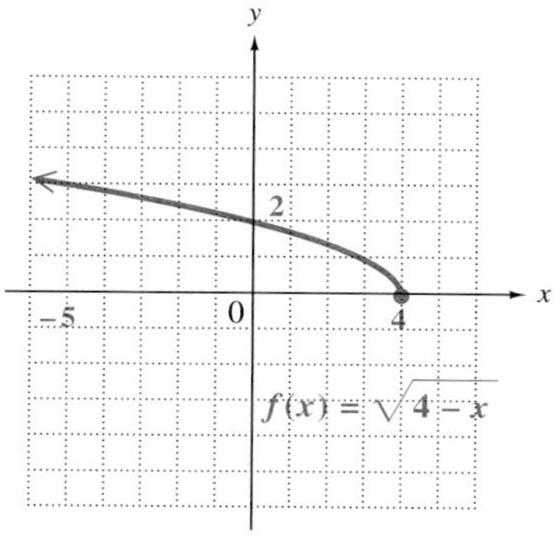

58. $3x + 2y \geq 0$
$y \leq 4$
$x \leq 4$

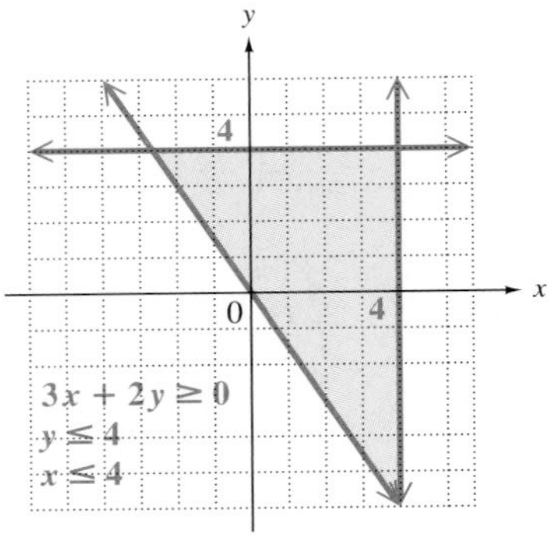

59. $4y > 3x - 12$
$x^2 < 16 - y^2$

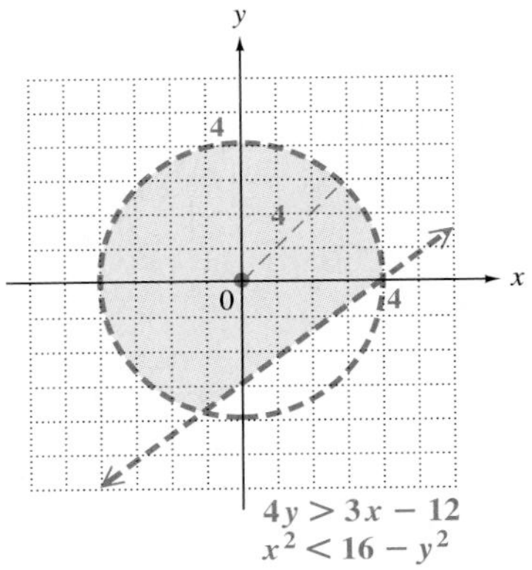

60. Explain why a set of points that form an ellipse does not satisfy the definition of a function.

There are cases where one x-value will yield two y-values. In a function, every x yields one and only one y.

The orbit of Mercury around the sun (a focus) is an ellipse with equation

$$\frac{x^2}{3352} + \frac{y^2}{3211} = 1,$$

where x and y are measured in million kilometers.

61. Find its apogee, its greatest distance from the sun. (*Hint:* Refer to Section 12.2, Exercise 37.)

69.8 million km

62. Find its perigee, its smallest distance from the sun.

46.0 million km

Chapter 12 Test

Study Skills Workbook
Activity 12

Match each function with its graph from choices A, B, C, and D.

1. $f(x) = \sqrt{x - 2}$
2. $f(x) = \sqrt{x + 2}$
3. $f(x) = \sqrt{x} + 2$
4. $f(x) = \sqrt{x} - 2$

A.

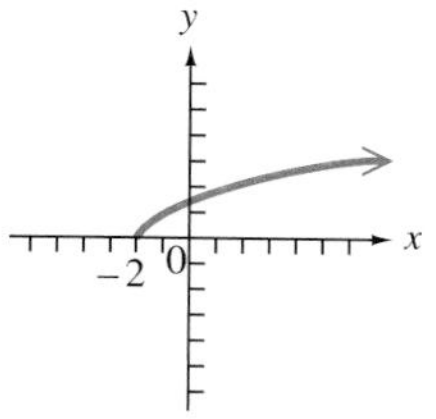

B.

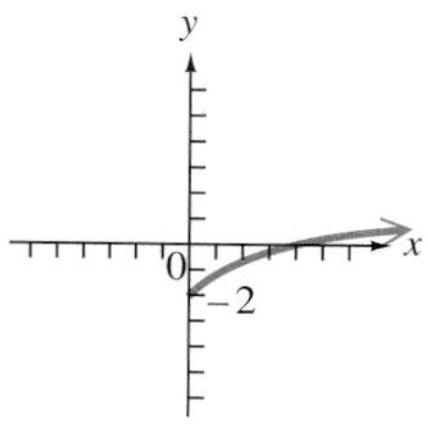

C.

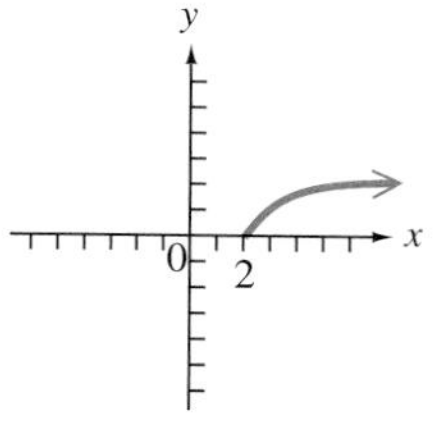

D.

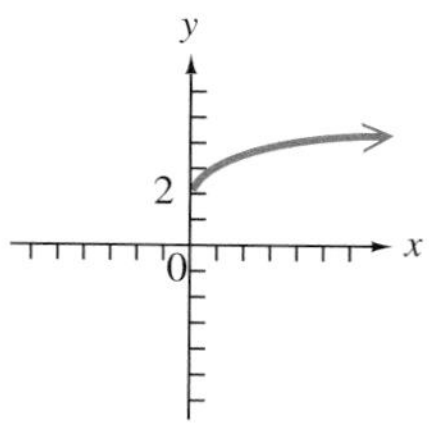

1. C
2. A
3. D
4. B

5. Sketch the graph of $f(x) = |x - 3| + 4$.

5.

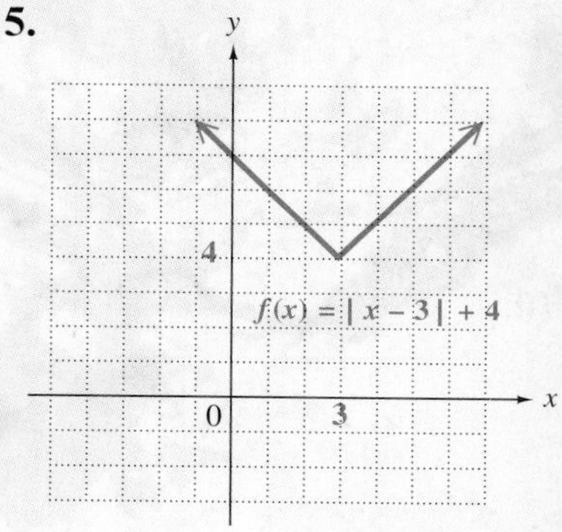

6. For $f(x) = 3x + 5$ and $g(x) = x^2 + 2$, find each of the following.
   (a) $(fg)(x)$
   (b) $(f - g)(2)$
   (c) $(f \circ g)(-2)$
   (d) $(f \circ g)(x)$
   (e) $(g \circ f)(x)$

6. (a) $3x^3 + 5x^2 + 6x + 10$
   (b) 5
   (c) 23
   (d) $3x^2 + 11$
   (e) $9x^2 + 30x + 27$

7. Find the center and radius of the circle whose equation is $(x - 2)^2 + (y + 3)^2 = 16$. Sketch the graph.

7. center: $(2, -3)$; radius: 4

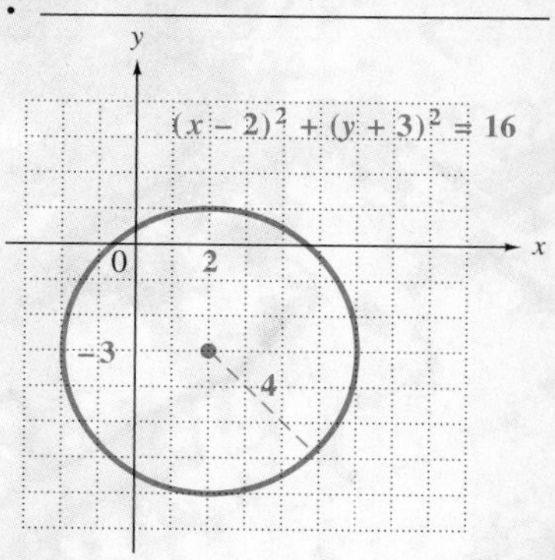

8. center: $(-4, 1)$; radius: 5

8. Find the center and radius of the circle whose equation is $x^2 + y^2 + 8x - 2y = 8$.

Graph.

9.

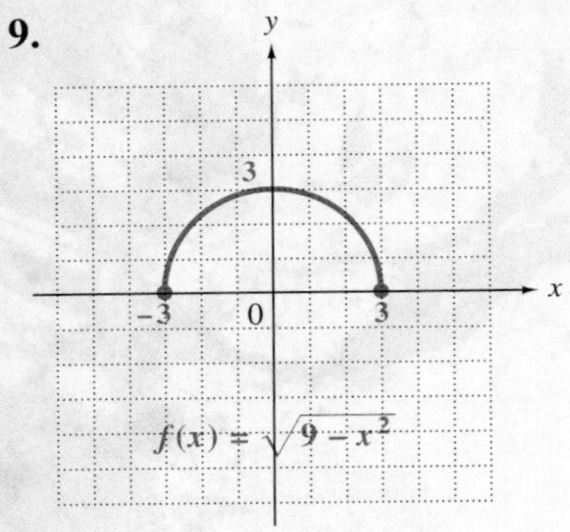

9. $f(x) = \sqrt{9 - x^2}$

10.

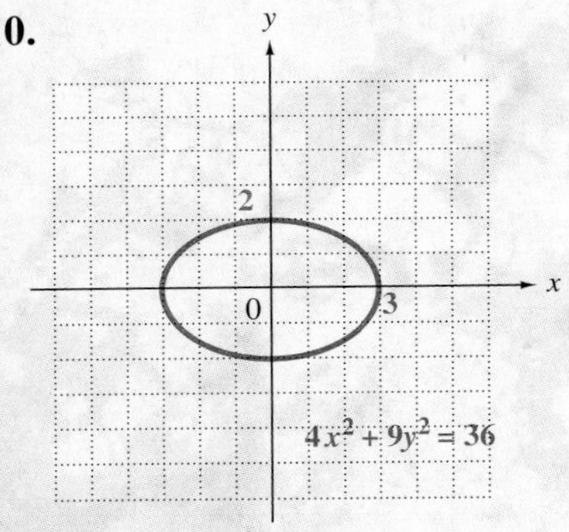

10. $4x^2 + 9y^2 = 36$

11.

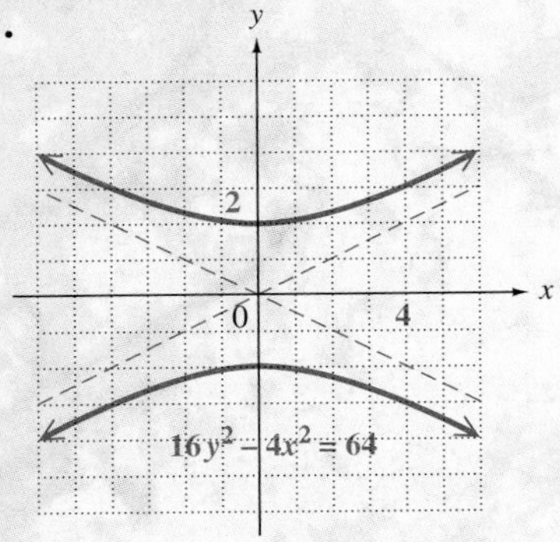

11. $16y^2 - 4x^2 = 64$

12. $\frac{y}{2} = -\sqrt{1 - \frac{x^2}{9}}$

12.

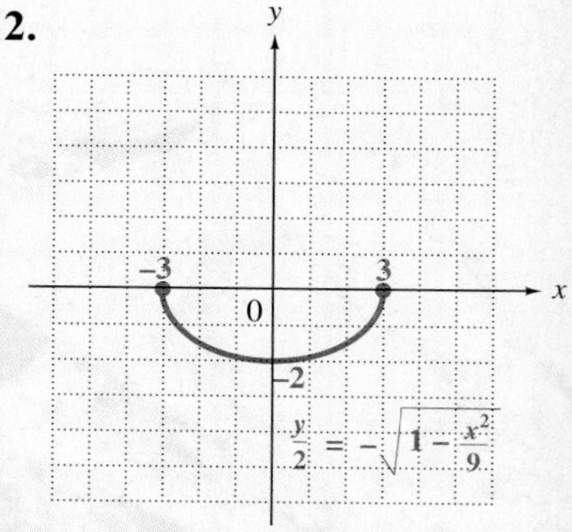

Identify the graph of each equation as a parabola, hyperbola, ellipse, *or* circle.

13. $6x^2 + 4y^2 = 12$

13. ellipse

14. $16x^2 = 144 + 9y^2$

14. hyperbola

15. $4y^2 + 4x = 9$

15. parabola

Solve each nonlinear system.

16. $2x - y = 9$
$xy = 5$

16. $\left\{\left(-\frac{1}{2}, -10\right), (5, 1)\right\}$

17. $\left\{(-2, -2), \left(\frac{14}{5}, -\frac{2}{5}\right)\right\}$

17. $x - 4 = 3y$
$x^2 + y^2 = 8$

18. $\{(-\sqrt{22}, -\sqrt{3}), (-\sqrt{22}, \sqrt{3}), (\sqrt{22}, -\sqrt{3}), (\sqrt{22}, \sqrt{3})\}$

18. $x^2 + y^2 = 25$
$x^2 - 2y^2 = 16$

19.

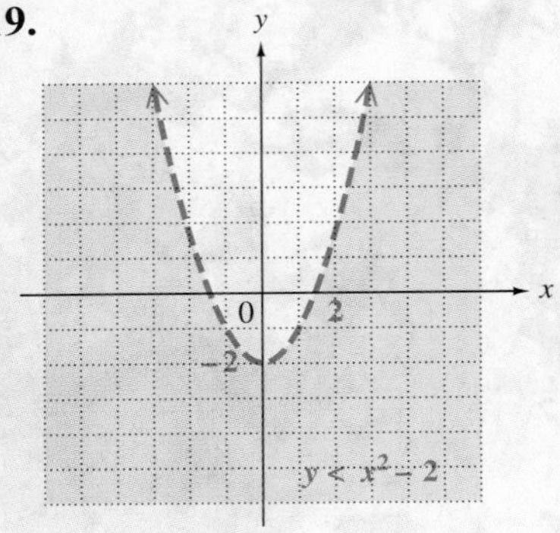

19. Graph the inequality $y < x^2 - 2$.

20.

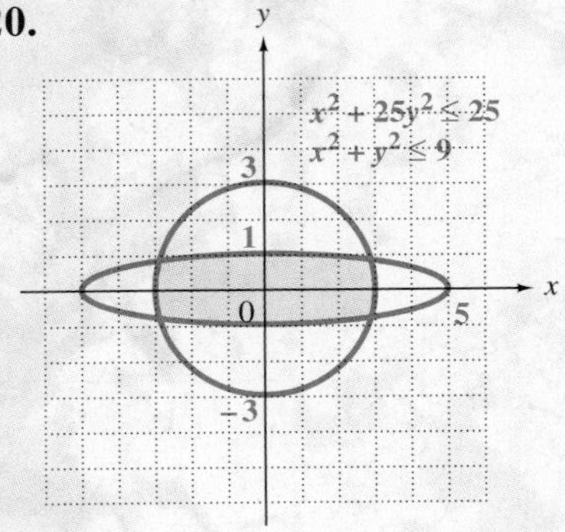

20. Graph the system.

$$x^2 + 25y^2 \le 25$$
$$x^2 + y^2 \le 9$$

Cumulative Review Exercises CHAPTERS R–12

1. Simplify $-10 + |-5| - |3| + 4$.

-4

Solve.

2. $4 - (2x + 3) + x = 5x - 3$

$\left\{\frac{2}{3}\right\}$

3. $-4k + 7 \geq 6k + 1$

$\left(-\infty, \frac{3}{5}\right]$

4. $|5m| - 6 = 14$

$\{-4, 4\}$

5. $|2p - 5| > 15$

$(-\infty, -5) \cup (10, \infty)$

6. Find the slope of the line through (2, 5) and (−4, 1).

$\frac{2}{3}$

7. Find the equation of the line through (−3, −2) and perpendicular to the graph of $2x - 3y = 7$.

$3x + 2y = -13$

Solve each system.

8. $3x - y = 12$
$2x + 3y = -3$

$\{(3, -3)\}$

9. $x + y - 2z = 9$
$2x + y + z = 7$
$3x - y - z = 13$

$\{(4, 1, -2)\}$

10. $xy = -5$
$2x + y = 3$

$\left\{(-1, 5), \left(\frac{5}{2}, -2\right)\right\}$

Solve each problem.

11. Al and Bev traveled from their apartment to a picnic 20 mi away. Al traveled on his bike while Bev, who left later, took her car. Al's average speed was half of Bev's average speed. The trip took Al $\frac{1}{2}$ hr longer than Bev. What was Bev's average speed?

40 mph

12. The president of InstaTune, a chain of franchised automobile tune-up shops, reports that people who buy a franchise and open a shop pay a weekly fee (in dollars) to company headquarters, according to the linear function defined by

$$f(x) = .07x + 135,$$

where $f(x)$ is the fee and x is the total amount of money taken in during the week by the shop. Find the weekly fee if \$2000 is taken in for the week. (*Source: Business Week.*)

\$275

Perform the indicated operations.

13. $(5y - 3)^2$

$25y^2 - 30y + 9$

14. $(2r + 7)(6r - 1)$

$12r^2 + 40r - 7$

15. $\dfrac{8x^4 - 4x^3 + 2x^2 + 13x + 8}{2x + 1}$

$4x^3 - 4x^2 + 3x + 5 + \dfrac{3}{2x + 1}$

Factor.

16. $12x^2 - 7x - 10$

$(3x + 2)(4x - 5)$

17. $2y^4 + 5y^2 - 3$

$(2y^2 - 1)(y^2 + 3)$

18. $z^4 - 1$

$(z^2 + 1)(z + 1)(z - 1)$

19. $a^3 - 27b^3$

$(a - 3b)(a^2 + 3ab + 9b^2)$

Perform each operation.

20. $\dfrac{5x - 15}{24} \cdot \dfrac{64}{3x - 9}$

$\dfrac{40}{9}$

21. $\dfrac{y^2 - 4}{y^2 - y - 6} \div \dfrac{y^2 - 2y}{y - 1}$

$\dfrac{y - 1}{y(y - 3)}$

22. $\dfrac{5}{c + 5} - \dfrac{2}{c + 3}$

$\dfrac{3c + 5}{(c + 5)(c + 3)}$

23. $\dfrac{p}{p^2 + p} + \dfrac{1}{p^2 + p}$

$\dfrac{1}{p}$

Solve.

24. Kareem and Jamal want to clean their office. Kareem can do the job alone in 3 hr, while Jamal can do it alone in 2 hr. How long will it take them if they work together?

$1\frac{1}{5}$ hr

Simplify. Assume all variables represent positive real numbers.

25. $\left(\dfrac{4}{3}\right)^{-1}$

$\dfrac{3}{4}$

26. $\dfrac{(2a)^{-2}a^4}{a^{-3}}$

$\dfrac{a^5}{4}$

27. $4\sqrt[3]{16} - 2\sqrt[3]{54}$

$2\sqrt[3]{2}$

28. $\dfrac{3\sqrt{5x}}{\sqrt{2x}}$

$\dfrac{3\sqrt{10}}{2}$

29. $\dfrac{5 + 3i}{2 - i}$

$\dfrac{7}{5} + \dfrac{11}{5}i$

Solve.

30. $2\sqrt{k} = \sqrt{5k + 3}$

$\emptyset$

31. $10q^2 + 13q = 3$

$\left\{\frac{1}{5}, -\frac{3}{2}\right\}$

32. $(4x - 1)^2 = 8$

$\left\{\frac{1 + 2\sqrt{2}}{4}, \frac{1 - 2\sqrt{2}}{4}\right\}$

33. $3k^2 - 3k - 2 = 0$

$\left\{\frac{3 + \sqrt{33}}{6}, \frac{3 - \sqrt{33}}{6}\right\}$

34. $2(x^2 - 3)^2 - 5(x^2 - 3) = 12$

$\left\{-\frac{\sqrt{6}}{2}, \frac{\sqrt{6}}{2}, -\sqrt{7}, \sqrt{7}\right\}$

35. $F = \frac{kwv^2}{r}$ for v

$v = \frac{\pm\sqrt{rFkw}}{kw}$

36. If $f(x) = x^3 + 4$, find $f^{-1}(x)$.

$f^{-1}(x) = \sqrt[3]{x - 4}$

37. Evaluate $3^{\log_3 4}$.

4

38. Evaluate $e^{\ln 7}$.

7

39. Use properties of logarithms to write

$$2 \log(3x + 7) - \log 4$$

as a single logarithm.

$\log \frac{(3x + 7)^2}{4}$

40. Solve $\log(x + 2) + \log(x - 1) = 1$.

$\{3\}$

41. If \$10,000 is invested at 5% for 4 yr, how much will there be in the account if interest is compounded

(a) quarterly, **\$12,198.90**

(b) continuously? **\$12,214.03**

The bar graph shows historic and projected annual on-line retail sales (in billions of dollars) over the Internet. A reasonable model for sales y in billions of dollars is the exponential function defined by

$$y = 1.38(1.65)^x.$$

The years are coded such that x is the number of years since 1995.

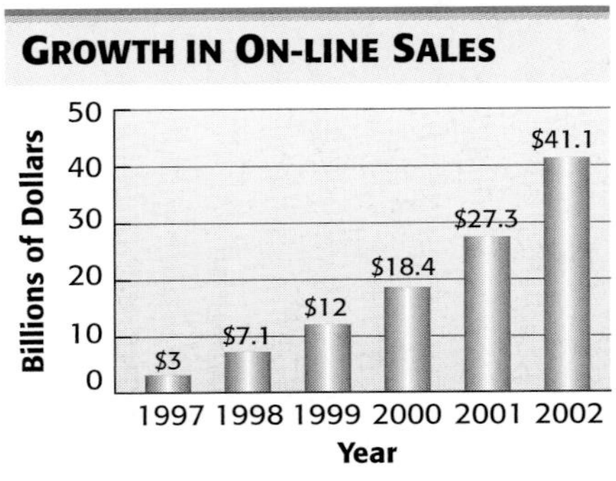

Source: Jupiter Communications.

42. Use the model to estimate sales in the year 2000. (*Hint:* Let $x = 5$.)

$16.9 billion

43. Use the model to estimate sales in the year 2003.

$75.8 billion

44. If $f(x) = x^2 + 2x - 4$ and $g(x) = 3x + 2$, find

(a) $(f - g)(x)$

$x^2 - x - 6$

(b) $(g \circ f)(1)$

-1

(c) $(f \circ g)(x)$.

$9x^2 + 18x + 4$

Graph.

45. $f(x) = -3x + 5$

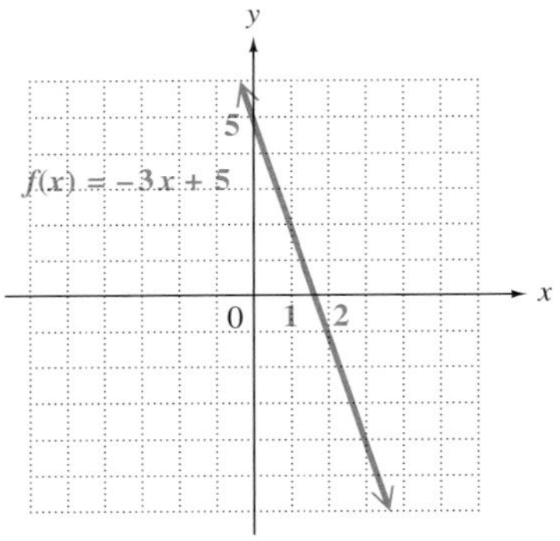

46. $f(x) = -2(x - 1)^2 + 3$

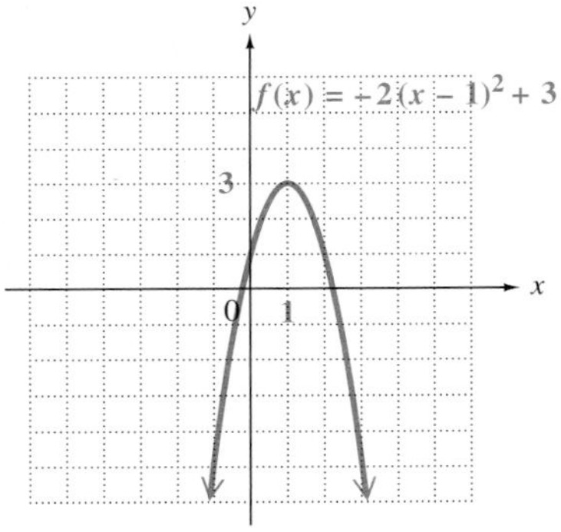

47. $\frac{x^2}{25} + \frac{y^2}{16} \le 1$

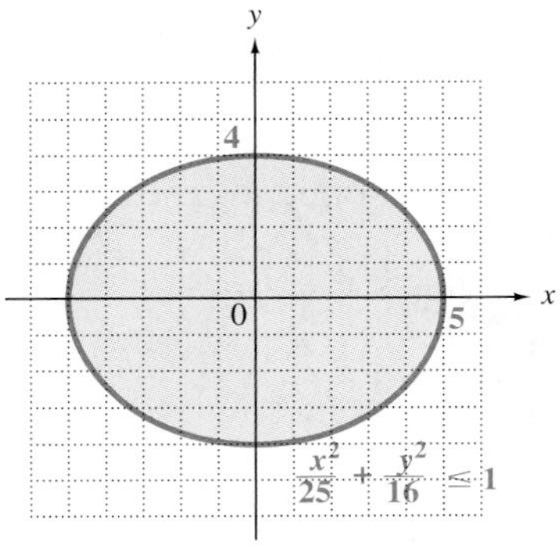

48. $f(x) = \sqrt{x - 2}$

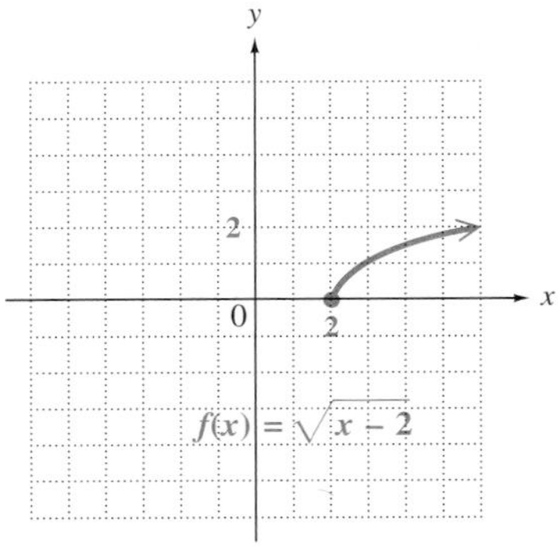

49. $\frac{x^2}{4} - \frac{y^2}{16} = 1$

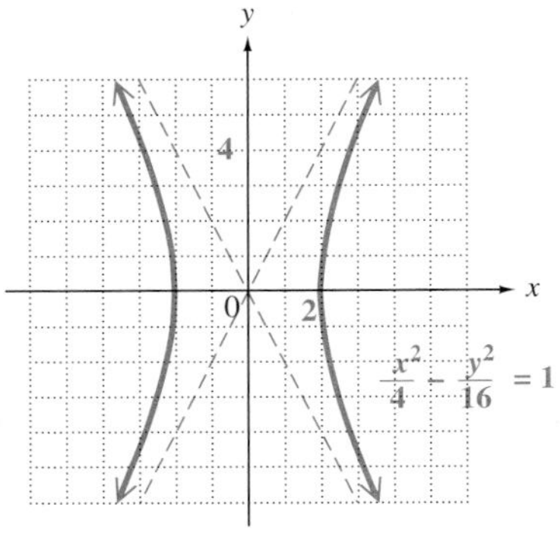

50. $f(x) = 3^x$

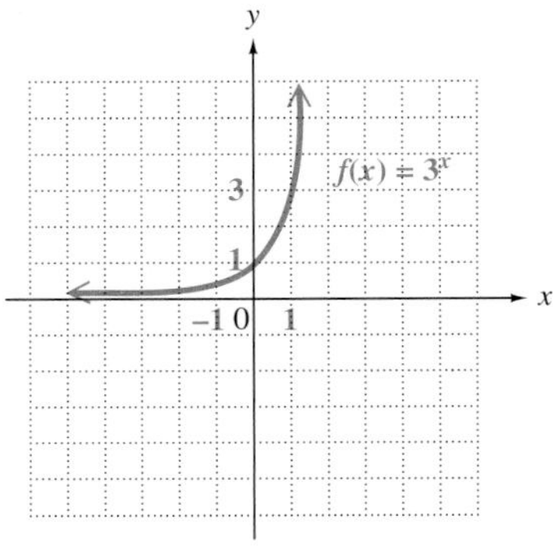

Appendix A
Sets

A SETS

1 List the elements of a set. A **set** is a collection of things. The objects in a set are called the **elements** of the set. A set is represented by listing its elements between **set braces,** { }. The order in which the elements of a set are listed is unimportant.

Example 1 Listing the Elements of Sets

Represent each set by listing the elements.

(a) The set of states in the United States that border on the Pacific Ocean = {California, Oregon, Washington, Hawaii, Alaska}.

(b) The set of all counting numbers less than 6 = $\{1, 2, 3, 4, 5\}$.

Work Problem 1 at the Side.

2 Learn the vocabulary and symbols used to discuss sets. Capital letters are used to name sets. To state that 5 is an element of

$$S = \{1, 2, 3, 4, 5\},$$

write $5 \in S$. The statement $6 \notin S$ means that 6 is not an element of S.

A set with no elements is called the **empty set,** or the **null set.** The symbols $\emptyset$ or { } are used for the empty set. If we let A be the set of all cats that fly, then A is the empty set.

$$A = \emptyset \quad \text{or} \quad A = \{\ \}$$

CAUTION

Do not make the common error of writing the empty set as $\{\emptyset\}$.

In any discussion of sets, there is some set that includes all the elements under consideration. This set is called the **universal set** for that situation. For example, if the discussion is about presidents of the United States, then the set of all presidents of the United States is the universal set. The universal set is denoted U.

3 Decide whether a set is finite or infinite. In Example 1, there are five elements in the set in part (a) and five in part (b). If the number of elements in a set is either 0 or a counting number, then the set is a **finite set.** On the other hand, the set of natural numbers, for example, is an **infinite set,** because there is no final natural number. We can list the elements of the set of natural numbers as

$$N = \{1, 2, 3, 4, \ldots\},$$

where the three dots indicate that the set continues indefinitely. Not all infinite sets can be listed in this way. For example, there is no way to list the elements in the set of all real numbers between 1 and 2.

OBJECTIVES

1. List the elements of a set.
2. Learn the vocabulary and symbols used to discuss sets.
3. Decide whether a set is finite or infinite.
4. Decide whether a given set is a subset of another set.
5. Find the complement of a set.
6. Find the union and the intersection of two sets.

1 Represent each set by listing the elements.

(a) The set of states whose names begin with the letter O

(b) The set of letters of the alphabet that follow T

(c) The set of even natural numbers less than 10

(d) The set of odd counting numbers between 15 and 20

ANSWERS

1. (a) {Oregon, Ohio, Oklahoma}
(b) {U, V, W, X, Y, Z}
(c) $\{2, 4, 6, 8\}$
(d) $\{17, 19\}$

Example 2 **Distinguishing between Finite and Infinite Sets**

List the elements of each set, if possible. Decide whether each set is *finite* or *infinite*.

(a) The set of all integers
One way to list the elements is $\{\ldots, -2, -1, 0, 1, 2, \ldots\}$. The set is infinite.

(b) The set of all natural numbers between 0 and 5
List the elements of this set as $\{1, 2, 3, 4\}$. The set is finite.

(c) The set of all irrational numbers
This is an infinite set whose elements cannot be listed.

Work Problem 2 at the Side.

Two sets are **equal** if they have exactly the same elements. Thus, the set of natural numbers and the set of positive integers are equal sets. Also, the sets

$$\{1, 2, 4, 7\} \quad \text{and} \quad \{4, 2, 7, 1\}$$

are equal. The order of the elements does not make a difference.

4 **Decide whether a given set is a subset of another set.** If all elements of a set A are also elements of a new set B, then we say A is a **subset** of B, written $A \subseteq B$. We use the symbol $A \nsubseteq B$ to mean that A is not a subset of B.

Example 3 **Using Subset Notation**

Let $A = \{1, 2, 3, 4\}$, $B = \{1, 4\}$, and $C = \{1\}$. Then

$$B \subseteq A, \quad C \subseteq A, \quad \text{and} \quad C \subseteq B,$$

but

$$A \nsubseteq B, \quad A \nsubseteq C, \quad \text{and} \quad B \nsubseteq C.$$

Work Problem 3 at the Side.

The set $M = \{a, b\}$ has four subsets: $\{a, b\}$, $\{a\}$, $\{b\}$, and $\emptyset$. The empty set is defined to be a subset of any set. How many subsets does $N = \{a, b, c\}$ have? There is one subset with 3 elements: $\{a, b, c\}$. There are three subsets with 2 elements:

$$\{a, b\}, \quad \{a, c\}, \quad \text{and} \quad \{b, c\}.$$

There are three subsets with 1 element:

$$\{a\}, \quad \{b\}, \quad \text{and} \quad \{c\}.$$

There is one subset with 0 elements: $\emptyset$. Thus, set N has eight subsets.
The following generalization can be made.

Number of Subsets of a Set

A set with n elements has 2^n subsets.

To illustrate the relationships between sets, **Venn diagrams** are often used. A rectangle represents the universal set, U. The sets under discussion are represented by regions within the rectangle. The Venn diagram in Figure 1 shows that $B \subseteq A$.

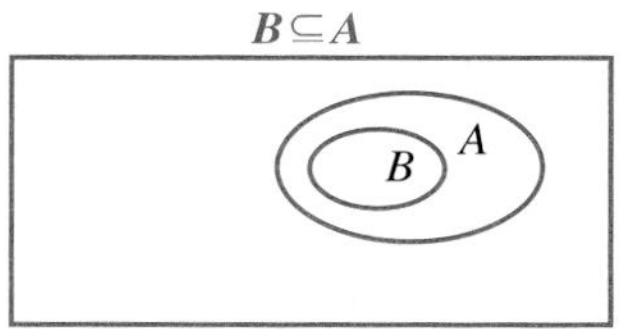

Figure 1

2 List the elements of each set, if possible. Decide whether each set is *finite* or *infinite*.

(a) The set of whole numbers

(b) The set of odd natural numbers between 10 and 20

(c) The set of integers greater than 3

(d) The set of rational numbers

3 Let

$A = \{2, 4, 6, 8, 10, 12\}$,
$B = \{2, 4, 8, 10\}$, and
$C = \{4, 10, 12\}$.

Tell whether each statement is *true* or *false*.

(a) $B \subseteq A$

(b) $C \subseteq B$

(c) $A \nsubseteq C$

(d) $B \nsubseteq C$

Answers

2. **(a)** $\{0, 1, 2, 3, \ldots\}$; infinite
(b) $\{11, 13, 15, 17, 19\}$; finite
(c) $\{4, 5, 6, \ldots\}$; infinite
(d) This is an infinite set whose elements cannot be listed.

3. **(a)** true **(b)** false **(c)** true **(d)** true

5 **Find the complement of a set.** For every set A, there is a set A', the **complement** of A, that contains all the elements of U that are not in A. The shaded region in the Venn diagram in Figure 2 represents A'.

A' is shaded.

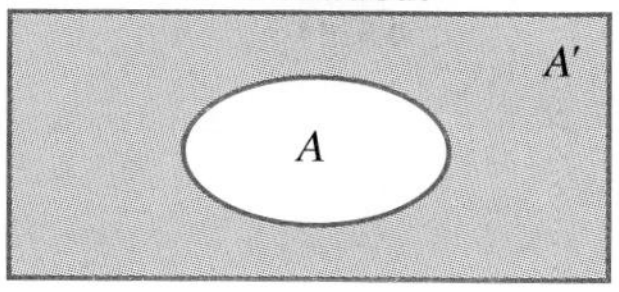

Figure 2

Example 4 **Determining Complements of Sets**

Given $U = \{a, b, c, d, e, f, g\}$, $A = \{a, b, c\}$, $B = \{a, d, f, g\}$, and $C = \{d, e\}$, then

$$A' = \{d, e, f, g\}, \quad B' = \{b, c, e\}, \quad \text{and} \quad C' = \{a, b, c, f, g\}.$$

Work Problem 4 at the Side.

6 **Find the union and the intersection of two sets.** The **union** of two sets A and B, written $A \cup B$, is the set of all elements of A together with all elements of B. Thus, for the sets in Example 4,

$$A \cup B = \{a, b, c, d, f, g\} \quad A = \{a, b, c\}, B = \{a, d, f, g\}$$

and

$$A \cup C = \{a, b, c, d, e\}. \quad A = \{a, b, c\}, C = \{d, e\}$$

In Figure 3 the shaded region is the union of sets A and B.

$A \cup B$ is shaded.

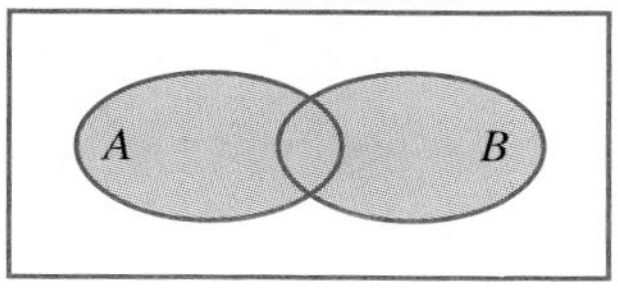

Figure 3

Example 5 **Finding the Union of Two Sets**

If $M = \{2, 5, 7\}$ and $N = \{1, 2, 3, 4, 5\}$, then

$$M \cup N = \{1, 2, 3, 4, 5, 7\}.$$

Work Problem 5 at the Side.

The **intersection** of two sets A and B, written $A \cap B$, is the set of all elements that belong to both A and B. For example, if

$$A = \{\textbf{Jose}, \textbf{Ellen}, \text{Marge}, \text{Kevin}\}$$

and

$$B = \{\textbf{Jose}, \text{Patrick}, \textbf{Ellen}, \text{Sue}\},$$

then

$$A \cap B = \{\textbf{Jose}, \textbf{Ellen}\}.$$

4 Let

$U = \{0, 1, 2, 3, 4, 5, 6, 7, 8\}$,
$M = \{0, 2, 4, 6, 8\}$,
$N = \{1, 3, 5, 7\}$, and
$Q = \{0, 1, 2, 3, 4\}$.

List the elements in each set.

(a) M'

(b) N'

(c) Q'

5 Using the sets given in Margin Problem 4, find the following.

(a) $M \cup N$

(b) $N \cup Q$

ANSWERS

4. **(a)** $\{1, 3, 5, 7\}$ **(b)** $\{0, 2, 4, 6, 8\}$
(c) $\{5, 6, 7, 8\}$

5. **(a)** $\{0, 1, 2, 3, 4, 5, 6, 7, 8\} = U$
(b) $\{0, 1, 2, 3, 4, 5, 7\}$

6 Using the sets given in Margin Problem 4, find the following.

(a) $M \cap Q$

(b) $N \cap Q$

(c) $M \cap N$

7 Let

$$U = \{1, 2, 3, 4, 6, 8, 10\},$$
$$A = \{1, 3, 4, 6\},$$
$$B = \{2, 4, 6, 8, 10\}, \text{ and}$$
$$C = \{2, 8\}.$$

Find the following.

(a) $B \cup C$

(b) $A \cap B$

(c) $A \cap C$

(d) A'

(e) $A \cup B$

ANSWERS

6. (a) $\{0, 2, 4\}$ **(b)** $\{1, 3\}$ **(c)** $\emptyset$

7. (a) $\{2, 4, 6, 8, 10\} = B$ **(b)** $\{4, 6\}$ **(c)** $\emptyset$ **(d)** $\{2, 8, 10\}$ **(e)** $\{1, 2, 3, 4, 6, 8, 10\} = U$

The shaded region in Figure 4 represents the intersection of the sets A and B.

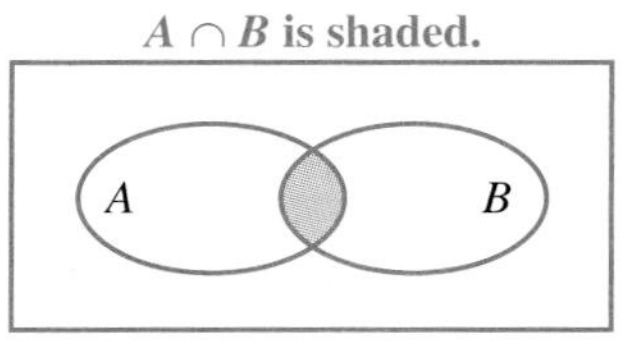

Figure 4

Example 6 Finding the Intersection of Two Sets

Suppose that

$$P = \{3, 9, 27\},$$
$$Q = \{2, 3, 10, 18, 27, 28\}, \text{ and}$$
$$R = \{2, 10, 28\}.$$

List the elements in each set.

(a) $P \cap Q = \{3, 27\}$ **(b)** $Q \cap R = \{2, 10, 28\} = R$ **(c)** $P \cap R = \emptyset$

Work Problem 6 at the Side.

Sets like P and R in Example 6 that have no elements in common are called **disjoint sets.** The Venn diagram in Figure 5 shows a pair of disjoint sets.

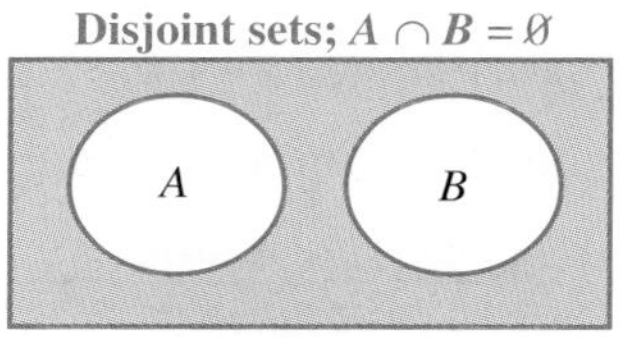

Figure 5

Example 7 Using Set Operations

Let

$$U = \{2, 5, 7, 10, 14, 20\},$$
$$A = \{2, 10, 14, 20\},$$
$$B = \{5, 7\}, \text{ and}$$
$$C = \{2, 5, 7\}.$$

Find the following.

(a) $A \cup B = \{2, 5, 7, 10, 14, 20\} = U$

(b) $A \cap B = \emptyset$

(c) $B \cup C = \{2, 5, 7\} = C$

(d) $B \cap C = \{5, 7\} = B$

(e) $A' = \{5, 7\} = B$

Work Problem 7 at the Side.

Appendix A EXERCISES

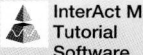

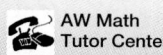

FOR EXTRA HELP: Student's Solutions Manual | MyMathLab.com | InterAct Math Tutorial Software | AW Math Tutor Center | www.mathxl.com MathXL

List the elements of each set. See Examples 1 and 2.

1. The set of all natural numbers less than 8

{1, 2, 3, 4, 5, 6, 7}

2. The set of all integers between 4 and 10

{5, 6, 7, 8, 9}

3. The set of seasons

{winter, spring, summer, fall}

4. The set of months of the year

{January, February, March, April, May, June, July, August, September, October, November, December}

5. The set of women presidents of the United States

∅

6. The set of all living humans who are more than 200 years old

∅

7. The set of letters of the alphabet between K and M

{L}

8. The set of letters of the alphabet between D and H

{E, F, G}

9. The set of positive even integers

{2, 4, 6, 8, 10, . . .}

10. The set of all multiples of 5

{. . . , −15, −10, −5, 0, 5, 10, 15, . . .}

11. Which of the sets described in Exercises 1–10 are infinite sets?

The sets in Exercises 9 and 10 are infinite sets.

12. Which of the sets described in Exercises 1–10 are finite sets?

The sets in Exercises 1–8 are finite sets.

Tell whether each statement is true *or* false.

13. $5 \in \{1, 2, 5, 8\}$ **true**

14. $6 \in \{1, 2, 3, 4, 5\}$ **false**

15. $2 \in \{1, 3, 5, 7, 9\}$ **false**

16. $1 \in \{6, 2, 5, 1\}$ **true**

17. $7 \notin \{2, 4, 6, 8\}$ **true**

18. $7 \notin \{1, 3, 5, 7\}$ **false**

19. $\{2, 4, 9, 12, 13\} = \{13, 12, 9, 4, 2\}$ **true**

20. $\{7, 11, 4\} = \{7, 11, 4, 0\}$ **false**

Let

$$A = \{1, 3, 4, 5, 7, 8\}, \quad B = \{2, 4, 6, 8\}, \quad C = \{1, 3, 5, 7\},$$
$$D = \{1, 2, 3\}, \quad E = \{3, 7\}, \quad \text{and} \quad U = \{1, 2, 3, 4, 5, 6, 7, 8, 9, 10\}.$$

Tell whether each statement is true *or* false. *See Examples 3, 5, 6, and 7.*

21. $A \subseteq U$ **true**

22. $D \subseteq A$ **false**

23. $\emptyset \subseteq A$ **true**

24. $\{1, 2\} \subseteq D$ **true**

25. $C \subseteq A$ **true**

26. $A \subseteq C$ **false**

27. $D \subseteq B$ **false**

28. $E \subseteq C$ **true**

29. $D \nsubseteq E$ **true**

30. $E \nsubseteq A$ **false**

31. There are exactly 4 subsets of E. **true**

32. There are exactly 8 subsets of D. **true**

33. There are exactly 12 subsets of C. **false**

34. There are exactly 16 subsets of B. **true**

35. $\{4, 6, 8, 12\} \cap \{6, 8, 14, 17\} = \{6, 8\}$ **true**

36. $\{2, 5, 9\} \cap \{1, 2, 3, 4, 5\} = \{2, 5\}$ **true**

37. $\{3, 1, 0\} \cap \{0, 2, 4\} = \{0\}$ **true**

38. $\{4, 2, 1\} \cap \{1, 2, 3, 4\} = \{1, 2, 3\}$ **false**

39. $\{3, 9, 12\} \cap \emptyset = \{3, 9, 12\}$ **false**

40. $\{3, 9, 12\} \cup \emptyset = \emptyset$ **false**

41. $\{4, 9, 11, 7, 3\} \cup \{1, 2, 3, 4, 5\} = \{1, 2, 3, 4, 5, 7, 9, 11\}$ **true**

42. $\{1, 2, 3\} \cup \{1, 2, 3\} = \{1, 2, 3\}$ **true**

43. $\{3, 5, 7, 9\} \cup \{4, 6, 8\} = \emptyset$ **false**

44. $\{5, 10, 15, 20\} \cup \{5, 15, 30\} = \{5, 15\}$ **false**

Let

$$U = \{\text{a, b, c, d, e, f, g, h}\}, \quad A = \{\text{a, b, c, d, e, f}\}, \quad B = \{\text{a, c, e}\}, \quad C = \{\text{a, f}\}, \quad \text{and} \quad D = \{\text{d}\}.$$

List the elements in each set. See Examples 4–7.

45. A' **{g, h}**

46. B' **{b, d, f, g, h}**

47. C' **{b, c, d, e, g, h}**

48. D' **{a, b, c, e, f, g, h}**

49. $A \cap B$ **{a, c, e} = B**

50. $B \cap A$ **{a, c, e} = B**

51. $A \cap D$ **{d} = D**

52. $B \cap D$ **∅**

53. $B \cap C$ **{a}**

54. $A \cup B$ **{a, b, c, d, e, f} = A**

55. $B \cup D$ **{a, c, d, e}**

56. $B \cup C$ **{a, c, e, f}**

57. $C \cup B$ **{a, c, e, f}**

58. $C \cup D$ **{a, d, f}**

59. $A \cap \emptyset$ **∅**

60. $B \cup \emptyset$ **{a, c, e} = B**

61. Name every pair of disjoint sets among *A–D* above.
B and D; C and D

Appendix B Determinants and Cramer's Rule

B Determinants and Cramer's Rule

Objectives

1. Evaluate 2 × 2 determinants.
2. Use expansion by minors to evaluate 3 × 3 determinants.
3. Understand the derivation of Cramer's rule.
4. Apply Cramer's rule to solve linear systems.

Recall from Section 5.6 that an ordered array of numbers within square brackets is called a *matrix* (plural *matrices*). Matrices are named according to the number of rows and columns they contain. A *square matrix* has the same number of rows and columns.

Columns; Rows

$$\begin{bmatrix} 2 & 3 & 5 \\ 7 & 1 & 2 \end{bmatrix} \quad 2 \times 3 \text{ matrix} \qquad \begin{bmatrix} -1 & 0 \\ 1 & -2 \end{bmatrix} \quad 2 \times 2 \text{ square matrix}$$

Associated with every *square matrix* is a real number called the **determinant** of the matrix. A determinant is symbolized by the entries of the matrix placed between two vertical lines, such as

$$\begin{vmatrix} 2 & 3 \\ 7 & 1 \end{vmatrix} \quad 2 \times 2 \text{ determinant} \qquad \begin{vmatrix} 7 & 4 & 3 \\ 0 & 1 & 5 \\ 6 & 0 & 1 \end{vmatrix}. \quad 3 \times 3 \text{ determinant}$$

Like matrices, determinants are named according to the number of rows and columns they contain.

1 Evaluate 2 × 2 determinants. As mentioned above, the value of a determinant is a *real number*. The value of the 2 × 2 determinant

$$\begin{vmatrix} a & b \\ c & d \end{vmatrix}$$

is defined as follows.

Value of a 2 × 2 Determinant

$$\begin{vmatrix} a & b \\ c & d \end{vmatrix} = ad - bc$$

Example 1 Evaluating a 2 × 2 Determinant

Evaluate the determinant.

$$\begin{vmatrix} -1 & -3 \\ 4 & -2 \end{vmatrix}$$

Here $a = -1$, $b = -3$, $c = 4$, and $d = -2$, so

$$\begin{vmatrix} -1 & -3 \\ 4 & -2 \end{vmatrix} = -1(-2) - (-3)4 = 2 + 12 = 14.$$

Work Problem 1 at the Side.

1 Evaluate each determinant.

(a) $\begin{vmatrix} -4 & 6 \\ 2 & 3 \end{vmatrix}$

(b) $\begin{vmatrix} 3 & -1 \\ 0 & 2 \end{vmatrix}$

(c) $\begin{vmatrix} -2 & 5 \\ 1 & 5 \end{vmatrix}$

Answers

1. **(a)** -24 **(b)** 6 **(c)** -15

A 3 × 3 determinant can be evaluated in a similar way.

Value of a 3 × 3 Determinant

$$\begin{vmatrix} a_1 & b_1 & c_1 \\ a_2 & b_2 & c_2 \\ a_3 & b_3 & c_3 \end{vmatrix} = (a_1b_2c_3 + b_1c_2a_3 + c_1a_2b_3) - (a_3b_2c_1 + b_3c_2a_1 + c_3a_2b_1)$$

This rule for evaluating a 3 × 3 determinant is hard to remember. A method for calculating a 3 × 3 determinant that is easier to use is based on the rule. Rearranging terms and using the distributive property gives

$$\begin{vmatrix} a_1 & b_1 & c_1 \\ a_2 & b_2 & c_2 \\ a_3 & b_3 & c_3 \end{vmatrix} = a_1(b_2c_3 - b_3c_2) - a_2(b_1c_3 - b_3c_1) + a_3(b_1c_2 - b_2c_1). \quad (1)$$

Each of the quantities in parentheses represents a 2 × 2 determinant that is the part of the 3 × 3 determinant remaining when the row and column of the multiplier are eliminated, as shown below.

$$a_1(b_2c_3 - b_3c_2) \qquad \begin{vmatrix} a_1 & b_1 & c_1 \\ a_2 & b_2 & c_2 \\ a_3 & b_3 & c_3 \end{vmatrix}$$

$$a_2(b_1c_3 - b_3c_1) \qquad \begin{vmatrix} a_1 & b_1 & c_1 \\ a_2 & b_2 & c_2 \\ a_3 & b_3 & c_3 \end{vmatrix}$$

$$a_3(b_1c_2 - b_2c_1) \qquad \begin{vmatrix} a_1 & b_1 & c_1 \\ a_2 & b_2 & c_2 \\ a_3 & b_3 & c_3 \end{vmatrix}$$

These 2 × 2 determinants are called **minors** of the elements in the 3 × 3 determinant. In the determinant above, the minors of a_1, a_2, and a_3 are, respectively,

$$\begin{vmatrix} b_2 & c_2 \\ b_3 & c_3 \end{vmatrix}, \quad \begin{vmatrix} b_1 & c_1 \\ b_3 & c_3 \end{vmatrix}, \quad \text{and} \quad \begin{vmatrix} b_1 & c_1 \\ b_2 & c_2 \end{vmatrix}.$$

2 Use expansion by minors to evaluate 3 × 3 determinants. A 3 × 3 determinant can be evaluated by multiplying each element in the first column by its minor and combining the products as indicated in equation (1). This is called **expansion of the determinant by minors** about the first column.

Example 2 Evaluating a 3 × 3 Determinant

Evaluate the determinant using expansion by minors about the first column.

$$\begin{vmatrix} 1 & 3 & -2 \\ -1 & -2 & -3 \\ 1 & 1 & 2 \end{vmatrix}$$

In this determinant, $a_1 = 1$, $a_2 = -1$, and $a_3 = 1$. Multiply each of these numbers by its minor, and combine the three terms using the definition. Notice that the second term in the definition is *subtracted.*

Continued on Next Page

$$\begin{vmatrix} 1 & 3 & -2 \\ -1 & -2 & -3 \\ 1 & 1 & 2 \end{vmatrix} = 1\begin{vmatrix} -2 & -3 \\ 1 & 2 \end{vmatrix} - (-1)\begin{vmatrix} 3 & -2 \\ 1 & 2 \end{vmatrix} + 1\begin{vmatrix} 3 & -2 \\ -2 & -3 \end{vmatrix}$$

$$\begin{aligned} &= 1[-2(2) - (-3)1] + 1[3(2) - (-2)1] \\ &\quad + 1[3(-3) - (-2)(-2)] \\ &= 1(-1) + 1(8) + 1(-13) \\ &= -1 + 8 - 13 \\ &= -6 \end{aligned}$$

Work Problem 2 at the Side.

To get equation (1) we could have rearranged terms in the definition of the determinant and used the distributive property to factor out the three elements of the second or third column or of any of the three rows. Therefore, expanding by minors about any row or any column results in the same value for a 3 × 3 determinant. To determine the correct signs for the terms of other expansions, the following **array of signs** is helpful.

Array of Signs for a 3 × 3 Determinant

$$\begin{matrix} + & - & + \\ - & + & - \\ + & - & + \end{matrix}$$

The signs alternate for each row and column beginning with a + in the first row, first column position. For example, if the expansion is to be about the second column, the first term would have a minus sign associated with it, the second term a plus sign, and the third term a minus sign.

Example 3 **Evaluating a 3 × 3 Determinant**

Evaluate the determinant of Example 2 using expansion by minors about the second column.

$$\begin{vmatrix} 1 & 3 & -2 \\ -1 & -2 & -3 \\ 1 & 1 & 2 \end{vmatrix} = -3\begin{vmatrix} -1 & -3 \\ 1 & 2 \end{vmatrix} + (-2)\begin{vmatrix} 1 & -2 \\ 1 & 2 \end{vmatrix} - 1\begin{vmatrix} 1 & -2 \\ -1 & -3 \end{vmatrix}$$

$$\begin{aligned} &= -3(1) - 2(4) - 1(-5) \\ &= -3 - 8 + 5 \\ &= -6 \end{aligned}$$

As expected, the result is the same as in Example 2.

Work Problem 3 at the Side.

2 Evaluate each determinant using expansion by minors about the first column.

(a) $\begin{vmatrix} 0 & -1 & 0 \\ 2 & 4 & 2 \\ 3 & 1 & 5 \end{vmatrix}$

(b) $\begin{vmatrix} 2 & 1 & 4 \\ -3 & 0 & 2 \\ -2 & 1 & 5 \end{vmatrix}$

3 Evaluate each determinant using expansion by minors about the second column.

(a) $\begin{vmatrix} 2 & 1 & 3 \\ -1 & 0 & 4 \\ 2 & 4 & 3 \end{vmatrix}$

(b) $\begin{vmatrix} 5 & -1 & 2 \\ 0 & 4 & 3 \\ -1 & 2 & 0 \end{vmatrix}$

ANSWERS
2. (a) 4 **(b)** −5
3. (a) −33 **(b)** −19

Calculator Tip The graphing calculator function det(A) assigns to each square matrix A one and only one real number, the determinant of A. For example, Figure 1 shows how a graphing calculator displays the correct value for the determinant in Example 1. Similarly, Figure 2 supports the results of Examples 2 and 3.

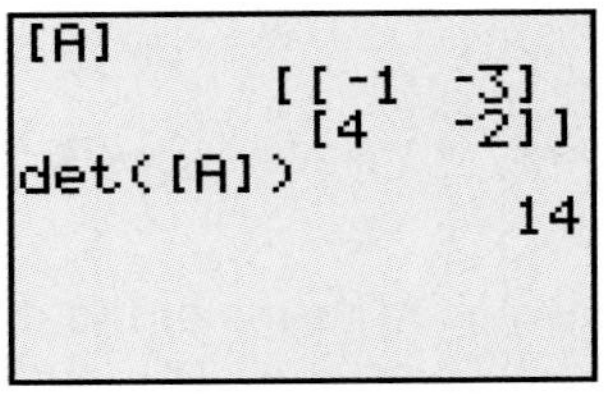

Figure 1

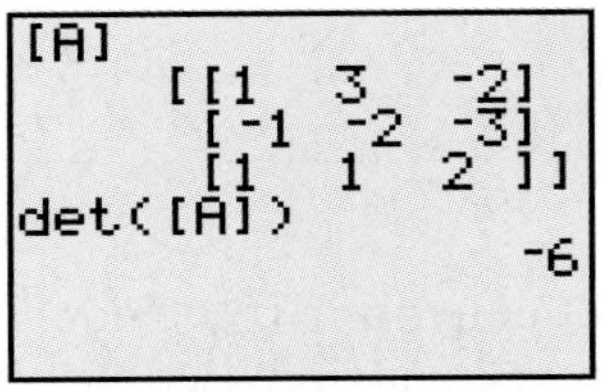

Figure 2

3 Understand the derivation of Cramer's rule. Determinants can be used to solve a system of the form

$$a_1x + b_1y = c_1 \quad (1)$$
$$a_2x + b_2y = c_2. \quad (2)$$

The result will be a formula that can be used to solve any system of two equations with two variables. To get this general solution, we eliminate y and solve for x by first multiplying each side of equation (1) by b_2 and each side of equation (2) by $-b_1$. Then we add these results and solve for x.

$$a_1b_2x + b_1b_2y = c_1b_2 \qquad \text{Multiply equation (1) by } b_2.$$
$$-a_2b_1x - b_1b_2y = -c_2b_1 \qquad \text{Multiply equation (2) by } -b_1.$$
$$(a_1b_2 - a_2b_1)x = c_1b_2 - c_2b_1$$
$$x = \frac{c_1b_2 - c_2b_1}{a_1b_2 - a_2b_1} \quad (\text{if } a_1b_2 - a_2b_1 \neq 0)$$

To solve for y, we multiply each side of equation (1) by $-a_2$ and each side of equation (2) by a_1 and add.

$$-a_1a_2x - a_2b_1y = -a_2c_1 \qquad \text{Multiply equation (1) by } -a_2.$$
$$a_1a_2x + a_1b_2y = a_1c_2 \qquad \text{Multiply equation (2) by } a_1.$$
$$(a_1b_2 - a_2b_1)y = a_1c_2 - a_2c_1$$
$$y = \frac{a_1c_2 - a_2c_1}{a_1b_2 - a_2b_1} \quad (\text{if } a_1b_2 - a_2b_1 \neq 0)$$

Both numerators and the common denominator of these values for x and y can be written as determinants because

$$a_1c_2 - a_2c_1 = \begin{vmatrix} a_1 & c_1 \\ a_2 & c_2 \end{vmatrix},$$

$$c_1b_2 - c_2b_1 = \begin{vmatrix} c_1 & b_1 \\ c_2 & b_2 \end{vmatrix},$$

and

$$a_1b_2 - a_2b_1 = \begin{vmatrix} a_1 & b_1 \\ a_2 & b_2 \end{vmatrix}.$$

Using these results, the solutions for x and y become

$$x = \frac{\begin{vmatrix} c_1 & b_1 \\ c_2 & b_2 \end{vmatrix}}{\begin{vmatrix} a_1 & b_1 \\ a_2 & b_2 \end{vmatrix}} \quad \text{and} \quad y = \frac{\begin{vmatrix} a_1 & c_1 \\ a_2 & c_2 \end{vmatrix}}{\begin{vmatrix} a_1 & b_1 \\ a_2 & b_2 \end{vmatrix}}, \quad \begin{vmatrix} a_1 & b_1 \\ a_2 & b_2 \end{vmatrix} \neq 0.$$

For convenience, denote the three determinants in the solution as

$$\begin{vmatrix} a_1 & b_1 \\ a_2 & b_2 \end{vmatrix} = D, \quad \begin{vmatrix} c_1 & b_1 \\ c_2 & b_2 \end{vmatrix} = D_x, \quad \text{and} \quad \begin{vmatrix} a_1 & c_1 \\ a_2 & c_2 \end{vmatrix} = D_y.$$

Notice that the elements of D are the four coefficients of the variables in the given system; the elements of D_x are obtained by replacing the coefficients of x by the respective constants; the elements of D_y are obtained by replacing the coefficients of y by the respective constants.

These results are summarized as **Cramer's rule.**

Cramer's Rule for 2 × 2 Systems

Given the system

$$\begin{aligned} a_1x + b_1y &= c_1 \\ a_2x + b_2y &= c_2 \quad \text{with} \quad a_1b_2 - a_2b_1 = D \neq 0, \end{aligned}$$

then

$$x = \frac{\begin{vmatrix} c_1 & b_1 \\ c_2 & b_2 \end{vmatrix}}{\begin{vmatrix} a_1 & b_1 \\ a_2 & b_2 \end{vmatrix}} = \frac{D_x}{D} \quad \text{and} \quad y = \frac{\begin{vmatrix} a_1 & c_1 \\ a_2 & c_2 \end{vmatrix}}{\begin{vmatrix} a_1 & b_1 \\ a_2 & b_2 \end{vmatrix}} = \frac{D_y}{D}.$$

NOTE

Swiss mathematician and physicist Gabriel Cramer (1704–1752) was looking for a method to determine the equation of a curve given several points on the curve. In 1750, he wrote down the general equation for a curve and then substituted each point for which he had two coordinates into the equation. For the resulting system of equations, he gave "a rule very convenient and general to solve any number of equations and unknowns which are of no more than first degree." This is the rule that now bears his name. (*Source:* Lial, Margaret L., Hornsby, John, and Schneider, David I., *College Algebra,* Eighth Edition, Addison-Wesley, 2001.)

4 Apply Cramer's rule to solve linear systems. To use Cramer's rule to solve a system of equations, find the three determinants, D, D_x, and D_y, and then write the necessary quotients for x and y.

CAUTION

As indicated in the box, Cramer's rule does not apply if $D = a_1b_2 - a_2b_1$ is 0. When $D = 0$, the system is inconsistent or has dependent equations. For this reason, it is a good idea to evaluate D first.

4 Solve each system using Cramer's rule.

(a) $x + y = 5$
$x - y = 1$

(b) $2x - 3y = -26$
$3x + 4y = 12$

(c) $4x - 5y = -8$
$3x + 7y = -6$

ANSWERS
4. (a) $\{(3, 2)\}$ **(b)** $\{(-4, 6)\}$ **(c)** $\{(-2, 0)\}$

Example 4 Using Cramer's Rule to Solve a 2 × 2 System

Use Cramer's rule to solve the system.

$$5x + 7y = -1$$
$$6x + 8y = 1$$

By Cramer's rule, $x = \frac{D_x}{D}$ and $y = \frac{D_y}{D}$. As previously mentioned, it is a good idea to find D first since if $D = 0$, Cramer's rule does not apply. If $D \neq 0$, then find D_x and D_y.

$$D = \begin{vmatrix} 5 & 7 \\ 6 & 8 \end{vmatrix} = 5(8) - 7(6) = -2$$

$$D_x = \begin{vmatrix} -1 & 7 \\ 1 & 8 \end{vmatrix} = -1(8) - 7(1) = -15$$

$$D_y = \begin{vmatrix} 5 & -1 \\ 6 & 1 \end{vmatrix} = 5(1) - (-1)6 = 11$$

From Cramer's rule,

$$x = \frac{D_x}{D} = \frac{-15}{-2} = \frac{15}{2} \quad \text{and} \quad y = \frac{D_y}{D} = \frac{11}{-2} = -\frac{11}{2}.$$

The solution set is $\{(\frac{15}{2}, -\frac{11}{2})\}$, as can be verified by checking in the given system.

Work Problem 4 at the Side.

In a similar manner, Cramer's rule can be applied to systems of three equations with three variables.

Cramer's Rule for 3 × 3 Systems

Given the system

$$a_1x + b_1y + c_1z = d_1$$
$$a_2x + b_2y + c_2z = d_2$$
$$a_3x + b_3y + c_3z = d_3$$

with

$$D_x = \begin{vmatrix} d_1 & b_1 & c_1 \\ d_2 & b_2 & c_2 \\ d_3 & b_3 & c_3 \end{vmatrix}, \quad D_y = \begin{vmatrix} a_1 & d_1 & c_1 \\ a_2 & d_2 & c_2 \\ a_3 & d_3 & c_3 \end{vmatrix},$$

$$D_z = \begin{vmatrix} a_1 & b_1 & d_1 \\ a_2 & b_2 & d_2 \\ a_3 & b_3 & d_3 \end{vmatrix}, \quad D = \begin{vmatrix} a_1 & b_1 & c_1 \\ a_2 & b_2 & c_2 \\ a_3 & b_3 & c_3 \end{vmatrix} \neq 0,$$

then

$$x = \frac{D_x}{D}, \quad y = \frac{D_y}{D}, \quad \text{and} \quad z = \frac{D_z}{D}.$$

Example 5 **Using Cramer's Rule to Solve a 3 × 3 System**

Use Cramer's rule to solve the system.

$$\begin{aligned} x + y - z + 2 &= 0 \\ 2x - y + z + 5 &= 0 \\ x - 2y + 3z - 4 &= 0 \end{aligned}$$

To use Cramer's rule, first rewrite the system in the form

$$\begin{aligned} x + y - z &= -2 \\ 2x - y + z &= -5 \\ x - 2y + 3z &= 4. \end{aligned}$$

Expand by minors about row 1 to find D.

$$\begin{aligned} D &= \begin{vmatrix} 1 & 1 & -1 \\ 2 & -1 & 1 \\ 1 & -2 & 3 \end{vmatrix} \\ &= 1\begin{vmatrix} -1 & 1 \\ -2 & 3 \end{vmatrix} - 1\begin{vmatrix} 2 & 1 \\ 1 & 3 \end{vmatrix} + (-1)\begin{vmatrix} 2 & -1 \\ 1 & -2 \end{vmatrix} \\ &= 1(-1) - 1(5) - 1(-3) \\ &= -3 \end{aligned}$$

Expanding D_x by minors about row 1 gives

$$\begin{aligned} D_x &= \begin{vmatrix} -2 & 1 & -1 \\ -5 & -1 & 1 \\ 4 & -2 & 3 \end{vmatrix} \\ &= -2\begin{vmatrix} -1 & 1 \\ -2 & 3 \end{vmatrix} - 1\begin{vmatrix} -5 & 1 \\ 4 & 3 \end{vmatrix} + (-1)\begin{vmatrix} -5 & -1 \\ 4 & -2 \end{vmatrix} \\ &= -2(-1) - 1(-19) - 1(14) \\ &= 7. \end{aligned}$$

Work Problem 5 at the Side.

Using the results for D and D_x and the results from Problem 5 at the side, apply Cramer's rule to get

$$x = \frac{D_x}{D} = \frac{7}{-3} = -\frac{7}{3}, \quad y = \frac{D_y}{D} = \frac{-22}{-3} = \frac{22}{3}, \quad z = \frac{D_z}{D} = \frac{-21}{-3} = 7.$$

Check that the solution set is $\{(-\frac{7}{3}, \frac{22}{3}, 7)\}$.

Work Problem 6 at the Side.

As mentioned earlier, Cramer's rule does not apply when $D = 0$. The next example illustrates this case.

5 Find D_y and D_z for Example 5.

6 Solve each system using Cramer's rule.

(a) $$\begin{aligned} x + y + z &= 2 \\ 2x - z &= -3 \\ y + 2z &= 4 \end{aligned}$$

(b) $$\begin{aligned} 3x - 2y + 4z &= 5 \\ 4x + y + z &= 14 \\ x - y - z &= 1 \end{aligned}$$

ANSWERS

5. $D_y = -22$ and $D_z = -21$

6. (a) $\{(-1, 2, 1)\}$ **(b)** $\{(3, 2, 0)\}$

7 Solve by Cramer's rule (if applicable).

$$\begin{aligned} x - y + z &= 6 \\ 3x + 2y + z &= 4 \\ 2x - 2y + 2z &= 14 \end{aligned}$$

Example 6 **Determining When Cramer's Rule Does Not Apply**

Use Cramer's rule to solve the system.

$$\begin{aligned} 2x - 3y + 4z &= 8 \\ 6x - 9y + 12z &= 24 \\ x + 2y - 3z &= 5 \end{aligned}$$

First, find D.

$$\begin{aligned} D &= \begin{vmatrix} 2 & -3 & 4 \\ 6 & -9 & 12 \\ 1 & 2 & -3 \end{vmatrix} \\ &= 2\begin{vmatrix} -9 & 12 \\ 2 & -3 \end{vmatrix} - 6\begin{vmatrix} -3 & 4 \\ 2 & -3 \end{vmatrix} + 1\begin{vmatrix} -3 & 4 \\ -9 & 12 \end{vmatrix} \\ &= 2(3) - 6(1) + 1(0) \\ &= 0 \end{aligned}$$

Since $D = 0$ here, Cramer's rule does not apply and we must use another method to solve the system. Multiplying each side of the first equation by 3 shows that the first two equations have the same solution set, so this system has dependent equations and an infinite solution set.

Work Problem 7 at the Side.

ANSWERS

7. Cramer's rule does not apply.

Appendix B EXERCISES

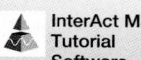

FOR EXTRA HELP — Student's Solutions Manual · MyMathLab.com · InterAct Math Tutorial Software · AW Math Tutor Center · www.mathxl.com

Decide whether each statement is true *or* false.

1. A matrix is an array of numbers, while a determinant is just a number.

true

2. A square matrix has the same number of rows as columns.

true

3. The determinant $\begin{vmatrix} a & b \\ c & d \end{vmatrix}$ is equal to $ad + bc$.

false

4. The value of $\begin{vmatrix} 0 & 0 \\ x & y \end{vmatrix}$ is 0 for any replacements for x and y.

true

Evaluate each determinant. See Example 1.

5. $\begin{vmatrix} -2 & 5 \\ -1 & 4 \end{vmatrix}$

-3

6. $\begin{vmatrix} 3 & -6 \\ 2 & -2 \end{vmatrix}$

6

7. $\begin{vmatrix} 1 & -2 \\ 7 & 0 \end{vmatrix}$

14

8. $\begin{vmatrix} -5 & -1 \\ 1 & 0 \end{vmatrix}$

1

9. $\begin{vmatrix} 0 & 4 \\ 0 & 4 \end{vmatrix}$

0

10. $\begin{vmatrix} 8 & -3 \\ 0 & 0 \end{vmatrix}$

0

Evaluate each determinant using expansion by minors about the first column. See Example 2.

11. $\begin{vmatrix} -1 & 2 & 4 \\ -3 & -2 & -3 \\ 2 & -1 & 5 \end{vmatrix}$

59

12. $\begin{vmatrix} 2 & -3 & -5 \\ 1 & 2 & 2 \\ 5 & 3 & -1 \end{vmatrix}$

-14

13. $\begin{vmatrix} 1 & 0 & -2 \\ 0 & 2 & 3 \\ 1 & 0 & 5 \end{vmatrix}$

14

14. $\begin{vmatrix} 2 & -1 & 0 \\ 0 & -1 & 1 \\ 1 & 2 & 0 \end{vmatrix}$

-5

15. $\begin{vmatrix} 1 & 0 & 0 \\ 0 & 1 & 0 \\ 0 & 0 & 1 \end{vmatrix}$

1

16. $\begin{vmatrix} 0 & 0 & 1 \\ 0 & 1 & 0 \\ 1 & 0 & 0 \end{vmatrix}$

-1

Evaluate each determinant by expansion about any row or column. (Hint: If possible, choose a row or column with 0s.) See Example 3.

17. $\begin{vmatrix} 4 & 4 & 2 \\ 1 & -1 & -2 \\ 1 & 0 & 2 \end{vmatrix}$

-22

18. $\begin{vmatrix} 3 & -1 & 2 \\ 1 & 5 & -2 \\ 0 & 2 & 0 \end{vmatrix}$

16

19. $\begin{vmatrix} 2 & 0 & 1 \\ -1 & 0 & 2 \\ 5 & 0 & 4 \end{vmatrix}$

0

20. $\begin{vmatrix} 2 & -4 & 0 \\ 3 & -5 & 0 \\ 6 & -7 & 0 \end{vmatrix}$

0

21. $\begin{vmatrix} -6 & 3 & 5 \\ -3 & 2 & 2 \\ 0 & 0 & 0 \end{vmatrix}$

0

22. $\begin{vmatrix} 0 & 0 & 0 \\ 4 & 0 & -2 \\ 2 & -1 & 3 \end{vmatrix}$

0

23. $\begin{vmatrix} 3 & 5 & -2 \\ 1 & -4 & 1 \\ 3 & 1 & -2 \end{vmatrix}$

20

24. $\begin{vmatrix} 1 & 3 & 2 \\ 3 & -1 & -2 \\ 1 & 10 & 20 \end{vmatrix}$

−124

25. For the system

$$8x - 4y = 8$$
$$x + 3y = 22,$$

$D_x = 112$, $D_y = 168$, and $D = 28$. What is the solution set of the system?

{(4, 6)}

26. For the system

$$x + 3y - 6z = 7$$
$$2x - y + z = 1$$
$$x + 2y + 2z = -1,$$

the solution set is $\{(1, 0, -1)\}$ and $D = -43$. Find the values of D_x, D_y, and D_z.

$D_x = -43$; $D_y = 0$; $D_z = 43$

Use Cramer's rule to solve each system. See Example 4.

27. $3x + 5y = -5$
$-2x + 3y = 16$

{(−5, 2)}

28. $5x + 2y = -3$
$4x - 3y = -30$

{(−3, 6)}

29. $3x + 2y = 3$
$2x - 4y = 2$

{(1, 0)}

30. $7x - 2y = 6$
$4x - 5y = 15$

{(0, −3)}

31. $8x + 3y = 1$
$6x - 5y = 2$

$\left\{\left(\frac{11}{58}, -\frac{5}{29}\right)\right\}$

32. $3x - y = 9$
$2x + 5y = 8$

$\left\{\left(\frac{53}{17}, \frac{6}{17}\right)\right\}$

Use Cramer's rule (where applicable) to solve each system. If Cramer's rule does not apply, say so. See Examples 5 and 6.

33. $2x + 3y + 2z = 15$
$x - y + 2z = 5$
$x + 2y - 6z = -26$

{(−2, 3, 5)}

34. $x - y + 6z = 19$
$3x + 3y - z = 1$
$x + 9y + 2z = -19$

{(4, −3, 2)}

35. $2x + 2y + z = 10$
$4x - y + z = 20$
$-x + y - 2z = -5$

{(5, 0, 0)}

36. $x + 3y - 4z = -12$
$3x + y - z = -5$
$5x - y + z = -3$

{(−1, 3, 5)}

37. $2x - 3y + 4z = 8$
$6x - 9y + 12z = 24$
$-4x + 6y - 8z = -16$

Cramer's rule does not apply.

38. $7x + y - z = 4$
$2x - 3y + z = 2$
$-6x + 9y - 3z = -6$

Cramer's rule does not apply.

39. $3x + 5z = 0$
$2x + 3y = 1$
$-y + 2z = -11$

{(20, −13, −12)}

40. $-x + 2y = 4$
$3x + y = -5$
$2x + z = -1$

{(−2, 1, 3)}

41. $x - 3y = 13$
$2y + z = 5$
$-x + z = -7$

$\left\{\left(\frac{62}{5}, -\frac{1}{5}, \frac{27}{5}\right)\right\}$

Appendix C
Synthetic Division

C SYNTHETIC DIVISION

OBJECTIVES

1. Use synthetic division to divide by a polynomial of the form $x - k$.
2. Use the remainder theorem to evaluate a polynomial.
3. Decide whether a given number is a solution of an equation.

1 Use synthetic division to divide by a polynomial of the form $x - k$. Often when one polynomial is divided by a second, the second polynomial is of the form $x - k$, where the coefficient of the x-term is 1. There is a shortcut method for doing these divisions. To see how it works, look at the left below, where the division of $3x^3 - 2x + 5$ by $x - 3$ is shown. Notice that 0 was inserted for the missing x^2-term.

$$
\begin{array}{r}
3x^2 + 9x + 25 \\
x - 3\,\overline{)\,3x^3 + 0x^2 - 2x + 5} \\
\underline{3x^3 - 9x^2} \qquad\qquad \\
9x^2 - 2x \qquad \\
\underline{9x^2 - 27x} \qquad \\
25x + 5 \\
\underline{25x - 75} \\
80
\end{array}
\qquad
\begin{array}{rrrrr}
 & 3 & 9 & 25 & \\
1 - 3\,) & 3 & 0 & -2 & 5 \\
 & \underline{3} & \underline{-9} & & \\
 & & 9 & -2 & \\
 & & \underline{9} & \underline{-27} & \\
 & & & 25 & 5 \\
 & & & \underline{25} & \underline{-75} \\
 & & & & 80
\end{array}
$$

On the right, the same division is shown written without the variables. This is why it is *essential* to use 0 as a placeholder in synthetic division. All the numbers in color on the right are repetitions of the numbers directly above them, so they may be omitted, as shown on the left below.

$$
\begin{array}{rrrrr}
 & 3 & 9 & 25 & \\
1 - 3\,) & 3 & 0 & -2 & 5 \\
 & & \underline{-9} & & \\
 & & 9 & -2 & \\
 & & & \underline{-27} & \\
 & & & 25 & 5 \\
 & & & & \underline{-75} \\
 & & & & 80
\end{array}
\qquad
\begin{array}{rrrrr}
 & 3 & 9 & 25 & \\
1 - 3\,) & 3 & 0 & -2 & 5 \\
 & & \underline{-9} & & \\
 & & 9 & & \\
 & & & \underline{-27} & \\
 & & & 25 & \\
 & & & & \underline{-75} \\
 & & & & 80
\end{array}
$$

The numbers in color on the left are again repetitions of the numbers directly above them; they too may be omitted, as shown on the right above.

Now the problem can be condensed. If the 3 in the dividend is brought down to the beginning of the bottom row, the top row can be omitted since it duplicates the bottom row.

$$
\begin{array}{rrrrr}
1 - 3\,) & 3 & 0 & -2 & 5 \\
 & & -9 & -27 & -75 \\
\hline
 & 3 & 9 & 25 & 80
\end{array}
$$

The 1 at the upper left can be omitted, since it represents $1x$, which will *always* be the first term in the divisor. Also, to simplify the arithmetic, subtraction in the second row is replaced by addition. We compensate for this by changing the -3 at the upper left to its additive inverse, 3. The result of doing all this is shown on the next page.

1 Divide, using synthetic division.

(a) $\dfrac{3z^2 + 10z - 8}{z + 4}$

(b) $(2x^2 + 3x - 5) \div (x + 1)$

$$\begin{array}{r|rrrrl} \text{Additive inverse} \rightarrow 3 & 3 & 0 & -2 & 5 & \\ & & 9 & 27 & 75 & \leftarrow \text{Change signs.} \\ \hline & 3 & 9 & 25 & 80 & \leftarrow \text{Remainder} \end{array}$$

The quotient is read from the bottom row.

$$3x^2 + 9x + 25 + \frac{80}{x - 3}$$

The first three numbers in the bottom row are the coefficients of the quotient polynomial with degree 1 less than the degree of the dividend. The last number gives the remainder.

Synthetic Division

This shortcut method is called **synthetic division.** It is used *only* when dividing a polynomial by a binomial of the form $x - k$.

Example 1 Using Synthetic Division

Use synthetic division to divide $5x^2 + 16x + 15$ by $x + 2$.

As mentioned above, use synthetic division only when dividing by a polynomial of the form $x - k$. Get $x + 2$ in this form by writing it as

$$x + 2 = x - (-2),$$

where $k = -2$. Now write the coefficients of $5x^2 + 16x + 15$, placing -2 to the left.

$$x + 2 \text{ leads to } -2. \rightarrow \begin{array}{r|rrrl} -2 & 5 & 16 & 15 & \leftarrow \text{Coefficients} \end{array}$$

Bring down the 5, and multiply: $-2 \cdot 5 = -10$.

$$\begin{array}{r|rrr} -2 & 5 & 16 & 15 \\ & & -10 & \\ \hline & 5 & & \end{array}$$

Add 16 and -10, getting 6. Multiply 6 and -2 to get -12.

$$\begin{array}{r|rrr} -2 & 5 & 16 & 15 \\ & & -10 & -12 \\ \hline & 5 & 6 & \end{array}$$

Add 15 and -12, getting 3.

$$\begin{array}{r|rrrl} -2 & 5 & 16 & 15 & \\ & & -10 & -12 & \\ \hline & 5 & 6 & 3 & \leftarrow \text{Remainder} \end{array}$$

Read the result from the bottom row.

$$\frac{5x^2 + 16x + 15}{x + 2} = 5x + 6 + \frac{3}{x + 2}$$

Work Problem 1 at the Side.

ANSWERS

1. **(a)** $3z - 2$ **(b)** $2x + 1 + \dfrac{-6}{x + 1}$

Example 2 Using Synthetic Division with a Missing Term

Use synthetic division to find $(-4x^5 + x^4 + 6x^3 + 2x^2 + 50) \div (x - 2)$.

Use the steps given above, inserting a 0 for the missing x-term.

$$\begin{array}{r|rrrrrr} 2 & -4 & 1 & 6 & 2 & 0 & 50 \\ & & -8 & -14 & -16 & -28 & -56 \\ \hline & -4 & -7 & -8 & -14 & -28 & -6 \end{array}$$

Read the result from the bottom row.

$$\frac{-4x^5 + x^4 + 6x^3 + 2x^2 + 50}{x - 2} = -4x^4 - 7x^3 - 8x^2 - 14x - 28 + \frac{-6}{x - 2}$$

Work Problem 2 at the Side.

2 Use the remainder theorem to evaluate a polynomial. We can use synthetic division to evaluate polynomials. For example, in the synthetic division of Example 2, where the polynomial was divided by $x - 2$, the remainder was -6.

Replacing x in the polynomial with 2 gives

$$\begin{aligned} -4x^5 + x^4 + 6x^3 + 2x^2 + 50 &= -4 \cdot 2^5 + 2^4 + 6 \cdot 2^3 + 2 \cdot 2^2 + 50 \\ &= -4 \cdot 32 + 16 + 6 \cdot 8 + 2 \cdot 4 + 50 \\ &= -128 + 16 + 48 + 8 + 50 \\ &= -6, \end{aligned}$$

the same number as the remainder; that is, dividing by $x - 2$ produced a remainder equal to the result when x is replaced with 2. This always happens, as the following remainder theorem states.

Remainder Theorem

If the polynomial $P(x)$ is divided by $x - k$, then the remainder is equal to $P(k)$.

This result is proved in more advanced courses.

Example 3 Using the Remainder Theorem

Let $P(x) = 2x^3 - 5x^2 - 3x + 11$. Find $P(-2)$.

Use the remainder theorem; divide $P(x)$ by $x - (-2)$.

$$\begin{array}{r|rrrr} \text{Value of } x \rightarrow -2 & 2 & -5 & -3 & 11 \\ & & -4 & 18 & -30 \\ \hline & 2 & -9 & 15 & -19 \end{array} \leftarrow \text{Remainder}$$

By this result, $P(-2) = -19$.

Work Problem 3 at the Side.

2 Divide, using synthetic division.

(a) $\dfrac{3a^3 - 2a + 21}{a + 2}$

(b) $(-4x^4 + 3x^3 + 18x + 2) \div (x - 2)$

3 Let $P(x) = x^3 - 5x^2 + 7x - 3$. Use synthetic division to find each value.

(a) $P(1)$ (Divide by $x - 1$.)

(b) $P(-2)$

ANSWERS

2. **(a)** $3a^2 - 6a + 10 + \dfrac{1}{a + 2}$

(b) $-4x^3 - 5x^2 - 10x - 2 + \dfrac{-2}{x - 2}$

3. **(a)** 0 **(b)** -45

4 Use synthetic division to decide whether 2 is a solution of each equation.

(a) $3x^3 - 11x^2 + 17x - 14 = 0$

(b) $4x^5 - 7x^4 - 11x^2 + 2x + 6 = 0$

ANSWERS

4. (a) yes **(b)** no

3 Decide whether a given number is a solution of an equation. The remainder theorem can also be used to show that a given number is a solution of an equation.

Example 4 Using the Remainder Theorem

Show that -5 is a solution of the equation

$$2x^4 + 12x^3 + 6x^2 - 5x + 75 = 0.$$

One way to show that -5 is a solution is to substitute -5 for x in the equation. However, an easier way is to use synthetic division and the remainder theorem.

$$\text{Proposed solution} \rightarrow \begin{array}{r|rrrrr} -5 & 2 & 12 & 6 & -5 & 75 \\ & & -10 & -10 & 20 & -75 \\ \hline & 2 & 2 & -4 & 15 & \mathbf{0} \end{array} \leftarrow \text{Remainder}$$

Since the remainder is 0, the polynomial has a value of 0 when $x = -5$, so -5 is a solution of the given equation.

Work Problem 4 at the Side.

The synthetic division in Example 4 also shows that $x - (-5)$ divides the polynomial with 0 remainder. Thus $x - (-5) = x + 5$ is a *factor* of the polynomial and

$$2x^4 + 12x^3 + 6x^2 - 5x + 75 = (x + 5)(2x^3 + 2x^2 - 4x + 15).$$

The second factor is the quotient polynomial found in the last row of the synthetic division.

Appendix C EXERCISES

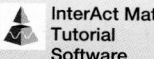

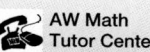

FOR EXTRA HELP: Student's Solutions Manual; MyMathLab.com; InterAct Math Tutorial Software; AW Math Tutor Center; www.mathxl.com

Choose the letter of the correct setup to perform synthetic division on the indicated quotient.

1. $\dfrac{x^2 + 3x - 6}{x - 2}$

A. $-2\overline{)1 \quad 3 \quad -6}$ B. $-2\overline{)-1 \quad -3 \quad 6}$

C. $2\overline{)1 \quad 3 \quad -6}$ D. $2\overline{)-1 \quad -3 \quad 6}$

C

2. $\dfrac{x^3 - 3x^2 + 2}{x - 1}$

A. $1\overline{)1 \quad -3 \quad 2}$ B. $-1\overline{)1 \quad -3 \quad 2}$

C. $1\overline{)1 \quad -3 \quad 0 \quad 2}$ D. $1\overline{)-1 \quad 3 \quad 0 \quad -2}$

C

Use synthetic division to find each quotient. See Examples 1 and 2.

3. $\dfrac{x^2 - 6x + 5}{x - 1}$

$x - 5$

4. $\dfrac{x^2 - 4x - 21}{x + 3}$

$x - 7$

5. $\dfrac{4m^2 + 19m - 5}{m + 5}$

$4m - 1$

6. $\dfrac{3k^2 - 5k - 12}{k - 3}$

$3k + 4$

7. $\dfrac{2a^2 + 8a + 13}{a + 2}$

$2a + 4 + \dfrac{5}{a + 2}$

8. $\dfrac{4y^2 - 5y - 20}{y - 4}$

$4y + 11 + \dfrac{24}{y - 4}$

9. $(p^2 - 3p + 5) \div (p + 1)$

$p - 4 + \dfrac{9}{p + 1}$

10. $(z^2 + 4z - 6) \div (z - 5)$

$z + 9 + \dfrac{39}{z - 5}$

11. $\dfrac{4a^3 - 3a^2 + 2a - 3}{a - 1}$

$4a^2 + a + 3$

12. $\dfrac{5p^3 - 6p^2 + 3p + 14}{p + 1}$

$5p^2 - 11p + 14$

13. $(x^5 - 2x^3 + 3x^2 - 4x - 2) \div (x - 2)$

$x^4 + 2x^3 + 2x^2 + 7x + 10 + \dfrac{18}{x - 2}$

14. $(2y^5 - 5y^4 - 3y^2 - 6y - 23) \div (y - 3)$

$2y^4 + y^3 + 3y^2 + 6y + 12 + \dfrac{13}{y - 3}$

15. $(-4r^6 - 3r^5 - 3r^4 + 5r^3 - 6r^2 + 3r) \div (r - 1)$

$-4r^5 - 7r^4 - 10r^3 - 5r^2 - 11r - 8 + \dfrac{-8}{r - 1}$

16. $(-3t^5 + 2t^4 - 5t^3 + 6t^2 - 3t - 2) \div (t - 2)$

$-3t^4 - 4t^3 - 13t^2 - 20t - 43 + \dfrac{-88}{t - 2}$

17. $(-3y^5 + 2y^4 - 5y^3 - 6y^2 - 1) \div (y + 2)$

$-3y^4 + 8y^3 - 21y^2 + 36y - 72 + \dfrac{143}{y + 2}$

18. $(m^6 + 2m^4 - 5m + 11) \div (m - 2)$

$m^5 + 2m^4 + 6m^3 + 12m^2 + 24m + 43 + \dfrac{97}{m - 2}$

19. $\dfrac{y^3 + 1}{y - 1}$

$y^2 + y + 1 + \dfrac{2}{y - 1}$

20. $\dfrac{z^4 + 81}{z - 3}$

$z^3 + 3z^2 + 9z + 27 + \dfrac{162}{z - 3}$

Use the remainder theorem to find P(k). See Example 3.

21. $P(x) = 2x^3 - 4x^2 + 5x - 3;\ k = 2$

7

22. $P(x) = x^3 + 3x^2 - x + 5;\ k = -1$

8

23. $P(r) = -r^3 - 5r^2 - 4r - 2;\ k = -4$

-2

24. $P(z) = -z^3 + 5z^2 - 3z + 4;\ k = 3$

13

25. $P(x) = 2x^3 - 4x^2 + 5x - 33;\ k = 3$

0

26. $P(x) = x^3 - 3x^2 + 4x - 4;\ k = 2$

0

Use synthetic division to decide whether the given number is a solution of each equation. See Example 4.

27. $x^3 - 2x^2 - 3x + 10 = 0;\ x = -2$

yes

28. $x^3 - 3x^2 - x + 10 = 0;\ x = -2$

no

29. $m^4 + 2m^3 - 3m^2 + 8m - 8 = 0;\ m = -2$

no

30. $r^4 - r^3 - 6r^2 + 5r + 10 = 0;\ r = -2$

yes

31. $3x^3 + 2x^2 - 2x + 11 = 0;\ x = -2$

no

32. $3z^3 + 10z^2 + 3z - 9 = 0;\ z = -2$

no

33. Explain why it is important to insert 0s as placeholders for missing terms before performing synthetic division.

Since the variables are not present, a missing term will not be noticed in synthetic division, so the quotient will be wrong if placeholders are not inserted.

34. Explain why a 0 remainder in synthetic division of $P(x)$ by k indicates that k is a solution of the equation $P(x) = 0$.

By the remainder theorem, a 0 remainder means that $P(k) = 0$; that is, k is the number that makes $P(x) = 0$.

Appendix D
Review of Exponents, Polynomials, and Factoring

(TRANSITION FROM INTRODUCTORY TO INTERMEDIATE ALGEBRA)

D Review of Exponents, Polynomials, and Factoring

Objectives

1. Review the basic rules for exponents.
2. Review addition, subtraction, and multiplication of polynomials.
3. Review factoring techniques.

1 Review the basic rules for exponents. In Sections 6.2 and 6.5 we introduced the following definitions and rules for working with exponents.

Definitions and Rules for Exponents

If no denominators are 0, for any integers m and n:

		Examples
Product rule	$a^m \cdot a^n = a^{m+n}$	$7^4 \cdot 7^3 = 7^7$
Zero exponent	$a^0 = 1$	$(-3)^0 = 1$
Negative exponent	$a^{-n} = \dfrac{1}{a^n}$	$5^{-3} = \dfrac{1}{5^3}$
Quotient rule	$\dfrac{a^m}{a^n} = a^{m-n}$	$\dfrac{2^2}{2^5} = 2^{-3} = \dfrac{1}{2^3}$
Power rules (a)	$(a^m)^n = a^{mn}$	$(4^2)^3 = 4^6$
(b)	$(ab)^m = a^m b^m$	$(3k)^4 = 3^4k^4$
(c)	$\left(\dfrac{a}{b}\right)^m = \dfrac{a^m}{b^m}$	$\left(\dfrac{2}{3}\right)^{10} = \dfrac{2^{10}}{3^{10}}$
Negative to positive rules	$\dfrac{a^{-m}}{b^{-n}} = \dfrac{b^n}{a^m}$	$\dfrac{5^{-3}}{3^{-5}} = \dfrac{3^5}{5^3}$
	$\left(\dfrac{a}{b}\right)^{-m} = \left(\dfrac{b}{a}\right)^m$	$\left(\dfrac{4}{7}\right)^{-2} = \left(\dfrac{7}{4}\right)^2$

Example 1 **Applying Definitions and Rules for Exponents**

Apply the definitions and rules for exponents to simplify each of the following, expressing the final answer using only positive exponents. Assume all variables represent nonzero real numbers.

(a) $(x^2y^{-3})(x^{-5}y^7) = (x^{2+(-5)})(y^{-3+7})$

$$= x^{-3}y^4$$

$$= \frac{1}{x^3}y^4$$

$$= \frac{y^4}{x^3}$$

(b) $(-5)^0 + (-5^0) = 1 + (-1)$ $\quad -5^0 = -1 \cdot 5^0 = -1 \cdot 1 = -1$

$$= 0$$

Continued on Next Page

1 Simplify each expression. Write answers using only positive exponents. Assume all variables represent nonzero real numbers.

(a) $(a^{-4}bc^2)(a^2b^{-2}c^4)$

(b) $4^0 + (-4)^0$

(c) $\dfrac{(x^3y^{-2})^3}{(x^4y^{-3})^2}$

(d) $\left(\dfrac{2x^2y^{-2}}{x^{-4}y}\right)^{-3}$

2 Add or subtract as indicated.

(a) $(5x^3 - 3x^2 + x + 4)$
$+ (2x^3 - x^2 - 3x - 1)$

(b) $(7y^2 - 11y + 8)$
$- (-3y^2 + 4y + 6)$

ANSWERS

1. (a) $\dfrac{c^6}{a^2b}$ (b) 2 (c) x (d) $\dfrac{y^9}{8x^{18}}$
2. (a) $7x^3 - 4x^2 - 2x + 3$
   (b) $10y^2 - 15y + 2$

(c) $\dfrac{(t^5s^{-4})^2}{(t^{-3}s^5)^3} = \dfrac{t^{10}s^{-8}}{t^{-9}s^{15}} = \dfrac{t^{10}t^9}{s^{15}s^8} = \dfrac{t^{19}}{s^{23}}$

(d) $\left(\dfrac{-3x^{-4}y}{x^5y^{-4}}\right)^{-2} = \left(\dfrac{x^5y^{-4}}{-3x^{-4}y}\right)^2 = \dfrac{x^{10}y^{-8}}{9x^{-8}y^2} = \dfrac{x^{18}}{9y^{10}}$

(e) $(2x^2y^3z)^2(x^4y^2)^3 = (4x^4y^6z^2)(x^{12}y^6) = 4x^{16}y^{12}z^2$

Work Problem 1 at the Side.

2 **Review addition, subtraction, and multiplication of polynomials.** These arithmetic operations with polynomials were covered in Sections 6.1, 6.3, and 6.4. We review them here.

Adding and Subtracting Polynomials

To add polynomials, add like terms. To subtract polynomials, change all signs on the second polynomial and add the result to the first polynomial.

Example 2 **Adding and Subtracting Polynomials**

Add or subtract as indicated.

(a) $(-4x^3 + 3x^2 - 8x + 2) + (5x^3 - 8x^2 + 12x - 3)$

$$= (-4 + 5)x^3 + (3 - 8)x^2 + (-8 + 12)x + (2 - 3)$$
$$= x^3 - 5x^2 + 4x - 1$$

(b) $-4(x^2 + 3x - 6) - (2x^2 - 3x + 7)$

$$= -4x^2 - 12x + 24 - 2x^2 + 3x - 7$$
$$= -6x^2 - 9x + 17$$

(c) Subtract.

$$\begin{array}{r} 2t^2 - 3t - 4 \\ -8t^2 + 4t - 1 \\ \hline \end{array}$$

Change the sign of each term in $-8t^2 + 4t - 1$, and add.

$$\begin{array}{rl} 2t^2 - 3t - 4 & \\ 8t^2 - 4t + 1 & \text{Change signs.} \\ \hline 10t^2 - 7t - 3 & \text{Add.} \end{array}$$

Work Problem 2 at the Side.

Multiplying Polynomials

To multiply two polynomials, multiply each term of the second polynomial by each term of the first polynomial and add the products. In particular, when multiplying two binomials, use the FOIL method. (See Section 6.3.)

There are also several special product rules that are useful when multiplying binomials.

Special Product Rules

$$(a + b)^2 = a^2 + 2ab + b^2$$
$$(a - b)^2 = a^2 - 2ab + b^2$$
$$(a + b)(a - b) = a^2 - b^2$$

Example 3 Multiplying Polynomials

Find each product.

(a) $(4y - 1)(3y + 2) = 4y(3y) + 4y(2) - 1(3y) - 1(2)$ FOIL

$= 12y^2 + 8y - 3y - 2$

$= 12y^2 + 5y - 2$

(b) $(3x + 5y)(3x - 5y) = (3x)^2 - (5y)^2$ $(a + b)(a - b) = a^2 - b^2$

$= 9x^2 - 25y^2$

(c) $(2t + 3)^2 = (2t)^2 + 2(2t)(3) + 3^2$ $(a + b)^2 = a^2 + 2ab + b^2$

$= 4t^2 + 12t + 9$

(d) $(5x - 1)^2 = (5x)^2 - 2(5x)(1) + 1^2$ $(a - b)^2 = a^2 - 2ab + b^2$

$= 25x^2 - 10x + 1$

(e) $(3x + 2)(9x^2 - 6x + 4)$

Multiply vertically.

$$\begin{array}{rrrrl} & 9x^2 & -\ 6x & +\ 4 & \\ & & 3x & +\ 2 & \\ \hline & 18x^2 & -\ 12x & +\ 8 & \leftarrow 2(9x^2 - 6x + 4) \\ 27x^3 & -\ 18x^2 & +\ 12x & & \leftarrow 3x(9x^2 - 6x + 4) \\ \hline 27x^3 & & & +\ 8 & \text{Add like terms.} \end{array}$$

The product is the sum of cubes, $27x^3 + 8$.

Work Problem 3 at the Side.

3 Review factoring techniques. Factoring, which involves writing a polynomial as a product, was covered in Chapter 7. Here are some general guidelines to use when factoring.

Factoring a Polynomial

1. Is there a common factor? If so, factor it out.
2. How many terms are in the polynomial?

   Two terms: Check to see whether it is a difference of squares or the sum or difference of cubes. If so, factor as in Section 7.5.

   Three terms: Is it a perfect square trinomial? If the trinomial is not a perfect square, check to see whether the coefficient of the squared term is 1. If so, use the method of Section 7.2. If the coefficient of the squared term of the trinomial is not 1, use the general factoring methods of Sections 7.3 and 7.4.

   Four terms: Try to factor the polynomial by grouping using the methods of Sections 7.1 and 7.3.
3. Can any factors be factored further? If so, factor them.

3 Find each product.

(a) $(2x + 5)(3x - 2)$

(b) $(2t + 7y)(2t - 7y)$

(c) $(6r - 5)^2$

(d) $(2x - 3)(4x^2 + 6x + 9)$

ANSWERS

3. (a) $6x^2 + 11x - 10$ **(b)** $4t^2 - 49y^2$ **(c)** $36r^2 - 60r + 25$ **(d)** $8x^3 - 27$

4 Factor each polynomial completely.

(a) $12x^2 - 5x - 2$

(b) $z^2 - 12z + 36$

(c) $8p^3 + 125$

(d) $xy + 6y + xz + 6z$

Example 4 Factoring Polynomials

Factor each polynomial completely.

(a) $6x^2y^3 - 12x^3y^2 = 6x^2y^2(y - 2x)$ $6x^2y^2$ is the greatest common factor.

(b) $3x^2 - x - 2$

To find the factors, find two terms that multiply to give $3x^2$ ($3x$ and x) and two terms that multiply to give -2 ($+2$ and -1). Make sure that the sum of the outer and inner products in the factored form is $-x$.

$$3x^2 - x - 2 = (3x + 2)(x - 1)$$

To check, multiply the factors using the FOIL method.

(c) $100t^2 - 81 = (10t)^2 - 9^2$ Difference of squares

$= (10t + 9)(10t - 9)$ $a^2 - b^2 = (a + b)(a - b)$

(d) $4x^2 + 20xy + 25y^2$

The terms $4x^2$ and $25y^2$ are both perfect squares, so factor as a perfect square trinomial.

$$4x^2 + 20xy + 25y^2 = (2x + 5y)^2$$

To check, take twice the product of the two terms in the squared binomial.

$$2(2x)(5y) = 20xy$$

Twice — First term — Last term

Since $20xy$ is the middle term of the trinomial, the trinomial is a perfect square and can be factored as $(2x + 5y)^2$.

(e) $1000x^3 - 27 = (10x)^3 - 3^3$ Difference of cubes

$= (10x - 3)[(10x)^2 + 10x(3) + 3^2]$ $a^3 - b^3 = (a - b)(a^2 + ab + b^2)$

$= (10x - 3)(100x^2 + 30x + 9)$

(f) $6xy - 3x + 4y - 2$

Since there are four terms, try factoring by grouping.

$6xy - 3x + 4y - 2 = (6xy - 3x) + (4y - 2)$ Group terms.

$= 3x(2y - 1) + 2(2y - 1)$ Factor each group.

$= (2y - 1)(3x + 2)$ Factor out $2y - 1$.

In the final step, factor out the greatest common factor, the binomial $2y - 1$.

Work Problem 4 at the Side.

ANSWERS

4. (a) $(4x + 1)(3x - 2)$ **(b)** $(z - 6)^2$
(c) $(2p + 5)(4p^2 - 10p + 25)$
(d) $(x + 6)(y + z)$

Appendix D EXERCISES

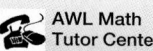

FOR EXTRA HELP: Student's Solutions Manual · MyMathLab.com · InterAct Math Tutorial Software · AWL Math Tutor Center · www.mathxl.com

Apply the definitions and rules for exponents to simplify each expression. Write the final answers using only positive exponents. Assume that all variables represent positive real numbers. See Example 1.

1. $(a^4b^{-3})(a^{-6}b^2)$

$\frac{1}{a^2b}$

2. $(t^{-3}s^{-5})(t^8s^{-2})$

$\frac{t^5}{s^7}$

3. $(5x^{-2}y)^2(2xy^4)^2$

$\frac{100y^{10}}{x^2}$

4. $(7x^{-3}y^4)^3(2x^{-1}y^{-4})^2$

$\frac{1372y^4}{x^{11}}$

5. $-6^0 + (-6)^0$

0

6. $(-12)^0 - 12^0$

0

7. $\frac{(2w^{-1}x^2y^{-1})^3}{(4w^5x^{-2}y)^2}$

$\frac{x^{10}}{2w^{13}y^5}$

8. $\frac{(5p^{-3}q^2r^{-4})^2}{(10p^4q^{-1}r^5)^{-1}}$

$\frac{250q^3}{p^2r^3}$

9. $\left(\frac{-4a^{-2}b^4}{a^3b^{-1}}\right)^{-3}$

$\frac{a^{15}}{-64b^{15}}$

10. $\left(\frac{r^{-3}s^{-8}}{-6r^2s^{-4}}\right)^{-2}$

$36r^{10}s^8$

11. $(7x^{-4}y^2z^{-2})^{-2}(7x^4y^{-1}z^3)^2$

$\frac{x^{16}z^{10}}{y^6}$

12. $(3m^{-5}n^2p^{-4})^3(3m^4n^{-3}p^5)^{-2}$

$\frac{3n^{12}}{m^{23}p^{22}}$

Add or subtract as indicated. See Example 2.

13. $(2a^4 + 3a^3 - 6a^2 + 5a - 12) + (-8a^4 + 8a^3 - 14a^2 + 21a - 3)$

$-6a^4 + 11a^3 - 20a^2 + 26a - 15$

14. $(-6r^4 - 3r^3 + 12r^2 - 9r + 9) + (8r^4 - 13r^3 - 14r^2 - 10r - 3)$

$2r^4 - 16r^3 - 2r^2 - 19r + 6$

15. $(6x^3 - 12x^2 + 3x - 4) - (-2x^3 + 6x^2 - 3x + 12)$

$8x^3 - 18x^2 + 6x - 16$

16. $(10y^3 - 4y^2 + 8y + 7) - (7y^3 + 5y^2 - 2y - 13)$

$3y^3 - 9y^2 + 10y + 20$

17. Add.

$$\begin{array}{r} 5x^2y + 2xy^2 + y^3 \\ \underline{-4x^2y - 3xy^2 + 5y^3} \\ x^2y - xy^2 + 6y^3 \end{array}$$

18. Add.

$$\begin{array}{r} 6ab^3 - 2a^2b^2 + 3b^5 \\ \underline{8ab^3 + 12a^2b^2 - 8b^5} \\ 14ab^3 + 10a^2b^2 - 5b^5 \end{array}$$

19. $3(5x^2 - 12x + 4) - 2(9x^2 + 13x - 10)$

$-3x^2 - 62x + 32$

20. $-4(2t^3 - 3t^2 + 4t - 1) - 3(-8t^3 + 3t^2 - 2t + 9)$

$16t^3 + 3t^2 - 10t - 23$

21. Subtract.

$$\begin{array}{r} 6x^3 - 2x^2 + 3x - 1 \\ \underline{-4x^3 + 2x^2 - 6x + 3} \\ 10x^3 - 4x^2 + 9x - 4 \end{array}$$

22. Subtract.

$$\begin{array}{r} -9y^3 - 2y^2 + 3y - 8 \\ \underline{-8y^3 + 4y^2 + 3y + 1} \\ -y^3 - 6y^2 - 9 \end{array}$$

Find each product. See Example 3.

23. $(3x + 1)(2x - 7)$

$6x^2 - 19x - 7$

24. $(5z + 3)(2z - 3)$

$10z^2 - 9z - 9$

25. $(4x - 1)(x - 2)$

$4x^2 - 9x + 2$

26. $(7t - 3)(t - 4)$
$7t^2 - 31t + 12$

27. $(4t + 3)(4t - 3)$
$16t^2 - 9$

28. $(6x + 1)(6x - 1)$
$36x^2 - 1$

29. $(2y^2 + 4)(2y^2 - 4)$
$4y^4 - 16$

30. $(3b^3 + 2t)(3b^3 - 2t)$
$9b^6 - 4t^2$

31. $(4x - 3)^2$
$16x^2 - 24x + 9$

32. $(9t + 2)^2$
$81t^2 + 36t + 4$

33. $(6r + 5y)^2$
$36r^2 + 60ry + 25y^2$

34. $(8m - 3n)^2$
$64m^2 - 48mn + 9n^2$

35. $(c + 2d)(c^2 - 2cd + 4d^2)$
$c^3 + 8d^3$

36. $(f + 3g)(f^2 - 3fg + 9g^2)$
$f^3 + 27g^3$

37. $(4x - 1)(16x^2 + 4x + 1)$
$64x^3 - 1$

38. $(5r - 2)(25r^2 + 10r + 4)$
$125r^3 - 8$

39. $(7t + 5s)(2t^2 + 5st - s^2)$
$14t^3 + 45st^2 + 18s^2t - 5s^3$

40. $(8p + 3q)(2p^2 - 4pq + q^2)$
$16p^3 - 26p^2q - 4pq^2 + 3q^3$

Factor each polynomial completely. See Example 4.

41. $8x^3y^4 + 12x^2y^3 + 36xy^4$
$4xy^3(2x^2y + 3x + 9y)$

42. $10m^5n + 4m^2n^3 + 18m^3n^2$
$2m^2n(5m^3 + 2n^2 + 9mn)$

43. $x^2 - 2x - 15$
$(x + 3)(x - 5)$

44. $x^2 + x - 12$
$(x + 4)(x - 3)$

45. $2x^2 - 9x - 18$
$(2x + 3)(x - 6)$

46. $3x^2 + 2x - 8$
$(3x - 4)(x + 2)$

47. $36t^2 - 25$

$(6t + 5)(6t - 5)$

48. $49r^2 - 9$

$(7r + 3)(7r - 3)$

49. $16t^2 + 24t + 9$

$(4t + 3)^2$

50. $25t^2 + 90t + 81$

$(5t + 9)^2$

51. $4m^2p - 12mnp + 9n^2p$

$p(2m - 3n)^2$

52. $16p^2r - 40pqr + 25q^2r$

$r(4p - 5q)^2$

53. $x^3 + 1$

$(x + 1)(x^2 - x + 1)$

54. $x^3 + 27$

$(x + 3)(x^2 - 3x + 9)$

55. $8t^3 + 125$

$(2t + 5)(4t^2 - 10t + 25)$

56. $27s^3 + 64$

$(3s + 4)(9s^2 - 12s + 16)$

57. $t^6 - 125$

$(t^2 - 5)(t^4 + 5t^2 + 25)$

58. $w^6 - 27$

$(w^2 - 3)(w^4 + 3w^2 + 9)$

59. $5xt + 15xr + 2yt + 6yr$

$(5x + 2y)(t + 3r)$

60. $3am + 18mb + 2an + 12nb$

$(3m + 2n)(a + 6b)$

61. $6ar + 12br - 5as - 10bs$

$(6r - 5s)(a + 2b)$

62. $7mt + 35ms - 2nt - 10ns$

$(7m - 2n)(t + 5s)$

63. $t^4 - 1$

$(t^2 + 1)(t + 1)(t - 1)$

64. $r^4 - 81$

$(r^2 + 9)(r + 3)(r - 3)$

65. $4x^2 + 12xy + 9y^2 - 1$

$(2x + 3y - 1)(2x + 3y + 1)$

66. $81t^2 + 36ty + 4y^2 - 9$

$(9t + 2y - 3)(9t + 2y + 3)$

Answers to Selected Exercises

In this section we provide the answers that we think most students will obtain when they work the exercises using the methods explained in the text. If your answer does not look exactly like the one given here, it is not necessarily wrong. In many cases there are equivalent forms of the answer that are correct. For example, if the answer section shows $\frac{3}{4}$ and your answer is .75, you have obtained the correct answer but written it in a different (yet equivalent) form. Unless the directions specify otherwise, .75 is just as valid an answer as $\frac{3}{4}$.

In general, if your answer does not agree with the one given in the text, see whether it can be transformed into the other form. If it can, then it is the correct answer. If you still have doubts, talk with your instructor.

Diagnostic Pretest

(page xxix)

1. **(a)** 18 **(b)** $\frac{253}{24}$ or $10\frac{13}{24}$ **2.** 28.322 **3.** **(a)** .0099 **(b)** 472% **4.** 56 **5.** 0 **6.** 4 **7.** $\{-2\}$ **8.** New York: 7,420,166; Los Angeles: 3,597,556 **9.** 58°, 122°

10. $\left(-\infty, \frac{1}{2}\right]$

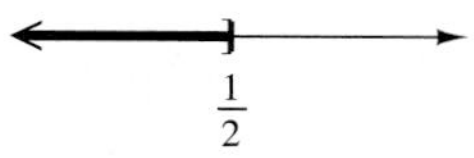

11. $(-4, 5]$

12. $\left\{-\frac{5}{8}, \frac{13}{2}\right\}$

13. x-intercept: $(-5, 0)$; y-intercept: $(0, 3)$

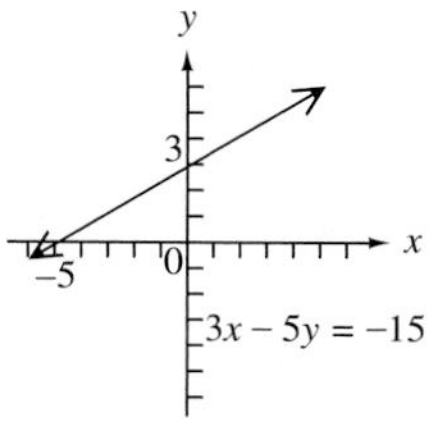

14. $-\frac{11}{7}$

15.

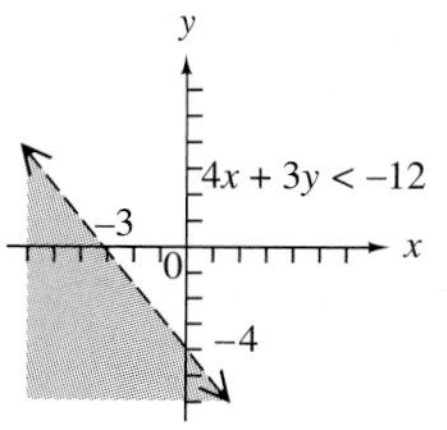

16. B; Set A includes two ordered pairs with the same first component and different second components, so it is not a function. **17.** $\{(-8, -1)\}$ **18.** $\{(5, -3)\}$ **19.** $\{(1, -2, 3)\}$

20. 20 lb of nuts, 12 lb of raisins **21.** $-2m^3 - 9m - 5$ **22.** $49z^2 + 42zw + 9w^2$ **23.** $-\frac{3}{10}$ **24.** **(a)** 4.45×10^8 **(b)** .000234 **25.** $(3x - 4)(x + 2)$ **26.** $\{-3, 5\}$ **27.** 15 in. by 11 in. **28.** $\frac{z + 4}{z + 1}$ **29.** $\frac{5x^2 + 11x + 12}{(x + 3)(x - 3)}$ **30.** $4x + 1$ **31.** $\frac{16m^{10}}{n^6}$ **32.** $5y^2z^3\sqrt[3]{2yz^2}$ **33.** $\{7\}$ **34.** 89 **35.** $\left\{-5, -\frac{1}{3}\right\}$ **36.** $\left\{\frac{-5 + \sqrt{37}}{6}, \frac{-5 - \sqrt{37}}{6}\right\}$

37. east: 60 mi; south: 45 mi

38. vertex: (3, 5)
domain: $(-\infty, \infty)$
range: $(-\infty, 5]$

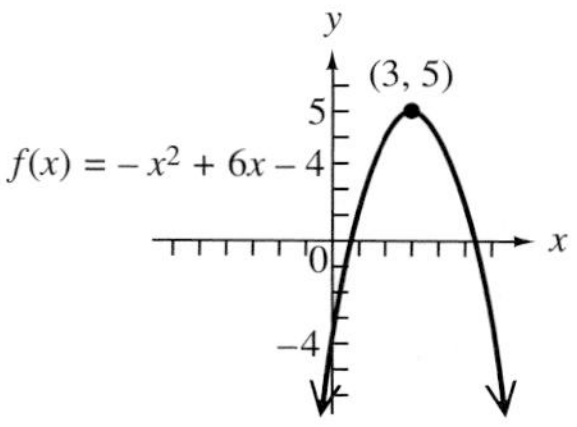

39. $f^{-1}(x) = \sqrt[3]{x + 8}$ **40.** $\{2\}$ **41.** $\{27\}$ **42.** $\{8\}$ **43.** **(a)** 12 **(b)** 13 **(c)** $4x^2 - 4x + 4$ **(d)** $2x^2 + 5$

44.

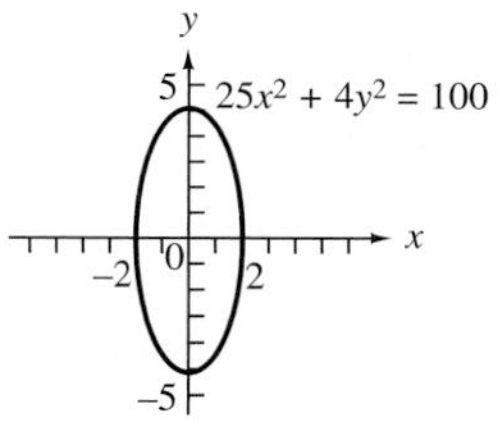

45. $\{(-1, -3), (3, 5)\}$

Chapter R

Section R.1 (page 11)

1. true **3.** False; the fraction $\frac{17}{51}$ can be simplified to $\frac{1}{3}$. **5.** False; *product* indicates multiplication, so the product of 8 and 2 is 16. **7.** prime **9.** composite **11.** composite **13.** neither **15.** $2 \cdot 3 \cdot 5$ **17.** $2 \cdot 2 \cdot 3 \cdot 3 \cdot 7$ **19.** $2 \cdot 2 \cdot 31$ **21.** 29 **23.** $\frac{1}{2}$ **25.** $\frac{5}{6}$ **27.** $\frac{1}{5}$ **29.** $\frac{6}{5}$ **31.** A **33.** $\frac{24}{35}$ **35.** $\frac{6}{25}$ **37.** $\frac{6}{5}$ **39.** $\frac{232}{15}$ or $15\frac{7}{15}$ **41.** $\frac{10}{3}$ **43.** 12 **45.** $\frac{1}{16}$ **47.** $\frac{84}{47}$ or $1\frac{37}{47}$ **49.** Multiply the first fraction (the dividend) by the reciprocal of the second fraction (the divisor) to divide two fractions. **51.** $\frac{2}{3}$ **53.** $\frac{8}{9}$ **55.** $\frac{27}{8}$ or $3\frac{3}{8}$ **57.** $\frac{17}{36}$

59. $\frac{11}{12}$ **61.** $\frac{4}{3}$ **63.** 6 cups **65.** $618\frac{3}{4}$ ft **67.** $\frac{9}{16}$ in. **69.** $\frac{5}{16}$ in. **71.** $\frac{1}{20}$ **73.** More than $1\frac{1}{25}$ million

Section R.2 (page 23)

1. (a) 6 **(b)** 9 **(c)** 1 **(d)** 7 **(e)** 4 **3. (a)** 46.25 **(b)** 46.2 **(c)** 46 **(d)** 50 **5.** C **7.** B **9.** $\frac{4}{10}$ **11.** $\frac{64}{100}$ **13.** $\frac{138}{1000}$ **15.** $\frac{3805}{1000}$ **17.** 139; 143.094 **19.** 27; 25.61 **21.** 10; 15.33 **23.** 82; 81.716 **25.** 15; 15.211 **27.** .006; .006 **29.** 90; 116.48 **31.** 6; 7.15 **33.** 2; 2.05 **35.** 6000; 5711.6 **37.** .2; .162 **39.** To add or subtract decimals, line up the decimal points in a column, add or subtract as usual, and move the decimal point straight down in the sum or difference. **41.** .125 **43.** .25 **45.** $.\overline{5}$; .556 **47.** $.1\overline{6}$; .167 **49.** To convert a decimal to a percent, move the decimal point two places to the right and attach a percent symbol (%). **51.** .54 **53.** 1.17 **55.** .024 **57.** .0625 **59.** .008 **61.** 75% **63.** .4% **65.** 128% **67.** 30% **69.** 75% **71.** $83.\overline{3}\,\%$ **73. (a)** $\frac{2}{32}$ **(b)** $\frac{2}{32}$

Chapter 1

Section 1.1 (page 31)

1. true **3.** False; using the guidelines for order of operations gives $4 + 3(8 - 2) = 4 + 3(6) = 4 + 18 = 22$. **5.** False; the correct translation is $4 = 16 - 12$. **7.** 49 **9.** 144 **11.** 64 **13.** 1000 **15.** 81 **17.** 1024 **19.** $\frac{16}{81}$ **21.** .000064 **23.** The 4 would be applied last because we work first inside the parentheses. **25.** 58 **27.** 13 **29.** 32 **31.** 19 **33.** $\frac{49}{30}$ **35.** 12 **37.** 36.14 **39.** 26 **41.** 4 **43.** 95 **45.** 12 **47.** 14 **49.** $\frac{19}{2}$ **51.** false **53.** true **55.** true **57.** false **59.** false **61.** true **63.** $15 = 5 + 10$ **65.** $9 > 5 - 4$ **67.** $16 \neq 19$ **69.** $2 \leq 3$ **71.** Seven is less than nineteen. True **73.** One-third is not equal to three-tenths. True **75.** Eight is greater than or equal to eleven. False **77.** $30 > 5$ **79.** $3 \leq 12$ **81.** United States and Netherlands **83.** United States, Netherlands, and France

Section 1.2 (page 37)

1. 10 **3.** $12 + x$; 21 **5.** expression; equation **7.** The equation would be $5x - 9 = 49$. **9.** Answers will vary. Two such pairs are $x = 0, y = 6$ and $x = 1, y = 4$. To find a pair, choose one number, substitute it for a variable, then calculate the value for the other variable. **11. (a)** 64 **(b)** 144 **13. (a)** $\frac{7}{8}$ **(b)** $\frac{13}{12}$ **15. (a)** 9.569 **(b)** 14.353 **17. (a)** 52 **(b)** 114 **19. (a)** 12 **(b)** 33 **21. (a)** 6 **(b)** $\frac{9}{5}$ **23. (a)** $\frac{4}{3}$ **(b)** $\frac{13}{6}$ **25. (a)** $\frac{2}{7}$ **(b)** $\frac{16}{27}$ **27. (a)** 12 **(b)** 55 **29. (a)** 1 **(b)** $\frac{28}{17}$ **31. (a)** 3.684 **(b)** 8.841 **33.** $12x$ **35.** $x - 2$ **37.** $7 - 4x$ **39.** $2x - 6$ **41.** $\frac{12}{x + 3}$ **43.** $6(x - 4)$ **45.** The word *and* does not signify addition here. In the phrase "the product of a number and 6," *and* connects two quantities to be multiplied. **47.** no **49.** yes **51.** yes **53.** no **55.** yes **57.** yes **59.** $x + 8 = 18$ **61.** $2x + 5 = 5$ **63.** $16 - \frac{3}{4}x = 13$ **65.** $3x = 2x + 8$ **67.** expression **69.** equation **71.** $10.50; less by $.33 **73.** $12.41; more by $.04

Section 1.3 (page 47)

1. 4 **3.** 0 **5.** One example is $\sqrt{12}$. There are others. **7. (a)** 3, 7 **(b)** 0, 3, 7 **(c)** $-9, 0, 3, 7$ **(d)** $-9, -1\frac{1}{4}, -\frac{3}{5}, 0, 3, 5.9, 7$ **(e)** $-\sqrt{7}, \sqrt{5}$ **(f)** All are real numbers. **9.** 93,000 **11.** $-31{,}532$

13.

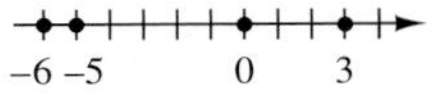

15.

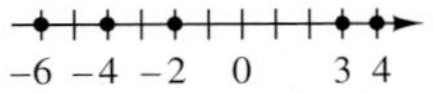

17.

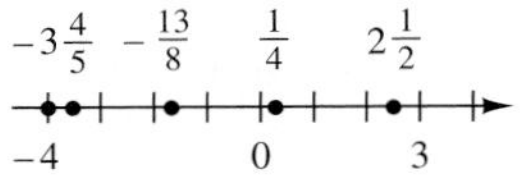

19. -11 **21.** -21 **23.** -100 **25.** $-\frac{2}{3}$ **27.** false **29.** true **31. (a)** 2 **(b)** 2 **33. (a)** -6 **(b)** 6 **35. (a)** $\frac{3}{4}$ **(b)** $\frac{3}{4}$ **37.** 7 **39.** -12 **41.** -14 **43.** 9 **45.** false **47.** true **49.** No; the statement is false for one number, 0. **51.** video/audio equipment from 1995–1996 **53.** 1996–1997

Section 1.4 (page 53)

1. Add -2 and 5. **3.** Add -1 and -3. **5.** 2 **7.** -3 **9.** -10 **11.** -13 **13.** -15.9 **15.** 5 **17.** 13 **19.** 0 **21.** -8 **23.** $\frac{3}{10}$ **25.** $\frac{1}{2}$ **27.** $-\frac{3}{4}$ **29.** -1.6 **31.** -8.7 **33.** -25 **35.** -12 **37.** true **39.** false **41.** true **43.** false **45.** true **47.** false
49. It must be negative and have the larger absolute value.
50. The sum of a positive number and 5 cannot be -7.
51. It must be positive and have the larger absolute value.
52. The sum of a negative number and -8 cannot be 2.
53. Add the absolute values of the numbers. The sum will be negative. **55.** $-5 + 12 + 6$; 13 **57.** $[-19 + (-4)] + 14$; -9 **59.** $[-4 + (-10)] + 12$; -2 **61.** $[8 + (-18)] + 4$; -6 **63.** $-\$80$ **65.** -184 m **67.** 37 yd **69.** 120°F **71.** $-\$107$ **73.** $286.60

Section 1.5 (page 61)

1. -8; -6 **3.** $7 - 12$; $12 - 7$ **5.** -4 **7.** -10 **9.** -16 **11.** 11 **13.** 19 **15.** -4 **17.** 5 **19.** 0 **21.** $\frac{3}{4}$ **23.** $-\frac{11}{8}$ **25.** $\frac{15}{8}$ **27.** 13.6 **29.** -11.9 **31.** -2.8 **33.** -6.3 **35.** -28 **37.** -18 **39.** $\frac{37}{12}$ **41.** -42.04 **43.** For example, let $a = 1, b = 1$ or let $a = 2, b = 2$. In general, choose $a = b$. **45.** 8 **47.** For example, $-8 - (-2) = -6$. **49.** $4 - (-8)$; 12 **51.** $-2 - 8$; -10 **53.** $[9 + (-4)] - 7$; -2 **55.** $[8 - (-5)] - 12$; 1 **57.** -58°F **59.** 14,776 ft **61.** $-\$80$ **63.** $105,000 **65.** $-\$3100$ **67.** $6800 **69.** positive **71.** positive

Section 1.6 (page 73)

1. greater than 0 **3.** less than 0 **5.** greater than 0 **7.** -28 **9.** -30 **11.** 0 **13.** $\frac{5}{6}$ **15.** -2.38 **17.** $\frac{3}{2}$ **19.** -3 **21.** -2 **23.** 16 **25.** 0 **27.** 25.63 **29.** $\frac{3}{2}$ **31.** C **33.** 3 **35.** 7 **37.** 4 **39.** -3 **41.** -1 **43.** negative; impossible to tell **45.** 68 **47.** -228 **49.** 1 **51.** 0 **53.** -6 **55.** 0 **57.** $-12 + 4(-7)$; -40 **59.** $-1 - 2(-8)(2)$; 31 **61.** $-3[3 - (-7)]$; -30

63. $\frac{3}{10}[-2+(-28)]; -9$ **65.** $\frac{-20}{-8+(-2)}; 2$

67. $\frac{-18+(-6)}{2(-4)}; 3$ **69.** $\frac{-\frac{2}{3}\left(-\frac{1}{5}\right)}{\frac{1}{7}}; \frac{14}{15}$ **71.** $4x=-36$

73. $\frac{x}{4}=-1$ **75.** $x-7=5$ **77.** $\frac{6}{x}=-3$

78. 42 **79.** 5 **80.** $8\frac{2}{5}$ **81.** $8\frac{2}{5}$ **82.** 2 **83.** $-12\frac{1}{2}$

Section 1.7 (page 83)

1. B **3.** C **5.** B **7.** G **9.** commutative property **11.** associative property **13.** inverse property **15.** inverse property **17.** identity property **19.** commutative property **21.** distributive property **23.** identity property **25.** distributive property **27.** **(a)** 0 **(b)** 1, −1 **29.** $25-(6-2)=25-4=21$ and $(25-6)-2=19-2=17$. Since these results are different, subtraction is not associative. **31.** $7+r$ **33.** s **35.** $-6x+(-6)7; -6x-42$ **37.** $w+[5+(-3)]; w+2$ **39.** We must multiply $\frac{3}{4}$ by 1 in the form $\frac{3}{3}$: $\frac{3}{4}\cdot\frac{3}{3}=\frac{9}{12}$. **41.** 2 **43.** $5(3+17); 100$ **45.** $4t+12$ **47.** $-8r-24$ **49.** $-5y+20$ **51.** $-16y-20z$ **53.** $8(z+w)$ **55.** $7(2v+5r)$ **57.** $24r+32s-40y$ **59.** $-24x-9y-12z$ **61.** $-4t-5m$ **63.** $5c+4d$ **65.** $3q-5r+8s$ **67.** Answers will vary. For example, "putting on your socks" and "putting on your shoes" **69.** false **71.** (foreign sales) clerk; foreign (sales clerk) **73.** 0 **74.** $-3(5)+(-3)(-5)$ **75.** −15 **76.** The product $-3(-5)$ must equal 15, since it is the additive inverse of −15.

Section 1.8 (page 91)

1. false **3.** true **5.** C **7.** A **9.** $4r+11$ **11.** $5+2x-6y$ **13.** $-7+3p$ **15.** −12 **17.** 5 **19.** 1 **21.** −1 **23.** 74 **25.** Answers will vary. For example, $-3x$ and $4x$ **27.** like **29.** unlike **31.** like **33.** unlike **35.** We cannot "add" unlike terms, so we must be able to identify like terms in order to combine them. **37.** $11-2x$ **39.** $-\frac{1}{3}t-\frac{28}{3}$ **41.** $-4.1r+4.2$ **43.** $-2y^2+3y^3$ **45.** $-19p+16$ **47.** $-\frac{3}{2}y+16$ **49.** $-16y+63$ **51.** $(x+3)+5x; 6x+3$ **53.** $(13+6x)-(-7x); 13+13x$ **55.** $2(3x+4)-(-4+6x); 12$ **57.** Wording may vary. One example is "the difference between 9 times a number and the sum of the number and 2." **59.** $1000+5x$ (dollars) **60.** $750+3y$ (dollars) **61.** $1000+5x+750+3y$ (dollars) **62.** $1750+5x+3y$ (dollars)

Chapter 1 Review Exercises (page 97)

1. 625 **2.** .00000081 **3.** .009261 **4.** $\frac{125}{8}$ **5.** 27 **6.** 200 **7.** −7 **8.** $\frac{20}{3}$ **9.** $13<17$ **10.** $5+2\neq 10$ **11.** Six is less than fifteen. **12.** One example is $-4+(-7)\geq\frac{12}{-3}$. **13.** 30 **14.** 60 **15.** 14 **16.** 13 **17.** $x+6$ **18.** $8-x$ **19.** $6x-9$ **20.** $12+\frac{3}{5}x$ **21.** yes **22.** no **23.** $2x-6=10$ **24.** $4x=8$ **25.** equation **26.** expression

27. 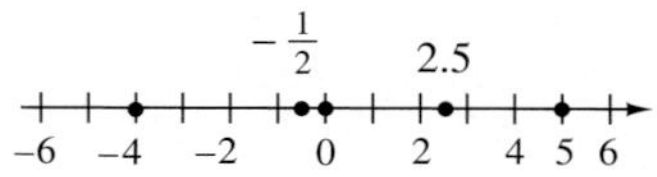

28. 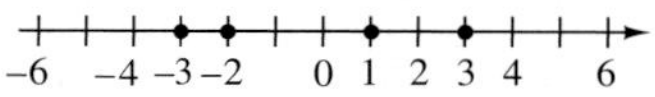

29. 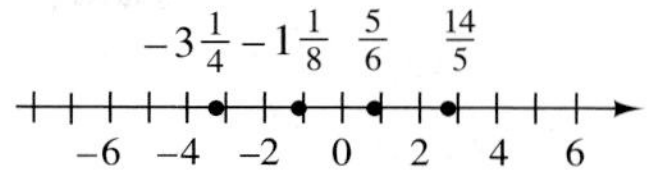

30. 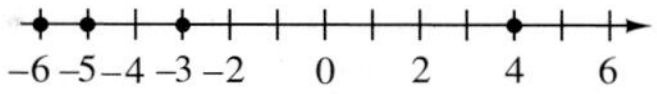

31. −10 **32.** −9 **33.** $-\frac{3}{4}$ **34.** $-|23|$ **35.** true **36.** true **37.** true **38.** false **39.** −3 **40.** −19 **41.** −7 **42.** 9 **43.** −6 **44.** −4 **45.** −17 **46.** $-\frac{29}{36}$ **47.** −10 **48.** −19 **49.** $(-31+12)+19; 0$ **50.** $[-4+(-8)]+13; 1$ **51.** −$8 **52.** 87°F **53.** −11 **54.** −1 **55.** 7 **56.** $-\frac{43}{35}$ **57.** 10.31 **58.** −12 **59.** 2 **60.** 1 **61.** $-4-(-6); 2$ **62.** $[4+(-8)]-5; -9$ **63.** 74.2% **64.** 1 min, 28.89 sec **65.** The first step is to change subtracting −6 to adding its opposite, 6, so the problem becomes $-8+6$. This sum is −2. **66.** Yes; for example, $-2-(-6)=-2+6=4$, a positive number. **67.** $25.1 billion **68.** −$11.3 billion **69.** $5.0 billion **70.** −$2.2 billion **71.** 36 **72.** −105 **73.** $\frac{1}{2}$ **74.** 10.08 **75.** −20 **76.** −10 **77.** −24 **78.** −35 **79.** 4 **80.** −20 **81.** $-\frac{3}{4}$ **82.** 11.3 **83.** −1 **84.** undefined **85.** 1 **86.** .5 **87.** −18 **88.** −18 **89.** 125 **90.** −423 **91.** $-4(5)-9; -29$ **92.** $\frac{5}{6}[12+(-6)]; 5$ **93.** $\frac{12}{8+(-4)}; 3$ **94.** $\frac{-20(12)}{15-(-15)}; -8$ **95.** $\frac{x}{x+5}=-2$ **96.** $8x-3=-7$ **97.** identity property **98.** identity property **99.** inverse property **100.** inverse property **101.** associative property **102.** associative property **103.** distributive property **104.** commutative property **105.** $(7+1)y; 8y$ **106.** $-12\cdot 4--12(t); -48+12t$ **107.** $3(2s+4y); 6s+12y$ **108.** $-1(-4r)+(-1)(5s); 4r-5s$ **109.** $17p^2$ **110.** $16r^2+7r$ **111.** $-19k+54$ **112.** $5s-6$ **113.** $-45t-23$ **114.** $-45t^2-23.4t$ **115.** $-2(3x)-7x; -13x$ **116.** $\frac{x+9}{x-6}$ **117.** No. The use of *and* there indicates the two quantities that are to be multiplied. **118.** Answers may vary. For example, "3 times the difference between 4 times a number and 6" **119.** 16 **120.** $\frac{25}{36}$ **121.** −26 **122.** $\frac{8}{3}$ **123.** $-\frac{1}{24}$ **124.** $\frac{7}{2}$ **125.** 2 **126.** 77.6 **127.** $-1\frac{1}{2}$ **128.** 11 **129.** $-\frac{28}{15}$ **130.** 24 **131.** −11 **132.** −6 **133.** $2x-1400=25{,}800$; x represents the amount spent in 1999. **134.** $\frac{x}{3x-14}$; x represents the number.

Chapter 1 Test (page 103)

1. true **2.** false **3.** 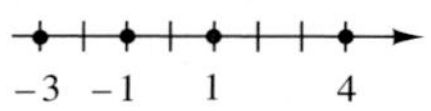

4. $-|-8|$ (or −8) **5.** −1.277 **6.** $\frac{-6}{2+(-8)}; 1$ **7.** negative **8.** 4 **9.** $-2\frac{5}{6}$ **10.** 2 **11.** 6 **12.** 108 **13.** 11 **14.** $\frac{30}{7}$

15. -70 **16.** 3 **17.** 178°F **18.** D **19.** A **20.** E **21.** B **22.** C **23.** $-9x^2 - 6x - 8$ **24.** identity and distributive properties **25. (a)** -18 **(b)** -18 **(c)** The distributive property tells us that the two methods produce equal results.

Chapter 2

Section 2.1 (page 111)

1. A and C **3.** A and B **5.** {4} **7.** {10} **9.** {12} **11.** {−10} **13.** {3} **15.** {−2} **17.** {4} **19.** {0} **21.** ∅ **23.** {all real numbers} **25.** {4} **27.** ∅ **29.** {all real numbers} **31.** $\left\{\frac{7}{15}\right\}$ **33.** {7} **35.** {−4} **37.** {13} **39.** {all real numbers} **41.** {18} **43.** {12} **45.** Since the opposite of x is 5, x must be -5. **47.** Answers will vary. One example is $x - 6 = -8$.

Section 2.2 (page 117)

1. {4} **3.** {−8} **5.** $\frac{3}{2}$ **7.** 10 **9.** $-\frac{2}{9}$ **11.** -1 **13.** 6 **15.** -4 **17.** .12 **19.** -1 **21.** If each side of an equation were multiplied by 0, the resulting equation would be $0 = 0$. This is true, but does not help to solve the equation. **23.** $\left\{\frac{15}{2}\right\}$ **25.** {−5} **27.** $\left\{-\frac{18}{5}\right\}$ **29.** {12} **31.** {0} **33.** {−12} **35.** {40} **37.** {−48} **39.** {−35} **41.** $\left\{-\frac{27}{35}\right\}$ **43.** {3} **45.** {−5} **47.** {7} **49.** {−2} **51.** $\left\{-\frac{3}{5}\right\}$ **53.** Answers will vary. One example is $\frac{3}{2}x = -6$. **55.** $3x = 18 + 5x$; -9; The number is -9.

Section 2.3 (page 123)

1. {−1} **3.** {5} **5.** {1} **7.** $\left\{-\frac{5}{3}\right\}$ **9.** {−1} **11.** ∅ **13.** {all real numbers} **15.** No, it is incorrect to divide each side by a variable. If $-3x$ is added to each side, the equation becomes $4x = 0$, so $x = 0$ is the correct solution, and {0} is the correct solution set. **17.** Simplify each side separately. Use the addition property to get all variable terms on one side of the equation and all numbers on the other, then combine terms. Use the multiplication property to get the equation in the form $x =$ a number. Check the solution. **19.** {7} **21.** {0} **23.** $\left\{\frac{3}{25}\right\}$ **25.** {60} **27.** {4} **29.** {5000} **31.** 800 **32.** Yes, you will get $(100 \cdot 2) \cdot 4 = 800$. This is a result of the associative property of multiplication. **33.** No, because $(100a)(100b) = 10{,}000ab \neq 100ab$. **34.** The distributive property involves the operation of addition as well. **35.** Yes; the associative property of multiplication is used. **36.** no **37.** $\left\{-\frac{72}{11}\right\}$ **39.** {0} **41.** {−6} **43.** {15} **45.** {all real numbers} **47.** ∅ **49.** $12 - q$ **51.** $\frac{t}{10}$

Section 2.4 (page 133)

1. The procedure should include the following steps: read the problem carefully; assign a variable to represent the unknown to be found; write down variable expressions for any other unknown quantities; translate into an equation; solve the equation; state the answer; check your solution. **3.** D; there cannot be a fractional number of cars. **5.** 6 **7.** -3 **9.** 45 Democrats; 55 Republicans **11.** 6562 men; 3779 women **13.** dog: 343 lb; lioness: 280 lb **15.** Airborne Express: 3; Federal Express: 9; United Parcel Service: 1 **17.** 36 million mi **19.** A and B: 40°; C: 100° **21.** 1950 Denver nickel: \$14.00; 1945 Philadelphia nickel: \$12.00 **23.** ice cream: 44,687.9 lb; topping: 537.1 lb **25.** 18° **27.** 39° **29.** 50° **31.** 68, 69 **33.** 10, 12 **35.** 101, 102 **37.** 10, 11 **39.** \$2.78 billion, \$3.33 billion, \$3.53 billion

Section 2.5 (page 143)

1. (a) The perimeter of a plane geometric figure is the distance around the figure. **(b)** The area of a plane geometric figure is the measure of the surface covered or enclosed by the figure. **3.** four **5.** area **7.** perimeter **9.** area **11.** area **13.** $P = 26$ **15.** $A = 64$ **17.** $b = 4$ **19.** $t = 5.6$ **21.** $I = 1575$ **23.** $r = 2.6$ **25.** $A = 50.24$ **27.** $V = 150$ **29.** $V = 52$ **31.** $V = 7234.56$ **33.** about 154,000 ft^2 **35.** perimeter: 13 in.; area: 10.5 in.^{2} **37.** 132.665 ft^2 **39.** 23,800.10 ft^2 **41.** length: 36 in.; volume: 11,664 in.^{3} **43.** 48°, 132° **45.** 51°, 51° **47.** 105°, 105° **49.** $t = \frac{d}{r}$ **51.** $H = \frac{V}{LW}$ **53.** $b = P - a - c$ **55.** $r = \frac{I}{pt}$ **57.** $h = \frac{2A}{b}$ **59.** $W = \frac{P - 2L}{2}$ or $W = \frac{P}{2} - L$ **61.** $h = \frac{3V}{\pi r^2}$ **63.** $F = \frac{9}{5}C + 32$

Section 2.6 (page 153)

1. (a) C **(b)** D **(c)** B **(d)** A **3.** $\frac{6}{7}$ **5.** $\frac{18}{55}$ **7.** $\frac{5}{16}$ **9.** $\frac{4}{15}$ **11.** 17-oz size **13.** 64-oz can **15.** 500-count **17.** 28-oz size **19.** A percent is a ratio where the basis of comparison is 100. For example, 27% represents the ratio of 27 to 100. **21.** {35} **23.** {7} **25.** {−1} **27.** {5} **29.** $\left\{\frac{13}{7}\right\}$ **31.** 4 gal **33.** 74.13 francs **35.** \$9.90 **37.** $25\frac{2}{3}$ in. **39.** 46,700 fish **41.** 124.8 **43.** 120% **45.** 600 **47.** 1.4% **49.** C **51.** 4.5% **53.** 65.9% **55.** \$304 **57.** 284% **59.** \$262 **61.** \$276 **63.** 30 **64. (a)** $5x = 12$ **(b)** $\left\{\frac{12}{5}\right\}$ **65.** $\left\{\frac{12}{5}\right\}$ **66.** Both methods give the same solution set.

Chapter 2 Review Exercises (page 161)

1. {9} **2.** {4} **3.** {−6} **4.** $\left\{\frac{3}{2}\right\}$ **5.** {20} **6.** $\left\{-\frac{61}{2}\right\}$ **7.** {15} **8.** {0} **9.** ∅ **10.** {all real numbers} **11.** $-\frac{7}{2}$ **12.** 20 **13.** Hawaii: 6425 mi^2; Rhode Island: 1212 mi^2 **14.** Seven Falls: 300 ft; Twin Falls: 120 ft **15.** 80° **16.** 11, 13 **17.** $h = 11$ **18.** $A = 28$ **19.** $r = 4.75$ **20.** $V = 904.32$ **21.** $L = \frac{A}{W}$ **22.** $h = \frac{2A}{b + B}$ **23.** 135°, 45° **24.** 100°, 100° **25.** perimeter: 326.5 ft; area: 6538.875 ft^2 **26.** diameter: approximately 19.9 ft; radius: approximately 9.95 ft; area: approximately 311 ft^2 **27.** $\frac{3}{2}$ **28.** $\frac{5}{14}$ **29.** $\frac{3}{4}$ **30.** $\frac{1}{12}$ **31.** $\left\{\frac{7}{2}\right\}$ **32.** $\left\{-\frac{8}{3}\right\}$ **33.** $\left\{\frac{25}{19}\right\}$ **34.** 40% means $\frac{40}{100}$ or $\frac{2}{5}$. It is the same as the ratio of 2 to 5. **35.** $6\frac{2}{3}$ lb **36.** 36 oz **37.** 54 ft **38.** 375 km **39.** 17.48 **40.** 175% **41.** $33\frac{1}{3}$% **42.** 2500 **43.** \$27,630.11

44. \$350.46 **45.** {7} **46.** $r = \frac{I}{pt}$ **47.** {2} **48.** {−9}
49. {70} **50.** $\left\{\frac{13}{4}\right\}$ **51.** ∅ **52.** {all real numbers} **53.** 80 ft
54. 6 **55.** Rita: 84 mi; Bobby: 28 mi **56.** Mike: 1200 votes; William: 600 votes **57.** United States: 97; Russia: 88
58. gold: 16; silver: 25; bronze: 17 **59.** 44 m **60.** 70 ft
61. $20\frac{1}{2}$ in. **62.** 26 in. **63.** 32-oz size **64.** 51°, 51°

Chapter 2 Test (page 165)

1. {6} **2.** {−6} **3.** $\left\{\frac{13}{4}\right\}$ **4.** {−10.8} **5.** ∅ **6.** {21}
7. {30} **8.** {all real numbers} **9.** East: 132; West: 120
10. 26 points **11.** Hawaii: 4021 mi^2; Maui: 728 mi^2; Kauai: 551 mi^2 **12.** 50° **13. (a)** $W = \frac{P - 2L}{2}$ or $W = \frac{P}{2} - L$
(b) 18 **14.** 100°, 80° **15.** 75°, 75° **16.** {6} **17.** {−29}
18. 8 slices for \$2.19 **19.** 2300 mi **20.** 236%

Cumulative Review Exercises: Chapters R–2 (page 167)

1. $\frac{3}{8}$ **2.** $\frac{3}{4}$ **3.** $\frac{31}{20}$ **4.** $\frac{551}{40}$ or $13\frac{31}{40}$ **5.** 6 **6.** $\frac{6}{5}$
7. 34.03 **8.** 27.31 **9.** 30.51 **10.** 56.3 **11.** 35 yd
12. $7\frac{1}{2}$ cups **13.** $99\frac{5}{8}$ lb **14.** \$3849.94 **15.** true **16.** true
17. 7 **18.** 1 **19.** 13 **20.** −40 **21.** −12 **22.** undefined
23. −6 **24.** 28 **25.** 1 **26.** 0 **27.** $\frac{73}{18}$ **28.** −64 **29.** −134
30. $-\frac{29}{6}$ **31.** distributive property **32.** commutative property
33. inverse property **34.** identity property **35.** $7p - 14$
36. $2k - 11$ **37.** {7} **38.** {−4} **39.** {−1} **40.** $\left\{-\frac{3}{5}\right\}$
41. {2} **42.** {−13} **43.** {26} **44.** {−12} **45.** $c = P - a - b$
46. $s = \frac{P}{4}$ **47.** \$4090.56 **48.** \$3750 **49.** \$230.50 **50.** \$98.45
51. 30 cm **52.** 16 in.

Chapter 3

Section 3.1 (page 179)

1. D **3.** B **5.** F **7.** Use a parenthesis when an endpoint is not included; use a bracket when it is included.

9. $[5, \infty)$

11. $(7, \infty)$
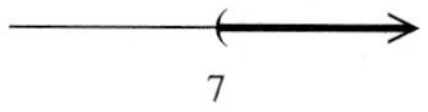

13. $(-4, \infty)$

15. $(-\infty, -40]$
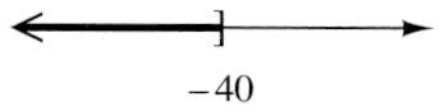

17. $(-\infty, 4]$

19. $\left(-\infty, -\frac{15}{2}\right)$
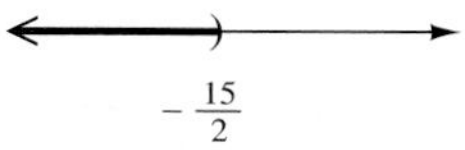

21. $\left[\frac{1}{2}, \infty\right)$
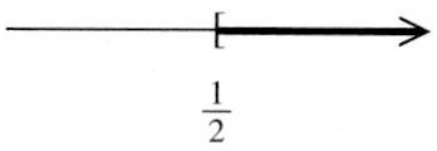

23. $(3, \infty)$
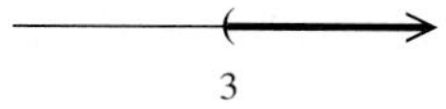

25. $(-\infty, 4)$
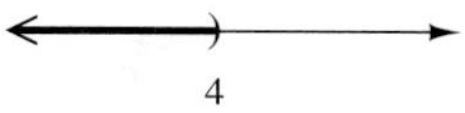

27. $\left(-\infty, \frac{23}{6}\right]$
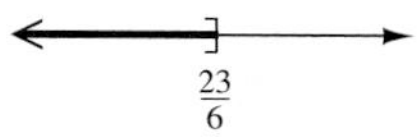

29. $\left(-\infty, \frac{76}{11}\right)$
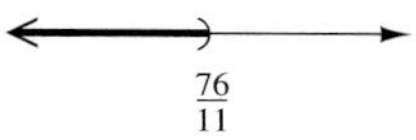

31. {−9}
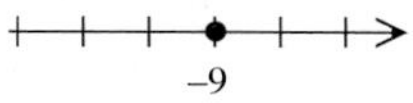

32. $(-9, \infty)$
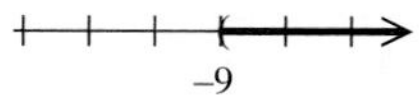

33. $(-\infty, -9)$
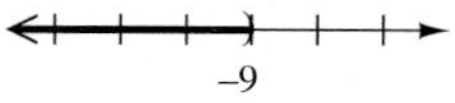

34. We obtain the set of all real numbers.
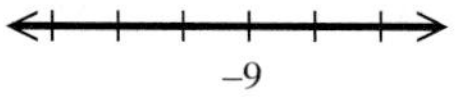

35. $(-\infty, -3)$

37. $(1, 11)$
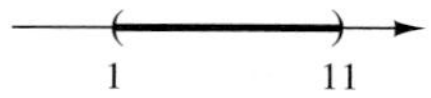

39. $[-14, 10]$
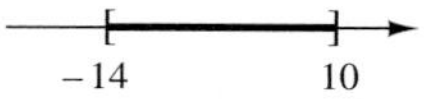

41. $[-5, 6]$
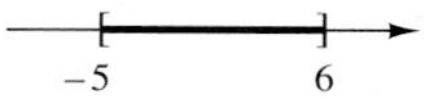

43. $(-6, -4)$

45. $\left[-\frac{13}{3}, \frac{11}{3}\right]$
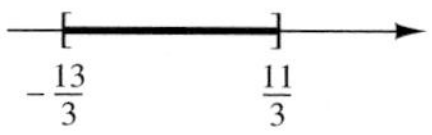

47. from about 8:00 A.M. to 10:15 A.M. and after about 9:00 P.M. **49.** about 65°F–67°F **51.** at least 82 **53.** 628.6 mi **55.** 921 deliveries **57. (a)** 130 to 157 beats per min **(b)** Answers will vary.

Section 3.2 (page 191)

1. true **3.** False; The union is $(-\infty, 6) \cup (6, \infty)$. **5.** {4} or D
7. ∅ **9.** {1, 2, 3, 4, 5, 6} or A **11.** {1, 3, 5, 6}

13.
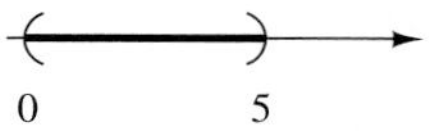

15.
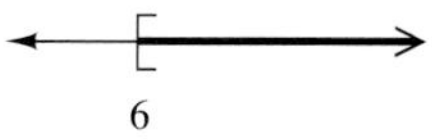

17.
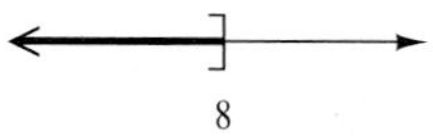

19. Answers will vary. One example is: The intersection of two streets is the region common to *both* streets.

21. $(-3, 2)$

23. $(-\infty, 2]$
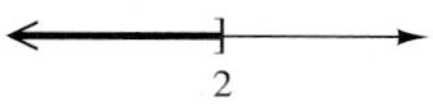

25. ∅

27. $[5, 9]$ 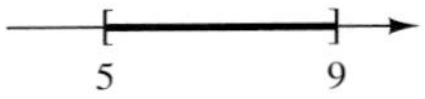

29. $(-\infty, 4]$ 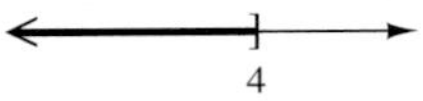

31. $(-\infty, 8]$ 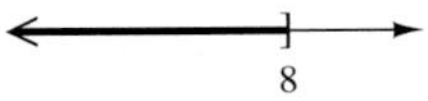

33. $[-2, \infty)$ 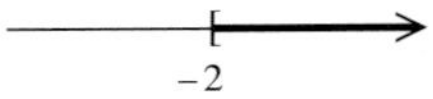

35. $(-\infty, \infty)$ 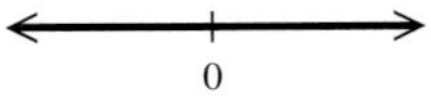

37. $(-\infty, -5) \cup (5, \infty)$ 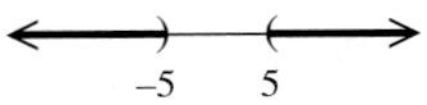

39. $(-\infty, 2) \cup (2, \infty)$ 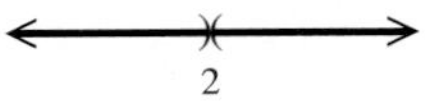

41. $[-4, -1]$ **43.** $[-9, -6]$ **45.** $(-\infty, 3)$ **47.** $[3, 9)$

49. intersection; $(-5, -1)$ 

51. union; $(-\infty, 4)$ 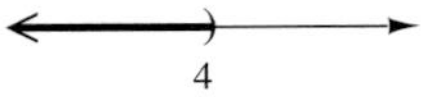

53. intersection; $[4, 12]$ 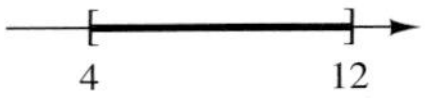

55. union; $(-\infty, 0] \cup [2, \infty)$ 

57. Mario, Joe **58.** none of them **59.** none of them **60.** Luigi, Than **61.** none

Section 3.3 (page 201)

1. E; C; D; B; A **3.** Use *or* for the equality statement and the $>$ statement. Use *and* for the $<$ statement. **5.** $\{-12, 12\}$ **7.** $\{-5, 5\}$ **9.** $\{-6, 12\}$ **11.** $\{-4, 3\}$ **13.** $\left\{-3, \frac{11}{2}\right\}$ **15.** $\left\{-\frac{19}{2}, \frac{9}{2}\right\}$ **17.** $\{-10, -2\}$ **19.** $\left\{-8, \frac{32}{3}\right\}$

21. $(-\infty, -3) \cup (3, \infty)$ 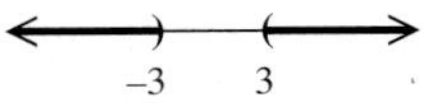

23. $(-\infty, -4] \cup [4, \infty)$ 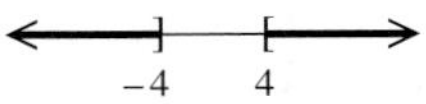

25. $(-\infty, -12) \cup (8, \infty)$ 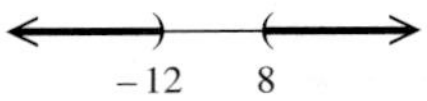

27. $\left(-\infty, -\frac{7}{3}\right] \cup [3, \infty)$ 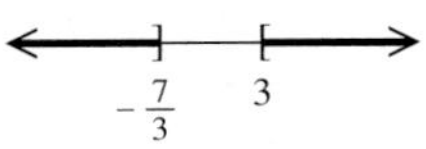

29. $(-\infty, -2) \cup (8, \infty)$ 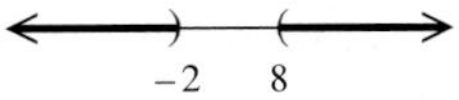

31. **(a)** 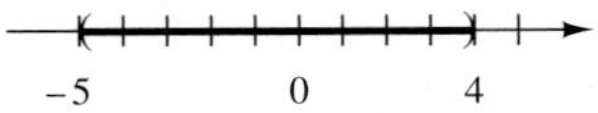

(b) 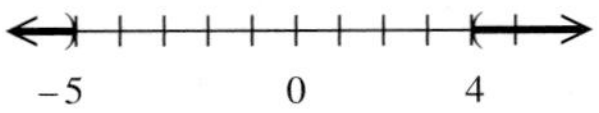

33. $[-3, 3]$ 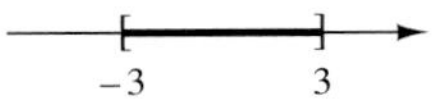

35. $(-4, 4)$ 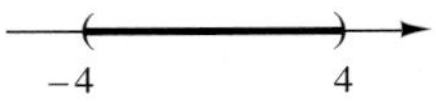

37. $[-12, 8]$ 

39. $\left(-\frac{7}{3}, 3\right)$ 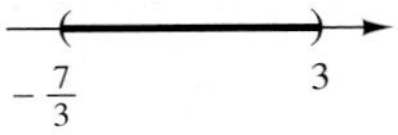

41. $[-2, 8]$ 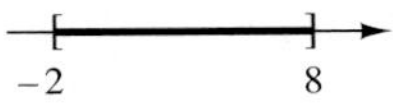

43. $(-\infty, -5) \cup (13, \infty)$ 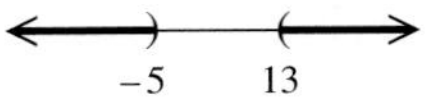

45. $\{-6, -1\}$ 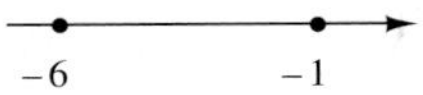

47. $\left[-\frac{10}{3}, 4\right]$ 

49. $\left[-\frac{7}{6}, -\frac{5}{6}\right]$ 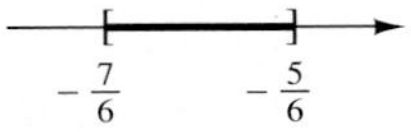

51. $\{-5, 5\}$ **53.** $\{-5, -3\}$ **55.** $(-\infty, -3) \cup (2, \infty)$ **57.** $[-10, 0]$ **59.** $\{-1, 3\}$ **61.** $\left\{-3, \frac{5}{3}\right\}$ **63.** $\left\{-\frac{1}{3}, -\frac{1}{15}\right\}$ **65.** $\left\{-\frac{5}{4}\right\}$ **67.** $\emptyset$ **69.** $\left\{-\frac{1}{4}\right\}$ **71.** $\emptyset$ **73.** $(-\infty, \infty)$ **75.** $\left\{-\frac{3}{7}\right\}$ **77.** $(-\infty, \infty)$ **79.** $\left(-\infty, -\frac{7}{10}\right) \cup \left(-\frac{7}{10}, \infty\right)$ **81.** $|x - 1000| \le 100$; $900 \le x \le 1100$ **83.** 472.9 ft **84.** 1201 Walnut, Fidelity Bank and Trust Building, City Hall, Kansas City Power and Light, Hyatt Regency **85.** City Center Square, Commerce Tower, Federal Office Building, 1201 Walnut, Fidelity Bank and Trust Building, City Hall, Kansas City Power and Light, Hyatt Regency **86.** **(a)** $|x - 472.9| \ge 75$ **(b)** $x \ge 547.9$ or $x \le 397.9$ **(c)** AT&T Town Pavilion, One Kansas City Place **(d)** It makes sense because it includes all buildings *not* listed earlier.

Summary Exercises on Solving Linear and Absolute Value Equations and Inequalities (page 207)

1. $\{12\}$ **2.** $\{-5, 7\}$ **3.** $\{7\}$ **4.** $\left\{-\frac{2}{5}\right\}$ **5.** $\emptyset$ **6.** $(-\infty, -1]$ **7.** $\left[-\frac{2}{3}, \infty\right)$ **8.** $\{-1\}$ **9.** $\{-3\}$ **10.** $\left\{1, \frac{11}{3}\right\}$ **11.** $(-\infty, 5]$ **12.** $(-\infty, \infty)$ **13.** $\{2\}$ **14.** $(-\infty, -8] \cup [8, \infty)$ **15.** $\emptyset$ **16.** $(-\infty, \infty)$ **17.** $(-5.5, 5.5)$ **18.** $\left\{\frac{13}{3}\right\}$ **19.** $\left\{-\frac{96}{5}\right\}$ **20.** $(-\infty, 32]$ **21.** $(-\infty, -24)$ **22.** $\left\{\frac{3}{8}\right\}$ **23.** $\left\{\frac{7}{2}\right\}$ **24.** $(-6, 8)$ **25.** $(-\infty, \infty)$ **26.** $(-\infty, 5)$ **27.** $(-\infty, -4) \cup (7, \infty)$ **28.** $\{24\}$ **29.** $\left\{-\frac{1}{5}\right\}$ **30.** $\left(-\infty, -\frac{5}{2}\right]$ **31.** $\left[-\frac{1}{3}, 3\right]$ **32.** $[1, 7]$ **33.** $\left\{-\frac{1}{6}, 2\right\}$ **34.** $\{-3\}$ **35.** $(-\infty, -1] \cup \left[\frac{5}{3}, \infty\right)$ **36.** $\left[\frac{3}{4}, \frac{15}{8}\right]$ **37.** $\left\{-\frac{5}{2}\right\}$ **38.** $\{60\}$ **39.** $\left[-\frac{9}{2}, \frac{15}{2}\right]$ **40.** $(1, 9)$ **41.** $(-\infty, \infty)$ **42.** $\left\{\frac{1}{3}, 9\right\}$ **43.** $(-\infty, \infty)$ **44.** $\left\{-\frac{10}{9}\right\}$ **45.** $\{-2\}$ **46.** $\emptyset$ **47.** $(-\infty, -1) \cup (2, \infty)$ **48.** $[-3, -2]$

Chapter 3 Review Exercises (page 213)

1. $(-9, \infty)$

2. $(-\infty, -3]$

3. $\left(\frac{3}{2}, \infty\right)$

4. $\left(-\infty, -\frac{14}{9}\right)$

5. $[-3, \infty)$

6. $[-3, 12]$

7. $[3, 5)$

8. $\left(-3, \frac{7}{2}\right)$

9. 38 m or less **10.** 99 tickets or less **11.** any grade greater than or equal to 61% **12.** Because the statement $-8 < -13$ is *false*, the inequality has no solution. **13.** $\{a, c\}$ **14.** $\{a\}$ **15.** $\{a, c, e, f, g\}$ **16.** $\{a, b, c, d, e, f, g\}$

17. $(6, 9)$

18. $(8, 14)$

19. $(-\infty, -3] \cup (5, \infty)$

20. $(-\infty, \infty)$

21. $\emptyset$

22. $(-\infty, -2] \cup [7, \infty)$

23. $(-3, 4)$ **24.** $(-\infty, 2)$ **25.** $(4, \infty)$ **26.** $(1, \infty)$ **27. (a)** managerial and professional specialty **(b)** managerial and professional specialty, mathematical and computer scientists

28. $\{-7, 7\}$ **29.** $\{-11, 7\}$ **30.** $\left\{-\frac{1}{3}, 5\right\}$ **31.** $\emptyset$ **32.** $\{0, 7\}$

33. $\left\{-\frac{3}{2}, \frac{1}{2}\right\}$ **34.** $\left\{-\frac{3}{4}, \frac{1}{2}\right\}$ **35.** $\left\{-\frac{1}{2}\right\}$

36. $(-14, 14)$

37. $[-1, 13]$

38. $[-3, -2]$

39. $(-\infty, \infty)$

40. $\left(-\infty, -\frac{8}{5}\right) \cup (2, \infty)$

41. $(-\infty, \infty)$

42. $\left(-\infty, \frac{7}{6}\right]$ **43.** $[-4, 5)$ **44.** $\left(-\infty, \frac{14}{17}\right)$ **45.** any amount greater than or equal to \$1100 **46.** $(-\infty, 2]$

47. $(-\infty, -1) \cup \left(\frac{11}{7}, \infty\right)$ **48.** $\{-5, 15\}$ **49.** $[-16, 10]$

50. $(-\infty, \infty)$ **51.** $\left\{-4, -\frac{2}{3}\right\}$

52.

53.

54. (a) $\emptyset$ **(b)** $(-\infty, \infty)$ **(c)** $\emptyset$

Chapter 3 Test (page 217)

1. Reverse the direction of the inequality symbol.
2. $[1, \infty)$

3. $(-\infty, 28)$

4. $[-3, 3]$

5. C **6. (a)** 1993–1998 **(b)** 1985–1989 **(c)** 1990, 1993–1995 **7.** 82% **8.** $[500, \infty)$ **9. (a)** $\{1, 5\}$ **(b)** $\{1, 2, 5, 7, 9, 12\}$ **10.** $\{2\}$

11. $[2, 9)$

12. $(-\infty, 3) \cup [6, \infty)$

13. $\left[-\frac{5}{2}, 1\right]$

14. $\left(-\infty, -\frac{7}{6}\right) \cup \left(\frac{17}{6}, \infty\right)$

15. $\emptyset$ **16.** $\left\{-\frac{5}{3}, 3\right\}$ **17.** $\left\{-\frac{5}{7}, \frac{11}{3}\right\}$

Cumulative Review Exercises: Chapters R–3 (page 219)

1. $\frac{3}{4}$ **2.** true **3.** $\frac{37}{60}$ **4.** $\frac{48}{5}$ **5.** 11 **6.** -8 **7.** -36

8. -125 **9.** $\frac{81}{16}$ **10.** -36 **11.** $\frac{3}{16}$ **12.** distributive property **13.** commutative property **14.** $2k - 11$ **15.** $\{-1\}$ **16.** $\{-12\}$

17. $\{26\}$ **18.** $\left\{\frac{3}{4}, \frac{7}{2}\right\}$ **19.** $y = \frac{24 - 3x}{4}$ **20.** $n = \frac{A - P}{iP}$

21. $[-14, \infty)$ 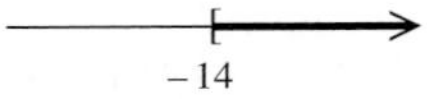

22. $\left[\frac{5}{3}, 3\right)$ 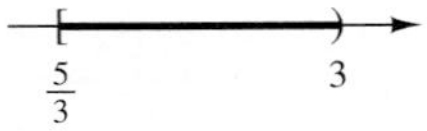

23. $(-\infty, 0) \cup (2, \infty)$ 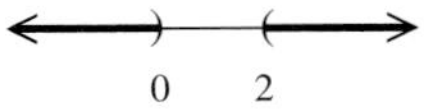

24. $\left(-\infty, -\frac{1}{7}\right] \cup [1, \infty)$ 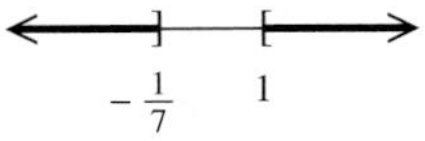

25. 140°, 40° **26.** $6\frac{1}{3}$ g **27.** 74 or greater **28.** 420 mi **29.** **(a)** 122 **(b)** 7.6% **30.** 4 cm; 9 cm; 27 cm

Chapter 4

Section 4.1 (page 233)

1. Snoopy; 31% **3.** Since 26% is twice as much as 13%, we can expect twice as many adults to favor Charlie Brown. **5.** Ohio (OH): about 680 million eggs; Iowa (IA): about 550 million eggs **7.** Indiana (IN) and Pennsylvania (PA); about 490 million eggs each **9.** from 1975 to 1980; about $.75 **11.** The price of a gallon of gas was decreasing. **13.** does; do not **15.** y **17.** 6 **19.** yes **21.** yes **23.** no **25.** yes **27.** no **29.** No. For two ordered pairs (x, y) to be equal, the x-values must be equal and the y-values must be equal. Here we have $4 \neq -1$ and $-1 \neq 4$. **31.** 11 **33.** $-\frac{7}{2}$ **35.** -4 **37.** -5 **39.** 4; 6; -6; (0, 4); (6, 0); $(-6, 8)$ **41.** 3; -5; -15; (0, 3); $(-5, 0)$; $(-15, -6)$ **43.** -9; -9; -9 **45.** -6; -6; -6 **47.** 8; 8; 8 **49.** (2, 4) **51.** $(-5, 4)$ **53.** (3, 0) **55.** negative; negative **57.** positive; negative **59.** If $xy < 0$, then either $x < 0$ and $y > 0$ or $x > 0$ and $y < 0$. If $x < 0$ and $y > 0$, then the point lies in quadrant II. If $x > 0$ and $y < 0$, then the point lies in quadrant IV.

61.–70.

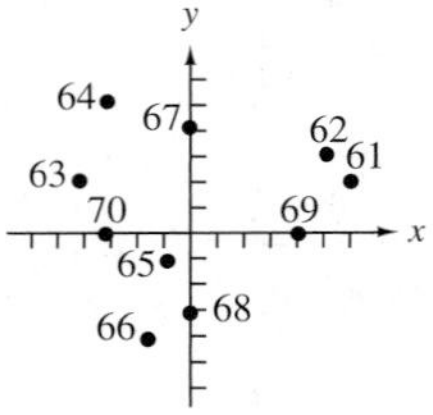

71. -3; 6; -2; 4

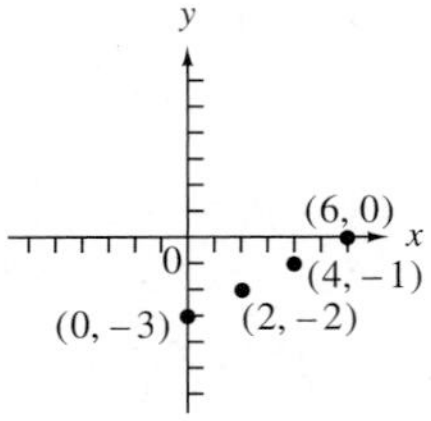

73. -3; 4; -6; $-\frac{4}{3}$

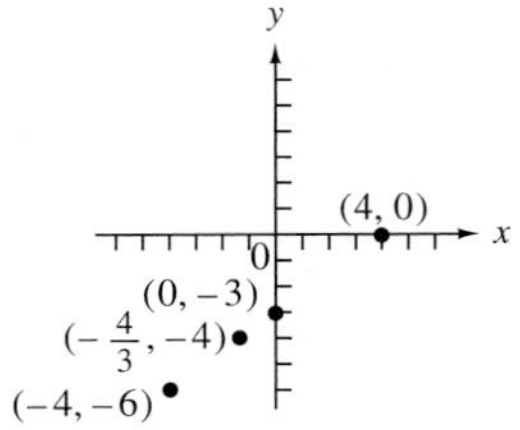

75. -4; -4; -4; -4

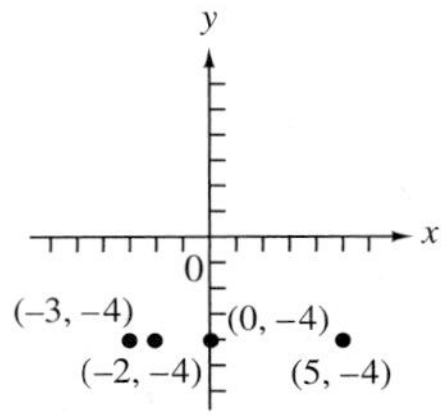

77. The points in each graph appear to lie on a straight line. **79.** **(a)** (1996, 53.3), (1997, 52.8), (1998, 52.1), (1999, 51.6) **(b)** (1995, 54.0) means that in 1995, the graduation rate for 4-year college students within 5 years was 54.0%.

(c) **4-YEAR COLLEGE STUDENTS GRADUATING WITHIN 5 YEARS**

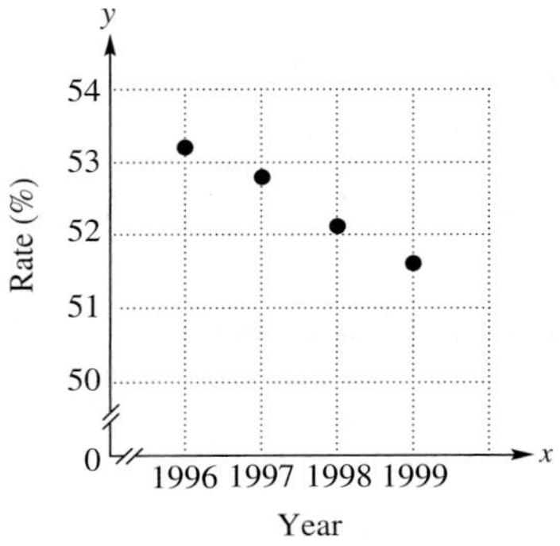

(d) The points appear to lie on a straight line. Graduation rates for 4-year college students within 5 years are decreasing. **81.** **(a)** 170; 154; 138; 122 **(b)** (20, 170), (40, 154), (60, 138), (80, 122) **(c)** The points lie in a linear pattern.

TARGET HEART RATE ZONE

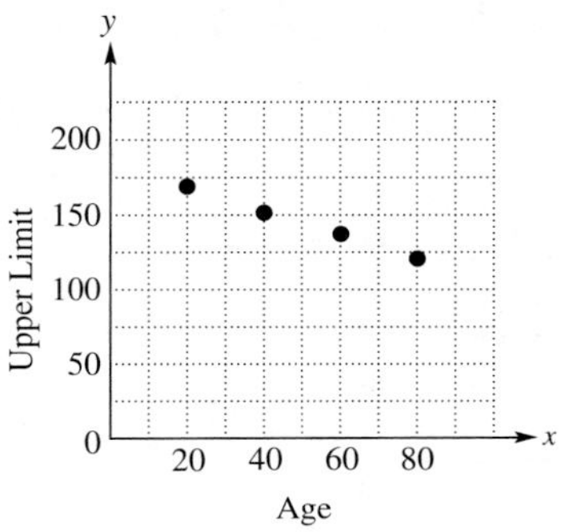

Section 4.2 (page 247)

1. 5; 5; 3

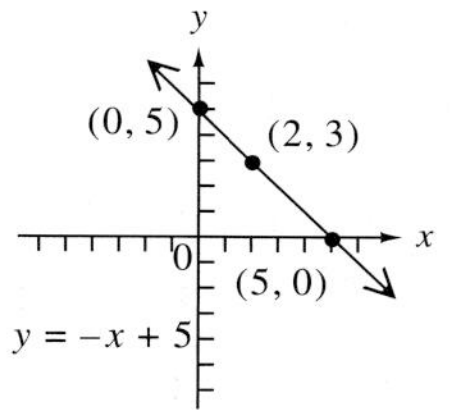

3. 1; 3; −1

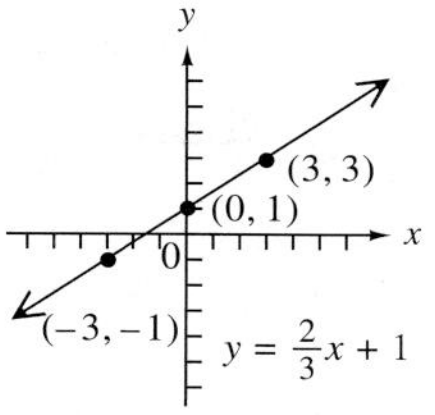

5. −6; −2; −5

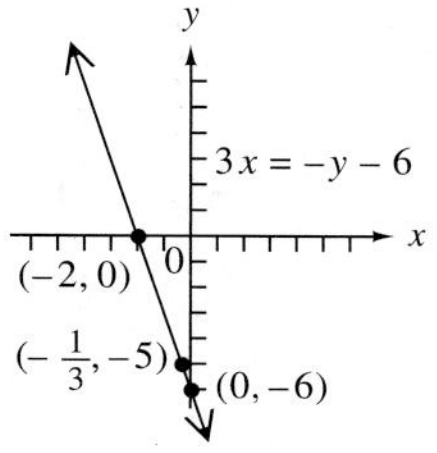

7. A **9.** D **11.** (12, 0); (0, −8) **13.** (0, 0); (0, 0)
15. Choose a value *other than* 0 for either x or y. For example, if $x = -5$, $y = 4$.

17.

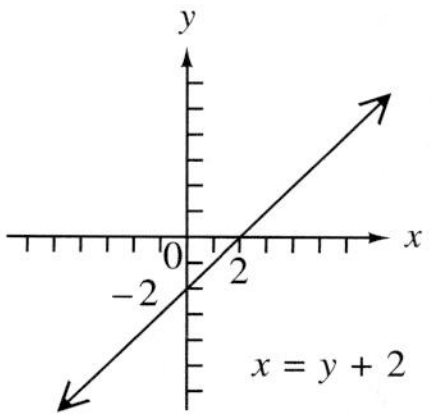

19.

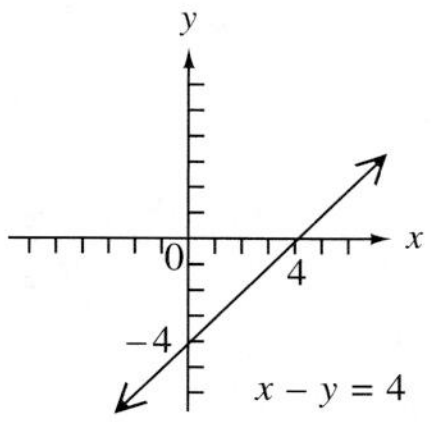

21.

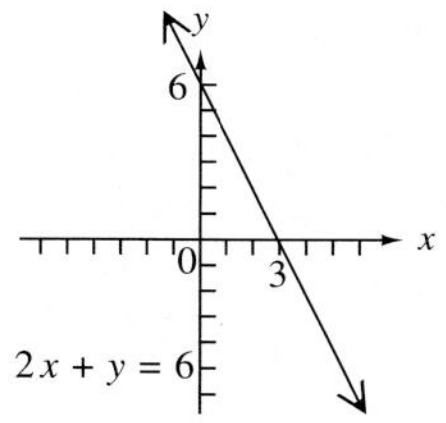

23.

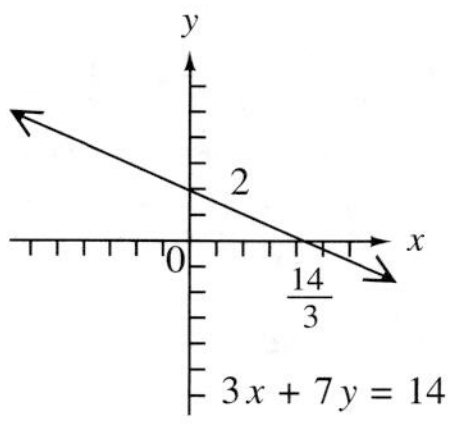

25.

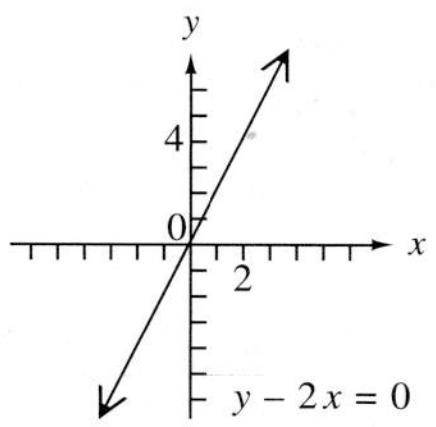

27.

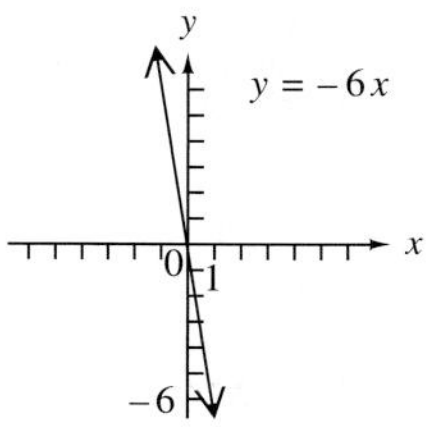

29.

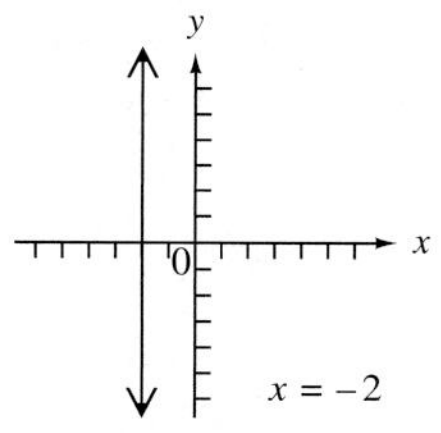

31.

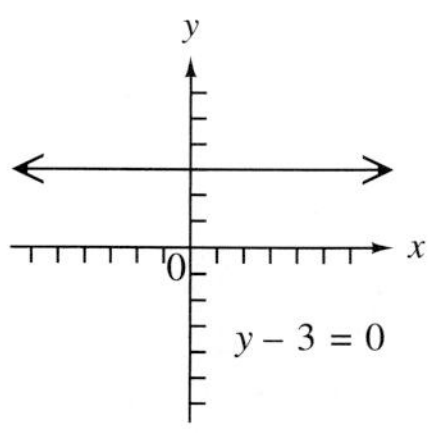

33. (a) 151.5 cm, 174.9 cm, 159.3 cm

(b)

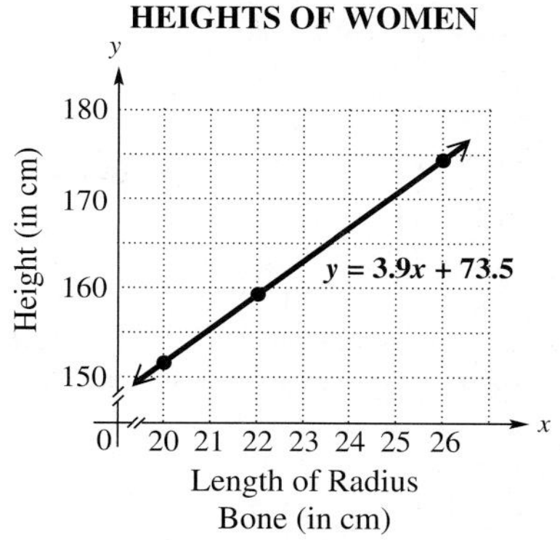

(c) 24 cm; 24 cm **35. (a)** 130 **(b)** 133 **(c)** They are quite close. **37.** between 133 and 162 **39. (a)** 1993: 49.8 gal; 1995: 51.4 gal; 1997: 53 gal **(b)** 1993: 50.1 gal; 1995: 51.6 gal; 1997: 53 gal **(c)** The corresponding values are quite close. **41. (a)** \$30,000 **(b)** \$15,000 **(c)** \$5000 **(d)** After 5 yr, the SUV has a value of \$5000. **43. (a)** The equation is a fairly good model. **(b)** The actual debt for 1996 is about 500 billion dollars; this is about 30 billion dollars more than the amount given by the equation. **(c)** No. Data for future years might not follow the same pattern, so the linear equation would not be a reliable model.

Section 4.3 (page 261)

1. Rise is the vertical change between two different points on a line. Run is the horizontal change between two different points on a line. **3.** 4 **5.** $-\frac{1}{2}$ **7.** 0 **9.** Yes, the answer would be the same. It doesn't matter which point you start with. The slope would be expressed as the quotient of −6 and −4, which simplifies to $\frac{3}{2}$.

10.–13. Answers will vary.

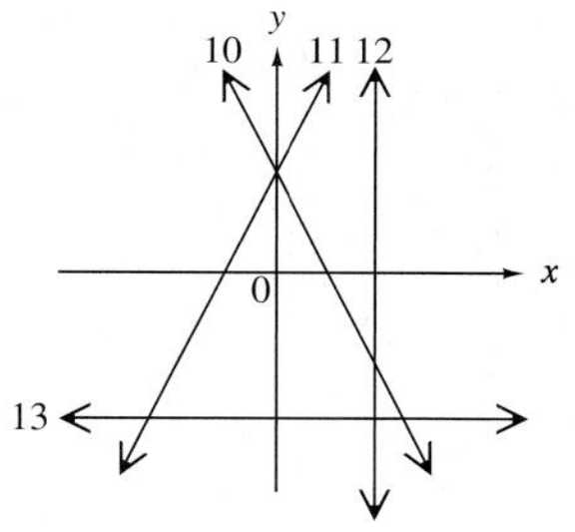

15. His answer is incorrect. Because he found the difference $3 - 5 = -2$ in the numerator, he should have subtracted in the same order in the denominator to get $-1 - 2 = -3$. The correct slope is $\frac{-2}{-3} = \frac{2}{3}$. **17.** $\frac{5}{4}$ **19.** $\frac{3}{2}$ **21.** −3 **23.** 0 **25.** undefined **27.** $-\frac{1}{2}$ **29.** 5 **31.** $\frac{1}{4}$ **33.** $\frac{3}{2}$ **35.** undefined **37. (a)** negative **(b)** 0 **39. (a)** positive **(b)** negative **41. (a)** 0 **(b)** negative **43.** $\frac{4}{3}$; $\frac{4}{3}$; parallel **45.** $\frac{5}{3}$; $\frac{3}{5}$; neither **47.** $\frac{3}{5}$; $-\frac{5}{3}$; perpendicular **49.** $\frac{8}{27}$ **50.** 232 thousand or 232,000 **51.** positive; increased **52.** 232,000 students **53.** −2 **54.** negative; decreased **55.** 2 students per computer **57.** 19.5 ft **59. (a)** −1.7 million recipients per yr **(b)** The negative slope means the numbers of recipients *decreased* by 1.7 million each year.

61. **(a)** 9652 thousand; 10,257 thousand; 11,269 thousand; 13,897 thousand; 16,838 thousand **(b)** no; no

62. $\frac{1}{3}$ **63.** $\frac{1}{3}$ **64.** $\frac{1}{3}$ **65.** $\frac{1}{3} = \frac{1}{3} = \frac{1}{3}$ is true. **66.** They are collinear. **67.** They are not collinear.

Section 4.4 (page 275)

1. D **3.** B **5.** $y = 3x - 3$ **7.** $y = -x + 3$ **9.** $y = 4x - 3$
11. $y = 3$ **13.** A vertical line has undefined slope, so there is no value for m. Also, there is no y-intercept, so there can be no value for b.

15. $y = \frac{1}{2}x + 4$

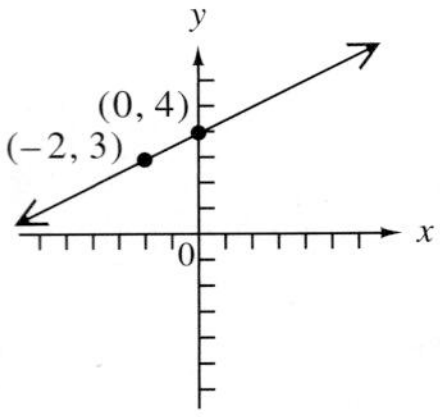

17. $y = -\frac{2}{5}x - \frac{23}{5}$

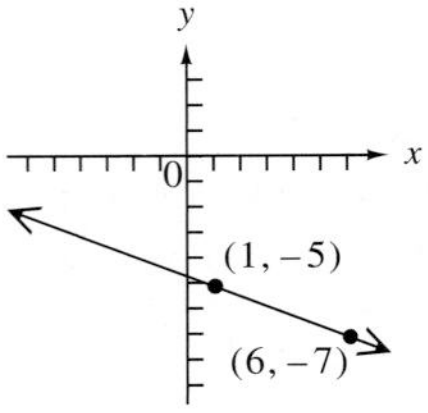

19. $y = 3x + 2$

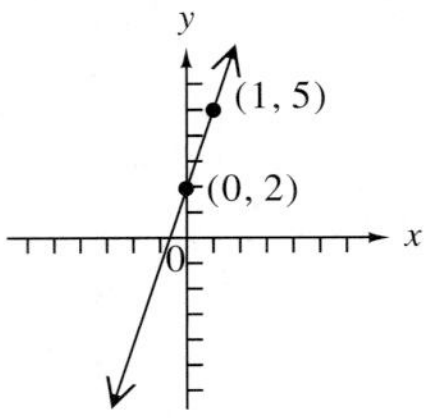

21. $y = 2$

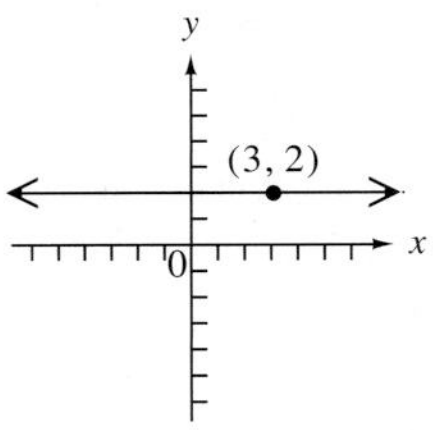

23. $x = 3$ (no slope-intercept form)

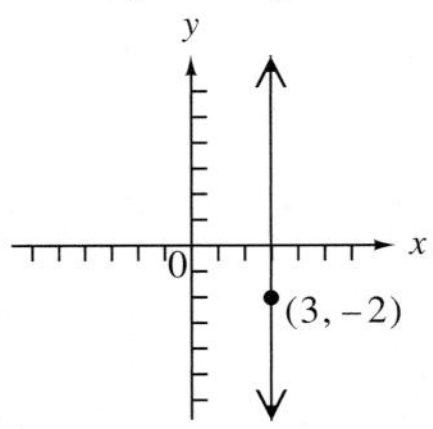

25. the y-axis **27.** $y = 2x - 7$ **29.** $y = -2x - 4$
31. $y = \frac{2}{3}x + \frac{19}{3}$ **33.** $y = x$ (There are other forms as well.)

35. $y = x - 3$ **37.** $y = -\frac{5}{7}x - \frac{54}{7}$ **39.** $y = -\frac{2}{3}x - 2$
41. $x = 3$ (no slope-intercept form) **43.** $y = \frac{1}{3}x + \frac{4}{3}$
45. (0, 32); (100, 212) **46.** $\frac{9}{5}$ **47.** $F - 32 = \frac{9}{5}(C - 0)$
48. $F = \frac{9}{5}C + 32$ **49.** $C = \frac{5}{9}(F - 32)$ **50.** 86°
51. 10° **52.** −40° **53.** $y = \frac{3}{4}x - \frac{9}{2}$ **55.** $y = -\frac{1}{2}x + 9$
57. $y = -2x - 3$ **59.** **(a)** \$400 **(b)** \$.25 **(c)** $y = .25x + 400$ **(d)** \$425 **(e)** 1500 **61.** **(a)** $y = 39x + 99$ **(b)** (5, 294); The cost of a 5-month membership is \$294. **(c)** \$567 **63.** **(a)** (1, 10,017), (3, 11,025), (5, 12,432), (7, 13,785), (9, 15,380)
(b) yes

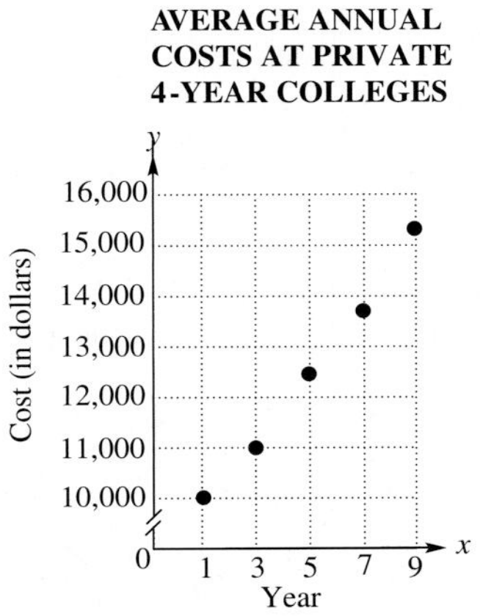

(c) $y = 725.8x + 8847.6$ or $y = 725.8x + 8847.8$ (depending on the point used) **(d)** \$18,283 **65.** **(a)** $y = .58x - 1098.2$ **(b)** 59.5%; This result is very close to the actual figure of 59.3%.

Section 4.5 (page 285)

1. solid; below **3.** dashed; above **5.** The graph of $Ax + By = C$ divides the plane into two regions. In one of these regions, the ordered pairs satisfy $Ax + By < C$; in the other, they satisfy $Ax + By > C$.

7.

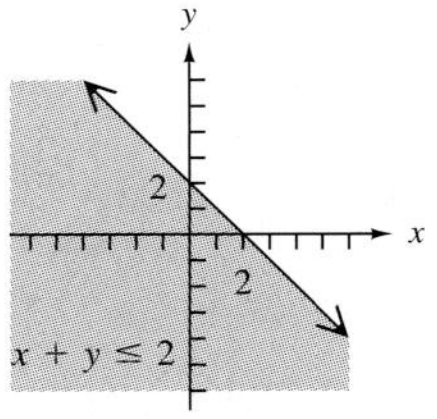

9.

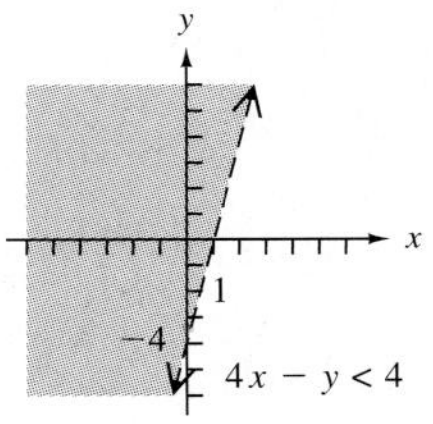

11.

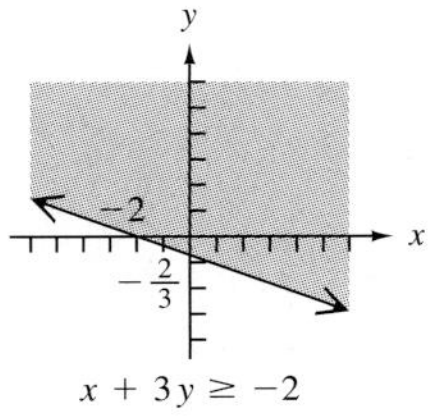

13.

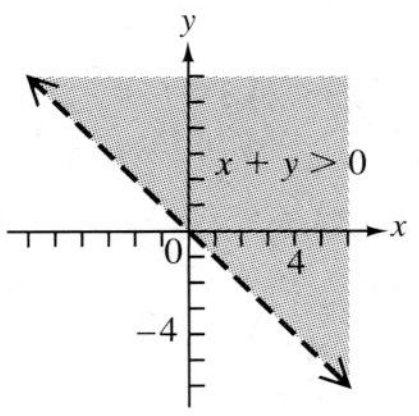

15.

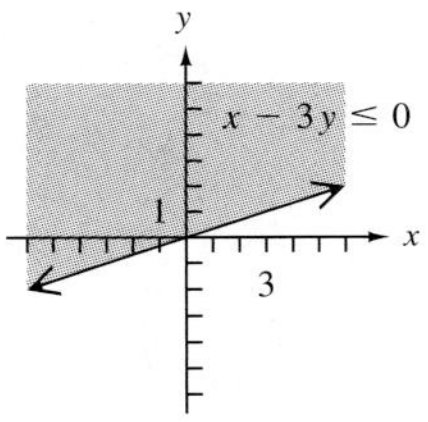

17.

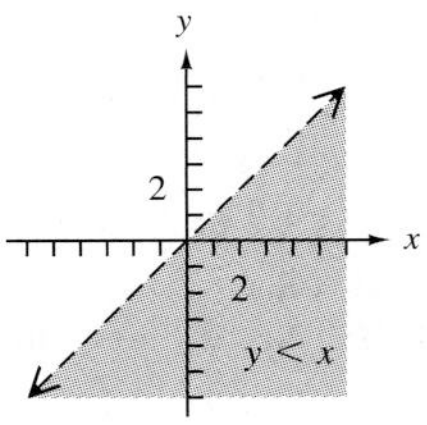

19.

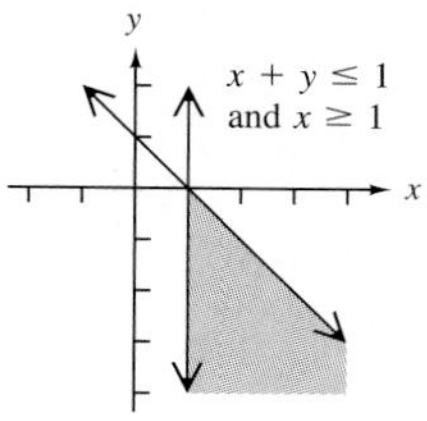

21.

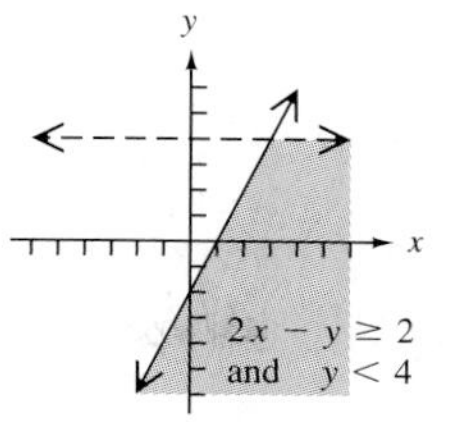

23.

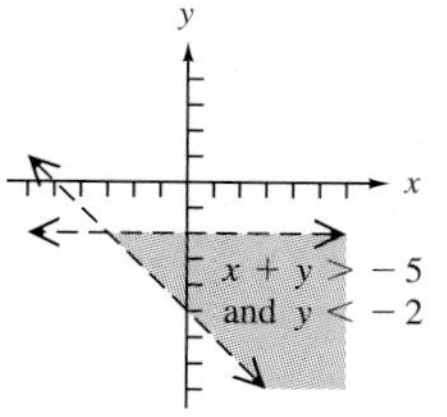

25.

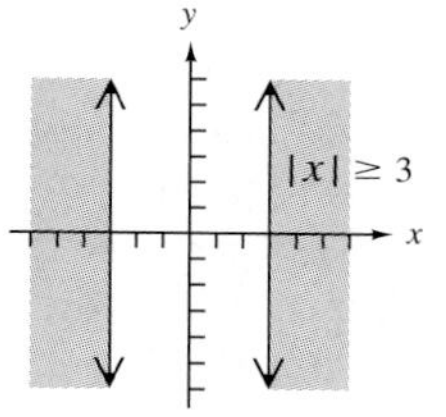

27.

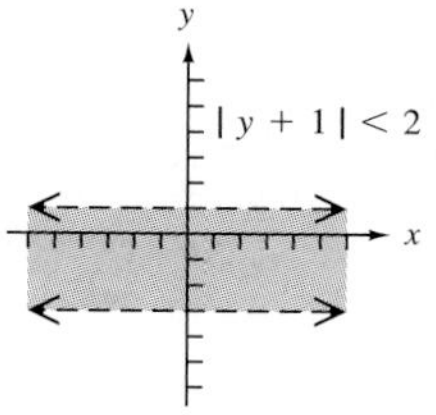

29.

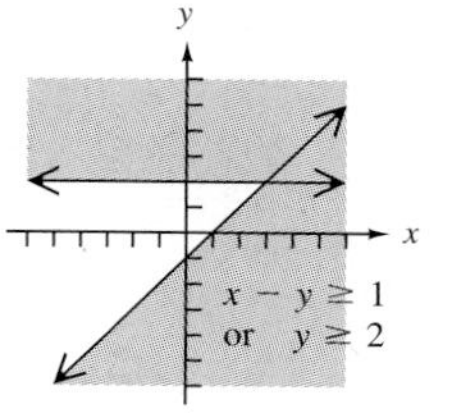

31.

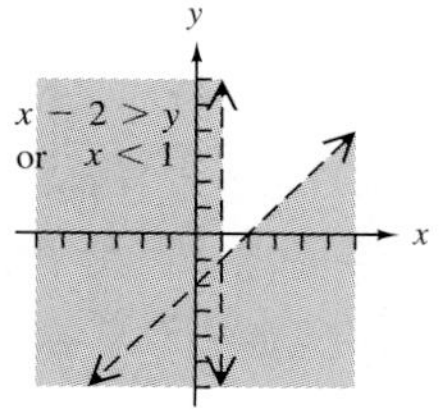

33.

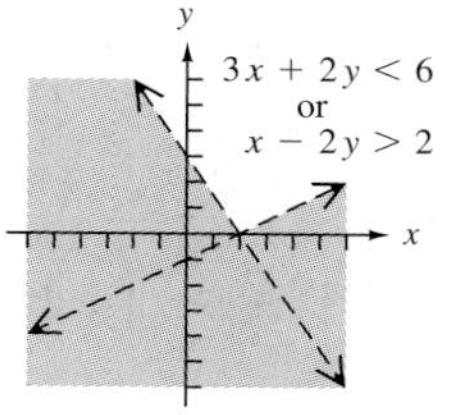

35. (a)

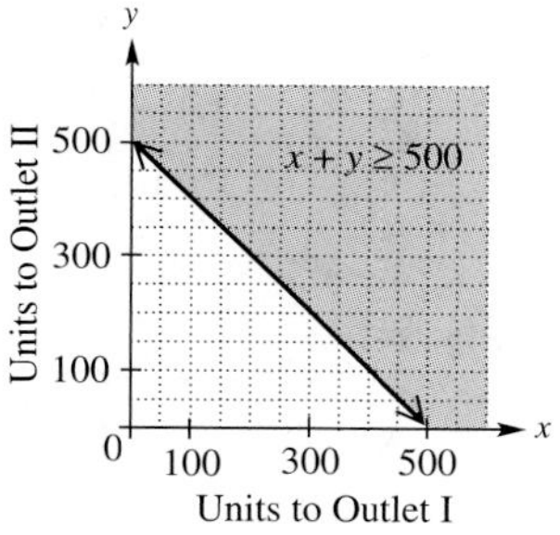

(b) (500, 0) and (200, 400); Other answers are possible.

Section 4.6 (page 299)

1. independent variable **3. (a)** A relation is a set of ordered pairs. **(b)** The domain is the set of all first components (x-values). **(c)** The range is the set of all second components (y-values). **(d)** A function is a relation in which each domain element is paired with one and only one range element. **5.** function; domain: $\{8, 5, 9, 3\}$; range: $\{0, 4, 3, 9\}$ **7.** not a function; domain: $\{9, -3\}$; range: $\{-2, 5, 1\}$ **9.** function; domain: $(-\infty, 0)$; range: $(0, \infty)$ **11.** function; domain: $(-\infty, \infty)$; range: $(-\infty, 4]$ **13.** not a function; domain: $[3, \infty)$; range: $(-\infty, \infty)$ **15.** function; domain: $(-\infty, \infty)$ **17.** not a function; domain: $[0, \infty)$ **19.** not a function; domain: $(-\infty, \infty)$ **21.** function; domain: $(-\infty, \infty)$ **23.** function; domain: $(-\infty, 0) \cup (0, \infty)$ **25.** function; domain: $(-\infty, \infty)$ **27.** function; domain: $(-\infty, 9) \cup (9, \infty)$ **29.** function; domain: $\left(-\infty, -\frac{1}{2}\right) \cup \left(-\frac{1}{2}, \infty\right)$ **31. (a)** $[0, 3000]$ **(b)** 25 hr; 25 hr **(c)** 2000 gal **(d)** $f(0) = 0$; The pool is empty at time 0. **33.** Here is one example. The cost of gasoline; number of gallons purchased; cost; number of gallons **35.** 4 **37.** -11

39. $-3p + 4$ **41.** $3x + 4$ **43.** $-3x - 2$ **45.** $-\frac{p^2}{9} + \frac{4p}{3} + 1$ **47.** line; -2; linear; $-2x + 4$; -2; 3; -2 **49. (a)** $f(x) = \frac{12 - x}{3}$ **(b)** 3 **51. (a)** $f(x) = 3 - 2x^2$ **(b)** -15 **53. (a)** $f(x) = \frac{8 - 4x}{-3}$ **(b)** $\frac{4}{3}$ **55. (a)** \$0; \$1.50; \$3.00; \$4.50 **(b)** $1.50x$

(c)

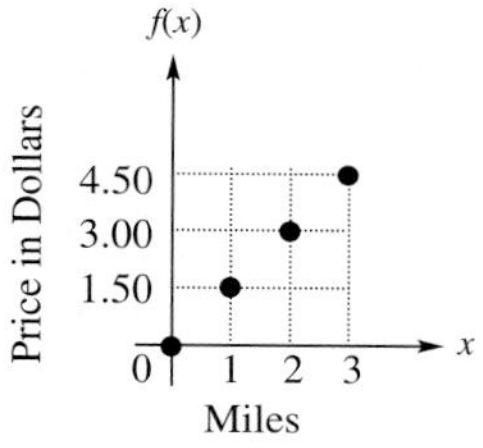

Chapter 4 Review Exercises (page 309)

1. \$1.05 per gal; \$1.75 per gal **2.** \$.70 per gal; about 67%
3. between April and June 2000; about \$.40 per gal
4. August–October 1999 and February–April 2000
5. -1; 2; 1 **6.** 2; $\frac{3}{2}$; $\frac{14}{3}$ **7.** yes **8.** no **9.** yes

10.–13.

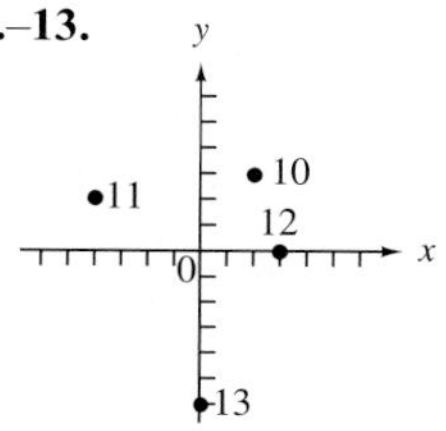

14. x is positive in quadrants I and IV; y is negative in quadrants III and IV. Thus, if x is positive and y is negative, (x, y) must lie in quadrant IV. **15.** In the ordered pair $(k, 0)$, the y-value is 0, so the point lies on the x-axis. In the ordered pair $(0, k)$, the x-value is 0, so the point lies on the y-axis.

16. $\left(-\frac{5}{2}, 0\right)$; $(0, 5)$ **17.** $\left(-\frac{7}{2}, 0\right)$; $(0, -7)$ **18.** $\left(\frac{8}{3}, 0\right)$; $(0, 4)$

19.

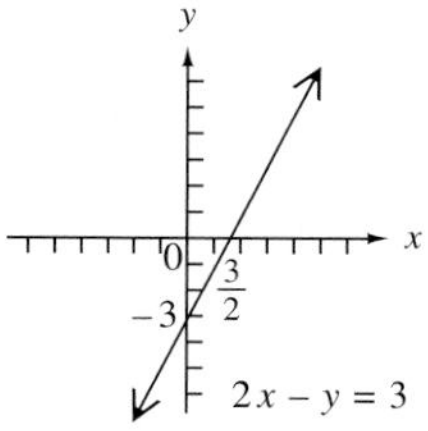

20.

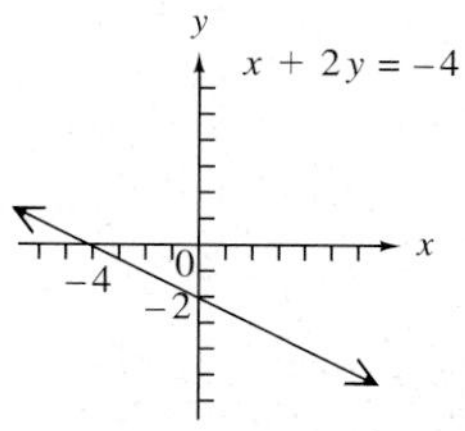

21.

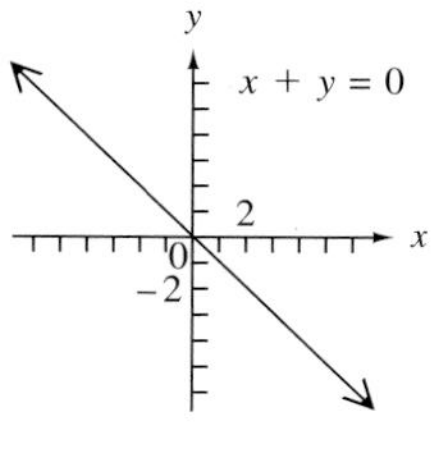

22. $-\frac{1}{2}$ **23.** undefined **24.** 3 **25.** $\frac{3}{2}$ **26.** $-\frac{1}{3}$ **27.** 0 **28.** $\frac{3}{2}$ **29. (a)** 2 **(b)** $\frac{1}{3}$ **30.** parallel **31.** perpendicular **32.** neither **33.** 12 ft **34.** \$1321 per yr **35.** $y = \frac{3}{5}x - 8$

36. $y = -\frac{1}{3}x + 5$ **37.** $y = 12$ **38.** $x = 2$ **39.** $y = -9x + 13$

40. $y = \frac{7}{5}x + \frac{16}{5}$ **41.** $y = 4x - 26$ **42.** $y = -\frac{5}{2}x + 1$

43. **(a)** $y = -.96x + 5.6$ **(b)** .8 million or 800,000 tons **(c)** near the end of 2001; The graphed line intersects the x-axis right before 2002.

44.

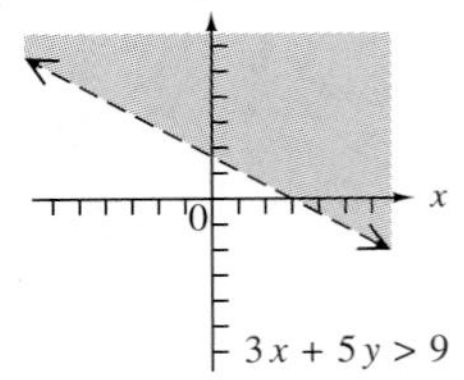

45.

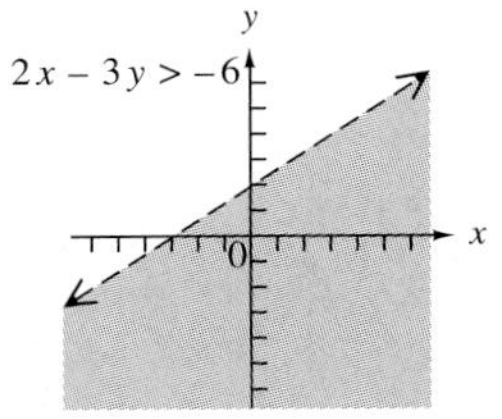

46.

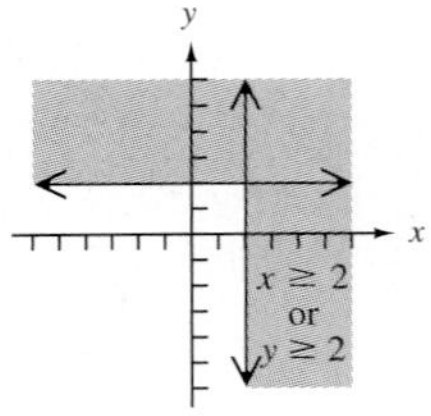

47. domain: $\{-4, 1\}$; range: $\{2, -2, 5, -5\}$; not a function **48.** domain: $[-4, 4]$; range: $[0, 2]$; function **49.** function; linear function; domain: $(-\infty, \infty)$ **50.** not a function; domain: $(-\infty, \infty)$ **51.** function; domain: $(-\infty, \infty)$ **52.** function; domain: $(-\infty, -7) \cup (-7, \infty)$ **53.** not a function; domain: $[0, \infty)$ **54.** function; domain: $(-\infty, 36) \cup (36, \infty)$ **55.** If no vertical line intersects the graph in more than one point, then it is the graph of a function. **56.** -6 **57.** -15 **58.** $-2p^2 + 3p - 6$ **59.** $-2k^2 - 3k - 6$ **60.** $f(x) = 2x^2$; 18 **61.** A **62.** C, D **63.** A, B, D **64.** D **65.** C **66.** B

67. $\left(-\frac{5}{2}, 0\right)$; $(0, -5)$; -2

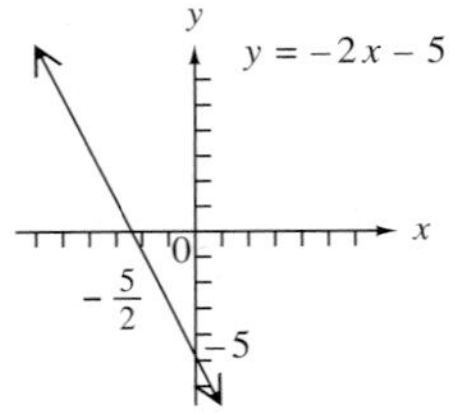

68. $(0, 0)$; $(0, 0)$; $-\frac{1}{3}$

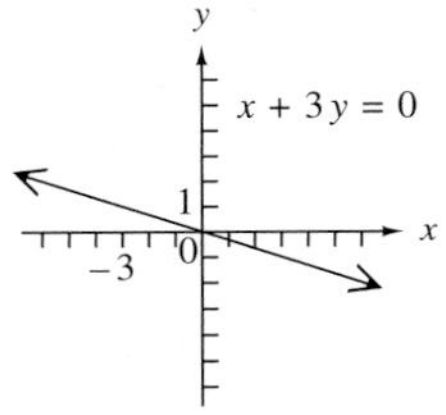

69. no x-intercept; $(0, 5)$; 0

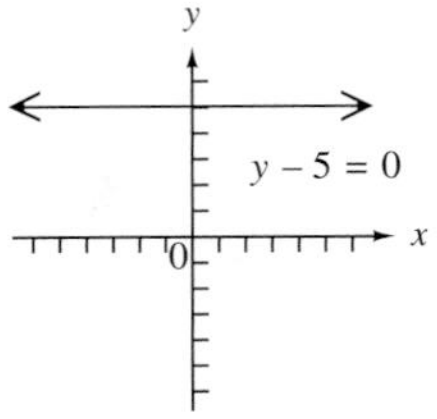

70. $y = -\frac{1}{4}x - \frac{5}{4}$ **71.** $y = -3x + 30$ **72.** $y = -\frac{4}{7}x - \frac{23}{7}$

73.

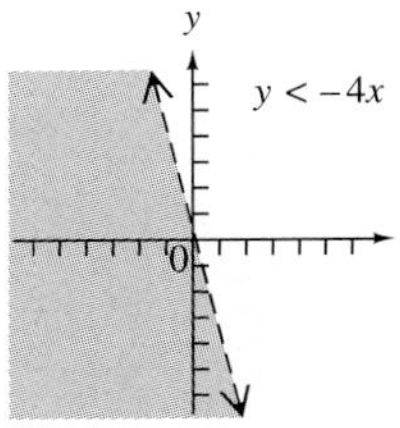

74.

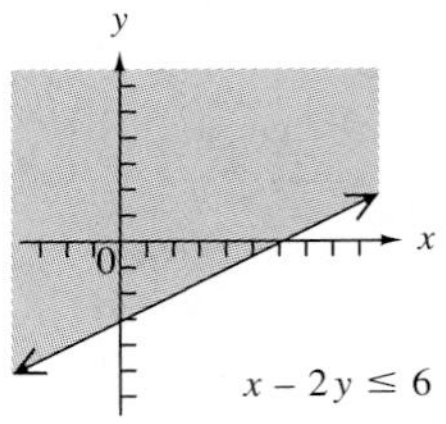

75. about \$1.5 billion **76.** It will have negative slope since the total spent on video rentals is decreasing over these years. **77.** (1996, 11.1), (2000, 9.6) **78.** $y = -.375x + 759.6$ **79.** $-.375$; Yes, the slope is negative. **80.** 10.7, 10.4, 10.0 **81.** The actual amounts are fairly close to those given by the equation. **82.** \$8.9 billion **83.** Answers will vary.

Chapter 4 Test (page 315)

1. $-6, -10, -5$ **2.** no **3.** To find the x-intercept, let $y = 0$, and to find the y-intercept, let $x = 0$.

4. x-intercept: $(2, 0)$; y-intercept: $(0, 6)$

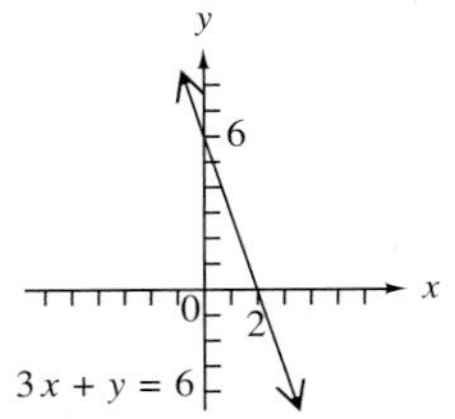

5. x-intercept: $(0, 0)$; y-intercept: $(0, 0)$

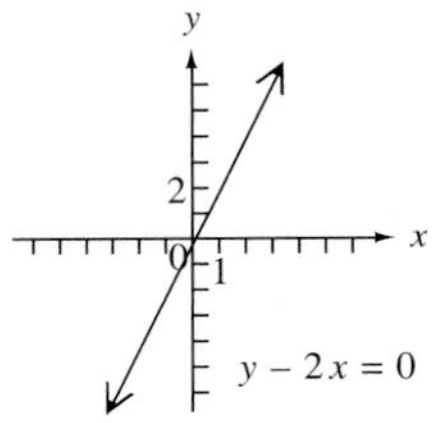

6. x-intercept: $(-3, 0)$; y-intercept: none

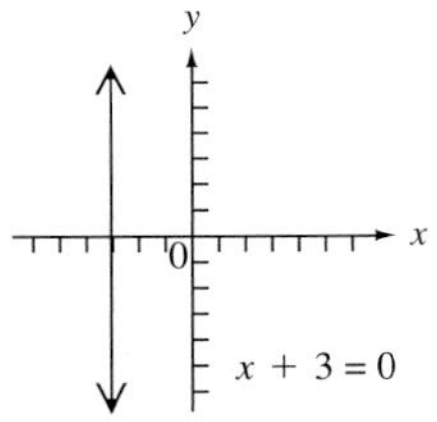

7. x-intercept: $(4, 0)$; y-intercept: $(0, -4)$

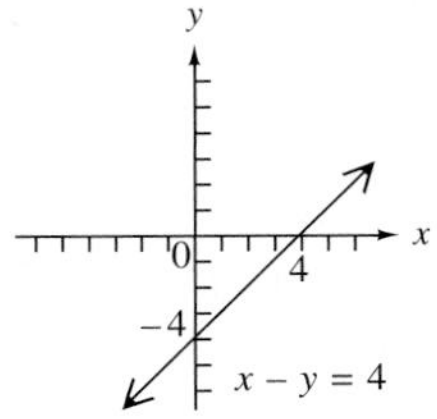

8. $-\frac{8}{3}$ **9.** -2 **10.** undefined **11.** $\frac{5}{2}$ **12.** $y = 2x + 6$

13. $y = \frac{5}{2}x - 4$ **14.** **(a)** $y = -\frac{3}{5}x - \frac{11}{5}$ **(b)** $y = -\frac{1}{2}x - \frac{3}{2}$

15.

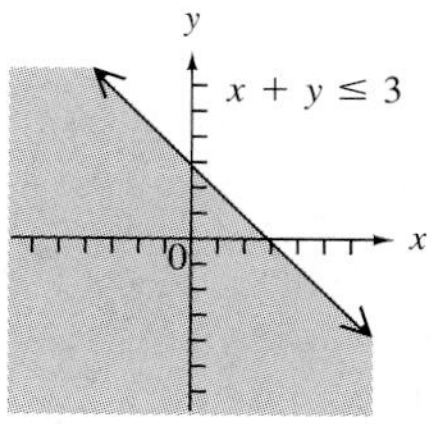

16. D **17.** **(a)** $(-\infty, \infty)$ **(b)** -2 **18.** B; The set in A includes, for example, the two ordered pairs (8.8, 1993) and (8.8, 1994). In a function, no value of the independent variable can correspond to more than one value of the dependent variable. **19.** The slope is positive since food and drink sales are increasing. **20.** (0, 43), (30, 376); 11.1 **21.** 1990: \$265 billion; 1995: \$320.5 billion **22.** In 2000, food and drink sales were \$376 billion.

Cumulative Review Exercises: Chapters R–4 (page 319)

1. $\frac{301}{40}$ or $7\frac{21}{40}$ **2.** 6 **3.** 7 **4.** $\frac{73}{18}$ or $4\frac{1}{18}$ **5.** true **6.** -43 **7.** distributive property **8.** $-p + 2$ **9.** $\left\{\frac{7}{6}\right\}$ **10.** $\{-1\}$ **11.** $h = \frac{3V}{\pi r^2}$ **12.** $\left(-\frac{1}{2}, \infty\right)$ **13.** (2, 3) **14.** $(-\infty, 2) \cup (3, \infty)$ **15.** $\left\{-\frac{16}{5}, 2\right\}$ **16.** $(-11, 7)$ **17.** $(-\infty, -2] \cup [7, \infty)$ **18.** high school diploma: \$22,895; bachelor's degree: \$40,478 **19.** 13 mi **20.** **(a)** 89.45; 81.95; 78.20 **(b)** In 1980, the winning time was 85.7 sec. **21.** **(a)** \$10,000 **(b)** about \$30,000 **22.** $(-4, 0)$; (0, 3) **23.** $\frac{3}{4}$

24.

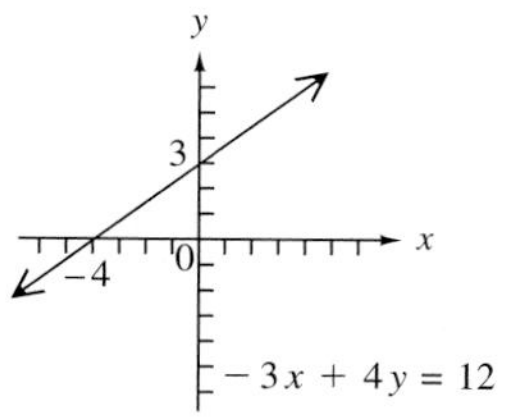

25. $y = 3x - 11$ **26.** $y = 4$ **27.** 10.5 **28.** the segment for 1992 through 2000

Chapter 5

Section 5.1 (page 327)

1. B, because the ordered pair must be in quadrant II. **3.** There is no way that the sum of two numbers can be both 2 and 4 at the same time. **5.** no **7.** yes **9.** yes **11.** no

We show the graphs here only for Exercises 13–17.

13. $\{(4, 2)\}$

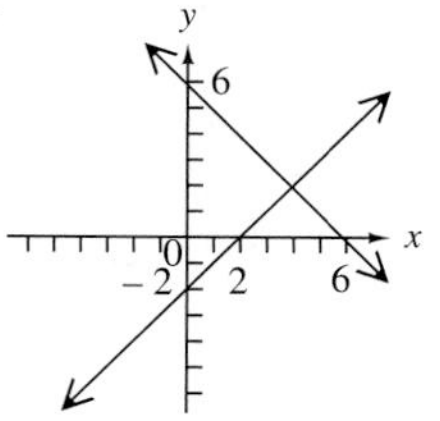

15. $\{(0, 4)\}$

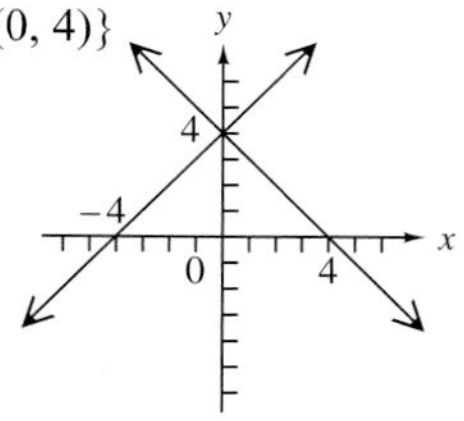

17. $\{(4, -1)\}$

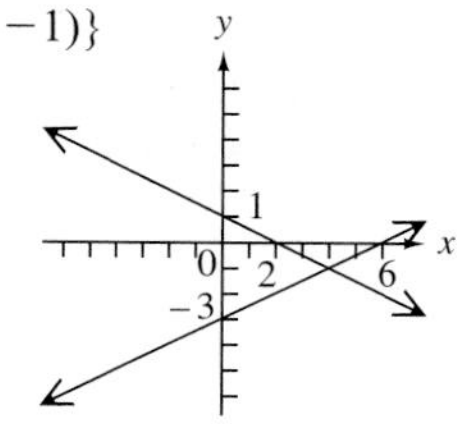

19. $\{(1, 3)\}$ **21.** $\{(0, 2)\}$ **23.** $\{(4, -3)\}$ **25.** $y = -\frac{3}{2}x + 3$; $y = -\frac{3}{2}x + \frac{5}{2}$; The graphs are parallel lines. **26.** $y = 2x - 4$; $y = 2x - 4$; The graphs are the same line. **27.** $y = \frac{1}{3}x - \frac{5}{3}$; $y = -2x + 8$; The graphs are intersecting lines. **28.** Exercise 25: no solution; Exercise 26: infinite number of solutions; Exercise 27: one solution **29.** $\emptyset$; inconsistent system **31.** $\{(x, y) \mid 2x - y = 4\}$; dependent equations **33.** $\emptyset$; inconsistent system **35.** If the coordinates of the point of intersection are not integers, the solution will be difficult to determine from a graph. **37.** **(a)** years 0 to 6 **(b)** year 6; about \$650 **39.** 1991; about 350 million **41.** between 1988 and 1990

Section 5.2 (page 337)

1. No, it is not correct, because the solution set is $\{(3, 0)\}$. The y-value must also be determined. **3.** The first student had less work to do, because the coefficient of y in the first equation is -1. The second student had to divide by 2, introducing fractions into the expression for x. **5.** $\{(7, 3)\}$ **7.** $\{(-2, 4)\}$ **9.** $\{(-4, 8)\}$ **11.** $\{(3, -2)\}$ **13.** $\{(x, y) \mid 3x - y = 5\}$ **15.** $\left\{\left(\frac{1}{3}, -\frac{1}{2}\right)\right\}$ **17.** $\emptyset$ **19.** $\{(x, y) \mid 3x - 4y = 2\}$ **21.** $\{(4, -6)\}$ **23.** $\{(7, 0)\}$ **25.** $\{(x, y) \mid 2x - y = -12\}$ **27.** $\emptyset$ **29.** **(a)** $\{(3, 2)\}$ **(b)** $\{(-1, -3)\}$; In each case, only one step is needed to find the solution because the value of one variable is known. **31.** $\{(0, 3)\}$ **33.** $\{(24, -12)\}$ **35.** $\{(3, 2)\}$ **37.** To find the total cost, multiply the number of bicycles (x) by the cost per bicycle (400 dollars) and add the fixed cost (5000 dollars). Thus, $y_1 = 400x + 5000$ gives this total cost (in dollars). **38.** $y_2 = 600x$ **39.** $y_1 = 400x + 5000$, $y_2 = 600x$; solution set: $\{(25, 15{,}000)\}$ **40.** 25; 15,000; 15,000 **41.** 1993

Section 5.3 (page 347)

1. true **3.** true **5.** $\{(-1, 3)\}$ **7.** $\{(-1, -3)\}$ **9.** $\{(-2, 3)\}$ **11.** $\left\{\left(\frac{1}{2}, 4\right)\right\}$ **13.** $\{(3, -6)\}$ **15.** $\{(7, 4)\}$ **17.** $\{(0, 4)\}$ **19.** $\{(-4, 0)\}$ **21.** $\{(0, 0)\}$ **23.** $\{(-6, 5)\}$ **25.** $\left\{\left(-\frac{6}{5}, \frac{4}{5}\right)\right\}$ **27.** $\left\{\left(\frac{1}{8}, -\frac{5}{6}\right)\right\}$ **29.** $\{(11, 15)\}$ **31.** $\emptyset$ **33.** $\{(x, y) \mid x - 3y = -4\}$ **35.** $\emptyset$ **37.** $\{(x, y) \mid 2x + y = 0\}$ **39.** $1141 = 1991a + b$ **40.** $1339 = 1996a + b$ **41.** $1991a + b = 1141$, $1996a + b = 1339$; solution set: $\{(39.6, -77{,}702.6)\}$ **42.** $y = 39.6x - 77{,}702.6$ **43.** 1220.2 (million); This is slightly less than the actual figure. **44.** It is not realistic to expect the data to lie in a perfectly straight line; as a result, the quantity obtained from an equation determined in this way will probably be "off" a bit. We cannot put too much faith in models such as this one, because not all sets of data points are linear in nature.

Section 5.4 (page 357)

1. The statement means that when -1 is substituted for x, 2 is substituted for y, and 3 is substituted for z in the three equations, the resulting three statements are true. **3.** $\{(3, 2, 1)\}$ **5.** $\{(1, 4, -3)\}$ **7.** $\left\{\left(1, \frac{3}{10}, \frac{2}{5}\right)\right\}$ **9.** $\{(0, 2, -5)\}$ **11.** $\left\{\left(-\frac{7}{3}, \frac{22}{3}, 7\right)\right\}$ **13.** $\{(4, 5, 3)\}$ **15.** $\{(2, 2, 2)\}$

17. $\left\{\left(\frac{8}{3}, \frac{2}{3}, 3\right)\right\}$ **19.** Answers will vary. Some possible answers are **(a)** two perpendicular walls and the ceiling in a normal room, **(b)** the floors of three different levels of an office building, and **(c)** three pages of this book (since they intersect in the spine). **21.** $\emptyset$ **23.** $\{(x, y, z) \mid x - y + 4z = 8\}$ **25.** $\{(x, y, z) \mid 2x + y - z = 6\}$ **27.** $\{(0, 0, 0)\}$ **29.** $128 = a + b + c$ **30.** $140 = 2.25a + 1.5b + c$ **31.** $80 = 9a + 3b + c$ **32.** $a + b + c = 128$; $2.25a + 1.5b + c = 140$; $9a + 3b + c = 80$; $\{(-32, 104, 56)\}$ **33.** $f(x) = -32x^2 + 104x + 56$ **34.** height; time **35.** 56 ft **36.** 140.5 ft

Section 5.5 (page 369)

1. wins: 95; losses: 67 **3.** length: 78 ft; width: 36 ft **5.** Exxon-Mobil: \$214 billion; General Motors: \$185 billion **7.** $x = 40$ and $y = 50$, so the angles measure 40° and 50°. **9.** NHL: \$219.74; NBA: \$203.38 **11.** single: \$2.09; double: \$3.19 **13. (a)** 6 oz **(b)** 15 oz **(c)** 24 oz **(d)** 30 oz **15.** $\$.99x$ **17.** 6 gal of 25%; 14 gal of 35% **19.** 6 L of pure acid; 48 L of 10% acid **21.** 14 kg of nuts; 16 kg of cereal **23.** \$1000 at 2%; \$2000 at 4% **25.** $25y$ **27.** freight train: 50 km per hr; express train: 80 km per hr **29.** boat: 21 mph; current: 3 mph **31.** Turner: \$80.4 million; 'N Sync: \$76.6 million **33.** 76 general admission; 108 with student ID **35.** 8 for a citron; 5 for a wood apple **37.** $x + y + z = 180$; angle measures: 70°, 30°, 80° **39.** first: 20°; second: 70°; third: 90° **41.** shortest: 12 cm; middle: 25 cm; longest: 33 cm **43.** Independent: 38; Democrat: 34; Republican: 28 **45.** \$10 tickets: 350; \$18 tickets: 250; \$30 tickets: 50 **47.** type A: 80; type B: 160; type C: 250

Section 5.6 (page 381)

1. (a) 0, 5, −3 **(b)** 1, −3, 8 **(c)** yes; The number of rows is the same as the number of columns (three). **(d)** $\begin{bmatrix} 1 & 4 & 8 \\ 0 & 5 & -3 \\ -2 & 3 & 1 \end{bmatrix}$ **(e)** $\begin{bmatrix} 1 & -\frac{3}{2} & -\frac{1}{2} \\ 0 & 5 & -3 \\ 1 & 4 & 8 \end{bmatrix}$ **(f)** $\begin{bmatrix} 1 & 15 & 25 \\ 0 & 5 & -3 \\ 1 & 4 & 8 \end{bmatrix}$

3. $\left[\begin{array}{rr|r} 1 & 2 & 11 \\ 2 & -1 & -3 \end{array}\right]$; $\left[\begin{array}{rr|r} 1 & 2 & 11 \\ 0 & -5 & -25 \end{array}\right]$; $\left[\begin{array}{rr|r} 1 & 2 & 11 \\ 0 & 1 & 5 \end{array}\right]$; $x + 2y = 11$; $y = 5$; $\{(1, 5)\}$ **5.** $\{(4, 1)\}$ **7.** $\{(1, 1)\}$ **9.** $\{(-1, 4)\}$ **11.** $\emptyset$

13. $\left[\begin{array}{rrr|r} 1 & 1 & -1 & -3 \\ 0 & -1 & 3 & 10 \\ 0 & -6 & 7 & 38 \end{array}\right]$; $\left[\begin{array}{rrr|r} 1 & 1 & -1 & -3 \\ 0 & 1 & -3 & -10 \\ 0 & -6 & 7 & 38 \end{array}\right]$; $\left[\begin{array}{rrr|r} 1 & 1 & -1 & -3 \\ 0 & 1 & -3 & -10 \\ 0 & 0 & -11 & -22 \end{array}\right]$; $\left[\begin{array}{rrr|r} 1 & 1 & -1 & -3 \\ 0 & 1 & -3 & -10 \\ 0 & 0 & 1 & 2 \end{array}\right]$; $x + y - z = -3$; $y - 3z = -10$; $z = 2$; $\{(3, -4, 2)\}$ **15.** $\{(4, 0, 1)\}$ **17.** $\{(-1, 23, 16)\}$ **19.** $\{(3, 2, -4)\}$ **21.** $\{(x, y) \mid x - 2y + z = 4\}$ **23.** \$3000 at 5%; \$1000 at 6%; \$6000 at 8%

Chapter 5 Review Exercises (page 387)

1. yes **2.** no **3.** $\{(3, 1)\}$ **4.** $\{(0, -2)\}$ **5.** $\{(x, y) \mid x - 2y = 2\}$ **6.** $\emptyset$ **7.** It is not a solution of the system because it is not a solution of the second equation, $2x + y = 4$. **8.** $\{(2, 1)\}$ **9.** $\{(3, 5)\}$ **10.** $\{(6, 4)\}$ **11.** $\emptyset$ **12.** $\{(7, 1)\}$ **13.** $\{(-5, -2)\}$ **14.** $\{(-4, 3)\}$ **15.** $\{(x, y) \mid 3x - 4y = 9\}$ **16. (a)** 2 **(b)** 9 **17.** $\{(9, 2)\}$ **18.** $\left\{\left(\frac{10}{7}, -\frac{9}{7}\right)\right\}$ **19.** $\{(8, 9)\}$ **20.** $\{(1, -5, 3)\}$ **21.** $\emptyset$ **22.** $\{(1, 2, 3)\}$ **23.** length: 200 ft; width: 85 ft **24.** 3 weekend days; 3 weekdays **25.** plane: 300 mph; wind: 20 mph **26.** 30 lb of nuts; 70 lb of candy **27.** 4 vats of green algae; 7 vats of brown algae **28.** 85°, 60°, 35° **29.** 5 L of 8%; 3 L of 20%; none of 10% **30.** Mantle: 54; Maris: 61; Blanchard: 21 **31.** $\{(3, -2)\}$ **32.** $\{(-1, 5)\}$ **33.** $\{(0, 0, -1)\}$ **34.** $\{(12, 9)\}$ **35.** $\left\{\left(\frac{82}{23}, -\frac{4}{23}\right)\right\}$ **36.** $\{(3, -1)\}$ **37.** $\{(5, 3)\}$ **38.** $\{(0, 4)\}$ **39.** $\emptyset$ **40.** 20 L **41.** U.S.: 97; Russia: 88; China: 59 **42.** $2a + b + c = -5$ **43.** $-a + c = -1$ **44.** $3a + 3b + c = -18$ **45.** $a = 1, b = -7, c = 0$; $x^2 + y^2 + x - 7y = 0$ **46.** The relation is not a function because a vertical line intersects its graph more than once.

Chapter 5 Test (page 391)

1. $\{(6, 1)\}$

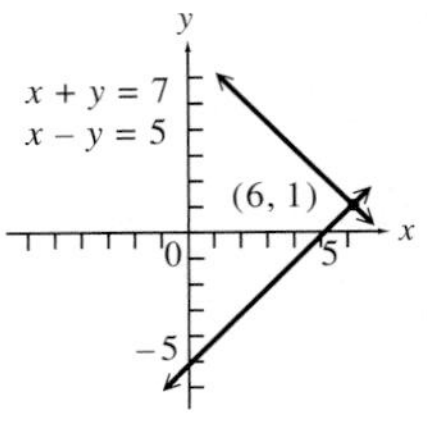

2. $\{(6, -4)\}$ **3.** $\{(x, y) \mid 12x - 5y = 8\}$ **4.** $\left\{\left(-\frac{9}{4}, \frac{5}{4}\right)\right\}$ **5.** $\{(3, 3)\}$ **6.** $\{(0, -2)\}$ **7.** $\emptyset$ **8.** $\left\{\left(-\frac{2}{3}, \frac{4}{5}, 0\right)\right\}$ **9.** $\{(3, -2, 1)\}$ **10.** *Pretty Woman:* \$178.4 million; *Runaway Bride:* \$152.3 million **11.** 45 mph, 75 mph **12.** 4 L of 20%; 8 L of 50% **13.** AC adaptor: \$8; rechargeable flashlight: \$15 **14.** 60 oz of Orange Pekoe; 30 oz of Irish Breakfast; 10 oz of Earl Grey **15.** $\left\{\left(\frac{2}{5}, \frac{7}{5}\right)\right\}$ **16.** $\{(-1, 2, 3)\}$

Cumulative Review Exercises: Chapters R–5 (page 393)

1. 81 **2.** −81 **3.** −81 **4.** 13 **5.** −13 **6.** −13 **7.** −199 **8.** 455 **9.** 14 **10.** $\left\{-\frac{15}{4}\right\}$ **11.** $\{11\}$ **12.** $x = \frac{d - by}{a - c}$ or $x = \frac{by - d}{c - a}$ **13.** $\left\{\frac{2}{3}, 2\right\}$ **14.** $\left(-\infty, \frac{240}{13}\right]$ **15.** $\left[-2, \frac{2}{3}\right]$ **16.** $(-\infty, \infty)$ **17.** 2010; 1813; 62.8%; 57.2% **18.** not guilty: 105; guilty: 95 **19.** 46°, 46°, 88° **20.** $y = 6$ **21.** $x = 4$ **22.** $-\frac{4}{3}$ **23.** $\frac{3}{4}$ **24.** $4x + 3y = 10$ **25.** $f(x) = -\frac{4}{3}x + \frac{10}{3}$

26.

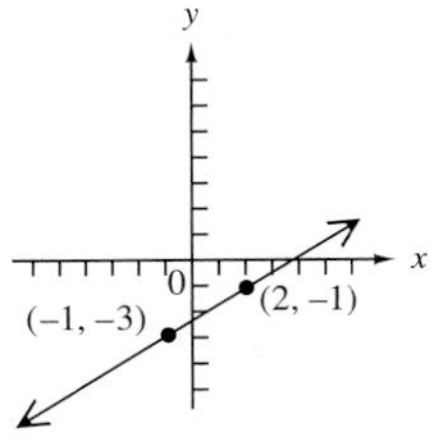

27.

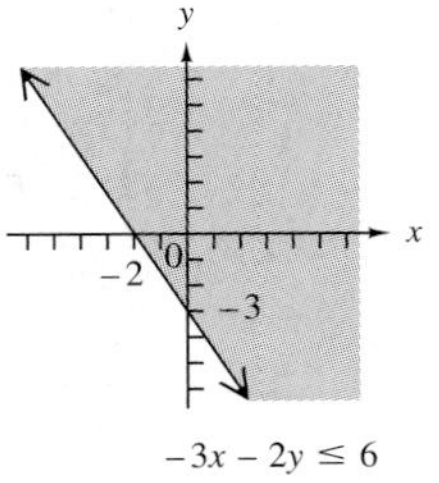

28. $\{(3, -3)\}$ **29.** $\{(5, 3, 2)\}$ **30.** Tickle Me Elmo: \$27.63; Snacktime Kid: \$36.26 **31.** 50 lb of \$1.20 candy; 30 lb of \$2.40 candy **32.** $x = 8$ or 800 parts; \$3000 **33.** about \$400

Chapter 6

Section 6.1 (page 401)

1. 7; 5 **3.** 8 **5.** 26 **7.** 1; 6 **9.** 1; 1 **11.** 2; -19, -1 **13.** 2; 1, 8 **15.** $2m^5$ **17.** $-r^5$ **19.** cannot be simplified; $.2m^5 - .5m^2$ **21.** $-5x^5$ **23.** $5p^9 + 4p^7$ **25.** $-2y^2$ **27.** already simplified; 4; binomial **29.** already simplified; $6m^5 + 5m^4 - 7m^3 - 3m^2$; 5; none of these **31.** $x^4 + \frac{1}{3}x^2 - 4$; 4; trinomial **33.** 7; 0; monomial **35. (a)** -1 **(b)** 5 **37. (a)** 19 **(b)** -2 **39. (a)** 36 **(b)** -12 **41. (a)** -124 **(b)** 5 **43.** 175 ft **44.** 87 ft; (1, 87) **45.** \$6.40 **46.** \$27 **47.** $5m^2 + 3m$ **49.** $4x^4 - 4x^2$ **51.** $\frac{7}{6}x^2 - \frac{2}{15}x + \frac{5}{6}$ **53.** $12m^3 - 13m^2 + 6m + 11$ **55.** $8r^2 + 5r - 12$ **57.** $5m^2 - 14m + 6$ **59.** $4x^3 + 2x^2 + 5x$ **61.** $-18y^5 + 7y^4 + 5y^3 + 3y^2 + y$ **63.** $-2m^3 + 7m^2 + 8m - 9$ **65.** $8x^2 + 8x + 6$ **67.** $8t^2 + 8t + 13$ **69.** $-11x^2 - 3x - 3$ **71.** The degree of a term is determined by the exponents on the *variables*, but 3 is not a variable. The degree of $3^4 = 3^4x^0$ is 0. **73.** $13a^2b - 7a^2 - b$ **75.** $c^4d - 5c^2d^2 + d^2$ **77.** $12m^3n - 11m^2n^2 - 4mn^2$

Section 6.2 (page 411)

1. 1 **3.** false **5.** false **7.** $(-2)^5$ **9.** $\left(\frac{1}{2}\right)^6$ **11.** $(-8p)^2$ **13.** The expression $(-3)^4 = (-3)(-3)(-3)(-3) = 81$, while $-3^4 = -(3 \cdot 3 \cdot 3 \cdot 3) = -81$. **15.** base: 3; exponent: 5; 243 **17.** base: -3; exponent: 5; -243 **19.** base: $-6x$; exponent: 4 **21.** base: x; exponent: 4 **23.** The product rule does not apply to $5^2 + 5^3$ because it is a *sum*, not a product. $5^2 + 5^3 = 25 + 125 = 150$ **25.** 5^8 **27.** 4^{12} **29.** $(-7)^9$ **31.** t^{24} **33.** $-56r^7$ **35.** $42p^{10}$ **37.** $14x^4$; $45x^8$ **39.** $5a^2$; $-140a^6$ **41.** 4^6 **43.** t^{20} **45.** 7^3r^3 **47.** $5^5x^5y^5$ **49.** $8q^3r^3$ **51.** $\frac{1}{2^3}$ **53.** $\frac{a^3}{b^3}$ **55.** $\frac{9^8}{5^8}$ **57.** $(-2)^3x^6y^3$ **59.** $3^2a^6b^4$ **61.** $12x^5$ **63.** $\frac{5^5}{2^5}$ **65.** $\frac{9^5}{8^3}$ **67.** $2^{12}x^{12}$ **69.** $(-6)^5p^5$ **71.** $6^5x^{10}y^{15}$ **73.** x^{21} **75.** $2^2w^4x^{26}y^7$ **77.** $-r^{18}s^{17}$ **79.** $\frac{5^3a^6b^{15}}{c^{18}}$ **81.** $25m^6p^{14}q^5$ **83.** $16x^{10}y^{16}z^{10}$

Section 6.3 (page 419)

1. $x^2 + 7x + 12$ **3.** $2x^3 + 7x^2 + 7x + 2$ **5.** distributive **7.** $-6m^2 - 4m$ **9.** $6p - \frac{9}{2}p^2 + 9p^4$ **11.** $6y^5 + 4y^6 + 10y^9$ **13.** $12x^3 + 26x^2 + 10x + 1$ **15.** $20m^4 - m^3 - 8m^2 - 17m - 15$ **17.** $6x^6 - 3x^5 - 4x^4 + 4x^3 - 5x^2 + 8x - 3$ **19.** $5x^4 - 13x^3 + 20x^2 + 7x + 5$ **21.** $n^2 + n - 6$ **23.** $8r^2 - 10r - 3$ **25.** $9x^2 - 4$ **27.** $9q^2 + 6q + 1$ **29.** $6t^2 + 23st + 20s^2$ **31.** $-.3t^2 + .22t + .24$ **33.** $x^2 - \frac{5}{12}x - \frac{1}{6}$ **35.** $\frac{15}{16} - \frac{1}{4}r - 2r^2$ **37.** $6y^5 - 21y^4 - 45y^3$ **39.** $30x + 60$ yd^2 **40.** $30x + 60 = 600$; 18 **41.** 10 yd by 60 yd **42.** \$2100 **43.** 140 yd **44.** \$1260 **45.** The answers are $x^2 - 16$, $y^2 - 4$, and $r^2 - 49$. Each product is the difference of the square of the first term and the square of the last term of the binomials.

Section 6.4 (page 425)

1. (a) $4x^2$ **(b)** $12x$ **(c)** 9 **(d)** $4x^2 + 12x + 9$ **3.** $a^2 - 2ac + c^2$ **5.** $p^2 + 4p + 4$ **7.** $16x^2 - 24x + 9$ **9.** $.64t^2 + 1.12ts + .49s^2$ **11.** $25x^2 + 4xy + \frac{4}{25}y^2$ **13.** $16a^2 - 12ab + \frac{9}{4}b^2$ **15.** $-16r^2 + 16r - 4$ **17. (a)** $49x^2$ **(b)** 0 **(c)** $-9y^2$ **(d)** $49x^2 - 9y^2$; Because 0 is the identity element for addition, it is not necessary to write "+ 0." **19.** $q^2 - 4$ **21.** $4w^2 - 25$ **23.** $100x^2 - 9y^2$ **25.** $4x^4 - 25$ **27.** $49x^2 - \frac{9}{49}$ **29.** $9p^3 - 49p$ **31.** $(a + b)^2$ **32.** a^2 **33.** $2ab$ **34.** b^2 **35.** $a^2 + 2ab + b^2$ **36.** They both represent the area of the entire large square. **37.** 1225 **38.** $30^2 + 2(30)(5) + 5^2$ **39.** 1225 **40.** They are equal. **41.** $m^3 - 15m^2 + 75m - 125$ **43.** $8a^3 + 12a^2 + 6a + 1$ **45.** $81r^4 - 216r^3t + 216r^2t^2 - 96rt^3 + 16t^4$ **47.** $x^2 + y^2$ is the sum of squares, while $(x + y)^2$ is the square of a sum. $(x + y)^2 = x^2 + 2xy + y^2$, and thus contains another term, $2xy$. **49.** $x^3 + 6x^2 + 12x + 8$

Section 6.5 (page 435)

1. negative **3.** negative **5.** positive **7.** 0 **9.** 1 **11.** -1 **13.** 0 **15.** 0 **17.** 2 **19.** $\frac{1}{64}$ **21.** 16 **23.** $\frac{49}{36}$ **25.** $\frac{8}{15}$ **27.** $-\frac{7}{18}$ **29.** 1 **30.** $\frac{5^2}{5^2}$ **31.** 5^0 **32.** $5^0 = 1$; This supports the definition of a 0 exponent. **33.** $\frac{1}{9}$ **35.** $\frac{1}{6^5}$ **37.** 6^3 **39.** $2r^4$ **41.** $\frac{5^2}{4^3}$ **43.** $\frac{p^5}{q^8}$ **45.** r^9 **47.** $\frac{x^5}{6}$ **49.** $3y^2$ **51.** x^3 **53.** 7^3 **55.** $\frac{1}{x^2}$ **57.** $\frac{4^3x}{3^2}$ **59.** $\frac{x^2z^4}{y^2}$ **61.** $6x$ **63.** $\frac{1}{m^{10}n^5}$ **65.** $\frac{5}{16x^5}$ **67.** $\frac{36q^2}{m^4p^2}$

Section 6.6 (page 439)

1. $6x^2 + 8$; 2; $3x^2 + 4$ **3.** $3x^2 + 4$; 2 (These may be reversed.); $6x^2 + 8$ **5.** To use the method of this section, the divisor must be just one term. This is true of the first problem, but not the second. **7.** $30x^3 - 10x + 5$ **9.** $-4m^3 + 2m^2 - 1$ **11.** $4t^4 - 2t^2 + 2t$ **13.** $a^4 - a + \frac{2}{a}$ **15.** $-2x^3 + \frac{2x^2}{3} - x$ **17.** $1 + 5x - 9x^2$ **19.** $\frac{4x^2}{3} + x + \frac{2}{3x}$ **21.** $9r^3 - 12r^2 - 2r + 1 - \frac{2}{3r}$ **23.** $-m^2 + 3m - \frac{4}{m}$ **25.** $-4b^2 + 3ab - \frac{5}{a}$ **27.** $\frac{12}{x} - \frac{6}{x^2} + \frac{14}{x^3} - \frac{10}{x^4}$ **29.** No, $\frac{2}{3}x$ means $\frac{2x}{3}$, which is not the same as $\frac{2}{3x}$. In the first case we multiply by x; in the second case we divide by x. Yes, $\frac{4}{3}x^2 = \frac{4x^2}{3}$. In both cases we are multiplying by x^2. **31.** $15x^5 - 35x^4 + 35x^3$ **33.** 1423 **34.** $(1 \times 10^3) + (4 \times 10^2) + (2 \times 10^1) + (3 \times 10^0)$ **35.** $x^3 + 4x^2 + 2x + 3$ **36.** They are similar in that the coefficients of the powers of ten are equal to the coefficients of the powers of x. They are different in that one is a number while the other is a polynomial. They are equal if $x = 10$.

Section 6.7 (page 445)

1. The divisor is $2x + 5$; the quotient is $2x^3 - 4x^2 + 3x + 2$. **3.** Divide $12m^2$ by $2m$ to get $6m$. **5.** $x + 2$ **7.** $2y - 5$

9. $p - 4 + \frac{44}{p + 6}$ **11.** $r - 5$ **13.** $2a - 14 + \frac{74}{2a + 3}$
15. $4x^2 - 7x + 3$ **17.** 33 **18.** 33 **19.** They are the same.
20. The answers should agree. **21.** $3y^2 - 2y + 2$
23. $3k - 4 + \frac{2}{k^2 - 2}$ **25.** $x^2 + 1$ **27.** $2p^2 - 5p + 4 + \frac{6}{3p^2 + 1}$
29. $x^3 + 3x^2 - x + 5$ **31.** $x^2 + 1$ **33.** $2x^2 + \frac{3}{5}x + \frac{1}{5}$
35. $x^2 + x - 3$ units

Section 6.8 (page 451)

1. 1.37504×10^{10} **3.** 6.6636×10^{10}; 1.43714×10^{11}
5. in scientific notation **7.** not in scientific notation; 5.6×10^6
9. not in scientific notation; 4×10^{-3} **11.** not in scientific notation; 8×10^1 **13.** A number is written in scientific notation if it is the product of a number whose absolute value is between 1 and 10 (inclusive of 1) and a power of 10. **15.** 5.876×10^9
17. 8.235×10^4 **19.** 7×10^{-6} **21.** -2.03×10^{-3}
23. 750,000 **25.** 5,677,000,000,000 **27.** -6.21 **29.** .00078
31. .000000005134 **33.** 6×10^{11}; 600,000,000,000
35. 1.5×10^7; 15,000,000 **37.** 6.426×10^4; 64,260
39. 3×10^{-4} **41.** 4×10^1 **43.** 2.6×10^{-3} **45.** about 3.3
47. about \$63,000,000,000 **49.** about .276 lb

Chapter 6 Review Exercises (page 457)

1. $22m^2$; degree 2; monomial **2.** $p^3 - p^2 + 4p + 2$; degree 3; none of these **3.** already in descending powers; degree 5; none of these **4.** $-8y^5 - 7y^4 + 9y$; degree 5; trinomial
5. $-5a^3 + 4a^2$ **6.** $2r^3 - 3r^2 + 9r$ **7.** $11y^2 - 10y + 9$
8. $-13k^4 - 15k^2 - 4k - 6$ **9.** $10m^3 - 6m^2 - 3$
10. $-y^2 - 4y + 26$ **11.** $10p^2 - 3p - 11$ **12.** $7r^4 - 4r^3 - 1$
13. 4^{11} **14.** $(-5)^{11}$ **15.** $-72x^7$ **16.** $10x^{14}$ **17.** 19^5x^5
18. $(-4)^7y^7$ **19.** $5p^4t^4$ **20.** $\frac{7^6}{5^6}$ **21.** $3^3x^6y^9$ **22.** t^{42}
23. $6^2x^{16}y^4z^{16}$ **24.** The product rule for exponents does not apply here because we want the sum of 7^2 and 7^4, not their product.
25. $10x^2 + 70x$ **26.** $-6p^5 + 15p^4$ **27.** $6r^3 + 8r^2 - 17r + 6$
28. $8y^3 + 27$ **29.** $5p^5 - 2p^4 - 3p^3 + 25p^2 + 15p$
30. $6k^2 - 9k - 6$ **31.** $12p^2 - 48pq + 21q^2$
32. $2m^4 + 5m^3 - 16m^2 - 28m + 9$ **33.** $a^2 + 8a + 16$
34. $9p^2 - 12p + 4$ **35.** $4r^2 + 20rs + 25s^2$
36. $r^3 + 6r^2 + 12r + 8$ **37.** $8x^3 - 12x^2 + 6x - 1$
38. $36m^2 - 25$ **39.** $4z^2 - 49$ **40.** $25a^2 - 36b^2$
41. $4x^4 - 25$ **42.** $(a + b)^2 = (a + b)(a + b) = a^2 + 2ab + b^2$. The term $2ab$ is not in $a^2 + b^2$. **43.** 2 **44.** $\frac{1}{32}$ **45.** $\frac{5^2}{6^2}$ or $\frac{25}{36}$
46. $-\frac{3}{16}$ **47.** 6^2 **48.** x^2 **49.** $\frac{1}{p^{12}}$ **50.** r^4 **51.** 2^8
52. $\frac{1}{9^6}$ **53.** 5^8 **54.** $\frac{1}{8^{12}}$ **55.** $\frac{1}{m^2}$ **56.** y^7 **57.** r^{13} **58.** $(-5)^2m^6$
59. $\frac{y^{12}}{2^3}$ **60.** $\frac{1}{a^3b^5}$ **61.** $2 \cdot 6^2 \cdot r^5$ **62.** $\frac{2^3n^{10}}{3m^{13}}$ **63.** $\frac{5y^2}{3}$
64. $-2x^2y$ **65.** $-y^3 + 2y - 3$ **66.** $p - 3 + \frac{5}{2p}$
67. $-x^9 + 2x^8 - 4x^3 + 7x$ **68.** $-2m^2n + mn^2 + \frac{6n^3}{5}$
69. $2r + 7$ **70.** $4m + 3 + \frac{5}{3m - 5}$ **71.** $2a + 1 + \frac{-8a + 12}{5a^2 - 3}$
72. $k^2 + 2k + 4 + \frac{-2k - 12}{2k^2 + 1}$ **73.** 4.8×10^7
74. 2.8988×10^{10} **75.** 6.5×10^{-5} **76.** 8.24×10^{-8}
77. 24,000 **78.** 78,300,000 **79.** .000000897
80. .00000000000995 **81.** 800 **82.** 4,000,000 **83.** .025
84. .01 **85.** .0000000000016 **86.** 2×10^{11} **87.** 0
88. $\frac{3^5}{p^3}$ **89.** $\frac{1}{7^2}$ **90.** $49 - 28k + 4k^2$ **91.** $y^2 + 5y + 1$
92. $\frac{6^4r^8s^4}{5^4}$ **93.** $-8m^7 - 10m^6 - 6m^5$ **94.** 2^5
95. $5xy^3 - \frac{8y^2}{5} + 3x^2y$ **96.** $\frac{r^2}{6}$ **97.** $8x^3 + 12x^2y + 6xy^2 + y^3$
98. $\frac{3}{4}$ **99.** $a^3 - 2a^2 - 7a + 2$ **100.** $8y^3 - 9y^2 + 5$
101. $10r^2 + 21r - 10$ **102.** $144a^2 - 1$ **103.** $2x^2 + x - 6$
104. $25x^8 + 20x^6 + 4x^4$

Chapter 6 Test (page 461)

1. $4t^4 + t^3 - 6t^2 - t$ **2.** $-2y^2 - 9y + 17$
3. $-12t^2 + 5t + 8$ **4.** $(-2)^5$ or -2^5 **5.** $\frac{6^3}{m^6}$
6. $-27x^5 + 18x^4 - 6x^3 + 3x^2$ **7.** $2r^3 + r^2 - 16r + 15$
8. $t^2 - 5t - 24$ **9.** $8x^2 + 2xy - 3y^2$ **10.** $25x^2 - 20xy + 4y^2$
11. $100v^2 - 9w^2$ **12.** $x^3 + 3x^2 + 3x + 1$ **13.** $\frac{1}{625}$
14. 2 **15.** $\frac{7}{12}$ **16.** 8^5 **17.** x^2y^6 **18.** $4y^2 - 3y + 2 + \frac{5}{y}$
19. $-3xy^2 + 2x^3y^2 + 4y^2$ **20.** $2x + 9$
21. $3x^2 + 6x + 11 + \frac{26}{x - 2}$ **22.** **(a)** 3.44×10^{11}
(b) 5.57×10^{-6} **23.** **(a)** 29,600,000 **(b)** .0000000607
24. $9x^2 + 54x + 81$ **25.** Answers will vary. One example is $(-4x^4 + 3x^3 + 2x + 1) + (4x^4 - 8x^3 + 2x + 7) = -5x^3 + 4x + 8$.

Cumulative Review Exercises: Chapters R–6 (page 463)

1. $\frac{19}{24}$ **2.** $-\frac{1}{20}$ **3.** 3.72 **4.** 62.006 **5.** \$1836 **6.** -8 **7.** 24
8. $\frac{1}{2}$ **9.** -4 **10.** associative property **11.** inverse property
12. distributive property **13.** $\{10\}$ **14.** $\left\{\frac{13}{4}\right\}$ **15.** $\emptyset$
16. $r = \frac{d}{t}$ **17.** $\{-5\}$ **18.** $\{20\}$ **19.** mouse: 160; elephant: 10
20. 4 **21.** $[10, \infty)$ **22.** $\left(-\infty, -\frac{14}{5}\right)$ **23.** $[-4, 2)$ **24.** $(2, 10]$
25. $\left\{1, \frac{5}{2}\right\}$ **26.** $(-\infty, -4) \cup (-1, \infty)$ **27.** $(0, 2)$ and $(-3, 0)$; $\frac{2}{3}$
28.

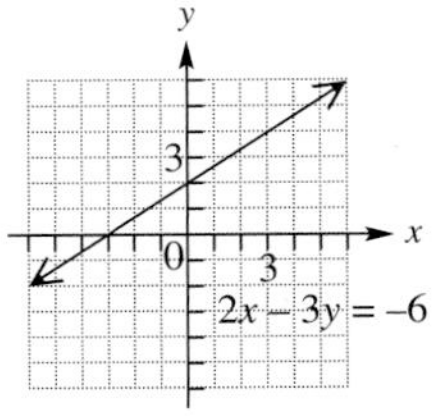

29. $f(x) = \frac{2}{3}x + 2$; 0 **30.** $\{(2, 1)\}$ **31.** $\{(1, 4)\}$ **32.** $\{(2, 1, 4)\}$
33. $\frac{5}{4}$ or $1\frac{1}{4}$ **34.** 1 **35.** $\frac{2b}{a^{10}}$ **36.** 3.45×10^4
37. $11x^3 - 14x^2 - x + 14$ **38.** $63x^2 + 57x + 12$
39. $25x^2 + 80x + 64$ **40.** $y^2 - 2y + 6$

Chapter 7

Section 7.1 (page 473)

1. 4 **3.** 4 **5.** 6 **7.** 1 **9.** 8 **11.** $10x^3$ **13.** xy^2 **15.** 6 **17.** $3m^2$ **19.** $2z^4$ **21.** $2mn^4$ **23.** $y + 2$ **25.** $a - 2$ **27.** $2 + 3xy$ **29.** $x(x - 4)$ **31.** $3t(2t + 5)$ **33.** $\frac{1}{4}d(d - 3)$ **35.** $6x^2(2x + 1)$ **37.** $5y^6(13y^4 + 7)$ **39.** no common factor (except 1) **41.** $8m^2n^2(n + 3)$ **43.** $2x(2x^2 - 5x + 3)$ **45.** $13y^2(y^6 + 2y^2 - 3)$ **47.** $9qp^3(5q^3p^2 + 4p^3 + 9q)$ **49.** $(x + 2)(c + d)$ **51.** $(2a + b)(a^2 - b)$ **53.** $(5 + n)(m + 4)$ **55.** $(2y - 7)(3x + 4)$ **57.** $(z + 2)(7z - a)$ **59.** $(3r + 2y)(6r - x)$ **61.** $(w + 1)(w^2 + 9)$ **63.** $(a + 2)(3a^2 - 2)$ **65.** $(4m - p^2)(4m^2 - p)$ **67.** $(y + 3)(y + x)$ **69.** $(z - 2)(2z - 3w)$ **71.** commutative property **72.** $2x(y - 4) - 3(y - 4)$ **73.** No, because it is not a product. It is the difference between $2x(y - 4)$ and $3(y - 4)$. **74.** $(2x - 3)(y - 4)$; yes

Section 7.2 (page 479)

1. a and b must have different signs. **3.** A prime polynomial is one that cannot be factored using only integers in the factors. **5.** 1 and 12, -1 and -12, 2 and 6, -2 and -6, 3 and 4, -3 and -4; the pair with a sum of 7 is 3 and 4. **7.** 1 and -24, -1 and 24, 2 and -12, -2 and 12, 3 and -8, -3 and 8, 4 and -6, -4 and 6; the pair with a sum of -5 is 3 and -8. **9.** C **11.** $x + 11$ **13.** $x - 8$ **15.** $y - 5$ **17.** $x + 11$ **19.** $y - 9$ **21.** $(y + 8)(y + 1)$ **23.** $(b + 3)(b + 5)$ **25.** $(m + 5)(m - 4)$ **27.** $(x + 8)(x - 5)$ **29.** $(y - 5)(y - 3)$ **31.** $(z - 8)(z - 7)$ **33.** $(r - 6)(r + 5)$ **35.** $(a - 12)(a + 4)$ **37.** prime **39.** $(r + 2a)(r + a)$ **41.** $(x + y)(x + 3y)$ **43.** $(t + 2z)(t - 3z)$ **45.** $(v - 5w)(v - 6w)$ **47.** $4(x + 5)(x - 2)$ **49.** $2t(t + 1)(t + 3)$ **51.** $2x^4(x - 3)(x + 7)$ **53.** $a^3(a + 4b)(a - b)$ **55.** $mn(m - 6n)(m - 4n)$ **57.** The factored form $(2x + 4)(x - 3)$ is incorrect because $2x + 4$ has a common factor, which must be factored out for the trinomial to be completely factored.

Section 7.3 (page 483)

1. $(m + 6)(m + 2)$ **3.** $(a + 5)(a - 2)$ **5.** $(2t + 1)(5t + 2)$ **7.** $(3z - 2)(5z - 3)$ **9.** $(2s - t)(4s + 3t)$ **11.** B **13. (a)** 2; 12; 24; 11 **(b)** 3; 8 (Order is irrelevant.) **(c)** $3m$; $8m$ **(d)** $2m^2 + 3m + 8m + 12$ **(e)** $(2m + 3)(m + 4)$ **(f)** $(2m + 3)(m + 4) = 2m^2 + 11m + 12$ **15.** $(2x + 1)(x + 3)$ **17.** $(4r - 3)(r + 1)$ **19.** $(4m + 1)(2m - 3)$ **21.** $(3m + 1)(7m + 2)$ **23.** $(2b + 1)(3b + 2)$ **25.** $(4y - 3)(3y - 1)$ **27.** $3(4x - 1)(2x - 3)$ **29.** $2m(m - 4)(m + 5)$ **31.** $4z^3(8z + 3)(z - 1)$ **33.** $(3p + 4q)(4p - 3q)$ **35.** $(3a - 5b)(2a + b)$ **37.** $(5 - x)(1 - x)$ **39.** The student stopped too soon. He needs to factor out the common factor $4x - 1$ to get $(4x - 1)(4x - 5)$ as the correct answer.

Section 7.4 (page 489)

1. B **3.** A **5.** A **7.** $2a + 5b$ **9.** $x^2 + 3x - 4$; $x + 4$, $x - 1$, or $x - 1$, $x + 4$ **11.** $2z^2 - 5z - 3$; $2z + 1$, $z - 3$, or $z - 3$, $2z + 1$ **13.** The binomial $2x - 6$ cannot be a factor because it has a common factor of 2, but the polynomial does not. **15.** $(3a + 7)(a + 1)$ **17.** $(2y + 3)(y + 2)$ **19.** $(3m - 1)(5m + 2)$ **21.** $(3s - 1)(4s + 5)$ **23.** $(5m - 4)(2m - 3)$ **25.** $(4w - 1)(2w - 3)$ **27.** $(4y + 1)(5y - 11)$ **29.** prime **31.** $2(5x + 3)(2x + 1)$ **33.** $q(5m + 2)(8m - 3)$ **35.** $3n^2(5n - 3)(n - 2)$ **37.** $y^2(5x - 4)(3x + 1)$ **39.** $(5a + 3b)(a - 2b)$ **41.** $(4s + 5t)(3s - t)$ **43.** $m^4n(3m + 2n)(2m + n)$ **45.** $-1(x + 7)(x - 3)$ **47.** $-1(3x + 4)(x - 1)$ **49.** $-1(a + 2b)(2a + b)$ **51.** $5 \cdot 7$ **52.** $(-5)(-7)$ **53.** The product of $3x - 4$ and $2x - 1$ is $6x^2 - 11x + 4$. **54.** The product of $4 - 3x$ and $1 - 2x$ is $6x^2 - 11x + 4$. **55.** The factors in Exercise 53 are the opposites of the factors in Exercise 54. **56.** $(3 - 7t)(5 - 2t)$

Section 7.5 (page 497)

1. 1; 4; 9; 16; 25; 36; 49; 64; 81; 100; 121; 144; 169; 196; 225; 256; 289; 324; 361; 400 **3.** 2 **5.** $(y + 5)(y - 5)$ **7.** $(3r + 2)(3r - 2)$ **9.** $\left(6m + \frac{4}{5}\right)\left(6m - \frac{4}{5}\right)$ **11.** $4(3x + 2)(3x - 2)$ **13.** $(14p + 15)(14p - 15)$ **15.** $(4r + 5a)(4r - 5a)$ **17.** prime **19.** $(p^2 + 7)(p^2 - 7)$ **21.** $(x^2 + 1)(x + 1)(x - 1)$ **23.** $(p^2 + 16)(p + 4)(p - 4)$ **25.** The teacher was justified, because it was not factored completely; $x^2 - 9$ can be factored as $(x + 3)(x - 3)$. The complete factored form is $(x^2 + 9)(x + 3)(x - 3)$. **27.** No, it is not a perfect square because the middle term should be $30y$, not $14y$. **29.** $(w + 1)^2$ **31.** $(x - 4)^2$ **33.** $\left(t + \frac{1}{2}\right)^2$ **35.** $(x - .5)^2$ **37.** $2(x + 6)^2$ **39.** $(4x - 5)^2$ **41.** $(7x - 2y)^2$ **43.** $(8x + 3y)^2$ **45.** $2h(5h - 2y)^2$ **47.** 1; 8; 27; 64; 125; 216; 343; 512; 729; 1000 **49.** C, D **51.** $(a + 1)(a^2 - a + 1)$ **53.** $(a - 1)(a^2 + a + 1)$ **55.** $(p + q)(p^2 - pq + q^2)$ **57.** $(y - 6)(y^2 + 6y + 36)$ **59.** $(k + 10)(k^2 - 10k + 100)$ **61.** $(3x - 1)(9x^2 + 3x + 1)$ **63.** $(5a + 2)(25a^2 - 10a + 4)$ **65.** $(y - 2x)(y^2 + 2xy + 4x^2)$ **67.** $(3a - 4b)(9a^2 + 12ab + 16b^2)$ **69.** $(2p + 9q)(4p^2 - 18pq + 81q^2)$ **71.** $2(2t - 1)(4t^2 + 2t + 1)$ **73.** $5(2w + 3)(4w^2 - 6w + 9)$ **75.** $(x + y^2)(x^2 - xy^2 + y^4)$ **77.** $(5k - 2m^3)(25k^2 + 10km^3 + 4m^6)$ **79.** $(x^3 - 1)(x^3 + 1)$ **80.** $(x - 1)(x^2 + x + 1)(x + 1)(x^2 - x + 1)$ **81.** $(x^2 - 1)(x^4 + x^2 + 1)$ **82.** $(x - 1)(x + 1)(x^4 + x^2 + 1)$ **83.** The result in Exercise 34 is completely factored. **84.** Show that $x^4 + x^2 + 1 = (x^2 + x + 1)(x^2 - x + 1)$. **85.** difference of squares **86.** $(x - 3)(x^2 + 3x + 9)(x + 3)(x^2 - 3x + 9)$

Summary Exercises on Factoring (page 501)

1. $8m^3(4m^6 + 2m^2 + 3)$ **2.** $2(m + 3)(m - 8)$ **3.** $7k(2k + 5)(k - 2)$ **4.** prime **5.** $(6z + 1)(z + 5)$ **6.** $(m + n)(m - 4n)$ **7.** $(7z + 4y)(7z - 4y)$ **8.** $10nr(10nr + 3r^2 - 5n)$ **9.** $4x(4x + 5)$ **10.** $(4 + m)(5 + 3n)$ **11.** $(5y - 6z)(2y + z)$ **12.** $(y^2 + 9)(y + 3)(y - 3)$ **13.** $(m - 3)(m + 5)$ **14.** $(2y + 1)(3y - 4)$ **15.** $8z(4z - 1)(z + 2)$ **16.** $5y(3y + 1)$ **17.** $(z - 6)^2$ **18.** $(3m + 8)(3m - 8)$ **19.** $(t + 4)(t^2 - 4t + 16)$ **20.** $(4z - 1)^2$ **21.** $6(y - 2)(y + 1)$ **22.** $\left(x + \frac{1}{4}\right)^2$ **23.** $(p - 6)(p - 11)$ **24.** $(a + 8)(a + 9)$ **25.** prime **26.** $3(6m - 1)^2$ **27.** $(z + 2a)(z - 5a)$ **28.** $(2a + 1)(a^2 - 7)$ **29.** $(2k - 3)^2$ **30.** $(4x - 7)(16x^2 + 28x + 49)$ **31.** $(4r + 3m)^2$ **32.** $(3k - 2)(k + 2)$ **33.** prime **34.** $(a^2 + 25)(a + 5)(a - 5)$ **35.** $4(2k - 3)^2$ **36.** $(4k + 1)(2k - 3)$ **37.** $6y^4(3y + 4)(2y - 5)$ **38.** $5z(z - 2)(z - 7)$ **39.** $(8p - 1)(p + 3)$ **40.** $(4k - 3h)(2k + h)$ **41.** $6(3m + 2z)(3m - 2z)$ **42.** $(2k - 5z)^2$ **43.** $2(3a - 1)(a + 2)$ **44.** $(3h - 2g)(5h + 7g)$ **45.** $(m + 9)(m - 9)$ **46.** $(z + 6w)(z^2 - 6wz + 36w^2)$ **47.** $5m^2(5m - 13n)(5m - 3n)$ **48.** $(3y - 1)(3y + 5)$ **49.** $(m - 2)^2$ **50.** prime **51.** $(2p - 1)(4p^2 + 2p + 1)$ **52.** $5(2m - 3)(m + 4)$ **53.** $(2 - q)(2 - 3p)$ **54.** $\left(k + \frac{8}{11}\right)\left(k - \frac{8}{11}\right)$ **55.** $4(4p + 5m)(4p - 5m)$ **56.** $(m + 4)(m^2 - 6)$ **57.** $(10a + 9y)(10a - 9y)$ **58.** $(8a - b)(a + 3b)$ **59.** $(a + 4)^2$ **60.** $(2y + 5)(2y - 5)$

Section 7.6 (page 509)

1. $\{-5, 2\}$ **3.** $\left\{3, \frac{7}{2}\right\}$ **5.** $\left\{-\frac{5}{6}, 0\right\}$ **7.** $\left\{0, \frac{4}{3}\right\}$ **9.** $\left\{-\frac{1}{2}, \frac{1}{6}\right\}$ **11.** $\{-.8, 2\}$ **13.** $\{9\}$ **15.** Set each *variable* factor equal to 0, to get $2x = 0$ or $3x - 4 = 0$. The solutions are 0 and $\frac{4}{3}$. **17.** $\{-2, -1\}$ **19.** $\{1, 2\}$ **21.** $\{-8, 3\}$ **23.** $\{-1, 3\}$ **25.** $\{-2, -1\}$ **27.** $\{-4\}$ **29.** $\left\{-2, \frac{1}{3}\right\}$ **31.** $\left\{-\frac{4}{3}, \frac{1}{2}\right\}$ **33.** $\left\{-\frac{2}{3}\right\}$ **35.** $\{-3, 3\}$ **37.** $\left\{-\frac{7}{4}, \frac{7}{4}\right\}$ **39.** $\{-11, 11\}$ **41.** $\{0, 7\}$ **43.** $\left\{0, \frac{1}{2}\right\}$ **45.** $\{2, 5\}$ **47.** $\left\{-4, \frac{1}{2}\right\}$ **49.** $\left\{-12, \frac{11}{2}\right\}$ **51.** $\{-2, 0, 2\}$ **53.** $\left\{-\frac{7}{3}, 0, \frac{7}{3}\right\}$ **55.** $\left\{-\frac{5}{2}, \frac{1}{3}, 5\right\}$ **57.** $\left\{-\frac{7}{2}, -3, 1\right\}$ **59. (a)** 64; 144; 4; 6 **(b)** No time has elapsed, so the object hasn't fallen (been released) yet. **(c)** Time cannot be negative.

Section 7.7 (page 517)

1. Read; variable; equation; Solve; answer; Check; original **3.** *Step 3:* $45 = (2x + 1)(x + 1)$; *Step 4:* $x = 4$ or $x = -\frac{11}{2}$; *Step 5:* base: 9 units; height: 5 units; *Step 6:* $9 \cdot 5 = 45$ **5.** *Step 3:* $80 = (x + 8)(x - 8)$; *Step 4:* $x = 12$ or $x = -12$; *Step 5:* length: 20 units; width: 4 units; *Step 6:* $20 \cdot 4 = 80$ **7.** length: 7 in.; width: 4 in. **9.** length: 13 in.; width: 10 in. **11.** height: 13 in.; width: 10 in. **13.** mirror: 7 ft; painting: 9 ft **15.** 20, 21 **17.** $-3, -2$ or 4, 5 **19.** $-3, -1$ or 7, 9 **21.** $-2, 0, 2$ or 6, 8, 10 **23.** 12 cm **25.** 12 mi **27.** 8 ft **29. (a)** 1 sec **(b)** $\frac{1}{2}$ sec and $1\frac{1}{2}$ sec **(c)** 3 sec **(d)** The negative solution, -1, does not make sense since t represents time, which cannot be negative. **31. (a)** 4.68 million; The result using the model is a little less than 5 million, the actual number for 1990. **(b)** 10 **(c)** 63.2 million; The result is a little more than 62 million, the actual number for 1998. **(d)** 120.54 million **32.** 107 billion dollars; 65% **33.** 1995: 66.9 billion dollars; 1997: 148.5 billion dollars; 1999: 230.1 billion dollars **34.** The answers using the linear equation are not at all close to the actual data. **35.** 1995: 104 billion dollars; 1997: 111.2 billion dollars; 1999: 266.4 billion dollars **36.** The answers in Exercise 35 are fairly close to the actual data. The quadratic equation models the data better. **37.** (0, 97.5), (1, 104.3), (2, 104.7), (3, 164.3), (4, 271.3)

38. no

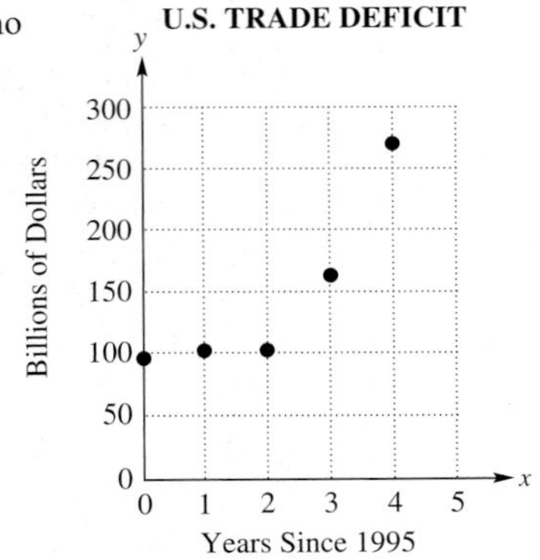

39. 399.5 billion dollars **40. (a)** The actual deficit is about 30 billion dollars less than the prediction. **(b)** No, the equation is based on data for the years 1995–1999. Data for later years might not follow the same pattern.

Chapter 7 Review Exercises (page 527)

1. $7(t + 2)$ **2.** $30z(2z^2 + 1)$ **3.** $35x^2(x + 2)$ **4.** $50m^2n^2(2n - mn^2 + 3)$ **5.** $(x - 4)(2y + 3)$ **6.** $(2y + 3)(3y + 2x)$ **7.** $(x + 3)(x + 2)$ **8.** $(y - 5)(y - 8)$ **9.** $(q + 9)(q - 3)$ **10.** $(r - 8)(r + 7)$ **11.** $(r + 8s)(r - 12s)$ **12.** $(p + 12q)(p - 10q)$ **13.** $8p(p + 2)(p - 5)$ **14.** $3x^2(x + 2)(x + 8)$ **15.** $(m + 3n)(m - 6n)$ **16.** $(y - 3z)(y - 5z)$ **17.** $p^5(p - 2q)(p + q)$ **18.** $3r^3(r + 3s)(r - 5s)$ **19.** prime **20.** $3(x^2 + 2x + 2)$ **21.** r and $6r$, $2r$ and $3r$ **22.** Factor out z. **23.** $(2k - 1)(k - 2)$ **24.** $(3r - 1)(r + 4)$ **25.** $(3r + 2)(2r - 3)$ **26.** $(5z + 1)(2z - 1)$ **27.** prime **28.** $4x^3(3x - 1)(2x - 1)$ **29.** $-3(x + 2)(2x - 5)$ **30.** $rs(5r + 6s)(2r + s)$ **31.** B **32.** D **33.** $(n + 8)(n - 8)$ **34.** $(5b + 11)(5b - 11)$ **35.** $(7y + 5w)(7y - 5w)$ **36.** $36(2p + q)(2p - q)$ **37.** prime **38.** $(z + 5)^2$ **39.** $(r - 6)^2$ **40.** $(3t - 7)^2$ **41.** $(4m + 5n)^2$ **42.** $(5x - 1)(25x^2 + 5x + 1)$ **43.** $(10p + 3)(100p^2 - 30p + 9)$ **44.** $8(z + 2y)(z^2 - 2yz + 4y^2)$ **45.** $\left\{-\frac{3}{4}, 1\right\}$ **46.** $\{-7, -3, 4\}$ **47.** $\left\{0, \frac{5}{2}\right\}$ **48.** $\{-3, -1\}$ **49.** $\{1, 4\}$ **50.** $\{3, 5\}$ **51.** $\left\{-\frac{4}{3}, 5\right\}$ **52.** $\left\{-\frac{8}{9}, \frac{8}{9}\right\}$ **53.** $\{0, 8\}$ **54.** $\{-1, 6\}$ **55.** $\{7\}$ **56.** $\{6\}$ **57.** $\left\{-\frac{2}{5}, -2, -1\right\}$ **58.** $\{-3, 3\}$ **59.** length: 10 ft; width: 4 ft **60.** 5 ft **61.** length: 6 m; width: 2 m **62.** length: 6 m; height: 5 m **63.** 6, 7 or $-5, -4$ **64.** 26 mi **65.** 112 ft **66.** 192 ft **67.** 256 ft **68.** after 8 sec **69. (a)** \$537 million **(b)** No, the prediction seems high. If eBay revenues in the last half of 2000 are comparable to those for the first half of the year, annual revenue in 2000 would be about \$366 million. **70.** D **71.** The factor $2x + 8$ has a common factor of 2. The complete factored form is $2(x + 4)(3x - 4)$. **72.** $(z - x)(z - 10x)$ **73.** $(3k + 5)(k + 2)$ **74.** $(3m + 4p)(5m - 4)$ **75.** $(y^2 + 25)(y + 5)(y - 5)$ **76.** $3m(2m + 3)(m - 5)$ **77.** $8abc(3b^2c - 7ac^2 + 9ab)$ **78.** prime **79.** $(10x - y)(100x^2 + 10xy + y^2)$ **80.** $2a^3(a + 2)(a - 6)$ **81.** $(2r + 3q)(6r - 5q)$ **82.** $(10a + 3)(10a - 3)$ **83.** $(7t + 4)^2$ **84.** $\{0, 7\}$ **85.** $\{-5, 2\}$ **86.** $\left\{-\frac{2}{5}\right\}$ **87.** 15 m, 36 m, 39 m **88.** length: 6 m; width: 4 m **89.** $-5, -4, -3$ or 5, 6, 7 **90. (a)** 256 ft **(b)** 1024 ft **91.** width: 10 m; length: 17 m **92.** 6 m

Chapter 7 Test (page 533)

1. D **2.** $6x(2x - 5)$ **3.** $m^2n(2mn + 3m - 5n)$ **4.** $(2x + y)(a - b)$ **5.** $(x - 7)(x - 2)$ **6.** $(3x + 1)(2x - 7)$ **7.** $3(x + 1)(x - 5)$ **8.** $(5z - 1)(2z - 3)$ **9.** prime **10.** prime **11.** $(y + 7)(y - 7)$ **12.** $(3y + 8)(3y - 8)$ **13.** $(x + 8)^2$ **14.** $(2x - 7y)^2$ **15.** $(x - 8)(x^2 + 8x + 64)$ **16.** $8(k + 2)(k^2 - 2k + 4)$ **17.** $-2(x + 1)^2$ **18.** $3t^2(2t + 9)(t - 4)$ **19.** $4t(t + 4)^2$ **20.** $(x^2 + 9)(x + 3)(x - 3)$ **21.** $(p + 3)(p + 3) = p^2 + 6p + 9 \neq p^2 + 9$ **22.** $\{-3, 9\}$ **23.** $\left\{\frac{1}{2}, 6\right\}$ **24.** $\left\{-\frac{2}{5}, \frac{2}{5}\right\}$ **25.** $\{10\}$ **26.** $\{0, 3\}$ **27.** 6 ft by 9 ft **28.** $-2, -1$ **29.** 17 ft **30.** 181

Cumulative Review Exercises: Chapters R–7 (page 535)

1. 0 **2.** 6 **3.** $\left[\frac{1}{2}, \infty\right)$ **4.** $P = \frac{A}{1 + rt}$ **5.** 345; 210; 38%; 15% **6.** gold: 12; silver: 9; bronze: 8 **7.** 107 million **8.** 110° and 70° **9. (a)** negative; positive **(b)** negative; negative **10.** $\left(-\frac{1}{4}, 0\right)$, $(0, 3)$ **11.** 12

12.

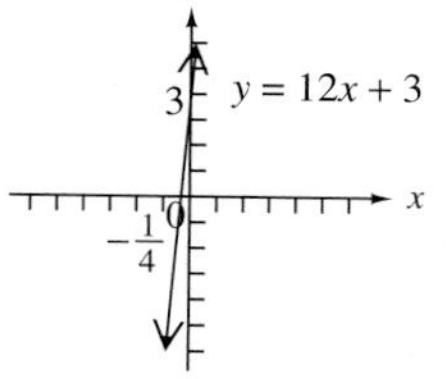

13. 103; A slope of 103 means that the number of radio stations increased by about 103 stations per year. **14.** $\{(2, 9)\}$
15. $\{(-3, 1, 6)\}$ **16.** 76 general admission; 108 with student ID

17. $\frac{1}{p^2}$ **18.** $k^2 - 4k + 4$ **19.** $45x^2 + 3x - 18$
20. $4x^3 + 6x^2 - 3x + 10$ **21.** 5.5×10^4; 2.0×10^6
22. $(2a - 1)(a + 4)$ **23.** $(2m + 3)(5m + 2)$
24. $(4t + 3v)(2t + v)$ **25.** $(2p - 3)^2$ **26.** $(5r + 9t)(5r - 9t)$

27. $2pq(3p + 1)(p + 1)$ **28.** $\left\{-\frac{2}{3}, \frac{1}{2}\right\}$ **29.** $\{0, 8\}$

30. 5 m, 12 m, 13 m

Chapter 8

Section 8.1 (page 545)

1. C **3.** D **5.** E **7.** Replacing x with 2 makes the denominator 0 and the value of the expression undefined. To find the values excluded from the domain, set the denominator equal to 0 and solve the equation. All solutions of the equation are excluded from the domain. **9.** 7 **11.** $-\frac{1}{7}$ **13.** 0 **15.** $-2, \frac{3}{2}$ **17.** none
19. none **21.** **(a)** numerator: x^2, $4x$; denominator: x, 4 **(b)** First factor the numerator, getting $x(x + 4)$, then divide the numerator and denominator by the common factor of $x + 4$ to get $\frac{x}{1}$ or x.

23. B **25.** x **27.** $\frac{x - 3}{x + 5}$ **29.** $\frac{x + 3}{2x(x - 3)}$ **31.** already in lowest terms **33.** $\frac{6}{7}$ **35.** $\frac{z}{6}$ **37.** $\frac{2}{t - 3}$ **39.** $\frac{x - 3}{x + 1}$ **41.** $\frac{4x + 1}{4x + 3}$

43. $a^2 - ab + b^2$ **45.** $\frac{c + 6d}{c - d}$ **47.** $\frac{a + b}{a - b}$ **49.** -1 *In Exercises 51–55, there are other acceptable ways to express each answer.*

51. $-(x + y)$ **53.** $-\frac{x + y}{x - y}$ **55.** $-\frac{1}{2}$ **57.** already in lowest terms **59.** $\frac{x + 4}{x - 2}$ **61.** $\frac{2x + 3}{x + 2}$ **63.** $-\frac{35}{8}$ **65.** $\frac{7x}{6}$

67. $-\frac{p + 5}{2p}$ (There are other ways.) **69.** $\frac{-m(m + 7)}{m + 1}$ (There are other ways.) **71.** -2 **73.** $\frac{x + 4}{x - 4}$ **75.** $\frac{2x + 3y}{2x - 3y}$

77. $\frac{k + 5p}{2k + 5p}$ **79.** $(k - 1)(k - 2)$

Section 8.2 (page 555)

1. To add or subtract rational expressions that have a common denominator, first add or subtract the numerators. Then place the result over the common denominator. Write the answer in lowest terms. **3.** $\frac{9}{t}$ **5.** $\frac{2}{x}$ **7.** 1 **9.** $x - 5$ **11.** $\frac{1}{p + 3}$ **13.** $a - b$
15. $72x^4y^5$ **17.** $z(z - 2)$ **19.** $2(y + 4)$ **21.** $(x + 9)^2(x - 9)$
23. $(m + n)(m - n)$ **25.** $x(x - 4)(x + 1)$
27. $(t + 5)(t - 2)(2t - 3)$ **29.** $2y(y + 3)(y - 3)$

31. Yes, they could both be correct because the expressions are equivalent. Multiplying $\frac{3}{5 - y}$ by 1 in the form $\frac{-1}{-1}$ gives $\frac{-3}{y - 5}$.

33. $\frac{31}{3t}$ **35.** $\frac{5 - 22x}{12x^2y}$ **37.** $\frac{1}{x(x - 1)}$ **39.** $\frac{5a^2 - 7a}{(a + 1)(a - 3)}$

41. 3 **43.** $\frac{3}{x - 4}$ or $\frac{-3}{4 - x}$ **45.** $\frac{w + z}{w - z}$ or $\frac{-w - z}{z - w}$

47. $\frac{-13}{12(3 + x)}$ **49.** $\frac{2(2x - 1)}{x - 1}$ **51.** $\frac{7}{y}$ **53.** $\frac{6}{x - 2}$

55. $\frac{3x - 2}{x - 1}$ **57.** $\frac{4x - 7}{x^2 - x + 1}$ **59.** $\frac{2x + 1}{x}$

61. $\frac{2x(x + 12y)}{(x + 2y)(x - y)(x + 6y)}$ **63.** $c(x) = \frac{10x}{49(101 - x)}$ **65.** $\frac{8}{9}$

66. $\frac{3}{7} + \frac{5}{9} - \frac{6}{63}$; They are the same. **67.** $\frac{8}{9}$; yes **68.** Answers will vary. Suppose the name is Bush, so that $x = 4$. The problem is $\frac{3}{2} + \frac{5}{4} - \frac{6}{8}$. The predicted answer is $\frac{8}{4} = 2$, which is correct.

69. It causes $\frac{3}{x - 2}$ and $\frac{6}{x^2 - 2x}$ to be undefined, since 0 appears in the denominators. **70.** 0

Section 8.3 (page 563)

1. Begin by simplifying the numerator. Then simplify the denominator. Write as a division problem, and proceed. **3.** $\frac{2x}{x - 1}$

5. $\frac{2(k + 1)}{3k - 1}$ **7.** $\frac{5x^2}{9z^3}$ **9.** $\frac{1 + x}{-1 + x}$ **11.** $\frac{y + x}{y - x}$ **13.** $4x$

15. $x + 4y$ **17.** $\frac{3y}{2}$ **19.** $\frac{x^2 + 5x + 4}{x^2 + 5x + 10}$ **21.** $\frac{m^2 + 6m - 4}{m(m - 1)}$

22. $\frac{m^2 - m - 2}{m(m - 1)}$ **23.** $\frac{m^2 + 6m - 4}{m^2 - m - 2}$ **24.** $m(m - 1)$

25. $\frac{m^2 + 6m - 4}{m^2 - m - 2}$ **26.** Method 1 involves simplifying the numerator and the denominator separately and then performing a division. Method 2 involves multiplying the fraction by a form of 1, the identity element for multiplication. (Preferences will vary.)

27. $\frac{x^2y^2}{y^2 + x^2}$ **29.** $\frac{y^2 + x^2}{xy^2 + x^2y}$ or $\frac{y^2 + x^2}{xy(y + x)}$ **31.** $\frac{1}{2xy}$

Section 8.4 (page 569)

1. $x = 0$

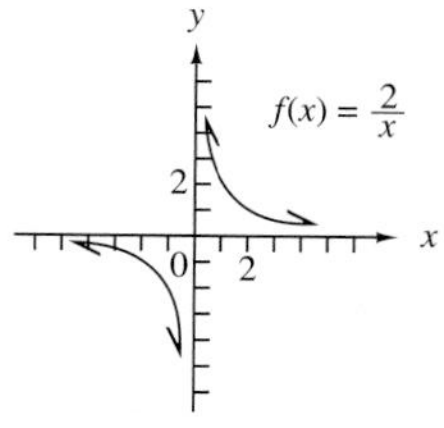

3. $x = 2$

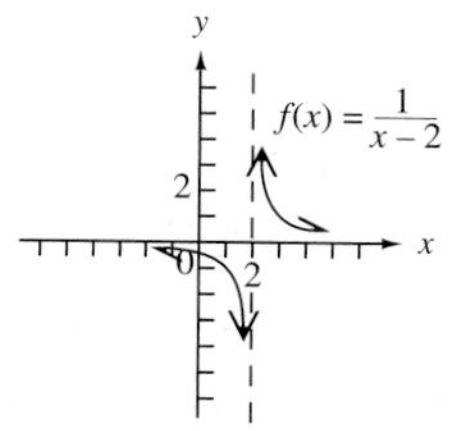

5. **(a)** $-1, 2$ **(b)** $\{x \mid x \neq -1, 2\}$ **7.** **(a)** $-\frac{5}{3}, 0, -\frac{3}{2}$
(b) $\left\{x \mid x \neq -\frac{5}{3}, 0, -\frac{3}{2}\right\}$ **9.** **(a)** 0 **(b)** $\{x \mid x \neq 0\}$

11. **(a)** $4, \frac{7}{2}$ **(b)** $\left\{x \mid x \neq 4, \frac{7}{2}\right\}$ **13.** **(a)** $0, 1, -3, 2$
(b) $\{x \mid x \neq 0, 1, -3, 2\}$ **15.** $\{1\}$ **17.** $\{-6, 4\}$

19. $\left\{-\frac{7}{12}\right\}$ **21.** $\emptyset$ **23.** $\{-3\}$ **25.** $\{5\}$ **27.** $\{5\}$ **29.** $\emptyset$

31. $\left\{\frac{27}{56}\right\}$ **33.** $\emptyset$ **35.** $\{-10\}$ **37.** $\emptyset$ **39.** $\{0\}$

41. $\left\{x \mid x \neq -\frac{3}{2}, \frac{3}{2}\right\}$ **43.** Substituting -1 for x gives a true statement, $\frac{4}{3} = \frac{4}{3}$. Substituting -2 for x leads to 0 in the first and third denominators. **44.** $C = -4$; $\{-2\}$; -1 is rejected. **45.** $C = 24$; $\{-4\}$; 3 is rejected. **46.** Answers will vary. However, in every case, $-B$ will be the rejected solution, and $\{-A\}$ will be the solution set. **47. (a)** 0 **(b)** 1.6 **(c)** 4.1 **(d)** The waiting time also increases.

Summary Exercises on Operations and Equations with Rational Expressions (page 573)

1. equation; $\{20\}$ **2.** operation; $\frac{2(x+5)}{5}$ **3.** operation; $-\frac{22}{7x}$ **4.** operation; $\frac{y+x}{y-x}$ **5.** equation; $\left\{\frac{1}{2}\right\}$ **6.** equation; $\{7\}$ **7.** operation; $\frac{43}{24x}$ **8.** equation; $\{1\}$ **9.** operation; $\frac{5x-1}{-2x+2}$ or $\frac{5x-1}{-2(x-1)}$ **10.** operation; $\frac{25}{4(r+2)}$ **11.** operation; $\frac{x^2+xy+2y^2}{(x+y)(x-y)}$ **12.** operation; $\frac{24p}{p+2}$ **13.** operation; $-\frac{5}{36}$ **14.** equation; $\{0\}$ **15.** operation; $\frac{b+3}{3}$ **16.** operation; $\frac{5}{3z}$ **17.** operation; $\frac{2x+10}{x(x-2)(x+2)}$ **18.** equation; $\{2\}$ **19.** operation; $\frac{-x}{3x+5y}$ **20.** equation; $\{-13\}$ **21.** operation; $\frac{3y+2}{y+3}$ **22.** equation; $\left\{\frac{5}{4}\right\}$ **23.** equation; $\emptyset$ **24.** operation; $\frac{2z-3}{2z+3}$ **25.** operation; $\frac{-1}{x-3}$ or $\frac{1}{3-x}$ **26.** operation; $\frac{t-2}{8}$ **27.** equation; $\{-10\}$ **28.** operation; $\frac{13x+28}{2x(x+4)(x-4)}$ **29.** equation; $\emptyset$ **30.** operation; $\frac{k(2k^2-2k+5)}{(k-1)(3k^2-2)}$

Section 8.5 (page 583)

1. A **3.** D **5.** 65.625 **7.** $\frac{25}{4}$ **9.** $G = \frac{Fd^2}{Mm}$ **11.** $a = \frac{bc}{c+b}$ **13.** $v = \frac{PVt}{pT}$ **15.** $r = \frac{nE - IR}{In}$ **17.** $b = \frac{2A}{h} - B$ or $b = \frac{2A - Bh}{h}$ **19.** $r = \frac{eR}{E-e}$ **21.** Multiply each side by $a - b$. **23.** 1996 **25.** 1996 **27.** 23 teachers **29.** \$95.75 **31.** $x = \frac{7}{2}$; $AC = 8$; $DF = 12$ **33.** 1.99 m per sec **35.** 4.059 hr **37.** 367.197 m per min **39.** $\frac{500}{x-10} = \frac{600}{x+10}$ **41.** 3 mph **43.** 900 mi **45.** 480 mi **47.** 190 mi **49.** $6\frac{2}{3}$ min **51.** 12 hr **53.** 20 hr **55.** $2\frac{4}{5}$ hr

Section 8.6 (page 595)

1. direct **3.** inverse **5.** inverse **7.** inverse **9.** direct **11.** joint **13.** combined **15.** 36 **17.** .625 **19.** $222\frac{2}{9}$ **21.** increases; decreases **23.** If y varies inverely as x, x is in the denominator; however, if y varies directly as x, x is in the numerator. Also, for $k > 0$, with inverse variation, as x increases, y decreases. With direct variation, y increases as x increases. **25.** $\$1.69\frac{9}{10}$ **27.** about 450 cm^3 **29.** about \$9211 **31.** $21\frac{1}{3}$ foot-candles **33.** \$420 **35.** 448.1 lb **37.** approximately 68,600 calls **39.** 11.8 lb **41.** (0, 0), (1, 1.75) **42.** 1.75 **43.** $y = 1.75x + 0$ or $y = 1.75x$ **44.** $a = 1.75$, $b = 0$ **45.** It is the price per gallon and the slope of the line. **46.** It can be written in the form $y = kx$ (where $k = a$). The value of a is called the constant of variation.

Chapter 8 Review Exercises (page 603)

1. (a) -6 **(b)** $\{x \mid x \neq -6\}$ **2. (a)** 2, 5 **(b)** $\{x \mid x \neq 2, 5\}$ **3. (a)** 9 **(b)** $\{x \mid x \neq 9\}$ **4.** $\frac{x}{2}$ **5.** $\frac{5m+n}{5m-n}$ **6.** $\frac{-1}{2+r}$ **7.** The reciprocal of a rational expression is another rational expression such that the two rational expressions have a product of 1. **8.** $\frac{3y^2(2y+3)}{2y-3}$ **9.** $\frac{-3(w+4)}{w}$ **10.** $\frac{z(z+2)}{z+5}$ **11.** 1 **12.** $96b^5$ **13.** $9r^2(3r+1)$ **14.** $(3x-1)(2x+5)(3x+4)$ **15.** $\frac{16z-3}{2z^2}$ **16.** 12 **17.** $\frac{71}{30(a+2)}$ **18.** $\frac{13r^2+5rs}{(5r+s)(2r-s)(r+s)}$ **19.** $\frac{3+2t}{4-7t}$ **20.** -2 **21.** $\frac{1}{3q+2p}$ **22.** $\frac{y+x}{xy}$ **23.** C; $x = 0$ **24.** $\{-3\}$ **25.** $\{-2\}$ **26.** $\{0\}$ **27.** $\emptyset$ **28.** Although her algebra was correct, 3 is not a solution because it is not in the domain of the equation. Thus, $\emptyset$ is correct. **29.** In simplifying the expression, we are combining terms to get a single fraction with a denominator of $6x$, while in solving the equation, we are finding a value for x that makes the equation true. **30.** $\frac{15}{2}$ **31.** $m = \frac{Fd^2}{GM}$ **32.** $M = \frac{m\mu}{\nu - \mu}$ **33.** 6000 passenger-km per day **34.** 16 km per hr **35.** $4\frac{4}{5}$ min **36.** $3\frac{3}{5}$ hr **37.** 800 gal **38.** 430 mm **39.** $71\frac{1}{9}$ lb **40.** 15 ft **41.** $\frac{1}{x-2y}$ **42.** $\frac{x+5}{x+2}$ **43.** $\frac{6m+5}{3m^2}$ **44.** $\frac{k-3}{36k^2+6k+1}$ **45.** $\frac{3-5x}{6x+1}$ **46.** $\frac{11}{3-x}$ or $\frac{-11}{x-3}$ **47.** $\frac{1}{3}$ **48.** $\frac{5a^2+4ab+12b^2}{(a+3b)(a-2b)(a+b)}$ **49.** $\left\{\frac{1}{3}\right\}$ **50.** $r = \frac{AR}{R-A}$ or $r = \frac{-AR}{A-R}$ **51.** $\{1, 4\}$ **52. (a)** 8.32 **(b)** 44.9 **53.** $8\frac{4}{7}$ min

Chapter 8 Test (page 607)

1. $-2, \frac{4}{3}$; $\left\{x \mid x \neq -2, \frac{4}{3}\right\}$ **2.** $\frac{2x-5}{x(3x-1)}$ **3.** $\frac{3(x+3)}{4}$ **4.** $\frac{y+4}{y-5}$ **5.** $\frac{x+5}{x}$ **6.** $t^2(t+3)(t-2)$ **7.** $\frac{7-2t}{6t^2}$ **8.** $\frac{13x+35}{(x-7)(x+7)}$ **9.** $\frac{4}{x+2}$ **10.** $\frac{72}{11}$ **11.** $-\frac{1}{a+b}$

12. $\frac{2y^2 + x^2}{xy(y - x)}$ **13.** $x = -1$

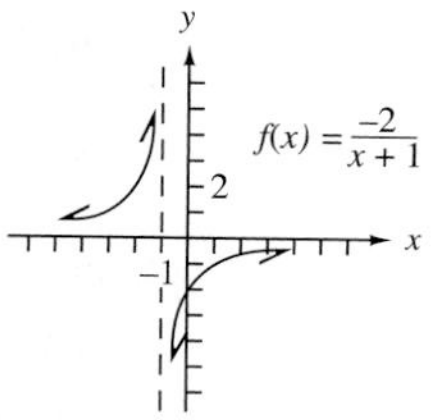

14. **(a)** operation; $\frac{11(x - 6)}{12}$ **(b)** equation; $\{6\}$ **15.** $\left\{\frac{1}{2}\right\}$

16. $\{5\}$ **17.** $\ell = \frac{2S}{n} - a$ or $\ell = \frac{2S - na}{n}$

18. $3\frac{3}{14}$ hr **19.** 15 mph **20.** **(a)** 3 units **(b)** 0 **21.** 256 ft

22. .8 lb

Cumulative Review Exercises: Chapters R–8 (page 609)

1. -199 **2.** 12 **3.** $\left\{-\frac{15}{4}\right\}$ **4.** $\left\{\frac{2}{3}, 2\right\}$

5. $x = \frac{d - by}{a - c}$ or $x = \frac{by - d}{c - a}$ **6.** $\left(-\infty, \frac{240}{13}\right]$

7. $(-\infty, -2] \cup \left[\frac{2}{3}, \infty\right)$ **8.** \$4000 at 4%; \$8000 at 3% **9.** 6 m

10. x-intercept: $(-2, 0)$; y-intercept: $(0, 4)$

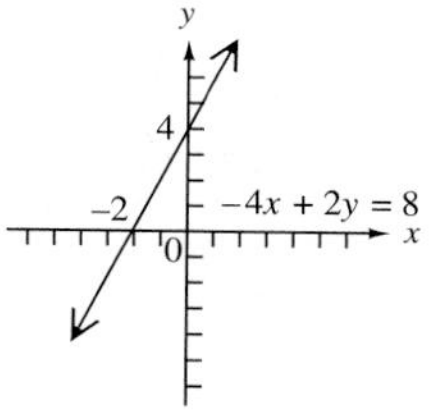

11. $-\frac{3}{2}$ **12.** $-\frac{3}{4}$ **13.** $y = -\frac{3}{2}x + \frac{1}{2}$

14.

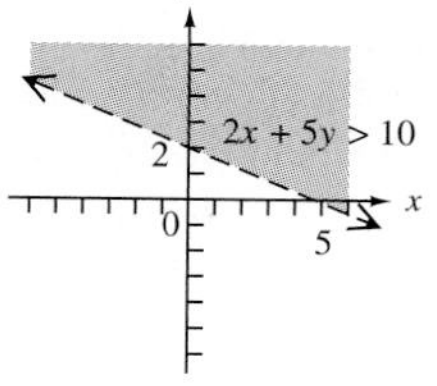

15.

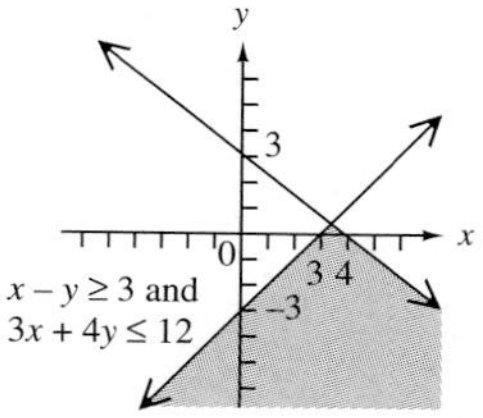

16. function; domain: $\{1990, 1992, 1994, 1996, 1998, 2000\}$; range: $\{1.25, 1.61, 1.80, 1.21, 1.94, 2.26\}$ **17.** not a function; domain: $[-2, \infty)$; range: $(-\infty, \infty)$ **18.** function; domain: $(-\infty, \infty)$; range: $(-\infty, \infty)$ **19.** **(a)** $f(x) = \frac{5x - 8}{3}$ or $f(x) = \frac{5}{3}x - \frac{8}{3}$ **(b)** -1 **20.** $3x + 15$ **21.** $\{(-1, 3)\}$ **22.** $\{(-2, 3, 1)\}$ **23.** $\emptyset$ **24.** automobile: 42 km per hr; airplane: 600 km per hr **25.** $\frac{a^{10}}{b^{10}}$ **26.** $\frac{m}{n}$ **27.** $4y^2 - 7y - 6$ **28.** $-6x^6 + 18x^5 - 12x^4$ **29.** $12f^2 + 5f - 3$ **30.** $49t^6 - 64$ **31.** $\frac{1}{16}x^2 + \frac{5}{2}x + 25$ **32.** $x^2 + 4x - 7$ **33.** **(a)** 7.6×10^{-5} **(b)** 5,600,000,000 **34.** $(2x + 5)(x - 9)$ **35.** $25(2t^2 + 1)(2t^2 - 1)$ **36.** $(2p + 5)(4p^2 - 10p + 25)$ **37.** $\left\{-\frac{7}{3}, 1\right\}$ **38.** $\frac{y + 4}{y - 4}$ **39.** $\frac{2x - 3}{2(x - 1)}$ **40.** $\frac{a(a - b)}{2(a + b)}$ **41.** 3 **42.** $\frac{2(x + 2)}{2x - 1}$ **43.** $\{-4\}$

44. $q = \frac{fp}{p - f}$ or $q = \frac{-fp}{f - p}$ **45.** 150 mph **46.** $1\frac{1}{5}$ hr

Chapter 9

Section 9.1 (page 621)

1. true **3.** False. Zero has only one square root. **5.** true **7.** E **9.** D **11.** A **13.** C **15.** C **17.** **(a)** not a real number **(b)** negative **(c)** 0 **19.** $-3, 3$ **21.** $-8, 8$ **23.** $-12, 12$ **25.** $-\frac{5}{14}, \frac{5}{14}$ **27.** $-30, 30$ **29.** 1 **31.** 7 **33.** -11 **35.** $-\frac{12}{11}$ **37.** not a real number **39.** rational; 5 **41.** irrational; 5.385 **43.** rational; -8 **45.** irrational; -17.321 **47.** not a real number **49.** irrational; 34.641 **51.** 1 **53.** 6 **55.** -4 **57.** -8 **59.** 6 **61.** -3 **63.** not a real number **65.** 2 **67.** -9 **69.** $\frac{8}{9}$ **71.** $\frac{2}{3}$ **73.** $\frac{1}{2}$

75. $[-3, \infty)$; $[0, \infty)$

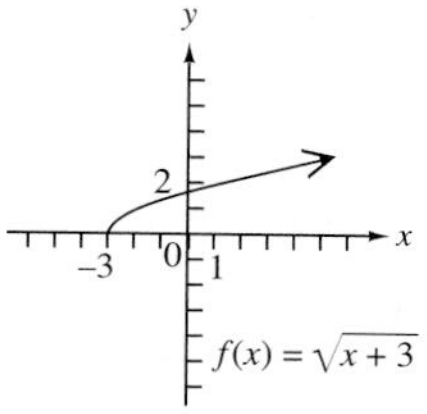

77. $[0, \infty)$; $[-2, \infty)$

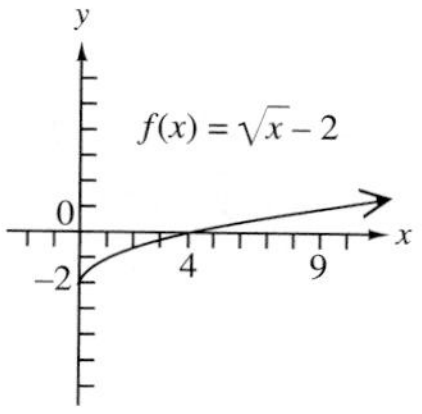

79. $(-\infty, \infty)$; $(-\infty, \infty)$

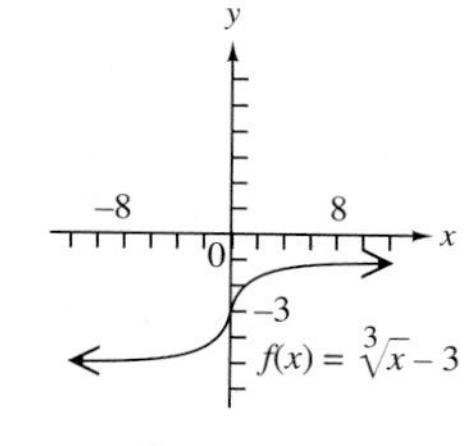

81. $|x|$ **83.** x **85.** x^5 **87.** $|x^3|$ **89.** 97.381 **91.** 16.863 **93.** 2.1 **95.** 1.5 **97.** -4 and 4 **98.** 4 **99.** $4, -4$ **100.** $\{-4, 4\}$ **101.** $\pm\sqrt{16}$ represents the two numbers $\sqrt{16} = 4$ and $-\sqrt{16} = 4$. **102.** $\sqrt{x^2}$ is always nonnegative, so it must be simplified as $|x|$ because x may be negative.

Section 9.2 (page 631)

1. 13 **3.** 9 **5.** 2 **7.** $-\frac{8}{9}$ **9.** -3 **11.** not a real number **13.** D **15.** C **17.** A **19.** 100,000 **21.** 256 **23.** $\frac{1}{512}$ **25.** $\frac{2}{5}$ **27.** $\frac{9}{4}$ **29.** not a real number **31.** 13 **33.** 100,000 **35.** 25 **37.** $\sqrt{12}$ **39.** $(\sqrt[4]{8})^3$ **41.** $(\sqrt[8]{9q})^5 - (\sqrt[3]{2x})^2$ **43.** $\frac{1}{(\sqrt{2m})^3}$ **45.** $(\sqrt[3]{2y + x})^2$ **47.** $\frac{1}{(\sqrt[3]{3m^4 + 2k^2})^2}$ **49.** 64 **51.** 64 **53.** x^{10} **55.** a^6 **57.** 9 **59.** 4 **61.** y **63.** $k^{2/3}$ **65.** $a^{1/2}$

67. $\frac{x^{4/5}}{16y^{12}}$ **69.** $9x^8y^{10}$ **71.** $\frac{1}{x^{10/3}}$ **73.** $\frac{1}{m^{1/4}n^{3/4}}$
75. $2x - 1 - 2x^{3/2}$ **77.** $\sqrt[6]{x^5}$ **79.** $y\sqrt{7y}$ **81.** $\sqrt[15]{t^8}$ **83.** $\sqrt[8]{m}$
85. $x^{-1/2}$ **86.** $m^{5/2}$ **87.** $k^{-3/4}$ **88.** $x^{-1/2}(3 - 4x)$
89. $m^{5/2}(m^{1/2} - 3)$ **90.** $k^{-3/4}(9 + 2k^{1/2})$ **91.** 4.5 hr

Section 9.3 (page 641)

1. True; both are equal to $4\sqrt{3}$ and approximately 6.92820323.
3. True; both are equal to $6\sqrt{2}$ and approximately 8.485281374.
5. Because there are only two factors of $\sqrt[3]{x}$, $\sqrt[3]{x} \cdot \sqrt[3]{x} = (\sqrt[3]{x})^2$ or $\sqrt[3]{x^2}$. **7.** $\sqrt{30}$ **9.** $\sqrt[3]{14xy}$ **11.** $\sqrt[4]{36}$ **13.** $\frac{8}{11}$
15. $\frac{\sqrt{3}}{5}$ **17.** $\frac{\sqrt{x}}{5}$ **19.** $\frac{p^3}{9}$ **21.** $\frac{3}{4}$ **23.** $-\frac{\sqrt[3]{r^2}}{2}$ **25.** $2\sqrt{3}$
27. $12\sqrt{2}$ **29.** $-4\sqrt{2}$ **31.** $-2\sqrt{7}$ **33.** not a real number
35. $4\sqrt[3]{2}$ **37.** $-2\sqrt[3]{2}$ **39.** $2\sqrt[3]{5}$ **41.** $-4\sqrt[4]{2}$ **43.** $2\sqrt[5]{2}$
45. His reasoning was incorrect. Here 8 is a term, not a factor.
47. $6k\sqrt{2}$ **49.** $\frac{3\sqrt[3]{3}}{4}$ **51.** $11x^3$ **53.** $-3t^4$ **55.** $-10m^4z^2$
57. $5a^2b^3c^4$ **59.** $\frac{1}{2}r^2t^5$ **61.** $5x\sqrt{2x}$ **63.** $-10r^5\sqrt{5r}$
65. $x^3y^4\sqrt{13x}$ **67.** $2z^2w^3$ **69.** $-2zt^2\sqrt[3]{2z^2t}$ **71.** $3x^3y^4$
73. $-3r^3s^2\sqrt[4]{2r^3s^2}$ **75.** $\frac{y^5\sqrt{y}}{6}$ **77.** $\frac{x^5\sqrt[3]{x}}{3}$ **79.** $4\sqrt{3}$
81. $x^2\sqrt{x}$ **83.** $\sqrt[6]{432}$ **85.** $\sqrt[12]{6912}$ **87.** 5 **89.** $8\sqrt{2}$
91. $\sqrt{37}$ **93.** $2\sqrt{10}$ **95.** $6\sqrt{2}$ **97.** $\sqrt{5y^2 - 2xy + x^2}$
99. 27.0 in.

Section 9.4 (page 647)

1. B **3.** 15; each radicand is a whole number power corresponding to the index of the radical. **5.** -4 **7.** $7\sqrt{3}$ **9.** $24\sqrt{2}$
11. 0 **13.** $20\sqrt{5}$ **15.** $12\sqrt{2x}$ **17.** $-11m\sqrt{2}$ **19.** $\sqrt[4]{2}$
21. $2\sqrt[4]{x}$ **23.** $19\sqrt[4]{2}$ **25.** $x\sqrt[4]{xy}$ **27.** $(4 + 3xy)\sqrt[3]{xy^2}$
29. $\frac{7\sqrt{2}}{6}$ **31.** $\frac{5\sqrt{2}}{3}$ **33.** Both are approximately 11.3137085.
35. Both are approximately 31.6227766. **37.** A; 42 m
39. $12\sqrt{5} + 5\sqrt{3}$ in. **41.** $24\sqrt{2} + 12\sqrt{3}$ in.

Section 9.5 (page 655)

1. E **3.** A **5.** D **7.** $6 - 4\sqrt{3}$ **9.** $6 - \sqrt{6}$ **11.** 2 **13.** 9
15. $3\sqrt{2} - 5\sqrt{3} + 2\sqrt{6} - 10$ **17.** $3x - 4$ **19.** $4x - y$
21. $16x + 24\sqrt{x} + 9$ **23.** $81 - \sqrt[3]{4}$ **25.** $6 - 4\sqrt{3}$ is not equal to $2\sqrt{3}$ because 6 and $4\sqrt{3}$ are not like terms, so they cannot be combined. **27.** $\sqrt{7}$ **29.** $5\sqrt{3}$ **31.** $\frac{\sqrt{6}}{2}$ **33.** $\frac{9\sqrt{15}}{5}$
35. $-\sqrt{2}$ **37.** $\frac{-8\sqrt{3k}}{k}$ **39.** $\frac{6\sqrt{3}}{y}$ **41.** Both methods lead to the same result, $\frac{6\sqrt{3}}{y}$, but multiplying the numerator and denominator by $\sqrt{y}$ produces this result more directly, with less simplification required. **43.** $\frac{\sqrt{14}}{2}$ **45.** $-\frac{\sqrt{14}}{10}$ **47.** $\frac{2\sqrt{6x}}{x}$
49. $-\frac{7r\sqrt{2rs}}{s}$ **51.** $\frac{12x^3\sqrt{2xy}}{y^5}$ **53.** $\frac{\sqrt[3]{18}}{3}$ **55.** $\frac{\sqrt[3]{12}}{3}$

57. $-\frac{\sqrt[3]{2pr}}{r}$ **59.** $\frac{2\sqrt[4]{x^3}}{x}$ **61.** Multiply the numerator and denominator by $4 - \sqrt{3}$, so the denominator becomes $(4 + \sqrt{3})(4 - \sqrt{3}) = 16 - 3 = 13$, a rational number.
63. $\frac{2(4 - \sqrt{3})}{13}$ **65.** $3(\sqrt{5} - \sqrt{3})$ **67.** $\sqrt{3} + \sqrt{7}$
69. $\sqrt{7} - \sqrt{6} - \sqrt{14} + 2\sqrt{3}$ **71.** $\frac{4\sqrt{x}(\sqrt{x} + 2\sqrt{y})}{x - 4y}$
73. $\frac{x\sqrt{2} - \sqrt{3xy} - \sqrt{2xy} + y\sqrt{3}}{2x - 3y}$ **75.** Square each side to show that each square is equal to $\frac{2 - \sqrt{3}}{4}$. **77.** $\frac{5 + 2\sqrt{6}}{4}$
79. $\frac{4 + 2\sqrt{2}}{3}$ **81.** $\frac{6 + 2\sqrt{6x}}{3}$ **83.** $\frac{319}{6(8\sqrt{5} + 1)}$
84. $\frac{9a - b}{(\sqrt{b} - \sqrt{a})(3\sqrt{a} - \sqrt{b})}$ **85.** $\frac{(3\sqrt{a} + \sqrt{b})(\sqrt{b} + \sqrt{a})}{b - a}$
86. In Exercise 84, we multiplied the numerator and denominator by the conjugate of the numerator, while in Exercise 85 we multiplied by the conjugate of the denominator.

Section 9.6 (page 663)

1. No; there is no solution. **3.** $\{19\}$ **5.** $\left\{\frac{38}{3}\right\}$ **7.** $\emptyset$ **9.** $\{5\}$
11. $\{1\}$ **13.** $\{9\}$ **15.** You cannot just square each term. The right-hand side should be $(8 - x)^2 = 64 - 16x + x^2$. **17.** $\{4\}$
19. $\{-3, -1\}$ **21.** $\emptyset$ **23.** $\{-1\}$ **25.** $\left\{\frac{1}{2}\right\}$ **27.** $\{5\}$
29. $\{7\}$ **31.** $\emptyset$ **33.** 3 **35.** $\{-13\}$ **37.** $\{14\}$ **39.** $\emptyset$
41. $\{7\}$ **43.** $\{2, 14\}$ **45.** $\left\{\frac{1}{4}, 1\right\}$ **47.** 1985: 0; 1990: 10 million; 1995: 40 million; 2000: 90 million
49. The approximation is reasonably good; 1990.

Section 9.7 (page 673)

1. i **3.** $-i$ **5.** $a + bi$ is a complex number if a and b are real numbers and i is the imaginary unit. Therefore, for every real number a, if $b = 0$, $a = a + 0i$ is a complex number. **7.** $13i$
9. $-12i$ **11.** $i\sqrt{5}$ **13.** $4i\sqrt{3}$ **15.** -15 **17.** -10 **19.** $\sqrt{3}$
21. $5i$ **23.** $-1 + 7i$ **25.** 0 **27.** $7 + 3i$ **29.** -2 **31.** $1 + 13i$
33. $6 + 6i$ **35.** $4 + 2i$ **37.** -81 **39.** -16 **41.** $-10 - 30i$
43. $10 - 5i$ **45.** $-9 + 40i$ **47.** 153 **49.** (a) $a - bi$ (b) a^2; b^2 **51.** $1 + i$ **53.** $-1 + 2i$ **55.** $2 + 2i$
57. $-\frac{5}{13} - \frac{12}{13}i$ **59.** (a) $4x + 1$ (b) $4 + i$ **60.** (a) $-2x + 3$ (b) $-2 + 3i$ **61.** (a) $3x^2 + 5x - 2$ (b) $5 + 5i$
62. (a) $-\sqrt{3} + \sqrt{6} + 1 - \sqrt{2}$ (b) $\frac{1}{5} - \frac{7}{5}i$
63. Because $i^2 = -1$, two pairs of like terms can be combined in Exercise 61(b). **64.** Because $i^2 = -1$, additional terms can be combined in the numerator and denominator. **65.** $\frac{5}{41} + \frac{4}{41}i$
67. -1 **69.** i **71.** 1 **73.** $-i$ **75.** Since $i^{20} = (i^4)^5 = 1^5 = 1$, the student multiplied by 1, which is justified by the identity property for multiplication. **77.** $\frac{1}{2} + \frac{1}{2}i$
79. $(1 + 5i)^2 - 2(1 + 5i) + 26$ will simplify to 0 when the operations are applied.

Chapter 9 Review Exercises (page 681)

1. 42 **2.** -17 **3.** not a real number **4.** 6 **5.** -2 **6.** $|x|$ **7.** x **8.** $|x|^5$ or $|x^5|$ **9.** domain: $[1, \infty)$; range: $[0, \infty)$ **10.** domain: $(-\infty, \infty)$; range: $(-\infty, \infty)$

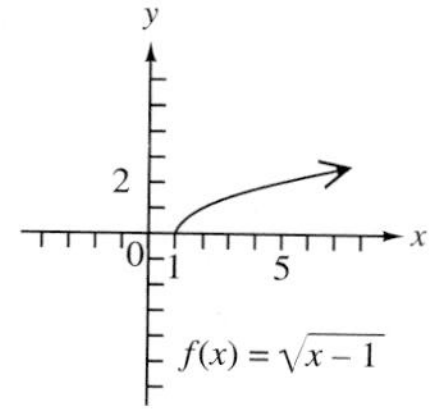

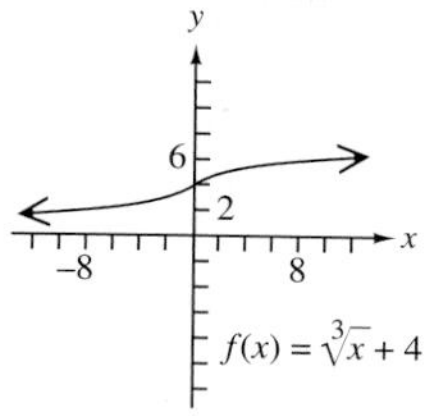

11. n must be even, and a must be negative. **12.** It is not a real number. **13.** 6.325 **14.** 8.775 **15.** 17.607 **16.** 10 mi **17.** 1.6 sec **18.** 7 **19.** -2 **20.** not a real number **21.** By a power rule for exponents and the definition of $x^{1/n}$, $a^{m/n} = (a^m)^{1/n} = \sqrt[n]{a^m}$. **22.** 32 **23.** -4 **24.** $-\frac{216}{125}$ **25.** -32 **26.** $\frac{1000}{27}$ **27.** 49 **28.** 96 **29.** $\frac{k^{17/12}}{2}$ **30.** $\sqrt[5]{2^4}$ or $\sqrt[5]{16}$ **31.** 3^9 **32.** $7^4\sqrt{7}$ **33.** $m^4\sqrt[3]{m}$ **34.** $k^2\sqrt[4]{k}$ **35.** $\sqrt[6]{m}$ **36.** $2y\sqrt[4]{y}$ **37.** $\sqrt[15]{y^8}$ **38.** $\sqrt[12]{y^5}$ **39.** $\sqrt{66}$ **40.** $\sqrt{5r}$ **41.** $\sqrt[3]{30}$ **42.** $\sqrt[4]{21}$ **43.** $2\sqrt{5}$ **44.** $-5\sqrt{5}$ **45.** $-3x\sqrt[3]{4xy}$ **46.** $4pq^2\sqrt[3]{p}$ **47.** $\frac{7}{9}$ **48.** $\frac{y\sqrt{y}}{12}$ **49.** $\frac{m^5}{3}$ **50.** $\frac{\sqrt[3]{r^2}}{2}$ **51.** $\sqrt[12]{2}$ **52.** $\sqrt[10]{x^3}$ **53.** $\sqrt{130}$ **54.** $\sqrt{53}$ **55.** $-11\sqrt{2}$ **56.** $23\sqrt{5}$ **57.** $7\sqrt{3y}$ **58.** $26m\sqrt{6m}$ **59.** $19\sqrt[3]{2}$ **60.** $-8\sqrt[4]{2}$ **61.** $1 - \sqrt{3}$ **62.** 2 **63.** $9 - 7\sqrt{2}$ **64.** $86 + 8\sqrt{55}$ **65.** $15 - 2\sqrt{26}$ **66.** $12 - 2\sqrt{35}$ **67.** $-3\sqrt{6}$ **68.** $\frac{3\sqrt{7py}}{y}$ **69.** $-\frac{\sqrt[3]{45}}{5}$ **70.** $\frac{3m\sqrt[3]{4n}}{n^2}$ **71.** $\frac{\sqrt{2} - \sqrt{7}}{-5}$ **72.** $\frac{-5(\sqrt{6} + \sqrt{3})}{3}$ **73.** $\{2\}$ **74.** $\{6\}$ **75.** $\emptyset$ **76.** $\{0, 5\}$ **77.** $\{9\}$ **78.** $\{3\}$ **79.** $\{7\}$ **80.** $\left\{-\frac{1}{2}\right\}$ **81.** $\{6\}$ **82.** $5i$ **83.** $10i\sqrt{2}$ **84.** $4i\sqrt{10}$ **85.** $-10 - 2i$ **86.** $14 + 7i$ **87.** $-\sqrt{35}$ **88.** -45 **89.** 3 **90.** $5 + i$ **91.** $32 - 24i$ **92.** $1 - i$ **93.** $4 + i$ **94.** $-i$ **95.** 1 **96.** $-i$ **97.** $-13ab^2$ **98.** $\frac{1}{100}$ **99.** $\frac{1}{y^{1/2}}$ **100.** $\frac{x^{3/4}}{z^{3/4}}$ **101.** k^6 **102.** $3z^3t^2\sqrt[3]{2t^2}$ **103.** $57\sqrt{2}$ **104.** $6x\sqrt[3]{y^2}$ **105.** $\sqrt{35} + \sqrt{15} - \sqrt{21} - 3$ **106.** $-\frac{\sqrt{3}}{6}$ **107.** $\frac{\sqrt[3]{60}}{5}$ **108.** $\frac{2\sqrt{z}(\sqrt{z} + 2)}{z - 4}$ **109.** $7i$ **110.** $3 - 7i$ **111.** $-5i$ **112.** $\{5\}$ **113.** $\left\{\frac{3}{2}\right\}$ **114.** 7.9 ft **115. (a)** \$496 million, which agrees closely with the estimate. **(b)** In year 3.9 or late in 1998, which agrees well with the actual year.

Chapter 9 Test (page 685)

1. -29 **2.** 5 **3.** C **4.** 12.09 **5.** domain: $[-6, \infty)$; range: $[0, \infty)$

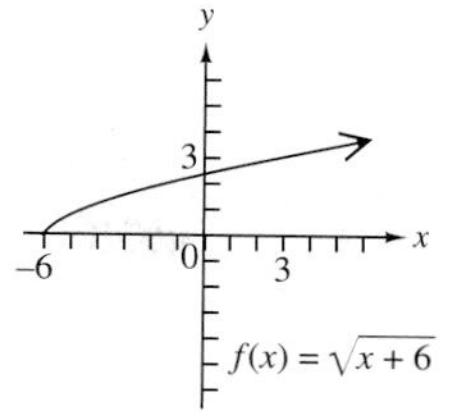

6. $\frac{1}{256}$ **7.** $\frac{9y^{3/10}}{x^2}$ **8.** $3x^2y^3\sqrt{6x}$ **9.** $2ab^3\sqrt[4]{2a^3b}$ **10.** $\sqrt[6]{200}$ **11.** $26\sqrt{5}$ **12.** $66 + \sqrt{5}$ **13.** $-2(\sqrt{7} - \sqrt{5})$ **14.** $\frac{-\sqrt{10}}{4}$ **15.** $\frac{2\sqrt[3]{25}}{5}$ **16.** $\sqrt{26}$ **17.** $\sqrt{145}$ **18.** $\{-1\}$ **19.** $\{6\}$ **20.** $-5 - 8i$ **21.** $3 + 4i$ **22.** $-i$

Cumulative Review Exercises: Chapters R–9 (page 687)

1. $\left\{\frac{4}{5}\right\}$ **2.** $\left\{\frac{11}{10}, \frac{7}{2}\right\}$ **3.** $(-6, \infty)$ **4.** $(1, 3)$ **5.** $(-2, 1)$ **6.** $12x + 11y = 18$ **7.** C **8. (a)** $(0, 6)$ **(b)** $(2, 0)$ **9.** \$120 **10.**

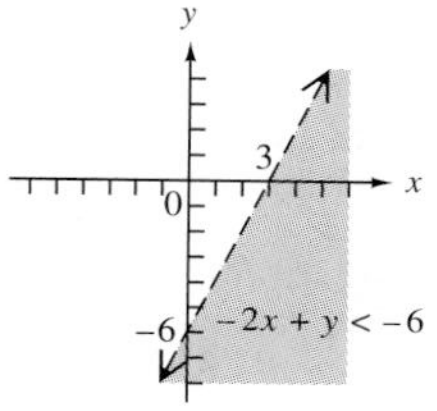

11. Both angles measure 80°. **12.** $\{(7, -2)\}$ **13.** $\emptyset$ **14.** infinite number of solutions **15.** 2-oz letter: \$.55; 3-oz letter: \$.78 **16.** $-k^3 - 3k^2 - 8k - 9$ **17.** $8x^2 + 17x - 21$ **18.** $z - 2 + \frac{3}{z}$ **19.** $3y^3 - 3y^2 + 4y + 1 + \frac{-10}{2y + 1}$ **20.** $(2p - 3q)(p - q)$ **21.** $(3k^2 + 4)(6k^2 - 5)$ **22.** $(x + 8)(x^2 - 8x + 64)$ **23.** $\frac{y}{y + 5}$ **24.** $\frac{4x + 2y}{(x + y)(x - y)}$ **25.** $-\frac{9}{4}$ **26.** $-\frac{1}{a + b}$ **27.** $\left\{-3, -\frac{5}{2}\right\}$ **28.** $\left\{-\frac{2}{5}, 1\right\}$ **29.** $\frac{1}{243}$ **30.** $x^{1/12}$ **31.** $8\sqrt{5}$ **32.** $\frac{-9\sqrt{5}}{20}$ **33.** $4(\sqrt{6} + \sqrt{5})$ **34.** $6\sqrt[3]{4}$ **35.** $\sqrt{29}$ **36.** $\{6\}$ **37.** 15 mph **38.** $\frac{80}{39}$ or $2\frac{2}{39}$ L **39.** 17 dimes and 12 quarters **40.** Brenda: 8 mph; Chuck: 4 mph

Chapter 10

Section 10.1 (page 695)

1. The equation is also true for $x = -4$. **3. (a)** The zero-factor property states that if a product equals 0, then at least one of the factors equals 0. **(b)** The square root property states that if the square of a quantity equals a number, then the quantity equals the positive or negative square root of the number. **5.** $\{9, -9\}$ **7.** $\{\sqrt{17}, -\sqrt{17}\}$ **9.** $\{4\sqrt{2}, -4\sqrt{2}\}$ **11.** $\{\sqrt{3}, -\sqrt{3}\}$ **13.** $\{2\sqrt{5}, -2\sqrt{5}\}$ **15.** $\{2\sqrt{6}, -2\sqrt{6}\}$ **17.** $\{-7, 3\}$ **19.** $\{4 + \sqrt{3}, 4 - \sqrt{3}\}$ **21.** $\{-5 + 4\sqrt{3}, -5 - 4\sqrt{3}\}$

23. $\left\{-3, \frac{5}{3}\right\}$ **25.** $\left\{\frac{1+\sqrt{7}}{3}, \frac{1-\sqrt{7}}{3}\right\}$

27. $\left\{\frac{-1+2\sqrt{6}}{4}, \frac{-1-2\sqrt{6}}{4}\right\}$

29. $\left\{\frac{-1+3\sqrt{2}}{3}, \frac{-1-3\sqrt{2}}{3}\right\}$ **31.** $\{2i\sqrt{3}, -2i\sqrt{3}\}$

33. $\{5+i\sqrt{3}, 5-i\sqrt{3}\}$ **35.** $\left\{\frac{1+2i\sqrt{2}}{6}, \frac{1-2i\sqrt{2}}{6}\right\}$

37. 6.3 sec **39.** 9 in.

Section 10.2 (page 703)

1. 16 **3.** multiplying $(t+2)(t-5)$ to get $t^2-3t-10$ **5.** D

7. 49 **9.** $\frac{25}{4}$ **11.** $\frac{1}{16}$ **13.** $\{1, 3\}$ **15.** $\{-3, -2\}$

17. $\{-1+\sqrt{6}, -1-\sqrt{6}\}$ **19.** $\{-5+\sqrt{7}, -5-\sqrt{7}\}$

21. $\left\{\frac{-1+\sqrt{5}}{2}, \frac{-1-\sqrt{5}}{2}\right\}$ **23.** $\left\{-\frac{3}{2}, \frac{1}{2}\right\}$

25. $\left\{\frac{2+\sqrt{14}}{2}, \frac{2-\sqrt{14}}{2}\right\}$ **27.** $\left\{\frac{-1+\sqrt{7}}{3}, \frac{-1-\sqrt{7}}{3}\right\}$

29. $\left\{\frac{-7+\sqrt{97}}{6}, \frac{-7-\sqrt{97}}{6}\right\}$ **31.** $\{-4, 2\}$

33. $\{1+\sqrt{6}, 1-\sqrt{6}\}$ **35.** $\{-2+3i, -2-3i\}$

37. $\left\{\frac{-2+2i\sqrt{2}}{3}, \frac{-2-2i\sqrt{2}}{3}\right\}$

39. $\{-3+i\sqrt{3}, -3-i\sqrt{3}\}$ **41.** x^2 **42.** x **43.** $6x$ **44.** 1

45. 9 **46.** $(x+3)^2$ or x^2+6x+9

Section 10.3 (page 711)

1. The student was incorrect, since the fraction bar should extend under the term $-b$. **3.** $\{3, 5\}$ **5.** $\left\{\frac{-2+\sqrt{2}}{2}, \frac{-2-\sqrt{2}}{2}\right\}$

7. $\left\{\frac{1+\sqrt{3}}{2}, \frac{1-\sqrt{3}}{2}\right\}$ **9.** $\{5+\sqrt{7}, 5-\sqrt{7}\}$

11. $\left\{\frac{-1+\sqrt{2}}{2}, \frac{-1-\sqrt{2}}{2}\right\}$ **13.** $\left\{\frac{-1+\sqrt{7}}{3}, \frac{-1-\sqrt{7}}{3}\right\}$

15. $\{1+\sqrt{5}, 1-\sqrt{5}\}$ **17.** $\left\{\frac{-2+\sqrt{10}}{2}, \frac{-2-\sqrt{10}}{2}\right\}$

19. $\{-1+3\sqrt{2}, -1-3\sqrt{2}\}$ **21.** $\left\{\frac{3+i\sqrt{59}}{2}, \frac{3-i\sqrt{59}}{2}\right\}$

23. $\{3+i\sqrt{5}, 3-i\sqrt{5}\}$ **25.** $\left\{\frac{1+i\sqrt{6}}{2}, \frac{1-i\sqrt{6}}{2}\right\}$

27. $\left\{\frac{-2+i\sqrt{2}}{3}, \frac{-2-i\sqrt{2}}{3}\right\}$ **29.** B **31.** C **33.** A **35.** D

37. The equations in Exercises 29, 30, 33, and 34 can be solved by factoring.

Section 10.4 (page 721)

1. Multiply by the LCD, x. **3.** Substitute a variable for r^2+r.
5. The potential solution -1 does not check. The solution set is $\{4\}$.

7. $\{-4, 7\}$ **9.** $\left\{-\frac{2}{3}, 1\right\}$ **11.** $\left\{-\frac{14}{17}, 5\right\}$ **13.** $\left\{-\frac{11}{7}, 0\right\}$

15. $\left\{\frac{-1+\sqrt{13}}{2}, \frac{-1-\sqrt{13}}{2}\right\}$ **17.** $\frac{1}{m}$ job per hr **19.** 25 mph

21. 80 km per hr **23.** 3.6 hr **25.** 9 min **27.** $\{3\}$ **29.** $\left\{\frac{8}{9}\right\}$

31. $\{16\}$ **33.** $\left\{\frac{2}{5}\right\}$ **35.** $\{-3, 3\}$ **37.** $\left\{-\frac{3}{2}, -1, 1, \frac{3}{2}\right\}$

39. $\{-2\sqrt{3}, -2, 2, 2\sqrt{3}\}$ **41.** $\{-6, -5\}$ **43.** $\{-4, 1\}$

45. $\left\{-\frac{1}{3}, \frac{1}{6}\right\}$ **47.** $\{-8, 1\}$ **49.** $\{-64, 27\}$ **51.** $\{25\}$

53. It would cause both denominators to be 0, and division by 0 is undefined. **54.** $\frac{12}{5}$ **55.** $\left(\frac{x}{x-3}\right)^2 + 3\left(\frac{x}{x-3}\right) - 4 = 0$

56. The numerator can never equal the denominator, since the denominator is 3 less than the numerator. **57.** $\left\{\frac{12}{5}\right\}$; The values for t are -4 and 1. The value 1 is impossible because it leads to a contradiction $\left(\text{since } \frac{x}{x-3} \text{ is never equal to } 1\right)$. **58.** $\left\{\frac{12}{5}\right\}$; The values for s are $\frac{1}{x}$ and $\frac{-4}{x}$. The value $\frac{1}{x}$ is impossible, since $\frac{1}{x} \neq \frac{1}{x-3}$ for all x.

Section 10.5 (page 729)

1. Solve for w^2 by dividing each side by g. **3.** $m = \sqrt{p^2 - n^2}$

5. $t = \frac{\pm\sqrt{dk}}{k}$ **7.** $d = \frac{\pm\sqrt{skI}}{I}$ **9.** $v = \frac{\pm\sqrt{kAF}}{F}$

11. $r = \frac{\pm\sqrt{3\pi Vh}}{\pi h}$ **13.** $t = \frac{-B \pm \sqrt{B^2 - 4AC}}{2A}$ **15.** $h = \frac{D^2}{k}$

17. $\ell = \frac{p^2 g}{k}$ **19.** eastbound ship: 80 mi; southbound ship: 150 mi

21. 2.3, 5.3, 5.8 **23.** 1 ft **25.** 20 in. by 12 in. **27.** 2.4 sec and 5.6 sec **29.** 9.2 sec **31.** It reaches its *maximum* height at 5 sec because this is the only time it reaches 400 ft. **33.** \$.80
35. **(a)** 2.4 million **(b)** 2.4 million; They are the same.
37. 1995; The graph indicates that sales reached 2 million in 1996.
39. 5.5 m per sec **41.** 5 or 14

Section 10.6 (page 739)

1. **(a)** B **(b)** C **(c)** A **(d)** D **3.** (0, 0) **5.** (0, 4) **7.** (1, 0)
9. $(-3, -4)$ **11.** In Exercise 9, the parabola is shifted 3 units to the left and 4 units down. The parabola in Exercise 10 is shifted 5 units to the right and 8 units down. **13.** down; wider **15.** up; narrower **17.** **(a)** I **(b)** IV **(c)** II **(d)** III

19.

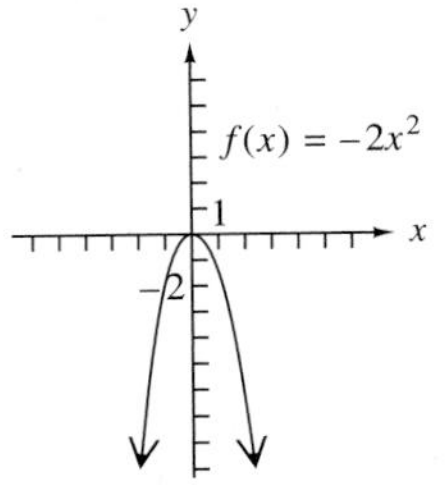

21.

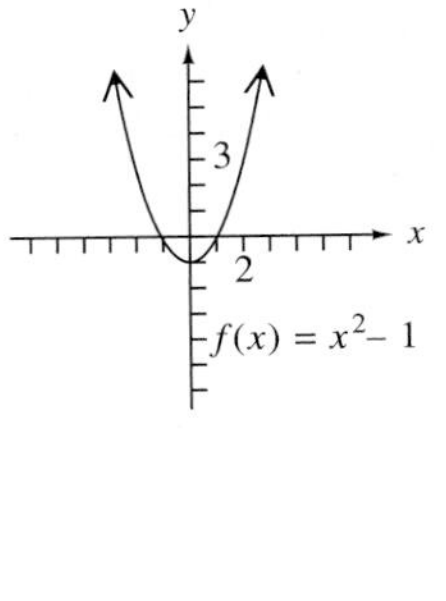

23.

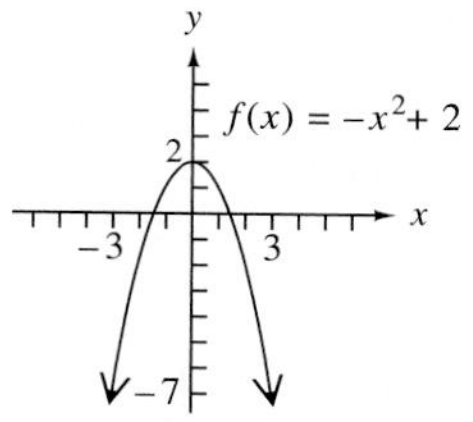

25. axis: $x = 4$; domain: $(-\infty, \infty)$; range: $[0, \infty)$

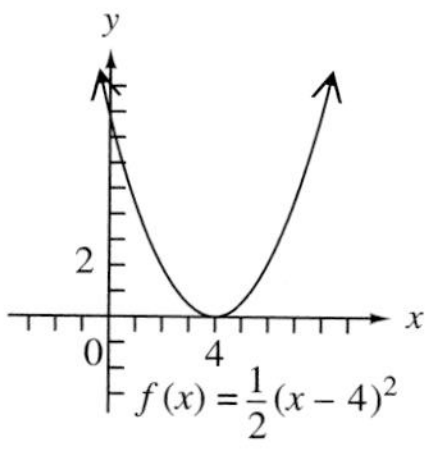

27. axis: $x = -2$; domain: $(-\infty, \infty)$; range: $[-1, \infty)$

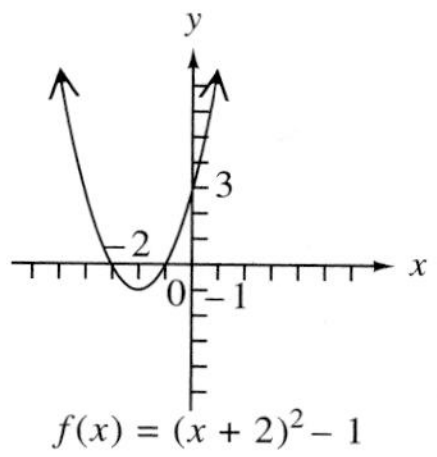

29. axis: $x = -3$; domain: $(-\infty, \infty)$; range: $(-\infty, 4]$

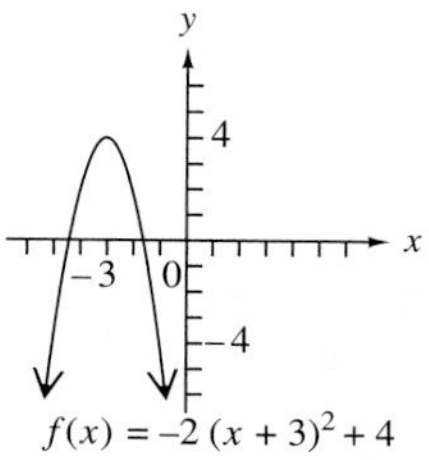

31. axis: $x = -2$; domain: $(-\infty, \infty)$; range: $(-\infty, 1]$

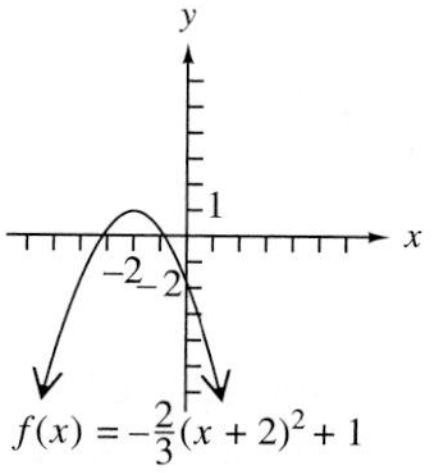

33. It is shifted 6 units up.

34.

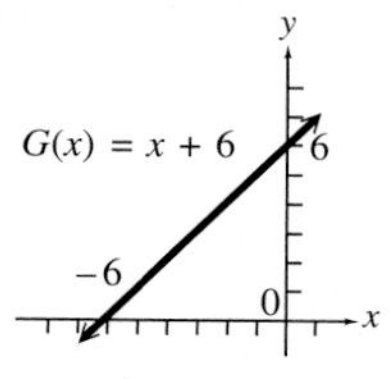

35. It is shifted 6 units up. **36.** It is shifted 6 units to the right.

37.

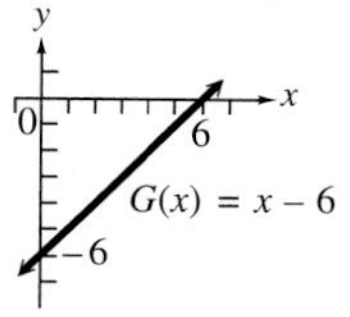

38. It is shifted 6 units to the right. **39.** quadratic; positive **41.** quadratic; negative **43.** linear; positive **45. (a)**

COMPANY BANKRUPTCY FILINGS

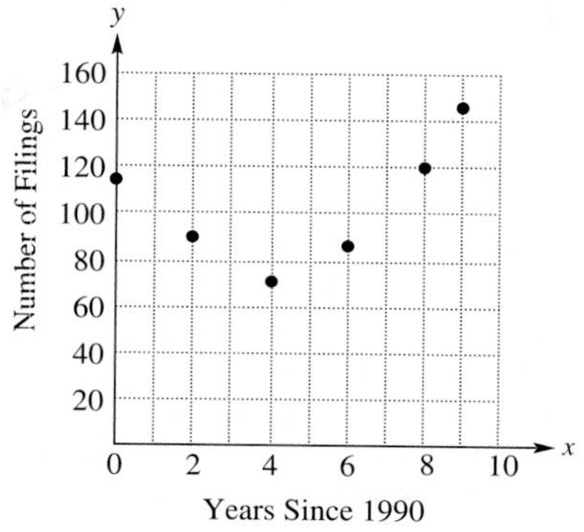

(b) quadratic; positive **(c)** $y = 2.969x^2 - 23.125x + 115$ **(d)** 181 **(e)** Yes. About 15 companies filed for bankruptcy each month, so at this rate, filings for 2000 would be about 180. **47. (a)** 171.2 **(b)** The approximation using the model is low.

Section 10.7 (page 753)

1. If x is squared, it has a vertical axis; if y is squared, it has a horizontal axis. **3.** Use the discriminant of the corresponding quadratic equation. If it is positive, there are two x-intercepts. If it is 0, there is just one x-intercept (the vertex), and if it is negative, there are no x-intercepts. **5.** $(-1, 3)$; up; narrower; no x-intercepts **7.** $\left(\frac{5}{2}, \frac{37}{4}\right)$; down; same; two x-intercepts **9.** $(-3, -9)$; to the right; wider

11. domain: $(-\infty, \infty)$; range: $[-1, \infty)$

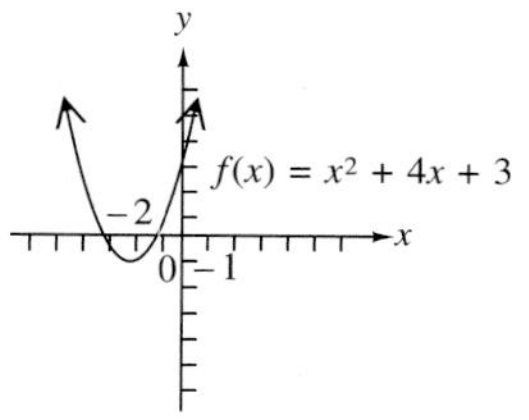

13. domain: $(-\infty, \infty)$; range: $(-\infty, -3]$

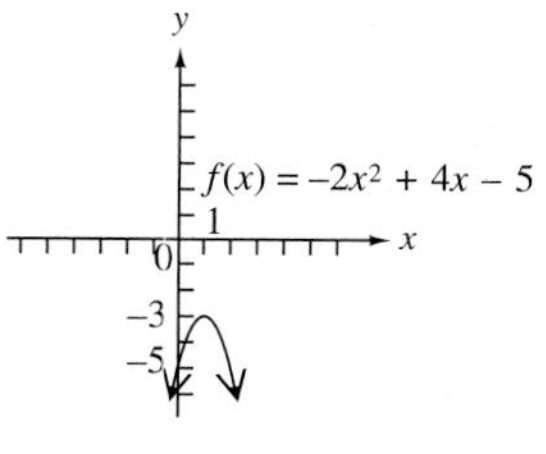

15. domain: $(-\infty, 1]$; range: $(-\infty, \infty)$

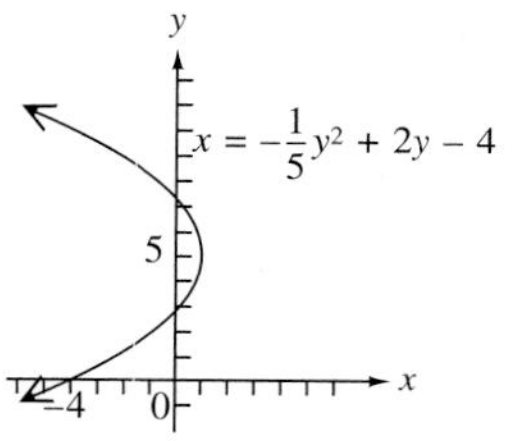

17. domain: $[-7, \infty)$; range: $(-\infty, \infty)$

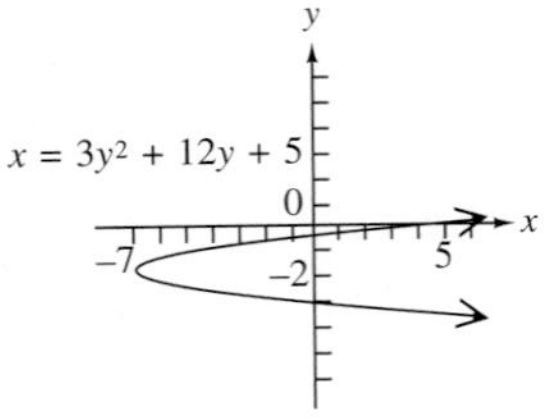

19. F **21.** C **23.** D **25.** 160 ft by 320 ft **27.** 30 and 30 **29.** 16 ft; 2 sec **31. (a)** $R(x) = 20{,}000 + 200x - 4x^2$ **(b)** 25 **(c)** \$22,500 **33. (a)** minimum **(b)** 1995; 1.7% **35. (a)** The coefficient of x^2 is negative because the parabola opens down. **(b)** (18.45, 3860) **(c)** In 2018 Social Security assets will reach their maximum value of \$3860 billion.

Section 10.8 (page 763)

1. (a) $\{1, 3\}$ **(b)** $(-\infty, 1) \cup (3, \infty)$ **(c)** $(1, 3)$
3. (a) $\left\{-3, \frac{5}{2}\right\}$ **(b)** $\left[-3, \frac{5}{2}\right]$ **(c)** $(-\infty, -3] \cup \left[\frac{5}{2}, \infty\right)$
5. Include the endpoints if the symbol is $\geq$ or $\leq$. Exclude the endpoints if the symbol is $>$ or $<$.

7. $(-\infty, -1) \cup (5, \infty)$ 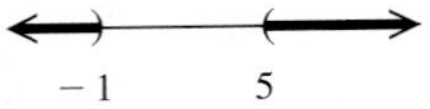

9. $(-4, 6)$ 

11. $(-\infty, 1] \cup [3, \infty)$ 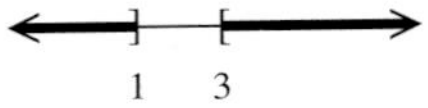

13. $\left(-\infty, -\frac{3}{2}\right] \cup \left[\frac{3}{5}, \infty\right)$ 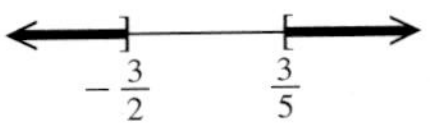

15. $\left(-\frac{2}{3}, \frac{1}{3}\right)$ 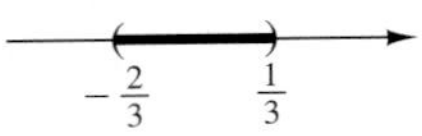

17. $\left(-\infty, -\frac{1}{2}\right] \cup \left[\frac{1}{3}, \infty\right)$ 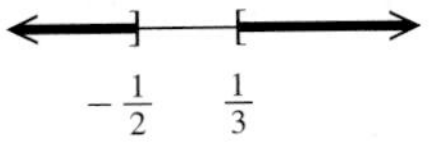

19. $(-\infty, 3 - \sqrt{3}] \cup [3 + \sqrt{3}, \infty)$ 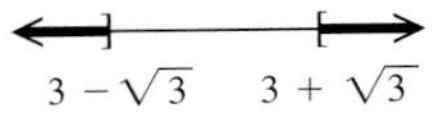

21. $(-\infty, \infty)$ **23.** $\emptyset$

25. $(-\infty, 1) \cup (2, 4)$ 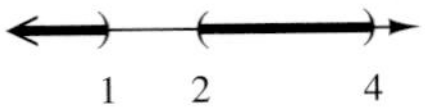

27. $\left[-\frac{3}{2}, \frac{1}{3}\right] \cup [4, \infty)$ 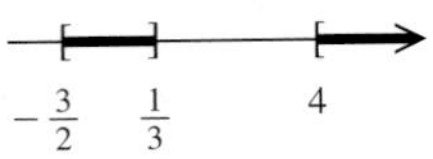

29. $(-\infty, 1) \cup (4, \infty)$ 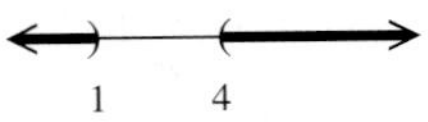

31. $\left[-\frac{3}{2}, 5\right)$ 

33. $(2, 6]$ 

35. $\left(-\infty, \frac{1}{2}\right) \cup \left(\frac{5}{4}, \infty\right)$ 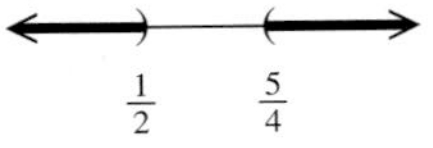

37. $[-4, -2)$ 

39. $\left(0, \frac{1}{2}\right) \cup \left(\frac{5}{2}, \infty\right)$ 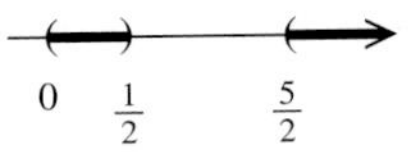

41. 3 sec and 13 sec **42.** between 3 sec and 13 sec **43.** at 0 sec (the time when it is initially projected) and at 16 sec (the time when it hits the ground) **44.** between 0 and 3 sec and between 13 and 16 sec

Chapter 10 Review Exercises (page 771)

1. $\{11, -11\}$ **2.** $\{\sqrt{3}, -\sqrt{3}\}$ **3.** $\{3 + \sqrt{10}, 3 - \sqrt{10}\}$
4. $\left\{-\frac{15}{2}, \frac{5}{2}\right\}$ **5.** $\left\{\frac{-1 + \sqrt{14}}{2}, \frac{-1 - \sqrt{14}}{2}\right\}$
6. $\left\{\frac{2 + 5i}{3}, \frac{2 - 5i}{3}\right\}$ **7.** By the square root property, $x = \sqrt{12}$ or $x = -\sqrt{12}$. **8.** 3.1 sec **9.** $\{-5, -1\}$
10. $\{-2 + \sqrt{11}, -2 - \sqrt{11}\}$ **11.** $\{-1 + \sqrt{6}, -1 - \sqrt{6}\}$
12. $\left\{\frac{-4 + \sqrt{22}}{2}, \frac{-4 - \sqrt{22}}{2}\right\}$ **13.** $\left\{-\frac{7}{2}\right\}$
14. $\left\{\frac{3 + i\sqrt{87}}{8}, \frac{3 - i\sqrt{87}}{8}\right\}$ **15.** $\left\{-\frac{7}{2}, 3\right\}$
16. $\left\{\frac{-5 + \sqrt{53}}{2}, \frac{-5 - \sqrt{53}}{2}\right\}$ **17.** $\left\{\frac{1 + \sqrt{41}}{2}, \frac{1 - \sqrt{41}}{2}\right\}$
18. $\left\{\frac{-3 + i\sqrt{23}}{4}, \frac{-3 - i\sqrt{23}}{4}\right\}$ **19.** $\left\{\frac{2 + i\sqrt{2}}{3}, \frac{2 - i\sqrt{2}}{3}\right\}$
20. $\left\{\frac{-7 + \sqrt{37}}{2}, \frac{-7 - \sqrt{37}}{2}\right\}$ **21.** C **22.** A **23.** D
24. B **25.** $\left\{-\frac{5}{2}, 3\right\}$ **26.** $\left\{-\frac{1}{2}, 1\right\}$ **27.** $\{-4\}$
28. $\left\{-\frac{11}{6}, -\frac{19}{12}\right\}$ **29.** $\left\{-\frac{343}{8}, 64\right\}$ **30.** $\{-2, -1, 1, 2\}$
31. 7 mph **32.** 40 mph **33.** 4.6 hr **34.** Greg: 2.6 hr; Carter: 3.6 hr **35.** $v = \frac{\pm\sqrt{rFkw}}{kw}$ **36.** $y = \frac{6p^2}{z}$
37. $t = \frac{3m \pm \sqrt{9m^2 + 24m}}{2m}$ **38.** 9 ft, 12 ft, 15 ft
39. 12 cm by 20 cm **40.** 1 in. **41.** 3 min **42.** 5.2 sec **43.** .7 sec and 4.0 sec **44.** \$.50 **45.** 4.5% **46. (a)** 305; It is close to the number shown in the graph. **(b)** $x \approx 9$, which represents 1999; Based on the graph, the number of e-mail boxes did not quite reach 200 million in 1999. **47.** $(1, 0)$ **48.** $(3, 7)$
49. $\left(\frac{2}{3}, -\frac{2}{3}\right)$ **50.** $(-4, 3)$
51. domain: $(-\infty, \infty)$; range: $[-3, \infty)$

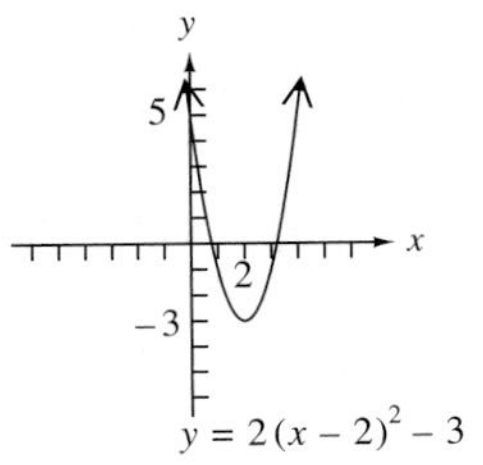

52. domain: $(-\infty, \infty)$; range: $(-\infty, 3]$

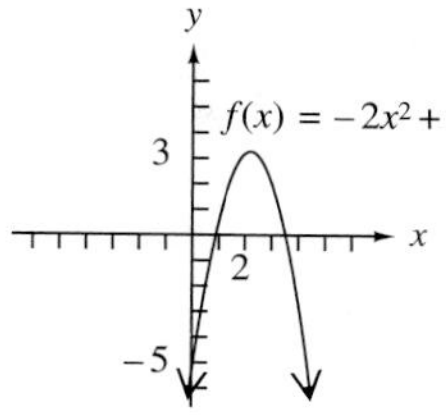

53. domain: $[-4, \infty)$; range: $(-\infty, \infty)$

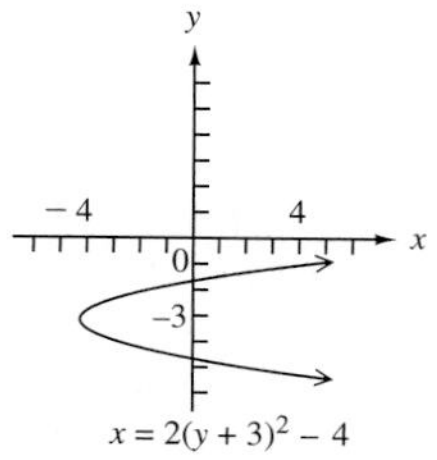

54. domain: $(-\infty, 4]$; range: $(-\infty, \infty)$

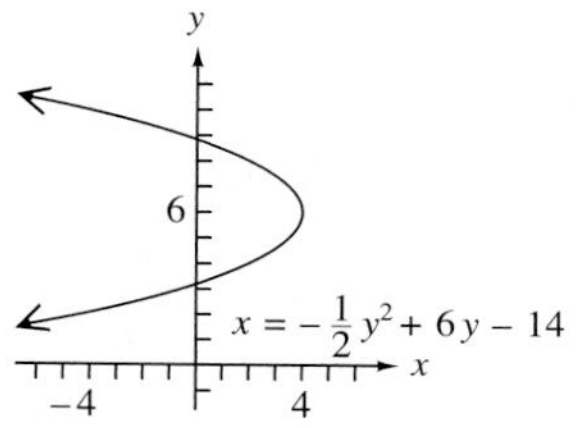

55. **(a)** $c = 12.39$, $16a + 4b + c = 15.78$, $49a + 7b + c = 22.71$ **(b)** $f(x) = .2089x^2 + .0118x + 12.39$ **(c)** \$25.85; The result using the model is a little high. **56.** 5 sec; 400 ft **57.** length: 50 m; width: 50 m

58. $\left(-\infty, -\frac{3}{2}\right) \cup (4, \infty)$

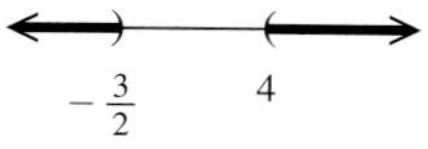

59. $[-4, 3]$

60. $(-\infty, -5] \cup [-2, 3]$

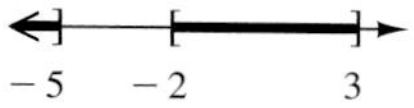

61. $\emptyset$ **62.** $\left(-\infty, \frac{1}{2}\right) \cup (2, \infty)$

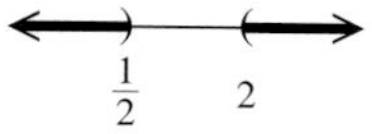

63. $[-3, 2)$

64. $R = \dfrac{\pm\sqrt{Vh - r^2h}}{h}$ **65.** $\left\{\dfrac{3 + i\sqrt{3}}{3}, \dfrac{3 - i\sqrt{3}}{3}\right\}$

66. $\{-2, -1, 3, 4\}$ **67.** $(-\infty, -6) \cup \left(-\frac{3}{2}, 1\right)$

68. $\left\{\dfrac{-11 + \sqrt{7}}{3}, \dfrac{-11 - \sqrt{7}}{3}\right\}$ **69.** $d = \dfrac{\pm\sqrt{SkI}}{I}$

70. $\{4\}$ **71.** $\left\{-\frac{5}{3}, -\frac{3}{2}\right\}$ **72.** $\left(-5, -\frac{23}{5}\right]$

73. domain: $(-\infty, \infty)$; range: $[-3, \infty)$

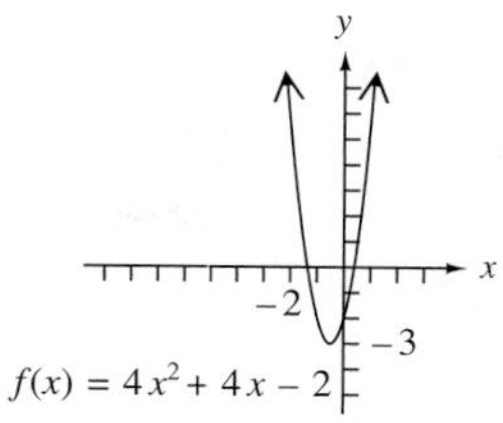

74. **(a)** 21.92 trillion ft^3 **(b)** 2005

Chapter 10 Test (page 777)

1. $\{3\sqrt{6}, -3\sqrt{6}\}$ **2.** $\left\{-\frac{8}{7}, \frac{2}{7}\right\}$ **3.** $\{-1 + \sqrt{2}, -1 - \sqrt{2}\}$

4. $\left\{\dfrac{3 + \sqrt{17}}{4}, \dfrac{3 - \sqrt{17}}{4}\right\}$ **5.** $\left\{\dfrac{2 + i\sqrt{11}}{3}, \dfrac{2 - i\sqrt{11}}{3}\right\}$

6. $\left\{\frac{2}{3}\right\}$ **7.** A **8.** discriminant: 88; There are two irrational solutions. **9.** $\left\{-\frac{2}{3}, 6\right\}$ **10.** $\left\{\dfrac{-7 + \sqrt{97}}{8}, \dfrac{-7 - \sqrt{97}}{8}\right\}$

11. $\left\{-2, -\frac{1}{3}, \frac{1}{3}, 2\right\}$ **12.** $\left\{-\frac{5}{2}, 1\right\}$ **13.** $r = \dfrac{\pm\sqrt{\pi S}}{2\pi}$

14. Maretha: 11.1 hr; Lillaana: 9.1 hr **15.** 7 mph **16.** 2 ft **17.** 16 m **18.** **(a)** 6.5% **(b)** 1996; 3.5% **19.** A **20.** $(0, -2)$

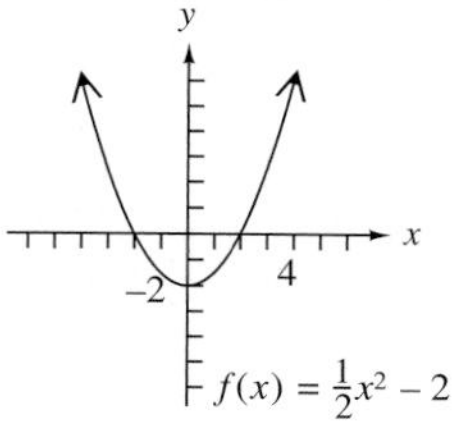

21. vertex: $(2, 3)$; domain: $(-\infty, \infty)$; range: $(-\infty, 3]$

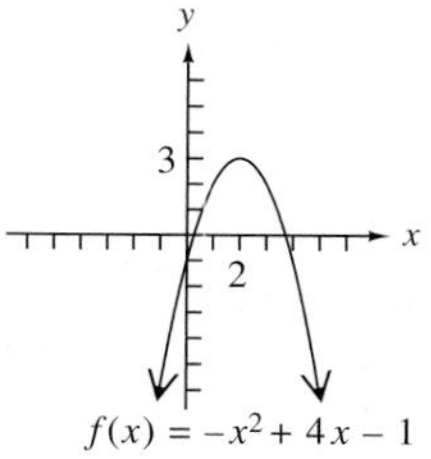

22. vertex: $(-5, -2)$; domain: $[-5, \infty)$; range: $(-\infty, \infty)$

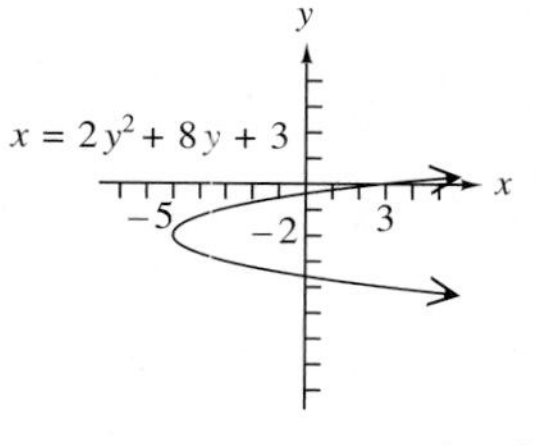

23. 140 ft by 70 ft; 9800 ft^2

24. $(-\infty, -5) \cup \left(\frac{3}{2}, \infty\right)$

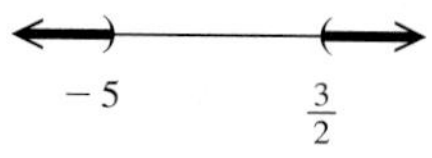

25. $(-\infty, 4) \cup [9, \infty)$

Cumulative Review Exercises: Chapters R–10 (page 781)

1. **(a)** $-2, 0, 7$ **(b)** $-\frac{7}{3}, -2, 0, .7, 7, \frac{32}{3}$ **(c)** all except $\sqrt{-8}$ **(d)** All are complex numbers. **2.** 6 **3.** 41 **4.** 930 **5.** 720 **6.** 990 **7.** 930 **8.** $\{1\}$ **9.** $[1, \infty)$ **10.** $\left[2, \frac{8}{3}\right]$ **11.** slope: $\frac{1}{2}$; y-intercept: $\left(0, -\frac{7}{4}\right)$ **12.** $x + 3y = -1$ **13.** function; domain: $(-\infty, \infty)$; range: $(-\infty, \infty)$

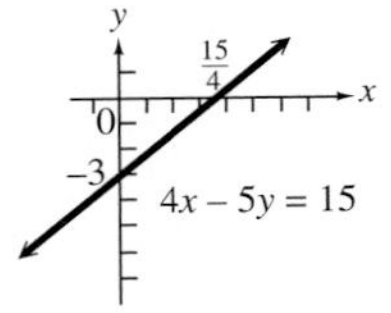

14. not a function

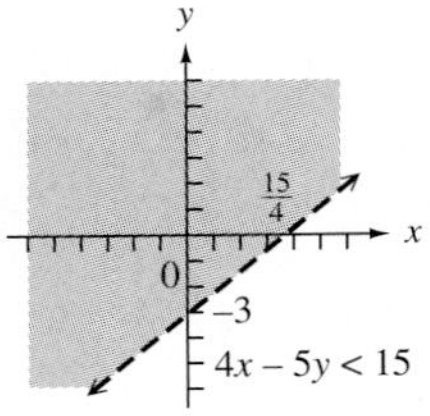

15. function; domain: $(-\infty, \infty)$; range: $(-\infty, 3]$

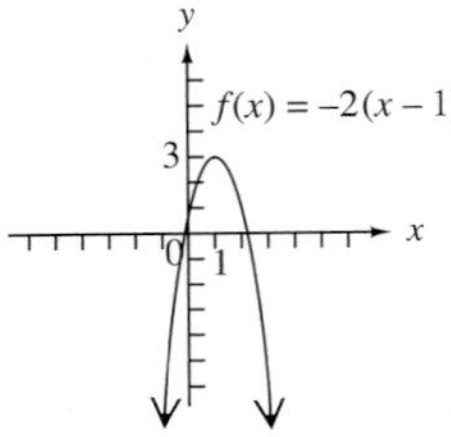

16. **(a)** $y = 1.2795x + 116.26$ **(b)** 158.48; It is a little too high. **17.** No, because the graph is a vertical line, which is not the graph of a function by the vertical line test. **18.** $\{(1, -2)\}$ **19.** $\{(3, -4, 2)\}$ **20.** **(a)** $x + y = 34.2$; $x = 4y - .3$ **(b)** AOL: \$27.3 billion; Time Warner: \$6.9 billion **21.** $\frac{x^8}{y^4}$ **22.** $\frac{4}{xy^2}$ **23.** $\frac{4}{9}t^2 + 12t + 81$ **24.** $-3t^3 + 5t^2 - 12t + 15$ **25.** $4x^2 - 6x + 11 + \frac{4}{x+2}$ **26.** $\$3.1 \times 10^{12}$ **27.** $x(4 + x)(4 - x)$ **28.** $(4m - 3)(6m + 5)$ **29.** $(3x - 5y)^2$ **30.** $-\frac{5}{18}$ **31.** $-\frac{8}{k}$ **32.** $\frac{r - s}{r}$ **33.** $\frac{3\sqrt[3]{4}}{4}$ **34.** $\sqrt{7} + \sqrt{5}$ **35.** $\left\{\frac{2}{3}\right\}$ **36.** $\left\{\frac{2 + \sqrt{10}}{2}, \frac{2 - \sqrt{10}}{2}\right\}$ **37.** $\{-3, 5\}$ **38.** $\emptyset$ **39.** $\{-3, -1, 1, 3\}$ **40.** southbound car: 57 mi; eastbound car: 76 mi

Chapter 11

Section 11.1 (page 791)

1. It is not one-to-one because both Illinois and Wisconsin are paired with the same range element, 40. **3.** Two or more siblings might be in the class. They would be paired with the same mother. **5.** B **7.** A **9.** $\{(6, 3), (10, 2), (12, 5)\}$ **11.** not one-to-one **13.** $f^{-1}(x) = \frac{x - 4}{2}$ **15.** $g^{-1}(x) = x^2 + 3, x \geq 0$ **17.** not one-to-one **19.** $f^{-1}(x) = \sqrt[3]{x + 4}$ **21.** **(a)** 8 **(b)** 3 **23.** **(a)** 1 **(b)** 0 **25.** **(a)** one-to-one **27.** **(a)** not one-to-one

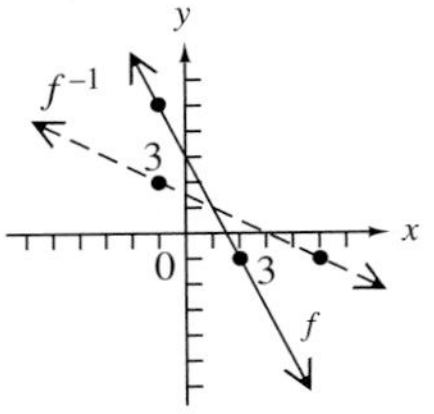

29. **(a)** one-to-one

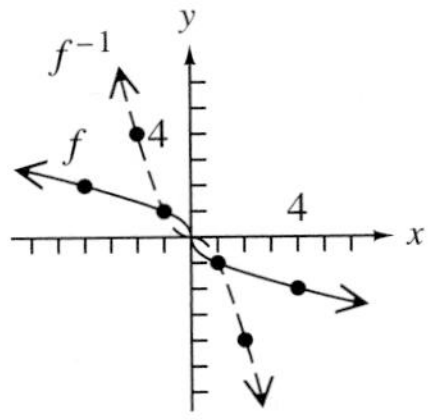

31.

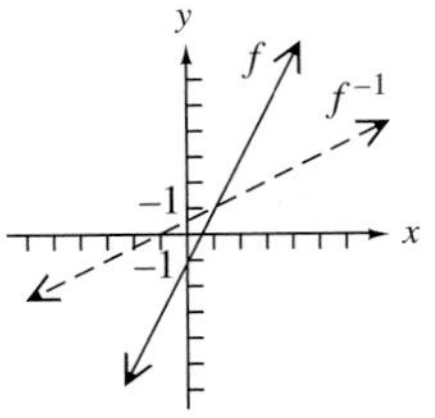

33.

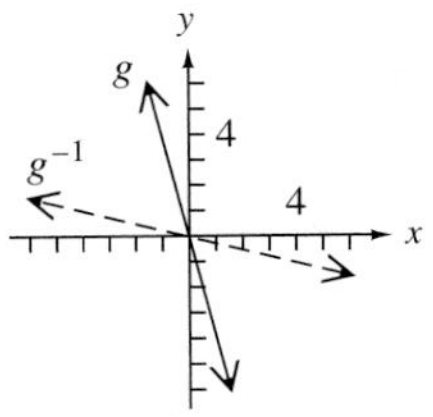

35.

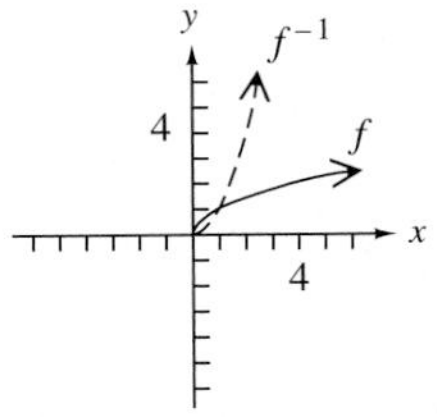

37.

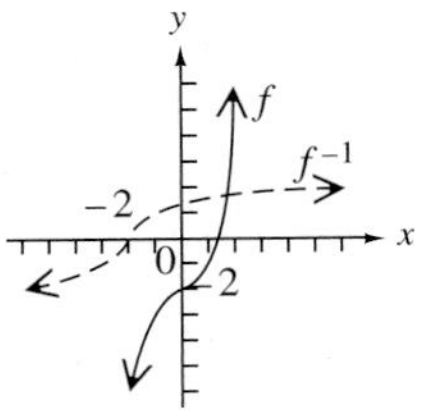

Section 11.2 (page 801)

1. C **3.** A **5.**

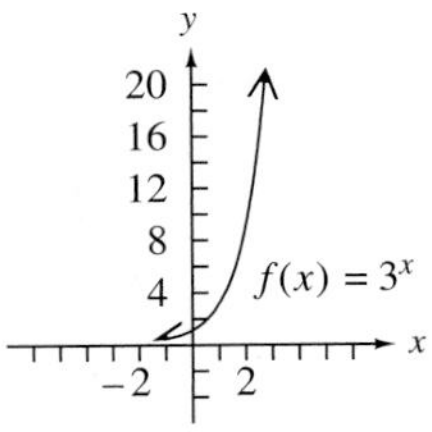

7.

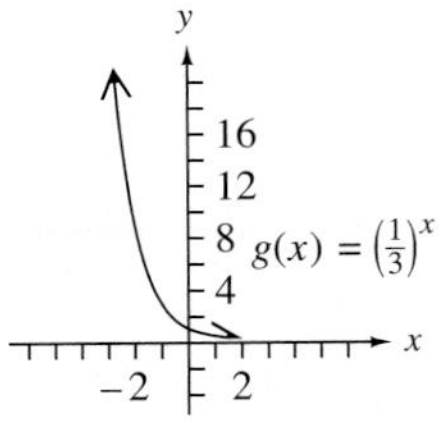

9.

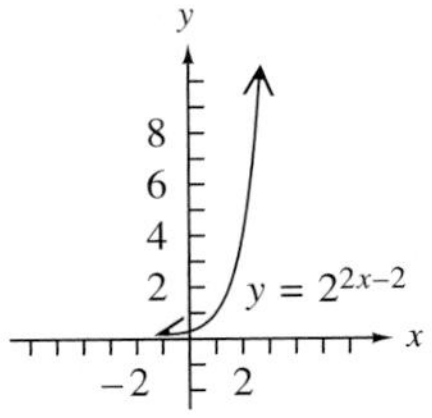

11. $\{2\}$ **13.** $\left\{\frac{3}{2}\right\}$ **15.** $\{7\}$ **17.** $\{-3\}$ **19.** $\{-1\}$ **21.** $\{-3\}$ **23.** **(a)** rises; falls **(b)** It is one-to-one and thus has an inverse. **25.** **(a)** 1.0°C **(b)** .4°C **27.** **(a)** 3.0°C **(b)** .7°C

Section 11.3 (page 809)

1. (a) C **(b)** F **(c)** B **(d)** A **(e)** E **(f)** D **3.** $\log_4 1024 = 5$ **5.** $\log_{1/2} 8 = -3$ **7.** $\log_{10} .001 = -3$ **9.** $\log_{625} 5 = \frac{1}{4}$ **11.** $4^3 = 64$ **13.** $10^{-4} = \frac{1}{10{,}000}$ **15.** $6^0 = 1$ **17.** $9^{1/2} = 3$ **19.** Since the radical $\sqrt{9} = 9^{1/2} = 3$, the exponent to which 9 must be raised is 1/2. **21.** $\left\{\frac{1}{3}\right\}$ **23.** $\{81\}$ **25.** $\left\{\frac{1}{5}\right\}$ **27.** $\{1\}$ **29.** $\{x \mid x > 0, x \neq 1\}$ **31.** $\{5\}$ **33.** $\left\{\frac{5}{3}\right\}$ **35.** $\{4\}$ **37.** $\left\{\frac{3}{2}\right\}$

39.

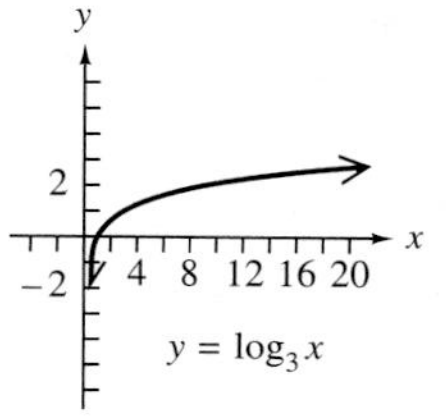

41.

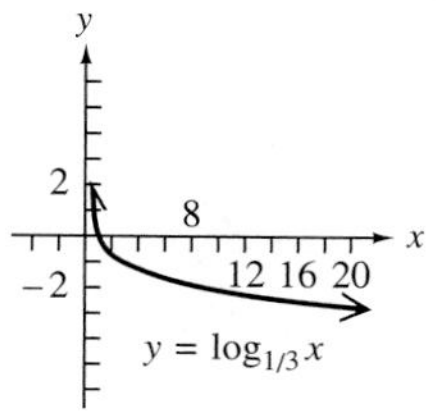

43. Answers will vary. **45.** 8 **47.** 24 **49.** Since every real number power of 1 equals 1, if $y = \log_1 x$, then $x = 1^y$ and so $x = 1$ for every y. This contradicts the definition of a function. **51.** $f(x) = 3^x$ **53. (a)** 645 sites **(b)** 962 sites **(c)** 1218 sites **55.** about 4 times as powerful

Section 11.4 (page 819)

1. false; $\log_b x + \log_b y = \log_b xy$ **3.** true **5.** $\log_7 4 - \log_7 5$ **7.** $\frac{1}{4}\log_2 8$ or $\frac{3}{4}$ **9.** $\log_4 3 + \frac{1}{2}\log_4 x - \log_4 y$

11. $\frac{1}{3}\log_3 4 - 2\log_3 x - \log_3 y$

13. $\frac{1}{2}\log_3 x + \frac{1}{2}\log_3 y - \frac{1}{2}\log_3 5$

15. $\frac{1}{3}\log_2 x + \frac{1}{5}\log_2 y - 2\log_2 r$ **17.** The distributive property tells us that the *product* $a(x + y)$ equals the sum $ax + ay$. In the notation $\log_a(x + y)$, the parentheses do not indicate multiplication. They indicate that $x + y$ is the result of raising a to some power. **19.** $\log_b xy$ **21.** $\log_a \frac{m^3}{n}$ **23.** $\log_a \frac{rt^3}{s}$ **25.** $\log_a \frac{125}{81}$ **27.** $\log_{10}(x^2 - 9)$ **29.** $\log_p \frac{x^3 y^{1/2}}{z^{3/2} a^3}$ **31.** For the power rule $\log_b x^r = r \log_b x$ to be true, x must be in the domain of $g(x) = \log_b x$, so $x > 0$. **33.** 4 **34.** It is the exponent to which 3 must be raised in order to obtain 81. **35.** 81 **36.** It is the exponent to which 2 must be raised in order to obtain 19. **37.** 19 **38.** m

Section 11.5 (page 825)

1. C **3.** C **5.** 19.2 **7.** 1.6335 **9.** 2.5164 **11.** −1.4868 **13.** 9.6776 **15.** 2.0592 **17.** −2.8896 **19.** 5.9613 **21.** 4.1506 **23.** 2.3026 **25.** Answers will vary. Suppose the name is Paul Bunyan, with $m = 4$ and $n = 6$. **(a)** $\log_4 6$ is the exponent to which 4 must be raised in order to obtain 6. **(b)** 1.29248125 **(c)** 6 (the value of n) **27.** An error message appears because we cannot find the common logarithm of a negative number. **29.** bog **31.** 5.9 **33.** 1.0×10^{-2} **35.** 2.5×10^{-5} **37. (a)** 35.0 yr **(b)** 14.2 yr **(c)** 9.0 yr **39. (a)** 107 dB **(b)** 100 dB **(c)** 98 dB **41. (a)** 55% **(b)** 90% **43. (a)** 5.6 yr **(b)** $t > 0$ and $\frac{87 - L}{63}$ is positive and in the domain of the function only if $24 < L < 87$.

Section 11.6 (page 837)

1. $\log 5^x = \log 125$ **2.** $x \log 5 = \log 125$ **3.** $x = \frac{\log 125}{\log 5}$ **4.** $\frac{\log 125}{\log 5} = 3$; $\{3\}$ **5.** $\{.827\}$ **7.** $\{.833\}$ **9.** $\{1.201\}$ **11.** $\{2.269\}$ **13.** $\{566.866\}$ **15.** $\{-18.892\}$ **17.** $\{4\}$ **19.** $\{43.301\}$ **21.** Natural logarithms are a better choice because e is the base. **23.** $\left\{\frac{2}{3}\right\}$ **25.** $\left\{\frac{33}{2}\right\}$ **27.** $\{-1 + \sqrt[3]{49}\}$ **29.** 2 cannot be a solution because $\log(2 - 3) = \log(-1)$, and -1 is not in the domain of $\log x$. **31.** $\left\{\frac{1}{3}\right\}$ **33.** $\{2\}$ **35.** $\emptyset$ **37.** $\{8\}$ **39.** $\left\{\frac{4}{3}\right\}$ **41.** $\{8\}$ **43. (a)** \$2539.47 **(b)** 10.2 yr **45.** \$4934.71 **47.** 15.4 yr **49.** about 180 g **51.** 1.4315 **53.** 3.3030 **55.** −.0947 **57.** .325

Chapter 11 Review Exercises (page 845)

1. not one-to-one **2.** one-to-one **3.** This function is not one-to-one because two sodas in the list have 41 mg of caffeine. **4.** $f^{-1}(x) = \frac{x - 7}{-3}$ or $\frac{7 - x}{3}$ **5.** $f^{-1}(x) = \frac{x^3 + 4}{6}$ **6.** not one-to-one

7.

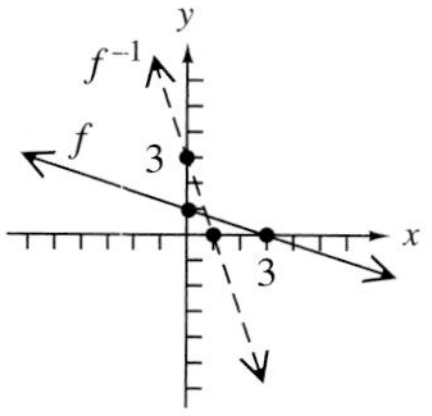

8.

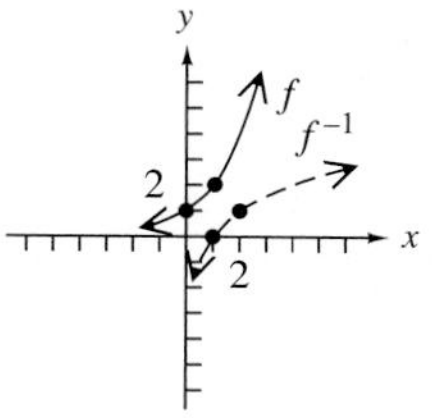

9.

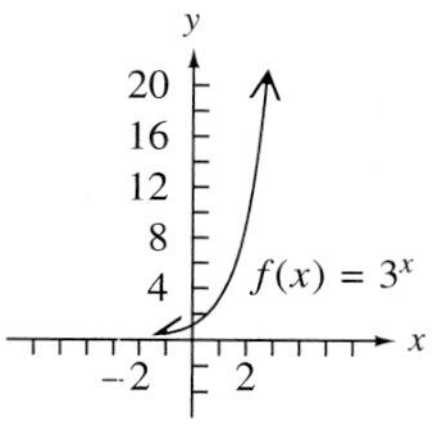

10.

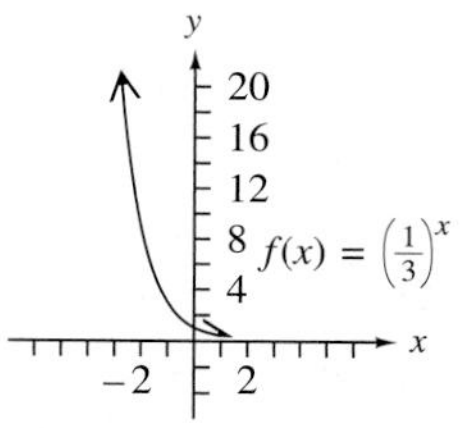

11.

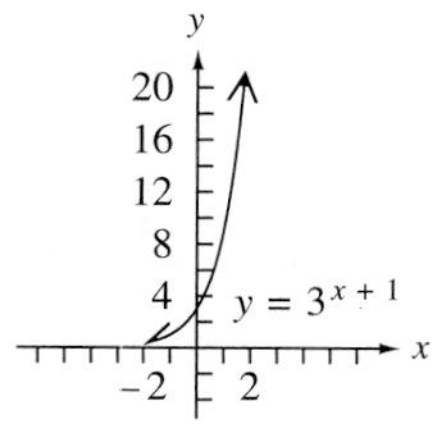

12. $\{4\}$ **13.** $\left\{\frac{3}{7}\right\}$ **14.** $\{0\}$ **15. (a)** 1.2 million tons **(b)** 3.8 million tons **(c)** 21.8 million tons **16. (a)** $5^4 = 625$ **(b)** $\log_5 .04 = -2$ **17. (a)** $\log_b a$ represents the exponent on b that equals a. **(b)** a

18.

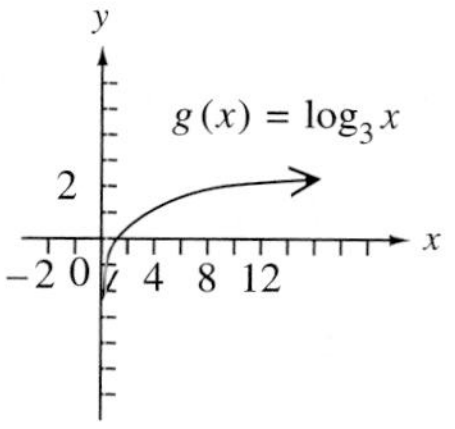

19.

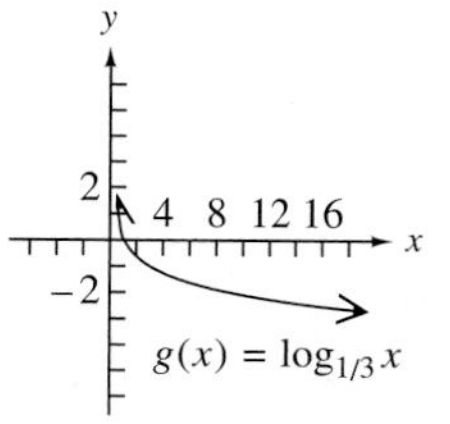

20. $\{2\}$ **21.** $\{-2\}$ **22.** $\{8\}$ **23.** $\{b \mid b > 0, b \neq 1\}$
24. $\log_4 3 + 2\log_4 x$ **25.** $2\log_2 p + \log_2 r - \frac{1}{2}\log_2 z$
26. $\log_b \frac{3x}{y^2}$ **27.** $\log_3 \frac{x+7}{4x+6}$ **28.** 1.4609 **29.** $-.5901$
30. 3.3638 **31.** -1.3587 **32.** 6.4 **33.** 8.4 **34.** 2.5×10^{-5}
35. (a) 18 yr **(b)** 12 yr **(c)** 7 yr **(d)** 6 yr **(e)** Each comparison shows approximately the same number. For example, in part (a) the doubling time is 18 yr (rounded) and $\frac{72}{4} = 18$. Thus, the formula $t = \frac{72}{100r}$ (called the *rule of 72*) is an excellent approximation of the doubling time formula. (It is used by bankers for that purpose.) **36. (a)** $g(92) = -3.4$; $g(99) = 7.1$
(b) $g(92)$ agrees closely with the y-value from the graph of about -3; $g(99)$ also is reasonably close to the y-value from the graph of about 7.5. **37.** $\{2.042\}$ **38.** $\{4.907\}$ **39.** $\{18.310\}$ **40.** $\left\{\frac{1}{9}\right\}$
41. $\{-6 + \sqrt[3]{25}\}$ **42.** $\{2\}$ **43.** $\left\{\frac{3}{8}\right\}$ **44.** $\{4\}$ **45.** $\{1\}$
46. \$7112.11 **47.** Plan A; it would pay \$2.92 more. **48.** \$4267
49. about 11% **50.** .9251 **51.** 1.7925 **52.** 1.4315 **53.** $\{72\}$
54. $\{5\}$ **55.** $\left\{\frac{1}{9}\right\}$ **56.** $\left\{\frac{4}{3}\right\}$ **57.** $\{3\}$ **58.** $\left\{\frac{1}{8}\right\}$
59. $\left\{\frac{11}{3}\right\}$ **60.** 6.8 yr

Chapter 11 Test (page 849)

1. (a) not one-to-one **(b)** one-to-one **2.** $f^{-1}(x) = x^3 - 7$

3.

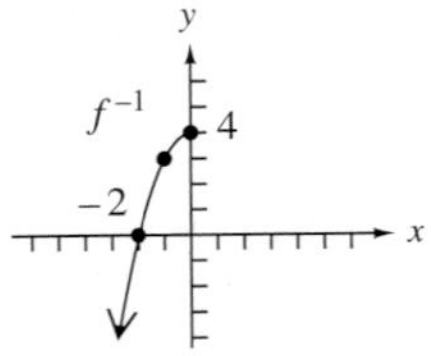

4.

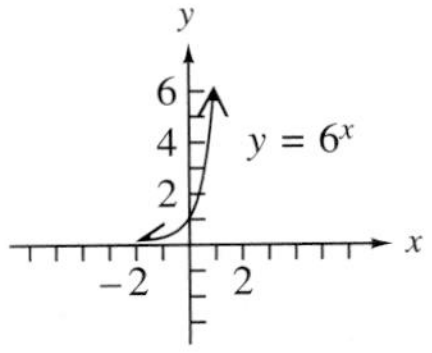

5.

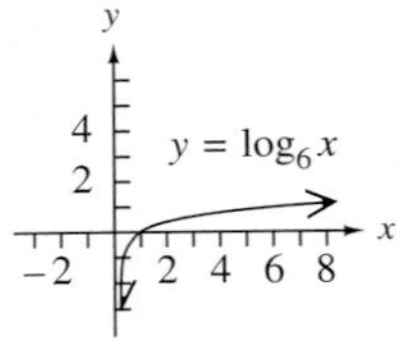

6. Interchange the x- and y-values of the ordered pairs, because the functions are inverses. **7.** $\{-4\}$ **8.** $\left\{-\frac{13}{3}\right\}$ **9.** 30.0 million; 37.7 million **10.** $\log_4 .0625 = -2$ **11.** $7^2 = 49$ **12.** $\{32\}$
13. $\left\{\frac{1}{2}\right\}$ **14.** $\{2\}$ **15.** $2\log_3 x + \log_3 y$ **16.** $\log_b \frac{r^{1/4}s^2}{t^{2/3}}$
17. (a) 1.3284 **(b)** $-.8440$ **(c)** 2.1245 **18.** $\{3.9656\}$
19. $\{3\}$ **20. (a)** \$12,507.51 **(b)** 15.5 yr

Cumulative Review Exercises: Chapters R–11 (page 851)

1. $-2, 0, 6, \frac{30}{3}$ (or 10) **2.** $-\frac{9}{4}, -2, 0, .6, 6, \frac{30}{3}$ (or 10)
3. $-\sqrt{2}, \sqrt{11}$ **4.** 16 **5.** -39 **6.** $\left\{-\frac{2}{3}\right\}$ **7.** $[1, \infty)$
8. $\{-2, 7\}$ **9.** $\left\{-\frac{16}{3}, \frac{16}{3}\right\}$ **10.** $\left[\frac{7}{3}, 3\right]$
11. $(-\infty, -3) \cup (2, \infty)$

12.

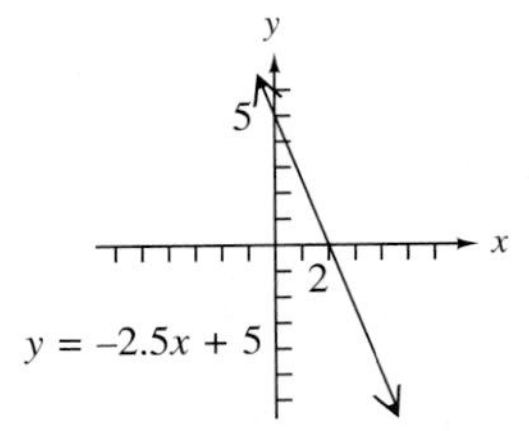

13.

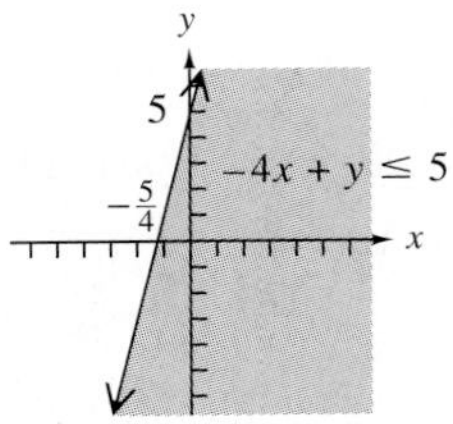

14. (a) yes **(b)** -4000; The number of acres harvested decreased by 4000 acres per year during 1997–1999. **15.** $y = \frac{3}{4}x - \frac{19}{4}$
16. $\{(4, 2)\}$ **17.** $\{(1, -1, 4)\}$ **18.** 6 lb of \$1.00 candy and 10 lb of \$1.96 candy **19.** $6p^2 + 7p - 3$ **20.** $16k^2 - 24k + 9$
21. $-5m^3 + 2m^2 - 7m + 4$ **22.** $2t^3 + 5t^2 - 3t + 4$
23. $x(8 + x^2)$ **24.** $(3y - 2)(8y + 3)$ **25.** $z(5z + 1)(z - 4)$
26. $(4a + 5b^2)(4a - 5b^2)$ **27.** $(2c + d)(4c^2 - 2cd + d^2)$
28. $(4r + 7q)^2$ **29.** $-\frac{1875p^{13}}{8}$ **30.** $\frac{x+5}{x+4}$
31. $\frac{-3k - 19}{(k+3)(k-2)}$ **32.** $\frac{22 - p}{p(p-4)(p+2)}$ **33.** $\left\{-\frac{1}{3}\right\}$
34. $12\sqrt{2}$ **35.** $-\frac{1}{4}$ **36.** $-27\sqrt{2}$ **37.** $\{0, 4\}$ **38.** 41
39. $\left\{\frac{1 \pm \sqrt{13}}{6}\right\}$ **40.** $(-\infty, -4) \cup (2, \infty)$ **41.** $\{\pm 1, \pm 2\}$

42.

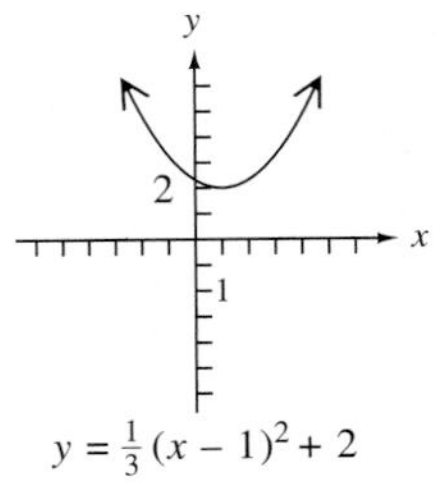

43.

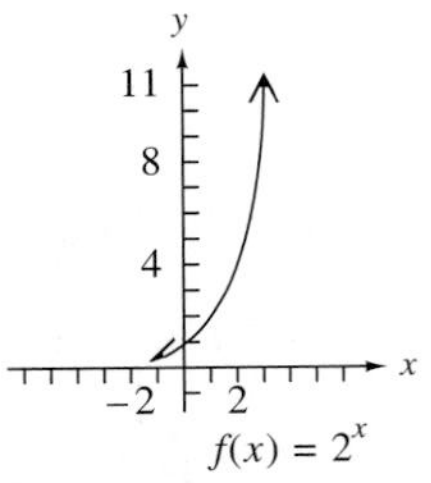

44.

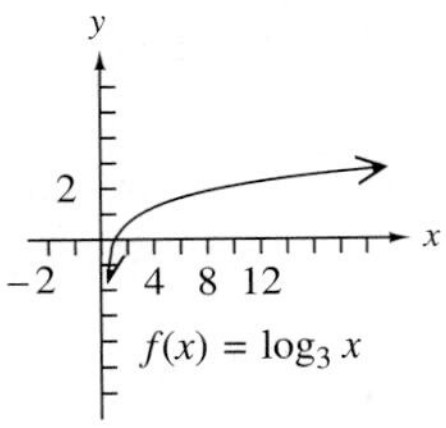

45. $\{-1\}$ **46.** $\{1\}$ **47.** $5^3 = 125$
48. $3\log x + \frac{1}{2}\log y - \log z$ **49.** .110 or 11%
50. (a) 25,000 **(b)** 37,300 **(c)** 68,000

Chapter 12

Section 12.1 (page 863)

1. 0 **3.** 0; 0 **5.** B **7.** A
9. $(-\infty, \infty)$; $[0, \infty)$

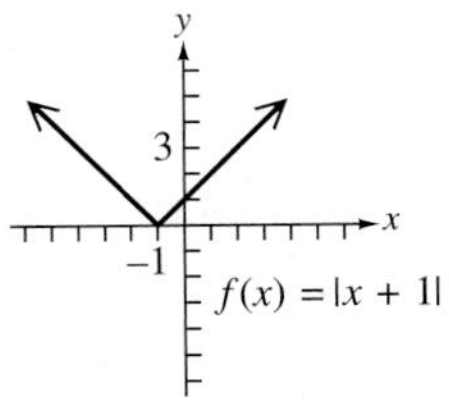

11. $(-\infty, 0) \cup (0, \infty)$; $(-\infty, 1) \cup (1, \infty)$

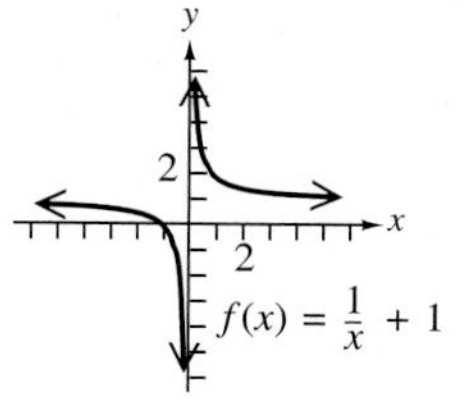

13. $[2, \infty)$; $[0, \infty)$

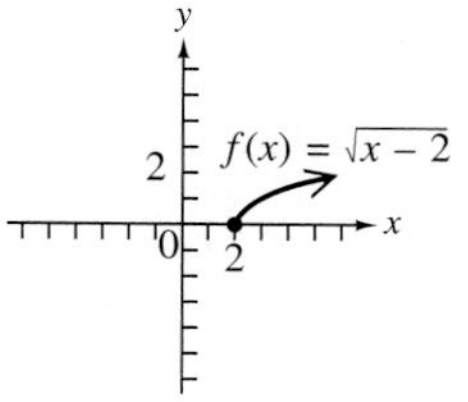

15. $(-\infty, 2) \cup (2, \infty)$; $(-\infty, 0) \cup (0, \infty)$

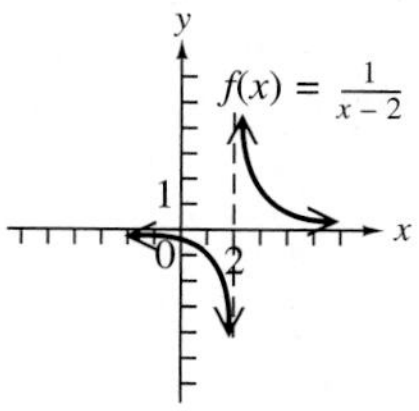

17. $[-3, \infty)$; $[-3, \infty)$

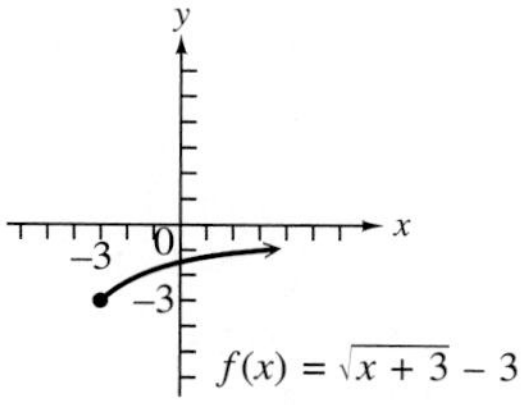

19. $x^2 + 2x - 9$ **21.** $2x^3 - 18x$ **23.** 6 **25.** -20 **27.** $x^2 - x - 6$ **29.** $x + 3, x \neq 3$ **31.** 6 **33.** 4 **35.** 16 **37.** 83 **39.** 13 **41.** $4x^2 + 12x + 13$ **43.** $x^2 + 10x + 29$ **45.** $2x + 8$ **47.** $(f \circ g)(x) = 63{,}360x$; It computes the number of inches in x mi. **49.** $(A \circ r)(t) = 4\pi t^2$; This is the area of the circular layer as a function of time.

Section 12.2 (page 873)

1. (a) $(0, 0)$ **(b)** 5 **(c)**

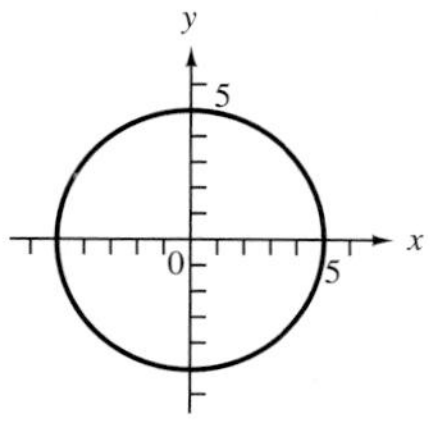

3. B **5.** D **7.** $(x + 4)^2 + (y - 3)^2 = 4$ **9.** $(x + 8)^2 + (y + 5)^2 = 5$ **11.** $(-2, -3)$; $r = 2$ **13.** $(-5, 7)$; $r = 9$ **15.** $(2, 4)$; $r = 4$ **17.** The thumbtack acts as the center and the length of the string acts as the radius.

19.

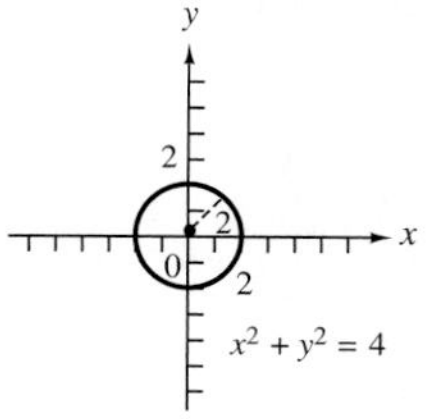

21.

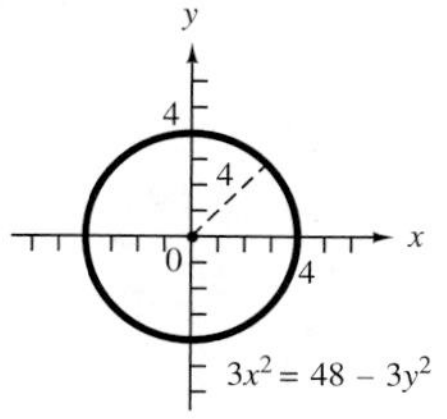

23.

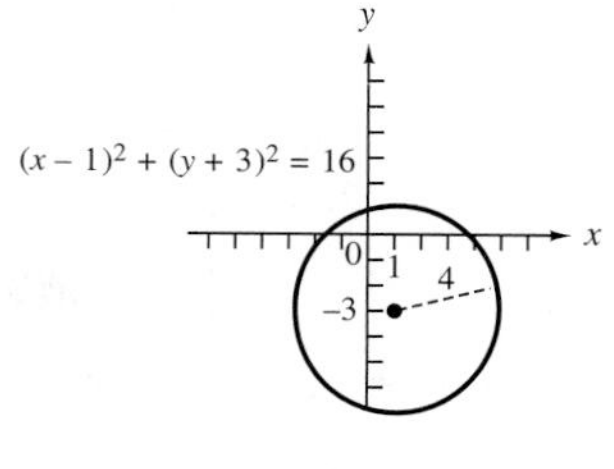

25.

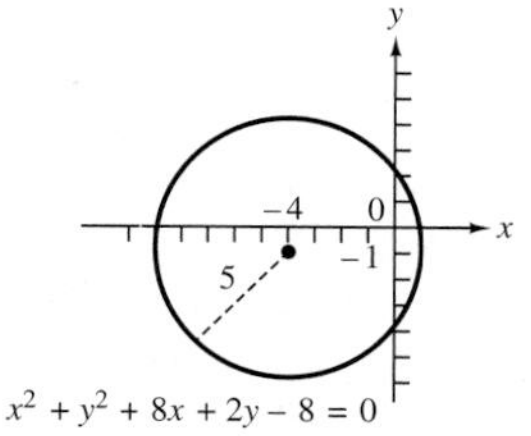

27.

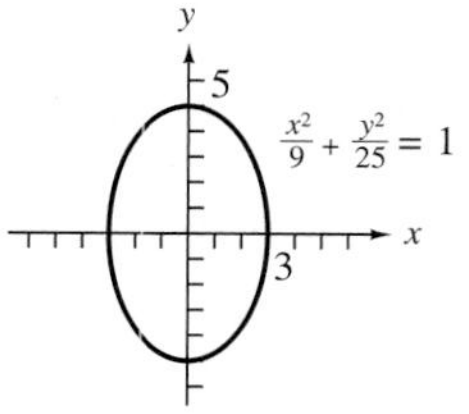

29.

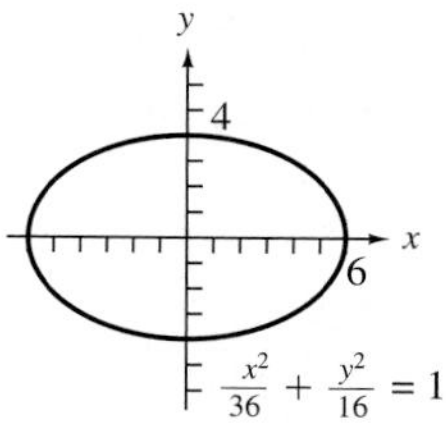

31.

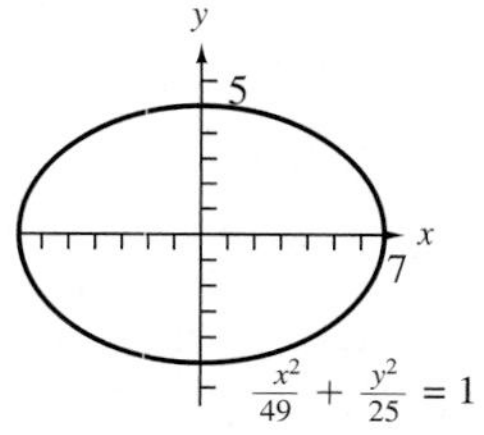

33.

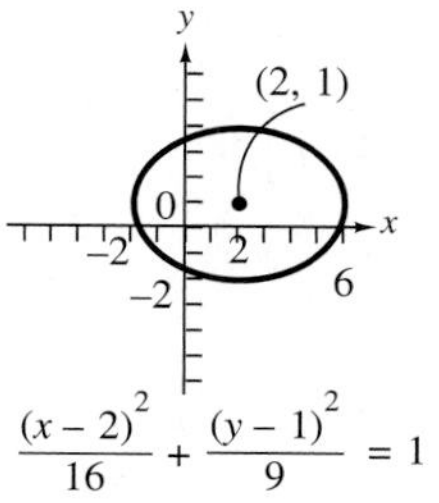

35. (a) 10 m **(b)** 36 m **37. (a)** 154.7 million mi **(b)** 128.7 million mi (Answers are rounded.)

Section 12.3 (page 883)

1. C **3.** D **5.** When written in one of the forms given in the box titled "Equations of Hyperbolas" in this section, it will open up and down if the $-$ sign precedes the x^2-term; it will open left and right if the $-$ sign precedes the y^2-term.

7.

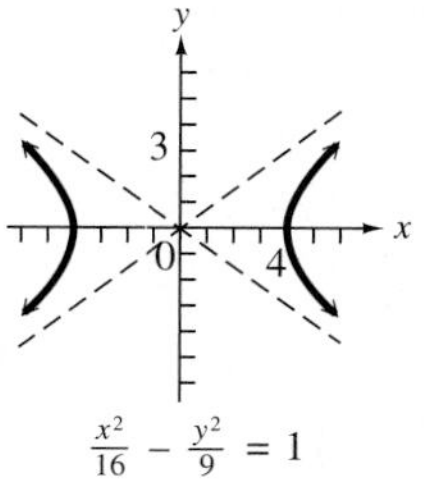

9.

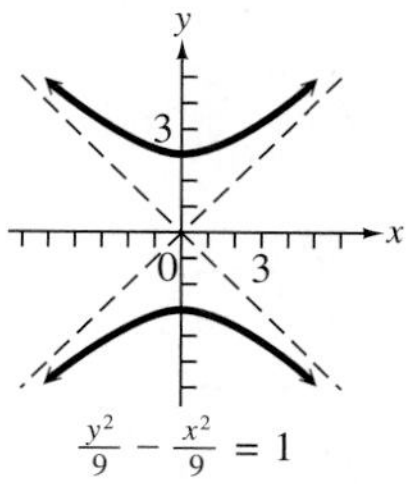

11.

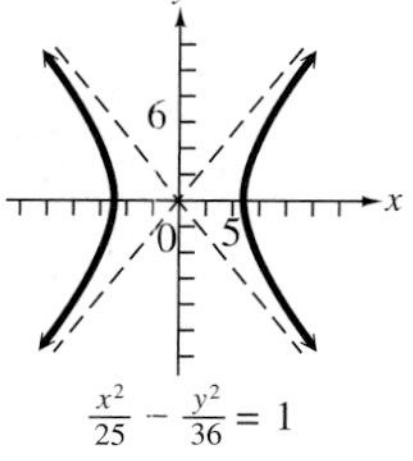

13. hyperbola

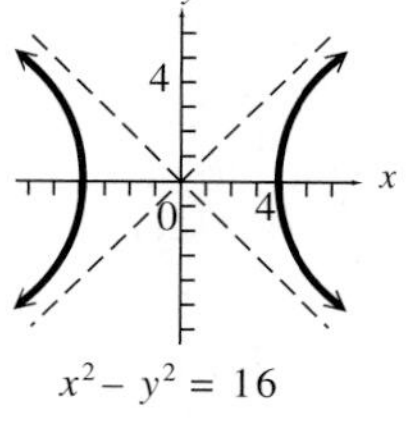

15. ellipse

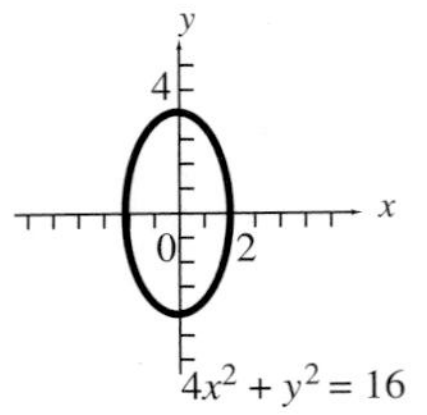

17. circle

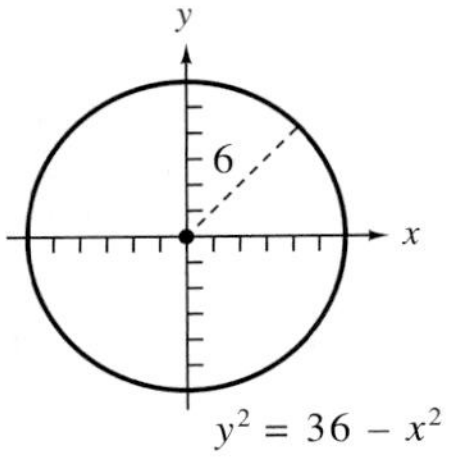

19. hyperbola

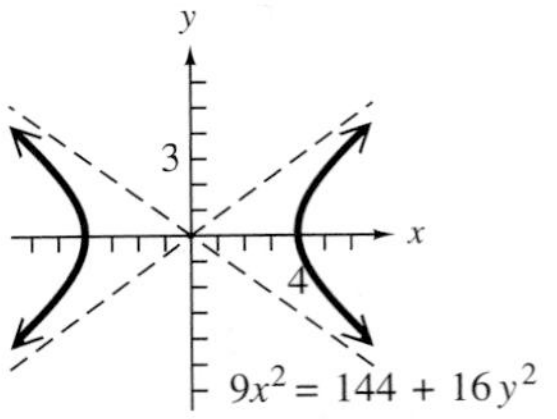

21. ellipse

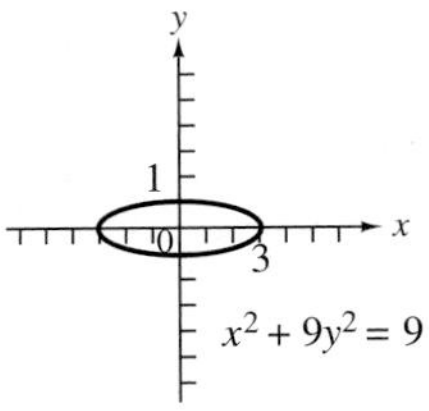

23. $[-3, 3]$; $[0, 3]$

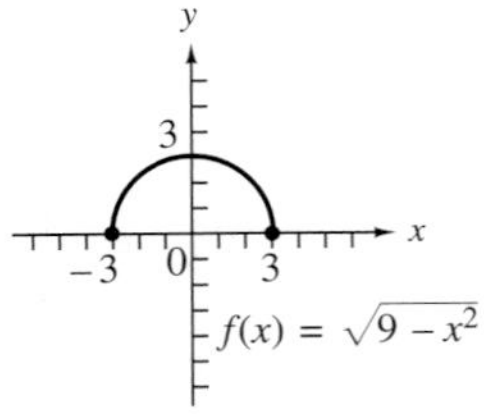

25. $[-5, 5]$; $[-5, 0]$

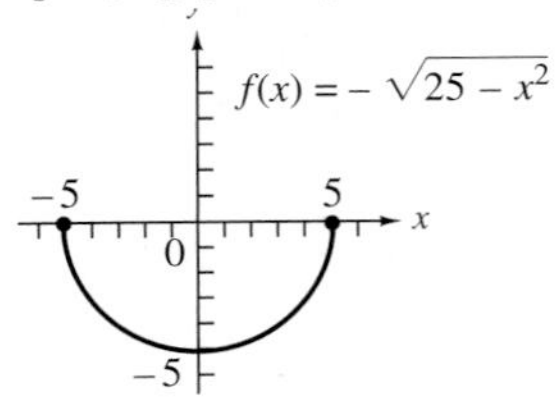

27. $[-4, \infty)$; $[0, \infty)$

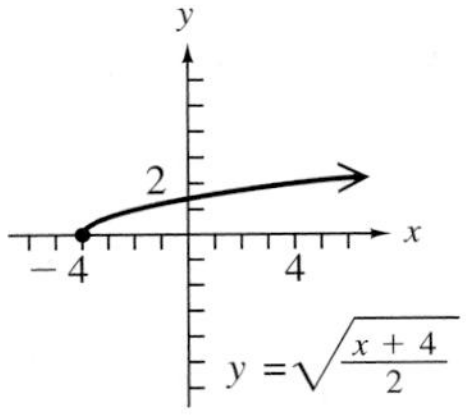

29. (a) 50 m **(b)** 69.3 m **31.** for V greater than 4325.68 m per sec

Section 12.4 (page 893)

1. Substitute $x - 1$ for y in the first equation. Then solve for x. Find the corresponding y-values by substituting back into $y = x - 1$. In the first equation, both variables are squared and in the second, both variables are to the first power, so the elimination method is not appropriate. **3.** one **5.** none

7.

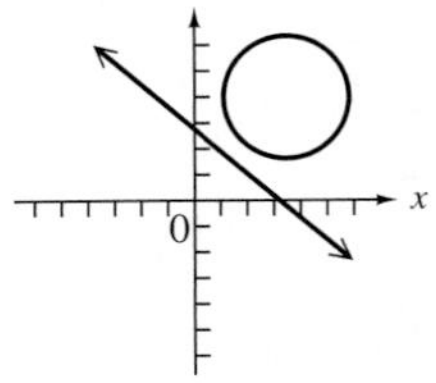

9.

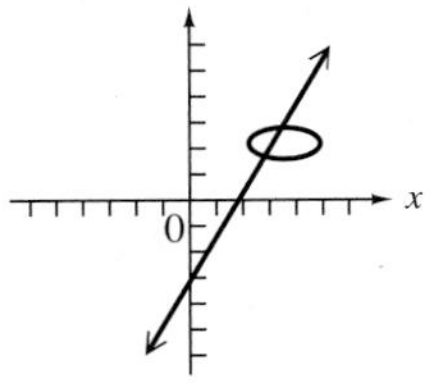

11.

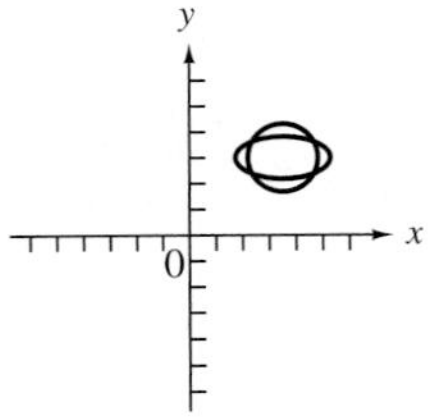

13. $\left\{(0, 0), \left(\frac{1}{2}, \frac{1}{2}\right)\right\}$ **15.** $\{(-6, 9), (-1, 4)\}$

17. $\left\{\left(-\frac{1}{5}, \frac{7}{5}\right), (1, -1)\right\}$ **19.** $\left\{(-2, -2), \left(-\frac{4}{3}, -3\right)\right\}$

21. $\{(-3, 1), (1, -3)\}$ **23.** $\left\{\left(-\frac{3}{2}, -\frac{9}{4}\right), (-2, 0)\right\}$

25. $\{(-\sqrt{3}, 0), (\sqrt{3}, 0), (-\sqrt{5}, 2), (\sqrt{5}, 2)\}$

27. $\{(-2, 0), (2, 0)\}$ **29.** $\{(i\sqrt{2}, -3i\sqrt{2}), (-i\sqrt{2}, 3i\sqrt{2}), (-\sqrt{6}, -\sqrt{6}), (\sqrt{6}, \sqrt{6})\}$ **31.** $\{(-2i\sqrt{2}, -2\sqrt{3}), (-2i\sqrt{2}, 2\sqrt{3}), (2i\sqrt{2}, -2\sqrt{3}), (2i\sqrt{2}, 2\sqrt{3})\}$

33. $\{(-\sqrt{5}, -\sqrt{5}), (\sqrt{5}, \sqrt{5})\}$ **35.** $\{(i, 2i), (-i, -2i), (2, -1), (-2, 1)\}$ **37.** length: 12 ft; width: 7 ft **39.** \$20; 800 calculators **41.** 1981; 470 thousand

Section 12.5 (page 901)

1. C **3.** Graph the corresponding equation as a solid curve if the inequality is $\leq$ or $\geq$, or as a dashed curve if the inequality is $<$ or $>$. Use a test point to decide which side of the boundary satisfies the inequality, and shade it. The shaded region is the solution set.

5.

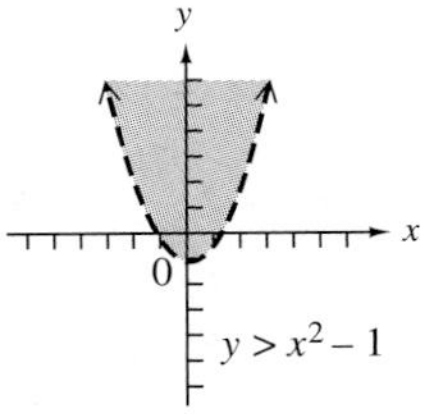

7.

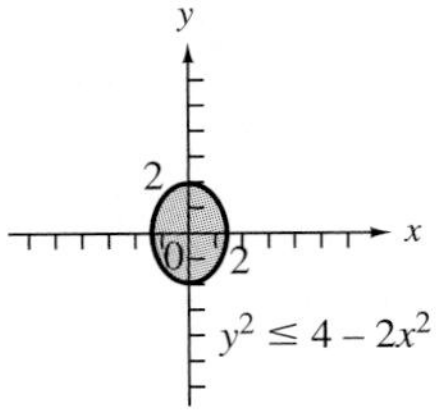

9.

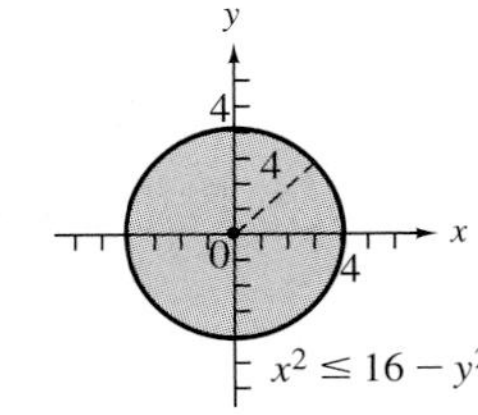

11.

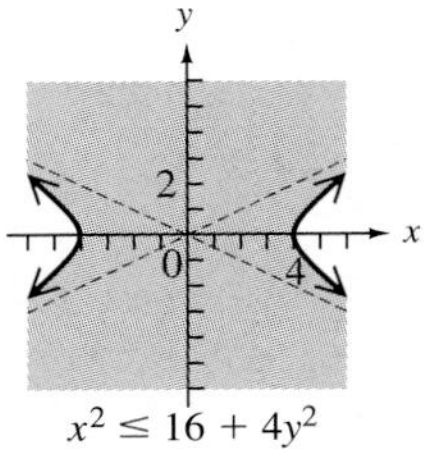

13.

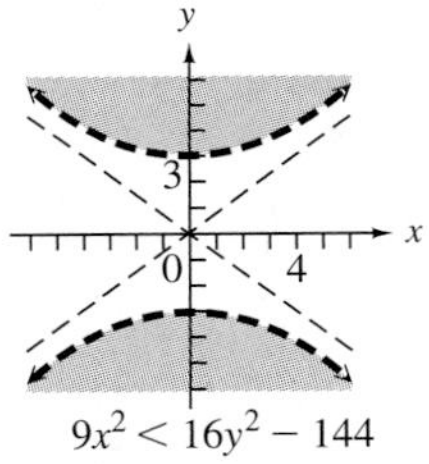

15.

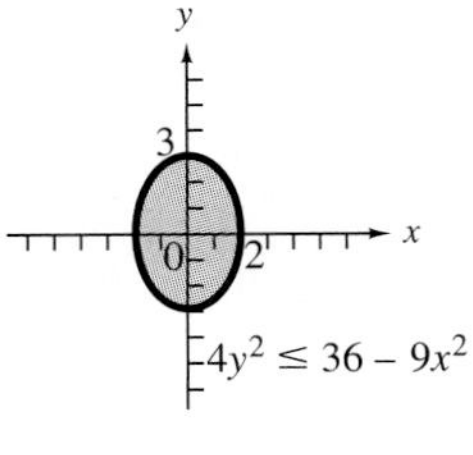

17.

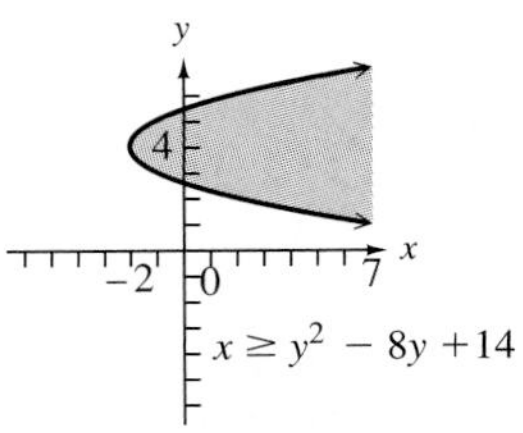

19.

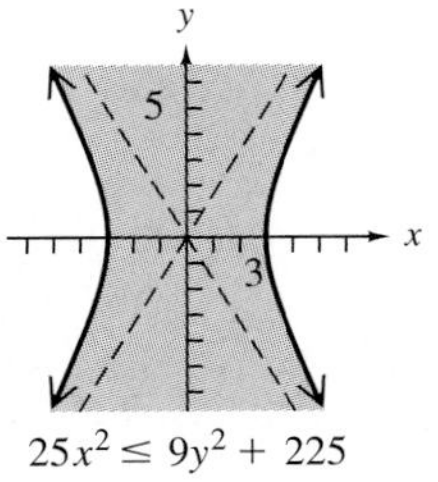

21.

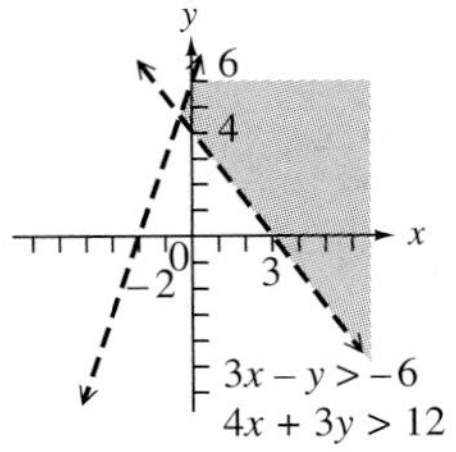

23.

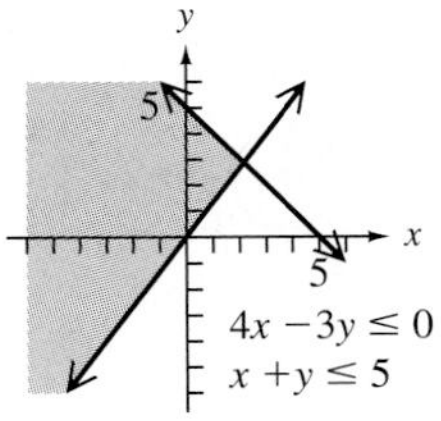

25.
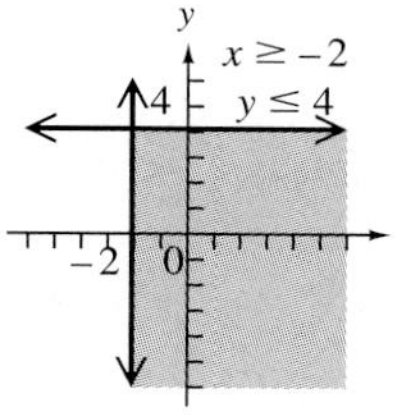

27.
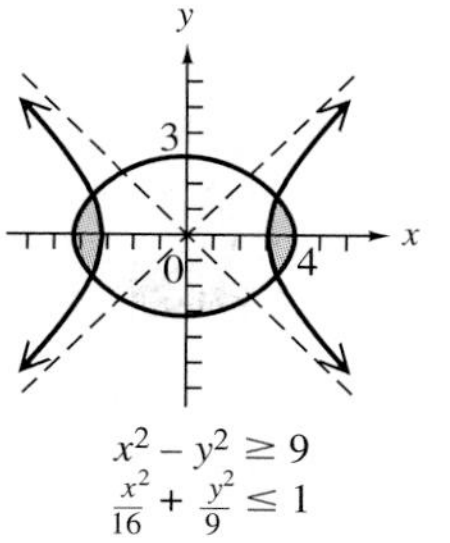

29.
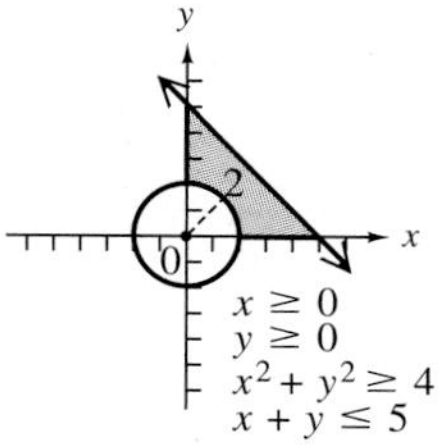

31.
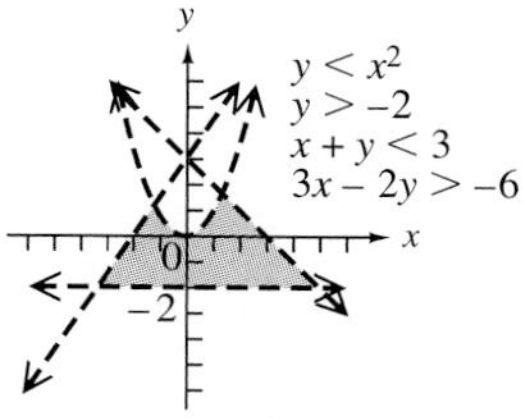

Chapter 12 Review Exercises (page 909)

1.
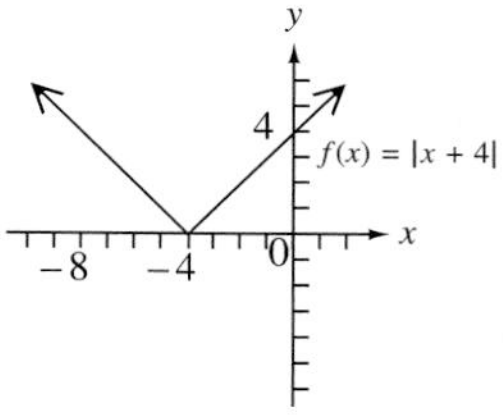

2.
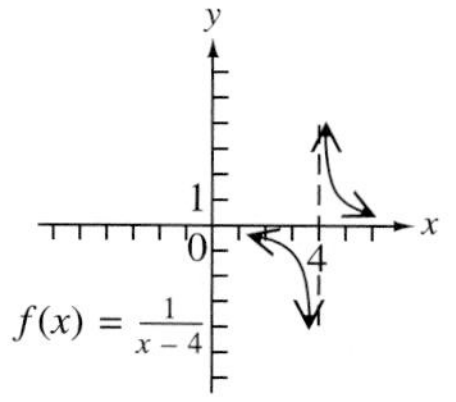

3.
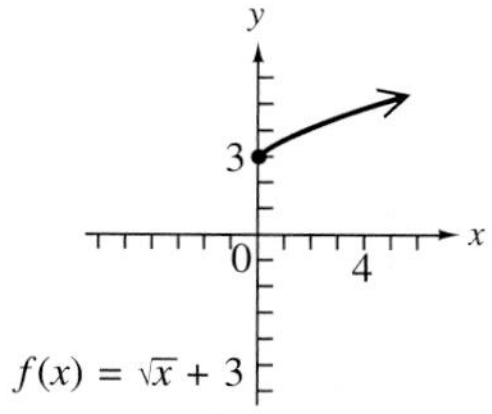

4. $3x^2 + 7x + 6$ **5.** -2 **6.** 20 **7.** 42 **8.** $75x^2 + 220x + 160$ **9.** $15x^2 + 10x + 2$ **10.** No, composition of functions is not a commutative operation. For example, the results of Exercises 8 and 9 show that $(f \circ g)(x) \neq (g \circ f)(x)$ in this case. **11.** $(x + 2)^2 + (y - 4)^2 = 9$ **12.** $(x + 1)^2 + (y + 3)^2 = 25$ **13.** $(x - 4)^2 + (y - 2)^2 = 36$ **14.** $(-3, 2), r = 4$ **15.** $(4, 1), r = 2$ **16.** $(-1, -5), r = 3$ **17.** $(3, -2), r = 5$

18.
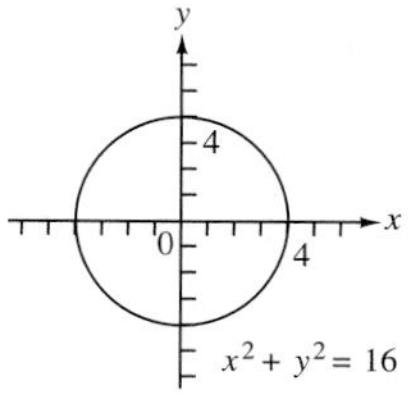

19.
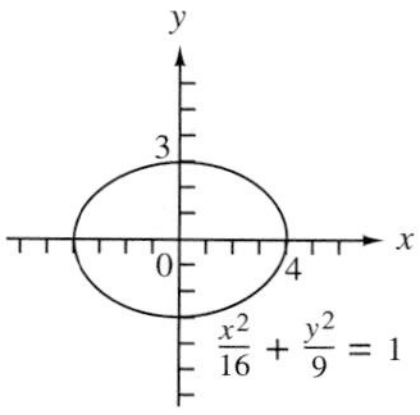

20.
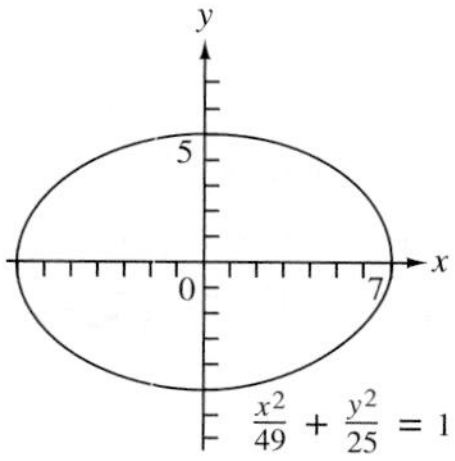

21. $\dfrac{x^2}{65{,}286{,}400} + \dfrac{y^2}{2{,}560{,}000} = 1$

22. A circular racetrack is most appropriate because the crawfish can move in any direction. Distance from the center determines the winner.

23.
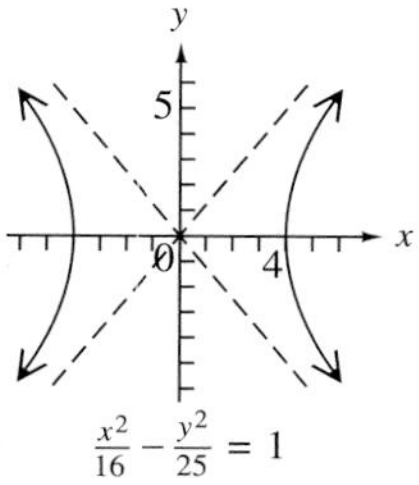

24.
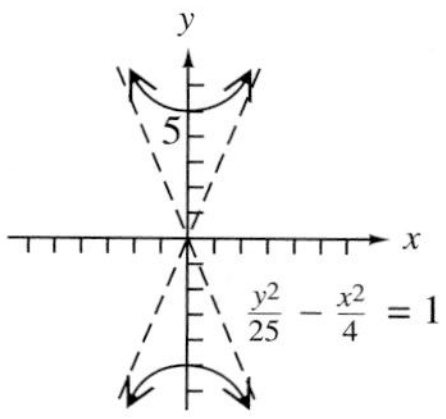

25.
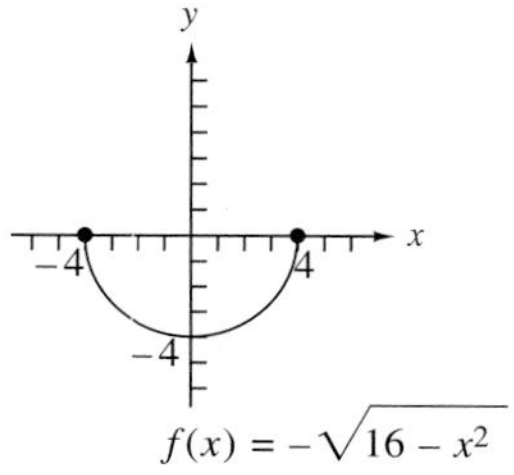

26. circle **27.** parabola **28.** hyperbola **29.** ellipse **30.** parabola **31.** hyperbola **32.** $\dfrac{x^2}{625} - \dfrac{y^2}{1875} = 1$

33. $\{(6, -9), (-2, -5)\}$ **34.** $\{(1, 2), (-5, 14)\}$
35. $\{(4, 2), (-1, -3)\}$ **36.** $\{(-2, -4), (8, 1)\}$
37. $\{(-\sqrt{2}, 2), (-\sqrt{2}, -2), (\sqrt{2}, -2), (\sqrt{2}, 2)\}$
38. $\{(-\sqrt{6}, -\sqrt{3}), (-\sqrt{6}, \sqrt{3}), (\sqrt{6}, -\sqrt{3}), (\sqrt{6}, \sqrt{3})\}$
39. 0, 1, or 2 **40.** 0, 1, 2, 3, or 4

41.
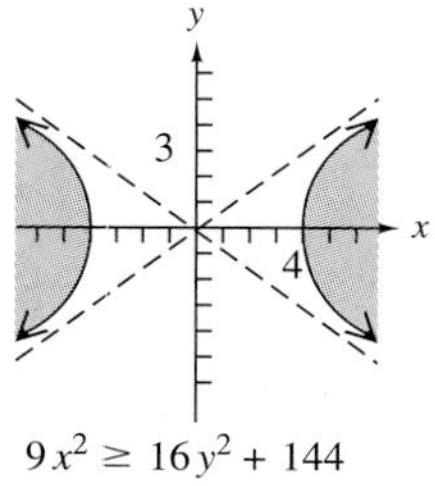

42.
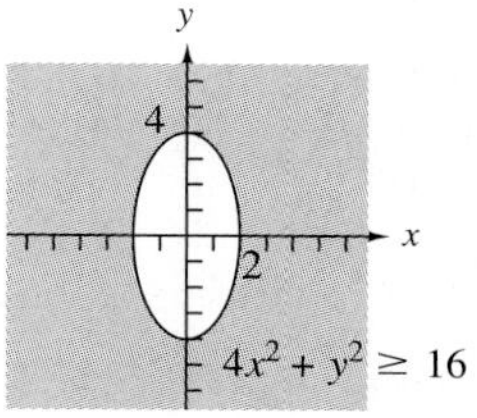

43.
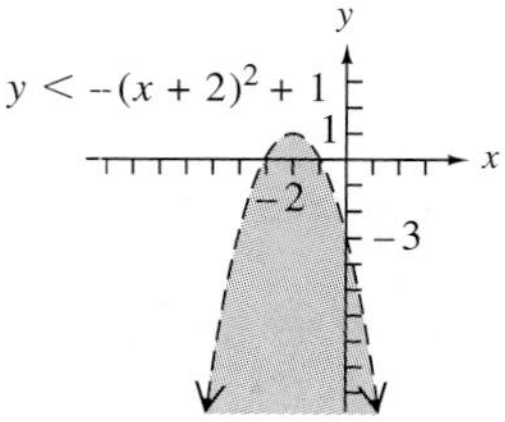

44.
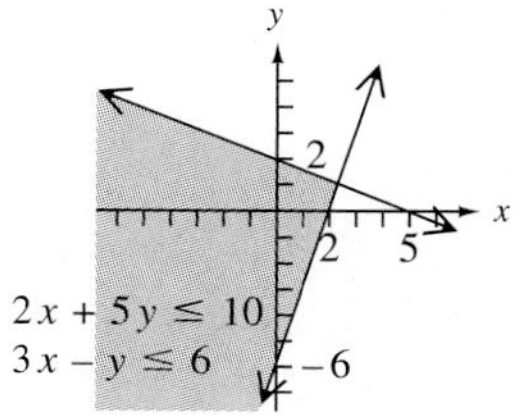

45.

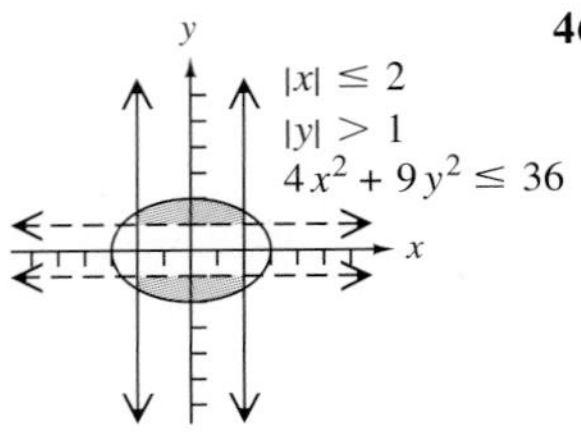

46.

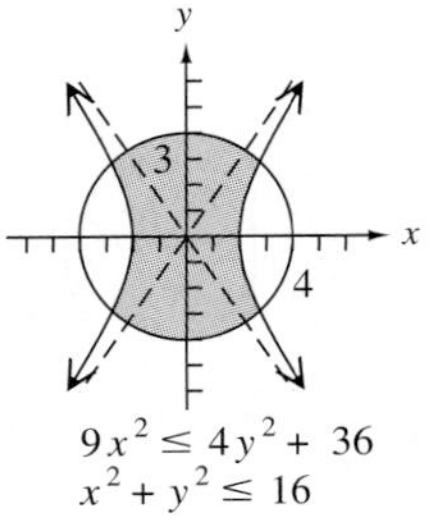

47. $2a + 4b + c = -20$ **48.** $5a + b + c = -26$ **49.** $-a + b + c = -2$ **50.** $\{(-4, -2, -4)\}$; $x^2 + y^2 - 4x - 2y - 4 = 0$ **51.** center: (2, 1); radius: 3

52.

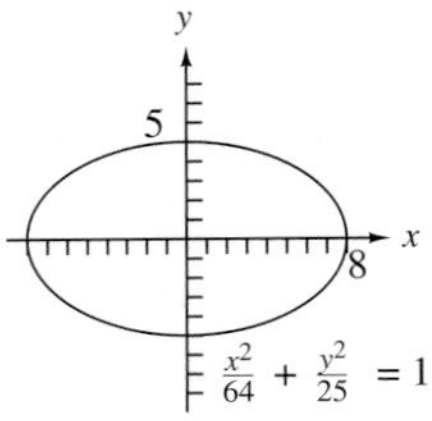

53.

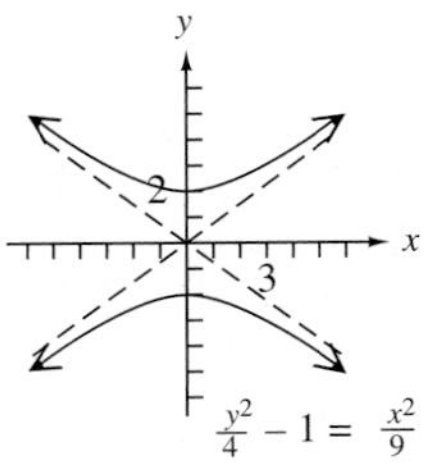

54.

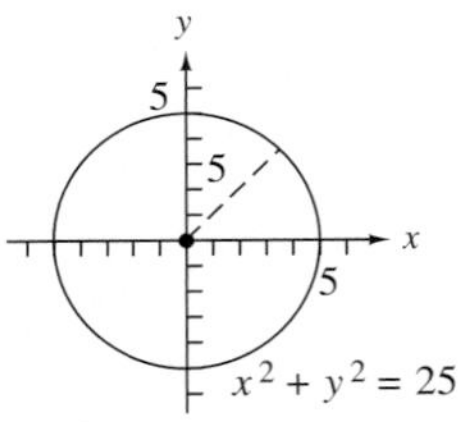

55.

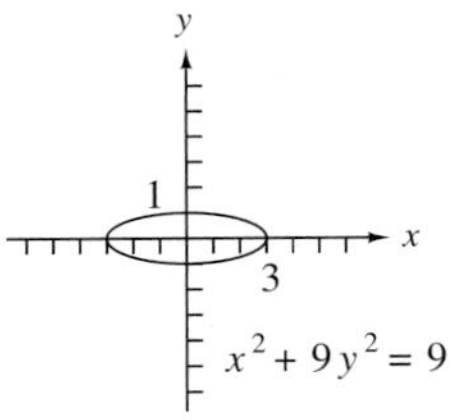

56.

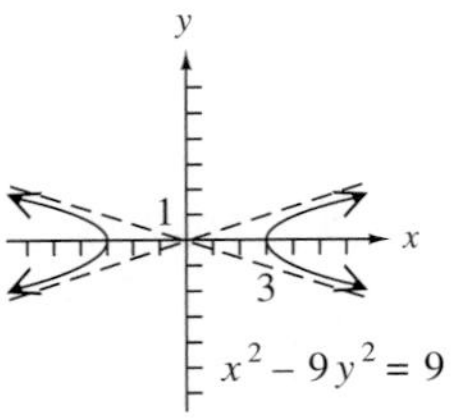

57.

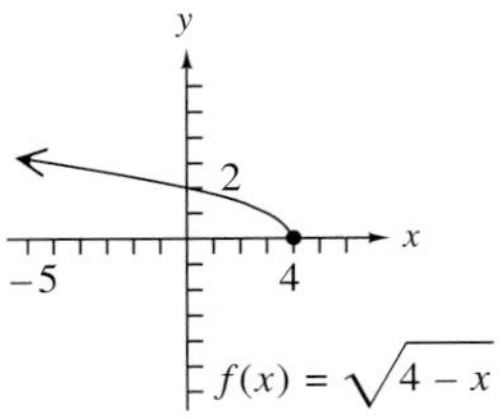

58.

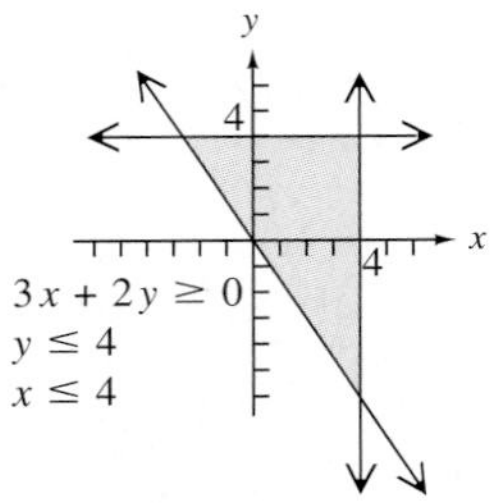

59.

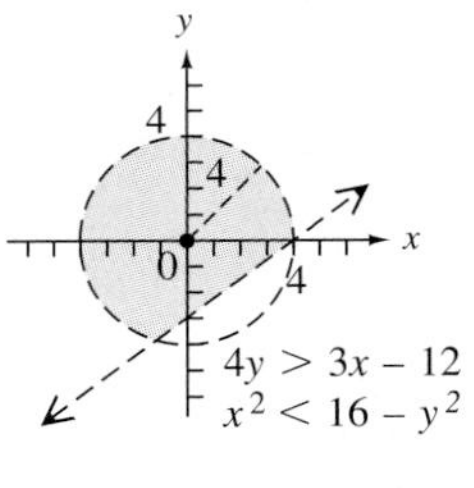

60. There are cases where one x-value will yield two y-values. In a function, every x yields one and only one y. **61.** 69.8 million km **62.** 46.0 million km

Chapter 12 Test (page 915)

1. C **2.** A **3.** D **4.** B

5.

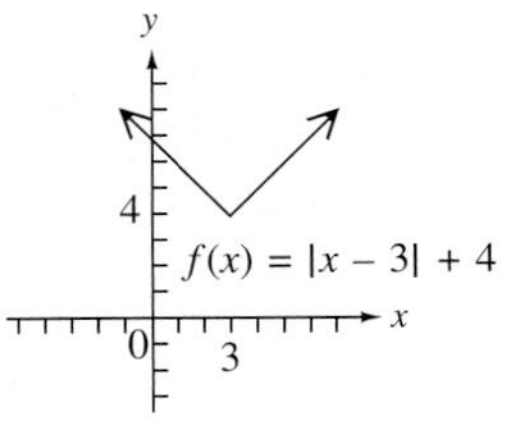

6. (a) $3x^3 + 5x^2 + 6x + 10$ **(b)** 5 **(c)** 23 **(d)** $3x^2 + 11$ **(e)** $9x^2 + 30x + 27$

7. center: $(2, -3)$; radius: 4

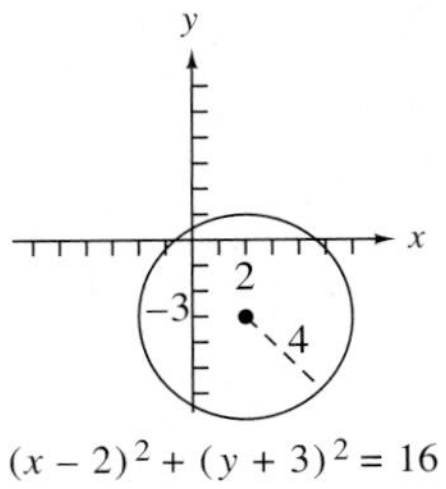

8. center: $(-4, 1)$; radius: 5

9.

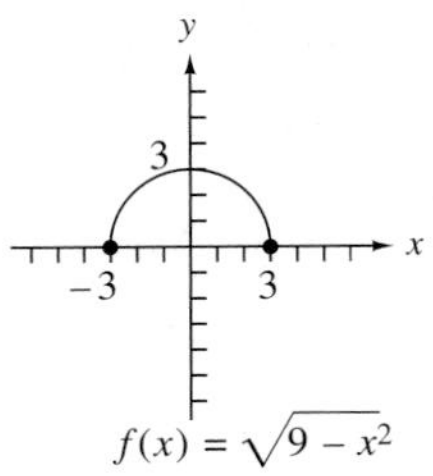

10.

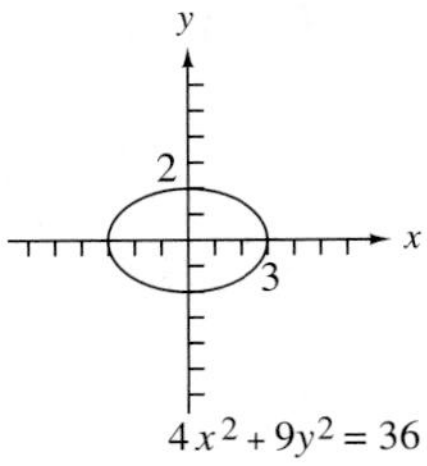

11.

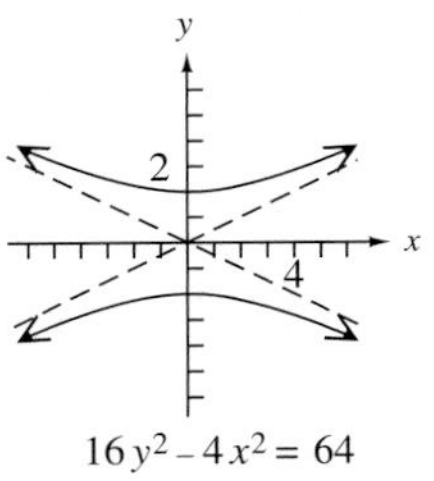

12.

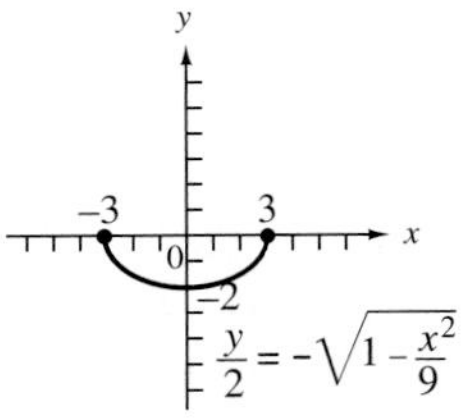

13. ellipse **14.** hyperbola **15.** parabola

16. $\left\{\left(-\frac{1}{2}, -10\right), (5, 1)\right\}$ **17.** $\left\{(-2, -2), \left(\frac{14}{5}, -\frac{2}{5}\right)\right\}$

18. $\{(-\sqrt{22}, -\sqrt{3}), (-\sqrt{22}, \sqrt{3}), (\sqrt{22}, -\sqrt{3}), (\sqrt{22}, \sqrt{3})\}$

19.

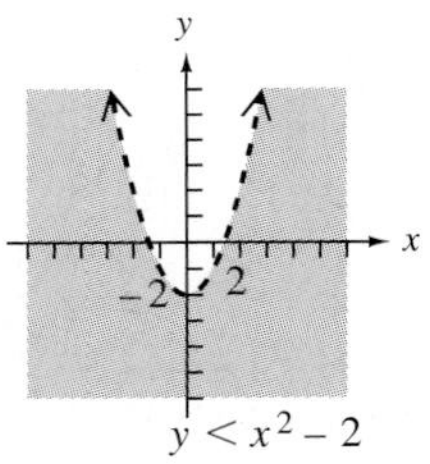

20.

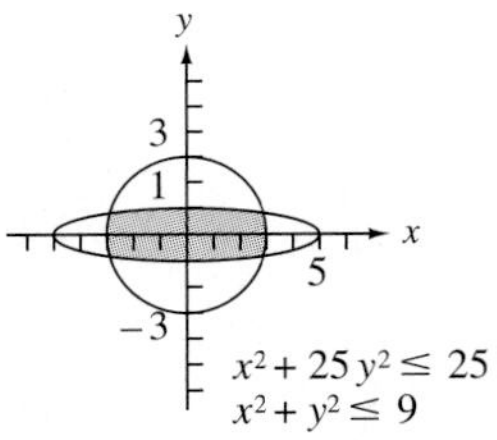

Cumulative Review Exercises: Chapters R–12 (page 919)

1. -4 **2.** $\left\{\frac{2}{3}\right\}$ **3.** $\left(-\infty, \frac{3}{5}\right]$ **4.** $\{-4, 4\}$

5. $(-\infty, -5) \cup (10, \infty)$ **6.** $\frac{2}{3}$ **7.** $3x + 2y = -13$

8. $\{(3, -3)\}$ **9.** $\{(4, 1, -2)\}$ **10.** $\left\{(-1, 5), \left(\frac{5}{2}, -2\right)\right\}$

11. 40 mph **12.** \$275 **13.** $25y^2 - 30y + 9$ **14.** $12r^2 + 40r - 7$

15. $4x^3 - 4x^2 + 3x + 5 + \frac{3}{2x + 1}$ **16.** $(3x + 2)(4x - 5)$

17. $(2y^2 - 1)(y^2 + 3)$ **18.** $(z^2 + 1)(z + 1)(z - 1)$

19. $(a - 3b)(a^2 + 3ab + 9b^2)$ **20.** $\frac{40}{9}$ **21.** $\frac{y - 1}{y(y - 3)}$

22. $\frac{3c+5}{(c+5)(c+3)}$ **23.** $\frac{1}{p}$ **24.** $1\frac{1}{5}$ hr **25.** $\frac{3}{4}$ **26.** $\frac{a^5}{4}$

27. $2\sqrt[3]{2}$ **28.** $\frac{3\sqrt{10}}{2}$ **29.** $\frac{7}{5}+\frac{11}{5}i$ **30.** $\emptyset$ **31.** $\left\{\frac{1}{5}, -\frac{3}{2}\right\}$

32. $\left\{\frac{1+2\sqrt{2}}{4}, \frac{1-2\sqrt{2}}{4}\right\}$ **33.** $\left\{\frac{3+\sqrt{33}}{6}, \frac{3-\sqrt{33}}{6}\right\}$

34. $\left\{-\frac{\sqrt{6}}{2}, \frac{\sqrt{6}}{2}, -\sqrt{7}, \sqrt{7}\right\}$ **35.** $v = \frac{\pm\sqrt{rFkw}}{kw}$

36. $f^{-1}(x) = \sqrt[3]{x-4}$ **37.** 4 **38.** 7 **39.** $\log \frac{(3x+7)^2}{4}$

40. $\{3\}$ **41.** **(a)** \$12,198.90 **(b)** \$12,214.03 **42.** \$16.9 billion **43.** \$75.8 billion **44.** **(a)** $x^2 - x - 6$ **(b)** -1 **(c)** $9x^2 + 18x + 4$

45.

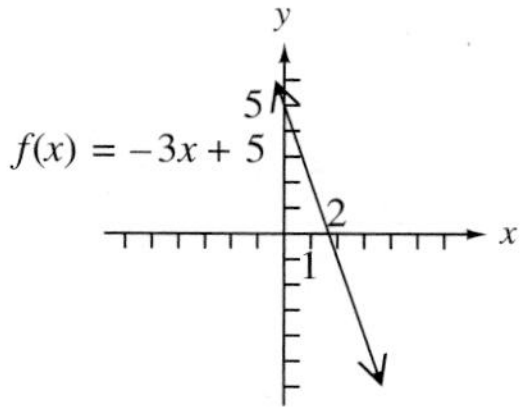

46.

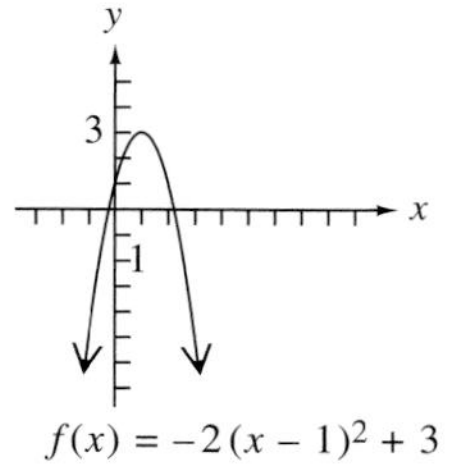

47.

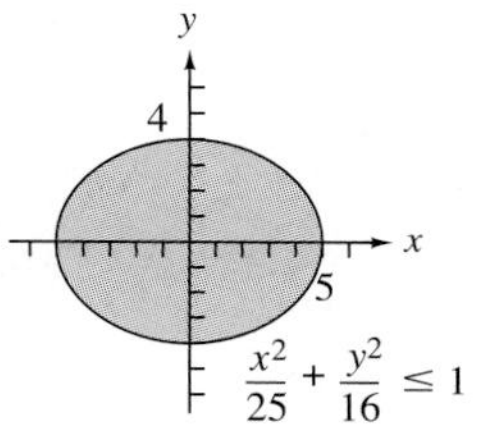

48.

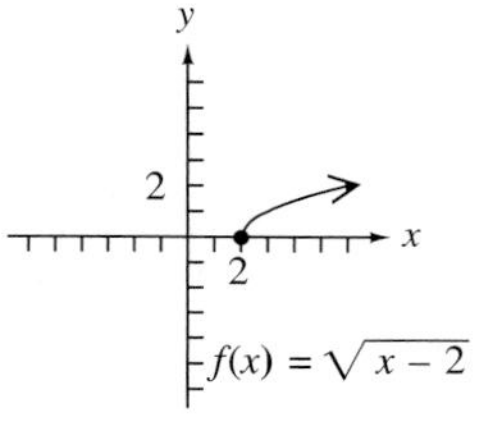

49.

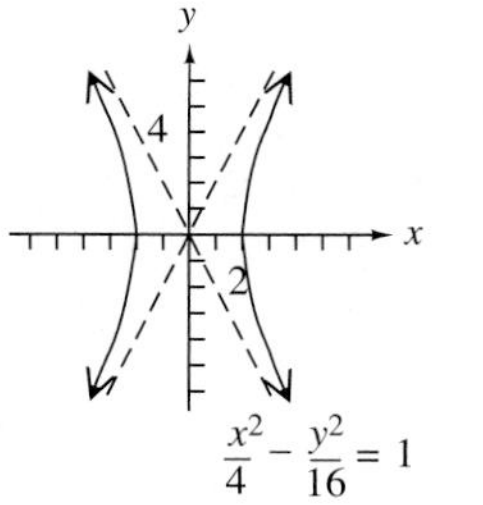

50.

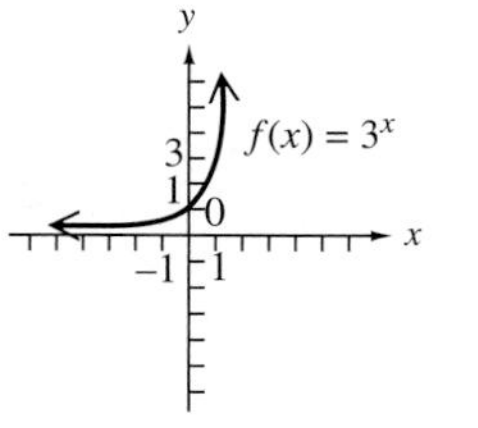

Appendix A

(page A–5)

1. $\{1, 2, 3, 4, 5, 6, 7\}$ **3.** {winter, spring, summer, fall} **5.** $\emptyset$ **7.** {L} **9.** $\{2, 4, 6, 8, 10, \ldots\}$ **11.** The sets in Exercises 9 and 10 are infinite sets. **13.** true **15.** false **17.** true **19.** true **21.** true **23.** true **25.** true **27.** false **29.** true **31.** true **33.** false **35.** true **37.** true **39.** false **41.** true **43.** false **45.** {g, h} **47.** {b, c, d, e, g, h} **49.** $\{a, c, e\} = B$ **51.** $\{d\} = D$ **53.** {a} **55.** {a, c, d, e} **57.** {a, c, e, f} **59.** $\emptyset$ **61.** B and D; C and D

Appendix B

(page A–15)

1. true **3.** false **5.** -3 **7.** 14 **9.** 0 **11.** 59 **13.** 14 **15.** 1 **17.** -22 **19.** 0 **21.** 0 **23.** 20 **25.** $\{(4, 6)\}$ **27.** $\{(-5, 2)\}$ **29.** $\{(1, 0)\}$ **31.** $\left\{\left(\frac{11}{58}, -\frac{5}{29}\right)\right\}$

33. $\{(-2, 3, 5)\}$ **35.** $\{(5, 0, 0)\}$ **37.** Cramer's rule does not apply. **39.** $\{(20, -13, -12)\}$ **41.** $\left\{\left(\frac{62}{5}, -\frac{1}{5}, \frac{27}{5}\right)\right\}$

Appendix C

(page A–21)

1. C **3.** $x - 5$ **5.** $4m - 1$ **7.** $2a + 4 + \frac{5}{a+2}$ **9.** $p - 4 + \frac{9}{p+1}$ **11.** $4a^2 + a + 3$

13. $x^4 + 2x^3 + 2x^2 + 7x + 10 + \frac{18}{x-2}$

15. $-4r^5 - 7r^4 - 10r^3 - 5r^2 - 11r - 8 + \frac{-8}{r-1}$

17. $-3y^4 + 8y^3 - 21y^2 + 36y - 72 + \frac{143}{y+2}$

19. $y^2 + y + 1 + \frac{2}{y-1}$ **21.** 7 **23.** -2 **25.** 0 **27.** yes **29.** no **31.** no **33.** Since the variables are not present, a missing term will not be noticed in synthetic division, so the quotient will be wrong if placeholders are not inserted.

Appendix D

(page A–27)

1. $\frac{1}{a^2b}$ **3.** $\frac{100y^{10}}{x^2}$ **5.** 0 **7.** $\frac{x^{10}}{2w^{13}y^5}$ **9.** $\frac{a^{15}}{-64b^{15}}$ **11.** $\frac{x^{16}z^{10}}{y^6}$ **13.** $-6a^4 + 11a^3 - 20a^2 + 26a - 15$ **15.** $8x^3 - 18x^2 + 6x - 16$ **17.** $x^2y - xy^2 + 6y^3$ **19.** $-3x^2 - 62x + 32$ **21.** $10x^3 - 4x^2 + 9x - 4$ **23.** $6x^2 - 19x - 7$ **25.** $4x^2 - 9x + 2$ **27.** $16t^2 - 9$ **29.** $4y^4 - 16$ **31.** $16x^2 - 24x + 9$ **33.** $36r^2 + 60ry + 25y^2$ **35.** $c^3 + 8d^3$ **37.** $64x^3 - 1$ **39.** $14t^3 + 45st^2 + 18s^2t - 5s^3$ **41.** $4xy^3(2x^2y + 3x + 9y)$ **43.** $(x+3)(x-5)$ **45.** $(2x+3)(x-6)$ **47.** $(6t+5)(6t-5)$ **49.** $(4t+3)^2$ **51.** $p(2m - 3n)^2$ **53.** $(x+1)(x^2 - x + 1)$ **55.** $(2t+5)(4t^2 - 10t + 25)$ **57.** $(t^2 - 5)(t^4 + 5t^2 + 25)$ **59.** $(5x + 2y)(t + 3r)$ **61.** $(6r - 5s)(a + 2b)$ **63.** $(t^2+1)(t+1)(t-1)$ **65.** $(2x + 3y - 1)(2x + 3y + 1)$

Index

D

E

F

G

H

I

N

O

P

Q

R

W

X

Y

Z